Climate Change 2022
Mitigation of Climate Change

Working Group III Contribution to the Sixth Assessment Report of the Intergovernmental Panel on Climate Change
Volume 1

Edited by

Priyadarshi R. Shukla
Co-Chair, Working Group III

Jim Skea
Co-Chair, Working Group III

Raphael Slade
Head of TSU (Science)

Roger Fradera
Head of TSU (Operations)

Minal Pathak
Senior Scientist

Alaa Al Khourdajie
Senior Scientist

Malek Belkacemi
IT/Web Manager

Renée van Diemen
Senior Scientist

Apoorva Hasija
Publication Manager

Géninha Lisboa
TSU Administrator

Sigourney Luz
Communications Manager

Juliette Malley
Senior Administrator

David McCollum
Senior Scientist

Shreya Some
Scientist

Purvi Vyas
Science Officer

T0389018

Shaftesbury Road, Cambridge CB2 8EA, United Kingdom

One Liberty Plaza, 20th Floor, New York, NY 10006, USA

477 Williamstown Road, Port Melbourne, VIC 3207, Australia

314–321, 3rd Floor, Plot 3, Splendor Forum, Jasola District Centre, New Delhi – 110025, India

103 Penang Road, #05-06/07, Visioncrest Commercial, Singapore 238467

Cambridge University Press is part of Cambridge University Press & Assessment, a department of the University of Cambridge.

We share the University's mission to contribute to society through the pursuit of education, learning and research at the highest international levels of excellence.

www.cambridge.org

Information on this title: www.cambridge.org/9781009157933

DOI: 10.1017/9781009157926

First published 2022

Printed in the United Kingdom by TJ Books Limited, Padstow Cornwall

A catalogue record for this publication is available from the British Library.

ISBN – 2 Volume Set: 978-1-009-15793-3 Paperback

ISBN – Volume 1: 978-1-009-42390-8 Paperback

ISBN – Volume 2: 978-1-009-42391-5 Paperback

Cambridge University Press & Assessment has no responsibility for the persistence or accuracy of URLs for external or third-party internet websites referred to in this publication and does not guarantee that any content on such websites is, or will remain, accurate or appropriate.

Electronic copies of this report are available from the IPCC website www.ipcc.ch.

Front cover photograph: Matt Bridgestock, Director and Architect at John Gilbert Architects

All International Energy Agency (IEA) Data, IEA Further Data and Derived Data has been sourced from https://www.iea.org/data-and-statistics.

Contents

Foreword
and Preface

Foreword

Climate Change 2022: Mitigation of Climate Change is the third part of the Sixth Assessment Report (AR6) of the Intergovernmental Panel on Climate Change (IPCC) and was prepared by its Working Group III. The volume provides an updated global assessment of current and projected emissions from all sources and sectors, mitigation options that reduce emissions or remove greenhouse gases from the atmosphere, and progress towards meeting climate ambitions. It assesses what is required to achieve net zero emissions as pledged by many countries.

This report shows that greenhouse gas emissions over the last decade are at the highest levels in human history. It shows that urgent action is needed. Unless there are immediate and deep emissions reductions across all sectors, limiting global warming to 1.5°C will be beyond reach. Global greenhouse gas emissions implied by Nationally Determined Contributions announced prior to COP26 make it likely that warming will exceed 1.5°C and will also make it harder to limit warming to below 2°C.

But there are positive signs and increased evidence of climate action. Options are available now in every sector that can at least halve emissions by 2030. Some countries have already achieved a steady decrease in emissions consistent with limiting warming to 2°C. Costs for some forms of renewable energy have fallen, use of renewables continues to rise and, in some countries and regions, electricity systems are already predominantly powered by renewables.

This IPCC report highlights for the first time the social and demand-side aspects of climate mitigation. As long as the necessary policies, infrastructure and technologies are in place, changes to lifestyles and behaviour have the potential for large reductions in global greenhouse gas emissions and, at the same time, lead to improved wellbeing.

The report calls attention to the deep links between climate mitigation and sustainable development. It draws attention to the way that climate action is intimately connected to addressing the nature crisis. Attention to equity and just transitions can support deeper ambition for accelerated climate action.

The findings in this report have considerably enhanced our understanding of available mitigation pathways. The timing of this report is critical. It provides crucial information that informs the first Global Stocktake under the Paris Agreement. It demands the urgent attention of policymakers and the general public.

As an intergovernmental body jointly established in 1988 by the World Meteorological Organization (WMO) and the United Nations Environment Programme (UNEP), the IPCC has successfully provided policymakers with the most authoritative and objective scientific and technical assessments, which are policy relevant without being policy prescriptive. Beginning in 1990, this series of IPCC Assessment Reports, Special Reports, Technical Papers, Methodology Reports and other products have become standard works of reference.

This Working Group III assessment was made possible thanks to the commitment and dedication of many hundreds of experts, representing a wide range of regions and scientific disciplines. WMO and UNEP are proud that so many of the experts belong to their communities and networks.

We express our deep gratitude to all authors, review editors and expert reviewers for devoting their knowledge, expertise and time. We note the particular challenges presented by the COVID-19 pandemic and the burdens placed on experts. We would like to thank the staff of the Working Group III Technical Support Unit and the IPCC Secretariat for their dedication.

We are also thankful to the governments that supported their scientists' participation in developing this report and that contributed to the IPCC Trust Fund to provide for the essential participation of experts from developing countries and countries with economies in transition.

We would like to express our appreciation to the government of Ethiopia for hosting the scoping meeting for the IPCC's Sixth Assessment Report, to the governments of the United Kingdom of Great Britain and Northern Ireland, India, Ecuador and Italy for hosting drafting sessions for the Working Group III contribution. The latter two meetings were held in a virtual format due to the COVID-19 pandemic. We also express our thanks to the government of the United Kingdom for hosting the Fourteenth Session of Working Group III for approval of the Working Group III Report. The generous financial support by the government of the United Kingdom, and the hosting of the Working Group III Technical Support Unit by Imperial College London (United Kingdom) and Ahmedabad University (India), is gratefully acknowledged.

We would particularly like to thank Dr. Hoesung Lee, Chairman of the IPCC, for his direction and guidance of the IPCC and we express our deep gratitude to Professor Priyadarshi R. Shukla and Professor Jim Skea, the Co-Chairs of Working Group III, for their tireless leadership throughout the development and production of this report.

Petteri Taalas
Secretary-General
World Meteorological Organization

Inger Andersen
Executive Director
United Nations Environment Programme

Preface

The Working Group III (WG III) contribution to the Sixth Assessment Report (AR6) of the Intergovernmental Panel on Climate Change (IPCC) provides a comprehensive and transparent assessment of the scientific literature on climate change mitigation. It builds upon the WG III contribution to the IPCC's Fifth Assessment Report (AR5) in 2014, the WG I and WG II contributions to the AR6, and the three AR6 Special Reports: *Global Warming of 1.5°C*; *Climate Change and Land*; and *The Ocean and Cryosphere in a Changing Climate*.

The report assesses progress in climate change mitigation and options for reducing emissions and enhancing sinks. It evaluates the societal implications of mitigation actions, without recommending any specific options.

Scope of the Report

The scoping of the WG III contribution to AR6 was driven by three guiding principles: to achieve a better synthesis between higher-level whole system and grounded bottom-up insights into technologies and other approaches for reducing emissions; to make wider use of social science disciplines, especially for gaining insight into issues related to lifestyle, behaviour, consumption and socio-technical transitions; and to link climate change mitigation better to other agreed policy goals both nationally and internationally.

The core of the report remains, as in AR5, a set of chapters devoted to different sectors, broadly aligned with the categorisation used in the IPCC Guidelines for National Greenhouse Gas Inventories. These chapters cover emission trends and drivers, mitigation costs and potentials, regional specificities, and sector specific barriers, policies, financing and enabling conditions. A systems level perspective was followed where appropriate. A cross-sectoral perspectives chapter integrates findings from the sectoral chapters and assesses approaches falling outside the scope of individual sectors.

As in the AR5, there is a chapter on recent trends and drivers, with the scope expanded to cover historic emissions and recent policy developments. Following the pattern established in the WG III AR5 report, and the Special Report on Global Warming of 1.5°C, this report assesses published emission scenarios with a 21st century perspective. Modelled emission scenarios are categorised according to climate outcomes, allowing a handshake with the WG I assessment. To meet the goal of linking top-down and bottom-up insights, the report includes an additional pathways chapter that provides a mid-century perspective, focussing on national and regional scales and the alignment between development pathways and mitigation actions.

As in the AR5, this report addresses mitigation enablers such as international cooperation, finance and investment, and policies and institutions, with a greater emphasis placed on the role of institutions than in the AR5. A new chapter is dedicated to the assessment of innovation systems, technology development and technology transfer. A further novelty is a chapter that assesses the literature on human behaviour, lifestyle and culture, and its implications for mitigation action. This chapter touches on patterns of development and human well-being, and circular and sharing economy concepts. It brings a wide range of disciplines, notably from the social sciences, within the scope of the WG III assessment.

Linkages with development and specifically the Sustainable Development Goals (SDGs) permeate the WG III report. This framing is set up in Chapter 1, and the threads are drawn together in the final chapter where linkages between mitigation and the SDGs are systematically assessed.

The AR6 has benefited from close and unprecedented collaboration between the three IPCC WGs: with WG I on scenarios and with WG II on urban systems, land use and development pathways. This collaboration is manifested in a number of Cross-Working Group boxes covering topics such as the economic benefits from avoided impacts along mitigation pathways, climate change and urban areas, mitigation and adaptation through the bioeconomy, and solar radiation modification.

Structure of the Report

This report consists of a Summary for Policymakers, a Technical Summary, 17 Chapters, six Annexes, and Index, as well as online Supplementary Material to chapters.

Chapters 1 (Introduction and framing) and 17 (Accelerating the transition in the context of sustainable development), the first and final chapters of the report, set climate change mitigation in the context of sustainable development. Chapter 1 sets out the evolving policy landscape for climate mitigation, provides the reader with the framing of, and context for, the report, and highlights key concepts. Chapter 17 adopts an integrative perspective on sustainable development and climate change responses, identifying synergies and trade-offs, and explores joint responses to climate change and sustainable development challenges.

Chapters 2–4 take a high-level view of trends and future pathways using three different time frames. Chapter 2 (Emissions trends and drivers) covers historic and current emission trends and socio-economic and demographic drivers of emissions. It also maps developments in technologies and policies since the AR5. Chapter 3 (Mitigation pathways compatible with long-term goals) assesses modelled emission pathways compatible with the Paris Agreement and higher warming levels. It addresses socio-cultural-techno-economic assumptions, technological and behavioural aspects of mitigation pathways, and links to adaptation and sustainable development. Chapter 4 (Mitigation and development pathways in the near- to mid-term) takes a mid-century perspective, considering national, regional and international scales and the implications of mitigation for national development objectives including employment, competitiveness, poverty eradication and the SDGs. Annex III (Scenarios and modelling methods) provides methodological background to Chapters 3 and 4.

Chapter 5 (Demand, services and social aspects of mitigation), a new chapter in AR6, explores how mitigation interacts with meeting human needs and access to services. It explores, *inter alia*: sustainable production and consumption; patterns of development and indicators of wellbeing; the role of culture, social norms, practices and behaviour changes; the sharing economy and circular economy; and policies facilitating behavioural and lifestyle change.

Chapters 6–12 (Energy systems; Agriculture, Forestry, and Other Land Uses (AFOLU); Urban systems and other settlements; Buildings; Transport; Industry; Cross-sectoral perspectives) assess the potential for emissions reductions in specific systems and sectors, taking into account trends in emissions and their key drivers, global and regional costs and potentials, links to climate adaptation and associated risks and co-benefits, and sector specific barriers, policies, financing and enabling conditions. Specificities include fugitive emissions and carbon capture and storage (Energy), provision of food, feed, fibre, wood, biomass for energy and other ecosystem services (AFOLU), demographic changes and urban form (Urban systems and other settlements), mitigation strategies including efficiency, sufficiency and renewables (Buildings), access to mobility (Transport), and resource efficiency (Industry). Chapter 12 (Cross-sectoral perspectives) synthesises costs and potentials, and co-benefits and trade-offs, across sectors; it also addresses cross-cutting approaches such as carbon dioxide removal and mitigation opportunities in the food system.

Chapters 13–16 address enabling conditions for mitigation action. Chapter 13 (National and sub-national policies and institutions) provides insights from national and subnational plans and strategies, including trends in legislation and institutions. Chapter 14 (International cooperation) assesses international cooperation and institutions, including linkages with non-climate organisations and processes, international sectoral agreements, and institutions for finance and investment and capacity building. Chapter 15 (Investment and finance) assesses scenarios of, and needs for, mitigation investment and financial flows, and the means of mobilising climate finance at the national and sub-national levels. Chapter 16 (Innovation, technology development and transfer) examines the role of innovation, technology development, diffusion and transfer in contributing to sustainable development and the aims of the Paris Agreement. It addresses specific challenges in emerging economies and least developed countries.

The Assessment Process

This WG III contribution to the AR6 has been prepared in accordance with IPCC rules and procedures. A scoping meeting was held in May 2017 and the outlines for the contributions of the three WGs were approved at the 46th Session of the Panel in September 2017.

Governments and IPCC observer organisations nominated experts for the author teams. The team of 199 Coordinating Lead Authors and Lead Authors, plus 38 Review Editors, selected by the WG III Bureau, was accepted at the 55th Session of the IPCC Bureau in January 2018. More than 350 Contributing Authors provided text for the author teams.

Drafts were subject to two rounds of formal review and revision followed by a final round of government comments on the Summary for Policymakers. More than 59,000 written comments were submitted by more than 1,600 expert reviewers and 42 governments. For each chapter, the review process was monitored by Review Editors to ensure that all comments received appropriate consideration.

During the review periods and in the run-up to the approval session, webinars were held with governments and two of the UNFCCC non-governmental organisation (NGO) constituencies, the Business and Industry NGOs (BINGOs), and the Environmental NGOs (ENGOs). These informal webinars offered an opportunity for authors to present draft material to IPCC audiences and to receive additional feedback.

The Report was accepted by the Panel at its 56th Session. The Summary for Policymakers was approved line-by-line and the underlying chapters were accepted at the 14th Session of IPCC WG III from 21 March – 4 April 2022, hosted virtually by the United Kingdom of Great Britain and Northern Ireland (UK).

Acknowledgements

The report was made possible thanks to the expertise, hard work and commitment to excellence shown by Coordinating Lead Authors and Lead Authors, with inputs from many Contributing Authors. Their efforts and stamina are particularly commendable given the additional demands and stresses imposed by virtual working as a consequence of the COVID pandemic.

We gratefully acknowledge the support of the Chapter Scientists, who worked tirelessly alongside the authors to deliver their chapters to the highest possible standards. Their time, dedication and hard work is greatly appreciated.

We would like to express our appreciation to the Government and Expert Reviewers for the time and energy they invested to provide constructive and useful comments on the draft reports. Our Review Editors were also critical in the AR6 process, helping author teams to process comments, and assuring an objective discussion of relevant issues.

We wish to thank the governments and other institutions for generous support which enabled the authors, Review Editors and Government and Expert Reviewers to participate.

We would like to thank the Vice-Chairs of the WG III Bureau, who provided invaluable scientific input and thoughtful advice throughout the AR6 process: Amjad Abdulla, Carlo Carraro, Diriba Korecha Dadi, Ramón Pichs-Madruga, Nagmeldin G.E. Mahmoud, Andy Reisinger and Diana Ürge-Vorsatz. Specific thanks are due to Andy Reisinger, who together with the Co-Chairs acted as an editor of the Summary for Policymakers, and to Ramón Pichs-Madruga and Diana Ürge-Vorsatz, who took on roles of editors of the Technical Summary.

We thank the Integrated Assessment Modelling Consortium (IAMC) and the International Institute for Applied Systems Analysis (IIASA) for facilitating the development, and hosting, of the AR6 Scenario Explorer and Database. Particular thanks are due to Edward Byers and Keywan Riahi of IIASA who led this initiative. We thank the International Energy Agency (IEA), in particular Roberta Quadrelli and her team, for providing us with access to their data products. We also thank Monica Crippa and her team at the Joint Research Centre of the European Commission for access to the EDGAR (Emissions Database for Global Atmospheric Research), and William Lamb and Jan Minx who led the assessment of emissions data across the report.

We acknowledge support from countries hosting WG III Lead Author Meetings (LAMs): the UK for hosting the first LAM in Edinburgh (March 2019); India for hosting the second LAM in New Delhi (September 2019); Ecuador for hosting the third LAM virtually (April 2020); and Italy for hosting the fourth LAM, also held virtually (April 2021). We thank the government of Ethiopia for hosting the Scoping Meeting for the report in Addis Ababa (May 2017).

We are especially grateful for the support of the UK government, in particular the Department of Business, Energy and Industrial Strategy (BEIS) and the Engineering and Physical Sciences Research Council (EPSRC), for funding the WG III Technical Support Unit (TSU). Jolene Cook, Eleanor Webster, Rhian Rees-Owen, Sarah Honour, Cathy Johnson, Julie Maclean, Alice Montgomery, Caroline Prescott, and Andrew Russell at BEIS, and Jim Fleming, Kathryn Magnay, Strachan McCormick, Kate Bowman and Jasmine Cain at EPSRC were always ready to dedicate time and energy to the needs of the team. BEIS also organised the venue hosting the core team for the 14th Session of IPCC WG III.

We are grateful for the close collaboration with authors, Bureau members and members of the Technical Support Units from WGs I and II, and Task Force on National Greenhouse Gas Inventories (TFI).. We especially thank WG I Co-Chairs Valérie Masson-Delmotte and Panmao Zhai, WG II Co-Chairs Hans-Otto Portner and Debra Roberts, and the Co-Chairs of the Task Force on Greenhouse Gas Inventories, Eduardo Calvo Buendía and Kiyoto Tanabe, for their collegial spirit and mutual support during the assessment. We extend our gratitude to the IPCC leadership. The Executive Committee, notably Vice-Chairs Ko Barrett, Thelma Krug, Youba Sokona, strengthened the work of all three WGs. We thank IPCC Chair, Hoesung Lee, for his leadership.

We would like to thank the Secretary of the IPCC, Abdalah Mokssit, and Deputy Secretaries, Ermira Fida and Kerstin Stendahl, and their colleagues Mudathir Abdallah, Jesbin Baidya, Laura Biagioni, Annie Courtin, Oksana Ekzarkho, Judith Ewa, Joelle Fernandez, Emelie Larrode, Jennifer Lew Schneider, Jonathan Lynn, Andrej Mahecic, Nina Peeva, Sophie Schlingemann, Mxolisi Shongwe, Melissa Walsh, and Werani Zabula, for their guidance in implementing IPCC processes, their logistical support, their close collaboration on communications, and for enabling the participation of experts from developing countries through the IPCC Trust Fund.

We wish to thank Sue Escott of Escott-Hunt and staff at the UN Foundation for their insight and hard work to ensure the effective communication of the messages in the report. Thanks are expressed to John Schwartz and his team at Soapbox Communications Ltd for graphics design support and for typesetting the final report, in particular Ian Blenkinsop, Margherita Cardoso, Autumn Forecast, Žiga Kropivšek, Sharon Mah, Jenny McCarten, Polly O'Hara, Francesca Romano and Alice Woodward, to Georgie Bowden for her careful compilation of the report index, and to Matt Lloyd, Jenny van der Meijden, and the team at Cambridge University Press for final publication of the report.

We are grateful to the members of the core team at the 14th Session of WG III, especially the IPCC Vice Chairs, WG I and II Vice-Chairs Greg Flato, Jan Fuglestvedt and Mark Howden, WG I, II and SYR TSU members, in particular Nada Caud, Sarah Connors, Melissa Gomis, Tijama Kerscher, Katherine Leitzell, Noëmie Leprince-Ringuet, Sina Löschke, Tom Maycock, Katja Mintenbeck, Komila Nabiyeva, Clotilde Péan, Anna Pirani, Elvira Poloczanska, Jussi Savolainen, and Melinda Tignor, as well as Sophie Berger, Kiane de Kleijne, and Chloe Ludden.

It is a pleasure to acknowledge the tireless work, resilience and good humour of the staff of the WG III TSU throughout the many challenges faced during the assessment cycle. Our thanks go to Raphael Slade, Roger Fradera, Minal Pathak, Alaa Al Khourdajie, Malek Belkacemi, Renée van Diemen, Apoorva Hasija, Géninha Lisboa, Sigourney Luz, Juliette Malley, David McCollum, Shreya Some, and Purvi Vyas, and also to past team members: Elizabeth Huntley, Katie Kissick, Suvadip Neogi and Joanna Portugal-Pereira. Your professionalism, creativity and indomitable spirit has been exemplary and continually inspiring. Finally, on behalf of all participants, we thank colleagues, family and friends for their understanding and support throughout the production of this report, which has taken place during unprecedented times.

Sincerely,

Jim Skea
Co-Chair Working Group III

Priyadarshi R. Shukla
Co-Chair Working Group III

In memoriam

Cristóbal Díaz Morejón
(1949–2021)

Lead Author of Chapter 17 on Accelerating the transition in the context of sustainable development

Cristóbal Díaz Morejón was an internationally renowned expert across a range of environmental disciplines. Over the course of a busy and successful career he led projects on the salinity of soils, water resource management, environmental strategy, desertification and droughts, and energy efficiency, amongst others. He represented Cuba in many international meetings on water resources and sustainable development. In 1994 he was awarded a Medal by the Academy of Sciences of Cuba on its 30th Anniversary, and in 2004, the "Juan Tomas Roig" Medal for 25 years dedicated to research. A contributor to IPCC reports since 2004, he was an intelligent, knowledgeable, dedicated and kind colleague, and will be sorely missed.

Summary for
Policymakers

Summary for Policymakers

SPM

Drafting Authors: Jim Skea (United Kingdom), Priyadarshi R. Shukla (India), Andy Reisinger (New Zealand), Raphael Slade (United Kingdom), Minal Pathak (India), Alaa Al Khourdajie (United Kingdom/Syria), Renée van Diemen (the Netherlands/United Kingdom), Amjad Abdulla (Maldives), Keigo Akimoto (Japan), Mustafa Babiker (Sudan/Saudi Arabia), Quan Bai (China), Igor A. Bashmakov (the Russian Federation), Christopher Bataille (Canada), Göran Berndes (Sweden), Gabriel Blanco (Argentina), Kornelis Blok (the Netherlands), Mercedes Bustamante (Brazil), Edward Byers (Austria/Ireland), Luisa F. Cabeza (Spain), Katherine Calvin (the United States of America), Carlo Carraro (Italy), Leon Clarke (the United States of America), Annette Cowie (Australia), Felix Creutzig (Germany), Diriba Korecha Dadi (Ethiopia), Dipak Dasgupta (India), Heleen de Coninck (the Netherlands), Fatima Denton (the Gambia), Shobhakar Dhakal (Nepal/Thailand), Navroz K. Dubash (India), Oliver Geden (Germany), Michael Grubb (United Kingdom), Céline Guivarch (France), Shreekant Gupta (India), Andrea N. Hahmann (Chile/Denmark), Kirsten Halsnaes (Denmark), Paulina Jaramillo (the United States of America), Kejun Jiang (China), Frank Jotzo (Australia), Tae Yong Jung (Republic of Korea), Suzana Kahn Ribeiro (Brazil), Smail Khennas (Algeria), Şiir Kılkış (Turkey), Silvia Kreibiehl (Germany), Volker Krey (Germany/Austria), Elmar Kriegler (Germany), William F. Lamb (Germany/United Kingdom), Franck Lecocq (France), Shuaib Lwasa (Uganda), Nagmeldin Mahmoud (Sudan), Cheikh Mbow (Senegal), David McCollum (the United States of America), Jan Christoph Minx (Germany), Catherine Mitchell (United Kingdom), Rachid Mrabet (Morocco), Yacob Mulugetta (Ethiopia/United Kingdom), Gert-Jan Nabuurs (the Netherlands), Gregory F. Nemet (the United States of America/Canada), Peter Newman (Australia), Leila Niamir (Iran/Germany), Lars J. Nilsson (Sweden), Sudarmanto Budi Nugroho (Indonesia), Chukwumerije Okereke (Nigeria/United Kingdom), Shonali Pachauri (India), Anthony Patt (Switzerland), Ramón Pichs-Madruga (Cuba), Joana Portugal-Pereira (Brazil), Lavanya Rajamani (India), Keywan Riahi (Austria), Joyashree Roy (India/Thailand), Yamina Saheb (France/Algeria), Roberto Schaeffer (Brazil), Karen C. Seto (the United States of America), Shreya Some (India), Linda Steg (the Netherlands), Ferenc L. Toth (Austria/Hungary), Diana Ürge-Vorsatz (Hungary), Detlef P. van Vuuren (the Netherlands), Elena Verdolini (Italy), Purvi Vyas (India), Yi-Ming Wei (China), Mariama Williams (Jamaica/the United States of America), Harald Winkler (South Africa).

Contributing Authors: Parth Bhatia (India), Sarah Burch (Canada), Jeremy Emmet-Booth (New Zealand), Jan S. Fuglestvedt (Norway), Meredith Kelller (the United States of America), Jarmo Kikstra (Austria/the Netherlands), Michael König (Germany), Malte Meinshausen (Australia/Germany), Zebedee Nicholls (Australia), Kaj-Ivar van der Wijst (the Netherlands).

This Summary for Policymakers should be cited as:

IPCC, 2022: Summary for Policymakers [P.R. Shukla, J. Skea, A. Reisinger, R. Slade, R. Fradera, M. Pathak, A. Al Khourdajie, M. Belkacemi, R. van Diemen, A. Hasija, G. Lisboa, S. Luz, J. Malley, D. McCollum, S. Some, P. Vyas, (eds.)]. In: *Climate Change 2022*: *Mitigation of Climate Change. Contribution of Working Group III to the Sixth Assessment Report of the Intergovernmental Panel on Climate Change* [P.R. Shukla, J. Skea, R. Slade, A. Al Khourdajie, R. van Diemen, D. McCollum, M. Pathak, S. Some, P. Vyas, R. Fradera, M. Belkacemi, A. Hasija, G. Lisboa, S. Luz, J. Malley, (eds.)]. Cambridge University Press, Cambridge, UK and New York, NY, USA. doi: 10.1017/9781009157926.001.

A. Introduction and Framing

The Working Group III (WGIII) contribution to the IPCC's Sixth Assessment Report (AR6) assesses literature on the scientific, technological, environmental, economic and social aspects of mitigation of climate change.[1] Levels of confidence[2] are given in () brackets. Numerical ranges are presented in square [] brackets. References to Chapters, Sections, Figures and Boxes in the underlying report and Technical Summary (TS) are given in {} brackets.

The report reflects new findings in the relevant literature and builds on previous IPCC reports, including the WGIII contribution to the IPCC's Fifth Assessment Report (AR5), the WGI and WGII contributions to AR6 and the three Special Reports in the Sixth Assessment cycle,[3] as well as other UN assessments. Some of the main developments relevant for this report include {TS.1, TS.2}:

- **An evolving international landscape.** The literature reflects, among other factors: developments in the UN Framework Convention on Climate Change (UNFCCC) process, including the outcomes of the Kyoto Protocol and the adoption of the Paris Agreement {13, 14, 15, 16}; the UN 2030 Agenda for Sustainable Development including the Sustainable Development Goals (SDGs) {1, 3, 4, 17}; and the evolving roles of international cooperation {14}, finance {15} and innovation {16}.

- **Increasing diversity of actors and approaches to mitigation.** Recent literature highlights the growing role of non-state and sub-national actors including cities, businesses, Indigenous Peoples, citizens including local communities and youth, transnational initiatives, and public-private entities in the global effort to address climate change {5, 13, 14, 15, 16, 17}. Literature documents the global spread of climate policies and cost declines of existing and emerging low emission technologies, along with varied types and levels of mitigation efforts, and sustained reductions in greenhouse gas (GHG) emissions in some countries {2, 5, 6, 8, 12, 13, 16}, and the impacts of, and some lessons from, the COVID-19 pandemic. {1, 2, 3, 5, 13, 15, Box TS.1, Cross-Chapter Box 1 in Chapter 1}

- **Close linkages between climate change mitigation, adaptation and development pathways.** The development pathways taken by countries at all stages of economic development impact GHG emissions and hence shape mitigation challenges and opportunities, which vary across countries and regions. Literature explores how development choices and the establishment of enabling conditions for action and support influence the feasibility and the cost of limiting emissions {1, 3, 4, 5, 13, 15, 16}. Literature highlights that climate change mitigation action designed and conducted in the context of sustainable development, equity, and poverty eradication, and rooted in the development aspirations of the societies within which they take place, will be more acceptable, durable and effective {1, 3, 4, 5}. This report covers mitigation from both targeted measures, and from policies and governance with other primary objectives.

- **New approaches in the assessment.** In addition to the sectoral and systems chapters {3, 6, 7, 8, 9, 10, 11, 12}, the report includes, for the first time in a WGIII report, chapters dedicated to demand for services, and social aspects of mitigation {5, Box TS.11}, and to innovation, technology development and transfer {16}. The assessment of future pathways in this report covers near term (to 2030), medium term (up to 2050), and long term (to 2100) time scales, combining assessment of existing pledges and actions {4, 5}, with an assessment of emissions reductions, and their implications, associated with long-term temperature outcomes up to the year 2100 {3}.[4] The assessment of modelled global pathways addresses ways of shifting development pathways towards sustainability. Strengthened collaboration between IPCC Working Groups is reflected in Cross-Working Group Boxes that integrate physical science, climate risks and adaptation, and the mitigation of climate change.[5]

---

[1] The Report covers literature accepted for publication by 11 October 2021.

[2] Each finding is grounded in an evaluation of underlying evidence and agreement. A level of confidence is expressed using five qualifiers, typeset in italics: *very low*, *low*, *medium*, *high* and *very high*. The assessed likelihood of an outcome or a result is described as: *virtually certain* 99–100% probability; *very likely* 90–100%; *likely* 66–100%; *more likely than not* 50–100%; *about as likely as not* 33–66%; *unlikely* 0–33%; *very unlikely* 0–10%; *exceptionally unlikely* 0–1%. Additional terms may also be used when appropriate, consistent with the IPCC uncertainty guidance: https://www.ipcc.ch/site/assets/uploads/2018/05/uncertainty-guidance-note.pdf.

[3] The three Special Reports are: Global Warming of 1.5°C: an IPCC Special Report on the impacts of global warming of 1.5°C above pre-industrial levels and related global greenhouse gas emission pathways, in the context of strengthening the global response to the threat of climate change, sustainable development, and efforts to eradicate poverty (2018); Climate Change and Land: an IPCC Special Report on climate change, desertification, land degradation, sustainable land management, food security, and greenhouse gas fluxes in terrestrial ecosystems (2019); IPCC Special Report on the Ocean and Cryosphere in a Changing Climate (2019).

[4] The term 'temperature' is used in reference to 'global surface temperatures' throughout this SPM as defined in footnote 8 of the AR6 WGI SPM (see note 14 of Table SPM.2). Emission pathways and associated temperature changes are calculated using various forms of models, as summarised in Box SPM.1 and Chapter 3, and discussed in Annex III.

[5] Namely: Economic Benefits from Avoided Climate Impacts along Long-Term Mitigation Pathways {Cross-Working Group Box 1 in Chapter 3}; Urban: Cities and Climate Change {Cross-Working Group Box 2 in Chapter 8}; and Mitigation and Adaptation via the Bioeconomy {Cross-Working Group Box 3 in Chapter 12}.

- **Increasing diversity of analytic frameworks from multiple disciplines including social sciences.** This report identifies multiple analytic frameworks to assess the drivers of, barriers to and options for, mitigation action. These include: economic efficiency, including the benefits of avoided impacts; ethics and equity; interlinked technological and social transition processes; and socio-political frameworks, including institutions and governance {1, 3, 13, Cross-Chapter Box 12 in Chapter 16}. These help to identify risks and opportunities for action, including co-benefits and just and equitable transitions at local, national and global scales. {1, 3, 4, 5, 13, 14, 16, 17}

Section B of this Summary for Policymakers (SPM) assesses *Recent developments and current trends*, including data uncertainties and gaps. Section C, *System transformations to limit global warming*, identifies emission pathways and alternative mitigation portfolios consistent with limiting global warming to different levels, and assesses specific mitigation options at the sectoral and system level. Section D addresses *Linkages between mitigation, adaptation, and sustainable development*. Section E, *Strengthening the response*, assesses knowledge of how enabling conditions of institutional design, policy, finance, innovation and governance arrangements can contribute to climate change mitigation in the context of sustainable development.

B. Recent Developments and Current Trends

B.1 **Total net anthropogenic GHG emissions[6] have continued to rise during the period 2010–2019, as have cumulative net CO_2 emissions since 1850. Average annual GHG emissions during 2010–2019 were higher than in any previous decade, but the rate of growth between 2010 and 2019 was lower than that between 2000 and 2009. (*high confidence*) (Figure SPM.1) {Figure 2.2, Figure 2.5, Table 2.1, 2.2, Figure TS.2}**

B.1.1 Global net anthropogenic GHG emissions were 59 ± 6.6 $GtCO_2$-eq[7,8] in 2019, about 12% (6.5 $GtCO_2$-eq) higher than in 2010 and 54% (21 $GtCO_2$-eq) higher than in 1990. The annual average during the decade 2010–2019 was 56 ± 6.0 $GtCO_2$-eq, 9.1 $GtCO_2$-eq yr^{-1} higher than in 2000–2009. This is the highest increase in average decadal emissions on record. The average annual rate of growth slowed from 2.1% yr^{-1} between 2000 and 2009 to 1.3% yr^{-1} between 2010 and 2019. (*high confidence*) (Figure SPM.1) {Figure 2.2, Figure 2.5, Table 2.1, 2.2, Figure TS.2}

B.1.2 Growth in anthropogenic emissions has persisted across all major groups of GHGs since 1990, albeit at different rates. By 2019, the largest growth in absolute emissions occurred in CO_2 from fossil fuels and industry followed by CH_4, whereas the highest relative growth occurred in fluorinated gases, starting from low levels in 1990 (*high confidence*). Net anthropogenic CO_2 emissions from land use, land-use change and forestry (CO_2-LULUCF) are subject to large uncertainties and high annual variability, with *low confidence* even in the direction of the long-term trend.[9] (Figure SPM.1) {Figure 2.2, Figure 2.5, 2.2, Figure TS.2}

B.1.3 Historical cumulative net CO_2 emissions from 1850 to 2019 were 2400 ± 240 $GtCO_2$ (*high confidence*). Of these, more than half (58%) occurred between 1850 and 1989 [1400 ± 195 $GtCO_2$], and about 42% between 1990 and 2019 [1000 ± 90 $GtCO_2$]. About 17% of historical cumulative net CO_2 emissions since 1850 occurred between 2010 and 2019 [410 ± 30 $GtCO_2$].[10] By comparison, the current central estimate of the remaining carbon budget from 2020 onwards for limiting warming to 1.5°C with a probability of 50% has been assessed as 500 $GtCO_2$, and as 1150 $GtCO_2$ for a probability of 67% for limiting warming to 2°C. Remaining carbon budgets depend on the amount of non-CO_2 mitigation (± 220 $GtCO_2$) and are further subject to geophysical uncertainties. Based on central estimates only, cumulative net CO_2 emissions between 2010 and 2019 compare to about four-fifths of the size of the remaining carbon budget from 2020 onwards for a 50% probability of limiting global warming to 1.5°C, and about one-third of the remaining carbon budget for a 67% probability to limit global warming to 2°C. Even when taking uncertainties into account, historical emissions between 1850 and 2019 constitute a large share of total carbon budgets for these global

---

[6] Net GHG emissions in this report refer to releases of greenhouse gases from anthropogenic sources minus removals by anthropogenic sinks, for those species of gases that are reported under the common reporting format of the United Nations Framework Convention on Climate Change (UNFCCC): CO_2 from fossil fuel combustion and industrial processes (CO_2-FFI); net CO_2 emissions from land use, land-use change and forestry (CO_2-LULUCF); methane (CH_4); nitrous oxide (N_2O); and fluorinated gases (F-gases) comprising hydrofluorocarbons (HFCs), perfluorocarbons (PFCs), sulphur hexafluoride (SF_6), as well as nitrogen trifluoride (NF_3). Different datasets for GHG emissions exist, with varying time horizons and coverage of sectors and gases, including some that go back to 1850. In this report, GHG emissions are assessed from 1990, and CO_2 sometimes also from 1850. Reasons for this include data availability and robustness, scope of the assessed literature, and the differing warming impacts of non-CO_2 gases over time.

[7] GHG emission metrics are used to express emissions of different greenhouse gases in a common unit. Aggregated GHG emissions in this report are stated in CO_2-equivalent (CO_2-eq) using the Global Warming Potential with a time horizon of 100 years (GWP100) with values based on the contribution of Working Group I to the AR6. The choice of metric depends on the purpose of the analysis, and all GHG emission metrics have limitations and uncertainties, given that they simplify the complexity of the physical climate system and its response to past and future GHG emissions. {Cross-Chapter Box 2 in Chapter 2, Supplementary Material 2.SM.3, Box TS.2; AR6 WGI Chapter 7 Supplementary Material}

[8] In this SPM, uncertainty in historic GHG emissions is reported using 90% uncertainty intervals unless stated otherwise. GHG emission levels are rounded to two significant digits; as a consequence, small differences in sums due to rounding may occur.

[9] Global databases make different choices about which emissions and removals occurring on land are considered anthropogenic. Currently, net CO_2 fluxes from land reported by global bookkeeping models used here are estimated to be about 5.5 $GtCO_2$ yr^{-1} higher than the aggregate global net emissions based on national GHG inventories. This difference, which has been considered in the literature, mainly reflects differences in how anthropogenic forest sinks and areas of managed land are defined. Other reasons for this difference, which are more difficult to quantify, can arise from the limited representation of land management in global models and varying levels of accuracy and completeness of estimated LULUCF fluxes in national GHG inventories. Neither method is inherently preferable. Even when the same methodological approach is applied, the large uncertainty of CO_2-LULUCF emissions can lead to substantial revisions to estimated emissions. {Cross-Chapter Box 3 in Chapter 3, 7.2, SRCCL SPM A.3.3}

[10] For consistency with WGI, historical cumulative CO_2 emissions from 1850 to 2019 are reported using 68% confidence intervals.

warming levels.[11,12] Based on central estimates only, historical cumulative net CO_2 emissions between 1850 and 2019 amount to about four-fifths[12] of the total carbon budget for a 50% probability of limiting global warming to 1.5°C (central estimate about 2900 GtCO_2), and to about two thirds[12] of the total carbon budget for a 67% probability to limit global warming to 2°C (central estimate about 3550 GtCO_2). {Figure 2.7, 2.2, Figure TS.3, WGI Table SPM.2}

B.1.4   Emissions of CO_2-FFI dropped temporarily in the first half of 2020 due to responses to the COVID-19 pandemic (*high confidence*), but rebounded by the end of the year (*medium confidence*). The annual average CO_2-FFI emissions reduction in 2020 relative to 2019 was about 5.8% [5.1–6.3%], or 2.2 [1.9–2.4] GtCO_2 (*high confidence*). The full GHG emissions impact of the COVID-19 pandemic could not be assessed due to a lack of data regarding non-CO_2 GHG emissions in 2020. {Cross-Chapter Box 1 in Chapter 1, Figure 2.6, 2.2, Box TS.1, Box TS.1 Figure 1}

Global net anthropogenic emissions have continued to rise across all major groups of greenhouse gases.

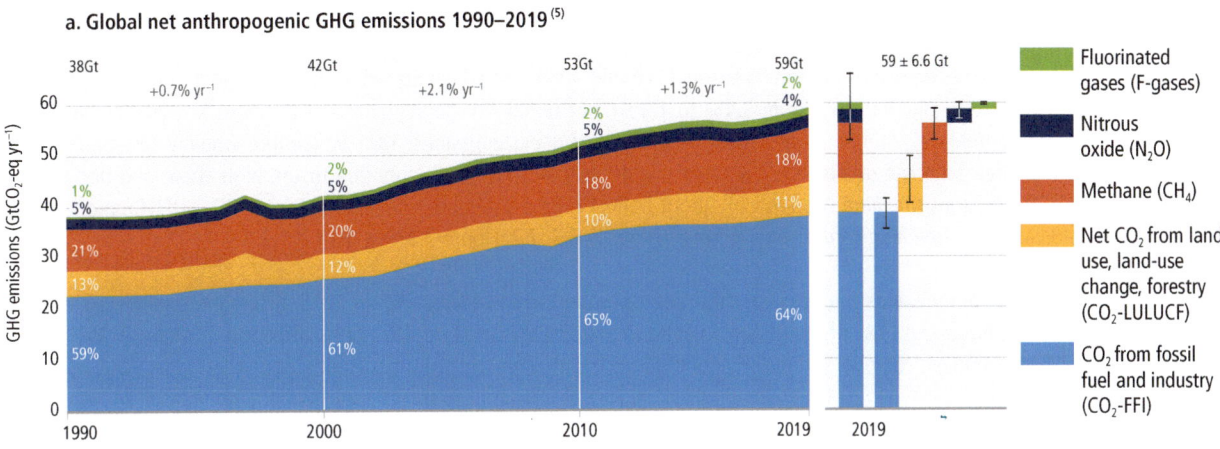

a. Global net anthropogenic GHG emissions 1990–2019 [(5)]

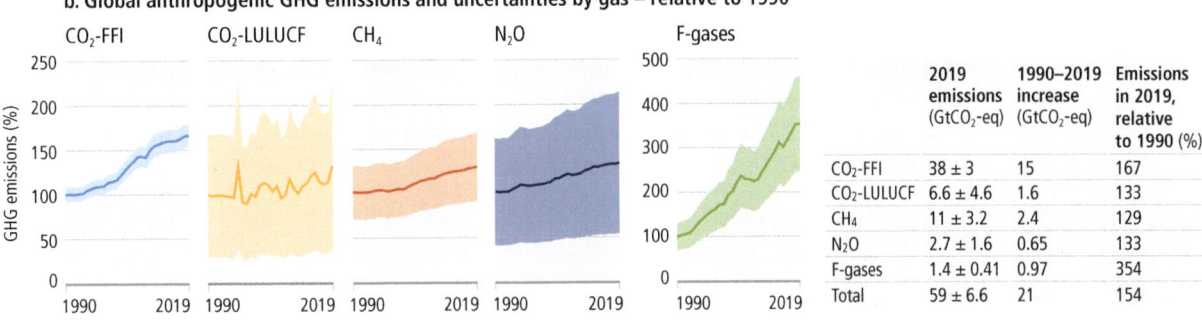

b. Global anthropogenic GHG emissions and uncertainties by gas – relative to 1990

The solid line indicates central estimate of emissions trends. The shaded area indicates the uncertainty range.

	2019 emissions (GtCO$_2$-eq)	1990–2019 increase (GtCO$_2$-eq)	Emissions in 2019, relative to 1990 (%)
CO$_2$-FFI	38 ± 3	15	167
CO$_2$-LULUCF	6.6 ± 4.6	1.6	133
CH$_4$	11 ± 3.2	2.4	129
N$_2$O	2.7 ± 1.6	0.65	133
F-gases	1.4 ± 0.41	0.97	354
Total	59 ± 6.6	21	154

Figure SPM.1 | Global net anthropogenic GHG emissions (GtCO$_2$-eq yr^{-1}) 1990–2019. Global net anthropogenic GHG emissions include CO_2 from fossil fuel combustion and industrial processes (CO_2-FFI); net CO_2 from land use, land-use change and forestry (CO_2-LULUCF)[9]; methane (CH$_4$); nitrous oxide (N$_2$O); and fluorinated gases (HFCs, PFCs, SF$_6$, NF$_3$).[6] **Panel a** shows aggregate annual global net anthropogenic GHG emissions by groups of gases from 1990 to 2019 reported in GtCO$_2$-eq converted based on global warming potentials with a 100-year time horizon (GWP100-AR6) from the IPCC Sixth Assessment Report Working Group I (Chapter 7). The fraction of global emissions for each gas is shown for 1990, 2000, 2010 and 2019; as well as the aggregate average annual growth rate between these decades. At the right side of Panel a, GHG emissions in 2019 are broken down into individual components with the associated uncertainties (90% confidence interval) indicated by the error bars: CO_2-FFI ±8%; CO_2-LULUCF ±70%; CH$_4$ ±30%; N$_2$O ±60%; F-gases ±30%; GHG ±11%. Uncertainties in GHG emissions are assessed in Supplementary Material 2.2. The single-year peak of emissions in 1997 was due to higher CO_2-LULUCF emissions from a forest and peat fire event in South East Asia. **Panel b** shows global anthropogenic CO_2-FFI, net CO_2-LULUCF, CH$_4$, N$_2$O and F-gas emissions individually for the period 1990–2019, normalised relative to 100 in 1990. Note the different scale for the included F-gas emissions compared to other gases, highlighting its rapid growth from a low base. Shaded areas indicate the uncertainty range. Uncertainty ranges as shown here are specific for individual groups of greenhouse gases and cannot be compared. The table shows the central estimate for: absolute emissions in 2019; the absolute change in emissions between 1990 and 2019; and emissions in 2019 expressed as a percentage of 1990 emissions. {2.2, Figure 2.5, Supplementary Material 2.2, Figure TS.2}

---

[11]   The carbon budget is the maximum amount of cumulative net global anthropogenic CO_2 emissions that would result in limiting global warming to a given level with a given likelihood, taking into account the effect of other anthropogenic climate forcers. This is referred to as the 'total carbon budget' when expressed starting from the pre-industrial period, and as the 'remaining carbon budget' when expressed from a recent specified date. The total carbon budgets reported here are the sum of historical emissions from 1850 to 2019 and the remaining carbon budgets from 2020 onwards, which extend until global net zero CO_2 emissions are reached. {Annex I: Glossary; WGI SPM}

[12]   Uncertainties for total carbon budgets have not been assessed and could affect the specific calculated fractions.

B.2   **Net anthropogenic GHG emissions have increased since 2010 across all major sectors globally. An increasing share of emissions can be attributed to urban areas. Emissions reductions in CO$_2$ from fossil fuels and industrial processes (CO$_2$-FFI), due to improvements in energy intensity of GDP and carbon intensity of energy, have been less than emissions increases from rising global activity levels in industry, energy supply, transport, agriculture and buildings. (*high confidence*) {2.2, 2.4, 6.3, 7.2, 8.3, 9.3, 10.1, 11.2}**

B.2.1   In 2019, approximately 34% (20 GtCO$_2$-eq) of total net anthropogenic GHG emissions came from the energy supply sector, 24% (14 GtCO$_2$-eq) from industry, 22% (13 GtCO$_2$-eq) from agriculture, forestry and other land use (AFOLU), 15% (8.7 GtCO$_2$-eq) from transport and 6% (3.3 GtCO$_2$-eq) from buildings.[13] If emissions from electricity and heat production are attributed to the sectors that use the final energy, 90% of these indirect emissions are allocated to the industry and buildings sectors, increasing their relative GHG emissions shares from 24% to 34%, and from 6% to 16%, respectively. After reallocating emissions from electricity and heat production, the energy supply sector accounts for 12% of global net anthropogenic GHG emissions. (*high confidence*) {Figure 2.12, 2.2, 6.3, 7.2, 9.3, 10.1, 11.2, Figure TS.6}

B.2.2   Average annual GHG emissions growth between 2010 and 2019 slowed compared to the previous decade in energy supply (from 2.3% to 1.0%) and industry (from 3.4% to 1.4%), but remained roughly constant at about 2% yr^{-1} in the transport sector (*high confidence*). Emissions growth in AFOLU, comprising emissions from agriculture (mainly CH$_4$ and N$_2$O) and forestry and other land use (mainly CO$_2$) is more uncertain than in other sectors due to the high share and uncertainty of CO$_2$-LULUCF emissions (*medium confidence*). About half of total net AFOLU emissions are from CO$_2$-LULUCF, predominantly from deforestation[14] (*medium confidence*). {Figure 2.13, 2.2, 6.3, 7.2, Figure 7.3, 9.3, 10.1, 11.2, TS.3}

B.2.3   The global share of emissions that can be attributed to urban areas is increasing. In 2015, urban emissions were estimated to be 25 GtCO$_2$-eq (about 62% of the global share) and in 2020, 29 GtCO$_2$-eq (67–72% of the global share).[15] The drivers of urban GHG emission are complex and include population size, income, state of urbanisation and urban form. (*high confidence*) {8.1, 8.3}

B.2.4   Global energy intensity (total primary energy per unit GDP) decreased by 2% yr^{-1} between 2010 and 2019. Carbon intensity (CO$_2$ from fossil fuel combustion and industrial processes (CO$_2$-FFI) per unit primary energy) decreased by 0.3% yr^{-1}, with large regional variations, over the same period mainly due to fuel switching from coal to gas, reduced expansion of coal capacity, and increased use of renewables. This reversed the trend observed for 2000–2009. For comparison, the carbon intensity of primary energy is projected to decrease globally by about 3.5% yr^{-1} between 2020 and 2050 in modelled scenarios that limit warming to 2°C (>67%), and by about 7.7% yr^{-1} globally in scenarios that limit warming to 1.5°C (>50%) with no or limited overshoot.[16] (*high confidence*) {Figure 2.16, 2.2, 2.4, Table 3.4, 3.4, 6.3}

---

[13]   Sector definitions can be found in Annex II.9.1.

[14]   Land overall constituted a net sink of −6.6 (±4.6) GtCO$_2$ yr^{-1} for the period 2010–2019, comprising a gross sink of −12.5 (±3.2) GtCO$_2$ yr^{-1} resulting from responses of all land to both anthropogenic environmental change and natural climate variability, and net anthropogenic CO$_2$-LULUCF emissions +5.7 (±4.0) GtCO$_2$ yr^{-1} based on bookkeeping models. {Table 2.1, 7.2, Table 7.1}

[15]   This estimate is based on consumption-based accounting, including both direct emissions from within urban areas, and indirect emissions from outside urban areas related to the production of electricity, goods and services consumed in cities. These estimates include all CO$_2$ and CH$_4$ emission categories except for aviation and marine bunker fuels, land-use change, forestry and agriculture. {8.1, Annex I: Glossary}

[16]   See Box SPM.1 for the categorisation of modelled long-term emission scenarios based on projected temperature outcomes and associated probabilities adopted in this report.

B.3 **Regional contributions[17] to global GHG emissions continue to differ widely. Variations in regional, and national per capita emissions partly reflect different development stages, but they also vary widely at similar income levels. The 10% of households with the highest per capita emissions contribute a disproportionately large share of global household GHG emissions. At least 18 countries have sustained GHG emission reductions for longer than 10 years.** (*high confidence*) (Figure SPM.2) {Figure 1.1, Figure 2.9, Figure 2.10, Figure 2.25, 2.2, 2.3, 2.4, 2.5, 2.6, Figure TS.4, Figure TS.5}

B.3.1 GHG emissions trends over 1990–2019 vary widely across regions and over time, and across different stages of development, as shown in Figure SPM.2. Average global per capita net anthropogenic GHG emissions increased from 7.7 to 7.8 tCO_2-eq, ranging from 2.6 tCO_2-eq to 19 tCO_2-eq across regions. Least developed countries (LDCs) and Small Island Developing States (SIDS) have much lower per capita emissions (1.7 tCO_2-eq and 4.6 tCO_2-eq, respectively) than the global average (6.9 tCO_2-eq), excluding CO_2-LULUCF.[18] (*high confidence*) (Figure SPM.2) {Figure1.2, Figure 2.9, Figure 2.10, 2.2, Figure TS.4}

B.3.2 Historical contributions to cumulative net anthropogenic CO_2 emissions between 1850 and 2019 vary substantially across regions in terms of total magnitude, but also in terms of contributions to CO_2-FFI (1650 ± 73 $GtCO_2$-eq) and net CO_2-LULUCF (760 ± 220 $GtCO_2$-eq) emissions.[10] Globally, the major share of cumulative CO_2-FFI emissions is concentrated in a few regions, while cumulative CO_2-LULUCF[9] emissions are concentrated in other regions. LDCs contributed less than 0.4% of historical cumulative CO_2-FFI emissions between 1850 and 2019, while SIDS contributed 0.5%. (*high confidence*) (Figure SPM.2) {Figure 2.10, 2.2, TS.3, Figure 2.7}

B.3.3 In 2019, around 48% of the global population lives in countries emitting on average more than 6 tCO_2-eq per capita, excluding CO_2-LULUCF. 35% live in countries emitting more than 9 tCO_2-eq per capita. Another 41% live in countries emitting less than 3 tCO_2-eq per capita. A substantial share of the population in these low-emitting countries lack access to modern energy services.[19] Eradicating extreme poverty, energy poverty, and providing decent living standards[20] to all in these regions in the context of achieving sustainable development objectives, in the near-term, can be achieved without significant global emissions growth. (*high confidence*) (Figure SPM.2) {Figure 1.2, 2.2, 2.4, 2.6, 3.7, 4.2, 6.7, Figure TS.4, Figure TS.5}

B.3.4 Globally, the 10% of households with the highest per capita emissions contribute 34–45% of global consumption-based household GHG emissions,[21] while the middle 40% contribute 40–53%, and the bottom 50% contribute 13–15%. (*high confidence*) {2.6, Figure 2.25}

B.3.5 At least 18 countries have sustained production-based GHG and consumption-based CO_2 emission reductions for longer than 10 years. Reductions were linked to energy supply decarbonisation, energy efficiency gains, and energy demand reduction, which resulted from both policies and changes in economic structure. Some countries have reduced production-based GHG emissions by a third or more since peaking, and some have achieved several years of consecutive reduction rates of around 4% yr^{-1}, comparable to global reductions in scenarios limiting warming to 2°C (>67%) or lower. These reductions have only partly offset global emissions growth. (*high confidence*) (Figure SPM.2) {Figure TS.4, 2.2, 1.3.2}

---

17 See Annex II, Part 1 for regional groupings adopted in this report.

18 In 2019, LDCs are estimated to have emitted 3.3% of global GHG emissions, and SIDS are estimated to have emitted 0.6% of global GHG emissions, excluding CO_2-LULUCF. These country groupings cut across geographic regions and are not depicted separately in Figure SPM.2. {Figure 2.10}

19 In this report, access to modern energy services is defined as access to clean, reliable and affordable energy services for cooking and heating, lighting, communications, and productive uses. {Annex I: Glossary}

20 In this report, decent living standards are defined as a set of minimum material requirements essential for achieving basic human well-being, including nutrition, shelter, basic living conditions, clothing, health care, education, and mobility. {5.1}

21 Consumption-based emissions refer to emissions released to the atmosphere to generate the goods and services consumed by a certain entity (e.g., a person, firm, country, or region). The bottom 50% of emitters spend less than USD3 PPP (purchasing power parity) per capita per day. The top 10% of emitters (an open-ended category) spend more than USD23 PPP per capita per day. The wide range of estimates for the contribution of the top 10% results from the wide range of spending in this category and differing methods in the assessed literature. {2.6, Annex I: Glossary}

Emissions have grown in most regions but are distributed unevenly, both in the present day and cumulatively since 1850.

a. Global net anthropogenic GHG emissions by region (1990–2019)

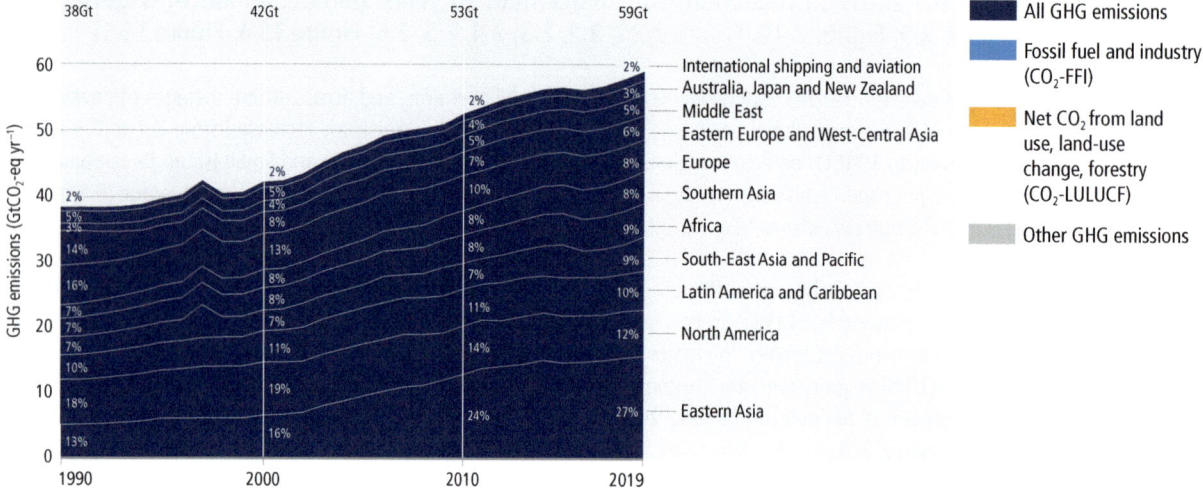

b. Historical cumulative net anthropogenic CO_2 emissions per region (1850–2019)

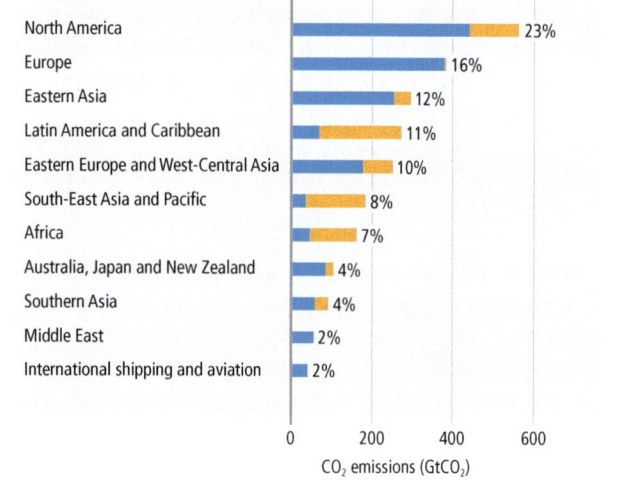

c. Net anthropogenic GHG emissions per capita and for total population, per region (2019)

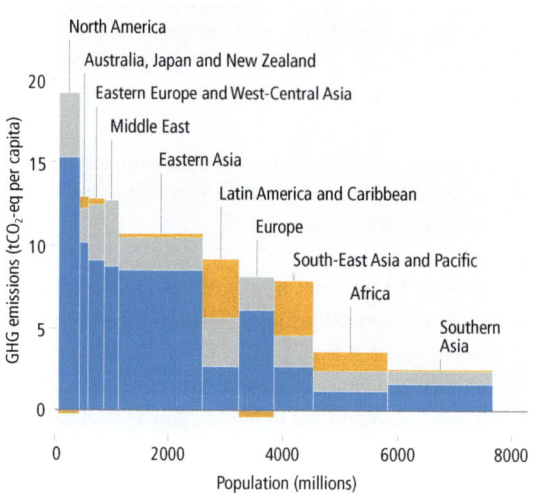

d. Regional indicators (2019) and regional production vs consumption accounting (2018)

	Africa	Australia, Japan, New Zealand	Eastern Asia	Eastern Europe, West-Central Asia	Europe	Latin America and Caribbean	Middle East	North America	South-East Asia and Pacific	Southern Asia
Population (million persons, 2019)	1292	157	1471	291	620	646	252	366	674	1836
GDP per capita (USD1000ppp2017 per person)[1]	5.0	43	17	20	43	15	20	61	12	6.2
Net GHG 2019[2] (production basis)										
% GHG contributions	9%	3%	27%	6%	8%	10%	5%	12%	9%	8%
GHG emissions intensity (tCO2-eq / USD1000ppp 2017)	0.78	0.30	0.62	0.64	0.18	0.61	0.64	0.31	0.65	0.42
GHG per capita (tCO2-eq per person)	3.9	13	11	13	7.8	9.2	13	19	7.9	2.6
CO2-FFI, 2018, per person										
Production-based emissions (tCO2-FFI per person, based on 2018 data)	1.2	10	8.4	9.2	6.5	2.8	8.7	16	2.6	1.6
Consumption-based emissions (tCO2-FFI per person, based on 2018 data)	0.84	11	6.7	6.2	7.8	2.8	7.6	17	2.5	1.5

[1] GDP per capita in 2019 in USD2017 currency purchasing power basis.
[2] Includes CO2-FFI, CO2-LULUCF and Other GHGs, excluding international aviation and shipping.

The regional groupings used in this figure are for statistical purposes only and are described in Annex II, Part I.

Figure SPM.2 | Regional GHG emissions, and the regional proportion of total cumulative production-based CO_2 emissions from 1850 to 2019.

Figure SPM.2 (continued): Regional GHG emissions, and the regional proportion of total cumulative production-based CO$_2$ emissions from 1850 to 2019. Panel a shows global net anthropogenic GHG emissions by region (in GtCO$_2$-eq yr^{-1} (GWP100-AR6)) for the time period 1990–2019.[6] Percentage values refer to the contribution of each region to total GHG emissions in each respective time period. The single-year peak of emissions in 1997 was due to higher CO$_2$-LULUCF emissions from a forest and peat fire event in South East Asia. Regions are as grouped in Annex II. **Panel b** shows the share of historical cumulative net anthropogenic CO$_2$ emissions per region from 1850 to 2019 in GtCO$_2$. This includes CO$_2$ from fossil fuel combustion and industrial processes (CO$_2$-FFI) and net CO$_2$ emissions from land use, land-use change, forestry (CO$_2$-LULUCF). Other GHG emissions are not included.[6] CO$_2$-LULUCF emissions are subject to high uncertainties, reflected by a global uncertainty estimate of ±70% (90% confidence interval). **Panel c** shows the distribution of regional GHG emissions in tonnes CO$_2$-eq per capita by region in 2019. GHG emissions are categorised into: CO$_2$-FFI; net CO$_2$-LULUCF; and other GHG emissions (methane, nitrous oxide, fluorinated gases, expressed in CO$_2$-eq using GWP100-AR6). The height of each rectangle shows per capita emissions, the width shows the population of the region, so that the area of the rectangles refers to the total emissions for each region. Emissions from international aviation and shipping are not included. In the case of two regions, the area for CO$_2$-LULUCF is below the axis, indicating net CO$_2$ removals rather than emissions. CO$_2$-LULUCF emissions are subject to high uncertainties, reflected by a global uncertainty estimate of ±70% (90% confidence interval). **Panel d** shows population, GDP per person, emission indicators by region in 2019 for percentage GHG contributions, total GHG per person, and total GHG emissions intensity, together with production-based and consumption-based CO$_2$-FFI data, which is assessed in this report up to 2018. Consumption-based emissions are emissions released to the atmosphere in order to generate the goods and services consumed by a certain entity (e.g., region). Emissions from international aviation and shipping are not included. {1.3, Figure 1.2, 2.2, Figure 2.9, Figure 2.10, Figure 2.11, Annex II}

B.4   **The unit costs of several low-emission technologies have fallen continuously since 2010. Innovation policy packages have enabled these cost reductions and supported global adoption. Both tailored policies and comprehensive policies addressing innovation systems have helped overcome the distributional, environmental and social impacts potentially associated with global diffusion of low-emission technologies. Innovation has lagged in developing countries due to weaker enabling conditions. Digitalisation can enable emission reductions, but can have adverse side effects unless appropriately governed. (*high confidence*) (Figure SPM.3) {2.2, 6.3, 6.4, 7.2, 12.2, 16.2, 16.4, 16.5, Cross-Chapter Box 11 in Chapter 16}**

B.4.1   From 2010 to 2019, there have been sustained decreases in the unit costs of solar energy (85%), wind energy (55%), and lithium-ion batteries (85%), and large increases in their deployment, e.g., >10× for solar and >100× for electric vehicles (EVs), varying widely across regions (Figure SPM.3). The mix of policy instruments which reduced costs and stimulated adoption includes public R&D, funding for demonstration and pilot projects, and demand pull instruments such as deployment subsidies to attain scale. In comparison to modular small-unit size technologies, the empirical record shows that multiple large-scale mitigation technologies, with fewer opportunities for learning, have seen minimal cost reductions and their adoption has grown slowly. (*high confidence*) {1.3, 1.5, Figure 2.5, 2.5, 6.3, 6.4, 7.2, 11.3, 12.2, 12.3, 12.6, 13.6, 16.3, 16.4, 16.6}

B.4.2   Policy packages tailored to national contexts and technological characteristics have been effective in supporting low-emission innovation and technology diffusion. Appropriately designed policies and governance have helped address distributional impacts and rebound effects. Innovation has provided opportunities to lower emissions and reduce emission growth and created social and environmental co-benefits (*high confidence*). Adoption of low-emission technologies lags in most developing countries, particularly least developed ones, due in part to weaker enabling conditions, including limited finance, technology development and transfer, and capacity. In many countries, especially those with limited institutional capacities, several adverse side effects have been observed as a result of diffusion of low-emission technology, for example, low-value employment, and dependency on foreign knowledge and suppliers. Low-emission innovation along with strengthened enabling conditions can reinforce development benefits, which can, in turn, create feedbacks towards greater public support for policy. (*medium confidence*) {9.9, 13.6, 13.7, 16.3, 16.4, 16.5, 16.6, Cross-Chapter Box 12 in Chapter 16, TS.3}

B.4.3   Digital technologies can contribute to mitigation of climate change and the achievement of several SDGs (*high confidence*). For example, sensors, internet of things, robotics, and artificial intelligence can improve energy management in all sectors, increase energy efficiency, and promote the adoption of many low-emission technologies, including decentralised renewable energy, while creating economic opportunities (*high confidence*). However, some of these climate change mitigation gains can be reduced or counterbalanced by growth in demand for goods and services due to the use of digital devices (*high confidence*). Digitalisation can involve trade-offs across several SDGs, for example, increasing electronic waste, negative impacts on labour markets, and exacerbating the existing digital divide. Digital technology supports decarbonisation only if appropriately governed (*high confidence*). {5.3, 10, 12.6, 16.2, Cross-Chapter Box 11 in Chapter 16, TS.5, Box TS.14}

The unit costs of some forms of renewable energy and of batteries for passenger EVs have fallen, and their use continues to rise.

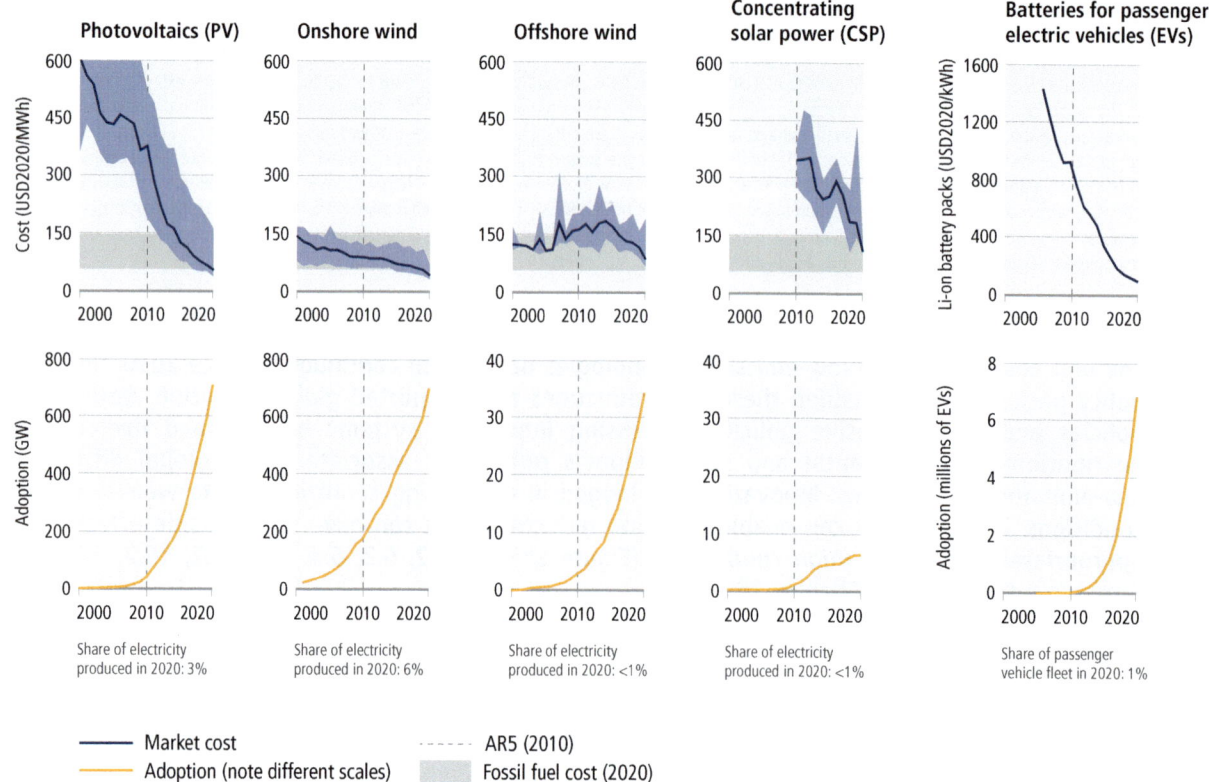

Figure SPM.3 | Unit cost reductions and use in some rapidly changing mitigation technologies. The **top panel** shows global costs per unit of energy (USD per MWh) for some rapidly changing mitigation technologies. Solid blue lines indicate average unit cost in each year. Light blue shaded areas show the range between the 5th and 95th percentiles in each year. Grey shading indicates the range of unit costs for new fossil fuel (coal and gas) power in 2020 (corresponding to USD55–148 per MWh). In 2020, the levelised costs of energy (LCOE) of the four renewable energy technologies could compete with fossil fuels in many places. For batteries, costs shown are for 1 kWh of battery storage capacity; for the others, costs are LCOE, which includes installation, capital, operations, and maintenance costs per MWh of electricity produced. The literature uses LCOE because it allows consistent comparisons of cost trends across a diverse set of energy technologies to be made. However, it does not include the costs of grid integration or climate impacts. Further, LCOE does not take into account other environmental and social externalities that may modify the overall (monetary and non-monetary) costs of technologies and alter their deployment. The **bottom panel** shows cumulative global adoption for each technology, in GW of installed capacity for renewable energy and in millions of vehicles for battery-electric vehicles. A vertical dashed line is placed in 2010 to indicate the change since AR5. Shares of electricity produced and share of passenger vehicle fleet are indicated in text for 2020 based on provisional data, i.e., percentage of total electricity production (for PV, onshore wind, offshore wind, CSP) and of total stock of passenger vehicles (for EVs). The electricity production share reflects different capacity factors; for example, for the same amount of installed capacity, wind produces about twice as much electricity as solar PV. {2.5, 6.4} Renewable energy and battery technologies were selected as illustrative examples because they have recently shown rapid changes in costs and adoption, and because consistent data are available. Other mitigation options assessed in the report are not included as they do not meet these criteria.

B.5   **There has been a consistent expansion of policies and laws addressing mitigation since AR5. This has led to the avoidance of emissions that would otherwise have occurred and increased investment in low-GHG technologies and infrastructure. Policy coverage of emissions is uneven across sectors. Progress on the alignment of financial flows towards the goals of the Paris Agreement remains slow and tracked climate finance flows are distributed unevenly across regions and sectors.** (*high confidence*) {5.6, 13.2, 13.4, 13.5, 13.6, 13.9, 14.3, 14.4, 14.5, Cross-Chapter Box 10 in Chapter 14, 15.3, 15.5}

B.5.1   The Kyoto Protocol led to reduced emissions in some countries and was instrumental in building national and international capacity for GHG reporting, accounting and emissions markets (*high confidence*). At least 18 countries that had Kyoto targets for the first commitment period have had sustained absolute emission reductions for at least a decade from 2005, of which two were countries with economies in transition (*very high confidence*). The Paris Agreement, with near universal participation, has led to policy development and target-setting at national and sub-national levels, in particular in relation to mitigation, as well as enhanced transparency of climate action and support (*medium confidence*). {14.3, 14.6}

B.5.2   The application of diverse policy instruments for mitigation at the national and sub-national levels has grown consistently across a range of sectors (*high confidence*). By 2020, over 20% of global GHG emissions were covered by carbon taxes or emissions trading systems, although coverage and prices have been insufficient to achieve deep reductions (*medium confidence*). By 2020, there were 'direct' climate laws focused primarily on GHG reductions in 56 countries covering 53% of global emissions (*medium confidence*). Policy coverage remains limited for emissions from agriculture and the production of industrial materials and feedstocks (*high confidence*). {5.6, 7.6, 11.5, 11.6, 13.2, 13.6}

B.5.3   In many countries, policies have enhanced energy efficiency, reduced rates of deforestation and accelerated technology deployment, leading to avoided and in some cases reduced or removed emissions (*high confidence*). Multiple lines of evidence suggest that mitigation policies have led to avoided global emissions of several $GtCO_2$-eq yr^{-1} (*medium confidence*). At least 1.8 $GtCO_2$-eq yr^{-1} can be accounted for by aggregating separate estimates for the effects of economic and regulatory instruments. Growing numbers of laws and executive orders have impacted global emissions and were estimated to result in 5.9 $GtCO_2$-eq yr^{-1} less emissions in 2016 than they otherwise would have been. (*medium confidence*) (Figure SPM.3) {2.2, 2.8, 6.7, 7.6, 9.9, 10.8, 13.6, Cross-chapter Box 10 in Chapter 14}

B.5.4   Annual tracked total financial flows for climate mitigation and adaptation increased by up to 60% between 2013/14 and 2019/20 (in USD2015), but average growth has slowed since 2018[22] (*medium confidence*). These financial flows remained heavily focused on mitigation, are uneven, and have developed heterogeneously across regions and sectors (*high confidence*). In 2018, public and publicly mobilised private climate finance flows from developed to developing countries were below the collective goal under the UNFCCC and Paris Agreement to mobilise USD100 billion per year by 2020 in the context of meaningful mitigation action and transparency on implementation (*medium confidence*). Public and private finance flows for fossil fuels are still greater than those for climate adaptation and mitigation (*high confidence*). Markets for green bonds, ESG (environmental, social and governance) and sustainable finance products have expanded significantly since AR5. Challenges remain, in particular around integrity and additionality, as well as the limited applicability of these markets to many developing countries. (*high confidence*) {Box 15.4, 15.3, 15.5, 15.6, Box 15.7}

---

[22]   Estimates of financial flows (comprising both private and public, domestic and international flows) are based on a single report which assembles data from multiple sources and which has applied various changes to their methodology over the past years. Such data can suggest broad trends but is subject to uncertainties.

B.6 **Global GHG emissions in 2030 associated with the implementation of Nationally Determined Contributions (NDCs) announced prior to COP26[23] would make it *likely* that warming will exceed 1.5°C during the 21st century.[24] *Likely* limiting warming to below 2°C would then rely on a rapid acceleration of mitigation efforts after 2030. Policies implemented by the end of 2020[25] are projected to result in higher global GHG emissions than those implied by NDCs. (*high confidence*) (Figure SPM.4) {3.3, 3.5, 4.2, Cross-Chapter Box 4 in Chapter 4}**

B.6.1 Policies implemented by the end of 2020 are projected to result in higher global GHG emissions than those implied by NDCs, indicating an implementation gap. A gap remains between global GHG emissions in 2030 associated with the implementation of NDCs announced prior to COP26 and those associated with modelled mitigation pathways assuming immediate action (for quantification see Table SPM.1).[26] The magnitude of the emissions gap depends on the global warming level considered and whether only unconditional or also conditional elements of NDCs[27] are considered.[28] (*high confidence*) {3.5, 4.2, Cross-Chapter Box 4 in Chapter 4}

B.6.2 Global emissions in 2030 associated with the implementation of NDCs announced prior to COP26 are lower than the emissions implied by the original NDCs[29] (*high confidence*). The original emissions gap has fallen by about 20% to one-third relative to pathways that limit warming to 2°C (>67%) with immediate action (category C3a in Table SPM.2), and by about 15–20% relative to pathways limiting warming to 1.5°C (>50%) with no or limited overshoot (category C1 in Table SPM.2) (*medium confidence*). (Figure SPM.4) {3.5, 4.2, Cross-Chapter Box 4 in Chapter 4}

Table SPM.1 | Projected global emissions in 2030 associated with policies implemented by the end of 2020 and NDCs announced prior to COP26, and associated emissions gaps. *Emissions projections for 2030 and absolute differences in emissions are based on emissions of 52–56 $GtCO_2$-eq yr^{-1} in 2019 as assumed in underlying model studies. (*medium confidence*) {4.2, Table 4.3, Cross-Chapter Box 4 in Chapter 4}

	Implied by policies implemented by the end of 2020 ($GtCO_2$-eq yr^{-1})	Implied by NDCs announced prior to COP26	
		Unconditional elements ($GtCO_2$-eq yr^{-1})	Including conditional elements ($GtCO_2$-eq yr^{-1})
Median projected global emissions (min–max)*	57 [52–60]	53 [50–57]	50 [47–55]
Implementation gap between implemented policies and NDCs (median)		4	7
Emissions gap between NDCs and pathways that limit warming to 2°C (>67%) with immediate action		10–16	6–14
Emissions gap between NDCs and pathways that limit warming to 1.5°C (>50%) with no or limited overshoot with immediate action		19–26	16–23

[23] NDCs announced prior to COP26 refer to the most recent Nationally Determined Contributions submitted to the UNFCCC up to the literature cut-off date of this report, 11 October 2021, and revised NDCs announced by China, Japan and the Republic of Korea prior to October 2021 but only submitted thereafter. 25 NDC updates were submitted between 12 October 2021 and the start of COP26.

[24] This implies that mitigation after 2030 can no longer establish a pathway with less than 67% probability to exceed 1.5°C during the 21st century, a defining feature of the class of pathways that limit warming to 1.5°C (>50%) with no or limited overshoot assessed in this report (category C1 in Table SPM.2). These pathways limit warming to 1.6°C or lower throughout the 21st century with a 50% likelihood.

[25] The policy cut-off date in studies used to project GHG emissions of 'policies implemented by the end of 2020' varies between July 2019 and November 2020. {Table 4.2}

[26] Immediate action in modelled global pathways refers to the adoption between 2020 and at latest before 2025 of climate policies intended to limit global warming to a given level. Modelled pathways that limit warming to 2°C (>67%) based on immediate action are summarised in category C3a in Table SPM.2. All assessed modelled global pathways that limit warming to 1.5°C (>50%) with no or limited overshoot assume immediate action as defined here (Category C1 in Table SPM.2).

[27] In this report, 'unconditional' elements of NDCs refer to mitigation efforts put forward without any conditions. 'Conditional' elements refer to mitigation efforts that are contingent on international cooperation, for example bilateral and multilateral agreements, financing or monetary and/or technological transfers. This terminology is used in the literature and the UNFCCC's NDC Synthesis Reports, not by the Paris Agreement. {4.2.1, 14.3.2}

[28] Two types of gaps are assessed: the implementation gap is calculated as the difference between the median of global emissions in 2030 implied by policies implemented by the end of 2020 and those implied by NDCs announced prior to COP26. The emissions gap is calculated as the difference between GHG emissions implied by the NDCs (minimum/maximum emissions in 2030) and the median of global GHG emissions in modelled pathways limiting warming to specific levels based on immediate action and with stated likelihoods as indicated (Table SPM.2).

[29] Original NDCs refer to those submitted to the UNFCCC in 2015 and 2016. Unconditional elements of NDCs announced prior to COP26 imply global GHG emissions in 2030 that are 3.8 [3.0–5.3] $GtCO_2$-eq yr^{-1} lower than those from the original NDCs, and 4.5 [2.7–6.3] $GtCO_2$-eq yr^{-1} lower when conditional elements of NDCs are included. NDC updates at or after COP26 could further change the implied emissions.

B.6.3 Modelled global emission pathways consistent with NDCs announced prior to COP26 that limit warming to 2°C (>67%) (category C3b in Table SPM.2) imply annual average global GHG emissions reduction rates of 0–0.7 GtCO$_2$-eq yr^{-1} during the decade 2020–2030, with an unprecedented acceleration to 1.4–2.0 GtCO$_2$-eq yr^{-1} during 2030–2050 (*medium confidence*). Continued investments in unabated high-emitting infrastructure and limited development and deployment of low-emitting alternatives prior to 2030 would act as barriers to this acceleration and increase feasibility risks (*high confidence*). {3.3, 3.5, 3.8, Cross-Chapter Box 5 in Chapter 4}

B.6.4 Modelled global emission pathways consistent with NDCs announced prior to COP26 will *likely* exceed 1.5°C during the 21st century. Those pathways that then return warming to 1.5°C by 2100 with a likelihood of 50% or greater imply a temperature overshoot of 0.15°C–0.3°C (42 pathways in category C2 in Table SPM.2). In such pathways, global cumulative net-negative CO$_2$ emissions are −380 [−860 to −200] GtCO$_2$[30] in the second half of the century, and there is a rapid acceleration of other mitigation efforts across all sectors after 2030. Such overshoot pathways imply increased climate-related risk, and are subject to increased feasibility concerns,[31] and greater social and environmental risks, compared to pathways that limit warming to 1.5°C (>50%) with no or limited overshoot. (*high confidence*) (Figure SPM.4, Table SPM.2) {3.3, 3.5, 3.8, 12.3; AR6 WGII SPM B.6}

Projected global GHG emissions from NDCs announced prior to COP26 would make it *likely* that warming will exceed 1.5°C and also make it harder after 2030 to limit warming to below 2°C.

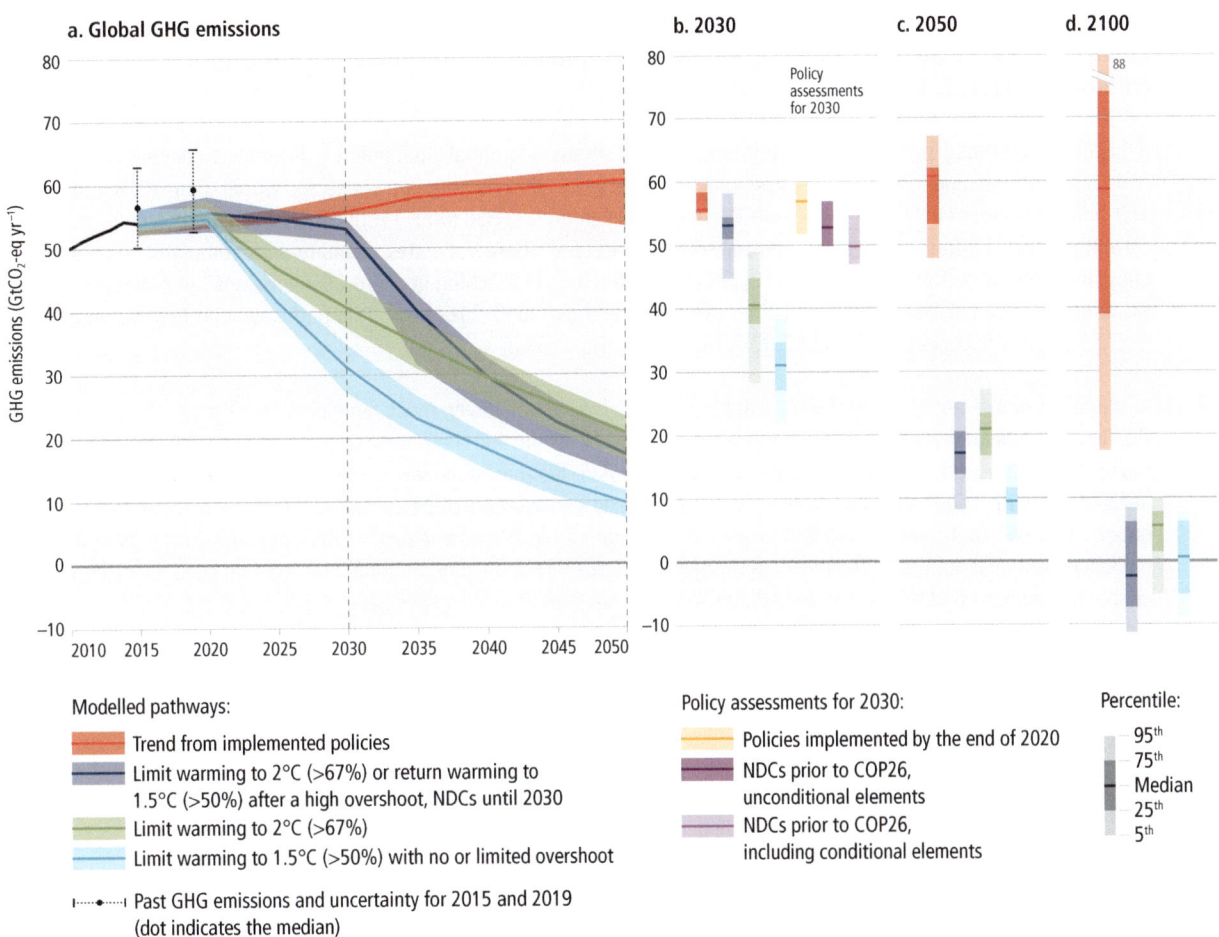

Figure SPM.4 | Global GHG emissions of modelled pathways (funnels in Panel a, and associated bars in Panels b, c, d) and projected emission outcomes from near-term policy assessments for 2030 (Panel b).

---

[30] Median and *very likely* range [5th to 95th percentile].

[31] Returning to below 1.5°C in 2100 from GHG emissions levels in 2030 associated with the implementation of NDCs is infeasible for some models due to model-specific constraints on the deployment of mitigation technologies and the availability of net negative CO$_2$ emissions.

Figure SPM.4 (continued): Global GHG emissions of modelled pathways (funnels in Panel a, and associated bars in Panels b, c, d) and projected emission outcomes from near-term policy assessments for 2030 (Panel b). Panel a shows global GHG emissions over 2015–2050 for four types of assessed modelled global pathways:

- Trend from implemented policies: Pathways with projected near-term GHG emissions in line with policies implemented until the end of 2020 and extended with comparable ambition levels beyond 2030 (29 scenarios across categories C5–C7, Table SPM.2).

- Limit to 2°C (>67%) or return warming to 1.5°C (>50%) after a high overshoot, NDCs until 2030: Pathways with GHG emissions until 2030 associated with the implementation of NDCs announced prior to COP26, followed by accelerated emissions reductions *likely* to limit warming to 2°C (C3b, Table SPM.2) or to return warming to 1.5°C with a probability of 50% or greater after high overshoot (subset of 42 scenarios from C2, Table SPM.2).

- Limit to 2°C (>67%) with immediate action: Pathways that limit warming to 2°C (>67%) with immediate action after 2020[26] (C3a, Table SPM.2).

- Limit to 1.5°C (>50%) with no or limited overshoot: Pathways limiting warming to 1.5°C with no or limited overshoot (C1, Table SPM.2 C1). All these pathways assume immediate action after 2020.

Past GHG emissions for 2010–2015 used to project global warming outcomes of the modelled pathways are shown by a black line[32] and past global GHG emissions in 2015 and 2019 as assessed in Chapter 2 are shown by whiskers. **Panels b, c and d** show snapshots of the GHG emission ranges of the modelled pathways in 2030, 2050, and 2100, respectively. Panel b also shows projected emissions outcomes from near-term policy assessments in 2030 from Chapter 4.2 (Tables 4.2 and 4.3; median and full range). GHG emissions are in CO_2-equivalent using GWP100 from AR6 WGI. {3.5, 4.2, Table 4.2, Table 4.3, Cross-Chapter Box 4 in Chapter 4}

B.7   **Projected cumulative future CO_2 emissions over the lifetime of existing and currently planned fossil fuel infrastructure without additional abatement exceed the total cumulative net CO_2 emissions in pathways that limit warming to 1.5°C (>50%) with no or limited overshoot. They are approximately equal to total cumulative net CO_2 emissions in pathways that limit warming to 2°C (>67%). (*high confidence*) {2.7, 3.3}**

B.7.1   If historical operating patterns are maintained,[33] and without additional abatement,[34] estimated cumulative future CO_2 emissions from existing fossil fuel infrastructure, the majority of which is in the power sector, would, from 2018 until the end of its lifetime, amount to 660 [460–890] $GtCO_2$. They would amount to 850 [600–1100] $GtCO_2$ when unabated emissions from currently planned infrastructure in the power sector is included. These estimates compare with cumulative global net CO_2 emissions from all sectors of 510 [330–710] $GtCO_2$ until the time of reaching net zero CO_2 emissions[35] in pathways that limit warming to 1.5°C (>50%) with no or limited overshoot, and 890 [640–1160] $GtCO_2$ in pathways that limit warming to 2°C (>67%). (*high confidence*) (Table SPM.2) {2.7, Figure 2.26, Figure TS.8}

B.7.2   In modelled global pathways that limit warming to 2°C (>67%) or lower, most remaining fossil fuel CO_2 emissions until the time of global net zero CO_2 emissions are projected to occur outside the power sector, mainly in industry and transport. Decommissioning and reduced utilisation of existing fossil fuel-based power sector infrastructure, retrofitting existing installations with CCS,[36] switches to low-carbon fuels, and cancellation of new coal installations without CCS are major options that can contribute to aligning future CO_2 emissions from the power sector with emissions in the assessed global modelled least-cost pathways. The most appropriate strategies will depend on national and regional circumstances, including enabling conditions and technology availability. (*high confidence*) (Box SPM.1) {Table 2.7, 2.7, 3.4, 6.3, 6.5, 6.7}

---

[32] See Box SPM.1 for a description of the approach to project global warming outcomes of modelled pathways and its consistency with the climate assessment in AR6 WGI.

[33] Historical operating patterns are described by load factors and lifetimes of fossil fuel installations as observed in the past (average and range).

[34] Abatement here refers to human interventions that reduce the amount of greenhouse gases that are released from fossil fuel infrastructure to the atmosphere.

[35] Total cumulative CO_2 emissions up to the time of global net zero CO_2 emissions are similar but not identical to the remaining carbon budget for a given temperature limit assessed by Working Group I. This is because the modelled emission scenarios assessed by Working Group III cover a range of temperature levels up to a specific limit, and exhibit a variety of reductions in non-CO_2 emissions that also contribute to overall warming. {Box 3.4}

[36] In this context, capture rates of new installations with CCS are assumed to be 90–95%+ {11.3.5}. Capture rates for retrofit installations can be comparable, if plants are specifically designed for CCS retrofits {11.3.6}.

C.   System Transformations to Limit Global Warming

C.1   **Global GHG emissions are projected to peak between 2020 and at the latest before 2025 in global modelled pathways that limit warming to 1.5°C (>50%) with no or limited overshoot and in those that limit warming to 2°C (>67%) and assume immediate action (see Table SPM.2 footnote i).[37] In both types of modelled pathways, rapid and deep GHG emissions reductions follow throughout 2030, 2040 and 2050 (*high confidence*). Without a strengthening of policies beyond those that are implemented by the end of 2020, GHG emissions are projected to rise beyond 2025, leading to a median global warming of 3.2 [2.2 to 3.5] °C by 2100[38,39] (*medium confidence*). (Table SPM.2, Figure SPM.4, Figure SPM.5) {3.3, 3.4}**

C.1.1   Net global GHG emissions are projected to fall from 2019 levels by 27% [13–45%] by 2030 and 63% [52–76%][40] by 2050 in global modelled pathways that limit warming to 2°C (>67%) and assuming immediate action (category C3a, Table SPM.2). This compares with reductions of 43% [34–60%] by 2030 and 84% [73–98%] by 2050 in pathways that limit warming to 1.5°C (>50%) with no or limited overshoot (C1, Table SPM.2) (*high confidence*).[41] In modelled pathways that return warming to 1.5°C (>50%) after a high overshoot,[42] GHG emissions are reduced by 23% [0–44%] in 2030 and by 75% [62–91%] in 2050 (C2, Table SPM.2) (*high confidence*). Modelled pathways that are consistent with NDCs announced prior to COP26 until 2030 and assume no increase in ambition thereafter have higher emissions, leading to a median global warming of 2.8 [2.1–3.4] °C by 2100 (*medium confidence*).[23] (Figure SPM.4) {3.3}

C.1.2   In modelled pathways that limit warming to 2°C (>67%) assuming immediate action, global net CO_2 emissions are reduced compared to modelled 2019 emissions by 27% [11–46%] in 2030 and by 52% [36–70%] in 2040; and global CH_4 emissions are reduced by 24% [9–53%] in 2030 and by 37% [20–60%] in 2040. In pathways that limit warming to 1.5°C (>50%) with no or limited overshoot global net CO_2 emissions are reduced compared to modelled 2019 emissions by 48% [36–69%] in 2030 and by 80% [61–109%] in 2040; and global CH_4 emissions are reduced by 34% [21–57%] in 2030 and 44% [31–63%] in 2040. There are similar reductions of non-CO_2 emissions by 2050 in both types of pathways: CH_4 is reduced by 45% [25–70%]; N_2O is reduced by 20% [–5 to +55%]; and F-gases are reduced by 85% [20–90%].[43] Across most modelled pathways, this is the maximum technical potential for anthropogenic CH_4 reductions in the underlying models (*high confidence*). Further emissions reductions, as illustrated by the IMP-SP pathway, may be achieved through changes in activity levels and/or technological innovations beyond those represented in the majority of the pathways (*medium confidence*). Higher emissions reductions of CH_4 could further reduce peak warming. (*high confidence*) (Figure SPM.5) {3.3}

C.1.3   In modelled pathways consistent with the continuation of policies implemented by the end of 2020, GHG emissions continue to rise, leading to global warming of 3.2 [2.2–3.5] °C by 2100 (within C5–C7, Table SPM.2) (*medium confidence*). Pathways that exceed warming of >4°C (≥50%) (C8, SSP5-8.5, Table SPM.2) would imply a reversal of current technology and/or mitigation policy trends (*medium confidence*). Such warming could occur in emission pathways consistent with policies implemented by the end of 2020 if climate sensitivity is higher than central estimates (*high confidence*). (Table SPM.2, Figure SPM.4) {3.3, Box 3.3}

---

[37]   All reported warming levels are relative to the period 1850–1900. If not otherwise specified, 'pathways' always refer to pathways computed with a model. Immediate action in the pathways refers to the adoption of climate policies between 2020 and at latest 2025 intended to limit global warming at a given level.

[38]   Long-term warming is calculated from all modelled pathways assuming mitigation efforts consistent with national policies that were implemented by the end of 2020 (scenarios that fall into policy category P1b of Chapter 3) and that pass through the 2030 GHG emissions ranges of such pathways assessed in Chapter 4 (see footnote 25). {3.2, Table 4.2}

[39]   Warming estimates refer to the 50th and [5th–95th] percentile across the modelled pathways and the median temperature change estimate of the probabilistic WGI climate model emulators (see Table SPM.2 footnote a).

[40]   In this report, emissions reductions are reported relative to 2019 modelled emission levels, while in SR1.5 emissions reductions were calculated relative to 2010. Between 2010 and 2019 global GHG and global CO_2 emissions have grown by 12% (6.5 $GtCO_2$-eq) and 13% (5.0 $GtCO_2$) respectively. In global modelled pathways assessed in this report that limit warming to 1.5°C (>50%) with no or limited overshoot, GHG emissions are projected to be reduced by 37% [28–57%] in 2030 relative to 2010. In the same type of pathways assessed in SR1.5, reported GHG emissions reductions in 2030 were 39–51% (interquartile range) relative to 2010. In absolute terms, the 2030 GHG emissions levels of pathways that limit warming to 1.5°C (>50%) with no or limited overshoot are higher in AR6 (31 [21–36] $GtCO_2$-eq) than in SR1.5 (28 [26–31 interquartile range] $GtCO_2$-eq). (Figure SPM.1, Table SPM.2) {3.3, SR1.5 Figure SPM.3b}

[41]   Scenarios in this category limit peak warming to 2°C throughout the 21st century with close to, or more than, 90% likelihood.

[42]   This category contains 91 scenarios with immediate action and 42 scenarios that are consistent with the NDCs until 2030.

[43]   These numbers for CH_4, N_2O, and F-gases are rounded to the nearest 5% except numbers below 5%.

Table SPM.2 | Key characteristics of the modelled global emissions pathways. Summary of projected CO_2 and GHG emissions, projected net zero timings and the resulting global warming outcomes. Pathways are categorised (rows), according to their likelihood of limiting warming to different peak warming levels (if peak temperature occurs before 2100) and 2100 warming levels. Values shown are for the median [p50] and 5th–95th percentiles [p5–p95], noting that not all pathways achieve net zero CO_2 or GHGs.

Category[b,c,d] [# pathways]	Category/subset label[e,f]	WGI SSP & WGIII IPs/IMPs alignment[e,f]	GHG emissions (GtCO$_2$-eq yr⁻¹)[g] 2030	2040	2050	GHG emissions reductions from 2019 (%)[h] 2030	2040	2050	Peak CO$_2$ emissions (% peak before 2100)	Peak GHG emissions (% peak before 2100)	Net zero CO$_2$ (% net zero pathways)	Net zero GHGs (% net zero pathways)[k,l]	Cumulative CO$_2$ emissions (GtCO$_2$)[m] 2020 to net zero CO$_2$	2020–2100	Cumulative net-negative CO$_2$ emissions (GtCO$_2$) Year of net zero CO$_2$ to 2100	Global mean temperature changes 50% probability (°C)[n] at peak warming	2100	Likelihood of peak global warming staying below (%)[o] <1.5°C	<2.0°C	<3.0°C
C1 [97]	**limit warming to 1.5°C (>50%) with no or limited overshoot**		31 [21–36]	17 [6–23]	9 [1–15]	43 [34–60]	69 [58–90]	84 [73–98]	2020–2025 (100%) [2020–2025]			2095–2100 (52%) [2050–...]	510 [330–710]	320 [-210 to 570]	-220 [-660 to -20]	1.6 [1.4–1.6]	1.3 [1.1–1.5]	38 [33–58]	90 [86–97]	100 [99–100]
C1a [50]	... with net zero GHGs	SSP1-1.9, SP, LD	33 [22–37]	18 [6–24]	8 [0–15]	41 [31–59]	66 [58–89]	85 [72–100]			2050–2055 (100%) [2035–2070]	2070–2075 (100%) [2050–2090]	550 [340–760]	160 [-220 to 620]	-360 [-680 to -140]	1.6 [1.4–1.6]	1.2 [1.1–1.4]	38 [34–60]	90 [85–98]	100 [99–100]
C1b [47]	... without net zero GHGs	Ren	29 [21–36]	16 [7–21]	9 [4–13]	48 [35–61]	70 [62–87]	84 [76–93]			...–... [0%]	[...–...]	460 [320–590]	360 [10–540]	-60 [-440 to 0]	1.6 [1.5–1.6]	1.4 [1.3–1.5]	37 [33–56]	89 [87–96]	100 [99–100]
C2 [133]	**return warming to 1.5°C (>50%) after a high overshoot**	Neg	42 [31–55]	25 [17–34]	14 [5–21]	23 [0–44]	55 [40–71]	75 [62–91]	2020–2030 [2020–2030]	2020–2025 (100%) [2020–2025]	2055–2060 (100%) [2045–2070]	2070–2075 (87%) [2055–...]	720 [530–930]	400 [-90 to 620]	-360 [-680 to -60]	1.7 [1.5–1.8]	1.4 [1.2–1.5]	24 [15–42]	82 [71–93]	100 [99–100]
C3 [311]	**limit warming to 2°C (>67%)**		44 [32–55]	29 [20–36]	20 [13–26]	21 [1–42]	46 [34–63]	64 [53–77]	2020–2030 [2020–2030]	2020–2025 (100%) [2020–2025]	2070–2075 (93%) [2055–...]	...–... (30%) [2075–...]	890 [640–1160]	800 [510–1140]	-40 [-290 to 0]	1.7 [1.6–1.8]	1.6 [1.5–1.8]	20 [13–41]	76 [68–91]	99 [98–100]
C3a [204]	... with action starting in 2020	SSP1-2.6	40 [30–49]	29 [21–36]	20 [14–27]	27 [13–45]	47 [35–63]	63 [52–76]	2020–2025 (100%) [2020–2025]		2070–2075 (91%) [2055–...]	...–... (24%) [2080–...]	860 [640–1180]	790 [480–1150]	-30 [-280 to 0]	1.7 [1.6–1.8]	1.6 [1.5–1.8]	21 [14–42]	78 [69–91]	100 [98–100]

Column explanatory notes:

Category/subset label: Modelled global emissions pathways categorised by projected global warming levels (GWL). Detailed likelihood definitions are provided in SPM Box 1. The five illustrative scenarios (SSPx-yy) considered by AR6 WGI and the Illustrative (Mitigation) Pathways assessed in WGIII are aligned with the temperature categories and are indicated in a separate column. Global emission pathways contain regionally differentiated information. This assessment focuses on their global characteristics.

GHG emissions: Projected median annual GHG emissions in the year across the scenarios, with the 5th–95th percentile in brackets. Modelled GHG emissions in 2019: 55 [53–58] GtCO$_2$-eq.

GHG emissions reductions: Projected median GHG emissions reductions of pathways in the year across the scenarios compared to modelled 2019, with the 5th–95th percentile in brackets. Negative numbers indicate increase in emissions compared to 2019.

Emissions milestones (peak): Median 5-year intervals at which projected CO$_2$ & GHG emissions peak, with the 5th–95th percentile interval in square brackets. Percentage of peaking pathways is denoted in round brackets. Three dots (…) denotes emissions peak in 2100 or beyond for that percentile.

Emissions milestones (net zero): Median 5-year intervals at which projected CO$_2$ & GHG emissions of pathways in this category reach net zero, with the 5th–95th percentile interval in square brackets. Percentage of net zero pathways is denoted in round brackets. Three dots (…) denotes net zero not reached for that percentile.

Cumulative CO$_2$ emissions: Median cumulative net CO$_2$ emissions across the projected scenarios in this category until reaching net zero or until 2100, with the 5th–95th percentile interval in square brackets.

Cumulative net-negative CO$_2$ emissions: Median cumulative net-negative CO$_2$ emissions between the year of net zero CO$_2$ and 2100. More net-negative results in greater temperature declines after peak.

Global mean temperature changes: Projected temperature change of pathways in this category (50% probability across the range of climate uncertainties), relative to 1850–1900, at peak warming and in 2100, for the median value across the scenarios and the 5th–95th percentile interval in square brackets.

Likelihood of peak global warming staying below: Median likelihood that the projected pathways in this category stay below a given global warming level, with the 5th–95th percentile interval in square brackets.

Table SPM.2 (continued):

Modelled global emissions pathways categorised by projected global warming levels (GWL). Detailed likelihood definitions are provided in SPM Box 1.

The five illustrative scenarios (SSPx-yy) considered by AR6 WGI and the Illustrative (Mitigation) Pathways assessed in WGIII are aligned with the temperature categories and are indicated in a separate column. Global emission pathways contain regionally differentiated information. This assessment focuses on their global characteristics.

Category [# pathways]	Category/subset label	WGI SSP & WGIII IPs/IMPs alignment [e,f]	GHG emissions (GtCO₂-eq yr⁻¹) [g] 2030	2040	2050	GHG emissions reductions from 2019 (%) [h] 2030	2040	2050	Emissions milestones [i,j] Peak CO₂ emissions (% peak before 2100)	Peak GHG emissions (% peak before 2100)	Net zero CO₂ (% net zero pathways)	Net zero GHGs (% net zero pathways) [i,l]	Cumulative CO₂ emissions (GtCO₂) [m] 2020 to net zero CO₂	2020–2100	Cumulative net-negative CO₂ emissions (GtCO₂) Year of net zero CO₂ to 2100	Global mean temperature changes 50% probability (°C) [n] at peak warming	2100	Likelihood of peak global warming staying below (%) [o] <1.5°C	<2.0°C	<3.0°C
p50 [p5–p95] [a]			Projected median annual GHG emissions in the year across the scenarios, with the 5th–95th percentile in brackets. Modelled GHG emissions in 2019: 55 [53–58] GtCO₂-eq.			Projected median GHG emissions reductions of pathways in the year across the scenarios compared to modelled 2019, with the 5th–95th percentile in brackets. Negative numbers indicate increase in emissions compared to 2019.			Median 5-year intervals at which projected CO₂ & GHG emissions peak, with the 5th–95th percentile interval in square brackets. Percentage of peaking pathways is denoted in round brackets. Three dots (…) denotes emissions peak in 2100 or beyond for that percentile.		Median 5-year intervals at which projected CO₂ & GHG emissions of pathways in this category reach net zero, with the 5th–95th percentile interval in square brackets. Percentage of net zero pathways is denoted in round brackets. Three dots (…) denotes net zero not reached for that percentile.		Median cumulative net CO₂ emissions across the projected scenarios in this category until reaching net zero or until 2100, with the 5th–95th percentile interval in square brackets.		Median cumulative net-negative CO₂ emissions between the year of net zero CO₂ and 2100. More net-negative results in greater temperature declines after peak.	Projected temperature change of pathways in this category (50% probability across the range of climate uncertainties), relative to 1850–1900, at peak warming and in 2100, for the median value across the scenarios and the 5th–95th percentile interval in square brackets.		Median likelihood that the projected pathways in this category stay below a given global warming level, with the 5th–95th percentile interval in square brackets.		
C3b [97]	… NDCs until 2030	GS	52 [47–56]	29 [20–36]	18 [10–25]	5 [0–14]	46 [34–63]	68 [56–82]			2065–2070 (97%) [2055–2090]	…–… (41%) [2075–…]	910 [720–1150]	800 [560–1050]	−60 [−300 to 0]	1.8 [1.6–1.8]	1.6 [1.5–1.7]	17 [12–35]	73 [67–87]	99 [98–99]
C4 [159]	limit warming to 2°C (>50%)		50 [41–56]	38 [28–44]	28 [19–35]	10 [0–27]	31 [20–50]	49 [35–65]	2020–2025 (100%) [2020–2030]		2080–2085 (86%) [2065–…]	…–… (31%) [2075–…]	1210 [970–1490]	1160 [700–1490]	−30 [−390 to 0]	1.9 [1.7–2.0]	1.8 [1.5–2.0]	11 [7–22]	59 [50–77]	98 [95–99]
C5 [212]	limit warming to 2.5°C (>50%)		52 [46–56]	45 [37–53]	39 [30–49]	6 [−1 to 18]	18 [4–33]	29 [11–48]			…–… (41%) [2080–…]	…–… (12%) [2090–…]	1780 [1400–2360]	1780 [1260–2360]	0 [−160 to 0]	2.2 [1.9–2.5]	2.1 [1.9–2.5]	4 [0–10]	37 [18–59]	91 [83–98]
C6 [97]	limit warming to 3°C (>50%)	SSP2-4.5 ModAct	54 [50–62]	53 [48–61]	52 [45–57]	2 [−10 to 11]	3 [−14 to 14]	5 [−2 to 18]	2030–2035 (96%) [2020–2090]	2020–2025 (97%) [2020–2090]	no net zero		no net zero	2790 [2440–3520]	no net zero	temperature does not peak by 2100	2.7 [2.4–2.9]	0 [0–0]	8 [2–18]	71 [53–88]
C7 [164]	limit warming to 4°C (>50%)	SSP3-7.0 CurPol	62 [53–69]	67 [56–76]	70 [58–83]	−11 [−18 to 3]	−19 [−31 to 1]	−24 [−41 to −2]	2085–2090 (57%) [2040–…]	2090–2095 (56%) [2040–…]	no net zero		no net zero	4220 [3160–5000]	no net zero		3.5 [2.8–3.9]	0 [0–0]	0 [0–2]	22 [7–60]
C8 [29]	exceed warming of 4°C (≥50%)	SSP5-8.5	71 [69–81]	80 [78–96]	88 [82–112]	−20 [−34 to −17]	−35 [−65 to −29]	−46 [−92 to −36]	2080–2085 (90%) [2070–…]		no net zero		no net zero	5600 [4910–7450]	no net zero		4.2 [3.7–5.0]	0 [0–0]	0 [0–0]	4 [0–11]

Table SPM.2 (continued):

a Values in the table refer to the 50th and [5th–95th] percentile values across the pathways falling within a given category as defined in Box SPM.1. For emissions-related columns these values relate to the distribution of all the pathways in that category. Harmonised emissions values are given for consistency with projected global warming outcomes using climate emulators. Based on the assessment of climate emulators in AR6 WGI (WG1 Chapter 7, Box 7.1), two climate emulators are used for the probabilistic assessment of the resulting warming of the pathways. For the 'Temperature change' and 'Likelihood' columns, the single upper-row values represent the 50th percentile across the pathways in that category and the median [50th percentile] across the warming estimates of the probabilistic MAGICC climate model emulator. For the bracketed ranges, the median warming for every pathway in that category is calculated for each of the two climate model emulators (MAGICC and FaIR). Subsequently, the 5th and 95th percentile values across all pathways for each emulator are calculated. The coolest and warmest outcomes (i.e., the lowest p5 of two emulators, and the highest p95, respectively) are shown in square brackets. These ranges therefore cover both the uncertainty of the emissions pathways as well as the climate emulators' uncertainty.

b For a description of pathways categories see Box SPM.1.

c All global warming levels are relative to 1850–1900. (See footnote n below and Box SPM.1[45] for more details.)

d C3 pathways are sub-categorised according to the timing of policy action to match the emissions pathways in Figure SPM.4. Two pathways derived from a cost-benefit analysis have been added to C3a, whilst 10 pathways with specifically designed near-term action until 2030, whose emissions fall below those implied by NDCs announced prior to COP26, are not included in either of the two subsets.

e Alignment with the categories of the illustrative SSP scenarios considered in AR6 WGI, and the Illustrative (Mitigation) Pathways (IPs/IMPs) of WGIII. The IMPs have common features such as deep and rapid emissions reductions, but also different combinations of sectoral mitigation strategies. See Box SPM.1 for an introduction of the IPs and IMPs, and Chapter 3 for full descriptions. {3.2, 3.3, Annex III.II.4}

f The Illustrative Mitigation Pathway 'Neg' has extensive use of carbon dioxide removal (CDR) in the AFOLU, energy and the industry sectors to achieve net negative emissions. Warming peaks around 2060 and declines to below 1.5°C (50% likelihood) shortly after 2100. Whilst technically classified as C3, it strongly exhibits the characteristics of C2 high-overshoot pathways, hence it has been placed in the C2 category. See Box SPM.1 for an introduction of the IPs and IMPs.

g The 2019 range of harmonised GHG emissions across the pathways [53–58 GtCO$_2$-eq] is within the uncertainty ranges of 2019 emissions assessed in Chapter 2 [53–66 GtCO$_2$-eq].[49] (Figure SPM.1, Figure SPM.2, Box SPM.1)

h Rates of global emission reduction in mitigation pathways are reported on a pathway-by-pathway basis relative to harmonised modelled global emissions in 2019 rather than the global emissions reported in SPM Section B and Chapter 2; this ensures internal consistency in assumptions about emission sources and activities, as well as consistency with temperature projections based on the physical climate science assessment by WGI.[49] {Annex III.II.2.5}. Negative values (e.g., in C7, C8) represent an increase in emissions.

i Emissions milestones are provided for five-year intervals in order to be consistent with the underlying five-year time-step data of the modelled pathways. Peak emissions (CO$_2$ and GHGs) are assessed for five-year reporting intervals starting in 2020. The interval 2020–2025 signifies that projected emissions peak as soon as possible between 2020 and at latest before 2025. The upper five-year interval refers to the median interval within which the emissions peak or reach net zero. Ranges in square brackets underneath refer to the range across the pathways, comprising the lower bound of the 5th percentile five-year interval and the upper bound of the 95th percentile five-year interval. Numbers in round brackets signify the fraction of pathways that reach specific milestones.

j Percentiles reported across all pathways in that category include those that do not reach net zero before 2100 (fraction of pathways reaching net zero is given in round brackets). If the fraction of pathways that reach net zero before 2100 is lower than the fraction of pathways covered by a percentile (e.g., 0.95 for the 95th percentile), the percentile is not defined and denoted with '…'. The fraction of pathways reaching net zero includes all with reported non-harmonised, and/or harmonised emissions profiles that reach net zero. Pathways were counted when at least one of the two profiles fell below 100 MtCO$_2$ yr^{-1} until 2100.

k The timing of net zero is further discussed in SPM C2.4 and Cross-Chapter Box 3 in Chapter 3 on net zero CO$_2$ and net zero GHG emissions.

l For cases where models do not report all GHGs, missing GHG species are infilled and aggregated into a Kyoto basket of GHG emissions in CO$_2$-eq defined by the 100-year global warming potential. For each pathway, reporting of CO$_2$, CH$_4$, and N$_2$O emissions was the minimum required for the assessment of the climate response and the assignment to a climate category. Emissions pathways without climate assessment are not included in the ranges presented here. {See Annex III.II.5}

m Cumulative emissions are calculated from the start of 2020 to the time of net zero and 2100, respectively. They are based on harmonised net CO$_2$ emissions, ensuring consistency with the WGI assessment of the remaining carbon budget.[50] {Box 3.4}

n Global mean temperature change for category (at peak, if peak temperature occurs before 2100, and in 2100) relative to 1850–1900, based on the median global warming for each pathway assessed using the probabilistic climate model emulators calibrated to the AR6 WGI assessment.[12] (See also Box SPM.1) {Annex III.II.2.5; WGI Cross-Chapter Box 7.1}

o Probability of staying below the temperature thresholds for the pathways in each category, taking into consideration the range of uncertainty from the climate model emulators consistent with the AR6 WGI assessment. The probabilities refer to the probability at peak temperature. Note that in the case of temperature overshoot (e.g., category C2 and some pathways in C1), the probabilities of staying below at the end of the century are higher than the probabilities at peak temperature.

C.1.4   Global modelled pathways falling into the lowest temperature category of the assessed literature (C1, Table SPM.2) are on average associated with a higher median peak warming in AR6 compared to pathways in the same category in SR1.5. In the modelled pathways in AR6, the likelihood of limiting warming to 1.5°C has on average declined compared to SR1.5. This is because GHG emissions have risen since 2017, and many recent pathways have higher projected emissions by 2030, higher cumulative net CO_2 emissions and slightly later dates for reaching net zero CO_2 or net zero GHG emissions. High mitigation challenges, for example, due to assumptions of slow technological change, high levels of global population growth, and high fragmentation as in the Shared Socio-economic Pathway SSP3, may render modelled pathways that limit warming to 2°C (>67%) or lower infeasible. (*medium confidence*) (Table SPM.2, Box SPM.1) {3.3, 3.8, Annex III Figure II.1, Annex III Figure II.3}

Box SPM.1 | Assessment of Modelled Global Emission Scenarios

A wide range of modelled global emission pathways and scenarios from the literature is assessed in this report, including pathways and scenarios with and without mitigation.[44] Emissions pathways and scenarios project the evolution of GHG emissions based on a set of internally consistent assumptions about future socio-economic conditions and related mitigation measures.[45] These are quantitative projections and are neither predictions nor forecasts. Around half of all modelled global emission scenarios assume cost-effective approaches that rely on least-cost emission abatement options globally. The other half look at existing policies and regionally and sectorally differentiated actions. Most do not make explicit assumptions about global equity, environmental justice or intra-regional income distribution. Global emission pathways, including those based on cost-effective approaches, contain regionally differentiated assumptions and outcomes, and have to be assessed with the careful recognition of these assumptions. This assessment focuses on their global characteristics. The majority of the assessed scenarios (about 80%) have become available since the SR1.5, but some were assessed in that report. Scenarios with and without mitigation were categorised based on their projected global warming over the 21st century, following the same scheme as in the SR1.5 for warming up to and including 2°C. {1.5, 3.2, 3.3, Annex III.II.2, Annex III.II.3}

Scenario categories are defined by their likelihood of exceeding global warming levels (at peak and in 2100) and referred to in this report as follows:[46,47]

- Category C1 comprises modelled scenarios that limit warming to 1.5°C in 2100 with a likelihood of greater than 50%, and reach or exceed warming of 1.5°C during the 21st century with a likelihood of 67% or less. In this report, these scenarios are referred to as scenarios that limit warming to 1.5°C (>50%) with no or limited overshoot. Limited overshoot refers to exceeding 1.5°C global warming by up to about 0.1°C and for up to several decades.[48]
- Category C2 comprises modelled scenarios that limit warming to 1.5°C in 2100 with a likelihood of greater than 50%, and exceed warming of 1.5°C during the 21st century with a likelihood of greater than 67%. In this report, these scenarios are also referred to as scenarios that return warming to 1.5°C (>50%) after a high overshoot. High overshoot refers to temporarily exceeding 1.5°C global warming by 0.1°C–0.3°C for up to several decades.
- Category C3 comprises modelled scenarios that limit peak warming to 2°C throughout the 21st century with a likelihood of greater than 67%. In this report, these scenarios are also referred to as scenarios that limit warming to 2°C (>67%).
- Categories C4, C5, C6 and C7 comprise modelled scenarios that limit warming to 2°C, 2.5°C, 3°C, 4°C, respectively, throughout the 21st century with a likelihood of greater than 50%. In some scenarios in C4 and many scenarios in C5–C7, warming continues beyond the 21st century.

---

[44]   In the literature, the terms 'pathways' and 'scenarios' are used interchangeably, with the former more frequently used in relation to climate goals. For this reason, this SPM uses mostly the term (emissions and mitigation) pathways. {Annex III.II.1.1}

[45]   Key assumptions relate to technology development in agriculture and energy systems and socio-economic development, including demographic and economic projections. IPCC is neutral with regard to the assumptions underlying the scenarios in the literature assessed in this report, which do not cover all possible futures. Additional scenarios may be developed. The underlying population assumptions range from 8.5 to 9.7 billion in 2050 and 7.4 to 10.9 billion in 2100 (5–95th percentile) starting from 7.6 billion in 2019. The underlying assumptions on global GDP growth (ppp) range from 2.5 to 3.5% per year in the 2019–2050 period and 1.3 to 2.1% per year in the 2050–2100 (5–95th percentile). Many underlying assumptions are regionally differentiated. {1.5; 3.2; 3.3; Figure 3.9; Annex III.II.1.4; Annex III.II.3}

[46]   The future scenario projections presented here are consistent with the total observed increase in global surface temperature between 1850–1900 and 1995–2014 as well as to 2011–2020 (with best estimates of 0.85°C and 1.09°C, respectively) assessed in WGI. The largest contributor to historical human-induced warming is CO_2, with historical cumulative CO_2 emissions from 1850 to 2019 being 2400 ± 240 $GtCO_2$. {WGI SPM A.1.2, WGI Table SPM.2, WGI Table 5.1, WGIII SPM Section B}.

[47]   In case no explicit likelihood is provided, the reported warming levels are associated with a likelihood of >50%.

[48]   Scenarios in this category are found to have simultaneous likelihood to limit peak global warming to 2°C throughout the 21st century of close to and more than 90%.

Box SPM.1 (continued)

- Category C8 comprises modelled scenarios that exceed warming of 4°C during the 21st century with a likelihood of 50% or greater. In these scenarios warming continues to rise beyond the 21st century.

Categories of modelled scenarios are distinct and do not overlap; they do not contain categories consistent with lower levels of global warming, for example, the category of C3 scenarios that limit warming to 2°C (>67%) does not include the C1 and C2 scenarios that limit or return warming to 1.5°C (>50%). Where relevant, scenarios belonging to the group of categories C1–C3 are referred to in this report as scenarios that limit warming to 2°C (>67%) or lower.

Methods to project global warming associated with the scenarios were updated to ensure consistency with the AR6 WGI assessment of physical climate science.[49] {3.2, Annex III.II.2.5; AR6 WGI Cross-Chapter Box 7.1}

The range of assessed scenarios results in a range of 21st century projected global warming.

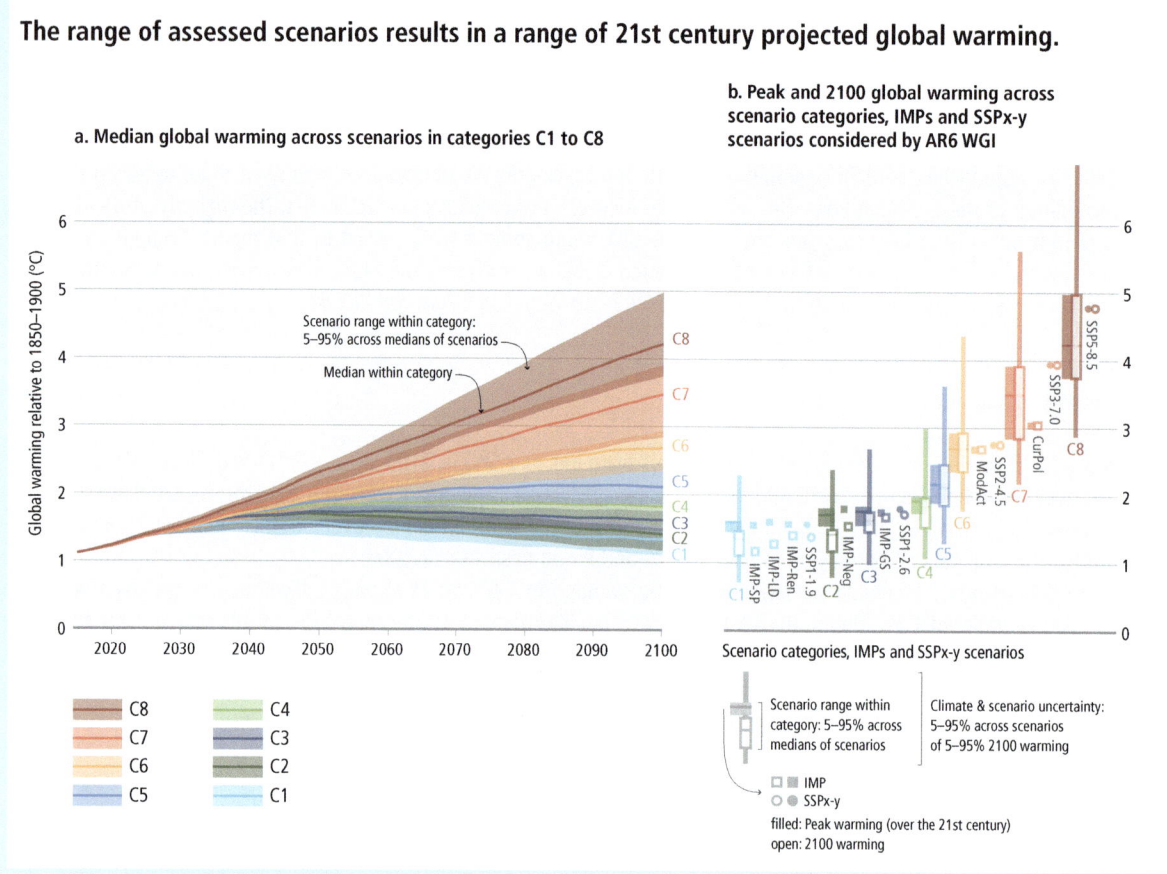

Box SPM.1, Figure 1 | Projected global mean warming of the ensemble of modelled scenarios included in the climate categories C1–C8 and IMPs (based on emulators calibrated to the WGI assessment), as well as five illustrative scenarios (SSPx-y) as considered by AR6 WGI. Panel a shows the p5–p95 range of projected median warming across global modelled pathways within a category, with the category medians (line). **Panel b** shows the peak and 2100 emulated temperature outcomes for the categories C1 to C8 and for IMPs, and the five illustrative scenarios (SSPx-y) as considered by AR6 WGI. The boxes show the p5–p95 range within each scenario category, as in panel a. The combined p5–p95 range across scenarios and the climate uncertainty for each category C1–C8 is also shown for 2100 warming (thin vertical lines). (Table SPM.2) {Figure 3.11; AR6 WGI Figure SPM.8}

---

[49] This involved improved methodologies to use climate emulators (MAGICC7 and FAIR v1.6), which were evaluated and calibrated to closely match the global warming response to emissions as assessed in AR6 WGI. It included harmonisation of global GHG emissions in 2015 in modelled scenarios (51–56 GtCO₂-eq; 5th to 95th percentiles) with the corresponding emission value underlying the CMIP6 projected climate response assessed by WGI (54 GtCO₂-eq), based on similar data sources of historical emissions that are updated over time. The assessment of past GHG emissions in Chapter 2 of the report is based on a more recent dataset providing emissions of 57 [±6.3] GtCO₂-eq in 2015 (B.1). Differences are well within the assessed uncertainty range, and arise mainly from differences in estimated CO₂-LULUCF emissions, which are subject to large uncertainties, high annual variability and revisions over time. Projected rates of global emission reduction in mitigation scenarios are reported relative to modelled global emissions in 2019 rather than the global emissions reported in Chapter 2; this ensures internal consistency in assumptions about emission sources and activities, as well as consistency with temperature projections based on the physical climate science assessment by WG I. {Annex III.II.2.5}

Box SPM.1 (continued)

These updated methods affect the categorisation of some scenarios. On average across scenarios, peak global warming is projected to be lower by up to about 0.05 [±0.1] °C than if the same scenarios were evaluated using the SR1.5 methodology, and global warming in 2100 is projected to be lower by about 0.1 [±0.1] °C. {Annex III.II.2.5.1, Annex III Figure II.3}

Resulting changes to the emission characteristics of scenario categories described in Table SPM.2 interact with changes in the characteristics of the wider range of emission scenarios published since the SR1.5. Proportionally more scenarios assessed in AR6 are designed to limit temperature overshoot and more scenarios limit large-scale net negative CO_2 emissions than in SR1.5. As a result, AR6 scenarios in the lowest temperature category (C1) generally reach net zero GHG emissions later in the 21st century than scenarios in the same category assessed in SR1.5, and about half do not reach net zero GHG by 2100. The rate of decline of GHG emissions in the near term by 2030 in category C1 scenarios is very similar to the assessed rate in SR1.5, but absolute GHG emissions of category C1 scenarios in AR6 are slightly higher in 2030 than in SR1.5, since the reductions start from a higher emissions level in 2020. (Table SPM.2) {Annex III, 2.5, 3.2, 3.3}

The large number of global emissions scenarios assessed, including 1202 scenarios with projected global warming outcomes using climate emulators, come from a wide range of modelling approaches. They include the five illustrative scenarios (Shared Socio-economic Pathways; SSPs) assessed by WGI for their climate outcomes but cover a wider and more varied set in terms of assumptions and modelled outcomes. For this assessment, Illustrative Mitigation Pathways (IMPs) were selected from this larger set to illustrate a range of different mitigation strategies that would be consistent with different warming levels. The IMPs illustrate pathways that achieve deep and rapid emissions reductions through different combinations of mitigation strategies. The IMPs are not intended to be comprehensive and do not address all possible themes in the underlying report. They differ in terms of their focus, for example, placing greater emphasis on renewables (IMP-Ren), deployment of carbon dioxide removal that results in net negative global GHG emissions (IMP-Neg), and efficient resource use as well as shifts in consumption patterns globally, leading to low demand for resources, while ensuring a high level of services and satisfying basic needs (IMP-LD) (Figure SPM.5). Other IMPs illustrate the implications of a less rapid introduction of mitigation measures followed by a subsequent gradual strengthening (IMP-GS), and how shifting global pathways towards sustainable development, including by reducing inequality, can lead to mitigation (IMP-SP). The IMPs reach different climate goals as indicated in Table SPM.2 and Box SPM.1, Figure 1. {1.5, 3.1, 3.2, 3.3, 3.6, Figure 3.7, Figure 3.8, Box 3.4, Annex III.II.2.4}

C.2 **Global net zero CO_2 emissions are reached in the early 2050s in modelled pathways that limit warming to 1.5°C (>50%) with no or limited overshoot, and around the early 2070s in modelled pathways that limit warming to 2°C (>67%). Many of these pathways continue to net negative CO_2 emissions after the point of net zero. These pathways also include deep reductions in other GHG emissions. The level of peak warming depends on cumulative CO_2 emissions until the time of net zero CO_2 and the change in non-CO_2 climate forcers by the time of peaking. Deep GHG emissions reductions by 2030 and 2040, particularly reductions of methane emissions, lower peak warming, reduce the likelihood of overshooting warming limits and lead to less reliance on net negative CO_2 emissions that reverse warming in the latter half of the century. Reaching and sustaining global net zero GHG emissions results in a gradual decline in warming. (*high confidence*) (Table SPM.2) {3.3, 3.5, Box 3.4, Cross-Chapter Box 3 in Chapter 3, AR6 WGI SPM D1.8}**

C.2.1 Modelled global pathways limiting warming to 1.5°C (>50%) with no or limited overshoot are associated with projected cumulative net CO_2 emissions[50] until the time of net zero CO_2 of 510 [330–710] $GtCO_2$. Pathways limiting warming to 2°C (>67%) are associated with 890 [640–1160] $GtCO_2$ (Table SPM.2). (*high confidence*) {3.3, Box 3.4}

C.2.2 Modelled global pathways that limit warming to 1.5°C (>50%) with no or limited overshoot involve more rapid and deeper near-term GHG emissions reductions through to 2030, and are projected to have less net negative CO_2 emissions and less carbon dioxide removal (CDR) in the longer term, than pathways that return warming to 1.5°C (>50%) after a high overshoot (C2 category). Modelled pathways that limit warming to 2°C (>67%) have on average lower net negative CO_2 emissions compared to pathways that limit warming to 1.5°C (>50%) with no or limited overshoot and pathways that return warming

---

[50] Cumulative net CO_2 emissions from the beginning of the year 2020 until the time of net zero CO_2 in assessed pathways are consistent with the remaining carbon budgets assessed by WGI, taking account of the ranges in the WGIII temperature categories and warming from non-CO_2 gases. {Box 3.4}

to 1.5°C (>50%) after a high overshoot (C1 and C2 categories respectively). Modelled pathways that return warming to 1.5°C (>50%) after a high overshoot (C2 category) show near-term GHG emissions reductions similar to pathways that limit warming to 2°C (>67%) (C3 category). For a given peak global warming level, greater and more rapid near-term GHG emissions reductions are associated with later net zero CO_2 dates. (*high confidence*) (Table SPM.2) {3.3, Table 3.5, Cross-Chapter Box 3 in Chapter 3, Annex I: Glossary}

C.2.3   Future non-CO_2 warming depends on reductions in non-CO_2 GHGs, aerosols and their precursors, and ozone precursor emissions. In modelled global low-emission pathways, the projected reduction of cooling and warming aerosol emissions over time leads to net warming in the near- to mid-term. In these mitigation pathways, the projected reductions of cooling aerosols are mostly due to reduced fossil fuel combustion that was not equipped with effective air pollution controls. Non-CO_2 GHG emissions at the time of net zero CO_2 are projected to be of similar magnitude in modelled pathways that limit warming to 2°C (>67%) or lower. These non-CO_2 GHG emissions are about 8 [5–11] $GtCO_2$-eq yr^{-1}, with the largest fraction from CH_4 (60% [55–80%]), followed by N_2O (30% [20–35%]) and F-gases (3% [2–20%]).[51] Due to the short lifetime of CH_4 in the atmosphere, projected deep reduction of CH_4 emissions up until the time of net zero CO_2 in modelled mitigation pathways effectively reduces peak global warming. (*high confidence*) {3.3; AR6 WGI SPM D1.7}

C.2.4   At the time of global net zero GHG emissions, net negative CO_2 emissions counterbalance metric-weighted non-CO_2 GHG emissions. Typical emissions pathways that reach and sustain global net zero GHG emissions based on the 100-year global warming potential (GWP-100)[7] are projected to result in a gradual decline of global warming. About half of the assessed pathways that limit warming to 1.5°C (>50%) with no or limited overshoot (C1 category) reach net zero GHG emissions during the second half of the 21st century. These pathways show greater reduction in global warming after the peak to 1.2 [1.1–1.4] °C by 2100 than modelled pathways in the same category that do not reach net zero GHG emissions before 2100 and that result in warming of 1.4 [1.3–1.5] °C by 2100. In modelled pathways that limit warming to 2°C (>67%) (C3 category), there is no significant difference in warming by 2100 between those pathways that reach net zero GHGs (around 30%) and those that do not (*high confidence*). In pathways that limit warming to 2°C (>67%) or lower and that do reach net zero GHG, net zero GHG occurs around 10–40 years later than net zero CO_2 emissions (*medium confidence*). {Cross-Chapter Box 2 in Chapter 2, 3.3, Cross-Chapter Box 3 in Chapter 3; AR6 WGI SPM D1.8}

C.3   All global modelled pathways that limit warming to 1.5°C (>50%) with no or limited overshoot, and those that limit warming to 2°C (>67%), involve rapid and deep and in most cases immediate GHG emission reductions in all sectors. Modelled mitigation strategies to achieve these reductions include transitioning from fossil fuels without CCS to very low- or zero-carbon energy sources, such as renewables or fossil fuels with CCS, demand side measures and improving efficiency, reducing non-CO_2 emissions, and deploying carbon dioxide removal (CDR) methods to counterbalance residual GHG emissions. Illustrative Mitigation Pathways (IMPs) show different combinations of sectoral mitigation strategies consistent with a given warming level. (*high confidence*) (Figure SPM.5) {3.2, 3.3, 3.4, 6.4, 6.6}

C.3.1   There is a variation in the contributions of different sectors in modelled mitigation pathways, as illustrated by the Illustrative Mitigation Pathways (IMPs). However, modelled pathways that limit warming to 2°C (>67%) or lower share common characteristics, including rapid and deep GHG emission reductions. Doing less in one sector needs to be compensated by further reductions in other sectors if warming is to be limited. (*high confidence*) (Figure SPM.5) {3.2, 3.3, 3.4}

C.3.2   In modelled pathways that limit warming to 1.5°C (>50%) with no or limited overshoot, the global use of coal, oil and gas in 2050 is projected to decline with median values of about 95%, 60% and 45% respectively, compared to 2019. The interquartile ranges are (80 to 100%), (40 to 75%) and (20 to 60%) and the p5–p95 ranges are [60 to 100%], [25 to 90%] and [−30 to +85%], respectively. In modelled pathways that limit warming to 2°C (>67%), these projected declines have a median value and interquartile range of 85% (65 to 95%), 30% (15 to 50%) and 15% (−10 to +40%) respectively by 2050. The use of coal, oil and gas without CCS in modelled pathways that limit warming to 1.5°C (>50%) with no or limited overshoot is projected to be reduced to a greater degree, with median values of about 100%, 60% and 70% in 2050 compared to 2019. The interquartile ranges are (95 to 100%), (45 to 75%) and (60 to 80%) and the p5–p95 ranges about [85 to 100%], [25 to 90%] and [35 to 90%] for coal, oil and gas respectively. In these global modelled pathways, in 2050 almost all electricity is supplied from zero- or low-carbon sources, such as renewables or fossil fuels with CCS, combined with increased

---

[51]   All numbers here rounded to the closest 5%, except values below 5% (for F-gases).

electrification of energy demand. As indicated by the ranges, choices in one sector can be compensated for by choices in another while being consistent with assessed warming levels.[52] (*high confidence*) {3.4, 3.5, Table 3.6, Figure 3.22, Figure 6.35}

C.3.3   In modelled pathways that reach global net zero CO_2 emissions: at the point they reach net zero, 5–16 $GtCO_2$ of emissions from some sectors are compensated for by net negative CO_2 emissions in other sectors. In most global modelled pathways that limit warming to 2°C (>67%) or lower, the AFOLU sector, via reforestation and reduced deforestation, and the energy supply sector reach net zero CO_2 emissions earlier than the buildings, industry and transport sectors. (*high confidence*) (Figure SPM.5e,f) {3.4}

C.3.4   In modelled pathways that reach global net zero GHG emissions, at the point they reach net zero GHG, around 74% [54 to 90%] of global emissions reductions are achieved by CO_2 reductions in energy supply and demand, 13% [4 to 20%] by CO_2 mitigation options in the AFOLU sector, and 13% [10 to 18%] through the reduction of non-CO_2 emissions from land-use, energy and industry (*medium confidence*). (Figure SPM.5f) {3.3, 3.4}

C.3.5   Methods and levels of CDR deployment in global modelled mitigation pathways vary depending on assumptions about costs, availability and constraints.[53] In modelled pathways that report CDR and that limit warming to 1.5°C (>50%) with no or limited overshoot, global cumulative CDR during 2020–2100 from bioenergy with carbon dioxide capture and storage (BECCS) and direct air carbon dioxide capture and storage (DACCS) is 30–780 $GtCO_2$ and 0–310 $GtCO_2$, respectively. In these modelled pathways, the AFOLU sector contributes 20–400 $GtCO_2$ net negative emissions. Total cumulative net negative CO_2 emissions including CDR deployment across all options represented in these modelled pathways are 20–660 $GtCO_2$. In modelled pathways that limit warming to 2°C (>67%), global cumulative CDR during 2020–2100 from BECCS and DACCS is 170–650 $GtCO_2$ and 0–250 $GtCO_2$ respectively, the AFOLU sector contributes 10–250 $GtCO_2$ net negative emissions, and total cumulative net negative CO_2 emissions are around 40 [0–290] $GtCO_2$. (Table SPM.2) (*high confidence*) {Table 3.2, 3.3, 3.4}

C.3.6   All mitigation strategies face implementation challenges, including technology risks, scaling, and costs. Many challenges, such as dependence on CDR, pressure on land and biodiversity (e.g., bioenergy) and reliance on technologies with high upfront investments (e.g., nuclear), are significantly reduced in modelled pathways that assume using resources more efficiently (e.g., IMP-LD) or that shift global development towards sustainability (e.g., IMP-SP). (*high confidence*) (Figure SPM.5) {3.2, 3.4, 3.7, 3.8, 4.3, 5.1}

---

[52]   Most but not all models include the use of fossil fuels for feedstock with varying underlying standards.

[53]   Aggregate levels of CDR deployment are higher than total net negative CO_2 emissions given that some of the deployed CDR is used to counterbalance remaining gross emissions. Total net negative CO_2 emissions in modelled pathways might not match the aggregated net negative CO_2 emissions attributed to individual CDR methods. Ranges refer to the 5–95th percentile across modelled pathways that include the specific CDR method. Cumulative levels of CDR from AFOLU cannot be quantified precisely given that: (i) some pathways assess CDR deployment relative to a baseline; and (ii) different models use different reporting methodologies that in some cases combine gross emissions and removals in AFOLU. Total CDR from AFOLU equals or exceeds the net negative emissions mentioned.

Modelled mitigation pathways that limit warming to 1.5°C, and 2°C, involve deep, rapid and sustained emissions reductions.

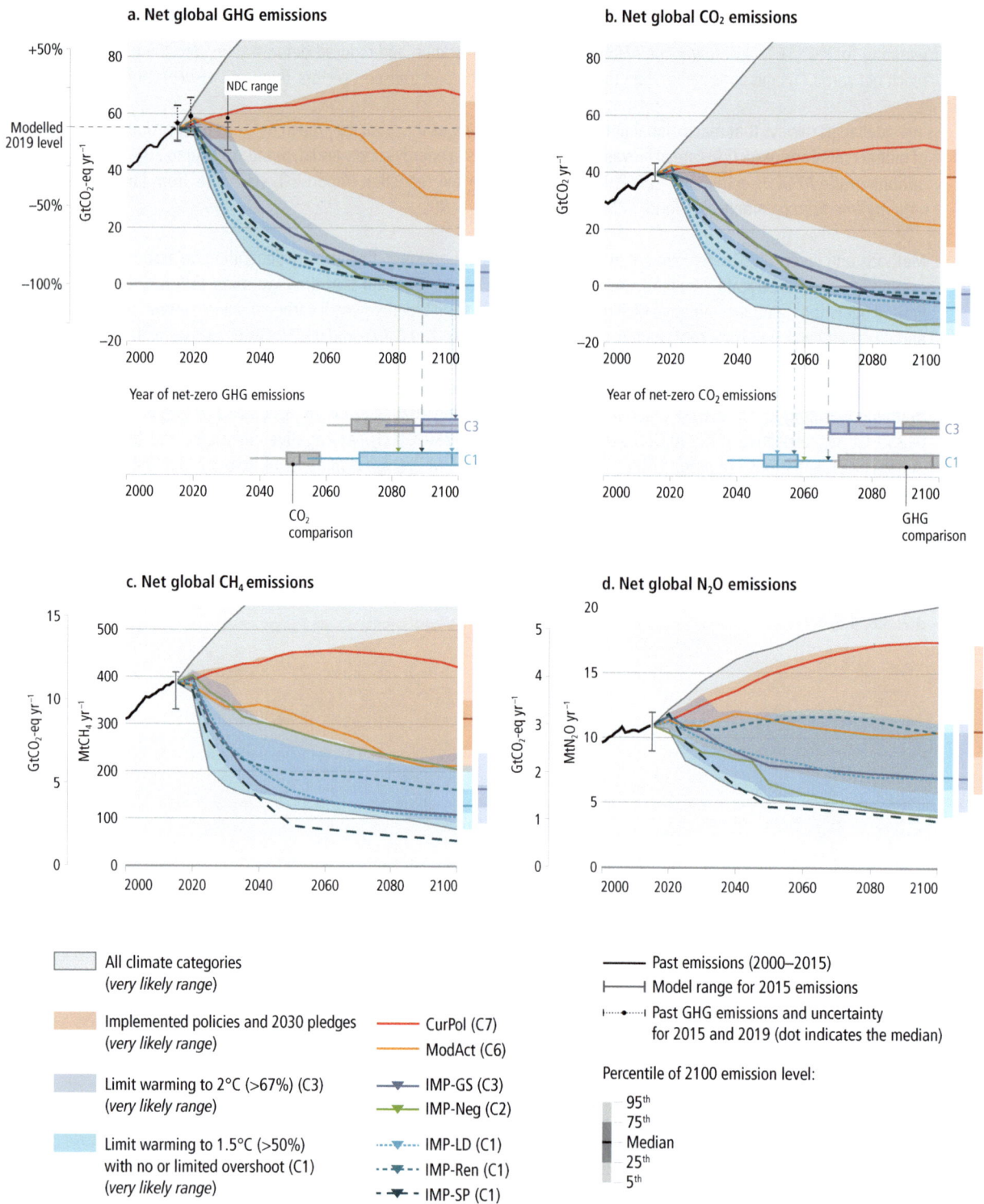

Figure SPM.5 | Illustrative Mitigation Pathways (IMPs) and net zero CO_2 and GHG emissions strategies.

Net zero CO₂ and net zero GHG emissions are possible through different modelled mitigation pathways.

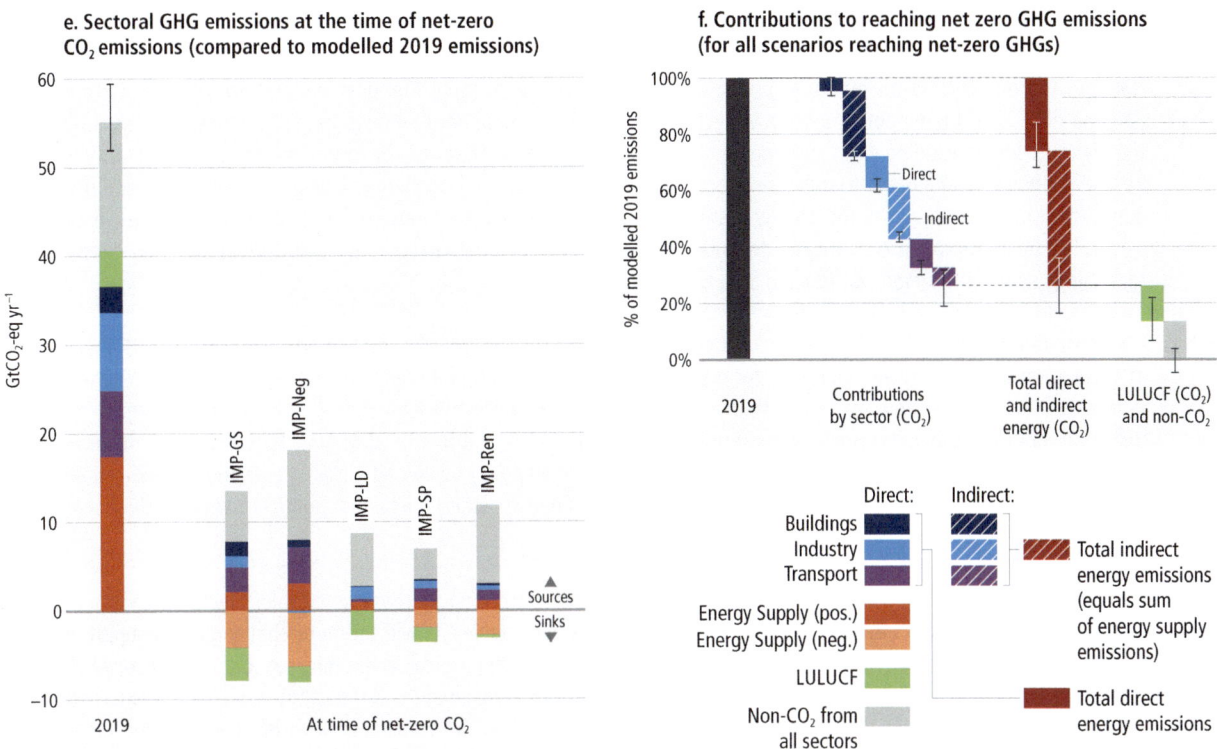

e. Sectoral GHG emissions at the time of net-zero CO₂ emissions (compared to modelled 2019 emissions)

f. Contributions to reaching net zero GHG emissions (for all scenarios reaching net-zero GHGs)

Figure SPM.5 (continued): Illustrative Mitigation Pathways (IMPs) and net zero CO₂ and GHG emissions strategies. Panels a and b show the development of global GHG and CO₂ emissions in modelled global pathways (upper sub-panels) and the associated timing of when GHG and CO₂ emissions reach net zero (lower sub-panels). **Panels c and d** show the development of global CH₄ and N₂O emissions, respectively. Coloured ranges denote the 5th to 95th percentile across pathways. The red ranges depict emissions pathways assuming policies that were implemented by the end of 2020 and pathways assuming implementation of NDCs (announced prior to COP26). Ranges of modelled pathways that limit warming to 1.5°C (>50%) with no or limited overshoot are shown in light blue (category C1) and pathways that limit warming to 2°C (>67%) are shown in light purple (category C3). The grey range comprises all assessed pathways (C1–C8) from the 5th percentile of the lowest warming category (C1) to the 95th percentile of the highest warming category (C8). The modelled pathway ranges are compared to the emissions from two pathways illustrative of high emissions (CurPol and ModAct) and five IMPs: IMP-LD, IMP-Ren, IMP-SP, IMP-Neg and IMP-GS. Emissions are harmonised to the same 2015 base year. The vertical error bars in 2015 show the 5–95th percentile uncertainty range of the non-harmonised emissions across the pathways, and the uncertainty range, and median value, in emission estimates for 2015 and 2019. The vertical error bars in 2030 (panel a) depict the assessed range of the NDCs, as announced prior to COP26 (Figure SPM.4).[23] **Panel e** shows the sectoral contributions of CO₂ and non-CO₂ emissions sources and sinks at the time when net zero CO₂ emissions are reached in the IMPs. Positive and negative emissions for different IMPs are compared to the GHG emissions from the year 2019. Energy supply (neg.) includes BECCS and DACCS. DACCS features in only two of the five IMPs (IMP-REN and IMP-GS) and contributes <1% and 64%, respectively, to the net negative emissions in Energy Supply (neg.). **Panel f** shows the contribution of different sectors and sources to the emissions reductions from a 2019 baseline for reaching net zero GHG emissions. Bars denote the median emissions reductions for all pathways that reach net zero GHG emissions. The whiskers indicate the p5–p95 range. The contributions of the service sectors (transport, buildings, industry) are split into direct (demand-side) as well as indirect (supply-side) CO₂ emissions reductions. Direct emissions represent demand-side emissions due to the fuel use in the respective demand sector. Indirect emissions represent upstream emissions due to industrial processes and energy conversion, transmission and distribution. In addition, the contributions from the LULUCF sector and reductions from non-CO₂ emissions sources (green and grey bars) are displayed. {3.3, 3.4}

C.4 **Reducing GHG emissions across the full energy sector requires major transitions, including a substantial reduction in overall fossil fuel use, the deployment of low-emission energy sources, switching to alternative energy carriers, and energy efficiency and conservation. The continued installation of unabated fossil fuel[54] infrastructure will 'lock-in' GHG emissions.** (*high confidence*) {2.7, 6.6, 6.7, 16.4}

C.4.1   Net-zero CO_2 energy systems entail: a substantial reduction in overall fossil fuel use, minimal use of unabated fossil fuels, and use of CCS in the remaining fossil fuel system;[54] electricity systems that emit no net CO_2; widespread electrification of the energy system including end uses; energy carriers such as sustainable biofuels, low-emissions hydrogen, and derivatives in applications less amenable to electrification; energy conservation and efficiency; and greater physical, institutional, and operational integration across the energy system. CDR will be needed to counterbalance residual emissions in the energy sector. The most appropriate strategies depend on national and regional circumstances, including enabling conditions and technology availability. (*high confidence*) {3.4, 6.6, 11.3, 16.4}

C.4.2   Unit cost reductions in key technologies, notably wind power, solar power, and storage, have increased the economic attractiveness of low-emission energy sector transitions through 2030. Maintaining emission-intensive systems may, in some regions and sectors, be more expensive than transitioning to low emission systems. Low-emission energy sector transitions will have multiple co-benefits, including improvements in air quality and health. The long-term economic attractiveness of deploying energy system mitigation options depends, *inter alia*, on policy design and implementation, technology availability and performance, institutional capacity, equity, access to finance, and public and political support. (*high confidence*) (Figure SPM.3) {3.4, 6.4, 6.6, 6.7, 13.7}

C.4.3   Electricity systems powered predominantly by renewables are becoming increasingly viable. Electricity systems in some countries and regions are already predominantly powered by renewables. It will be more challenging to supply the entire energy system with renewable energy. Even though operational, technological, economic, regulatory, and social challenges remain, a variety of systemic solutions to accommodate large shares of renewables in the energy system have emerged. A broad portfolio of options, such as integrating systems, coupling sectors, energy storage, smart grids, demand-side management, sustainable biofuels, electrolytic hydrogen and derivatives, and others will ultimately be needed to accommodate large shares of renewables in energy systems. (*high confidence*) {Box 6.8, 6.4, 6.6}

C.4.4   Limiting global warming to 2°C or below will leave a substantial amount of fossil fuels unburned and could strand considerable fossil fuel infrastructure (*high confidence*). Depending on its availability, CCS could allow fossil fuels to be used longer, reducing stranded assets (*high confidence*). The combined global discounted value of the unburned fossil fuels and stranded fossil fuel infrastructure has been projected to be around USD1–4 trillion from 2015 to 2050 to limit global warming to approximately 2°C, and it will be higher if global warming is limited to approximately 1.5°C (*medium confidence*). In this context, coal assets are projected to be at risk of being stranded before 2030, while oil and gas assets are projected to be more at risk of being stranded towards mid-century. A low-emission energy sector transition is projected to reduce international trade in fossil fuels. (*high confidence*) {6.7, Figure 6.35}

C.4.5   Global methane emissions from energy supply, primarily fugitive emissions from production and transport of fossil fuels, accounted for about 18% [13–23%] of global GHG emissions from energy supply, 32% [22–42%] of global CH_4 emissions, and 6% [4–8%] of global GHG emissions in 2019 (*high confidence*). About 50–80% of CH_4 emissions from these fossil fuels could be avoided with currently available technologies at less than USD50 tCO_2-eq^{-1} (*medium confidence*). {6.3, 6.4.2, Box 6.5, 11.3, 2.2.2, Table 2.1, Figure 2.5, Annex1: Glossary}

C.4.6   CCS is an option to reduce emissions from large-scale fossil-based energy and industry sources, provided geological storage is available. When CO_2 is captured directly from the atmosphere (DACCS), or from biomass (BECCS), CCS provides the storage component of these CDR methods. CO_2 capture and subsurface injection is a mature technology for gas processing and enhanced oil recovery. In contrast to the oil and gas sector, CCS is less mature in the power sector, as well as in cement and chemicals production, where it is a critical mitigation option. The technical geological CO_2 storage capacity is estimated to be on the order of 1000 $GtCO_2$, which is more than the CO_2 storage requirements through 2100 to limit global warming to 1.5°C, although the regional availability of geological storage could be a limiting factor. If the geological storage site is appropriately selected and managed, it is estimated that the CO_2 can be permanently isolated from the atmosphere. Implementation of CCS currently faces technological, economic, institutional, ecological-environmental and socio-cultural barriers. Currently, global rates of CCS deployment are far below those in modelled pathways limiting global warming to 1.5°C or 2°C. Enabling

---

[54]   In this context, 'unabated fossil fuels' refers to fossil fuels produced and used without interventions that substantially reduce the amount of GHG emitted throughout the life cycle; for example, capturing 90% or more CO_2 from power plants, or 50–80% of fugitive methane emissions from energy supply. {Box 6.5, 11.3}

conditions such as policy instruments, greater public support and technological innovation could reduce these barriers. (*high confidence*) {2.5, 6.3, 6.4, 6.7, 11.3, 11.4, Cross-Chapter Box 8 in Chapter 12, Figure TS.31; SRCCL Chapter 5}

C.5   **Net zero CO_2 emissions from the industrial sector are challenging but possible. Reducing industry emissions will entail coordinated action throughout value chains to promote all mitigation options, including demand management, energy and materials efficiency, circular material flows, as well as abatement technologies and transformational changes in production processes. Progressing towards net zero GHG emissions from industry will be enabled by the adoption of new production processes using low- and zero-GHG electricity, hydrogen, fuels, and carbon management. (*high confidence*) {11.2, 11.3, 11.4, Box TS.4}**

C.5.1   The use of steel, cement, plastics, and other materials is increasing globally, and in most regions. There are many sustainable options for demand management, materials efficiency, and circular material flows that can contribute to reduced emissions, but how these can be applied will vary across regions and different materials. These options have a potential for being more used in industrial practice and would need more attention from industrial policy. These options, as well as new production technologies, are generally not considered in recent global scenarios nor in national economy-wide scenarios due to relative newness. As a consequence, the mitigation potential in some scenarios is underestimated compared to bottom-up industry-specific models. (*high confidence*) {3.4, 5.3, Figure 5.7, 11.2, Box 11.2, 11.3, 11.4, 11.5.2, 11.6}

C.5.2   For almost all basic materials – primary metals,[55] building materials and chemicals – many low- to zero-GHG intensity production processes are at the *pilot* to *near-commercial* and in some cases *commercial* stage but they are not yet established industrial practice. Introducing new sustainable production processes for basic materials could increase production costs but, given that only a small fraction of consumer costs are based on materials, such new processes are expected to translate into minimal cost increases for final consumers. Hydrogen direct reduction for primary steelmaking is *near-commercial* in some regions. Until new chemistries are mastered, deep reduction of cement process emissions will rely on already commercialised cementitious material substitution and the availability of CCS. Reducing emissions from the production and use of chemicals would need to rely on a life cycle approach, including increased plastics recycling, fuel and feedstock switching, and carbon sourced through biogenic sources, and, depending on availability, carbon capture and use (CCU), direct air CO_2 capture, as well as CCS. Light industry, mining and manufacturing have the potential to be decarbonised through available abatement technologies (e.g., material efficiency, circularity), electrification (e.g., electrothermal heating, heat pumps) and low- or zero-GHG emitting fuels (e.g., hydrogen, ammonia, and bio-based and other synthetic fuels). (*high confidence*) {Table 11.4, Box 11.2, 11.3, 11.4}

C.5.3   Action to reduce industry sector emissions may change the location of GHG-intensive industries and the organisation of value chains. Regions with abundant low-GHG energy and feedstocks have the potential to become exporters of hydrogen-based chemicals and materials processed using low-carbon electricity and hydrogen. Such reallocation will have global distributional effects on employment and economic structure. (*medium confidence*) {Box 11.1}

C.5.4   Emissions-intensive and highly traded basic materials industries are exposed to international competition, and international cooperation and coordination may be particularly important in enabling change. For sustainable industrial transitions, broad and sequential national and sub-national policy strategies reflecting regional contexts will be required. These may combine policy packages including: transparent GHG accounting and standards; demand management; materials and energy efficiency policies; R&D and niche markets for commercialisation of low-emission materials and products; economic and regulatory instruments to drive market uptake; high quality recycling, low-emissions energy and other abatement infrastructure (e.g., for CCS); and socially inclusive phase-out plans of emissions-intensive facilities within the context of just transitions. The coverage of mitigation policies could be expanded nationally and sub-nationally to include all industrial emission sources, and both available and emerging mitigation options. (*high confidence*) {11.6}

---

[55]   Primary metals refers to virgin metals produced from ore.

C.6 **Urban areas can create opportunities to increase resource efficiency and significantly reduce GHG emissions through the systemic transition of infrastructure and urban form through low-emission development pathways towards net-zero emissions. Ambitious mitigation efforts for established, rapidly growing and emerging cities will encompass (i) reducing or changing energy and material consumption, (ii) electrification, and (iii) enhancing carbon uptake and storage in the urban environment. Cities can achieve net-zero emissions, but only if emissions are reduced within and outside of their administrative boundaries through supply chains, which will have beneficial cascading effects across other sectors. (*very high confidence*) {8.2, 8.3, 8.4, 8.5, 8.6, Figure 8.21, 13.2}**

C.6.1 In modelled scenarios, global consumption-based urban CO_2 and CH_4 emissions[15] are projected to rise from 29 $GtCO_2$-eq in 2020 to 34 $GtCO_2$-eq in 2050 with moderate mitigation efforts (intermediate GHG emissions, SSP2-4.5), and up to 40 $GtCO_2$-eq in 2050 with low mitigation efforts (high GHG emissions, SSP3-7.0). With ambitious and immediate mitigation efforts, including high levels of electrification and improved energy and material efficiency, global consumption-based urban CO_2 and CH_4 emissions could be reduced to 3 $GtCO_2$-eq in 2050 in the modelled scenario with very low GHG emissions (SSP1-1.9).[56] (*medium confidence*) {8.3}

C.6.2 The potential and sequencing of mitigation strategies to reduce GHG emissions will vary depending on a city's land use, spatial form, development level, and state of urbanisation (*high confidence*). Strategies for established cities to achieve large GHG emissions savings include efficiently improving, repurposing or retrofitting the building stock, targeted infilling, and supporting non-motorised (e.g., walking, bicycling) and public transport. Rapidly growing cities can avoid future emissions by co-locating jobs and housing to achieve compact urban form, and by leapfrogging or transitioning to low-emissions technologies. New and emerging cities will have significant infrastructure development needs to achieve high quality of life, which can be met through energy efficient infrastructures and services, and people-centred urban design (*high confidence*). For cities, three broad mitigation strategies have been found to be effective when implemented concurrently: (i) reducing or changing energy and material use towards more sustainable production and consumption; (ii) electrification in combination with switching to low-emission energy sources; and (iii) enhancing carbon uptake and storage in the urban environment, for example through bio-based building materials, permeable surfaces, green roofs, trees, green spaces, rivers, ponds and lakes.[57] (*very high confidence*) {5.3, Figure 5.7, Supplementary Material Table 5.SM.2, 8.2, 8.4, 8.6, Figure 8.21, 9.4, 9.6, 10.2}

C.6.3 The implementation of packages of multiple city-scale mitigation strategies can have cascading effects across sectors and reduce GHG emissions both within and outside a city's administrative boundaries. The capacity of cities to develop and implement mitigation strategies varies with the broader regulatory and institutional settings, as well as enabling conditions, including access to financial and technological resources, local governance capacity, engagement of civil society, and municipal budgetary powers. (*very high confidence*) {Figure 5.7, Supplementary Material Table 5.SM.2, 8.4, 8.5, 8.6, 13.2, 13.3, 13.5, 13.7, Cross-Chapter Box 9 in Chapter 13}

C.6.4 A growing number of cities are setting climate targets, including net-zero GHG targets. Given the regional and global reach of urban consumption patterns and supply chains, the full potential for reducing consumption-based urban emissions to net zero GHG can be met only when emissions beyond cities' administrative boundaries are also addressed. The effectiveness of these strategies depends on cooperation and coordination with national and sub-national governments, industry, and civil society, and whether cities have adequate capacity to plan and implement mitigation strategies. Cities can play a positive role in reducing emissions across supply chains that extend beyond cities' administrative boundaries, for example through building codes and the choice of construction materials. (*very high confidence*) {8.4, Box 8.4, 8.5, 9.6, 9.9, 13.5, 13.9}

---

[56] These scenarios have been assessed by WGI to correspond to intermediate, high and very low GHG emissions.

[57] These examples are considered to be a subset of nature-based solutions or ecosystem-based approaches.

C.7. **In modelled global scenarios, existing buildings, if retrofitted, and buildings yet to be built, are projected to approach net zero GHG emissions in 2050 if policy packages, which combine ambitious sufficiency, efficiency, and renewable energy measures, are effectively implemented and barriers to decarbonisation are removed. Low ambition policies increase the risk of locking-in buildings' carbon for decades, while well-designed and effectively implemented mitigation interventions (in both new buildings and existing ones if retrofitted), have significant potential to contribute to achieving SDGs in all regions while adapting buildings to future climate.** (*high confidence*) {9.1, 9.3, 9.4, 9.5, 9.6, 9.9}

C.7.1 In 2019, global direct and indirect GHG emissions from buildings and emissions from cement and steel use for building construction and renovation were 12 GtCO$_2$-eq. These emissions include indirect emissions from offsite generation of electricity and heat, direct emissions produced onsite and emissions from cement and steel used for building construction and renovation. In 2019, global direct and indirect emissions from non-residential buildings increased by about 55% and those from residential buildings increased by about 50% compared to 1990. The latter increase, according to the decomposition analysis, was mainly driven by the increase of the floor area per capita, population growth and the increased use of emission-intensive electricity and heat while efficiency improvements have partly decreased emissions. There are great differences in the contribution of each of these drivers to regional emissions. (*high confidence*) {9.3}

C.7.2 Integrated design approaches to the construction and retrofit of buildings have led to increasing examples of zero energy or zero carbon buildings in several regions. However, the low renovation rates and low ambition of retrofitted buildings have hindered the decrease of emissions. Mitigation interventions at the design stage include buildings typology, form, and multi-functionality to allow for adjusting the size of buildings to the evolving needs of their users and repurposing unused existing buildings to avoid using GHG-intensive materials and additional land. Mitigation interventions include: at the construction phase, low-emission construction materials, highly efficient building envelope and the integration of renewable energy solutions;[58] at the use phase, highly efficient appliances/equipment, the optimisation of the use of buildings and their supply with low-emission energy sources; and at the disposal phase, recycling and re-using construction materials. (*high confidence*) {9.4, 9.5, 9.6, 9.7}

C.7.3 By 2050, bottom-up studies show that up to 61% (8.2 GtCO$_2$) of global building emissions could be mitigated. Sufficiency policies[59] that avoid the demand for energy and materials contribute 10% to this potential, energy efficiency policies contribute 42%, and renewable energy policies 9%. The largest share of the mitigation potential of new buildings is available in developing countries while in developed countries the highest mitigation potential is within the retrofit of existing buildings. The 2020–2030 decade is critical for accelerating the learning of know-how, building the technical and institutional capacity, setting the appropriate governance structures, ensuring the flow of finance, and in developing the skills needed to fully capture the mitigation potential of buildings. (*high confidence*) {9.3, 9.4, 9.5, 9.6, 9.7, 9.9}

---

[58] Integration of renewable energy solutions refers to the integration of solutions such as solar photovoltaics, small wind turbines, solar thermal collectors, and biomass boilers.

[59] Sufficiency policies are a set of measures and daily practices that avoid demand for energy, materials, land and water while delivering human well-being for all within planetary boundaries.

C.8 **Demand-side options and low-GHG emissions technologies can reduce transport sector emissions in developed countries and limit emissions growth in developing countries (*high confidence*). Demand-focused interventions can reduce demand for all transport services and support the shift to more energy efficient transport modes (*medium confidence*). Electric vehicles powered by low-emissions electricity offer the largest decarbonisation potential for land-based transport, on a life cycle basis (*high confidence*). Sustainable biofuels can offer additional mitigation benefits in land-based transport in the short and medium term (*medium confidence*). Sustainable biofuels, low-emissions hydrogen, and derivatives (including synthetic fuels) can support mitigation of CO_2 emissions from shipping, aviation, and heavy-duty land transport but require production process improvements and cost reductions (*medium confidence*). Many mitigation strategies in the transport sector would have various co-benefits, including air quality improvements, health benefits, equitable access to transportation services, reduced congestion, and reduced material demand (*high confidence*). {10.2, 10.4, 10.5, 10.6, 10.7}**

C.8.1 In scenarios that limit warming to 1.5°C (>50%) with no or limited overshoot, global transport-related CO_2 emissions fall by 59% (42–68% interquartile range) by 2050 relative to modelled 2020 emissions, but with regionally differentiated trends (*high confidence*). In global modelled scenarios that limit warming to 2°C (>67%), transport-related CO_2 emissions are projected to decrease by 29% [14–44% interquartile range] by 2050 compared to modelled 2020 emissions. In both categories of scenarios, the transport sector likely does not reach zero CO_2 emissions by 2100 so negative emissions are likely needed to counterbalance residual CO_2 emissions from the sector (*high confidence*). {3.4, 10.7}

C.8.2 Changes in urban form (e.g., density, land-use mix, connectivity, and accessibility) in combination with programmes that encourage changes in consumer behaviour (e.g., transport pricing) could reduce transport-related greenhouse gas emissions in developed countries and slow growth in emissions in developing countries (*high confidence*). Investments in public inter- and intra-city transport and active transport infrastructure (e.g., bicycle and pedestrian pathways) can further support the shift to less GHG-intensive transport modes (*high confidence*). Combinations of systemic changes, including teleworking, digitalisation, dematerialisation, supply chain management, and smart and shared mobility may reduce demand for passenger and freight services across land, air, and sea (*high confidence*). Some of these changes could lead to induced demand for transport and energy services, which may decrease their GHG emissions reduction potential (*medium confidence*). {5.3, 10.2, 10.8}

C.8.3 Electric vehicles powered by low-GHG emissions electricity have large potential to reduce land-based transport GHG emissions, on a life cycle basis (*high confidence*). Costs of electrified vehicles, including automobiles, two- and three-wheelers, and buses, are decreasing and their adoption is accelerating, but they require continued investments in supporting infrastructure to increase scale of deployment (*high confidence*). Advances in battery technologies could facilitate the electrification of heavy-duty trucks and complement conventional electric rail systems (*medium confidence*). There are growing concerns about critical minerals needed for batteries. Material and supply diversification strategies, energy and material efficiency improvements, and circular material flows can reduce the environmental footprint and material supply risks for battery production (*medium confidence*). Sourced sustainably and with low-GHG emissions feedstocks, bio-based fuels, blended or unblended with fossil fuels, can provide mitigation benefits, particularly in the short and medium term (*medium confidence*). Low-GHG emissions hydrogen and hydrogen derivatives, including synthetic fuels, can offer mitigation potential in some contexts and land-based transport segments (*medium confidence*). {3.4, 6.3, 10.3, 10.4, 10.7, 10.8, Box 10.6}

C.8.4 While efficiency improvements (e.g., optimised aircraft and vessel designs, mass reduction, and propulsion system improvements) can provide some mitigation potential, additional CO_2 emissions mitigation technologies for aviation and shipping will be required (*high confidence*). For aviation, such technologies include high energy density biofuels (*high confidence*), and low-emission hydrogen and synthetic fuels (*medium confidence*). Alternative fuels for shipping include low-emission hydrogen, ammonia, biofuels, and other synthetic fuels (*medium confidence*). Electrification could play a niche role for aviation and shipping for short trips (*medium confidence*) and can reduce emissions from port and airport operations (*high confidence*). Improvements to national and international governance structures would further enable the decarbonisation of shipping and aviation (*medium confidence*). Such improvements could include, for example, the implementation of stricter efficiency and carbon intensity standards for the sectors (*medium confidence*). {10.3. 10.5, 10.6, 10.7, 10.8, Box 10.5}

C.8.5 The substantial potential for GHG emissions reductions, both direct and indirect, in the transport sector largely depends on power sector decarbonisation, and low-emissions feedstocks and production chains (*high confidence*). Integrated transport and energy infrastructure planning and operations can enable sectoral synergies and reduce the environmental, social, and economic impacts of decarbonising the transport and energy sectors (*high confidence*). Technology transfer and financing can support developing countries leapfrogging or transitioning to low-emissions transport systems thereby providing multiple co-benefits (*high confidence*). {10.2, 10.3, 10.4, 10.5, 10.6, 10.7, 10.8}

C.9 **AFOLU mitigation options, when sustainably implemented, can deliver large-scale GHG emission reductions and enhanced removals, but cannot fully compensate for delayed action in other sectors. In addition, sustainably sourced agricultural and forest products can be used instead of more GHG-intensive products in other sectors. Barriers to implementation and trade-offs may result from the impacts of climate change, competing demands on land, conflicts with food security and livelihoods, the complexity of land ownership and management systems, and cultural aspects. There are many country-specific opportunities to provide co-benefits (such as biodiversity conservation, ecosystem services, and livelihoods) and avoid risks (for example, through adaptation to climate change).** (*high confidence*) {7.4, 7.6, 7.7, 12.5, 12.6}

C.9.1 The projected economic mitigation potential of AFOLU options between 2020 and 2050, at costs below USD100 tCO_2-eq^{-1}, is 8–14 $GtCO_2$-eq yr^{-1} [60] (*high confidence*). 30–50% of this potential is available at less than USD20 tCO_2-eq and could be upscaled in the near term across most regions (*high confidence*). The largest share of this economic potential [4.2–7.4 $GtCO_2$-eq yr^{-1}] comes from the conservation, improved management, and restoration of forests and other ecosystems (coastal wetlands, peatlands, savannas and grasslands), with reduced deforestation in tropical regions having the highest total mitigation. Improved and sustainable crop and livestock management, and carbon sequestration in agriculture (the latter including soil carbon management in croplands and grasslands, agroforestry and biochar), can contribute 1.8–4.1 $GtCO_2$-eq yr^{-1} reduction. Demand-side and material substitution measures, such as shifting to balanced, sustainable healthy diets,[61] reducing food loss and waste, and using bio-materials, can contribute 2.1 [1.1–3.6] $GtCO_2$-eq yr^{-1} reduction. In addition, demand-side measures together with the sustainable intensification of agriculture can reduce ecosystem conversion and CH_4 and N_2O emissions, and free up land for reforestation and restoration, and the production of renewable energy. The improved and expanded use of wood products sourced from sustainably managed forests also has potential through the allocation of harvested wood to longer-lived products, increasing recycling or material substitution. AFOLU mitigation measures cannot compensate for delayed emission reductions in other sectors. Persistent and region-specific barriers continue to hamper the economic and political feasibility of deploying AFOLU mitigation options. Assisting countries to overcome barriers will help to achieve significant mitigation (*medium confidence*). (Figure SPM.6) {7.1, 7.4, 7.5, 7.6}

C.9.2 AFOLU carbon sequestration and GHG emission reduction options have both co-benefits and risks in terms of biodiversity and ecosystem conservation, food and water security, wood supply, livelihoods and land tenure and land-use rights of Indigenous Peoples, local communities and small land owners. Many options have co-benefits but those that compete for land and land-based resources can pose risks. The scale of benefit or risk largely depends on the type of activity undertaken, deployment strategy (e.g., scale, method), and context (e.g., soil, biome, climate, food system, land ownership) that vary geographically and over time. Risks can be avoided when AFOLU mitigation is pursued in response to the needs and perspectives of multiple stakeholders to achieve outcomes that maximize co-benefits while limiting trade-offs. (*high confidence*) {7.4, 7.6, 12.3}

C.9.3 Realising the AFOLU mitigation potential entails overcoming institutional, economic and policy constraints and managing potential trade-offs (*high confidence*). Land-use decisions are often spread across a wide range of land owners; demand-side measures depend on billions of consumers in diverse contexts. Barriers to the implementation of AFOLU mitigation include insufficient institutional and financial support, uncertainty over long-term additionality and trade-offs, weak governance, insecure land ownership, low incomes and the lack of access to alternative sources of income, and the risk of reversal. Limited access to technology, data, and know-how is a barrier to implementation. Research and development are key for all measures. For example, measures for the mitigation of agricultural CH_4 and N_2O emissions with emerging technologies show promising results. However, the mitigation of agricultural CH_4 and N_2O emissions is still constrained by cost, the diversity and complexity of agricultural systems, and by increasing demands to raise agricultural yields, and increasing demand for livestock products. (*high confidence*) {7.4, 7.6}

C.9.4 Net costs of delivering 5–6 $GtCO_2$ yr^{-1} of forest-related carbon sequestration and emission reduction as assessed with sectoral models are estimated to reach to about USD400 billion yr^{-1} by 2050. The costs of other AFOLU mitigation measures are highly context specific. Financing needs in AFOLU, and in particular in forestry, include both the direct effects of any changes in

---

[60] The global top-down estimates and sectoral bottom-up estimates described here do not include the substitution of emissions from fossil fuels and GHG-intensive materials. 8–14 $GtCO_2$-eq yr^{-1} represents the mean of the AFOLU economic mitigation potential estimates from top-down estimates (lower bound of range) and global sectoral bottom-up estimates (upper bound of range). The full range from top-down estimates is 4.1–17.3 $GtCO_2$-eq yr^{-1} using a 'no policy' baseline. The full range from global sectoral studies is 6.7–23.4 $GtCO_2$-eq yr^{-1} using a variety of baselines. (*high confidence*)

[61] 'Sustainable healthy diets' promote all dimensions of individuals' health and well-being; have low environmental pressure and impact; are accessible, affordable, safe and equitable; and are culturally acceptable, as described in FAO and WHO. The related concept of 'balanced diets' refers to diets that feature plant-based foods, such as those based on coarse grains, legumes, fruits and vegetables, nuts and seeds, and animal-sourced food produced in resilient, sustainable and low-GHG emission systems, as described in SRCCL.

C.9.5 Context specific policies and measures have been effective in demonstrating the delivery of AFOLU carbon sequestration and GHG emission reduction options but the above-mentioned constraints hinder large scale implementation (*medium confidence*). Deploying land-based mitigation can draw on lessons from experience with regulations, policies, economic incentives, payments (e.g., for biofuels, control of nutrient pollution, water regulations, conservation and forest carbon, ecosystem services, and rural livelihoods), and from diverse forms of knowledge such as Indigenous knowledge, local knowledge and scientific knowledge. Indigenous Peoples, private forest owners, local farmers and communities manage a significant share of global forests and agricultural land and play a central role in land-based mitigation options. Scaling successful policies and measures relies on governance that emphasises integrated land-use planning and management framed by SDGs, with support for implementation. (*high confidence*) {7.4, Box 7.2, 7.6}

C.10 **Demand-side mitigation encompasses changes in infrastructure use, end-use technology adoption, and socio-cultural and behavioural change. Demand-side measures and new ways of end-use service provision can reduce global GHG emissions in end-use sectors by 40–70% by 2050 compared to baseline scenarios, while some regions and socioeconomic groups require additional energy and resources. Demand-side mitigation response options are consistent with improving basic well-being for all. (*high confidence*) (Figure SPM.6) {5.3, 5.4, Figure 5.6, Figure 5.14, 8.2, 9.4, 10.2, 11.3, 11.4, 12.4, Figure TS.22}**

C.10.1 Infrastructure design and access, and technology access and adoption, including information and communication technologies, influence patterns of demand and ways of providing services, such as mobility, shelter, water, sanitation, and nutrition. Illustrative global low-demand scenarios, accounting for regional differences, indicate that more efficient end-use energy conversion can improve services while reducing the need for upstream energy by 45% by 2050 compared to 2020. Demand-side mitigation potential differs between and within regions, and some regions and populations require additional energy, capacity, and resources for human well-being. The lowest population quartile by income worldwide faces shortfalls in shelter, mobility, and nutrition. (*high confidence*) {5.2, 5.3, 5.4, 5.5, Figure 5.6, Figure 5.10, Table 5.2, Figure TS.20, Figure TS.22}

C.10.2 By 2050, comprehensive demand-side strategies could reduce direct and indirect CO_2 and non-CO_2 GHG emissions in three end-use sectors (buildings, land transport, and food) globally by 40%–70% compared to the 2050 emissions projection of two scenarios consistent with policies announced by national governments until 2020. With policy support, socio-cultural options and behavioural change can reduce global GHG emissions of end-use sectors by at least 5% rapidly, with most of the potential in developed countries, and more until 2050, if combined with improved infrastructure design and access. Individuals with high socio-economic status contribute disproportionately to emissions and have the highest potential for emissions reductions, e.g., as citizens, investors, consumers, role models, and professionals. (*high confidence*) (Figure SPM.6) {5.2, 5.3, 5.4, 5.5, 5.6, Supplementary Material Table 5.SM.2, 8.4, 9.9, 13.2, 13.5, 13.8, Figure TS.20}

C.10.3 A range of 5–30% of global annual GHG emissions from end-use sectors are avoidable by 2050, compared to 2050 emissions projection of two scenarios consistent with policies announced by national governments until 2020, through changes in the built environment, new and repurposed infrastructures and service provision through compact cities, co-location of jobs and housing, more efficient use of floor space and energy in buildings, and reallocation of street space for active mobility (*high confidence*). (Figure SPM.6) {5.3.1, 5.3.3, 5.4, Figure 5.7, Figure 5.13, Table 5.1, Table 5.5, Supplementary Material Table 5.SM.2, 8.4, 9.5, 10.2, 11.3, 11.4, Table 11.6, Box TS.12}

C.10.4 Choice architecture[62] can help end-users adopt, as relevant to consumers, culture and country contexts, low-GHG-intensive options such as balanced, sustainable healthy diets[61] acknowledging nutritional needs; food waste reduction; adaptive heating and cooling choices for thermal comfort; building-integrated renewable energy; and electric light-duty vehicles, and shifts to walking, cycling, shared pooled and public transit; and sustainable consumption by intensive use of longer-lived repairable products (*high confidence*). Addressing inequality and many forms of status consumption[63] and focusing on wellbeing supports climate change mitigation efforts (*high confidence*). (Figure SPM.6) {2.4.3, 2.6.2, 4.2.5, 5.1, 5.2, 5.3, 5.4, Figure 5.4, Figure 5.10, Table 5.2, Supplementary Material Table 5.SM.2, 7.4.5, 8.2, 8.4, 9.4, 10.2, 12.4, Figure TS.20}

---

[62] 'Choice architecture' describes the presentation of choices to consumers, and the impact that presentation has on consumer decision-making.

[63] 'Status consumption' refers to the consumption of goods and services which publicly demonstrates social prestige.

Demand-side mitigation can be achieved through changes in socio-cultural factors, infrastructure design and use, and end-use technology adoption by 2050.

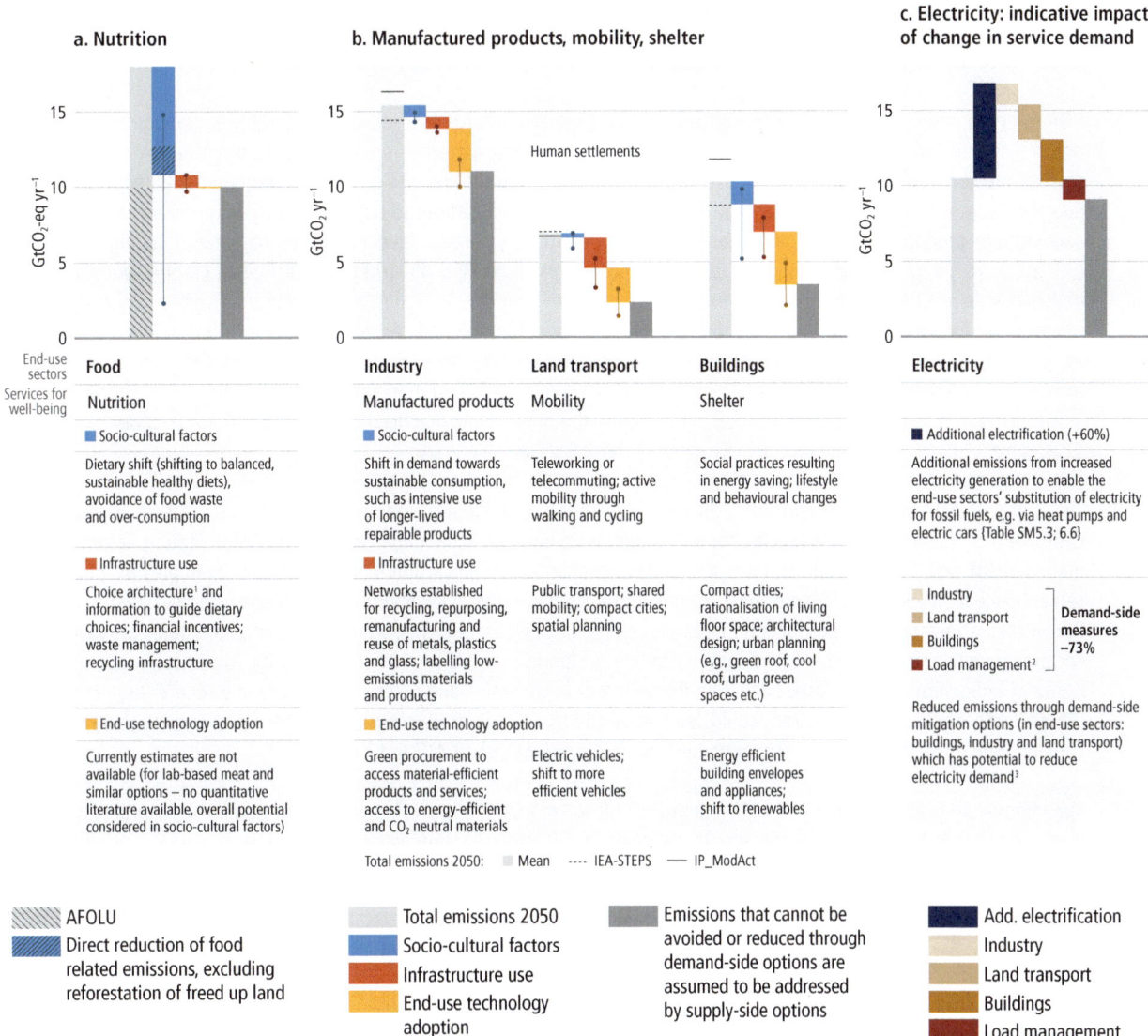

a. Nutrition

b. Manufactured products, mobility, shelter

c. Electricity: indicative impacts of change in service demand

		Food	Industry	Land transport	Buildings	Electricity
End-use sectors		Food	Industry	Land transport	Buildings	Electricity
Services for well-being		Nutrition	Manufactured products	Mobility	Shelter	

■ Socio-cultural factors

Dietary shift (shifting to balanced, sustainable healthy diets), avoidance of food waste and over-consumption

■ Socio-cultural factors

Shift in demand towards sustainable consumption, such as intensive use of longer-lived repairable products

Teleworking or telecommuting; active mobility through walking and cycling

Social practices resulting in energy saving; lifestyle and behavioural changes

■ Additional electrification (+60%)

Additional emissions from increased electricity generation to enable the end-use sectors' substitution of electricity for fossil fuels, e.g. via heat pumps and electric cars {Table SM5.3; 6.6}

■ Infrastructure use

Choice architecture[1] and information to guide dietary choices; financial incentives; waste management; recycling infrastructure

■ Infrastructure use

Networks established for recycling, repurposing, remanufacturing and reuse of metals, plastics and glass; labelling low-emissions materials and products

Public transport; shared mobility; compact cities; spatial planning

Compact cities; rationalisation of living floor space; architectural design; urban planning (e.g., green roof, cool roof, urban green spaces etc.)

■ Industry
■ Land transport
■ Buildings
■ Load management[2]

Demand-side measures −73%

Reduced emissions through demand-side mitigation options (in end-use sectors: buildings, industry and land transport) which has potential to reduce electricity demand[3]

■ End-use technology adoption

Currently estimates are not available (for lab-based meat and similar options – no quantitative literature available, overall potential considered in socio-cultural factors)

■ End-use technology adoption

Green procurement to access material-efficient products and services; access to energy-efficient and CO₂ neutral materials

Electric vehicles; shift to more efficient vehicles

Energy efficient building envelopes and appliances; shift to renewables

Total emissions 2050: ▢ Mean ---- IEA-STEPS ── IP_ModAct

▨ AFOLU
▨ Direct reduction of food related emissions, excluding reforestation of freed up land

▢ Total emissions 2050
■ Socio-cultural factors
■ Infrastructure use
■ End-use technology adoption

■ Emissions that cannot be avoided or reduced through demand-side options are assumed to be addressed by supply-side options

■ Add. electrification
■ Industry
■ Land transport
■ Buildings
■ Load management

[1] The presentation of choices to consumers, and the impact of that presentation on consumer decision-making.

[2] Load management refers to demand-side flexibility that cuts across all sectors and can be achieved through incentive design like time of use pricing/monitoring by artificial intelligence, diversification of storage facilities, etc.

[3] The impact of demand-side mitigation on electricity sector emissions depends on the baseline carbon intensity of electricity supply, which is scenario dependent.

Figure SPM.6 | Indicative potential of demand-side mitigation options by 2050. Figure SPM.6 covers the indicative potential of demand-side options for the year 2050. Figure SPM.7 covers cost and potentials for the year 2030. Demand-side mitigation response options are categorised into three broad domains: 'socio-cultural factors', associated with individual choices, behaviour, lifestyle changes, social norms, and culture; 'infrastructure use', related to the design and use of supporting hard and soft infrastructure that enables changes in individual choices and behaviour; and 'end-use technology adoption', referring to the uptake of technologies by end-users. Demand-side mitigation is a central element of the IMP-LD and IMP-SP scenarios (Figure SPM.5). **Panel a** (Nutrition) demand-side potentials in 2050 assessment is based on bottom-up studies and is estimated following the 2050 baseline for the food sector presented in peer-reviewed literature (more information in Supplementary Material 5.II, and Section 7.4.5). **Panel b** (Manufactured products, mobility, shelter) the assessment of potentials for total emissions in 2050 are estimated based on approximately 500 bottom-up studies representing all global regions (detailed list is in Supplementary Material Table 5.SM.2). Baseline is provided by the sectoral mean GHG emissions in 2050 of the two scenarios consistent with policies announced by national governments until 2020. The heights of the coloured columns represent the potentials represented by the median value. These are based on a range of values available in the case studies from literature shown in Supplementary Material 5.SM.II. The range is shown by the dots connected by dotted lines representing the highest and the lowest potentials reported in the literature. **Panel a** shows the demand-side potential of socio-cultural factors and infrastructure use. The median value of direct emissions (mostly non-CO₂) reduction through socio-cultural factors is 1.9 GtCO₂-eq without considering land-use change through reforestation of freed up land. If changes in land-use pattern enabled by this change in food demand are considered, the indicative potential could reach 7 GtCO₂-eq. Panel b illustrates mitigation potential in industry, land transport and buildings end-use sectors through demand-side options. Key options are presented in the summary table below the figure and the details are in Supplementary Material Table 5.SM.2. **Panel c** visualises how sectoral demand-side mitigation options (presented in panel b) change demand on the electricity distribution system. Electricity accounts for an increasing proportion of final energy demand in 2050 (additional electricity bar) in line with multiple bottom-up studies (detailed list is in Supplementary Material Table 5.SM.3), and Chapter 6 (Section 6.6). These studies are used to compute the impact of end-use electrification which increases overall electricity demand. Some of the projected increase in electricity demand can be avoided through demand-side mitigation options in the domains of socio-cultural factors and infrastructure use in end-use electricity use in buildings, industry, and land transport found in literature based on bottom-up assessments. Dark grey columns show the emissions that cannot be avoided through demand-side mitigation options. {5.3, Figure 5.7, Supplementary Material 5.SM.II}

C.11 **The deployment of carbon dioxide removal (CDR) to counterbalance hard-to-abate residual emissions is unavoidable if net zero CO_2 or GHG emissions are to be achieved. The scale and timing of deployment will depend on the trajectories of gross emission reductions in different sectors. Upscaling the deployment of CDR depends on developing effective approaches to address feasibility and sustainability constraints especially at large scales. (*high confidence*) {3.4, 7.4, 12.3, Cross-Chapter Box 8 in Chapter 12}**

C.11.1 CDR refers to anthropogenic activities that remove CO_2 from the atmosphere and store it durably in geological, terrestrial, or ocean reservoirs, or in products. CDR methods vary in terms of their maturity, removal process, time scale of carbon storage, storage medium, mitigation potential, cost, co-benefits, impacts and risks, and governance requirements (*high confidence*). Specifically, maturity ranges from lower maturity (e.g., ocean alkalinisation) to higher maturity (e.g., reforestation); removal and storage potential ranges from lower potential (<1 $GtCO_2$ yr^{-1}, e.g., blue carbon management) to higher potential (>3 $GtCO_2$ yr^{-1}, e.g., agroforestry); costs range from lower cost (e.g., USD-45–100 per tCO_2 for soil carbon sequestration) to higher cost (e.g., USD100–300 per tCO_2 for DACCS) (*medium confidence*). Estimated storage time scales vary from decades to centuries for methods that store carbon in vegetation and through soil carbon management, to 10,000 years or more for methods that store carbon in geological formations (*high confidence*). The processes by which CO_2 is removed from the atmosphere are categorised as biological, geochemical or chemical. Afforestation, reforestation, improved forest management, agroforestry and soil carbon sequestration are currently the only widely practiced CDR methods (*high confidence*). {7.4, 7.6, 12.3, Table 12.6, Cross-Chapter Box 8 in Chapter 12, Table TS.7; AR6 WGI 5.6}

C.11.2 The impacts, risks and co-benefits of CDR deployment for ecosystems, biodiversity and people will be highly variable depending on the method, site-specific context, implementation and scale (*high confidence*). Reforestation, improved forest management, soil carbon sequestration, peatland restoration and blue carbon management are examples of methods that can enhance biodiversity and ecosystem functions, employment and local livelihoods, depending on context (*high confidence*). In contrast, afforestation or production of biomass crops for BECCS or biochar, when poorly implemented, can have adverse socio-economic and environmental impacts, including on biodiversity, food and water security, local livelihoods and on the rights of Indigenous Peoples, especially if implemented at large scales and where land tenure is insecure (*high confidence*). Ocean fertilisation, if implemented, could lead to nutrient redistribution, restructuring of ecosystems, enhanced oxygen consumption and acidification in deeper waters (*medium confidence*). {7.4, 7.6, 12.3, 12.5}

C.11.3 The removal and storage of CO_2 through vegetation and soil management can be reversed by human or natural disturbances; it is also prone to climate change impacts. In comparison, CO_2 stored in geological and ocean reservoirs (via BECCS, DACCS, ocean alkalinisation) and as carbon in biochar is less prone to reversal. (*high confidence*) {6.4, 7.4, 12.3}

C.11.4 In addition to deep, rapid, and sustained emission reductions CDR can fulfil three different complementary roles globally or at country level: lowering net CO_2 or net GHG emissions in the near term; counterbalancing 'hard-to-abate' residual emissions (e.g., emissions from agriculture, aviation, shipping, industrial processes) in order to help reach net zero CO_2 or net zero GHG emissions in the mid-term; and achieving net negative CO_2 or GHG emissions in the long term if deployed at levels exceeding annual residual emissions. (*high confidence*) {3.3, 7.4, 11.3, 12.3, Cross-Chapter Box 8 in Chapter 12}

C.11.5 Rapid emission reductions in all sectors interact with future scale of deployment of CDR methods, and their associated risks, impacts and co-benefits. Upscaling the deployment of CDR methods depends on developing effective approaches to address sustainability and feasibility constraints, potential impacts, co-benefits and risks. Enablers of CDR include accelerated research, development and demonstration, improved tools for risk assessment and management, targeted incentives and development of agreed methods for measurement, reporting and verification of carbon flows. (*high confidence*) {3.4, 7.6, 12.3}

C.12   Mitigation options costing USD100 tCO$_2$-eq^{-1} or less could reduce global GHG emissions by at least half the 2019 level by 2030 (*high confidence*). Global GDP continues to grow in modelled pathways[64] but, without accounting for the economic benefits of mitigation action from avoided damages from climate change nor from reduced adaptation costs, it is a few percent lower in 2050 compared to pathways without mitigation beyond current policies. The global economic benefit of limiting warming to 2°C is reported to exceed the cost of mitigation in most of the assessed literature (*medium confidence*). (Figure SPM.7) {3.6, 3.8, Cross-Working Group Box 1 in Chapter 3, 12.2, Box TS.7}

C.12.1   Based on a detailed sectoral assessment of mitigation options, it is estimated that mitigation options costing USD100 tCO$_2$-eq^{-1} or less could reduce global GHG emissions by at least half of the 2019 level by 2030 (options costing less than USD20 tCO$_2$-eq^{-1} are estimated to make up more than half of this potential).[65] For a smaller part of the potential, deployment leads to net cost savings. Large contributions with costs less than USD20 tCO$_2$-eq^{-1} come from solar and wind energy, energy efficiency improvements, reduced conversion of natural ecosystems, and CH$_4$ emissions reductions (coal mining, oil and gas, waste). The mitigation potentials and mitigation costs of individual technologies in a specific context or region may differ greatly from the provided estimates. The assessment of the underlying literature suggests that the relative contribution of the various options could change beyond 2030. (*medium confidence*) (Figure SPM.7) {12.2}

C.12.2   The aggregate effects of climate change mitigation on global GDP are small compared to global projected GDP growth in assessed modelled global scenarios that quantify the macroeconomic implications of climate change mitigation, but that do not account for damages from climate change nor adaptation costs (*high confidence*). For example, compared to pathways that assume the continuation of policies implemented by the end of 2020, assessed global GDP reached in 2050 is reduced by 1.3–2.7% in modelled pathways assuming coordinated global action starting between now and 2025 at the latest to limit warming to 2°C (>67%). The corresponding average reduction in annual global GDP growth over 2020–2050 is 0.04–0.09 percentage points. In assessed modelled pathways, regardless of the level of mitigation action, global GDP is projected to at least double (increase by at least 100%) over 2020–2050. For modelled global pathways in other temperature categories, the reductions in global GDP in 2050 compared to pathways that assume the continuation of policies implemented by the end of 2020 are as follows: 2.6–4.2% (C1), 1.6–2.8% (C2), 0.8–2.1% (C4), 0.5–1.2% (C5). The corresponding reductions in average annual global GDP growth over 2020–2050, in percentage points, are as follows: 0.09–0.14 (C1), 0.05–0.09 (C2), 0.03–0.07 (C4), 0.02–0.04 (C5).[66] There are large variations in the modelled effects of mitigation on GDP across regions, depending notably on economic structure, regional emissions reductions, policy design and level of international cooperation[67] (*high confidence*). Country-level studies also show large variations in the effect of mitigation on GDP depending notably on the level of mitigation and on the way it is achieved (*high confidence*). Macroeconomic implications of mitigation co-benefits and trade-offs are not quantified comprehensively across the above scenarios and depend strongly on mitigation strategies (*high confidence*). {3.6, 4.2, Box TS.7, Annex III.I.2, Annex III.I.9, Annex III.I.10 and Annex III.II.3}

C.12.3   Estimates of aggregate economic benefits from avoiding damages from climate change, and from reduced adaptation costs, increase with the stringency of mitigation (*high confidence*). Models that incorporate the economic damages from climate change find that the global cost of limiting warming to 2°C over the 21st century is lower than the global economic benefits of reducing warming, unless: (i) climate damages are towards the low end of the range; or, (ii) future damages are discounted at high rates (*medium confidence*).[68] Modelled pathways with a peak in global emissions between now and 2025 at the latest, compared to modelled pathways with a later peak in global emissions, entail more rapid near-term transitions and higher up-front investments, but bring long-term gains for the economy, as well as earlier benefits of avoided climate change impacts (*high confidence*). The precise magnitude of these gains and benefits is difficult to quantify. {1.7, 3.6, Cross-Working Group Box 1 in Chapter 3, Box TS.7; AR6 WGII SPM B.4}

---

[64]   In modelled pathways that limit warming to 2°C (>67%) or lower.

[65]   The methodology underlying the assessment is described in the caption to Figure SPM.7.

[66]   These estimates are based on 311 pathways that report effects of mitigation on GDP and that could be classified in temperature categories, but that do not account for damages from climate change nor adaptation costs and that mostly do not reflect the economic impacts of mitigation co-benefits and trade-offs. The ranges given are interquartile ranges. The macroeconomic implications quantified vary largely depending on technology assumptions, climate/emissions target formulation, model structure and assumptions, and the extent to which pre-existing inefficiencies are considered. Models that produced the pathways classified in temperature categories do not represent the full diversity of existing modelling paradigms, and there are in the literature models that find higher mitigation costs, or conversely lower mitigation costs and even gains. {1.7, 3.2, 3.6, Annex III.I.2, Annex III.I.9, Annex III.I.10 and Annex III.II.3}

[67]   In modelled cost-effective pathways with a globally uniform carbon price, without international financial transfers or complementary policies, carbon intensive and energy exporting countries are projected to bear relatively higher mitigation costs because of a deeper transformation of their economies and changes in international energy markets. {3.6}

[68]   The evidence is too limited to make a similar robust conclusion for limiting warming to 1.5°C.

Many options available now in all sectors are estimated to offer substantial potential to reduce net emissions by 2030. Relative potentials and costs will vary across countries and in the longer term compared to 2030.

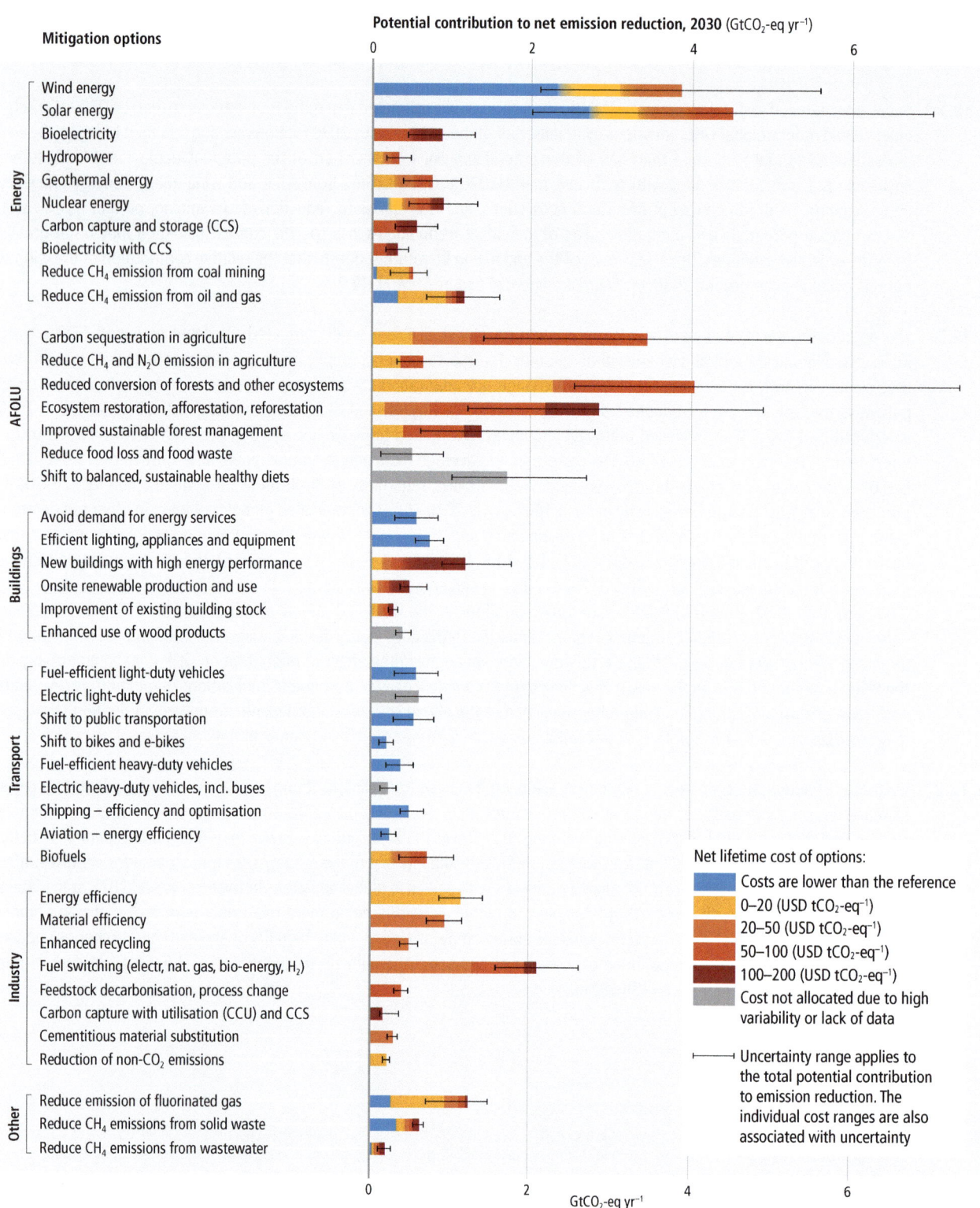

Figure SPM.7 | Overview of mitigation options and their estimated ranges of costs and potentials in 2030.

Figure SPM.7 (continued): Overview of mitigation options and their estimated ranges of costs and potentials in 2030. Costs shown are net lifetime costs of avoided greenhouse gas emissions. Costs are calculated relative to a reference technology. The assessments per sector were carried out using a common methodology, including definition of potentials, target year, reference scenarios, and cost definitions. The mitigation potential (shown in the horizontal axis) is the quantity of net GHG emission reductions that can be achieved by a given mitigation option relative to a specified emission baseline. Net GHG emission reductions are the sum of reduced emissions and/or enhanced sinks. The baseline used consists of current policy (around 2019) reference scenarios from the AR6 scenarios database (25/75 percentile values). The assessment relies on approximately 175 underlying sources, that together give a fair representation of emission reduction potentials across all regions. The mitigation potentials are assessed independently for each option and are not necessarily additive. {12.2.1, 12.2.2} The length of the solid bars represents the mitigation potential of an option. The error bars display the full ranges of the estimates for the total mitigation potentials. Sources of uncertainty for the cost estimates include assumptions on the rate of technological advancement, regional differences, and economies of scale, among others. Those uncertainties are not displayed in the figure. Potentials are broken down into cost categories, indicated by different colours (see legend). Only discounted lifetime monetary costs are considered. Where a gradual colour transition is shown, the breakdown of the potential into cost categories is not well known or depends heavily on factors such as geographical location, resource availability, and regional circumstances, and the colours indicate the range of estimates. Costs were taken directly from the underlying studies (mostly in the period 2015–2020) or recent datasets. No correction for inflation was applied, given the wide cost ranges used. The cost of the reference technologies were also taken from the underlying studies and recent datasets. Cost reductions through technological learning are taken into account.[69]

– When interpreting this figure, the following should be taken into account:

– The mitigation potential is uncertain, as it will depend on the reference technology (and emissions) being displaced, the rate of new technology adoption, and several other factors.

– Cost and mitigation potential estimates were extrapolated from available sectoral studies. Actual costs and potentials would vary by place, context and time.

– Beyond 2030, the relative importance of the assessed mitigation options is expected to change, in particular while pursuing long-term mitigation goals, recognising also that the emphasis for particular options will vary across regions (for specific mitigation options see SPM Sections C4.1, C5.2, C7.3, C8.3 and C9.1).

– Different options have different feasibilities beyond the cost aspects, which are not reflected in the figure (compare with SPM Section E.1).

– The potentials in the cost range USD100–200 tCO$_2$-eq^{-1} may be underestimated for some options.

– Costs for accommodating the integration of variable renewable energy sources in electricity systems are expected to be modest until 2030, and are not included because of complexities in attributing such costs to individual technology options.

– Cost range categories are ordered from low to high. This order does not imply any sequence of implementation.

– Externalities are not taken into account. {12.2, Table 12.3, 6.4, Table 7.3, Supplementary Material Table 9.SM.2, Supplementary Material Table 9.SM.3, 10.6, 11.4, Figure 11.13, Supplementary Material 12.SM.1.2.3}

---

[69] For nuclear energy, modelled costs for long-term storage of radioactive waste are included.

D. Linkages between Mitigation, Adaptation, and Sustainable Development

D.1 **Accelerated and equitable climate action in mitigating, and adapting to, climate change impacts is critical to sustainable development. Climate change actions can also result in some trade-offs. The trade-offs of individual options could be managed through policy design. The Sustainable Development Goals (SDGs) adopted under the UN 2030 Agenda for Sustainable Development can be used as a basis for evaluating climate action in the context of sustainable development.** (*high confidence*) (Figure SPM.8) {1.6, 3.7, 17.3, Figure TS.29}

D.1.1 Human-induced climate change is a consequence of more than a century of net GHG emissions from unsustainable energy use, land-use and land use change, lifestyle and patterns of consumption and production. Without urgent, effective and equitable mitigation actions, climate change increasingly threatens the health and livelihoods of people around the globe, ecosystem health and biodiversity. There are both synergies and trade-offs between climate action and the pursuit of other SDGs. Accelerated and equitable climate action in mitigating, and adapting to, climate change impacts is critical to sustainable development. (*high confidence*) {1.6, Cross-Chapter Box 5 in Chapter 4, 7.2, 7.3, 17.3; AR6 WGI SPM.A, Figure SPM.2; AR6 WGII SPM.B2, Figure SPM.3, Figure SPM.4b, Figure SPM.5}

D.1.2 Synergies and trade-offs depend on the development context including inequalities, with consideration of climate justice. They also depend on means of implementation, intra- and inter-sectoral interactions, cooperation between countries and regions, the sequencing, timing and stringency of mitigation actions, governance, and policy design. Maximising synergies and avoiding trade-offs pose particular challenges for developing countries, vulnerable populations, and Indigenous Peoples with limited institutional, technological and financial capacity, and with constrained social, human, and economic capital. Trade-offs can be evaluated and minimised by giving emphasis to capacity building, finance, governance, technology transfer, investments, and development and social equity considerations with meaningful participation of Indigenous Peoples and vulnerable populations. (*high confidence*) {1.6, 1.7, 3.7, 5.2, 5.6, 7.4, 7.6, 17.4}

D.1.3 There are potential synergies between sustainable development and energy efficiency, renewable energy, urban planning with more green spaces, reduced air pollution, and demand-side mitigation including shifts to balanced, sustainable healthy diets (*high confidence*). Electrification combined with low-GHG energy, and shifts to public transport can enhance health, employment, and can elicit energy security and deliver equity (*high confidence*). In industry, electrification and circular material flows contribute to reduced environmental pressures and increased economic activity and employment. However, some industrial options could impose high costs (*medium confidence*). (Figure SPM.8) {5.2, 8.2, 11.3, 11.5, 17.3, Figure TS.29}

D.1.4 Land-based options such as reforestation and forest conservation, avoided deforestation, restoration and conservation of natural ecosystems and biodiversity, improved sustainable forest management, agroforestry, soil carbon management and options that reduce CH_4 and N_2O emissions in agriculture from livestock and soil, can have multiple synergies with the SDGs. These include enhancing sustainable agricultural productivity and resilience, food security, providing additional biomass for human use, and addressing land degradation. Maximising synergies and managing trade-offs depend on specific practices, scale of implementation, governance, capacity building, integration with existing land use, and the involvement of local communities and Indigenous Peoples and through benefit-sharing, supported by frameworks such as Land Degradation Neutrality within the UNCCD. (*high confidence*) {3.7, 7.4, 12.5, 17.3}

D.1.5 Trade-offs in terms of employment, water use, land-use competition and biodiversity, as well as access to, and the affordability of, energy, food, and water can be avoided by well-implemented land-based mitigation options, especially those that do not threaten existing sustainable land uses and land rights, though more frameworks for integrated policy implementation are required. The sustainability of bioenergy and other bio-based products is influenced by feedstock, land management practice, climatic region, the context of existing land management, and the timing, scale and speed of deployment. (*medium confidence*) {3.5, 3.7, 7.4, 12.4, 12.5, 17.1}

D.1.6 CDR methods such as soil carbon sequestration and biochar[70] can improve soil quality and food production capacity. Ecosystem restoration and reforestation sequester carbon in plants and soil, and can enhance biodiversity and provide additional

---

[70] Potential risks, knowledge gaps due to the relative immaturity of use of biochar as a soil amendment and unknown impacts of widespread application, and co-benefits of biochar are reviewed in Section 7.4.3.2.

biomass, but can displace food production and livelihoods, which calls for integrated approaches to land-use planning, to meet multiple objectives including food security. However, due to limited application of some of the options today, there are some uncertainties about potential benefits. (*high confidence*) {3.7, 7.4, 7.6, 12.5, 17.3, Table TS.7}

Mitigation options have synergies with many Sustainable Development Goals, but some options can also have trade-offs. The synergies and trade-offs vary dependent on context and scale.

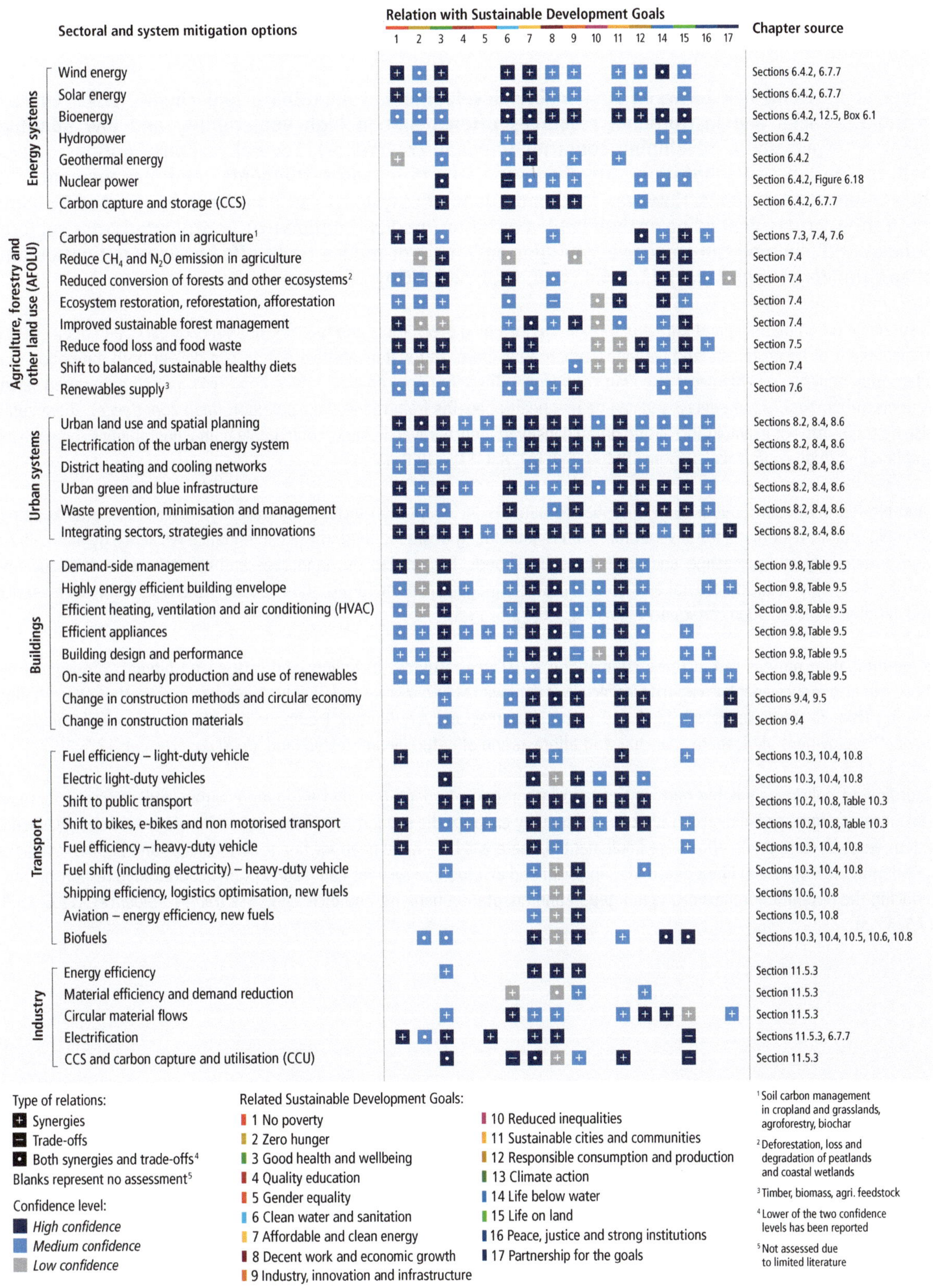

Sectoral and system mitigation options
Relation with Sustainable Development Goals
1 2 3 4 5 6 7 8 9 10 11 12 14 15 16 17
Chapter source
Energy systems
Wind energy
Solar energy
Bioenergy
Hydropower
Geothermal energy
Nuclear power
Carbon capture and storage (CCS)
Sections 6.4.2, 6.7.7
Sections 6.4.2, 6.7.7
Sections 6.4.2, 12.5, Box 6.1
Section 6.4.2
Section 6.4.2
Section 6.4.2, Figure 6.18
Section 6.4.2, 6.7.7
Agriculture, forestry and other land use (AFOLU)
Carbon sequestration in agriculture[1]
Reduce CH_4 and N_2O emission in agriculture
Reduced conversion of forests and other ecosystems[2]
Ecosystem restoration, reforestation, afforestation
Improved sustainable forest management
Reduce food loss and food waste
Shift to balanced, sustainable healthy diets
Renewables supply[3]
Sections 7.3, 7.4, 7.6
Section 7.4
Section 7.4
Section 7.4
Section 7.4
Section 7.5
Section 7.4
Section 7.6
Urban systems
Urban land use and spatial planning
Electrification of the urban energy system
District heating and cooling networks
Urban green and blue infrastructure
Waste prevention, minimisation and management
Integrating sectors, strategies and innovations
Sections 8.2, 8.4, 8.6
Sections 8.2, 8.4, 8.6
Sections 8.2, 8.4, 8.6
Sections 8.2, 8.4, 8.6
Sections 8.2, 8.4, 8.6
Sections 8.2, 8.4, 8.6
Buildings
Demand-side management
Highly energy efficient building envelope
Efficient heating, ventilation and air conditioning (HVAC)
Efficient appliances
Building design and performance
On-site and nearby production and use of renewables
Change in construction methods and circular economy
Change in construction materials
Section 9.8, Table 9.5
Section 9.8, Table 9.5
Section 9.8, Table 9.5
Section 9.8, Table 9.5
Section 9.8, Table 9.5
Section 9.8, Table 9.5
Sections 9.4, 9.5
Section 9.4
Transport
Fuel efficiency – light-duty vehicle
Electric light-duty vehicles
Shift to public transport
Shift to bikes, e-bikes and non motorised transport
Fuel efficiency – heavy-duty vehicle
Fuel shift (including electricity) – heavy-duty vehicle
Shipping efficiency, logistics optimisation, new fuels
Aviation – energy efficiency, new fuels
Biofuels
Sections 10.3, 10.4, 10.8
Sections 10.3, 10.4, 10.8
Sections 10.2, 10.8, Table 10.3
Sections 10.2, 10.8, Table 10.3
Sections 10.3, 10.4, 10.8
Sections 10.3, 10.4, 10.8
Sections 10.6, 10.8
Sections 10.5, 10.8
Sections 10.3, 10.4, 10.5, 10.6, 10.8
Industry
Energy efficiency
Material efficiency and demand reduction
Circular material flows
Electrification
CCS and carbon capture and utilisation (CCU)
Section 11.5.3
Section 11.5.3
Section 11.5.3
Sections 11.5.3, 6.7.7
Section 11.5.3
Type of relations:
Synergies
Trade-offs
Both synergies and trade-offs[4]
Blanks represent no assessment[5]
Confidence level:
High confidence
Medium confidence
Low confidence
Related Sustainable Development Goals:
1 No poverty
2 Zero hunger
3 Good health and wellbeing
4 Quality education
5 Gender equality
6 Clean water and sanitation
7 Affordable and clean energy
8 Decent work and economic growth
9 Industry, innovation and infrastructure
10 Reduced inequalities
11 Sustainable cities and communities
12 Responsible consumption and production
13 Climate action
14 Life below water
15 Life on land
16 Peace, justice and strong institutions
17 Partnership for the goals
[1] Soil carbon management in cropland and grasslands, agroforestry, biochar
[2] Deforestation, loss and degradation of peatlands and coastal wetlands
[3] Timber, biomass, agri. feedstock
[4] Lower of the two confidence levels has been reported
[5] Not assessed due to limited literature

Figure SPM.8 | Synergies and trade-offs between sectoral and system mitigation options and the SDGs.

Figure SPM.8 (continued): Synergies and trade-offs between sectoral and system mitigation options and the SDGs. The sectoral chapters (Chapters 6–11) include qualitative assessments of synergies and trade-offs between sectoral mitigation options and the SDGs. Figure SPM.8 presents a summary of the chapter-level assessment for selected mitigation options (see Supplementary Material Table 17.SM.1 for the underlying assessment). The last column provides a line of sight to the sectoral chapters, which provide details on context specificity and dependence of interactions on the scale of implementation. Blank cells indicate that interactions have not been assessed due to limited literature. They do not indicate the absence of interactions between mitigation options and the SDGs. Confidence levels depend on the quality of evidence and level of agreement in the underlying literature assessed by the sectoral chapters. Where both synergies and trade-offs exist, the lower of the confidence levels for these interactions is used. Some mitigation options may have applications in more than one sector or system. The interactions between mitigation options and the SDGs might differ depending on the sector or system, and also on the context and the scale of implementation. Scale of implementation particularly matters when there is competition for scarce resources. {6.3, 6.4, 6.7, 7.3, 7.4, 7.5, 7.6, 8.2, 8.4, 8.6, Figure 8.4, Supplementary Material Table 8.SM.1, Supplementary Material Table 8.SM.2, 9.4, 9.5, 9.8, Table 9.5, 10.3, 10.4, 10.5, 10.6, 10.8, Table 10.3, 11.5, 12.5, 17.3, Figure 17.1, Supplementary Material Table 17.SM.1, Annex II.IV.12}

D.2 **There is a strong link between sustainable development, vulnerability and climate risks. Limited economic, social and institutional resources often result in high vulnerability and low adaptive capacity, especially in developing countries (*medium confidence*). Several response options deliver both mitigation and adaptation outcomes, especially in human settlements, land management, and in relation to ecosystems. However, land and aquatic ecosystems can be adversely affected by some mitigation actions, depending on their implementation (*medium confidence*). Coordinated cross-sectoral policies and planning can maximise synergies and avoid or reduce trade-offs between mitigation and adaptation (*high confidence*). {3.7, 4.4, 13.8, 17.3; AR6 WGII}**

D.2.1 Sustainable urban planning and infrastructure design including green roofs and facades, networks of parks and open spaces, management of urban forests and wetlands, urban agriculture, and water-sensitive design can deliver both mitigation and adaptation benefits in settlements (*medium confidence*). These options can also reduce flood risks, pressure on urban sewer systems, urban heat island effects, and can deliver health benefits from reduced air pollution (*high confidence*). There could also be trade-offs. For example, increasing urban density to reduce travel demand, could imply high vulnerability to heat waves and flooding (*high confidence*). (Figure SPM.8) {3.7, 8.2, 8.4, 12.5, 13.8, 17.3}

D.2.2 Land-related mitigation options with potential co-benefits for adaptation include agroforestry, cover crops, intercropping, perennial plants, restoring natural vegetation and rehabilitating degraded land. These can enhance resilience by maintaining land productivity and protecting and diversifying livelihoods. Restoration of mangroves and coastal wetlands sequesters carbon, while also reducing coastal erosion and protecting against storm surges, thus, reducing the risks from sea level rise and extreme weather. (*high confidence*) {4.4, 7.4, 7.6, 12.5, 13.8}

D.2.3 Some mitigation options can increase competition for scarce resources including land, water and biomass. Consequently, these can also reduce adaptive capacity, especially if deployed at larger scale and with high expansion rates thus exacerbating existing risks, in particular where land and water resources are very limited. Examples include the large-scale or poorly planned deployment of bioenergy, biochar, and afforestation of naturally unforested land. (*high confidence*) {12.5, 17.3}

D.2.4 Coordinated policies, equitable partnerships and integration of adaptation and mitigation within and across sectors can maximise synergies and minimise trade-offs and thereby enhance the support for climate action (*medium confidence*). Even if extensive global mitigation efforts are implemented, there will be a large need for financial, technical, and human resources for adaptation. Absence or limited resources in social and institutional systems can lead to poorly coordinated responses, thus reducing the potential for maximising mitigation and adaptation benefits, and increasing risk (*high confidence*). {12.6, 13.8, 17.1, 17.3}

D.3 **Enhanced mitigation and broader action to shift development pathways towards sustainability will have distributional consequences within and between countries. Attention to equity and broad and meaningful participation of all relevant actors in decision-making at all scales can build social trust, and deepen and widen support for transformative changes.** (*high confidence*) {3.6, 4.2, 4.5, 5.2, 13.2, 17.3, 17.4}

D.3.1 Countries at all stages of economic development seek to improve the well-being of people, and their development priorities reflect different starting points and contexts. Different contexts include social, economic, environmental, cultural, or political conditions, resource endowment, capabilities, international environment, and history. The enabling conditions for shifting development pathways towards increased sustainability will therefore also differ, giving rise to different needs. (*high confidence*) (Figure SPM.2) {1.6, 1.7, 2.4, 2.6, Cross-Chapter Box 5 in Chapter 4, 4.3.2, 17.4}

D.3.2 Ambitious mitigation pathways imply large and sometimes disruptive changes in economic structure, with significant distributional consequences, within and between countries. Equity remains a central element in the UN climate regime, notwithstanding shifts in differentiation between states over time and challenges in assessing fair shares. Distributional consequences within and between countries include shifting of income and employment during the transition from high- to low-emissions activities. While some jobs may be lost, low-emissions development can also open more opportunities to enhance skills and create more jobs that last, with differences across countries and sectors. Integrated policy packages can improve the ability to integrate considerations of equity, gender equality and justice. (*high confidence*) {1.4, 1.6, 3.6, 4.2, 5.2, Box 11.1, 14.3, 15.2, 15.5, 15.6}

D.3.3 Inequalities in the distribution of emissions and in the impacts of mitigation policies within countries affect social cohesion and the acceptability of mitigation and other environmental policies. Equity and just transitions can enable deeper ambitions for accelerated mitigation. Applying just transition principles and implementing them through collective and participatory decision-making processes is an effective way of integrating equity principles into policies at all scales, in different ways depending on national circumstances (*medium confidence*). This is already taking place in many countries and regions, as national just transition commissions or task forces, and related national policies, have been established in several countries. A multitude of actors, networks, and movements are engaged (*high confidence*). {1.6, 1.7, 2.4, 2.6, 4.5, 13.2, 13.9, 14.3, 14.5}

D.3.4 Broadening equitable access to domestic and international finance, technologies that facilitate mitigation, and capacity, while explicitly addressing needs can further integrate equity and justice into national and international policies and act as a catalyst for accelerating mitigation and shifting development pathways (*medium confidence*). The consideration of ethics and equity can help address the uneven distribution of adverse impacts associated with 1.5°C and higher levels of global warming, in all societies (*high confidence*). Consideration of climate justice can help to facilitate shifting development pathways towards sustainability, including through equitable sharing of benefits and burdens of mitigation, increasing resilience to the impacts of climate change, especially for vulnerable countries and communities, and equitably supporting those in need (*high confidence*). {1.4, 1.6, 1.7, 3.6, 4.2, 4.5, Box 5.10, 13.4, 13.8, 13.9, 14.3, 14.5, 15.2, 15.5, 15.6, 16.5, 17.3, 17.4; SR1.5 SPM, AR6 WGII Chapter 18}

E. Strengthening the Response

E.1 **There are mitigation options which are feasible[71] to deploy at scale in the near term. Feasibility differs across sectors and regions, and according to capacities and the speed and scale of implementation. Barriers to feasibility would need to be reduced or removed, and enabling conditions[72] strengthened to deploy mitigation options at scale. These barriers and enablers include geophysical, environmental-ecological, technological, and economic factors, and especially institutional and socio-cultural factors. Strengthened near-term action beyond the NDCs (announced prior to UNFCCC COP26) can reduce and/or avoid long-term feasibility challenges of global modelled pathways that limit warming to 1.5°C (>50%) with no or limited overshoot. (*high confidence*) {3.8, 6.4, 8.5, 9.9, 10.8, 12.3, Figure TS.31, Annex II.IV.11}**

E.1.1 Several mitigation options, notably solar energy, wind energy, electrification of urban systems, urban green infrastructure, energy efficiency, demand-side management, improved forest- and crop/grassland management, and reduced food waste and loss, are technically viable, are becoming increasingly cost effective, and are generally supported by the public. This enables deployment in many regions (*high confidence*). While many mitigation options have environmental co-benefits, including improved air quality and reducing toxic waste, many also have adverse environmental impacts, such as reduced biodiversity, when applied at very large scale, for example very large scale bioenergy or large scale use of battery storage, that would have to be managed (*medium confidence*). Almost all mitigation options face institutional barriers that need to be addressed to enable their application at scale (*medium confidence*). {6.4, Figure 6.19, 7.4, 8.5, Figure 8.19, 9.9, Figure 9.20, 10.8, Figure 10.23, 12.3, Figure 12.4, Figure TS.31}

E.1.2 The feasibility of mitigation options varies according to context and time. For example, the institutional capacity to support deployment varies across countries; the feasibility of options that involve large-scale land-use changes varies across regions; spatial planning has a higher potential at early stages of urban development; the potential of geothermal is site specific; and capacities, cultural and local conditions can either inhibit or enable demand-side responses. The deployment of solar and wind energy has been assessed to become increasingly feasible over time. The feasibility of some options can increase when combined or integrated, such as using land for both agriculture and centralised solar production. (*high confidence*) {6.4, 6.6, Supplementary Material Table 6.SM, 7.4, 8.5, Supplementary Material Table 8.SM.2, 9.9, Supplementary Material Table 9.SM.1, 10.8, Appendix 10.3, 12.3, Tables 12.SM.2.1 to 12.SM.2.6}

E.1.3 Feasibility depends on the scale and speed of implementation. Most options face barriers when they are implemented rapidly at a large scale, but the scale at which barriers manifest themselves varies. Strengthened and coordinated near-term actions in cost-effective modelled global pathways that limit warming to 2°C (>67%) or lower, reduce the overall risks to the feasibility of the system transitions, compared to modelled pathways with relatively delayed or uncoordinated action.[73] (*high confidence*) {3.8, 6.4, 10.8, 12.3}

---

[71] In this report, the term 'feasibility' refers to the potential for a mitigation or adaptation option to be implemented. Factors influencing feasibility are context-dependent and may change over time. Feasibility depends on geophysical, environmental-ecological, technological, economic, socio-cultural and institutional factors that enable or constrain the implementation of an option. The feasibility of options may change when different options are combined and increase when enabling conditions are strengthened.

[72] In this report, the term 'enabling conditions' refers to conditions that enhance the feasibility of adaptation and mitigation options. Enabling conditions include finance, technological innovation, strengthening policy instruments, institutional capacity, multi-level governance, and changes in human behaviour and lifestyles.

[73] The future feasibility challenges described in the modelled pathways may differ from the real-world feasibility experiences of the past.

E.2   In all countries, mitigation efforts embedded within the wider development context can increase the pace, depth and breadth of emissions reductions (*medium confidence*). Policies that shift development pathways towards sustainability can broaden the portfolio of available mitigation responses, and enable the pursuit of synergies with development objectives (*medium confidence*). Actions can be taken now to shift development pathways and accelerate mitigation and transitions across systems (*high confidence*). {4.3, 4.4, Cross-Chapter Box 5 in Chapter 4, 5.2, 5.4, 13.9, 14.5, 15.6, 16.3, 16.4, 16.5}

E.2.1   Current development pathways may create behavioural, spatial, economic and social barriers to accelerated mitigation at all scales (*high confidence*). Choices made by policymakers, citizens, the private sector and other stakeholders influence societies' development pathways (*high confidence*). Actions that steer, for example, energy and land systems transitions, economy-wide structural change, and behaviour change, can shift development pathways towards sustainability[74] (*medium confidence*). {4.3, Cross-Chapter Box 5 in Chapter 4, 5.4, 13.9}

E.2.2   Combining mitigation with policies to shift development pathways, such as broader sectoral policies, policies that induce lifestyle or behaviour changes, financial regulation, or macroeconomic policies can overcome barriers and open up a broader range of mitigation options (*high confidence*). It can also facilitate the combination of mitigation and other development goals (*high confidence*). For example, measures promoting walkable urban areas combined with electrification and renewable energy can create health co-benefits from cleaner air and benefits from enhanced mobility (*high confidence*). Coordinated housing policies that broaden relocation options can make mitigation measures in transport more effective (*medium confidence*). {3.2, 4.3, 4.4, Cross-Chapter Box 5 in Chapter 4, 5.3, 8.2, 8.4}

E.2.3   Institutional and regulatory capacity, innovation, finance, improved governance and collaboration across scales, and multi-objective policies enable enhanced mitigation and shifts in development pathways. Such interventions can be mutually reinforcing and establish positive feedback mechanisms, resulting in accelerated mitigation. (*high confidence*) {4.4, 5.4, Figure 5.14, 5.6, 9.9, 13.9, 14.5, 15.6, 16.3, 16.4, 16.5, Cross-Chapter Box 12 in Chapter 16}

E.2.4   Enhanced action on all the above enabling conditions can be taken now (*high confidence*). In some situations, such as with innovation in technology at an early stage of development and some changes in behaviour towards low emissions, because the enabling conditions may take time to be established, action in the near term can yield accelerated mitigation in the mid-term (*medium confidence*). In other situations, the enabling conditions can be put in place and yield results in a relatively short time frame, for example the provision of energy related information, advice and feedback to promote energy saving behaviour (*high confidence*). {4.4, 5.4, Figure 5.14, 5.6, 6.7, 9.9, 13.9, 14.5, 15.6, 16.3, 16.4, 16.5, Cross-Chapter Box 12 in Chapter 16}

E.3   Climate governance, acting through laws, strategies and institutions, based on national circumstances, supports mitigation by providing frameworks through which diverse actors interact, and a basis for policy development and implementation (*medium confidence*). Climate governance is most effective when it integrates across multiple policy domains, helps realise synergies and minimise trade-offs, and connects national and sub-national policymaking levels (*high confidence*). Effective and equitable climate governance builds on engagement with civil society actors, political actors, businesses, youth, labour, media, Indigenous Peoples and local communities (*medium confidence*). {5.4, 5.6, 8.5, 9.9, 13.2, 13.7, 13.9}

E.3.1   Climate governance enables mitigation by providing an overall direction, setting targets, mainstreaming climate action across policy domains, enhancing regulatory certainty, creating specialised organisations and creating the context to mobilise finance (*medium confidence*). These functions can be promoted by climate-relevant laws, which are growing in number, or climate strategies, among others, based on national and sub-national context (*medium confidence*). Framework laws set an overarching legal basis, either operating through a target and implementation approach, or a sectoral mainstreaming approach, or both, depending on national circumstance (*medium confidence*). Direct national and sub-national laws that explicitly target mitigation and indirect laws that impact emissions through mitigation-related policy domains have both been shown to be relevant to mitigation outcomes (*medium confidence*). {13.2}

---

[74]   Sustainability may be interpreted differently in various contexts as societies pursue a variety of sustainable development objectives.

E.3.2 Effective national climate institutions address coordination across sectors, scales and actors, build consensus for action among diverse interests, and inform strategy setting (*medium confidence*). These functions are often accomplished through independent national expert bodies, and high-level coordinating bodies that transcend departmental mandates. Complementary sub-national institutions tailor mitigation actions to local context and enable experimentation but can be limited by inequities and resource and capacity constraints (*high confidence*). Effective governance requires adequate institutional capacity at all levels (*high confidence*). {4.4, 8.5, 9.9, 11.3, 11.5, 11.6, 13.2, 13.5, 13.7, 13.9}

E.3.3 The extent to which civil society actors, political actors, businesses, youth, labour, media, Indigenous Peoples, and local communities are engaged influences political support for climate change mitigation and eventual policy outcomes. Structural factors of national circumstances and capabilities (e.g., economic and natural endowments, political systems and cultural factors and gender considerations) affect the breadth and depth of climate governance. Mitigation options that align with prevalent ideas, values and beliefs are more easily adopted and implemented. Climate-related litigation, for example by governments, private sector, civil society and individuals, is growing - with a large number of cases in some developed countries, and with a much smaller number in some developing countries - and in some cases, has influenced the outcome and ambition of climate governance. (*medium confidence*) {5.2, 5.4, 5.5, 5.6, 9.9, 13.3, 13.4}

E.4 **Many regulatory and economic instruments have already been deployed successfully. Instrument design can help address equity and other objectives. These instruments could support deep emissions reductions and stimulate innovation if scaled up and applied more widely (*high confidence*). Policy packages that enable innovation and build capacity are better able to support a shift towards equitable low-emission futures than are individual policies (*high confidence*). Economy-wide packages, consistent with national circumstances, can meet short-term economic goals while reducing emissions and shifting development pathways towards sustainability (*medium confidence*). {Cross-Chapter Box 5 in Chapter 4, 13.6, 13.7, 13.9, 16.3, 16.4, 16.6}**

E.4.1 A wide range of regulatory instruments at the sectoral level have proven effective in reducing emissions. These instruments, and broad-based approaches including relevant economic instruments,[75] are complementary (*high confidence*). Regulatory instruments that are designed to be implemented with flexibility mechanisms can reduce costs (*medium confidence*). Scaling up and enhancing the use of regulatory instruments, consistent with national circumstances, could improve mitigation outcomes in sectoral applications, including but not limited to renewable energy, land use and zoning, building codes, vehicle and energy efficiency, fuel standards, and low-emissions industrial processes and materials (*high confidence*). {6.7, 7.6, 8.4, 9.9, 10.4, 11.5, 11.6, 13.6}

E.4.2 Economic instruments have been effective in reducing emissions, complemented by regulatory instruments mainly at the national and also sub-national and regional level (*high confidence*). Where implemented, carbon pricing instruments have incentivised low-cost emissions reduction measures, but have been less effective, on their own and at prevailing prices during the assessment period, in promoting the higher-cost measures necessary for further reductions (*medium confidence*). Equity and distributional impacts of such carbon pricing instruments can be addressed by using revenue from carbon taxes or emissions trading to support low-income households, among other approaches (*high confidence*). Practical experience has informed instrument design and helped to improve predictability, environmental effectiveness, economic efficiency, distributional goals and social acceptance (*high confidence*). Removing fossil fuel subsidies would reduce emissions, improve public revenue and macroeconomic performance, and yield other environmental and sustainable development benefits; subsidy removal may have adverse distributional impacts especially on the most economically vulnerable groups which, in some cases can be mitigated by measures such as redistributing revenue saved, all of which depend on national circumstances (*high confidence*); fossil fuel subsidy removal is projected by various studies to reduce global CO_2 emissions by 1–4%, and GHG emissions by up to 10% by 2030, varying across regions (*medium confidence*). {6.3, 13.6}

E.4.3 Low-emission technological innovation is strengthened through the combination of dedicated technology-push policies and investments (e.g., for scientific training, R&D, demonstration), with tailored demand-pull policies (e.g., standards, feed-in tariffs, taxes), which create incentives and market opportunities. Developing countries' abilities to deploy low-emission technologies, seize socio-economic benefits and manage trade-offs would be enhanced with increased financial resources and capacity for innovation which are currently concentrated in developed countries, alongside technology transfer. (*high confidence*) {16.2, 16.3, 16.4, 16.5}

---

[75] Economic instruments are structured to provide a financial incentive to reduce emissions and include, among others, market- and price-based instruments.

E.4.4   Effective policy packages would be comprehensive in coverage, harnessed to a clear vision for change, balanced across objectives, aligned with specific technology and system needs, consistent in terms of design and tailored to national circumstances. They are better able to realise synergies and avoid trade-offs across climate and development objectives. Examples include: emissions reductions from buildings through a mix of efficiency targets, building codes, appliance performance standards, information provision, carbon pricing, finance and technical assistance; and industrial GHG emissions reductions through innovation support, market creation and capacity building. (*high confidence*) {4.4, 6.7, 9.9, 11.6, 13.7, 13.9, 16.3, 16.4}

E.4.5   Economy-wide packages that support mitigation and avoid negative environmental outcomes include: long-term public spending commitments; pricing reform; and investment in education and training, natural capital, R&D and infrastructure (*high confidence*). They can meet short-term economic goals while reducing emissions and shifting development pathways towards sustainability (*medium confidence*). Infrastructure investments can be designed to promote low-emissions futures that meet development needs (*medium confidence*). {Cross-Chapter Box 5 in Chapter 4, 5.4, 5.6, 8.5, 13.6, 13.9, 16.3, 16.5, 16.6}

E.4.6   National policies to support technology development and diffusion, and participation in international markets for emission reduction, can bring positive spillover effects for other countries (*medium confidence*), although reduced demand for fossil fuels could result in costs to exporting countries (*high confidence*). There is no consistent evidence that current emission trading systems have led to significant emissions leakage, which can be attributed to design features aimed at minimising competitiveness effects, among other reasons (*medium confidence*). {13.6, 13.7, 13.8, 16.2, 16.3, 16.4}

E.5   Tracked financial flows fall short of the levels needed to achieve mitigation goals across all sectors and regions. The challenge of closing gaps is largest in developing countries as a whole. Scaling up mitigation financial flows can be supported by clear policy choices and signals from governments and the international community (*high confidence*). Accelerated international financial cooperation is a critical enabler of low-GHG and just transitions, and can address inequities in access to finance and the costs of, and vulnerability to, the impacts of climate change (*high confidence*). {15.2, 15.3, 15.4, 15.5, 15.6}

E.5.1   Average annual modelled investment requirements for 2020 to 2030 in scenarios that limit warming to 2°C or 1.5°C are a factor of three to six greater than current levels, and total mitigation investments (public, private, domestic and international) would need to increase across all sectors and regions (*medium confidence*). Mitigation investment gaps are wide for all sectors, and widest for the AFOLU sector in relative terms and for developing countries[76] (*high confidence*). Financing and investment requirements for adaptation, reduction of losses and damages, general infrastructure, regulatory environment and capacity building, and climate-responsive social protection further exacerbate the magnitude of the challenges for developing countries to attract financing (*high confidence*). {3.2, 14.4, 15.1, 15.2, 15.3, 15.4, 15.5}

E.5.2   There is sufficient global capital and liquidity to close global investment gaps, given the size of the global financial system, but there are barriers to redirect capital to climate action both within and outside the global financial sector, and in the macroeconomic headwinds facing developing regions. Barriers to the deployment of commercial finance from within the financial sector as well as macroeconomic considerations include: inadequate assessment of climate-related risks and investment opportunities; regional mismatch between available capital and investment needs; home bias factors; country indebtedness levels; economic vulnerability; and limited institutional capacities (*high confidence*). Challenges from outside the financial sector include: limited local capital markets; unattractive risk-return profiles, in particular due to missing or weak regulatory environments consistent with ambition levels; limited institutional capacity to ensure safeguards; standardisation, aggregation, scalability and replicability of investment opportunities and financing models; and, a pipeline ready for commercial investments. (*high confidence*) {15.2, 15.3, 15.5, 15.6}

E.5.3   Accelerated financial support for developing countries from developed countries and other sources is a critical enabler to enhance mitigation action and address inequities in access to finance, including its costs, terms and conditions, and economic vulnerability to climate change for developing countries (*high confidence*). Scaled-up public grants for mitigation and adaptation funding for vulnerable regions, especially in Sub-Saharan Africa, would be cost-effective and have high social returns in terms of access to basic energy (*high confidence*). Options for scaling up mitigation in developing regions include: increased levels of public finance and publicly mobilised private finance flows from developed to developing countries in the context of the USD100 billion-a-year goal; increase the use of public guarantees to reduce risks and leverage private flows

---

[76]   In modelled pathways, regional investments are projected to occur when and where they are most cost-effective to limit global warming. The model quantifications help to identify high-priority areas for cost-effective investments, but do not provide any indication on who would finance the regional investments.

at lower cost; local capital markets development; and building greater trust in international cooperation processes (*high confidence*). A coordinated effort to make the post-pandemic recovery sustainable and increased flows of financing over the next decade can accelerate climate action, including in developing regions and countries facing high debt costs, debt distress and macroeconomic uncertainty (*high confidence*). {15.2, 15.3, 15.4, 15.5, 15.6, Box 15.6}

E.5.4   Clear signalling by governments and the international community, including a stronger alignment of public sector finance and policy, and higher levels of public sector climate finance, reduces uncertainty and transition risks for the private sector. Depending on national contexts, investors and financial intermediaries, central banks, and financial regulators can support climate action and can shift the systemic underpricing of climate-related risk by increasing awareness, transparency and consideration of climate-related risk, and investment opportunities. Financial flows can also be aligned with funding needs through: greater support for technology development; a continued role for multilateral and national climate funds and development banks; lowering financing costs for underserved groups through entities such as green banks existing in some countries, funds and risk-sharing mechanisms; economic instruments which consider economic and social equity and distributional impacts; gender-responsive and women-empowerment programmes as well as enhanced access to finance for local communities and Indigenous Peoples and small land owners; and greater public-private cooperation. (*high confidence*) {15.2, 15.5, 15.6}

E.6   **International cooperation is a critical enabler for achieving ambitious climate change mitigation goals. The UNFCCC, Kyoto Protocol, and Paris Agreement are supporting rising levels of national ambition and encouraging development and implementation of climate policies, although gaps remain. Partnerships, agreements, institutions and initiatives operating at the sub-global and sectoral levels and engaging multiple actors are emerging, with mixed levels of effectiveness. (*high confidence*) {8.5, 14.2, 14.3, 14.5, 14.6, 15.6, 16.5}**

E.6.1   Internationally agreed processes and goals, such as those in the UNFCCC, Kyoto Protocol, and Paris Agreement – including transparency requirements for national reporting on emissions, actions and support, and tracking progress towards the achievement of Nationally Determined Contributions – are enhancing international cooperation, national ambition and policy development. International financial, technology and capacity building support to developing countries will enable greater implementation and encourage ambitious Nationally Determined Contributions over time. (*medium confidence*) {14.3}

E.6.2   International cooperation on technology development and transfer accompanied by capacity building, knowledge sharing, and technical and financial support can accelerate the global diffusion of mitigation technologies, practices and policies at national and sub-national levels, and align these with other development objectives (*high confidence*). Challenges in and opportunities to enhance innovation cooperation exist, including in the implementation of elements of the UNFCCC and the Paris Agreement as per the literature assessed, such as in relation to technology development and transfer, and finance (*high confidence*). International cooperation on innovation works best when tailored to specific institutional and capability contexts, when it benefits local value chains, when partners collaborate equitably and on voluntary and mutually agreed terms, when all relevant voices are heard, and when capacity building is an integral part of the effort (*medium confidence*). Support to strengthen technological innovation systems and innovation capabilities, including through financial support in developing countries would enhance engagement in and improve international cooperation on innovation (*high confidence*). {4.4, 14.2, 14.4, 16.3, 16.5, 16.6}

E.6.3   Transnational partnerships can stimulate policy development, low-emissions technology diffusion and emission reductions by linking sub-national and other actors, including cities, regions, non-governmental organisations and private sector entities, and by enhancing interactions between state and non-state actors. While this potential of transnational partnerships is evident, uncertainties remain over their costs, feasibility, and effectiveness. Transnational networks of city governments are leading to enhanced ambition and policy development and a growing exchange of experience and best practices (*medium confidence*). {8.5, 11.6, 14.5, 16.5, Cross-Chapter Box 12 in Chapter 16}

E.6.4   International environmental and sectoral agreements, institutions, and initiatives are helping, and in some cases may help, to stimulate low-GHG emissions investment and reduce emissions. Agreements addressing ozone depletion and transboundary air pollution are contributing to mitigation, and in other areas, such as atmospheric emissions of mercury, may contribute to mitigation (*high confidence*). Trade rules have the potential to stimulate international adoption of mitigation technologies and policies, but may also limit countries' ability to adopt trade-related climate policies (*medium confidence*). Current sectoral levels of ambition vary, with emission reduction aspirations in international aviation and shipping lower than in many other sectors (*medium confidence*). {14.5, 14.6}

Technical
Summary

TS

Technical Summary

Coordinating Lead Authors:

Minal Pathak (India), Raphael Slade (United Kingdom), Ramón Pichs-Madruga (Cuba), Diana Ürge-Vorsatz (Hungary), Priyadarshi R. Shukla (India), Jim Skea (United Kingdom)

Lead Authors:

Amjad Abdulla (Maldives), Alaa Al Khourdajie (United Kingdom/Syria), Mustafa Babiker (Sudan/Saudi Arabia), Quan Bai (China), Igor A. Bashmakov (the Russian Federation), Christopher Bataille (Canada), Göran Berndes (Sweden), Gabriel Blanco (Argentina), Luisa F. Cabeza (Spain), Carlo Carraro (Italy), Leon Clarke (the United States of America), Heleen de Coninck (the Netherlands), Felix Creutzig (Germany), Diriba Korecha Dadi (Ethiopia), Fatima Denton (the Gambia), Shobhakar Dhakal (Nepal/Thailand), Renée van Diemen (the Netherlands/United Kingdom), Navroz K. Dubash (India), Amit Garg (India), Oliver Geden (Germany), Michael Grubb (United Kingdom), Céline Guivarch (France), Kirsten Halsnaes (Denmark), Paulina Jaramillo (the United States of America), Tae Yong Jung (Republic of Korea), Suzana Kahn Ribeiro (Brazil), Şiir Kılkış (Turkey), Alexandre Koberle (Brazil/United Kingdom), Silvia Kreibiehl (Germany), Elmar Kriegler (Germany), William F. Lamb (Germany/United Kingdom), Franck Lecocq (France), Shuaib Lwasa (Uganda), Nagmeldin Mahmoud (Sudan), Eric Masanet (the United States of America), David McCollum (the United States of America), Jan Christoph Minx (Germany), Catherine Mitchell (United Kingdom), Kanako Morita (Japan), Rachid Mrabet (Morocco), Gert-Jan Nabuurs (the Netherlands), Peter Newman (Australia), Leila Niamir (Iran/Germany), Lars J. Nilsson (Sweden), Chukwumerije Okereke (Nigeria/United Kingdom), Anthony Patt (Switzerland), Joana Portugal-Pereira (Brazil), Lavanya Rajamani (India), Andy Reisinger (New Zealand), Keywan Riahi (Austria), Joyashree Roy (India/Thailand), Ambuj Sagar (India), Yamina Saheb (France/Algeria), Roberto Schaeffer (Brazil), Karen C. Seto (the United States of America), Pete Smith (United Kingdom), Shreya Some (India), Benjamin K. Sovacool (Denmark/United Kingdom), Linda Steg (the Netherlands), Massimo Tavoni (Italy), Ferenc L. Toth (Austria/Hungary), Purvi Vyas (India), Yi-Ming Wei (China), Jake Whitehead (Australia), Thomas Wiedmann (Australia/Germany), Harald Winkler (South Africa)

Review Editors:

Arnulf Jäger-Waldau (Italy/Germany), Tek Sapkota (Nepal/Canada)

This Technical Summary should be cited as:

M. Pathak, R. Slade, P.R. Shukla, J. Skea, R. Pichs-Madruga, D. Ürge-Vorsatz, 2022: Technical Summary. In: *Climate Change 2022: Mitigation of Climate Change. Contribution of Working Group III to the Sixth Assessment Report of the Intergovernmental Panel on Climate Change* [P.R. Shukla, J. Skea, R. Slade, A. Al Khourdajie, R. van Diemen, D. McCollum, M. Pathak, S. Some, P. Vyas, R. Fradera, M. Belkacemi, A. Hasija, G. Lisboa, S. Luz, J. Malley, (eds.)]. Cambridge University Press, Cambridge, UK and New York, NY, USA. doi: 10.1017/9781009157926.002.

Table of Contents

TS.1   Introduction

The Working Group III (WGIII) contribution to the IPCC's Sixth Assessment Report (AR6) assesses the current state of knowledge on the scientific, technological, environmental, economic and social aspects of climate change mitigation. It builds on previous IPCC reports, including the WGIII contribution to the IPCC's Fifth Assessment Report (AR5) and the three Special Reports of the Sixth Assessment cycle on: Global Warming of 1.5°C (SR1.5); Climate Change and Land (SRCCL); and the Ocean and Cryosphere in a Changing Climate (SROCC).[1]

The report assesses new literature, methodological and recent developments, and changes in approaches towards climate change mitigation since the IPCC AR5 report was published in 2014.

The global science and policy landscape on climate change mitigation has evolved since AR5. The development of the literature reflects, among other factors, the UN Framework Convention on Climate Change (UNFCCC), the outcomes of its Kyoto Protocol and the goals of the Paris Agreement {13, 14, 15}, and the UN 2030 Agenda for Sustainable Development {1, 4, 17}. Literature further highlights the growing role of non-state and sub-national actors in the global effort to address climate change, including cities, businesses, citizens, transnational initiatives and public-private entities {5, 8, 13}. It draws attention to the decreasing cost of some low-emission technologies {2, 6, 12} and the evolving role of international cooperation {14}, finance {15} and innovation {16}. Emerging literature examines the global spread of climate policies, strengthened mitigation actions in developing countries, sustained reductions in greenhouse gas (GHG) emissions in some developed countries and the continuing challenges for mitigation. {2, 13}

There are ever closer linkages between climate change mitigation, development pathways and the pursuit of Sustainable Development Goals (SDGs). Development pathways largely drive GHG emissions and hence shape the mitigation challenge and the portfolio of available responses {4}. The co-benefits and risks of mitigation responses also differ according to stages of development and national capabilities {1, 2, 3, 4, 13}. Climate change mitigation framed in the context of sustainable development, equity, and poverty eradication, and rooted in the development aspirations of the society within which they take place, will be more acceptable, durable and effective. {1, 4, 17}

This report includes new assessment approaches that go beyond those evaluated in the previous IPCC WGIII reports. In addition to sectoral and systems chapters {6, 7, 8, 9, 10, 11}, this report includes, for the first time, chapters dedicated to cross-sectoral perspectives {12}, demand, services and social aspects of mitigation (Box TS.11) {5}, and innovation, technology development and transfer {16}. The assessment of future pathways combines a forward-looking assessment of near- to medium-term perspectives up to 2050, including ways of shifting development pathways towards sustainability {4}, with an assessment of long-term outcome-oriented pathways up to 2100 {3}. Collaboration between the IPCC Working Groups is reflected in Cross-Working Group boxes which address topics such as the economic benefits from avoided impacts along mitigation pathways {Cross-Working Group Box 1 in Chapter 3}, climate change and urban areas {Cross-Working Group Box 2 in Chapter 8}, mitigation and adaptation through the bioeconomy {Cross-Working Group Box 3 in Chapter 12} and Solar Radiation Modification (SRM) {Cross-Working Group Box 4 in Chapter 14}. This assessment also gives greater attention than AR5 to social, economic and environmental dimensions of mitigation actions, and institutional, legal and financial aspects. {5, 13, 14, 15}

The report draws from literature on broad and diverse analytic frameworks across multiple disciplines. These include, *inter alia*: economic and environmental efficiency {1}; ethics and equity {4, 5, 17}; innovation and the dynamics of socio-technical transitions {16}; and socio-political-institutional frameworks {1, 5, 13, 14, 17}. These help to identify synergies and trade-offs with Sustainable Development Goals (SDGs), challenges and windows of opportunity for action including co-benefits, and equitable transitions at local, national and global scales. {1, 5, 13, 14, 16}

This Technical Summary (TS) of the WGIII contribution to the IPCC's Sixth Assessment Report (AR6) broadly follows the report chapter order and is structured as follows.

- TS Section 2 (TS.2) sets out how the global context for mitigation has changed and summarises signs of progress and continuing challenges.
- TS Section 3 (TS.3) evaluates emission trends and drivers including recent sectoral, financial, technological and policy developments.
- TS Section 4 (TS.4) identifies mitigation and development pathways in the near and mid-term to 2050, and in the longer term to 2100. This section includes an assessment of how mitigation pathways deploying different portfolios of mitigation responses are consistent with limiting global warming to different levels.
- TS Section 5 (TS.5) summarises recent advances in knowledge across sectors and systems including energy, urban and other settlements, transport, buildings, industry, and agriculture, forestry and other land-use (AFOLU).
- TS Section 6 (TS.6) examines how enabling conditions including behaviour and lifestyle, policy, governance and institutional capacity, international cooperation, finance, and innovation and technology can accelerate mitigation in the context of sustainable development.
- TS Section 7 (TS.7) evaluates how mitigation can be achieved in the context of sustainable development, while maximising co-benefits and minimising risks.

---

1   The three Special Reports are: Global Warming of 1.5°C: an IPCC Special Report on the impacts of global warming of 1.5°C above pre-industrial levels and related global greenhouse gas emission pathways, in the context of strengthening the global response to the threat of climate change, sustainable development, and efforts to eradicate poverty (2018); Climate Change and Land: an IPCC Special Report on climate change, desertification, land degradation, sustainable land management, food security, and greenhouse gas fluxes in terrestrial ecosystems (2019); IPCC Special Report on the Ocean and Cryosphere in a Changing Climate (2019).

Technical Summary

Throughout this Technical Summary the validity of findings, confidence in findings, and cross-references to Technical Summary sections, figures and tables are shown in ( ) brackets.[2] References to the underlying report are shown in { } brackets.

---

2 Each finding is grounded in an evaluation of the underlying evidence, typeset in italics. The validity of a finding is evaluated in terms of the evidence quality – '*limited*', '*medium*', '*robust*' – and the degree of agreement between sources – '*low*', '*medium*', '*high*'. A level of confidence is expressed using five qualifiers: *very low, low, medium, high* and *very high*. Generally, the level of confidence is highest where there is robust evidence from multiple sources and high agreement. For findings with, for example, '*robust evidence, medium agreement*', a confidence statement may not always be appropriate. The assessed likelihood of an outcome or a result is described as: *virtually certain* (99–100% probability); *very likely* (90–100%); *likely* (66–100%); *about as likely as not* (33–66%); *unlikely* (0–33%); *very unlikely* (0–10%); *exceptionally unlikely* (0–1%). Additional terms may also be used when appropriate, consistent with the IPCC uncertainty guidance: https://www.ipcc.ch/site/assets/uploads/2018/05/uncertainty-guidance-note.pdf.

TS.2   The Changed Global Context, Signs of Progress and Continuing Challenges

Since the IPCC's Fifth Assessment Report (AR5), important changes that have emerged include the specific objectives established in the Paris Agreement of 2015 (for temperature, adaptation and finance), rising climate impacts, and higher levels of societal awareness and support for climate action (*high confidence*). Meeting the long-term temperature goal in the Paris Agreement, however, implies a rapid inflection in GHG emission trends and accelerating decline towards 'net zero'. This is implausible without urgent and ambitious action at all scales. {1.2, 1.3, 1.5, 1.6, Chapters 3 and 4}

Effective and equitable climate policies are largely compatible with the broader goal of sustainable development and efforts to eradicate poverty as enshrined in the UN 2030 Agenda for Sustainable Development and its 17 Sustainable Development Goals (SDGs), notwithstanding trade-offs in some cases (*high confidence*). Taking urgent action to combat climate change and its impacts is one of the 17 SDGs (SDG 13). However, climate change mitigation also has synergies and/or trade-offs with many other SDGs. There has been a strong relationship between development and GHG emissions, as historically both per-capita and absolute emissions have risen with industrialisation. However, recent evidence shows countries can grow their economies while reducing emissions. Countries have different priorities in achieving the SDGs and reducing emissions as informed by their respective national conditions and capabilities. Given the differences in GHG emissions contributions, degree of vulnerability and impacts, as well as capacities within and between nations, equity and justice are important considerations for effective climate policy and for securing national and international support for deep decarbonisation. Achieving sustainable development and eradicating poverty would involve effective and equitable climate policies at all levels from local to global scale. Failure to address questions of equity and justice over time can undermine social cohesion and stability. International cooperation can enhance efforts to achieve ambitious global climate mitigation in the context of sustainable development. Pathways that illustrate movement towards fulfilling the SDGs are shown in Figure TS.1. {1.4, 1.6, Chapters 2, 3, 4, 5, 6, 7, 8, 9, 10, 11, 13 and 17}

The transition to a low-carbon economy depends on a wide range of closely intertwined drivers and constraints, including policies and technologies where notable advances over the past decade have opened up new and large-scale opportunities for deep decarbonisation, and for alternative development pathways which could deliver multiple social and developmental goals (*high confidence*). Drivers for, and constraints on, low-carbon societal transitions comprise economic and technological factors (the means by which services such as food, heating and shelter are provided and for whom, the emissions intensity of traded products, finance and investment), socio-political issues (political economy, equity and fairness, social innovation and behaviour change), and institutional factors (legal framework and institutions, and the quality of international cooperation). In addition to being deeply intertwined, all the factors matter to varying degrees, depending on the prevailing social, economic, cultural and political context. They often both drive and inhibit transitions at the same time, within and across different scales. The development and deployment of innovative technologies and systems at scale are important for achieving deep decarbonisation, and in recent years, the cost of several low-carbon technologies has declined sharply as deployment has risen rapidly. (Figure TS.7) {1.3, 1.4, Chapters 2, 4, 5, 13,14}

Accelerating mitigation to prevent dangerous anthropogenic interference with the climate system will require the integration of broadened assessment frameworks and tools that combine multiple perspectives, applied in a context of multi-level governance (*high confidence*). Analysing a challenge on the scale of fully decarbonising our economies entails integration of multiple analytic frameworks. Approaches to risk assessment and resilience, established across IPCC Working Groups, are complemented by frameworks for probing the challenges in implementing mitigation. *Aggregate frameworks* include cost-effectiveness analysis towards given objectives, and cost-benefit analysis, both of which have been developing to take fuller account of advances in understanding risks and innovation, the dynamics of sectors and systems and of climate impacts, and welfare economic theory including growing consensus on long-term discounting. *Ethical frameworks* consider the fairness of processes and outcomes which can help ameliorate distributional impacts across income groups, countries and generations. *Transition and transformation frameworks* explain and evaluate the dynamics of transitions to low-carbon systems arising from interactions amongst levels. *Psychological, behavioural and political frameworks* outline the constraints (and opportunities) arising from human psychology and the power of incumbent interests. A comprehensive understanding of climate mitigation must combine these multiple frameworks. Together with established risk frameworks, these collectively help to explain potential synergies and trade-offs in mitigation, implying a need for a wide portfolio of policies attuned to different actors and levels of decision-making, and underpin 'just transition' strategies in diverse contexts. {1.2.2, 1.7, 1.8, Figure 1.7}

The speed, direction, and depth of any transition will be determined by choices in the environmental, technological, economic, socio-cultural and institutional realms (*high confidence*). Transitions in specific systems can be gradual or can be rapid and disruptive. The pace of a transition can be impeded by 'lock-in' generated by existing physical capital, institutions, and social norms. The interaction between politics, economics and power relationships is central to explaining why broad commitments do not always translate to urgent action. At the same time, attention to, and support for, climate policies and low-carbon societal transitions has generally increased, as the impacts have become more salient. Both public and private financing and financial structures strongly affect the scale and balance of high- and low-carbon investments. Societal and behavioural norms, regulations and institutions are essential conditions to accelerate low-carbon transitions in multiple sectors, whilst addressing distributional concerns endemic to any major transition. The COVID-19 pandemic has also had far-reaching impacts on the global economic and social system, and recovery will present both challenges and opportunities for climate mitigation. (Box TS.1) {1.3, Box 1.1, 1.4, 1.8, Chapters 2, 3, 4, 5, 15, 17}

TS

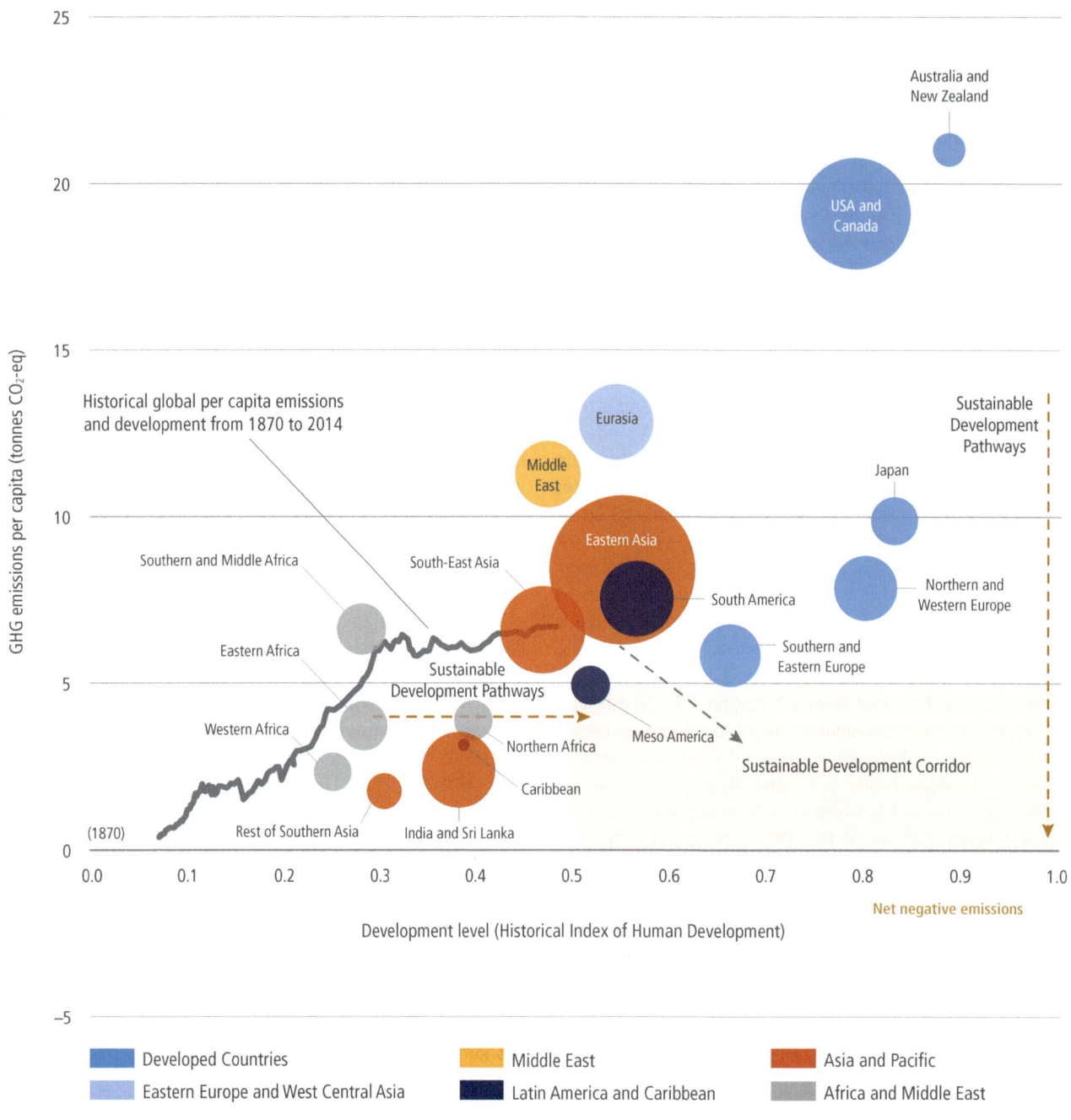

Figure TS.1 | Sustainable development pathways towards fulfilling the Sustainable Development Goals. The graph shows global average per-capita GHG emissions (vertical axis) and relative 'Historic Index of Human Development' (HIHD) levels (horizontal) have increased globally since the industrial revolution (grey line). The bubbles on the graph show regional per-capita GHG emissions and human development levels in the year 2015, illustrating large disparities. Pathways towards fulfilling the Paris Agreement (and SDG 13) involve global average per-capita GHG emissions below about 5 tCO₂-eq by 2030. Likewise, to fulfil SDGs 3, 4 and 8, HIHD levels (see footnote 7 in Chapter 1) need to be at least 0.5 or greater. This suggests a 'sustainable development zone' for year 2030 (in pale brown); the in-figure text also suggests a 'sustainable development corridor', where countries limit per-capita GHG emissions while improving levels of human development over time. The emphasis of pathways into the sustainable development zone differ (dashed brown arrows), but in each case transformations are needed in how human development is attained while limiting GHG emissions.

Achieving the global transition to a low-carbon, climate-resilient and sustainable world requires purposeful and increasingly coordinated planning and decisions at many scales of governance including local, sub-national, national and global levels (*high confidence*). Accelerating mitigation globally would imply strengthening policies adopted to date, expanding the effort across options, sectors, and countries, and broadening responses to include more diverse actors and societal processes at multiple – including international – levels. The effective governance of climate change entails strong action across multiple jurisdictions and decision-making levels, including regular evaluation and learning. Choices that cause climate change as well as the processes for making

and implementing relevant decisions involve a range of non-nation state actors such as cities, businesses, and civil society organisations. At global, national and sub-national levels, climate change actions are interwoven with, and embedded in, the context of much broader social, economic and political goals. Therefore, the governance required to address climate change has to navigate power, political, economic, and social dynamics at all levels of decision-making. Effective climate-governing institutions, and openness to experimentation on a variety of institutional arrangements, policies and programmes can play a vital role in engaging stakeholders and building momentum for effective climate action. {1.4, 1.9, Chapters 8, 13, 15, 17}

Table TS.1 | Signs of progress and continuing challenges.

Signs of progress	Continuing challenges
Emissions trends	
The rate of global GHG emissions growth has slowed in recent years, from 2.1% yr^{-1} between 2000 and 2009, to 1.3% yr^{-1} in between 2010 and 2019. (TS.3) {2.2}	**GHG emissions have continued to grow at high absolute rates**. Emissions increased by 8.9 GtCO$_2$-eq from 2000 to 2009 and by 6.5 GtCO$_2$-eq from 2010 to 2019, reaching 59 GtCO$_2$-eq in 2019. (TS.3) {2.2}
A growing number of countries have reduced both territorial carbon dioxide (CO$_2$) and GHG emissions and consumption-based CO$_2$ emissions in absolute terms for at least 10 years. These include mainly European countries, some of which have reduced production-based GHG emissions by a third or more since peaking. Some countries have achieved several years of rapid sustained CO$_2$ reduction rates of 4% yr^{-1}. (TS.3) {2.2}	**The combined emissions reductions achieved by some countries have been outweighed by rapid emissions growth elsewhere,** particularly among developing countries that have grown from a much lower base of per-capita emissions. Uncertainties in emissions levels and changes over time prevents a precise assessment of reductions in some cases. The per-capita emissions of developed countries remain high, particularly in Australia, Canada, and the United States of America. {2.2}
Lockdown policies in response to COVID-19 led to an estimated global drop of 5.8% in CO$_2$ emissions in 2020 relative to 2019. Energy demand reduction occurred across sectors, except in residential buildings due to teleworking and homeschooling. The transport sector was particularly impacted and international aviation emissions declined by 45%. (Box TS.1) {2.2}	**Atmospheric CO$_2$ concentrations continued to rise in 2020 and emissions have already rebounded as lockdown policies are eased.** Economic recovery packages currently include support for fossil fuel industries. (Boxes TS.1 and TS.8) {2.2}
Sectors	
Multiple low-carbon electricity generation and storage technologies have made rapid progress: costs have reduced, deployment has scaled up, and performance has improved. These include solar photovoltaics (PV), onshore and offshore wind, and batteries. In many contexts solar PV and onshore wind power are now competitive with fossil-based generation. (TS.3) {2.5, 6.3}	**Although deployment is increasing rapidly, low-carbon electricity generation deployment levels and rates are currently insufficient to meet stringent climate goals.** The combined market share of solar PV and wind generation technologies are still below 10%. Global low-carbon electricity generation will have to reach 100% by 2050, which is challenged by the continuous global increase in electricity demand. The contribution of biomass has absolute limits. (TS.5) {2.5}
The rate of emissions growth from coal slowed since 2010 as coal power plants were retired in the US and Europe, fewer new plants were added in China, and a large number of planned global plants were scrapped or converted to co-firing with biomass. (TS.3) {2.7, 6.3}	**Global coal emissions may not have peaked yet,** and a few countries and international development banks continue to fund and develop new coal capacity, especially abroad. The lifetime emissions of current fossil-based energy infrastructures may already exceed the remaining carbon budget for keeping warming below 1.5°C. (TS.3) {2.2, 2.7, 6.7}
Deforestation has declined since 2010 and net forest cover increased. Government initiatives and international moratoria were successful in reducing deforestation in the Amazon between 2004 and 2015, while regrowth and regeneration occurred in Europe, Eurasia and North America. (TS.5.6.1) {7.3.1}	**The long-term maintenance of low deforestation rates is challenging.** Deforestation in the Amazon has risen again over the past four years. Other parts of the world also face steady, or rapidly increasing, deforestation. {7.3.1}
Electrification of public transport services is demonstrated as a feasible, scalable and affordable mitigation option to decarbonise mass transportation. Electric vehicles (e-vehicles) are the fastest growing segment of the automobile industry, having achieved double-digit market share by 2020 in many countries. When charged with low-carbon electricity, these vehicles can significantly reduce emissions. {10.4}	**Transport emissions have remained roughly constant, growing at an average of 2% yr^{-1} between 2010 and 2019** due to the persistence of high travel demand, heavier vehicles, low efficiencies, and car-centric development. The full decarbonisation of e-vehicles requires that they are charged with zero-carbon electricity, and that car production, shipping, aviation and supply chains are decarbonised. (TS.3) {2.4}
There has been a significant global transition from coal and biomass use in buildings towards modern energy carriers and efficient conversion technologies. This led to efficiency improvements and some emissions reductions in developed countries, as well as significant gains in health and well-being outcomes in developing regions. Nearly zero energy buildings (nZEB) or low-energy buildings are achievable in all regions and climate zones for both new and existing buildings. {9.3, 9.8}	**There is a significant lock-in risk in all regions given the long lifespans of buildings and the low ambition of building policies.** This is the case for both existing buildings in developed countries, and also for new buildings in developing countries that are also challenged by the lack of technical capacity and effective governance. Emissions reductions in developed countries have been outweighed by the increase in population growth, floor area per capita and the demand for electricity and heat. {9.3, 9.9}
The decarbonisation of most industrial processes has been demonstrated using technologies that include electricity and hydrogen for energy and feedstocks, carbon capture and utilisation technologies, and innovation in circular material flows. (TS.5.5) {11.2}	**Industry emissions continue to increase, driven by a strong global demand for basic materials.** Without reductions in material demand growth and a very rapid scale-up of low-carbon innovations, the long lifetimes of industrial capital stock risks locking-in emissions for decades to come. (TS.5.5) {11.2}

Table TS.1 (continued):

Signs of progress	Continuing challenges
Policies and investment	
The Paris Agreement established a new global policy architecture to meet stringent climate goals, while avoiding many areas of deadlock that had arisen in trying to extend the Kyoto Protocol. (TS.6.3)	Current national pledges under the Paris Agreement[3] are insufficient to limit warming to 1.5°C (>50%) with no or limited overshoot, and would require an abrupt acceleration of mitigation efforts after 2030 to limit warming to 2°C (>67%). (TS.6.3)
Most wealthy countries, and a growing list of developing countries, have signalled an intention to achieve net zero GHG (or net zero CO_2) emissions by mid-century. National economy-wide GHG emissions targets covered 90% of global emissions in 2020 compared to 49% in 2010. Direct and indirect climate legislation has also steadily increased and this is supported by a growing list of financial investors. (TS.6.2)	**Many net-zero targets are ambiguously defined, and the policies needed to achieve them are not yet in place.** Opposition from status quo interests, as well as insufficient low-carbon financial flows, act as barriers to establishing and implementing stringent climate policies covering all sectors. (Box TS.6) {13.4}
The global coverage of mandatory policies – pricing and regulation – has increased, and sectoral coverage of mitigation policies has expanded. Emission trading and carbon taxes now cover over 20% of global CO_2 emissions. Allowance prices as of 1 April 2021 ranged from just over USD1 to USD50, covering between 9% and 80% of a jurisdiction's emissions {13.6.3}. Many countries have introduced sectoral regulations that block new investment in fossil fuel technologies. (TS.6)	**There is incomplete global policy coverage of non-CO_2 gases, CO_2 from industrial processes, and emissions outside the energy sector.** Few of the world's carbon prices are at a level consistent with various estimates of the carbon price needed to limit warming to 2°C or 1.5°C. {13.6}
There has been a marked increase in civic and private engagement with climate governance. This includes business measures to limit emissions, invest in reforestation and develop carbon-neutral value chains such as using wood for construction. There is an upsurge in climate activism, and growing engagement of groups such as labour unions {1.3.3, 5.2.3}. The media coverage of climate change has also grown steadily across platforms and has generally become more accurate over time. (TS.6.2)	**There is no conclusive evidence that an increase in engagement results in overall pro-mitigation outcomes.** A broad group of actors influence how climate governance develops over time, including a range of civic organisations, encompassing both pro-and anti-climate action groups. Accurate transference of the climate science has been undermined significantly by climate change counter-movements, in both legacy and new/social media environments through misinformation. (TS.6.2)

GHG emissions continued to rise to 2019, although the growth of global GHG emissions has slowed over the past decade (_high confidence_). Delivering the updated Nationally Determined Contributions (NDCs) to 2030 would turn this into decline, but the implied global emissions by 2030, still exceed pathways consistent with 1.5°C by a large margin and are near the upper end of the range of modelled pathways that limit warming to 2°C (>67%) or below. In all chapters of this report there is evidence of progress towards deeper mitigation, but there remain many obstacles to be overcome. Table TS.1 summarises some of the key signs of progress in emission trends, sectors, policies and investment, as well as the challenges that persist.

---

3   Current NDCs refer to Nationally Determined Contributions submitted to the UNFCCC, as well as publicly announced but not yet submitted mitigation pledges with sufficient detail on targets, reflected in studies published up to 11 October 2021. Revised NDCs submitted or announced after 11 October 2021 are not included. Intended Nationally Determined Contributions (INDCs) were converted to NDCs as countries ratified the Paris Agreement. Original INDCs and NDCs refer to those submitted to the UNFCCC in 2015 and 2016.

TS.3 Emission Trends and Drivers

Global net anthropogenic GHG emissions during the decade 2010–2019 were higher than any previous time in human history (*high confidence*). Since 2010, GHG emissions have continued to grow reaching 59 ± 6.6 $GtCO_2$-eq in 2019,[4] but the average annual growth in the last decade (1.3%, 2010–2019) was lower than in the previous decade (2.1%, 2000–2009) (*high confidence*). Average annual GHG emissions were 56 $GtCO_2$-eq yr[-1] for 2010–2019 (the highest decadal average on record) growing by about 9.1 $GtCO_2$-eq yr[-1] from the previous decade (2000–2009) (*high confidence*). (Figure TS.2) {2.2.2, Table 2.1, Figure 2.5}

Emissions growth has varied, but has persisted, across all groups of greenhouse gases (*high confidence*). The average annual emission levels of the last decade (2010–2019) were higher than in any previous decade for each group of greenhouse gases (*high confidence*). In 2019, CO_2 emissions were 45 ± 5.5 $GtCO_2$,[5] methane (CH_4) 11 ± 3.2 $GtCO_2$-eq, nitrous oxide (N_2O) 2.7 ± 1.6 $GtCO_2$-eq and fluorinated gases (F-gases[6]) 1.4 ± 0.41 $GtCO_2$-eq. Compared to 1990, the magnitude and speed of these increases differed across gases: CO_2 from fossil fuel and industry (FFI) grew by 15 $GtCO_2$-eq yr[-1] (67%), CH_4 by 2.4 $GtCO_2$-eq yr[-1] (29%), F-gases by 0.97 $GtCO_2$-eq yr[-1] (250%), N_2O by 0.65 $GtCO_2$-eq yr[-1] (33%). CO_2 emissions from net land use, land-use change and forestry (LULUCF) have shown

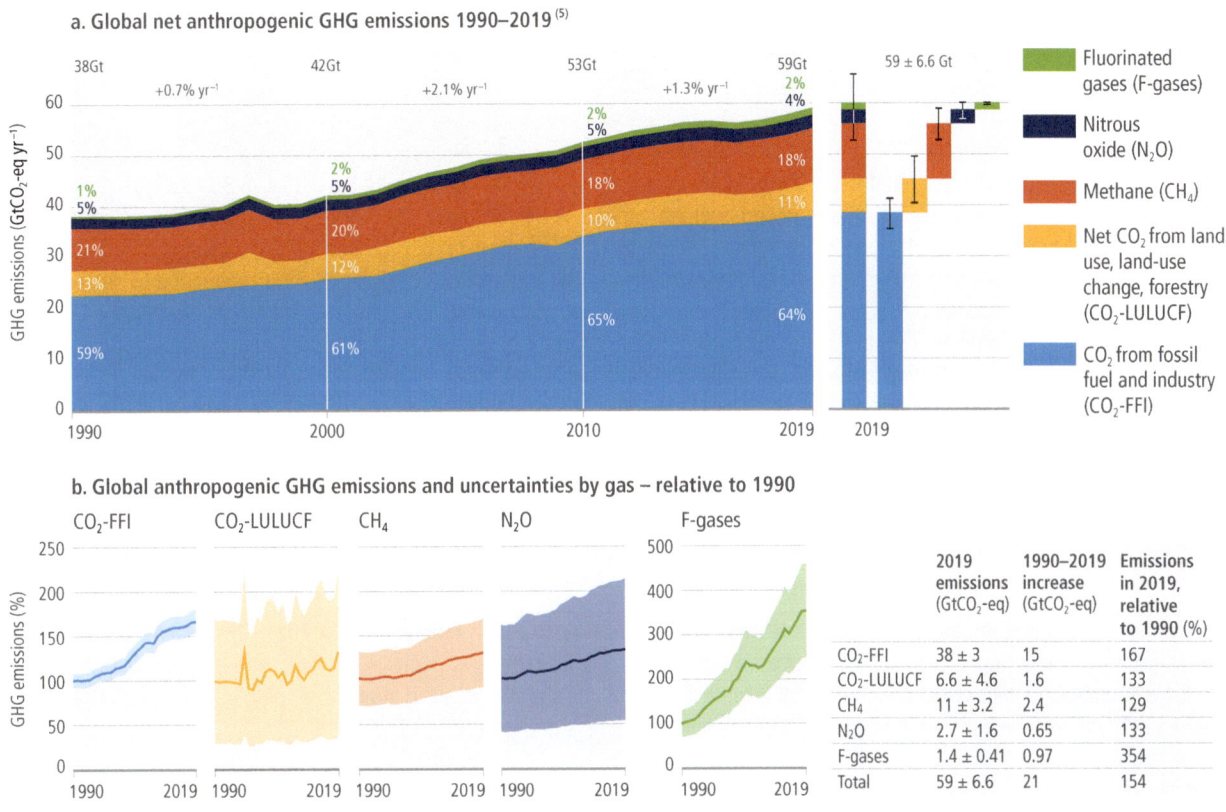

Figure TS.2 | Global net anthropogenic GHG emissions ($GtCO_2$-eq yr[-1]) 1990–2019. Global net anthropogenic GHG emissions include CO_2 from fossil fuel combustion and industrial processes (CO₂-FFI); net CO_2 from land use, land-use change and forestry (CO₂-LULUCF)[5]; methane (CH_4); nitrous oxide (N_2O); and fluorinated gases (HFCs, PFCs, SF₆, NF₃).[6] **Panel a** shows aggregate annual global net anthropogenic GHG emissions by groups of gases from 1990 to 2019 reported in $GtCO_2$-eq converted based on global warming potentials with a 100-year time horizon (GWP100-AR6) from the IPCC Sixth Assessment Report Working Group I (Chapter 7). The fraction of global emissions for each gas is shown for 1990, 2000, 2010 and 2019; as well as the aggregate average annual growth rate between these decades. At the right side of Panel a, GHG emissions in 2019 are broken down into individual components with the associated uncertainties (90% confidence interval) indicated by the error bars: CO₂-FFI ±8%; CO₂-LULUCF ±70%; CH_4 ±30%; N_2O ±60%; F-gases ±30%; GHG ±11%. Uncertainties in GHG emissions are assessed in Supplementary Material 2.2. The single-year peak of emissions in 1997 was due to higher CO₂-LULUCF emissions from a forest and peat fire event in South East Asia. **Panel b** shows global anthropogenic CO₂-FFI, net CO₂-LULUCF, CH_4, N_2O and F-gas emissions individually for the period 1990–2019, normalised relative to 100 in 1990. Note the different scale for the included F-gas emissions compared to other gases, highlighting its rapid growth from a low base. Shaded areas indicate the uncertainty range. Uncertainty ranges as shown here are specific for individual groups of greenhouse gases and cannot be compared. The table shows the central estimate for: absolute emissions in 2019; the absolute change in emissions between 1990 and 2019; and emissions in 2019 expressed as a percentage of 1990 emissions. {2.2, Figure 2.5, Supplementary Material 2.2, Figure TS.2}

---

4 Emissions of GHGs are weighed by global warming potentials (GWPs) with a 100-year time horizon (GWP100) from the Sixth Assessment Report. GWP100 is commonly used in wide parts of the literature on climate change mitigation and is required for reporting emissions under the United Nations Framework Convention on Climate Change (UNFCCC). All metrics have limitations and uncertainties. {Cross-Chapter Box 2, Annex II.II.8}

5 In 2019, CO_2 from fossil fuel and industry (FFI) was 38 ± 3.0 Gt; CO_2 from net land use, land-use change and forestry (LULUCF) was 6.6 ± 4.6 Gt.

6 Fluorinated gases, also known as 'F-gases', include: hydrofluorocarbons (HFCs), perfluorocarbons (PFCs), sulphur hexafluouride (SF₆) and nitrogen trifluouride (NF₃).

little long-term change, with large uncertainties preventing the detection of statistically significant trends. F-gases excluded from GHG emissions inventories such as *chlorofluorocarbons* and *hydrochlorofluorocarbons* are about the same size as those included (*high confidence*). (Figure TS.2) {2.2.1, 2.2.2, Table 2.1, Figures 2.2, 2.3 and 2.5}

Globally, gross domestic product (GDP) per capita and population growth remained the strongest drivers of CO_2 emissions from fossil fuel combustion in the last decade (*high confidence*). Trends since 1990 continued in the years 2010 to 2019 with GDP per capita and population growth increasing emissions by 2.3% yr^{-1} and 1.2% yr^{-1}, respectively. This growth outpaced the reduction in the use of energy per unit of GDP (−2% yr^{-1}, globally) as well as improvements in the carbon intensity of energy (−0.3% yr^{-1}). {2.4.1, Figure 2.19}

Box TS.1 | The COVID-19 Pandemic: Impact on Emissions and Opportunities for Mitigation

The COVID-19 pandemic triggered the deepest global economic contraction as well as CO_2 emission reductions since the Second World War {2.2.2}. While emissions and most economies rebounded in 2020, some impacts of the pandemic could last well beyond this. Owing to the very recent nature of this event, it remains unclear what the exact short- and long-term impacts on global emissions drivers, trends, macroeconomics and finance will be.

Starting in the spring of 2020 a major break in global emissions trends was observed due to lockdown policies implemented in response to the pandemic. Overall, global CO_2-FFI emissions are estimated to have declined by 5.8% (5.1–6.3%) in 2020, or about 2.2 (1.9–2.4%) $GtCO_2$ in total. This exceeds any previous global emissions decline since 1970 both in relative and absolute terms (Box TS.1, Figure 1). During periods of economic lockdown, daily emissions, estimated based on activity and power-generation data, declined substantially compared to 2019, particularly in April 2020 – as shown in Box TS.1, Figure 1 – but rebounded by the end of 2020. Impacts were differentiated by sector, with road transport and aviation particularly affected. Different databases estimate the total power-sector CO_2 reduction from 2019 to 2020 at 3% (IEA[7]) and 4.5% (EDGAR[8]). Approaches that predict near real-time estimates of the power-sector reduction are more uncertain and estimates range more widely between 1.8%, 4.1% and 6.8%, the latter taking into account the over-proportional reduction of coal generation due to low gas prices and merit order effects.

The lockdowns implemented in many countries accelerated some specific trends, such as the uptake in urban cycling. The acceptability of collective social change over a longer term towards less resource-intensive lifestyles, however, depends on the social mandate for change. This mandate can be built through public participation, discussion and debate, to produce recommendations that inform policymaking. {Box 5.2}

Most countries were forced to undertake unprecedented levels of short-term public expenditures in 2021. This is expected to slow economic growth and may squeeze financial resources for mitigation and relevant investments in the near future. Pandemic responses have increased sovereign debt across countries in all income bands and the sharp increase in most developing economies and regions has caused debt distress, widening the gap in developing countries' access to capital. {15.6.3}

The wider overall reduction in energy investment has prompted a relative shift towards low-carbon investment particularly for major future investment decisions by the private sector {15.2.1, 15.3.1, 15.6.1}. Some countries and regions have prioritised green stimulus expenditures, for example, as part of a 'Green New Deal' {Box 13.1}. This is motivated by assessments that investing in new growth industries can boost the macroeconomic effectiveness ('multipliers') of public spending, crowd-in and revive private investment, whilst also delivering on mitigation commitments. {15.2.3}

The impacts of COVID-19 may have temporarily set back development and the delivery of many SDGs. It also distracts political and financial capacity away from efforts to accelerate climate change mitigation and shift development pathways to increased sustainability. Yet, studies of previous post-shock periods suggest that waves of innovation that are ready to emerge can be accelerated by crises, which may prompt new behaviours, weaken incumbent systems, and initiate rapid reform. {1.6.5}

Institutional change can be slow but major economic dislocation can create significant opportunities for new ways of financing and enabling 'leapfrogging' investment {10.8}. Given the unambiguous risks of climate change, and consequent stranded asset risks from new fossil fuel investments {Box 6.11}, the most robust recoveries may well be those which align with lower carbon and resilient development pathways.

---

7   IEA: International Energy Agency

8   EDGAR: Emissions Database for Global Atmospheric Research

Box TS.1 (continued)

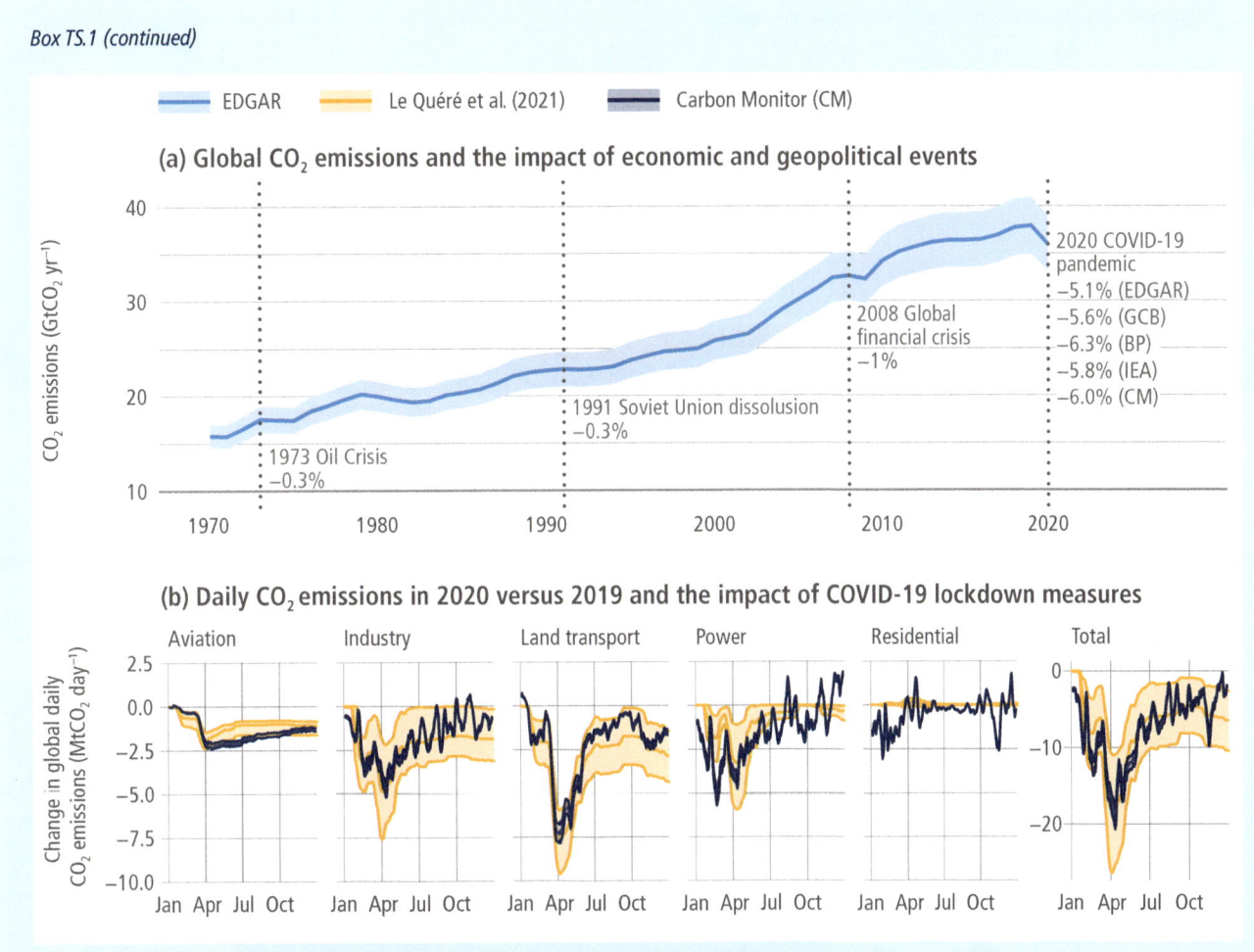

Box TS.1, Figure 1 | **Global carbon emissions in 2020 and the impact of COVID-19. Panel (a)** depicts carbon emissions from fossil fuel and industry over the past five decades. The single-year declines in emissions following major economic and geopolitical events are shown, as well as the decline recorded in five different datasets for emissions in 2020 compared to 2019. **Panel (b)** depicts the perturbation of daily carbon emissions in 2020 compared to 2019, showing the impact of COVID-19 lockdown policies. {Figure 2.6}

Cumulative net CO_2 emissions over the last decade (2010–2019) are about the same size as the remaining carbon budget to limit warming to 1.5°C (>67%) (*medium confidence*). 62% of total cumulative CO_2 emissions from 1850 to 2019 occurred since 1970 (1500 ± 140 $GtCO_2$), about 43% since 1990 (1000 ± 90 $GtCO_2$), and about 17% since 2010 (410 ± 30 $GtCO_2$). For comparison, the remaining carbon budget for keeping warming to 1.5°C with a 67% (50%) probability is about 400 (500) ± 220 $GtCO_2$ (Figure TS.3). {2.2.2, Figure 2.7, AR6 WGI Chapter 5.5, AR6 WGI Chapter 5, Table 5.8}

A growing number of countries have achieved GHG emission reductions over periods longer than 10 years – a few at rates that are broadly consistent with the global rates described in climate change mitigation scenarios that limit warming to 2°C (>67%) (*high confidence*). At least 18 countries have reduced CO_2 and GHG emissions for longer than 10 years. Reduction rates in a few countries have reached 4% in some years, in line with global rates observed in pathways that limit warming to 2°C (>67%). However, the total reduction in annual GHG emissions of these countries is small (about 3.2 $GtCO_2$-eq yr^{-1}) compared to global emissions growth

observed over the last decades. Complementary evidence suggests that countries have decoupled territorial CO_2 emissions from GDP, but fewer have decoupled consumption-based emissions from GDP. Decoupling has mostly occurred in countries with high per-capita GDP and high per-capita CO_2 emissions. (Figure TS.4, Box TS.2) {2.2.3, 2.3.3, Figure 2.11, Tables 2.3 and 2.4}

(a) Long term trend of anthropogenic CO₂ emissions sources

(b) Historic emissions vs. future carbon budgets

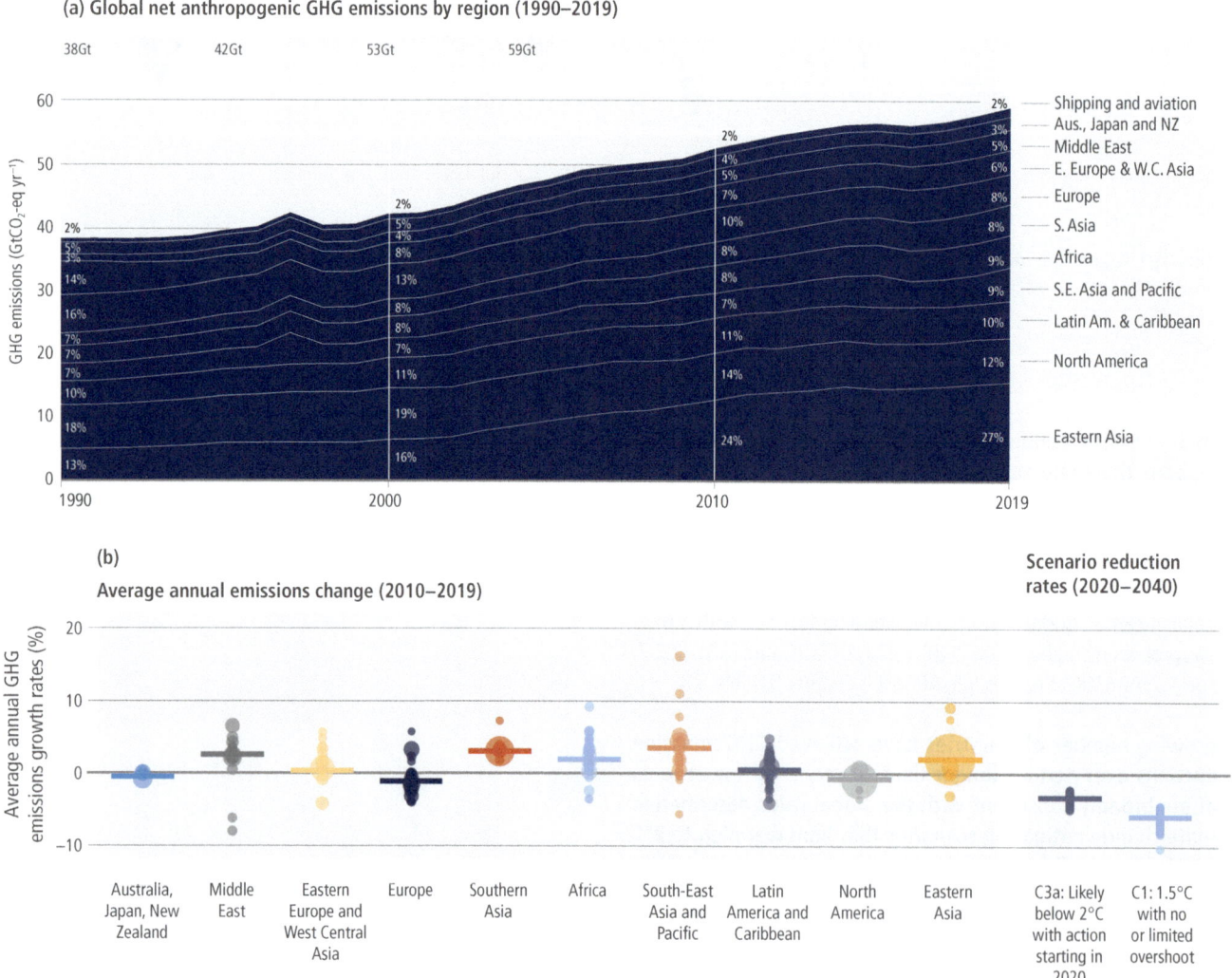

Figure TS.3 | Historic anthropogenic CO₂ emission and cumulative CO₂ emissions (1850–2019) as well as remaining carbon budgets for limiting warming to 1.5°C (>67%) and 2°C (>67%). Panel (a) shows historic annual anthropogenic CO₂ emissions (GtCO₂ yr⁻¹) by fuel type and process. **Panel (b)** shows historic cumulative anthropogenic CO₂ emissions for the periods 1850–1989, 1990–2009, and 2010–2019 as well as remaining future carbon budgets as of 1 January 2020 to limit warming to 1.5°C and 2°C at the 67th percentile of the transient climate response to cumulative CO₂ emissions. The whiskers indicate a budget uncertainty of ±220 GtCO₂-eq for each budget and the aggregate uncertainty range at one standard deviation for historical cumulative CO₂ emissions, consistent with WGI. {Figure 2.7}

(a) Global net anthropogenic GHG emissions by region (1990–2019)

(b)

Average annual emissions change (2010–2019)

Scenario reduction rates (2020–2040)

Figure TS.4 | Emissions have grown in most regions, although some countries have achieved sustained emission reductions in line with 2°C scenarios.

Figure TS.4 (continued): Emissions have grown in most regions, although some countries have achieved sustained emission reductions in line with 2°C scenarios. Change in regional GHG emissions and rates of change compatible with warming targets. **Panel (a):** Regional GHG emission trends (in $GtCO_2$-eq yr^{-1} (GWP100; AR6) for the time period 1990–2019. **Panel (b):** Historical GHG emissions change by region (2010–2019). Circles depict countries, scaled by total emissions in 2019, short horizontal lines depict the average change by region. Also shown are global rates of reduction over the period 2020–2040 in scenarios assessed in AR6 that limit global warming to 1.5°C and 2°C with different probabilities. The 5–95th percentile range of emissions changes for scenarios below 1.5°C with no or limited overshoot (scenario category C1) and scenarios below 2°C (>67%) with immediate action (scenario category C3a) are shown as a shaded area with a horizontal line at the mean value. Panel b excludes CO_2 LULUCF due to a lack of consistent historical national data, and International Shipping and Aviation, which cannot be allocated to regions. Global rates of reduction in scenarios are shown for illustrative purposes only and do not suggest rates of reduction at the regional or national level. {Figures 2.9 and 2.11}

Box TS.2 | Greenhouse Gas (GHG) Emission Metrics Provide Simplified Information About the Effects of Different Greenhouse Gases

Comprehensive mitigation policy relies on consideration of all anthropogenic forcing agents, which differ widely in their atmospheric lifetimes and impacts on the climate system. GHG emission metrics provide simplified information about the effect that emissions of different gases have on global temperature or other aspects of climate, usually expressed relative to the effect of emitting CO_2.[9] This information can support choices about priorities, trade-offs and synergies in mitigation policies and emission targets for non-CO_2 gases relative to CO_2 as well as baskets of gases expressed in CO_2-eq.

The choice of metric can affect the timing and emphasis placed on reducing emissions of short-lived climate forcers (SLCFs) relative to CO_2 within multi-gas abatement strategies as well as the costs of such strategies. Different metric choices can also alter the time at which net zero GHG emissions are calculated to be reached for any given emissions scenario. A wide range of GHG emission metrics has been published in the scientific literature, which differ in terms of: (i) the key measure of climate change they consider, (ii) whether they consider climate outcomes for a specified point in time or integrated over a specified time horizon, (iii) the time horizon over which the metric is applied, (iv) whether they apply to a single emission pulse, to emissions sustained over a period of time, or to a combination of both, and (v) whether they consider the climate effect from an emission compared to the absence of that emission, or compared to a reference emissions level or climate state. {Annex II}

Parties to the Paris Agreement decided to report aggregated emissions and removals (expressed as CO_2-eq) based on the Global Warming Potential (GWP) with a time horizon of 100 years (GWP100) using values from IPCC AR5 or from a subsequent IPCC report as agreed upon by the CMA,[10] and to account for future Nationally Determined Contributions (NDCs) in accordance with this approach. Parties may also report supplemental information on aggregate emissions and removals, expressed as CO_2-eq, using other GHG emission metrics assessed by the IPCC.

The WGIII contribution to AR6 uses updated GWP100 values from AR6 WGI to report aggregate emissions and removals unless stated otherwise. These reflect updated scientific understanding of the response of the climate system to emissions of different gases and include a methodological update to incorporate climate-carbon cycle feedbacks associated with the emission of non-CO_2 gases (see Annex II.II.8 for a list of GWP100 metric values). The choice of GWP100 was made *inter alia* for consistency with decisions under the Rulebook for the Paris Agreement and because it is the dominant metric used in the literature assessed by WGIII. Furthermore, for mitigation pathways that limit global warming to 2°C (>67%) or lower, using GWP100 to inform cost-effective abatement choices between gases would achieve such long-term temperature goals at close to least global cost within a few percent (*high confidence*).

However, GWP100 is not well-suited to estimate the cumulative effect on climate from sustained SLCF emissions and the resulting warming at specific points in time. This is because the warming caused by an individual SLCF emission pulse is not permanent, and hence, unlike CO_2, the warming from successive SLCF emission pulses over multiple decades or centuries depends mostly on their ongoing rate of emissions rather than cumulative emissions. Recently developed step/pulse metrics such as the CGTP (combined global temperature change potential) and GWP* (referred to as GWP-star and indicated by an asterisk) recognise that a sustained increase/decrease in the rate of SLCF emissions has indeed a similar effect on global surface temperature as one-off emission/ removal of CO_2. These metrics use this relationship to calculate the CO_2 emissions or removals that would result in roughly the same temperature change as a sustained change in the rate of SLCF emissions (CGTP) over a given time period, or as a varying time series of CH_4 emissions (GWP*). IFrom a mitigation perspective, this makes these metrics well-suited in principle to estimate the effect on the remaining carbon budget from more, or less, ambitious SLCF mitigation over multiple decades compared to a given reference scenario (*high confidence*). However, potential application in wider climate policy (e.g., to inform equitable and ambitious emission targets or to support sector-specific mitigation policies) is contested and relevant literature still limited.

---

9   Emission metrics also exist for aerosols, but these are not commonly used in climate policy. This assessment focuses on GHG emission metrics only.

10   The CMA is the Conference of the Parties serving as the Meeting of the Parties to the Paris Agreement. See 18/CMA.1 (Annex, para. 37) and 4/CMA.1 (Annex II, para. 1) regarding the use of GHG emission metrics in reporting of emissions and removals and accounting for Parties' NDCs.

Box TS.2 (continued)

All metrics have limitations and uncertainties, given that they simplify the complexity of the physical climate system and its response to past and future GHG emissions. For this reason, the WGIII contribution to the AR6 reports emissions and mitigation options for individual gases where possible; CO_2-equivalent emissions are reported in addition to individual gas emissions where this is judged to be policy-relevant. This approach aims to reduce the ambiguity regarding actual climate outcomes over time arising from the use of any specific GHG emission metric. {Cross-Chapter Box 2 in Chapter 2, SM.2.3, Annex II.II.8; AR6 WGI Chapter 7.6}

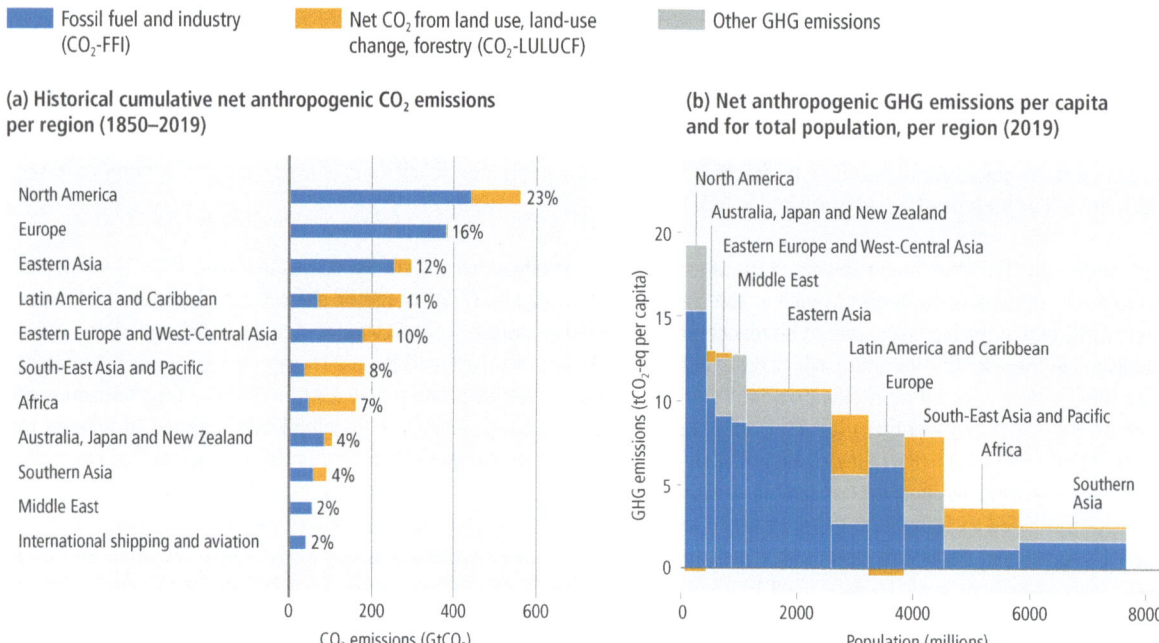

(c) Regional indicators (2019) and regional production vs consumption accounting (2018)

	Africa	Australia, Japan, New Zealand	Eastern Asia	Eastern Europe, West Central Asia	Europe	Latin America and Caribbean	Middle East	North America	South-East Asia and Pacific	Southern Asia
Population (million persons, 2019)	1292	157	1471	291	620	646	252	366	674	1836
GDP per capita (USD1000$_{PPP}$ 2017 per person)[1]	5.0	43	17	20	43	15	20	61	12	6.2
Net GHG 2019[2] (production basis)										
% GHG contributions	9%	3%	27%	6%	8%	10%	5%	12%	9%	8%
GHG emissions intensity (tCO$_2$-eq / USD1000$_{PPP}$ 2017)	0.78	0.30	0.62	0.64	0.18	0.61	0.64	0.31	0.65	0.42
GHG per capita (tCO$_2$-eq per person)	3.9	13	11	13	7.8	9.2	13	19	7.9	2.6
CO$_2$-FFI, 2018, per person										
Production-based emissions (tCO$_2$-FFI per person, based on 2018 data)	1.2	10	8.4	9.2	6.5	2.8	8.7	16	2.6	1.6
Consumption-based emissions (tCO$_2$-FFI per person, based on 2018 data)	0.84	11	6.7	6.2	7.8	2.8	7.6	17	2.5	1.5

[1] GDP per capita in 2019 in USD2017 currency purchasing power basis.
[2] Includes CO$_2$-FFI, CO$_2$-LULUCF and Other GHGs, excluding international aviation and shipping.

The regional groupings used in this figure are for statistical purposes only and are described in Annex II, Part I.

Figure TS.5 | Global emissions are distributed unevenly, both in the present day and cumulatively since 1850. Panel (a) shows the distribution of regional GHG emissions in tonnes CO$_2$-eq per capita by region in 2019. GHG emissions are categorised into: CO$_2$ fossil fuel and industry (CO$_2$-FFI); CO$_2$ land use, land-use change and forestry (CO$_2$-LULUCF); and other GHG emissions (CH$_4$, nitrous oxide, F-gas, expressed in CO$_2$-eq using GWP100). The height of each rectangle shows per-capita emissions, the width shows the population of the region, so that the area of the rectangles refers to the total emissions for each regional. Percentages refer to overall GHG contributions to total global emissions in 2019. Emissions from international aviation and shipping are not included. **Panel (b)** shows the share of historical net CO$_2$ emissions per region from 1850 to 2019. This includes CO$_2$-FFI and CO$_2$-LULUCF (GtCO$_2$). Other GHG emissions are not included. Emissions from international aviation and shipping are included. **Panel (c)** shows population, GDP per person, emission indicators by region in 2019 for percentage GHG contributions, total GHG per person, and total GHG emissions intensity, together with production-based and consumption-based CO$_2$-FFI data, which is assessed in this report up to 2018. Consumption-based emissions are emissions released to the atmosphere in order to generate the goods and services consumed by a certain entity (e.g., region). Emissions from international aviation and shipping are not included. {1.3, Figure 1.2a, 2.2, Figure 2.10}

Consumption-based CO_2 emissions in Developed Countries and the Asia and Pacific region are higher than in other regions (*high confidence*). In Developed Countries, consumption-based CO_2 emissions peaked at 15 $GtCO_2$ in 2007, declining to about 13 $GtCO_2$ in 2018. The Asia and Developing Pacific region, with 52% of the current global population, has become a major contributor to consumption-based CO_2 emission growth since 2000 (5.5% yr^{-1} for 2000–2018); in 2015 it exceeded the Developed Countries region, with 16% of global population, as the largest emitter of consumption-based CO_2. {2.3.2, Figure 2.14}

Carbon-intensity improvements in the production of traded products has led to a net reduction in CO_2 emissions embodied in international trade (*high confidence*). A decrease in the carbon intensity of traded products has offset increased trade volumes between 2006 and 2016. Emissions embodied in internationally traded products depend on the composition of the global supply chain across sectors and countries and the respective carbon intensity of production processes (emissions per unit of economic output). {2.3, 2.4}

Developed Countries tend to be net CO_2 emission importers, whereas developing countries tend to be net emission exporters (*high confidence*). Net CO_2 emission transfers from developing to Developed Countries via global supply chains have decreased between 2006 and 2016. Between 2004 and 2011, CO_2 emissions embodied in trade between developing countries have more than doubled (from 0.47 to 1.1 Gt) with the centre of trade activities shifting from Europe to Asia. {2.3.4, Figure 2.15}

Territorial emissions from developing country regions continue to grow, mostly driven by increased consumption and investment, albeit starting from a low base of per-capita emissions and with a lower historic contribution to cumulative emissions than developed countries (*high confidence*). Average 2019 per-capita CO_2-FFI emissions in three developing regions, Africa (1.2 tCO_2), Asia and Pacific (4.4 tCO_2), and Latin America and Caribbean (2.7 tCO_2), remained less than half of Developed Countries' 2019 CO_2-FFI emissions (9.5 tCO_2). In these three developing regions together, CO_2-FFI emissions grew by 26% between 2010 and 2019 (compared to 260% between 1990 and 2010). In contrast, in Developed Countries emissions contracted by 9.9% between 2010 and 2019 and by 9.6% between 1990 and 2010. Historically, these three developing regions together contributed 28% to cumulative CO_2-FFI emissions between 1850 and 2019, whereas Developed Countries contributed 57%, and least developed countries contributed 0.4%. (Figure TS.5) {2.2, Figures 2.9 and 2.10}

Globally, households with income in the top 10% contribute about 36–45% of global GHG emissions (*robust evidence, medium agreement*). About two thirds of the top 10% live in Developed Countries and one third in other economies. The lifestyle consumption emissions of the middle income and poorest citizens in emerging economies are between five and 50 times below their counterparts in high-income countries (*medium confidence*). Increasing inequality within a country can exacerbate dilemmas of redistribution and social cohesion, and affect the willingness of the rich and poor to accept policies to protect the environment, and to accept and afford lifestyle changes that favour mitigation (*medium confidence*). {2.6.1, 2.6.2, Figure 2.29}

Globally, GHG emissions continued to rise across all sectors and subsectors, and most rapidly in transport and industry (*high confidence*). In 2019, 34% (20 $GtCO_2$-eq) of global GHG emissions came from the energy sector, 24% (14 $GtCO_2$-eq) from industry, 22% (13 $GtCO_2$-eq) from agriculture, forestry and other land use (AFOLU), 15% (8.7 $GtCO_2$-eq) from transport, and 5.6% (3.3 $GtCO_2$-eq) from buildings. Once indirect emissions from energy use are considered, the relative shares of industry and buildings emissions rise to 34% and 16%, respectively. Average annual GHG emissions growth during 2010–2019 slowed compared to the previous decade in energy supply (from 2.3% to 1.0%) and industry (from 3.4% to 1.4%, direct emissions only), but remained roughly constant at about 2% yr^{-1} in the transport sector (*high confidence*). Emission growth in AFOLU is more uncertain due to the high share of CO_2-LULUCF emissions (*medium confidence*). (Figure TS.8) {2.2.4, Figure 2.13 and Figures 2.16–2.21}

There is a discrepancy, equating to 5.5 $GtCO_2$ yr^{-1}, between alternative methods of accounting for anthropogenic land CO_2 fluxes. Accounting for this discrepancy would assist in assessing collective progress in a global stocktake (*high confidence*). The principal accounting approaches are national GHG inventories (NGHGI) and global modelling[11] approaches. NGHGI, based on IPCC guidelines, consider a much larger area of forest to be under human management than global models. NGHGI consider the fluxes due to human-induced environmental change on this area to be anthropogenic and are thus reported. Global models, in contrast, consider these fluxes to be natural and are excluded from the total reported anthropogenic land CO_2 flux. The accounting method used will affect the assessment of collective progress in a global stocktake (*medium confidence*) {Cross-Chapter Box 6 in Chapter 7}. In the absence of these adjustments, allowing a like-with-like comparison, collective progress would appear better than it is. {7.2}

This accounting discrepancy also applies to Integrated Assessment Models (IAMs), with the consequence that anthropogenic land CO_2 fluxes reported in IAM pathways cannot be compared directly with those reported in national GHG inventories (*high confidence*). Methodologies enabling a more like-for-like comparison between models' and countries' approaches would support more accurate assessment of the collective progress achieved under the Paris Agreement. {3.4, 7.2.2}

Average annual growth in GHG emissions from energy supply decreased from 2.3% for 2000–2009 to 1.0% for 2010–2019 (*high confidence*). This slowing of growth is attributable to further improvements in energy efficiency and reductions in the carbon intensity of energy supply driven by fuel switching from coal to gas, reduced expansion of coal capacity, particularly in Eastern Asia, and the increased use of renewables (*medium confidence*). (Figure TS.6) {2.2.4, 2.4.2.1, Figure 2.17}

---

11   Bookkeeping models and dynamic global vegetation models.

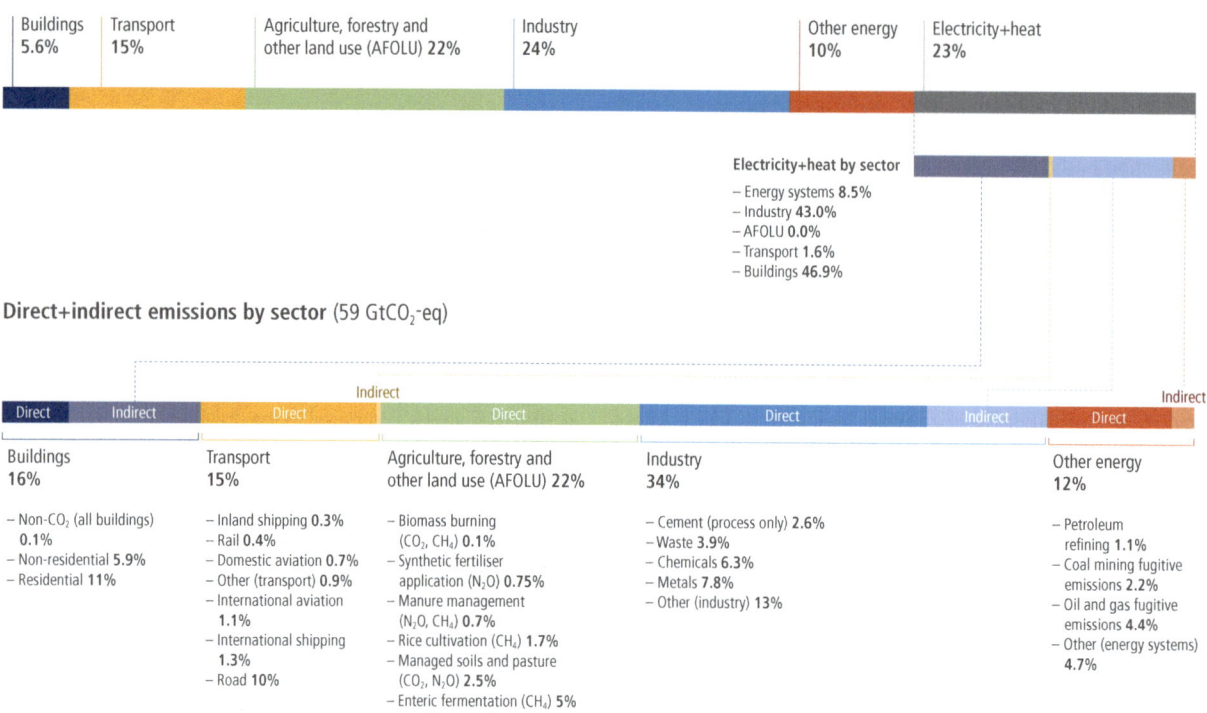

Figure TS.6 | Total anthropogenic direct and indirect GHG emissions for the year 2019 (in GtCO₂-eq) by sector and subsector. Direct emissions estimates assign emissions to the sector in which they arise (scope 1 reporting). Indirect emissions – as used here – refer to the reallocation of emissions from electricity and heat to the sector of final use (scope 2 reporting). Note that cement refers to process emissions only, as a lack of data prevents the full reallocation of indirect emissions to this sector. More comprehensive conceptualisations of indirect emissions including all products and services (scope 3 reporting) are discussed in Section 2.3. Emissions are converted into CO₂-equivalents based on global warming potentials with a 100-year time horizon (GWP100) from the IPCC Sixth Assessment Report. Percentages may not add up to 100 across categories due to rounding at the second significant digit. {Figure 2.12, 2.3}

The industry, buildings and transport sectors make up 44% of global GHG emissions, or 66% when the emissions from electricity and heat production are reallocated as *indirect emissions* (*high confidence*). This reallocation makes a substantial difference to overall industry and buildings emissions as shown in Figure TS.6. Industry, buildings, and transport emissions are driven, respectively, by the large rise in demand for basic materials and manufactured products, a global trend of increasing floor space per capita, building energy service use, travel distances, and vehicle size and weight. Between 2010 and 2019, aviation grew particularly fast on average at about 3.3% per annum. Globally, energy efficiency has improved in all three demand sectors, but carbon intensities have not. (Figure TS.6) {2.2.4, Figures 2.18, 2.19 and 2.20}

Providing access to modern energy services universally would increase global GHG emissions by a few percent at most (*high confidence*). The additional energy demand needed to support *decent living standards*[12] for all is estimated to be well below current average energy consumption (*medium evidence, high agreement*). More equitable income distribution could also reduce carbon emissions, but the nature of this relationship can vary by level of income and development (*limited evidence, medium agreement*). {2.4.3}

Evidence of rapid energy transitions exists in some case studies (*medium confidence*). Emerging evidence since AR5 on past energy transitions identifies a growing number of cases of accelerated technology diffusion at sub-global scales and describes mechanisms by which future energy transitions may occur more quickly than those in the past. Important drivers include technology transfer and cooperation, international policy and financial support, and harnessing synergies among technologies within a sustainable energy system perspective (*medium confidence*). A fast global low-carbon energy transition enabled by finance to facilitate low-carbon technology adoption in developing and particularly in least developed countries can facilitate achieving climate stabilisation targets (*high confidence*). {2.5.2, Table 2.5}

---

12 Decent Living Standards (DLS) – a benchmark of material conditions for human well-being – overlaps with many Sustainable Development Goals (SDGs). Minimum requirements of energy use consistent with enabling well-being for all is between 20 and 50 GJ per capita yr⁻¹ depending on the context. (Figure TS.22) {5.2.2, 5.2.2, Box 5.3}

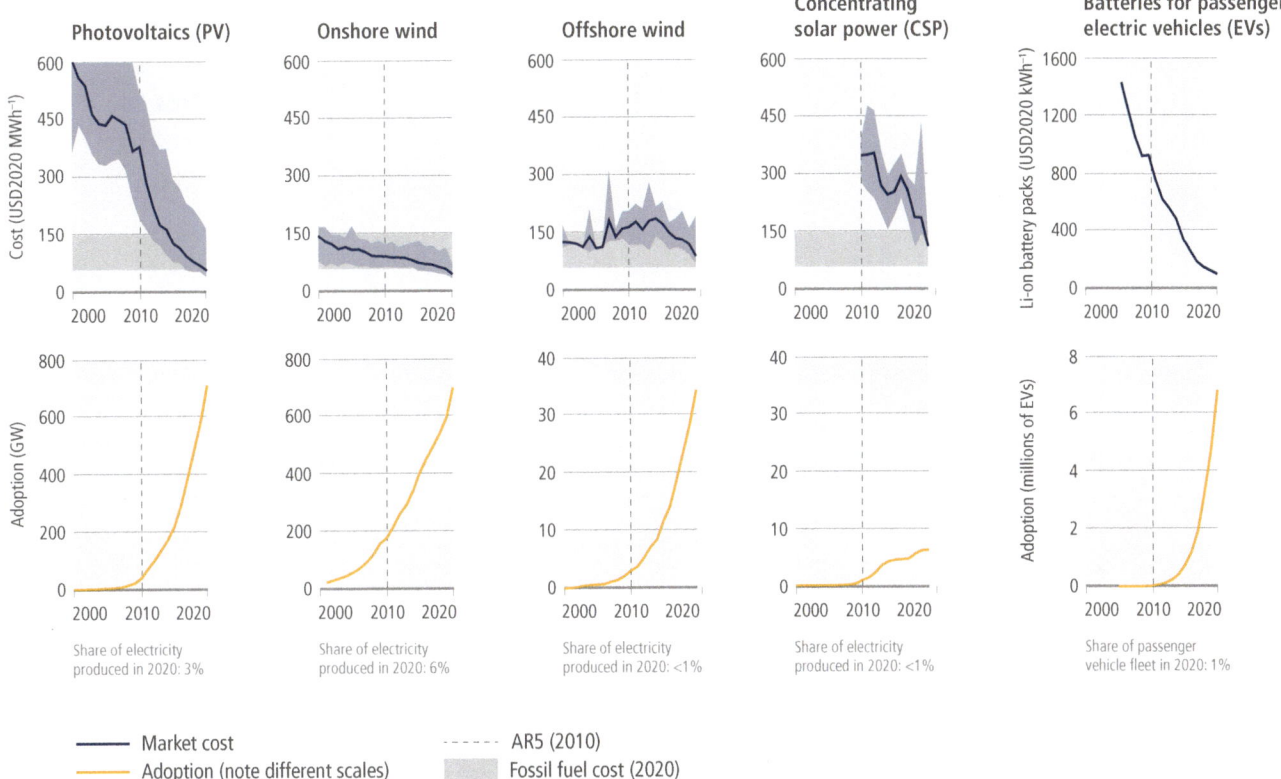

Figure TS.7 | The unit costs of batteries and some forms of renewable energy have fallen significantly, and their adoption continues to increase. The **top panel** shows global costs per unit of energy (USD per MWh) for some rapidly changing mitigation technologies. Solid blue lines indicate average unit cost in each year. Light blue shaded areas show the range between the 5th and 95th percentiles in each year. Grey shading indicates the range of unit costs for new fossil fuel (coal and gas) power in 2020 (corresponding to USD55–148 per MWh). In 2020, the levelised costs of energy (LCOE) of the four renewable energy technologies could compete with fossil fuels in many places. For batteries, costs shown are for 1 kWh of battery storage capacity; for the others, costs are LCOE, which includes installation, capital, operations, and maintenance costs per MWh of electricity produced. The literature uses LCOE because it allows consistent comparisons of cost trends across a diverse set of energy technologies to be made. However, it does not include the costs of grid integration or climate impacts. Further, LCOE does not take into account other environmental and social externalities that may modify the overall (monetary and non-monetary) costs of technologies and alter their deployment. The **bottom panel** shows cumulative global adoption for each technology, in GW of installed capacity for renewable energy and in millions of vehicles for battery-electric vehicles. A vertical dashed line is placed in 2010 to indicate the change since AR5. Shares of electricity produced and share of passenger vehicle fleet are indicated in text for 2020 based on provisional data, i.e., percentage of total electricity production (for PV, onshore wind, offshore wind, CSP) and of total stock of passenger vehicles (for EVs). The electricity production share reflects different capacity factors; for example, for the same amount of installed capacity, wind produces about twice as much electricity as solar PV. {2.5, 6.4} Renewable energy and battery technologies were selected as illustrative examples because they have recently shown rapid changes in costs and adoption, and because consistent data are available. Other mitigation options assessed in the report are not included as they do not meet these criteria.

Multiple low-carbon technologies have shown rapid progress since AR5 – in cost, performance, and adoption – enhancing the feasibility of rapid energy transitions (*high confidence*). The rapid deployment and unit cost decrease of modular technologies like solar, wind, and batteries have occurred much faster than anticipated by experts and modelled in previous mitigation scenarios, as shown in Figure TS.7 (*high confidence*). The political, economic, social, and technical feasibility of solar energy, wind energy and electricity storage technologies has improved dramatically over the past few years. In contrast, the adoption of nuclear energy and CO_2 capture and storage (CCS) in the electricity sector has been slower than the growth rates anticipated in stabilisation scenarios. Emerging evidence since AR5 indicates that small-scale technologies (e.g., solar, batteries) tend to improve faster and be adopted more quickly than large-scale technologies (nuclear, CCS) (*medium confidence*). (Figure TS.7, Box TS.15) {2.5.3, 2.5.4, Figures 2.22 and 2.23}

Robust incentives for investment in innovation, especially incentives reinforced by national policy and international agreements, are central to accelerating low-carbon technological change (*robust evidence, medium agreement*). Policies have driven innovation, including instruments for technology push (e.g., scientific training, research and development (R&D)) and demand pull (e.g., carbon pricing, adoption subsidies), as well as those promoting knowledge flows and especially technology transfer. The magnitude of the scale-up challenge elevates the importance of rapid technology development and adoption. This includes ensuring participation of developing countries in an enhanced global flow of knowledge, skills, experience, equipment, and technology; which in turn requires strong financial, institutional, and capacity-building support. {16.4, 16.5}

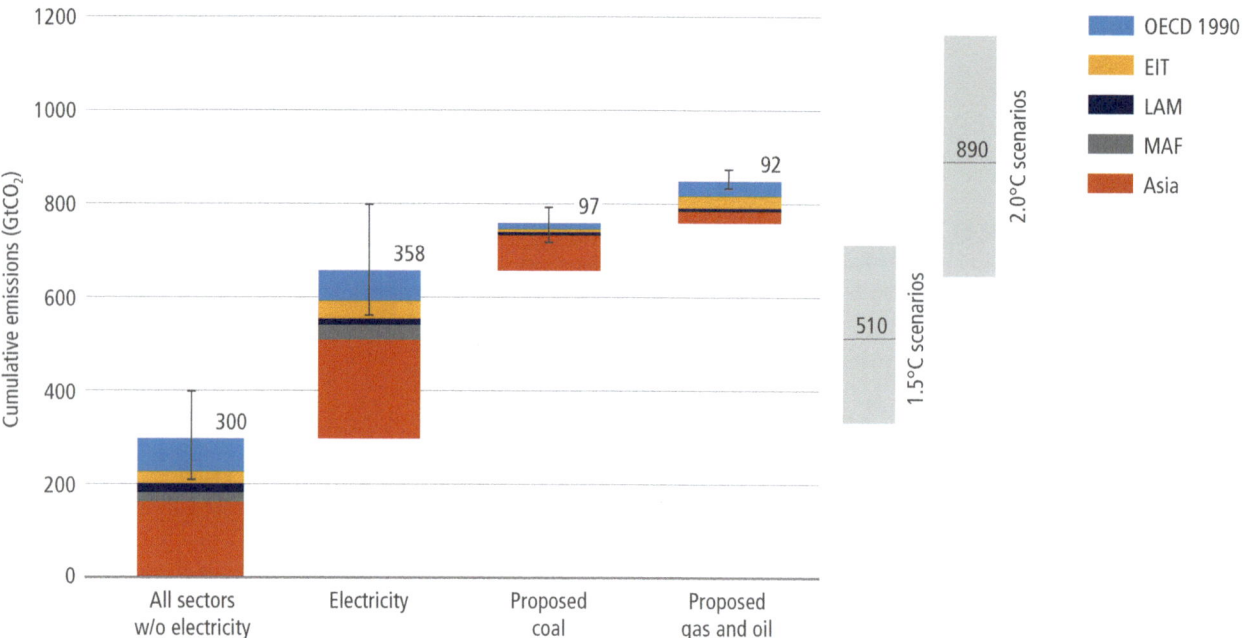

Figure TS.8 | Future CO$_2$ emissions from existing and currently planned fossil fuel infrastructure in the context of the Paris Agreement carbon budgets in GtCO$_2$ based on historic patterns of infrastructure lifetimes and Future CO$_2$ emissions estimates of existing infrastructure for the electricity sector as well as all other sectors (industry, transport, buildings, other fossil fuel infrastructures) and of proposed infrastructures for coal power as well as gas and oil power. Grey bars on the right depict the range (5–95th percentile) in overall cumulative net CO$_2$ emissions until reaching net zero CO$_2$ in pathways that limit warming to 1.5°C (>50%) with no or limited overshoot (1.5°C scenarios), and in pathways that limit warming to 2°C (>67%) (2°C scenarios). {Figure 2.26}

Estimates of future CO$_2$ emissions from existing fossil fuel infrastructures already exceed remaining cumulative net CO$_2$ emissions in pathways limiting warming to 1.5°C (>50%) with no or limited overshoot (*high confidence*). Assuming variations in historic patterns of use and decommissioning, estimated future CO$_2$ emissions from existing fossil fuel infrastructure alone are 660 (460–890) GtCO$_2$ and from existing and currently planned infrastructure 850 (600–1100) GtCO$_2$. This compares to overall cumulative net CO$_2$ emissions until reaching net zero CO$_2$ of 510 (330–710) GtCO$_2$ in pathways that limit warming to 1.5°C (>50%) with no or limited overshoot, and 890 (640–1160) GtCO$_2$ in pathways that limit warming to 2°C (>67%) (*high confidence*). While most future CO$_2$ emissions from existing and currently planned fossil fuel infrastructure are situated in the power sector, most remaining fossil fuel CO$_2$ emissions in pathways that limit warming to 2°C (>67%) and below are from non-electric energy – most importantly from the industry and transportation sectors (*high confidence*). Decommissioning and reduced utilisation of existing fossil fuel installations in the power sector as well as cancellation of new installations are required to align future CO$_2$ emissions from the power sector with projections in these pathways (*high confidence*). (Figure TS.8) {2.7.2, 2.7.3, Figure 2.26, Tables 2.6 and 2.7}

TS.4   Mitigation and Development Pathways

While previous WGIII assessments have explored mitigation pathways, since AR5 there has been an increasing emphasis in the literature on development pathways, and in particular at the national scale. Chapter 4 assesses near-term (2019–2030) to mid-term (2030–2050) pathways, complementing Chapter 3 which focuses on long-term pathways (up to 2100). While there is considerable literature on country-level mitigation pathways, including but not limited to NDCs, the country distribution of this literature is very unequal (*high confidence*). {4.2.1, Cross-Chapter Box 4 in Chapter 4}

TS.4.1   Mitigation and Development Pathways in the Near- to Mid-term

An emissions gap persists, exacerbated by an implementation gap, despite mitigation efforts including those in Nationally Determined Contributions (NDCs). In this report the *emissions gap* is understood as the difference between projected global emissions with Nationally Determined Contributions (NDCs) in 2030, and emissions in 2030 if mitigation pathways consistent with the Paris temperature goals were achieved. The term *implementation gap* refers to the gap between NDC mitigation pledges and the expected outcome of existing policies.

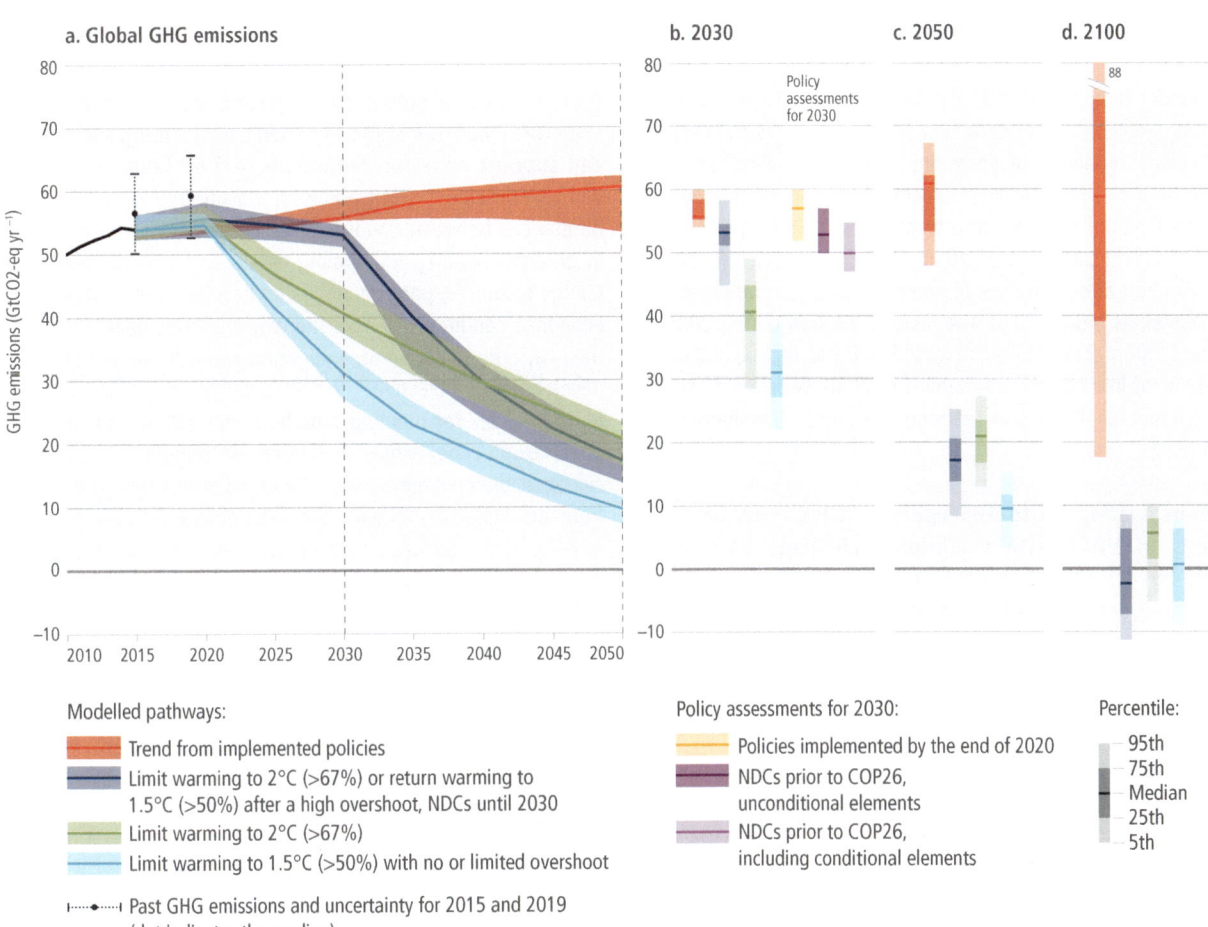

Figure TS.9 | Aggregate greenhouse gas (GHG) emissions of global mitigation pathways (coloured funnels and bars) and projected emission outcomes from current policies and emissions implied by unconditional and conditional elements of NDCs, based on updates available by 11 October 2021 (grey bars). Shaded areas show GHG emission medians and 25–75th percentiles over 2020–2050 for four types of pathways in the AR6 scenario database: (i) pathways with near-term emissions developments in line with current policies and extended with comparable ambition levels beyond 2030; (ii) pathways *likely* to limit warming to 2°C with near-term emissions developments reflecting 2030 emissions implied by current NDCs followed by accelerated emissions reductions; (iii) pathways *likely* to limit warming to 2°C based on immediate actions from 2020 onwards; (iv) pathways that limit warming to 1.5°C with no or limited overshoot. Right-hand panels show two snapshots of the 2030 and 2050 emission ranges of the pathways in detail (median, 25–75th and 5–95th percentiles). The 2030 snapshot includes the projected emissions from the implementation of the NDCs as assessed in Section 4.2 (Table 4.1; median and full range). Historic GHG emissions trends as used in model studies are shown for 2010–2015. GHG emissions are in CO₂-equivalent using GWP100 values from AR6. {3.5, Table 4.1, Cross-Chapter Box 4 in Chapter 4}

Pathways consistent with the implementation and extrapolation of countries' current[13] policies see GHG emissions reaching 57 (52–60) $GtCO_2$-eq yr^{-1} by 2030 and to 46–67 $GtCO_2$-eq yr^{-1} by 2050, leading to a median global warming of 2.4°C to 3.5°C by 2100 (*medium confidence*). NDCs with unconditional and conditional elements[14] lead to 53 (50–57) and 50 (47–55) $GtCO_2$-eq, respectively (*medium confidence*) {Table 4.1}. This leaves median estimated *emissions gaps* of 14–23 $GtCO_2$-eq to limit warming to 2°C and 25–34 $GtCO_2$-eq to limit warming to 1.5°C relative to mitigation pathways. (Figure TS.9) {Cross-Chapter Box 4, Figure 1 in Chapter 4}

Projected global emissions from aggregated NDCs place limiting global warming to 1.5°C beyond reach and make it harder after 2030 to limit warming to 2°C (*high confidence*). Pathways following NDCs until 2030 show a smaller reduction in fossil fuel use, slower deployment of low-carbon alternatives, and a smaller reduction in CO_2, CH_4 and overall GHG emissions in 2030 compared to immediate action scenarios. This is followed by a much faster reduction of emissions and fossil fuels after 2030, and a larger increase in the deployment of low-carbon alternatives during the medium term in order to get close to the levels of the immediate action pathways in 2050. Those pathways also deploy a larger amount of carbon dioxide removal (CDR) to compensate for higher emissions before 2030. The faster transition during 2030 to 2050 entails greater investment in fossil fuel infrastructure and lower deployment of low-carbon alternatives in 2030, which adds to the socio-economic challenges in realising the higher transition rates. (TS.4.2) {3.5}

Studies evaluating up to 105 updated NDCs[15] indicate that emissions in NDCs with conditional elements have been reduced by 4.5 (2.7–6.3) $GtCO_2$-eq. This closes the emission gaps by about one third to 2°C and about 20% to 1.5°C compared to the original NDCs submitted in 2015/16 (*medium confidence*) {4.2.2, Cross-Chapter Box 4 in Chapter 4}. An *implementation gap* also exists between the projected emissions with 'current policies' and the projected emissions resulting from the implementation of the unconditional and conditional elements of NDCs; this is estimated to be around 4 and 7 $GtCO_2$-eq in 2030, respectively (*medium confidence*) {4.2.2}. Many countries would therefore require additional policies and associated action on climate change to meet their autonomously determined mitigation targets as specified under the first NDCs (*limited evidence*). The disruptions triggered by the COVID-19 pandemic increase uncertainty over the range of projections relative to pre-COVID-19 literature. As indicated by a growing number of studies at the national and global level, how large near- to mid-term emissions implications of the COVID-19 pandemic are, to a large degree depends on how stimulus or recovery packages are designed. {4.2}

There is a need to explore how accelerated mitigation – relative to NDCs and current policies – could close both emission gaps and implementation gaps. There is increasing understanding of the technical content of accelerated mitigation pathways, differentiated by national circumstances, with considerable, though uneven, literature at country-level (*medium evidence, high agreement*). Transformative technological and institutional changes for the near term include demand reductions through efficiency and reduced activity, rapid decarbonisation of the electricity sector and low-carbon electrification of buildings, industry and transport (*robust evidence, medium agreement*). A focus on energy use and supply is essential, but not sufficient on its own – the land sector and food systems deserve attention. The literature does not adequately include demand-side options and systems analysis, and captures the impact from non-CO_2 GHGs (*medium confidence*). {4.2.5}

If obstacles to accelerated mitigation are rooted in underlying structural features of society, then transforming such structures can support emission reductions {4.2.6}. Countries and regions will have different starting points for transition pathways. Some critical differences between countries include climate conditions resulting in different heating and cooling needs, endowments with different energy resources, patterns of spatial development, and political and economic conditions {4.2.5}. The way countries develop determines their capacity to accelerate mitigation and achieve other sustainable development objectives simultaneously (*medium confidence*) {4.3.1, 4.3.2}. Yet meeting ambitious mitigation and development goals cannot be achieved through incremental change (*robust evidence, medium agreement*). Though development pathways result from the actions of a wide range of actors, it is possible to shift development pathways through policies and enhancing enabling conditions (*limited evidence, medium agreement*).

Shifting development pathways towards sustainability **offers ways to broaden the range of levers and enablers that a society can use to accelerate mitigation and increases the likelihood of making progress simultaneously on climate action and other development goals (Box TS.3) {Cross-Chapter Box 5 in Chapter 4, Figure 4.7, 4.3}.** There are practical options to shift development pathways in ways that advance mitigation and other sustainable development objectives, support political feasibility, increase resources to meet multiple goals, and reduce emissions (*limited evidence, high agreement*). Concrete examples, assessed in Chapter 4 of this report, include high-employment and low-emissions structural change; fiscal reforms for mitigation and social contract, combining housing policies to deliver both housing and transport mitigation; and changed economic, social and spatial patterns of agriculture sector development, providing the basis for sustained reductions in emissions from deforestation. {4.4.1, 4.4, 1.10}

---

13 Current NDCs refers to the most recent Nationally Determined Contributions submitted to the UNFCCC as well as those publicly announced (with sufficient detail on targets, but not yet submitted) up to 11 October 2021, and reflected in literature published up to 11 October 2021. Original INDCs and NDCs refer to those submitted to the UNFCCC in 2015 and 2016.

14 See {4.2.1} for descriptions of 'unconditional' and 'conditional' elements of NDCs.

15 Submitted by 11 October 2021.

Table TS.2 | Comparison of key characteristics of mitigation pathways with immediate action towards limiting warming to 1.5-2°C vs. pathways following NDCs announced prior to COP26 until 2030. Key characteristics are reported for five groups of mitigation pathways: (i) immediate action to limit warming to 1.5°C (>50%) with no or limited overshoot (C1 in Table TS.3; 97 scenarios), (ii) near term action following the NDCs until 2030 and returning warming to 1.5°C (> 50%) by 2100 after a high overshoot (subset of 42 scenarios following the NDCs until 2030 in C2), (iii) immediate action to limit warming to 2°C (>67%), (C3a in Table TS.3; 204 scenarios), (iv) near term action following the NDCs until 2030 followed by post-2030 action to limit warming to 2°C (>67%) (C3b in Table TS.3; 97 scenarios). Also shown are the characteristics for (v) the combined class of all scenarios that limit warming to 2°C (>67%). The groups (i), (iii), and the combination of (ii) and (iv) are depicted in Figure TS.9. Reported are median and interquartile ranges (in brackets) for selected global indicators. Numbers are rounded to the nearest five, with the exception of cumulative net negative CO_2 emissions rounded to the nearest 10. Changes from 2019 are relative to modelled 2019 values. Emissions reductions are based on harmonised model emissions used for the climate assessment. {Section 3.5} {Table 3.6}

Global indicators	1.5°C (>50%)	1.5°C (>50%) by 2100	2°C (>67%)		
	Immediate action, with no or limited overshoot	NDCs until 2030, with overshoot before 2100	Immediate action	NDCs until 2030	All
Cumulative net negative CO_2 emissions until 2100 (GtCO_2)	220 (70,430)	380 (300,470)	30 (0,130)	60 (20,210)	40 (10,180)
Change in GHG emissions in 2030 (% rel to 2019)	−45 (−50,−40)	−5 (−5,0)	−25 (−35,−20)	−5 (−10,0)	−20 (−30,−10)
in 2050 (% rel to 2019)	−85 (−90,−80)	−75 (−85,−70)	−65 (−70,−60)	−70 (−70,−60)	−65 (−70,−60)
Change in CO_2 emissions in 2030 (% rel to 2019)	−50 (−60,−40)	−5 (−5,0)	−25 (−35,−20)	−5 (−5,0)	−20 (−30,−5)
in 2050 (% rel to 2019)	−100 (−105,−95)	−85 (−95,−80)	−70 (−80,−65)	−75 (−80,−65)	−75 (−80,−65)
Change in net land use CO_2 emissions in 2030 (% rel to 2019)	−100 (−105,−95)	−30 (−60,−20)	−90 (−105,−75)	−20 (−80,−20)	−80 (−100,−30)
in 2050 (% rel to 2019)	−150 (−200,−100)	−135 (−165,−120)	−135 (−185,−100)	−130 (−145,−115)	−135 (−180,−100)
Change in CH_4 emissions in 2030 (% rel to 2019)	−35 (−40,−30)	−5 (−5,0)	−25 (−35,−20)	−10 (−15,−5)	−20 (−25,−10)
in 2050 (% rel to 2019)	−50 (−60,−45)	−50 (−60,−45)	−45 (−50,−40)	−50 (−65,−45)	−45 (−55,−40)
Change in primary energy from coal in 2030 (% rel to 2019)	−75 (−80,−65)	−10 (−20,−5)	−50 (−65,−35)	−15 (−20,−10)	−35 (−55,−20)
in 2050 (% rel to 2019)	−95 (−100,−80)	−90 (−100,−85)	−85 (−100,−65)	−80 (−90,−70)	−85 (−95,−65)
Change in primary energy from oil in 2030 (% rel to 2019)	−10 (−25,0)	5 (5,10)	0 (−10,10)	10 (5,10)	5 (0,10)
in 2050 (% rel to 2019)	−60 (−75,−40)	−50 (−65,−35)	−30 (−45,−15)	−40 (−55,−20)	−30 (−50,−15)
Change in primary energy from gas in 2030 (% rel to 2019)	−10 (−30,0)	15 (10,25)	10 (0,15)	15 (10,15)	10 (0,15)
in 2050 (% rel to 2019)	−45 (−60,−20)	−45 (−55,−30)	−10 (−35,15)	−30 (−45,−5)	−15 (−40,10)
Change in primary energy from nuclear in 2030 (% rel to 2019)	40 (10,70)	10 (0,25)	35 (5,50)	10 (0,30)	25 (0,45)
in 2050 (% rel to 2019)	90 (15,295)	100 (45,130)	85 (30,200)	75 (30,120)	80 (30,140)
Change in primary energy from modern biomass in 2030 (% rel to 2019)	75 (55,130)	45 (20,75)	60 (35,105)	45 (20,80)	55 (35,105)
in 2050 (% rel to 2019)	290 (215,430)	230 (170,420)	240 (130,355)	260 (95,435)	250 (115,405)
Change in primary energy from non-biomass renewables in 2030 (% rel to 2019)	225 (155,270)	100 (85,145)	150 (115,190)	115 (85,130)	130 (90,170)
in 2050 (% rel to 2019)	725 (545,950)	665 (535,925)	565 (415,765)	625 (545,700)	605 (470,735)
Change in carbon intensity of electricity in 2030 (% rel to 2019)	−75 (−80,−70)	−30 (−40,−30)	−60 (−70,−50)	−35 (−40,−30)	−50 (−65,−35)
in 2050 (% rel to 2019)	−100 (−100,−100)	−100 (−100,−100)	−95 (−100,−95)	−100 (−100,−95)	−95 (−100,−95)

Box TS.3 | Shifting Development Pathways to Increase Sustainability and Broaden Mitigation Options

In this report, *development pathways* refer to the patterns of development resulting from multiple decisions and choices made by many actors in the national and global contexts. Each society whether in developing or developed regions follows its own pattern of growth (Figure TS.13). Development pathways can also be described at smaller scales (e.g., for regions or cities) and for sectoral systems.

Development pathways are major drivers of GHG emissions {1, 2}. There is compelling evidence to show that continuing along existing development pathways will not achieve rapid and deep emission reductions. In the absence of shifts in development pathways, conventional mitigation policy instruments may not be able to limit global emissions to a degree sufficient to meet ambitious mitigation goals or they may only be able to do so at very high economic and social costs.

Policies to shift development pathways, on the other hand, make mitigation policies more effective. Shifting development pathways broadens the scope for synergies between sustainable development objectives and mitigation. Development pathways also determine the enablers and levers available for adaptation {AR6 WGII TS.E.1.2} and for achieving other SDGs.

There are many instances in which reducing GHG emissions and moving towards the achievement of other development objectives can go hand in hand {Chapter 3, Figure 3.33, Chapters 6–12, and 17}. Integrated policies can support the creation of synergies between *action to combat climate change and its impacts* (SDG 13 – climate action) and other SDGs. For example, when measures promoting walkable urban areas are combined with electrification and clean renewable energy, there are several co-benefits to be attained. These include reduced pressures on agricultural land from reduced urban growth, health co-benefits from cleaner air, and benefits from enhanced mobility {8.2, 8.4, 4.4.1}. Energy efficiency in buildings and energy poverty alleviation through improved access to clean fuels also deliver significant health benefits. {9.8.1 and 9.8.2}

However, decisions about mitigation actions, and their timing and scale, may entail trade-offs with the achievement of other national development objectives in the near, mid- and long term {Chapter 12}. In the near term, for example, regulations may ban vehicles from city centres to reduce congestion and local air pollution but reduce mobility and choice. Increasing green spaces within cities without caps on housing prices may involve trade-offs with affordable housing and push low-income residents outside the city {8.2.2}. In the mid- and long term, large-scale deployment of biomass energy raises concerns about food security and biodiversity conservation {3.7.1, 3.7.5, 7.4.4, 9.8.1, 12.5.2, 12.5.3}. Prioritising is one way to manage these trade-offs, addressing some national development objectives earlier than others. Another way is to adopt policy packages aimed at shifting development pathways towards increased sustainability (SDPS) as they expand the range of tools available to simultaneously achieve multiple development objectives and accelerate mitigation. (Box TS.3, Figure 1)

What does *shifting development pathways towards increased sustainability* entail?
Shifting development pathways towards increased sustainability implies making transformative changes that disrupt existing developmental trends. Such choices would not be marginal, but include technological, systemic and socio-behavioural changes {4.4}. Decision points also arise with new infrastructure, sustainable supply chains, institutional capacities for evidence-based and integrated decision-making, financial alignment towards low-carbon socially responsible investments, just transitions and shifts in behaviour and norms to support shifts away from fossil fuel consumption. Adopting multi-level governance modes, tackling corruption where it inhibits shifts to sustainability, and improving social and political trust are also key for aligning and supporting long-term environmentally just policies and processes. {4.4, Cross-Chapter Box 5 in Chapter 4}

How can development pathways be 'shifted'?
Shifting development paths is complex. Changes that involve 'dissimilar, unfamiliar and more complex science-based components' take more time, acceptance and legitimation and involve complex social learning, even when they promise large gains. Despite the complexities of the interactions that result in patterns of development, history also shows that societies can influence the direction of development pathways based on choices made by decision-makers, citizens, the private sector, and social stakeholders. Shifts in development pathways result from both sustained political interventions and bottom-up changes in public opinion. Collective action by individuals as part of social movements or lifestyle changes underpins system change. {5.2.3, 5.4.1, 5.4.5}

Sectoral transitions that aim to shift development pathways often have multiple objectives and deploy a diverse mix of policies and institutional measures. Context-specific governance conditions can significantly enable or disable sectoral transitions. {Cross-Chapter Box 12 in Chapter 16}

Box TS.3 (continued)

The necessary transformational changes are anticipated to be more acceptable if rooted in the development aspirations of the economy and society within which they take place and may enable a new social contract to address a complex set of interlinkages across sectors, classes, and the whole economy. Taking advantage of windows of opportunity and disruptions to mindsets and socio-technical systems could advance deeper transformations.

How can shifts in development pathways be implemented by actors in different contexts?

Shifting development pathways to increased sustainability is a shared aspiration. Yet since countries differ in starting points (e.g., social, economic, cultural, political) and historical backgrounds, they have different urgent needs in terms of facilitating the economic, social, and environmental dimensions of sustainable development and, therefore, give different priorities {4.3.2, 17.1}. The appropriate set of policies to shift development pathways thus depends on national circumstances and capacities.

Shifting development pathways towards sustainability needs to be supported by multilateral partnerships to strengthen suitable capacity, technological innovation (TS.6.5), and financial flows (TS.6.4). The international community can play a particularly key role by helping ensure the necessary broad participation in climate-mitigation efforts, including by countries at different development levels, through sustained support for policies and partnerships that support shifting development pathways towards sustainability while promoting equity and being mindful of different transition capacities. {4.3, 16.5, 16.6}

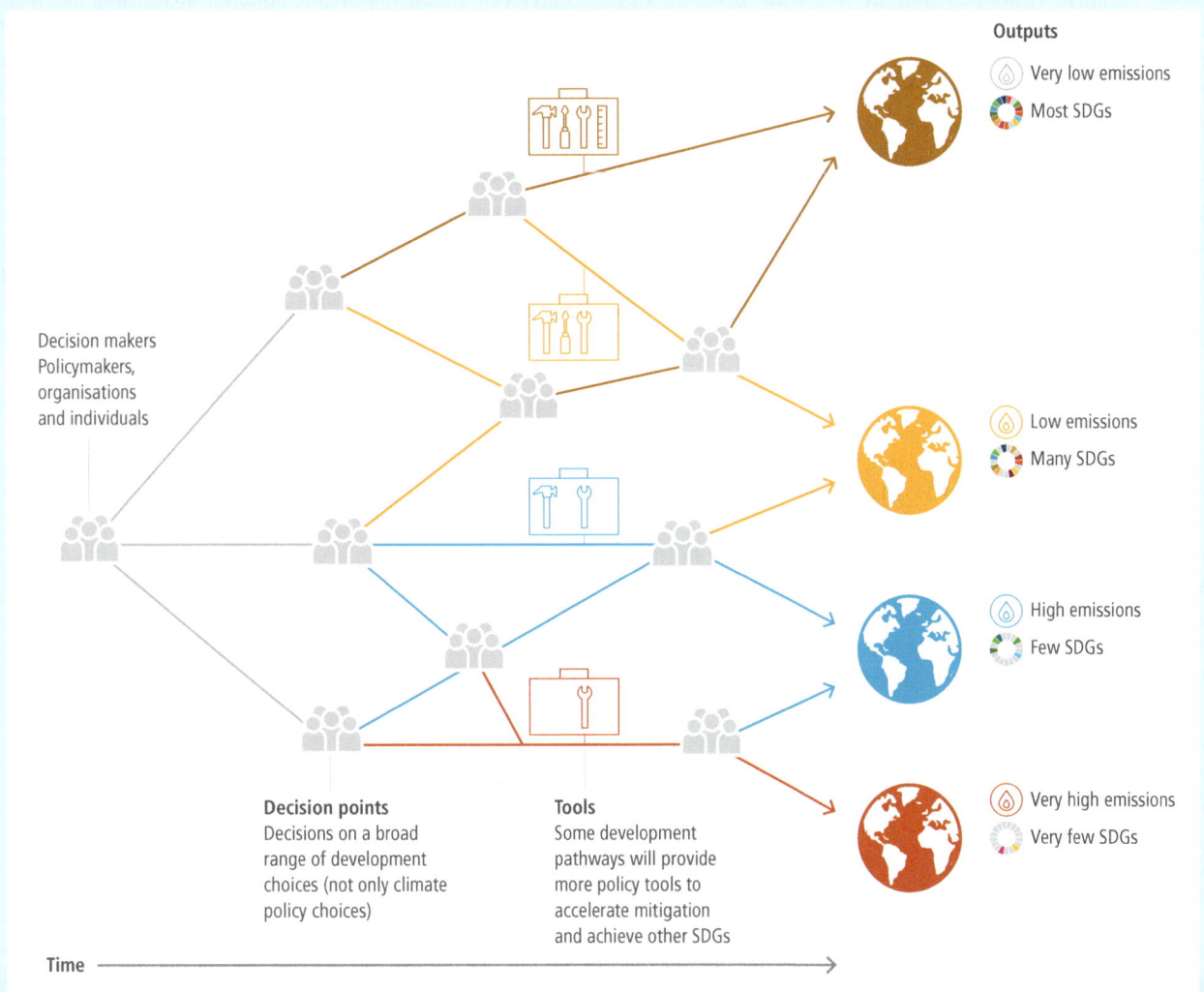

Box TS.3, Figure 1 | Shifting development pathways to increased sustainability: choices by a wide range of actors at key decision points on development pathways can reduce barriers and provide more tools to accelerate mitigation and achieve other Sustainable Development Goals. {4.7}

Policies can *shift* development pathways. There are examples of policies implemented in the pursuit of overall societal development objectives, such as job creation, macroeconomic stability, economic growth, and public health and welfare. In some countries, such policies are framed as part of a *Just Transition* (Box TS.3), however, they can have major influence on mitigative capacity, and hence can be seen as tools to broaden mitigation options (*medium confidence*) {4.3.3}. Coordinated policy mixes would need to orchestrate multiple actors – individuals, groups and collectives, corporate actors, institutions and infrastructure actors – to deepen decarbonisation and shift pathways towards sustainability. Shifts in one country may spill over to other countries. Shifting development pathways can jointly support mitigation and adaptation {4.4.2}. Some studies explore the risks of high complexity and potential delay attached to shifting development pathways. (Box TS.4, Figure TS.11) {4.4.3}

An increasing number of mitigation strategies up to 2050 (mid-term) have been developed by various actors. A growing number of such strategies aim at net zero GHG or CO_2 emissions, but it is not yet possible to draw global implications due to the limited size of sample (*medium evidence, low agreement*) {4.2.4}. Non-state actors are also engaging in a wide range of mitigation initiatives. When adding up emission reduction potentials, sub-national and non-state international cooperative initiatives could reduce emissions by up to about 20 $GtCO_2$-eq in 2030 (*limited evidence, medium agreement*) {4.2.3}. Yet perceived or real conflicts between mitigation and other SDGs can impede such action. If undertaken without precaution, accelerated mitigation is found to have significant implications for development objectives and macroeconomic costs at country level. The literature shows that the employment effect of mitigation policies tends to be limited on aggregate but can be significant at sectoral level (*limited evidence, medium agreement*). Detailed design of mitigation policies is critical for distributional impacts and avoiding lock-in (*high confidence*), though further research is needed in that direction. {4.2.6}

The literature identifies a broad set of enabling conditions that can both foster *shifting development pathways* and *accelerated mitigation* (*medium evidence, high agreement*). Policy integration is a necessary component of shifting development pathways, addressing multiple objectives. To this aim, mobilising a range of policies is preferable to single policy instruments (*high confidence*). {4.4.1}. Governance for climate mitigation and shifting development pathways is enhanced when tailored to national and local contexts. Improved institutions and effective governance enable ambitious action on climate and can help bridge implementation gaps (*medium evidence, high agreement*). Given that strengthening institutions may be a long-term endeavour, it needs attention in the near term {4.4.1}. Accelerated mitigation and shifting development pathways necessitates both redirecting existing financial flows from high- to low-emissions technologies and systems, and providing additional resources to overcome current financial barriers (*high confidence*) {4.4.1}. Opportunities exist in the near term to close the finance gap {15.2.2}. At the national level, public finance for actions promoting sustainable development helps broaden the scope of mitigation (*medium confidence*). Changes in behaviour and lifestyles are important to move beyond mitigation as incremental change, and when supporting shifts to more sustainable development pathways will broaden the scope of mitigation (*medium confidence*). {4.4.1, Figure 4.8}

Some enabling conditions can be put in place relatively quickly while some others may take time to establish underscoring the importance of early action (*high confidence*). Depending on context, some enabling conditions such as promoting innovation may take time to establish. Other enabling conditions, such as improved access to financing, can be put in place in a relatively short time frame, and can yield rapid results {4.4, Figure 5.14, 13.9, 14.5, 15.6, 16.3, 16.4, 16.5, Cross-Chapter Box 12 in Chapter 16}. Focusing on development pathways and considering how to shift them may also yield rapid results by providing tools to accelerate mitigation and achieve other sustainable development goals {4.4.1}. Charting just transitions to net zero may provide a vision, which policy measures can help achieve (Boxes TS.4 and TS.8).

Equity can be an important enabler, increasing the level of ambition for accelerated mitigation (*high confidence*) {4.5}. Equity deals with the distribution of costs and benefits and how these are shared, as per social contracts, national policy and international agreements. Transition pathways have distributional consequences such as large changes in employment and economic structure (*high confidence*). The *Just Transition* concept has become an international focal point tying together social movements, trade unions, and other key stakeholders to ensure equity is better accounted for in low-carbon transitions (Box TS.4). The effectiveness of cooperative action and the perception of fairness of such arrangements are closely related in that pathways that prioritise equity and allow broad stakeholder participation can enable broader consensus for the transformational change implicit in the need for deeper mitigation (*robust evidence, medium agreement*). (Box TS.4) {4.5, Figure 4.9}

TS

Box TS.4 | Just Transition

The Just Transition framework refers to a set of principles, processes and practices aimed at ensuring that no people, workers, places, sectors, countries or regions are left behind in the move from a high-carbon to a low-carbon economy. It includes respect and dignity for vulnerable groups; creation of decent jobs; social protection; employment rights; fairness in energy access and use and social dialogue and democratic consultation with relevant stakeholders.

The concept has evolved, becoming prominent in the United States of America in 1980, related to environmental regulations that resulted in job losses from highly polluting industries. Traced from a purely labour movement, trade union space, the Just Transition framework emphasises that decent work and environmental protection are not incompatible. During COP 24, with the Just Transition Silesia Declaration, the concept gained in recognition and was signed by 56 heads of state.

Implicit in a Just Transition is the notion of well-being, equity and justice – the realisation that transitions are inherently disruptive and deliberate effort may be required to ensure communities dependent on fossil-fuel based economies and industries do not suffer disproportionately {Chapter 4}. 'Just Transitions' are integral to the European Union as mentioned in the EU Green Deal, the Scottish Government's development plans and other national low-carbon transition strategies. The US Green New Deal Resolution puts structural inequality, poverty mitigation, and 'Just Transitions' at its centre. There is a growing awareness of the need for shifting finance towards Just Transition in the context of COVID-19, in particular, public finance and governance have a major role in allowing a Just Transition more broadly {Chapter 15}.

In the immediate aftermath of the COVID-19 pandemic, low oil prices created additional financial problems for fossil fuel producer countries faced with loss of revenue and reduced fiscal latitude and space. Public spending and social safety nets associated with the proceeds from producer economies can be affected as assets become stranded and spending on strategic sustainable development goals such as free education and health-care services are neglected. Fiscal challenges are intricately linked to 'Just Transitions' and the management associated with sustainable energy transition. There is no certainty on how energy systems will recover post-COVID-19. However, 'Just Transitions' will have equity implications if stimulus packages are implemented without due regard for the differentiated scales and speeds and national and regional contexts, especially in the context of developing countries.

A Just Transition entails targeted and proactive measures from governments, agencies, and other non-state authorities to ensure that any negative social, environmental, or economic impacts of economy-wide transitions are minimised, whilst benefits are maximised for those disproportionally affected. These proactive measures include eradication of poverty, regulating prosperity and creating jobs in 'green' sectors. In addition, governments, polluting industries, corporations, and those more able to pay higher associated taxes, can pay for transition costs by providing a welfare safety net and adequate compensation to people, communities, and regions that have been impacted by pollution, or are marginalised, or are negatively impacted by a transition from a high- to low-carbon economy and society. There is, nonetheless, increased recognition that resources that can enable the transition, international development institutions, as well as other transitional drivers such as tools, strategies and finance, are scarce. A sample of global efforts is summarised in Box TS.4, Figure 1.

Box TS.4 (continued)

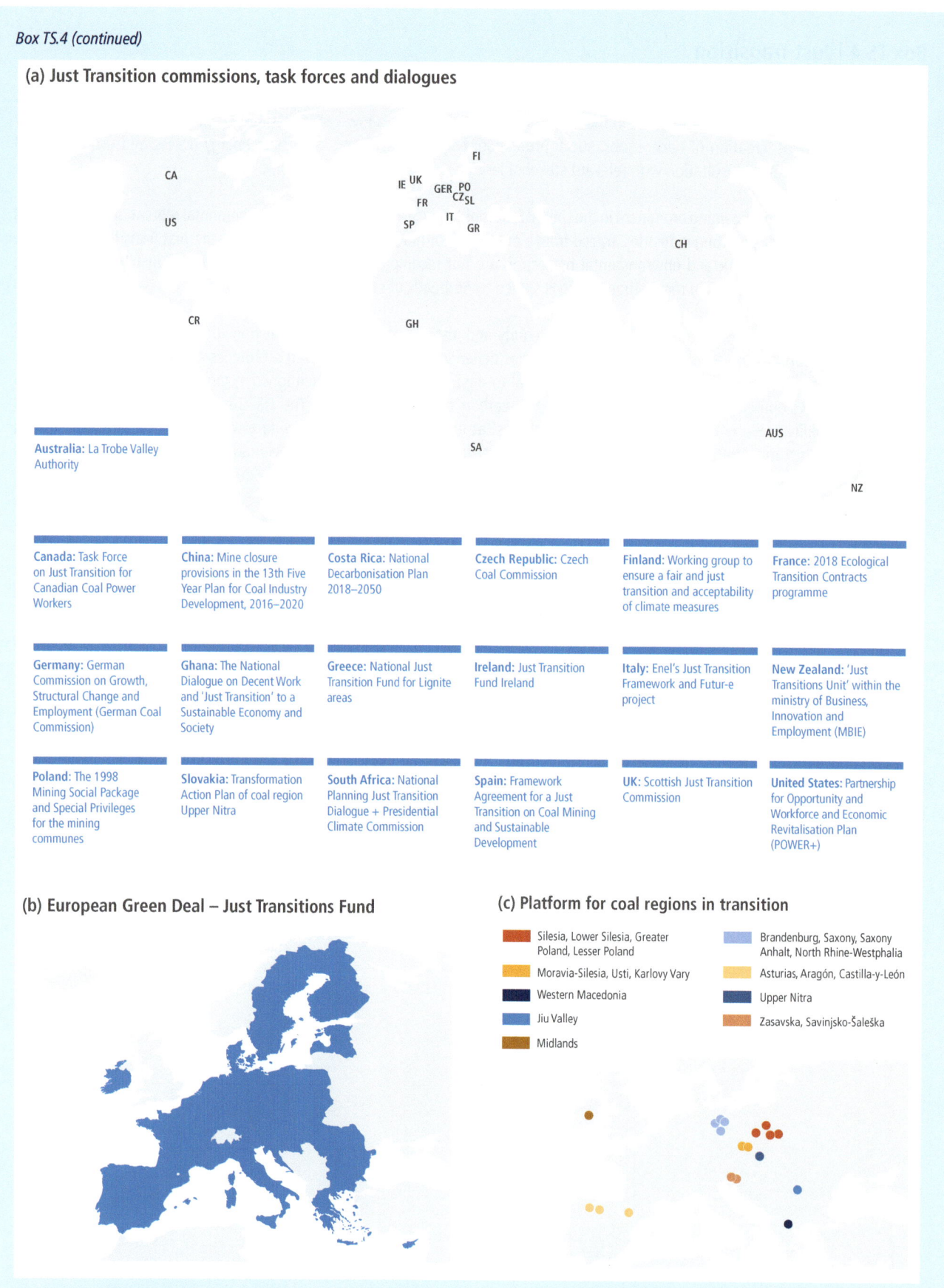

(a) Just Transition commissions, task forces and dialogues

Australia: La Trobe Valley Authority

Canada: Task Force on Just Transition for Canadian Coal Power Workers

China: Mine closure provisions in the 13th Five Year Plan for Coal Industry Development, 2016–2020

Costa Rica: National Decarbonisation Plan 2018–2050

Czech Republic: Czech Coal Commission

Finland: Working group to ensure a fair and just transition and acceptability of climate measures

France: 2018 Ecological Transition Contracts programme

Germany: German Commission on Growth, Structural Change and Employment (German Coal Commission)

Ghana: The National Dialogue on Decent Work and 'Just Transition' to a Sustainable Economy and Society

Greece: National Just Transition Fund for Lignite areas

Ireland: Just Transition Fund Ireland

Italy: Enel's Just Transition Framework and Futur-e project

New Zealand: 'Just Transitions Unit' within the ministry of Business, Innovation and Employment (MBIE)

Poland: The 1998 Mining Social Package and Special Privileges for the mining communes

Slovakia: Transformation Action Plan of coal region Upper Nitra

South Africa: National Planning Just Transition Dialogue + Presidential Climate Commission

Spain: Framework Agreement for a Just Transition on Coal Mining and Sustainable Development

UK: Scottish Just Transition Commission

United States: Partnership for Opportunity and Workforce and Economic Revitalisation Plan (POWER+)

(b) European Green Deal – Just Transitions Fund

(c) Platform for coal regions in transition

- Silesia, Lower Silesia, Greater Poland, Lesser Poland
- Moravia-Silesia, Usti, Karlovy Vary
- Western Macedonia
- Jiu Valley
- Midlands
- Brandenburg, Saxony, Saxony Anhalt, North Rhine-Westphalia
- Asturias, Aragón, Castilla-y-León
- Upper Nitra
- Zasavska, Savinjsko-Šaleška

Box TS.4 Figure 1 | Just Transitions around the world, 2020. Panel (a) shows commissions, task forces, and dialogues behind a Just Transition in many countries. **Panel (b)** shows the funds related to the Just Transition within the European Union Green Deal. **Panel (c)** shows the European Union's Platform for Coal Regions in Transition. {Figure 4.9}

TS.4.2   Long-term Mitigation Pathways

The characteristics of a wide range of long-term mitigation pathways, their common elements and differences are assessed in Chapter 3. Differences between pathways typically represent choices that can steer the system in alternative directions through the selection of different combinations of response options (*high confidence*). More than 2000 quantitative emissions pathways were submitted to the AR6 scenarios database, of which more than 1200 pathways included sufficient information for the associated warming to be assessed (consistent with AR6 WGI methods). (Box TS.5) {3.2, 3.3}

Many pathways in the literature show how to limit global warming to 2°C (>67%) with no overshoot or to limit warming to 1.5°C (>50%) with limited overshoot compared to 1850–1900. The likelihood of limiting warming to 1.5°C with no or limited overshoot has dropped in AR6 WGIII compared to AR6 SR1.5 because global GHG emissions have risen since 2017, leading to higher near-term emissions (2030) and higher cumulative CO_2 emissions until the time of net zero (*medium confidence*). Only a small number of published pathways limit global warming to 1.5°C without overshoot over the course of the 21st century. {3.3, Annex III.II.3}

Mitigation pathways limiting warming to 1.5°C with no or limited overshoot reach 50% CO_2 reductions in the 2030s, relative to 2019, then reduce emissions further to reach net zero CO_2 emissions in the 2050s. Pathways limiting warming to 2°C (>67%) reach 50% reductions in the 2040s and net zero CO_2 by the 2070s (*medium confidence*). (Figure TS.10, Box TS.6) {3.3}

Cost-effective mitigation pathways assuming immediate action to limit warming to 2°C (>67%) are associated with net global GHG emissions of 30–49 $GtCO_2$-eq yr^{-1} by 2030 and 14–27 $GtCO_2$-eq yr^{-1} by 2050 (*medium confidence*). This corresponds to reductions, relative to 2019 levels, of 13–45% by 2030 and 52–76% by 2050. Pathways that limit global warming to below 1.5°C with no or limited overshoot require a further acceleration in the pace of transformation, with net GHG emissions typically around 21–36 $GtCO_2$-eq yr^{-1} by 2030 and 1–15 $GtCO_2$-eq yr^{-1} by 2050; this corresponds to reductions of 34–60% by 2030 and 73–98% by 2050 relative to 2019 levels. {3.3}

Box TS.5 | Illustrative Mitigation Pathways (IMPs), and Shared Socio-economic Pathways (SSPs)

The Illustrative Mitigation Pathways (IMPs)
The over 2500 model-based pathways submitted to the AR6 scenarios database pathways explore different possible evolutions of future energy and land use (with and without climate policy) and the consequences for greenhouse gas emissions.

From the full range of pathways, five archetype scenarios – referred to in this report as *Illustrative Mitigation Pathways* (IMPs) – were selected to illustrate key mitigation-strategy themes that flow through several chapters in this report. A further two *pathways illustrative of high emissions* assuming continuation of current policies or moderately increased action were selected to show the consequences of current policies and pledges. Together these pathways provide illustrations of potential future developments that can be shaped by human choices, including: Where are current policies and pledges leading us? What is needed to reach specific temperature goals? What are the consequences of using different strategies to meet these goals? What are the consequences of delay? How can we shift development from current practices to give higher priority to sustainability and the SDGs?

Each of the IMPs comprises: a *storyline* and a *quantitative illustration*. The *storyline* describes the key characteristics of the pathway qualitatively; the *quantitative illustration* is selected from the literature on long-term scenarios to effectively represent the IMP numerically. The five Illustrative Mitigation Pathways (IMPs) each emphasise a different scenario element as its defining feature, and are named accordingly: heavy reliance on <u>ren</u>ewables (IMP-Ren), strong emphasis on <u>l</u>ow <u>d</u>emand for energy (IMP-LD), extensive use of carbon dioxide removal (CDR) in the energy and the industry sectors to achieve net <u>neg</u>ative emissions (IMP-Neg), mitigation in the context of broader sustainable development and <u>s</u>hifting development <u>p</u>athways (IMP-SP), and the implications of a less rapid and gradual <u>s</u>trengthening of near-term mitigation actions (IMP-GS). In some cases, sectoral chapters may use different quantifications that follow the same storyline narrative but contain data that better exemplify the chapter's assessment. Some IMP variants are also used to explore the sensitivity around alternative temperature goals. {3.2, 3.3}

The two additional *pathways illustrative of higher emissions* are <u>c</u>urrent <u>pol</u>icies (CurPol) and <u>mod</u>erate <u>act</u>ion (ModAct).

This framework is summarised in Box TS.5, Table.1 below, which also shows where the IMPs are situated with respect to the classification of emissions scenarios into warming levels (C1–C8) introduced in Chapter 3, and the CMIP6 (Coupled Model Intercomparison Project 6) scenarios used in the AR6 WGI report.

Box TS.5 (continued)

Box TS.5, Table.1 | *Illustrative Mitigation Pathways (IMPs)* and *pathways illustrative of higher emissions* in relation to scenarios' categories, and CMIP6 scenarios.

Classification of emissions scenarios into warming levels: C1–C8	Pathways illustrative of higher emissions	Illustrative mitigation pathways (IMPs)	CMIP6 scenarios
C8 exceeding warming of 4°C (≥50%)			SSP5-8.5
C7 limit warming to 4°C (>50%)	CurPol		SSP3-7.0
C6 limit warming to 3°C (>50%)	ModAct		SSP2-4.5
C5 limit warming to 2.5°C (>50%)			SSP4-3.7
C4 limit warming to 2°C (>50%)			
C3 limit warming to 2°C (>67%)		IMP-GS (Sensitivities: Neg; Ren)	SSP2-2.6
C2 return warming to 1.5°C (>50%) after a high overshoot		IMP-Neg	
C1 limit warming to 1.5°C (>50%) with no or limited overshoot		IMP-LD IMP-Ren IMP-SP	SSP1-1.9

The Shared Socio-economic Pathways (SSPs)

First published in 2017, the Shared Socio-economic Pathways (SSPs) are alternative projections of socio-economic developments that may influence future GHG emissions.

The initial set of SSP narratives described worlds with different challenges to mitigation and adaptation: SSP1 (*sustainability*), SSP2 (*middle of the road*), SSP3 (*regional rivalry*), SSP4 (*inequality*) and SSP5 (*rapid growth*). The SSPs were subsequently quantified in terms of energy, land-use change, and emission pathways for both (i) no-climate-policy reference scenarios and (ii) mitigation scenarios that follow similar radiative forcing pathways as the representative concentration pathways (RCPs) assessed in AR5 WGI. {3.2.3}

Most of the scenarios in the AR6 database are SSP-based. The majority of the assessed scenarios are consistent with SSP2. Using the SSPs permits a more systematic assessment of future GHG emissions and their uncertainties than was possible in AR5. The main emissions drivers across the SSPs include growth in population reaching 8.5–9.7 billion by 2050, and an increase in global GDP of 2.7–4.1% per year between 2015 and 2050. Final energy demand in the absence of any new climate policies is projected to grow to around 480 to 750 EJ yr^{-1} in 2050 (compared to around 390 EJ yr^{-1} in 2015) (*medium confidence*). The highest emissions scenarios in the literature result in global warming of >5°C by 2100, based on assumptions of rapid economic growth and pervasive climate policy failures (*high confidence*). {3.3}

Table TS.3 | GHG, CO₂ emissions and warming characteristics of different mitigation pathways submitted to the AR6 scenarios database, and as categorised in the climate assessment. {Table 3.2}

Category[b,c,d] [# pathways]	Category/subset label	WGI SSP & WGIII IPs/IMPs alignment[e,f]	GHG emissions (GtCO₂-eq yr⁻¹)[g] 2030	2040	2050	GHG emissions reductions from 2019 (%)[h] 2030	2040	2050	Peak CO₂ emissions (% peak before 2100)	Peak GHG emissions (% peak before 2100)	Net zero CO₂ (% net zero pathways)[i,j]	Net zero GHGs (% net zero pathways)[i,j]	Cumulative CO₂ emissions (GtCO₂) 2020 to net zero CO₂	2020–2100	Cumulative net-negative CO₂ emissions (GtCO₂) Year of net zero CO₂ to 2100[m]	Global mean temperature changes 50% probability (°C)[n] at peak warming	2100	Likelihood of peak global warming staying below (%)[o] <1.5°C	<2.0°C	<3.0°C
Modelled global emissions pathways categorised by projected global warming levels (GWL). Detailed likelihood definitions are provided in SPM Box 1. The five illustrative scenarios (SSPx-yy) considered by AR6 WGI and the Illustrative (Mitigation) Pathways assessed in WGIII are aligned with the temperature categories and are indicated in a separate column. Global emission pathways contain regionally differentiated information. This assessment focuses on their global characteristics.			Projected median annual GHG emissions in the year across the scenarios, with the 5th–95th percentile in brackets. Modelled GHG emissions in 2019: 55 [53–58] GtCO₂-eq.			Projected median GHG emissions reductions of pathways in the year across the scenarios compared to modelled 2019, with the 5th–95th percentile in brackets. Negative numbers indicate increase in emissions compared to 2019.			Median 5-year intervals at which projected CO₂ & GHG emissions peak, with the 5th–95th percentile interval in square brackets. Percentage of peaking pathways is denoted in round brackets. Three dots (...) denotes emissions peak in 2100 or beyond for that percentile.		Median 5-year intervals at which projected CO₂ & GHG emissions of pathways in this category reach net zero, with the 5th–95th percentile interval in square brackets. Percentage of net zero pathways is denoted in round brackets. Three dots (...) denotes net zero not reached for that percentile.		Median cumulative net CO₂ emissions across the projected scenarios in this category until reaching net zero or until 2100, with the 5th–95th percentile interval in square brackets.		Median cumulative net-negative CO₂ emissions between the year of net zero CO₂ and 2100. More net-negative results in greater temperature declines after peak.	Projected temperature change of pathways in this category (50% probability across the range of climate uncertainties), relative to 1850–1900, at peak warming and in 2100, for the median value across the scenarios and the 5th percentile interval in square brackets.		Median likelihood that the projected pathways in this category stay below a given global warming level, with the 5th–95th percentile interval in square brackets.		
C1 [97]	limit warming to 1.5°C (>50%) with no or limited overshoot	SSP1-1.9, SP LD Ren	31 [21–36]	17 [6–23]	9 [1–15]	43 [34–60]	69 [58–90]	84 [73–98]	2020–2025 (100%) [2020–2025]	2020–2025 (100%) [2020–2025]	2050–2055 (100%) [2035–2070]	2095–2100 (52%) [2050–...]	510 [330–710]	320 [–210 to 570]	–220 [–660 to –20]	1.6 [1.4–1.6]	1.3 [1.1–1.5]	38 [33–58]	90 [86–97]	100 [99–100]
C1a [50]	... with net zero GHGs		33 [22–37]	18 [6–24]	8 [0–15]	41 [31–59]	66 [58–89]	85 [72–100]			2050–2055 (100%) [2035–2070]	2070–2075 (100%) [2050–2090]	550 [340–760]	160 [–220 to 620]	–360 [–680 to –140]	1.6 [1.4–1.6]	1.2 [1.1–1.4]	38 [34–60]	90 [85–98]	100 [99–100]
C1b [47]	... without net zero GHGs		29 [21–36]	16 [7–21]	9 [4–13]	48 [35–61]	70 [62–87]	84 [76–93]				...–... [0%] [...–...]	460 [320–590]	360 [10–540]	–60 [–440 to 0]	1.6 [1.5–1.6]	1.4 [1.3–1.5]	37 [33–56]	89 [87–96]	100 [99–100]
C2 [133]	return warming to 1.5°C (>50%) after a high overshoot	Neg	42 [31–55]	25 [17–34]	14 [5–21]	23 [0–44]	55 [40–71]	75 [62–91]	2020–2030 (100%) [2020–2025]	2020–2025 (100%) [2020–2025]	2055–2060 (100%) [2045–2070]	2070–2075 (87%) [2055–...]	720 [530–930]	400 [–90 to 620]	–360 [–680 to –60]	1.7 [1.5–1.8]	1.4 [1.2–1.5]	24 [15–42]	82 [71–93]	100 [99–100]
C3 [311]	limit warming to 2°C (>67%)	SSP1-2.6	44 [32–55]	29 [20–36]	20 [13–26]	21 [1–42]	46 [34–63]	64 [53–77]	2020–2025 (100%) [2020–2030]	2020–2025 (100%) [2020–2025]	2070–2075 (93%) [2055–...]	...–... (30%) [2075–...]	890 [640–1160]	800 [510–1140]	–40 [–290 to 0]	1.7 [1.6–1.8]	1.6 [1.5–1.8]	20 [13–41]	76 [68–91]	99 [98–100]
C3a [204]	... with action starting in 2020		40 [30–49]	29 [21–36]	20 [14–27]	27 [13–45]	47 [35–63]	63 [52–76]	2020–2025 (100%) [2020–2025]	2020–2025 (100%) [2020–2025]	2070–2075 (91%) [2055–...]	...–... (24%) [2080–...]	860 [640–1180]	790 [480–1150]	–30 [–280 to 0]	1.7 [1.6–1.8]	1.6 [1.5–1.8]	21 [14–42]	78 [69–91]	100 [98–100]

Table TS.3 (continued):

Category[b,c,d] [# pathways]	Category/subset label	WGI SSP & WGIII IPs/IMPs alignment[e,f]	GHG emissions (GtCO2-eq yr^-1)[g]			GHG emissions reductions from 2019 (%)[h]			Emissions milestones[i]				Cumulative CO2 emissions (GtCO2)[m]		Cumulative net-negative CO2 emissions (GtCO2)	Global mean temperature changes 50% probability (°C)[n]		Likelihood of peak global warming staying below (%)[o]		
			2030	2040	2050	2030	2040	2050	Peak CO2 emissions (% peak before 2100)	Peak GHG emissions (% peak before 2100)	Net zero CO2 (% net zero pathways)	Net zero GHGs (% net zero pathways)[k,l]	2020 to net zero CO2	2020–2100	Year of net zero CO2 to 2100	at peak warming	2100	<1.5°C	<2.0°C	<3.0°C
Modelled global emissions pathways categorised by projected global warming levels (GWL). Detailed likelihood definitions are provided in SPM Box 1. The five Illustrative scenarios (SSPx-yy) considered by AR6 WGI and the Illustrative (Mitigation) Pathways assessed in WGIII are aligned with the temperature categories and are indicated in a separate column. Global emission pathways contain regionally differentiated information. This assessment focuses on their global characteristics.			Projected median annual GHG emissions in the year across the scenarios, with the 5th–95th percentile in brackets. Modelled GHG emissions in 2019: 55 [53–58] GtCO2-eq.			Projected median GHG emissions reductions of pathways in the year across the scenarios compared to modelled 2019, with the 5th–95th percentile in brackets. Negative numbers indicate increase in emissions compared to 2019.			Median 5-year intervals at which projected CO2 & GHG emissions peak, with the 5th–95th percentile interval in square brackets. Percentage of peaking pathways is denoted in round brackets. Three dots (...) denotes emissions peak in 2100 or beyond for that percentile.		Median 5-year intervals at which projected CO2 & GHG emissions reach net zero, with the 5th–95th percentile interval in square brackets. Percentage of net zero pathways is denoted in round brackets. Three dots (...) denotes net zero not reached for that percentile.		Median cumulative net CO2 emissions across the projected scenarios in this category until reaching net zero or until 2100, with the 5th–95th percentile interval in square brackets.		Median cumulative net-negative CO2 emissions between the year of net zero CO2 and 2100. More net-negative results in greater temperature declines after peak.	Projected temperature change of pathways in this category (50% probability across the range of climate uncertainties), relative to 1850–1900, at peak warming and in 2100, for the median value across the scenarios and the 5th–95th percentile interval in square brackets.		Median likelihood that the projected pathways in this category stay below a given global warming level, with the 5th–95th percentile interval in square brackets.		
C3b [97]	...NDCs until 2030	GS	52 [47–56]	29 [20–36]	18 [10–25]	5 [0–14]	46 [34–63]	68 [56–82]	2020–2025 (100%) [2020–2030]		2065–2070 (97%) [2055–2090]	...–... (41%) [2075–...]	910 [720–1150]	800 [560–1050]	−60 [−300 to 0]	1.8 [1.6–1.8]	1.6 [1.5–1.7]	17 [12–35]	73 [67–87]	99 [98–99]
C4 [159]	limit warming to 2°C (>50%)		50 [41–56]	38 [28–44]	28 [19–35]	10 [0–27]	31 [20–50]	49 [35–65]			2080–2085 (86%) [2065–...]	...–... (31%) [2075–...]	1210 [970–1490]	1160 [700–1490]	−30 [−390 to 0]	1.9 [1.7–2.0]	1.8 [1.5–2.0]	11 [7–22]	59 [50–77]	98 [95–99]
C5 [212]	limit warming to 2.5°C (>50%)		52 [46–56]	45 [37–53]	39 [30–49]	6 [−1 to 18]	18 [4–33]	29 [11–48]			...–... (41%) [2080–...]	...–... (12%) [2090–...]	1780 [1400–2360]	1780 [1260–2360]	0 [−160 to 0]	2.2 [1.9–2.5]	2.1 [1.9–2.5]	4 [0–10]	37 [18–59]	91 [83–98]
C6 [97]	limit warming to 3°C (>50%)	SSP2-4.5 ModAct	54 [50–62]	53 [48–61]	52 [45–57]	2 [−10 to 11]	3 [−14 to 14]	5 [−2 to 18]	2030–2035 (96%) [2020–2090]	2020–2025 (97%) [2020–2090]	no net zero		no net zero	2790 [2440–3520]	no net zero	temperature does not peak by 2100	2.7 [2.4–2.9]	0 [0–0]	8 [2–18]	71 [53–88]
C7 [164]	limit warming to 4°C (>50%)	SSP3-7.0 CurPol	62 [53–69]	67 [56–76]	70 [58–83]	−11 [−18 to 3]	−19 [−31 to 1]	−24 [−41 to −2]	2085–2090 (57%) [2040–...]	2090–2095 (56%)	no net zero		no net zero	4220 [3160–5000]	no net zero		3.5 [2.8–3.9]	0 [0–0]	0 [0–2]	22 [7–60]
C8 [29]	exceed warming of 4°C (≥50%)	SSP5-8.5	71 [69–81]	80 [78–96]	88 [82–112]	−20 [−34 to −17]	−35 [−65 to −29]	−46 [−92 to −36]	2080–2085 (90%) [2070–...]	2080–2085 (90%) [2070–...]	no net zero		no net zero	5600 [4910–7450]	no net zero		4.2 [3.7–5.0]	0 [0–0]	0 [0–0]	4 [0–11]

Table TS.3 (continued):

[a] Values in the table refer to the 50th and [5th–95th] percentile values across the pathways falling within a given category as defined in Box SPM.1. For emissions-related columns these values relate to the distribution of all the pathways in that category. Harmonised emissions values are given for consistency with projected global warming outcomes using climate emulators. Based on the assessment of climate emulators in AR6 WGI (WG1 Chapter 7, Box 7.1), two climate emulators are used for the probabilistic assessment of the resulting warming of the pathways. For the 'Temperature change' and 'Likelihood' columns, the single upper-row values represent the 50th percentile across the pathways in that category and the median [50th percentile] across the warming estimates of the probabilistic MAGICC climate model emulator. For the bracketed ranges, the median warming for every pathway in that category is calculated for each of the two climate model emulators (MAGICC and FaIR). Subsequently, the 5th and 95th percentile values across all pathways for each emulator are calculated. The coolest and warmest outcomes (i.e., the lowest p5 of two emulators, and the highest p95, respectively) are shown in square brackets. These ranges therefore cover both the uncertainty of the emissions pathways as well as the climate emulators' uncertainty.

[b] For a description of pathways categories see Box SPM.1 and Table 3.1.

[c] All global warming levels are relative to 1850–1900. (See footnote n below and Box SPM.1 for more details.)

[d] C3 pathways are sub-categorised according to the timing of policy action to match the emissions pathways in Figure SPM.4. Two pathways derived from a cost-benefit analysis have been added to C3a, whilst 10 pathways with specifically designed near-term action until 2030, whose emissions fall below those implied by NDCs announced prior to COP26, are not included in either of the two subsets.

[e] Alignment with the categories of the illustrative SSP scenarios considered in AR6 WGI, and the Illustrative (Mitigation) Pathways (IPs/IMPs) of WGIII. The IMPs have common features such as deep and rapid emissions reductions, but also different combinations of sectoral mitigation strategies. See Box SPM.1 for an introduction of the IPs and IMPs, and Chapter 3 for full descriptions. {3.2, 3.3, Annex III.II.4}

[f] The Illustrative Mitigation Pathway 'Neg' has extensive use of carbon dioxide removal (CDR) in the AFOLU, energy and the industry sectors to achieve net negative emissions. Warming peaks around 2060 and declines to below 1.5°C (50% likelihood) shortly after 2100. Whilst technically classified as C3, it strongly exhibits the characteristics of C2 high-overshoot pathways, hence it has been placed in the C2 category. See Box SPM.1 for an introduction of the IPs and IMPs.

[g] The 2019 range of harmonised GHG emissions across the pathways [53–58 GtCO$_2$-eq] is within the uncertainty ranges of 2019 emissions assessed in Chapter 2 [53–66 GtCO$_2$-eq]. (Figure SPM.1, Figure SPM.2, Box SPM.1)

[h] Rates of global emission reduction in mitigation pathways are reported on a pathway-by-pathway basis relative to harmonised modelled global emissions in 2019 rather than the global emissions reported in SPM Section B and Chapter 2; this ensures internal consistency in assumptions about emission sources and activities, as well as consistency with temperature projections based on the physical climate science assessment by WGI. {Annex III.II.2.5}. Negative values (e.g., in C7, C8) represent an increase in emissions.

[i] Emissions milestones are provided for five-year intervals in order to be consistent with the underlying five-year time-step data of the modelled pathways. Peak emissions (CO$_2$ and GHGs) are assessed for five-year reporting intervals starting in 2020. The interval 2020–2025 signifies that projected emissions peak as soon as possible between 2020 and at latest before 2025. The upper five-year interval refers to the median interval within which the emissions peak or reach net zero. Ranges in square brackets underneath refer to the range across the pathways, comprising the lower bound of the 5th percentile five-year interval and the upper bound of the 95th percentile five-year interval. Numbers in round brackets signify the fraction of pathways that reach specific milestones.

[j] Percentiles reported across all pathways in that category include those that do not reach net zero before 2100 (fraction of pathways reaching net zero is given in round brackets). If the fraction of pathways that reach net zero before 2100 is lower than the fraction of pathways covered by a percentile (e.g., 0.95 for the 95th percentile), the percentile is not defined and denoted with '…'. The fraction of pathways reaching net zero includes all with reported non-harmonised, and/or harmonised emissions profiles that reach net zero. Pathways were counted when at least one of the two profiles fell below 100 MtCO$_2$ yr^{-1} until 2100.

[k] The timing of net zero is further discussed in SPM C2.4 and Cross-Chapter Box 3 in Chapter 3 on net zero CO$_2$ and net zero GHG emissions.

[l] For cases where models do not report all GHGs, missing GHG species are infilled and aggregated into a Kyoto basket of GHG emissions in CO$_2$-eq defined by the 100-year global warming potential. For each pathway, reporting of CO$_2$, CH$_4$, and N$_2$O emissions was the minimum required for the assessment of the climate response and the assignment to a climate category. Emissions pathways without climate assessment are not included in the ranges presented here. {See Annex III.II.5}

[m] Cumulative emissions are calculated from the start of 2020 to the time of net zero and 2100, respectively. They are based on harmonised net CO$_2$ emissions, ensuring consistency with the WGI assessment of the remaining carbon budget. {Box 3.4}

[n] Global mean temperature change for category (at peak, if peak temperature occurs before 2100, and in 2100) relative to 1850–1900, based on the median global warming for each pathway assessed using the probabilistic climate model emulators calibrated to the AR6 WGI assessment. (See also Box SPM.1) {Annex III.II.2.5; WGI Cross-Chapter Box 7.1}

[o] Probability of staying below the temperature thresholds for the pathways in each category, taking into consideration the range of uncertainty from the climate model emulators consistent with the AR6 WGI assessment. The probabilities refer to the probability at peak temperature. Note that in the case of temperature overshoot (e.g., category C2 and some pathways in C1), the probabilities of staying below at the end of the century are higher than the probabilities at peak temperature.

Pathways following current NDCs until 2030 reach annual emissions of 47–57 GtCO$_2$-eq yr^{-1} by 2030, thereby making it impossible to limit warming to 1.5°C (>50%) with no or limited overshoot and strongly increasing the challenge of limiting warming to 2°C (>67%) (*high confidence*). A high overshoot of 1.5°C increases the risks from climate impacts and increases dependence on large-scale carbon dioxide removal (CDR) from the atmosphere. A future consistent with current NDCs implies higher fossil fuel deployment and lower reliance on low-carbon alternatives until 2030, compared to mitigation pathways describing immediate action that limits warming to 1.5°C (>50%) with no or limited overshoot, or limits warming to 2°C (>67%) and below. After following the NDCs to 2030, to limit warming to 2°C (>67%) the pace of global GHG emission reductions would need to abruptly increase from 2030 onward to an average of 1.3–2.1 GtCO$_2$-eq per year between 2030 and 2050. This is similar to the global CO$_2$ emission reductions in 2020 that occurred due to the COVID-19 pandemic lockdowns, and around 70% faster than in pathways where immediate action is taken to limit warming to 2°C (>67%). Accelerating emission reductions after following an NDC pathway to 2030 would also be particularly challenging because of the continued buildup of fossil fuel infrastructure that would take place between now and 2030. (TS4.1, Table TS.3) {3.5, 4.2}

Pathways accelerating action compared to current NDCs – that reduce annual GHG emissions to 47 (38–51) GtCO$_2$-eq by 2030 (which is 3–9 GtCO$_2$-eq below projected emissions from fully implementing current NDCs) – make it less challenging to limit warming to 2°C (>67%) after 2030 (*medium confidence*). The accelerated action pathways are characterised by a global, but regionally differentiated, roll-out of regulatory and pricing policies. Compared to current NDCs, they describe less fossil fuel use and more low-carbon fuel use until 2030; they narrow, but do not close the gap to pathways that assume immediate global action using all available least-cost abatement options. All delayed or accelerated action pathways limiting warming to below 2°C (>67%) converge to a global mitigation regime at some point after 2030 by putting a significant value on reducing carbon and other GHG emissions in all sectors and regions. {3.5}

In mitigation pathways, peak warming is determined by the cumulative net CO$_2$ emissions until the time of net zero CO$_2$ together with the warming contribution of other GHGs and climate forcers at that time (*high confidence*). Cumulative net CO$_2$ emissions from 2020 to the time of net zero CO$_2$ are 510 (330–710) GtCO$_2$ in pathways that limit warming to 1.5°C (>50%) with no or limited overshoot and 890 (640–1160) GtCO$_2$ in pathways limiting warming to 2°C (>67%). These estimates are consistent with the AR6 WGI assessment of remaining carbon budgets adjusting for methodological differences and non-CO$_2$ warming. {3.3, Box 3.4}

Rapid reductions in non-CO$_2$ GHGs, particularly CH$_4$, would lower the level of peak warming (*high confidence*). Non-CO$_2$ emissions – at the time of reaching net zero CO$_2$ – range between 4–11 GtCO$_2$-eq yr^{-1} in pathways limiting warming to 2°C (>67%) or below. CH$_4$ is reduced by around 20% (1–46%) in 2030 and almost 50% (26–64%) in 2050, relative to 2019. CH$_4$ emission reductions in pathways limiting warming to 1.5°C with no or limited overshoot are substantially higher by 2030, 33% (19–57%), but only moderately so by 2050, 50% (33–69%). CH$_4$ emissions reductions are thus attainable at comparatively low costs, but, at the same time, reductions are limited in scope in most 1.5°C–2°C pathways. Deeper CH$_4$ emissions reductions by 2050 could further constrain the peak warming. N$_2$O emissions are also reduced, but similar to CH$_4$, N$_2$O emission reductions saturate for more stringent climate goals. The emissions of cooling aerosols in mitigation pathways decrease as fossil fuels use is reduced. The overall impact on non-CO$_2$-related warming combines all these factors. {3.3}

Net zero GHG emissions imply net negative CO$_2$ emissions at a level that compensates for residual non-CO$_2$ emissions. Only 30% of the pathways limiting warming to 2°C (>67%) or below reach net zero GHG emissions in the 21st century (*high confidence*). In those pathways reaching net zero GHGs, net zero GHGs is achieved around 10–20 years later than net zero CO$_2$ is achieved (*medium confidence*). The reported quantity of residual non-CO$_2$ emissions depends on accounting choices, and in particular the choice of GHG metric (Box TS.2). Reaching and sustaining global net zero GHG emissions – when emissions are measured and reported in terms of GWP100 – results in a gradual decline in temperature (*high confidence*). (Box TS.6) {3.3}

Pathways that limit warming to 2°C (>67%) or lower exhibit substantial reductions in emissions from all sectors (*high confidence*). Pathways that limit warming to 1.5°C (>50%) with no or limited overshoot entail CO$_2$ emissions reductions between 2019 and 2050 of around 77% (31–96%) for energy demand, around 115% (90–167%) for energy supply, and around 148% (94–387%) for AFOLU.[16] In pathways that limit warming to 2°C (>67%), projected CO$_2$ emissions are reduced between 2019 and 2050 by around 49% for energy demand, 97% for energy supply, and 136% for AFOLU (*medium confidence*). {3.4}

If warming is to be limited, delaying or failing to achieve emissions reductions in one sector or region necessitates compensating reductions in other sectors or regions (*high confidence*). Mitigation pathways show differences in the timing of decarbonisation and when net zero CO$_2$ emissions are achieved across sectors and regions. At the time of *global net zero CO$_2$ emissions*, emissions in some sectors and regions are positive while others are negative; whether specific sectors and regions are positive or negative depends on the availability and cost of mitigation options in those regions, and the policies implemented. In cost-effective mitigation pathways, the energy supply sector typically reaches net zero CO$_2$ before the economy as a whole, while the demand sectors reach net zero CO$_2$ later, if ever (*high confidence*). (Figure TS.10) {3.4}

Pathways limiting warming to 2°C (>67%) or 1.5°C involve substantial reductions in fossil fuel consumption and a near elimination of coal use without CCS (*high confidence*). These pathways show an increase in low-carbon energy, with 88% (69–97%) of primary energy coming from low-carbon sources by 2100. {3.4}

---

16   Reductions greater than 100% in energy supply and AFOLU indicate that these sectors would become carbon sinks.

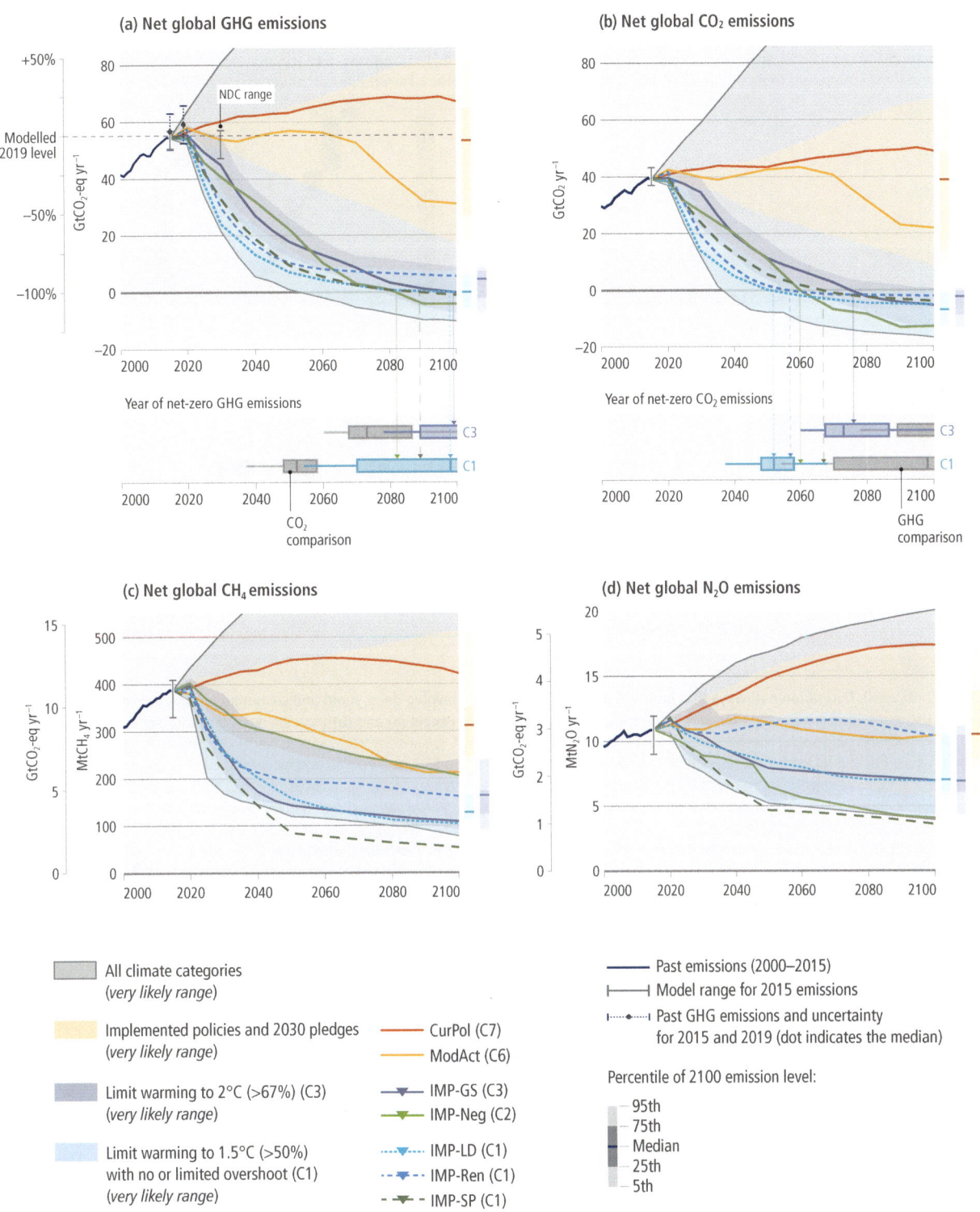

Figure TS.10 | Mitigation pathways that limit warming to 1.5°C, or 2°C, involve deep, rapid and sustained emissions reductions. Net zero CO₂ and net zero GHG emissions are possible through different mitigation portfolios.

Net zero CO₂ and net zero GHG emissions are possible through different modelled mitigation pathways.

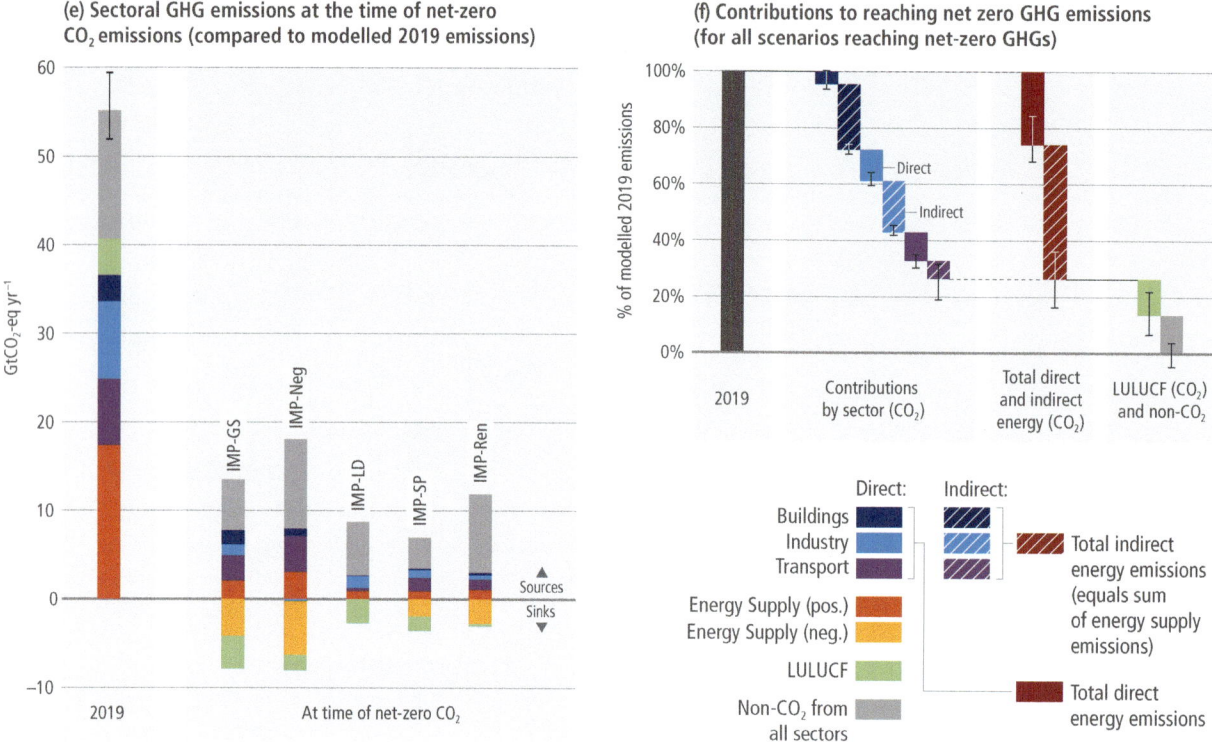

Figure TS.10 (continued): Mitigation pathways that limit warming to 1.5°C, or 2°C, involve deep, rapid and sustained emissions reductions. Net zero CO₂ and net zero GHG emissions are possible through different mitigation portfolios. Panels (a) and (b) show the development of global GHG and CO₂ emissions in modelled global pathways (upper sub-panels) and the associated timing of when GHG and CO₂ emissions reach net zero (lower sub-panels). **Panels (c) and (d)** show the development of global CH₄ and N₂O emissions, respectively. Coloured ranges denote the 5th to 95th percentile across pathways. The red ranges depict emissions pathways assuming policies that were implemented by the end of 2020 and pathways assuming implementation of NDCs (announced prior to COP26). Ranges of modelled pathways that limit warming to 1.5°C (>50%) with no or limited overshoot are shown in light blue (category C1) and pathways that limit warming to 2°C (>67%) are shown in light purple (category C3). The grey range comprises all assessed pathways (C1–C8) from the 5th percentile of the lowest warming category (C1) to the 95th percentile of the highest warming category (C8). The modelled pathway ranges are compared to the emissions from two pathways illustrative of high emissions (CurPol and ModAct) and five IMPs: IMP-LD, IMP-Ren, IMP-SP, IMP-Neg and IMP-GS. Emissions are harmonised to the same 2015 base year. The vertical error bars in 2015 show the 5–95th percentile uncertainty range of the non-harmonised emissions across the pathways, and the uncertainty range, and median value, in emission estimates for 2015 and 2019. The vertical error bars in 2030 (panel a) depict the assessed range of the NDCs, as announced prior to COP26.[17] **Panel (e)** shows the sectoral contributions of CO₂ and non-CO₂ emissions sources and sinks at the time when net zero CO₂ emissions are reached in the IMPs. Positive and negative emissions for different IMPs are compared to the GHG emissions from the year 2019. Energy supply (neg.) includes BECCS and DACCS. DACCS features in only two of the five IMPs (IMP-REN and IMP-GS) and contributes <1% and 64%, respectively, to the net negative emissions in Energy Supply (neg.). **Panel (f)** shows the contribution of different sectors and sources to the emissions reductions from a 2019 baseline for reaching net zero GHG emissions. Bars denote the median emissions reductions for all pathways that reach net zero GHG emissions. The whiskers indicate the p5–p95 range. The contributions of the service sectors (transport, buildings, industry) are split into direct (demand-side) as well as indirect (supply-side) CO₂ emissions reductions. Direct emissions represent demand-side emissions due to the fuel use in the respective demand sector. Indirect emissions represent upstream emissions due to industrial processes and energy conversion, transmission and distribution. In addition, the contributions from the LULUCF sector and reductions from non-CO₂ emissions sources (green and grey bars) are displayed. {3.3, 3.4}

Stringent emissions reductions at the level required for 2°C or 1.5°C are achieved through the increased electrification of buildings, transport, and industry, consequently all pathways entail increased electricity generation (*high confidence*). Nearly all electricity in pathways limiting warming to 2°C (>67%) or 1.5°C (>50%) is also from low- or no-carbon technologies, with different shares across pathways of: nuclear, biomass, non-biomass renewables, and fossil fuels in combination with CCS. {3.4}

Measures required to limit warming to 2°C (>67%) or below can result in large-scale transformation of the land surface (*high confidence*). These pathways are projected to reach net zero CO₂ emissions in the AFOLU sector between the 2020s and 2070.

---

17   NDCs announced prior to COP26 refer to the most recent Nationally Determined Contributions submitted to the UNFCCC up to the literature cut-off date of this report, 11 October 2021, and revised NDCs announced by China, Japan and the Republic of Korea prior to October 2021 but only submitted thereafter. 25 NDC updates were submitted between 12 October 2021 and the start of COP26.

Pathways limiting warming to 1.5°C with no or limited overshoot show an increase in forest cover of about 322 (−67 to 890) million ha in 2050 (*high confidence*). In these pathways the cropland area to supply biomass for bioenergy (including bioenergy with carbon capture and storage (BECCS)) is around 199 (56–482) million ha in 2050. The use of bioenergy can lead to either increased or reduced emissions, depending on the scale of deployment, conversion technology, fuel displaced, and how, and where, the biomass is produced (*high confidence*). {3.4}

Pathways limiting warming to 2°C (>67%) or 1.5°C (>50%) require some amount of CDR to compensate for residual GHG emissions, even alongside substantial direct emissions reductions are achieved in all sectors and regions (*high confidence*). CDR deployment in pathways serves multiple purposes: accelerating the pace of emissions reductions, offsetting residual emissions, and creating the option for net negative CO_2 emissions in case temperature reductions need to be achieved in the long term (*high confidence*). CDR options in pathways are mostly limited to BECCS, afforestation and direct air CO_2 capture and storage (DACCS). CDR through some measures in AFOLU can be maintained for decades but not over the very long term because these sinks will ultimately saturate (*high confidence*). {3.4}

Mitigation pathways show reductions in energy demand, relative to reference scenarios that assume continuation of current policies, through a diverse set of demand-side interventions (*high confidence*). Bottom-up and non-IAM studies show significant potential for demand-side mitigation. A stronger emphasis on demand-side mitigation implies less dependence on CDR and, consequently, reduced pressure on land and biodiversity. {3.4, 3.7}

Limiting warming requires shifting energy investments away from fossil fuels and towards low-carbon technologies (*high confidence*). The bulk of investments are needed in medium- and low-income regions. Investment needs in the electricity sector are on average 2.3 trillion USD2015 yr^{-1} over 2023–2052 for pathways limiting temperature to 1.5°C (>50%) with no or limited overshoot, and 1.7 trillion USD2015 yr^{-1} for pathways limiting warming to 2°C (>67%). {3.6.1}

Pathways *that* avoid overshoot of 2°C (>67%) warming require more rapid near-term transformations and are associated with higher upfront transition costs, but at the same time bring long-term gains for the economy as well as earlier benefits in avoided climate change impacts (*high confidence*). This conclusion is independent of the discount rate applied, though the modelled cost-optimal balance of mitigation action over time does depend on the discount rate. Lower discount rates favour earlier mitigation, reducing reliance on CDR and temperature overshoot. {3.6.1, 3.8}

Mitigation pathways *that* limit warming to 2°C (>67%) entail losses in global GDP with respect to reference scenarios of between 1.3% and 2.7% in 2050. In pathways limiting warming to 1.5°C (>50%) with no or limited overshoot, losses are between 2.6% and 4.2%. These estimates do not account for the economic benefits of avoided climate change impacts (*medium confidence*). In mitigation pathways limiting warming to 2°C (>67%), marginal abatement costs of carbon are about 90 (60–120) USD2015 tCO_2 in 2030 and about 210 (140–340) USD2015/tCO_2 in 2050. This compares with about 220 (170–290) USD2015 tCO_2 in 2030 and about 630 (430–990) USD2015 tCO_2 in 2050[18] in pathways that limit warming to 1.5°C (>50%) with no or limited overshoot. Reference scenarios, in the AR6 scenarios database, describe possible emission trajectories in the absence of new stringent climate policies. Reference scenarios have a broad range depending on socio-economic assumptions and model characteristics. {3.2.1, 3.6.1}

The global benefits of pathways limiting warming to 2°C (>67%) outweigh global mitigation costs over the 21st century, if aggregated economic impacts of climate change are at the moderate to high end of the assessed range, and a weight consistent with economic theory is given to economic impacts over the long term. This holds true even without accounting for benefits in other sustainable development dimensions or non-market damages from climate change (*medium confidence*). The aggregate global economic repercussions of mitigation pathways include: the macroeconomic impacts of investments in low-carbon solutions and structural changes away from emitting activities; co-benefits and adverse side effects of mitigation; avoided climate change impacts; and reduced adaptation costs. Existing quantifications of the global aggregate economic impacts show a strong dependence on socio-economic development conditions, as these shape exposure and vulnerability and adaptation opportunities and responses. Avoided impacts for poorer households and poorer countries represent a smaller share in aggregate economic quantifications expressed in GDP or monetary terms, whereas their well-being and welfare effects are comparatively larger. When aggregate economic benefits from avoided climate change impacts are accounted for, mitigation is a welfare-enhancing strategy (*high confidence*). {3.6.2}

The economic benefits on human health from air quality improvement arising from mitigation action can be of the same order of magnitude as mitigation costs, and potentially even larger (*medium confidence*). {3.6.3}

Differences in aggregate employment between mitigation pathways and reference scenarios are relatively small, although there may be substantial reallocations across sectors, with job creation in some sectors and job losses in others (*medium confidence*). The net employment effect (and whether employment increases or decreases) depends on the scenario assumptions, modelling framework, and modelled policy design. Mitigation has implications for employment through multiple channels, each of which impacts geographies, sectors and skill categories differently. {3.6.4}

---

18 Numbers in parentheses represent he interquartile range of the scenario samples.

The economic repercussions of mitigation vary widely across regions and households, depending on policy design and the level of international cooperation (*high confidence*). Delayed global cooperation increases policy costs across regions, especially in those that are relatively carbon intensive at present (*high confidence*). Pathways with uniform carbon values show higher mitigation costs in more carbon-intensive regions, in fossil fuel-exporting regions, and in poorer regions (*high confidence*). Aggregate quantifications expressed in GDP or monetary terms undervalue the economic effects on households in poorer countries; the actual effects on welfare and well-being are comparatively larger (*high confidence*). Mitigation at the speed and scale required to limit warming to 2°C (>67%) or below implies deep economic and structural changes, thereby raising multiple types of distributional concerns across regions, income classes, and sectors (*high confidence*). (Box TS.7) {3.6.1, 3.6.4}

Box TS.6 | Understanding Net Zero CO_2 and Net Zero GHG Emissions

Reaching net zero CO_2 emissions[19] globally along with reductions in other GHG emissions is necessary to halt global warming at any level. At the point of net zero, the amount of CO_2 human activity is putting into the atmosphere equals the amount of CO_2 human activity is removing from the atmosphere. Reaching and sustaining net zero CO_2 emissions globally would stabilise CO_2-induced warming. Moving to net negative CO_2 emissions globally would reduce peak cumulative net CO_2 emissions – which occurs at the time of reaching net zero CO_2 emissions – and lead to a peak and decline in CO_2-induced warming. {Cross-Chapter Box 3 in Chapter 3}

Reaching net zero CO_2 emissions sooner can reduce cumulative CO_2 emissions and result in less human-induced global warming. Overall human-induced warming depends not only on CO_2 emissions but also on the contribution from other anthropogenic climate forcers, including aerosols and other GHGs (e.g., CH_4 and F-gases). To halt total human-induced warming, emissions of other GHGs, in particular CH_4, need to be strongly reduced.

In the AR6 scenario database, global emissions pathways limi warming to 1.5°C (>50%) with no or limited overshoot reach net zero CO_2 emissions between 2050–2055 (2035–2070) (median and 5–95th percentile ranges; 100% of pathways); pathways limiting warming to 2°C (>67%) reach net zero CO_2 emissions between 2070–2075 (2055–…) (median and 5–95th percentile ranges; 90% of pathways). This is later than assessed in the AR6 SR1.5 primarily due to more pathways in the literature that approach net zero CO_2 emissions more gradually after a rapid decline of emissions until 2040. (Box TS.6, Figure 1)

It does not mean that the world has more time for emissions reductions while still limiting warming to 1.5°C than reported in the SR1.5. It only means that the exact timing of reaching net zero CO_2 after a steep decline of CO_2 emissions until 2040 can show some variation. The SR1.5 median value of 2050 is still close to the middle of the current range. If emissions are reduced less rapidly in the period up to 2030, an earlier net zero year is needed.

Reaching net zero GHG emissions requires net negative CO_2 emissions to balance residual CH_4, N_2O and F-gas emissions. If achieved globally, net zero GHG emissions would reduce global warming from an earlier peak. Around half global emission pathways limiting warming to 1.5°C (>50%), and a third of pathways limiting warming to 2°C (>67%), reach net zero GHG emissions (based on GWP100) in the second half of the century, around 10 to 40 years later than net zero CO_2 emissions. They show warming being halted at some peak value followed by a gradual decline towards the end of the century. The remainder of the pathways do not reach net zero GHG emissions during the 21st century and show little decline of warming after it stabilised.

Global net zero CO_2 or GHG emissions can be achieved even while some sectors and regions continue to be net emitters, provided that others achieve net GHG removal. Sectors and regions have different potentials and costs to achieve net zero or even net GHG removal. The adoption and implementation of net zero emission targets by countries and regions depends on multiple factors, including equity and capacity criteria and international and cross-sectoral mechanisms to balance emissions and removals. The formulation of net zero pathways by countries will benefit from clarity on scope, plans of action, and fairness. Achieving net zero emission targets relies on policies, institutions and milestones against which to track progress.

---

19   In this assessment the terms *net zero CO_2 emissions* and *carbon neutrality* have different meanings and are only equivalent at the global scale. At the scale of regions, or sectors, each term applies different system boundaries. This is also the case for the related terms *net zero GHG* and *GHG neutrality*. {Cross-Chapter Box 3 in Chapter 3}

Box TS.6 (continued)

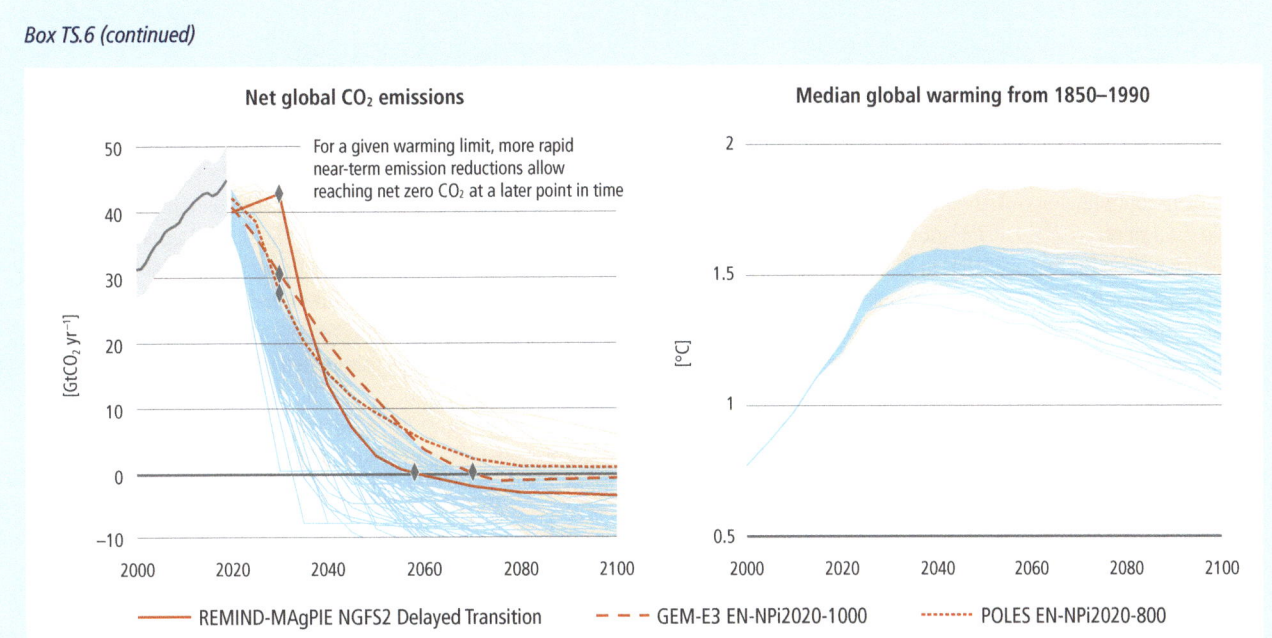

Box TS.6, Figure 1 | CO₂ Emissions (panel (a)) and temperature change (panel (b)) of three alternative pathways limiting warming to 2°C (>67%) and reaching net zero CO₂ emissions at different points in time. Limiting warming to a specific level can be consistent with a range of dates when net zero CO₂ emissions need to be achieved. This difference in the date of net zero CO₂ emissions reflects the different emissions profiles that are possible while staying within a specific carbon budget and the associated warming limit. Shifting the year of net zero to a later point in time (>2050), however, requires more rapid and deeper near-term emissions reductions (in 2030 and 2040) if warming is to be limited to the same level. Funnels show pathways limiting warming to 1.5°C (>50%) with no or limited overshoot (light blue) and limiting warming to 2°C (>67%) (beige).

Box TS.7 | The Long-term Economic Benefits of Mitigation from Avoided Climate Change Impacts

Integrated studies use either a cost-effectiveness analysis (CEA) approach (minimising the total mitigation costs of achieving a given policy goal) or a cost-benefit analysis (CBA) approach (balancing the cost and benefits of climate action). In the majority of studies that have produced the body of work on the cost of mitigation assessed in this report, a CEA approach is adopted, and the feedbacks of climate change impacts on the economic development pathways are not accounted for. This omission of climate impacts leads to overly optimistic economic projections in the reference scenarios, in particular in reference scenarios with no or limited mitigation action where the extent of global warming is the greatest. Mitigation cost estimates computed against no or limited policy reference scenarios therefore omit economic benefits brought by avoided climate change impact along mitigation pathways. {1.7, 3.6.1}

The difference in aggregate economic impacts from climate change between two given temperature levels represents the aggregate economic benefits arising from avoided climate change impacts due to mitigation action. Estimates of these benefits vary widely, depending on the methodology used and impacts included, as well as on assumed socio-economic development conditions, which shape exposure and vulnerability. The aggregate economic benefits of avoiding climate impacts increase with the stringency of the mitigation. Global economic impact studies with regional estimates find large differences across regions, with developing and transitional economies typically more vulnerable. Furthermore, avoided impacts for poorer households and poorer countries represent a smaller share in aggregate quantifications expressed in GDP terms or monetary terms, compared to their influence on well-being and welfare (*high confidence*). {3.6.2, Cross-Working Group Box 1 in Chapter 3}

Box TS.7 (continued)

CBA analysis and CBA integrated assessment models (IAMs) remain limited in their ability to represent all damages from climate change, including non-monetary damages, and capture the uncertain and heterogeneous nature of damages and the risk of catastrophic damages, such that other lines of evidence should be considered in decision-making. However, emerging evidence suggests that, even without accounting for co-benefits of mitigation on other sustainable development dimensions, the global benefits of pathways limiting warming to 2°C (>67%) outweigh global mitigation costs over the 21st century (*medium confidence*). Depending on the study, the reason for this result lies in assumptions of economic damages from climate change in the higher end of available estimates, in the consideration of risks of tipping points or damages to natural capital and non-market goods, or in the combination of updated representations of carbon cycle and climate modules, updated damage estimates and updated representations of economic and mitigation dynamics. In the studies that perform a sensitivity analysis, this result is found to be robust to a wide range of assumptions on social preferences (in particular on inequality aversion and pure rate of time preference), and holds except if assumptions of economic damages from climate change are in the lower end of available estimates and the pure rate of time preference is in the higher range of values usually considered (typically above 1.5%). However, although such pathways bring overall net benefits over time (in terms of aggregate discounted present value), they involve distributional consequences between and within generations. {3.6.2}

TS.5 Mitigation Responses in Sectors and Systems

Chapters 5 to 12 assess recent advances in knowledge in individual sectors and systems. These chapters – *Energy* (Chapter 6), *Urban and Other Settlements* (Chapter 8), *Transport* (Chapter 10), *Buildings* Chapter 9), *Industry* (Chapter 11), and *Agriculture, Forestry and Other Land Use (AFOLU)* (Chapter 7) – correspond broadly to the IPCC National Greenhouse Gas Inventory reporting categories and build on similar chapters in previous WGIII reports. Chapters 5 and 12 tie together the cross-sectoral aspects of this group of chapters including the assessment of costs and potentials, demand-side aspects of mitigation, and carbon dioxide removal (CDR).

TS.5.1 Energy

A broad-based approach to deploying energy-sector mitigation options can reduce emissions over the next ten years and set the stage for still deeper reductions beyond 2030 (*high confidence*). There are substantial, cost-effective opportunities to reduce emissions rapidly, including in electricity generation, but near-term reductions will not be sufficient to limit warming to 2°C (>67%) or limit warming to 1.5°C (>50%) with no or limited overshoot. {6.4, 6.6, 6.7}

Warming cannot be limited to 2°C or 1.5°C without rapid and deep reductions in energy system CO_2 and GHG emissions (*high confidence*). In scenarios limiting warming to 1.5°C (>50%) with no or limited overshoot (*likely* below 2°C), net energy system CO_2 emissions fall by 87–97% (interquartile range 60–79%) in 2050. In 2030, in scenarios limiting warming to 1.5°C with no or limited overshoot, net CO_2 and GHG emissions fall by 35–51% and 38–52% respectively. In scenarios limiting warming to 1.5°C with no or limited overshoot (*likely* below 2°C), net electricity sector CO_2 emissions reach zero globally between 2045 and 2055 (2050 and 2080) (*high confidence*). {6.7}

Limiting warming to 2°C or 1.5°C will require substantial energy system changes over the next 30 years. This includes reduced fossil fuel consumption, increased production from low- and zero-carbon energy sources, and increased use of electricity and alternative energy carriers (*high confidence*). Coal consumption without CCS falls by 67–82% (interquartile range) in 2030 in scenarios limiting warming to 1.5°C with no or limited overshoot. Oil and gas consumption fall more slowly. Low-carbon sources produce 93–97% of global electricity by 2050 in scenarios that limit warming to 2°C (>67%) or below. In scenarios limiting warming to 1.5°C with no or limited overshoot (*likely* below 2°C), electricity supplies 48–58% (36–47%) of final energy in 2050, up from 20% in 2019. {6.7}

Net zero energy systems will share common characteristics, but the approach in every country will depend on national circumstances (*high confidence*). Common characteristics of net-zero energy systems will include: (i) electricity systems that produce no net CO_2 or remove CO_2 from the atmosphere; (ii) widespread electrification of end uses, including light-duty transport, space heating, and cooking; (iii) substantially lower use of fossil fuels

than today; (iv) use of alternative energy carriers such as hydrogen, bioenergy, and ammonia to substitute for fossil fuels in sectors less amenable to electrification; (v) more efficient use of energy than today; (vi) greater energy system integration across regions and across components of the energy system; and (vii) use of CO_2 removal including DACCS and BECCS to offset residual emissions. {6.6}

Energy demands and energy sector emissions have continued to rise (*high confidence*). From 2015 to 2019, global final energy consumption grew by 6.6%, CO_2 emissions from the global energy system grew by 4.6%, and total GHG emissions from energy supply rose by 2.7%. Fugitive CH_4 emissions from oil, gas, and coal, accounted for 18% of GHG emissions in 2019. Coal electricity capacity grew by 7.6% between 2015 and 2019, as new builds in some countries offset declines in others. Total consumption of oil and oil products increased by 5%, and natural gas consumption grew by 15%. Declining energy intensity in almost all regions has been balanced by increased energy consumption. {6.3}

The unit costs for several key energy system mitigation options have dropped rapidly over the last five years, notably solar PV, wind power, and batteries (*high confidence*). From 2015 to 2020, the costs of electricity from PV and wind dropped 56% and 45%, respectively, and battery prices dropped by 64%. Electricity from PV and wind is now cheaper than electricity from fossil sources in many regions, electric vehicles are increasingly competitive with internal combustion engines, and large-scale battery storage on electricity grids is increasingly viable. (Figure TS.7) {6.3, 6.4}

Global wind and solar PV capacity and generation have increased rapidly driven by policy, societal pressure to limit fossil generation, low interest rates, and cost reductions (*high confidence*). Solar PV grew by 170% (to 680 TWh); wind grew by 70% (to 1420 TWh) from 2015 to 2019. Solar PV and wind together accounted for 21% of total low-carbon electricity generation and 8% of total electricity generation in 2019. Nuclear generation grew 9% between 2015 and 2019 and accounted for 10% of total generation in 2019 (2790 TWh); hydro-electric power grew by 10% and accounted for 16% (4290 TWh) of total generation. In total, low- and zero-carbon electricity generation technologies produced 37% of global electricity in 2019. {6.3, 6.4}

If investments in coal and other fossil infrastructure continue, energy systems will be locked-in to higher emissions, making it harder to limit warming to 2°C or 1.5°C (*high confidence*). Many aspects of the energy system – physical infrastructure; institutions, laws, and regulations; and behaviour – are resistant to change or take many years to change. New investments in coal-fired electricity without CCS are inconsistent with limiting warming to well below 2°C. {6.3, 6.7}

Limiting warming to 2°C or 1.5°C will strand fossil-related assets, including fossil infrastructure and unburned fossil fuel resources (*high confidence*). The economic impacts of stranded assets could amount to trillions of dollars. Coal assets are most vulnerable over the coming decade; oil and gas assets are more vulnerable toward mid-century. CCS can allow fossil fuels to be used longer, reducing potential stranded assets. (Box TS.8) {6.7}

Box TS.8 | Stranded Assets

Limiting warming to 2°C or 1.5°C is expected to result in the 'stranding' of carbon-intensive assets. Stranded assets can be broadly defined as assets which 'suffer from unanticipated or premature write-offs, downward revaluations or conversion to liabilities'. Climate policies, other policies and regulations, innovation in competing technologies, and shifts in fuel prices could all lead to stranded assets. The loss of wealth from stranded assets would create risks for financial market stabilityand reduce fiscal revenue for hydrocarbon-dependent economies, which in turn could affect macroeconomic stability and the prospects for a Just Transition. (Box TS.4) {6.7, 15.6, Chapter 17}

Two types of assets are at risk of being stranded: (i) in-ground fossil resources and (ii) human-made capital assets (e.g., power plants and cars). About 30% of oil, 50% of gas, and 80% of coal reserves will remain unburnable if warming is limited to 2°C. {6.7, Box 6.11}

Practically all long-lived technologies and investments that cannot be adapted to low-carbon and zero-emission modes could face stranding under climate policy – depending on their current age and expected lifetimes. Scenario evidence suggests that without carbon capture, the worldwide fleet of coal- and gas power plants would need to retire about 23 and 17 years earlier than expected lifetimes, respectively, in order to limit global warming to 1.5°C and 2°C {2.7}. Blast furnaces and cement factories without CCS {11.4}, new fleets of airplanes and internal combustion engine vehicles {10.4, 10.5}, and new urban infrastructures adapted to sprawl and motorisation may also be stranded. {Chapter 8; Box 10.1}

Many countries, businesses, and individuals stand to lose wealth from stranded assets. Countries, businesses, and individuals may therefore desire to keep assets in operation even if financial, social, or environmental concerns call for retirement. This creates political economic risks, including actions by asset owners to hinder climate policy reform {6.7; Box 6.11}. It will be easier to retire these assets if the risks are communicated, if sustainability reporting is mandated and enforced, and if corporations are protected with arrangements that shield them from short-term shareholder value maximisation.

Without early retirements, or reductions in utilisation, the current fossil infrastructure will emit more GHGs than is compatible with limiting warming to 1.5°C {2.7}. Including the pipeline of planned investments would push these future emissions into the uncertainty range of 2°C carbon budgets {2.7}. Continuing to build new coal-fired power plants and other fossil infrastructure will increase future transition costs and may jeopardise efforts to limit warming to 2°C (>67%) or 1.5°C with no or limited overshoot. One study has estimated that USD11.8 trillion in current assets will need to be stranded by 2050 for a 2°C world; further delaying action for another 10 years would result in an additional USD7.7 trillion in stranded assets by 2050. {15.5.2}

Experience from past stranding indicates that compensation for the devaluation costs of private-sector stakeholders by the public sector is common. Limiting new investments in fossil technologies hence also reduces public finance risks in the long term. {15.6.3}

A low-carbon energy transition will shift investment patterns and create new economic opportunities (*high confidence*). Total energy investment needs will rise, relative to today, over the next decades, if warming is limited to 2°C or lower (>67%), or if warming is limited to 1.5°C (>50%) with no or limited overshoot. These increases will be far less pronounced, however, than the reallocations of investment flows that are anticipated across subsectors, namely from fossil fuels (extraction, conversion, and electricity generation) without CCS and toward renewables, nuclear power, CCS, electricity networks and storage, and end-use energy efficiency. A significant and growing share of investments between now and 2050 will be made in emerging economies, particularly in Asia. {6.7}

Climate change will affect many future local and national low-carbon energy systems. The impacts, however, are uncertain, particularly at the regional scale (*high confidence*). Climate change will alter hydropower production, bioenergy and agricultural yields, thermal power plant efficiencies, and demands for heating and cooling, and it will directly impact power system infrastructure. Climate change will not affect wind and solar resources to the extent that it would compromise their ability to reduce emissions. {6.5}

Electricity systems powered predominantly by renewables will be increasingly viable over the coming decades, but it will be challenging to supply the entire energy system with renewable energy (*high confidence*). Large shares of variable solar PV and wind power can be incorporated in electricity grids through batteries, hydrogen, and other forms of storage; transmission; flexible non-renewable generation; advanced controls; and greater demand-side responses. Because some applications (e.g., aviation) are not currently amenable to electrification, it is anticipated that 100% renewable energy systems will need to include alternative fuels such as hydrogen or biofuels. Economic, regulatory, social, and operational challenges increase with higher shares of renewable electricity and energy. The ability to overcome these challenges in practice is not fully understood. (Box TS.9) {6.6}

Box TS.9 | The Transformation in Energy Carriers: Electrification and Hydrogen

To use energy, it must be 'carried' from where it was produced – at a power plant, for example, or a refinery, or a coal mine – to where it is used. As countries reduce CO_2 emissions, they will need to switch from gasoline and other petroleum-based fuels, natural gas, coal, and electricity produced from these fossil fuels to energy carriers with little or no carbon footprint. An important question is which new energy carriers will emerge to support low-carbon transitions.

Low-carbon energy systems are expected to rely heavily on end-use electrification, where electricity produced with low GHG emissions is used for building and industrial heating, transport and other applications that rely heavily on fossil fuels at present. But not all end-uses are expected to be commercially electrifiable in the short to medium term {11.3.5}, and many will require low GHG liquid and gaseous fuels, that is, hydrogen, ammonia, and biogenic and synthetic low GHG hydrocarbons made from low GHG hydrogen, oxygen and carbon sources (the latter from CCU,[20] biomass, or direct air capture {11.3.6}). The future role of hydrogen and hydrogen derivatives will depend on how quickly and how far production technology improves, that is, from electrolysis ('green'), biogasification, and fossil fuel reforming with CCS ('blue') sources. As a general rule, and across all sectors, it is more efficient to use electricity directly and avoid the progressively larger conversion losses from producing hydrogen, ammonia, or constructed low GHG hydrocarbons. What hydrogen does do, however, is add time and space option value to electricity produced using variable clean sources, for use as hydrogen, as stored future electricity via a fuel cell or turbine, or as an industrial feedstock. Furthermore, electrification and hydrogen involve a symbiotic range of general-purpose technologies, such as electric motors, power electronics, heat pumps, batteries, electrolysis, fuel cells, and so on, that have different applications across sectors but cumulative economies of innovation and production scale benefits. Finally, neither electrification nor hydrogen produce local air pollutants at point of end-use.

For almost 140 years we have primarily produced electricity by burning coal, oil, and gas to drive steam turbines connected to electricity generators. When switching to low-carbon energy sources – renewable sources, nuclear power, and fossil or bioenergy with CCS – electricity is expected to become a more pervasive energy carrier. Electricity is a versatile energy carrier, with much higher end-use efficiencies than fuels, and it can be used directly to avoid conversion losses.

An increasing reliance on electricity from variable renewable sources, notably wind and solar power, disrupts old concepts and makes many existing guidelines obsolete for power system planning, for example, that specific generation types are needed for baseload, intermediate load, and peak load to follow and meet demand. In future power systems with high shares of variable electricity from renewable sources, system planning and markets will focus more on demand flexibility, grid infrastructure and interconnections, storage on various timelines (on the minute, hourly, overnight and seasonal scale), and increased coupling between the energy sector and the building, transport and industrial sectors. This shifts the focus to energy systems that can handle variable supply rather than always follow demand. Hydrogen may prove valuable to improve the resilience of electricity systems with high penetration of variable renewable electricity. Flexible hydrogen electrolysis, hydrogen power plants and long-duration hydrogen storage may all improve resilience. Electricity-to-hydrogen-to-electricity round-trip efficiencies are projected to reach up to 50% by 2030. {6.4.3}

Electrification is expected to be the dominant strategy in buildings as electricity is increasingly used for heating and for cooking. Electricity will help to integrate renewable energy into buildings and will also lead to more flexible demand for heating, cooling, and electricity. District heating and cooling offers potential for demand flexibility through energy storage and supply flexibility through cogeneration. Heat pumps are increasingly used in buildings and industry for heating and cooling {9.3.3, Box 9.3}. The ease of switching to electricity means that hydrogen is not expected to be a dominant pathway for buildings {Box 9.6}. Using electricity directly for heating, cooling and other building energy demand is more efficient than using hydrogen as a fuel, for example, in boilers or fuel cells. In addition, electricity distribution is already well developed in many regions compared to essentially non-existent hydrogen infrastructure, except for a few chemicals industry pipelines. At the same time, hydrogen could potentially be used for on-site storage should technology advance sufficiently.

---

20 Carbon dioxide capture and utilisation (CCU) refers to a process in which CO_2 is captured and the carbon is then used in a product. The climate effect of CCU depends on the product lifetime, the product it displaces, and the CO_2 source (fossil, biomass or atmosphere). CCU is sometimes referred to as carbon dioxide capture and use, or carbon capture and utilisation.

Box TS.9 (continued)

Electrification is already occurring in several modes of personal and light-freight transport, and vehicle-to-grid solutions for flexibility have been extensively explored in the literature and small-scale pilots. The role of hydrogen in transport depends on how far technology develops. Batteries are currently a more attractive option than hydrogen and fuel cells for light-duty vehicles. Hydrogen and hydrogen-derived synthetic fuels, such as ammonia and methanol, may have a more important role in heavy vehicles, shipping, and aviation {10.3}. Current transport of fossil fuels may be replaced by future transport of hydrogen and hydrogen carriers such as ammonia and methanol, or energy-intensive basic materials processed with hydrogen (e.g., reduced iron) in regions with bountiful renewable resources. {Box 11.1}

Both light and heavy industry are potentially large and flexible users of electricity for both final energy use (e.g., directly and using heat pumps in light industry) and for feedstocks (e.g., hydrogen for steel-making and chemicals). For example, industrial process heat demand, ranging from below 100°C to above 1000°C, can be met through a wide range of electrically powered technologies instead of using fuels. Future demand for hydrogen (e.g., for nitrogen fertiliser or as a reduction agent in steel production) also offers electricity-demand flexibility for electrolysis through hydrogen storage and flexible production cycles {11.3.5}. The main use of hydrogen and hydrogen carriers in industry is expected to be as feedstock (e.g., for ammonia and organic chemicals) rather than for energy as industrial electrification increases.

Multiple energy supply options are available to reduce emissions over the next decade (*high confidence*). Nuclear power and hydropower are already established technologies. Solar PV and wind are now cheaper than fossil-generated electricity in many locations. Bioenergy accounts for about a tenth of global primary energy. Carbon capture is widely used in the oil and gas industry, with early applications in electricity production and biofuels. It will not be possible to widely deploy all of these and other options without efforts to address the geophysical, environmental-ecological, economic, technological, socio-cultural, and institutional factors that can facilitate or hinder their implementation (*high confidence*). (Figures TS.11 and TS.31) {6.4}

Enhanced integration across energy system sectors and across scales will lower costs and facilitate low-carbon energy system transitions (*high confidence*). Greater integration between the electricity sector and end-use sectors can facilitate integration of variable renewable energy options. Energy systems can be integrated across district, regional, national, and international scales (*high confidence*). {6.4, 6.6}

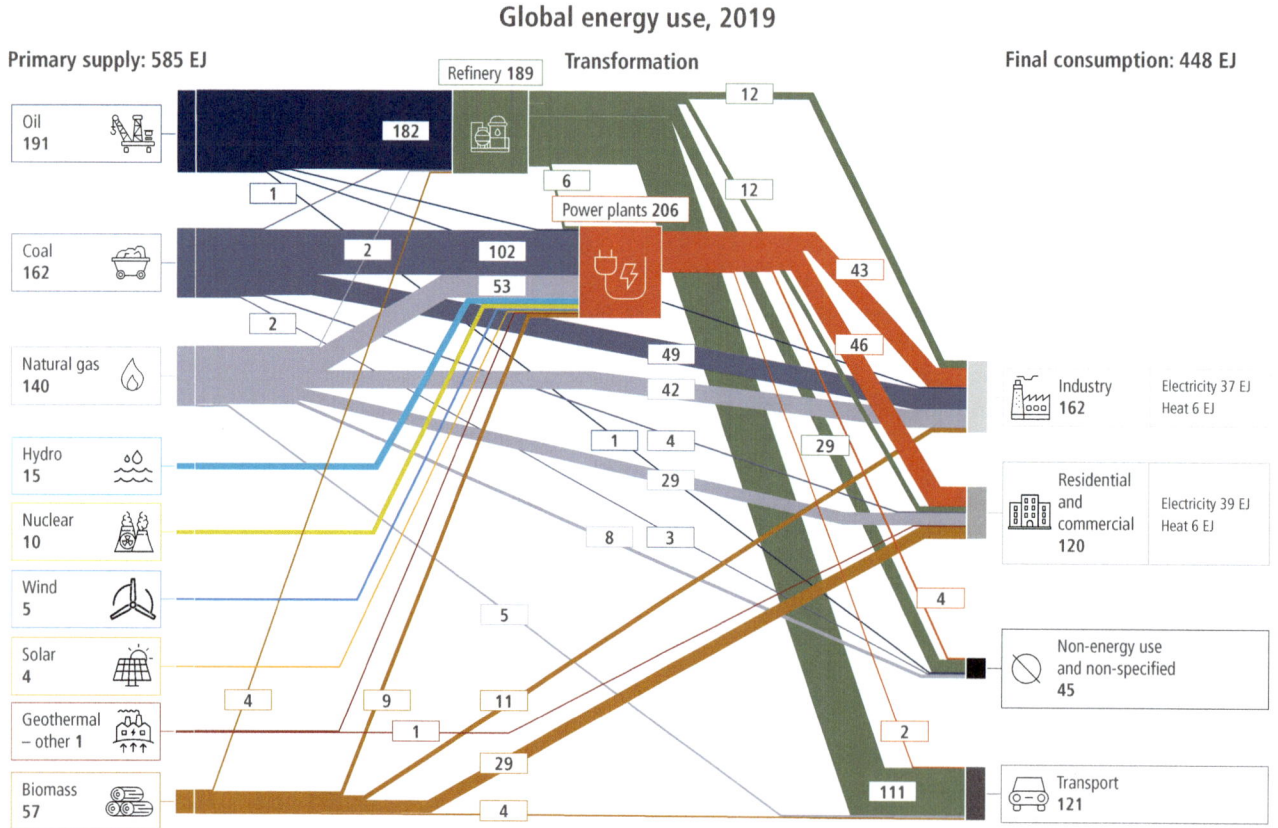

Figure TS.11 | Global energy flows within the 2019 global energy system (top panel) and within two illustrative future, net-zero CO₂ emissions global energy system (bottom panels).

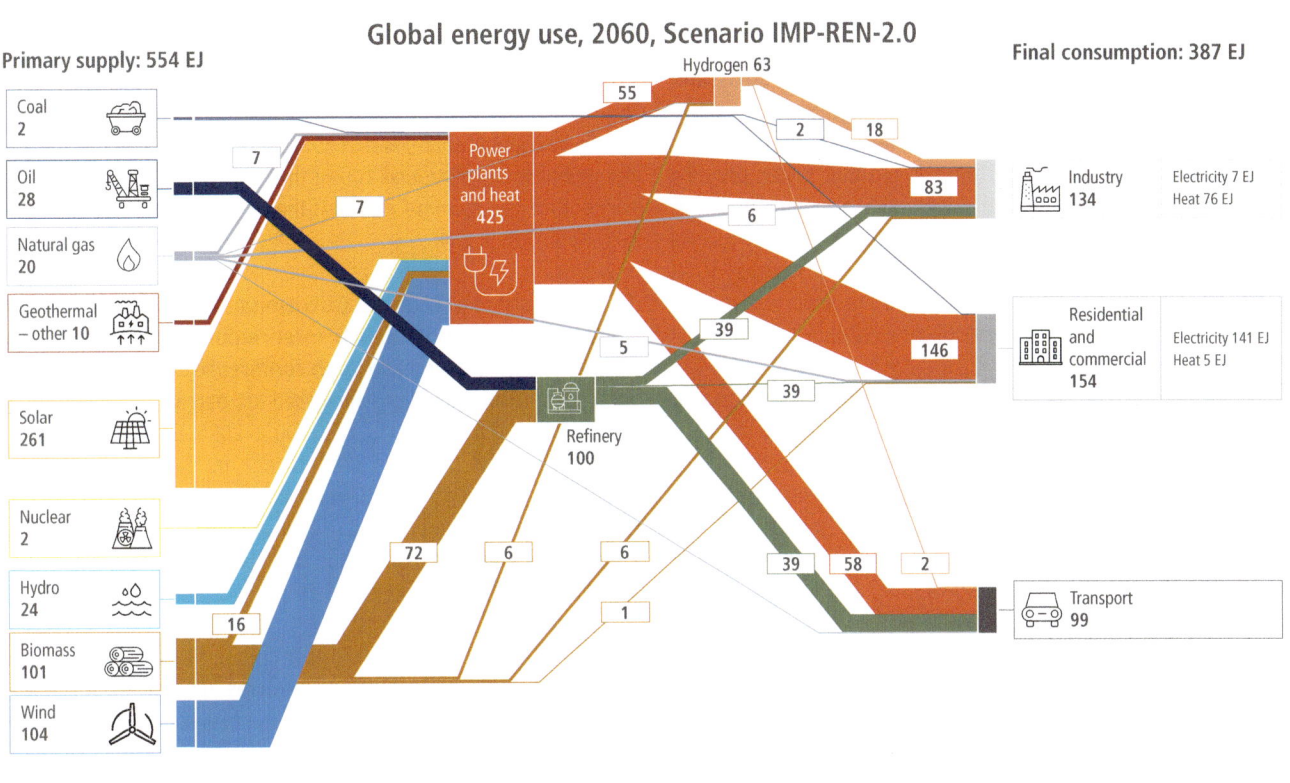

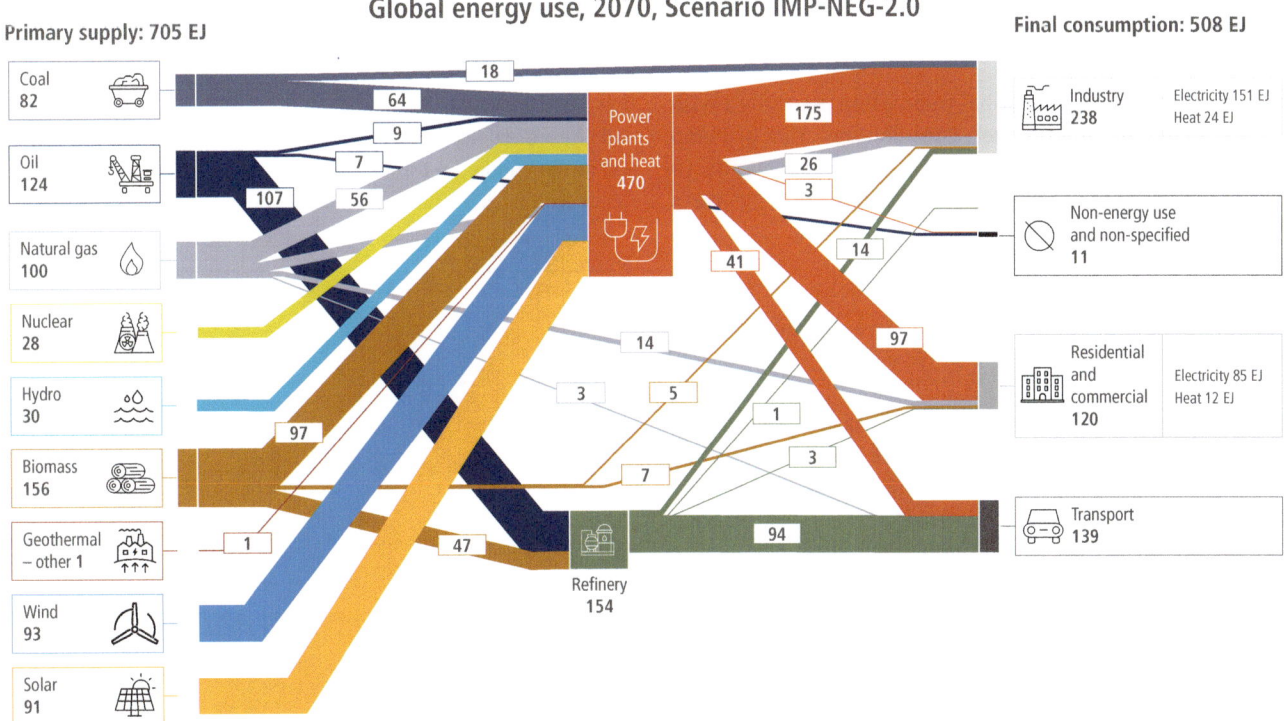

Figure TS.11 continued: Global energy flows within the 2019 global energy system (top panel) and within two illustrative future, net-zero CO₂ emissions global energy system (bottom panels). Source: IEA, AR6 Scenarios Database. Flows below 1 EJ are not represented. The illustrative net-zero scenarios correspond to the years in which net energy system CO₂ emissions reach zero – 2045 in IMP-Ren and 2060 in IMP-Neg-2.0. Source: data from IMP-Ren: Luderer et al.(2022); IMP-Neg-2.0: Riahi, K. et al. 2021.

TS

The viable speed and scope of a low-carbon energy system transition will depend on how well it can support SDGs and other societal objectives (*high confidence*). Energy systems are linked to a range of societal objectives, including energy access, air and water pollution, health, energy security, water security, food security, economic prosperity, international competitiveness, and employment. These linkages and their importance vary among regions. Energy-sector mitigation and efforts to achieve SDGs generally support one another, though there are important region-specific exceptions (*high confidence*). (Figure TS.29) {6.1, 6.7}

The economic outcomes of low-carbon transitions in some sectors and regions may be on par with, or superior to those of an emissions-intensive future (*high confidence*). Cost reductions in key technologies, particularly in electricity and light-duty transport, have increased the economic attractiveness of near-term low-carbon transitions. Long-term mitigation costs are not well understood and depend on policy design and implementation, and the future costs and availability of technologies. Advances in low-carbon energy resources and carriers such as next-generation biofuels, hydrogen produced from electrolysis, synthetic fuels, and carbon-neutral ammonia would substantially improve the economics of net zero energy systems (*medium confidence*). {6.4, 6.7}

TS.5.2   Urban Systems and Other Settlements

Although urbanisation is a global trend often associated with increased incomes and higher consumption, the growing concentration of people and activities is an opportunity to increase resource efficiency and decarbonise at scale (*very high confidence*). The same urbanisation level can have large variations in per-capita urban carbon emissions. For most regions, per-capita urban emissions are lower than per-capita national emissions (excluding aviation, shipping and biogenic sources) (*very high confidence*). {8.1.4, 8.3.3, 8.4, Box 8.1}

Most future urban population growth will occur in developing countries, where per-capita emissions are currently low, but are expected to increase with the construction and use of new infrastructure, and the built environment, and changes in incomes and lifestyles (*very high confidence*). The drivers of urban GHG emissions are complex and include an interplay of population size, income, state of urbanisation, and how cities are laid out (i.e., urban form). How new cities and towns are designed, constructed, managed, and powered will lock-in behaviour, lifestyles, and future urban GHG emissions. Urban strategies can improve well-being while minimising impact on GHG emissions. However, urbanisation can result in increased global GHG emissions through emissions outside the city's boundaries (*very high confidence*). {8.1.4, 8.3, Box 8.1, 8.4, 8.6}

The urban share of combined global CO_2 and CH_4) emissions is substantial and continues to increase (*high confidence*). In 2015, urban emissions were estimated to be 25GtCO$_2$-eq (about 62% of the global share) and in 2020 were 29 GtCO$_2$-eq (67–72% of the global share).[21] Around 100 of the highest-emitting urban areas account for approximately 18% of the global carbon footprint (*high confidence*). {8.1, 8.3}

The urban share of regional GHG emissions increased between 2000 and 2015, with much inter-regional variation in the magnitude of the increase (*high confidence*). Globally, the urban share of national emissions increased six percentage points, from 56% in 2000 to 62% in 2015. For 2000 to 2015, the urban emissions share increased from 28% to 38% in Africa, from 46% to 54% in Asia and Pacific, from 62% to 72% in Developed Countries, from 57% to 62% in Eastern Europe and West Central Asia, from 55% to 66% in Latin America and Caribbean, and from 68% to 69% in the Middle East (*high confidence*). {8.1.6, 8.3.3}

Per-capita urban GHG emissions increased between 2000 and 2015, with cities in developed countries accounting for nearly seven times more per capita than the lowest emitting region (*medium confidence*). From 2000 to 2015, global urban GHG emissions per capita increased from 5.5 to 6.2 tCO$_2$-eq per person (an increase of 11.8%). Emissions in Africa increased from 1.3 to 1.5 tCO$_2$-eq per person (22.6%); in Asia and Pacific from 3.0 to 5.1 tCO$_2$-eq per person (71.7%); in Eastern Europe and West Central Asia from 6.9 to 9.8 tCO$_2$-eq per person (40.9%); in Latin America and the Caribbean from 2.7 to 3.7 tCO$_2$-eq per person (40.4%); and in the Middle East from 7.4 to 9.6 tCO$_2$-eq per person (30.1%). Albeit starting from the highest level, developed countries showed a modest decline of 11.4 to 10.7 tCO$_2$-eq per person (–6.5%). (Figure TS.12) {8.3.3}

---

21 These estimates are based on consumption-based accounting, including both direct emissions from within urban areas, and indirect emissions from outside urban areas related to the production of electricity, goods, and services consumed in cities. Estimates include all CO_2 and CH_4 emission categories except for aviation and marine bunker fuels, land-use change, forestry, and agriculture. {8.1, Annex I: Glossary}

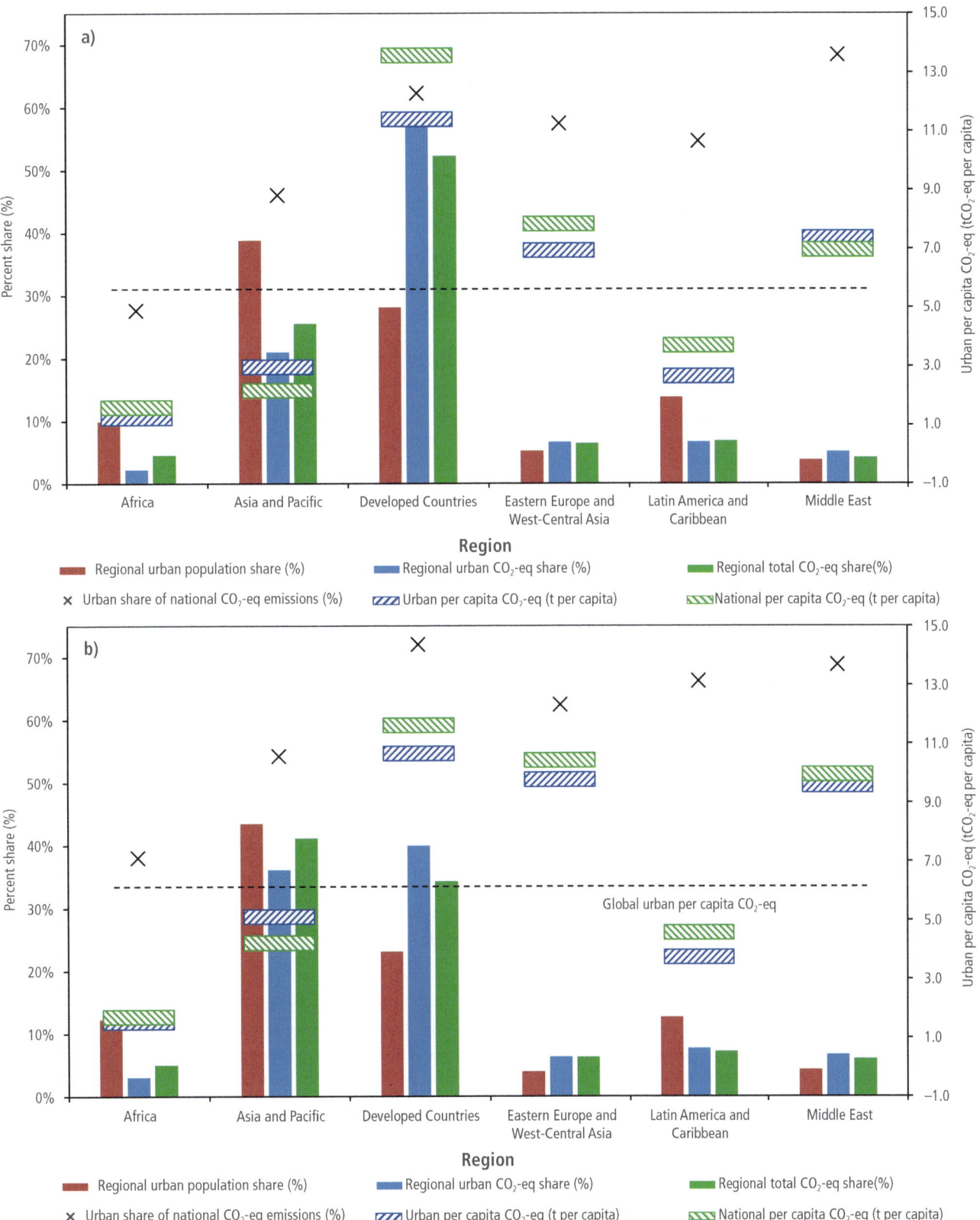

Figure TS.12 | Changes in six metrics associated with urban and national-scale combined CO₂ and CH₄ emissions represented in the AR6 WGIII six-region aggregation, with (a) 2000 and (b) 2015. The trends in Luqman et al. (2021) were combined with the work of Moran et al. (2018) to estimate the regional urban CO₂-eq share of global urban emissions, the urban share of national CO₂-eq emissions, and the urban per capita CO₂-eq emissions by region. This estimate is derived from consumption-based accounting that includes both direct emissions from within urban areas and indirect emissions from outside urban areas related to the production of electricity, goods, and services consumed in cities. It incorporates all CO₂ and CH₄ emissions except aviation, shipping and biogenic sources (i.e., land-use change, forestry, and agriculture). The dashed grey line represents the global average urban per capita CO₂-eq emissions. The regional urban population share, regional CO₂-eq share in total emissions, and national per capita CO₂-eq emissions by region are given for comparison. Source: adapted from Gurney et al. (2022).

(a)

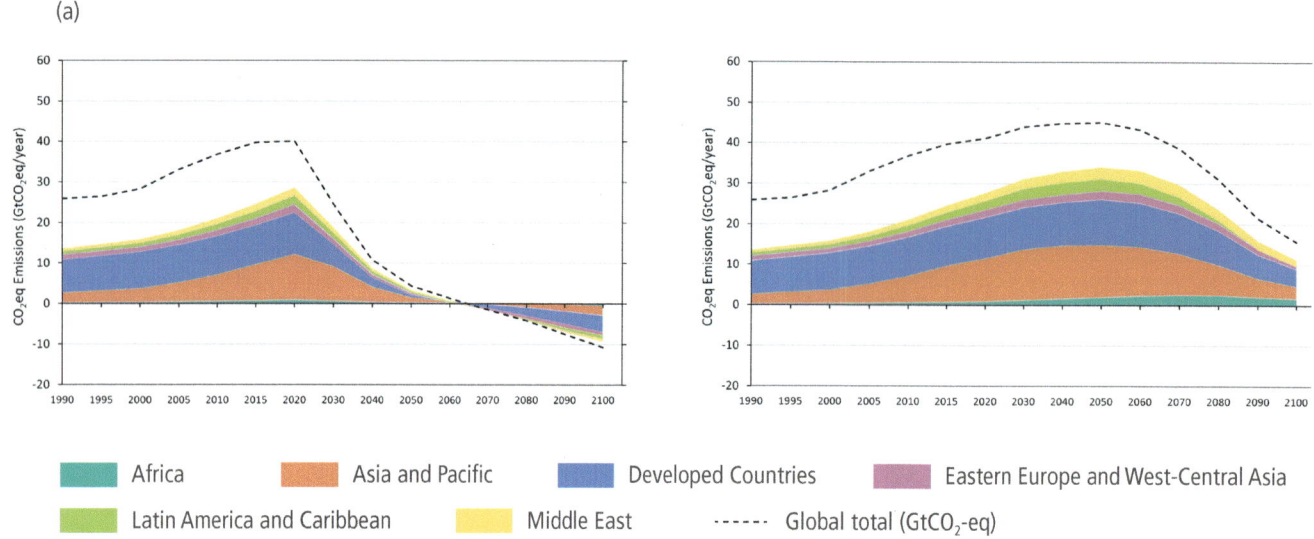

(b) Estimated urban emissions changes in two different scenarios (2020–2030)

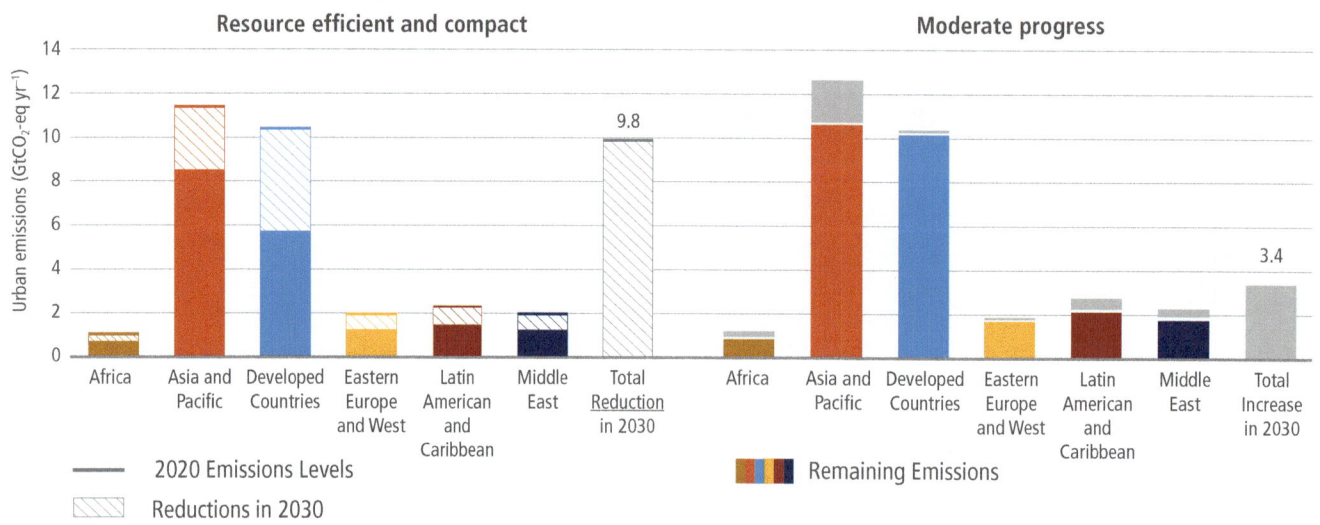

Figure TS.13 | Panel (a): carbon dioxide-equivalent emissions from global urban areas from 1990 to 2100. Urban areas are aggregated to six regional domains; Panel (b): comparison of urban emissions under different urbanisation scenarios (GtCO$_2$-eq yr^{-1}) for different regions.[21] {Figures 8.13 and 8.14}

The global share of future urban GHG emissions is expected to increase through 2050 with moderate to low mitigation efforts due to growth trends in population, urban land expansion, and infrastructure and service demands, but the extent of the increase depends on the scenario and the scale and timing of urban mitigation action (*medium confidence*). In modelled scenarios, global consumption-based urban CO$_2$ and CH$_4$ emissions are projected to rise from 29 GtCO$_2$-eq in 2020 to 34 GtCO$_2$-eq in 2050 with moderate mitigation efforts (intermediate GHG emissions, SSP2-4.5), and up to 40 GtCO$_2$-eq in 2050 with low mitigation efforts (high GHG emissions, SSP 3-7.0). With aggressive and immediate mitigation efforts to limit global warming to 1.5°C (>50%) with no or limited overshoot by the end of the century (very low emissions,

SSP1-1.9), including high levels of electrification, energy and material efficiency, renewable energy preferences, and socio-behavioural responses, urban GHG emissions could approach net-zero and reach a maximum of 3 GtCO$_2$-eq in 2050. Under a scenario with aggressive but not immediate urban mitigation policies to limit global warming to 2°C (>67%) (low emissions, SSP1-2.6), urban emissions could reach 17 GtCO$_2$-eq in 2050.[23] (Figure TS.13) {8.3.4}

Urban land areas could triple between 2015 and 2050, with significant implications for future carbon lock-in (*medium confidence*). There is a large range in the forecasts of urban land expansion across scenarios and models, which highlights an opportunity to shape future urban development towards low- or net zero GHG

---

22   These scenarios have been assessed by WGI to correspond to intermediate, high, and very low GHG emissions.

23   These scenarios have been assessed by WGI to correspond to intermediate, high, and very low GHG emissions.

emissions. By 2050, urban areas could increase up to 211% over the 2015 global urban extent, with the median projected increase ranging from 43% to 106%. While the largest absolute amount of new urban land is forecasted to occur in Asia and Pacific, and in Developed Countries, the highest rate of urban land growth is projected to occur in Africa, Eastern Europe and West Central Asia, and in the Middle East. Given past trends, the expansion of urban areas is expected to take place on agricultural lands and forests, with implications for the loss of carbon stocks. The infrastructure that will be constructed concomitant with urban land expansion will lock-in patterns of energy consumption that will persist for decades. {8.3.1, 8.3.4, 8.4.1, 8.6}

The construction of new, and upgrading of existing, urban infrastructure through 2030 will add to emissions (*medium evidence, high agreement*). The construction of new and upgrading of existing urban infrastructure using conventional practices and technologies can result in a significant increase in CO_2 emissions, ranging from 8.5 $GtCO_2$ to 14 $GtCO_2$ annually up to 2030 and more than double annual resource requirements for raw materials to about 90 billion tonnes per year by 2050, up from 40 billion tonnes in 2010. {8.4.1, 8.6}

Given the dual challenges of rising urban GHG emissions and future projections of more frequent extreme climate events, there is an urgent need to integrate urban mitigation and adaptation strategies for cities to address climate change (*very high confidence*). Mitigation strategies can enhance resilience against climate change impacts while contributing to social equity, public health, and human well-being. Urban mitigation actions that facilitate economic decoupling can have positive impacts on employment and local economic competitiveness. {8.2, Cross-Working Group Box 2 in Chapter 8, 8.4}

Cities can achieve net-zero GHG emissions only through deep decarbonisation and systemic transformation (*very high confidence*). Three broad mitigation strategies have been found to be effective in reducing emissions when implemented concurrently: (i) reducing or changing urban energy and material use towards more sustainable production and consumption across all sectors, including through compact and efficient urban forms and supporting infrastructure; (ii) electrification and switching to low-carbon energy sources; and (iii) enhancing carbon uptake and storage in the urban environment (*high confidence*). Given the regional and global reach of urban supply chains, cities can achieve net-zero emissions only if emissions are reduced both within and outside of their administrative boundaries through supply chains. {8.1.6, 8.3.4, 8.4, 8.6}

Packages of mitigation policies that implement multiple urban-scale interventions can have cascading effects across sectors, reduce GHG emissions outside a city's administrative boundaries, and reduce emissions more than the net sum of individual interventions, particularly if multiple scales of governance are included (*high confidence*). Cities have the ability to implement policy packages across sectors using an urban systems approach, especially those that affect key infrastructure

based on spatial planning, electrification of the urban energy system, and urban green and blue infrastructure. The institutional capacity of cities to develop, coordinate, and integrate sectoral mitigation strategies within their jurisdiction varies by context, particularly those related to governance, the regulatory system, and budgetary control. {8.4, 8.5, 8.6}

Integrated spatial planning to achieve compact and resource-efficient urban growth through co-location of higher residential and job densities, mixed land use, and transit-oriented development could reduce urban energy use between 23% and 26% by 2050 compared to the business-as-usual scenario (*high confidence*). Compact cities with shortened distances between housing and jobs, and interventions that support a modal shift away from private motor vehicles towards walking, cycling, and low-emissions shared, or public, transportation, passive energy comfort in buildings, and urban green infrastructure can deliver significant public health benefits and lower GHG emissions. {8.2, 8.3.4, 8.4, 8.6}

Urban green and blue infrastructure can mitigate climate change through carbon sinks, avoided emissions, and reduced energy use while offering multiple co-benefits (*high confidence*). Urban green and blue infrastructure, including urban forests and street trees, permeable surfaces, and green roofs[24] offer potentials to mitigate climate change directly through storing carbon, and indirectly by inducing a cooling effect that both reduces energy demand and reduces energy use for water treatment. Globally, urban trees store approximately 7.4 billion tonnes of carbon, and sequester approximately 217 million tonnes of carbon annually, although carbon storage is highly dependent on biome. Among the multiple co-benefits of green and blue infrastructure are reducing the urban heat island (UHI) effect and heat stress, reducing stormwater runoff, improving air quality, and improving the mental and physical health of urban dwellers. Many of these options also provide benefits to climate adaptation. (*high agreement, robust evidence*) {8.2, 8.4.4}

The potential and sequencing of mitigation strategies to reduce GHG emissions will vary depending on a city's land use, spatial form, development level, and state of urbanisation (i.e., whether it is an established city with existing infrastructure, a rapidly growing city with new infrastructure, or an emerging city with infrastructure buildup) (*high confidence*). New and emerging cities will have significant infrastructure development needs to achieve high quality of life, which can be met through energy-efficient infrastructures and services, and people-centred urban design (high confidence). The long lifespan of urban infrastructures locks in behaviour and committed emissions. Urban infrastructures and urban form can enable sociocultural and lifestyle changes that can significantly reduce carbon footprints. Rapidly growing cities can avoid higher future emissions through urban planning to co-locate jobs and housing to achieve compact urban form, and by leapfrogging to low-carbon technologies. Established cities will achieve the largest GHG emissions savings by replacing, repurposing, or retrofitting the building stock, targeted infilling and densifying, as well as through modal shift and the electrification of the urban energy system. New and emerging cities

---

24 These examples are considered to be a subset of 'nature-based solutions' or 'ecosystem-based approaches'.

have unparalleled potential to become low or net zero GHG emissions while achieving high quality of life by creating compact, co-located, and walkable urban areas with mixed land use and transit-oriented design, that also preserve existing green and blue assets. {8.2, 8.4, 8.6}

With over 880 million people living in informal settlements, there are opportunities to harness and enable informal practices and institutions in cities related to housing, waste, energy, water, and sanitation to reduce resource use and mitigate climate change (*low evidence, medium agreement*). The upgrading of informal settlements and inadequate housing to improve resilience and well-being offers a chance to create a low-carbon transition. However, there is limited quantifiable data on these practices and their cumulative impacts on GHG emissions. {8.1.4, 8.2.2, Cross-Working Group Box 2 in Chapter 8, 8.3.2, 8.4, 8.6, 8.7}

Achieving transformational changes in cities for climate change mitigation and adaptation will require engaging multiple scales of governance, including governments and non-state actors, and in connection with substantial financing beyond sectoral approaches (*very high confidence*). Large and complex infrastructure projects for urban mitigation are often beyond the capacity of local municipality budgets, jurisdictions, and institutions. Partnerships between cities and international institutions, national and regional governments, transnational networks, and local stakeholders play a pivotal role in mobilising global climate finance resources for a range of infrastructure projects with low-carbon emissions and related spatial planning programs across key sectors. {8.4, 8.5}

TS.5.3   Transport

Meeting climate mitigation goals would require transformative changes in the transport sector. In 2019, direct GHG emissions from the transport sector were 8.7 GtCO$_2$-eq (up from 5.0 GtCO$_2$-eq in 1990) and accounted for 23% of global energy-related CO$_2$ emissions. Road vehicles accounted for 70% of direct transport emissions, while 1%, 11%, and 12% of direct emissions came from rail, shipping, and aviation, respectively. Emissions from shipping and aviation continue to grow rapidly. Transport-related emissions in developing regions of the world have increased more rapidly than in Europe or North America, a trend that is expected to continue in coming decades (*high confidence*). {10.1, 10.5, 10.6}

Since AR5 there has been a growing awareness of the need for demand management solutions combined with new technologies, such as the rapidly growing use of electromobility for land transport and the emerging options in advanced biofuels and hydrogen-based fuels for shipping and aviation and in other specific land-based contexts (*high confidence*). There is a growing need for systemic infrastructure changes that enable behavioural modifications and reductions in demand for transport services that can in turn reduce energy demand. The response to the COVID-19 pandemic has also shown that behavioural interventions can

reduce transport-related GHG emissions. For example, COVID-19-based lockdowns have confirmed the transformative value of telecommuting replacing significant numbers of work and personal journeys as well as promoting local active transport. There are growing opportunities to implement strategies that drive behavioural change and support the adoption of new transport technology options. {Chapter 5, 10.2, 10.3, 10.4, 10.8}

Changes in urban form, behaviour programs, the circular economy, the shared economy, and digitalisation trends can support systemic changes that lead to reductions in demand for transport services or expand the use of more efficient transport modes (*high confidence*). Cities can reduce their transport-related fuel consumption by around 25% through combinations of more compact land use and the provision of less car-dependent transport infrastructure. Appropriate infrastructure, including protected pedestrian and bike pathways, can also support much greater localised active travel.[25] Transport demand management incentives are expected to be necessary to support these systemic changes. There is mixed evidence of the effect of circular economy initiatives, shared economy initiatives, and digitalisation on demand for transport services (Box TS.14). For example, while dematerialisation can reduce the amount of material that needs to be transported to manufacturing facilities, an increase in online shopping with priority delivery can increase demand for freight transport. Similarly, while teleworking could reduce travel demand, increased ride-sharing could increase vehicle kilometres travelled (VKT). {Chapters 1 and 5, 10.2, 10.8}

Battery electric vehicles (BEVs) have lower lifecycle greenhouse gas (GHG) emissions than internal combustion engine vehicles (ICEVs) when BEVs are charged with low-carbon electricity (*high confidence*). Electromobility is being rapidly implemented in micro-mobility (e-autorickshaws, e-scooters, e-bikes), in transit systems, especially buses, and to a lesser degree, in personal vehicles. BEVs could also have the added benefit of supporting grid operations. The commercial availability of mature lithium-ion batteries (LIBs) has underpinned this growth in electromobility. As global battery production increases, unit costs are declining. Further efforts to reduce the GHG footprint of battery production, however, are essential for maximising the mitigation potential of BEVs. The continued growth of electromobility for land transport would entail investments in electric charging and related grid infrastructure. Electromobility powered by low-carbon electricity has the potential to rapidly reduce transport GHG and can be applied with multiple co-benefits, especially in developing countries. {10.3, 10.4, 10.8}

Land-based, long-range, heavy-duty trucks can be decarbonised through battery-electric haulage (including the use of electric road systems), complemented by hydrogen- and biofuel-based fuels in some contexts. These same technologies and expanded use of available electric rail systems can support rail decarbonisation (*medium confidence*). Initial deployments of battery-electric, hydrogen- and bio-based haulage are underway, and commercial operations of some of these technologies are considered

---

25   'Active travel' is travel that requires physical effort, for example journeys made by walking or cycling.

feasible by 2030 (*medium confidence*). These technologies nevertheless face challenges regarding driving range, capital and operating costs, and infrastructure availability. In particular, fuel-cell durability, high energy consumption, and costs continue to challenge the commercialisation of hydrogen-based fuel-cell vehicles. Increased capacity for low-carbon hydrogen production would also be essential for hydrogen-based fuels to serve as an emissions reduction strategy (*high confidence*). (Box TS.15) {10.3, 10.4, 10.8}

Decarbonisation options for shipping and aviation still require R&D, though advanced biofuels, ammonia, and synthetic fuels are emerging as viable options (*medium confidence*). Increased efficiency has been insufficient to limit the emissions from shipping and aviation, and natural gas-based fuels are expected to be inadequate to meet stringent decarbonisation goals for these segments (*high confidence*). High-energy density, low-carbon fuels are required, but they have not yet reached commercial scale. Advanced biofuels could provide low-carbon jet fuel (*medium confidence*). The production of synthetic fuels using low-carbon hydrogen with CO_2 captured through DACCS/BECCS could provide jet and marine fuels but these options still require demonstration at scale (*low confidence*). Ammonia produced with low-carbon hydrogen could also serve as a marine fuel (*medium confidence*). Deployment of these fuels requires reductions in production costs. (Figure TS.14) {10.2, 10.3, 10.4, 10.5, 10.6, 10.8}

Scenarios from bottom-up and top-down models indicate that, without intervention, CO_2 emissions from transport could grow in the range of 16% and 50% by 2050 (*medium confidence*). The scenarios literature projects continued growth in demand for freight and passenger services, particularly in developing countries in Africa and Asia (*high confidence*). This growth is projected to take place across all transport modes. Increases in demand notwithstanding, scenarios that limit warming to 1.5°C degree with no or limited overshoot suggest that a 59% reduction (42–68% interquartile range) in transport-related CO_2 emissions by 2050, compared to modelled 2020 levels is required. While many global scenarios place greater reliance on emissions reduction in sectors other than transport, a quarter of the 1.5°C scenarios describe transport-related CO_2 emissions reductions in excess of 68% (relative to modelled 2020 levels) (*medium confidence*). Illustrative Mitigation Pathways IMP-Ren and IMP-LD (TS 4.2) describe emission reductions of 80% and 90% in the transport sector, respectively, by 2050. Transport-related emission reductions, however, may not happen uniformly across regions. For example, transport emissions from the Developed Countries, and Eastern Europe and West Central Asia countries decrease from 2020 levels by 2050 across all scenarios limiting global warming to 1.5°C by 2100, but could increase in Africa, Asia and Pacific (APC), Latin America and Caribbean, and the Middle East in some of these scenarios. {10.7}

The scenarios literature indicates that fuel and technology shifts are crucial in reducing carbon emissions to meet temperature goals (*high confidence*). In general terms, electrification tends to play the key role in land-based transport, but biofuels and hydrogen (and derivatives) could play a role in decarbonisation of freight in some contexts. Biofuels and hydrogen (and derivatives) are expected to be more prominent in shipping and aviation. The shifts towards these alternative fuels must occur alongside shifts towards clean technologies in other sectors. {10.7}

There is a growing awareness of the need to plan for the significant expansion of low-carbon energy infrastructure, including low-carbon power generation and hydrogen production, to support emissions reductions in the transport sector (*high confidence*). Integrated energy planning and operations that take into account energy demand and system constraints across all sectors (transport, buildings, and industry) offer the opportunity to leverage sectoral synergies and avoid inefficient allocation of energy resources. Integrated planning of transport and power infrastructure would be particularly useful in developing countries where 'greenfield' development doesn't suffer from constraints imposed by legacy systems. {10.3, 10.4, 10.8}

The deployment of low-carbon aviation and shipping fuels that support decarbonisation of the transport sector could require changes to national and international governance structures (*medium confidence*). The UNFCCC does not specifically cover emissions from international shipping and aviation. Reporting emissions from international transport is at the discretion of each country. While the International Civil Aviation Organization (ICAO) and International Maritime Organization (IMO) have established emissions reductions targets, only strategies to improve fuel efficiency and demand reductions have been pursued, and there has been minimal commitment to new technologies. {10.5, 10.6, 10.7}

There are growing concerns about resource availability, labour rights, non-climate environmental impacts, and costs of critical minerals needed for lithium-ion batteries (*medium confidence*). Emerging national strategies on critical minerals and the requirements from major vehicle manufacturers are leading to new, more geographically diverse mines. The standardisation of battery modules and packaging within and across vehicle platforms, as well as increased focus on design for recyclability are important. Given the high degree of potential recyclability of lithium-ion batteries, a nearly closed-loop system in the future could mitigate concerns about critical mineral issues (*medium confidence*). {10.3, 10.8}

Legislated climate strategies are emerging at all levels of government, and together with pledges for personal choices, could spur the deployment of demand- and supply-side transport mitigation strategies (*medium confidence*). At the local level, legislation can support local transport plans that include commitments or pledges from local institutions to encourage behaviour change by adopting an organisational culture that motivates sustainable behaviour with inputs from the creative arts. Such institution-led mechanisms could include bike-to-work campaigns, free transport passes, parking charges, or eliminating car benefits. Community-based solutions such as *solar sharing*, *community charging*, and *mobility as a service* can generate new opportunities to facilitate low-carbon transport futures. At the regional and national levels, legislation can include vehicle and fuel efficiency standards, R&D support, and large-scale investments in low-carbon transport infrastructure. (Figure TS.14) {10.8, Chapter 15}

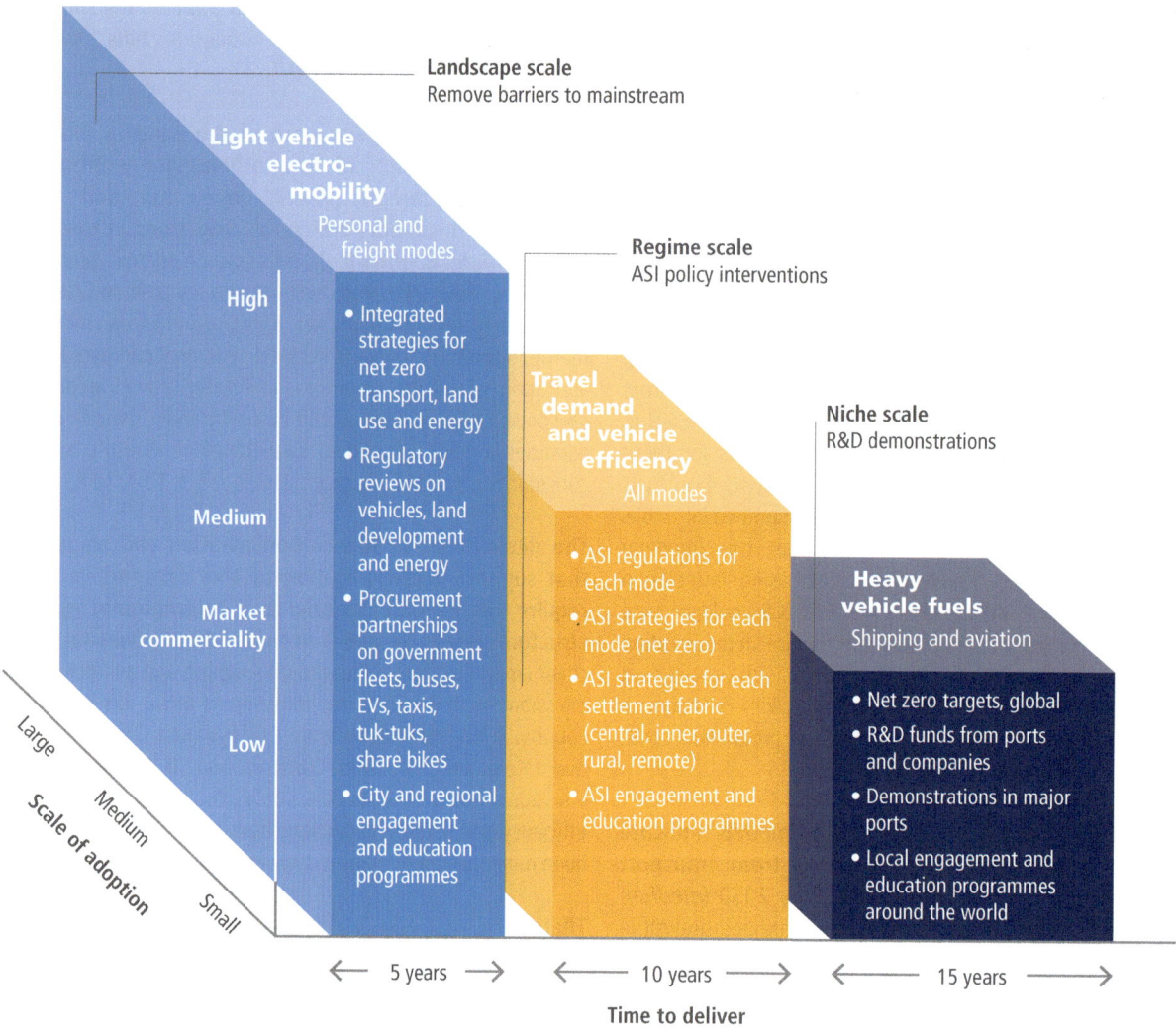

Figure TS.14 | Mitigation options and enabling conditions for transport. 'Niche' scale includes strategies that still require innovation. {Figure 10.22} ASI: Avoid-Shift-Improve; TRL: technology readiness level.

TS.5.4   Buildings

Global GHG emissions from buildings were 12 GtCO₂-eq in 2019, equivalent to 21% of global GHG emissions. Of this, 57% (6.8 GtCO₂-eq) were indirect emissions from off-site generation of electricity and heat, 24% (2.9 GtCO₂-eq) were direct emissions produced on-site and 18% (2.2 GtCO₂-eq) were embodied emissions from the production of cement and steel used in buildings (*high confidence*). Most building-sector emissions are CO₂. Final energy demand from buildings reached 128 EJ globally in 2019 (around 31% of global final energy demand), and electricity demand from buildings was slightly above 43 EJ globally (around 18% of global electricity demand). Residential buildings consumed 70% (90 EJ) of the global final energy demand from buildings. Over the period 1990–2019, global CO₂ emissions from buildings increased by 50%, global final energy demand from buildings grew by 38%, and global final electricity demand increased by 161%. {9.3}

In most regions, historical improvements in efficiency have been approximately matched by growth in floor area per capita (*high confidence*). At the global level, building-specific drivers of GHG emissions include: (i) population growth, especially in developing countries; (ii) increasing floor area per capita, driven by the increasing size of dwellings while the size of households kept decreasing, especially in developed countries; (iii) the inefficiency of newly constructed buildings, especially in developing countries, and the low renovation rates and low ambition level in developed countries when existing buildings are renovated; (iv) the increase in use, number and size of appliances and equipment, especially information and communication technologies (ICT) and cooling, driven by income; and, (v) the continued reliance on carbon-intensive electricity and heat. These factors taken together are projected to continue driving increased GHG emissions in the building sector in the future. {9.3, 9.6, 9.9}

Building-sector GHG emissions were assessed using the Sufficiency, Efficiency, Renewable (SER) framework. Sufficiency measures tackle the causes of GHG emissions by limiting the demand for energy and materials over the lifecycle of buildings and appliances (*high confidence*). In Chapter 9 of this report, *sufficiency* differs from *efficiency*: *sufficiency* is about long-term actions driven by non-technological solutions, which consume less energy in absolute terms; *efficiency*, in contrast is about continuous short-term marginal technological improvements. Sufficiency policies are a set of measures and daily practices that avoid demand for energy, materials, land and water while delivering human well-being-for-all within planetary boundaries. Use of the SER framework aims to reduce the cost of constructing and using buildings without reducing occupants' well-being and comfort. {9.1, 9.4, 9.5, 9.9}

Sufficiency interventions do not consume energy during the use phase of buildings and do not require maintenance nor replacement over the lifetime of buildings. Density, compacity, bioclimatic design to optimise the use of nature-based solutions, multi-functionality of space through shared space and to allow for adjusting the size of buildings to the evolving needs of households, circular use of materials and repurposing unused existing buildings to avoid using virgin materials, optimisation of the use of buildings through lifestyle changes, use of the thermal mass of buildings to reduce thermal needs, and moving from ownership to usership of appliances, are among the sufficiency interventions implemented in leading municipalities (*high confidence*). At a global level, up to 17% of the mitigation potential in the buildings sector could be captured by 2050 through sufficiency interventions (*medium confidence*). (Figure TS.15) {9.2, 9.3, 9.4, 9.5, 9.9}

The potential associated with sufficiency measures, as well as the replacement of appliances, equipment and lights by efficient ones, is below zero cost (*high confidence*). The construction of high-performance buildings is expected to become a business-as-usual technology by 2050 with costs below USD20 tCO$_2$$^{-1}$ in developed countries and below USD100 tCO$_2$$^{-1}$ in developing countries (*medium confidence*). For existing buildings, there have been many examples of deep retrofits where additional costs per CO$_2$ abated are not significantly higher than those of shallow retrofits. However, for the whole building stock they tend to be in cost intervals of USD–200 tCO$_2$$^{-1}$ and >USD200 tCO$_2$$^{-1}$ (*medium confidence*). Literature emphasises the critical role of the 2020–2030 decade in accelerating the learning of know-how and skills to reduce the costs and remove feasibility constraints for achieving high-efficiency buildings at scale and set the sector on the pathway to realise its full potential (*high confidence*). {9.3, 9.6, 9.9}.

The development, since AR5, of integrated approaches to the construction and retrofit of buildings has led to increasing the number of zero-energy or zero-carbon buildings in almost all climate zones. The complementarity and interdependency of measures leads to cost reductions, while optimising the mitigation potential achieved and avoiding the lock-in-effect (*medium confidence*). {9.6, 9.9}

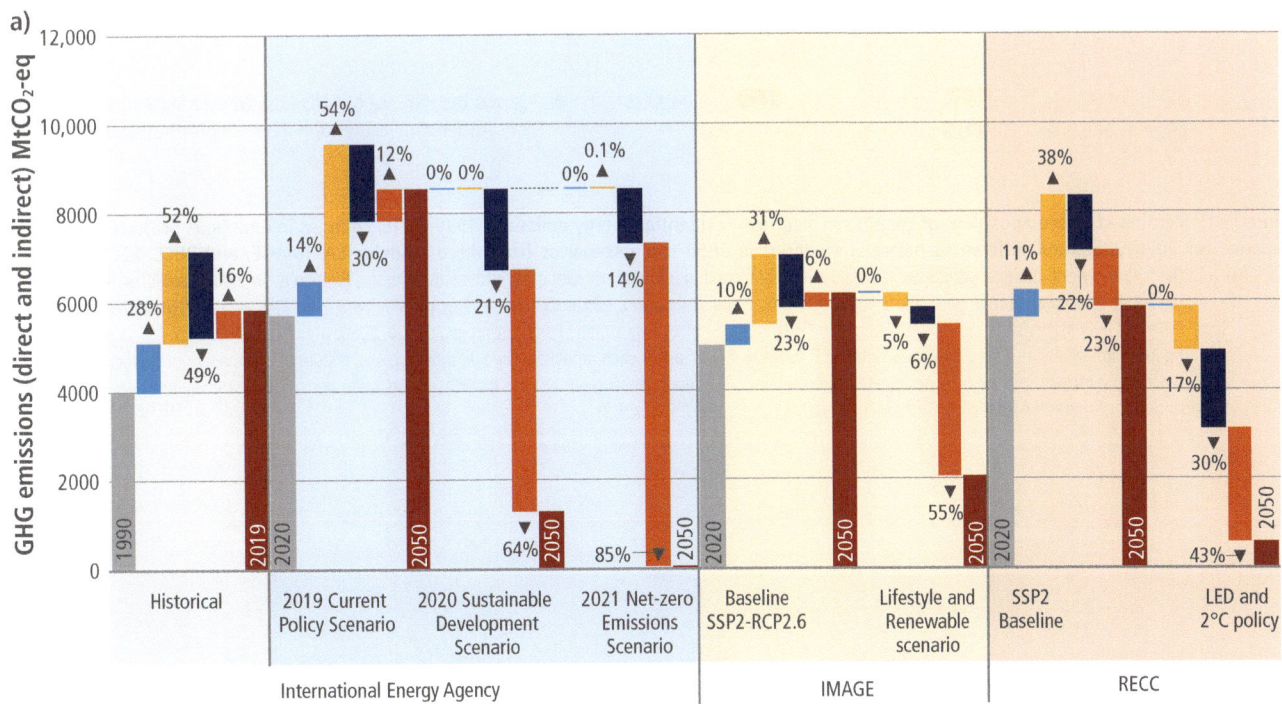

Figure TS.15 | Decompositions of changes in historical residential energy emissions 1990–2019, changes in emissions projected by baseline scenarios for 2020–2050, and differences between scenarios in 2050 using scenarios from three models: IEA, IMAGE, and RECC.

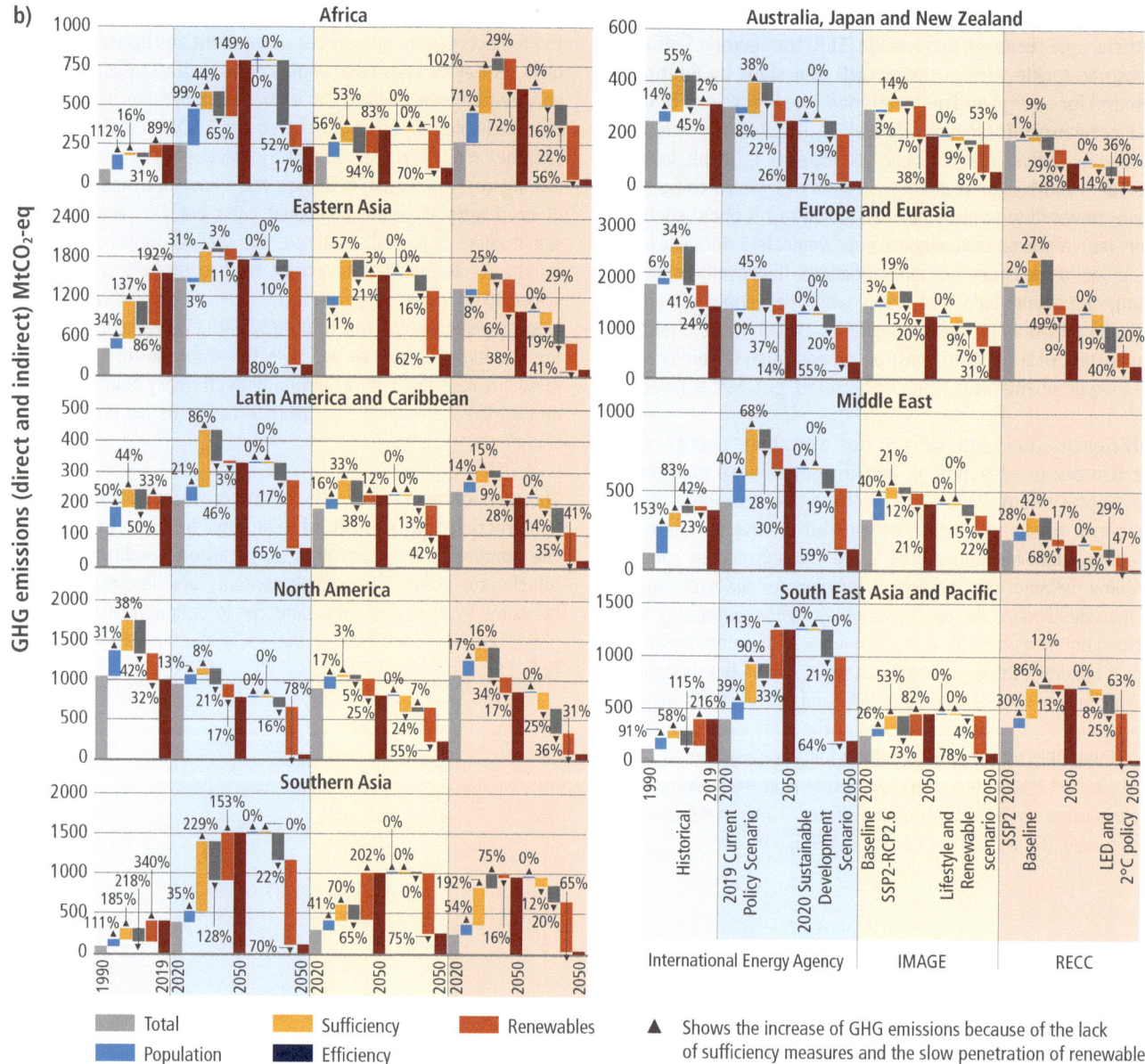

Figure TS.15 (continued): Decompositions of changes in historical residential energy emissions 1990–2019, changes in emissions projected by baseline scenarios for 2020–2050, and differences between scenarios in 2050 using scenarios from three models: IEA, IMAGE, and RECC. RECC-LED data for **(a)** global, and **(b)** for nine world regions, include only space heating and cooling and water heating in residential buildings. Emissions are decomposed using the equation, which shows changes in driver variables of population, sufficiency (floor area per capita), efficiency (final energy per floor area), and renewables (GHG emissions per final energy). 'Renewables' is a summary term describing changes in GHG intensity of energy supply. Emission projections to 2050, and differences between scenarios in 2050, demonstrate mitigation potentials from the dimensions of the SER framework realised in each model scenario. In most regions, historical improvements in efficiency have been approximately matched by growth in floor area per capita. Implementing sufficiency measures that limit growth in floor area per capita, particularly in developed regions, reduces the dependence of climate mitigation on technological solutions. {Figure 9.5, Box 9.2}

The decarbonisation of buildings is constrained by multiple barriers and obstacles as well as limited finance flows (*high confidence*). The lack of institutional capacity, especially in developing countries, and appropriate governance structures slow down the decarbonisation of the global building stock (*medium confidence*). The building sector is highly heterogenous with many different building types, sizes, and operational uses. The sub-segment representing rented property faces principal/agent problems where the tenant benefits from the decarbonisation's investment made by the landlord. The organisational context and the governance structure could trigger or hinder the decarbonisation of buildings. Global investment in the decarbonisation of buildings was estimated at USD164 billion in 2020. However, this is not enough by far to close the investment gap (*high confidence*). {9.9}

Policy packages could grasp the full mitigation potential of the global building stock. Building energy codes represent the main regulatory instrument to reduce emissions from both new and existing buildings (*high confidence*). The most advanced building energy codes include requirements on each of the three pillars of the SER framework in the *use* and *construction* phase of buildings. Building energy codes have proven to be effective if compulsory and combined with other regulatory instruments such as minimum energy performance standard for appliances and equipment, if the performance level is set at the level of the best available technologies in the market (*high confidence*). Market-based instruments such as carbon taxes with recycling of the revenues and personal or building carbon allowances could also contribute to fostering the decarbonisation of the building sector (*medium confidence*). {9.9}

Adapting buildings to future climate while ensuring well-being for all requires action. Expected heatwaves will inevitably increase cooling needs to limit the health impacts of climate change (*medium confidence*). Global warming will impact cooling and heating needs but also the performance, durability and safety of buildings, especially historical and coastal ones, through changes in temperature, humidity, atmospheric concentrations of CO_2 and chloride, and sea level rise. Adaptation measures to cope with climate change may increase the demand for energy and materials leading to an increase in GHG emissions if not mitigated. Sufficiency measures which anticipate climate change, and include natural ventilation, white walls, and nature-based solutions (e.g., green roofs) will decrease the demand for cooling. Shared cooled spaces with highly efficient cooling solutions are among the mitigation strategies which can limit the effect of the expected heatwaves on people's health. {9.7, 9.8}

2 hours per day saved for women and girls from collecting fuel in Africa

Up to 90% GHG emissions reduction in developed countries

Up to 80% of GHG emissions reduction in developing countries

24,500 avoided premature deaths and **22,300** disability-adjusted life years (DALYs) of avoided asthma in the EU

1.8 million fewer avoided premature deaths from HAP in developing world in 2030

90% of our time is spent indoors

Up to 28% higher selling prices for decarbonised building in developed countries

Up to 2.8 billion people in developing countries lifted from energy poverty

5 to 8 million households in Europe lifted from energy poverty

Up to 30 direct and indirect jobs per million USD invested in building retrofit or new energy efficient buildings

2 million direct jobs from transforming fuel-based lighting to solar LED lighting in developing countries

Key point: Achieving SDG targets requires implementation of ambitious climate mitigation policies which include sufficiency measures to align building design, size and use with SDGs, efficiency measures to ensure high penetration of best available technologies and supplying the remaining energy needs with renewable energy sources.

Figure TS.16 | Contribution of building-sector mitigation policies to meeting Sustainable Development Goals. {Figure 9.18}

Well-designed and effectively implemented mitigation actions in the buildings sector have significant potential to help achieve the SDGs (*high confidence*). As shown in Figure TS.16, the impacts of mitigation actions in the building sector go far beyond the goal of climate action (SDG 13) and contribute to meeting 15 other SDGs. Mitigation actions in the building sector bring health gains through improved indoor air quality and thermal comfort, and have positive significant macro- and micro-economic effects, such as increased productivity of labour, job creation, reduced poverty, especially energy poverty, and improved energy security (*high confidence*). (Figure TS.29) {9.8}

The COVID-19 pandemic emphasised the importance of buildings for human well-being and highlighted the inequalities in access for all to suitable, healthy buildings, which provide natural daylight and clean air to their occupants (*medium confidence*). Recent WHO health recommendations have also emphasise indoor air quality, preventive maintenance of centralised mechanical heating, ventilation, and cooling systems. There are opportunities for repurposing existing non-residential buildings, no longer in use due to the expected spread of teleworking triggered by the health crisis and enabled by digitalisation. (Box TS.14) {9.1}

TS.5.5   Industry

The industry chapter focuses on new developments since AR5 and emphasises the role of the energy-intensive and emissions-intensive basic materials industries in strategies for reaching net zero emissions. The Paris Agreement, the SDGs and the COVID-19 pandemic provide a new context for the evolution of industry and mitigation of industry greenhouse gas (GHG) emissions (*high confidence*). {11.1.1}

Net zero CO_2 industrial-sector emissions are possible but challenging (*high confidence*). Energy efficiency will continue to be important. Reduced materials demand, material efficiency, and circular economy solutions can reduce the need for primary production. Primary production options include switching to new processes that use low-to-zero GHG energy carriers and feedstocks (e.g., electricity, hydrogen, biofuels, and carbon dioxide capture and utilisation (CCU) to provide carbon feedstocks). Carbon capture and storage (CCS) will be required to mitigate remaining CO_2 emissions {11.3}. These options require substantial scaling up of electricity, hydrogen, recycling, CO_2, and other infrastructure, as well as phase-out or conversion of existing industrial plants. While improvements in the GHG intensities of major basic materials have nearly stagnated over the last 30 years, analysis of historical technology shifts and newly available technologies indicate these intensities can be significantly reduced by mid-century. {11.2, 11.3, 11.4}

Industry-sector emissions have been growing faster since 2000 than emissions in any other sector, driven by increased basic materials extraction and production (*high confidence*). GHG emissions attributed to the industrial sector originate from fuel combustion, process emissions, product use and waste, which jointly accounted for 14.1 $GtCO_2$-eq or 24% of all direct anthropogenic emissions in 2019, second behind the energy supply sector. Industry is a leading GHG emitter – 20 $GtCO_2$-eq or 34% of global emissions in 2019 – if indirect emissions from power and heat generation are included. The share of emissions originating from direct fuel combustion is decreasing and was 7 $GtCO_2$-eq, 50% of direct industrial emissions in 2019. {11.2.2}

Global material intensity – the in-use stock of manufactured capital in tonnes per unit of GDP – is increasing (*high confidence*). In-use stock of manufactured capital per capita has been growing faster than GDP per capita since 2000. Total global in-use stock of manufactured capital grew by 3.4% yr^{-1} in 2000–2019. At the same time, per-capita material stocks in several developed countries have stopped growing, showing a decoupling from GDP per capita. {11.2.1, 11.3.1}

The demand for plastic has been growing most strongly since 1970 (*high confidence*). The current >99% reliance on fossil feedstock, very low recycling, and high emissions from petrochemical processes is a challenge for reaching net zero emissions. At the same time, plastics are important for reducing emissions elsewhere, for example, light-weighting vehicles. There are as yet no shared visions for fossil-free plastics, but several possibilities. {11.4.1.3}

Scenario analyses show that significant reductions in global GHG emissions and even close to net zero emissions from GHG intensive industry (e.g., steel, plastics, ammonia, and cement) can be achieved by 2050 by deploying multiple available and emerging options (*medium confidence*). Significant reductions in industry emissions require a reorientation from the historic focus on important but incremental improvements (e.g., energy efficiency) to transformational changes in energy and feedstock sourcing, materials efficiency, and more circular material flows. {11.3, 11.4}

Key mitigation options such as materials efficiency, circular material flows and emerging primary processes, are not well represented in climate change scenario modelling and integrated assessment models (IAMs), albeit with some progress in recent years (*high confidence*). The character of these interventions (e.g., appearing in many forms across complex value chains, making cost estimates difficult) combined with the limited data on new fossil-free primary processes help explain why they are less represented in models than, for example, CCS. As a result, overall mitigation costs and the need for CCS may be overestimated. {11.4.2.1}

Electrification is emerging as a key mitigation option for industry (*high confidence*). Using electricity directly, or indirectly via hydrogen from electrolysis for high temperature and chemical feedstock requirements, offers many options to reduce emissions. It also can provide substantial grid-balancing services, for example, through electrolysis and storage of hydrogen for chemical process use or demand response. (Box TS.9) {11.3.5}

Carbon is a key building block in organic chemicals, fuels and materials and will remain important (*high confidence*). In order to reach net zero CO_2 emissions for the carbon needed in society (e.g., plastics, wood, aviation fuels, solvents, etc.), it is important to

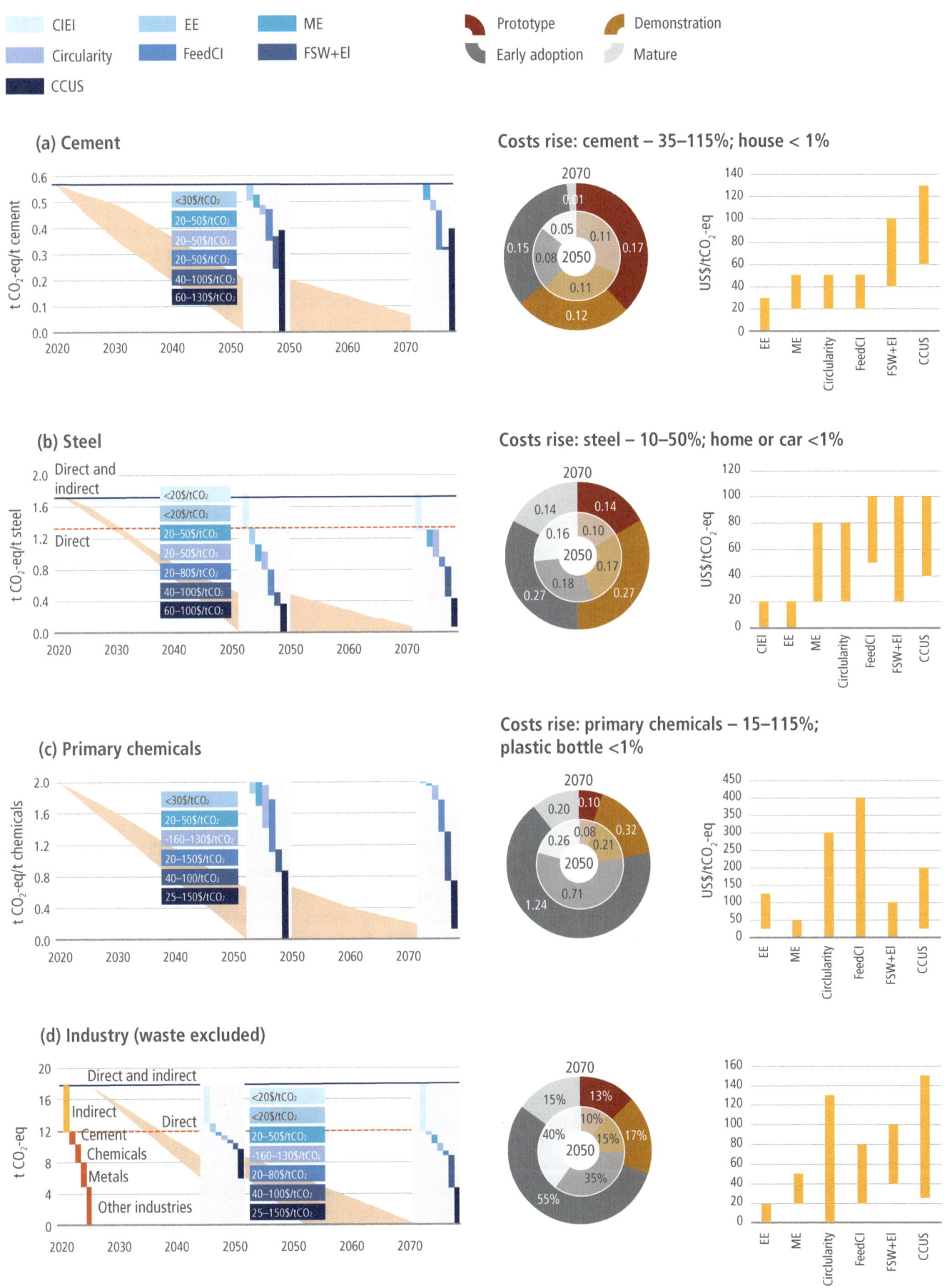

Figure TS.17 | Potentials and costs for zero-carbon mitigation options for industry and basic materials.

Figure TS.17 (continued): Potentials and costs for zero-carbon mitigation options for industry and basic materials. CIEI – carbon intensity of electricity for indirect emissions; EE – energy efficiency; ME – material efficiency; Circularity – material flows (clinker substituted by coal fly ash, blast furnace slag or other by-products and waste, steel scrap, plastic recycling, etc.); FeedCI – feedstock carbon intensity (hydrogen, biomass, novel cement, natural clinker substitutes); FSW+EI – fuel switch and processes electrification with low-carbon electricity. Ranges for mitigation options are shown based on bottom-up studies for grouped technologies packages, not for single technologies. In circles, contribution to mitigation from technologies based on their readiness are shown for 2050 (2040) and 2070. Direct emissions include fuel combustion and process emissions. Indirect emissions include emissions attributed to consumed electricity and purchased heat. For basic chemicals, only methanol, ammonia and high-value chemicals are considered. Total for industry does not include emissions from waste. Negative mitigation costs for some options such as Circularity are not reflected. {Figure 11.13}

close the use loops for carbon and carbon dioxide through increased circularity with mechanical and chemical recycling, more efficient use of biomass feedstock with addition of low-GHG hydrogen to increase product yields (e.g., for biomethane and methanol), and potentially direct air capture of CO_2 as a new carbon source. {11.3, 11.4.1}

Production costs for very low to zero emissions basic materials may be high but the cost for final consumers and the general economy will be low (*medium confidence*). Costs and emissions reductions potential in industry, and especially heavy industry, are highly contingent on innovation, commercialisation, and market-uptake policies. Technologies exist to take all industry sectors to very low or zero emissions, but require five to fifteen years of intensive innovation, commercialisation, and policy to ensure uptake. Mitigation costs are in the rough range of USD50–150 tCO$_2$-eq^{-1}, with wide variation within and outside this band. This affects competitiveness and requires supporting policy. Although production cost increases can be significant, they translate to very small increases in the costs for final products, typically less than a few percent depending on product, assumptions, and system boundaries. (Figure TS.17) {11.4.1.5}

Several technological options exist for very low to zero emissions steel, but their uptake will require integrated material efficiency, recycling, and production decarbonisation policies (*high confidence*). Material efficiency can potentially reduce steel demand by up to 40% based on design for less steel use, long life, reuse, constructability, and low-contamination recycling. Secondary production through high-quality recycling must be maximised. Production decarbonisation will also be required, starting with the retrofitting of existing facilities for partial fuel switching (e.g., to biomass or hydrogen), CCU and CCS, followed by very low and zero emissions production based on high-capture CCS or direct hydrogen, or electrolytic iron-ore reduction followed by an electric arc furnace. {11.3.2, 11.4.1.1}

Several current and emerging options can significantly reduce cement and concrete emissions. Producer, user, and regulator education, as well as innovation and commercialisation policy are needed (*medium confidence*). Cement and concrete are currently overused because they are inexpensive, durable, and ubiquitous, and consumption decisions typically do not give weight to their production emissions. Basic material efficiency efforts to use only well-made concrete thoughtfully and only where needed (e.g., using right-sized, prefabricated components) could reduce emissions by 24–50% through lower demand for clinker. Cementitious material substitution with various materials (e.g., ground limestone and calcined clays) can reduce process calcination emissions by up to 50% and occasionally much more. Until a very low GHG emissions alternative binder to Portland cement is commercialised – which is

not anticipated in the near to mid-term – CCS will be essential for eliminating the limestone calcination process emissions for making clinker, which currently represent 60% of GHG emissions in best-available technology plants. {11.3.2, 11.3.6, 11.4.1.2}

While several technological options exist for decarbonising the main industrial feedstock chemicals and their derivatives, the costs vary widely (*high confidence*). Fossil fuel-based feedstocks are inexpensive and still without carbon pricing, and their biomass- and electricity-based replacements are expected to be more expensive. The chemical industry consumes large amounts of hydrogen, ammonia, methanol, carbon monoxide, ethylene, propylene, benzene, toluene, and mixed xylenes and aromatics from fossil feedstock, and from these basic chemicals produces tens of thousands of derivative end-use chemicals. Hydrogen, biogenic or air-capture carbon, and collected plastic waste for the primary feedstocks can greatly reduce total emissions. Biogenic carbon feedstock is expected to be limited due to competing land uses. {11.4.1}

Light industry and manufacturing can be largely decarbonised through switching to low-GHG fuels (e.g., biofuels and hydrogen) and electricity (e.g., for electrothermal heating and heat pumps) (*high confidence*). Most of these technologies are already mature, for example for low-temperature heat, but a major challenge is the current low cost of fossil CH_4 and coal relative to low- and zero-GHG electricity, hydrogen, and biofuels. {11.4.1}

The pulp and paper industry has significant biogenic carbon emissions but relatively small fossil carbon emissions. Pulp mills have access to biomass residues and by-products and in paper mills the use of process heat at low to medium temperatures allows for electrification (*high confidence*). Competition for feedstock will increase if wood substitutes for building materials and petrochemicals feedstock. The pulp and paper industry can also be a source of biogenic carbon dioxide, carbon for organic chemicals feedstock, and for CDR using CCS. {11.4.1}

The geographical distribution of renewable resources has implications for industry (*medium confidence*). The potential for zero-emission electricity and low-cost hydrogen from electrolysis powered by solar and wind, or hydrogen from other very low emission sources, may reshape where currently energy- and emissions-intensive basic materials production is located, how value chains are organised, trade patterns, and what gets transported in international shipping. Regions with bountiful solar and wind resources, or low fugitive CH_4 co-located with CCS geology, may become exporters of hydrogen or hydrogen carriers such as methanol and ammonia, or home to the production of iron and steel, organic platform chemicals, and other energy-intensive basic materials. {11.2, 11.4, Box 11.1}

The level of policy maturity and experience varies widely across the mitigation options (*high confidence*). Energy efficiency is a well-established policy field with decades of experience from voluntary and negotiated agreements, regulations, energy auditing and demand-side management (DSM) programmes. In contrast, materials demand management and efficiency are not well understood and addressed from a policy perspective. Barriers to recycling that policy could address are often specific to the different material loops (e.g., copper contamination for steel and lack of technologies or poor economics for plastics) or waste-management systems. For electrification and fuel switching the focus has so far been mainly on innovation and developing technical supply-side solutions rather than creating market demand. {11.5.2, 11.6}

Industry has so far largely been sheltered from the impacts of climate policy and carbon pricing due to concerns about carbon leakage[26] and reducing competitiveness (*high confidence*). New approaches to industrial development policy are emerging for a transition to net zero GHG emissions. The transition requires a clear direction towards net zero, technology development, market demand for low-carbon materials and products, governance capacity and learning, socially inclusive phase-out plans, as well as international coordination of climate and trade policies (see also TS.6.5). It requires comprehensive and sequential industrial policy strategies leading to immediate action as well as preparedness for future decarbonisation, governance at different levels (from international to local) and integration with other policy domains. {11.6}

TS.5.6 Agriculture, Forestry, Other Land Uses, and Food Systems

TS.5.6.1 Agricultre, Forestry, and Other Land Use (AFOLU)

The agriculture, forestry and other land use (AFOLU)[27] sector encompasses managed ecosystems and offers significant mitigation opportunities while providing food, wood and other renewable resources as well as biodiversity conservation, provided the sector adapts to climate change. Land-based mitigation measures can reduce GHG emissions within the AFOLU sector, deliver CDR and provide biomass thereby enabling emission reductions in other sectors.[28] The rapid deployment of AFOLU measures features in all pathways that limit global warming to 1.5°C. Where carefully and appropriately implemented, AFOLU mitigation measures are positioned to deliver substantial co-benefits and help address many of the wider challenges associated with land management. If AFOLU measures are deployed badly, when taken together with the increasing need to produce sufficient food, feed, fuel and wood, they may exacerbate trade-offs with the conservation of habitats, adaptation, biodiversity and other services.

At the same time the capacity of the land to support these functions may be threatened by climate change (*high confidence*). {AR6 WGI Figure SPM.7; AR6 WGII, 7.1, 7.6}

The AFOLU sector, on average, accounted for 13–21% of global total anthropogenic GHG emissions in the period 2010–2019. At the same time managed and natural terrestrial ecosystems were a carbon sink, absorbing around one third of anthropogenic CO_2 emissions (*medium confidence*). Estimated anthropogenic net CO_2 emissions from AFOLU (based on bookkeeping models) result in a net source of $+5.9 \pm 4.1$ $GtCO_2$ yr^{-1} between 2010 and 2019 with an unclear trend. Based on FAOSTAT or national GHG inventories, the net CO_2 emissions from AFOLU were 0.0 to +0.8 $GtCO_2$ yr^{-1} over the same period. There is a discrepancy in the reported CO_2 AFOLU emissions magnitude because alternative methodological approaches that incorporate different assumptions are used {7.2.2}. If the responses of all managed and natural land to both anthropogenic environmental change and natural climate variability, estimated to be a gross sink of -12.5 ± 3.2 $GtCO_2$ yr^{-1} for the period 2010–2019, are added to land-use emissions, then land overall constituted a net sink of -6.6 ± 5.2 $GtCO_2$ yr^{-1} in terms of CO_2 emissions (*medium confidence*). (Table TS.4) {7.2, Table 7.1}

Land-use change drives net AFOLU CO_2 emission fluxes. The rate of deforestation, which accounts for 45% of total AFOLU emissions, has generally declined, while global tree cover and global forest-growing stock levels are *likely* increasing (*medium confidence*). There are substantial regional differences, with losses of carbon generally observed in tropical regions and gains in temperate and boreal regions. Agricultural CH_4 and N_2O emissions are estimated to average 157 ± 47.1 $MtCH_4$ yr^{-1} and 6.6 ± 4.0 MtN_2O yr^{-1} or 4.2 ± 1.3 and 1.8 ± 1.1 $GtCO_2$-eq yr^{-1} (using IPCC AR6 GWP100 values for CH_4 and N_2O) respectively between 2010 and 2019 {7.2.1, 7.2.3}. AFOLU CH_4 emissions continue to increase, the main source of which is enteric fermentation from ruminant animals. Similarly, AFOLU N_2O emissions are increasing, dominated by agriculture, notably from manure application, nitrogen deposition, and nitrogen fertiliser use (*high confidence*). In addition to being a net carbon sink and source of GHG emissions, land plays an important role in climate through albedo effects, evapotranspiration, and aerosol loading through emissions of volatile organic compounds (VOCs). The combined role of CH_4, N_2O and aerosols in total climate forcing, however, is unclear and varies strongly with bioclimatic region and management practice. {2.4.2.5, 7.2, 7.3}

---

26 See section TS.5.9.

27 AFOLU is a sector in the *2019 Refinement to the 2006 IPCC Guidelines for National Greenhouse Gas Inventories*. AFOLU anthropogenic greenhouse gas emissions and removals by sinks reported by governments under the UNFCCC are defined as all those occurring on 'managed land'. Managed land is land where human interventions and practices have been applied to perform production, ecological or social functions.

28 For example: in the *2019 Refinement to the 2006 IPCC Guidelines for National Greenhouse Gas Inventories*, CO_2 emissions from biomass used for energy are reported in the AFOLU sector, calculated as an implicit component of carbon stock changes. In the energy sector, CO_2 emissions from biomass combustion for energy are recorded as an information item that is not included in the sectoral total emissions for the that sector.

TS

Table TS.4 | Net anthropogenic emissions (annual averages for 2010–2019[a]) from agriculture, forestry and other land use (AFOLU). For context, the net flux due to the natural response of land to climate and environmental change is also shown for CO_2 in column E. Positive values represent emissions, negative values represent removals. Due to different approaches to estimate anthropogenic fluxes, AFOLU CO_2 estimates in the table below are not directly comparable to LULUCF in national greenhouse gas inventories (NGHGIs).

Gas	Units	Anthropogenic				Natural response	Natural and anthropogenic
		AFOLU net anthropogenic emissions	Non-AFOLU anthropogenic GHG emissions	Total net anthropogenic emissions (AFOLU and non-AFOLU) by gas	AFOLU as a % of total net anthropogenic emissions by gas	Natural land sinks including natural response of land to anthropogenic environmental change and climate variability	Net-land atmosphere CO_2 flux (i.e., anthropogenic AFOLU and natural fluxes across entire land surface)
		A	B	C = A + B	D = (A/C) *100	E	F = A + E
CO_2	$GtCO_2$-eq yr^{-1}	5.9 ± 4.1 (bookkeeping models, managed soils and pasture). 0 to 0.8 (NGHGI/ FAOSTAT data)	36.2 ± 2.9	42.0 ± 29.0	14%	−12.5 ± 3.2	−6.6 ± 4.6
CH_4	$MtCH_4$ yr^{-1}	157.0 ± 47.1	207.5 ± 62.2	364.4 ± 109.3			
	$GtCO_2$-eq yr^{-1}	4.2 ± 1.3	5.9 ± 1.8	10.2 ± 3.0	41%		
N_2O	MtN_2O yr^{-1}	6.6 ± 4.0	2.8 ± 1.7	9.4 ± 5.6			
	$GtCO_2$-eq yr^{-1}	1.8 ± 1.1	0.8 ± 0.5	2.6 ± 1.5	69%		
Total	$GtCO_2$-eq yr^{-1}	11.9 ± 4.4 (CO_2 component considers bookkeeping models only)	44 ± 3.4	55.9 ± 6.1	21%		

[a] Estimates are given for 2019 as this is the latest date when data are available for all gases, consistent with Chapter 2 of this report. Positive fluxes are emission from land to the atmosphere. Negative fluxes are removals. For all Table footnotes see Table 7.1. {Table 7.1}

The AFOLU sector offers significant near-term mitigation potential at relatively low cost and can provide 20–30% of the 2050 emissions reduction described in scenarios that limit warming to 2°C (>67%) or lower (*high evidence, medium agreement*). The AFOLU sector can provide 20–30% (interquartile range) of the global mitigation needed for a 1.5°C or 2°C pathway towards 2050, though there are highly variable mitigation strategies for how AFOLU potential can be deployed for achieving climate targets {Illustrative Mitigation Pathways in 7.5}. The estimated economic (<USD100 tCO$_2$-eq^{-1}) AFOLU sector mitigation potential is 8 to 14 GtCO$_2$-eq yr^{-1} between 2020–2050, with the bottom end of this range representing the mean from IAMs and the upper end representing the mean estimate from global sectoral studies. The economic potential is about half of the technical potential from AFOLU, and about 30–50% could be achieved under USD20 tCO$_2$-eq^{-1} {7.4}. The implementation of robust measurement, reporting and verification processes is paramount to improving the transparency of changes in land carbon stocks and this can help prevent misleading assumptions or claims on mitigation. {7.1, 7.4, 7.5}

Between 2020 and 2050, mitigation measures in forests and other natural ecosystems provide the largest share of the AFOLU mitigation potential (up to USD100 tCO$_2$-eq^{-1}), followed by agriculture and demand-side measures (*high confidence*). In the global sectoral studies, the protection, improved management, and restoration of forests, peatlands, coastal wetlands, savannas and grasslands have the potential to reduce emissions and/or sequester 7.3 mean (3.9–13.1) GtCO$_2$-eq yr^{-1}. Agriculture provides the second largest share of the mitigation potential, with 4.1 (1.7–6.7) GtCO$_2$-eq yr^{-1} (up to USD100 tCO$_2$-eq^{-1}) from cropland and grassland soil carbon management, agroforestry, use of biochar, improved rice cultivation, and livestock and nutrient management. Demand-side measures including shifting to sustainable healthy diets, reducing food waste, building with wood, biochemicals, and bio-textiles, have a mitigation potential of 2.2 (1.1–3.6) GtCO$_2$-eq yr^{-1}. Most mitigation options are available and ready to deploy. Emissions reductions can be achieved relatively quickly, whereas CDR needs upfront investment. Sustainable intensification in agriculture, shifting diets, and reducing food waste could enhance efficiencies and reduce agricultural land needs, and are therefore critical for enabling supply-side measures such as reforestation, restoration, as well as decreasing CH$_4$ and N$_2$O emissions from agricultural production. In addition, emerging technologies (e.g., vaccines or CH$_4$ inhibitors) have the potential to substantially increase the CH$_4$ mitigation potential beyond current estimates. AFOLU mitigation is not only relevant in countries with large land areas. Many smaller countries and regions, particularly with wetlands, have disproportionately high levels of AFOLU mitigation potential density. {7.4, 7.5}

The economic and political feasibility of implementing AFOLU mitigation measures is hampered by persistent barriers. Assisting countries to overcome barriers will help to achieve

significant short-term mitigation (*medium confidence*). Finance forms a critical barrier to achieving these gains as currently mitigation efforts rely principally on government sources and funding mechanisms which do not provide sufficient resources to enable the economic potential to be realised. Differences in cultural values, governance, accountability and institutional capacity are also important barriers. Climate change itself could reduce the mitigation potential from the AFOLU sector, although an increase in the capacity of natural sinks could occur despite changes in climate (*medium confidence*) {AR6 WGI Figure SPM.7 and Sections 7.4 and 7.6}. The continued loss of biodiversity makes ecosystems less resilient to climate change extremes and this may further jeopardise the achievement of the AFOLU mitigation potentials indicated in this chapter (*high confidence*). (Box TS.15) {7.6}

The provision of biomass for bioenergy (with/without BECCS) and other bio-based products represents an important share of the total mitigation potential associated with the AFOLU sector, though these mitigation effects accrue to other sectors (*high confidence*). Recent estimates of the technical bioenergy potential, when constrained by food security and environmental considerations, are within the ranges 5–50 and 50–250 EJ yr^{-1} by 2050 for residues and dedicated biomass production systems, respectively.[29] (TS.5.7) {7.4, 12.3}

Bioenergy is the most land-intensive energy option, but total land occupation of other renewable energy options can also become significant in high deployment scenarios. While not as closely connected to the AFOLU sector as bioenergy, other renewable energy options can influence AFOLU activities in both synergistic and detrimental ways (*high confidence*). The character of land occupation, and associated impacts, vary considerably among mitigation options and also for the same option depending on geographic location, scale, system design and deployment strategy. Land occupation can be large uniform areas, for example, reservoir hydropower dams and tree plantations, and more distributed occupation that is integrated with other land uses, for example, wind turbines and agroforestry in agriculture landscapes. Deployment can be partly decoupled from additional land use, for example, use of organic waste and residues and integration of solar PV into buildings and other infrastructure (*high confidence*). Wind and solar power can coexist with agriculture in beneficial ways (*medium confidence*). Indirect land occupation includes new agriculture areas following displacement of food production with bioenergy plantations and expansion of mining activities providing minerals required for manufacture of EV batteries, PV, and wind power. {7.4, 12.5}

The deployment of land-based mitigation measures can provide co-benefits, but there are also risks and trade-offs from inappropriate land management (*high confidence*). Such risks can best be managed if AFOLU mitigation is pursued in response to the needs and perspectives of multiple stakeholders to achieve outcomes that maximise synergies while limiting trade-offs (*medium confidence*). The results of implementing AFOLU measures are often variable and highly context-specific. Depending on local conditions (e.g., ecosystem, climate, food system, land ownership) and management strategies (e.g., scale, method), mitigation measures can positively or negatively affect biodiversity, ecosystem functioning, air quality, water availability and quality, soil productivity, rights infringements, food security, and human well-being. The agriculture and forestry sectors can devise management approaches that enable biomass production and use for energy in conjunction with the production of food and timber, thereby reducing the conversion pressure on natural ecosystems (*medium confidence*). Mitigation measures addressing GHGs may also affect other climate forcers such as albedo and evapotranspiration. Integrated responses that contribute to mitigation, adaptation, and other land challenges will have greater likelihood of being successful (*high confidence*); measures which provide additional benefits to biodiversity and human well-being are sometimes described as 'Nature-based Solutions'. {7.1, 7.4, 7.6, 12.4, 12.5}

AFOLU mitigation measures have been well understood for decades but deployment remains slow, and emissions trends indicate unsatisfactory progress despite beneficial contributions to global emissions reduction from forest-related options (*high confidence*). Globally, the AFOLU sector has so far contributed modestly to net mitigation, as past policies have delivered about 0.65 GtCO$_2$ yr^{-1} of mitigation during 2010–2019 or 1.4% of global gross emissions. The majority (>80%) of emission reduction resulted from forestry measures. Although the mitigation potential of AFOLU measures is large from a biophysical and ecological perspective, its feasibility is hampered by lack of institutional support, uncertainty over long-term additionality and trade-offs, weak governance, fragmented land ownership, and uncertain permanence effects. Despite these impediments to change, AFOLU mitigation options are demonstrably effective and with appropriate support can enable rapid emission reductions in most countries. {7.4, 7.6}

Concerted, rapid and sustained effort by all stakeholders, from policymakers and investors to land owners and managers is a pre-requisite for achieving high levels of mitigation in the AFOLU sector (*high confidence*). To date USD0.7 billion yr^{-1} is estimated to have been spent on AFOLU mitigation. This is well short of the more than USD400 billion yr^{-1} that is estimated to be necessary to deliver the up to 30% of global mitigation effort envisaged in deep mitigation scenarios (*medium confidence*). This estimate of the global funding requirement is smaller than current subsidies provided to agriculture and forestry. A gradual redirection of existing agriculture and forestry subsidies would greatly advance mitigation. Effective policy interventions and national (investment) plans as part of NDCs, specific to local circumstances and needs, are urgently needed to accelerate the deployment of AFOLU mitigation options. These interventions are effective when they include funding schemes and long-term consistent support for implementation with governments taking the initiative together with private funders and non-state actors. {7.6}

---

29 These potentials do not include avoided emissions resulting from bioenergy use associated with BECCS, which depends on energy substitution patterns, conversion efficiencies, and supply chain emissions for both the BECCS and substituted energy systems. Estimates of substitution effects of bioenergy indicate that this additional mitigation would be of the same magnitude as provided through CDR using BECCS. Bio-based products with long service life, for example, construction timber, can also provide mitigation through substitution of steel, concrete, and other products, and through carbon storage in the bio-based product pool. See section TS.5.7 for the CDR potential of BECCS. {7.4, 12.3}

Realising the mitigation potential of the AFOLU sector depends strongly on policies that directly address emissions and drive the deployment of land-based mitigation options, consistent with carbon prices in deep mitigation scenarios (*high confidence*). Examples of successful policies and measures include establishing and respecting tenure rights and community forestry, improved agricultural management and sustainable intensification, biodiversity conservation, payments for ecosystem services, improved forest management and wood-chain usage, bioenergy, voluntary supply chain management efforts, consumer behaviour campaigns, private funding and joint regulatory efforts to avoid, for example, leakage. The efficacy of different policies, however, will depend on numerous region-specific factors. In addition to funding, these factors include governance, institutions, long-term consistent execution of measures, and the specific policy setting. While the governance of land-based mitigation can draw on lessons from previous experience with regulating biofuels and forest carbon, integrating these insights requires governance that goes beyond project-level approaches emphasising integrated land-use planning and management within the frame of the Sustainable Development Goals. {7.4, Box 7.2, 7.6}

Addressing the many knowledge gaps in the development and testing of AFOLU mitigation options can rapidly advance the likelihood of achieving sustained mitigation (*high confidence*). Research priorities include improved quantification of anthropogenic and natural GHG fluxes and emissions modelling, better understanding of the impacts of climate change on the mitigation potential, permanence and additionality of estimated mitigation actions, and improved (real-time and cheap) measurement, reporting and verification. There is a need to include a greater suite of mitigation measures in IAMs, informed by more realistic assessments that take into account local circumstances and socio-economic factors and cross-sector synergies and trade-offs. Finally, there is a critical need for more targeted research to develop appropriate country-level, locally specific, policy and land-management response options. These options could support more specific NDCs with AFOLU measures that enable mitigation while also contributing to biodiversity conservation, ecosystem functioning, livelihoods for millions of farmers and foresters, and many other SDGs. {7.7, Figure 17.1}

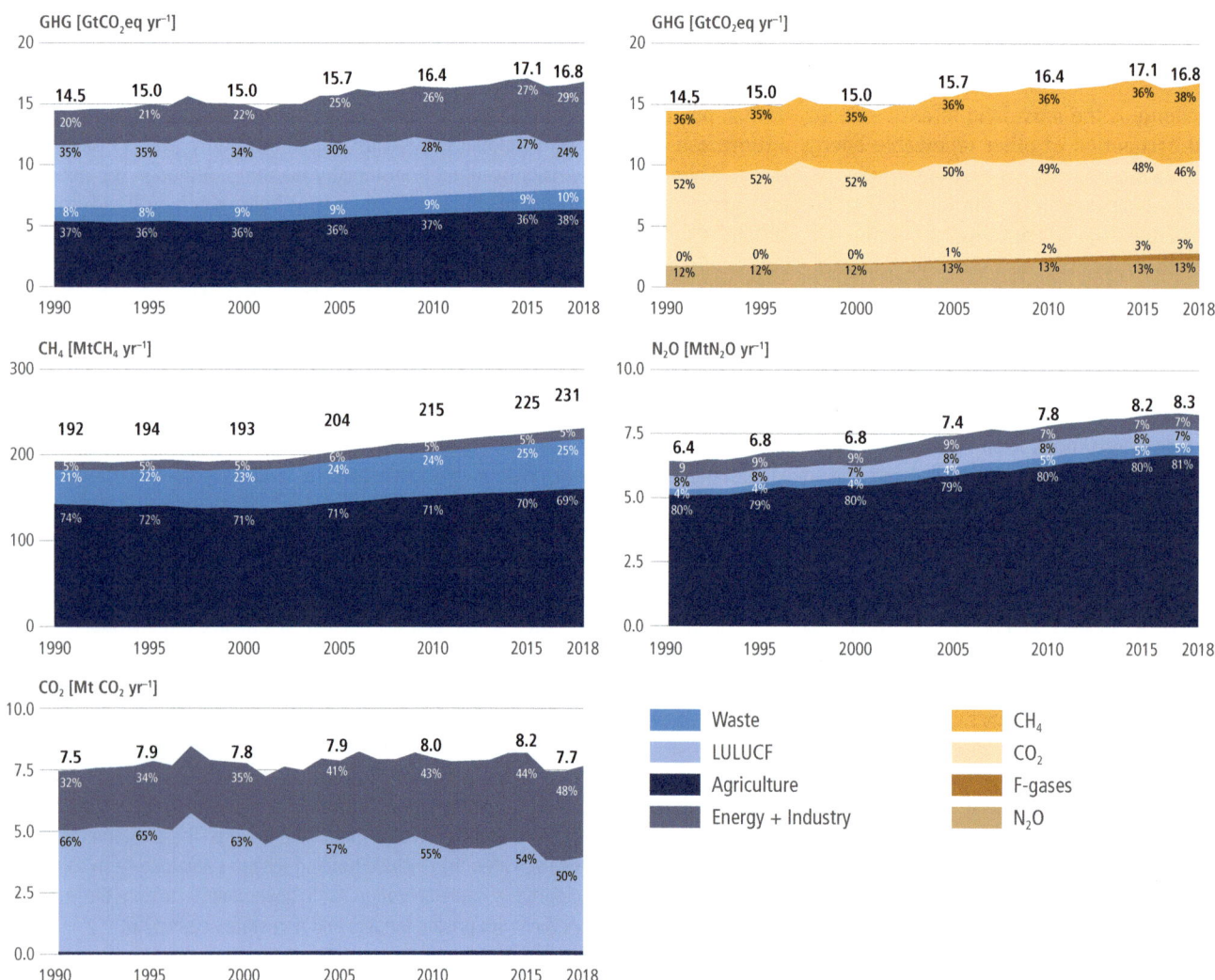

Figure TS.18 | Food-system GHG emissions from the agriculture, and land use, land-use change and forestry (LULUCF), waste, and energy and industry sectors. {Figure 12.5}

TS.5.6.2   Food Systems

Realising the full mitigation potential from the food system requires change at all stages from producer to consumer and waste management, which can be facilitated through integrated policy packages (*high confidence*). Food systems are associated with 23–42% of global GHG emissions, while there is still widespread food insecurity and malnutrition. Absolute GHG emissions from food systems increased from 14 to 17 GtCO$_2$-eq yr^{-1} in the period 1990–2018. Both supply- and demand-side measures are important to reduce the GHG intensity of food systems. Integrated food policy packages based on a combination of market-based, administrative, informative, and behavioural policies can reduce cost compared to uncoordinated interventions, address multiple sustainability goals, and increase acceptance across stakeholders and civil society (*limited evidence, medium agreement*). Food systems governance may be pioneered through local food policy

initiatives complemented by national and international initiatives, but governance on the national level tends to be fragmented, and thus has limited capacity to address structural issues like inequities in access. (Figure TS.18, Table TS.5, Table TS.6) {7.2, 7.4, 12.4}

Diets high in plant protein and low in meat and dairy are associated with lower GHG emissions (*high confidence*). Ruminant meat shows the highest GHG intensity. Beef from dairy systems has lower emissions intensity than beef from beef herds (8–23 and 17–94 kgCO$_2$-eq (100 g protein)$^{-1}$, respectively) when some emissions are allocated to dairy products. The wide variation in emissions reflects differences in production systems, which range from intensive feedlots with stock raised largely on grains through to rangeland and transhumance production systems. Where appropriate, a shift to diets with a higher share of plant protein, moderate intake of animal-source foods and reduced intake of saturated fats could lead to substantial decreases in GHG emissions. Benefits would also include reduced land

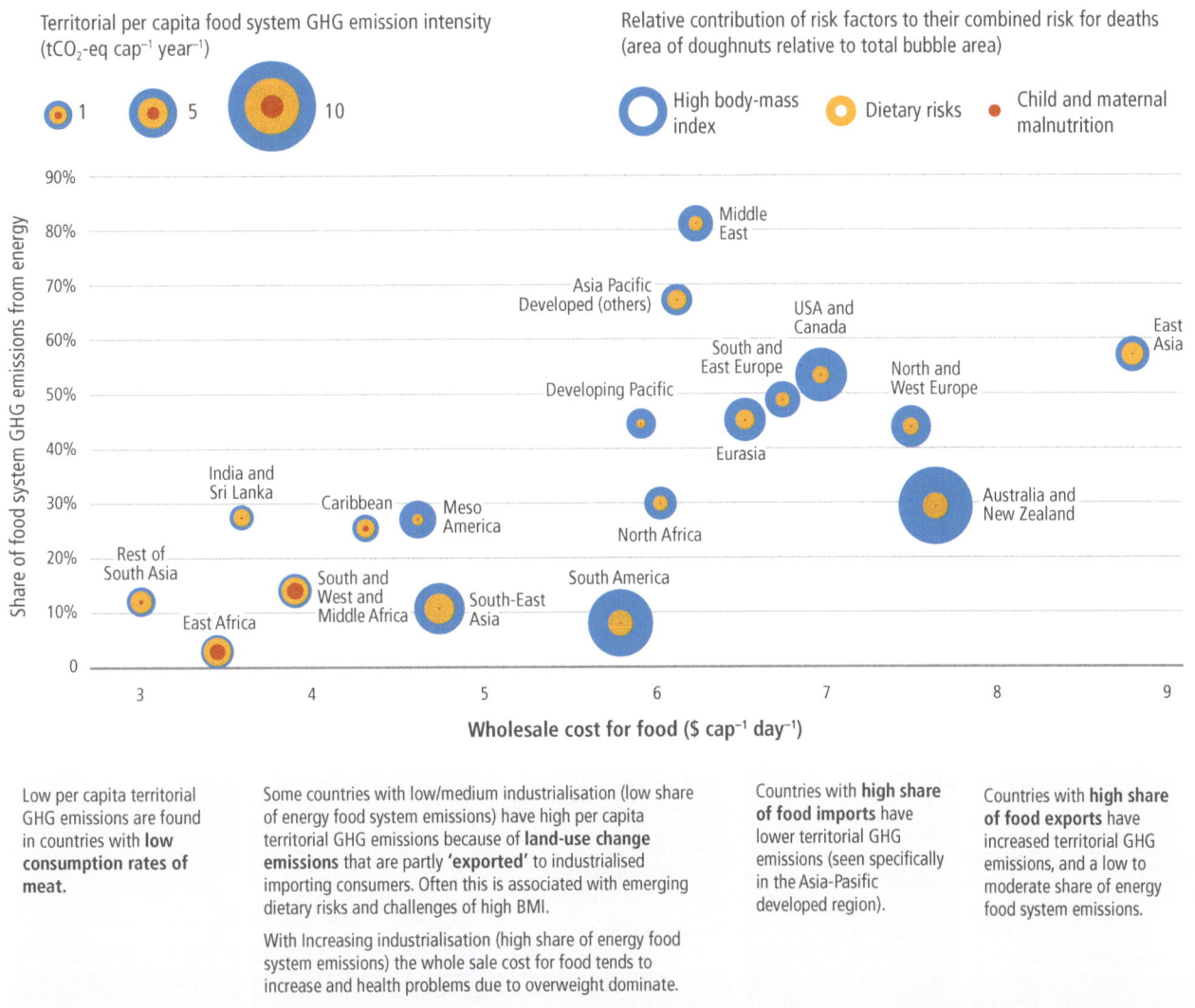

Low per capita territorial GHG emissions are found in countries with **low consumption rates of meat.**

Some countries with low/medium industrialisation (low share of energy food system emissions) have high per capita territorial GHG emissions because of **land-use change emissions** that are partly **'exported'** to industrialised importing consumers. Often this is associated with emerging dietary risks and challenges of high BMI.

With Increasing industrialisation (high share of energy food system emissions) the whole sale cost for food tends to increase and health problems due to overweight dominate.

Countries with **high share of food imports** have lower territorial GHG emissions (seen specifically in the Asia-Pasific developed region).

Countries with **high share of food exports** have increased territorial GHG emissions, and a low to moderate share of energy food system emissions.

Figure TS.19 | Regional differences in health outcome, territorial per-capita GHG emissions from national food systems, and share of food system GHG emission from energy use. GHG emissions are calculated according to the IPCC Tier 1 approach and are assigned to the country where they occur, not necessarily where the food is consumed. Health outcome is expressed as relative contribution of each of the following risk factors to their combined risk for deaths: Child and maternal malnutrition (red), Dietary risks (yellow) or High body-mass index (blue). {Figure 12.7}

Table TS.5 | Food system mitigation opportunities.

Food system mitigation options (I: incremental; T: transformative)		Direct and indirect effect on GHG mitigation (+/0/–) [a]		Co-benefits/adverse effects [b]	
Food from agriculture, aquaculture and fisheries	(I) Dietary shift, in particular increased share of plant-based protein sources	D+	↓ GHG footprint	A+ L+ H+	Animal welfare Land sparing Good nutritional properties, potentially ↓ risk from zoonotic diseases, pesticides and antibiotics
	(I/T) Digital agriculture	D+	↑ logistics	L+ R+	Land sparing ↑ resource-use efficiencies
	(T) Gene technology	D+	↑ productivity or efficiency	H+ E0	↑ nutritional quality ↓ use of agrochemicals; ↑ probability of off-target impacts
	(I) Sustainable intensification Land-use optimisation	D+ E0	↓ GHG footprint Mixed effects	L+ R–	Land sparing Might ↑ pollution/biodiversity loss
	(I) Agroecology	D+ E+	↓ GHG/area, positive micro-climatic effects ↓ energy, possibly ↓ transport FL+ Circular approaches	E+ R+	Focus on co-benefits/ecosystem services Circular, ↑ nutrient and water use efficiencies
Controlled environment agriculture	(T) Soil-less agriculture	D+ FL+ E–	↑ productivity, weather independent Harvest on demand Currently ↑ energy demand, but ↓ transport, building spaces can be used for renewable energy	R+ L+ H+	Controlled loops ↑ nutrient- and water-use efficiency Land sparing Crop breeding can be optimised for taste and/or nutritional quality
Emerging food production technologies	(T) Insects	D0 FW+	Good feed conversion efficiency Can be fed on food waste	H0	Good nutritional qualities but attention to allergies and food safety issues required
	(I/T) Algae and bivalves	D+	↓ GHG footprints	A+ L+ H+ R+	Animal welfare Land sparing Good nutritional qualities; risk of heavy-metal and pathogen contamination Biofiltration of nutrient-polluted waters
	(I/T) Plant-based alternatives to animal-based food products	D+	No emissions from animals, ↓ inputs for feed	A+ L+ H+	Animal welfare Land sparing Potentially ↓ risk from zoonotic diseases, pesticides and antibiotics; but ↑ processing demand
	(T) Cellular agriculture (including cultured meat, microbial protein)	D+ E– FLW+	No emissions from animals, high protein conversion efficiency ↑ energy need ↓ food loss and waste	A+ R+ H0	Animal welfare ↓ emissions of reactive nitrogen or other pollutants Potentially ↓ risk from zoonotic diseases, pesticides and antibiotics; ↑ research on safety aspects needed
Food processing and packaging	(I) Valorisation of by-products, FLW logistics and management	M+ FL+	Substitution of bio-based materials ↓ of food losses		
	(I) Food conservation	FW+ E0	↓ of food waste ↑ energy demand but also energy savings possible (e.g., refrigeration, transport)		
	(I) Smart packaging and other technologies	FW+ M0 E0	↓ of food waste ↑ material demand and ↑ material efficiency ↑ energy demand; energy savings possible	H+	Possibly ↑ freshness/reduced food safety risks
	(I) Energy efficiency	E+	↓ energy		
Storage and distribution	(I) Improved logistics	D+ FL+ FW–	↓ transport emissions ↓ losses in transport Easier access to food could ↑ food waste		
	(I) Specific measures to reduce food waste in retail and food catering	FW+ E+ M+	↓ of food waste ↓ downstream energy demand ↓ downstream material demand		
	(I) Alternative fuels/transport modes	D+	↓ emissions from transport		
	(I) Energy efficiency	E+	↓ energy in refrigeration, lightening, climatisation		
	(I) Replacing refrigerants	D+	↓ emissions from the cold chain		

[a] Direct and indirect GHG effects: D – direct emissions except emissions from energy use, E – energy demand, M – material demand, FL – food losses, FW – food waste; direction of effect on GHG mitigation: (+) increased mitigation, (0) neutral, (–) decreased mitigation.

[b] Co-benefits/adverse effects: H – health aspects, A – animal welfare, R – resource use, L – land demand, E – ecosystem services; (+) co-benefits, (–) adverse effects. {Table 12.8}

TS

occupation and nutrient losses to the surrounding environment, while at the same time providing health benefits and reducing mortality from diet-related non-communicable diseases. (Figure TS.19) {7.4.5, 12.4}

Emerging food technologies such as cellular fermentation, cultured meat, plant-based alternatives to animal-based food products, and controlled environment agriculture, can bring substantial reduction in direct GHG emissions from food production (*limited evidence, high agreement*). These technologies have lower land, water, and nutrient footprints, and address concerns over animal welfare. Realising the full mitigation potential depends on access to low-carbon energy as some emerging technologies are relatively more energy intensive. This also holds for deployment of cold-chain and packaging technologies, which can help reduce food loss and waste, but increase energy and materials use in the food system. (Table TS.5) {11.4.1.3, 12.4}

TS.5.7   Carbon Dioxide Removal (CDR)

CDR is a key element in scenarios that limit warming to 2°C (>67%) or 1.5°C (>50%) by 2100 (*high confidence*). Implementation strategies need to reflect that CDR methods differ in terms of removal process, timescale of carbon storage, technological maturity, mitigation potential, cost, co-benefits, adverse side effects, and governance requirements. (Box TS.10)

Table TS.6 | Assessment of food system policies targeting (post-farm gate) food-chain actors and consumers.

	Level G: global/multinational; N: national; L: local	Transformative potential	Environmental effectiveness	Feasibility	Distributional effects	Cost	Co-benefits[a] and adverse side effect	Implications for coordination, coherence and consistency in policy package[b]
Integrated food policy packages	NL				can be controlled	cost efficient	+ balanced, addresses multiple sustainability goals	Reduces cost of uncoordinated interventions; increases acceptance across stakeholders and civil society (*robust evidence, high agreement*)
Taxes on food products	GN				regressive	low#1	– unintended substitution effects	High enforcing effect on other food policies; higher acceptance if compensation or hypothecated taxes (*medium evidence, high agreement*)
GHG taxes on food	GN				regressive	low#2	– unintended substitution effects + high spillover effect	Supportive, enabling effect on other food policies, agricultural/fishery policies; requires changes in power distribution and trade agreements (*medium evidence, medium agreement*)
Trade policies	G				impacts global distribution	complex effects	+ counters leakage effects +/– effects on market structure and jobs	Requires changes in existing trade agreements (*medium evidence, high agreement*)
Investment into research and innovation	GN				none	medium	+ high spillover effect + converging with digital society	Can fill targeted gaps for coordinated policy packages (e.g., monitoring methods) (*robust evidence, high agreement*)
Food and marketing regulations	N					low		Can be supportive; might be supportive to realise innovation; voluntary standards might be less effective (*medium evidence, medium agreement*)
Organisational-level procurement policies	NL					low	+ can address multiple sustainability goals	Enabling effect on other food policies; reaches large share of population (*medium evidence, high agreement*)
Sustainable food-based dietary guidelines	GNL				none	low	+ can address multiple sustainability goals	Little attention so far on environmental aspects; can serve as benchmark for other policies (labels, food formulation standards, etc.) (*medium evidence, medium agreement*)
Food labels/ information	GNL				education level relevant	low	+ empowers citizens + increases awareness + multiple objectives	Effective mainly as part of a policy package; incorporation of other objectives (e.g., animal welfare, fair trade); higher effect if mandatory (*medium evidence, medium agreement*)
Nudges	NL				none	low	+ possibly counteracting information deficits in population subgroups	High enabling effect on other food policies (*medium evidence, high agreement*)

Effect of measures: ■ negative ■ none/unclear ■ slightly positive ■ positive

Notes: #1 Minimum level to be effective 20% price increase; #2 Minimum level to be effective USD50–80 tCO$_2$-eq. [a] In addition, all interventions are assumed to address health and climate change mitigation. [b] Requires coordination between policy areas, participation of stakeholders, transparent methods and indicators to manage trade-offs and prioritisation between possibly conflicting objectives; and suitable indicators for monitoring and evaluation against objectives.

All the illustrative mitigation pathways (IMPs) assessed in this report use land-based biological CDR (primarily afforestation/reforestation (A/R)) and/or bioenergy with carbon capture and storage (BECCS). Some also include direct air CO_2 capture and storage (DACCS) (*high confidence*). Across the scenarios limiting warming to 2°C (>67%) or below, cumulative volumes[30] of BECCS reach 328 (168–763) $GtCO_2$, CO_2 removal from AFOLU (mainly A/R) reaches 252 (20–418) $GtCO_2$, and DACCS reaches 29 (0–339) $GtCO_2$, for the 2020–2100 period. Annual volumes in 2050 are 2.75 (0.52–9.45) $GtCO_2$ yr^{-1} for BECCS, 2.98 (0.23–6.38) $GtCO_2$ yr^{-1} for the CO_2 removal from AFOLU (mainly A/R), and 0.02 (0–1.74) $GtCO_2$ yr^{-1} for DACCS. (Box TS.10) {12.3, Cross-Chapter Box 8 in Chapter 12}

Despite limited current deployment, estimated mitigation potentials for DACCS, enhanced weathering (EW) and ocean-based CDR methods (including ocean alkalinity enhancement and ocean fertilisation) are moderate to large (*medium confidence*). The potential for DACCS (5–40 $GtCO_2$ yr^{-1}) is limited mainly by requirements for low-carbon energy and by cost (100–300 (full range: 84–386) USD tCO_2^{-1}). DACCS is currently at a medium technology readiness level. EW has the potential to remove 2–4 (full range: <1 to around 100) $GtCO_2$ yr^{-1}, at costs ranging from 50 to 200 (full range: 24–578) USD tCO_2^{-1}. Ocean-based methods have a combined potential to remove 1–100 $GtCO_2$ yr^{-1} at costs of USD40–500 tCO_2^{-1}, but their feasibility is uncertain due to possible side effects on the marine environment. EW and ocean-based methods are currently at a low technology readiness level. {12.3}

CDR governance and policymaking can draw on widespread experience with emissions reduction measures (*high confidence*). Additionally, to accelerate research, development, and demonstration, and to incentivise CDR deployment, a political commitment to formal integration into existing climate policy frameworks is required, including reliable measurement, reporting and verification (MRV) of carbon flows. {12.3.3, 12.4, 12.5}

Box TS.10 | Carbon Dioxide Removal (CDR)

Carbon Dioxide Removal (CDR) is necessary to achieve net zero CO_2 and GHG emissions both globally and nationally, counterbalancing 'hard-to-abate' residual emissions. CDR is also an essential element of scenarios that limit warming to 1.5°C or below 2°C (>67%) by 2100, regardless of whether global emissions reach near zero, net zero or net negative levels. While national mitigation portfolios aiming at net zero emissions or lower will need to include some level of CDR, the choice of methods and the scale and timing of their deployment will depend on the achievement of gross emission reductions, and managing multiple sustainability and feasibility constraints, including political preferences and social acceptability.

CDR refers to anthropogenic activities removing CO_2 from the atmosphere and durably storing it in *geological*, *terrestrial*, or *ocean* reservoirs, or in products. It includes existing and potential anthropogenic enhancement of biological, geochemical or chemical CO_2 sinks, but excludes natural CO_2 uptake not directly caused by human activities (Annex I). Carbon Capture and Storage (CCS) and Carbon Capture and Utilisation (CCU) applied to fossil CO_2 do not count as removal technologies. CCS and CCU can only be part of CDR methods if the CO_2 is biogenic or directly captured from ambient air, and stored durably in geological reservoirs or products. {12.3}

There is a great variety of CDR methods and respective implementation options {Cross-Chapter Box 8, Figure 1 in Chapter 12}. Some of these methods (like afforestation and soil carbon sequestration) have been practiced for decades to millennia, although not necessarily with the intention to remove carbon from the atmosphere. Conversely, for methods such as DACCS and BECCS, experience is growing but still limited in scale. A categorisation of CDR methods can be based on several criteria, depending on the highlighted characteristics. In this report, the categorisation is focused on the role of CDR methods in the carbon cycle, that is on the removal process (*land-based biological*; *ocean-based biological*; *geochemical*; *chemical*) and on the time scale of storage (*decades to centuries*; *centuries to millennia*; *10,000 years or longer*), the latter being closely linked to different carbon storage media. Within one category (e.g., ocean-based biological CDR) options often differ with respect to other dynamic or context-specific dimensions such as mitigation potential, cost, potential for co-benefits and adverse side effects, and technology readiness level. (Table TS.7, TS.5.6, TS. 5.7) {12.3}

It is useful to distinguish between CO_2 removal from the atmosphere as the outcome of deliberate activities implementing CDR options, and the net emissions outcome achieved with the help of CDR deployment (i.e., gross emissions minus gross removals). As part of ambitious mitigation strategies at global or national levels, gross CDR can fulfil three different roles in complementing emissions abatement: (i) lowering net CO_2 or GHG emissions in the near term; (ii) counterbalancing 'hard-to-abate' residual emissions such as CO_2 from industrial activities and long-distance transport, or CH_4 and nitrous oxide from agriculture, in order to help reach net zero CO_2 or GHG emissions in the mid-term; (iii) achieving net negative CO_2 or GHG emissions in the long term if deployed at levels exceeding annual residual emissions {2.7, 3.3, 3.4, 3.5}. These roles of CDR are not mutually exclusive: for example, achieving net zero CO_2 or GHG emissions globally might involve individual developed countries attaining net negative CO_2 emissions at the time of global net zero, thereby allowing developing countries a smoother transition. {Cross-Chapter Box 8, Figure 2 in Chapter 12}

---

30   As a median value [5–95th percentile range].

Table TS.7 | Summary of status, costs, potentials, risk and impacts, co-benefits, trade-offs and spillover effects and the role in mitigation pathways for CDR methods {12.3.2, 7.4}. (TRL = technology readiness level.)

CDR method	Status (TRL)	Cost[1] (USD tCO$_2$$^{-1}$)	Mitigation potential[1] (GtCO$_2$ yr^{-1})	Risk and impacts	Co-benefits	Trade-offs and spillover effects	Role in mitigation pathways	Section
Afforestation/ reforestation	8–9	0–240	0.5–10	Reversal of carbon removal through wildfire, disease, pests may occur. Reduced catchment water yield and lower groundwater level if species and biome are inappropriate.	Enhanced employment and local livelihoods, improved biodiversity, improved renewable wood products provision, soil carbon and nutrient cycling. Possibly less pressure on primary forest.	Inappropriate deployment at large scale can lead to competition for land with biodiversity conservation and food production.	Substantial contribution in IAMs and also in bottom-up sectoral studies.	{7.4}
Soil carbon sequestration in croplands and grasslands	8–9	–45–100	0.6–9.3	Risk of increased nitrous oxide emissions due to higher levels of organic nitrogen in the soil; risk of reversal of carbon sequestration.	Improved soil quality, resilience and agricultural productivity.	Attempts to increase carbon sequestration potential at the expense of production. Net addition per hectare is very small; hard to monitor.	In development – not yet in global mitigation pathways simulated by IAMs in bottom-up studies: with medium contribution.	{7.4}
Peatland and coastal wetland restoration	8–9	Insufficient data	0.5–2.1	Reversal of carbon removal in drought or future disturbance. Risk of increased CH$_4$ emissions.	Enhanced employment and local livelihoods, increased productivity of fisheries, improved biodiversity, soil carbon and nutrient cycling.	Competition for land for food production on some peatlands used for food production.	Not in IAMs but some bottom-up studies with medium contribution.	{7.4}
Agroforestry	8–9	Insufficient data	0.3–9.4	Risk that some land area lost from food production; requires very high skills.	Enhanced employment and local livelihoods, variety of products improved soil quality, more resilient systems.	Some trade-off with agricultural crop production, but enhanced biodiversity, and resilience of system.	No data from IAMs, but in bottom-up sectoral studies with medium contribution.	{7.4}
Improved forest management	8–9	Insufficient data	0.1–2.1	If improved management is understood as merely intensification involving increased fertiliser use and introduced species, then it could reduce biodiversity and increase eutrophication.	In case of sustainable forest management, it leads to enhanced employment and local livelihoods, enhanced biodiversity, improved productivity.	If it involves increased fertiliser use and introduced species it could reduce biodiversity and increase eutrophication and upstream GHG emissions.	No data from IAMs, but in bottom-up sectoral studies with medium contribution.	{7.4}
Biochar	6–7	10–345	0.3–6.6	Particulate and GHG emissions from production; biodiversity and carbon stock loss from unsustainable biomass harvest.	Increased crop yields and reduced non-CO$_2$ emissions from soil; and resilience to drought.	Environmental impacts associated particulate matter; competition for biomass resource.	In development – not yet in global mitigation pathways simulated by IAMs.	{7.4}
Direct air carbon capture and storage (DACCS)	6	100–300 (84–386)	5–40	Increased energy and water use.	Water produced (solid sorbent DAC designs only).	Potentially increased emissions from water supply and energy generation.	In a few IAMs; DACCS complements other CDR methods.	{12.3}
Bioenergy with carbon capture and storage (BECCS)	5–6	15–400	0.5–11	Inappropriate deployment at very large scale leads to additional land and water use to grow biomass feedstock. Biodiversity and carbon stock loss if from unsustainable biomass harvest.	Reduction of air pollutants, fuel security, optimal use of residues, additional income, health benefits, and if implemented well, it can enhance biodiversity.	Competition for land with biodiversity conservation and food production.	Substantial contribution in IAMs and bottom-up sectoral studies. Note – mitigation through avoided GHG emissions resulting from bioenergy use is of the same magnitude as the mitigation from CDR (TS.5.6).	{7.4}
Enhanced weathering (EW)	3–4	50–200 (24–578)	2–4 (<1–95)	Mining impacts; air quality impacts of rock dust when spreading on soil.	Enhanced plant growth, reduced erosion, enhanced soil carbon, reduced soil acidity, enhanced soil water retention.	Potentially increased emissions from water supply and energy generation.	In a few IAMs; EW complements other CDR methods.	{12.3}

TS

Table TS.7 (continued):

CDR method	Status (TRL)	Cost[1] (USD tCO₂⁻¹)	Mitigation potential[1] (GtCO₂ yr⁻¹)	Risk and impacts	Co-benefits	Trade-offs and spillover effects	Role in mitigation pathways	Section
'Blue carbon management' in coastal wetlands	2–3	Insufficient data	<1	If degraded or lost, coastal blue carbon ecosystems are expected to release most of their carbon back to the atmosphere; potential for sediment contaminants, toxicity, bioaccumulation and biomagnification in organisms; issues related to altering degradability of coastal plants; use of sub-tidal areas for tidal wetland carbon removal; effect of shoreline modifications on sediment redeposition and natural marsh accretion; abusive use of coastal blue carbon as means to reclaim land for purposes that degrade capacity for carbon removal.	Provide many non-climatic benefits and can contribute to ecosystem-based adaptation, coastal protection, increased biodiversity, reduced upper ocean acidification; could potentially benefit human nutrition or produce fertiliser for terrestrial agriculture, anti-methanogenic feed additive, or as an industrial or materials feedstock.	If degraded or lost, coastal blue carbon ecosystems are likely to release most of their carbon back to the atmosphere. The full delivery of the benefits at their maximum global capacity will require years to decades to be achieved.	Not incorporated in IAMs, but in some bottom-up studies: small contribution.	{7.4, 12.3.1}
Ocean fertilisation	1–2	50–500	1–3	Nutrient redistribution, restructuring of the ecosystem, enhanced oxygen consumption and acidification in deeper waters, potential for decadal-to-millennial-scale return to the atmosphere of nearly all the extra carbon removed, risks of unintended side effects.	Increased productivity and fisheries, reduced upper-ocean acidification.	Sub-surface ocean acidification, deoxygenation; altered meridional supply of macro-nutrients as they are utilised in the iron-fertilised region and become unavailable for transport to, and utilisation in other regions, fundamental alteration of food webs, biodiversity.	No data.	{12.3.1}
Ocean alkalinity enhancement (OAE)	1–2	40–260	1–100	Increased seawater pH and saturation states and may impact marine biota. Possible release of nutritive or toxic elements and compounds. Mining impacts.	Limiting ocean acidification.	Potentially increased emissions of CO₂ and dust from mining, transport and deployment operations.	No data.	{12.3.1}

[1] Range based on authors' estimates (as assessed from literature) are shown, with full literature ranges shown in ( ) brackets.

TS

TS.5.8   Demand-side Aspects of Mitigation

The assessment of the social science literature and regional case studies reveals how social norms, culture, and individual choices interact with infrastructure and other structural changes over time. This provides new insight into climate change mitigation strategies, and how economic and social activity might be organised across sectors to support emission reductions. To enhance well-being, people demand services and not primary energy and physical resources per se. Focusing on demand for services and the different social and political roles people play broadens the participation in climate action. (Box TS.11)

Demand-side mitigation and new ways of providing services can help *Avoid* and *Shift* final service demands and *Improve* service delivery. Rapid and deep changes in demand make it easier for every sector to reduce GHG emissions in the near and mid-term (*high confidence*). {5.2, 5.3}

The indicative potential of demand-side strategies to reduce emissions of direct and indirect CO_2 and non-CO_2 GHG emissions in three end-use sectors (buildings, land transport, and food) is 40–70% globally by 2050 (*high confidence*). Technical mitigation potentials compared to the 2050 emissions projection of two scenarios

consistent with policies announced by national governments until 2020 amount to 6.8 $GtCO_2$ for building use and construction, 4.6 $GtCO_2$ for land transport and 8.0 $GtCO_2$-eq for food demand, and amount to 4.4 $GtCO_2$ for industry. Mitigation strategies can be classified as *Avoid-Shift-Improve* (ASI) options, that reflect opportunities for socio-cultural, infrastructural, and technological change. The greatest *Avoid* potential comes from reducing long-haul aviation and providing short-distance low-carbon urban infrastructures. The greatest *Shift* potential would come from switching to plant-based diets. The greatest *Improve* potential comes from within the building sector, and in particular increased use of energy-efficient end-use technologies and passive housing. (Figures TS.20 and TS.21) {5.3.1, 5.3.2, Figures 5.7 and 5.8, Table 5.1 and Table SM.5.2}

Socio-cultural and lifestyle changes can accelerate climate change mitigation (*medium confidence*). Among 60 identified actions that could change individual consumption, individual mobility choices have the largest potential to reduce carbon footprints. Prioritising car-free mobility by walking and cycling and adoption of electric mobility could save 2 tCO_2-eq cap^{-1} yr^{-1}. Other options with high mitigation potential include reducing air travel, cooling setpoint adjustments, reduced appliance use, shifts to public transit, and shifting consumption towards plant-based diets. {5.3.1, 5.3.1.2, Figure 5.8}

Box TS.11 | A New Chapter in AR6 WGIII Focusing on the Social Science of Demand, and Social Aspects of Mitigation

The WGIII contribution to the Sixth Assessment Report of the IPCC (AR6) features a distinct chapter on demand, services and social aspects of mitigation {5}. The scope, theories, and evidence for such an assessment are addressed in Sections 5.1 and 5.4 within Chapter 5 and a Social Science Primer as an Appendix to Chapter 5.

The literature on social science – from sociology, psychology, gender studies and political science for example – and climate change mitigation is growing rapidly. A bibliometric search of the literature identified 99,065 peer-reviewed academic papers, based on 34 search queries with content relevant to Chapter 5. This literature is expanding by 15% per year, with twice as many publications in the AR6 period (2014–2020) as in all previous years.

The models of stakeholders' decisions assessed by IPCC have continuously evolved. From AR1 to AR4, rational choice was the implicit assumption: agents with perfect information and unlimited processing capacity maximising self-focused expected utility and differing only in wealth, risk attitude, and time discount rate. The AR5 introduced a broader range of goals (material, social, and psychological) and decision processes (calculation-based, affect-based, and rule-based processes). However, its perspective was still individual- and agency-focused, neglecting structural, cultural, and institutional constraints and the influence of physical and social context.

A social science perspective is important in two ways. By adding new actors and perspectives, it (i) provides more options for climate mitigation; and (ii) helps to identify and address important social and cultural barriers and opportunities to socio-economic, technological, and institutional change. Demand-side mitigation involves five sets of social actors: individuals (e.g., consumption choices, habits), groups and collectives (e.g., social movements, values), corporate actors (e.g., investments, advertising), institutions (e.g., political agency, regulations), and infrastructure actors (e.g., very long-term investments and financing). Actors either contribute to the status-quo of global high-carbon consumption, and a GDP growth-oriented economy, or help generate the desired change to a low-carbon energy-services, well-being, and equity-oriented economy. Each set of actors has novel implications for the design and implementation of both demand- and supply-side mitigation policies. They show important synergies, making energy demand mitigation a dynamic problem where the packaging and/or sequencing of different policies play a role in their effectiveness {5.5, 5.6}. Incremental interventions change social practices, simultaneously affecting emissions and well-being. The transformative change requires coordinated action across all five sets of actors (Table 5.4), using social science insights about intersection of behaviour, culture, institutional and infrastructural changes for policy design and implementation. *Avoid*, *Shift*, and *Improve* choices by individuals, households and communities support mitigation {5.3.1.1, Table 5.1}. They are instigated by role models, changing social norms driven by policies and social movements. They also require appropriate infrastructures designed by urban planners and building and transport professionals, corresponding investments, and a political culture supportive of demand-side mitigation action.

Demand side mitigation is about more than behavioural change. Reconfiguring the way services are provided while simultaneously changing social norms and preferences will help reduce emissions and access. Transformation happens through societal, technological and institutional changes.

(a) Tilting the balance towards less resource intensive service provisioning

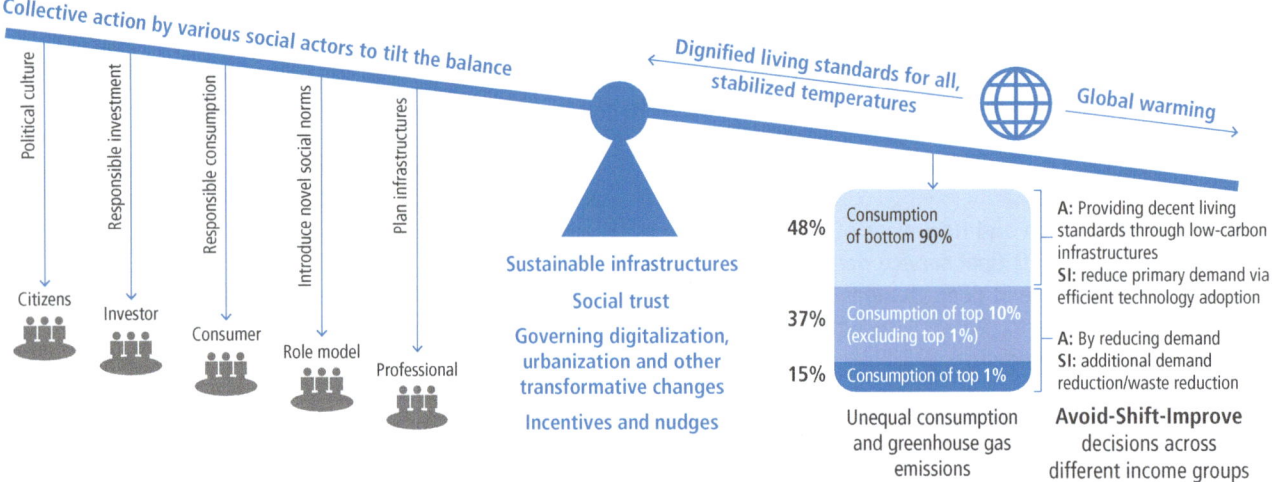

(b) Using wide range of demand-side options

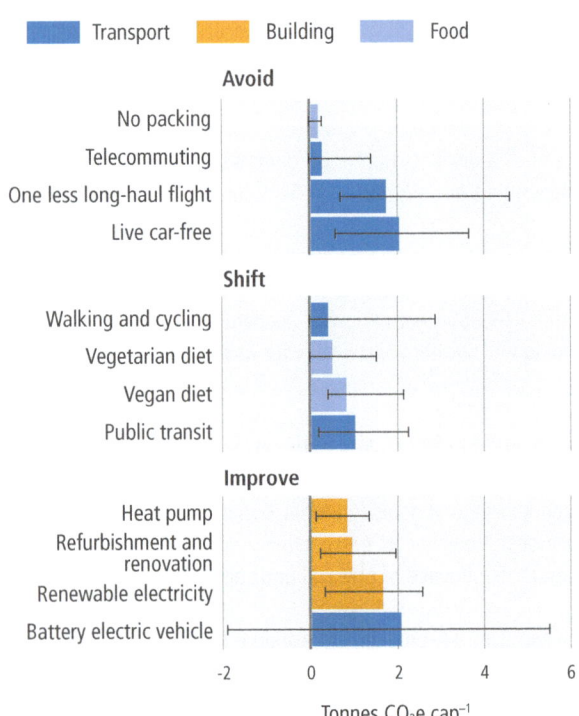

Low-carbon lifestyle transition can be classified into Avoid, Shift, and Improve options. Individual potential to reduce emissions is highest in mobility systems.

(c) Achieving a Low Demand scenario by 2050

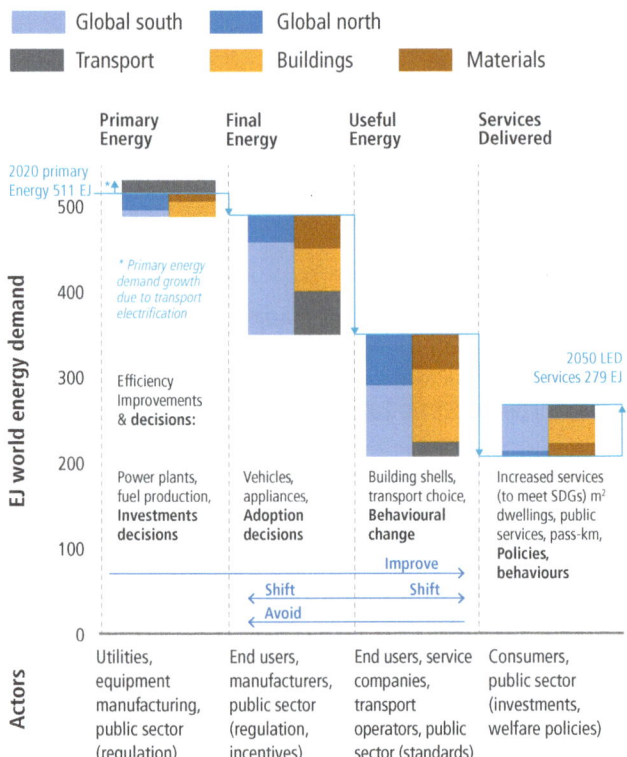

Improved service provisioning systems enable increases in service levels and at the same time a reduction in upstream energy demand by 45%.

Figure TS.20 | Demand-side strategies for mitigation. Demand-side mitigation is about more than behavioural change and transformation happens through societal, technological and institutional changes. {Figure 5.10, Figure 5.14}

Demand-side mitigation can be achieved through changes in socio-cultural factors, infrastructure design and use, and end-use technology adoption by 2050.

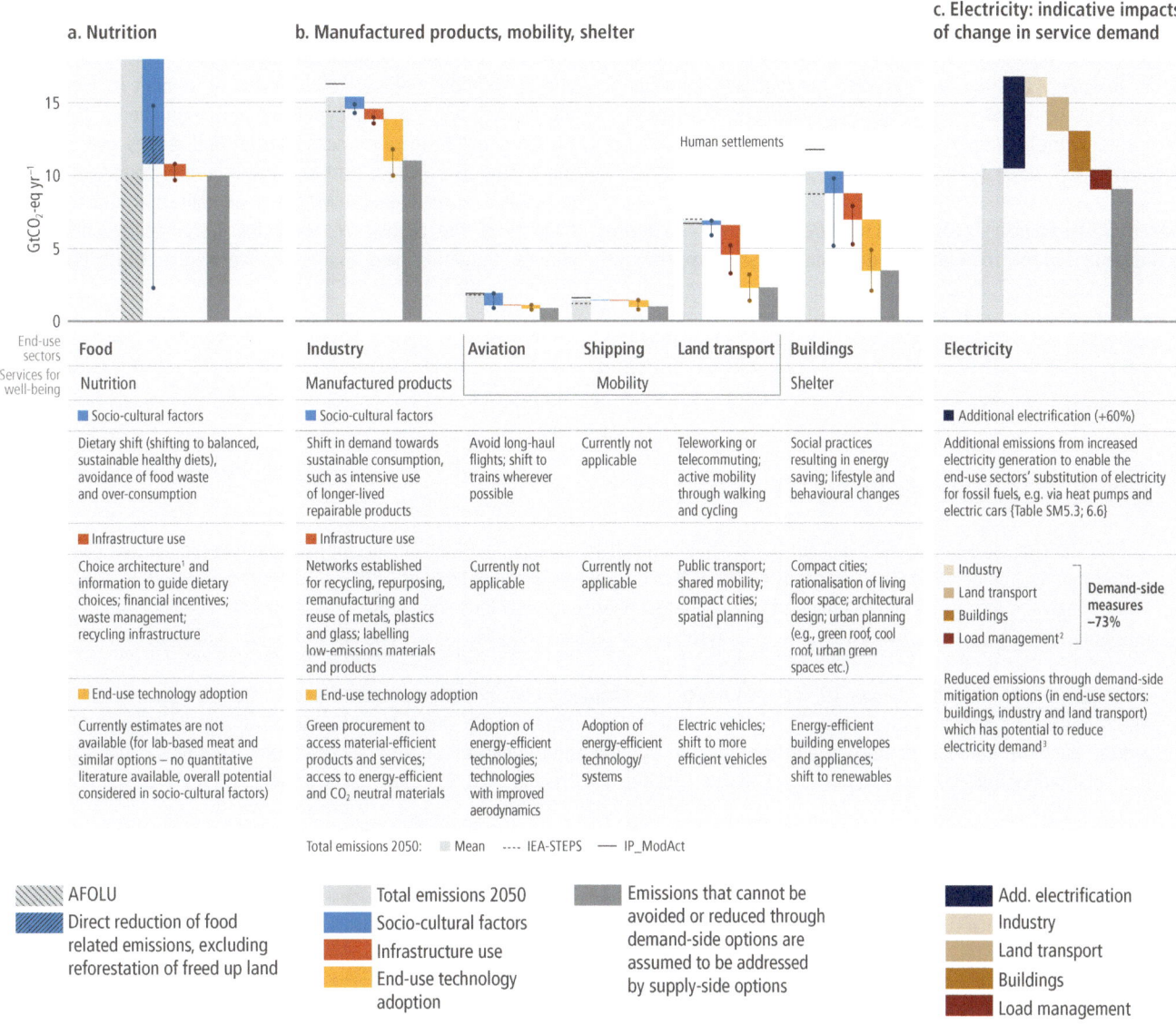

Figure TS.21 | Demand-side mitigation can be achieved through changes in socio-cultural factors, infrastructure design and use, and technology adoption. Mitigation response options related to demand for services have been categorised into three domains: 'socio-cultural factors', related to social norms, culture, and individual choices and behaviour; 'infrastructure use', related to the provision and use of supporting infrastructure that enables individual choices and behaviour; and 'technology adoption', which refers to the uptake of technologies by end users. Potentials in 2050 are estimated using the International Energy Agency's 2020 World Energy Outlook STEPS (Stated Policy Scenarios) as a baseline. This scenario is based on a sector-by-sector assessment of specific policies in place, as well as those that have been announced by countries by mid-2020. This scenario was selected due to the detailed representation of options across sectors and sub-sectors. The heights of the coloured columns represent the potentials on which there is a high level of agreement in the literature, based on a range of case studies. The range shown by the dots connected by dotted lines represents the highest and lowest potentials reported in the literature which have low to medium levels of agreement. The demand-side potential of socio-cultural factors in the food system has two parts. The economic potential of direct emissions (mostly non-CO_2) demand reduction through socio-cultural factors alone is 1.9 GtCO$_2$-eq without considering land-use change by diversion of agricultural land from food production to carbon sequestration. If further changes in land use enabled by this change in demand are considered, the indicative potential could reach 7 GtCO$_2$-eq. The electricity panel presents separately the mitigation potential from changes in electricity demand and changes associated with enhanced electrification in end-use sectors. Electrification increases electricity demand, while it is avoided though demand-side mitigation strategies. Load management refers to demand-side flexibility that can be achieved through incentive design such as time-of-use pricing/monitoring by artificial intelligence, diversification of storage facilities, and so on. NZE (IEA Net-Zero Emissions by 2050 scenario) is used to compute the impact of end-use sector electrification, while the impact of demand-side response options is based on bottom-up assessments. Dark grey columns show the emissions that cannot be avoided through demand-side mitigation options. The table indicates which demand-side mitigation options are included. Options are categorised according to: socio-cultural factors, infrastructure use, and technology adoption. Figure SPM.7 covers potential of demand-side options for the year 2050. Figure SPM.8 covers both supply- and demand-side options and their potentials for the year 2030. {5.3, Figure 5.7, 5.SM.II}

Leveraging improvements in end-use service delivery through behavioural and technological innovations, and innovations in market organisation, leads to large reductions in upstream resource use (*high confidence*). Analysis of indicative potentials range from a factor 10- to 20-fold improvement in the case of available energy (exergy) analysis, with the highest improvement potentials at the end-user and service-provisioning levels. Realisable service level efficiency improvements could reduce upstream energy demand by 45% in 2050. (Figure TS.20) {5.3.2, Figure 5.10}

Decent living standards (DLS) and *well-being for all* (SDG 3) are achievable if high-efficiency low-demand mitigation pathways are followed (*medium confidence*). Minimum requirements of energy use consistent with enabling *well-being for all* is between 20 and 50 GJ cap^{-1} yr^{-1} depending on the context. (Figure TS.22) {5.2.2.1, 5.2.2.2, Box 5.3}

Alternative service provision systems, for example, those enabled through digitalisation, sharing economy initiatives and circular economy initiatives, have to date made a limited contribution to climate change mitigation (*medium confidence*). While digitalisation through specific new products and applications holds potential for improvement in service-level efficiencies, without public policies and regulations, it also has the potential to increase consumption and energy use. Reducing the energy use of data centres, networks, and connected devices is possible in managing low-carbon digitalisation. Claims on the benefits of the circular economy for sustainability and climate change mitigation have limited evidence. (Box TS.12, Box TS.14) {5.3.4, Figures 5.12 and 5.13}

Box TS.12 | Circular Economy (CE)

In AR6, the circular economy (CE) concept {Annex I} is highlighted as an increasingly important mitigation approach that can help deliver human well-being by minimising waste of energy and resources. While definitions of CE vary, its essence is to shift away from linear 'make and dispose' economic models to those that emphasise product longevity, reuse, refurbishment, recycling, and material efficiency, thereby enabling more circular material systems that reduce embodied energy and emissions. {5.3.4, 8.4, 8.5, 9.5, 11.3.3}

Whereas IPCC AR4 {WGIII, Chapter 10} included a separate chapter on waste-sector emissions and waste-management practices, and AR5 {WGIII, Chapter 10} reviewed the importance of 'reduce, reuse, recycle' and related policies, AR6 focuses on how CE can reduce waste in materials production and consumption by optimising materials' end-use service utility. Specific examples of CE implementations, policies, and mitigation potentials are included in Chapters 5, 8, 9, 11 and 12. {5.3, 8.4, 9.5, 11.3, 12.6}

CE is shown to empower new social actors in mitigation actions, given that it relies on the synergistic actions of producers, sellers, and consumers {11.3.3}. As an energy and resource demand-reduction strategy, it is consistent with high levels of human well-being {5.3.4.3} and ensures better environmental quality (Figure TS.22) {5.2.1}. It also creates jobs through increased sharing, reuse, refurbishment, and recycling activities. Therefore, CE contributes to several SDGs, including clean water and sanitation (SDG 6), affordable energy and clean energy (SDG 7), decent work and economic growth (SDG 8), responsible production and consumption (SDG 12) and climate action (SDG 13). {11.5.3.2}

Emissions savings derive from reduced primary material production and transport. For example, in buildings, lifetime extension, material efficiency, and reusable components reduce embodied emissions by avoiding demand for structural materials {9.3, 9.5}. At regional scales, urban/industrial symbiosis reduce primary material demand through by-product exchange networks {11.3.3}. CE strategies also exhibit enabling effects, such as material-efficient and circular vehicle designs that also improve fuel economy {10.2.2.2}. There is growing interest in 'circular bioeconomy' concepts applied to bio-based materials {Box 12.2} and even a 'circular carbon economy', wherein carbon captured via CCU {11.3.6} or CDR {3.4.6} is converted into reusable materials, which is especially relevant for the transitions of economies dependent on fossil fuel revenue. {12.6}

While there are many recycling policies, CE-oriented policies for more efficient material use with higher value retention are comparatively far fewer; these policy gaps have been attributed to institutional failures, lack of coordination, and lack of strong advocates {5.3, 9.5.3.6, Boxes 11.5 and 12.2}. Reviews of mitigation potentials reveal unevenness in the savings of CE applications and potential risks of rebound effects {5.3}. Therefore, CE policies that identify system determinants maximise potential emissions reductions, which vary by material, location, and application.

There are knowledge gaps for assessing CE opportunities within mitigation models due to CE's many cross-sectoral linkages and data gaps related to its nascent state {3.4.4}. Opportunity exists to bridge knowledge from the industrial ecology field, which has historically studied CE, to the mitigation modelling community for improved analysis of interventions and policies for AR7. For instance, a global CE knowledge-sharing platform is helpful for CE performance measurement, reporting and accounting. {5.3, 9.5, 11.7}

Providing better services with less energy and resource input has high technical potential and is consistent with providing well-being for all (*medium confidence*). The assessment of 19 demand-side mitigation options and 18 different constituents of well-being showed that positive impacts on well-being outweigh negative ones by a factor of 11. {5.2, 5.2.3, Figure 5.6}

Demand-side mitigation options bring multiple interacting benefits (*high confidence*). Energy services to meet human needs for nutrition, shelter, health, and so on, are met in many different ways with different emissions implications that depend on local contexts, cultures, geography, available technologies, and social preferences. In the near term, many less-developed countries, and poor people everywhere, require better access to safe and low-emissions energy sources to ensure decent living standards and increase energy savings from service improvements by about 20–25%. (Figure TS.22) {5.2, 5.4.5, Figures 5.3, 5.4, 5.5 and 5.6, Boxes 5.2 and 5.3}

Granular technologies and decentralised energy end-use, characterised by modularity, small unit sizes and small unit costs, diffuse faster into markets and are associated with faster technological learning benefits, greater efficiency, more opportunities to escape technological lock-in, and greater employment (*high confidence*). Examples include solar PV systems, batteries, and thermal heat pumps. {5.3, 5.5, 5.5.3}

Wealthy individuals contribute disproportionately to higher emissions and have a high potential for emissions reductions while maintaining decent living standards and well-being (*high confidence*). Individuals with high socio-economic status are capable of reducing their GHG emissions by becoming role models of low-carbon lifestyles, investing in low-carbon businesses, and advocating for stringent climate policies. {5.4.1, 5.4.3, 5.4.4, Figure 5.14}

Demand-side solutions require both motivation and capacity for change (*high confidence*). Motivation by individuals or households worldwide to change energy consumption behaviour is generally low. Individual behavioural change is insufficient for climate change mitigation unless embedded in structural and cultural change. Different factors influence individual motivation and capacity for change in different demographics and geographies. These factors go beyond traditional socio-demographic and economic predictors and include psychological variables such as awareness, perceived risk, subjective and social norms, values, and perceived behavioural control. Behavioural nudges promote easy behaviour change, for example, '*Improve*' actions such as making investments in energy efficiency, but fail to motivate harder lifestyle changes (*high confidence*). {5.4}

Behavioural interventions, including the way choices are presented to end users (an intervention practice known as choice architecture), work synergistically with price signals, making the combination more effective (*medium confidence*). Behavioural interventions through nudges, and alternative ways of redesigning and motivating decisions, alone provide small to medium contributions to reduce energy consumption and GHG emissions. Green defaults, such as automatic enrolment in 'green energy' provision, are highly effective. Judicious labelling, framing, and communication of social norms can also increase the effect of mandates, subsidies, or taxes. {5.4, 5.4.1, Table 5.3, 5.3}

Cultural change, in combination with new or adapted infrastructure, is necessary to enable and realise many *Avoid* and *Shift* options (*medium confidence*). By drawing support from diverse actors, narratives of change can enable coalitions to form, providing the basis for social movements to campaign in favour of (or against) societal transformations. People act and contribute to climate change mitigation in their diverse capacities as consumers, citizens, professionals, role models, investors, and policymakers. {5.4, 5.5, 5.6}

Collective action as part of social or lifestyle movements underpins system change (*high confidence*). Collective action and social organising are crucial to shift the possibility space of public policy on climate change mitigation. For example, climate strikes have given voice to youth in more than 180 countries. In other instances, mitigation policies allow the active participation of all stakeholders, resulting in building social trust, new coalitions, legitimising change, and thus initiate a positive cycle in climate governance capacity and policies. {5.4.2, Figure 5.14}

Transition pathways and changes in social norms often start with pilot experiments led by dedicated individuals and niche groups (*high confidence*). Collectively, such initiatives can find entry points to prompt policy, infrastructure, and policy reconfigurations, supporting the further uptake of technological and lifestyle innovations. Individuals' agency is central as social change agents and narrators of meaning. These bottom-up socio-cultural forces catalyse a supportive policy environment, which enables changes. {5.5.2}

The current effects of climate change, as well as some mitigation strategies, are threatening the viability of existing business practices, while some corporate efforts also delay mitigation action (*medium confidence*). Policy packages that include job creation programmes can help to preserve social trust, livelihoods, respect, and dignity of all workers and employees involved. Business models that protect rent-extracting behaviour may sometimes delay political action. Corporate advertisement and brand-building strategies may also attempt to deflect corporate responsibility to individuals or aim to appropriate climate-care sentiments in their own brand–building. {5.4.3, 5.6.4}

Middle actors – professionals, experts, and regulators – play a crucial, albeit underestimated and underutilised, role in establishing low-carbon standards and practices (*medium confidence*). Building managers, landlords, energy-efficiency advisers, technology installers, and car dealers influence patterns of mobility and energy consumption by acting as middle actors or intermediaries in the provision of building or mobility services and need greater capacity and motivation to play this role. (Figure TS.20a) {5.4.3}

Figure TS.22 | Demand-side mitigation options, well-being and SDGs. [Figure 5.6]

Mitigation strategies / Well-being dimensions	Food (2)	Water (6)	Air (7,11)	Health (3)	Sanitation (6)	Energy (7)	Shelter (11)	Mobility (11)	Education (4)	Communication	Social protection (1,2,8,10)	Participation (5,10,16)	Personal Security (5,16)	Social cohesion (10,16)	Political stability (11,16)	Economic stability (8)	Material provision (9,12)
Sufficiency (adequate floor space, etc.)	[+1]	[+2]	[+2]	[+3]	[+1]	[+3]	[+1]	[+1]	[+1]	[+2]	[+1]	[+1]		[+2]		[+2]	[+2]
Efficiency	[+2]	[+2]	[+3/-1]	[+3/-1]	[+1]	[+3]	[+2]		[+1]	[+1]		[+1]	[+1]	[+2/-1]		[+2]	[+2/-1]
Lower carbon and renewable energy	[+2/-1]	[+2/-1]	[+3]	[+3]		[+3]	[+1]	[+1]	[+1]	[+2]	[+1]	[+1]	[+1]	[+2/-1]	[+1]	[+2/-1]	[+2]
Food waste	[+1]	[+2]	[+1]	[+2]	[+1]	[+1]	[+1]		[+1]	[+1]	[-1/+1]	[+1]			[+1]	[+1]	
Over-consumption	[+1]	[+1/-1]	[+1/-1]	[+3]		[+1/-1]				[+1]		[+2]			[+1]		
Plant based diets	[+2]	[+2]	[+3]	[+3]					[-1]	[-1]	[+3]	[+1]	[+1/-1]	[-1]	[+2]	[+2]	[-1]
Teleworking and online education system	[+1]		[+3]	[+2]		[+2]	[+1]	[+2]	[+1]	[+2]	[+1]	[+2]	[+1/-1]	[+2]	[+2]	[+2]	
Non-motorised transport	[+2]	[+1]	[+1]	[+3]		[+2]		[+3]	[+1]	[+3]	[+1]	[+1]	[+2]	[+2]	[+2]	[+2]	
Shared mobility	[+1]		[+3]	[+2]	[+1]	[+1]	[+1]	[+2]		[+1]	[+2]	[+1]	[+1/-1]	[+1/-1]		[+2]	[+2]
Electric vehicles (EVs)	[+1]	[+1/-1]	[+2]	[+1]	[+1]	[+3]	[+1/-1]	[+2]		[+1/-1]	[+3]	[+2]	[+1]	[+2/-2]	[-1]	[+2]	[-1]
Compact city	[+2/-1]	[+1]	[+2/-1]	[+2]	[+1]	[+3/-1]	[-1]	[+3]	[+1]	[+1/-1]	[+2]	[+1]	[+1]	[+1/-1]	[+1]	[+1]	[+1]
Circular and shared economy	[+2]	[+1]	[+3]	[+3]	[+1]	[+3]	[+2/-1]	[+3]	[+1]	[+2]	[+1]	[+1]	[+2]	[+1]		[+2]	[+3]
Systems approach in urban policy and practice	[+1]	[+2]	[+2]	[+3]	[+1]	[+3]	[+2]	[+3]	[+1]	[+1]	[-1]	[+1]	[+2]	[+1]		[+1]	[+3]
Nature-Based Solutions	[+2]	[+1/-1]	[+3/-1]	[+3]	[+1]	[+3]	[+1/-1]	[+1]	[+2]	[+1]	[+2]	[+3]	[+1]	[+2/-2]		[+3]	[+1]
Using less material by design	[+2]	[+2]	[+3]	[+2]	[+2]	[+3]	[+2]	[+2]	[+1]	[+2]	[+1]	[+1]	[+1]	[+1]	[+1]	[+2]	[+3]
Product life extension	[+2]	[+2]	[+3]	[+2]	[+2]	[+3]	[+2]	[+2]	[+1]	[+2]	[+1]	[+1]	[+1]	[+1]	[+1]	[+2]	[+3]
Energy efficiency	[+2]	[+2]	[+3]	[+1]	[+2]	[+3]	[+2]	[+2]	[+1]	[+2]	[+2]	[+2]	[+1]		[+1]	[+2]	[+2]
Circular economy	[+2]	[+2]	[+3]	[+1]	[+2]	[+3]	[+2]	[+2]	[+1]	[+2]	[+1]	[+1]	[+2]	[+1]	[+1]	[+2]	[-3]

Legend:
- High positive impact [+3]
- Medium positive impact [+2]
- Low positive impact [+1]
- Overall neutral
- No impact
- Low negative impact [-1]
- Medium negative impact [-2]
- ● Confidence level

TS

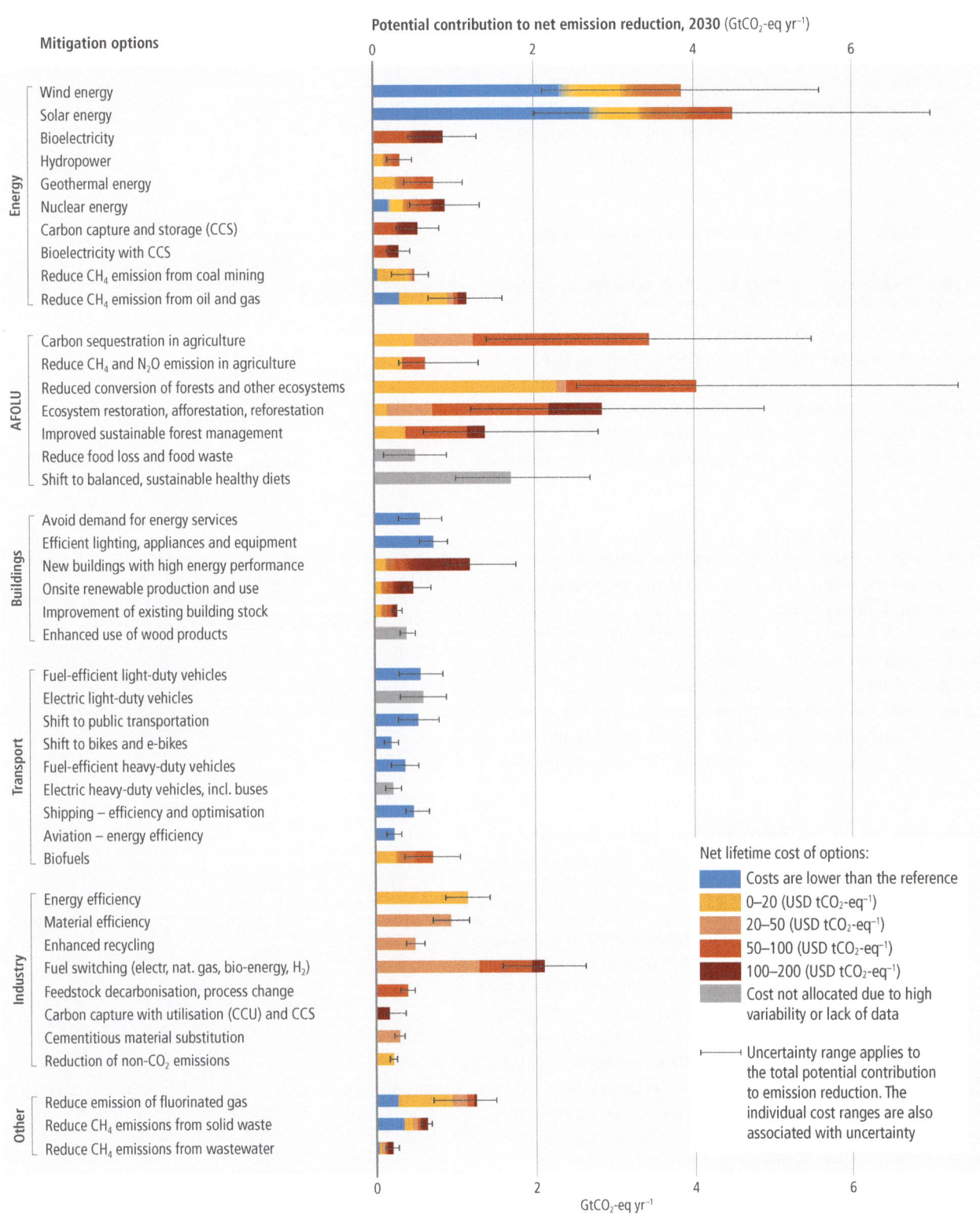

Figure TS.23 | Overview of emission mitigation options and their cost and potential for the year 2030. The mitigation potential of each option is the quantity of net greenhouse gas emission reductions that can be achieved by a given mitigation option relative to specified emission baselines that reflects what would be considered current policies in the period 2015–2019. Mitigation options may overlap or interact and cannot simply be summed together. The potential for each option is broken down into cost categories (see legend). Only monetary costs and revenues are considered. If costs are less than zero, lifetime monetary revenues are higher than lifetime monetary costs. For wind energy, for example, negative cost indicates that the cost is lower than that of fossil-based electricity production. The error bars refer to the total potential for each option. The breakdown into cost categories is subject to uncertainty. Where a smooth colour transition is shown, the breakdown of the potential into cost categories is not well researched, and the colours indicate only into which cost category the potential can predominantly be found in the literature. {Figure SPM.8, 6.4, Table 7.3, Supplementary Material Table 9.SM.2, Supplementary Material Table 9.SM.3, 10.6, 11.4, Figure 11.13, 12.2, Supplementary Material 12.SM.1.2.3}

Social influencers and thought leaders can increase the adoption of low-carbon technologies, behaviours, and lifestyles (*high confidence*). Preferences are malleable and can align with a cultural shift. The modelling of such shifts by salient and respected community members can help bring about changes in different service provisioning systems. Between 10% and 30% of committed individuals are required to set new social norms. {5.2.1, 5.4}

TS.5.9 Mitigation Potential Across Sectors and Systems

The total emission mitigation potential achievable by the year 2030, calculated based on sectoral assessments, is sufficient to reduce global greenhouse gas (GHG) emissions to half of the current (2019) level or less (*high confidence*). This potential – 31–44 $GtCO_2$-eq – requires the implementation of a wide range of mitigation options. Options with mitigation costs lower than USD20 tCO_2^{-1} make up more than half of this potential and are available for all sectors. The market benefits of some options exceed their costs. (Figure TS.23) {12.2, Table 12.3}

Cross-sectoral considerations in mitigation finance are critical for the effectiveness of mitigation action as well as for balancing the often conflicting social, developmental, and environmental policy goals at the sectoral level (*medium confidence*). True resource mobilisation plans that properly address mitigation costs and benefits at sectoral level cannot be developed in isolation of their cross-sectoral implications. There is an urgent need for multilateral financing institutions to align their frameworks and delivery mechanisms, including the use of blended financing to facilitate cross-sectoral solutions as opposed to causing competition for resources among sectors. {12.6.4}

Carbon leakage is a cross-sectoral and cross-country consequence of differentiated climate policy (*robust evidence, medium agreement*). Carbon leakage occurs when mitigation measures implemented in one country/sector leads to increased emissions in other countries/sectors. Global commodity value chains and associated international transport are important mechanisms through which carbon leakage occurs. Reducing emissions from the value chain and transportation can offer opportunities to mitigate three elements of cross-sectoral spillovers and related leakage: (i) domestic cross-sectoral spillovers within the same country; (ii) international spillovers within a single sector resulting from substitution of domestic production of carbon-intensive goods with their imports from abroad; and (iii) international cross-sectoral spillovers among sectors in different countries. {12.6.3}

TS.6   Implementation and Enabling Conditions

Chapters 13 to 16 address the enabling conditions that can accelerate or impede rapid progress on mitigation. Chapters 13 and 14 focus on policy, governance and institutional capacity, and international cooperation, respectively taking a national and international perspective; Chapter 15 focuses on investment and finance; and Chapter 16 focuses on innovation and technology. The assessment of social aspects of mitigation draws on material assessed in Chapter 5.

TS.6.1   Policy and Institutions

Long-term deep emission reductions, including the reduction of emissions to net zero, is best achieved through institutions and governance that nurture new mitigation policies, while at the same time reconsidering existing policies that support the continued emission of GHGs (*high confidence*). To do so effectively, the scope of climate governance needs to include both direct efforts to target GHG emissions and indirect opportunities to tackle GHG emissions that result from efforts directed towards other policy objectives. {13.2, 13.5, 13.6, 13.7, 13.9}

Institutions and governance underpin mitigation by providing the legal basis for action. This includes setting up implementing organisations and the frameworks through which diverse actors interact (*medium evidence, high agreement*). Institutions can create mitigation and sectoral policy instruments; policy packages for low-carbon system transition; and economy-wide measures for systemic restructuring. {13.2, 13.7, 13.9}

Policies have had a discernible impact on mitigation for specific countries, sectors, and technologies (*high confidence*), avoiding emissions of several $GtCO_2$-eq yr^{-1} (*medium confidence*). Both market-based and regulatory policies have distinct but complementary roles. The share of global GHG emissions subject to mitigation policy has increased rapidly in recent years, but big gaps remain in policy coverage, and the stringency of many policies falls short of what is needed to achieve the desired mitigation outcomes. (Box TS.13) {13.6, Cross-Chapter Box 10 in Chapter 14}

Climate laws enable mitigation action by signalling the direction of travel, setting targets, mainstreaming mitigation into sector policies, enhancing regulatory certainty, creating law-backed agencies, creating focal points for social mobilisation, and attracting international finance (*medium evidence, high agreement*). By 2020, 'direct' climate laws primarily focused on GHG reductions were present in 56 countries covering 53% of global emissions (Figure TS.24). More than 690 laws, including 'indirect' laws, however, may also have an effect on mitigation. Among direct laws, 'framework' laws set an overarching legal basis for mitigation either by pursuing a target and implementation approach, or by seeking to mainstream climate objectives through sectoral plans and integrative institutions. (Figure TS.24) {13.2}

Institutions can enable improved governance by coordinating across sectors, scales and actors, building consensus for action, and setting strategies (*medium evidence, high agreement*). Institutions are more stable and effective when they are congruent with national contexts, leading to mitigation-focused institutions in some countries and the pursuit of multiple objectives in others. Sub-national institutions play a complementary role to national institutions by developing locally relevant visions and plans, addressing policy gaps or limits in national institutions, building local administrative structures and convening actors for place-based decarbonisation. {13.2}

Mitigation strategies, instruments and policies that fit with dominant ideas, values and belief systems within a country or within a sector are more easily adopted and implemented (*medium confidence*). Ideas, values and beliefs may change over time. Policies that bring perceived direct benefits, such as subsidies, usually receive greater support. The awareness of co-benefits for the public increases support of climate policies (*high confidence*). {13.2, 13.3, 13.4}

Climate governance is constrained and enabled by domestic structural factors, but it is still possible for actors to make substantial changes (*medium evidence, high agreement*). Key structural factors are domestic material endowments (such as fossil fuels and land-based resources); domestic political systems; and prevalent ideas, values and belief systems. Developing Countries face additional material constraints in climate governance due to development challenges and scarce economic or natural resources. A broad group of actors influence how climate governance develop over time, including a range of civic organisations, encompassing both pro- and anti-climate action groups. {13.3, 13.4}

Sub-national actors are important for mitigation because municipalities and regional governments have jurisdiction over climate-relevant sectors such as land use, waste and urban policy. They are able to experiment with climate solutions and can forge partnerships with the private sector and internationally to leverage enhanced climate action (*high confidence*). More than 10,500 cities and nearly 250 regions representing more than 2 billion people have pledged largely voluntary action to reduce emissions. Indirect gains include innovation, establishing norms and developing capacity. However, sub-national actors often lack national support, funding, and capacity to mobilise finance and human resources, and create new institutional competences. {13.5}

Climate litigation is growing and can affect the outcome and ambition of climate governance (*medium evidence, high agreement*). Since 2015, at least 37 systemic cases have been initiated against states that challenge the overall effort of a state to mitigate or adapt to climate change. If successful, such cases can lead to an increase in a country's overall ambition to tackle climate change. Climate litigation has also successfully challenged governments' authorisations of high-emitting projects, setting precedents in favour of climate action. Climate litigation against private sector and financial institutions is also on the rise. {13.4}

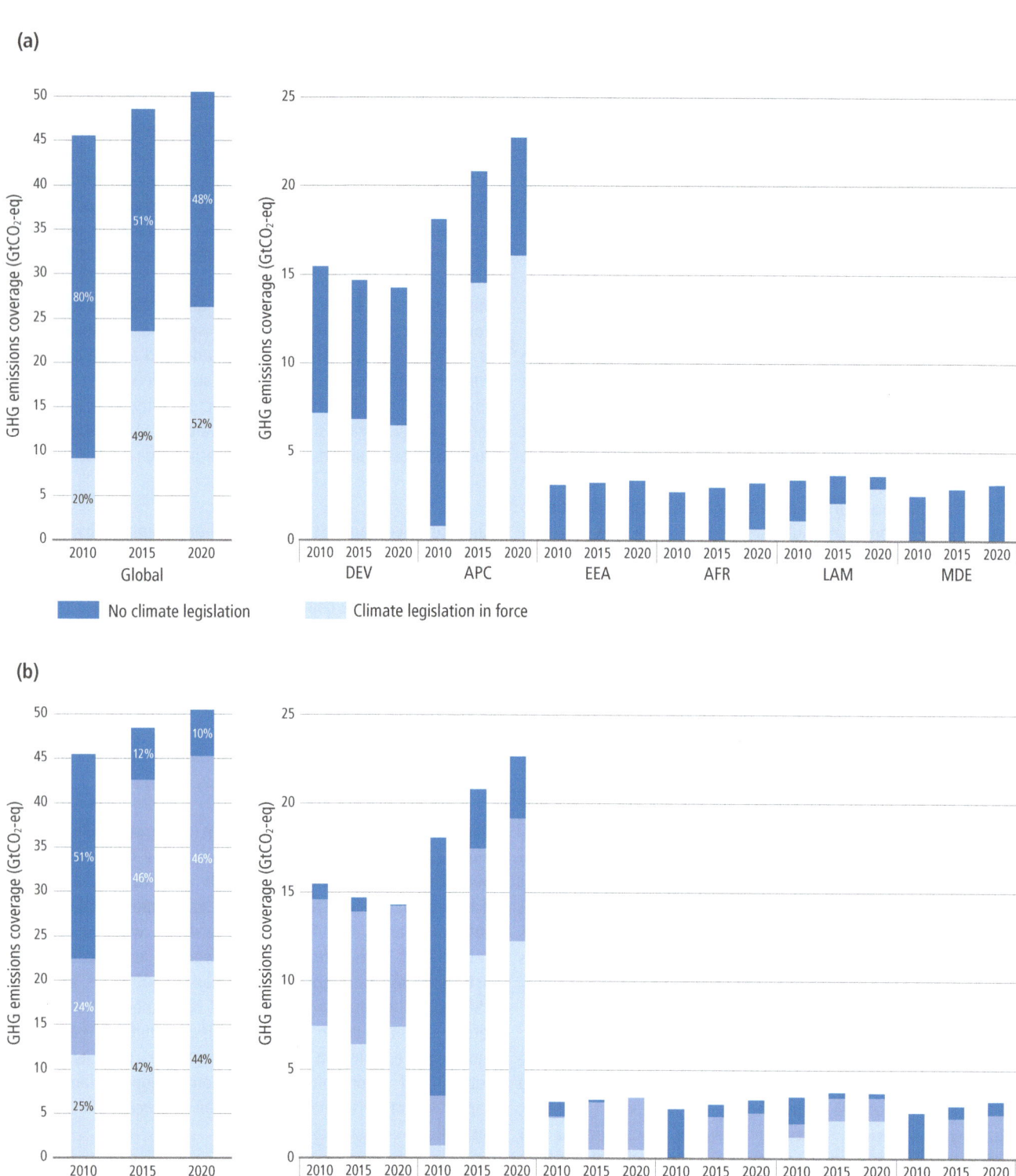

(a)

(b)

Figure TS.24 | Prevalence of legislation and emissions targets across regions. Panel (a): shares of global GHG emissions under national climate change legislations – in 2010, 2015 and 2020. Climate legislation is defined as an act passed by a parliament that includes the reduction of GHGs in its title or objectives. **Panel (b):** shares of global GHG emissions under national climate emission targets – in 2010, 2015 and 2020. Emissions reductions targets were taken into account as a legislative target when they were defined in a law or as part of a country's submission under the Kyoto Protocol, or as an executive target when they were included in a national policy or official submissions under the UNFCCC. Targets were included if they were economy-wide or included at least the energy sector. The proportion of national emissions covered are scaled to reflect coverage and whether targets are in GHG or CO₂ terms. Emissions data used are for 2019. 2020 data was excluded as emissions shares across regions deviated from past patterns due to COVID-19. AR6 regions: DEV = Developed countries; APC = Asia and Pacific; EEA = Eastern Europe and West Central Asia; AFR = Africa; LAM = Latin America and the Caribbean; ME = Middle East. {Figure 13.1 and 13.2}

The media shapes the public discourse about climate mitigation. This can usefully build public support to accelerate mitigation action but may also be used to impede decarbonisation (*medium evidence, high agreement*). Global media coverage (across a study of 59 countries) has been growing, from about 47,000 articles in 2016–17 to about 87,000 in 2020–21. Generally, the media representation of climate science has increased and become more accurate over time. On occasion, the propagation of scientifically misleading information by organised counter-movements has fuelled polarisation, with negative implications for climate policy. {13.4}

Explicit attention to equity and justice is salient to both social acceptance and fair and effective policymaking for mitigation (*high confidence*). Distributional implications of alternative climate policy choices can be usefully evaluated at city, local and national scales as an input to policymaking. It is anticipated that institutions and governance frameworks that enable consideration of justice and Just Transitions can build broader support for climate policymaking. {13.2, 13.6, 13.8, 13.9}

Carbon pricing is effective in promoting implementation of low-cost emissions reductions (*high confidence*). While the coverage of emissions trading and carbon taxes has risen to over 20 percent of global CO_2 emissions, both coverage and price are lower than is needed for deep reductions. Market mechanisms ideally are designed to be effective as well as efficient, balance distributional goals and find social acceptance. Practical experience has driven progress in market mechanism design, especially of emissions trading schemes. Carbon pricing is limited in its effect on adoption of higher-cost mitigation options, and where decisions are often not sensitive to price incentives, such as in energy efficiency, urban planning, and infrastructure (*robust evidence, medium agreement*). Subsidies have been used to improve energy efficiency, encourage the uptake of renewable energy and other sector-specific emissions-saving options. {13.6}

Carbon pricing is most effective if revenues are redistributed or used impartially (*high confidence*). A carbon levy earmarked for green infrastructures or saliently returned to taxpayers corresponding to widely accepted notions of fairness increases the political acceptability of carbon pricing. {5.6, Box 5.11}

Removing fossil fuel subsidies would reduce emissions, improve public revenue and macroeconomic performance, and yield other environmental and sustainable development benefits. Subsidy removal may have adverse distributional impacts especially on the most economically vulnerable groups which, in some cases can be mitigated by measures such as redistributing revenue saved, all of which depend on national circumstances (*high confidence*); fossil fuel subsidy removal is projected by various studies (using alternative methodologies) to reduce global CO_2 emissions by 1–4%, and GHG emissions by up to 10% by 2030, varying across regions (*medium confidence*). {6.3, 13.6} {13.6}

Regulatory instruments play an important role in achieving specific mitigation outcomes in sectoral applications (*high confidence*). Regulation is effective in particular applications and often enjoys greater political support, but tends to be more economically costly than pricing instruments (*robust evidence, medium agreement*). Flexible forms of regulation (e.g., performance standards) have achieved aggregate goals for renewable energy generation, vehicle efficiency and fuel standards, and energy efficiency in buildings and industry. Infrastructure investment decisions are significant for mitigation because they lock-in high- or low-emissions trajectories over long periods. Information and voluntary programs can contribute to overall mitigation outcomes (*medium evidence, high agreement*). Designing for overlap and interactions among mitigation policies enhances their effectiveness. {13.6}

National mitigation policies interact internationally with effects that both support and hinder mitigation action (*medium evidence, high agreement*). Reductions in demand for fossil fuels tend to negatively affect fossil fuel-exporting countries. Creation of markets for emission reduction credits tends to benefit countries able to supply credits. Policies to support technology development and diffusion tend to have positive spillover effects. There is no consistent evidence of significant emissions leakage or competitiveness effects between countries, including for emissions-intensive trade-exposed industries covered by emission-trading systems (*medium confidence*). {13.6}

Policy packages are better able to support socio-technical transitions and shifts in development pathways toward low-carbon futures than are individual policies (*high confidence*). For best effect, they need to be harnessed to a clear vision for change and designed with attention to local governance context. Comprehensiveness in coverage, coherence to ensure complementarity, and consistency of policies with the overarching vision and its objectives are important design criteria. Integration across objectives occurs when a policy package is informed by a clear problem framing and identification of the full range of relevant policy subsystems. The climate policy landscape is outlined in Table TS.8, which maps framings of desired national policy outcomes to policymaking approaches. {13.7, Figure 13.6}

TS

Table TS.8 | Mapping the landscape of climate policy. {Figure 13.6}

Approach to policymaking	Framing of outcome	
	Enhancing mitigation	**Addressing multiple objectives of mitigation and development**
Shifting incentives	'Direct mitigation focus' {2.8, 13.6} **Objective:** reduce GHG emissions now. **Literature:** how to design and implement policy instruments, with attention to distributional and other concerns. **Examples:** carbon tax, cap and trade, border carbon adjustment (BCA), disclosure policies.	'Co-benefits' {5.6.2, 12.4.4, 17.3} **Objective:** synergies between mitigation and development. **Literature:** scope for and policies to realise synergies and avoid trade-offs across climate and development objectives. **Examples:** appliance standards, fuel taxes, community forest management, sustainable dietary guidelines, green building codes, packages for air pollution, packages for public transport.
Enabling transition	'Socio-technical transitions' {1.7.3, 5.5, 6.7, 10.8, Cross-Chapter Box 12 in Chapter 16} **Objective:** accelerate low-carbon shifts in socio-technical systems. **Literature:** understand socio-technical transition processes, integrated policies for different stages of a technology 'S curve' and explore structural, social and political elements of transitions. **Examples:** packages for renewable-energy transition and coal phase-out; diffusion of electric vehicles, process and fuel switching in key industries.	'System transitions to shift development pathways' {7.4.5, 11.6.6, 13.9, 17.3.3, Cross-Chapter Box 5 in Chapter 4, Cross-Chapter Box 12 in Chapter 16} **Objective:** accelerate system transitions and shift development pathways to expand mitigation options and meet other development goals. **Literature:** examines how structural development patterns and broad cross-sector and economy-wide measures drive ability to mitigate while achieving development goals through integrated policies and aligning enabling conditions. **Examples:** packages for sustainable urbanisation, land-energy-water nexus approaches, green industrial policy, regional Just Transition plans.

The co-benefits and trade-offs of integrating adaptation and mitigation are most usefully identified and assessed prior to policymaking rather than being accidentally discovered (*high confidence*). This requires strengthening relevant national institutions to reduce silos and overlaps, increasing knowledge exchange at the country and regional levels, and supporting engagement with bilateral and multilateral funding partners. Local governments are well placed to develop policies that generate social and environmental co-benefits but to do so require legal backing and adequate capacity and resources. {13.8}

Climate change mitigation is accelerated when attention is given to integrated policy and economy-wide approaches, and when enabling conditions (*governance, institutions, behaviour and lifestyle, innovation, policy,* and *finance*), are present (*robust evidence, medium agreement*). Accelerating climate mitigation includes simultaneously weakening high-carbon systems and encouraging low-carbon systems; ensuring interaction between adjacent systems (e.g., energy and agriculture); overcoming resistance to policies (e.g., from incumbents in high-carbon-emitting industries), including by providing transitional support to the vulnerable and negatively affected by distributional impacts; inducing changes in consumer practices and routines; providing transition support; and addressing coordination challenges in policy and governance. Table TS.9 elucidates the complexity of policymaking in driving sectoral transitions by summarising case studies of sectoral transitions from Chapters 5 to 12. These real-world sectoral transitions reinforce critical lessons on policy integration. (Table TS.9) {13.7, 13.9}

Economy-wide packages, including economic-stimulus packages, can contribute to shifting sustainable development pathways and achieving net zero outcomes whilst meeting short-term economic goals (*medium evidence, high agreement*). The 2008–9 global recession showed that policies for sustained economic recovery go beyond short-term fiscal stimulus to include long-term commitments of public spending on the low-carbon economy, pricing reform, addressing affordability, and minimising distributional impacts. COVID-19 spurred stimulus packages and multi-objective recovery policies may also have potential to meet short-term economic goals while enabling longer-term sustainability goals. (Table TS.8) {13.9}

TS

Table TS.9 | Case studies of integrated policymaking for sectoral transitions. Real-world sectoral transitions reinforce critical lessons on policy integration: a high-level strategic goal (column A), the need for a clear sectoral outcome framing (column B), a carefully coordinated mix of policy instruments and governance actions (column C), and the importance of context-specific governance factors (column D). Illustrative examples, drawn from sectors, help elucidate the complexity of policymaking in driving sectoral transitions. {Cross-Chapter Box 9 in Chapter 13, Table 1}

A. Illustrative case	B. Objective	C. Policy mix	D. Governance context	
			Enablers	**Barriers**
Shift in mobility service provision in Kolkata, India {Box 5.8}	– Improve system efficiency, sustainability and comfort – Shift public perceptions of public transport	– Strengthen coordination between modes – Formalise and green auto-rickshaws – Procure fuel-efficient, comfortable low-floor AC buses – Ban cycling on busy roads – Deploy policy actors as change-agents, mediating between interest groups	– Cultural norms around informal transport-sharing, linked to high levels of social trust – Historically crucial role of buses in transit – App-cab companies shifting norms and formalising mobility-sharing – Digitalisation and safety on board	– Complexity: multiple modes with separate networks and meanings – Accommodating and addressing legitimate concerns from social movements about the exclusionary effects of 'premium' fares, cycling bans on busy roads
LPG subsidy ('Zero Kero') programme, Indonesia {Box 6.3}	– Decrease fiscal expenditures on kerosene subsidies for cooking	– Subsidise provision of liquefied petroleum gas (LPG) cylinders and initial equipment – Convert existing kerosene suppliers to LPG suppliers	– Provincial government and industry support in targeting beneficiaries and implementation – Synergies in kerosene and LPG distribution infrastructures	– Continued user preference for traditional solid fuels – Reduced GHG benefits as subsidy shifted between fossil fuels
Action Plan for Prevention and Control of Deforestation in the Legal Amazon, Brazil {Box 7.9}	– Control deforestation and promote sustainable development	– Expand protected areas; homologation of indigenous lands – Improve inspections, satellite-based monitoring – Restrict public credit for enterprises and municipalities with high deforestation rates – Set up a REDD+ mechanism (Amazon Fund)	– Participatory agenda-setting process – Cross-sectoral consultations on conservation guidelines – Mainstreaming of deforestation in government programmes and projects	– Political polarisation leading to erosion of environmental governance – Reduced representation and independence of civil society in decision-making bodies – Lack of clarity around land ownership
Climate smart cocoa (CSC) production, Ghana {Box 7.12}	– Promote sustainable intensification of cocoa production – Reduce deforestation – Enhance incomes and adaptive capacities	– Distribute shade tree seedlings – Provide access to agronomic information and agrochemical inputs – Design a multi-stakeholder program including MNCs, farmers and NGOs	– Local resource governance mechanisms ensuring voice for smallholders – Community governance allowed adapting to local context – Private-sector role in popularising CSC	– Lack of secure tenure (tree rights) – Bureaucratic and legal hurdles to register trees – State monopoly on cocoa marketing, export
Coordination mechanism for joining fragmented urban policymaking in Shanghai, China {Box 8.3}	– Integrate policymaking across objectives, towards low-carbon urban development	– Combine central targets and evaluation with local flexibility for initiating varied policy experiments – Establish a local leadership team for coordinating cross-sectoral policies involving multiple institutions – Create a direct programme fund for implementation and capacity-building	– Strong vertical linkages between central and local levels – Mandate for policy learning to inform national policy – Experience with mainstreaming mitigation in related areas (e.g., air pollution)	– Challenging starting point – low share of renewable energy, high dependency on fossil fuels – Continued need for high investments in a developing context
Policy package for building energy efficiency, EU {Box SM.9.1}	– Reduce energy consumption, integrating renewable energy and mitigating GHG emissions from buildings	– Energy performance standards, set at nearly zero energy for new buildings – Energy performance standards for appliances – Energy performance certificates shown during sale – Long-term renovation strategies	– Binding EU-level targets, directives and sectoral effort-sharing regulations – Supportive urban policies, coordinated through city partnerships – Funds raised from allowances auctioned under the Emissions Trading Scheme (ETS)	– Inadequate local technical capacity to implement multiple instruments – Complex governance structure leading to uneven stringency

Table TS.9 (continued):

A. Illustrative case	B. Objective	C. Policy mix	D. Governance context	
			Enablers	Barriers
African electromobility – trackless trams with solar in Bulawayo and e-motorbikes in Kampala {Box 10.4}	– Leapfrog into a decarbonised transport future – Achieve multiple social benefits beyond mobility provision	– Develop urban centres with solar at station precincts – Public-private partnerships for financing – Sanction demonstration projects for new electric transit and new electric motorbikes (for freight)	– 'Achieving SDGs' was an enabling policy framing – Multi-objective policy process for mobility, mitigation and manufacturing – Potential for funding through climate finance – Co-benefits such as local employment generation	– Economic decline in the first decade of the 21st century – Limited fiscal capacity for public funding of infrastructure – Inadequate charging infrastructure for e-motorbikes
Initiative for a climate-friendly industry in North Rhine Westphalia (NRW), Germany {Box 11.3}	– Collaboratively develop innovative strategies towards a net zero GHG industrial sector, while securing competitiveness	– Build platform to bring together industry, scientists and government in self-organised innovation teams – Intensive cross-branch cooperation to articulate policy/infrastructure needs	– NRW is Germany's industrial heartland, with an export-oriented industrial base – Established government-industry ties – Active discourse between industry and public	– Compliance rules preventing in-depth co-operation
Food2030 strategy, Finland {Box 12.2}	– Local, organic and climate-friendly food production – Responsible and healthy food consumption – A competitive food supply chain	– Target funding and knowledge support for innovations – Apply administrative means (legislation, guidance) to increase organic food production and procurement – Use education and information instruments to shift behaviour (media campaigns, websites)	– Year-long deliberative stakeholder engagement process across sectors – Institutional structures for agenda-setting, guiding policy implementation and reflexive discussions	– Weak role of integrated impact assessments (IAMs) to inform agenda-setting – Monitoring and evaluation close to ministry in charge – Lack of standardised indicators of food system sustainability

Box TS.13 | Policy Attribution: Methodologies For – and Estimations of – the Macro-level Impact of Mitigation Policies on Indices of GHG Mitigation

Policy attribution examines the extent to which *GHG emission reductions*, the *proximate drivers of emissions*, and the deployment of *technologies that reduce emissions* may be reasonably attributed to policies implemented prior to the observed changes. Such policies include regulatory instruments such as energy-efficiency programmes or technical standards and codes, carbon pricing, financial support for low-carbon energy technologies and efficiency, voluntary agreements, and regulation of land-use practices.

The vast majority of literature reviewed for this report examines the effect of particular instruments in particular contexts {13.6, 14.3, 16.4}, and only a small number directly or plausibly infer global impacts of policies. Policies also differ in design, scope, and stringency, may change over time as they require amendments or new laws, and often partially overlap with other instruments. These factors complicate analysis, because they give rise to the potential for double counting emissions reductions that have been observed. These lines of evidence on the impact of polices include:

- **GHG Emissions.** Evidence from econometric assessments of the impact of policies in countries which took on Kyoto Protocol targets; decomposition analyses that identify policy-related, absolute reductions from historical levels in particular countries. {13.6.2, 14.3.3, Cross-Chapter Box 10 in Chapter 14}
- **Proximate emission drivers.** Trends in the factors that drive emissions including reduced rates of deforestation {7.6.2}, industrial energy efficiency {Box 16.3}, buildings energy efficiency {Figure 2.22}, and the policy-driven displacement of fossil fuel combustion by renewable energy. (Box TS.13, Table 1; Box TS.13, Figure 1) {Chapters 2 and 6, Cross-Chapter Box 10 in Chapter 14}
- **Technologies.** The literature indicates unambiguously that the rapid expansion of low-carbon energy technologies is substantially attributable to policy. {6.7.5, 16.5}

As illustrated in Box TS.13, Figure 1, these multiple lines of evidence point to policies having had a discernible impact on mitigation for specific countries, sectors, and technologies (*high confidence*), avoiding emissions of several GtCO$_2$-eq yr^{-1} globally (*medium confidence*).

Box TS.13 (continued)

Box TS.13, Table 1 | The effects of policy on GHG emissions, drivers of emissions, and technology deployment.

Sector	Effects on emissions	Effects on immediate drivers	Effects on low-carbon technology
Energy supply {Chapter 6}	Carbon pricing, emissions standards, and technology support have led to declining emissions associated with the supply of energy.	Carbon pricing and technology support have led to improvements in the efficiency of energy conversion.	A variety of market-based instruments, especially technology-support policies have led to high diffusion rates and cost reductions for renewable energy technologies.
AFOLU {Chapter 7}	Regulation of land-use rights and practices have led to falling aggregate AFOLU-sector emissions.	Regulation of land-use rights and practices, payments for ecosystem service, and offsets, have led to decreasing rates of deforestation (*medium confidence*).	
Buildings {Chapter 9}	Regulatory standards have led to reduced emissions from new buildings.	Regulatory standards, financial support for building renovation and market-based instruments have led to improvements in building and building-system efficiencies.	Technology support and regulatory standards have led to adoption of low-carbon heating systems and high-efficiency appliances.
Transport {Chapter 10}	Vehicle standards, land-use planning, and carbon pricing have led to avoided emissions in ground transportation.	Vehicle standard, carbon pricing, and support for electrification have led to automobile efficiency improvements.	Technology support and emissions standards have increased diffusion rates and cost reductions for electric vehicles.
Industry {Chapter 11}		Carbon pricing has led to efficiency improvements in industrial facilities.	

Note: statements describe the effects of policies across those countries where policies are in place. Unless otherwise noted, all findings are of *high confidence*.

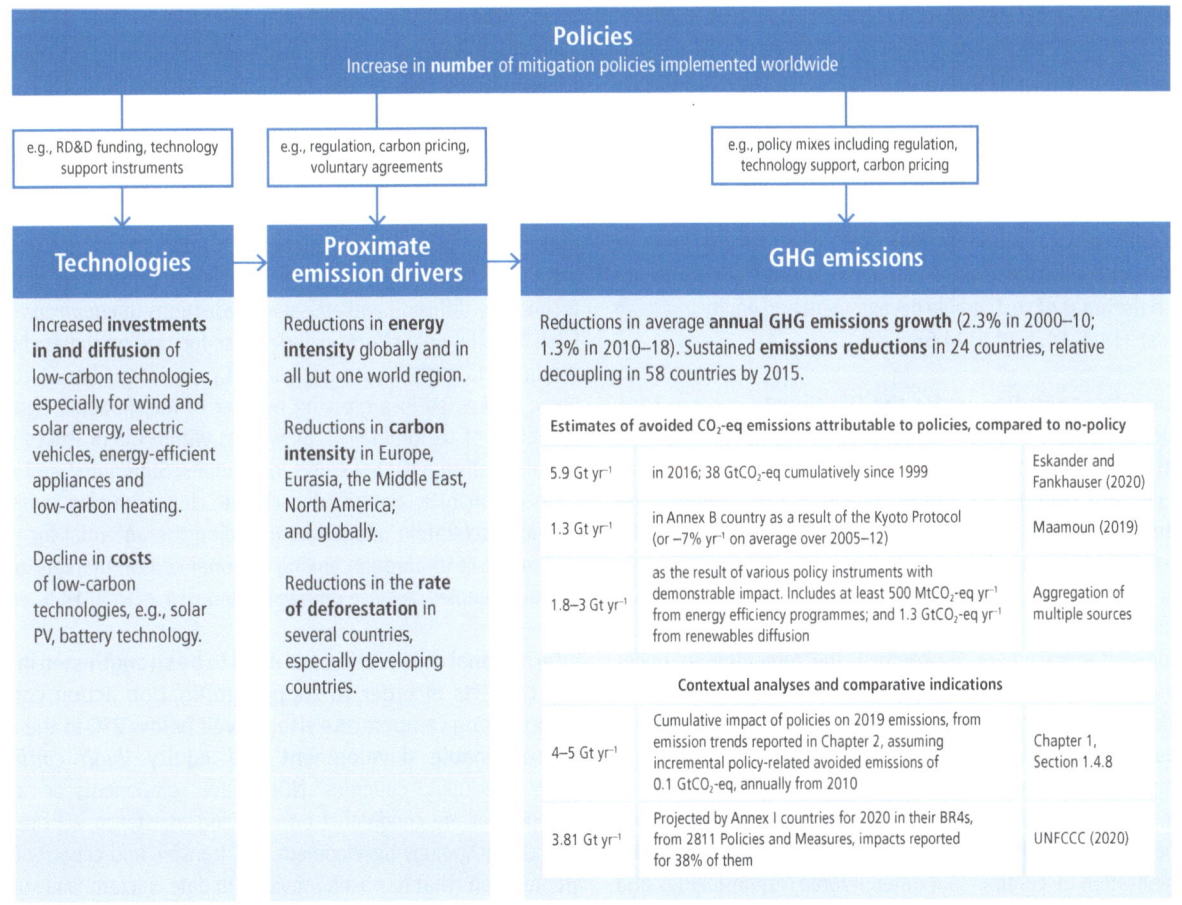

Box TS.13, Figure 1 | Policy impacts on key outcome indices: GHG emissions, proximate emission drivers, and technologies, including several lines of evidence on GHG abatement attributable to policies. {Cross-Chapter Box 10, Figure 1 in Chapter 14}

TS.6.2   International Cooperation

International cooperation is having positive and measurable results (*high confidence*). The Kyoto Protocol led to measurable and substantial avoided emissions, including in 20 countries with Kyoto first-commitment period targets that have experienced a decade of declining absolute emissions. It also built national capacity for GHG accounting, catalysed the creation of GHG markets, and increased investments in low-carbon technologies. Other international agreements and institutions have led to avoided CO_2 emissions from land-use practices, as well as avoided emissions of some non-CO_2 greenhouse gases (*medium confidence*). {14.3, 14.5, 14.6}

New forms of international cooperation have emerged since AR5 in line with an evolving understanding of effective mitigation policies, processes, and institutions. Both new and pre-existing forms of cooperation are vital for achieving climate mitigation goals in the context of sustainable development (*high confidence*). While previous IPCC assessments have noted important synergies between the outcomes of climate mitigation and achieving sustainable development objectives, there now appear to be synergies between the two processes themselves (*medium confidence*). Since AR5, international cooperation has shifted towards facilitating national-level mitigation action through numerous channels, including though processes established under the UNFCCC regime and through regional and sectoral agreements and organisations. {14.2, 14.3, 14.5, 14.6}

Participation in international agreements and transboundary networks is associated with the adoption of climate policies at the national and sub-national levels, as well as by non-state actors (*high confidence*). International cooperation helps countries achieve long-term mitigation targets when it supports development and diffusion of low-carbon technologies, often at the level of individual sectors, which can simultaneously lead to significant benefits in the areas of sustainable development and equity (*medium confidence*). {14.2, 14.3, 14.5, 14.6}

International cooperation under the UN climate regime took an important new direction with the entry into force of the 2015 Paris Agreement, which strengthened the objective of the UN climate regime, including its long-term temperature goal, while adopting a different architecture to that of the Kyoto Protocol (*high confidence*). The core national commitments under the Kyoto Protocol were legally binding quantified emission targets for developed countries tied to well-defined mechanisms for monitoring and enforcement. By contrast, the commitments under the Paris Agreement are primarily procedural, extend to all parties, and are designed to trigger domestic policies and measures, enhance transparency, and stimulate climate investments, particularly in developing countries, and to lead iteratively to rising levels of ambition across all countries. Issues of equity remain of central importance in the UN climate regime, notwithstanding shifts in the operationalisation of 'common but differentiated responsibilities and respective capabilities' from Kyoto to Paris. {14.3}

There are conflicting views on whether the Paris Agreement's commitments and mechanisms will lead to the attainment of its stated goals (*medium confidence*). Arguments in support of the Paris Agreement are that the processes it initiates and supports will in multiple ways lead, and indeed have already led, to rising levels of ambition over time. The recent proliferation of national mid-century net zero GHG targets can be attributed in part to the Paris Agreement. Moreover, its processes and commitments will enhance countries' abilities to achieve their stated level of ambition, particularly among developing countries. Arguments against the Paris Agreement are that it lacks a mechanism to review the adequacy of individual Parties' Nationally Determined Contributions (NDCs), that collectively current NDCs are inconsistent in their level of ambition with achieving the Paris Agreement's long-term temperature goal, that its processes will not lead to sufficiently rising levels of ambition in the NDCs, and that NDCs will not be achieved because the targets, policies and measures they contain are not legally binding at the international level. To some extent, arguments on both sides are aligned with different analytic frameworks, including assumptions about the main barriers to mitigation that international cooperation can help overcome. The extent to which countries increase the ambition of their NDCs and ensure they are effectively implemented will depend in part on the successful implementation of the support mechanisms in the Paris Agreement, and in turn will determine whether the goals of the Paris Agreement are met (*high confidence*). {14.2, 14.3, 14.4}

International cooperation outside the UNFCCC processes and agreements provides critical support for mitigation in particular regions, sectors and industries, for particular types of emissions, and at the sub- and trans-national levels (*high confidence*). Agreements addressing ozone depletion, transboundary air pollution, and release of mercury are all leading to reductions in the emissions of specific greenhouse gases. Cooperation is occurring at multiple governance levels including cities. Transnational partnerships and alliances involving non-state and sub-national actors are also playing a growing role in stimulating low-carbon technology diffusion and emissions reductions (*medium confidence*). Such transnational efforts include those focused on climate litigation; the impacts of these are unclear but promising. Climate change is being addressed in a growing number of international agreements operating at sectoral levels, as well as within the practices of many multilateral organisations and institutions. Sub-global and regional cooperation, often described as climate clubs, can play an important role in accelerating mitigation, including the potential for reducing mitigation costs through linking national carbon markets, although actual examples of these remain limited. {14.2, 14.4, 14.5, 14.6}

International cooperation will need to be strengthened in several key respects in order to support mitigation action consistent with limiting temperature rise to well below 2°C in the context of sustainable development and equity (*high confidence*). Many developing countries' NDCs have components or additional actions that are conditional on receiving assistance with respect to finance, technology development and transfer, and capacity-building, greater than what has been provided to date. Sectoral and sub-global cooperation is providing critical support, and yet there is room for further progress. In some cases, notably with respect to aviation and shipping, sectoral agreements have adopted climate mitigation goals that fall far short of what would be required to achieve the long-term temperature goal of the Paris Agreement. Moreover, there are cases where international cooperation may be hindering mitigation efforts, namely evidence that trade and investment agreements, as well as agreements within the energy sector, impede national mitigation efforts (*medium confidence*). International cooperation is emerging but so far fails to fully address transboundary issues associated with solar radiation modification (SRM) and carbon dioxide removal (CDR). {14.2, 14.3, 14.4, 14.5, 14.6, Cross-Working Group Box 4 in Chapter 14}

TS.6.3   Societal Aspects of Mitigation

Social equity reinforces capacity and motivation for mitigating climate change (*medium confidence*). Impartial governance such as fair treatment by law-and-order institutions, fair treatment by gender, and income equity, increases social trust, thus enabling demand-side climate policies. High-status (often high-carbon) item consumption may be reduced by taxing absolute wealth without compromising well-being. {5.2, 5.4.2, 5.6}

Policies that increase the political access and participation of women, racialised, and marginalised groups, increase the democratic impetus for climate action (*high confidence*). Including more differently situated knowledge and diverse perspectives makes climate mitigation policies more effective. {5.2, 5.6}

Greater contextualisation and granularity in policy approaches better addresses the challenges of rapid transitions towards zero-carbon systems (*high confidence*). Larger systems take more time to evolve, grow, and change compared to smaller ones. Creating and scaling up entirely new systems takes longer than replacing existing technologies and practices. Late adopters tend to adopt faster than early pioneers. Obstacles and feasibility barriers are high in the early transition phases. Barriers decrease as a result of technical and social learning processes, network building, scale economies, cultural debates, and institutional adjustments. {5.5, 5.6}

Mitigation policies that integrate and communicate with the values people hold are more successful (*high confidence*). Values differ between cultures. Measures that support autonomy, energy security and safety, equity and environmental protection, and fairness resonate well in many communities and social groups. Changing from a commercialised, individualised, entrepreneurial training model to an education cognisant of planetary health and human well-being can accelerate climate change awareness and action. {5.4.1, 5.4.2}

Changes in consumption choices that are supported by structural changes and political action enable the uptake of low-carbon choices (*high confidence*). Policy instruments applied in coordination can help to accelerate change in a consistent desired direction. Targeted technological change, regulation, and public policy can help in steering digitalisation, the sharing economy, and circular economy towards climate change mitigation. (Boxes TS.12 and TS.14) {5.3, 5.6}

Complementarity in policies helps in the design of an optimal demand-side policy mix (*medium confidence*). In the case of energy efficiency, for example, this may involve CO_2 pricing, standards and norms, and information feedback. {5.3, 5.4, 5.6}

TS.6.4   Investment and Finance

Finance to reduce net GHG emissions and enhance resilience to climate impacts is a critical enabling factor for the low-carbon transition. Fundamental inequities in access to finance as well as finance terms and conditions, and countries' exposure to physical impacts of climate change overall, result in a worsening outlook for a global Just Transition (*high confidence*). Decarbonising the economy requires global action to address fundamental economic inequities and overcome the climate investment trap that exists for many developing countries. For these countries the costs and risks of financing often represent a significant challenge for stakeholders at all levels. This challenge is exacerbated by these countries' general economic vulnerability and indebtedness. The rising public fiscal costs of mitigation, and of adapting to climate shocks, is affecting many countries and worsening public indebtedness and country credit ratings at a time when there were already significant stresses on public finances. The COVID-19 pandemic has made these stresses worse and tightened public finances still further. Other major challenges for commercial climate finance include: the mismatch between capital and investment needs, home bias[31] considerations, differences in risk perceptions for regions, as well as limited institutional capacity to ensure safeguards are effective (*high confidence*). {15.2, 15.6.3}

Investors, central banks, and financial regulators are driving increased awareness of climate risk. This increased awareness can support climate policy development and implementation (*high confidence*) {15.2, 15.6}. Climate-related financial risks arise from physical impacts of climate change (already relevant in the short term), and from a disorderly transition to a low-carbon economy. Awareness of these risks is increasing, leading also to concerns about financial stability. Financial regulators and institutions have responded with multiple regulatory and voluntary initiatives to assess and address these risks. Yet despite these initiatives, climate-related financial risks remain greatly underestimated by financial institutions and markets, limiting the capital reallocation needed for the low-carbon transition. Moreover, risks relating to national and international inequity – which act as a barrier to the transformation – are not yet reflected in decisions by the financial community. Stronger steering by regulators and policymakers has the potential to close this gap. Despite the increasing attention of investors to climate change, there is limited evidence that this attention has directly impacted emission reductions. This leaves high uncertainty, both near term (2021–30) and longer term (2021–50), on the feasibility of an alignment of financial flows with the Paris Agreement goals (*high confidence*). {15.2, 15.6}

Progress on the alignment of financial flows with low-GHG emissions pathways remains slow. There is a climate financing

---

31   Most of climate finance stays within national borders, especially private climate flows (over 90%). The reasons for this range from national policy support, differences in regulatory standards, exchange rate, political and governance risks, to information market failures.

gap which reflects a persistent misallocation of global capital (*high confidence*) {15.2, 15.3}. Persistently high levels of both public and private fossil fuel-related financing continue to be of major concern despite promising recent commitments. This reflects policy misalignment, the current perceived risk-return profile of fossil fuel-related investments, and political economy constraints (*high confidence*). Estimates of climate finance flows[32] exhibit highly divergent patterns across regions and sectors and a slowing growth {15.3}. When the perceived risks are too high, the misallocation of abundant savings persists and investors refrain from investing in infrastructure and industry in search of safer financial assets, even earning low or negative real returns (*high confidence*). {15.2, 15.3}

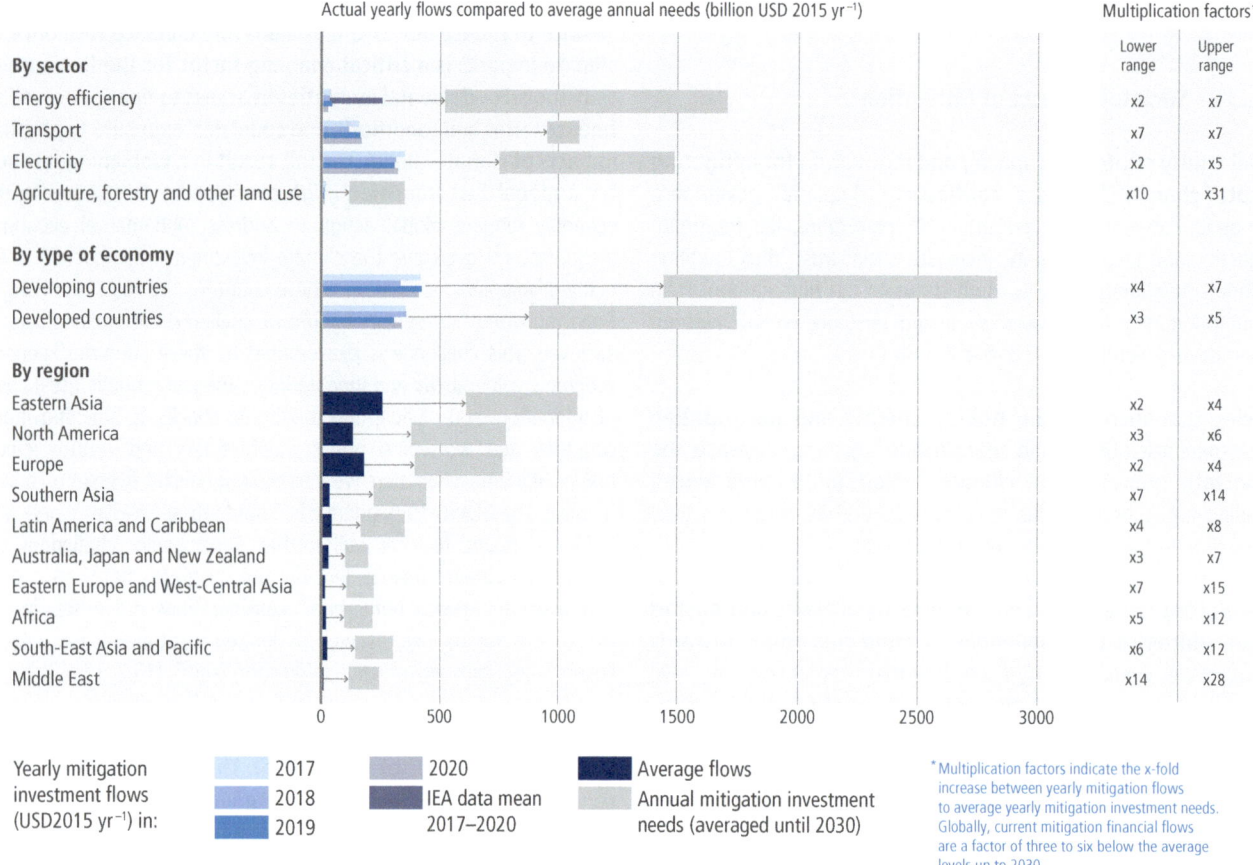

Figure TS.25 | Breakdown of recent average (downstream) mitigation investments and model-based investment requirements for 2020–2030 (USD billion) in scenarios that likely limit warming to 2°C or lower. Mitigation investment flows and model-based investment requirements by sector / segment (energy efficiency in buildings and industry, transport including efficiency, electricity generation, transmission and distribution including electrification, and agriculture, forestry and other land use), by type of economy, and by region (see Annex II Part I Section 1: By region is based on intermediate level (R10) classification scheme. By type of economy is based on intermediate level (R10) classification scheme, which considers 'North America', 'Europe', and 'Australia, Japan and New Zealand' as developed countries, and the other seven regions as developing countries). Breakdown by sector / segment may differ slightly from sectoral analysis in other contexts due to the availability of investment needs data. The granularity of the models assessed in Chapter 3, and other studies, do not allow for a robust assessment of the specific investment needs of LDCs or SIDSs. Investment requirements in developing countries might be underestimated due to missing data points as well as underestimated technology costs. In modelled pathways, regional investments are projected to occur when and where they are cost cost-effective to limit global warming. The model quantifications help to identify high-priority areas for cost-effective investments, but do not provide any indication on who would finance the regional investments. Investment requirements and flows covering downstream / mitigation technology deployment only. Data includes investments with a direct mitigation effect, and in the case of electricity, additional transmission and distribution investments. See section 15.4.2 Quantitative assessment of financing needs for detailed data on investment requirements. Data on mitigation investment flows are based on a single series of reports (Climate Policy Initiative, CPI) which assembles data from multiple sources. Investment flows for energy efficiency are adjusted based on data from the International Energy Agency (IEA). Data on mitigation investments do not include technical assistance (i.e., policy and national budget support or capacity building), other non-technology deployment financing. Adaptation only flows are also excluded. Data on mitigation investment requirements for electricity are based on emission pathways C1, C2 and C3 (Table SPM.1). For electricity investment requirements, the upper end refers to the mean of C1 pathways and the lower end to the mean of C3 pathways. Data points for energy efficiency, transport and AFOLU cannot always be linked to C1–C3 scenarios. Data do not include needs for adaptation or general infrastructure investment or investment related to meeting the SDGs other than mitigation, which may be at least partially required to facilitate mitigation. The multiplication factors show the ratio of average annual model-based mitigation investment requirements (2020–2030) and most recent annual mitigation investments (averaged for 2017–2020). The lower and upper multiplication factors refer to the lower and upper ends of the range of investment needs.

Given the multiple sources and lack of harmonised methodologies, the data can only be indicative of the size and pattern of investment gaps. The gap between most recent flows and required investments is only a single indicator. A more comprehensive (and qualitative) assessment is required in order to understand the magnitude of the challenge of scaling up investment in sectors and regions. The analysis also does not consider the effects of misaligned flows. {15.3, 15.4, 15.5, Table 15.2, Table 15.3, Table 15.4}

---

32   Climate finance flows refers to local, national, or transnational financing from public, private, and alternative sources, to support mitigation and adaptation actions addressing climate change.

Global climate finance is heavily focused on mitigation (more than 90% on average between 2017–2020) (*high confidence*) {15.4, 15.5}. This is despite the significant economic effects of climate change's expected physical impacts, and the increasing awareness of these effects on financial stability. To meet the needs for rapid deployment of mitigation options, global mitigation investments are expected to need to increase by the factor of three to six (*high confidence*). The gaps represent a major challenge for developing countries, especially Least-Developed Countries (LDCs), where flows have to increase by the factor of four to seven for specific sectors such as AFOLU, and for specific groups with limited access to, and high costs of, climate finance (*high confidence*) (Figure TS.25) {15.4, 15.5}. The actual size of sectoral and regional climate financing gaps is only one component driving the magnitude of the challenge. Financial and economic viability, access to capital markets, appropriate regulatory frameworks, and institutional capacity to attract and facilitate investments and ensure safeguards are decisive to scaling-up funding. Soft costs for regulatory environment and institutional capacity, upstream funding needs as well as R&D and venture capital for development of new technologies and business models are often overlooked despite their critical role to facilitate the deployment of scaled-up climate finance (*high confidence*). {15.4.1, 15.5.2}

The relatively slow implementation of commitments by countries and stakeholders in the financial sector to scale up climate finance reflects neither the urgent need for ambitious climate action, nor the economic rationale for ambitious climate action (*high confidence*). Delayed climate investments and financing – and limited alignment of investment activity with the Paris Agreement – will result in significant carbon lock-ins, stranded assets, and other additional costs. This will particularly impact urban infrastructure and the energy and transport sectors (*high confidence*). A common understanding of debt sustainability and debt transparency, including negative implications of deferred climate investments on future GDP, and how stranded assets and resources may be compensated, has not yet been developed (*medium confidence*). {15.6}

There is a mismatch between capital availability in the developed world and the future emissions expected in developing countries (*high confidence*). This emphasises the need to recognise the explicit and positive social value of global cross-border mitigation financing. A significant push for international climate finance access for vulnerable and poor countries is particularly important given these countries' high costs of financing, debt stress and the impacts of ongoing climate change (*high confidence*). {15.2, 15.3.2.3, 15.5.2, 15.6.1, 15.6.7}

Innovative financing approaches could help reduce the systemic under-pricing of climate risk in markets and foster demand for investment opportunities aligned with the Paris Agreement goals. Approaches include de-risking investments, robust 'green' labelling and disclosure schemes, in addition to a regulatory focus on transparency and reforming international monetary system financial sector regulations (*medium confidence*). Green bond markets and markets for sustainable finance products have grown significantly since AR5 and the landscape continues to evolve. Underpinning this evolution is investors' preference for scalable and identifiable low-carbon investment opportunities. These relatively new labelled financial products will help by allowing a smooth integration into existing asset allocation models (*high confidence*). Green bond markets and markets for sustainable finance products have also increased significantly since AR5, but challenges nevertheless remain, in particular, there are concerns about 'greenwashing' and the limited application of these markets to developing countries (*high confidence*). {15.6.2, 15.6.6}

New business models (e.g., pay-as-you-go) can facilitate the aggregation of small-scale financing needs and provide scalable investment opportunities with more attractive risk-return profiles (*high confidence*). Support and guidance for enhancing transparency can promote capital markets' climate financing by providing quality information to price climate risks and opportunities. Examples include SDG and environmental, social and governance (ESG) disclosure, scenario analysis and climate risk assessments, including the Task Force on Climate-related Financial Disclosures (TCFD). The outcome of these market-correcting approaches on capital flows cannot be taken for granted, however, without appropriate fiscal, monetary and financial policies. Mitigation policies will be required to enhance the risk-weighted return of low-emission and climate-resilient options, accelerate the emergence and support for financial products based on real projects, such as green bonds, and phase-out fossil fuel subsidies. Greater public-private cooperation can also encourage the private sector to increase and broaden investments, within a context of safeguards and standards, and this can be integrated into national climate change policies and plans (*high confidence*). {15.1, 15.2.4, 15.3.1, 15.3.2, 15.3.3, 15.5.2, 15.6.1, 15.6.2, 15.6.6, 15.6.7, 15.6.8}

Ambitious global climate policy coordination and stepped-up public climate financing over the next decade (2021–2030) can help redirect capital markets and overcome challenges relating to the need for parallel investments in mitigation. It can also help address macroeconomic uncertainty and alleviate developing countries' debt burden post-COVID-19 (*high confidence*). Providing strong climate policy signals helps guide investment decisions. Credible signalling by governments and the international community can reduce uncertainty for financial decision-makers and help reduce transition risk. In addition to indirect and direct subsidies, the public sector's role in addressing market failures, barriers, provision of information, and risk-sharing can encourage the efficient mobilisation of private sector finance (*high confidence*) {15.2, 15.6.1, 15.6.2}. The mutual benefits of coordinated support for climate mitigation and adaptation in the next decade for both developed and developing regions could potentially be very high in the post-COVID era. Climate-compatible stimulus packages could significantly reduce the macro-financial uncertainty generated by the pandemic and increase the sustainability of the world economic recovery {15.2, 15.3.2.3, 15.5.2, 15.6.1, 15.6.7}. Political leadership and intervention remain central to addressing uncertainty, which is a fundamental barrier for the redirection of financial flows. Existing policy misalignments – for example, in fossil fuel subsidies – undermine the credibility of public commitments, reduce perceived transition risks and limit financial sector action (*high confidence*). {15.2, 15.3.3, 15.6.1, 15.6.2, 15.6.3}

TS

The greater the urgency of action to remain on a 1.5°C pathway, the greater need for parallel investment decisions in upstream and downstream parts of the value chain (*high confidence*). Greater urgency also reduces the lead times to build trust in regulatory frameworks. Consequently, many investment decisions will need to be made based on the long-term global goals. This highlights the importance of trust in political leadership which, in turn, affects risk perception and ultimately financing costs (*high confidence*). {15.6.1, 15.6.2}

Accelerated international cooperation on finance is a critical enabler of a low-carbon and Just Transition (*very high confidence*). Scaled-up public grants for adaptation and mitigation, and funding for low-income and vulnerable regions, especially in Sub-Saharan Africa, may have the highest returns. Key options include: increased public finance flows from developed to developing countries beyond USD100 billion a year; shifting from a direct lending modality towards public guarantees to reduce risks and greatly leverage private flows at lower cost; local capital markets development; and, changing the enabling operational definitions. A coordinated effort to green the post-pandemic recovery is also essential in countries facing much higher debt costs (*high confidence*). {15.2, 15.6}

TS.6.5 Innovation, Technology Development and Transfer

Innovation in climate mitigation technologies has seen enormous activity and significant progress in recent years. Innovation has also led to, and exacerbated, trade-offs in relation to sustainable development. Innovation can leverage action to mitigate climate change by reinforcing other interventions. In conjunction with other enabling conditions, innovation can support system transitions to limit warming and help shift development pathways. The currently widespread implementation of solar PV and LED lighting, for instance, could not have happened without technological innovation. Technological innovation can also bring about new and improved ways of delivering services that are essential to human well-being (*high confidence*) {16.1, 16.3, 16.4, 16.6}. At the same time as delivering benefits, innovation can result in trade-offs that undermine both progress on mitigation and progress towards other Sustainable Development Goals (SDGs). Trade-offs include negative externalities' – for instance, greater environmental pollution and social inequalities – rebound effects leading to lower net emission reductions or even increases in emissions, and increased dependency on foreign knowledge and providers (*high confidence*). Effective governance and policy have the potential to avoid and minimise such misalignments (*medium evidence, high agreement*). {16.2, 16.3, 16.4, 16.5.1, 16.6}

A systemic view of innovation to direct and organise the processes has grown over the last decade. This systemic view of innovation takes into account the role of actors, institutions, and their interactions, and can inform how innovation systems that vary across technologies, sectors and countries, can be strengthened (*high confidence*) {16.2, 16.3, 16.5}. Where a systemic view of innovation has been taken, it has enabled the development and implementation of indicators that are better able to provide insights in innovation processes. This, in turn, has enabled the analysis and strengthening of innovation systems. Traditional quantitative innovation indicators mainly include R&D investments and patents. Figure TS.26 illustrates that energy-related research, development and demonstration (RD&D) has risen slowly in the last

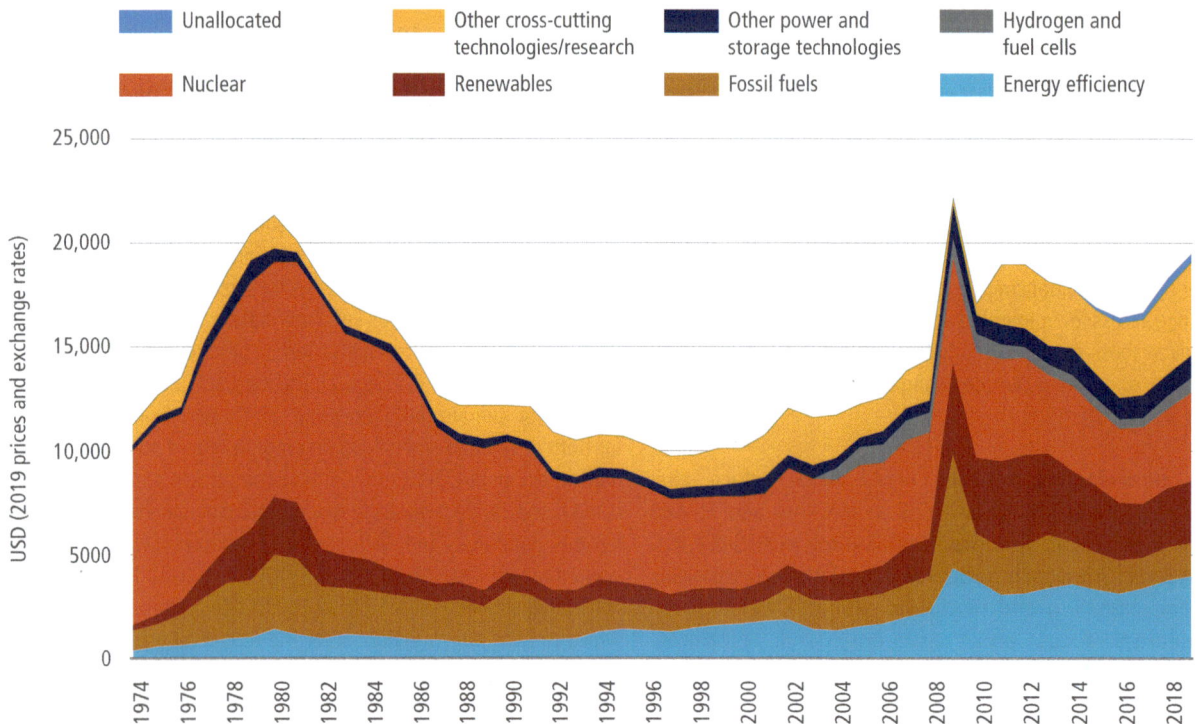

Figure TS.26 | Fraction of public energy research, development and demonstration (RD&D) spending by technology over time for IEA (largely OECD) countries between 1974 and 2018. {Box 16.3, Figure 1}

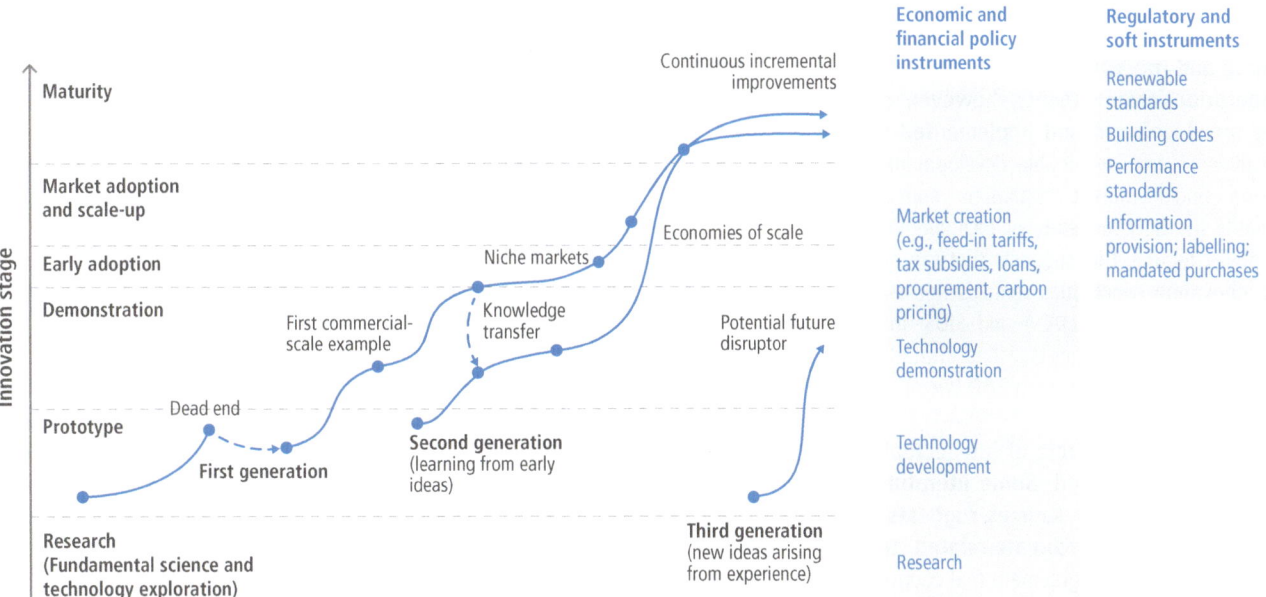

Figure TS.27 | Technology innovation process and the (illustrative) roles of different public policy instruments (on the right-hand side). {Figure 16.1} Note that demand-pull instruments in the regulatory instrument category, for instance, can also shape the early stages of the innovation process. Their position in the latter stages is highlighted in this figure because typically these instruments have been introduced in latter stages of the development of the technology. {16.4.4}

two decades, and that there has been a reorientation of the portfolio of funded energy technologies. Systemic indicators of innovation, however, go well beyond these approaches. They include structural innovation system elements including actors and networks, as well as indicators for how innovation systems function, such as access to finance, employment in relevant sectors, and lobbying activities {16.3.4, Table 16.7}. For example, in Latin America, monitoring systemic innovation indicators for the effectiveness of agroecological mitigation approaches has provided insights on the appropriateness and social alignment of new technologies and practices {Box 16.5}. Climate-energy-economy models, including integrated assessment models (IAMs), generally employ a stylised and necessarily incomplete view of innovation, and have yet to incorporate a systemic representation of innovation systems. {16.2.4, Box 16.1}

A systemic perspective on technological change can provide insights to policymakers supporting their selection of effective innovation policy instruments (*high confidence*) {16.4, 16.5}. A combination of scaled-up innovation investments with demand-pull interventions can achieve faster technology unit cost reductions and more rapid scale-up than either approach in isolation. These innovation policy instruments would nonetheless have to be tailored to local development priorities, to the specific context of different countries, and to the technology being supported. The timing of interventions and any trade-offs with sustainable development also need to be addressed. Public R&D funding and support, as well as innovation procurement, have shown to be valuable for fostering innovation in small-to-medium clean-tech firms (Figure TS.27) {16.4.4.3}. Innovation outcomes of policy instruments not necessarily aimed at innovation, such as feed-in tariffs, auctions, emissions

trading schemes, taxes and renewable portfolio standards, vary from negligible to positive for climate change mitigation. Some specific designs of environmental taxation can also result in negative distributional outcomes {16.4.4}. Most of the available literature and evidence on innovation systems come from industrialised countries and larger developing countries. However, there is a growing body of evidence from developing countries and Small Island Developing States (SIDS). {16.4, 16.5, 16.7}

Experience and analyses show that technological change is inhibited if technological innovation system functions are not adequately fulfilled; this inhibition occurs more often in developing countries (*high confidence*). Examples of such functions are knowledge development, resource mobilisation, and activities that shape the needs, requirements and expectations of actors within the innovation system (guidance of the search). Capabilities play a key role in these functions, the buildup of which can be enhanced by domestic measures, but also by international cooperation. For instance, innovation cooperation on wind energy has contributed to the accelerated global spread of this technology. As another example, the policy guidance by the Indian government, which also promoted development of data, testing capabilities and knowledge within the private sector, has been a key determinant of the success of an energy-efficiency programme for air conditioners and refrigerators in India. {16.3, 16.5, 16.6, Cross-Chapter Box 12 in Chapter 16, Box 16.3}

Consistent with innovation system approaches, the sharing of knowledge and experiences between developed and developing countries can contribute to addressing global climate and the SDGs. The effectiveness of such international cooperation arrangements, however, depends on the way they are developed and implemented (*high confidence*). The effectiveness and sustainable development benefits of technology sharing under market conditions appears to be determined primarily by the complexity of technologies, local capabilities and the policy regime. This suggests that the development of planning and innovation capabilities remains necessary, especially in Least-Developed Countries (LDCs) and SIDS. International diffusion of low-emission technologies is also facilitated by knowledge spillovers from regions engaged in clean R&D (*medium confidence*). {16.2}

The evidence on the role of intellectual property rights (IPR) in innovation is mixed. Some literature suggests that it is a barrier while other sources suggests that it is an enabler to the diffusion of climate-related technologies (*medium confidence*). There is agreement that countries with well-developed institutional capacity may benefit from a strengthened IPR regime, but that countries with limited capabilities might face greater barriers to innovation as a consequence. This enhances the continued need for capacity-building. Ideas to improve the alignment of the global IPR regime and addressing climate change include specific arrangements for LDCs, case-by-case decision-making and patent-pooling institutions. {16.2.3, 16.5, Box 16.10}

Although some initiatives have mobilised investments in developing countries, gaps in innovation cooperation remain, including in the Paris Agreement instruments. These gaps could be filled by enhancing financial support for international technology cooperation, by strengthening cooperative approaches, and by helping build suitable capacity in developing countries across all technological innovation system functions (*high confidence*). The implementation of current arrangements of international cooperation for technology development and transfer, as well as capacity-building, are insufficient to meet climate objectives and contribute to sustainable development. For example, despite building a large market for mitigation technologies in developing countries, the lack of a systemic perspective in the implementation of the Clean Development Mechanism (CDM), operational since the mid-2000s, has only led to some technology transfer, especially to larger developing countries, but limited capacity building and minimal technology development (*medium confidence*). In the current climate regime, a more systemic approach to innovation cooperation could be introduced by linking technology institutions, such as the Technology Mechanism, and financial actors, such as the Financial Mechanism. {16.5.3}

Countries are exposed to sustainable development challenges in parallel with the challenges that relate to climate change. Addressing both sets of challenges simultaneously presents multiple and recurrent obstacles that systemic approaches to technological change could help resolve, provided they are well managed (*high confidence*). Obstacles include both entrenched power relations dominated by vested interests that

control and benefit from existing technologies, and governance structures that continue to reproduce unsustainable patterns of production and consumption (*medium confidence*). Studies also highlight the potential of cultural factors to strongly influence the pace and direction of technological change. Sustainable solutions require adoption and mainstreaming of locally novel technologies that can meet local needs, and simultaneously address the SDGs. Acknowledging the systemic nature of technological innovation – which involve many levels of actors, stages of innovation and scales – can lead to new opportunities to shift development pathways towards sustainability. {16.4, 16.5, 16.6}

Strategies for climate change mitigation can be most effective in accelerating transformative change when actions taken to strengthen one set of enabling conditions also reinforce and strengthen the effectiveness of other enabling conditions (*medium confidence*). Applying transition or system dynamics to decisions can help policymakers take advantage of such high-leverage intervention points, address the specific characteristics of technological stages, and respond to societal dynamics. Inspiration can be drawn from the global unit-cost reductions of solar PV, which were accelerated by a combination of factors interacting in a mutually reinforcing way across a limited group of countries (*high confidence*) {Box 16.2, Cross-Chapter Box 12 in Chapter 16}. Transitions can be accelerated by policies appropriately targeted, which may be grouped in different 'pillars of policy'. The relative importance of different 'pillars' differs according to the stage of the transition. (Figure TS.28) {1.2.3}

Better and more comprehensive data on innovation indicators can provide timely insights for policymakers and policy design locally, nationally and internationally, especially for developing countries, where such insights are often missing. Data needed include those that can show the strength of technological, sectoral and national innovation systems. It is also necessary to validate current results and generate insights from theoretical frameworks and empirical studies for developing countries' contexts. Innovation studies on adaptation and mitigation other than energy and *ex-post* assessments of the effectiveness of various innovation-related policies and interventions, including R&D, would also provide benefits. Furthermore, methodological developments to improve the ability of IAMs to capture energy innovation system dynamics and the relevant institutions and policies (including design and implementation), would allow for more realistic assessment. {16.2, 16.3, 16.7}

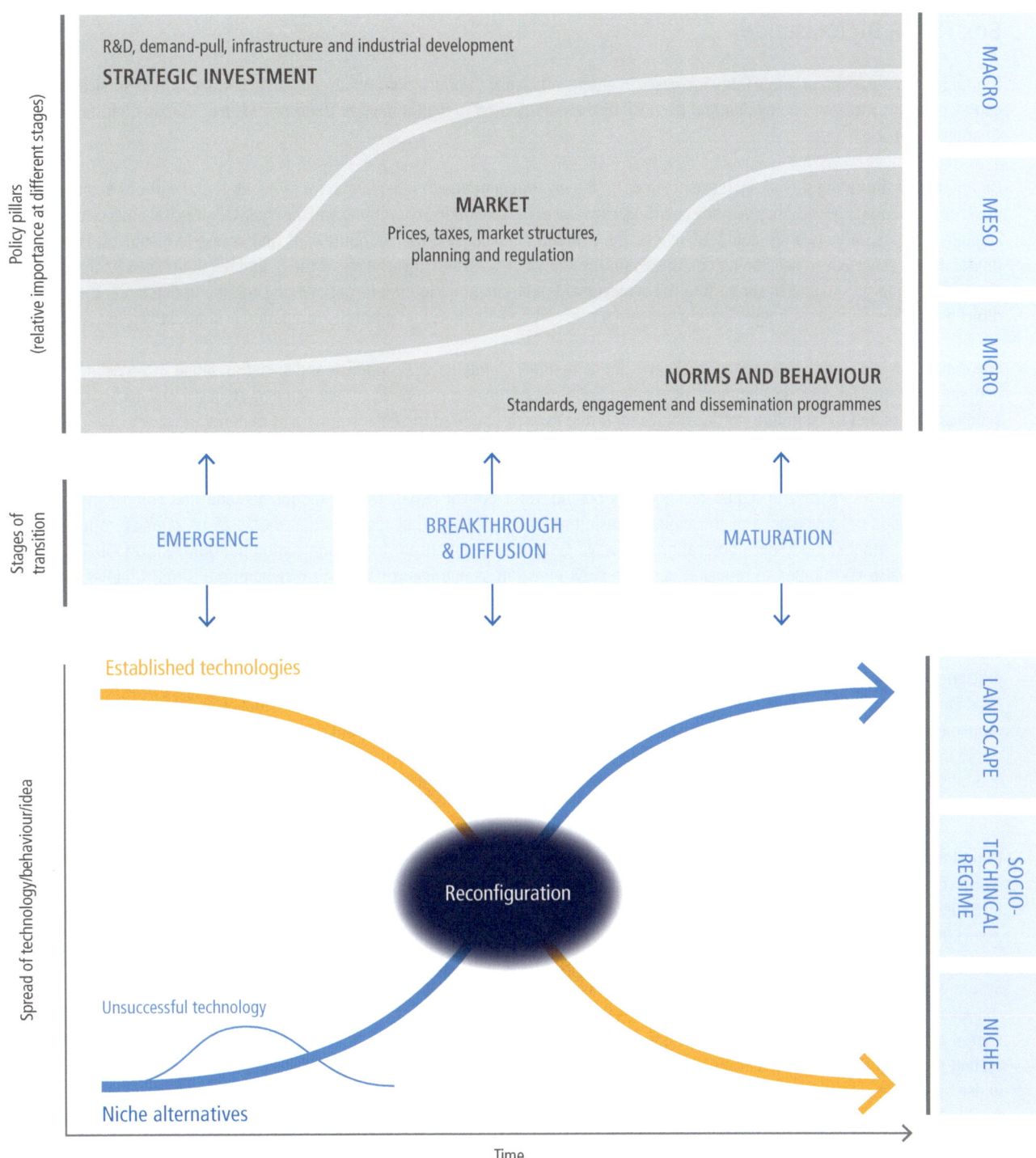

Figure TS.28 | Transition dynamics: levels, policies and processes. {Figure 1.7} The relative importance of different 'pillars of policy' differs according to the stage of the transition. The lower panel illustrates growth of innovative technologies or practices, which if successful, emerge from niches into an S-shaped dynamic of exponential growth. The diffusion stage often involves new infrastructure and reconfiguration of existing market and regulatory structures. During the phase of more widespread diffusion, growth levels off to linear, then slows as the industry and market matures. The processes displace incumbent technologies/practices which decline, initially slowly, but then at an accelerating pace. Many related literatures identify three main levels with different characteristics, most generally termed *micro, meso* and *macro*.

Box TS.14 | Digitalisation

Digital technologies can promote large increases in energy efficiency through coordination and an economic shift to services, but they can also greatly increase energy demand because of the energy used in digital devices (*high confidence*). {Cross-Chapter Box 11 in Chapter 16, 16.2}

Digital devices, including servers, increase pressure on the environment due to the demand for rare metals and end-of-life disposal. The absence of adequate governance in many countries can lead to harsh working conditions and unregulated disposal of electronic waste. Digitalisation also affects firms' competitiveness, the demand for skills, and the distribution of, and access to resources. The existing digital divide, especially in developing countries, and the lack of appropriate governance of the digital revolution can hamper the role that digitalisation could play in supporting the achievement of stringent mitigation targets. At present, the understanding of both the direct and indirect impacts of digitalisation on energy use, carbon emissions and potential mitigation is limited (*medium confidence*).

The digital transformation is a megatrend that is fundamentally changing all economies and societies, albeit in very different ways depending on the level of development of a given country and on the nature of its economic system. Digital technologies have significant potential to contribute to decarbonisation due to their ability to increase energy and material efficiency, make transport and building systems less wasteful, and improve the access to services for consumers and citizens. Yet, if left unmanaged, the digital transformation will probably increase energy demand, exacerbate inequities and the concentration of power, leaving developing economies with less access to digital technologies behind, raise ethical issues, reduce labour demand and compromise citizens' welfare. Appropriate governance of the digital transformation can ensure that digitalisation works as an enabler, rather than as a barrier and further strain in decarbonisation pathways. Governance can ensure that digitalisation not only reduces GHG emissions intensity but also contributes to reducing absolute GHG emission, constraining run-away consumption. {Cross-Chapter Box 11 in Chapter 16, 16.2}

Digital technologies have the potential to reduce energy demand in all end-use sectors through steep improvements in energy efficiency. This includes material input savings and increased coordination as they allow the use of fewer inputs to perform a given task. Smart appliances and energy management, supported by choice architectures, economic incentives and social norms, effectively reduce energy demand and associated GHG emissions by 5–10% while maintaining equal service levels. Data centres can also play a role in energy-system management, for example by waste-heat utilisation where district heat systems are close by; temporal and spatial scheduling of electricity demand can provide about 6% of the total potential demand response. {5.5, Cross-Chapter Box 11, Table 1 in Chapter 16}

Digital technologies, analytics and connectivity consume large amounts of energy, implying higher direct energy demand and related carbon emissions. Global energy demand from digital appliances reached 7.14 EJ in 2018. The demand for computing services increased by 550% between 2010 and 2018 and is now estimated at 1% of global electricity consumption. Due to efficiency improvements, the associated energy demand increased only modestly, by about 6% from 2000 to 2018. {Box 9.5}

System-wide effects endanger energy and GHG-emission savings. Rising demand can diminish energy savings, and also produce run-away effects associated with additional consumption and GHG emissions if left unregulated. Savings are varied in smart and shared mobility systems, as ride-hailing increases GHG emissions due to deadheading, whereas shared pooled mobility and shared cycling reduce GHG emissions, as occupancy levels and/or weight per person kilometre transported improve. Systemic effects have wider boundaries of analysis and are more difficult to quantify and investigate but are nonetheless very relevant. Systemic effects tend to have negative impacts, but policies and adequate infrastructures and choice architectures can help manage and contain these. {5.3, 5.4, 5.6}

TS.7 Mitigation in the Context of Sustainable Development

Accelerating climate mitigation *in the context of sustainable development* involves not only expediting the pace of change but also addressing the underlying drivers of vulnerability and emissions. Addressing these drivers can enable diverse communities, sectors, stakeholders, regions and cultures to participate in just, equitable and inclusive processes that improve the health and well-being of people and the planet. Looking at climate change from a justice perspective also means placing the emphasis on: (i) the protection of vulnerable populations from the impacts of climate change, (ii) mitigating the effects of low-carbon transformations, and (iii) ensuring an equitable decarbonised world (*high confidence*). {17.1}

The SDG framework[33] can serve as a template to evaluate the long-term implications of mitigation on sustainable development and vice versa (*high confidence*). Understanding the co-benefits and trade-offs associated with mitigation is key to understanding how societies prioritise among the various sectoral policy options (*medium confidence*). Areas with anticipated trade-offs include food and biodiversity, energy affordability/access, and mineral-resource extraction. Areas with anticipated co-benefits include health, especially regarding air pollution, clean energy access and water availability. The possible implementation of the different sectoral mitigation options therefore depends on how societies prioritise mitigation versus other products and services: not least, how societies prioritise food, material well-being, nature conservation and biodiversity protection, as well as considerations such as their future dependence on CDR. Figure TS.29 summarises the assessment of where key synergies and trade-offs exist between mitigation options and the SDGs. (Figures TS.29 and TS.31, Table TS.7) {12.3, 12.4, 12.5, 12.6.1, Figures 3.39 and 17.1}

The beneficial and adverse impacts of deploying climate-change mitigation and adaptation responses are highly context-specific and scale-dependent. There are synergies and trade-offs between adaptation and mitigation as well as synergies and trade-offs with sustainable development (*high confidence*). Strong links also exist between sustainable development, vulnerability and climate risks, as limited economic, social and institutional resources often result in low adaptive capacities and high vulnerability, especially in developing countries. Resource limitations in these countries can similarly weaken the capacity for climate mitigation and adaptation. The move towards climate-resilient societies requires transformational or deep systemic change. This has important implications for countries' sustainable development pathways (*medium evidence, high agreement*). (Box TS.3, Figure TS.29) {4.5, Figure 4.9, 17.3.3}

Many of the potential trade-offs between mitigation and other sustainable development outcomes depend on policy design and can be compensated or avoided with additional policies and investments, or through policies that integrate mitigation with other SDGs (*high confidence*). Targeted SDG policies and investments, for example, in the areas of healthy nutrition, sustainable consumption and production, and international collaboration, can support climate change mitigation policies and resolve or alleviate trade-offs. Trade-offs can also be addressed by complementary policies and investments, as well as through the design of cross-sectoral policies integrating mitigation with the SDGs, and in particular: good health and well-being (SDG 3), zero hunger and nutrition (SDG 2), responsible consumption and production (SDG 12), reduced inequalities (SDG 10), and life on land (SDG 15). (Figures TS.29 and TS.30) {3.7}

***Decent living standards*, which encompasses many SDG dimensions, are achievable at lower energy use than previously thought (*high confidence*).** Mitigation strategies that focus on lowering demand for energy and land-based resources exhibit reduced trade-offs and negative consequences for sustainable development relative to pathways involving either high emissions and climate impacts or pathways with high consumption and emissions that are ultimately compensated by large quantities of BECCS. Figure TS.30 illustrates how, in the case of pathways limiting warming to 1.5°C (>67%), sustainable development policies can lead to overall benefits compared to mitigation policies alone. (Figures TS.22 and TS.30) {3.7, 5.2}

The timing of mitigation actions and their effectiveness will have significant consequences for broader sustainable development outcomes in the longer term (*high confidence*). Ambitious mitigation can be considered a precondition for achieving the SDGs. {3.7}

Adopting coordinated cross-sectoral approaches to climate mitigation can target synergies and minimise trade-offs, both between sectors and between sustainable development objectives (*high confidence*). This requires integrated planning using multiple-objective-multiple-impact policy frameworks. Strong inter-dependencies and cross-sectoral linkages create both opportunities for synergies and need to address trade-offs related to mitigation options and technologies. This can only be done if coordinated sectoral approaches to climate change mitigation policies are adopted that mainstream these interactions and ensure local people are involved in the development of new products, as well as production and consumption practices. For instance, there can be many synergies in urban areas between mitigation policies and the SDGs but capturing these depends on the overall planning of urban structures and on local integrated policies such as combining affordable housing and spatial planning with walkable urban areas, green electrification and clean renewable energy (*medium confidence*). Integrated planning and cross-sectoral alignment of climate change policies are also particularly evident in developing countries' NDCs under the Paris Agreement, where key priority sectors such as agriculture and energy are closely aligned with the proposed mitigation and adaptation actions and the SDGs. {12.6.2, Supplementary Material Table 17.SM.1, 17.3.3}

---

33   The 17 SDGs are at the heart of the UN 2030 Agenda for Sustainable Development, adopted by all United Nations Member States in 2015.

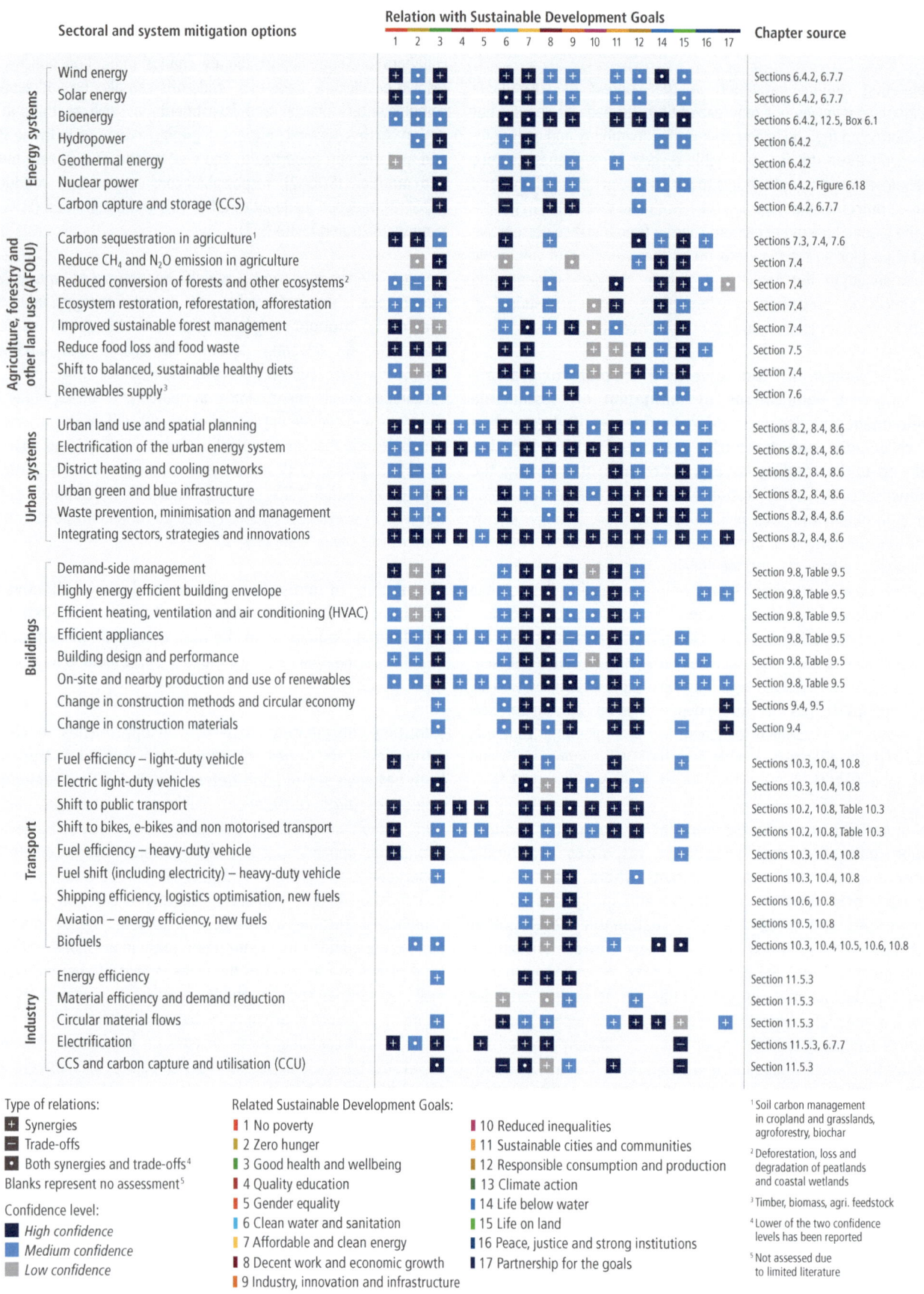

Figure TS.29 | Mitigation options have synergies with many Sustainable Development Goals (SDGs), but there are trade-offs associated with some options especially when implemented at scale.

Figure TS.29 (continued): Mitigation options have synergies with many Sustainable Development Goals (SDGs), but there are trade-offs associated with some options especially when implemented at scale. The synergies and trade-offs vary widely and depend on the context. Figure presents a summary of the chapter-level qualitative assessment of the synergies and trade-offs for selected mitigation options. Overlaps may exist in the mitigation options assessed and presented by sector and system, and interlinkages with the SDGs might differ depending on the application of that option by sector. Interactions of mitigation options with the SDGs are context-specific and dependent on the scale of implementation. For some mitigation options, these scaling and context-specific issues imply that there are both synergies and trade-offs in relation to specific SDGs. The SDGs are displayed as coloured squares. They indicate whether a synergy, trade-off, or both synergies and trade-offs exist between the SDG and the mitigation option. Confidence levels are indicated through the solidity of the squares. A solid square indicates high confidence, a partially filled square indicates medium confidence, and an outlined square indicates low confidence. The final column in the figure provides a line of sight to the chapters that provide details on context-specificity and scale of implementation. {6.3, 6.4, 6.7, 7.3, 7.4, 7.5, 7.6, 8.2, 8.4, 8.6, 9.4, 9.5, 9.8, Table 9.5, 10.3, 10.4, 10.5, 10.6, 10.8, 11.5, Table 10.3, 17.3, Figure 17.1, Supplementary Material Table 17.SM.1, Annex II.IV.12}

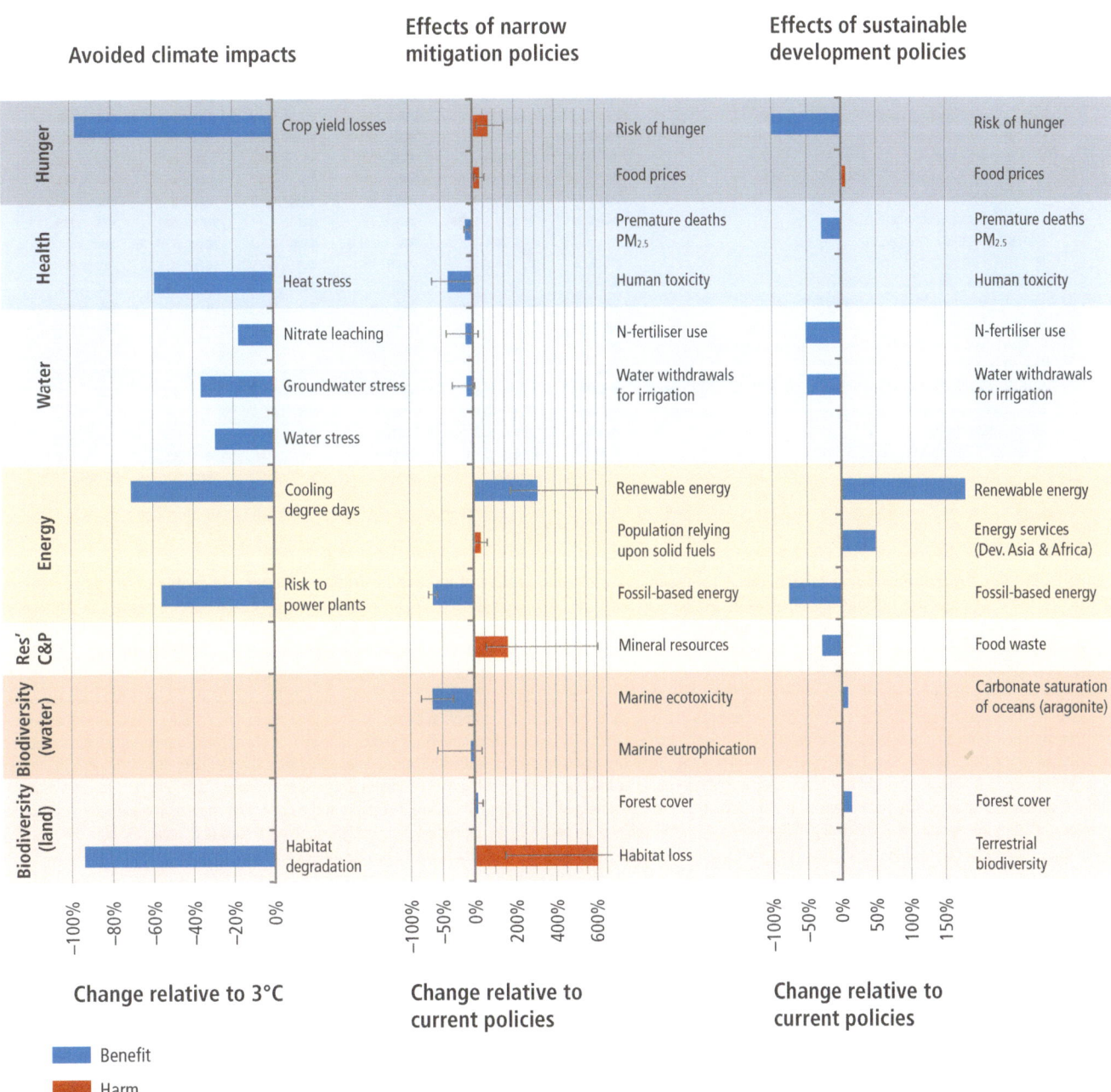

Figure TS.30 | Impacts on SDGs of mitigation limiting warming to 1.5°C (>50%) with narrow mitigation policies vs broader sustainable development policies. Left: benefits of mitigation from avoided impacts. **Middle:** sustainability co-benefits and trade-offs of narrow mitigation policies (averaged over multiple models). **Right:** sustainability co-benefits and trade-offs of mitigation policies integrating Sustainable Development Goals. Scale: 0% means no change compared to 3°C (left) or current policies (middle and right). Green values correspond to proportional improvements, red values to proportional worsening. Note: only the left panel considers climate impacts on sustainable development; the middle and right panels do not. 'Res' C&P' stands for Responsible Consumption and Production (SDG 12). {Figure 3.39}

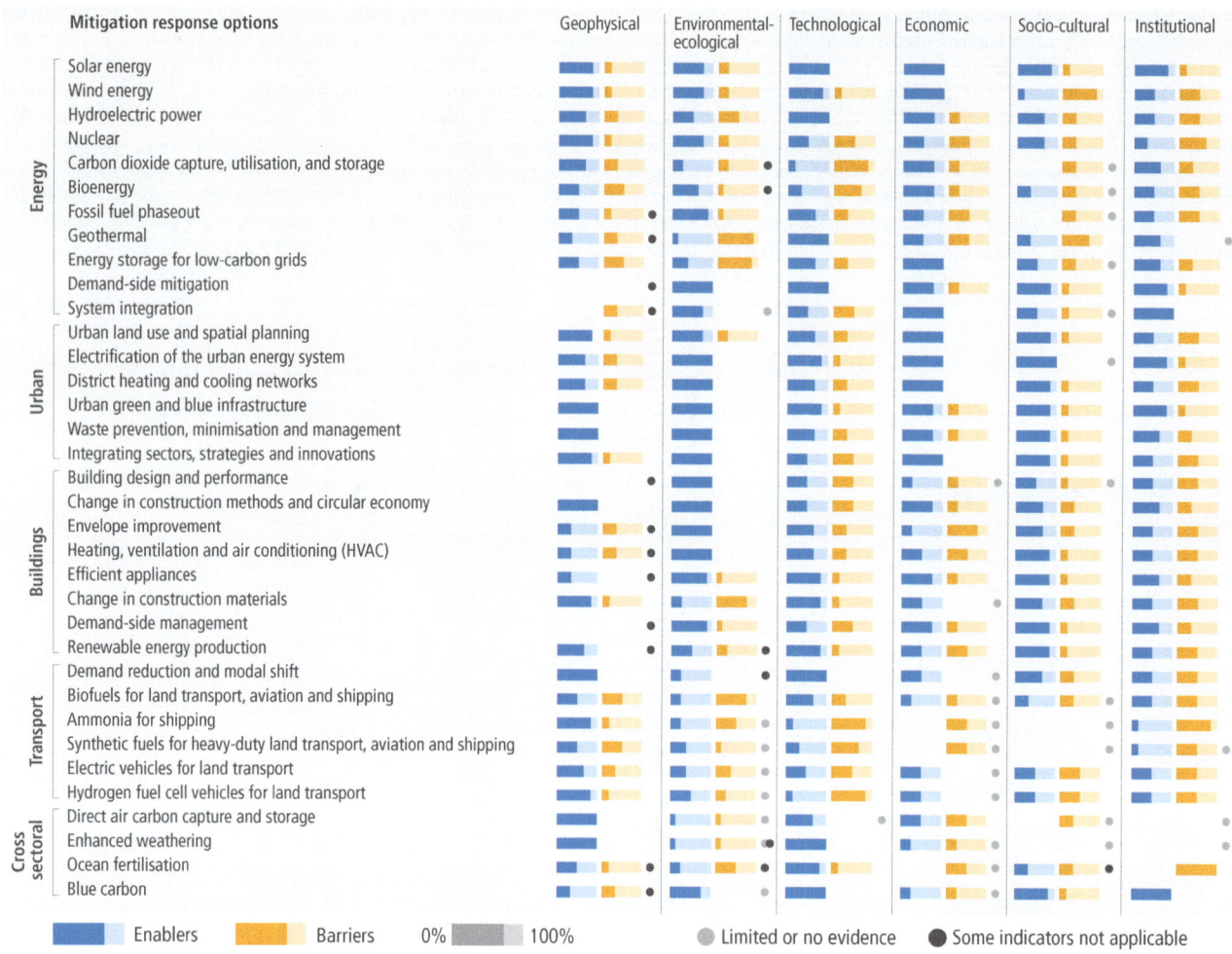

Figure TS.31 | Geophysical, environmental-ecological, technological, economic, socio-cultural and institutional factors can enable or act as barriers to the deployment of response options. Chapter-level assessment for selected mitigation options. Overlaps may exist in the mitigation options assessed and presented by sector and system, and feasibility might differ depending on the demarcation of that option in each sector. Chapters 6, 8, 9, 10, and 12 assess mitigation response options across six feasibility dimensions: *geophysical, environmental-ecological, technological, economic, socio-cultural and institutional*. AFOLU (Chapter 7) and industry (Chapter 11) are not included because of the heterogeneity of options in these sectors. For each dimension, a set of feasibility indicators was identified. Examples of indicators include impacts on land use, air pollution, economic costs, technology scalability, public acceptance and political acceptance (see Box TS.15, and Annex II.IV.11 for a detailed explanation). An indicator could refer to a barrier or an enabler to implementation, or could refer to both a barrier or an enabler, depending on the context, speed, and scale of implementation. Dark blue bars indicate the extent of enablers to deployment within each dimension. This is shown relative to the maximum number of possible enablers, as indicated by the light blue shading. Dark orange bars indicate the extent of barriers to deployment within each dimension. This is shown relative to light orange shading. A light grey dot indicates that there is limited or no evidence to assess the option. A dark grey dot indicates that one of the feasibility indicators within that dimension is not relevant for the deployment of the option. The relevant sections in the underlying chapters include references to the literature on which the assessment is based and indicate whether the feasibility of an option varies depending on context (e.g., region), scale (e.g., small, medium or full scale), speed (e.g., implementation in 2030 versus 2050) and warming level (e.g., 1.5°C versus 2°C). {6.4, 8.5, 9.10, 10.8, 12.3, Annex II.IV.11}

The feasibility of deploying response options is shaped by barriers and enabling conditions across geophysical, environmental-ecological, technological, economic, socio-cultural, and institutional dimensions (*high confidence*). Accelerating the deployment of response options depends on reducing or removing barriers across these dimensions, as well on establishing and strengthening enabling conditions. Feasibility is context-dependent, and also depends on the scale and the speed of implementation. For example: the institutional, legal and administrative capacity to support deployment varies across countries; the feasibility of options that involve large-scale land-use changes is highly context-dependent; spatial planning has a higher potential in early stages of urban development; the geophysical potential of geothermal is site-

specific; and cultural and local conditions may either inhibit or enable demand-side responses. Figure TS.31 summarises the assessment of barriers and enablers for a broad range of sector-specific, and cross-sectoral response options. (Box TS.15) {6.4, 7.4, 8.5, 9.10, 10.8, 12.3}

Alternative mitigation pathways are also associated with different feasibility challenges (*high confidence*). These challenges are multi-dimensional, context-dependent, malleable to policy and to technological and societal trends. They can also be reduced by putting in place appropriate enabling conditions. Figure TS.32 highlights the dynamic and transient nature of feasibility risks. These risks are transient and concentrated in the decades before mid-century. Figure TS.32 also illustrates how different

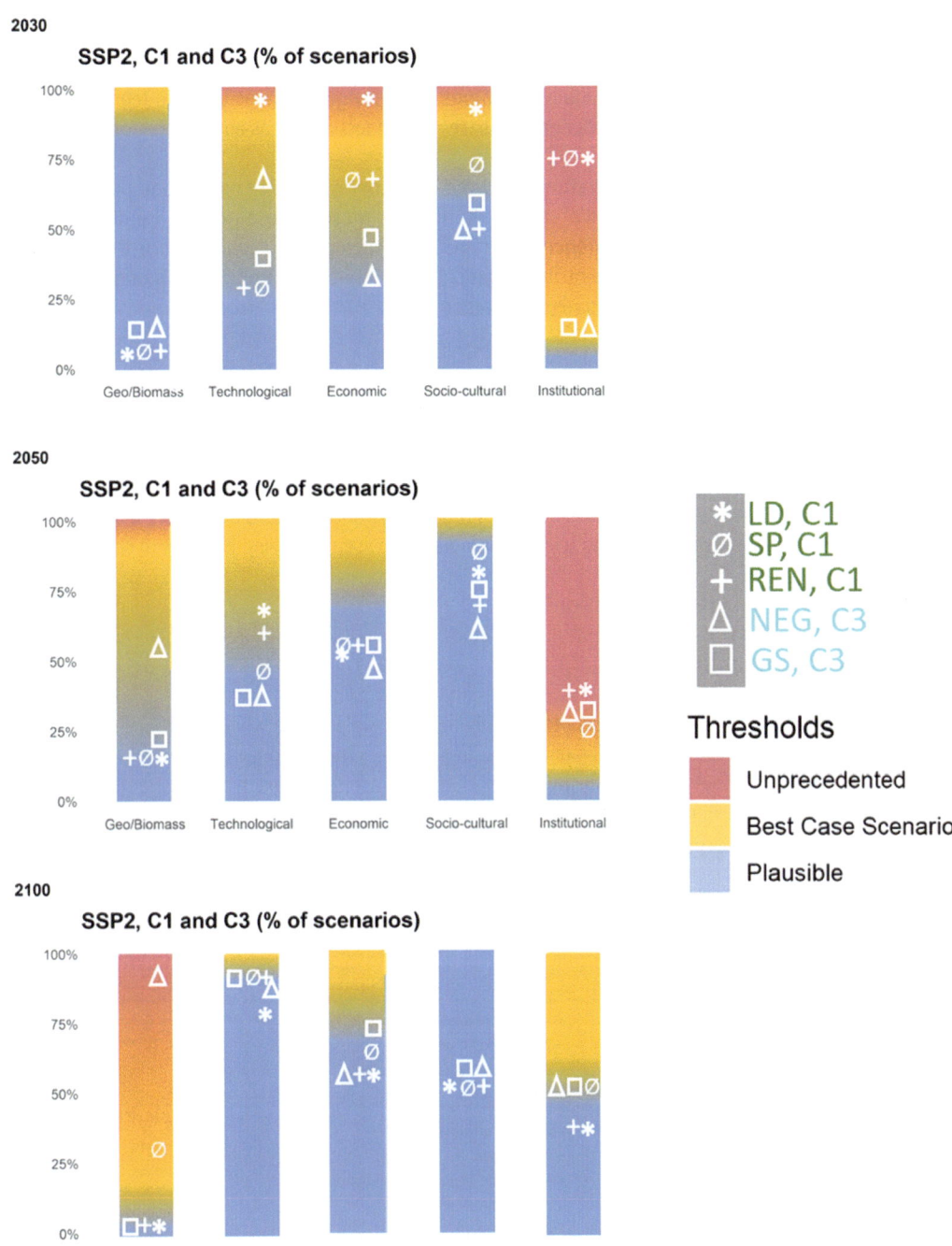

Figure TS.32 | The feasibility of mitigation scenarios. Figure TS.32 shows the proportion of scenarios in the AR6 scenarios database – falling within the warming level classifications C1 and C3 (**C1:** below 1.5°C (>50%), no or limited overshoot; **C3:** below 2°C (>67%)) – that exceed threshold values in 2030, 2050 and 2100 for five dimensions of feasibility (Boxes TS.5 and TS.15). The feasibility dimensions shown are: *geophysical, technological, economic, socio-cultural and institutional*. The thresholds shown are: (i) *plausible* – range of values based on past historical trends or other peer reviewed assessments; (ii) *best-case scenario* – range of values assuming major political support or technological breakthrough; (iii) *unprecedented* – values going beyond those observed or reported in peer-reviewed assessments. Overlayed are the Illustrative Mitigation Pathways consistent with SSP2 (LD, SP, Ren: C1 category; Neg, GS: C3 category). The positioning of the illustrative pathways is simply indicative of the general trade-offs over time and across the feasibility dimensions, it is not determined mathematically. (Box TS.5) {3.8}

feasibility dimensions pose differentiated challenges: for example, institutional feasibility challenges are shown as *unprecedented* for a high proportion of scenarios, in line with the qualitative literature, but moving from 2030 to 2050 and 2100 these challenges decrease.

The feasibility challenges associated with mitigation pathways are predominantly *institutional* and *economic* rather than *technological* and *geophysical* (*medium confidence*). The rapid pace of technological development and deployment in mitigation scenarios is not incompatible with historical records, but rather, institutional capacity is a key limiting factor for a successful transition. Emerging economies appear to have highest feasibility challenges in the near to mid-term. This suggests a key role of policy and technology as enabling factors. (Figure TS.32) {3.8}

Pathways relying on a broad portfolio of mitigation strategies are more robust and resilient (*high confidence*). Portfolios of technological solutions reduce the feasibility risks associated with the low-carbon transition. (Figures TS.31 and TS.32, Box TS.15) {3.8}

Box TS.15 | A Harmonised Approach to Assessing Feasibility

The assessment of feasibility in this report aims to identify barriers and enablers to the deployment of mitigation options and pathways. The assessment organises evidence to support policy decisions, and decisions on actions, that would improve the feasibility of mitigation options and pathways by removing relevant barriers and by strengthening enablers of change.

The feasibility of mitigation response options
Mitigation response options are assessed against six dimensions of feasibility. Each dimension comprises a key set of indicators that can be evaluated by combining various strands of literature. {Annex II.IV.11, Table 6.1}

The assessment – undertaken by the sectoral chapters in this report – evaluates to what extent each indicator (listed in Box TS.15, Table.1) would be an enabler or barrier to implementation using a scoring methodology (described in detail in Annex II.IV.11). When appropriate, it is also indicated whether the feasibility of an option varies across context, scale, time and temperature goal. The resulting scores provide insight into the extent to which each feasibility dimension enables or inhibits the deployment of the relevant option. It also provides insight into the nature of the effort needed to reduce or remove barriers, thereby improving the feasibility of individual options. {Annex II.IV.11}

Box TS.15, Table.1 | Feasibility dimensions and indicators to assess the barriers and enablers of implementing mitigation options.

Feasibility dimension	Indicators
Geophysical feasibility	Availability of required geophysical resources: – Physical potential – Geophysical resource availability – Land use
Environmental-ecological feasibility	Impacts on environment: – Air pollution – Toxic waste, ecotoxicity and eutrophication – Water quantity and quality – Biodiversity
Technological feasibility	Extent to which the technology can be implemented at scale soon: – Simplicity – Technology scalability – Maturity and technology readiness
Economic feasibility	Financial costs and economic effects: – Costs now, in 2030 and in the long term – Employment effects and economic growth
Socio-cultural feasibility	Public engagement and support, and social impacts: – Public acceptance – Effects on health and well-being – Distributional effects
Institutional feasibility	Institutional conditions that affect the implementation of the response option: – Political acceptance – Institutional capacity and governance, cross-sectoral coordination – Legal and administrative capacity

Box TS.15 (continued)

The feasibility of mitigation scenarios

Scenarios provide internally consistent projections of emission-reduction drivers and help contextualise the scale of deployment and interactions of mitigation strategies. Recent research has proposed and operationalised frameworks for the feasibility assessment of mitigation scenarios. In this report the feasibility assessment of scenarios uses an approach that involves developing a set of multi-dimensional metrics capturing the *timing*, *disruptiveness* and the *scale* of the transformative change within five dimensions: *geophysical, technological, economic, socio-cultural and institutional,* as illustrated in Box TS.15, Figure 1.

More than 20 indicators were chosen to represent feasibility dimensions that could be related to scenario metrics. Thresholds of feasibility risks of different intensity were obtained through empirical analysis of historical data and assessed literature. Details of indicators, thresholds, and how they were applied is reported in Annex II.IV.11. {3.8}

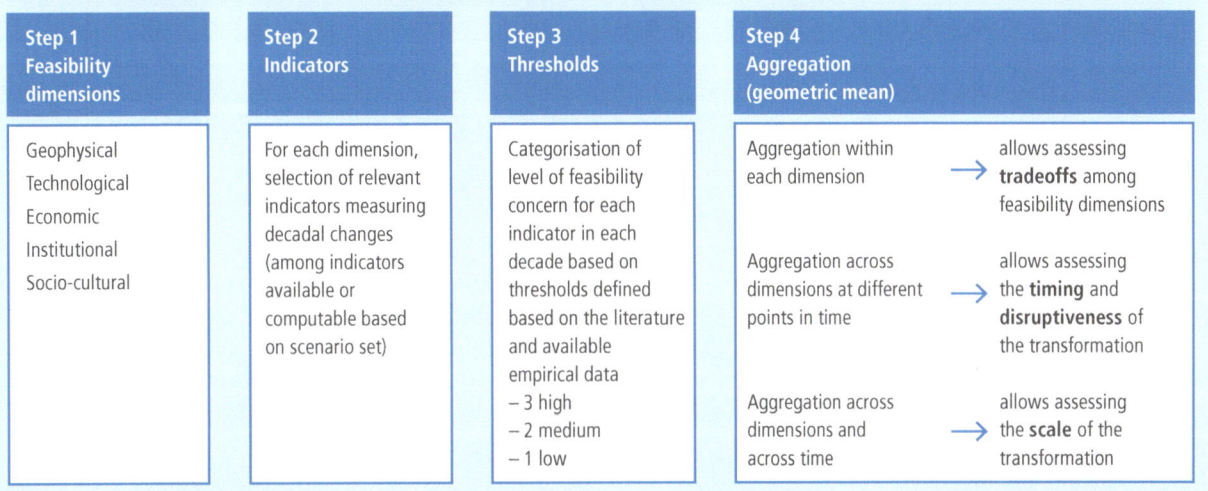

Step 1 Feasibility dimensions	Step 2 Indicators	Step 3 Thresholds	Step 4 Aggregation (geometric mean)	
Geophysical Technological Economic Institutional Socio-cultural	For each dimension, selection of relevant indicators measuring decadal changes (among indicators available or computable based on scenario set)	Categorisation of level of feasibility concern for each indicator in each decade based on thresholds defined based on the literature and available empirical data – 3 high – 2 medium – 1 low	Aggregation within each dimension	allows assessing **tradeoffs** among feasibility dimensions
			Aggregation across dimensions at different points in time	allows assessing the **timing** and **disruptiveness** of the transformation
			Aggregation across dimensions and across time	allows assessing the **scale** of the transformation

Box TS.15, Figure 1 | Steps involved in evaluating the feasibility of scenarios. {Figure 3.41} Note: in this approach the *environmental-ecological* dimension is captured through different scenarios' categories.

A wide range of factors have been found to enable sustainability transitions, ranging from technological innovations to shifts in markets, and from policies and governance arrangements to shifts in belief systems and market forces (*high confidence*). Many of these factors have come together in a co-evolutionary process that has unfolded globally, internationally and locally over several decades (*low evidence, high agreement*). Those same conditions that may serve to impede the transition (i.e., organisational structure, behaviour, technological lock-in) can also 'flip' to enable both the transition and the framing of sustainable development policies to create a stronger basis for policy support (*high confidence*). It is important to note that strong shocks to these systems, including accelerating climate change impacts, economic crises and political changes, may provide crucial openings for accelerated transitions to sustainable systems. For example, rebuilding more sustainably after an extreme event, or renewed public debate about the drivers of social and economic vulnerability to multiple stressors (*medium confidence*). {17.4}

While transition pathways will vary across countries it is anticipated that they will be challenging in many contexts (*high confidence*). Climate change is the result of decades of unsustainable production and consumption patterns, as well as governance arrangements and political economic institutions that lock-in resource-intensive development patterns (*high confidence*). Resource shortages, social divisions, inequitable distributions of wealth, poor infrastructure and limited access to advanced technologies and skilled human resources can constrain the options

and capacity of developing countries to achieve sustainable and Just Transitions (*medium evidence, high agreement*) {17.1.1}. Reframing development objectives and shifting development pathways towards sustainability can help transform these patterns and practices, allowing space to transform unsustainable systems (*medium evidence, high agreement*). {1.6, Cross-Chapter Box 5 in Chapter 4, 17.1, 17.3}

The landscape of transitions to sustainable development is changing rapidly, with multiple transitions already underway. This creates the room to manage these transitions in ways that prioritise the needs of workers in vulnerable sectors (e.g., land, energy) to secure their jobs and maintain secure and healthy lifestyles (*medium evidence, high agreement*). {17.3.2}

Actions aligning sustainable development, climate mitigation and partnerships can support transitions. Strengthening different stakeholders' 'response capacities' to mitigate and adapt to a changing climate will be critical for a sustainable transition (*high confidence*). {17.1}

Accelerating the transition to sustainability will be enabled by explicit consideration being given to the principles of justice, equality and fairness (*high confidence*). {5.2, 5.4, 5.6, 13.2, 13.6, 13.8, 13.9, 17.4}

Chapters

1

Introduction and Framing

Coordinating Lead Authors:

Michael Grubb (United Kingdom) and Chukwumerije Okereke (Nigeria/United Kingdom)

Lead Authors:

Jun Arima (Japan), Valentina Bosetti (Italy), Ying Chen (China), James Edmonds (the United States of America), Shreekant Gupta (India), Alexandre Köberle (Brazil/United Kingdom), Snorre Kverndokk (Norway), Arunima Malik (Australia), Linda Yanti Sulistiawati (Indonesia)

Contributing Authors:

Lilia Caiado Couto (Brazil), Felix Creutzig (Germany), Dipak Dasgupta (India), Kirsten Halsnæs (Denmark), Şiir Kılkış (Turkey), Jonathan Köhler (Germany), Silvia Kreibiehl (Germany), Robert Lempert (the United States of America), Kennedy Mbeva (Kenya), Jan Christoph Minx (Germany), Peter Newman (Australia), Matthew Paterson (United Kingdom), Kate Ricke (the United States of America), Diana Ürge-Vorsatz (Hungary), Jeremy Webb (New Zealand)

Review Editors:

Ismail Elgizouli Idris (the Sudan), Jason Lowe (United Kingdom)

Chapter Scientists:

Lilia Caiado Couto (Brazil), Ben Hinder (United Kingdom), Vimla Kanhye (Mauritius)

This chapter should be cited as:

Grubb, M., C. Okereke, J. Arima, V. Bosetti, Y. Chen, J. Edmonds, S. Gupta, A. Köberle, S. Kverndokk, A. Malik, L. Sulistiawati, 2022: Introduction and Framing. In IPCC, 2022: *Climate Change 2022: Mitigation of Climate Change. Contribution of Working Group III to the Sixth Assessment Report of the Intergovernmental Panel on Climate Change* [P.R. Shukla, J. Skea, R. Slade, A. Al Khourdajie, R. van Diemen, D. McCollum, M. Pathak, S. Some, P. Vyas, R. Fradera, M. Belkacemi, A. Hasija, G. Lisboa, S. Luz, J. Malley, (eds.)]. Cambridge University Press, Cambridge, UK and New York, NY, USA. doi: 10.1017/9781009157926.003

Table of Contents

Executive Summary

Global greenhouse gas (GHG) emissions continued to rise to 2019: the aggregate reductions implied by current Nationally Determined Contributions (NDCs) to 2030 would still make it impossible to limit warming to 1.5°C with no or limited overshoot, and would only be compatible with *likely limiting warming* below 2°C if followed by much steeper decline, hence limiting warming to either level implies accelerated mitigation actions at all scales (*robust evidence, high agreement*). Since the IPCC's Fifth Assessment Report (AR5), important changes that have emerged include the specific objectives established in the Paris Agreement of 2015 (for temperature, adaptation and finance), rising climate impacts, and higher levels of societal awareness and support for climate action. The growth of global GHG emissions has slowed over the past decade, and delivering the updated NDCs to 2030 would turn this into decline, but the implied global emissions by 2030 exceed pathways consistent with 1.5°C by a large margin, and are near the upper end of the range of modelled pathways which keep temperatures *likely* limit warming to 2°C (with >65% probability). Continuing investments in carbon-intensive activities at scale will heighten the multitude of risks associated with climate change and impede societal and industrial transformation towards low-carbon development. Meeting the long-term temperature objective in the Paris Agreement therefore implies a rapid turn to an accelerating decline of GHG emissions towards 'net zero', which is implausible without urgent and ambitious action at all scales. The unprecedented COVID-19 pandemic has had far-reaching impacts on the global economic and social system, and recovery will present both challenges and opportunities for climate mitigation. {1.2, 1.3, 1.5, 1.6, Chapters 3 and 4}

While there are some trade-offs, effective and equitable climate policies are largely compatible with the broader goal of sustainable development and efforts to eradicate poverty as enshrined in the 17 Sustainable Development Goals (SDGs) (*robust evidence, high agreement*). Climate mitigation is one of many goals that societies pursue in the context of sustainable development, as evidenced by the wide range of the SDGs. Climate mitigation has synergies and/or trade-offs with many other SDGs. There has been a strong relationship between development and GHG emissions, as historically both per capita and absolute emissions have risen with industrialisation. However, recent evidence shows countries can grow their economies while reducing emissions. Countries have different priorities in achieving the SDGs and reducing emissions as informed by their respective national conditions and capabilities. Given the differences in GHG emissions contributions, degree of vulnerabilities and impacts, as well as capacities within and between nations, equity and justice are important considerations for effective climate policy and for securing national and international support for deep decarbonisation. Achieving sustainable global development and eradicating poverty as enshrined in the 17 SDGS would involve effective and equitable climate policies at all levels from local to global scale. Failure to address questions of equity and justice over time can undermine social cohesion and stability. International cooperation can enhance efforts to achieve ambitious global climate mitigation in the context of sustainable development. {1.4, 1.6, Chapters 2, 3, 4, 5, 13 and 17}

The transition to a low-carbon economy depends on a wide range of closely intertwined drivers and constraints, including policies and technologies where notable advances over the past decade have opened up new and large-scale opportunities for deep decarbonisation, and for alternative development pathways which could deliver multiple social and developmental goals (*robust evidence, medium agreement*). Drivers for and constraints against low-carbon societal transition comprise *economic and technological* factors (the means by which services such as food, heating and shelter are provided and for whom, the emissions intensity of traded products, finance, and investment), *socio-political issues* (political economy, equity and fairness, social innovation and behaviour change), and *institutional factors* (legal framework and institutions, and the quality of international cooperation). In addition to being deeply intertwined all the factors matter to varying degrees, depending on the prevailing social, economic, cultural and political context. They often exert both push and pull forces at the same time, within and across different scales. The development and deployment of innovative technologies and systems at scale are important for achieving deep decarbonisation. In recent years, the cost of several low-carbon technologies has declined sharply, alongside rapid deployment. Over 20 countries have also sustained emission reductions, and many more have accelerated energy efficiency and/or land-use improvements. Overall, however, the global contribution is so far modest, at a few billion tonnes (tCO_2-eq) of avoided emissions annually. {1.3, 1.4, Chapters 2, 4, 13 and 14}

Accelerating mitigation to prevent dangerous anthropogenic interference within the climate system will require the integration of broadened assessment frameworks and tools that combine multiple perspectives, applied in a context of multi-level governance (*robust evidence, medium agreement*). Analysing a challenge on the scale of fully decarbonising our economies entails integration of multiple analytic frameworks. Approaches to risk assessment and resilience, established across IPCC Working Groups, are complemented by frameworks for probing the challenges in implementing mitigation. *Aggregate frameworks* include cost-effectiveness analysis towards given objectives, and cost-benefit analysis, both of which have been developing to take fuller account of advances in understanding risks and innovation, the dynamics of emitting systems and of climate impacts, and welfare economic theory including growing consensus on long-term discounting. *Ethical frameworks* consider the fairness of processes and outcomes which can help ameliorate distributional impacts across income groups, countries and generations. *Transition and transformation frameworks* explain and evaluate the dynamics of transitions to low-carbon systems arising from interactions amongst levels, with inevitable resistance from established socio-technical structures. *Psychological, behavioural and political frameworks* outline the constraints (and opportunities) arising from human psychology and the power of incumbent interests. A comprehensive understanding of climate mitigation must combine these multiple frameworks. Together with established risk frameworks, collectively these help to explain potential synergies and trade-offs in mitigation, imply a need for a wide portfolio of policies attuned to different actors and levels of decision-making, and underpin Just Transition strategies in diverse contexts. {1.2.2, 1.7, 1.8}

The speed, direction and depth of any transition will be determined by choices in the, environmental, technological, economic, socio-cultural and institutional realms (*robust evidence, high agreement*). Transitions in specific systems can be gradual or rapid and disruptive. The pace of a transition can be impeded by 'lock-in' generated by existing physical capital, institutions, and social norms. The interaction between power, politics and economy is central in explaining why broad commitments do not always translate to urgent action. At the same time, attention to and support for climate policies and low-carbon societal transition has generally increased, as the impacts have become more salient. Both public and private financing and financial structures strongly affect the scale and balance of high- and low-carbon investments. COVID-19 has strained public finances, and integrating climate finance into ongoing recovery strategies, nationally and internationally, can accelerate the diffusion of low-carbon technologies and also help poorer countries to minimise future stranded assets. Societal and behavioural norms, regulations and institutions are essential conditions to accelerate low-carbon transitions in multiple sectors, whilst addressing distributional concerns endemic to any major transition. {1.3.3, 1.4, 1.8, Chapters 2, 4 and 15, and Cross-Chapter Box 1 in this chapter}

Achieving the global transition to a low-carbon, climate-resilient and sustainable world requires purposeful and increasingly coordinated planning and decisions at many scales of governance including local, sub-national, national and global levels (*robust evidence, high agreement*). Accelerating mitigation globally would imply strengthening policies adopted to date, expanding the effort across options, sectors, and countries, and broadening responses to include more diverse actors and societal processes at multiple – including international – levels. Effective governance of climate change entails strong action across multiple jurisdictions and decision-making levels, including regular evaluation and learning. Choices that cause climate change as well as the processes for making and implementing relevant decisions involve a range of non-nation state actors such as cities, businesses, and civil society organisations. At global, national and sub-national levels, climate change actions are interwoven with and embedded in the context of much broader social, economic and political goals. Therefore, the governance required to address climate change has to navigate power, political, economic, and social dynamics at all levels of decision-making. Effective climate-governing institutions, and openness to experimentation on a variety of institutional arrangements, policies and programmes can play a vital role in engaging stakeholders and building momentum for effective climate action. {1.4, 1.9, Chapters 8, 15 and 17}

1.1   Introduction

This report (AR6 WGIII) aims to assess new literature on climate mitigation including implications for global sustainable development. In this Sixth Assessment Cycle the IPCC has also published three Special Reports,[1] all of which emphasise the rising threat of climate change and the implications for more ambitious mitigation efforts at all scales. At the same time, the Paris Agreement (PA) and the UN 2030 Agenda for Sustainable Development with its 17 Sustainable Development Goals (SDGs), both adopted in 2015, set out a globally agreed agenda within which climate mitigation efforts must be located. Along with a better understanding of the physical science basis of climate change (AR6 WGI), and vulnerabilities, impacts, and adaptation (AR6 WGII), the landscape of climate mitigation has evolved substantially since the Fifth Assessment Report (AR5).

Since (IPCC 2014a), climate mitigation policies around the world have grown in both number and shape (Chapter 13). However, while the average rate of annual increase of CO_2 emissions has declined (Section 1.3.2), GHG emissions globally continued to rise, underlining the urgency of the mitigation challenge (Chapters 2 and 3). Over 20 countries have cut absolute emissions alongside sustained economic growth, but the scale of mitigation action across countries remains varied and is generally much slower than the pace required to meet the goals of the Paris Agreement (Sections 1.3.2 and 2.7.2). Per capita GHG emissions between countries even at similar stages of economic development (based on GDP per capita) vary by a factor of three (Figure 1.6) and by more than two on consumption basis (Section 2.3).

The Special Report on Global Warming of 1.5°C (SR1.5) underlined that humanity is now living with the 'unifying lens of the Anthropocene' (IPCC 2018a, pp. 52–53), that requires a sharpened focus on the impact of human activity on the climate system and the planet more broadly given 'planetary boundaries' (Steffen et al. 2015) including interdependencies of climate change and biodiversity (Dasgupta 2021). Recent literature assessed by Working Groups I and II of this AR6 underlines the urgency of climate action as cumulative CO_2 emissions, along with other greenhouses gases (GHGs), drives the temperature change. Across AR6, global temperature changes are defined relative to the period 1850–1900, as in SR1.5 and collaboration with WGI enabled the use of AR6-calibrated emulators to assure consistency across the three Working Groups. The remaining 'carbon budgets' (see Annex I: Glossary) associated with 1.5°C and 2°C temperature targets equate to about one (for 1.5°C) to three (for 2°C) decades of current emissions, as from 2020, but with significant variation depending on multiple factors including other gases (Figure 2.7, and Cross-Working Group Box 1 in Chapter 3). For an outline of the WGIII approach to mitigation scenarios, emission pathways implied by the Paris goals, and the timing of peak and 'net zero' (see Glossary and FAQ 1.3), see Section 1.5 and Chapter 3.

Strong differences remain in responsibilities for, and capabilities to, take climate action within and between countries. These differences, as well as differences in the impact of climate change, point to the role of collective action in achieving urgent and ambitious global climate mitigation in the context of sustainable development, with attention to issues of equity and fairness as highlighted in several chapters of the report (Chapters 4, 5, 14, 15 and 17).

Innovation and industrial development of key technologies in several relevant sectors have transformed prospects for mitigation at much lower cost than previously assessed (Chapters 2 and 6–12). Large reductions in the cost of widely available renewable energy technologies, along with energy efficient technologies and behavioural changes (Chapters 5 and 9–11), can enable societies to provide services with much lower emissions. However, there are still significant differences in the ability to access and utilise low-carbon technologies across the world (Chapters 4, 15 and 16). New actors, including cities, businesses, and numerous non-state transnational alliances have emerged as important players in the global effort to tackle climate change (Chapters 13–16).

Along with continued development of concepts, models and technologies, there have been numerous insights from both the successes and failures of mitigation action that can inform future policy design and climate action. However, to date, policies and investments are still clearly inadequate to put the world in line with the PA's aims (Chapters 13 and 15).

The greater the inertia in emission trends and carbon-intensive investments, the more that CO_2 will continue to accumulate (Hilaire et al. 2019; IPCC 2019a). Overall, the literature points to the need for a more dynamic consideration of intertwined challenges concerning the transformation of key GHG-emitting systems: to minimise the trade-offs, and maximise the synergies, of delivering deep decarbonisation whilst enhancing sustainable development.

This chapter introduces readers to the AR6 WGIII Report and provides an overview of progress and challenges, in three parts. Part A (1.1–1.5) introduces the climate mitigation challenge, provides key findings and developments since previous assessment, and reviews the main drivers for, and constraints against accelerated climate action. Part B (1.6–1.8) provides an assessment of the key frameworks for understanding the climate mitigation challenge covering broad approaches such as sustainable development and more specific economic, political and ethical framings. Part C (1.9–1.12) briefly highlights the role of governance for steering and coordinating efforts to accelerate globally effective and equitable climate mitigation, notes the gaps in knowledge that have been identified in the process of assessment, and provides a road map to the rest of the report.

---

[1]   These are the Special Report on Global Warming of 1.5°C (SR1.5) (IPCC 2018b); the Special Report on the Ocean and Cryosphere in a Changing Climate (SROCC) (IPCC 2019b); and the Special Report on Climate Change and Land (SRCCL) (IPCC 2019c).

1.2   Previous Assessments

1.2.1   Key Findings from Previous Assessment Reports

Successive WGIII IPCC assessments have emphasised the importance of climate mitigation along with the need to consider broader societal goals especially sustainable development. Key insights from AR5 and the subsequent three Special Reports (IPCC 2018b, 2019b, 2019c) are summarised below.

The AR5 projected that in baseline scenarios (i.e., based on prevailing trends without explicit additional mitigation efforts), agriculture, forestry and other land use (AFOLU) would be the only sector where emissions could fall by 2100, with some CO_2 removal (IPCC 2014b, p. 17). Direct CO_2 emissions from energy were projected to double or even triple by 2050 (IPCC 2014b, p. 20) due to global population and economic growth, resulting in global mean surface temperature increases in 2100 from 3.7°C to 4.8°C compared to pre-industrial levels. The AR5 noted that mitigation effort and the costs associated with ambitious mitigation differ significantly across countries, and in 'globally cost-effective' scenarios, the biggest reductions (relative to projections) occur in the countries with the highest future emissions in the baseline scenarios (IPCC 2014b, p. 17). Since most physical capital (e.g., power plants, buildings, transport infrastructure) involved in GHG emissions is long-lived, the timing of the shift in investments and strategies will be crucial (IPCC 2014b, p. 18).

A key message from recent Special Reports is the urgency to mitigate GHG emissions in order to avoid rapid and potentially irreversible changes in natural and human systems (IPCC 2018b, 2019b, 2019c). Successive IPCC reports have drawn upon increasing sophistication of modelling tools to project emissions in the absence of ambitious decarbonisation action, as well as the emission pathways that meet long-term temperature targets. The SR1.5 examined pathways limiting warming to 1.5°C, compared to the historical baseline of 1850–1900, finding that 'in pathways with no or limited overshoot of 1.5°C, global net anthropogenic CO_2 emissions decline by about 45% from 2010 levels by 2030, reaching net zero around 2050' (2045–2055 interquartile range); with 'overshoot' referring to higher temperatures, then brought down by 2100 through 'net negative' emissions. It found this would require rapid and far-reaching transitions in energy, land, urban and infrastructure (including transport and buildings), and industrial systems (*high confidence*) (IPCC 2018b).

The SR1.5 found that the Nationally Determined Contributions (NDCs) as declared under the Paris Agreement (PA) would not limit warming to 1.5°C; despite significant updates to NDCs in 2020/21, this remains the case, although delivery of these more ambitious NDCs would somewhat enhance the prospects for staying below 2°C (Section 1.3.3).

The AR5 WGIII and the Special Reports analysed economic costs associated with climate action. The estimates vary widely depending on the assumptions made as to how ordered the transition is, temperature target, technology availability, and the metric or model used, among others (Chapter 6). Modelled direct mitigation costs of pathways to 1.5°C, with no/limited overshoot, span a wide range,

but were typically three to four times higher than in pathways to 2°C (*high confidence*), before taking account of benefits, including significant reduction in loss of life and livelihoods, and avoided climate impacts (IPCC 2018b).

Successive IPCC reports highlight a strong connection between climate mitigation and sustainable development. Climate mitigation and adaptation goals have synergies and trade-offs with efforts to achieve sustainable development, including poverty eradication. A comprehensive assessment of climate policy therefore involves going beyond a narrow focus on specific mitigation and adaptation options to incorporate climate issues into the design of comprehensive strategies for equitable sustainable development. At the same time, some climate mitigation policies can run counter to sustainable development and eradicating poverty, which highlights the need to consider trade-offs alongside benefits. Examples include synergies between climate policy and improved air quality, reducing premature deaths and morbidity (IPCC 2014b, Figure SPM.6) (AR6 WGI Sections 6.6.3 and 6.7.3), but there would be trade-offs if policy raises net energy bills, with distributional implications. The Special Report on Climate Change and Land (SRCCL) also emphasises important synergies and trade-offs, bringing new light on the link between healthy and sustainable food consumption and emissions caused by the agricultural sector. Land-related responses that contribute to climate change adaptation and mitigation can also combat desertification and land degradation, and enhance food security (IPCC 2019a).

Previous Assessment Reports (ARs) have detailed the contribution of various sectors and activities to global GHG emissions. When indirect emissions (mainly from electricity, heat and other energy conversions) are included, the four main consumption (end-use) drivers are industry, AFOLU, buildings and transport (Figure 2.14), though the magnitude of these emissions can vary widely between countries. These – together with the energy and urban systems which feed and shape end-use sectors – define the sectoral chapters in this AR6 WGIII report.

Estimates of emissions associated with production and transport of internationally traded goods were first presented in AR5 WGIII, which estimated the 'embodied emission transfers' from upper-middle-income countries to industrialised countries through trade at about 10% of CO_2 emissions in each of these groups (IPCC 2014a, Figure TS.5). The literature on this and discussion on their accounting has grown substantially since then (Chapters 2 and 8).

The atmosphere is a shared global resource and an integral part of the 'global commons'. In the depletion/restoration of this resource, myriad actors at various scales are involved, for instance, individuals, communities, firms and states. *Inter alia*, international cooperation to tackle ozone depletion and acid rain offer useful examples. The AR5 noted that greater cooperation would ensue if policies are perceived as fair and equitable by all countries along the spectrum of economic development – implying a need for equitable sharing of the effort. A key takeaway from AR5 is that climate policy involves value judgement and ethics. (IPCC 2014a Box TS.1: 'People and countries have rights and owe duties towards each other. These are matters of justice, equity, or fairness. They fall within the subject matter of moral and political philosophy, jurisprudence, and economics.' p. 37). International cooperation and collective action on climate change alongside local, national, regional and global policies will be crucial to solve the problem, and this report notes cooperative approaches beyond simple 'global commons' framings (Chapters 13 and 14).

The AR5 (all Working Group reports) also underlined that climate policy inherently involves risk and uncertainty (in nature, economy, society and individuals). To help evaluate responses, there exists a rich suite of analytical tools, for example, cost-benefit analysis, cost-effectiveness analysis, multi-criteria analysis, expected utility theory, and catastrophe and risk models. All have pros and cons, and have been further developed in subsequent literature and in AR6 (Sections 1.2.2 and 1.7).

Recent assessments (IPCC 2014a, 2018b) began to consider the role of individual behavioural choices and cultural norms in driving energy and food patterns. Notably, SR1.5 (Section 4.4.3) outlined emerging evidence on the potential for changes in behaviour, lifestyle and culture to contribute to decarbonisation (and lower the cost); for the first time, AR6 devotes a whole chapter (Chapter 5) to consider these and other underlying drivers of energy demand, food choices and social aspects.

1.2.2 Developments in Climate Science, Impacts and Risk

The assessment of the Physical Science Basis (IPCC AR6 WGI) documents sustained and widespread changes in the atmosphere, cryosphere, biosphere and ocean, providing unequivocal evidence of a world that has warmed, associated with rising atmospheric CO_2 concentrations reaching levels not experienced in at least the last 2 million years. Aside from temperature, other clearly discernible, human-induced changes beyond natural variations include declines in Arctic Sea ice and glaciers, thawing of permafrost, and a strengthening of the global water cycle (AR6 WGI SPM A.2, B.3 and B.4). Oceanic changes include rising sea level, acidification, deoxygenation, and changing salinity (WGI SPM B.3). Over land, in recent decades, both frequency and severity have increased for hot extremes but decreased for cold extremes; intensification of heavy precipitation is observed in parallel with a decrease in available water in dry seasons, along with an increased occurrence of weather conditions that promote wildfires.

In defining the objective of international climate negotiations as being to 'prevent dangerous anthropogenic interference' (UNFCCC 1992, Art. 2), the UNFCCC underlines the centrality of risk framing in considering the threats of climate change and potential response measures. Against the background of 'unequivocal' (AR4) evidence of human-induced climate change, and the growing experience of direct impacts, the IPCC has sought to systematise a robust approach to risk and risk management.

In AR6 the IPCC employs a common risk framing across all three working groups and provides guidance for more consistent and transparent usage (AR6 WGI Cross-Chapter Box 3 in Chapter 1; AR6 WGII Section 1.4.1; IPCC risk guidance). AR6 defines risk as 'the potential for adverse consequences for human or ecological systems, recognising the diversity of values and objectives associated with such systems' (Annex I), encompassing risks from both potential impacts of climate change and human responses to it (Reisinger et al. 2020). The risk framing includes steps for identifying, evaluating, and prioritising current and future risks; for understanding the interactions among different sources of risk; for distributing effort and equitable sharing of risks; for monitoring and adjusting actions over time while continuing to assess changing circumstances; and for communications among analysts, decision-makers, and the public.

Climate change risk assessments face challenges including a tendency to mischaracterise risks and pay insufficient attention to the potential for surprises (Weitzman 2011; Aven and Renn 2015; Stoerk et al. 2018). Concepts of resilience and vulnerability provide overlapping, alternative entry points to understanding and addressing the societal challenges caused and exacerbated by climate change (AR6 WGII, Section 1.2.1).

The AR6 WGII devotes a full chapter (Chapter 17) to 'Decision-Making Options for Managing Risk', detailing the analytic approaches and drawing upon the *Cynefin* classification of *known*, *knowable*, *complex* and *chaotic* systems (Section 17.3.1). With deep uncertainty, risk management often aims to identify specific combinations of response actions and enabling institutions that increase the potential for favourable outcomes despite irreducible uncertainties (AR6 WGII Chapter 17 Cross-Chapter Box DEEP; also Marchau et al. (2019); Doukas and Nikas (2020)).

Literature trying to quantify the cost of climate damages has continued to develop. Different methodologies systematically affect outcomes, with recent estimates based on empirical approaches – econometric measurements based on actual impacts – 'categorically higher than estimates from other approaches' (AR6 WGII, Cross-Working Group Box ECONOMIC in Chapter 16, and Section 16.6.2). This, along with other developments strengthen foundations for calculating a 'social cost of carbon'. This informs a common metric for comparing different risks and estimating benefits compared to the costs of GHG reductions and other risk-reducing options (Section 1.7.1); emissions mitigation itself also involves multiple uncertainties, which alongside risks can also involve potential opportunities (Section 1.7.3).

Simultaneously, the literature increasingly emphasises the importance of multi-objective risk assessment and management (e.g., representative key risks in AR6 WGII Chapter 16), which may or may not correlate with any single estimate of economic value (AR6 WGII, Section 1.4.1; IPCC risk guidance). Given the deep uncertainties and risks, the goals established (notably in the Paris Agreement and SDGs) reflect negotiated outcomes informed by the scientific assessment of risks.

1.3　The Multilateral Context, Emissions Trends and Key Developments

Since AR5, there have been notable multilateral efforts which help determine the context for current and future climate action. This section summarises key features of this evolving context.

1.3.1　The 2015 Agreements

In 2015 the world concluded four major agreements that are very relevant to climate action. These include: the Paris Agreement under the 1992 United Nations Framework Convention on Climate Change (UNFCCC), the UN agreements on Disaster Risk Reduction (Sendai) and Finance for Development (Addis Ababa), and the Sustainable Development Goals (SDGs).

The Paris Agreement (PA). The Paris Agreement aims to 'hold the increase in the global average temperature to well below 2°C above pre-industrial levels and pursuing efforts to limit the temperature increase to 1.5°C above pre-industrial levels' (UNFCCC 2015), alongside goals for adaptation (IPCC AR6 WGII), and 'aligning financial flows' (see 'finance goal', below) , so as 'to strengthen the global response to the threat of climate change, in the context of sustainable development and efforts to eradicate poverty.'

The Paris Agreement is predicated on encouraging progressively ambitious climate action from all countries on the basis of Nationally Determined Contributions (Clémençon 2016; Rajamani 2016). The NDC approach requires countries to set their own level of ambitions for climate change mitigation but within a collaborative and legally binding process to foster ambition towards the agreed goals (Bodansky 2016; Falkner 2016a). The PA entered into force in November 2016 and as of February 2021 it already had 190 Parties (out of 197 Parties to the UNFCCC).

The PA also underlines 'the principle of common but differentiated responsibilities and respective capabilities, in the light of different national circumstances' (PA Art. 2, para. 2), and correspondingly that 'developed country Parties should continue taking the lead by undertaking economy-wide absolute emission reductions'. It states that developing country Parties should continue enhancing their mitigation efforts, and are encouraged to move over time towards economy-wide emission reduction or limitation targets in the light of different national circumstances.

In order to achieve the its long term temperature goal, the Paris Agreement aims 'to achieve a balance between anthropogenic emissions by sources and removals by sinks of greenhouse gases in the second half of this century' (PA Art. 4 para. 1). The PA provides for five-yearly stocktakes in which Parties have to take collective stock on progress towards achieving its purposes and its long-term goal in the light of equity and available best science (PA Art. 14). The first global stocktake is scheduled for 2023 (PA Art. 14, para. 3).

The Paris Agreement's finance goal aims to make 'finance flows consistent with a pathway towards low greenhouse gas emissions and climate-resilient development' (PA Art. 2.1C). In keeping with the acknowledged context of global sustainable development and poverty eradication, and the corresponding aims of aligning finance and agreed differentiating principles as indicated above, '…the developed country parties are to assist developing country parties with financial resources' (PA Art. 9). The Green Climate Fund (GCF), an operating entity of the UNFCCC Financial Mechanism to finance mitigation and adaptation efforts in developing countries (GCF 2020), was given an important role in serving the Agreement and supporting PA goals. The GCF gathered pledges worth USD10.3 billion, from developed and developing countries, regions, and one city (Paris) (Antimiani et al. 2017; Bowman and Minas 2019). Financing has since increased but remains short of the goal to mobilise USD100 billion by 2020 (Chapter 15).

Initiatives contributing to the Paris Agreement goals include the Non-State Actor Zone for Climate Action (NAZCA: now renamed as Global Climate Action) portal, launched at COP20 (December 2014) in Lima, Peru, to support city-based actions for mitigating climate change (IISD 2015) and Marrakech Partnership for Global Climate Action which is a UNFCCC-backed series of events intended to facilitate collaboration between governments and the cities, regions, businesses and investors that must act on climate change.

Details of the Paris Agreement, evaluation of the Kyoto Protocol, and other key multilateral developments since AR5 that are relevant to climate mitigation including the CORSIA aviation agreement adopted under ICAO, the IMO shipping strategy, and the Kigali Amendment to the Montreal Protocol on hydrofluorocarbons (HFCs), are discussed in Chapter 14.

SDGs. In September 2015, the UN endorsed a universal agenda – 'Transforming our World: the 2030 Agenda for Sustainable Development'. The agenda adopted 17 non-legally-binding SDGs and 169 targets to support people, peace, prosperity, partnerships and the planet. While climate change is explicitly listed as SDG 13, the pursuit of the implementation of the UNFCCC is relevant for a number of other goals including SDG 7 (clean energy for all), SDG 9 (sustainable industry), and SDG 11 (sustainable cities), SDG 12 (responsible consumption and production) as well as those relating to life below water (SDG 14) and on land (SDG 15) (Biermann et al. 2017). Mitigation actions could have multiple synergies and trade-offs across the SDGs (Pradhan et al. 2017) (Chapter 17) and their net effects depend on the pace and magnitude of changes, the specific mitigation choices and the management of the transition. This suggests that mitigation must be pursued in the broader context of sustainable development as explained in Section 1.6.

Finance. The Paris Agreement's finance goal (above) reflects a broadened focus, beyond the costs of climate adaptation and mitigation, to recognising that a structural shift towards low-carbon climate-resilient development pathways requires large-scale investments that engage the wider financial system (Sections 15.1 and 15.2.4). The SR1.5 report estimated that 1.5°C pathways would require *increased investment* of 0.5–1% of global GDP between now and 2050, which is up to 2.5% of global savings/investment over the period. For low- and middle-income countries, SDG-compatible infrastructure investments in the most relevant sectors are estimated to be around 4–5% of their GDP, and 'infrastructure investment paths compatible with full decarbonisation in the second half of the century need not cost more than more-polluting alternatives' (Rozenberg and Fay 2019).

The parallel 2015 UN Addis Ababa Conference on Finance for Development, and its resulting Action Agenda, aims to 'address the challenge of financing … to end poverty and hunger, and to achieve sustainable development in its three dimensions through promoting inclusive economic growth, protecting the environment, and promoting social inclusion.' The Conference recognises the significant potential of regional cooperation and provides a forum for discussing the solutions to common challenges faced by developing countries (Section 15.6.4).

Alongside this, private and blended climate finance is increasing but is still short of projected requirements consistent with Paris Agreement goals (Section 15.3.2.1). The financing gap is particularly acute for adaptation projects, especially in vulnerable developing countries. From a macro-regulatory perspective, there is growing recognition that substantial financial value may be at risk from changing regulation and technology in a low-carbon transition, with potential implications for global financial stability (Section 15.6.3). To date, the most significant governance development is the Financial Stability Board's Task Force on Climate-related Financial Disclosures (TCFD) and its recommendations that investors and companies consider climate change risks in their strategies and capital allocation, so investors can make informed decisions (TCFD 2018), welcomed by over 500 financial institutions and companies as signatories, albeit with patchy implementation (Sections 1.4.4 and 15.6.3).

Talanoa Dialogue and Just Transition. As mandated at Paris COP21 and launched at COP23, the 'Talanoa Dialogue' (UNFCCC 2018a) emphasised holistic approaches across multiple economic sectors for climate change mitigation. At COP24 also, the Just Transition Silesia Declaration, focusing on the need to consider social aspects in designing policies for climate change mitigation was signed by 56 heads of state (UNFCCC 2018b). This underlined the importance of aiming for Just Transitions in reducing emissions, at the same time preserving livelihoods and managing economic risks for countries and communities that rely heavily on emissions-intensive technologies for domestic growth (Markkanen and Anger-Kraavi 2019), and for maintaining ecosystem integrity through nature-based solutions.

1.3.2   Global and Regional Emissions

Global GHG emissions have continued to rise since AR5, though the average rate of emissions growth slowed, from 2.4% (from 2000–2010) to 1.3% for 2010–2019 (Figure 1.1). After a period of exceptionally rapid growth from 2000 as charted in AR5, global fossil fuel- and industry-related (FFI) CO_2 emissions almost plateaued between 2014 and 2016 (while the global economy continued to expand (World Bank 2020), but increased again over 2017–19, the average annual growth rate for all GHGs since 2014 being around 0.8% yr^{-1} (IPCC/EDGAR emissions database; see also Chapter 11, Figure 11.2)). Important driving factors include population and GDP growth, as illustrated in panels (b) and (c) of Figure 1.1 respectively. The pause in emissions growth reflected the interplay of strong energy efficiency improvements and low-carbon technology deployment, but these did not expand fast enough to offset the continued pressures for overall growth at global level (UNEP 2018a; IEA 2019a). However, since 2013/14, the decline in global emissions intensity (GHG/GDP) has accelerated somewhat, and global emissions growth has averaged slightly slower than population growth (Figure 1.1d), which if sustained would imply a peak of global CO_2 (GHG) emissions per capita, at about 5 tCO_2 per person (7 tCO_2-eq per person) respectively.

Due to its much shorter lifetime, methane has a disproportionate impact on near-term temperature, and is estimated to account for almost a third of the warming observed to date (AR6 WGI SPM; AR6 WGIII Chapter 2, Figure 2.4). Methane reductions could be particularly important in relation to near- and medium-term temperatures, including through counteracting the impact of reducing short-lived aerosol pollutants which have an average cooling effect.[2]

The land-use component of CO_2 emissions has different drivers and particularly large uncertainties (Figures 2.2 and 2.5), hence is shown separately. Also, compared to AR5, new evidence showed that the AFOLU CO_2 estimates by the global models assessed in this report are not necessarily comparable with national GHG inventories, due to different approaches to estimate the 'anthropogenic' CO_2 sink. Possible ways to reconcile these discrepancies are discussed in Chapter 7.

Regional trends have varied. Emissions from most countries continued to grow, but in absolute terms, 32 countries reduced energy and industry CO_2 emissions for at least a decade, and 24 reduced overall GHG (CO_2-eq) emissions over the same period, but only half of them by more than 10% over the period in each case (Chapter 2).[3] In total,

---

[2]   Indeed, cooling effects of anthropogenic aerosols (organic carbon, black carbon, sulphates, nitrates), which are also important components of local air pollution (Myhre et al. 2013) (AR6 WGI SPM D1.7) may in global average be of similar magnitude to warming from methane at present. Mitigation which reduces such aerosol masking could thereby increase global temperatures, and reducing methane emissions would offset this much more rapidly than reducing CO_2 because of its relatively short lifetime, with the combined effects which could counterbalance each other (AR6 WGI SPM D1.7). Methane is thus particularly important in determining whether or when 1.5°C is reached for example.

[3]   With some exclusions for countries which were very small or undergoing economic collapse: fossil-fuel-and industry (CO_2-FFI) emissions in 2018 were below 2008 levels in 32 developed countries, but only in 24 when including other GHGs. Reductions were by less than 10% in half these countries. Data from Chapter 2: see Section 2.2.3, as analysed in Lamb et al. (2021). An earlier study found 18 developed countries that had reduced CO_2-FFI emissions over 2005–2015 (Le Quéré et al. 2019). Decomposition analysis of national trends in Xia et al. (2021), identified 23 industrialised countries (UNFCCC Annex I) with CO_2-FFI emissions in 2017 lower than in 2000 (Figure 1.3), of which 22 had increased GDP over the period. The previously rising trend of 'outsourced/embodied emissions' associated with goods imported into developed countries peaked in 2006, but detailed data on this are only available for CO_2-FFI up to 2018 (Section 2.3). See Chapter 3 for reduction rates associated with 1.5°C and 2°C.

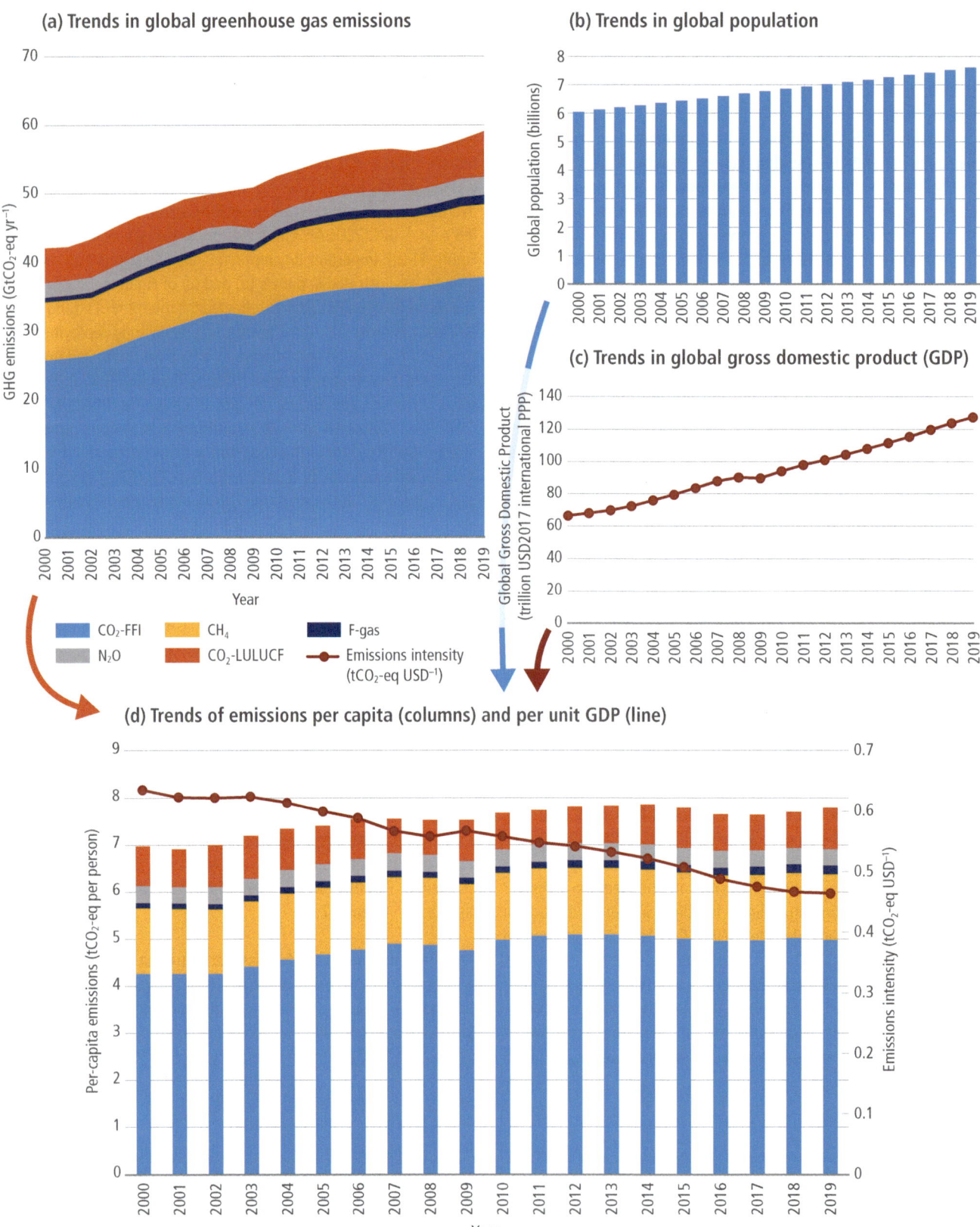

Figure 1.1 | Global emission trends since 2000 by groups of gases: absolute, per capita, and intensity. Note: shows CO₂ from fossil fuel combustion and industrial processes (FFI); CO₂ from agriculture, forestry and other land use (AFOLU); methane (CH₄); nitrous oxide (N₂O); fluorinated gases (F-gases). Gases reported in GtCO₂-eq converted based on AR6 global warming potentials with a 100-year time horizon (GWP100).

developed country emissions barely changed from 2010, whilst those from the rest of the world grew.

Figure 1.2 shows the distribution of regional emissions (a) per capita and (b) per GDP based on purchasing power parity (GDP$_{ppp}$) of different country groupings in 2019. Plotted against population and GDP respectively, the area of each block is proportional to the

(a) Distribution of regional emissions (territorial, 2019): CO$_2$-FFI (bottom-bar above x-axis, darker), plus non-CO$_2$ GHGs (top bar, lighter), plus CO$_2$-LULUCF (top-most or below-axis (negative) bars)

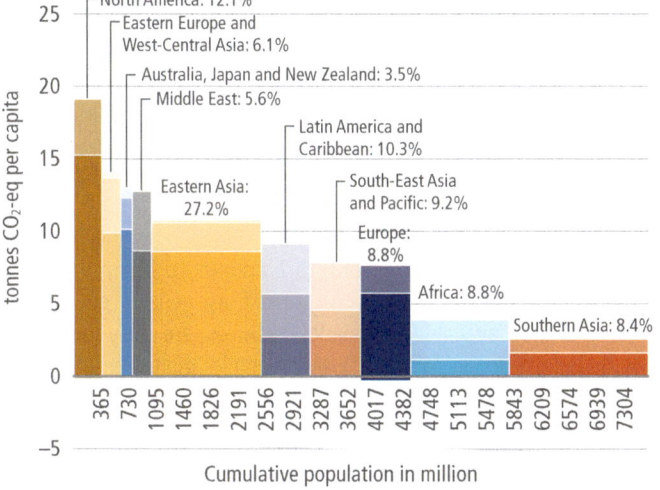

(b) Distribution of regional emissions (territorial, 2019): CO$_2$-FFI (bottom-bar above x-axis, darker), plus non-CO$_2$ GHGs (top bar, lighter), plus CO$_2$-LULUCF (top-most or below-axis (negative) bars)

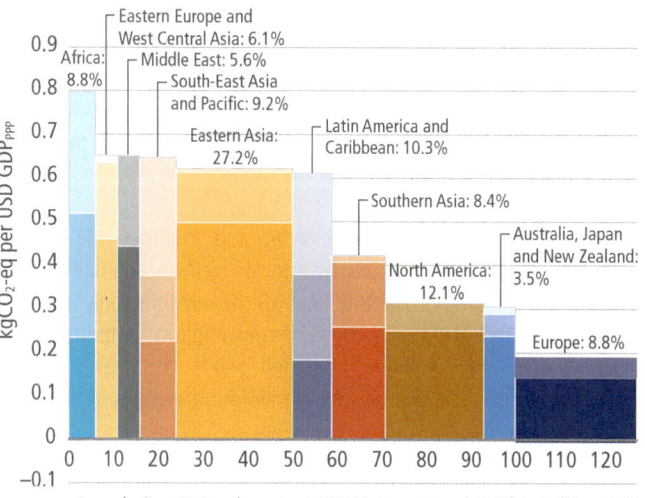

(c) Distribution of regional emissions (consumption-based footprint, 2018): CO$_2$-FFI only

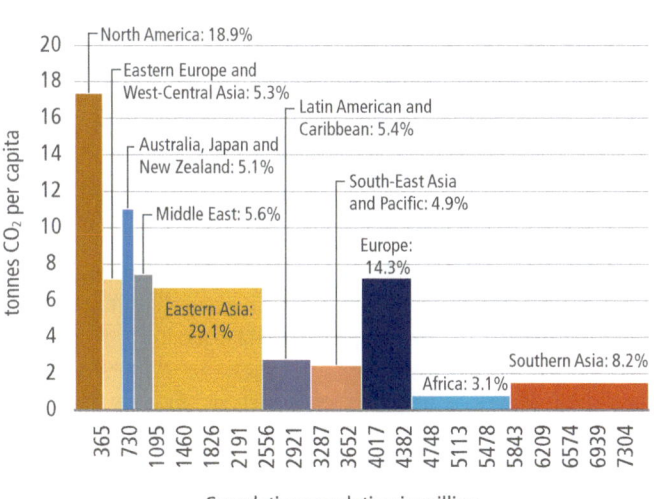

(d) Distribution of regional emissions (consumption-based footprint, 2018): CO$_2$-FFI only

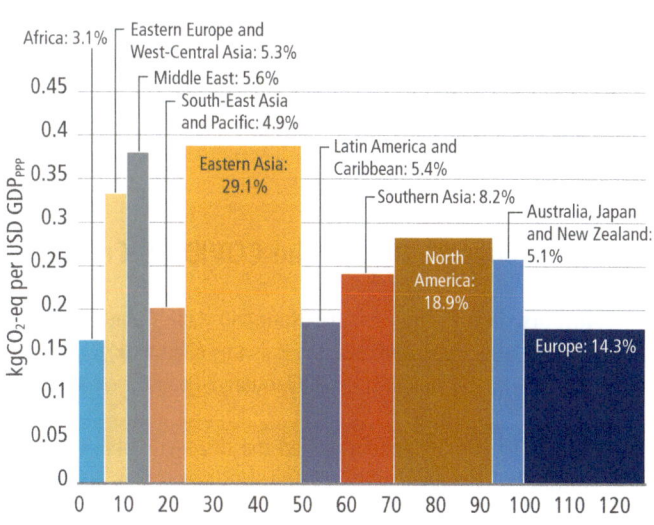

Figure 1.2 | Distribution of regional greenhouse gas (GHG) emissions for 10 broad global regions according to territorial accounting (panels (a) and (b), GHG emissions) and consumption-based accounting (panels (c) and (d), CO$_2$-FFI emissions only). GHG emissions are categorised into: fossil fuel and industry (CO$_2$-FFI); land use, land-use change and forestry (CO$_2$-LULUCF); and other greenhouse gases (methane, nitrous oxide and F-gas – converted to 100-year global warming potentials). Per-capita GHGs for territorial **(panel a)** and CO$_2$-FFI emissions vs population for consumption-based accounting **(panel c)**. Panels **(b)** and **(d)**: GHG emissions per unit GDP$_{ppp}$ vs GDP$_{ppp}$, weighted with purchasing power parity for territorial accounting (panel b), CO$_2$-FFI emissions per unit GDP$_{ppp}$ for consumption-based accounting (panel d). The area of the rectangles refers to the total emissions for each regional category, with the height capturing per-capita emissions (panels a and c) or emissions per unit GDP$_{ppp}$ (panels (b) and (d)), and the width proportional to the population of the regions and GDP$_{ppp}$. Emissions from international aviation and shipping (2.4% of the total GHG emissions) are not included.

1

region's emissions. Compared to the equivalent presentations in 2004 (AR4 WGIII Figure SPM.3) and 2010 (AR5 WGIII Figure 1.8), East Asia now forms substantially the biggest group, whilst at about 8 tCO_2-FFI (/10 tCO_2-eq all GHGs) per person, its emissions per capita remain about half that of North America. In contrast, a third of the world's population, in Southern Asia and Africa, emit on average under 2 (2.5 tCO_2-eq) per person, little more than in the previous assessments. Particularly for these regions, there continue to be substantial differences in GDP, life expectancy and other measures of well-being (Figure 1.6).

Emissions per unit GDP are much less diverse than per capita and have also converged significantly. Poorer countries tend to show higher energy/emissions per unit GDP partly because of higher reliance on basic industries, and this remains the case, though in general their energy/GDP has declined faster.

Many developed country regions are net importers of energy-intensive goods, and emissions are affected by the accounting of such 'embodied emissions'. Panels (c) and (d) show results (only available for CO_2-FFI, to 2018) on the basis of consumption footprints which include emissions embodied in traded goods. This makes modest changes to the relative position of different regions (for further discussion see Section 2.3).

While extreme poverty has fallen in more than half of the world's economies in recent years, nearly one fifth of countries faced poverty rates above 30% in 2015 (below USD1.90 a day), reflecting large income inequality (Laborde Debucquet and Martin 2017; Rozenberg and Fay 2019). Diffenbaugh and Burke (2019) find that global warming already has increased global economic inequality, even if between-country inequalities have decreased over recent decades. The distributional implications between regional groups in the Shared Socio-economic Pathways (SSPs) diverge according to the scenario (Frame et al. 2019).

An important recent development has been commitments by many countries, now covering a large majority of global emissions, to reach net zero CO_2 or greenhouse gas emissions (Chapter 3).[4] Furthermore, globally, net zero targets (whether CO_2 or GHG) have been adopted by about 823 cities and 101 regions (Chapter 8).

1.3.3   Some Other Key Trends and Developments

The COVID-19 pandemic profoundly impacted economy and human society, globally and within countries. As detailed in Cross-Chapter Box 1 in this chapter, some of its impacts will be long-lasting, permanent even, and there are also lessons relevant to climate change. The direct impact on emissions projected for rest of this decade are modest, but the necessity for economic recovery packages creates a central role for government-led investment, and may change the economic fundamentals involved for some years to come.

The COVID-19 aftermath consequently also changes the economic context for mitigation (Sections 15.2 and 15.4). Many traditional forms of economic analysis (expressed as general equilibrium) assume that available economic resources are fully employed, with limited scope for beneficial economic 'multiplier effects' of government-led investment. After COVID-19 however, no country is in this state. Very low interest rates amplify opportunities for large-scale investments which could bring 'economic multiplier' benefits, especially if they help to build the industries and infrastructures for further clean growth (Hepburn et al. 2020). However, the capability to mobilise low-interest finance varies markedly across countries and large public debts – including bringing some developing countries close to default – undermine both the political appetite and feasibility of large-scale clean investments. In practice the current orientation of COVID-19 recovery packages is very varied, pointing to a very mixed picture about whether or not countries are exploiting this opportunity (Cross-Chapter Box 1 in this chapter).

Cross-Chapter Box 1 | The COVID-19 Crisis: Lessons, Risks and Opportunities for Mitigation

Authors: Diana Ürge-Vorsatz (Hungary), Lilia Caiado Couto (Brazil), Felix Creutzig (Germany), Dipak Dasgupta (India), Michael Grubb (United Kingdom), Kirsten Halsnæs (Denmark), Şiir Kılkış (Turkey), Alexandre Köberle (Brazil/United Kingdom), Silvia Kreibiehl (Germany), Jan Christoph Minx (Germany), Peter Newman (Australia), Chukwumerije Okereke (Nigeria/United Kingdom)

The COVID-19 pandemic triggered the deepest global economic contraction as well as CO_2 emission reductions since the Second World War (Le Quéré et al. 2020b), (AR6 WGI, Box 6.1) (Section 2.2.2.1). While emissions and most economies are expected to rebound in 2021–2022 (IEA 2021), some impacts of the pandemic (e.g., aspects of economy, finance and transport-related emission drivers) may last far longer. COVID-19 pushed more than 100 million people back into extreme poverty, and reversed progress towards some other SDGs including health, life expectancy and child literacy (UN DESA 2021). Health impacts and the consequences of deep economy-wide shocks may last many years even without significant future recurrence (Section 15.6.3). These changes, as well as the pandemic response actions, bring both important risks as well as opportunities for accelerating mitigation (Chapters 1, 5, 10 and 15).

---

[4]   Continually updated information on net zero commitments is available at https://www.zerotracker.net.

Cross-Chapter Box 1 (continued)

Lessons. Important lessons can be drawn from the pandemic to climate change including the value of forward-looking risk management, the role of scientific assessment, preparatory action and international process and institutions (Chapter 5 and Section 1.3). There had been long-standing warnings of pandemic risks and precursors – with both pandemic and climate risks being identified by social scientists as 'uncomfortable knowledge' or 'unknown knowns', which tend to be marginalised in practical policy (Rayner 2012; Sarewitz 2020). This echoes long-standing climate literature on potential 'high impact' events, including those *perceived* as low probability (Dietz 2011; Weitzman 2011). The costs of preparatory action, mainly in those countries that had suffered from earlier pandemics were negligible in comparison, suggesting the importance not just of knowledge but its effective communication and embodiment in society (Chapter 5). Klenert et al. (2020) offer five early lessons for climate policy, concerning: the cost of delay; the bias in human judgement; the inequality of impacts; the need for multiple forms of international cooperation; and finally, 'transparency in value judgements at the science–policy interface'.

Emissions and behavioural changes. Overall, global CO_2 FFI emissions declined by about 5.8% (5.1–6.3%) from 2019 to 2020, or about 2.2 (1.8–2.4) $GtCO_2$ in total (Section 2.2.2). Analysis from previous economic crises suggest significant rebound in emissions without policy-induced structural shifts (Jaeger et al. 2020) (Section 2.2.2.1 and Figure 2.5). Initial projections suggest the COVID aftermath may reduce emissions by 4–5% over 2025–2030 (Shan and Et.al 2020; Reilly et al. 2021), below a 'no-pandemic' baseline. The long-term impacts on behaviour, technology and associated emissions remain to be seen, but may be particularly significant in transport – lockdowns reduced mobility-related emissions, alongside two major growth areas: electronic communications replacing many work and personal travel requirements (Chapter 10 and Section 4.4.3.4); and revitalised local active transport and e-micromobility (Earley and Newman 2021). Temporary 'clear skies' may also have raised awareness of the potential environment and health co-benefits of reduced fossil fuel use particularly in urban areas (Section 8.7), with evidence also indicating that air pollution itself amplified vulnerability to COVID-19 (Gudka et al. 2020; Wu et al. 2020). The significant impacts on passenger aviation are projected to extend not just through behavioural changes, but also fleet changes from retiring older planes, and reduced new orders indicating expectations of reduced demand and associated GHG emissions until 2030 (Sections 5.1.2 and 10.5) (AR6 WGI Box 6.1 in Chapter 6). However, air cargo has recovered more rapidly (IATA 2020), possibly enhanced by online ordering.

Fiscal, growth and inequality impacts. Aspects of the global and regional economic crises from COVID-19 may prevail much longer than the crisis itself, potentially compromising mitigation. Most countries have undertaken unprecedented levels of short-term public expenditures. The International Monetary Fund (IMF) projects sovereign debt to GDP to have increased by 20% in advanced economies and 10% in emerging economies by the end of 2021 (IMF 2020). This is likely to slow economic growth, and may squeeze financial resources for mitigation and relevant investments for many years to come (Sections 15.2.3 and 15.6.3). COVID-19 further lowered interest rates which should facilitate low-carbon investment, but pandemic responses have increased sovereign debt across countries in all income bands (IMF 2021), and, particularly in some developing economies and regions, it has caused debt distress (Bulow et al. 2021), widening the gap in developing countries' access to capital (Hourcade et al. 2021b) (Section 15.6.3). After decades of global progress in reducing poverty, COVID-19 has pushed hundreds of millions of people below poverty thresholds and raises the spectre of intersecting health and climate crises that are devastating for the most vulnerable (Section 5.1.2 and Box 5.1). Like those of climate change, pandemic impacts fall heavily on disadvantaged groups, exacerbate the uneven distribution of future benefits, amplify existing inequities, and introduce new ones. Increased poverty also hinders efforts towards sustainable low-carbon transitions (Section 1.6).

Impacts on profitability and investment. COVID-19-induced demand reduction in electricity disproportionally affected coal power plants, whilst transport reduction most affected oil (IEA 2020a). This accelerated pre-existing decline in the relative profitability of most fossil fuel industries (Ameli et al. 2021). Renewables were the only energy sector to increase output (IEA 2020a). Within the context of a wider *overall* reduction in energy investment this prompted a substantial *relative* shift towards low-carbon investment particularly by the private sector (IEA 2020b; Rosembloom and Markard 2020) (Sections 15.2.1, 15.3.1 and 15.6.1).

Post-pandemic recovery pathways provide an opportunity to attract finance into accelerated and transformative low-carbon public investment (Sections 15.2 and 15.6.3). In most countries, COVID-19 has increased unemployment and/or state-supported employment. There is a profound difference between short-term 'bail outs' to stem unemployment, and the orientation of new public investment. The public debt is mirrored by large pools of private capital. During deep crises like that of COVID-19, economic multipliers of stimulus packages can be high (Hepburn et al., 2020), so much so that fiscal injections can then generate multipliers from 1.5 to 2.5, weakening the alleged crowding-out effect of public stimulus (Auerbach and Gorodnichenko 2012; Blanchard and Leigh 2013) (Section 15.2.3).

Cross-Chapter Box 1 (continued)

Recovery packages are motivated by assessments of the macroeconomic effectiveness ('multipliers') of public spending in ways that can crowd-in and revive private investment (Hepburn et al. 2020). There are clear reasons why a low-carbon response can create more enduring jobs, better aligned to future growth sectors: by also crowding-in and reviving private investment (e.g., from capital markets and institutional investors, including the growing profile of environmental, social and governance (ESG) and green bond markets (Section 15.6)), this can boost the effectiveness of public spending (IMF 2020). Stern and Valero (2021) argue that investment in low-carbon innovation and its diffusion, complemented by investments in sustainable infrastructure, are key to shaping environmentally sustainable and inclusive growth in the aftermath of the COVID-19 pandemic crisis. This would be the case both for high-income economies on the global innovation frontier, and to promote sustainable development in poorer economies.

A study with a global general equilibrium model (Liu et al. 2021) finds that because the COVID-19 economic aftermath combines negative impacts on employment and consumption, a shift from employment and consumption taxes to carbon- or other resource-related taxes would enhance GDP by 1.7% in 2021 relative to 'no policy', in addition to reducing CO_2 and other pollutants. A post-Keynesian model of wider 'green recovery' policies (Pollitt et al. 2021) finds a short-run benefit of around 3.5% GDP (compared to 'no policy'), and even about 1% above a recovery boosted by cuts in consumption taxes, the latter benefit sustained through 2030 – outperforming an equivalent conventional stimulus package while reducing global CO_2 emissions by 12%.

Orientation of recovery packages. The large public spending on supporting or stimulating economies, exceeding USD12 trillion by October 2020, dwarfs clean-energy investment needs and hence could either help to solve the combined crises, or result in high-carbon lock-in (Andrijevic et al. 2020). The short-term 'bail outs' to date do not foster climate-resilient long-term investments and have not been much linked to climate action, (Sections 15.2.3 and 15.6.3): in the G20 counties, 40% of energy-related support spending went to the fossil fuel industry compared to 37% on low-carbon energy (EPT 2020). Recovery packages are also at risk of being 'colourless' (Hepburn et al., 2020), though some countries and regions have prioritised green stimulus expenditures for example as part of a 'Green New Deal' (Rochedo et al. 2021) (Sections 13.9.6 and 15.6.3).

Integrating analyses. The response to COVID-19 also reflects the relevance of combining multiple analytic frameworks spanning economic efficiency, ethics and equity, transformation dynamics, and psychological and political analyses (Section 1.7). As with climate impacts, not only has the global burden of disease been distributed unevenly, but capabilities to prevent and treat disease were asymmetrical and those in greatest vulnerability often had the least access to human, physical, and financial resources (Ruger and Horton 2020). 'Green' versus 'brown' recovery has corresponding distributional consequences between these and 'green' producers, suggesting need for differentiated policies with international coordination (Le Billon et al. 2021). This illustrates the role of Just Transition approaches to global responses including the value of integrated, multi-level governance (Sections 1.7, 4.5 and 17.1).

Crises and opportunities: the wider context for mitigation and transformation. The impacts of COVID-19 have been devastating in many ways, in many countries, and may distract political and financial capacity away from efforts to mitigate climate change. Yet, studies of previous post-shock periods suggest that waves of innovation that are ready to emerge can be accelerated by crises, which may prompt new behaviours, weaken incumbent ('meso-level') systems, and prompt rapid reforms (Roberts and Geels 2019a) (Section 1.6.5). Lessons from the collective effort to 'flatten the curve' during the pandemic, illustrating aspects of science–society interactions for public health in many countries, may carry over to climate mitigation, and open new opportunities (Section 5.1.2). COVID-19 appears to have accelerated the emergence of renewable power, electromobility and digitalisation (Newman 2020) (Sections 5.1.2, 6.3 and 10.2). Institutional change is often very slow but major economic dislocation can create significant opportunities for new ways of financing and enabling 'leapfrogging' investment to happen (Section 10.8). Given the unambiguous risks of climate change, and consequent stranded asset risks from new fossil fuel investments (Box 6.11), the most robust recoveries are likely to be those which emerge on lower carbon and resilient pathways (Obergassel et al. 2021). Noting the critical global post-COVID-19 challenge as the double impact of heightened credit risk in developing countries, along with indebtedness in developed countries, Hourcade et al. (2021a) estimate that a 'multilateral' sovereign guarantee structure to underwrite low-carbon investments could leverage projects up to 15 times its value, contributing to shifting development pathways consistent with the SDGs and Paris goals.

COVID-19 can thus be taken as a reminder of the urgency of addressing climate change, a warning of the risk of future stranded assets (Rempel and Gupta 2021) (Chapter 17), but also an opportunity for a cleaner recovery.

In addition to developments in climate science, emissions, the international agreements in 2015, and the recent impact of COVID-19, a few other key developments have strong implications for climate mitigation.

Cheaper renewable energy technologies. Most striking, the cost of solar photovoltaic (PV) has fallen by a factor of 5 to 10 in the decade since the IPCC Special Report on Renewable Energy (IPCC 2011a) and other data inputting to the AR5 assessments. The SR1.5 reported major cost reductions, the IEA (2020) World Energy Outlook described PV as now 'the cheapest electricity in history' for projects that 'tap low cost finance and high quality resources.' Costs and deployment both vary widely between different countries (Chapters 6, 9 and 12) but costs are still projected to continue falling (Vartiainen et al. 2020). Rapid technological developments have occurred in many other low-carbon technologies including batteries and electric vehicles (Section 1.4.3), IT and related control systems, with progress also where electrification is not possible (Chapters 2, 6 and 11).

Civil society pressures for stronger action. Civic engagement increased leading up to the Paris Agreement (Bäckstrand and Lövbrand 2019) and after. Youth movements in several countries show young people's awareness about climate change, evidenced by the school strikes for the climate (Hagedorn et al. 2019; Buettner 2020; Thackeray et al. 2020; Walker 2020). Senior figures across many religions (Francis 2015; IFEES 2015) stressed the duty of humanity to protect future generations and the natural world, and warned about the inequities of climate change. Growing awareness of local environmental problems such as air pollution in Asia and Africa (Karlsson et al. 2020), and the threat to indigenous people's rights and existence has also fuelled climate activism (Etchart 2017). Grass-roots movements (Cheon and Urpelainen 2018; Fisher et al. 2019), build political pressure for accelerating climate change mitigation, as does increasing climate litigation (Setzer and Vanhala 2019) (Chapters 13 and 14).

Climate policies also encounter resistance. However, there are multiple sources of resistance to climate action in practice. Corporations and trade associations often lobby against measures they deem detrimental (Section 1.4.6). The emblematic 'yellow vest' movement in France was triggered by higher fuel costs as a result of a CO_2 tax hike (Lianos 2019; Driscoll 2021), though it had broader aspect of income inequality and other social issues. There is often a mismatch between concerns on climate change and people's willingness to pay for mitigation. For example, whilst most Americans believe climate change is happening, 68% said in a survey they would oppose climate policies that added just USD10 per month to electricity bills (EPIC et al. 2019), and worry about energy costs can eclipse those about climate change elsewhere (Poortinga et al. 2018) (Chapter 13).

Global trends contrary to multilateral cooperation. State-centred politics and geopolitical/geo-economic tensions seem to have become more prominent across many countries and issues (WEF 2019). In some cases, multilateral cooperation could be threatened by trends such as rising populism, nationalism, authoritarianism and growing protectionism (Abrahamsen et al. 2019), making it

more difficult to tackle global challenges including protecting the environment (Schreurs 2016; Parker et al. 2017; WEF 2019).

Transnational alliances. Partly countering this trend, cities, businesses and a wide range of other non-state actors also have emerged with important international networks to foster mitigation. City-based examples include the Cities Alliance in addressing climate change, Carbon Neutral Cities Alliance and the Covenant of Mayors (Chapter 8); there are numerous other alliances and networks such as those in finance (Chapter 15) and technology (Chapter 16), amongst many others (Chapters 13 and 14).

Finally, under the Paris Agreement process, during 2020/21, many countries strengthened their Nationally Determined Contributions (NDCs). Including updates until October 2021, these would imply global GHG emissions declining by 2030 to between 1–4% below 2019 levels (unconditional NDCs), or 4–10% (for NDCs conditional on international support) (Table 4.3). This is a significant change but would still not be compatible with 1.5°C pathways, and even if delivered in full, to limit warming to 2°C (>67%), emissions would have to fall very rapidly after 2030 (Section 3.2.5).

Thus, developments since AR5 highlight the complexity of the mitigation challenge. There is no far-sighted, globally optimising decision-maker and indeed climate policymaking at all levels is subject to conflicting pressures in multiple ways. The next section overviews the drivers and constraints.

1.4 Drivers and Constraints of Climate Mitigation and System Transitions/Transformation

This section provides a brief assessment of key factors and dynamics that drive, shape and/or limit climate mitigation in (i) **economic factors**: which include sectors and services, trade and leakage, finance and investment, and technological innovation; (ii) **socio-political issues**: which include political economy, social innovation, and equity and fairness; and (iii) **institutional factors**, which comprise policy, legal frameworks and international cooperation.

The AR5 introduced six 'enabling conditions' for shifting development pathways which are presented in Chapter 4 of this report and some of which overlap with the drivers reviewed here. However, the terminology of drivers and constraints have been chosen here to reflect the fact that each of these factors can serve as an enabling condition or a constraint to ambitious climate action depending on the context and how they are deployed. Often one sees the factors exerting both push and pull forces at the same time in the same and across different scales. For example, finance and investments can serve as a barrier or an enabler to climate action (Battiston et al. 2021). Similarly, political economy factors can align in favour of ambitious climate action or act in ways that inhibit strong cooperation and low-carbon transition. The other key insight from the assessment of the system drivers and constraints undertaken below is that none of the factors or conditions by themselves is more or less important than the others. In addition to being deeply intertwined all the factors matter in different measures with each exacting more or less force depending on the prevailing social, economic, cultural and political context. Often achieving accelerated mitigation would require effort to bring several of the factors in alignment in and across multiple levels of political or governance scales.

1.4.1   Services, Sectors and Urbanisation

Human activities drive emissions primarily through the demand for a wide range of services such as food, shelter, heating/cooling, goods, travel, communication, and entertainment. This demand is fulfilled by various activities often grouped into sectors such as agriculture, industry and commerce. The literature uses a wide range of sectoral definitions to organise data and analysis (Chapter 2). Energy sectors are typically organised into primary energy producers, energy transformation processes (such as power generation and fuel refining), and major energy users such as buildings, industry and transport (Chapters 2 and 5). Other research (Chapter 8) organises data around interacting urban and rural human activities. Land-based activities can be organised into agriculture, forestry and other land-use (AFOLU), or land use, land-use change and forestry (LULUCF) (Chapter 7). Each set of sectoral definitions and analysis offers its own insights.

Sectoral perspectives help to identify and understand the drivers of emissions, opportunities for emissions mitigation, and interactions with resources, other goals and other sectors, including the co-evolution of systems across scales (Kyle et al. 2016; Moss et al. 2016; Mori et al. 2017; IPBES 2019). Interactions between sectors and agents pursuing multiple goals is a major theme pervading this assessment.

The 'nexus' between energy, water, and land – all key contributors to human well-being – also helps to provide, regulate and support ecosystem and cultural services (Bazilian et al. 2011; Ringler et al. 2013; Smajgl et al. 2016; Albrecht et al. 2018; Brouwer et al. 2018; D'Odorico et al. 2018; Van Vuuren et al. 2019), with important implications for cities in managing new systems of transformation (Thornbush et al. 2013; Wolfram et al. 2016) (Chapter 8). Other important nexuses shaping our planet's future (Fajardy et al. 2018) include agriculture, forestry, land use and ecosystem services (Chazdon 2008; Settele et al. 2016; Torralba et al. 2016; Nesshöver et al. 2017; Keesstra et al. 2018).

Historically, energy-related GHG emissions were considered a by-product of the increasing scale of human activity, driven by population size, economic activity and technology. That simple notion has evolved greatly over time to become much more complex and diverse, with increasing focus on the provision of energy services (Cullen and Allwood 2010; Bardi et al. 2019; Brockway et al. 2019; Garrett et al. 2020). The demand for agricultural products has historically driven conversion of natural lands (land-use change). AFOLU along with food processing accounts for 21–37% of total net anthropogenic GHG emissions (SRCCL SPM A3).[5]

Continued growth in population and income are expected to continue driving up demand for goods and services (Chapters 2, 3 and 5), with an important role for urbanisation which is proceeding at an unprecedented speed and scale. In the last decade, the urban population grew by 70 million people each year, or about 1.3 million people per week, with urban area expanding by about 102 km^2 per day (Chapter 8). Urban areas account for most (45–87%) of the global carbon footprint (8.1) and the strong and positive correlation between urbanisation and incomes means higher consumption from urban lifestyles will continue driving direct and indirect GHG emissions. Cities provide a conduit to many of the services such as transportation, housing, water, food, medical care and recreation, and other services and urban carbon emissions are driven not only by population and income but also by the form and structure of urban areas (Sections 8.1 and 8.3–8.6). This creates opportunities for decarbonisation through urban planning and purposeful 'experimentation' (Newman et al. 2017) (Chapter 8).

Human needs and wants evolve over time making the transition toward climate and sustainable development goals either more or less difficult. For example, changes in the composition of goods consumed, such as shifting diets toward a more vegetarian balance, can reduce land-use emissions without compromising the quality of life (Stehfest et al. 2009; Gough 2017; van Vuuren et al. 2018; van den Berg et al. 2019; Hargreaves et al. 2021; SRCCL SPM B2.3).

Human behaviour and choices, including joint achievement of wider social goals, will play an important part in enabling or hindering climate mitigation and sustainable development (Shi et al. 2016), for example, shifting passenger transportation preferences in ways that combine climate, health and sustainable development goals (Romanello et al. 2021).

1.4.2   Trade, Consumption and Leakage

Emissions associated with international trade account for 20–33 % of global emissions, as calculated using multi-regional input-output analysis (Wiedmann and Lenzen 2018). Whether international trade drives an increase or decrease in global GHG emissions depends on the emissions intensity of traded products as well as the influence of trade on relocation of production, with studies reaching diverse conclusions about the net effect of trade openness on CO_2 emissions (Section 2.4.5). Tariff reduction of low-carbon technologies could facilitate effective mitigation (de Melo and Vijil 2014; Ertugrul et al. 2016; Islam et al. 2016; WTO 2016).

The magnitude of carbon leakage (see Glossary) caused by unilateral mitigation in a fragmented climate policy world depends on trade and substitution patterns of fossil fuels and the design of policies (IPCC 2014a, Box 5.4), but its potential significance in trade-exposed energy-intensive sectors (Bauer et al. 2013; Carbone and Rivers 2017; Naegele and Zaklan 2019) can make it an important constraint on policy. See Section 13.6.6.1 in Chapter 13 for channels and evidence. Akimoto et al. (2018) argue that differences in marginal abatement

---

[5]   AFOLU accounted for about 13% of CO_2, 44% of CH_4 and 82% of N_2O global anthropogenic GHG emissions in 2007–2016.

costs of NDCs could cause carbon leakage in energy-intensive, trade-exposed sectors, and could weaken effective global mitigation.

Policy responses to cope with carbon leakage include border carbon adjustment (BCAs) and differentiated carbon taxes (Liu et al. 2020). Some BCA options focusing on levelling the cost of carbon paid by consumers on products could be designed in line with the WTO (Ismer et al. 2016), while others may not be (Mehling et al. 2019). All proposals could involve difficulty of tracing and verifying the carbon content of inputs (Onder 2012; Denis-Ryan et al. 2016). An international consensus and certification practice on the carbon content would help to overcome WTO compatibility (Holzer 2014). See Chapter 13 and Mehling et al. (2019) on the context of trade law and the PA.

Official inventories report territorial emissions, which do not consider the impacts embodied in imports of goods. Global supply chains undoubtedly lead to a growth in trade volumes (Federico and Tena-Junguito 2017), alternative methods have been suggested to account for emissions associated with international trade, such as shared responsibility (Lenzen et al. 2007), technology-adjusted consumption-based accounting (Kander et al. 2015), value-added-based responsibility (Piñero et al. 2019) and exergy-based responsibility based on thermodynamics (Khajehpour et al. 2019). Consumption-based emissions (i.e., attribution of emissions related to domestic consumption and imports to final destination) are not officially reported in global emissions datasets but data has improved (Tukker and Dietzenbacher 2013; Afionis et al. 2017). This analysis has been used extensively for consumption-based accounting of emissions, and other environmental impacts (Wiedmann and Lenzen 2018; Malik et al. 2019) (Section 2.3).

Increasing international trade has resulted in a general shifting of fossil fuel-driven emissions-intensive production from developed to developing countries (Arto and Dietzenbacher 2014; Malik and Lan 2016), and between developing countries (Zhang et al. 2019). High-income developed countries thus tend to be net importers of emissions, whereas low/middle-income developing countries net exporters (Peters et al. 2011) (Figure 1.2c, d). This trend is shifting, with a growth in trade between non-OECD countries (Meng et al. 2018; Zhang et al. 2019), and a decline in emissions intensity of traded goods (Wood et al. 2020b).

The Paris Agreement primarily deals with national commitments relating to domestic emissions and removals, hence emissions from international aviation and shipping are not covered. Aviation and shipping accounted for approximately 2.7% of greenhouse gas emissions in 2019 (before COVID-19); see Section 10.5.2 for discussion. In addition to CO_2 emissions, aircraft-produced contrail cirrus clouds, and emissions of black carbon and short-lived aerosols (e.g., sulphates) from shipping are especially harmful for the Arctic (Section 10.8 and Box 10.6).

1.4.3   Technology

The rapid developments in technology over the past decade enhance potential for transformative changes, in particular to help deliver climate goals simultaneously with other SDGs.

The fall in renewable energy costs alongside rapid growth in capacity (Figure 1.3; see also Figures 6.8 and 6.11 in Chapter 6) has been accompanied by varied progress in many other technology areas such as electric vehicles, fuel cells for both stationary and mobile applications (Dodds 2019), thermal energy (Chapter 6), and battery and other storage technologies (Freeman et al. 2017) (Chapters 6, 9 and 12; Figure TS.7). Nuclear contributions may be enhanced by new generations of reactors (e.g., Generation III) and small modular reactors (Knapp and Pevec 2018) (Chapter 6).

Large-scale hydrogen developments could provide a complementary energy channel with long-term storage. Like electricity, hydrogen (H_2) is an energy vector with multiple potential applications, including in industrial processes such as steel and non-metallic materials production (Chapter 11), for long-range transportation (Chapter 10), and low-temperature heating in buildings (Chapter 9). Emissions depend on how it is produced, and deploying H_2 delivery infrastructure economically is a challenge when the future scale of hydrogen demand is so uncertain (Chapter 6). H_2 from natural gas with CO_2 capture and storage (CCS) may help to kick-start the H_2 economy (Sunny et al. 2020).

CO_2-based fuels and feedstocks such as synthetic methane, methanol, diesel, jet fuel and other hydrocarbons, potentially from carbon capture and utilisation (CCU), represent drop-in solutions with limited new infrastructure needs (Artz et al. 2018; Bobeck et al. 2019; Yugo and Soler 2019) (Chapter 10). Deployment and development of CCS technologies (with large-scale storage of captured CO_2) have been much slower than projected in previous assessments (IEA 2019b; Page et al. 2019) (Chapter 11).

Potential constraints on new energy technologies may include their material requirements, notably rare earth materials for electronics or lithium for batteries (Wanger 2011; Flexer et al. 2018), stressing the importance of recycling (IPCC 2011b; Rosendahl and Rubiano 2019). Innovation is enabling greater recycling and reuse of energy-intensive materials (Shemi et al. 2018), and introducing radically new and more environmentally friendly materials, however, still not all materials can be recycled (Allwood 2014).

By sequestering carbon in biomass and soils, soil carbon management, and other terrestrial strategies could offset hard-to-reduce emissions in other sectors. However, large-scale bioenergy deployment could increase risks of desertification, land degradation, and food insecurity (IPCC 2019a), and higher water withdrawals (Hasegawa et al. 2018; Fuhrman et al. 2020), though this may be at least partially offset by innovation in agriculture, diet shifts and plant-based proteins contributing to meeting demand for food, feed, fibre and bioenergy (or bioenergy with carbon capture and storage (BECCS) with CCS) (Havlik et al. 2014; Popp et al. 2017; Köberle et al. 2020) (Chapters 5 and 7).

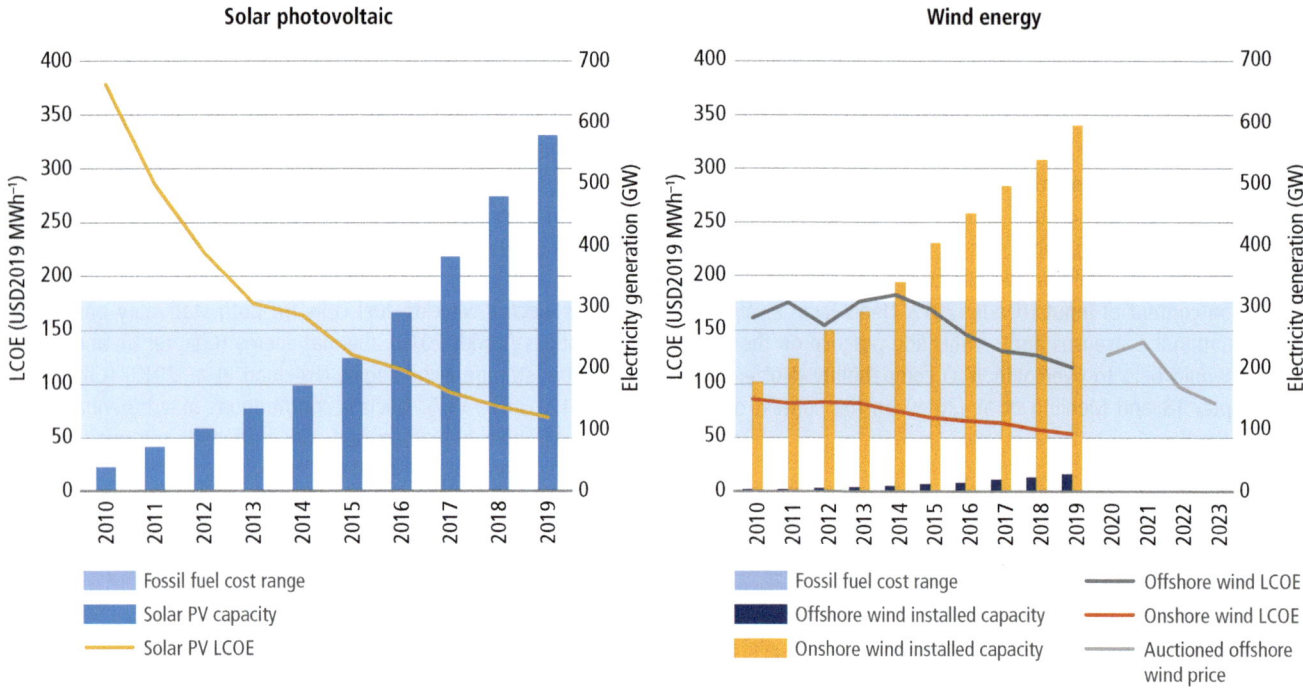

Figure 1.3 | Cost reductions and adoption in solar photovoltaic and wind energy. Fossil fuel Levelised Cost of Electricity (LCOE) is indicated by blue shading at USD50–177 MWh^{-1} (IRENA 2020b). Source: data from IRENA (2021a,b).

A broad class of more speculative technologies propose to counteract effects of climate change by removing CO_2 from the atmosphere (CDR), or by directly modifying the Earth's energy balance at a large scale (solar radiation modification or SRM). CDR technologies include ocean iron fertilisation, enhanced weathering and ocean alkalinisation (Council 2015a), along with direct air carbon capture and storage (DACCS). They could potentially draw down atmospheric CO_2 much faster than the Earth's natural carbon cycle, and reduce reliance on biomass-based removal (Köberle 2019; Realmonte et al. 2019), but some present novel risks to the environment and DACCS is currently more expensive than most other forms of mitigation (Fuss et al. 2018) (Cross-Chapter Box 8 in Chapter 12). Solar radiation modification (SRM) could potentially cool the planet rapidly at low estimated direct costs by reflecting incoming sunlight (Council 2015b), but entails uncertain side effects and thorny international equity and governance challenges (Netra et al. 2018; Florin et al. 2020; National Academies of Sciences 2021) (Chapter 14). Understanding the climate response to SRM remains subject to large uncertainties (AR6 WGI). Some literature uses the term 'geoengineering' for both CDR or SRM when applied at a planetary scale (Shepherd 2009; GESAMP 2019). In this report, CDR and SRM are discussed separately, reflecting their very different geophysical characteristics.

Large improvements in information storage, processing, and communication technologies, including artificial intelligence, will affect emissions. They can enhance energy-efficient control, reduce transaction costs for energy production and distribution, improve demand-side management (DSM) (Raza and Khosravi 2015), and reduce the need for physical transport (Smidfelt Rosqvist and Winslott Hiselius 2016) (Chapters 5, 6 and 9–11). However, data centres and related IT systems (including blockchain), are electricity-intensive and will raise demand for energy (Avgerinou et al. 2017) – cryptocurrencies may be a major global source of CO_2 if the electricity production is not decarbonised (Mora et al. 2018) – and there is also a concern that Information technologies can compound and exacerbate current inequalities (Chapters 5, 16 and Cross-Chapter Box 11 in Chapter 16). IT may affect broader patterns of work and leisure (Boppart and Krusell 2020), and the emissions intensity of how people spend their leisure time will become more important (Chapters 5 and 9). Because higher efficiency tends to reduces costs, it often involves some 'rebound' offsetting at least some of the emission savings (Sudbury and Hutchinson 2016; Belkhir and Elmeligi 2018; Cohen and Cavoli 2019).

Technology can enable both emissions reductions and/or increased emissions (Chapter 16). Governments play an important role in most major innovations, in both 'technology-push' (Mazzucato 2013) and induced by 'demand-pull' (Grubb et al. 2021a), so policy is important in determining its pace, direction and utilisation (Roberts and Geels 2019a) (Sections 1.7.1 and 1.7.3). Overall, the challenge will be to enhance the synergies and minimise the trade-offs and rebounds, including taking account of ethical and distributional dimensions (Gonella et al. 2019).

1.4.4   Finance and Investment

Finance is both an enabler and a constraint on mitigation, and since AR5, attention to the financial sector's role in mitigation has grown. This is partly in the context of the Paris Agreement finance articles and the Green Climate Fund, the pledge to mobilise USD100 billion yr^{-1} by 2020, and the Addis Abbaba Action Agenda (Section 1.3.1).

However, there is a persistent but uncertain gap in mitigation finance (Cui and Huang 2018) (Table 15.15.1), even though tracked climate finance overwhelmingly goes toward mitigation compared to adaptation (UNEP 2020) (Section 15.3; Working Group II). Green bond issuance has increased recently in parallel with efforts to reform the international financial system by supporting development of local capital markets (Section 15.6.4).

Climate finance is a multi-actor, multi-objective domain that includes central banks, commercial banks, asset managers, underwriters, development banks, and corporate planners. Climate change presents both risks and opportunities for the financial sector. The risks include physical risks related to the impacts of climate change itself; transition risks related to the exposure to policy, technology and behavioural changes in line with a low-carbon transition; and liability risks from litigation for climate-related damages (Box 15.2). These could potentially lead to stranded assets (the loss of economic value of existing assets before the end of their useful lifetimes (Bos and Gupta 2019) (Sections 6.7 and 15.6.3). Such risks continue to be underestimated by financial institutions (Section 15.6.1). The continuing expansion of fossil fuel infrastructure and insufficient transparency on how these are valued raises concerns that systemic risk may be accumulating in the financial sector in relation to a potential low-carbon transition that may already be under way (Battiston et al. 2017) (Section 15.6.3). The Financial Stability Board's Taskforce on Climate-related Financial Disclosures' (TCFD) recommendations on transparency aim to ensure that investors and companies consider climate change risks in their strategies and capital allocation (TCFD 2018). This is helping 'investors to reassess core assumptions' and may lead to 'significant' capital reallocation (Fink 2020). However, metrics and indicators of assets risk exposure are inadequate (Monasterolo 2017; Campiglio et al. 2018) and transparency alone is insufficient to drive the required asset reallocation in the absence of clear regulatory frameworks (Ameli et al. 2020; Chenet et al. 2021). A coalition of central banks have formed the Network for Greening the Financial Sector, to support and advance the transformation of the financial system (Allen et al. 2020; NGFS 2020), with some of them conducting climate-related institutional stress tests.

Governments cannot single-handedly fund the transition (Section 15.6.7), least of all in low-income developing countries with large sovereign debt and poor access to global financial markets. Long-term sources of private capital are required to close the financing gap across sectors and geographies (Section 15.6.7). Future investment needs are greatest in emerging and developing economies (Section 15.5.2) which already face higher costs of capital, hindering capacity to finance a transition (Buhr et al. 2018; Ameli et al. 2020). Requisite North–South financial flows are impeded by both geographic and technological risk premiums (Iyer et al. 2015), and the COVID-19 pandemic has further compromised the ability of developing and emerging economies to finance development activities or attract additional climate finance from developed countries (Section 15.6.3, and Cross-Chapter Box 1 in this chapter). Climate-related investments in developing countries also suffer from structural barriers such as sovereign risk and exchange rate volatility (Farooquee and Shrimali 2016; Guzman et al. 2018) which affect not only climate-related investment but investment in general (Yamahaki et al. 2020) including in needed infrastructure development (Gray and Irwin 2003). A Green Climate Fund (GCF) report notes the paradox that USD14 trillion of negative-yielding debt in OECD countries might be expected to flow to much larger low-carbon, climate-resilient investment opportunities in developing countries, but 'this is not happening' (Hourcade et al. 2021b).

There is often a disconnect between stated national climate ambition and finance flows, and overseas direct investment (ODI) from donor countries may be at odds with national climate pledges such as NDCs. One report found funds supported by foreign state-owned enterprises into 56 recipient countries in Asia and Africa in 2014–2017 went mostly to fossil fuel-based projects not strongly aligned with low-carbon priorities of recipient countries' NDCs (Zhou et al. 2018). Similarly, Steffen and Schmidt (2019) found that even within multilateral development banks, 'public- and private-sector branches differ considerably', with public-sector lending used mainly in non-renewable and hydropower projects. Political leadership is therefore essential to steer financial flows to support low-carbon transition (Section 15.6). Voituriez et al. (2019) identify significant mitigation potential if financing countries simply applied their own environmental standards to their overseas investments.

1.4.5   Political Economy

The politics of interest (most especially economic interest) of key actors at sub-national, national and global levels can be important determinants of climate (in)action (O'Hara 2009; Lo 2010; Tanner and Allouche 2011; Sovacool et al. 2015; Lohmann 2017; Clapp et al. 2018; Newell and Taylor 2018; Lohmann 2019). Political economy approaches can be crudely divided into 'economic approaches to politics', and those used by other social scientists (Paterson and P-Laberge 2018). The former shows how electoral concerns lead to weak treaties (Battaglini and Harstad 2016) and when policy negotiations cause status-quo biases and the use of inefficient policy instruments (Austen-Smith et al. 2019) or delays and excessive harmonisation (Harstad 2007). The latter emphasises the central role of structures of power and production, and a commitment to economic growth and capital accumulation in relation to climate action, given the historically central role of fossil fuels to economic development and the deep embedding of fossil energy in daily life (Newell and Paterson 2010; Huber 2012; Di Muzio 2015; Malm 2015).

The economic centrality of fossil fuels raises obvious questions regarding the possibility of decarbonisation. Economically, this is well understood as a problem of decoupling. But the constraint is also political, in terms of the power of incumbent fossil fuel interests to block initiatives towards decarbonisation (Jones and Levy 2009; Newell and Paterson 2010; Geels 2014). The effects of climate policy are key considerations in deciding the level of policy ambition and direction and strategies of states (Lo 2010; Alam et al. 2013; Ibikunle and Okereke 2014), regions (Goldthau and Sitter 2015), and business actors (Wittneben et al. 2012), and there is a widespread cultural assumption that continued fossil fuel use is central to this (Strambo and Espinosa 2020). Decarbonisation strategies are often centred around projects to develop new sources of economic activity: carbon markets creating new commodities (Newell and Paterson 2010); investment generated in new urban infrastructure (Whitehead 2013); and/or innovations in a range of new energy technologies (Fankhauser et al. 2013; Lachapelle et al. 2017; Meckling and Nahm 2018).

One factor limiting the ambition of climate policy has been the ability of incumbent industries to shape government action on climate change (Newell and Paterson 1998; Jones and Levy 2009; Geels 2014; Breetz et al. 2018). Incumbent industries are often more concentrated than those benefiting from climate policy and lobby more effectively to prevent losses than those who would gain (Meng and Rode 2019). Drawing upon wider networks (Brulle 2014), campaigns by oil and coal companies against climate action in the United States of America and Australia are perhaps the most well known and largely successful of these (Pearse 2017; Brulle et al. 2020; Mildenberger 2020; Stokes 2020), although similar dynamics have been demonstrated in Brazil and South Africa (Hochstetler 2020), Canada (Harrison 2018), and Norway and Germany (Fitzgerald et al. 2019), for example. In other contexts, resistance by incumbent companies is more subtle but nevertheless has weakened policy design on emissions trading systems (Rosembloom and Markard 2020), and limited the development of alternative-fuelled automobiles (Levy and Egan 2003; Wells and Nieuwenhuis 2012).

The interaction of politics, power and economics is central in explaining why countries with higher per-capita emissions, which logically have more opportunities to reduce emissions, in practice often take the opposite stance, and conversely, why some low-emitting countries may find it easier to pursue climate action because they have fewer vested interests in high-carbon economies. These dynamics can arise from the vested interest of state-owned enterprises (SOEs) (Wittneben et al. 2012; Polman 2015; Wright and Nyberg 2017), the alignment and coalitions of countries in climate negotiations (Gupta 2016; Okereke and Coventry 2016), and the patterns of opposition to or support for climate policy among citizens (Baker 2015; Swilling et al. 2016; Heffron and McCauley 2018; Ransan-Cooper et al. 2018; Turhan et al. 2019).

1.4.6   Equity and Fairness

Equity and fairness can serve as both drivers and barriers to climate mitigation at different scales of governance. Literature regularly highlights equity and justice issues as critical components in local politics and international diplomacy regarding all SDGs, such as goals for no poverty, zero hunger, gender equality, affordable clean energy, reducing inequality, but also for climate action (SDG 13) (Marmot and Bell 2018; Spijkers 2018). Equity issues help explain why it has proved hard to reach more substantive global agreements, as it is hard to agree on a level of greenhouse gas (GHG) mitigation (or emissions) and how to distribute mitigation efforts among countries (Kverndokk 2018) for several reasons. First, an optimal trade-off between mitigation costs and damage costs of climate change depends on ethical considerations, and simulations from integrated assessment models using different ethical parameters producing different optimal mitigation paths (IPCC 2018b) (Section 3.6.1.2). Second, treaties that

are considered unfair may be hard to implement (Klinsky et al. 2017; Liu et al. 2017). Lessons from experimental economics show that people may not accept a distribution that is considered unfair, even if there is a cost of not accepting (Gampfer 2014). As equity issues are important for reaching deep decarbonisation, the transition towards sustainable development (Evans and Phelan 2016; Heffron and McCauley 2018; Okereke 2018) depends on taking equity seriously in climate policies and international negotiations (Okereke and Coventry 2016; Klinsky et al. 2017; Martinez et al. 2019).

Climate change and climate policies affect countries and people differently. Low-income countries tend to be more dependent on primary industries (agriculture and fisheries, etc.) than richer countries, and their infrastructure may be less robust to tackle more severe weather conditions. Within a country, the burdens may not be equally distributed either, due to policy measures implemented and from differences in vulnerability and adaptive capacity following from e.g. income and wealth distribution, race and gender. For instance, unequal social structures can result in women being more vulnerable to the effects of climate change compared to men, especially in poor countries (Arora-Jonsson 2011; Jost et al. 2016; Rao et al. 2019). Costs of mitigation also differ across countries. Studies show there are large disparities of economic impacts of NDCs across regions, and also between relatively similar countries when it comes to the level of development, due to large differences in marginal abatement costs for the emission-reduction goal of NDCs (Fujimori et al. 2016; Hof et al. 2017; Akimoto et al. 2018; Evans & Gabbatiss 2019). Equalising the burdens from climate policies may give more support for mitigation policies (Maestre-Andrés et al. 2019).

Taking equity into account in designing an international climate agreement is complicated as there is no single universally accepted equity criterion, and countries may strategically choose a criterion that favours them (Lange et al. 2007, 2010). Still, several studies analyse the consequences of different social preferences in designing climate agreements, such as, for instance, inequality aversion, sovereignty and altruism (Anthoff et al. 2010; Kverndokk et al. 2014).

International transfers from rich to poor countries to support mitigation and adaptation activities may help with equalising burdens, as agreed upon in the UNFCCC (1992) (Chapters 14 and 15), such that they may be motivated by strategic as well as equity reasons (Kverndokk 2018) (Section 1.4.4).

1.4.7   Social Innovation and Behaviour Change

Social and psychological factors affect both perceptions and behaviour (Weber 2015; Whitmarsh et al. 2021). Religion, values, culture, gender, identity, social status and habits strongly influence individual behaviours and choices, and therefore sustainable consumption (Sections 1.6.3.1 and 5.2). Identities can provide powerful attachments to consumption activities and objects that inhibit shifts away from them (Brekke et al. 2003; Bénabou and Tirole 2011; Stoll-Kleemann and Schmidt 2017; Ruby et al. 2020). Consumption is a habit-driven and social practice rather than simply a set of individual decisions, making shifts in consumption harder to pursue (Evans et al. 2012; Shove and Spurling 2013; Kurz et al. 2015; Warde 2017; Verplanken and Whitmarsh 2021). Finally, shifts towards low-carbon behaviour are also inhibited by social-psychological and political dynamics that cause individuals to ignore the connections from daily consumption practices to climate change impacts (Norgaard 2011; Brulle and Norgaard 2019).

As a notable example, plant-based alternatives to meat could reduce emissions from diets (Eshel et al. 2019; Willett et al. 2019). However, diets are deeply entrenched in cultures and identities, and hard to change (Fresco 2015; Mylan 2018). Changing diets also raises cross-cultural ethical issues, in addition to meat's role in providing nutrition (Plumwood 2004). Henceforth, some behaviours that are harder to change will only be transformed by the transition itself: triggered by policies, the transition will bring about technologies that, in turn, will entrench new sustainable behaviours.

Behaviour can be influenced through a number of mechanisms besides economic policy and regulation, such as information campaigns, advertising and 'nudging'. Innovations and infrastructure also impact behaviour, as with bicycle lanes to reduce road traffic. Wider social innovations also have indirect impacts. Education is increasing across the world, and higher education will have impacts on fertility, consumption and the attitude towards the environment (Osili and Long 2008; Hamilton 2011; McCrary and Royer 2011). Reducing poverty and improvements in health and reproductive choice will also have implications for fertility, energy use and consumption globally. Finally, social capital and the ability to work collectively may have large consequences for mitigation and the ability to adapt to climate change (Adger 2009; IPCC 2014a Section 4.3.5).

1.4.8   Policy Impacts

Transformation to different systems will hinge on conscious policy to change the direction in which energy, land use, agriculture and other key sectors develop (Bataille et al. 2016) (Chapters 13 and 16). Policy plays a central role in in land-related systems (Chapter 7), urban development (Chapter 8), improving energy efficiency in buildings (Chapter 9) and transport/mobility (Chapter 10), and decarbonising industrial systems (Chapter 11).

Policy has been and will be central not only because GHG emissions are almost universally under-priced in market economies (Stern and Stiglitz 2017; World Bank 2019), and because of inadequate economic incentives to innovation (Jaffe et al. 2005), but also due to various delay mechanisms (Karlsson and Gilek 2020) and multiple sources of path-dependence and lock-in to existing systems (Section 1.8.2), including: 'Infrastructure developments and long-lived products that lock societies into GHG-intensive emissions pathways may be difficult or very costly to change, reinforcing the importance of early

action for ambitious mitigation (*robust evidence*, *high agreement*).' (AR5 WGIII p.18).

Many hundreds of policies have been introduced explicitly to mitigate GHG emissions, improve energy efficiency or land use, or to foster low-carbon industries and innovation, with demonstrable impact. The role of policy to date has been most evident in energy efficiency (Sections 5.4 and 5.6) and electricity (Chapter 6). The IPCC Special Report on Renewable Energy already found that: 'Government policies play a crucial role in accelerating the deployment of RE technologies' (IPCC 2011a, p. 24). Policy packages since then have driven rapid expansion in renewables capacity and cost reductions (e.g., through the German *Energiewende*), and emission reductions from electricity (most dramatically with the halving of CO_2 emissions from the UK power sector, driven by multiple policy instruments and regulatory changes), as detailed in Chapter 6 (Section 6.7.5).

Chapter 13 charts the international evolution of policies and many of the lessons drawn. Attributing the overall impact on emissions is complex, but an emerging literature of several hundred papers indicates impacts on multiple drivers of emissions. Collectively, policies are likely to have curtailed global emissions growth by several $GtCO_2$-eq annually already by the mid-2010s (Cross-Chapter Box 10 in Chapter 14). This suggests initial evidence that policy has driven some decoupling (Figure 1.1d) and started to 'bend the curve' of global emissions, but more specific attribution to observed trends is not as yet possible.[6]

However, some policies (e.g., subsidies to fossil fuel production or consumption) increase emissions, whilst others (e.g., investment protection) may constrain efforts at mitigation. Also, wider economic and developmental policies have important direct and indirect impacts on emissions. Policy is thus both a driver and a constraint on mitigation.

Synergies and trade-offs arise partly because of the nexus of GHG emissions with other adverse impacts (e.g., local air pollution) and critical resources (e.g., water and food) (Conway et al. 2015; Andrews-Speed and Dalin 2017), which also imply interacting policy domains.

The literature shows increasing emphasis on policy packages, including those spanning the different levels of niche/behaviour; existing regimes governing markets and public actors; and strategic and landscape levels (Section 1.7.3). Chapters 13, 16 and 17 appraise policies for transformation in the context of sustainable development, indicating the importance of policy as a driver at multiple levels and across many actors, with potential for benefits as well as costs at many levels.

National-level legislation may be particularly important to the credibility and long-term stability of policy to reduce the risks, and hence cost,

---

[6]   Linking estimated policy impacts to trends is complex, and as yet very tentative. An important factor is that many mitigation policies involve investments in low-carbon or energy-efficient technology, the savings from which persist. As a purely illustrative example: the annual increase in global emissions during 2000–2010 averaged around 1 $GtCO_2$-eq yr^{-1}, but with large fluctuations. If policies by 2010 reduced the *annual increase* in that year by 100 $MtCO_2$-eq (0.1 $GtCO_2$-eq) below what it would otherwise have been, this is hard to discern. But if these savings sustain, and in each subsequent year, policies cut another 100 $MtCO_2$-eq off the annual increase compared to the previous year, global emissions after a decade would be around 5 $GtCO_2$-eq yr^{-1} below what they would have been without any such policies, and on average close to stabilising. However each step would be difficult to discern in the noise of annual fluctuations.

of finance (Chapters 13 and 15), and for encouraging private-sector innovation at scale (Chapter 16), for example, if it offers greater stability and mid-term predictability for carbon prices; Nash and Steurer (2019) find that seven national climate change acts in European countries all act as 'living policy processes, though to varying extents'.

The importance of policy at multiple levels does not lessen the importance of international policy, for reasons including long-term stability, equity, and scope, but examples of effective implementation policy at international levels remain fewer and governance weaker (Chapter 14).

1.4.9   Legal Framework and Institutions

Institutions are rules and norms held in common by social actors that guide, constrain and shape human interaction (IPCC 2018b). Institutions can be formal, such as laws and policies, or informal, such as norms and conventions. Institutions can both facilitate or constrain climate policymaking and implementation in multiple ways. Institutions set the economic incentives for action or inaction on climate change at national, regional and individual levels (Dorsch and Flachsland 2017; Sullivan 2017).

Institutions entrench specific political decision-making processes, often empowering some interests over others, including powerful interest groups who have vested interests in maintaining the current high-carbon economic structures (Okereke and Russel 2010; Wilhite 2016; Engau et al. 2017); see also Section 1.4.6 and Chapter 13 on the sub-national and national governance challenges including coordination, mediating politics and strategy setting.

Some suggest that societal transformation towards a low-carbon future requires new politics that involves thinking in intergenerational time horizons, as well as new forms of partnerships between private and public actors (Westman and Broto 2018), and associated institutions and social innovations to increase involvement of non-state actors in climate governance (Fuhr et al. 2018). However literature is divided as to how much democratisation of climate politics, with greater emphasis on equity and community participation, would advance societal transformation in the face of climate change (Stehr 2005), or may actually hinder radical climate action in some circumstances (Povitkina 2018).

Since 2016, the number of climate litigation cases has increased rapidly. The UN Environment Programme's Global Climate Litigation Report: 2020 Status Review (UNEP 2020) noted that between March 2017 and 1 July 2020, the number of cases nearly doubled with at least 1550 climate cases filed in eight countries. Several important cases such as Urgenda Foundation vs The State of the Netherlands ('Urgenda') and Juliana et al. vs United States ('Juliana') have had ripple effects, inspiring other similar cases (Lin and Kysar 2020).

Numerous international climate governance initiatives engage national and sub-national governments, NGOs and private corporations, constituting a 'regime complex' (Raustiala and Victor 2004; Keohane and Victor 2011). They may have longer-run and second-order effects if commitments are more precise and binding (Kahler 2017). However, without targets, incentives, defined baselines or monitoring, reporting, and verification, they are not likely to fill the 'mitigation gap' (Michaelowa and Michaelowa 2017).

1.4.10   International Cooperation

Tackling climate change is often mentioned as an important reason for strong international cooperation in the 21st century (Falkner 2016; Keohane and Victor 2016; Bodansky et al. 2017; Cramton et al. 2017b). Mitigation costs are borne by countries taking action, while the benefits of reduced climate change are not limited to them, being in economic terms 'global and non-excludable'. Hence anthropogenic climate change is typically seen as a global commons problem (Falkner 2016; Wapner and Elver 2017). Moreover, the belief that mitigation will raise energy costs and may adversely affect competitiveness creates incentives for free riding, where states avoid taking their fair share of action (Barrett 2005; Keohane and Victor 2016). International cooperation has the potential to address these challenges through collective action (Tulkens 2019) and international institutions offer the opportunity for actors to engage in meaningful communication and exchange of ideas about potential solutions (Cole 2015). International cooperation is also vital for the creation and diffusion of norms and the framework for stabilising expectations among actors (Pettenger 2016).

Some key roles of the UNFCCC have been detailed by its former heads (Kinley et al. 2021). In addition to specific agreements (most recently the PA) it has enhanced transparency through reporting and data, and generated or reinforced several important norms for global climate action including the principles of equity, common but differentiated responsibility and respective capabilities, and the precautionary principles for maintaining global cooperation among states with unevenly distributed emissions sources, climate impacts, and varying mitigation costs across countries (Keohane and Victor, 2016). In addition to formal negotiations, the annual Conference of the Parties (COPs) have increased awareness, and motivated more ambitious actions, sometimes through the formation of 'coalitions of the willing', for example. It provides a structure for measuring and monitoring action towards a global goal (Milkoreit and Haapala 2019). International cooperation (including the UNFCCC) can also promote technology development and transfer and capacity building; mobilise finance for mitigation and adaptation; and help address concerns on climate justice (Okereke and Coventry 2016; Chan et al. 2018) (Chapters 14–16).

A common criticism of international institutions is their limited (if any) powers to enforce compliance (Zahar 2017). As a global legal institution, the PA has little enforcement mechanism (Sindico 2015), but enforcement is not a necessary condition for an instrument to be legally binding (Bodansky 2016; Rajamani 2016). In reality implementation of specific commitments tends to be high once countries have ratified and a treaty or an agreement is in force (Bodansky 2016; Rajamani 2016). Often, the problem is not so much of 'power to enforce compliance or sanction non-compliance', but the level of ambition (Chapter 14).

However, whilst in most respects a driver, international cooperation has also been characterised as 'organised hypocrisy' where proclamations are not matched with corresponding action (Egnell 2010). Various reasons for inadequate progress after 30 years of climate negotiations, have been identified (Stoddard et al. 2021). International cooperation can also seem to be a barrier to ambitious action when negotiation is trapped in 'relative-gains' calculus, in which countries seek to game the regime or gain leverage over one another (Purdon 2017), or where states lower ambition to the 'least common dominator' to accommodate participation of the least ambitious states (Falkner 2016). Geden (2016) and Dubash (2020) offer more nuanced assessments.

International collaboration works best if an agreement can be made self-reinforcing with incentives for mutual gains and joint action (Barrett 2016; Keohane and Victor 2016), but the structure of the climate challenge makes this hard to achieve. The evidence from the Montreal Protocol on ozone-depleting substances and from the Kyoto Protocol on GHGs, is that legally binding targets have been *effective* in that participating Parties complied with them (Shishlov et al. 2016; Albrecht and Parker 2019), and (for Kyoto) these account for most of the countries that have sustained emission reductions for at least the past 10 to 15 years (Sections 1.3.2 and 2.2). However, such binding commitments may deter *participation* if there are no clear incentives to sustain participation and especially if other growing emitters are omitted by design, as with the Kyoto Protocol. Consequently the USA refused to ratify (and Canada withdrew), particularly on the grounds that developing countries had no targets; with participation in Kyoto's second period commitments declining further, the net result was limited global progress in emissions under Kyoto (Bodansky 2016; Okereke and Coventry 2016; Scavenius and Rayner 2018) despite full legal compliance in both commitment periods (Chapter 14).

The negotiation of the Paris Agreement was thus done in the context of serious questions about how best to structure international climate cooperation to achieve better results. This new agreement is designed to sidestep the fractious bargaining which characterised international climate cooperation (Marcu 2017). It contains a mix of hard, soft and non-obligations, the boundaries between which are blurred, but each of which plays a distinct and valuable role (Rajamani 2016). The provisions of the PA could encourage flexible responses to changing conditions, but limit assurances of ambitious national commitments and their fulfilment (Pickering et al. 2018). The extent to which this new arrangement will drive ambitious climate policy in the long run remains to be seen (Chapter 14).

Whilst the PA abandoned common accounting systems and time frames, outside of the UNFCCC many other platforms and metrics for comparing mitigation efforts have emerged (Aldy 2015). Countries may assess others' efforts in determining their actions through multiple platforms including the Climate Change Cooperation Index (C3-I), Climate Change Performance Index (CCPI), Climate Laws, Institutions and Measures Index (CLIMI) (Bernauer and Böhmelt 2013) and Energy Transition Index (Singh et al. 2019). International cooperative initiatives between and among non-state (e.g., business, investors and civil society) and sub-national (e.g., city and state) actors have also been emerging, taking the forms of public-private partnerships,

private-sector governance initiatives, NGO transnational initiatives, and sub-national transnational initiatives (Bulkeley and Schroeder 2012; Hsu et al. 2018). Literature is mostly positive about the role of these transnational initiatives in facilitating climate action across scales although criticism and caution about their accountability and effectiveness remain (Chan et al. 2016; Michaelowa and Michaelowa 2017; Roger et al. 2017; Widerberg and Pattberg 2017) (Chapter 14).

1.5 Emissions Scenarios and Illustrative Mitigation Pathways (IMPs)

Scenarios are a powerful tool for exploring an uncertain future world against the background of alternative choices and development. Scenarios can be constructed using both narrative and quantitative methods. When these two methods are combined they provide complementary information and insights. Quantitative and narrative models are frequently used to represent scenarios to explore choices and challenges. The IPCC has a long history of assessing scenarios (Nakicenovic et al. 2000; van Vuuren et al. 2011, 2014) (see also AR6 WGI Section 1.6 for a history of scenarios within the IPCC). This WGIII assessment employs a wide range of qualitative and quantitative scenarios including quantitative scenarios developed through a wide and heterogeneous set of tools ranging from spreadsheets to complex computational models (Annex III: Scenarios and Modelling Methods provides further discussion and examples of computational models).

The concept of an **illustrative pathway (IP)** was introduced in the IPCC Special Report on Global Warming of 1.5°C (IPCC 2018b) to highlight a subset of the quantitative scenarios, drawn from a larger pool of published literature, with specific characteristics that would help represent some of the key findings emerging from the assessment in terms of different strategies, ambitions and options available to achieve the Paris goals.

Integrated assessment models (IAMs) are the primary tools for quantitatively evaluating the technological and macroeconomic implications of decarbonisation, particularly for global long-term pathways. They broadly divide into 'stylised aggregate benefit-cost models', and more complex 'detailed process' IAMs (Weyant 2017), often mirroring the benefit-cost and cost-effective approaches outlined in Section 1.7.1, with more detailed classification in, for example, Nikas et al. (2019). IAMs embody a number of structural and socio-demographic assumptions and include multiple modelling approaches, ranging from economic optimising behaviour to simulation (see Annex III). Detailed process models can include energy system models used to analyse decarbonisation and 'net zero' scenarios by international agencies (e.g., IEA 2020a).

Calculating cost-effective trajectories towards given goals typically involves detailed process IAMs. Often these calculate the dynamic portfolio of technologies consistent with a given climate target. Some track records of technology forecasting in IAMs are outlined in Section 2.5.4, and Box 16.1. Climate targets may be imposed in models in a variety of ways that include, but are not limited to, constraints on emissions or cumulated emissions (carbon budgets), and the pricing of emissions. The time-path of mitigation costs calculated through these models may be translated into 'shadow prices' that (like the social cost of carbon; SCC) offer a benchmark to assess the cost-effectiveness of investments, as used by some governments and companies (Section 1.8.2).

Scenarios in the IPCC and AR6. For AR6, WGIII received submissions of more than 2500 model-based scenarios published in the scientific literature. Such scenarios, which explore different possible evolutions of future energy and land use (with or without climate policy) and associated emissions, are made available through an interactive AR6 scenario database. The main characteristics of pathways in relation to 'net zero' emissions and remaining 'carbon budgets' are summarised in Box 3.5 in Chapter 3. The warming contribution of CO_2 is very closely related to cumulative CO_2 emissions, but the remaining 'carbon budget' for a given warming depends strongly *inter alia* on emissions of other GHGs; for targets below 2°C this may affect the corresponding 'carbon budget' by about ±220 $GtCO_2$, compared to central estimates of around 500 $GtCO_2$ (for 1.5°C) and 1350 $GtCO_2$ (for 2°C) (AR6 WGI, Table SPM.2) (Cross-Working Group Box 1 in Chapter 3).

Pathways and 'net zero'. The date at which the world needs aggregate emissions to reach net zero for Paris-consistent temperature goals depends both on progress in reducing non-CO_2 GHG emissions and near-term progress in reducing CO_2 emissions. Faster progress in the near term extends the date at which net zero must be reached, while conversely, slower near-term progress brings the date even closer to the present. Some of the modelled 1.5°C pathways with limited overshoot cut global CO_2 emissions in half until 2030, which allows for a more gradual decline thereafter, reaching net zero CO_2 after 2050; also, net zero GHGs occurs later,

with remaining emissions of some non-CO_2 GHGs compensated by 'net negative' CO_2 (see Glossary and FAQ 1.3, and Cross-Chapter Box 3 in Chapter 3).

Drawing from the scenarios database, five **Illustrative Mitigation Pathways (IMPs)** were defined for this report (Figure 3.5 and Table 1.1). These are introduced here, with a more complete description and discussion provided in Section 3.2.5. These IMPs were chosen to illustrate key themes with respect to mitigation strategies across the entire WGIII assessment. The IMPs embody both a storyline, which describes in narrative form the key socio-economic characteristics of that scenario, and a quantitative illustration providing numerical values that are internally consistent and comparable across chapters of this report. Quantitative IMPs can be associated directly with specific human activities and provide a quantitative point of reference that links activities in different parts of socio-economic systems. Some parts of the report draw on these quantitative scenarios, whilst others use only the narratives. No assessment of the likelihood of each IMP has been made (as they reflect both human choice and deep uncertainty).

The IMPs are organised around two dimensions: the *level of ambition* consistent with meeting Paris goals, and the scenario features (Figure 1.4). The IMPs explore different pathways potentially consistent with meeting the long-term temperature goals of the Paris Agreement. As detailed in Section 3.2.5 and in Chapter 4, a pathway of Gradual Strengthening of current policies (**IMP-GS**) to 2030, if followed by very fast reductions, may stay below 2°C. The **IMP-NEG** pathway, with somewhat deeper emission cutbacks to 2030, might enable 1.5°C to be reached but only after significant overshoot, through the subsequent extensive use of CDR in the energy and

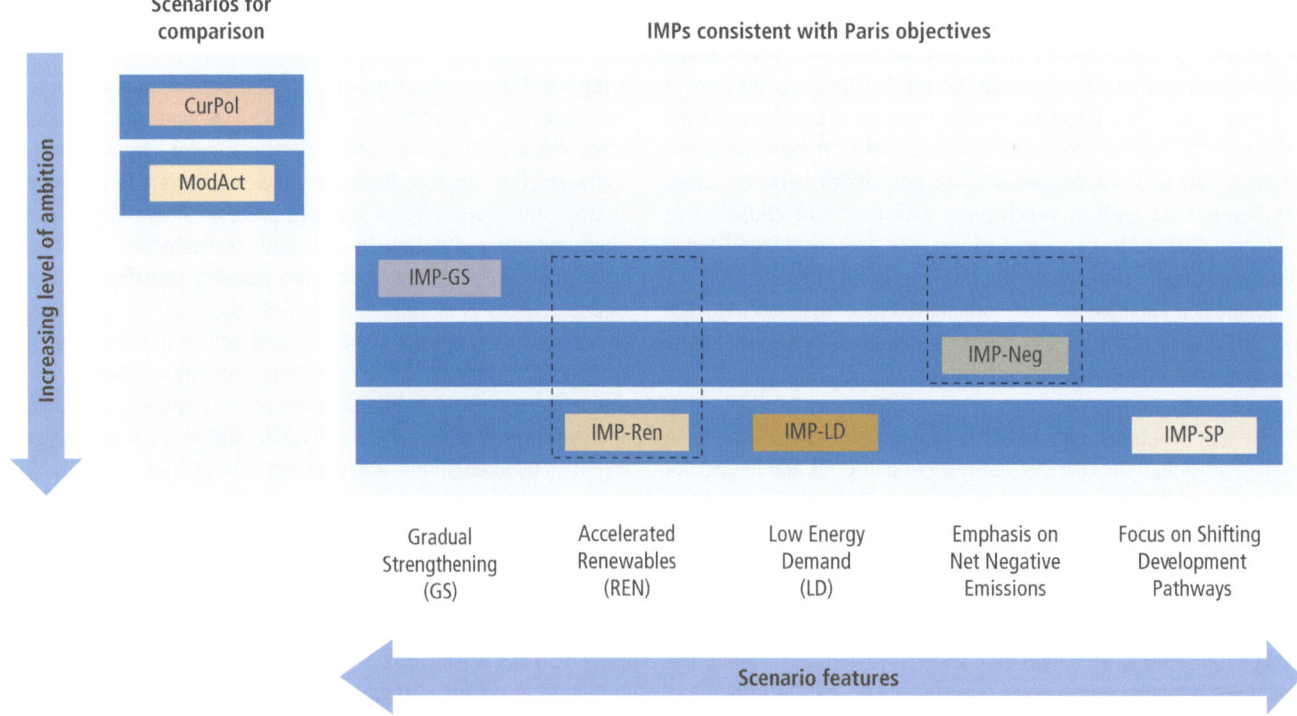

Figure 1.4 | Illustrative Mitigation Pathways (IMPs) used in AR6: illustration of key features and levels of ambition.

Table 1.1 | Illustrative Mitigation Pathways used in AR6.

Scenarios			Full name	Main policy characteristics
CurPol			Current Policies	Implementation of current climate *policies* (mostly as reported in Nationally Determined Contributions (NDCs)), neglecting stated subsequent goals and objectives (e.g., for 2030); only Gradual Strengthening after 2030; grey COVID recovery.
ModAct			Moderate Action	Implementation of current policies *and* achievement of 2030 NDCs, with further strengthening post-2030. Similarly to the situation implied by the diversity of NDCs (both policies and pledges), a fragmented policy landscape remains; mixed COVID recovery.
IMPs	1.5°C/ <2°C	GS	Gradual Strengthening	Until 2030, primarily current NDCs are implemented; after that a strong universal regime leads to coordinated and rapid decarbonisation actions.
		Neg	Net Negative Emissions	Successful international climate policy regime reduces emissions below ModAct or GS to 2030, but with a focus on the long-term temperature goal, negative emissions kick in at growing scales thereafter, so that mitigation in all sectors also includes a growing and ultimately large reliance on negative emissions, with large 'net global negative' after 2050 to meet 1.5°C after significant overshoot.
		Ren	Renewables	Successful international climate policy regime with immediate action, particularly policies and incentives (including international finance) favouring renewable energy; less emphasis on negative-emission technologies. Rapid deployment and innovation of renewables and systems; electrification of all end use.
		LD	Low Demand	Successful international climate policy regime with immediate action on the demand side; policies and financial incentives favouring reduced demand that in turn leads to early emission reductions; this reduces the decarbonisation effort on the supply side.
		SP	Shifting Pathways	Successful international climate policy regime with a focus on additional SDG policies aiming, for example, at poverty reduction and broader environmental protection. Major transformations shift development towards sustainability and reduced inequality, including deep GHG emissions reduction.

the industry sectors to achieve net negative global emissions, as discussed in Chapters 3, 6, 7, 10 and 12.

Three other IMPs illustrate different features of technology scenarios with more short-term rapid emission reductions, which could deliver outcomes compatible with the temperature range in the Paris Agreement without large overshoot. Based on the assessment in Section 5.3.3, one key mitigation strategy would be to rely on the opportunities for reducing demand (**IMP-*LD***). Chapters 6 and 7–11 show how energy systems based on accelerated deep renewable energy penetration and electrification can also provide a pathway to deep mitigation (**IMP-*REN***). Chapters 3, 4 and 17 provide insights into how shifting development pathways can lead to deep emission reductions and achieve sustainable development goals (**IMP-*SP***).

These pathways can be implemented with different levels of ambition, that can be measured through the classes (C) of temperature levels from the scenarios database, see Chapter 3 (Table 3.2). In the IMP framework, Section 3.2.5 presents and explores quantitative scenarios that can limit warming to 1.5°C (with a probability of 50% or greater, i.e., C1 for the illustrated quantification of LD, SP and REN, and C2 for NEG scenario), along with other GS pathways which keep warming below 2°C with a probability of 67% or greater (C3). In addition to these primary IMPs, the full scenario database contains sensitivity cases that explore alternative warming levels.

In addition to the IMPs two additional scenarios were selected, which illustrate the consequences of current policies and pledges. Current Policies (**CurPol**) explores the consequences of continuing along the path of implemented climate policies in 2020 and only a Gradual Strengthening after that, drawing on numerous such scenarios in the literature. Moderate Action (**ModAct**) explores the impact of implementing NDCs to 2030, but without further strengthening:

both result in global mean temperature above 2°C. They provide benchmarks against which to compare the IMPs.

Table 1.1 summarises the main storyline elements of the reference scenarios and each IMP.

What the IMPs do and don't do. The IMPs are, as their name implies, a set of scenarios meant to illustrate some important themes that run through the entire WGIII assessment. They illustrate that the climate outcomes that individuals and society will face in the century ahead depend on individual and societal choices. In addition, they illustrate that there are multiple ways to successful achievement of Paris long-term temperature goals.

IMPs are not intended to be comprehensive. They are not intended to illustrate all possible themes in this report. They do not, for example, attempt to illustrate the range of alternative socio-economic pathways against which efforts to implement Paris goals may be set, or to reflect variations in potential regional development pathways. They do not explore issues around income distribution or environmental justice, but assume implicitly that *where* and *how* action occurs can be separated from who pays, in ways to adequately address such issues. They are essentially pathways of technological evolution and demand shifts reflecting broad global trends in social choice. The IMPs do not directly assess issues of realisation linked to the 'drivers and constraints' summarised in our previous section, and the quantifications use, for the most part, models that are grounded mainly in the Aggregate Economics Frameworks (Section 7.1). As such they reflect primarily the geophysical, economic and technological Dimensions of Assessment, but can be assessed in relation to the full set of Feasibility criteria (Section 1.8.1).

Together the IMPs provide illustrations of potential future developments that can be shaped by human choices, including:

Where are current policies and pledges leading? What is needed to reach specific temperature goals under varying assumptions? What are the consequences of different strategies to meet climate targets (i.e., demand-side strategy, a renewable energy strategy or a strategy with a role for net negative emissions)? What are the consequences of delay? What are the implications for other SDGs of various climate mitigation pathways?

1.6   Achieving Mitigation in the Context of Sustainable Development

This chapter now sets out approaches to understanding the mitigation challenge, working from its broad location in the context of wider aspirations for sustainable development, then identifying specific analytic approaches, before summarising the corresponding main dimensions used for the assessment of options and pathways in much of the report.

1.6.1   The Climate Change and Development Connection

Climate change mitigation is one of many goals that societies pursue in the context of sustainable development, as evidenced by the wide range of the Sustainable Development Goals (SDGs). Climate change and sustainable development, as well as development more broadly, are interwoven along multiple and complex lines of relationship (Okereke et al. 2009; Fankhauser and McDermott 2016; Okereke and Massaquoi 2017; Gomez-Echeverri 2018a), as highlighted in several previous IPCC reports (IPCC 2007, 2011a, 2014a, 2018b, 2019a). With its significant negative impact on natural systems, food security and infrastructure, loss of lives and territories, species extinction, conflict health, among several other risks, climate change poses a serious threat to development and wellbeing in both rich and poor countries (IPCC 2007, 2011a, 2014a, 2018b, 2019b). Without serious efforts at mitigation and adaptation, climate change could push millions further into poverty and limit the opportunities for economic development (Chapters 4 and 17). It follows that ambitious climate mitigation is necessary to secure a safe climate within which development and well-being can be pursued and sustained.

At the same time, rapid and large-scale economic development (which has in the past driven climate change through land-use change and dependence on fossil fuels), is widely seen as needed to improve global well-being and lift millions especially in low- and middle-income countries out of poverty (Chen et al. 2017; Mugambiwa and Tirivangasi 2017; Lu et al. 2019; Baarsch et al. 2020) (Figure 1.6). This strand of literature emphasises the importance of economic growth including for tackling climate change itself, pointing to the relationship between economic development and climate resilience as well as the role of industry-powered technologies such as electric vehicles in reducing GHG levels and promoting well-being (Heinrichs et al. 2014; Kasztelan 2017). Yet, others argue that the character of social and economic development produced by the nature of capitalist society (Pelling and Manuel-Navarrete 2011; Koch 2012; Malm 2016) is ultimately unsustainable.

There are at least two major implications of the very close link between climate change and development as outlined above. The first is that the choice of development paths made by countries and regions have significant consequences for GHG emissions and efforts to combat climate change (Chapters 2, 3, 4, 5 and 14). The second is that climate mitigation at local, national and global levels cannot be effectively achieved by a narrow focus on 'climate-specific' sectors, actors and policies, but rather through a much broader attention to the mix of development choices and the resulting development paths and trajectories (O'Neill et al. 2014) (Chapters 4, 6 and 10).

As a key staple of IPCC reports and the global climate policy landscape (IPCC 2007, 2014b; van Vuuren et al. 2017; Gidden et al. 2019; Quilcaille et al. 2019) (Chapter 2), integrated assessment models and global scenarios (such as the Shared Socio-economic Pathways – SSPs) highlight the interaction between development paths, climate change and emission stabilisation (Section 3.6). The close links are also recognised in the PA (Section 1.3.1).

The impact of climate change in limiting well-being is most acutely felt by the world's poorest people, communities, and nations, who have the smallest carbon footprint, constrained capacity to respond and limited voice in important decision-making circles (Okereke and Ehresman 2015; Tosam and Mbih 2015; Mugambiwa and Tirivangasi 2017). The wide variation in the contribution to, and impact of climate change within and across countries makes equity, inequality, justice, and poverty eradication, inescapable aspects of the relationship between sustainable development and climate change (Okereke and Coventry 2016; Klinsky et al. 2017; Reckien et al. 2017; Bos and Gupta 2019; Kayal et al. 2019; Diffenbaugh and Burke 2019; Baarsch et al. 2020). This underpins the conclusion, as commonly expressed, that climate action needs to be pursued in the context of sustainable development, equity and poverty eradication (Smit et al. 2001; Tschakert and Olsson 2005; IPCC 2014a, 2018b; Klinsky and Winkler 2014).

1.6.2   Concepts and Frameworks for Integrating Climate Mitigation and Development

At one level, sustainable development can be seen as a meta framework for integrating climate action with other global sustainability goals (Casadio Tarabusi and Guarini 2013; Antal and Van Den Bergh 2016). Fundamentally, the concept of sustainable development underscores the interlinkages and interdependence of human and natural systems and the need to balance economic, social, and environmental (including climate pollution) aspects in development planning and processes (Nunan 2017; Gomez-Echeverri 2018b; Zhenmin and Espinosa 2019).

Despite the appeal of the concept, tensions remain over the interpretation and practical application, with acute disagreements regarding what the balancing entails in real life, how to measure well-being, which goals to set, and the means through which such goals might be pursued (Arrow et al. 2011; Dasgupta et al. 2015; Michelsen et al. 2016; Okereke and Massaquoi 2017; UNEP 2018b; Haberl et al. 2019; Shang et al. 2019; Sugiawan et al. 2019).

Moreover, countries differ enormously in their respective situation regarding their development path – a condition which affects their capability, goals, priorities and approach to the pursuit of sustainability (Shi et al. 2016; Ramos-Mejía et al. 2018; Okereke et al. 2019). Most of the literature recognises that despite its limitations, sustainable development with its emphasis on integrating social, economic and environmental goals, provides a more comprehensive approach to the pursuit of planetary health and human well-being. Sustainable development is then not a static objective but a dynamic framework for measuring human progress (Costanza et al. 2016; Fotis and Polemis 2018), relevant for all countries even if different groups of nations experience the challenge of sustainability in different ways.

Much like sustainable development, concepts like low-carbon development (Mulugetta and Urban 2010; Yuan et al. 2011; Wang et al. 2017; Tian et al. 2019), climate-compatible development (CCD) (Mitchell and Maxwell 2010; Tompkins et al. 2013; Stringer et al. 2014; Bickersteth et al. 2017) and more recently climate-resilient development (CRD) (Fankhauser and McDermott 2016; Henly-Shepard et al. 2018; IPCC 2018b) have all emerged as ideas, tools and frameworks, intended to bring together the goals of climate mitigation and the SDGs, as well as development more broadly. Figure 1.5 suggests that the prospects for realising a climate-resilient and equitable world are enhanced by a process of transformation and development trajectories that seek to limit global warming while also achieving the SDGs. The SDGs represent medium-term goals, and long-term sustainability requires continued

effort to keep the world along a climate-resilient development path. A key feature of development or transformation pathways that achieve a climate-resilient world is that they maximise the synergies and minimise the trade-offs between climate mitigation and other sustainable development goals (Klausbruckner et al. 2016; Thornton and Comberti 2017; Wüstemann et al. 2017; Dagnachew et al. 2018; Fuso Nerini et al. 2018; Mainali et al. 2018). Crucially, the nature of trade-offs and timing of related decisions will vary across countries depending on circumstances including the level of development, capability and access to resources (Cross-Chapter Box 5, Shifting Development Paths to Increase Sustainability, in Chapter 4).

Other concepts such as 'Doughnut Economics' (Raworth 2018), ecological modernisation, and mainstreaming are also used to convey ideals of development pathways that take sustainability, climate mitigation, and environmental limits seriously (Dale et al. 2015a). Mainstreaming focuses on incorporating climate change into national development activities, such as the building of infrastructure (Wamsler and Pauleit 2016; Runhaar et al. 2018). The 'green economy' and green growth – growth without undermining ecological systems, partly by gaining economic value from cleaner technologies and systems and is inclusive and equitable in its outcomes – has gained popularity in both developed and developing countries as an approach for harnessing economic growth to address environmental issues (Bina 2013; Georgeson et al. 2017; Capasso et al. 2019; Song et al. 2020; Hao et al. 2021). However, critics argue that green economy ultimately emphasises economic growth to the detriment of other important aspects of human welfare such as social

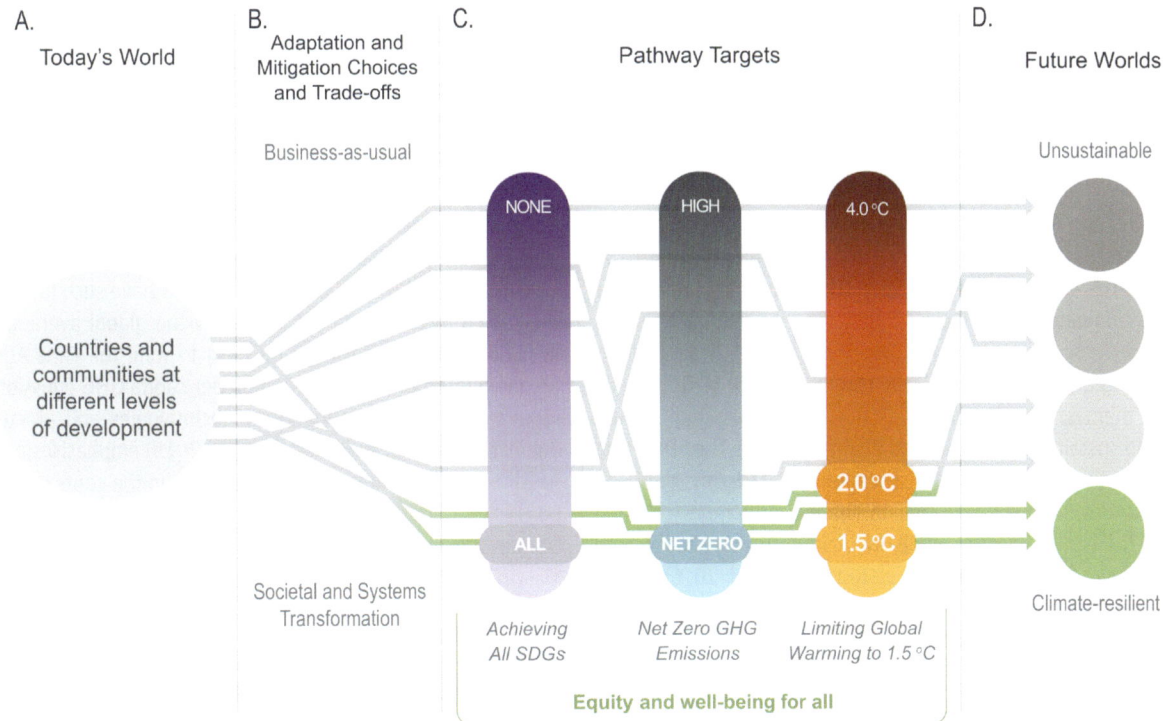

Figure 1.5 | A climate-resilient and equitable world requires limiting global warming while achieving the Sustainable Development Goals (SDGs).
Source: IPCC (2018b).

justice (Death 2014; Adelman 2015; Kamuti 2015), and challenge the central idea that it is possible to decouple economic activity and growth (measured as GDP increment) from increasing use of biophysical resources (raw materials, energy) (Jackson and Victor 2019; Parrique et al. 2019; Haberl et al. 2020; Hickel and Kallis 2020; Vadén et al. 2020).

Literature on degrowth, post growth, and post development questions the sustainability and imperative of more growth especially in already industrialised countries and argues that prosperity and the 'Good Life' are not immutably tied to economic growth (Asara et al. 2015; Escobar 2015; Latouche 2018; Kallis 2019) (Section 5.2.1). The concept of Just Transition also stresses the need to integrate justice concerns so as to not impose hardship on already marginalised populations within and between countries (Evans and Phelan 2016; Goddard and Farrelly 2018; Heffron and McCauley 2018; Smith, Jackie and Patterson 2018; McCauley and Heffron 2018) (Section 1.7.2). The key insight is that pursuing climate goals in the context of sustainable development requires holistic thinking including on how to measure well-being, serious consideration of the notion of ecological limits, at least some level of decoupling and certainly choices and decision-making approaches that exploit and maximise the synergy and minimise the trade-off between climate mitigation and other sustainable development goals. It also requires consideration of equity and justice within and between countries. However, ideas of a synergistic relationship between development and climate mitigation can sometimes offer limited practical guidelines for reconciling the tensions that are often present in practical policymaking (Ferguson et al. 2014; Dale et al. 2015b; Kasztelan 2017; Kotzé 2018).

1.6.3 Climate Mitigation, Equity and the Sustainable Development Goals (SDGs)

Climate action can be conceptualised as both a stand-alone and cross-cutting issue in the 2030 SDGs (Makomere and Liti Mbeva 2018), given that several of the other goals such as ending poverty (SDG 1), zero hunger (SDG 2), good health and well-being (SDG 3), and affordable and clean energy (SDG 7), among many others, are related to climate change (Figure 3.39).

In addition to galvanising global collective action, the SDGs provide concrete themes, targets and indicators for measuring human progress to sustainability (Kanie and Biermann 2017). The SDGs also provide a basis for exploring the synergies and trade-offs between sustainable development and climate change mitigation (Pradhan et al. 2017; Fuso Nerini et al. 2018; Mainali et al. 2018; Makomere and Liti Mbeva 2018). Progress to date (Sachs et al. 2016) shows fulfilling SDGs is a challenge for all groups of countries – developed

and developing – even though the challenge differs between countries and regions (Pradhan et al. 2017).

Historically, the industrialisation associated with economic development has involved a strong relationship with GHG emissions (Section 5.2.1). Figure 1.6 shows per-capita GHG emissions on the vertical axis and Historical Index of Human Development (HIHD) levels (Prados de la Escosura 2015) on the horizontal axis.[7] The grey line shows historic global average GHG emissions per capita and levels of human development over time, from 1870 to 2014. The current positions of different regions are shown by bubbles, with sizes representing total GHG emissions. Figure 1.6 also shows the estimated position of the SDGs zone for the year 2030, and a 'sustainable development corridor' as countries reach towards higher HDI and lower emissions. To fulfil the SDGs, including SDG 13 (climate action), the historic relationship needs to change.

The top of the SDG zone is situated around the global per-capita GHG emissions level of 5 tCO_2-eq required for the world to be path towards fulfilling the Paris Agreement.[8] The horizontal position of the SDG zone is estimated based on the HIHD levels (Prados de la Escosura 2015) of countries that have been shown to either have achieved, or have some challenges, when it comes to SDG 3, SDG 4 and SDG 8 (Sachs et al. 2016), as these SDGs are related to the constituent parts of the HIHD. Beyond 2030, the sustainable development corridor allows for increasing levels of human development while lowering per-capita GHG emissions.

Figure 1.6 shows that at present, regions with HIHD levels of around 0.5 all have emissions at or above about 5 tCO_2-eq per capita (even more so on a consumption footprint basis; see Figure 1.1c,d), but there are wide variations within this. Indeed, there are regions with HIHD levels above 0.8 which have GHG per-capita emissions lower than several with HIHD levels of around 0.5. The mitigation challenge involves countries at many different stages of development seeking paths towards higher welfare with low emissions.

From Figure 1.6, there are two distinct dimensions to sustainable development pathways for fulfilling the SDGs. In terms of per-capita GHG emissions (the vertical), some regions have such low levels that they could increase and still be below the global average required in 2030 for the world to be on path to fulfil the Paris Agreement. Meanwhile, other regions with high per-capita GHG emissions would require a rapid transformation in technologies and practices. It is against this background that Dubash (2019) emphasises placing the need for urgent action on climate change in the context of domestic political priorities and the institutions within which national frameworks are crystallised.

---

[7] The Historical Index of Human Development (HIHD) emulates the widely used Human Development Index (HDI) as they both summarise in indexes the key human development dimensions consisting of a healthy life, knowledge and a decent standard of living. HDI is based on: life expectancy, expected years of schooling of children, the mean years of schooling of the adult population, and gross national income (GNI) per capita adjusted for purchasing power; the HIHD is based on: life expectancy at birth, adult literacy rates, educational enrolment rates, and GDP per capita, and is used in Figure 1.6 because it is available for a longer time series (Prados de la Escosura 2015).

[8] Based on global population projections of between 8 and 8.5 billion people in 2030, and GHG emissions levels from the C1, C2 and C3 categories of scenarios in Table 3.2 and Box 3.7.

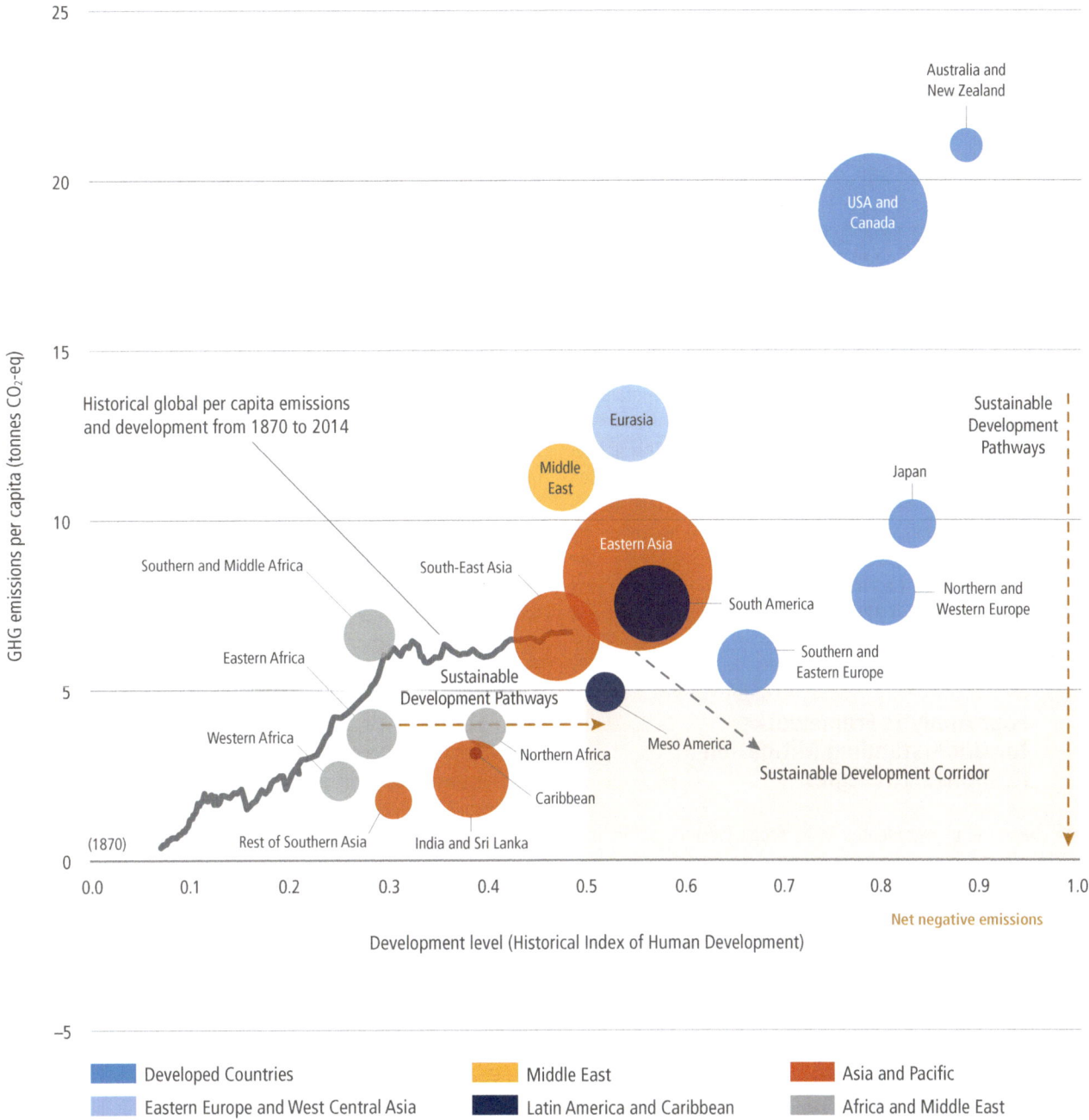

Figure 1.6 | Sustainable development pathways towards fulfilling the Sustainable Development Goals (SDGs). The graph shows global average per-capita GHG emissions (vertical axis) and relative 'Historic Index of Human Development' (HIHD) levels (horizontal) have increased globally since the industrial revolution (grey line). The bubbles on the graph show regional per-capita GHG emissions and human development levels in the year 2015, illustrating large disparities. Pathways towards fulfilling the Paris Agreement (and SDG 13) involve global average per-capita GHG emissions below about 5 tCO$_2$-eq by 2030. Likewise, to fulfil SDGs 3, 4 and 8, HIHD levels (see footnote 7) need to be at least 0.5 or greater. This suggests a 'sustainable development zone' for year 2030 (in pale brown); the in-figure text also suggests a 'sustainable development corridor', where countries limit per-capita GHG emissions while improving levels of human development over time. The emphasis of pathways into the sustainable development zone differ (dashed brown arrows), but in each case transformations are needed in how human development is attained while limiting GHG emissions.

Concerns over equity in the context of growing global inequality and very tight remaining global carbon budgets have motivated an emphasis on equitable access to sustainable development (Peters et al. 2015; Kartha et al. 2018b; Matthews et al. 2019; van den Berg et al. 2019). This literature emphasises the need for less developed countries to have sufficient room for development while addressing climate change (Winkler et al. 2013; Pan et al. 2014; Gajevic Sayegh 2017; Robinson and Shine 2018; Warlenius 2018). Meanwhile, many

countries reliant on fossil fuels, related technologies and economic activities, are eager to ensure tax revenues are maintained, workers and industries have income and justice is embedded in the economic transformations required to limit GHG emissions (Cronin et al. 2021).

Correlation between CO$_2$ emission intensity, or absolute emission and gross domestic product growth, is not rigid, unambiguous and deterministic (Ojekunle et al. 2015), but the extent to which SDGs and economic growth expectations can be fulfilled while decoupling GHG emissions remains a concern (Haberl et al. 2020; Hickel and Kallis 2020). Below some thresholds of absolute poverty, more consumption is necessary for development to lead to well-being (Section 5.2.1.1), which may not be the case at higher levels of consumption (Lamb and Steinberger 2017; Steinberger et al. 2020) (Section 1.7.2).

In conclusion, achieving climate stabilisation in the context of sustainable development and efforts to eradicate poverty requires collective action and exploiting synergies between climate action and sustainable development, while minimising the impact of trade-offs (Najam 2005; Okereke and Massaquoi 2017; Makomere and Liti Mbeva 2018; Dooley et al. 2021). It also requires a focus on equity considerations to avoid climate-induced harm, as well as unfairness that can result from urgent actions to cut emissions (Pan et al. 2014; Robiou du Pont et al. 2017; Kartha et al. 2018a). This is ever more important as the diminishing carbon budget has intensified debates on which countries should have the greatest claim to the 'remaining space' for emissions (Raupach et al. 2014) or production (McGlade and Ekins 2015), amplified by persistent concerns over the insufficiency of support for means of implementation, to support ambitious mitigation efforts (Pickering et al. 2015; Weikmans and Roberts 2019).

1.7   Four Analytic Frameworks for Understanding Mitigation Response Strategies

Climate change is unprecedented in its scope (sectors, actors and countries), depth (major transformations) and time scales (over generations). As such, it creates unique challenges for analysis. It has been called 'the greatest market failure in history' (Stern 2007); the 'perfect moral storm' (Gardiner 2006) and a 'super wicked problem' (Lazarus 2009; Levin et al. 2012) – one which appears difficult to solve through the traditional tools and assumptions of social organisation and analysis.

To complement the extensive literature on risks and decision-making under uncertainty reviewed in AR6 WGII (notably, Chapter 19), this section summarises insights and developments in key analytic frameworks and tools particularly relevant to understanding specific mitigation strategies, policies and other actions, including explaining the observed if limited progress to date. Organised partly as reflected in the quotes above, these include *aggregated* (principally, economic) frameworks to evaluate system-level choices; *ethical* perspectives on values and equity including stages of development and distributional concerns; and *transition* frameworks which focus on the processes and actors involved in major technological and social transitions. These need to be complemented by a fourth set of approaches which shine more light on *psychological/behavioural and political* factors. All these frameworks are relevant, and together they point to the multiple perspectives and actions required if the positive drivers of emission reduction summarised in Section 4 are to outweigh the barriers and overcome the constraints.

1.7.1   Aggregated Approaches: Economic Efficiency and Global Dynamics of Mitigation

Some of the most established and influential approaches to understanding the *aggregate* causes and consequences of climate change and mitigation across societies, draw upon economic theories and modelling to generate global emission pathways in the absence of climate policies and to study alternative mitigation pathways (described in detail in Section 3.2.5, and Appendix 3). The underlying economic concepts aggregate wealth or other measures of welfare based on utilitarian ethical foundations, and in most applications, a number of additional assumptions detailed in AR5 (Chapters 2 and 3).

1.7.1.1   Cost-benefit Analysis and Cost-effectiveness Analysis

Such global aggregate economic studies coalesce around two main questions. One, as pioneered by Nordhaus (1992, 2008) attempts to monetise overall climate damages and mitigation costs so as to strike a 'cost-benefit optimum' pathway. More detailed and empirically-grounded 'cost-effectiveness analysis' explores pathways that would minimise mitigation costs (Ekholm 2014; IPCC 2014a Section 2.5; Weyant 2017) for given targets (e.g., as agreed in international negotiations, see Section 3.2 in Chapter 3). Both approaches recognise that resources are limited and climate change competes with other priorities in government policymaking, and are generally examined with some form of Integrated Assessment Model (IAM) (Section 1.5 and Appendix III). Depending on the regional disaggregation of the modelling tools used and on the scope of the analyses, these studies may or may not address distributional aspects within and across nations associated with climate policies (Bauer et al. 2020).

For at least 10 to 15 years after the first computed global cost-benefit estimate (Nordhaus 1992), the dominant conclusions from these different approaches seemed to yield very different recommendations, with cost-benefit studies suggesting lenient mitigation compared to the climate targets typically recommended from scientific risk assessments (Weyant 2017). Over the past 10 to 15 years, literature has made important strides towards reconciling these two approaches, both in the analytic methods and the conclusions arising.

Damages and risks. Incorporating impacts which may be extremely severe but are uncertain (known as 'fat tails' (Weitzman 2009, 2011)), strengthens the economic case for ambitious action to avoid risks of extreme climate impacts (Ackerman et al. 2010; Fankhauser et al. 2013; Dietz and Stern 2015). The salience of risks has also been amplified by improved understanding of climate 'tipping points' (Lontzek et al. 2015; Lenton et al. 2019); valuations should reflect that cutting emissions reduces not only average expected damages, but also the risk of catastrophic events (IWG 2021).

Discounting. The role of time discounting in weighting future climate change impacts against today's costs of mitigating emissions has been long recognised (Weitzman 1994, 2001; Nordhaus 2007; Stern 2007; Dasgupta 2008). Its importance is underlined in analytical Integrated Assessment Models (IAMs) (Golosov et al. 2014; van den Bijgaart et al. 2016; van der Ploeg and Rezai 2019) (Annex III). Economic literature suggests applying risk-free, public, and long-term interest rates when evaluating overall climate strategy (Weitzman 2001; Dasgupta 2008; Arrow et al. 2013; Groom and Hepburn 2017). Expert elicitations indicate values around 2% (majority) to 3% (Drupp et al. 2018). This is lower than in many of the studies reviewed in earlier IPCC assessments, and many IAM studies since, and by increasing the weight accorded to the future would increase current 'optimal effort'. The US Interagency Working Group on the Social Cost of Carbon used 3% as its central value (IAWG 2016; Li and Pizer 2018; Adler et al. 2017). Individual projects may require specific risk adjustments.

Distribution of impacts. The economic damages from climate change at the nationally aggregated and sub-national level are very diverse (Moore et al. 2017; Ricke et al. 2018; Carleton et al. 2020). A 'global damage function' necessarily implies aggregating impacts across people and countries with different levels of income, and over generations, a process which obscures the strategic considerations that drive climate policymaking (Keohane and Oppenheimer 2016). Economics acknowledges there is no single, objectively defined 'social welfare function' (IPCC 1995, 2014a). This applies also to the distribution of responses: both underline the relevance of equity (next section) and global negotiations to determine national and collective objectives.

Obvious limitations arise from these multiple difficulties in assessing an objective, globally acceptable single estimate of climate change damages (e.g., Arrow et al. 2013; Pindyck 2013; Auffhammer 2018; Stern et al. 2021), with some arguing that agreement on a specific value can never be expected (Rosen and Guenther 2015; Pezzey 2018). A new generation of cost-benefits analysis, based on projections of actual observed damages, results in stronger mitigation efforts as optimal (Glanemann et al. 2020; Hänsel et al. 2020). Overall, the combination of improved damage functions with the wider consensus on low discount rates (as well as lower mitigation costs due to innovation) has increasingly yielded 'optimal' results from benefit-cost studies in line with the range established in the Paris Agreement (Cross-Working Group Box 1 in Chapter 3).

Hybrid cost-benefit approaches that extend the objective of the optimisation beyond traditional welfare, adding some form of temperature targets as in Llavador et al. (2015) and Held (2019) also represent a step in bridging the gap between the two approaches and result in proposed strategies much more in line with those coming from the cost-effectiveness literature. Approaching from the opposite side, cost-effectiveness studies have looked into incorporating benefits from avoided climate damages, to improve the assessment of net costs (Drouet et al. 2021).

Cost-benefit IAMs utilise damage functions to derive a social cost of CO_2 emissions' (SCC – the additional cost to society of a pulse of CO_2 emissions). One review considered that 'the best estimate' of the optimal (near-term) level 'still ranges from a few tens to a few hundreds of dollars per ton of carbon' (Tol 2018), with various recent studies in the hundreds, taking account of risks (Taconet et al. 2019), learning (Ekholm 2018) and distribution (Ricke et al. 2018). In addition to the importance of uncertainty/risk, aggregation, and realistic damage functions as noted, on which some progress has been made,

some reviews additionally critique how IAMs represent abatement costs in terms of energy efficiency and innovation (e.g., Farmer et al. 2015; Rosen and Guenther 2015; Keen 2021) (Sections 1.7.3 and 1.7.4). IAMs may better reflect associated 'rebound' at system level (Saunders et al. 2021), and inefficient implementation would raise mitigation costs (Homma et al. 2019); conversely, *co-benefits* – most extensively estimated for air quality, valued at a few tens of USD per tCO_2-eq across 16 studies (Karlsson et al. 2020) – complement global with additional local benefits (Table 1.2).

Whereas many of these factors affect primarily cost-benefit evaluation, discounting also determines the cost-effective trajectory: Emmerling et al. (2019) find that, for a remaining budget of 1000 $GtCO_2$, reducing the discount rate from 5% to 2% would more than double current efforts, limit 'overshoot', greatly reduce a late rush to negative emissions, and improve intergenerational justice by more evenly distributing policy costs across the 21st century.

1.7.1.2   Dynamic Efficiency and Uncertainty

Care is required to clarify what is optimised (Dietz and Venmans 2019). Optimising a path towards a given temperature goal *by a fixed date* (e.g., 2100) gives time-inconsistent results backloaded to large, last-minute investment in carbon dioxide removal (CDR). 'Cost-effective' optimisations generate less initial effort than *equivalent* cost-benefit models (Dietz and Venmans 2019; Gollier 2021) as they do not incorporate benefits of reducing impacts earlier.

'Efficient pathways' are affected by inertia and innovation. Inertia implies amplifying action on long-lived investments and infrastructure that could otherwise lock-in emissions for many decades (Vogt-Schilb et al. 2018; Baldwin et al. 2020). Chapter 3 (Section 3.5) discusses interactions between near-, medium- and long-term actions in global pathways, particularly vis-à-vis inertia. Also, to the extent that early action induces low-carbon innovation, it 'multiplies' the optimal effort (for given damage assumptions), because it facilitates subsequent cheaper abatement. For example, a 'learning-by-doing' analysis concludes that early deployment of expensive PV was of net global economic benefit, due to induced innovation (Newbery 2018).

Research thus increasingly emphasises the need to understand climate transformation in terms of dynamic, rather than static, efficiency (Gillingham and Stock 2018). This means taking account of inertia, learning and various additional sources of 'path-dependence'. Including induced innovation in stylised IAMs can radically change the outlook (Acemoglu et al. 2012, 2016), albeit with limitations (Pottier et al. 2014); many more detailed-process IAMs now do include endogenous technical change (as reviewed in Yang et al. 2018 and Grubb et al. 2021b) (Annex III).

These dynamic and uncertainty effects typically justify greater upfront effort (Kalkuhl et al. 2012; Bertram et al. 2015), including accelerated international diffusion (Schultes et al. 2018), and strengthen optimal initial effort in cost-benefit models (Baldwin et al. 2020; Grubb et al. 2021b). Approaches to risk premia common in finance would similarly amplify the initial mitigation effort, declining as uncertainties reduce (Daniel et al. 2019).

1.7.1.3   Disequilibrium, Complex Systems and Evolutionary Approaches

Other approaches to aggregate evaluation draw on various branches of intrinsically non-equilibrium theories (e.g., Chang 2014). These including long-standing theories from the 1930s (e.g., Schumpeter 1934; Keynes 1936) to understand situations of structurally underemployed resources, potential financial instabilities (Minsky 1986), and related economic approaches which emphasise time dimensions (e.g., recent reviews in Legrand and Hagemann 2017; Stern 2018). More recently developing have been formal economic theories of endogenous growth building on, for example, Romer (1986), and developments of Schumpeterian creative destruction (Aghion et al. 2021) and evolutionary economic theories which abandon any notion of full or stable resource utilisation even as a reference concept (Nelson and Winter 1982; Freeman and Perez 1988; Carlsson and Stankiewicz 1991; Freeman and Louçã 2001; Perez 2001).

The latter especially are technically grounded in complex system theories (e.g., Arthur 1989, 1999; Beinhocker 2007; Hidalgo and Hausmann 2009). These take inherently dynamic views of economies as continually evolving systems with continuously unfolding and path-dependent properties, and emphasise uncertainty in contrast to any predictable or default optimality. Such approaches have been variously applied in policy evaluation (Walton 2014; Moore et al. 2018), and specifically for global decarbonisation (e.g., Barker and Crawford-Brown 2014) using global simulation models. Because these have no natural reference 'least lost' trajectory, they illustrate varied and divergent pathways and tend to emphasise the diversity of possibilities and relevant policies, particularly linked to innovation and potentially 'sensitive intervention points' (Farmer et al. 2019) (Section 1.7.3). They also illustrate that different representations of innovation and financial markets together can explain why estimated impacts of mitigation on GDP can differ very widely (potentially even in sign), between different model types (Chapter 15, Section 15.6.3 and Box 15.7).

1.7.2   Ethical Approaches

Gardiner's (2011) book on climate change as 'The Perfect Moral Storm' identified three 'tempests'. Its *global* dimension, in a world of sovereign states which have only fragmentary responsibility and control, makes it 'difficult to generate the moral consideration and necessary political will'. Its impacts are *intergenerational* but future generations have no voice in contemporary affairs, the usual mechanism for addressing distributional injustices, amplified by the intrinsic inequity of wealthy big emitters impacting particularly poorer victims. He argues that these are exacerbated by a third, *theoretical* failure to acknowledge a central need for 'moral sensitivity, compassion, transnational and transgenerational care, and other forms of ethical concern to rise to the surface' to help guide effective climate action. As noted in Section 1.4.6, however, equity and ethics are both a driver of and constraint on mitigation.

1.7.2.1   Ethics and Values

A large body of literature examines the critical role of values, ethics, attitudes, and behaviours as foundational frames for understanding and assessing climate action, sustainable development and societal transformation (IPCC 2014a Chapter 3). Most of this work is offered as a counterpoint or critique to mainstream literature's focus on the safeguarding of economic growth of nations, corporations and individuals (Castree 2017; Gunster 2017). These perspectives highlight the dominance of economic utilitarianism in western philosophical thought as a key driver for unsustainable consumption and global environmental change (Hoeing et al. 2015; Popescu 2016).

Entrenching alternative values that promote deep decarbonisation, environmental conservation and protection across all levels of society is then viewed as foundational component of climate-resilient and sustainable development and for achieving human rights, and a safe climate world (Evensen 2015; Jolly et al. 2015; Popescu 2016; Tàbara et al. 2019). The UN Human Rights Office of the High Commissioner has highlighted the potentially crucial role of human rights in relation to climate change (UNHCR 2018). While acknowledging the role of policy, technology, and finance, the 'managerialist' approaches, that emphasise 'technical governance' and fail to challenge the deeper values that underpin society, may not secure the deep change required to avert dangerous climate change and other environmental challenges (Hartzell-Nichols 2014; Steinberger et al. 2020).

Social justice perspectives emphasise the distribution of responsibilities, rights, and mutual obligations between nations in navigating societal transformations (Gawel and Kuhlicke 2017; Leach et al. 2018; Patterson et al. 2018). Current approaches to climate action may fail to match what is required by science because they tend to circumvent constraints on human behaviour, especially constraints on economic interest and activity. Related literature explores governance models that are centred on environmental limits, planetary boundaries and the moral imperative to prioritise the poor in earth systems governance (Carley and Konisky 2020; Kashwan et al. 2020), with emphasis on trust and solidarity as foundations for global cooperation on climate change (Jolly et al. 2015). A key obstacle is that the economic interests of states tend to be stronger than the drivers for urgent climate action (Bain 2017).

Short-term interests of stakeholders are acknowledged to impede the reflection and deliberation needed for climate mitigation and adaptation planning (Hackmann 2016; Sussman et al. 2016; Schlosberg et al. 2017; Herrick 2018). Situationally appropriate mitigation and adaptation policies at both national and international level may require more ethical self-reflection (Herrick 2018), including self-transcendent values such as universalism and benevolence, and moderation which are positively related to pro-environmental behaviours (Jonsson and Nilsson 2014; Katz-Gerro et al. 2015; Braito et al. 2017; Howell and Allen 2017).

Another strong theme in the literature concerns recognition of interdependence including the intimate relationship between humans and the non-human world (Hannis 2016; Gupta and Racherla 2018; Howell and Allen 2017), with such ecological interdependence offered as an organising principle for enduring transformation to sustainability. A key policy implication of this is moving away from valuing nature only in market and monetary terms to strongly incorporating existential and non-material value of nature in natural-resource accounting (Neuteleers and Engelen 2015; Shackleton et al. 2017; Himes-Cornell et al. 2018). There has been increasing attention on ways to design climate policy frameworks to help reconcile ecological virtue (with its emphasis on the collective) with individual freedoms and personal autonomy (Kasperbauer 2016; Nash et al. 2017; Xiang et al. 2019). In such a framework, moderation, fairness, and stewardship are all understood and promoted as directly contributing to the 'good life'. Such approaches are deemed vital to counteract tendencies to 'free ride', and to achieve behavioural changes often associated with tackling climate change (Section 5.2.1).

Some literature suggests that attention to emotions, especially with regards to climate communication, could help societies and individuals act in ways that focus less on monetary gain and more on climate and environmental sustainability (Bryck and Ellis 2016; Chapman et al. 2017; Nabi et al. 2018; Zummo et al. 2020).

1.7.2.2 Equity and Representation: International Public Choice Across Time and Space

Equity perspectives highlight three asymmetries relevant for climate change (Okereke and Coventry 2016; Okereke 2017) (Section 1.4.6). *Asymmetry in contribution* highlights different contributions to climate change both in historical and current terms, and applies both within and between states as well as between generations (Caney 2016; Heyward and Roser 2016). *Asymmetry in impacts* highlights the fact that the damages will be borne disproportionately across countries, regions, communities, individuals and gender; moreover, it is often those that have contributed the least that stand to bear the greatest impact of climate change (IPCC 2014a; Shi et al. 2016). *Asymmetry in capacity* highlights differences of power between groups and nations to participate in climate decision and governance, including the capacity to implement mitigation and adaptation measures.

If attention is not paid to equity, efforts designed to tackle climate change may end up exacerbating inequities among communities and between countries (Heffron and McCauley 2018). The implication is that to be sustainable in the long run, mitigation involves a central place for consideration of justice, both within and between countries (Chapters 4 and 14). Arguments that the injustices following from climate change are symptomatic of a more fundamental structural injustice in social relations, are taken to imply a need to address the deeper inequities within societies (Routledge et al. 2018).

Climate change and climate policies affect countries and people differently, with the poor likely to be more affected (Section 1.6.1). Ideas of Just Transitions (outlined in Section 1.8.2.) often have a national focus in the literature, but also imply that mitigation should not increase the asymmetries between rich and poor countries, implying a desire for transitions which seek to reduce (or at least avoid adverse) distributional affects. Thus, it comes into play in the timing of zero emissions (Chapters 3 and 14). International climate finance in which rich countries finance mitigation and adaptation in poor countries is also essential for reducing the asymmetries between rich and poor countries (Section 1.6.3 and Chapter 15).

Equity across generations – the distribution between the present and future generations – also matters. One aspect is discounting (Section 1.7.1). Another approach has been to study the burdens on each generation following from the transition to low-carbon economies (IPCC 2014a Chapter 3) (Cross-Working Group Box 3 in Chapter 12). Suggestions include shifting more investments into 'natural capital', so that future generations will inherit less physical capital but a better environment, or financing mitigation efforts today using governmental debt redeemed by future generations (Heijdra et al. 2006; Broome 2012; Karp and Rezai 2014; Hoel et al. 2019).

1.7.3 Transition and Transformation Processes

This report uses the term *transition* as the process, and *transformation* as the overall change or outcome, of large-scale shifts in technological, economic and social systems, called socio-technical systems in the innovation literature. Typically, new technologies, ideas and associated systems initially grow slowly in absolute terms, but may then 'take-off' in a phase of exponential growth as they emerge from a position of niche into mainstream diffusion, as indicated by the 'S-curve' growth in Figure 1.7 (lower panel). These dynamics arise from interactions between innovation (in technologies, companies and other organisations), markets, infrastructure and institutions, at multiple levels (Geels et al. 2017; Kramer 2018). Consequently, interdisciplinary perspectives are needed (Turnheim et al. 2015; Geels et al. 2016; Hof et al. 2020). Beyond aggregated economic perspectives on dynamics (Section 1.7.1.2), these emphasise the multiple actors and processes involved.

Technological Innovation Systems (TIS) frameworks (Section 16.4) focus on processes and policies of early innovation and 'emergence', which combine experimentation and commercialisation, involving *Strategic Niche Management* (Rip and Kemp 1998; Geels and Raven 2006). Literatures on the wider processes of transition highlight different stages (e.g., Cross-Chapter Box 12 in Chapter 16) and scales across three main levels, most generally termed *micro, meso and macro* (Rotmans et al. 2001).

The widely-used *Multi-Level Perspective* or MLP (Geels 2002) identifies the meso level as the established 'socio-technical (ST) regime', a set of interrelated sub-systems which define rules and regulatory structures around existing technologies and practices. The micro level is an ecosystem of varied niche alternatives, and overlaying the ST regime is a macro 'landscape' level. Transitions often start with niche alternatives (Grin et al. 2010; Köhler et al. 2019), which may break through to wider diffusion (second stage in Figure 1.8), especially if external landscape developments 'create pressures on the regime that lead to cracks, tensions and windows of opportunity' (Rotmans et al. 2001; Geels 2010); an example is climate change putting sustained pressure on current regimes of energy production and consumption (Kuzemko et al. 2016). There are continual interactions between landscape, regime and niches, with varied implications for *Transition Management* (Rotmans et al. 2001; Loorbach 2010).

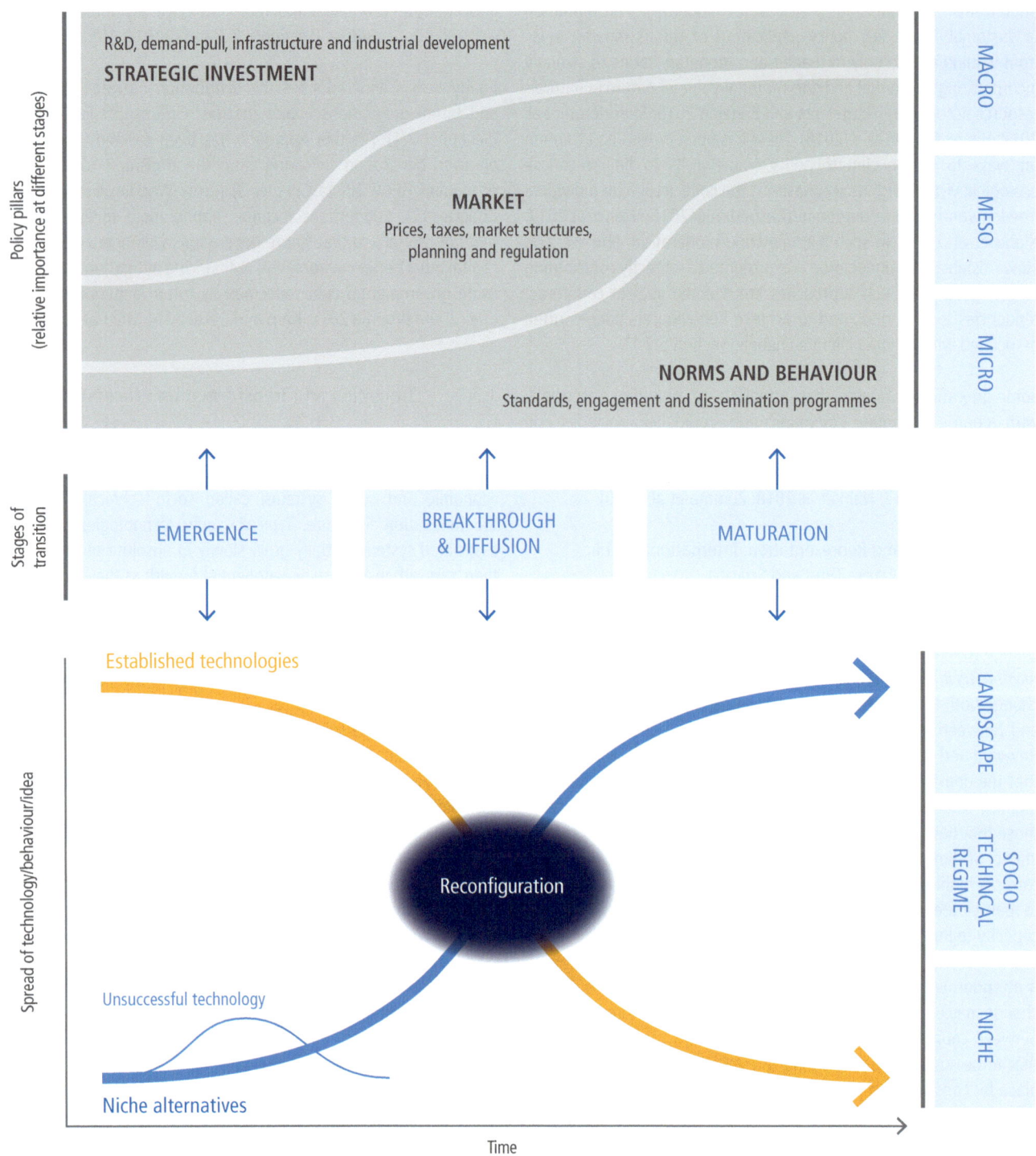

Figure 1.7 | Transition dynamics: levels, policies and processes. Note: the lower panel illustrates growth of innovative technologies or practices, which if successful emerge from niches into an S-shape dynamic of exponential growth. The diffusion stage often involves new infrastructure and reconfiguration of existing market and regulatory structures (known in the literature as the 'socio-technical regime'). During the phase of more widespread diffusion, growth levels off to linear, then slows as the industry and market matures. The processes displace incumbent technologies/practices which decline, initially slowly but then at an accelerating pace. Many related literatures identify three main levels with different characteristics, most generally termed micro, meso and macro. Transitions can be accelerated by policies appropriately targeted, which may be similarly grouped and sequenced (upper panel) in terms of three corresponding pillars of policy (Section 1.7.3): generally all are relevant, but their relative importance differs according to the stage of the transition.

In contrast to standard economic metrics of marginal or smooth change (e.g., elasticities), transition theories emphasise interdisciplinary approaches and the non-linear dynamics, social, economic and environmental aspects of transitions to sustainability (Cherp et al. 2018; Köhler et al. 2018). This may explain persistent tendencies to underestimate the exponential pace of change now being observed in renewable electricity (Chapters 2 and 6) and emerging in mobility (Chapter 10).

Recent decades have seen parallel broadening of economic perspectives and theories. Building also on the New Institutional Economics literatures, Building on the New Institutional Economics literature (Williamson 2000), Grubb et al. (2014, 2015) classify these into three 'domains of economic decision-making' associated with different branches of economic theory, respectively (i) *behavioural and organisational*; (ii) *neoclassical and welfare*; and (iii) *evolutionary and institutional*. Like MLP, these are related to different social and temporal scales, as applied also in studying the 'adaptive finance' in UK electricity transition (Hall et al. 2017). There are significant differences but these approaches all point to understanding the characteristics of different actors, notably, individuals/local actors; larger corporate organisations (public or private); and (mainly) public authorities, each with different decision-making characteristics.

Sustainability may require purposeful actions at the different levels to foster the growth of sustainable technologies and practices, including support for niche alternatives (Grin et al. 2010). The middle level (established 'socio-technical regime') tends to resist major change, reforms generally involve pressures from the other two levels. Thus, transitions can be accelerated by policies appropriately targeting relevant actors at the different levels (Köhler et al. 2019), the foundations for 'three pillars of policy' (Grubb et al. 2014), which logically evolve in the course of transition (Figure 2.6a). Incumbent industries have to adapt if they are to thrive within the growth of new systems. Policy may need to balance existing socio-technical systems with strategic investment and institutional development of the emerging niches (e.g., the maintenance of energy provision and energy security with the development of renewables), and help manage declining industries (Koasidis et al. 2020).

There is usually a social dimension to such transitions. Key elements include capacity to transform (Folke et al. 2010), planning, and interdisciplinarity (Woiwode 2013). The Second World War demonstrated the extent to which crises can motivate (sometimes positive) change across complex social and technical systems, including industry, and agriculture which then doubled its productivity over 15 years (Roberts and Geels 2019b). In practice, climate change may involve a combination of (reactive) transformational adaptation, and (proactive) societal transformation (Feola 2015), the latter seen as reorientation (including values and norms) in a sustainable direction (Section 5.4), including, for example, 'democratisation' in energy systems (Sorman et al. 2020). Business change management principles could be relevant to support positive social change (Stephan et al. 2016). Overall, effective transitions rest on appropriate enabling conditions, which can also link socio-technical transitions to broader development pathways (Cross-Chapter Box 12 in Chapter 16).

Transition theories tend to come from very different disciplines and approaches compared to either economics or other social sciences, with less quantification, notwithstanding evolutionary and complex system models (Section 1.7.1.3). However, a few distinct types of quantitative models of 'socio-technical energy transition' (Li et al. 2015) have emerged. For policy evaluation, transitions can be viewed as processes in which dynamic efficiency (Section 1.7.2) dominates over static allocative efficiency, with potential 'positive intervention points' (Farmer et al. 2019). Given inherent uncertainties, there are obvious risks (e.g., Alic and Sarewitz 2016). All this may make an evaluation framework of *risks and opportunities* more appropriate than traditional cost-benefit (Mercure et al. 2021), and (drawing on lessons from renewables and electric vehicles) create foundations for sector-based international 'positive sum cooperation' in climate mitigation (Sharpe and Lenton 2021).

1.7.4 Approaches From Psychology and Politics of Changing Course

The continued increase in global emissions to 2019, despite three decades of scientific warnings of ever-greater clarity and urgency, motivates growing attention in the literature to the psychological 'faults of our rationality' (Bryck and Ellis 2016), and the political nature of climate mitigation.

1.7.4.1 Psychological and Behavioural Dimensions

The AR5 emphasised that decision processes often include both deliberate ('calculate the costs and benefits') and intuitive thinking, the latter utilising emotion- and rule-based responses that are conditioned by personal past experience, social context, and cultural factors (e.g., Kahneman 2003), and that laypersons tend to judge risks differently than experts – for example, 'intuitive' reactions are often characterised by biases to the status quo and aversion to perceived risks and ambiguity (Kahneman and Tversky 1979). Many of these features of human reasoning create 'psychological distance' from climate change (Spence et al. 2012; Marshall 2014). These can impede adequate personal responses, in addition to the collective nature of the problem, where such problems can take the form of 'uncomfortable knowledge', neglected and so becoming 'unknown knowns' (Sarewitz 2020). These decision processes, and the perceptions that shape them, have been studied through different lenses from psychology (Weber 2016) to sociology (Guilbeault et al. 2018), and media studies (Boykoff 2011). Karlsson and Gilek (2020) identify science denialism and 'decision thresholds' as key mechanisms of delay.

Experimental economics (Allcott 2011) also helps explain why cost-effective energy efficiency measures or other mitigation technologies are not taken up as fast or as widely as the benefits might suggest, including procrastination and inattention, as 'we often resist actions with clear long-term benefits if they are unpleasant in the short run' (Allcott and Mullainathan 2010). Incorporating behavioural and social dynamics in models is required particularly to better represent the demand side (Nikas et al. 2020), for example, Safarzyńska (2018) demonstrates how behavioural factors change responses to carbon pricing relative to other instruments. A key perspective is to eschew 'either/or' between economic and behavioural frameworks, as the greatest effects often involve combining behavioural dimensions (e.g., norms, social influence networks, convenience and quality assurance) with financial incentives and information (Stern et al. 2010). Randomised, controlled field trials can help predict the effects of behavioural interventions (Levitt and List 2009; McRae and Meeks 2016; Gillan 2017). Chapter 5 explores both positive and negative dimensions of behaviour in more depth, including the development of norms and interactions with the wider social context, with emphasis upon the services associated with human well-being, rather than the economic activities per se.

1.7.4.2 Socio-political and Institutional Approaches

Political and institutional dynamics shape climate change responses in important ways, not least because incumbent actors have frequently blocked climate policy (Section 1.4.5). Institutional perspectives probe networks of opposition (Brulle 2019) and emphasise that their ability to block – as well as the ability of others to foster low-carbon transitions – are structured by specific institutional forms across countries (Lamb and Minx 2020). National institutions have widely been developed to promote traditionally fossil fuel-based sectors like electricity and transport as key to economic development, contributing to carbon lock-in (Seto et al. 2016) and inertia (Rosenschöld et al. 2014).

The influence of interest groups on policymaking varies across countries. Comparative political economy approaches tend to find that countries where interests are closely coordinated by governments ('coordinated market economies') have been able to generate transformative change more than those with a more arms-length, even combative relationship between interest groups and governments ('liberal market economies') (Lachapelle and Paterson 2013; Ćetković and Buzogány 2016; Zou et al. 2016; Meckling 2018). 'Developmental states' often have the capacity for strong intervention but any low-carbon interventions may be overwhelmed by other pressures and very rapid economic growth (Wood et al. 2020a).

Institutional features affecting climate policy include levels and types of democracy (Povitkina 2018), electoral systems, or levels of institutional centralisation (federal vs unitary states, presidential vs parliamentary systems) (Lachapelle and Paterson 2013; Steurer and Clar 2018; Clulow 2019). Countries that have constructed an overarching architecture of climate governance institutions (e.g., cross-department and multi-level coordination, and semi-autonomous climate agencies), are more able to develop the strategic approaches to climate governance needed to foster transformative change (Dubash 2021).

Access of non-governmental organisations (NGOs) to policy processes enables new ideas to be adopted, but too close an NGO-government relation may stifle innovation and transformative action (Dryzek et al. 2003). NGO campaigns on fracking (Neville et al. 2019) or divestment (Mangat et al. 2018) have raised attention to ideas such as 'stranded assets' in policy arenas (Green 2018; Piggot

2018; Newell et al. 2020; Paterson 2021). Attempts to depoliticise climate change may narrow the space for democratic participation and contestation, thus impacting policy responses (Swyngedouw 2010, 2011; Kenis and Lievens 2014). Some institutional innovations have more directly targeted enhanced public deliberation and participation, notably in citizens' climate assemblies (Howarth et al. 2020) and in the use of legal institutions to litigate against those opposing climate action (Peel and Osofksy 2020). This literature shows that transformative pathways are possible within a variety of institutional settings, although institutional innovation will be necessary everywhere to pursue zero carbon transitions (Section 4.4, Chapter 13 and Cross-Chapter Box 12).

Balancing the forces outlined in Section 4.6 in Chapter 4 typically involves building coalitions of actors who benefit economically from climate policy (Levin et al. 2012). Policy stability is critical to enabling long-term investments in decarbonisation (Rietig and Laing 2017; Rosenbloom et al. 2018). Policy design can encourage coalitions to form that sustain momentum by supporting further policy development to accelerate decarbonisation (Roberts et al. 2018), for example, by generating concentrated benefits to coalition members (Bernstein and Hoffmann 2018; Meckling 2019; Millar et al. 2020), as with renewable feed-in tariffs (FiTs) in Germany (Michaelowa et al. 2018). Coalitions may also be sustained by overarching framings, especially to involve actors (e.g., NGOs) for whom the benefits of climate policy are not narrowly economic. However, policy design can also provoke coalitions to oppose climate policy, as in the FiT programme in Ontario (Stokes 2013; Raymond 2020) or the yellow vest protests against carbon taxation in France (Berry and Laurent 2019). The Just Transitions frame can thus also be understood in terms of coalition-building, as well as ethics, as the pursuit of low-carbon transitions which spread the economic benefits broadly, through 'green jobs', and the redistributive policies embedded in them both nationally and globally (Healy and Barry 2017; Winkler 2020). Appropriate policy design will be different at different stages of the transition process (Meckling et al. 2017; Breetz et al. 2018).

Integration. Politics is ultimately the way in which societies make decisions – which in turn, reflect diverse forces and assumed frameworks. Effective policy requires understandings which combine economic efficiency, ethics and equity, the dynamics and processes of large-scale transitions, and the role of psychology and politics. No one framework is adequate to such a broad-ranging goal, nor are single tools. Chapter 13 (Figure 13.6) presents a 'framing' table for policy instruments depending on the extent to which they focus on mitigation per se or wider socio-economic development, and whether they aim to shift marginal incentives or drive larger transitions. Holistic analysis needs to bridge modelling, qualitative transition theories illuminated by case studies, and practice-based action research (Geels et al. 2016).

These analytic frameworks also point to arenas of potential synergies and trade-offs (when broadly known), and opportunities and risks (when uncertainties are greater), associated with mitigation. This offers theoretical foundations for mitigation strategies which can also generate co-benefits. Climate policy may help to motivate policies with beneficial synergies (such as

Table 1.2 | Potential for net co-benefits arising from synergies and trade-offs, opportunities and risks.

	Positives	**Negatives**
Broadly known (e.g., air pollution, distributional).	Synergies	Trade-offs
Deep uncertainties (e.g., radical innovations).	Opportunities	Risks
	Select options with maximum synergies, and foster and exploit opportunities.	Ameliorate trade-offs (e.g., revenue redistribution), and minimise or allocate risks appropriately.

Net co-benefits from appropriate mitigation choices

the consumer cost savings from energy efficiency, better forest management, transitions to cleaner vehicles) and opportunities (such as stimulating innovation), by focusing on options for which the positives outweigh the negatives, or can be made to be, through smart policy (e.g., Karlsson et al. 2020). More broadly, climate concerns may help to attract international investment, and help overcoming bureaucratic or political obstacles to better policy, and support synergies between mitigation, adaptation, and other SDGs, a foundation for shifting development pathways towards sustainability (Chapter 17 and Section 1.6.1).

1.8 Feasibility and Multi-dimensional Assessment of Mitigation

1.8.1 Building on the SR1.5 Assessment Framework: Feasibility and Enabling Conditions

While previous ARs dealt with the definition of alternative mitigation pathways mostly exploring the technological potentials, the latest research focused on what kind of mitigation pathways are feasible in a broader sense, underlining the multi-dimensional nature of the mitigation challenge. Building on frameworks introduced by Majone (1975) and Gilabert and Lawford-Smith (2012), SR1.5 introduced multi-dimensional approaches to analysing 'feasibility' and 'enabling conditions', which AR6 develops and applies broadly in relation to six 'dimensions of feasibility assessment' (Figure 1.8). Two reflect the physical environment:

- *Geophysical*, not only the global risks from climate change but also, for technology assessment, the global availability of critical resources.
- *Environmental and ecological*, including local environmental constraints and co-benefits of different technologies and pathways.

The other four dimensions correspond broadly to the four analytic frameworks outlined in Section 1.7:

- *Economic*, particularly aggregate economic and financial indicators, and SDGs reflecting different stages and goals of economic development.
- *Socio-cultural*, including particularly ethical and justice dimensions, and social and cultural norms.
- *Technological*, including innovation needs and transitional dynamics associated with new and emergent technologies and associated systems.

- *Institutional and political,* including political acceptability, legal and administrative feasibility, and the capacity and governance requirements at different levels to deliver sustained mitigation in the wider context of sustainable development.

The AR6 emphasises that all pathways involve different challenges and require choices to be made. Continuing 'business as usual' is still a choice, which in addition to the obvious geophysical risks, involves not making the best use of new technologies, risks of future stranded assets, greater local pollution, and multiple other environmental threats.

The dimensions as listed provide a basis for this assessment both in the sectoral chapters (6–11), providing a common framework for cross-sectoral assessment detailed further in Chapter 12, and in the evaluation of global pathways (Section 3.2). More specific indicators under each of these dimensions offer consistency in assessing the challenges, choices, and enabling requirements facing different aspects of mitigating climate change.

Figure 1.8 also illustrates variants on these dimensions appropriate for evaluating domestic and international policies (Chapters 13 and 14). The SR1.5 (Section 4.4) also introduced a framework of 'Enabling Conditions for systemic change', which as illustrated also has key dimensions in common with those of our feasibility assessment. In AR6 these enabling conditions are applied particularly in the context of shifting development pathways (Chapter 4.4).

Some fundamental criteria may span across several dimensions. Most obviously, issues of ethics and equity are intrinsic to the economic, socio-cultural (values, including intergenerational justice) and institutional (e.g., procedural justice) dimensions. Geopolitical issues could also clearly involve several dimensions, for example, concerning the politics of international trade, finance and resource distribution (economic dimension); international versus nationalistic identity (socio-cultural); and multilateral governance (institutional).

In this report, chapters with a strong demand-side dimension also suggest a simple policy hierarchy, reflecting that avoiding wastage – demands superfluous to human needs and wants – can carry benefits across multiple indicators. Consequently, Chapters 5 and 10 organise key actions in a hierarchy of **Avoid** (unnecessary demand) – **Shift** (to less resource-intensive modes) – **Improve** (technologies for existing modes), with a closely-related policy hierarchy in Chapter 9 (buildings).

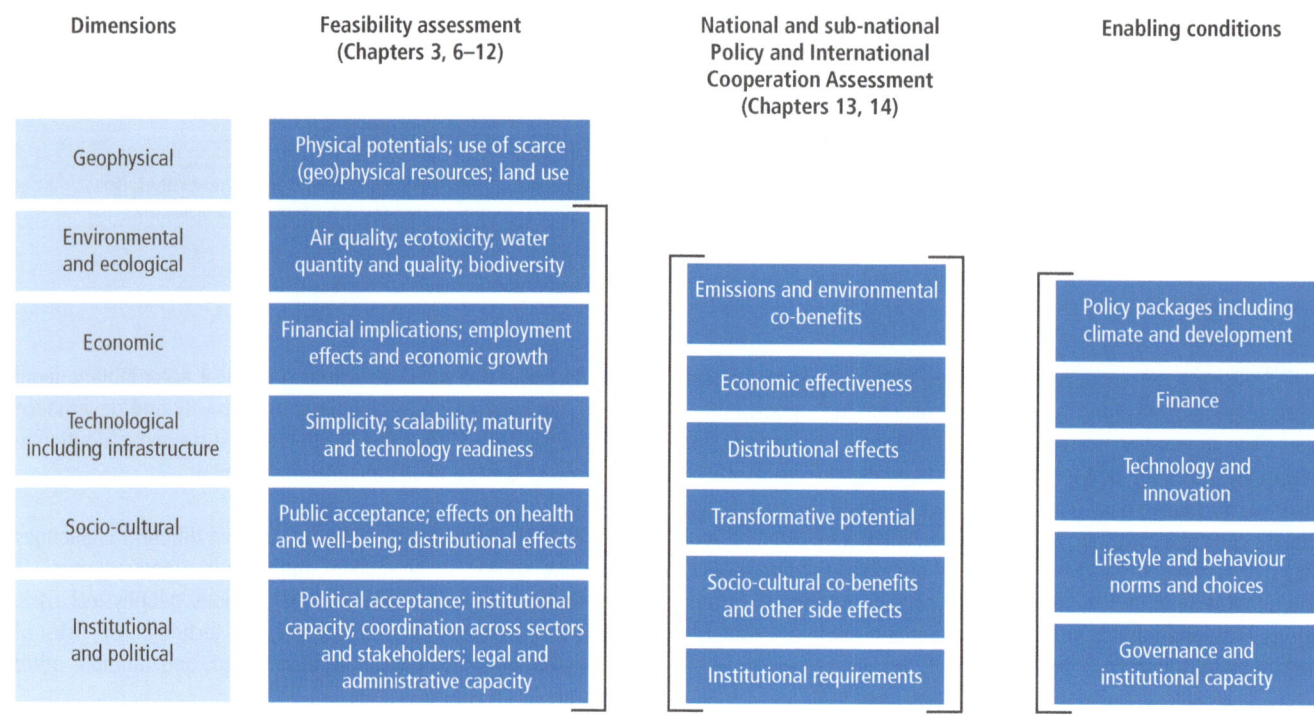

Figure 1.8 | Feasibility and related dimensions of assessment.

1.8.2 Illustrations of Multi-dimensional Assessment: Lock-in, Policies and 'Just Transition'

The rest of this section illustrates briefly how such multi-dimensional assessment, utilising the associated analytic frameworks, can shed light on a few key issues which arise across many chapters of this assessment.

Carbon Lock-in. The continued rise of global emissions reflects in part the strongly *path-dependent* nature of socio-economic systems, which implies a historic tendency to 'carbon lock-in' (Unruh 2000). An interdisciplinary review (Seto et al. 2016) identifies a dozen main components organised into four types, across the relevant dimensions of assessment as summarised in Table 1.3.

Along with the long lifetime of various physical assets detailed in AR5, AR6 underlines the exceptional degree of path-dependence in urban systems (Chapter 8) and associated buildings (Chapter 9) and transport (Chapter 10) sectors, but it is a feature across almost all the major emitting sectors. The (typically expected) operating lifetimes of existing carbon-emitting assets would involve anticipated emissions (often but inaccurately called 'committed' emissions in the literature), substantially exceeding the remaining carbon budgets associated with 1.5°C pathways (Chapter 2.7). Ongoing GHG-intensive investments, including those from basic industrialisation in poorer countries, are adding to this.

The fact that investors anticipate a level of fossil fuel use that is not compatible with severe climate constraints creates a clear risk of *'stranded assets'* facing these investors (Box 6.2), and others who depend on them, which itself raises issues of equity. A multi-dimensional/multi-framework assessment helps to explain why such investments have continued, even in rich countries, and the consequent risks, and the complexity of shifting such investments in all countries. It may also inform approaches that could exploit path-dependence in clean energy systems, if there is sufficient investment in building up the low-GHG industries, infrastructures and networks required.

Carbon pricing. Appraisal of policy instruments also requires such multi-dimensional assessment. Stern's (2007) reference to climate change as 'the greatest market failure in history' highlights that damages inflicted by climate change are not properly costed in most economic decision-making. Economic perspectives emphasise the value of removing fossil fuel subsidies, and pricing emissions to 'internalise' in economic decision-making the 'external' damages imposed by GHG emissions, and/or to meet agreed goals. Aggregate economic frameworks generally indicate carbon pricing (on principles which extend to other gases) as the most cost-effective way to reduce emissions, notwithstanding various market failures which complicate this logic.[9] The High-Level Commission on carbon pricing (Stern and Stiglitz 2017) estimated an appropriate range as USD40–80 tCO_2 in 2020, rising steadily thereafter. In practice the extent and level of carbon pricing implemented to date is far lower than this or

---

[9] Beyond GHG externalities, Stern (2015) lists such market failures as: inadequate R&D; failures in risk/capital markets; network effects creating coordination failures; wider information failures; and co-benefits.

Table 1.3 | Carbon lock-in – types and key characteristics. Source: adapted from Seto et al. (2016).

Lock-in type	Key characteristics
Economic	– Large investments with long lead times and sunk costs, made on the basis of anticipated use of resources, capital, and equipment to pay back the investment and generate profits. – Initial choices account for private but not social costs and benefits.
Socio-cultural, equity and behaviour	– Lock-in through social structure (e.g., norms and social processes). – Lock-in through individual decision-making (e.g., psychological processes). – Single, calculated choices become a long string of non-calculated and self-reinforcing habits. – Interrupting habits is difficult but possible (e.g., family size, thermostat setting) to change. – Individuals and communities become dependent on the fossil fuel economy, meaning that change may have adverse distributional impacts.
Technology and infrastructure	– Learning-by-doing and scale effects, including the cumulative nature of innovation, reinforces established technologies. – Interaction of technologies and networks (physical, organisational, financial) on which they depend. – Random, unintentional events including network and learning-effect final outcomes (e.g., lock-in to the QWERTY keyboard).
Institutional and political	– Powerful economic, social, and political actors seek to reinforce the status quo that favours their interests. – Laws and Institutions, including regulatory structures, are designed to stabilise and lock-in a desired trajectory, and also to provide long-term predictability (socio-technical regimes in transition theories). – Beneficial and intended outcomes for some actors. – Not random chance but intentional choice (e.g., support for renewable electricity in Germany) can develop political consistencies that reinforce a direction of travel.

than most economic analyses now recommend (Section 3.6.1), and nowhere is carbon pricing the only instrument deployed.

A socio-cultural and equity perspective emphasises that the faith in and role of markets varies widely between countries – many energy systems do not in fact operate on a basis of competitive markets – and that because market-based carbon pricing involves large revenue transfers, it must also contend with major distributional effects and political viability (Prinn et al. 2017; Klenert et al. 2018), both domestic (Chapter 13) and international (Chapter 14). A major review (Maestre-Andrés et al. 2019) finds persistent distributional concerns (rich incumbents have also been vocal in using arguments about impacts on the poor (Rennkamp 2019)), but suggests these may be addressed by combining redistribution of revenues with support for low-carbon innovation. Measures could include redistributing the tax revenue to favour of low-income groups or differentiated carbon taxes (Metcalf 2009; Klenert and Mattauch 2016; Stiglitz 2019), including 'dual track' approaches (van den Bergh et al. 2020). To an extent though, all these depend on levels of trust, and institutional capacity.

Technological and transitions perspectives in turn find carbon-pricing incentives may only stimulate incremental improvements, but other instruments may be much more effective for driving deeper innovation and transitions (Chapters 14, 15 and 16), whilst psychological and behavioural studies emphasise many factors beyond only pricing (Sections 5.4.1 and 5.4.2). In practice, a wide range of policy instruments are used (Chapter 13).

Finally, in economic theory, negotiations on a common carbon price (or other common policies) may have large benefits (less subject to 'free riding') compared to a focus on negotiating national targets (Cramton et al. 2017a). The fact that this has never even been seriously considered (outside some efforts in the EU) may reflect the exceptional sovereignty sensitivities around taxation and cultural differences around the role of markets. However, carbon-pricing concepts can be important outside of the traditional market ('tax or trading') applications. A 'social cost of carbon' can be used to

evaluate government and regulatory decisions, to compensate for inadequate carbon prices in actual markets, and by companies to reflect the external damage of their emissions and strategic risks of future carbon controls (Zhou and Wen 2020). An agreed 'social value of mitigation activities' could form a basic index for underwriting risks in low-carbon investments internationally (Hourcade et al. 2021a).

Thus, practical assessment of carbon pricing inherently needs multi-dimensional analysis. The realities of political economy and lobbying have to date severely limited the implementation of carbon pricing (Mildenberger 2020), leading some social scientists to ask '*Can we price carbon?*' (Rabe 2018). Slowly growing adoption (World Bank 2019) suggests 'yes', but only through complex evolution of efforts: a study of 66 implemented carbon-pricing policies show important effects of regional clustering, international processes, and seizing political windows of opportunity (Skovgaard et al. 2019).

Just Transitions. Finally, whilst 'transition' frameworks may explain potential dynamics that could transform systems, a multi-dimensional/multi-framework assessment underlines the motivation for Just Transitions (Sections 1.6.2.3 and 4.5). This can be defined as a transition from a high-carbon to a low-carbon economy which is considered sufficiently equitable for the affected individuals, workers, communities, sectors, regions and countries (Jasanoff 2018; Newell and Mulvaney 2013). As noted, sufficient equity is not only an ethical issue but an enabler of deeper ambition for accelerated mitigation (Klinsky and Winkler 2018; Urpelainen and Van de Graaf 2018; Hoegh-Guldberg et al. 2019). Perception of fairness influences the effectiveness of cooperative action (Winkler et al. 2018), and this can apply to affected individuals, workers, communities, sectors, regions and countries (Newell and Mulvaney 2013; Jasanoff 2018).

A Just Transitions framing can also enable coalitions which integrate low-carbon transformations with concerns for climate adaptation (Patterson et al. 2018). All this explains the emergence of 'Just Transition Commissions' in several of the more ambitious developed countries and complex social packages for coal phase-out in Europe

(Sovacool et al. 2019; Green and Gambhir 2020) (Section 4.5), as well as reference to the concept in the PA and its emphasis in the Talanoa Dialogue and Silesia Declaration (Section 1.2.2).

Whilst the broad concepts of Just Transitions have roots going back decades, its specific realisation in relation to climate change is of course complex: Section 4.5 identifies at least eight distinct elements proposed in the literature, even before considering the international dimensions.

1.9   Governing Climate Change

Previous sections have highlighted the multiple factors that drive and constrain climate action, the complex interconnection between climate mitigation and other societal objectives, and the diversity of analytical frames for interpreting these connections. Despite the complexities, there are signs of progress including increased societal awareness, change in social attitudes, policy commitments by a broad range of actors and sustained emission reductions in some jurisdictions. Nevertheless, emission trends at the global level remains incompatible with the goals agreed in the Paris Agreement. Fundamentally, the challenge of how best to urgently scale up and speed up the climate-mitigation effort at all scales – from local to global – to the pace needed to address the climate challenge is that of governance understood as 'modes and mechanisms to steer society' (Jordan et al. 2015). The concept of governance encompasses the ability to plan and create the organisations needed to achieve a desired goal (Güney 2017) and the process of interaction among actors involved in a common problem for making and implementing decisions (Kooiman 2003; Hufty 2012).

Climate change governance has been projected as conscious transformation at unprecedented scale and speed involving a contest of ideas and experimentation across scales of authority and jurisdiction (Hildén et al. 2017; Kivimaa et al. 2017; Laakso et al. 2017; Gordon 2018; van der Heijden 2018). Yet, there remains a sense that achieving the urgent transition to a low-carbon, climate-resilient and sustainable world requires significant innovation in governance (Hoffmann 2011; Stevenson and Dryzek 2013; Aykut 2016).

Starting from an initial focus on multilateral agreements, climate change governance has long evolved into a complex polycentric structure that spans from the global to national and sub-national levels, with 'multiple parallel initiatives involving a range of actors at different levels of governance' (Okereke et al. 2009) and relying on both formal and informal networks and policy channels (Bulkeley et al. 2014; Jordan et al. 2015). At the international level, implementation of the Paris Agreement and the UNFCCC more broadly is proceeding in parallel with other activities in an increasingly diverse landscape of loosely coordinated institutions, constituting 'regime complex' (Keohane and Victor 2011), and new cooperative efforts demonstrate an evolution in the shifting authority given to actors at different levels of governance (Chan et al. 2018).

Multi-level governance has been used to highlight the notion that the processes involved in making and implementing decisions on climate change are no longer the exclusive preserve of government actors but rather involve a range of non-nation state actors such as cities, businesses, and civil society organisations (IPCC 2014a; Bäckstrand et al. 2017; Jordan et al. 2018) (Chapter 13, and Sections 13.3.1 and 13.5.2). Increased multi-level participation of sub-national actors, along with a diversity of other transnational and non-state actors has helped to facilitate increased awareness, experimentation, innovation, learning and achieving benefits at multiple scales. Multi-level participation in governance systems can help to build coalitions to support climate change mitigation policies (Roberts et al. 2018) and fragmentation has the potential to take cooperative and even synergistic forms (Biermann et al. 2009).

However, there is no guarantee that multi-level governance can successfully deal with complex human-ecological systems (York et al. 2005; Biermann et al. 2017; Di Gregorio et al. 2019). Multi-level governance can contribute to an extremely polarised discussion and policy blockage rather than enabling policy innovation (Fisher and Leifeld 2019). A fragmented governance landscape may lead to coordination and legitimacy gaps undermining the regime (Nasiritousi and Bäckstrand 2019). The realities of the 'drivers and constraints' detailed in Section 4, the 'glocal' nature of climate change, the divided authority in world politics, diverse preferences of public and private entities across the spectrum, and pervasive suspicions of free riding, imply the challenge as how to incrementally deepen cooperation in a polycentric global system, rather than seeking a single, integrated governance (Keohane and Victor 2016).

Crucially, climate governance takes place in the context of embedded power relations, operating in global, national and local contexts. Effective rules and institutions to govern climate change are more likely to emerge where and when power structures and interests favour action. However widespread and enduring cooperation can only be expected when the benefits outweigh the cost of cooperation and when the interests of key actors are sufficiently aligned (Barrett 1994; Finus and Rübbelke 2008; Victor 2011; Mainali et al. 2018; Tulkens 2019). Investigating the distribution and role of hard and soft power resources, capacities and power relations within and across different jurisdictional levels is therefore important to uncover hindrances to effective climate governance (Marquardt 2017). Institutions at international and national levels are also critical as they have the ability to mediate the power and interest of actors, and sustain cooperation based on equity and fair rules and outcomes. Governance, in fact, helps to align and moderate the interests of actors as well as to shift perceptions, including the negative, burden-sharing narratives that often accompany discussion about climate action, especially in international negotiations. It is also useful for engaging the wider public and international networks in imagining low-carbon societies (e.g., Levy and Spicer 2013; Milkoreit 2017; Nikoleris et al. 2017; Wapner and Elver 2017; Bengtsson Sonesson et al. 2019; Fatemi et al. 2020). Experimentation also represents an important source of governance innovation and capability formation, linked to global knowledge and technology flows, which could reshape emergent socio-technical regimes and so contribute to alternative development pathways (Berkhout et al. 2010; Roberts et al. 2018; Turnheim et al. 2018; Lo and Castán Broto 2019).

1.10   Conclusions

Global conditions have changed substantially since the IPCC's Fifth Assessment Report in 2014. The Paris Agreement and the SDGs provided a new international context, but global intergovernmental cooperation has been under intense stress. Growing direct impacts of climate change are unambiguous and movements of protest and activism – in countries and transnational organisations at many levels – have grown. Global emissions growth had slowed but not stopped up to 2018/19, albeit with more diverse national trends. Growing numbers of countries have adopted 'net zero' CO_2 and/or GHG emission goals and decarbonisation or low-carbon growth strategies, but the current NDCs to 2030 collectively would barely reduce global emissions below present levels (Section 1.3.3). An unfolding technology revolution is making significant contributions in some countries, but as yet its global impact is limited. Global climate change can only be tackled within, and if integrated with, the wider context of sustainable development, and related social goals including equity concerns. Countries and their populations have many conflicting priorities. Developing countries in particular have multiple urgent needs associated with earlier stages of sustainable development as reflected in the non-climate SDGs. Developed countries are amongst the most unsustainable in terms of overall consumption, but also face social constraints particularly arising from distributional impacts of climate policies.

The assessment of the key drivers for, and barriers against mitigation undertaken in this chapter underscore the complexity and multi-dimensional nature of climate mitigation. Historically, much of the academic analysis of mitigating climate change, particularly global approaches, has focused on modelling costs and pathways, and discussion about 'optimal' policy instruments. Developments since AR5 have continued to highlight the role of a wide range of factors intersecting the political, economic, social and institutional domains. Yet despite such complexities, there are signs of progress emerging from years of policy effort in terms of technology, social attitudes, and emission reductions in some countries, with tentative signs of impact on the trajectory of global emissions. The challenge remains how best to urgently scale up and speed up the climate mitigation effort at all scales – from local to global – to achieve the level of mitigation needed to address the problem as indicated by climate science. A related challenge is how to ensure that mitigation effort and any associated benefits of action are distributed fairly within and between countries and aligned to the overarching objective of global sustainable development. Lastly, globally effective and efficient mitigation will require international cooperation especially in the realms of finance and technology.

Multiple frameworks of analytic assessment, adapted to the realities of climate change mitigation, are therefore required. We identified four main groups. *Aggregate economic* frameworks – including environmental costs or goals, and with due attention to implied behavioural, distributional and dynamic assumptions – can provide insights about trade-offs, cost-effectiveness and policies for delivering agreed goals. *Ethical frameworks* are equally essential to inform both international and domestic discourse and decisions, including the relationship with international (and intergenerational)

responsibilities, related financial systems, and domestic policy design in all countries. Explicit frameworks for analysing *transition and transformation* across multiple sectors need to draw on both socio-technical transition literatures, and those on social transformation. Finally, literatures on *psychology, behaviour and political sciences* can illuminate obstacles that have impeded progress to date and suggest ways to overcome them.

No single analytical framework, or single discipline, on its own can offer a comprehensive assessment of climate change mitigation. Together they point to the relevance of growing literatures and discourses on Just Transitions, and the role of governance at multiple levels. Ultimately all these frameworks are needed to inform the decisions required to deepen and connect the scattered elements of progress to date, and hence accelerate progress towards agreed goals and multiple dimensions of climate change mitigation in the context of sustainable development.

1.11   Knowledge Gaps

Despite huge expansion in the literature (Callaghan et al. 2020), knowledge gaps remain. Modeling still struggles to bring together detailed physical and economic climate impacts and mitigation, with limited representation of financial and distributional dynamics. There are few interdisciplinary tools which apply theories of transition and transformation to questions of economic and social impacts, compounded by remaining uncertainties concerning the role of new technological sets, international instruments, policy and political evaluation.

One scan of future research needs suggests three priority areas (Roberts et al. 2020): (i) human welfare-focused development (e.g., reducing inequality); (ii) how the historic position of states within international power relations conditions their ability to respond to climate change; (iii) transition dynamics and the flexibility of institutions to drive towards low-carbon development pathways. There remain gaps in understanding how international dynamics and agreements filter down to affect constituencies and local implementation. Literature on the potential for supply-side agreements, in which producers agree to restrict the supply of fossil fuels (e.g., Asheim et al. 2019) is limited but gaining increasing academic attention.

Nature is under pressure both at land and at sea, as demonstrated by declining biodiversity (IPBES 2019). Climate policies could increase the pressure on land and oceans (IPCC 2019c,b), with insufficient attention to relationships between biodiversity and climate agreements and associated policies. IPBES aims to coordinate with the IPCC more directly, but literature will be required to support these reports.

Compounding these gaps is the fact that socially oriented, agriculture-related options, where human and non-human systems intersect most obviously, remain under-researched (e.g., Balasubramanya and Stifel 2020). Efforts to engage with policies here, especially framed around ecosystem services, have often neglected their 'practical fitness' in favour of focusing on their 'institutional fitness', which needs to be addressed in future research (Stevenson et al. 2021).

The relative roles of short-term mitigation policies and long-term investments, including government and financial decision-making tools, remains inadequately explored. Strategic investments may include city planning, public transport, EV-charging networks, and CCU/CCS. Understanding how international treaties can increase incentives to make such investments is all the more salient in the aftermath of COVID-19, on which research is necessarily young but rapidly growing. Finally, the economic, institutional and political strategies to close the gap between NDCs, actual implementation, and mitigation goals – informed by the PA and the UNFCCC Global Stocktake – require much further research.

1.12   Roadmap to the Report

This Sixth Assessment Report covers mitigation in five main parts (Figure 1.9), namely: introduction and frameworks; emission trends, scenarios and pathways; sectors; institutional dimensions including national and international policy, financial and technological mitigation drivers; and conclusions.

Chapters 2 to 5 cover the big picture trends, drivers and projections at national and global levels. Chapter 2 analyses emission trends and drivers to date. Chapter 3 presents long-term global scenarios, including the projected economic and other characteristics of mitigation through to the balancing of sources and sinks through the second half of this century, and the implications for global temperature change and risks. Chapter 4 explores the shorter-term prospects including NDCs, and the possibilities for accelerating mitigation out to 2050 in the context of sustainable development at the national, regional and international scales. Chapter 5, a new chapter for IPCC Assessments, focuses upon the role of services and derived demand for energy and land use, and the social dimensions.

Chapters 6 to 12 examine sectoral contributions and possibilities for mitigation. Chapter 6 summarises characteristics and trends in the energy sector, specifically supply, including the remarkable changes in the cost of some key technologies since AR5. Chapter 7 examines the roles of AFOLU, drawing upon and updating the recent Special Report, including the potential tensions between the multiple uses of land. Chapter 8 presents a holistic view of the trends and pressures of urban systems, as both a challenge and an opportunity for mitigation. Chapters 9 and 10 then examine two sectors which entwine with, but go well beyond, urban systems: buildings (Chapter 9) including construction materials and zero-carbon buildings; and transport (Chapter 10), including shipping and aviation and a wider look at mobility as a general service. Chapter 11 explores the contribution of industry, including supply chain developments, resource efficiency/circular economy, and the cross-system implications of decarbonisation for industrial systems. Finally, Chapter 12 takes a cross-sectoral perspective and explores cross-cutting issues like the interactions of biomass energy, food and land, and carbon dioxide removal.

Four chapters then review thematic issues in implementation and governance of mitigation. Chapter 13 explores national and sub-national policies and institutions, bringing together lessons of policies examined in the sectoral chapters, as well as insights from service and demand-side perspectives (Chapter 5), along with governance approaches and capacity-building, and the role and relationships of sub-national actors. Chapter 14 then considers the roles and status of international cooperation, including the UNFCCC agreements and international institutions, sectoral agreements and multiple forms of international partnerships, and the ethics and governance challenges of solar radiation modification. Chapter 15 explores investment and finance, including current trends, the investment needs for deep decarbonisation, and the complementary roles of public and private finance. This includes climate-related investment opportunities and risks (e.g., 'stranded assets'), linkages between finance and investments in adaptation and mitigation; and the impact of COVID-19. A new chapter on innovation (Chapter 16) looks at technology development, accelerated deployment and global diffusion as systemic issues that hold potential for transformative changes, and the challenges of managing such changes at multiple levels including the role of international cooperation.

Finally, Chapter 17 considers accelerating the transition in the context of sustainable development, including practical pathways for joint responses to climate change and sustainable development challenges. This includes major regional perspectives, mitigation-adaptation interlinkages, and enabling conditions including the roles of technology, finance and cooperation for sustainable development.

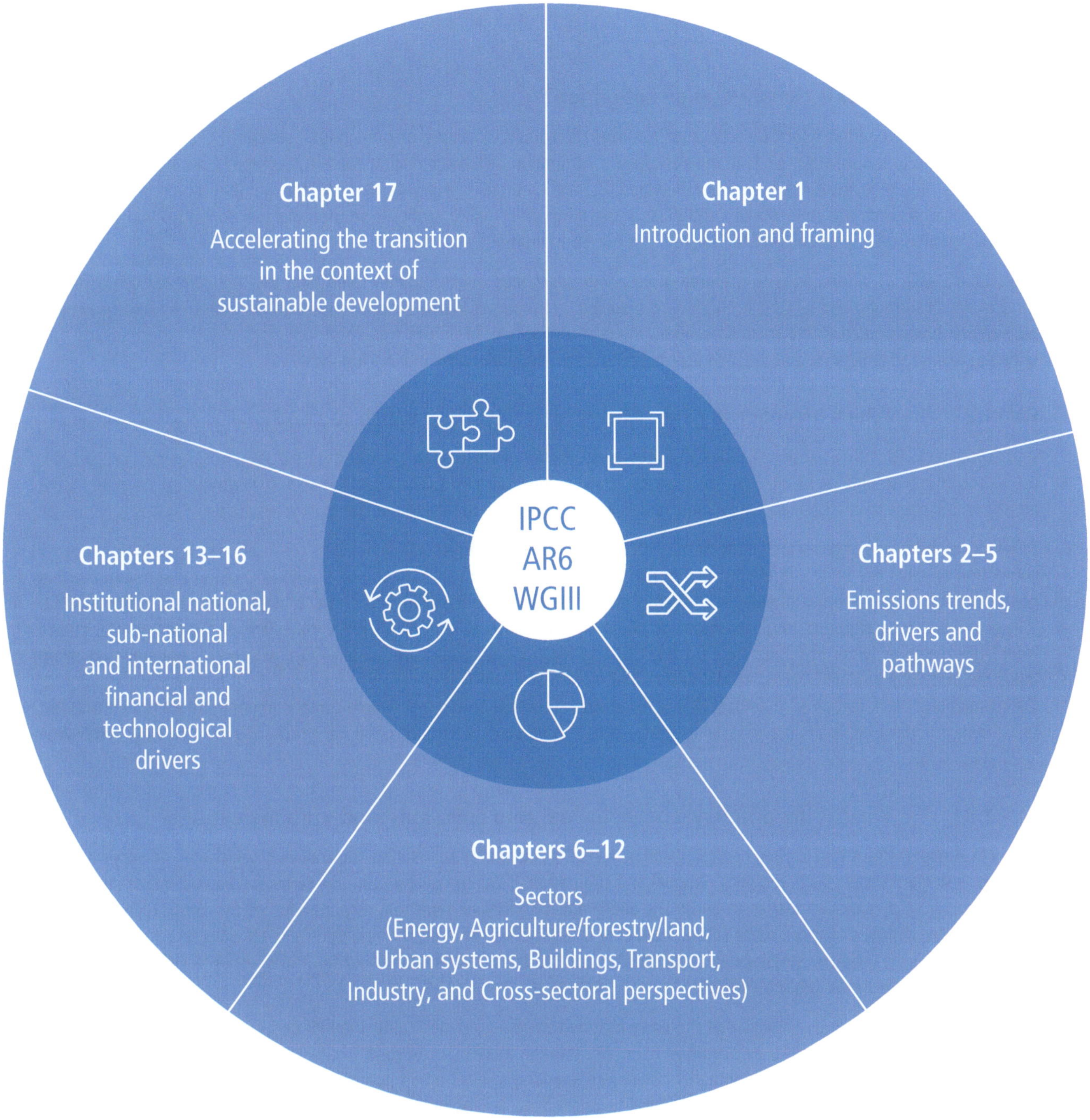

Figure 1.9 | The structure of the AR6 mitigation report.

Frequently Asked Questions (FAQs)

FAQ 1.1 | What is climate change mitigation?

Climate change mitigation refers to actions or activities that limit emissions of greenhouse gases (GHGs) from entering the atmosphere and/or reduce their levels in the atmosphere. Mitigation includes reducing the GHGs emitted from energy production and use (e.g., that reduces use of fossil fuels), and land use, and methods to mitigate warming, for example, by carbon sinks which remove emissions from the atmosphere through land-use or other (including artificial) mechanisms (Sections 12.3 and 14.4.5; see AR6 WGI for physical science, and WGIII Chapter 7 for AFOLU mitigation).

The ultimate goal of mitigation is to preserve a biosphere which can sustain human civilisation and the complex of ecosystem services which surround and support it. This means reducing anthropogenic GHG emissions towards net zero to limit the warming, with global goals agreed in the Paris Agreement. Effective mitigation strategies require an understanding of mechanisms that underpin release of emissions, and the technical, policy and societal options for influencing these.

FAQ 1.2 | Which greenhouse gases (GHGs) are relevant to which sectors?

Anthropogenic GHGs such as carbon dioxide (CO_2), methane (CH_4), nitrous oxide (N_2O), and fluorinated gases (e.g., hydrofluorocarbons, perfluorocarbons, sulphur hexafluoride) are released from various sources. CO_2 makes the largest contribution to global GHG emissions, but some have extremely long atmospheric lifetimes extending to tens of thousands of years, such as F-gases (Chapter 2).

Different combinations of gases are emitted from different activities. The largest source of CO_2 is combustion of fossil fuels in energy conversion systems like boilers in electric power plants, engines in aircraft and automobiles, and in cooking and heating within homes and businesses (approximately 64% of emissions, Figure SPM.2). Fossil fuels are also a major source of methane (CH_4), the second biggest contributor to global warming. While most GHGs come from fossil fuel combustion, about one quarter comes from land-related activities like agriculture (mainly CH_4 and N_2O) and deforestation (mainly CO_2), with additional emissions from industrial processes (mainly CO_2, N_2O and F-gases), and municipal waste and wastewater (mainly CH_4) (Chapter 2). In addition to these emissions, black carbon – an aerosol that is, for example, emitted during incomplete combustion of fossil fuels – contributes to warming of the Earth's atmosphere, whilst some other short-lived pollutants temporarily cool the surface (IPCC AR6 WGI Section 6.5.4.3).

FAQ 1.3 | What is the difference between 'net zero emissions' and 'carbon neutrality'?

Annex I (Glossary) states that 'carbon neutrality and net zero CO_2 emissions are overlapping concepts' which 'can be applied at the global or sub-global scales (e.g., regional, national and sub-national)'. At the global scale the terms are equivalent. At sub-global scales, net zero CO_2 typically applies to emissions under direct control or territorial responsibility of the entity reporting them (e.g., a country, district or sector); while carbon neutrality is also applied to firms, commodities and activities (e.g., a service or an event) and generally includes emissions and removals beyond the entity's direct control or territorial responsibility, termed 'Scope 3' or 'value chain emissions' (Bhatia et al. 2011).

This means the emissions and removals that should be included are wider for 'neutrality' than for net zero goals, but also that offset mechanisms could be employed to help achieve neutrality through abatement beyond what is possible under the direct control of the entity. Rules and environmental integrity criteria are intended to ensure additionality and avoid double counting of offsets consistent with 'neutrality' claims (see 'carbon neutrality' and 'offset' in Glossary, for detail and a list of criteria).

While the term 'carbon' neutrality in this report is defined as referring specifically to CO_2 neutrality, use of this term in practice can be ambiguous, as some users apply it to neutrality of all GHG emissions. GHG neutrality means an entity's gross emissions of all GHG must be balanced by the removal of an equivalent amount of CO_2 from the atmosphere. This requires the selection of a suitable metric that aggregates emissions from non-CO_2 gases, such as the commonly used GWP100 metric (for a discussion of GHG metrics, see AR6 WGI Box 1.3 and Cross-Chapter Box 2 in Chapter 2 of this report).

References

Abrahamsen, R., L.R. Andersen, and O.J. Sending, 2019: Introduction: Making liberal internationalism great again? *Int. J. Canada's J. Glob. Policy Anal.*, **74(1)**, 5–14, doi:10.1177/0020702019827050.

Acemoglu, D., P. Aghion, L. Bursztyn, and D. Hemous, 2012: The environment and directed technical change. *Am. Econ. Rev.*, **102(1)**, 131–166, doi:10.1257/aer.102.1.131.

Acemoglu, D., U. Akcigit, D. Hanley, and W. Kerr, 2016: Transition to Clean Technology. *J. Polit. Econ.*, **124(1)**, 52–104, doi:10.1086/684511.

Ackerman, F., E.A. Stanton, and R. Bueno, 2010: Fat tails, exponents, extreme uncertainty: Simulating catastrophe in DICE. *Ecol. Econ.*, **69(8)**, 1657–1665, doi:10.1016/J.ECOLECON.2010.03.013.

Adelman, S., 2015: Tropical forests and climate change: a critique of green governmentality. *Int. J. Law Context*, **11(2)**, 195–212, doi:10.1017/s1744552315000075.

Adger, W.N., 2009: Social Capital, Collective Action, and Adaptation to Climate Change. *Econ. Geogr.*, **79(4)**, 387–404, doi:10.1111/j.1944-8287.2003.tb00220.x.

Adler, M. et al., 2017: Priority for the worse-off and the social cost of carbon. *Nat. Clim. Change*, **7(6)**, 443–449, doi:10.1038/nclimate3298.

Afionis, S., M. Sakai, K. Scott, J. Barrett, and A. Gouldson, 2017: Consumption-based carbon accounting: does it have a future? *Wiley Interdiscip. Rev. Clim. Change*, **8(1)**, e438, doi:10.1002/wcc.438.

Aghion, P., C. Antonin, and S. Bunel, 2021: *The Power of Creative Destruction*. Harvard University Press, Cambridge, MA, USA, and London, UK, 400 pp. doi.org/10.4159/9780674258686.

Akimoto, K., F. Sano, and T. Tomoda, 2018: GHG emission pathways until 2300 for the 1.5°C temperature rise target and the mitigation costs achieving the pathways. *Mitig. Adapt. Strateg. Glob. Change*, **23(6)**, 839–852, doi:10.1007/s11027-017-9762-z.

Alam, K. et al., 2013: Planning "Exceptionalism"? Political Economy of Climate Resilient Development in Bangladesh, in *Climate Change Adaptation Actions in Bangladesh* [Shaw, R., Mallick, F., and Islam, A. (eds)]. Springer, Tokyo, Japan, 387–417 pp. doi: 10.1007/978-4-431-54249-0_20.

Albrecht, F., and C.F. Parker, 2019: Healing the Ozone Layer: The Montreal Protocol and the Lessons and Limits of a Global Governance Success Story. In: *Great Policy Successes* [Hart, P. and Compton, M. (eds)], Oxford University Press, Oxford, UK, pp. 304–322. doi: 10.1093/oso/9780198843719.003.0016.

Albrecht, T.R., A. Crootof, and C.A. Scott, 2018: The Water-Energy-Food Nexus: A systematic review of methods for nexus assessment. *Environ. Res. Lett.*, **13(4)**, doi:10.1088/1748-9326/aaa9c6.

Aldy, J.E., 2015: Pricing climate risk mitigation. *Nat. Clim. Change*, **5(5)**, 396–398, doi:10.1038/nclimate2540.

Alic, J.A. and D. Sarewitz, 2016: Rethinking innovation for decarbonizing energy systems. *Energy Res. Soc. Sci.*, **21**, 212–221, doi:10.1016/j.erss.2016.08.005.

Allcott, H., 2011: Social norms and energy conservation. *J. Public Econ.*, **95**(9–10), 1082–1095, doi:10.1016/J.JPUBECO.2011.03.003.

Allcott, H., and S. Mullainathan, 2010: Behavior and Energy Policy. *Science*, **327**(5970), 1204–1205, doi:10.1126/science.1180775.

Allen, T. et al., 2020: Climate-Related Scenarios for Financial Stability Assessment: An Application to France. *SSRN Electron. J.*, doi:10.2139/ssrn.3653131.

Allwood, J.M., 2014: Squaring the Circular Economy: The Role of Recycling within a Hierarchy of Material Management Strategies. In: *Handbook of Recycling* [Worrell, E. and M.A. Reuter (eds.)]. Elsevier, pp. 445–477, doi:10.1016/B978-0-12-396459-5.00030-1.

Ameli, N., P. Drummond, A. Bisaro, M. Grubb, and H. Chenet, 2020: Climate finance and disclosure for institutional investors: why transparency is not enough. *Clim. Change*, **160(4)**, 565–589, doi:10.1007/s10584-019-02542-2.

Ameli, N., S. Kothari, and M. Grubb, 2021: Misplaced expectations from climate disclosure initiatives. *Nat. Clim. Change*, **11(11)**, 917–924, doi:10.1038/s41558-021-01174-8.

Andrews-Speed, P. and C. Dalin, 2017: Elements of the water–energy–food nexus in China. In: *Routledge Handbook of the Resource Nexus* [Bleischwitz, R., H. Hoff, C. Spataru, E. Van der Voet, and S.D. VanDeveer (eds.)]. Routledge, Abingdon, UK, pp. 347–367, doi:10.4324/9781315560625-23.

Andrijevic, M., C.-F. Schleussner, M.J. Gidden, D.L. McCollum, and J. Rogelj, 2020: COVID-19 recovery funds dwarf clean energy investment needs. *Science*, **370(6514)**, 298–300, doi:10.1126/science.abc9697.

Antal, M. and J.C.J.M. Van Den Bergh, 2016: Green growth and climate change: conceptual and empirical considerations. *Clim. Policy*, **16(2)**, 165–177, doi:10.1080/14693062.2014.992003.

Anthoff, D. and R.S.J. Tol, 2010: On international equity weights and national decision making on climate change. *J. Environ. Econ. Manage.*, **60(1)**, 14–20, doi:10.1016/j.jeem.2010.04.002.

Antimiani, A., V. Costantini, A. Markandya, E. Paglialunga, and G. Sforna, 2017: The Green Climate Fund as an effective compensatory mechanism in global climate negotiations. *Environ. Sci. Policy*, **77** (July), 49–68, doi:10.1016/j.envsci.2017.07.015.

Arora-Jonsson, S., 2011: Virtue and vulnerability: Discourses on women, gender and climate change. *Glob. Environ. Change*, **21(2)**, 744–751, doi:10.1016/J.GLOENVCHA.2011.01.005.

Arrow, K. et al., 2013: Determining benefits and costs for future generations. *Science*, **341(6144)**, 349–350, doi:10.1126/science.1235665.

Arrow, K.J., A. Sen, and K. Suzumura, 2011: *Handbook of Social Choice and Welfare Volume 2*. North-Holland, Oxford, UK,, 952 pp.

Arthur, B., 1989: Competing technologies, increasing returns, and lock-in by historical events. *Econ. J.*, **99**, 116–131, doi: 10.2307/2234208.

Arthur, W.B., 1999: Complexity and the Economy. *Science*, **284(5411)**, 107–109, doi:10.1126/science.284.5411.107.

Arto, I. and E. Dietzenbacher, 2014: Drivers of the growth in global greenhouse gas emissions. *Environ. Sci. Technol.*, **48(10)**, 5388–5394, doi:10.1021/es5005347.

Artz, J. et al., 2018: Sustainable Conversion of Carbon Dioxide: An Integrated Review of Catalysis and Life Cycle Assessment. *Chem. Rev.*, **118(2)**, 434–504, doi:10.1021/acs.chemrev.7b00435.

Asara, V., I. Otero, F. Demaria, and E. Corbera, 2015: Socially sustainable degrowth as a social–ecological transformation: repoliticizing sustainability. *Sustain. Sci.*, **10(3)**, 375–384, doi:10.1007/s11625-015-0321-9.

Asheim, G.B. et al., 2019: The case for a supply-side climate treaty. *Science*, **365(6451)**, 325–327, doi:10.1126/science.aax5011.

Auerbach, A.J. and Y. Gorodnichenko, 2012: Measuring the Output Responses to Fiscal Policy. *Am. Econ. J. Econ. Policy*, **4(2)**, 1–27, doi:10.1257/pol.4.2.1.

Auffhammer, M., 2018: Quantifying Economic Damages from Climate Change. *J. Econ. Perspect.*, **32(4)**, 33–52, doi:10.1257/JEP.32.4.33.

Austen-Smith, D., W. Dziuda, B. Harstad, and A. Loeper, 2019: Gridlock and inefficient policy instruments. *Theor. Econ.*, **14(4)**, 1483–1534, doi:10.3982/TE3329.

Aven, T. and O. Renn, 2015: An evaluation of the treatment of risk and uncertainties in the IPCC reports on climate change. *Risk Anal.*, **35(4)**, 701–712, doi:10.1111/risa.12298.

Avgerinou, M., P. Bertoldi, and L. Castellazzi, 2017: Trends in Data Centre Energy Consumption under the European Code of Conduct for Data Centre Energy Efficiency. *Energies*, **10(10)**, 1470, doi:10.3390/en10101470.

Aykut, S.C., 2016: Taking a wider view on climate governance: moving beyond the 'iceberg,' the 'elephant,' and the 'forest.' *WIREs Clim. Change*, **7(3)**, 318–328, doi:10.1002/wcc.391.

Baarsch, F. et al., 2020: The impact of climate change on incomes and convergence in Africa. *World Dev.*, **126**, 104699, doi:10.1016/j.worlddev.2019.104699.

Bäckstrand, K. and E. Lövbrand, 2019: The Road to Paris: Contending Climate Governance Discourses in the Post-Copenhagen Era. *J. Environ. Policy Plan.*, **21(5)**, 519–532, doi:10.1080/1523908X.2016.1150777.

Bäckstrand, K., J.W. Kuyper, B.-O. Linnér, and E. Lövbrand, 2017: Non-state actors in global climate governance: from Copenhagen to Paris and beyond. *Env. Polit.*, **26(4)**, 561–579, doi:10.1080/09644016.2017.1327485.

Bain, C., 2017: The greening of self-interest: why is China standing firm on its climate commitments despite US regression?, MA thesis, University of British Columbiapp. 57.

Baker, L., 2015: Renewable energy in South Africa's minerals-energy complex: a 'low carbon' transition?' *Rev. Afr. Polit. Econ.*, **42(144)**, 245–261, doi:10.1080/03056244.2014.953471.

Balasubramanya, S. and D. Stifel, 2020: Viewpoint: Water, agriculture & poverty in an era of climate change: Why do we know so little? *Food Policy*, **93**, 101905, doi:10.1016/J.FOODPOL.2020.101905.

Baldwin, E., Y. Cai, and K. Kuralbayeva, 2020: To build or not to build? Capital stocks and climate policy*. *J. Environ. Econ. Manage.*, **100**, 102235, doi:10.1016/j.jeem.2019.05.001.

Bardi, U., S. Falsini, and I. Perissi, 2019: Toward a General Theory of Societal Collapse: A Biophysical Examination of Tainter's Model of the Diminishing Returns of Complexity. *Biophys. Econ. Resour. Qual.*, **4(1)**, 3, doi:10.1007/s41247-018-0049-0.

Barker, T. and D. Crawford-Brown, 2014: Decarbonising the world's economy: Assessing the feasibility of policies to reduce greenhouse gas emissions. *Decarbonising World's Econ. Assess. Feasibility Policies to Reduce Greenh. Gas Emiss.*, 1–361, doi:10.1142/P955.

Barker, T., and D. Crawford-Brown, 2014: *Decarbonising the World's Economy*. Imperial College Press, London, UK, pp. 1–361.

Barrett, S., 1994: Self-Enforcing International Environmental Agreements. *Oxf. Econ. Pap.*, **46(0)**, 878–894.

Barrett, S., 2005: The theory of international environmental agreements. In: *Handbook of Environmental Economics Volume 3* [Mäler, K.-G. and J.R. Vincent, (eds.)]. Vol. 3 of, Elsevier, Amsterdam, Netherlands, pp. 1457–1516.

Barrett, S., 2016: Coordination vs. voluntarism and enforcement in sustaining international environmental cooperation. *Proc. Natl. Acad. Sci.*, **113(51)**, 14515–14522, doi:10.1073/PNAS.1604989113.

Bataille, C. et al., 2016: The need for national deep decarbonization pathways for effective climate policy. *Clim. Policy*, **16(sup1)**, S7–S26, doi:10.1080/14693062.2016.1173005.

Battaglini, M. and B. Harstad, 2016: Participation and Duration of Environmental Agreements. *J. Polit. Econ.*, **124(1)**, 160–204, doi:10.1086/684478.

Battiston, S., A. Mandel, I. Monasterolo, F. Schütze, and G. Visentin, 2017: A climate stress-test of the financial system. *Nat. Clim. Change*, **7(4)**, 283–288, doi:10.1038/nclimate3255.

Battiston, S., I. Monasterolo, K. Riahi, and B.J. van Ruijven, 2021: Accounting for finance is key for climate mitigation pathways. *Science*, **372(6545)**, 918–920, doi:10.1126/science.abf3877.

Bauer, N. et al., 2013: CO$_2$ emission mitigation and fossil fuel markets: Dynamic and international aspects of climate policies. *Technol. Forecast. Soc. Change*, **90**.

Bauer, N. et al., 2020: Quantification of an efficiency-sovereignty trade-off in climate policy. *Nature*, **588(7837)**, 261–266, doi:10.1038/S41586-020-2982-5.

Bazilian, M. et al., 2011: Considering the energy, water and food nexus: Towards an integrated modelling approach. *Energy Policy*, **39(12)**, 7896–7906, doi:10.1016/j.enpol.2011.09.039.

Beinhocker, E.D., 2007: *The origin of wealth: evolution, complexity, and the radical remaking of economics*. Harvard Business School Press, Boston, MA, USA, 526 pp.

Belkhir, L. and A. Elmeligi, 2018: Assessing ICT global emissions footprint: Trends to 2040 & recommendations. *J. Clean. Prod.*, **177**, 448–463, doi:10.1016/j.jclepro.2017.12.239.

Bénabou, R. and J. Tirole, 2011: Identity, morals, and taboos: Beliefs as assets. *Q.J. Econ.*, **126(2)**, 805–855, doi:10.1093/qje/qjr002.

Bengtsson Sonesson, L. et al., 2019: Carbon Ruins: An exhibition of the fossil age. Climaginaries. https://www.climaginaries.org/carbonruins.

Berkhout, F. et al., 2010: Sustainability experiments in Asia: Innovations shaping alternative development pathways? *Environ. Sci. Policy*, **13(4)**, 261–271, doi:10.1016/j.envsci.2010.03.010.

Bernauer, T. and T. Böhmelt, 2013: National climate policies in international comparison: The Climate Change Cooperation Index. *Environ. Sci. Policy*, **25**, 196–206, doi:10.1016/j.envsci.2012.09.007.

Bernstein, S. and M. Hoffmann, 2018: The politics of decarbonization and the catalytic impact of subnational climate experiments. *Policy Sciences*, **51(2)**, 189–211, doi:10.1007/s11077-018-9314-8.

Berry, A., and É. Laurent, 2019: *Taxe carbone, le retour, à quelles conditions?*, RAPPEL Paris, France, 38pp.

Bertram, C. et al., 2015: Carbon lock-in through capital stock inertia associated with weak near-term climate policies. *Technol. Forecast. Soc. Change*, **90(PA)**, 62–72, doi:10.1016/j.techfore.2013.10.001.

Bickersteth, S. et al., 2017: *Mainstreaming climate compatible development*. Climate and Development Knowledge Network, London, UK, 302pp. https://cdkn.org/wp-content/uploads/2017/08/Mainstreaming-climate-compatible-development-web-final.pdf.

Biermann, F., P. Pattberg, H. van Asselt, and F. Zelli, 2009: The Fragmentation of Global Governance Architectures: A Framework for Analysis. *Glob. Environ. Polit.*, **9(4)**, 14–40, doi:10.1162/glep.2009.9.4.14.

Biermann, F., N. Kanie, and R.E. Kim, 2017: Global governance by goal-setting: the novel approach of the UN Sustainable Development Goals. *Curr. Opin. Environ. Sustainability*, **26–27**, 26–31, doi:10.1016/j.cosust.2017.01.010.

Bina, O., 2013: The Green Economy and Sustainable Development: An Uneasy Balance? *Environ. Plan. C Gov. Policy*, **31(6)**, 1023–1047, doi:10.1068/c1310j.

Blanchard, O. and D. Leigh, 2013: Growth Forecast Errors and Fiscal Multipliers. *IMF Work. Pap.*, **13(1)**, 1, doi:10.5089/9781475576443.001.

Bobeck, J., J. Peace, F. M. Ahmad, and R. Munson, 2019: *Carbon Utilization - A Vital and Effective Pathway for Decarbonization*. Center for Climate and Energy Solutions, Arlington, VA, 42pp. https://www.c2es.org/document/carbon-utilization-a-vital-and-effective-pathway-for-decarbonization/.

Bodansky, D., 2016: The Legal Character of the Paris Agreement. *Rev. Eur. Comp. Int. Environ. Law*, **25(2)**, 142–150, doi:10.1111/reel.12154.

Bodansky, D., J. Brunnée, and L. Rajamani, 2017: *International Climate Change Law*. Oxford University Press, Oxford UK.

Boppart, T. and P. Krusell, 2020: Labor Supply in the Past, Present, and Future: A Balanced-Growth Perspective. *J. Polit. Econ.*, **128(1)**, 118–157, doi:10.1086/704071.

Bos, K. and J. Gupta, 2019: Stranded assets and stranded resources: Implications for climate change mitigation and global sustainable development. *Energy Res. Soc. Science*, **56**, 101215, doi:10.1016/j.erss.2019.05.025.

Bowman, M. and S. Minas, 2019: Resilience through interlinkage: the green climate fund and climate finance governance. *Clim. Policy*, **19(3)**, 342–353, doi:10.1080/14693062.2018.1513358.

Boykoff, M.T., 2011: *Who Speaks for the Climate?: Making Sense of Media Reporting on Climate Change*. Cambridge University Press, Cambridge, UK, 241pp.

Braito, M.T. et al., 2017: Human-nature relationships and linkages to environmental behaviour. *Environ. Values*, **26(3)**, 365–389, doi:10.3197/096327117X14913285800706.

Breetz, H., M. Mildenberger, and L. Stokes, 2018: The political logics of clean energy transitions. *Bus. Polit.*, **20(4)**, 492–522, doi:10.1017/bap.2018.14.

Brekke, K.A., S. Kverndokk, and K. Nyborg, 2003: An economic model of moral motivation. *J. Public Econ.*, **87(9–10)**, 1967–1983, doi:10.1016/S0047-2727(01)00222-5.

Brockway, P.E., A. Owen, L.I. Brand-Correa, and L. Hardt, 2019: Estimation of global final-stage energy-return-on-investment for fossil fuels with comparison to renewable energy sources. *Nat. Energy*, **4**(7), 612–621.

Broome, J., 2012: *Climate matters: ethics in a warming world*. W.W. Norton & Co., New York, USA, 192pp.

Brouwer, F. et al., 2018: Energy modelling and the Nexus concept. *Energy Strateg. Rev.*, **19**, 1–6, doi:10.1016/j.esr.2017.10.005.

Brulle, R.J., 2014: Institutionalizing delay: foundation funding and the creation of US climate change counter-movement organizations. *Clim. Change*, **122**(4), 681–694, doi:10.1007/s10584-013-1018-7.

Brulle, R.J., 2019: Networks of Opposition: A Structural Analysis of US Climate Change Countermovement Coalitions 1989–2015. *Sociol. Inq.*, **91(3)**, 603–624, doi:10.1111/soin.12333.

Brulle, R.J. and K.M. Norgaard, 2019: Avoiding Cultural Trauma: Climate Change and Social Inertia. *Env. Polit.*, **28(5)**, 886–908, doi:10.1080/09644016.2018.1562138.

Brulle, R.J., M. Aronczyk, and J. Carmichael, 2020: Corporate promotion and climate change: an analysis of key variables affecting advertising spending by major oil corporations, 1986–2015. *Clim. Change*, **159(1)**, 87–101, doi:10.1007/s10584-019-02582-8.

Bryck, K. and N. Ellis, 2016: An Engineering Approach to Sustainable Decision Making. *Environ. Values*, **25(6)**, 639–662, doi:10.3197/0963271 16X14736981715580.

Buettner, A., 2020: 'Imagine what we could do'– the school strikes for climate and reclaiming citizen empowerment. *Continuum*, **34(6)**, 828–839, doi:10.1080/10304312.2020.1842123.

Buhr, B. et al., 2018: *Climate Change and the Cost of Capital in Developing Countries*, Imperial College Business School and SOAS University of London, London, UK, 38 pp https://imperialcollegelondon.app.box.com/s/e8x6t16y9bajb85inazbk5mdrqtvxfzd.

Bulkeley, H. and H. Schroeder, 2012: Beyond state/non-state divides: Global cities and the governing of climate change. *Eur. J. Int. Relations*, **18(4)**, 743–766, doi:10.1177/1354066111413308.

Bulkeley, H. et al., 2014: *Transnational Climate Change Governance*. Cambridge University Press, Cambridge, UK, pp 212.

Bulow, J., C. Reinhart, K. Rogoff, and C. Trebesch, 2021: The debt pandemic: new steps are needed to improve sovereign debt workouts. *IMF Financ. Dev.*,. https://www.imf.org/external/pubs/ft/fandd/2020/09/debt-pandemic-reinhart-rogoff-bulow-trebesch.htm (Accessed March 12, 2021).

Callaghan, M.W., J.C. Minx, and P.M. Forster, 2020: A topography of climate change research. *Nat. Clim. Change*, **10(2)**, 118–123, doi:10.1038/s41558-019-0684-5.

Campiglio, E. et al., 2018: Climate change challenges for central banks and financial regulators. *Nat. Clim. Change*, **8(6)**, 462–468, doi:10.1038/s41558-018-0175-0.

Caney, S., 2016: The Struggle for Climate Justice in a Non-Ideal World. *Midwest Stud. Philos.*, **40(1)**, 9–26, doi:10.1111/misp.12044.

Capasso, M., T. Hansen, J. Heiberg, A. Klitkou, and M. Steen, 2019: Green growth – A synthesis of scientific findings. *Technol. Forecast. Soc. Change*, **146**, 390–402, doi:10.1016/j.techfore.2019.06.013.

Carbone, J.C. and N. Rivers, 2017: The Impacts of Unilateral Climate Policy on Competitiveness: Evidence From Computable General Equilibrium Models. *Rev. Environ. Econ. Policy*, **11(1)**, 24–42, doi:10.1093/reep/rew025.

Carleton, T. et al., 2020: *Valuing the Global Mortality Consequences of Climate Change Accounting for Adaptation Costs and Benefits*. National Bureau of Economic Research,Cambridge, MA, USA, 49 pp.

Carley, S. and D.M. Konisky, 2020: The justice and equity implications of the clean energy transition. *Nat. Energy*, **5(8)**, 569–577, doi:10.1038/s41560-020-0641-6.

Carlsson, B. and R. Stankiewicz, 1991: On the nature, function and composition of technological systems. *J. Evol. Econ.*, **1(2)**, 93–118, doi:10.1007/BF01224915.

Casadio Tarabusi, E. and G. Guarini, 2013: An Unbalance Adjustment Method for Development Indicators. *Soc. Indic. Res.*, **112(1)**, 19–45, doi:10.1007/s11205-012-0070-4.

Castree, N., 2017: Unfree Radicals: Geoscientists, the Anthropocene, and Left Politics. *Antipode*, **49**, 52–74, doi:10.1111/anti.12187.

Ćetković, S. and A. Buzogány, 2016: Varieties of capitalism and clean energy transitions in the European Union: When renewable energy hits different economic logics. *Clim. Policy*, **16(5)**, 642–657, doi:10.1080/14693062.2015.1135778.

Chan, S., C. Brandi, and S. Bauer, 2016: Aligning Transnational Climate Action with International Climate Governance: The Road from Paris. *Rev. Eur. Comp. Int. Environ. Law*, **25(2)**, 238–247, doi:10.1111/reel.12168.

Chan, S., R. Falkner, M. Goldberg, and H. van Asselt, 2018: Effective and geographically balanced? An output-based assessment of non-state climate actions. *Clim. Policy*, **18(1)**, 24–35, doi:10.1080/14693062.2016.1248343.

Chang, H.-J., 2014: *Economics: The User's Guide*. 1st ed. Pelican, New Orleans, USA, 502 pp.

Chapman, D.A., B. Lickel, and E.M. Markowitz, 2017: Reassessing emotion in climate change communication. *Nat. Clim. Change*, **7(12)**, 850–852, doi:10.1038/s41558-017-0021-9.

Chazdon, R., 2008: Beyond deforestation: restoring forests and ecosystem services on degraded lands. *Science*, **320(5882)**, 1458–1460, doi: 10.1126/science.1155365.

Chen, K. et al., 2017: Impact of climate change on heat-related mortality in Jiangsu Province, China. *Environ. Pollut.*, **224**, 317–325, doi:10.1016/j.envpol.2017.02.011.

Chenet, H., J. Ryan-Collins, and F. van Lerven, 2021: Finance, climate-change and radical uncertainty: Towards a precautionary approach to financial policy. *Ecol. Econ.*, **183**, 106957, doi:10.1016/j.ecolecon.2021.106957.

Cheon, A. and J. Urpelainen, 2018: *Activism and the fossil fuel industry*. 1st ed. Routledge, Abingdon, UK, 242 pp.

Cherp, A., V. Vinichenko, J. Jewell, E. Brutschin, and B. Sovacool, 2018: Integrating techno-economic, socio-technical and political perspectives on national energy transitions: A meta-theoretical framework. *Energy Res. Soc. Science*, **37**, 175–190, doi:10.1016/j.erss.2017.09.015.

Clapp, J., P. Newell, and Z.W. Brent, 2018: The global political economy of climate change, agriculture and food systems. *J. Peasant Stud.*, **45(1)**, 80–88, doi:10.1080/03066150.2017.1381602.

Clémençon, R., 2016: The Two Sides of the Paris Climate Agreement: Dismal Failure or Historic Breakthrough? *J. Environ. Dev.*, **25(1)**, 3–24, doi:10.1177/1070496516631362.

Clulow, Z., 2019: Democracy, electoral systems and emissions: explaining when and why democratization promotes mitigation. *Clim. Policy*, **19(2)**, 244–257, doi:10.1080/14693062.2018.1497938.

Cohen, T. and C. Cavoli, 2019: Automated vehicles: exploring possible consequences of government (non)intervention for congestion and accessibility. *Transp. Rev.*, **39(1)**, 129–151, doi:10.1080/01441647.2018.1524401.

Cole, D.H., 2015: Advantages of a polycentric approach to climate change policy. *Nat. Clim. Change*, **5(2)**, 114–118, doi:10.1038/nclimate2490.

Conway, D. et al., 2015: Climate and southern Africa's water–energy–food nexus. *Nat. Clim. Change*, **5(9)**, 837–846, doi:10.1038/nclimate2735.

Costanza, R., L. Fioramonti, and I. Kubiszewski, 2016: The UN Sustainable Development Goals and the dynamics of well-being. *Front. Ecol. Environ.*, **14(2)**, 59, doi:10.1002/fee.1231.

National Research Council, 2015a: *Climate Intervention: Carbon Dioxide Removal and Reliable Sequestration*. The National Academies Press, Washington, DC, USA.

National Research Council, 2015b: *Climate Intervention: Reflecting Sunlight to Cool Earth*. The National Academies Press, Washington, DC, USA.

Cramton, P., D.J.C. MacKay, A. Ockenfels, and S. (eds) Stoft, 2017a: *Global Carbon Pricing: the path to climate cooperation*. [Cramton, P., D.J. MacKay, A. Ockenfels, and S. Stoft, (eds.)]. MIT Press, Cambridge, MA, USA, 268pp.

Cramton, P., A. Ockenfels, and J. Tirole, 2017b: Policy Brief – Translating the Collective Climate Goal Into a Common Climate Commitment. *Rev. Environ. Econ. Policy*, **11(1)**, 165–171, doi:10.1093/reep/rew015.

Cronin, J. et al., 2021: Embedding justice in the 1.5°C transition: A transdisciplinary research agenda. *Renew. Sustain. Energy Transit.*, **1**, 100001, doi:10.1016/j.rset.2021.100001.

Cui, L. and Y. Huang, 2018: Exploring the Schemes for Green Climate Fund Financing: International Lessons. *World Dev.*, **101**, 173–187, doi:10.1016/j.worlddev.2017.08.009.

Cullen, J.M. and J.M. Allwood, 2010: The efficient use of energy: Tracing the global flow of energy from fuel to service. *Energy Policy*, **38(1)**, 75–81, doi:10.1016/j.enpol.2009.08.054.

D'Odorico, P. et al., 2018: The Global Food-Energy-Water Nexus. *Rev. Geophys.*, **56(3)**, 456–531, doi:10.1029/2017RG000591.

Dagnachew, A.G., P.L. Lucas, A.F. Hof, and D.P. van Vuuren, 2018: Trade-offs and synergies between universal electricity access and climate change mitigation in Sub-Saharan Africa. *Energy Policy*, **114**, 355–366, doi:10.1016/j.enpol.2017.12.023.

Dale, G., M.V. Mathai, and J.A. Puppim de Oliveira, 2015a: *Green growth: ideology, political economy and the alternatives*. Zed Books, London, UK. 323 pp.

Daniel, K.D., R.B. Litterman, and G. Wagner, 2019: Declining CO_2 price paths. *Proc. Natl. Acad. Sci.*, **116(42)**, 20886–20891, doi:10.1073/pnas.1817444116.

Dasgupta, P., 2008: Discounting climate change. *J. Risk Uncertain.*, **37(2–3)**, 141–169, doi:10.1007/s11166-008-9049-6.

Dasgupta, P. et al., 2015: How to measure sustainable progress. *Science*, **350(6262)**, 748, doi:10.1126/science.350.6262.748.

David Tàbara, J., J. Jäger, D. Mangalagiu, and M. Grasso, 2019: Defining transformative climate science to address high-end climate change. *Reg. Environ. Change*, **19(3)**, 807–818, doi:10.1007/s10113-018-1288-8.

de Melo, J. and M. Vijil, 2014: *Barriers to Trade in Environmental Goods and Environmental Services: How Important are They? How Much Progress at Reducing Them?* Fondazione Eni Enrico Mattei (FEEM)Milan, Italy, 59pp.

Death, C., 2014: The Green Economy in South Africa: Global Discourses and Local Politics. *Politikon*, **41(1)**, 1–22, doi:10.1080/02589346.2014.885668.

Denis-Ryan, A., C. Bataille, and F. Jotzo, 2016: Managing carbon-intensive materials in a decarbonizing world without a global price on carbon. *Clim. Policy*, **16(sup1)**, S110–S128, doi:10.1080/14693062.2016.1176008.

Di Gregorio, M. et al., 2019: Multi-level governance and power in climate change policy networks. *Glob. Environ. Change*, **54**, 64–77, doi:10.1016/j.gloenvcha.2018.10.003.

Di Muzio, T., 2015: *The 1% and The Rest of Us*. Bloomsbury Academic, London, UK, 258 pp.

Dietz, S., 2011: High impact, low probability? An empirical analysis of risk in the economics of climate change. *Clim. Change*, **108(3)**, 519–541, doi:10.1007/s10584-010-9993-4.

Dietz, S. and N. Stern, 2015: Endogenous Growth, Convexity of Damage and Climate Risk: How Nordhaus' Framework Supports Deep Cuts in Carbon Emissions. *Econ. J.*, **125(583)**, 574–620, doi:10.1111/ecoj.12188.

Dietz, S. and F. Venmans, 2019: Cumulative carbon emissions and economic policy: In search of general principles. *J. Environ. Econ. Manage.*, **96**, 108–129, doi:10.1016/j.jeem.2019.04.003.

Diffenbaugh, N.S. and M. Burke, 2019: Global warming has increased global economic inequality. *Proc. Natl. Acad. Sci.*, **116(20)**, 9808–9813, doi:10.1073/pnas.1816020116.

Dodds, T., 2019: Reporting with WhatsApp: Mobile Chat Applications' Impact on Journalistic Practices. *Digit. Journal.*, **7(6)**, 725–745, doi:10.1080/2167 0811.2019.1592693.

Dooley, K. et al., 2021: Ethical choices behind quantifications of fair contributions under the Paris Agreement. *Nat. Clim. Change*, **11(4)**, 300–305, doi:10.1038/s41558-021-01015-8.

Dorsch, M.J. and C. Flachsland, 2017: A Polycentric Approach to Global Climate Governance. *Glob. Environ. Polit.*, **17(2)**, 45–64, doi:10.1162/GLEP_a_00400.

Doukas, H. and A. Nikas, 2020: Decision support models in climate policy. *Eur. J. Oper. Res.*, **280(1)**, 1–24, doi:10.1016/j.ejor.2019.01.017.

Driscoll, D., 2021: Populism and Carbon Tax Justice: The Yellow Vest Movement in France. *Soc. Probl.*, spab036 doi:10.1093/socpro/spab036.

Drouet, L. et al., 2021: Net zero emission pathways reduce the physical and economic risks of climate change. *Nat. Clim. Change*, **11**(12), 1070–1076 doi:10.1038/s41558-021-01218-z.

Drupp, M.A., M.C. Freeman, B. Groom, and F. Nesje, 2018: Discounting disentangled. *Am. Econ. J. Econ. Policy*, **10(4)**, 109–134, doi:10.1257/pol.20160240.

Dryzek, J., D. Downes, C. Hunold, D. Schlosberg, and H.K. Hernes, 2003: *Green States and Social Movements*. Oxford University Press, Oxford, UK, 240pp.

Dubash, N., 2019: An Introduction to India's Evolving Climate Change Debate: From Diplomatic Insulation to Policy Integration. In: *India in a Warming World: Integrating Climate Change and Development* [Dubash, N.K. (ed.)]. Oxford University Press, Oxford, UK, pp. 1–28.

Dubash, N.K., 2020: Revisiting climate ambition: The case for prioritizing current action over future intent. *WIREs Clim. Change*, **11(1)**, doi:10.1002/wcc.622.

Dubash, N.K., 2021: Varieties of climate governance: the emergence and functioning of climate institutions. *Env. Polit.*, **30(sup1)**, 1–25, doi:10.1080/09644016.2021.1979775.

Earley, R. and P. Newman, 2021: Transport in the Aftermath of COVID-19: Lessons Learned and Future Directions. *J. Transp. Technol.*, **11(02)**, 109–127, doi:10.4236/jtts.2021.112007.

Egnell, R., 2010: The organised hypocrisy of international state-building. *Conflict, Secur. Dev.*, **10(4)**, 465–491, doi:10.1080/14678802.2010.50052.

Ekholm, T., 2014: Hedging the climate sensitivity risks of a temperature target. *Clim. Change*, **127(2)**, 153–167, doi:10.1007/s10584-014-1243-8.

Ekholm, T., 2018: Climatic Cost-benefit Analysis Under Uncertainty and Learning on Climate Sensitivity and Damages. *Ecol. Econ.*, **154**, 99–106, doi:10.1016/j.ecolecon.2018.07.024.

Emmerling, J. et al., 2019: The role of the discount rate for emission pathways and negative emissions. *Environ. Res. Lett.*, **14(10)**, 104008, doi:10.1088/1748-9326/ab3cc9.

Engau, C., D.C. Sprengel, and V.H. Hoffmann, 2017: Fasten your seatbelts: European airline responses to climate change turbulence. In: *Corporate Responses to Climate Change* [Sullivan, R. (ed.)]. Routledge, Abingdon, UK, pp. 279–300.

EPIC, 2019: *Is the Public Willing to Pay to Help Fix Climate Change?* Chicago, MA, USA, 12 pp.

EPT, 2020: Track funds for energy in recovery packages. *Energy Policy Tracker*,. https://www.energypolicytracker.org/ (Accessed June 1, 2020).

Ertugrul, H.M., M. Cetin, F. Seker, and E. Dogan, 2016: The impact of trade openness on global carbon dioxide emissions: Evidence from the top ten emitters among developing countries. *Ecol. Indic.*, **67**, 543–555, doi:10.1016/j.ecolind.2016.03.027.

Escobar, A., 2015: Degrowth, postdevelopment, and transitions: a preliminary conversation. *Sustainability Science*, **10(3)**, 451–462, doi:10.1007/s11625-015-0297-5.

Eshel, G., P. Stainier, A. Shepon, and A. Swaminathan, 2019: Environmentally Optimal, Nutritionally Sound, Protein and Energy Conserving Plant Based Alternatives to US Meat. *Sci. Rep.*, **9(1)**, doi:10.1038/s41598-019-46590-1.

Etchart, L., 2017: The role of indigenous peoples in combating climate change. *Palgrave Commun.*, **3(1)**, 17085, doi:10.1057/palcomms.2017.85.

Evans, D., A. McMeekin, and D. Southerton, 2012: Sustainable Consumption, Behaviour Change Policies and Theories of Practice. *Collegium*, **12**, 113–129.

Evans, G. and L. Phelan, 2016: Transition to a post-carbon society: Linking environmental justice and just transition discourses. *Energy Policy*, **99**, 329–339, doi:10.1016/j.enpol.2016.05.003.

Evans, S., and J. Gabbattiss, 2019: Article 6 Could Make or Break the Paris Agreement to Limit Climate Change. *Carbon Br.*,. https://www.carbonbrief. org/in-depth-q-and-a-how-article-6-carbon-markets-could-make-or-break-the-paris-agreement (Accessed November 29, 2019).

Evensen, D.T., 2015: Policy Decisions on Shale Gas Development ('Fracking'): The Insufficiency of Science and Necessity of Moral Thought. *Environ. Values*, **24(4)**, 511–534, doi:10.3197/096327115X14345368709989.

Fajardy, M., S. Chiquier, and N. Mac Dowell, 2018: Investigating the BECCS resource nexus: delivering sustainable negative emissions. *Energy Environ. Science*, **11(12)**, 3408–3430, doi:10.1039/C8EE01676C.

Falkner, R., 2016: The Paris Agreement and the new logic of international climate politics. *Int. Aff.*, **92(5)**, 1107–1125, doi:10.1111/1468-2346.12708.

Fankhauser, S. et al., 2013: Who will win the green race? In search of environmental competitiveness and innovation. *Glob. Environ. Change*, **23(5)**, 902–913, doi:10.1016/j.gloenvcha.2013.05.007.

Fankhauser, S. and T.K.J. McDermott, 2016: Climate-resilient development: an introduction. In: *The Economics of Climate-Resilient Development* [Fankhauser, S. and T.K.J. McDermott (eds.)]. Edward Elgar Publishing, Cheltenham, UK, pp 1–12.

Farmer, J.D., C. Hepburn, P. Mealy, and A. Teytelboym, 2015: A Third Wave in the Economics of Climate Change. *Environ. Resour. Econ.*, **62(2)**, 329–357, doi:10.1007/s10640-015-9965-2.

Farmer, J.D. et al., 2019: Sensitive intervention points in the post-carbon transition. *Science*, **364(6436)**, 132–134, doi:10.1126/science.aaw7287.

Farooquee, A.A. and G. Shrimali, 2016: Making renewable energy competitive in India: Reducing financing costs via a government-sponsored hedging facility. *Energy Policy*, **95**, 518–528, doi:10.1016/j.enpol.2016.02.005.

Fatemi, M.N., S.A. Okyere, S.K. Diko, and M. Kita, 2020: Multi-Level Climate Governance in Bangladesh via Climate Change Mainstreaming: Lessons for Local Climate Action in Dhaka City. *Urban Science*, **4(2)**, 24, doi:10.3390/urbansci4020024.

Federico, G. and A. Tena-Junguito, 2017: A tale of two globalizations: gains from trade and openness 1800–2010. *Rev. World Econ.*, **153(3)**, 601–626, doi:10.1007/s10290-017-0279-z.

Feola, G., 2015: Societal transformation in response to global environmental change: A review of emerging concepts. *Ambio*, **44(5)**, 376–390, doi:10.1007/s13280-014-0582-z.

Ferguson, D.B., J. Rice, and C.A. Woodhouse, 2014: *Linking Environmental Research and Practice: Lessons From The Integration of Climate Science and Water Management in the Western United States,* Climate Assessment for the Southwest, Tucson AZ, 21pp. https://climas.arizona.edu/publication/report/linking-environmental-research-and-practice.

Fink, L., 2020: A Fundamental Reshaping of Finance. *BlackRock Letter to CEOs*,. https://www.blackrock.com/us/individual/larry-fink-ceo-letter (Accessed August 3, 2021).

Finus, M., and D.T.G. Rübbelke, 2008: *Coalition Formation and the Ancillary Benefits of Climate Policy*. Fondazione Eni Enrico Mattei, Milan, Italy, 34 pp, doi: 10.2139/ssrn.1259699.

Fisher, D.R. and P. Leifeld, 2019: The polycentricity of climate policy blockage. *Clim. Change*, **155(4)**, 469–487, doi:10.1007/s10584-019-02481-y.

Fisher, D.R. et al., 2019: The science of contemporary street protest: New efforts in the United States. *Sci. Adv.*, **5(10)**, 15pp, doi:10.1126/sciadv.aaw5461.

Fitzgerald, L.M., I. Braunger, and H. Brauers, 2019: *Destabilisation of Sustainable Energy Transformations: Analysing Natural Gas Lock-in in the Case of Germany*. STEPS Working Paper, no. 106, Brighton, UK, pp 34.

Flexer, V., C.F. Baspineiro, and C.I. Galli, 2018: Lithium recovery from brines: A vital raw material for green energies with a potential environmental impact in its mining and processing. *Sci. Total Environ.*, **639**, 1188–1204, doi:10.1016/j.scitotenv.2018.05.223.

Florin, M.-V., P. Rouse, A.-M. Hubert, M. Honegger, and J. Reynolds, 2020: *International governance issues on climate engineering Information for policymakers*. EPFL International Risk Governance Center, Lausanne, Switzerland, pp 152. https://infoscience.epfl.ch/record/277726.

Folke, C. et al., 2010: Resilience Thinking: Integrating Resilience, Adaptability and Transformability. *Ecol. Soc.*, **15(4)**, 20.

Forster, P.M. et al., 2020: Current and future global climate impacts resulting from COVID-19. *Nat. Clim. Change*, **10(10)**, 913–919, doi:10.1038/s41558-020-0883-0.

Fotis, P. and M. Polemis, 2018: Sustainable development, environmental policy and renewable energy use: A dynamic panel data approach. *Sustainable Dev.*, **26(6)**, 726–740, doi:10.1002/sd.1742.

Frame, D.J. et al., 2019: Emissions and emergence: A new index comparing relative contributions to climate change with relative climatic consequences. *Environ. Res. Lett.*, **14(8)**, 84009, doi:10.1088/1748-9326/ab27fc.

Francis, 2015: *Laudato Si' of the Holy Father Francis on Care for Our Common Home*. Vatican Press, Rome, Italy, 184 pp.

Freeman, C., and C.L.B.-F. Perez, 1988: Structural crises of adjustment: business cycles. In: *Technical Change and Economic Theory* [Dosi, G., C. Freeman, R. Nelson, G. Silverberg, and L. Soete (eds.)]. Pinter Publishers, London, UK, pp. 38–66.

Freeman, C., and F. Louçã, 2002: *As Time Goes By*. Oxford University Press, Oxford, UK, 426 pp.

Freeman, G.M., T.E. Drennen, and A.D. White, 2017: Can parked cars and carbon taxes create a profit? The economics of vehicle-to-grid energy storage for peak reduction. *Energy Policy*, **106**, 183–190, doi:10.1016/j.enpol.2017.03.052.

Fresco, L., 2015: *Hamburgers in Paradise: The Stories behind the Food We Eat*. Princeton University Press, Princeton, NJ, USA, 560 pp.

Fuhr, H., T. Hickmann, and K. Kern, 2018: The role of cities in multi-level climate governance: local climate policies and the 1.5°C target. *Curr. Opin. Environ. Sustainability*, **30**, 1–6, doi: https://doi.org/10.1016/j.cosust.2017.10.006.

Fuhrman, J. et al., 2020: Food–energy–water implications of negative emissions technologies in a +1.5 °C future. *Nat. Clim. Change*, **10(10)**, 920–927, doi:10.1038/s41558-020-0876-z.

Fujimori, S. et al., 2016: Will international emissions trading help achieve the objectives of the Paris Agreement? *Environ. Res. Lett.*, **11(10)**, doi:10.1088/1748-9326/11/10/104001.

Fuso Nerini, F. et al., 2018: Mapping synergies and trade-offs between energy and the Sustainable Development Goals. *Nat. Energy*, **3(1)**, 10–15, doi:10.1038/s41560-017-0036-5.

Fuss, S. et al., 2018: Negative emissions – Part 2: Costs, potentials and side effects. *Environ. Res. Lett.*, **13(6)**, 063002, doi:10.1088/1748-9326/AABF9F.

Gajevic Sayegh, A., 2017: Climate justice after Paris: a normative framework. *J. Glob. Ethics*, **13(3)**, 344–365, doi:10.1080/17449626.2018.1425217.

Gampfer, R., 2014: Do individuals care about fairness in burden sharing for climate change mitigation? Evidence from a lab experiment. *Clim. Change*, **124(1–2)**, 65–77, doi:10.1007/s10584-014-1091-6.

Gardiner, S.M., 2006: A perfect moral storm: Climate change, intergenerational ethics and the problem of moral corruption. *Environ. Values*, **15(3)**, 397–413, doi:10.3197/096327106778226293.

Gardiner, S.M., 2011: *A Perfect Moral Storm: The Ethical Tragedy of Climate Change*. Oxford University Press, Oxford, UK, 512 pp.

Garrett, T.J., M. Grasselli, and S. Keen, 2020: Past world economic production constrains current energy demands: Persistent scaling with implications for economic growth and climate change mitigation. *PLoS One*, **15(8)**, e0237672, doi:10.1371/journal.pone.0237672.

Gawel, E. and C. Kuhlicke, 2017: Efficiency–Equity–Trade–Off as a Challenge for Shaping Urban Transformations. In: *Urban Transformations* [Kabisch, S. et al. (eds.).]. Springer, Cambridge, UK pp. 45–60.

GCF, 2020: Green Climate Fund Website. *Green Climate Fund*. https://www.greenclimate.fund/about (Accessed October 1, 2020).

Geden, O., 2016: The Paris Agreement and the inherent inconsistency of climate policymaking. *WIREs Clim. Change*, **7(6)**, 790–797, doi:10.1002/wcc.427.

Geels, B.F.W., B. Sovacool, T. Schwanen, and S. Sorrell, 2017: Accelerating innovation is as important as climate policy. *Science*, **357(6357)**, 1242–1244.

Geels, F. and R. Raven, 2006: Non-linearity and Expectations in Niche-Development Trajectories: Ups and Downs in Dutch Biogas Development (1973–2003). *Technol. Anal. Strateg. Manag.*, **18(3–4)**, 375–392, doi:10.1080/09537320600777143.

Geels, F.W., 2002: Technological transitions as evolutionary reconfiguration processes: a multi-level perspective and a case-study. *Res. Policy*, **31(8–9)**, 1257–1274, doi:10.1016/S0048-7333(02)00062-8.

Geels, F.W., 2010: Ontologies, socio-technical transitions (to sustainability), and the multi-level perspective. *Res. Policy*, **39(4)**, 495–510, doi:10.1016/j.respol.2010.01.022.

Geels, F.W., 2014: Regime Resistance against Low-Carbon Transitions: Introducing Politics and Power into the Multi-Level Perspective. *Theory, Cult. Soc.*, **31(5)**, 21–40, doi:10.1177/0263276414531627.

Geels, F.W., F. Berkhout, and D.P. van Vuuren, 2016: Bridging analytical approaches for low-carbon transitions. *Nat. Clim. Change*, **6(6)**, 576–583, doi:10.1038/nclimate2980.

Georgeson, L., M. Maslin, and M. Poessinouw, 2017: The global green economy: a review of concepts, definitions, measurement methodologies and their interactions. *Geo Geogr. Environ.*, **4(1)**, e00036, doi:10.1002/geo2.36.

GESAMP, 2019: *High Level Review of a Wide Range of Proposed Marine Geoengineering Techniques* [Boyd, P.W. and C.M.G. Vivian (eds.)]. International Maritime Organisation, London, UK, pp 145.

Gheorghe H., P. and F.C. Ciurlau, 2016: Can environmental sustainability be attained by incorporating nature within the capitalist economy? *Econ. Manag. Financ. Mark.*, **11(4)**.

Gidden, M.J. et al., 2019: Global emissions pathways under different socioeconomic scenarios for use in CMIP6: a dataset of harmonized emissions trajectories through the end of the century. *Geosci. Model Dev.*, **12(4)**, 1443–1475, doi:10.5194/gmd-12-1443-2019.

Gilabert, P. and H. Lawford-Smith, 2012: Political Feasibility: A Conceptual Exploration. *Polit. Stud.*, **60(4)**, 809–825, doi:10.1111/j.1467-9248.2011.00936.x.

Gillan, J.M., 2017: *Dynamic Pricing, Attention, and Automation: Evidence from a Field Experiment in Electricity Consumption*. Berkeley, CA, USA, 57pp.

Gillingham, K. and J.H. Stock, 2018: The Cost of Reducing Greenhouse Gas Emissions. *J. Econ. Perspect.*, **32(4)**, 53–72, doi:10.1257/jep.32.4.53.

Glanemann, N., S.N. Willner, and A. Levermann, 2020: Paris Climate Agreement passes the cost-benefit test. *Nat. Commun.*, **11(1)**, 110, doi:10.1038/s41467-019-13961-1.

Goddard, G. and M.A. Farrelly, 2018: Just transition management: Balancing just outcomes with just processes in Australian renewable energy transitions. *Appl. Energy*, **225**, 110–123, doi:10.1016/j.apenergy.2018.05.025.

Goldthau, A. and N. Sitter, 2015: *A Liberal Actor in a Realist World*. Oxford University Press, Oxford, UK, 180pp.

Gollier, C., 2021: The cost-efficiency carbon pricing puzzle. *CEPR Discuss. Pap. No. DP15919*, pp. 1–33.

Golosov, M., J. Hassler, P. Krusell, and A. Tsyvinski, 2014: Optimal Taxes on Fossil Fuel in General Equilibrium. *Econometrica*, **82(1)**, 41–88, doi:10.3982/ECTA10217.

Gomez-Echeverri, L., 2018a: Climate and development: enhancing impact through stronger linkages in the implementation of the Paris Agreement

and the Sustainable Development Goals (SDGs). *Philos. Trans. R. Soc. A Math. Phys. Eng. Sci.*, **376(2119)**, doi:10.1098/rsta.2016.0444.

Gomez-Echeverri, L., 2018b: Climate and development: enhancing impact through stronger linkages in the implementation of the Paris Agreement and the Sustainable Development Goals (SDGs). *Philos. Trans. R. Soc. A Math. Phys. Eng. Sci.*, **376(2119)**, 20160444, doi:10.1098/rsta.2016.0444.

Gonella, F. et al., 2019: Is technology optimism justified? A discussion towards a comprehensive narrative. *J. Clean. Prod.*, **223**, 456–465, doi:10.1016/J.JCLEPRO.2019.03.126.

Gordon, D.J., 2018: Global urban climate governance in three and a half parts: Experimentation, coordination, integration (and contestation). *WIREs Clim. Change*, **9(6)**, e546, doi:10.1002/wcc.546.

Gough, I., 2017: Recomposing consumption: defining necessities for sustainable and equitable well-being. *Philos. Trans. R. Soc. A Math. Phys. Eng. Sci.*, **375(2095)**, 20160379, doi:10.1098/rsta.2016.0379.

Gray, P. and T. Irwin, 2003: *Exchange Rate Risk Allocating Exchange Rate Risk in Private Infrastructure Projects*. Note No. 266. Washington, DC, USA: The World Bank, https://openknowledge.worldbank.org/handle/10986/11286.

Green, F., 2018: Anti-fossil fuel norms. *Clim. Change*, **150(1)**, 103–116, doi:10.1007/s10584-017-2134-6.

Green, F. and A. Gambhir, 2020: Transitional assistance policies for just, equitable and smooth low-carbon transitions: who, what and how? *Clim. Policy*, **20(8)**, 902–921, doi:10.1080/14693062.2019.1657379.

Grin, J., J. Rotmans, and J. Schot, 2010: *Transitions to Sustainable Development: New Directions in the Study of Long Term Transformative Change*. Routledge, Abingdon, UK, 419pp.

Groom, B. and C. Hepburn, 2017: Looking back at social discounting policy: The influence of papers, presentations, political preconditions, and personalities. *Rev. Environ. Econ. Policy*, **11(2)**, 336–356, doi:10.1093/reep/rex015.

Grubb, M., J.-C. Hourcade, and K. Neuhoff, 2014: *Planetary Economics: Energy, climate change and the three domains of sustainable development*. 1st ed. Routledge, Abingdon, UK, 520 pp.

Grubb, M., J.-C. Hourcade, and K. Neuhoff, 2015: The Three Domains structure of energy-climate transitions. *Technol. Forecast. Soc. Change*, **98**, 290–302, doi:10.1016/j.techfore.2015.05.009.

Grubb, M. et al., 2021a: Induced innovation in energy technologies and systems: A review of evidence and potential implications for CO_2 mitigation. *Environ. Res. Lett.*, **16(4)**, 43007, doi:10.1088/1748-9326/abde07.

Grubb, M., C. Wieners, and P. Yang, 2021b: Modelling Myths: on DICE and dynamic realism in integrated assessment models of climate change mitigation. *Wiley Interdiscip. Rev. Clim. Change*, **12(3)**, doi:https://doi.org/10.1002/wcc.698.

Gudka, S., N. Armstrong, and P. Newman, 2020: Cutting diesel exhaust could lessen Covid spread in cities,. *Sci. Am.*,. https://www.scientificamerican.com/article/cutting-diesel-exhaust-could-lessen-covid-spread-in-cities/ (Accessed January 1, 2021).

Guilbeault, D., J. Becker, and D. Centola, 2018: Social learning and partisan bias in the interpretation of climate trends. *Proc. Natl. Acad. Sci.*, **115(39)**, 9714–9719, doi:https://doi.org/10.1073/pnas.1722664115.

Güney, T., 2017: Governance and sustainable development: How effective is governance? *J. Int. Trade Econ. Dev.*, **26(3)**, 316–335, doi:10.1080/09638199.2016.1249391.

Gunster, S., 2017: This changes everything: capitalism vs the climate. *Environ. Commun.*, **11(1)**, 136–138, doi:10.1080/17524032.2016.1196534.

Gupta, J., 2016: The Paris Climate Change Agreement: China and India. *Clim. Law*, **6(1–2)**, 171–181, doi:10.1163/18786561-00601012.

Gupta, S.K., and U.S. Racherla, 2018: Interdependence among dimensions of sustainability: Evidence from the Indian leather industry. *Manag. Environ. Qual.*, **29(3)**, 406–415, doi:10.1108/MEQ-06-2017-0051.

Guzman, M., J.A. Ocampo, and J.E. Stiglitz, 2018: Real exchange rate policies for economic development. *World Dev.*, **110**, 51–62, doi:10.1016/j.worlddev.2018.05.017.

Haberl, H. et al., 2019: Contributions of sociometabolic research to sustainability science. *Nat. Sustainability*, **2(3)**, 173–184, doi:10.1038/s41893-019-0225-2.

Haberl, H. et al., 2020: A systematic review of the evidence on decoupling of GDP, resource use and GHG emissions, part II: synthesizing the insights. *Environ. Res. Lett.*, **15(6)**, 065003, doi:10.1088/1748-9326/ab842a.

Hackmann, B., 2016: Regime Learning in Global Environmental Governance. *Environ. Values*, **25(6)**, 663–686, doi:10.3197/096327116X14736981715625.

Hagedorn, G. et al., 2019: Concerns of young protesters are justified. *Science*, **364(6436)**, 139–140, doi:10.1126/science.aax3807.

Hall, S., T.J. Foxon, and R. Bolton, 2017: Investing in low-carbon transitions: energy finance as an adaptive market. *Clim. Policy*, **17(3)**, 280–298, doi:10.1080/14693062.2015.1094731.

Hamilton, L.C., 2011: Education, politics and opinions about climate change evidence for interaction effects. *Clim. Change*, **104(2)**, 231–242, doi:10.1007/s10584-010-9957-8.

Hannis, M., 2016: *Freedom and environment: Autonomy, human flourishing and the political philosophy of sustainability*. Taylor & Francis, Abingdon, UK, 74 pp.

Hänsel, M.C. et al., 2020: Climate economics support for the UN climate targets. *Nat. Clim. Change*, **10(8)**, 781–789, doi:10.1038/s41558-020-0833-x.

Hao, L.-N., M. Umar, Z. Khan, and W. Ali, 2021: Green growth and low carbon emission in G7 countries: How critical the network of environmental taxes, renewable energy and human capital is? *Sci. Total Environ.*, **752**, 141853, doi:10.1016/j.scitotenv.2020.141853.

Hargreaves, S.M., A. Raposo, A. Saraiva, and R.P. Zandonadi, 2021: Vegetarian Diet: An Overview through the Perspective of Quality of Life Domains. *Int. J. Environ. Res. Public Health*, **18(8)**, 4067, doi:10.3390/ijerph18084067.

Harrison, K., 2018: The Challenge of Transition in Liberal Market Economies: The United States and Canada. In: *National Pathways to Low Carbon Emission Economies* [Hübner, K. (ed.)]. Routledge, Abingdon, UK, pp 45–66.

Harstad, B., 2007: Harmonization and Side Payments in Political Cooperation. *Am. Econ. Rev.*, **97(3)**, 871–889, doi:10.1257/AER.97.3.871.

Hartzell-Nichols, L., 2014: The Price of Precaution and the Ethics of Risk. *Ethics, Policy & Environment*, **17(1)**, 116–118, doi:10.1080/21550085.2014.885183.

Hasegawa, T. et al., 2018: Risk of increased food insecurity under stringent global climate change mitigation policy. *Nat. Clim. Change*, **8(8)**, 699–703, doi:10.1038/s41558-018-0230-x.

Havlik, P. et al., 2014: Climate change mitigation through livestock system transitions. *Proc. Natl. Acad. Sci.*, **111(10)**, 3709–3714, doi:10.1073/pnas.1308044111.

Healy, N., and J. Barry, 2017: Politicizing energy justice and energy system transitions: Fossil fuel divestment and a 'just transition.' *Energy Policy*, **108**, 451–459, doi:10.1016/j.enpol.2017.06.014.

Heffron, R.J., and D. McCauley, 2018: What is the 'Just Transition'? *Geoforum*, **88**, 74–77, doi:10.1016/j.geoforum.2017.11.016.

Heijdra, B.J., J.P. Kooiman, and J.E. Ligthart, 2006: Environmental quality, the macroeconomy, and intergenerational distribution. *Resour. Energy Econ.*, **28(1)**, 74–104, doi:10.1016/j.reseneeco.2005.05.001.

Heinrichs, H., P. Jochem, and W. Fichtner, 2014: Including road transport in the EU ETS (European Emissions Trading System): A model-based analysis of the German electricity and transport sector. *Energy*, **69**, 708–720, doi:10.1016/j.energy.2014.03.061.

Held, H., 2019: Cost Risk Analysis: Dynamically Consistent Decision-Making under Climate Targets. *Environ. Resour. Econ.*, **72(1)**, 247–261, doi:10.1007/s10640-018-0288-y.

Henly-Shepard, S., Z. Zommers, E. Levine, and D. Abrahams, 2018: Climate-Resilient Development in Fragile Contexts. In: *Resilience: The science of adaptation to climate change* [Zommers, Z. and K. Alverson (eds.)]. Elsevier, Amsterdam, Netherlands, pp. 279–290.

Hepburn, C., B. O'Callaghan, N. Stern, J. Stiglitz, and D. Zenghelis, 2020: Will COVID-19 fiscal recovery packages accelerate or retard progress on climate change? *Oxford Rev. Econ. Policy*, **36(20)**, doi:10.1093/oxrep/graa015.

Herrick, C.N., 2018: Self-identity and sense of place: Some thoughts regarding climate change adaptation policy formulation. *Environ. Values*, **27(1)**, 81–102, doi:10.3197/096327118X15144698637531.

Heyward, J.C. and D. Roser, 2016: *Climate Justice in a Non-Ideal World*. Oxford University Press, Oxford, UK, 323 pp.

Hickel, J. and G. Kallis, 2020: Is Green Growth Possible? *New Polit. Econ.*, **25(4)**, 469–486, doi:10.1080/13563467.2019.1598964.

Hidalgo, C.A. and R. Hausmann, 2009: The building blocks of economic complexity. *Proc. Natl. Acad. Sci.*, **106(26)**, 10570–10575.

Hilaire, J. et al., 2019: Negative emissions and international climate goals – learning from and about mitigation scenarios. *Clim. Change*, **157(2)**, 189–219, doi:10.1007/s10584-019-02516-4.

Hildén, M., A. Jordan, and D. Huitema, 2017: Special issue on experimentation for climate change solutions editorial: The search for climate change and sustainability solutions – The promise and the pitfalls of experimentation. *J. Clean. Prod.*, **169**, 1–7, doi:https://doi.org/10.1016/j.jclepro.2017.09.019.

Himes-Cornell, A., L. Pendleton, and P. Atiyah, 2018: Valuing ecosystem services from blue forests: A systematic review of the valuation of salt marshes, sea grass beds and mangrove forests. *Ecosyst. Serv.*, **30**, 36–48, doi:10.1016/j.ecoser.2018.01.006.

Hochstetler, K., 2020: *Political Economies of Energy Transition*. Cambridge University Press, Cambridge, UK, 278pp.

Hoegh-Guldberg, O. et al., 2019: The human imperative of stabilizing global climate change at 1.5°C. *Science*, **365(6459)**, doi:10.1126/science.aaw6974.

Hoeing, A. et al., 2015: How nature is used and valued by villagers in two villages in Uut Murung. *J. Indones. Nat. Hist.*, **3(1)**, 8–18.

Hoel, M.O., S.A.C. Kittelsen, and S. Kverndokk, 2019: Correcting the Climate Externality: Pareto Improvements Across Generations and Regions. *Environ. Resour. Econ.*, **74(1)**, 449–472, doi:10.1007/s10640-019-00325-y.

Hof, A.F. et al., 2017: Global and regional abatement costs of Nationally Determined Contributions (NDCs) and of enhanced action to levels well below 2°C and 1.5°C. *Environ. Sci. Policy*, **71**, 30–40, doi:10.1016/J.ENVSCI.2017.02.008.

Hof, A.F., D.P. van Vuuren, F. Berkhout, and F.W. Geels, 2020: Understanding transition pathways by bridging modelling, transition and practice-based studies: Editorial introduction to the special issue. *Technol. Forecast. Soc. Change*, **151**, 119665, doi:10.1016/j.techfore.2019.05.023.

Hoffmann, M.J., 2011: *Climate Governance at the Crossroads*. Oxford University Press, Oxford, UK, 240pp.

Holzer, K., 2014: *Carbon-related Border Adjustment and WTO Law*. 1st ed. World Trade Institute, Bern, Switzerland, 352 pp.

Homma, T., G. K, J. Oda, and K. Akimoto, 2019: Analysis of International Competitiveness under the Current Climate and Energy Policies and the Nationally Determined Contributions. *J. Japan Soc. Energy Resour.*, **41(5)**.

Hourcade, J.-C., D. Dasgupta, and F. Ghersi, 2021a: Accelerating the speed and scale of climate finance in the post-pandemic context. *Clim. Policy*, **21**(10), 1383–1397, doi:10.1080/14693062.2021.1977599.

Hourcade, J.C. et al., 2021b: *Scaling up climate finance in the context of Covid-19*. Green Climate Fund, London, UK, 141pp.

Howarth, C. et al., 2020: Building a Social Mandate for Climate Action: Lessons from COVID-19. *Environ. Resour. Econ.*, **76(4)**, 1107–1115, doi:10.1007/s10640-020-00446-9.

Howell, R. and S. Allen, 2017: People and Planet: Values, Motivations and Formative Influences of Individuals Acting to Mitigate Climate Change. *Environ. Values*, **26(2)**, 131–155, doi:10.3197/096327117X14847335385436.

Hsu, A., O. Widerberg, M. Roelfsema, Lütkehermöller K, and F. Bakhtiari, 2018: *Bridging the emissions gap – The role of non-state and subnational actors. Pre-release version of a chapter of the forthcoming UN Environment*

Emissions Gap Report. Nairobi, Kenya, 27pp. http://www.un.org/Depts/Cartographic/english/htmain. (Accessed August 19, 2021).

Huber, B.R., 2012: How Did RGGI Do It? Political Economy and Emissions Auctions. *Ecology Law Quarterly*, **59**, doi:10.2139/ssrn.2018329.

Hufty, M., 2012: *Investigating Policy Processes: The Governance Analytical Framework (GAF)*. Graduate Institute of International and Development Studies (IHEID), Geneva, Switzerland, 22pp. https://papers.ssrn.com/sol3/papers.cfm?abstract_id=2019005 (Accessed September 15, 2020).

IATA, 2020: *Air Cargo Market Analysis: Robust end to 2020 for air cargo*. International Air Transport Association, Montreal, Canada, 4 pp. https://www.iata.org/en/iata-repository/publications/economic-reports/air-freight-monthly-analysis---december-2020/ (Accessed January 20, 2021).

IAWG, 2016: *Technical Update of the Social Cost of Carbon for Regulatory Impact Analysis*. Environmental Protection Agency, Washington, DC, USA. https://19january2017snapshot.epa.gov/climatechange/social-cost-carbon_.html (Accessed January 10, 2021).

Ibikunle, G. and C. Okereke, 2014: Governing carbon through the European Union Emissions Trading System: Opportunities, pitfalls and future prospects. In: *Carbon Governance, Climate Change and Business Transformation* [Bumpus, A., J. Tansey, B. Henriquez, and C. Okereke (eds.)]. Routledge, London, UK, pp. 143–157.

IEA, 2019a: *Global Energy & CO_2 Status Report The latest trends in energy and emissions in 2018*. Paris, France. 29pp https://iea.blob.core.windows.net/assets/23f9eb39-7493-4722-aced-61433cbffe10/Global_Energy_and_CO2_Status_Report_2018.pdf (Accessed April 15, 2021).

IEA, 2019b: *World Energy Outlook 2019*. Paris, France. 810pp https://www.iea.org/reports/world-energy-outlook-2019 (Accessed April 15, 2021).

IEA, 2020a: *World Energy Outlook 2020*. Paris, France, 464pp https://www.iea.org/reports/world-energy-outlook-2020 (Accessed April 15, 2021).

IEA, 2020b: *Sustainable recovery: World Energy Outlook Special Report*. Paris, France, pp 174. https://www.iea.org/reports/sustainable-recovery (Accessed April 15, 2021).

IEA, 2021: *Global Energy Review 2021*. Paris, France 34pp https://www.iea.org/reports/global-energy-review-2021 (Accessed May 15, 2021).

IFEES, 2015: *Islamic Declaration on Global Climate Change*. Istanbul, Turkey, 8pp. https://www.ifees.org.uk/about/islamic-declaration-on-global-climate-change/ (Accessed September 20, 2021).

IISD, 2015: UNFCCC's NAZCA Portal Features Over 500 City Actions. *SGD Knowl. Hub*,. http://sdg.iisd.org/news/unfcccs-nazca-portal-features-over-500-city-actions/ (Accessed January 22, 2022).

IMF, 2020: *World Economic Outlook – A Long and Difficult Ascent*. Washington, DC, USA, 204pp, https://www.imf.org/en/Publications/WEO/Issues/2020/09/30/world-economic-outlook-october-2020 (Accessed April 16, 2021).

IMF, 2021: Gross debt position % of GDP. *IMF Datamapper*. https://www.imf.org/external/datamapper/G_XWDG_G01_GDP_PT@FM/ADVEC/FM_EMG/FM_LIDC (Accessed June 13, 2021).

IPBES, 2019: *The global assessment report on Biodiversity and Ecosystem Services* [Díaz, S. et al. (eds.)]. IPBES secretariat, Bonn, Germany, 1148 pp.

IPCC, 1995: *Climate Change 1995: Economic and Social Dimensions of Climate Change. Contribution of Working Group III to the Second Assessment Report of the Intergovernmental Panel on Climate Change* [Bruce, J., H. Lee, and E. Haites (eds.)]. Cambridge University Press, Cambridge UK, 1076pp.

IPCC, 2007: *Climate Change 2007: Mitigation of Climate Change: Contribution of Working Group III to the Fourth Assessment Report of the Intergovernmental Panel on Climate Change* [Metz, B., O.R. Davidson, P.R. Bosch, R. Dave, and L.A. Meyer (eds.)]. Cambridge University Press, Cambridge, UK, 863pp.

IPCC, 2011a: *IPCC Special Report on Renewable Energy Sources and Climate Change Mitigation* [O. Edenhofer, R. Pichs-Madruga, Y. Sokona, K. Seyboth, P. Matschoss, S. Kadner, T. Zwickel, P. Eickemeier, G. Hansen, S. Schlömer, C. von Stechow (eds.)]. Cambridge University Press, Cambridge, UK and New York, NY, USA, 1088 pp.

IPCC, 2011b: Summary for Policymakers. In: *IPCC Special Report on Renewable Energy Sources and Climate Change Mitigation* [O. Edenhofer, R. Pichs-Madruga, Y. Sokona, K. Seyboth, P. Matschoss, S. Kadner, T. Zwickel, P. Eickemeier, G. Hansen, S. Schlömer, C. von Stechow (eds.)]. Cambridge University Press, Cambridge, UK and New York, NY, USA, pp. 3–27.

IPCC, 2013: *Climate Change 2013: The Physical Science Basis. Contribution of Working Group I to the Fifth Assessment Report of the Intergovernmental Panel on Climate Change* [Stocker, T.F., D. Qin, G.-K. Plattner, M. Tignor, S.K. Allen, J. Boschung, A. Nauels, Y. Xia, V. Bex and P.M. Midgley (eds.)]. Cambridge University Press, Cambridge, UK and New York, NY, USA, 1535 pp.

IPCC, 2014a: *Climate Change 2014: Mitigation of Climate Change. Contribution of Working Group III to the Fifth Assessment Report of the Intergovernmental Panel on Climate Change* [Edenhofer, O., R. Pichs-Madruga, Y. Sokona, E. Farahani, S. Kadner, K., T.Z. Seyboth, A. Adler, I. Baum, S. Brunner, P. Eickemeier, B. Kriemann, J. Savolainen, S. Schlömer, C. von Stechow, J.C., and Minx (eds.)]. Cambridge University Press, Cambridge, UK and New York, NY, USA, 151 pp.

IPCC, 2014b: Summary for Policymakers. In: *Climate Change 2014: Mitigation of Climate Change. Contribution of Working Group III to the Fifth Assessment Report of the Intergovernmental Panel on Climate Change* [Edenhofer, O., R. Pichs-Madruga, Y. Sokona, E. Farahani, S. Kadner, K., T.Z. Seyboth, A. Adler, I. Baum, S. Brunner, P. Eickemeier, B. Kriemann, J. Savolainen, S. Schlömer, C. von Stechow, J.C., and Minx (eds.)]. Cambridge University Press, Cambridge, UK and New York, NY, USA, 1–30.

IPCC, 2018a: Summary for Policymakers. In: *Global Warming of 1.5°C. An IPCC Special Report on the impacts of global warming of 1.5°C above pre-industrial levels and related global greenhouse gas emission pathways, in the context of strengthening the global response to the threat of climate change, sustainable development, and efforts to eradicate poverty* [Masson-Delmotte, V., P. Zhai, H.-O. Pörtner, D. Roberts, J. Skea, P.R. Shukla, A. Pirani, W. Moufouma-Okia, C. Péan, R. Pidcock, S. Connors, J.B.R. Matthews, Y. Chen, X. Zhou, M.I. Gomis, E. Lonnoy, T. Maycock, M. Tignor, and T. Waterfield (eds.)]. Cambridge University Press, Cambridge, UK, and New York, NY, USA.

IPCC, 2018b: *Global Warming of 1.5°C. An IPCC Special Report on the impacts of global warming of 1.5°C above pre-industrial levels and related global greenhouse gas emission pathways, in the context of strengthening the global response to the threat of climate change, sustainable development, and efforts to eradicate poverty* [Masson-Delmotte, V., P. Zhai, H.-O. Pörtner, D. Roberts, J. Skea, P.R. Shukla, A. Pirani, W. Moufouma-Okia, C. Péan, R. Pidcock, S. Connors, J.B.R. Matthews, Y. Chen, X. Zhou, M.I. Gomis, E. Lonnoy, T. Maycock, M. Tignor, and T. Waterfield (eds.)]. Cambridge University Press, Cambridge, UK, and New York, NY, USA.

IPCC, 2019a: Summary for Policymakers. In: *An IPCC Special Report on climate change, desertification, land degradation, sustainable land management, food security, and greenhouse gas fluxes in terrestrial ecosystems* [P.R. Shukla, J. Skea, E. Calvo Buendia, V. Masson-Delmotte, H.-O. Pörtner, D.C. Roberts, P. Zhai, R. Slade, S. Connors, R. van Diemen, M. Ferrat, E. Haughey, S. Luz, S. Neogi, M. Pathak, J. Petzold, J. Portugal Pereira, P. Vyas, E. Huntley, K. Kissick, M. Belkacemi, J. Malley (ed.)]. Cambridge University Press, Cambridge, UK, and New York, NY, USA. 43 pp.

IPCC, 2019b: *IPCC Special Report on the Ocean and Cryosphere in a Changing Climate* [H.-O. Pörtner, D.C. Roberts, V. Masson-Delmotte, P. Zhai, M. Tignor, E. Poloczanska, K. Mintenbeck, A. Alegría, M. Nicolai, A. Okem, J. Petzold, B. Rama, N.M. Weyer (eds.)]. Cambridge University Press, Cambridge, UK, and New York, NY, USA.

IPCC, 2019c: *Climate Change and Land: an IPCC Special Report on climate change, desertification, land degradation, sustainable land management, food security, and greenhouse gas fluxes in terrestrial ecosystems* [P.R. Shukla, J. Skea, E. Calvo Buendia, V. Masson-Delmotte, H.-O. Pörtner, D. C. Roberts, P. Zhai, R. Slade, S. Connors, R. van Diemen, M. Ferrat, E. Haughey, S. Luz, S. Neogi, M. Pathak, J. Petzold, J. Portugal Pereira,

P. Vyas, E. Huntley, K. Kissick, M. Belkacemi, J. Malley (eds.)]. Cambridge University Press, Cambridge, UK, and New York, NY, USA.

IRENA, 2020a: *Renewable Power Generation Costs in 2019*. Masdar City, UAE, 144pp https://www.irena.org/publications/2020/Jun/Renewable-Power-Costs-in-2019 (Accessed September 15, 2021).

IRENA, 2020b: *Renewable Electricity Capacity and Generation Statistics 2020*. Masdar City, UAE, https://www.irena.org/publications/2020/Jul/Renewable-energy-statistics-2020 (Accsed September 15 2021).

Islam, M., K. Kanemoto, and S. Managi, 2016: Impact of Trade Openness and Sector Trade on Embodied Greenhouse Gases Emissions and Air Pollutants. *J. Ind. Ecol.*, **20(3)**, 494–505, doi:10.1111/jiec.12455.

Ismer, R., M. Haussner, K. Neuhoff, and W.W. Acworth, 2016: Inclusion of Consumption into Emissions Trading Systems: Legal Design and Practical Administration. *SSRN Electron. J.*, doi:10.2139/ssrn.2784169.

IWG, 2021: *Technical Support Document: Social Cost of Carbon, Methane, and Nitrous Oxide Interim Estimates under Executive Order 13990*. Washington, DC, USA, 48pp. https://www.whitehouse.gov/wp-content/uploads/2021/02/TechnicalSupportDocument_SocialCostofCarbonMethaneNitrousOxide.pdf (Accessed September 2021).

Iyer, G.C. et al., 2015: Improved representation of investment decisions in assessments of CO_2 mitigation. *Nat. Clim. Change*, **5(5)**, 436–440, doi:10.1038/nclimate2553.

Jackson, T. and P.A. Victor, 2019: Unraveling the claims for (and against) green growth. *Science*, **366(6468)**, 950–951, doi:10.1126/science.aay0749.

Jaeger, J., M.I. Westphal, and C. Park, 2020: *Lessons Learned On Green Stimulus: Case studies from the global financial crisis*, World Resources Institute, Washington DC, USA. 32 pp, https://www.wri.org/research/lessons-learned-green-stimulus-case-studies-global-financial-crisis (Accessesd April 15, 2021).

Jaffe, A.B., R.G. Newell, and R.N. Stavins, 2005: A tale of two market failures: Technology and environmental policy. *Ecol. Econ.*, **54(2–3)**, 164–174, doi:10.1016/j.ecolecon.2004.12.027.

Jasanoff, S., 2018: Just transitions: A humble approach to global energy futures. *Energy Res. Soc. Sci.*, **35**, 11–14, doi:10.1016/j.erss.2017.11.025.

Jolly, W.M. et al., 2015: Climate-induced variations in global wildfire danger from 1979 to 2013. *Nat. Commun.*, **6(1)**, 7537, doi:10.1038/ncomms8537.

Jones, C.A. and D.L. Levy, 2009: Business Strategies and Climate Change. In: *Changing Climates in North American Politics*, The MIT Press, Cambridge, MA, USA, pp. 218–240.

Jonsson, A.K. and A. Nilsson, 2014: Exploring the relationship between values and Pro-Environmental behaviour: The infuence of locus of control. *Environ. Values*, **23(3)**, 297–314, doi:10.3197/096327114X13947900181752.

Jordan, A., D. Huitema, J. Schoenefeld, H. van Assett, and J. Forster, 2018: Governing Climate Change Polycentrically. In: *Governing Climate Change* [Jordan, A., D. Huitema, H. Van Assett, and J. Forster, (eds.)], Cambridge University Press, Cambridge, UK, pp. 3–26.

Jordan, A.J. et al., 2015: Emergence of polycentric climate governance and its future prospects. *Nat. Clim. Change*, **5(11)**, 977–982, doi:10.1038/nclimate2725.

Jost, C. et al., 2016: Understanding gender dimensions of agriculture and climate change in smallholder farming communities. *Clim. Dev.*, **8(2)**, 133–144, doi:10.1080/17565529.2015.1050978.

Kahler, M., 2017: Domestic Sources of Transnational Climate Governance. *Int. Interact.*, **43(1)**, 156–174, doi:10.1080/03050629.2017.1251687.

Kahneman, D., 2003: Maps of Bounded Rationality: Psychology for Behavioral Economics. *Am. Econ. Rev.*, **93(5)**, 1449–1475, doi:10.1257/000282803322655392.

Kahneman, D. and A. Tversky, 1979: Prospect theory: An analysis of decision under risk. *Econometrica*, **47**, 263–291, doi:10.2307/1914185.

Kalkuhl, M., O. Edenhofer, and K. Lessmann, 2012: Learning or lock-in: Optimal technology policies to support mitigation. *Resour. Energy Econ.*, **34(1)**, 1–23, doi:10.1016/j.reseneeco.2011.08.001.

Kallis, G., 2019: Socialism Without Growth. *Capital. Nat. Social.*, **30(2)**, 189–206, doi:10.1080/10455752.2017.1386695.

Kamuti, T., 2015: A Critique of the Green Economy: Approach in the Wildlife Ranching Sector in South Africa. *Afr. Insight*, **45(1)**, 146–168.

Kander, A., M. Jiborn, D.D. Moran, and T.O. Wiedmann, 2015: National greenhouse-gas accounting for effective climate policy on international trade. *Nat. Clim. Change*, **5(5)**, 431.

Kanie, N. and F. Biermann, *Governing through goals: sustainable development goals as governance innovation*. The MIT Press, Cambridge, MA, USA, 333 pp.

Karlsson, M. and M. Gilek, 2020: Mind the gap: Coping with delay in environmental governance. *Ambio*, **49(5)**, 1067–1075, doi:10.1007/s13280-019-01265-z.

Karlsson, M., E. Alfredsson, and N. Westling, 2020: Climate policy co-benefits: a review. *Clim. Policy*, **20(3)**, 292–316, doi:10.1080/14693062.2020.1724070.

Karp, L. and A. Rezai, 2014: The Political Economy of Environmental Policy with Overlapping Generations. *Int. Econ. Rev.*, **55(3)**, 711–733, doi:10.1111/iere.12068.

Kartha, S. et al., 2018a: Cascading biases against poorer countries. *Nat. Clim. Change*, **8(5)**, 348–349, doi:10.1038/s41558-018-0152-7.

Kartha, S., S. Caney, N.K. Dubash, and G. Muttitt, 2018b: Whose carbon is burnable? Equity considerations in the allocation of a 'right to extract.' *Clim. Change*, **150(1–2)**, 117–129, doi:10.1007/s10584-018-2209-z.

Kashwan, P., F. Biermann, A. Gupta, and C. Okereke, 2020: Planetary justice: Prioritizing the poor in earth system governance. *Earth Syst. Gov.*, **6**, 100075, doi:10.1016/j.esg.2020.100075.

Kasperbauer, T.J., 2016: The Implications of Psychological Limitations for the Ethics of Climate Change. *Environ. Values*, **25(3)**, 353–370, doi:10.3197/096327116X14598445991547.

Kasztelan, A., 2017: Green Growth, Green Economy and Sustainable Development: Terminological and Relational Discourse. *Prague Econ. Pap.*, **26(4)**, 487–499, doi:10.18267/j.pep.626.

Katz-Gerro, T., I. Greenspan, F. Handy, H.-Y. Lee, and A. Frey, 2015: Environmental Philanthropy and Environmental Behavior in Five Countries: Is There Convergence Among Youth? *Volunt. Int. J. Volunt. Nonprofit Organ.*, **26(4)**, 1485–1509, doi:10.1007/s11266-014-9496-4.

Kayal, M., H. Lewis, J. Ballard, and E. Kayal, 2019: Humanity and the 21st century's resource gauntlet: a commentary on Ripple et al.'s article 'World scientists' warning to humanity: a second notice'. *Rethink. Ecol.*, **4**, 21–30, doi:10.3897/rethinkingecology.4.32116.

Keen, S., 2021: The appallingly bad neoclassical economics of climate change. *Globalizations*, **18(7)**, 1149–1177, doi:10.1080/14747731.2020.1807856.

Keesstra, S. et al., 2018: The superior effect of nature based solutions in land management for enhancing ecosystem services. *Sci. Total Environ.*, **610–611**, 997–1009, doi:10.1016/j.scitotenv.2017.08.077.

Kenis, A. and M. Lievens, 2014: Searching for `the Political' in Environmental Politics. *Env. Polit.*, **23(4)**, 531–548, doi:10.1080/09644016.2013.870067.

Keohane, R.O. and D.G. Victor, 2011: The Regime Complex for Climate Change. *Perspect. Polit.*, **9(1)**, 7–23, doi:10.1017/S1537592710004068.

Keohane, R.O. and M. Oppenheimer, 2016: Paris: Beyond the Climate Dead End through Pledge and Review? *Polit. Gov.*, **4(3)**, 142–151, doi:10.17645/pag.v4i3.634.

Keohane, R.O. and D.G. Victor, 2016: Cooperation and discord in global climate policy. *Nat. Clim. Change*, **6(6)**, 570–575, doi:10.1038/nclimate2937.

Keynes, J.M., 1936: *The General Theory of Employment, Interest and Money*. 1st ed. Palgrave Macmillan, London, UK, 283pp.

Khajehpour, H., Y. Saboohi, and G. Tsatsaronis, 2019: Exergy-Based Responsibility Allocation of Climate Change. In: *University Initiatives in Climate Change Mitigation and Adaptation*, Springer, New York, NY, USA, pp. 291–315.

Kinley, R., M.Z. Cutajar, Y. de Boer, and C. Figueres, 2021: Beyond good intentions, to urgent action: Former UNFCCC leaders take stock of thirty years of international climate change negotiations. *Clim. Policy*, **21(5)**, 593–603, doi:10.1080/14693062.2020.1860567.

Kivimaa, P., M. Hildén, D. Huitema, A. Jordan, and J. Newig, 2017: Experiments in climate governance – A systematic review of research on energy and built environment transitions. *J. Clean. Prod.*, **169**, 17–29, doi:https://doi.org/10.1016/j.jclepro.2017.01.027.

Klausbruckner, C., H. Annegarn, L.R.F. Henneman, and P. Rafaj, 2016: A policy review of synergies and trade-offs in South African climate change mitigation and air pollution control strategies. *Environ. Sci. Policy*, **57**, 70–78, doi:10.1016/j.envsci.2015.12.001.

Klenert, D., and L. Mattauch, 2016: How to make a carbon tax reform progressive: The role of subsistence consumption. *Econ. Lett.*, **138**, 100–103, doi:10.1016/J.ECONLET.2015.11.019.

Klenert, D. et al., 2018: Making carbon pricing work for citizens. *Nat. Clim. Change*, **8(8)**, 669–677, doi:10.1038/s41558-018-0201-2.

Klenert, D., F. Funke, L. Mattauch, and B. O'Callaghan, 2020: Five Lessons from COVID-19 for Advancing Climate Change Mitigation. *Environ. Resour. Econ.*, **76(4)**, 751–778, doi:10.1007/s10640-020-00453-w.

Klinsky, S. and H. Winkler, 2014: Equity, sustainable development and climate policy. *Clim. Policy*, **14(1)**, 1–7, doi:10.1080/14693062.2014.859352.

Klinsky, S. and H. Winkler, 2018: Building equity in: strategies for integrating equity into modelling for a 1.5°C world. *Philos. Trans. Roy. Soc. A*, **376(2119)**, 20160461 doi:10.1098/rsta.2016.0461.

Klinsky, S. et al., 2017: Why equity is fundamental in climate change policy research. *Glob. Environ. Change*, **44**, 170–173, doi:10.1016/j.gloenvcha.2016.08.002.

Knapp, V. and D. Pevec, 2018: Promises and limitations of nuclear fission energy in combating climate change. *Energy Policy*, **120**, 94–99, doi:10.1016/j.enpol.2018.05.027.

Koasidis, K. et al., 2020: The UK and German Low-Carbon Industry Transitions from a Sectoral Innovation and System Failures Perspective. *Energies*, **13(19)**, 4994, doi:10.3390/en13194994.

Köberle, A.C., 2019: The Value of BECCS in IAMs: a Review. *Curr. Sustain. Energy Reports*, **6(4)**, 107–115, doi:10.1007/s40518-019-00142-3.

Köberle, A.C., P.R.R. Rochedo, A.F.P. Lucena, A. Szklo, and R. Schaeffer, 2020: Brazil's emission trajectories in a well-below 2°C world: the role of disruptive technologies versus land-based mitigation in an already low-emission energy system. *Clim. Change*, **162(4)**, 1823–1842, doi:10.1007/s10584-020-02856-6.

Koch, M., 2012: *Capitalism and Climate Change. Theoretical Discussion, Historical Development and Policy Responses*. Palgrave Macmillan UK, London, UK, 177 pp.Köhler, J. et al., 2018: Modelling Sustainability Transitions: An Assessment of Approaches and Challenges. *J. Artif. Soc. Soc. Simulation*, **21**, 8, doi:10.18564/jasss.3629.

Köhler, J. et al., 2019: An agenda for sustainability transitions research: State of the art and future directions. *Environ. Innov. Soc. Transitions*, **31**, 1–32, doi:https://doi.org/10.1016/j.eist.2019.01.004.

Kooiman, J., 2003: *Governing as Governance Governing as governance*. 1st ed. SAGE Publications Ltd, London, UK, 262 pp.

Kotzé, L.J., 2018: Chapter 3: The Sustainable Development Goals: an existential critique alongside three new-millennial analytical paradigms. In: *Sustainable Development Goals Law, Theory and Implementation* [French, D. and L.J. Kotzé (eds.)]. Edward Elgar Publishing Limited, Cheltenham, UK, pp. 41–65.

Kramer, G.J., 2018: Energy scenarios – Exploring disruption and innovation. *Energy Res. Soc. Sci.*, **37**, 247–250, doi:10.1016/j.erss.2017.10.047.

Kurz, T., B. Gardner, B. Verplanken, and C. Abraham, 2015: Habitual Behaviors or Patterns of Practice? Explaining and Changing Repetitive Climate-Relevant Actions. *WIREs Clim. Change*, **6(1)**, 113–128, doi:10.1002/wcc.327.

Kuzemko, C., M. Lockwood, C. Mitchell, and R. Hoggett, 2016: Governing for sustainable energy system change: Politics, contexts and contingency. *Energy Res. Soc. Sci.*, **12**, 96–105, doi:10.1016/j.erss.2015.12.022.

Kverndokk, S., 2018: Climate Policies, Distributional Effects and Transfers Between Rich and Poor Countries. *Int. Rev. Environ. Resour. Econ.*, **12(2–3)**, 129–176, doi:10.1561/101.00000100.

Kverndokk, S., E. Nævdal, and L. Nøstbakken, 2014: The trade-off between intra- and intergenerational equity in climate policy. *Eur. Econ. Rev.*, **69**, 40–58, doi:10.1016/j.euroecorev.2014.01.007.

Kyle, J., F. Sussman, A. Kindle, J. Kuna, and B. Hurley, 2016: Multi-Scale Economic Methodologies and Scenarios Workshop. Washington, DC, USA,.

Laakso, S., A. Berg, and M. Annala, 2017: Dynamics of experimental governance: A meta-study of functions and uses of climate governance experiments. *J. Clean. Prod.*, **169**, 8–16, doi:https://doi.org/10.1016/j.jclepro.2017.04.140.

Laborde Debucquet, D. and W. Martin, 2017: Formulas for failure? Were the Doha tariff formulas too ambitious for success?: In: *Agriculture, development, and the global trading system: 2000– 2015* [Bouët, A. and D. Laborde Debucquet (eds.)]. International Food Policy Research Institute (IFPRI), Washington DC, USA, 24 pp.

Lachapelle, E. and M. Paterson, 2013: Drivers of national climate policy. *Clim. Policy*, **13(5)**, 547–571, doi:10.1080/14693062.2013.811333.

Lachapelle, E., R. MacNeil, and M. Paterson, 2017: The political economy of decarbonisation: from green energy 'race' to green 'division of labour.' *New Polit. Econ.*, **22(3)**, 311–327, doi:10.1080/13563467.2017.1240669.

Lamb, W.F. and J.K. Steinberger, 2017: Human well-being and climate change mitigation. *WIREs Clim. Change*, **8(6)**, doi:10.1002/wcc.485.

Lamb, W.F. and J.C. Minx, 2020: The political economy of national climate policy: Architectures of constraint and a typology of countries. *Energy Res. Soc. Sci.*, **64**, 101429, doi:10.1016/j.erss.2020.101429.

Lamb, W.F. et al., 2021: A review of trends and drivers of greenhouse gas emissions by sector from 1990 to 2018. *Environ. Res. Lett.*, **16(7)**, 073005, doi:10.1088/1748-9326/ABEE4E.

Lange, A., C. Vogt, and A. Ziegler, 2007: On the importance of equity in international climate policy: An empirical analysis. *Energy Econ.*, **29(3)**, 545–562, doi:10.1016/j.eneco.2006.09.002.

Lange, A., A. Löschel, C. Vogt, and A. Ziegler, 2010: On the self-interested use of equity in international climate negotiations. *Eur. Econ. Rev.*, **54(3)**, 359–375, doi:10.1016/j.euroecorev.2009.08.006.

Latouche, S., 2018: The Path to Degrowth for a Sustainable Society. In: *Factor X Challenges, Implementation Strategies and Examples for a Sustainable Use of Natural Resources* [Lehmann, H. (eds)], Springer, New York, NY, USA, pp. 277–284.

Lazarus, R. J., 2009: *Super Wicked Problems and Climate Change: Restraining the Present to Liberate the Future*. Georgetown University Law Centre, Washington D.C, USA, 84 pp. https://scholarship.law.georgetown.edu/facpub/159 (Accessed January 15, 2020).

Le Billon, P., P. Lujala, D. Singh, V. Culbert, and B. Kristoffersen, 2021: Fossil fuels, climate change, and the COVID-19 crisis: pathways for a just and green post-pandemic recovery. *Clim. Policy*, **21**(10),1347-1356, doi:10.1080/14693062.2021.1965524.

Le Quéré, C. et al., 2019. "Drivers of declining CO2 emissions in 18 developed economies." *Nature Climate Change* 9, no. 3, 213–217.

Le Quéré, C. et al., 2020: Temporary reduction in daily global CO_2 emissions during the COVID-19 forced confinement. *Nat. Clim. Change*, **10(7)**, 647–653, doi:10.1038/s41558-020-0797-x.

Leach, M. et al., 2018: Equity and sustainability in the anthropocene: A social-ecological systems perspective on their intertwined futures. *Glob. Sustainability*, **1**, e13, doi:10.1017/sus.2018.12.

Legrand, M.D.P. and H. Hagemann, 2017: Retrospectives: Do Productive Recessions Show the Recuperative Powers of Capitalism? Schumpeter's Analysis of the Cleansing Effect. *J. Econ. Perspect.*, **31(1)**, 245–256, doi:10.1257/jep.31.1.245.

Lenton, T.M. et al., 2019: Climate tipping points – too risky to bet against. *Nature*, **575(7784)**, 592–595, doi:10.1038/d41586-019-03595-0.

Lenzen, M., J. Murray, F. Sack, and T. Wiedmann, 2007: Shared producer and consumer responsibility – Theory and practice. *Ecol. Econ.*, **61(1)**, 27–42.

Levin, K., B. Cashore, S. Bernstein, and G. Auld, 2012: Overcoming the tragedy of super wicked problems: constraining our future selves to ameliorate global climate change. *Policy Sciences*, **45(2)**, 123–152, doi:10.1007/s11077-012-9151-0.

Levitt, S.D. and J.A. List, 2009: Field experiments in economics: The past, the present, and the future. *Eur. Econ. Rev.*, **53(1)**, 1–18, doi:10.1016/j.euroecorev.2008.12.001.

Levy, D.L. and D. Egan, 2003: A Neo-Gramscian Approach to Corporate Political Strategy: Conflict and Accommodation in the Climate Change Negotiations. *J. Manag. Stud.*, **40(4)**, 803–829, doi:10.1111/1467-6486.00361.

Levy, D.L. and A. Spicer, 2013: Contested imaginaries and the cultural political economy of climate change. *Organization*, **20(5)**, 659–678, doi:10.1177/1350508413489816.

Li, F.G.N., E. Trutnevyte, and N. Strachan, 2015: A review of socio-technical energy transition (STET) models. *Technol. Forecast. Soc. Change*, **100**, 290–305, doi:10.1016/j.techfore.2015.07.017.

Li, Q. and W.A. Pizer, 2018: *The discount rate for public policy over the distant future*. National Bureau of Economic Research, Cambridge MA, USA, 51 pp.

Lianos, M., 2019: Yellow vests and European democracy. *Eur. Soc.*, **21(1)**, 1–3, doi:10.1080/14616696.2019.1570055.

Lin, J. and D.A. Kysar, 2020: *Climate Change Litigation in the Asia Pacific*. Cambridge University Press, Cambridge, UK.

Liu, L.-J. et al., 2021: Combining economic recovery with climate change mitigation: A global evaluation of financial instruments. *Econ. Anal. Policy*, **72**, 438–453, doi:10.1016/j.eap.2021.09.009.

Liu, L., T. Wu, and Y. Huang, 2017: An equity-based framework for defining national responsibilities in global climate change mitigation. *Clim. Dev.*, **9(2)**, 152–163, doi:10.1080/17565529.2015.1085358.

Liu, Z. et al., 2020: Near-real-time monitoring of global CO_2 emissions reveals the effects of the COVID-19 pandemic. *Nat. Commun.*, **11(1)**, 1–12, doi:10.1038/s41467-020-18922-7.

Llavador, H., J.E. Roemer, and J. Silvestre, 2015: *Sustainability for a Warming Planet*. Harvard University Press, Cambridge, MA, USA, 238 pp.

Lo, A.Y., 2010: Active conflict or passive coherence? The political economy of climate change in China. *Env. Polit.*, **19(6)**, 1012–1017, doi:10.1080/09644016.2010.518689.

Lo, K. and V. Castán Broto, 2019: Co-benefits, contradictions, and multi-level governance of low-carbon experimentation: Leveraging solar energy for sustainable development in China. *Glob. Environ. Change*, **59**, 101993, doi:10.1016/j.gloenvcha.2019.101993.

Lohmann, L., 2017: Toward a Political Economy of Neoliberal Climate Science. In: *The Routledge Handbook of the Political Economy of Science*, Routledge, Abingdon, UK, pp. 305–316.

Lohmann, L., 2019: Neoliberalism, law and nature. In: *Research Handbook on Law, Environment and the Global South*, Edward Elgar Publishing, Cheltenham, UK, pp. 32–63.

Lontzek, T.S., Y. Cai, K.L. Judd, and T.M. Lenton, 2015: Stochastic integrated assessment of climate tipping points indicates the need for strict climate policy. *Nat. Clim. Change*, **5(5)**, 441–444, doi:10.1038/nclimate2570.

Loorbach, D., 2010: Transition Management for Sustainable Development: A Prescriptive, Complexity-Based Governance Framework. *Governance*, **23(1)**, 161–183, doi.org/10.1111/j.1468-0491.2009.01471.x.

Lu, S., X. Bai, X. Zhang, W. Li, and Y. Tang, 2019: The impact of climate change on the sustainable development of regional economy. *J. Clean. Prod.*, **233**, 1387–1395, doi:10.1016/j.jclepro.2019.06.074.

Maestre-Andrés, S., S. Drews, and J. van den Bergh, 2019: Perceived fairness and public acceptability of carbon pricing: a review of the literature. *Clim. Policy*, **19(9)**, 1186–1204, doi:10.1080/14693062.2019.1639490.

Mainali, B., J. Luukkanen, S. Silveira, and J. Kaivo-oja, 2018: Evaluating Synergies and Trade-Offs among Sustainable Development Goals (SDGs): Explorative Analyses of Development Paths in South Asia and Sub-Saharan Africa. *Sustainability*, **10(3)**, 815, doi:10.3390/su10030815.

Majone, G., 1975: On the notion of political feasibility. *Eur. J. Polit. Res.*, **3(3)**, 259–274, doi:10.1111/j.1475-6765.1975.tb00780.x.

Makomere, R. and K. Liti Mbeva, 2018: Squaring the Circle: Development Prospects Within the Paris Agreement. *Carbon Clim. Law Rev.*, **12(1)**, 31–40, doi:10.21552/cclr/2018/1/7.

Malik, A. and J. Lan, 2016: The role of outsourcing in driving global carbon emissions. *Econ. Syst. Res.*, **28(2)**, 168–182, doi:10.1080/09535314.2016.1172475.

Malik, A., D. McBain, T.O. Wiedmann, M. Lenzen, and J. Murray, 2019: Advancements in Input-Output Models and Indicators for Consumption-Based Accounting. *J. Ind. Ecol.*, **23(2)**, 300–312, doi:10.1111/jiec.12771.

Malm, A., 2015: Exploding in the Air: Beyond the Carbon Trail of Neoliberal Globalisation. In: *Polarising Development: Alternatives to Neoliberalism and the Crisis* [Pradella, L. and T. Marois, (eds.)]. Pluto Press, London, UK, pp. 108–118.

Malm, A., 2016: *Fossil Capital: The Rise of Steam Power and the Roots of Global Warming*. Verso Books, London, UK, 615 pp.

Mangat, R., S. Dalby, and M. Paterson, 2018: Divestment discourse: war, justice, morality and money. *Env. Polit.*, **27(2)**, 187–208, doi:10.1080/09644016.2017.1413725.

Marchau, V.A.W.J., R.J. Lempert, W.E. Walker, P.J.T.M. Bloemen, and S.W. Popper, 2019: *Decision Making under Deep Uncertainty*. Springer International Publishing, New York, NY, USA, 405 pp.

Marcu, A., 2017: *Article 6 of the Paris Agreement: Reflections on Party Submissions before Marrakech*. International Centre for Trade and Sustainable Development (ICTSD), Geneva, Switzerland, 32pp, https://ercst.org/article-6-of-the-paris-agreement-reflections-on-submissions-by-parties-before-marrakech/ (Accessed February 15, 2021).

Markkanen, S. and A. Anger-Kraavi, 2019: Social impacts of climate change mitigation policies and their implications for inequality. *Clim. Policy*, **19(7)**, 827–844, doi:10.1080/14693062.2019.1596873.

Marmot, M. and R. Bell, 2018: The Sustainable Development Goals and Health Equity. *Epidemiology*, **29(1)**, 5–7, doi:10.1097/EDE.0000000000000773.

Marquardt, J., 2017: Conceptualizing power in multi-level climate governance. *J. Clean. Prod.*, **154**, 167–175, doi:10.1016/j.jclepro.2017.03.176.

Marshall, G., 2014: *Don't even think about it: why our brains are wired to ignore climate change*. Bloomsbury Publishing, London, UK, 260 pp.

Martinez, G.S. et al., 2019: Delegation size and equity in climate negotiations: An exploration of key issues. *Carbon Manag.*, **10(4)**, 431–435, doi:10.1080/17583004.2019.1630243.

Matthews, N.E., L. Stamford, and P. Shapira, 2019: Aligning sustainability assessment with responsible research and innovation: Towards a framework for Constructive Sustainability Assessment. *Sustain. Prod. Consum.*, **20**, 58–73, doi:10.1016/j.spc.2019.05.002.

Mazzucato, M., 2013: Financing innovation: creative destruction vs. destructive creation. *Ind. Corp. Change*, **22(4)**, 851–867, doi:10.1093/icc/dtt025.

McCauley, D. and R. Heffron, 2018: Just transition: Integrating climate, energy and environmental justice. *Energy Policy*, **119**, 1–7, doi:10.1016/j.enpol.2018.04.014.

McCrary, J. and H. Royer, 2011: The Effect of Female Education on Fertility and Infant Health: Evidence from School Entry Policies Using Exact Date of Birth. *Am. Econ. Rev.*, **101(1)**, 158–195, doi:10.1257/aer.101.1.158.

McGlade, C. and P. Ekins, 2015: The geographical distribution of fossil fuels unused when limiting global warming to 2°C. *Nature*, **517(7533)**, 187–190, doi:10.1038/nature14016.

McRae, S. and R. Meeks, 2016: *Price perception and electricity demand with nonlinear tariffs*. Ann Arbor, MI, USA https://www.semanticscholar.org/paper/Price-perception-and-electricity-demand-with-McRae-Meeks/57dd8dca3ebd0c9d835e604b3f233b2f6197d99d

Meckling, J., 2018: The developmental state in global regulation: Economic change and climate policy. *Eur. J. Int. Relations*, **24(1)**, 58–81, doi:10.1177/1354066117700966.

Meckling, J., 2019: Governing renewables: Policy feedback in a global energy transition. *Environ. Plan. C Polit. Sp.*, **37(2)**, 317–338, doi:10.1177/2399654418777765.

Meckling, J. and J. Nahm, 2018: When do states disrupt industries? Electric cars and the politics of innovation. *Rev. Int. Polit. Econ.*, **25(4)**, 505–529, doi:10.1080/09692290.2018.1434810.

Meckling, J., T. Sterner, and G. Wagner, 2017: Policy sequencing toward decarbonization. *Nat. Energy*, **2(12)**, 918–922, doi:10.1038/s41560-017-0025-8.

Mehling, M.A., H. Van Asselt, K. Das, S. Droege, and C. Verkuijl, 2019: Designing Border Carbon Adjustments for Enhanced Climate Action. *Am. J. Int. Law*, **113(3)**, 433–481, doi:10.1017/ajil.2019.22.

Meng, J. et al., 2018: The rise of South-South trade and its effect on global CO_2 emissions. *Nat. Commun.*, **9(1)**, doi:10.1038/s41467-018-04337-y.

Meng, K.C. and A. Rode, 2019: The Social Cost of Lobbying over Climate Policy. *Nat. Clim. Change*, **9(6)**, 472–476, doi:10.1038/s41558-019-0489-6.

Mercure, J.F. et al., 2021: Risk-opportunity analysis for transformative policy design and appraisal. *Glob. Environ. Change*, **70**, 102359, doi:10.1016/J.GLOENVCHA.2021.102359.

Metcalf, G.E., 2009: Market-based Policy Options to Control U.S. Greenhouse Gas Emissions. *J. Econ. Perspect.*, **23(2)**, 5–27, doi:10.1257/jep.23.2.5.

Michaelowa, A., M. Allen, and F. Sha, 2018: Policy Instruments for Limiting Global Temperature Rise to 1.5C – Can Humanity Rise to the Challenge? *Clim. Policy*, **18(3)**, 275–286, doi:10.1080/14693062.2018.1426977.

Michaelowa, K. and A. Michaelowa, 2017: Transnational Climate Governance Initiatives: Designed for Effective Climate Change Mitigation? *Int. Interact.*, **43(1)**, 129–155, doi:10.1080/03050629.2017.1256110.

Michelsen, G., M. Adomßent, P. Martens, and M. von Hauff, 2016: Sustainable Development – Background and Context. In: *Sustainability Science* [Heinrichs, H., P. Martens, G. Michelsen, and A. Wiek, (eds.)], Springer Netherlands, Heidelberg, Germany, pp. 5–29.

Mildenberger, M., 2020: *Carbon Captured: How Business and Labor Control Climate Politics*. MIT Press, Cambridge, MA, USA, 368 pp.

Milkoreit, M., 2017: Imaginary politics: Climate change and making the future. *Elem Sci Anth*, **5(0)**, 62, doi:10.1525/elementa.249.

Milkoreit, M. and K. Haapala, 2019: The global stocktake: design lessons for a new review and ambition mechanism in the international climate regime. *Int. Environ. Agreements Polit. Law Econ.*, **19(1)**, 89–106, doi:10.1007/s10784-018-9425-x.

Millar, H., E. Bourgeois, S. Bernstein, and M. Hoffmann, 2020: Self-reinforcing and self-undermining feedbacks in subnational climate policy implementation. *Env. Polit.*, **0(0)**, 1–20, doi:10.1080/09644016.2020.1825302.

Minsky, H.P., 1986: *Stabilizing an unstable economy*. Yale University Press, New Haven, CT, 432 pp.

Mitchell, T. and S. Maxwell, 2010: *Defining climate compatible development*. London, UK, 1–6 pp.

Monasterolo, I., 2017: *A climate stress-test of financial institutions*. Green Finance Research Advances, Vienna, Austria, Vienna University of Economics and Business, 17 pp.

Moore, F.C., U. Baldos, T. Hertel, and D. Diaz, 2017: New science of climate change impacts on agriculture implies higher social cost of carbon. *Nat. Commun.*, **8(1)**, 1607, doi:10.1038/s41467-017-01792-x.

Moore, G.F. et al., 2019: From complex social interventions to interventions in complex social systems: Future directions and unresolved questions for intervention development and evaluation. *Evaluation*, **25(1)**, 23–45, doi:10.1177/1356389018803219.

Mora, C. et al., 2018: Bitcoin emissions alone could push global warming above 2°C. *Nat. Clim. Change*, **8(11)**, 931–933, doi:10.1038/s41558-018-0321-8.

Mori, A.S., K.P. Lertzman, and L. Gustafsson, 2017: Biodiversity and ecosystem services in forest ecosystems: a research agenda for applied forest ecology. *J. Appl. Ecol.*, **54(1)**, 12–27, doi:10.1111/1365-2664.12669.

Moss, R. et al., 2016: *Understanding dynamics and resilience in complex interdependent systems*. Washington, DC, USA. https://www.globalchange.gov/browse/reports/understanding-dynamics-and-resilience-complex-interdependent-systems (Accessed July 23, 2021).

Mugambiwa, S.S. and H.M. Tirivangasi, 2017: Climate change: A threat towards achieving 'sustainable development goal number two' (end hunger, achieve food security and improved nutrition and promote sustainable agriculture) in South Africa. *Jamba J. Disaster Risk Stud.*, **9(1)**, a350, doi:10.4102/jamba.v9i1.350.

Mulugetta, Y. and F. Urban, 2010: Deliberating on low carbon development. *Energy Policy*, **38(12)**, 7546–7549, doi:10.1016/j.enpol.2010.05.049.

Myhre, G., C.E.L. Myhre, B.H. Samset, and T. Storelvmo, 2013: Aerosols and their Relation to Global Climate and Climate Sensitivity. *Nat. Educ. Knowl.*, **4(7)** https://www.nature.com/scitable/knowledge/library/aerosols-and-their-relation-to-global-climate-102215345/ (Accessed June 18, 2021).

Mylan, J., 2018: Sustainable Consumption in Everyday Life: A Qualitative Study of UK Consumer Experiences of Meat Reduction. *Sustainability*, **10(7)**, 2307, doi:10.3390/su10072307.

Nabi, R.L., A. Gustafson, and R. Jensen, 2018: Framing Climate Change: Exploring the Role of Emotion in Generating Advocacy Behavior. *Sci. Commun.*, **40(4)**, 442–468, doi:10.1177/1075547018776019.

Naegele, H. and A. Zaklan, 2019: Does the EU ETS cause carbon leakage in European manufacturing? *J. Environ. Econ. Manage.*, **93**, 125–147, doi:10.1016/j.jeem.2018.11.004.

Najam, A., 2005: Developing Countries and Global Environmental Governance: From Contestation to Participation to Engagement. *Int. Environ. Agreements Polit. Law Econ.*, **5(3)**, 303–321, doi:10.1007/s10784-005-3807-6.

Nakicenovic, N. et al., 2000: Emissions scenarios – Special Report of the Intergovernmental Panel on Climate Change. Cambridge University Press, Cambridge, UK, 27 pp.

Nash, N. et al., 2017: Climate-relevant behavioral spillover and the potential contribution of social practice theory. *Wiley Interdiscip. Rev. Clim. Change*, **8(6)**, doi:10.1002/wcc.481.

Nash, S.L. and R. Steurer, 2019: Taking stock of Climate Change Acts in Europe: living policy processes or symbolic gestures? *Clim. Policy*, **19(8)**, 1052–1065, doi:10.1080/14693062.2019.1623164.

Nasiritousi, N., and K. Bäckstrand, 2019: *International Climate Politics in the post-Paris era*, Stockholm University Stockholm, Sweden, 1–19 pp, https://nordregio.org/wp-content/uploads/2018/10/International-Climate-Politics-in-the-post-Paris-era_Nasiritousi.pdf (Accessed July 13, 2021).

National Academies of Sciences, 2021: *Reflecting Sunlight*. National Academies Press, Washington, DC, USA, 312 pp.

Nelson, R.R. and S.G. Winter, 1982: *An Evolutionary Theory of Economic Change*. Harvard University Press, Cambridge, USA, 454 pp.

Nesshöver, C. et al., 2017: The science, policy and practice of nature-based solutions: An interdisciplinary perspective. *Sci. Total Environ.*, **579**, 1215–1227, doi:10.1016/j.scitotenv.2016.11.106.

Netra, C. et al., 2018: *Governing solar radiation management*. Washington, DC, USA, 72 pp.

Neuteleers, S. and B. Engelen, 2015: Talking money: How market-based valuation can undermine environmental protection. *Ecol. Econ.*, **117**, 253–260, doi:10.1016/j.ecolecon.2014.06.022.

Neville, K.J., J. Cook, J. Baka, K. Bakker, and E.S. Weinthal, 2019: Can shareholder advocacy shape energy governance? The case of the US antifracking movement. *Rev. Int. Polit. Econ.*, **26(1)**, 104–133, doi:10.1080/09692290.2018.1488757.

Newbery, D., 2018: Evaluating the case for supporting renewable electricity. *Energy Policy*, **120**, 684–696, doi:10.1016/j.enpol.2018.05.029.

Newell, P. and M. Paterson, 1998: A climate for business: global warming, the state and capital. *Rev. Int. Polit. Econ.*, **5(4)**, 679–703, doi:10.1080/096922998347426.

Newell, P. and M. Paterson, 2010: *Climate Capitalism: Global Warming and the Transformation of the Global Economy*. Cambridge University Press, Cambridge, UK 222 pp.

Newell, P. and D. Mulvaney, 2013: The political economy of the 'just transition.', *Geogr. J.*, **179(2)**, 132–140, doi:10.1111/geoj.12008.

Newell, P. and O. Taylor, 2018: Contested landscapes: the global political economy of climate-smart agriculture. *J. Peasant Stud.*, **45(1)**, 108–129, doi:10.1080/03066150.2017.1324426.

Newell, P., M. Paterson, and M. Craig, 2021: The Politics of Green Transformations: An Introduction to the Special Section. *New Polit. Econ.*, **26**(6), 903–906, doi:10.1080/13563467.2020.1810215.

Newman, P., 2020: COVID, CITIES and CLIMATE: Historical Precedents and Potential Transitions for the New Economy. *Urban Science*, **4(3)**, 32, doi:10.3390/urbansci4030032.

Newman, P., T. Beatley, and H. Boyer, 2017: *Resilient Cities*. Island Press/Center for Resource Economics, Washington, DC, USA, 1–253 pp.

NGFS, 2020: *Climate Scenarios for central banks and supervisors*. Network for Greening Finance, Paris, France., 39 pp https://www.ngfs.net/en/ngfs-climate-scenarios-central-banks-and-supervisors (Accessed July 15, 2021).

Nikas, A., H. Doukas, and A. Papandreou, 2019: A Detailed Overview and Consistent Classification of Climate-Economy Models. In: *Understanding Risks and Uncertainties in Energy and Climate Policy: Multidisciplinary Methods and Tools for a Low Carbon Society* [Doukas, H., A. Flamos, and J. Lieu, (eds.)]. Springer International Publishing, Cham, Switzerland, pp. 1–54.

Nikas, A. et al., 2020: The desirability of transitions in demand: Incorporating behavioural and societal transformations into energy modelling. *Energy Res. Soc. Sci.*, **70**, 101780, doi:10.1016/j.erss.2020.101780.

Nikoleris, A., J. Stripple, and P. Tenngart, 2017: Narrating climate futures: shared socioeconomic pathways and literary fiction. *Clim. Change*, **143(3–4)**, 307–319, doi:10.1007/s10584-017-2020-2.

Nordhaus, W., 2007: Critical assumptions in the stern review on climate change. *Science*, **317(5835)**, 201–202, doi:10.1126/science.1137316.

Nordhaus, W., 2008: *A Question of Balance*. Yale University Press, New Haven, CT, USA.

Nordhaus, W.D.W. D., 1992: An optimal transition path for controlling greenhouse gases. *Science*, **258(5086)**, 1315–1319, doi:10.1126/science.258.5086.1315.

Norgaard, K.M., 2011: *Living in Denial: Climate Change, Emotions, and Everyday Life*. 1st ed. MIT Press, Cambridge, MA, USA, 304 pp.

Nunan, F., 2017: *Making Climate Compatible Development Happen*. 1st ed. Routledge, Abingdon, UK, 284 pp.

O'Hara, P.A., 2009: Political economy of climate change, ecological destruction and uneven development. *Ecol. Econ.*, **69(2)**, 223–234, doi:https://doi.org/10.1016/j.ecolecon.2009.09.015.

O'Neill, B.C. et al., 2014: A new scenario framework for climate change research: the concept of shared socioeconomic pathways. *Clim. Change*, **122(3)**, 387–400, doi:10.1007/s10584-013-0905-2.

Obergassel, W., L. Hermwille, and S. Oberthür, 2021: Harnessing international climate governance to drive a sustainable recovery from the COVID-19 pandemic. *Clim. Policy*, **21(10)**, 1298–1306, doi:10.1080/14693 062.2020.1835603.

Ojekunle, Z.O. et al., 2015: Global Climate Change: The Empirical Study of the Sensitivity Model in China's Sustainable Development, Part 2. *Energy Sources, Part A Recover. Util. Environ. Eff.*, **37(8)**, 861–869, doi:10.1080/1 5567036.2013.840695.

Okereke, C., 2017: A six-component model for assessing procedural fairness in the Intergovernmental Panel on Climate Change (IPCC). *Clim. Change*, **145(3–4)**, 509–522, doi:10.1007/s10584-017-2106-x.

Okereke, C., 2018: Equity and Justice in Polycentric Climate Governance. In: *Governing Climate Change* [Jordan, A., D. Huitema, H. Van Asselt, and J. Forster, (eds.)], Cambridge University Press, Cambridge, UK, pp. 320–337.

Okereke, C. and D. Russel, 2010: Regulatory Pressure and Competitive Dynamics: Carbon Management Strategies of UK Energy-Intensive Companies. *Calif. Manage. Rev.*, **52(4)**, 100–124, doi:10.1525/cmr.2010.52.4.100.

Okereke, C. and T.G. Ehresman, 2015: International environmental justice and the quest for a green global economy: introduction to special issue. *Int. Environ. Agreements Polit. Law Econ.*, **15(1)**, 5–11, doi:10.1007/s10784-014-9264-3.

Okereke, C. and P. Coventry, 2016: Climate justice and the international regime: before, during, and after Paris. *Wiley Interdiscip. Rev. Clim. Change*, **7(6)**, 834–851, doi:10.1002/wcc.419.

Okereke, C. and A.-B.S. Massaquoi, 2017: Climate change, environment and development. In: *Introduction to International Development: Approaches, Actors and Issues* [Haslam, P., J. Schafer, and P. Beaudet (eds.)]. Oxford University Press, Oxford, UK, pp. 320–334.

Okereke, C., H. Bulkeley, and H. Schroeder, 2009: Conceptualizing climate governance beyond the international regime. *Glob. Environ. Polit.*, **9(1)**, doi:10.1162/glep.2009.9.1.58.

Okereke, C. et al., 2019: Governing green industrialisation in Africa: Assessing key parameters for a sustainable socio-technical transition in the context of Ethiopia. *World Dev.*, **115**, 279–290, doi:10.1016/j.worlddev.2018.11.019.

Onder, H., 2012: *What does trade have to do with climate change?* VOX CEPR Policy Portal, London UK. https://voxeu.org/article/what-does-trade-have-do-climate-change (Accessed July 21, 2021).

Osili, U.O. and B.T. Long, 2008: Does female schooling reduce fertility? Evidence from Nigeria. *J. Dev. Econ.*, **87(1)**, 57–75, doi:10.1016/j.jdeveco.2007.10.003.

Page, B., G. Turan, and A. Zapantis, 2019: *Global Status of CCS 2019*. Docklands, Australia., 46 pp https://www.globalccsinstitute.com/wp-content/uploads/2019/12/GCC_GLOBAL_STATUS_REPORT_2019.pdf (Accessed June 13, 2021).

Pan, X., F. Teng, Y. Ha, and G. Wang, 2014: Equitable Access to Sustainable Development: Based on the comparative study of carbon emission rights allocation schemes. *Appl. Energy*, **130**, 632–640, doi:10.1016/j.apenergy.2014.03.072.

Parker, C.F., C. Karlsson, and M. Hjerpe, 2017: Assessing the European Union's global climate change leadership: from Copenhagen to the Paris Agreement. *J. Eur. Integr.*, **39(2)**, 239–252, doi:10.1080/07036337.2016.1275608.

Parrique, T. et al., 2019: *Decoupling Debunked: Evidence and arguments against green growth as a sole strategy for sustainability*. The European Environmental BureauBrussels, Belgium 80 pp.

Paterson, M., 2021: Climate change and international political economy: between collapse and transformation. *Rev. Int. Polit. Econ.*, **28(2)**, 394–405, doi:10.1080/09692290.2020.1830829.

Paterson, M. and X. P-Laberge, 2018: Political economies of climate change. *WIREs Clim. Change*, **9(2)**, e506, doi:10.1002/wcc.506.

Patterson, J.J. et al., 2018: Political feasibility of 1.5°C societal transformations: the role of social justice. *Curr. Opin. Environ. Sustainability*, **31**, 1–9, doi:10.1016/j.cosust.2017.11.002.

Pearse, R., 2017: *Pricing Carbon in Australia: Contestation, the State and Market Failure*. Routledge, Abingdon, UK, 156 pp.

Peel, J., and H. M. Osofsky, 2020: Climate Change Litigation. *Annu. Rev. Law Soc. Sci.*, **16(1)**, 21–38, doi:10.1146/annurev-lawsocsci-022420-122936.

Pelling, M. and D. Manuel-Navarrete, 2011: From Resilience to Transformation: the Adaptive Cycle in Two Mexican Urban Centers. *Ecol. Soc.*, **16(2)**, 11, https://www.jstor.org/stable/26268885.

Perez, C., 2001: *Technological Revolutions and Financial Capital*. Edward Elgar, Cheltenham, UK, 224 pp.

Peters, G.P., J.C. Minx, C.L. Weber, and O. Edenhofer, 2011: Growth in emission transfers via international trade from 1990 to 2008. *Proc. Natl. Acad. Sci.*, **108(21)**, 8903–8908, doi:10.1073/pnas.1006388108.

Peters, G.P., R.M. Andrew, S. Solomon, and P. Friedlingstein, 2015: Measuring a fair and ambitious climate agreement using cumulative emissions. *Environ. Res. Lett.*, **10(10)**, 105004, doi:10.1088/1748-9326/10/10/105004.

Pettenger, M.E., 2016: *The Social Construction of Climate Change*. Routledge, Abingdon, UK, 280 pp.

Pezzey, J.C. V, 2018: *High unknowability of climate damage valuation means the social cost of carbon will always be disputed*. Centre for Climate and Energy Policy, Canberra, Australia, 21 pp.

Pickering, J., F. Jotzo, and P.J. Wood, 2015: Sharing the Global Climate Finance Effort Fairly with Limited Coordination. *Glob. Environ. Polit.*, **15(4)**, 39–62, doi:10.1162/GLEP_a_00325.

Pickering, J., J.S. McGee, T. Stephens, and S.I. Karlsson-Vinkhuyzen, 2018: The impact of the US retreat from the Paris Agreement: Kyoto revisited? *Clim. Policy*, **18(7)**, 818–827, doi:10.1080/14693062.2017.1412934.

Piggot, G., 2018: The influence of social movements on policies that constrain fossil fuel supply. *Clim. Policy*, **18(7)**, 942–954, doi:10.1080/14693 062.2017.1394255.

Pindyck, R.S., 2013: Climate change policy: What do the models tell us? *J. Econ. Lit.*, **51(3)**, 860–872, doi:10.1257/jel.51.3.860.

Piñero, P., M. Bruckner, H. Wieland, E. Pongrácz, and S. Giljum, 2019: The raw material basis of global value chains: allocating environmental responsibility based on value generation. *Econ. Syst. Res.*, **31(2)**, 206–227, doi:10.1080/09535314.2018.1536038.

Plumwood, V., 2004: Gender, Eco-Feminism and the Environment. In: *Controversies in Environmental Sociology* [White, R. (ed.)]. Cambridge University Press, Cambridge, UK, pp. 43–60.

Pollitt, H., R. Lewney, B. Kiss-Dobronyi, and X. Lin, 2021: Modelling the economic effects of COVID-19 and possible green recovery plans: a post-Keynesian approach. *Clim. Policy*, **21(10)**, 1257–1271, doi:10.1080/14693 062.2021.1965525.

Polman, P., 2015: On the Business of Climate Change. *Fletcher Forum World Aff.*, **39(2)**.

Poortinga, W. et al., 2018: *European Attitudes to Climate Change and Energy: Topline Results from Round 8 of the European Social Survey*, European Social Survey, London, UK, 20 pp. https://www.europeansocialsurvey.org/docs/findings/ESS8_toplines_issue_9_climatechange.pdf (Accessed June 20, 2021)

Popp, A. et al., 2017: Land-use futures in the shared socio-economic pathways. *Glob. Environ. Change*, **42**, 331–345, doi:10.1016/j.gloenvcha.2016.10.002.

Pottier, A., J.-C. Hourcade, and E. Espagne, 2014: Modelling the redirection of technical change: The pitfalls of incorporeal visions of the economy. *Energy Econ.*, **42**, 213–218, doi:10.1016/j.eneco.2013.12.003.

Povitkina, M., 2018: The limits of democracy in tackling climate change. *Env. Polit.*, **27(3)**, 411–432, doi:10.1080/09644016.2018.1444723.

Pradhan, P., L. Costa, D. Rybski, W. Lucht, and J.P. Kropp, 2017: A Systematic Study of Sustainable Development Goal (SDG) Interactions. *Earth's Future*, **5(11)**, 1169–1179, doi:10.1002/2017EF000632.

Prados de la Escosura, L., 2015: World Human Development: 1870–2007. *Rev. Income Wealth*, **61(2)**, 220–247, doi:10.1111/roiw.12104.

Prinn, R.G., J.M. Reilly, V.J. Karplus, and J. Jenkins, 2017: *Insights for Accelerating Clean Energy Transitions,* The MIT Joint Program on the Science and Policy of Global Carbon Pricing under Political Constraints, Helsinki, Finland, 48 pp. http://globalchange.mit.edu (Accessed June 20, 2021).

Purdon, M., 2017: Neoclassical realism and international climate change politics: moral imperative and political constraint in international climate finance. *J. Int. Relations Dev.*, **20(2)**, 263–300, doi:10.1057/jird.2013.5.

Quilcaille, Y., T. Gasser, P. Ciais, F. Lecocq, and M. Obersteiner, 2019: Carbon budgets based on new climate projections of the SSP scenarios and observations. European Geosciences Union (EGU) General Assembly, Vienna, Austria, pp 24. http://pure.iiasa.ac.at/id/eprint/15835/ (Accessed Jun 20, 2021).

Rabe, B.G., 2018: *Can we price carbon?* MIT Press, Cambridge, MA, USA, 376 pp.

Rajamani, L., 2016: The 2015 Paris Agreement: Interplay Between Hard, Soft and Non-Obligations: Table 1. *J. Environ. Law*, **28(2)**, 337–358, doi:10.1093/jel/eqw015.

Ramos-Mejía, M., M.L. Franco-Garcia, and J.M. Jauregui-Becker, 2018: Sustainability transitions in the developing world: Challenges of socio-technical transformations unfolding in contexts of poverty. *Environ. Sci. Policy*, **84**, 217–223, doi:10.1016/j.envsci.2017.03.010.

Ransan-Cooper, H., S.A. Ercan, and S. Duus, 2018: When anger meets joy: how emotions mobilise and sustain the anti-coal seam gas movement in regional Australia. *Soc. Mov. Stud.*, **17(6)**, 635–657, doi:10.1080/14742 837.2018.1515624.

Rao, N., E.T. Lawson, W.N. Raditloaneng, D. Solomon, and M.N. Angula, 2019: Gendered vulnerabilities to climate change: insights from the semi-arid regions of Africa and Asia. *Clim. Dev.*, **11(1)**, 14–26, doi:10.1080/17565 529.2017.1372266.

Raupach, M.R. et al., 2014: Sharing a quota on cumulative carbon emissions. *Nat. Clim. Change*, **4(10)**, 873–879, doi:10.1038/nclimate2384.

Raustiala, K. and D.G. Victor, 2004: The Regime Complex for Plant Genetic Resources. *Int. Organ.*, **58(02), pp** 277–309, doi:10.1017/S0020818304582036.

Raworth, K., 2018: *Doughnut Economics: Seven Ways to Think Like a 21st-Century Economist*. Chelsea Green Publishing, Chelsea, USA, 323 pp.

Raymond, L., 2020: Carbon Pricing and Economic Populism: The Case of Ontario. *Clim. Policy*, **20(9)**, 1127–1140, doi:10.1080/14693 062.2020.1782824.

Rayner, S., 2012: Uncomfortable knowledge: The social construction of ignorance in science and environmental policy discourses. *Econ. Soc.*, **41(1)**, 107–125, doi:10.1080/03085147.2011.637335.

Raza, M.Q. and A. Khosravi, 2015: A review on artificial intelligence based load demand forecasting techniques for smart grid and buildings. *Renew. Sustain. Energy Rev.*, **50**, 1352–1372, doi:10.1016/j.rser.2015.04.065.

Realmonte, G. et al., 2019: An inter-model assessment of the role of direct air capture in deep mitigation pathways. *Nat. Commun.*, **10(1)**, 3277, doi:10.1038/s41467-019-10842-5.

Reckien, D. et al., 2017: Climate change, equity and the Sustainable Development Goals: an urban perspective. *Environ. Urban.*, **29(1)**, 159–182, doi:10.1177/0956247816677778.

Reilly, J.M., Y.-H.H. Chen, and H.D. Jacoby, 2021: The COVID-19 effect on the Paris agreement. *Humanit. Soc. Sci. Commun.*, **8(1)**, 16, doi:10.1057/s41599-020-00698-2.

Reisinger, A. et al., 2020: *The concept of risk in the IPCC Sixth Assessment Report: a summary of cross-Working Group discussions*. Geneva, Switzerland, 15 pp.

Rennkamp, B., 2019: Power, coalitions and institutional change in South African climate policy. *Clim. Policy*, **19(6)**, 756–770, doi:10.1080/14693 062.2019.1591936.

Ricke, K., L. Drouet, K. Caldeira, and M. Tavoni, 2018: Country-level social cost of carbon. *Nat. Clim. Change*, **8(10)**, 895–900, doi:10.1038/s41558-018-0282-y.

Rietig, K. and T. Laing, 2017: Policy Stability in Climate Governance: The case of the United Kingdom. *Environ. Policy Gov.*, **27(6)**, 575–587, doi:10.1002/eet.1762.

Ringler, C., A. Bhaduri, and R. Lawford, 2013: The nexus across water, energy, land and food (WELF): potential for improved resource use efficiency? *Curr. Opin. Environ. Sustainability*, **5(6)**, 617–624, doi:10.1016/j.cosust.2013.11.002.

Rip, A. and R. Kemp, 1998: Technological change. In: *Human choice and climate change*. Battelle Press, Colombus, Ohio, USA, pp. 327–399.

Roberts, C., and F. W. Geels, 2019a: Conditions and intervention strategies for the deliberate acceleration of socio-technical transitions: lessons from a comparative multi-level analysis of two historical case studies in Dutch and Danish heating. *Technol. Anal. Strateg. Manag.*, **31**(9), 1081–1103, doi:10.1080/09537325.2019.1584286.

Roberts, C. and F.W. Geels, 2019b: Conditions for politically accelerated transitions: Historical institutionalism, the multi-level perspective, and two historical case studies in transport and agriculture. *Technol. Forecast. Soc. Change*, **140**, 221–240, doi:10.1016/j.techfore.2018.11.019.

Roberts, C. et al., 2018: The politics of accelerating low-carbon transitions: Towards a new research agenda. *Energy Res. Soc. Sci.*, **44**, 304–311, doi:10.1016/j.erss.2018.06.001.

Roberts, J.T. et al., 2020: Four agendas for research and policy on emissions mitigation and well-being. *Glob. Sustainability*, **3**, e3, doi:10.1017/sus.2019.25.

Robinson, M. and T. Shine, 2018: Achieving a climate justice pathway to 1.5°C. *Nat. Clim. Change*, **8**(7), 564–569, doi:10.1038/s41558-018-0189-7.

Robiou du Pont, Y. et al., 2017: Equitable mitigation to achieve the Paris Agreement goals. *Nat. Clim. Change*, **7**(1), 38–43, doi:10.1038/nclimate3186.

Rochedo, P.R.R. et al., 2021: Is Green Recovery Enough? Analysing the Impacts of Post-COVID-19 Economic Packages. *Energies*, **14**(17), 5567, doi:10.3390/en14175567.

Roger, C., T. Hale, and L. Andonova, 2017: The Comparative Politics of Transnational Climate Governance. *Int. Interact.*, **43**(1), 1–25, doi:10.1080/03050629.2017.1252248.

Romanello, M. et al., 2021: The 2021 report of the Lancet Countdown on health and climate change: code red for a healthy future. *Lancet*, **398**(10311), 1619–1662, doi:10.1016/S0140-6736(21)01787-6.

Romer, P.M., 1986: Increasing Returns and Long-Run Growth. *J. Polit. Econ.*, **94**(5), 1002–1037, doi:10.1086/261420.

Rosembloom, D. and J. Markard, 2020: A COVID-19 recovery for climate. *Science*, **368**(6490), 2019–2020, doi:10.1126/science.abc4887.

Rosen, R.A. and E. Guenther, 2015: The economics of mitigating climate change: What can we know? *Technol. Forecast. Soc. Change*, **91**, 93–106, doi:10.1016/J.TECHFORE.2014.01.013.

Rosenbloom, D., B. Haley, and J. Meadowcroft, 2018: Critical choices and the politics of decarbonization pathways: Exploring branching points surrounding low-carbon transitions in Canadian electricity systems. *Energy Res. Soc. Sci.*, **37**, 22–36, doi:10.1016/j.erss.2017.09.022.

Rosendahl, K.E. and D.R. Rubiano, 2019: How Effective is Lithium Recycling as a Remedy for Resource Scarcity? *Environ. Resour. Econ.*, **74**(3), 985–1010, doi:10.1007/s10640-019-00356-5.

Rosenschöld, J.M. af, J.G. Rozema, and L.A. Frye-Levine, 2014: Institutional Inertia and Climate Change: A Review of the New Institutionalist Literature. *WIREs Clim. Change*, **5**(5), 639–648, doi:10.1002/wcc.292.

Rotmans, J., R. Kemp, and M. van Asselt, 2001: More evolution than revolution: transition management in public policy. *Foresight*, **3**(1), 15–31, doi:10.1108/14636680110803003.

Routledge, P., A. Cumbers, and K.D. Derickson, 2018: States of just transition: Realising climate justice through and against the state. *Geoforum*, **88**, 78–86, doi:10.1016/j.geoforum.2017.11.015.

Rozenberg, J. and M. Fay, 2019: *Beyond the Gap: How Countries Can Afford the Infrastructure They Need while Protecting the Planet*. World Bank, Washington, DC, USA, 199 pp.

Ruby, M.B., I. Walker, and H.M. Watkins, 2020: Sustainable Consumption: The Psychology of Individual Choice, Identity, and Behavior. *J. Soc. Issues*, **76**(1), 8–18, doi:10.1111/josi.12376.

Ruger, J.P. and R. Horton, 2020: Justice and health: The Lancet–Health Equity and Policy Lab Commission. *Lancet*, **395**(10238), 1680–1681, doi:10.1016/S0140-6736(20)30928-4.

Runhaar, H., B. Wilk, Å. Persson, C. Uittenbroek, and C. Wamsler, 2018: Mainstreaming climate adaptation: taking stock about 'what works' from empirical research worldwide. *Reg. Environ. Change*, **18**(4), 1201–1210, doi:10.1007/s10113-017-1259-5.

Sachs, J., G. Schmidt-Traub, C. Kroll, D. Durand-Delacre, and K. Teksoz, 2016: *An SDG Index and Dashboards – Global Report*. New York, NY, USA, 58 pp. https://www.sdgindex.org/reports/sdg-index-and-dashboards-2016/.

Safarzyńska, K., 2018: Integrating behavioural economics into climate-economy models: some policy lessons. *Clim. Policy*, **18**(4), 485–498, doi:10.1080/14693062.2017.1313718.

Sarewitz, D., 2020: Unknown Knowns. *Issues Sci. Technol.*, **37**(1), pp 18–19.

Saunders, H.D. et al., 2021: Energy Efficiency: What Has Research Delivered in the Last 40 Years? *Annu. Rev. Environ. Resour.*, **46**(1), doi:10.1146/annurev-environ-012320-084937.

Scavenius, T.B.B. and S. Rayner, 2018: *Institutional Capacity for Climate Change Response: A New Approach to Climate Politics*. Routledge, Abingdon, UK, 164 pp.

Schlosberg, D., L.B. Collins, and S. Niemeyer, 2017: Adaptation policy and community discourse: risk, vulnerability, and just transformation. *Env. Polit.*, **26**(3), 413–437, doi:10.1080/09644016.2017.1287628.

Schreurs, M.A., 2016: The Paris Climate Agreement and the Three Largest Emitters: China, the United States, and the European Union. *Polit. Gov.*, **4**(3), 219, doi:10.17645/pag.v4i3.666.

Schultes, A. et al., 2018: Optimal international technology cooperation for the low-carbon transformation. *Clim. Policy*, **18**(9), 1165–1176, doi:10.1080/14693062.2017.1409190.

Schumpeter, J.A., 1934a: *The Theory of Economic Development: An Inquiry Into Profits, Credit, Interest, and the Business Cycle*. Harvard University Press, Cambridge, MA, USA, 255 pp.

Seto, K.C. et al., 2016: Carbon Lock-In: Types, Causes, and Policy Implications. *Annu. Rev. Environ. Resour.*, **41**(1), 425–452, doi:10.1146/annurev-environ-110615-085934.

Settele, J., J. Bishop, and S.G. Potts, 2016: Climate change impacts on pollination. *Nat. Plants*, **2**(7), 16092, doi:10.1038/nplants.2016.92.

Setzer, J. and L.C. Vanhala, 2019: Climate change litigation: A review of research on courts and litigants in climate governance. *Wiley Interdiscip. Rev. Clim. Change*, **10**(3), e580, doi:10.1002/WCC.580.

Shackleton, R.T., P. Angelstam, B. van der Waal, and M. Elbakidze, 2017: Progress made in managing and valuing ecosystem services: a horizon scan of gaps in research, management and governance. *Ecosyst. Serv.*, **27**, 232–241, doi:10.1016/j.ecoser.2016.11.020.

Shan, Y., et. al, 2020: Impacts of COVID-19 and fiscal stimuli on global emissions and the Paris Agreement. *Nat. Clim. Change*, **11**(3), 200–206, doi:10.1038/s41558-020-00977-5.

Shang, C., T. Wu, G. Huang, and J. Wu, 2019: Weak sustainability is not sustainable: Socioeconomic and environmental assessment of Inner Mongolia for the past three decades. *Resour. Conserv. Recycl.*, **141**, 243–252, doi:10.1016/j.resconrec.2018.10.032.

Sharpe, S. and T.M. Lenton, 2021: Upward-scaling tipping cascades to meet climate goals: plausible grounds for hope. *Clim. Policy*, **21**(4), 421–433, doi:10.1080/14693062.2020.1870097.

Shemi, A., A. Magumise, S. Ndlovu, and N. Sacks, 2018: Recycling of tungsten carbide scrap metal: A review of recycling methods and future prospects. *Miner. Eng.*, **122**, 195–205, doi:10.1016/J.MINENG.2018.03.036.

Shepherd, J.G., 2009: *Geoengineering the climate: science, governance and uncertainty*. The Royal SocietyLondon, UK, 98 pp.

Shi, L. et al., 2016: Roadmap towards justice in urban climate adaptation research. *Nat. Clim. Change*, **6**(2), 131–137, doi:10.1038/nclimate2841.

Shishlov, I., R. Morel, and V. Bellassen, 2016: Compliance of the Parties to the Kyoto Protocol in the first commitment period. *Clim. Policy*, **16**(6), 768–782, doi:10.1080/14693062.2016.1164658.

Shove, E. and N. Spurling, 2013: *Sustainable practices: Social theory and climate change*. Routledge, Abingdon, UK, 224 pp.

Sindico, F., 2015: *Is the Paris Agreement Really Legally Binding? University of Strathclyde* Glasgow, UK, 4 pp.

Singh, H.V., R. Bocca, P. Gomez, S. Dahlke, and M. Bazilian, 2019: The energy transitions index: An analytic framework for understanding the evolving global energy system. *Energy Strateg. Rev.*, **26**, 100382, doi:10.1016/J. ESR.2019.100382.

Skovgaard, J., S.S. Ferrari, and Å. Knaggård, 2019: Mapping and clustering the adoption of carbon pricing policies: what polities price carbon and why? *Clim. Policy*, **19(9)**, 1173–1185, doi:10.1080/14693062.2019.1641460.

Smajgl, A., J. Ward, and L. Pluschke, 2016: The water–food–energy nexus – Realising a new paradigm. *J. Hydrol.*, **533**, 533–540, doi:10.1016/j. jhydrol.2015.12.033.

Smidfelt Rosqvist, L. and L. Winslott Hiselius, 2016: Online shopping habits and the potential for reductions in carbon dioxide emissions from passenger transport. *J. Clean. Prod.*, **131**, 163–169, doi:10.1016/j. jclepro.2016.05.054.

Smit, B., Pilifosova, O., Burton, I., B. Challenger, S. Huq, R.J.T. Klein, and G. Yohe, 2001: Adaptation to Climate Change and Variability in the Context of Sustainable Development. In: Climate Change 2001: Impacts, Adaptation, and Vulnerability. Contribution of Working Group II to the Third Assessment Report of the Intergovernmental Panel on Climate Change [McCarthy, J.J, O.F. Canziani, N.A. Leary, D.J. Dokken, and K.S. White (eds.)]. Cambridge University Press, Cambridge, UK, 877–912.

Smith, J. and Patterson, J., 2018: Global Climate Justice Activism: "The New Protagonists" and their Projects for a Just Transition. In: *Ecologically Unequal Exchange: Environmental Injustice in Comparative and Historical Perspective* [Frey, R.S, P.K. Gellert, and H.F. Dahms (eds.)]. Palgrave Macmillan, New York, USA, pp. 245–272.

Song, M., S. Zhu, J. Wang, and J. Zhao, 2020: Share green growth: Regional evaluation of green output performance in China. *Int. J. Prod. Econ.*, **219**, 152–163, doi:10.1016/j.ijpe.2019.05.012.

Sorman, A.H., E. Turhan, and M. Rosas-Casals, 2020: Democratizing energy, energizing democracy: Central dimensions surfacing in the debate. *Front. Energy Res.*, **8**, 279.

Sovacool, B.K., B.-O. Linnér, and M.E. Goodsite, 2015: The political economy of climate adaptation. *Nat. Clim. Change*, **5(7)**, 616, doi:10.1038/nclimate2665.

Sovacool, B.K., A. Hook, M. Martiskainen, and L. Baker, 2019: The whole systems energy injustice of four European low-carbon transitions. *Glob. Environ. Change*, **58**, 101958, doi:10.1016/j.gloenvcha.2019.101958.

Spence, A., W. Poortinga, and N. Pidgeon, 2012: The Psychological Distance of Climate Change. *Risk Anal.*, **32(6)**, 957–972, doi:10.1111/j.1539-6924.2011.01695.x.

Spijkers, O., 2018: Intergenerational Equity and the Sustainable Development Goals. *Sustainability*, **10(11)**, 3836, doi:10.3390/su10113836.

Steffen, B. and T.S. Schmidt, 2019: A quantitative analysis of 10 multilateral development banks' investment in conventional and renewable power-generation technologies from 2006 to 2015. *Nat. Energy*, **4(1)**, 75–82, doi:10.1038/s41560-018-0280-3.

Stehfest, E. et al., 2009: Climate benefits of changing diet. *Clim. Change*, **95(1)**, 83–102, doi:10.1007/s10584-008-9534-6.

Stehr, N., 2005: *Knowledge Politics: governing the consequences of science and technology*. Routledge, Abingdon, UK, 252 pp.

Steinberger, J.K., W.F. Lamb, and M. Sakai, 2020: Your money or your life? The carbon-development paradox. *Environ. Res. Lett.*, **15(4)**, 044016, doi:10.1088/1748-9326/ab7461.

Stephan, U., M. Patterson, C. Kelly, and J. Mair, 2016: Organizations Driving Positive Social Change. *J. Manage.*, **42(5)**, 1250–1281, doi:10.1177/0149206316633268.

Stern, N., 2007: *The economics of climate change: The Stern review*. Cambridge University Press, Cambridge, UK, 692 pp.

Stern, N., 2018: Public economics as if time matters: Climate change and the dynamics of policy. *J. Public Econ.*, **162**, 4–17, doi:10.1016/j. jpubeco.2018.03.006.

Stern, N. and J.E. Stiglitz, 2017: *Report of the high-level commission on carbon prices*. Washington, DC, USA, 53 pp.

Stern, N. and A. Valero, 2021: Research policy, Chris Freeman special issue innovation, growth and the transition to net-zero emissions. *Res. Policy*, **50(9)**, 104293, doi:10.1016/j.respol.2021.104293.

Stern, N., J.E. Stiglitz, and J. Stiglitz, 2021: *The Social Cost of Carbon, Risk, Distribution, Market Failures: An alternative approach*. Cambridge, MA, USA, 65 pp.

Stern, N.H., 2015: *Why are we waiting? The logic, urgency, and promise of tackling climate change*. MIT Press, Cambridge, MA, USA, 406 pp.

Stern, P.C., T. Dietz, G.T. Gardner, J. Gilligan, and M.P. Vandenbergh, 2010: Energy Efficiency Merits More Than a Nudge. *Science*, **328(5976)**, 308–309, doi:10.1126/science.328.5976.308.

Steurer, R. and C. Clar, 2018: The ambiguity of federalism in climate policy-making: how the political system in Austria hinders mitigation and facilitates adaptation. *J. Environ. Policy Plan.*, **20(2)**, 252–265, doi:10.10 80/1523908X.2017.1411253.

Stevenson, H. and J.S. Dryzek, 2013: *Democratizing Global Climate Governance*. Cambridge University Press, Cambridge, UK, 268 pp.

Stevenson, H., G. Auld, J.I. Allan, L. Elliott, and J. Meadowcroft, 2021: The Practical Fit of Concepts: Ecosystem Services and the Value of Nature. *Glob. Environ. Polit.*, **21(2)**, 3–22, doi:10.1162/GLEP_A_00587.

Stiglitz, J.E., 2019: Addressing climate change through price and non-price interventions. *Eur. Econ. Rev.*, **119**, 594–612, doi:10.1016/j. euroecorev.2019.05.007.

Stoddard, I. et al., 2021: Three Decades of Climate Mitigation: Why Haven't We Bent the Global Emissions Curve? *Annu. Rev. Environ. Resour.*, **46(1)**, 653–689, doi:10.1146/annurev-environ-012220-011104.

Stoerk, T., G. Wagner, and R.E.T. Ward, 2018: Policy Brief – Recommendations for Improving the Treatment of Risk and Uncertainty in Economic Estimates of Climate Impacts in the Sixth Intergovernmental Panel on Climate Change Assessment Report. *Rev. Environ. Econ. Policy*, **12(2)**, 371–376, doi:10.1093/reep/rey005.

Stokes, L.C., 2013: The politics of renewable energy policies: The case of feed-in tariffs in Ontario, Canada. *Energy Policy*, **56**, 490–500, doi:10.1016/j. enpol.2013.01.009.

Stokes, L.C., 2020: *Short Circuiting Policy: Interest Groups and the Battle Over Clean Energy and Climate Policy in the American States*. Oxford University Press, Oxford, UK, 320 pp.

Stoll-Kleemann, S. and U.J. Schmidt, 2017: Reducing Meat Consumption in Developed and Transition Countries to Counter Climate Change and Biodiversity Loss: A Review of Influence Factors. *Reg. Environ. Change*, **17(5)**, 1261–1277, doi:10.1007/s10113-016-1057-5.

Strambo, C. and A.C.G. Espinosa, 2020: Extraction and Development: Fossil Fuel Production Narratives and Counternarratives in Colombia. *Clim. Policy*, **20(8)**, 931–948, doi:10.1080/14693062.2020.1719810.

Stringer, L.C. et al., 2014: Advancing climate compatible development: lessons from southern Africa. *Reg Env. Change*, **14**, 713–725, doi:10.1007/s10113-013-0533-4.

Sudbury, A.W. and E.B. Hutchinson, 2016: A Cost Analysis Of Amazon Prime Air Drone Delivery. *J. Econ. Educ.*, **16(1)**. https://libjournals.mtsu.edu/index.php/jfee/article/view/1512 (Accessed August 3, 2021)

Sugiawan, Y., R. Kurniawan, and S. Managi, 2019: Are carbon dioxide emission reductions compatible with sustainable well-being? *Appl. Energy*, **242**(December 2018), 1–11, doi:10.1016/j.apenergy.2019.03.113.

Sullivan, R., 2017: *Corporate responses to climate change: achieving emissions reduction through regulation, self-regulation and economic incentives*. 1st ed. Routledge, Abingdon, UK, 27 pp.

Sunny, N., N. Mac Dowell, and N. Shah, 2020: What is needed to deliver carbon-neutral heat using hydrogen and CCS? *Energy Environ. Sci.*, **13(11)**, 4204–4224, doi:10.1039/D0EE02016H.

Sussman, R., R. Gifford, and W. Abrahamse, 2016: *Social Mobilization: How to Encourage Action on Climate Change*. Pacific Institute for Climate Solutions, Victoria, BC, Canada, 20 pp http://www.pics.uvic.ca/sites/default/files/uploads/publications/FINAL (Accessed August 5, 2021).

Swilling, M., J. Musango, and J. Wakeford, 2016: Developmental states and sustainability transitions: Prospects of a just Transition in South Africa. *J. Environ. Policy Plan.*, **18(5)**, 650–672, doi:10.1080/1523908X.2015.1107716.

Swyngedouw, E., 2010: Apocalypse Forever? *Theory, Cult. Soc.*, **27(2–3)**, 213–232, doi:10.1177/0263276409358728.

Swyngedouw, E., 2011: Depoliticized Environments: The End of Nature, Climate Change and the Post-Political Condition. *R. Inst. Philos. Suppl.*, **69**, 253–274, doi:10.1017/S1358246111000300.

Taconet, N., C. Guivarch, and A. Pottier, 2021: Social Cost of Carbon Under Stochastic Tipping Points. *Environ. Resour. Econ.*, **78(4)**, 709–737, doi:10.1007/s10640-021-00549-x.

Tanner, T., and J. Allouche, 2011: Towards a New Political Economy of Climate Change and Development. *IDS Bull.*, **42(3)**, 1–14, doi:10.1111/j.1759-5436.2011.00217.x.

TCFD, 2018: *Task Force on Financial Disclosures: Status Report*. Financial Stability Board, Basel, Switzerland, 116 pp.

Thackeray, S.J. et al., 2020: Civil disobedience movements such as School Strike for the Climate are raising public awareness of the climate change emergency. *Glob. Change Biol.*, **26(3)**, 1042–1044, doi:10.1111/gcb.14978.

Thornbush, M., O. Golubchikov, and S. Bouzarovski, 2013: Sustainable cities targeted by combined mitigation–adaptation efforts for future-proofing. *Sustain. Cities Soc.*, **9**, 1–9, doi:10.1016/j.scs.2013.01.003.

Thornton, T.F., and C. Comberti, 2017: Synergies and trade-offs between adaptation, mitigation and development. *Clim. Change*, **140(1)**, 5–18, doi:10.1007/s10584-013-0884-3.

Tian, X., F. Bai, J. Jia, Y. Liu, and F. Shi, 2019: Realizing low-carbon development in a developing and industrializing region: Impacts of industrial structure change on CO_2 emissions in southwest China. *J. Environ. Manage.*, **233**, 728–738, doi:10.1016/j.jenvman.2018.11.078.

Tol, R.S.J., 2018: The Economic Impacts of Climate Change. *Rev. Environ. Econ. Policy*, **12(1)**, 4–25, doi:10.1093/reep/rex027.

Tompkins, E.L. et al., 2013: *An investigation of the evidence of benefits from climate compatible development*. Sustainability Research Institute, University of Leeds, Leeds, UK, 31 pp.

Torralba, M., N. Fagerholm, P.J. Burgess, G. Moreno, and T. Plieninger, 2016: Do European agroforestry systems enhance biodiversity and ecosystem services? A meta-analysis. *Agric. Ecosyst. Environ.*, **230**, 150–161, doi:10.1016/j.agee.2016.06.002.

Tosam, M.J. and R.A. Mbih, 2015: Climate change, health, and sustainable development in Africa. *Environ. Dev. Sustainability*, **17(4)**, 787–800, doi:10.1007/s10668-014-9575-0.

Tschakert, P. and L. Olsson, 2005: Post-2012 climate action in the broad framework of sustainable development policies: the role of the EU. *Clim. Policy*, **5(3)**, 329–348, doi:10.1080/14693062.2005.9685561.

Tukker, A. and E. Dietzenbacher, 2013: Global Multiregional Input–Output Frameworks: An Introduction and Outlook. *Econ. Syst. Res.*, **25(1)**, 1–19, doi:10.1080/09535314.2012.761179.

Tulkens, H., 2019: *Economics, Game Theory and International Environmental Agreements*. World Scientific, Singapore, 432 pp.

Turhan, E., B. Özkaynak, and C.İ. Aydın, 2019: Coal, ash, and other tales: The making and remaking of the anti-coal movement in Aliağa, Turkey. In: *Transforming Socio-Natures in Turkey: Landscapes, State and Environmental Movements*, Taylor and Francis, Abingdon, UK, pp. 166–186.

Turnheim, B. et al., 2015: Evaluating sustainability transitions pathways: Bridging analytical approaches to address governance challenges. *Glob. Environ. Change*, **35**, 239–253, doi:10.1016/J.GLOENVCHA.2015.08.010.

Turnheim, B., P. Kivimaa, and F. Berkhout, 2018: *Innovating Climate Governance*. Cambridge University Press, Cambridge, UK, 262 pp.

UN DESA, 2021: *The Sustainable Development Goals Report*. The UN New York, NY, USA, 68pp https://unstats.un.org/sdgs/report/2021/.

UNEP, 2018a: *Emissions Gap Report 2018*. United Nations Environment Programme, Nairobi, Kenya., 112 pp

UNEP, 2018b: *Inclusive wealth report 2018: measuring progress towards sustainability*. Nairobi, Kenya, 14 pp.

UNEP, 2020: *Global Climate Litigation Report 2020 Status Review*. Nairobi, Kenya, pp 52.

UNFCCC, 1992: United Nations Framework Convention on Climate Change, Rio de Janiero, Brazil.

UNFCCC, 2015: Paris Agreement to the United Nations Framework Convention on Climate Change, Paris, France.

UNFCCC, 2018a: *Talanoa Call for Action by the Presidents of COP23 and COP24*. Katowice, Poland. https://unfccc.int/sites/default/files/resource/Talanoa Call for Action.pdf.

UNFCCC, 2018b: Silesia Declaration: Solidarity and Just Transition, Katowice, poland.

UNHRC, 2018: *Report of the Special Rapporteur on the issue of human rights obligations relating to the enjoyment of a safe, clean, healthy and sustainable environment*. New York, NY, USA, 22 pp. https://undocs.org/en/A/HRC/37/59 (Accessed June 22, 2021).

Unruh, G.C., 2000: Understanding carbon lock-in. *Energy Policy*, **28(12)**, 817–830, doi:10.1016/S0301-4215(00)00070-7.

Urpelainen, J. and T. Van de Graaf, 2018: United States non-cooperation and the Paris agreement. *Clim. Policy*, **18(7)**, 839–851, doi:10.1080/14693062.2017.1406843.

Vadén, T. et al., 2020: Decoupling for ecological sustainability: A categorisation and review of research literature. *Environ. Sci. Policy*, **112**, 236–244, doi:10.1016/j.envsci.2020.06.016.

van den Berg, N.J. et al., 2019: Improved modelling of lifestyle changes in Integrated Assessment Models: Cross-disciplinary insights from methodologies and theories. *Energy Strateg. Rev.*, **26**, 100420, doi:10.1016/j.esr.2019.100420.

van den Bergh, J.C.J.M. et al., 2020: A dual-track transition to global carbon pricing. *Clim. Policy*, **20(9)**, 1057–1069, doi:10.1080/14693062.2020.1797618.

van den Bijgaart, I., R. Gerlagh, and M. Liski, 2016: A simple formula for the social cost of carbon. *J. Environ. Econ. Manage.*, **77**, 75–94, doi:10.1016/j.jeem.2016.01.005.

van der Heijden, J., 2018: From leaders to majority: a frontrunner paradox in built-environment climate governance experimentation. *J. Environ. Plan. Manag.*, **61(8)**, 1383–1401, doi:10.1080/09640568.2017.1350147.

van der Ploeg, F., and A. Rezai, 2019: Simple Rules for Climate Policy and Integrated Assessment. *Environ. Resour. Econ.*, **72(1)**, 77–108, doi:10.1007/s10640-018-0280-6.

van Vuuren, D.P. et al., 2011: The representative concentration pathways: an overview. *Clim. Change*, **109(1–2)**, 5–31, doi:10.1007/s10584-011-0148-z.

van Vuuren, D.P. et al., 2014: A new scenario framework for Climate Change Research: scenario matrix architecture. *Clim. Change*, **122(3)**, 373–386, doi:10.1007/s10584-013-0906-1.

van Vuuren, D.P. et al., 2017: The Shared Socio-economic Pathways: Trajectories for human development and global environmental change. *Glob. Environ. Change*, **42**, 148–152, doi:10.1016/j.gloenvcha.2016.10.009.

van Vuuren, D.P. et al., 2018: Alternative pathways to the 1.5°C target reduce the need for negative emission technologies. *Nat. Clim. Change*, **8(5)**, 391–397, doi:10.1038/s41558-018-0119-8.

Van Vuuren, D.P. et al., 2019: Integrated scenarios to support analysis of the food–energy–water nexus. *Nat. Sustain.*, **2(12)**, 1132–1141, doi:10.1038/s41893-019-0418-8.

Vartiainen, E., G. Masson, C. Breyer, D. Moser, and E. Román Medina, 2020: Impact of weighted average cost of capital, capital expenditure, and other parameters on future utility-scale PV levelised cost of electricity. *Prog. Photovoltaics Res. Appl.*, **28(6)**, 439–453, doi:10.1002/pip.3189.

Verplanken, B. and L. Whitmarsh, 2021: Habit and Climate Change. *Curr. Opin. Behav. Sci.*, **42**, 42–46, doi:10.1016/j.cobeha.2021.02.020.

Victor, D.G., 2011: *Global Warming Gridlock: Creating More Effective Strategies for Protecting the Planet*. Cambridge University Press, Cambridge, UK, 358 pp.

Vogt-Schilb, A., G. Meunier, and S. Hallegatte, 2018: When starting with the most expensive option makes sense: Optimal timing, cost and sectoral allocation of abatement investment. *J. Environ. Econ. Manage.*, **88**, 210–233, doi:10.1016/J.JEEM.2017.12.001.

Voituriez, T., W. Yao, and M.L. Larsen, 2019: Revising the 'host country standard" principle: a step for China to align its overseas investment with the Paris Agreement.' *Clim. Policy*, **19(10)**, 1205–1210, doi:10.1080/14693062.2019.1650702.

Walker, C., 2020: Uneven solidarity: the school strikes for climate in global and intergenerational perspective. *Sustain. Earth*, **3(1)**, 5, doi:10.1186/s42055-020-00024-3.

Walton, M., 2014: Applying complexity theory: A review to inform evaluation design. *Eval. Program Plann.*, **45**, 119–126, doi:10.1016/J.EVALPROGPLAN.2014.04.002.

Wamsler, C. and S. Pauleit, 2016: Making headway in climate policy mainstreaming and ecosystem-based adaptation: two pioneering countries, different pathways, one goal. *Clim. Change*, **137(1–2)**, 71–87, doi:10.1007/s10584-016-1660-y.

Wang, L., L. Zhao, G. Mao, J. Zuo, and H. Du, 2017: Way to accomplish low carbon development transformation: A bibliometric analysis during 1995–2014. *Renew. Sustain. Energy Rev.*, **68**, 57–69, doi:10.1016/j.rser.2016.08.021.

Wanger, T.C., 2011: The Lithium future-resources, recycling, and the environment. *Conserv. Lett.*, **4(3)**, 202–206, doi:10.1111/j.1755-263X.2011.00166.x.

Wapner, P.K. and H. Elver, 2017: *Reimagining climate change*. 1st ed. Routledge, Abingdon, UK, 198 pp.

Warde, A., 2017: Sustainable Consumption: Practices, Habits and Politics. In: *Consumption: A Sociological Analysis* [Warde, A. (ed.)]. Palgrave Macmillan UK, London, UK, pp. 181–204.

Warlenius, R., 2018: Decolonizing the Atmosphere: The Climate Justice Movement on Climate Debt. *J. Environ. Dev.*, **27(2)**, 131–155, doi:10.1177/1070496517744593.

Weber, E.U., 2015: Climate Change Demands Behavioral Change: What Are the Challenges? *Soc. Res.*, **82(3)**, 561–580.

Weber, E.U., 2016: What shapes perceptions of climate change? New research since 2010. *Wiley Interdiscip. Rev. Clim. Change*, **7(1)**, 125–134, doi:10.1002/wcc.377.

WEF, 2019: *The Global Risks Report 2019, 14th Edition*. Insight Report. World Economic Forum (WEF), Geneva, Switzerland, 80 pp.

Weikmans, R. and J.T. Roberts, 2019: The international climate finance accounting muddle: is there hope on the horizon? *Clim. Dev.*, **11(2)**, 97–111, doi:10.1080/17565529.2017.1410087.

Weitzman, M.L., 1994: On the "environmental" discount rate. *J. Environ. Econ. Manage.*, **26(2)**, 200–209, doi:10.1006/jeem.1994.1012.

Weitzman, M.L., 2001: Gamma discounting. *Am. Econ. Rev.*, **91(1)**, 260–271, doi:10.1257/aer.91.1.260.

Weitzman, M. L., 2009: On Modeling and Interpreting the Economics of Catastrophic Climate Change. *Rev. Econ. Stat.*, **91**(1), 1–19, doi:10.1162/rest.91.1.1.

Weitzman, M.L., 2011: Fat-tailed uncertainty in the economics of catastrophic climate change. *Rev. Environ. Econ. Policy*, **5(2)**, 275–292, doi:10.1093/reep/rer006.

Wells, P. and P. Nieuwenhuis, 2012: Transition failure: Understanding continuity in the automotive industry. *Technol. Forecast. Soc. Change*, **79(9)**, 1681–1692, doi:10.1016/j.techfore.2012.06.008.

Westman, L. and V.C. Broto, 2018: Climate governance through partnerships: A study of 150 urban initiatives in China. *Glob. Environ. Change*, **50**, 212–221, doi:10.1016/j.gloenvcha.2018.04.008.

Weyant, J., 2017: Some Contributions of Integrated Assessment Models of Global Climate Change. *Rev. Environ. Econ. Policy*, **11**(1), 115–137, doi:10.1093/reep/rew018.

Whitehead, M., 2013: Neoliberal Urban Environmentalism and the Adaptive City: Towards a Critical Urban Theory and Climate Change. *Urban Stud.*, **50(7)**, 1348–1367, doi:10.1177/0042098013480965.

Whitmarsh, L., W. Poortinga, and S. Capstick, 2021: Behaviour Change to Address Climate Change. *Curr. Opin. Psychol.*, **42**, 76–81, doi:10.1016/j.copsyc.2021.04.002.

Widerberg, O. and P. Pattberg, 2017: Accountability Challenges in the Transnational Regime Complex for Climate Change. *Rev. Policy Res.*, **34(1)**, 68–87, doi:10.1111/ropr.12217.

Wiedmann, T. and M. Lenzen, 2018: Environmental and social footprints of international trade. *Nat. Geosci.*, **11(5)**, 314–321, doi:10.1038/s41561-018-0113-9.

Wilhite, H., 2016: *The political economy of low carbon transformation: breaking the habits of capitalism*. Routledge, Abingdon, UK, 66 pp.

Willett, W. et al., 2019: Food in the Anthropocene: the EAT–Lancet Commission on healthy diets from sustainable food systems. *Lancet*, **393(10170)**, 447–492, doi:10.1016/S0140-6736(18)31788-4.

Williamson, O.E., 2000: The New Institutional Economics: Taking Stock, Looking Ahead. *J. Econ. Lit.*, **38(3)**, 595–613, doi:10.1257/jel.38.3.595.

Winkler, H., 2020: Towards a theory of just transition: A neo-Gramscian understanding of how to shift development pathways to zero poverty and zero carbon. *Energy Res. Soc. Sci.*, **70**, 101789, doi:10.1016/j.erss.2020.101789.

Winkler, H., T. Letete, and A. Marquard, 2013: Equitable access to sustainable development: operationalizing key criteria. *Clim. Policy*, **13(4)**, 411–432, doi:10.1080/14693062.2013.777610.

Winkler, H. et al., 2018: Countries start to explain how their climate contributions are fair: more rigour needed. *Int. Environ. Agreements Polit. Law Econ.*, **18(1)**, 99–115, doi:10.1007/s10784-017-9381-x.

Wittneben, B.B.F., C. Okereke, S.B. Banerjee, and D.L. Levy, 2012: Climate Change and the Emergence of New Organizational Landscapes. *Organ. Stud.*, **33(11)**, 1431–1450, doi:10.1177/0170840612464612.

Woiwode, C., 2013: New Departures in Tackling Urban Climate Change: Transdisciplinarity for Social Transformation (a critical appraisal of the WBGU's 2011 Report). *Integr. Rev.*, **9(2)**.

Wolfram, M., N. Frantzeskaki, and S. Maschmeyer, 2016: Cities, systems and sustainability: status and perspectives of research on urban transformations. *Curr. Opin. Environ. Sustainability*, **22**, 18–25, doi:10.1016/j.cosust.2017.01.014.

Wood, G. et al., 2020a: The comparative institutional analysis of energy transitions. *Socio-Economic Rev.*, **18(1)**, 257–294, doi:10.1093/ser/mwz026.

Wood, R. et al., 2020b: Beyond peak emission transfers: historical impacts of globalization and future impacts of climate policies on international emission transfers. *Clim. Policy*, **20(sup1)**, S14–S27, doi:10.1080/14693062.2019.1619507.

World Bank, 2019: *State and Trends of Carbon Pricing 2019*. World Bank, Washington, DC, USA, 97 pp.

World Bank, 2020: *GDP growth (annual %)*. World Bank national accounts data, Washington, DC, USA. https://data.worldbank.org/indicator/NY.GDP.MKTP.KD.ZG (Accessed June 3, 2021).

Wright, C. and D. Nyberg, 2017: An inconvenient truth: How organizations translate climate change into business as usual. *Acad. Manag. J.*, **60(5)**, 1633–1661, doi:10.5465/amj.2015.0718.

WTO, 2016: *World Trade Statistical Review 2016*. World Trade Organization (WTO), Geneva, Switzerland, 165 pp.

Wu, X., R.C. Nethery, M.B. Sabath, D. Braun, and F. Dominici, 2020: Air pollution and COVID-19 mortality in the United States: Strengths and limitations of an ecological regression analysis. *Sci. Adv.*, **6(45)**, eabd4049, doi:10.1126/SCIADV.ABD4049.

Wüstemann, H. et al., 2017: Synergies and trade-offs between nature conservation and climate policy: Insights from the "Natural Capital Germany – TEEB DE" study. *Ecosyst. Serv.*, **24**, 187–199, doi:10.1016/j.ecoser.2017.02.008.

Xia, Q., H. Wang, X. Liu, and X. Pan, 2021: Drivers of global and national CO_2 emissions changes 2000–2017. *Clim. Policy*, **21(5)**, 604–615, doi:10.1080/14693062.2020.1864267.

Xiang, P., H. Zhang, L. Geng, K. Zhou, and Y. Wu, 2019: Individualist-collectivist differences in climate change inaction: The role of perceived intractability. *Front. Psychol.*, **10**, doi:10.3389/fpsyg.2019.00187.

Yamahaki, C., A. V. Felsberg, A. C. Köberle, A. C. Gurgel, and J. Stewart-Richardson, 2022: Structural and specific barriers to the development of a green bond market in Brazil. *J. Sustain. Financ. Invest.*, **12**(2), 389–406, doi:10.1080/20430795.2020.1769985.

Yang, P. et al., 2018: Social cost of carbon under shared socioeconomic pathways. *Glob. Environ. Change*, **53**, 225–232, doi:10.1016/j.gloenvcha.2018.10.001.

York, A.M., M.A. Janssen, and E. Ostrom, 2005: Incentives Affecting Land Use Decisions of Nonindustrial Private Forest Landowners. In: *Handbook of Global Environmental Politics* [Peter Dauvergne (eds)], Edward Elgar Publishing, Northampton, MA, USA, 560 pp.

Yuan, H., P. Zhou, and D. Zhou, 2011: What is Low-Carbon Development? A Conceptual Analysis. *Energy Procedia*, **5**, 1706–1712, doi:10.1016/j.egypro.2011.03.290.

Yugo, M., and A. Soler, 2019: *A look into the role of e-fuels in the transport system in Europe (2030-2050) (literature review)*. Concawe, Brussels, Belgium, 19 pp.

Zahar, A., 2017: A Bottom-Up Compliance Mechanism for the Paris Agreement. *Chinese J. Environ. Law*, **1(1)**, 69–98, doi:10.1163/24686042-12340005.

Zhang, Y., Y. Li, K. Hubacek, X. Tian, and Z. Lu, 2019: Analysis of CO_2 transfer processes involved in global trade based on ecological network analysis. *Appl. Energy*, **233–234**, 576–583, doi:10.1016/j.apenergy.2018.10.051.

Zhenmin, L., and P. Espinosa, 2019: Tackling climate change to accelerate sustainable development. *Nat. Clim. Change*, **9(7)**, 494–496, doi:10.1038/s41558-019-0519-4.

Zhou, L., S. Gilbert, Y.E. Wang, M.M. Cabré, and K.P. Gallagher, 2018: *Moving the Green Belt and Road Initiative: From Words to Actions*. World Resources Institute, Washington, DC, USA, 44 pp. https://www.wri.org/research/moving-green-belt-and-road-initiative-words-actions (Accessed August 2, 2021).

Zhou, P. and W. Wen, 2020: Carbon-constrained firm decisions: From business strategies to operations modeling. *Eur. J. Oper. Res.*, **281(1)**, 1–15, doi:10.1016/j.ejor.2019.02.050.

Zou, C., Q. Zhao, G. Zhang, and B. Xiong, 2016: Energy revolution: From a fossil energy era to a new energy era. *Nat. Gas Ind. B*, **3(1)**, 1–11, doi:10.1016/j.ngib.2016.02.001.

Zummo, L., E. Gargroetzi, and A. Garcia, 2020: Youth voice on climate change: using factor analysis to understand the intersection of science, politics, and emotion. *Environ. Educ. Res.*, **26(8)**, 1207–1226, doi:10.1080/13504622.2020.1771288.

1

Emissions Trends and Drivers

2

Coordinating Lead Authors:
Shobhakar Dhakal (Nepal/Thailand), Jan Christoph Minx (Germany), Ferenc L. Toth (Austria/Hungary)

Lead Authors:
Amr Abdel-Aziz (Egypt), Maria Josefina Figueroa Meza (Venezuela/Denmark), Klaus Hubacek (the Netherlands/the United States of America), Inge G.C. Jonckheere (Italy/Belgium), Yong-Gun Kim (Republic of Korea), Gregory F. Nemet (the United States of America/Canada), Shonali Pachauri (India), Xianchun C. Tan (China), Thomas Wiedmann (Australia/Germany)

Contributing Authors:
Alaa Al Khourdajie (United Kingdom/Syria), Robbie M. Andrew (Norway), Giovanni Baiocchi (the United States of America/Italy), Igor A. Bashmakov (the Russian Federation), Alexandre Bizeul (France), Kornelis Blok (the Netherlands), Lazarus Chapungu (Zimbabwe), Harry Clark (New Zealand), William Collins (United Kingdom), Annette Cowie (Australia), Monica Crippa (Italy), Hancheng Dai (China), Steven J. Davis (the United States of America), Stéphane de la Rue du Can (the United States of America), Niklas Döbbeling (Germany), Kuishuang Feng (the United States of America), Vivien Fisch-Romito (France), Piers M. Forster (United Kingdom), Jan S. Fuglestvedt (Norway), Victor García Tapia (Spain), Oliver Geden (Germany), Yong Geng (China), Veronika Ginzburg (the Russian Federation), Giacomo Grassi (Italy/European Union), Baihe Gu (China), Céline Guivarch (France), Diego Guizzardi (Italy), Joanna I. House (United Kingdom), Suzana Kahn Ribeiro (Brazil), Smail Khennas (Algeria/United Kingdom), William F. Lamb (Germany/United Kingdom), Gunnar Luderer (Germany), Giulio Mattioli (Germany/Italy), Francesco Mattion (Italy), Rachid Mrabet (Morocco), Gert-Jan Nabuurs (the Netherlands), Jos Olivier (the Netherlands), Anne Owen (United Kingdom), Glen P. Peters (Norway/Australia), Julia Pongratz (Germany), Roberta Quadrelli (Italy), Andy Reisinger (New Zealand), Keywan Riahi (Austria), Matt Rigby (United Kingdom), Joeri Rogelj (Belgium/United Kingdom), Yamina Saheb (France/Algeria), Marielle Saunois (France), Roberto Schaeffer (Brazil), Karen C. Seto (the United States of America), Yuli Shan (China), Raphael Slade (United Kingdom), Steven J. Smith (the United States of America), Efisio Solazzo (Italy), Jan Steckel (Germany), Anders Hammer Strømman (Norway), Laixiang Sun (the United States of America), Pouya Taghavi-Moharamli (Canada), Hanqin Tian (the United States of America), Detlef P. van Vuuren (the Netherlands), Dominik Wiedenhofer (Austria)

Review Editors:
Barbara Amon (Germany), David I. Stern (Australia)

Chapter Scientists:
Lazarus Chapungu (Zimbabwe), William F. Lamb (Germany/United Kingdom)

This chapter should be cited as:
Dhakal, S., J.C. Minx, F.L. Toth, A. Abdel-Aziz, M.J. Figueroa Meza, K. Hubacek, I.G.C. Jonckheere, Yong-Gun Kim, G.F. Nemet, S. Pachauri, X.C. Tan, T. Wiedmann, 2022: Emissions Trends and Drivers. In IPCC, 2022: *Climate Change 2022: Mitigation of Climate Change. Contribution of Working Group III to the Sixth Assessment Report of the Intergovernmental Panel on Climate Change* [P.R. Shukla, J. Skea, R. Slade, A. Al Khourdajie, R. van Diemen, D. McCollum, M. Pathak, S. Some, P. Vyas, R. Fradera, M. Belkacemi, A. Hasija, G. Lisboa, S. Luz, J. Malley, (eds.)]. Cambridge University Press, Cambridge, UK and New York, NY, USA. doi: 10.1017/9781009157926.004

Table of Contents

Executive Summary

Global net anthropogenic greenhouse gas (GHG) emissions during the last decade (2010–2019) were higher than at any previous time in human history (*high confidence*). Since 2010, GHG emissions have continued to grow, reaching 59 ± 6.6 GtCO$_2$-eq in 2019,[1] but the average annual growth in the last decade (1.3%, 2010–2019) was lower than in the previous decade (2.1%, 2000–2009) (*high confidence*). Average annual GHG emissions were 56 ± 6.0 GtCO$_2$-eq yr^{-1} for the decade 2010–2019 growing by about 9.1 GtCO$_2$-eq yr^{-1} from the previous decade (2000–2009) – the highest decadal average on record (*high confidence*). {2.2.2, Table 2.1, Figure 2.2, Figure 2.5}

Emissions growth has varied, but persisted across all groups of GHGs (*high confidence*). The average annual emission levels of the last decade (2010–2019) were higher than in any previous decade for each group of GHGs (*high confidence*). In 2019, CO$_2$ emissions were 45 ± 5.5 GtCO$_2$,[2] CH$_4$ 11 ± 3.2 GtCO$_2$-eq, N$_2$O 2.7 ± 1.6 GtCO$_2$-eq and fluorinated gases (F-gases: HFCs, PFCs, SF$_6$, NF$_3$) 1.4 ± 0.41 GtCO$_2$-eq. Compared to 1990, the magnitude and speed of these increases differed across gases: CO$_2$ from fossil fuel and industry (FFI) grew by 15 GtCO$_2$-eq yr^{-1} (67%), CH$_4$ by 2.4 GtCO$_2$-eq yr^{-1} (29%), F-gases by 0.97 GtCO$_2$-eq yr^{-1} (254%), and N$_2$O by 0.65 GtCO$_2$-eq yr^{-1} (33%). CO$_2$ emissions from net land use, land-use change and forestry (LULUCF) have shown little long-term change, with large uncertainties preventing the detection of statistically significant trends. F-gases excluded from GHG emissions inventories such as *chlorofluorocarbons* and *hydrochlorofluorocarbons* are about the same size as those included (*high confidence*). {2.2.1, 2.2.2, Table 2.1, Figures 2.2, 2.3 and 2.5}

Globally, gross domestic product (GDP) per capita and population growth remained the strongest drivers of CO$_2$ emissions from fossil fuel combustion in the last decade (*robust evidence, high agreement*). Trends since 1990 continued in the years 2010 to 2019 with GDP per capita and population growth increasing emissions by 2.3% and 1.2% yr^{-1}, respectively. This growth outpaced the reduction in the use of energy per unit of GDP (–2% yr^{-1}, globally) as well as improvements in the carbon intensity of energy (–0.3% yr^{-1}) (*high confidence*). {2.4.1, Figure 2.16}

The global COVID-19 pandemic led to a steep drop in CO$_2$ emissions from fossil fuel and industry (*high confidence*). Global CO$_2$-FFI emissions dropped in 2020 by about 5.8% (5.1–6.3%) or about 2.2 (1.9–2.4) GtCO$_2$ compared to 2019. Emissions, however, have rebounded globally by the end of December 2020 (*medium confidence*). {2.2.2, Figure 2.6}

Cumulative net CO$_2$ emissions of the last decade (2010–2019) are about the same size as the remaining carbon budget for keeping warming to 1.5°C (*medium confidence*). Cumulative net CO$_2$ emissions since 1850 are increasing at an accelerating rate: about 62% of total cumulative CO$_2$ emissions from 1850 to 2019 occurred since 1970 (1500 ± 140 GtCO$_2$); about 43% since 1990 (1000 ± 90 GtCO$_2$); and about 17% since 2010 (410 ± 30 GtCO$_2$). For comparison, the remaining carbon budget for keeping warming to 1.5°C with a 67% (50%) probability is about 400 (500) ± 220 GtCO$_2$ (*medium confidence*). {2.2.2, Figure 2.7; AR6 WGI 5.5; AR6 WGI Table 5.8}

A growing number of countries have achieved GHG emission reductions longer than 10 years – a few at rates that are broadly consistent with climate change mitigation scenarios that limit warming to well below 2°C (*high confidence*). There are at least 18 countries that have reduced CO$_2$ and GHG emissions for longer than 10 years. Reduction rates in a few countries have reached 4% in some years, in line with rates observed in pathways that limit warming to 2°C (>67%). However, the total reduction in annual GHG emissions of these countries is small (about 3.2 GtCO$_2$-eq yr^{-1}) compared to global emissions growth observed over the last decades. Complementary evidence suggests that countries have decoupled territorial CO$_2$ emissions from GDP, but fewer have decoupled consumption-based emissions from GDP. This decoupling has mostly occurred in countries with high per capita GDP and high per capita CO$_2$ emissions. {2.2.3, 2.3.3, Figure 2.11, Table 2.3, Table 2.4}

Consumption-based CO$_2$ emissions in Developed Countries and the Asia and Pacific region are higher than in other regions (*high confidence*). In Developed Countries, consumption-based CO$_2$ emissions peaked at 15 GtCO$_2$ in 2007, declining to about 13 GtCO$_2$ in 2018. The Asia and Pacific region, with 52% of current global population, has become a major contributor to consumption-based CO$_2$ emission growth since 2000 (5.5% yr^{-1} for 2000–2018); it exceeded the Developed Countries region, which accounts for 16% of current global population, as the largest emitter of consumption-based CO$_2$. {2.3.2, Figure 2.14}

Carbon intensity improvements in the production of traded products have led to a net reduction in CO$_2$ emissions embodied in international trade (*robust evidence, high agreement*). A decrease in the carbon intensity of traded products has offset increased trade volumes between 2006 and 2016. Emissions embodied in internationally traded products depend on the composition of the global supply chain across sectors and countries and the respective carbon intensity of production processes (emissions per unit of economic output). {2.3, 2.4}

---

[1]   Emissions of GHGs are weighed by global warming potentials with a 100-year time horizon (GWP100) from the Sixth Assessment Report (Forster et al. 2021). GWP100 is commonly used in wide parts of the literature on climate change mitigation and is required for reporting emissions under the United Nations Framework Convention on Climate Change (UNFCCC). All metrics have limitations and uncertainties. (Cross-Chapter Box 2 in Chapter 2 and Annex II, Part II, Section 8).

[2]   In 2019, CO$_2$ from fossil fuel and industry (FFI) were 38 ± 3.0 Gt, CO$_2$ from net land use, land-use change and forestry (LULUCF) 6.6 ± 4.6 Gt.

Developed Countries tend to be net CO$_2$ emission importers, whereas developing countries tend to be net emission exporters (*robust evidence, high agreement*). Net CO$_2$ emission transfers from developing to Developed Countries via global supply chains have decreased between 2006 and 2016. Between 2004 and 2011, CO$_2$ emission embodied in trade between developing countries have more than doubled (from 0.47 to 1.1 Gt) with the centre of trade activities shifting from Europe to Asia. {2.3.4, Figure 2.15}

Emissions from developing countries have continued to grow, starting from a low base of per capita emissions and with a lower contribution to cumulative emissions than Developed Countries (*robust evidence, high agreement*). Average 2019 per capita CO$_2$-FFI emissions in three developing regions – Africa (1.2 tCO$_2$ per capita), Asia and Pacific (4.4 tCO$_2$ per capita), and Latin America and Caribbean (2.7 tCO$_2$ per capita) – remained less than half that of Developed Countries (9.5 tCO$_2$ per capita) in 2019. CO$_2$-FFI emissions in the three developing regions together grew by 26% between 2010 and 2019, compared to 260% between 1990 and 2010, while in Developed Countries emissions contracted by 9.9% between 2010 and 2019, and by 9.6% between 1990 and 2010. Historically, the three developing regions together contributed 28% to cumulative CO$_2$-FFI emissions between 1850 and 2019, whereas Developed Countries contributed 57% and Least-Developed Countries contributed 0.4%. {2.2.3, Figures 2.9 and 2.10}

Globally, GHG emissions continued to rise across all sectors and subsectors; most rapidly in transport and industry (*high confidence*). In 2019, 34% (20 GtCO$_2$-eq) of global GHG emissions came from the energy sector, 24% (14 GtCO$_2$-eq) from industry, 22% (13 GtCO$_2$-eq) from agriculture, forestry and other land use (AFOLU), 15% (8.7 GtCO$_2$-eq) from transport and 5.6% (3.3 GtCO$_2$-eq) from buildings. Once indirect emissions from energy use are considered, the relative shares of industry and buildings emissions rise to 34% and 16%, respectively. Average annual GHG emissions growth during 2010 to 2019 slowed compared to the previous decade in energy supply (from 2.3% to 1.0%) and industry (from 3.4% to 1.4%, direct emissions only), but remained roughly constant at about 2% per year in the transport sector (*high confidence*). Emission growth in AFOLU is more uncertain due to the high share of CO$_2$-LULUCF emissions (*medium confidence*). {2.4.2, Figure 2.13, Figures 2.16 to 2.21}

Average annual growth in GHG emissions from energy supply decreased from 2.3% for 2000–2009 to 1.0% for 2010–2019 (*high confidence*). This slowing of growth is attributable to further improvements in energy efficiency (annually, 1.9% less energy per unit of GDP was used globally between 2010 and 2019). Reductions in global carbon intensity by −0.2% yr^{-1} contributed further – reversing the trend during 2000 to 2009 (+0.2% yr^{-1}) (*medium confidence*). These carbon intensity improvements were driven by fuel switching from coal to gas, reduced expansion of coal capacity, particularly in Eastern Asia, and the increased use of renewables. {2.2.4, 2.4.2.1, Figure 2.17}

GHG emissions in the industry, buildings and transport sectors continue to grow, driven by an increase in the global demand for products and services (*high confidence*). These final demand sectors make up 44% of global GHG emissions, or 66% when the emissions from electricity and heat production are reallocated as indirect emissions to related sectors, mainly to industry and buildings. Emissions are driven by the large rise in demand for basic materials and manufactured products, a global trend of increasing floor space per capita, building energy service use, travel distances, and vehicle size and weight. Between 2010 and 2019, domestic and international aviation were particularly fast growing at average annual rates of +3.3% and +3.4%. Global energy efficiencies have improved in all three demand sectors, but carbon intensities have not. {2.2.4; Figures 2.18 to 2.20}

Providing access to modern energy services universally would increase global GHG emissions by, at most, a few percent (*medium confidence*). The additional energy demand needed to support decent living standards[3] for all is estimated to be well below current average energy consumption (*medium evidence, high agreement*). More equitable income distributions can reduce carbon emissions, but the nature of this relationship can vary by level of income and development (*limited evidence, medium agreement*). {2.4.3}

Evidence of rapid energy transitions exists, but only at sub-global scales (*medium evidence, medium agreement*). Emerging evidence since the Fifth Assessment Report of the Intergovernmental Panel on Climate Change (IPCC AR5) on past energy transitions identifies a growing number of cases of accelerated technology diffusion at sub-global scales and describes mechanisms by which future energy transitions may occur more quickly than those in the past. Important drivers include technology transfer and cooperation, intentional policy and financial support, and harnessing synergies among technologies within a sustainable energy system perspective (*medium evidence, medium agreement*). A fast global low-carbon energy transition enabled by finance to facilitate low-carbon technology adoption in developing, and particularly in least-developed countries, can facilitate achieving climate stabilisation targets (*robust evidence, high agreement*). {2.5.2, Table 2.5}

Multiple low-carbon technologies have shown rapid progress since AR5 – in cost, performance, and adoption – enhancing the feasibility of rapid energy transitions (*robust evidence, high agreement*). The rapid deployment and cost decrease of modular technologies like solar, wind, and batteries have occurred much faster than anticipated by experts and modelled in previous mitigation scenarios (*robust evidence, high agreement*). The political, economic, social, and technical feasibility of solar energy, wind energy and electricity storage technologies has improved dramatically over the past few years. In contrast, the adoption of nuclear energy and carbon capture and storage (CCS) in the electricity sector has been slower than the growth rates anticipated in stabilisation scenarios. Emerging evidence since AR5 indicates that small-scale technologies (e.g., solar, batteries) tend to improve faster and be adopted more

---

[3]　Decent Living Standards (DLS) – a benchmark of material conditions for human well-being – overlaps with many Sustainable Development Goals (SDGs). Minimum requirements of energy use consistent with enabling well-being for all is between 20 and 50 GJ per capita yr^{-1} depending on the context. {5.2.2, 5.2.2, Box 5.3, Figure 5.6}

quickly than large-scale technologies (nuclear, CCS) (*medium evidence, medium agreement*). {2.5.3, 2.5.4, Figures 2.22 and 2.23}

Robust incentives for investment in innovation, especially incentives reinforced by national policy and international agreements, are central to accelerating low-carbon technological change (*robust evidence, medium agreement*). Policies have driven innovation, including instruments for technology push (e.g., scientific training, research and development) and demand pull (e.g., carbon pricing, adoption subsidies), as well as those promoting knowledge flows and especially technology transfer. The magnitude of the scale-up challenge elevates the importance of rapid technology development and adoption. This includes ensuring participation of developing countries in an enhanced global flow of knowledge, skills, experience, and equipment. Also, technology itself requires strong financial, institutional, and capacity-building support (*robust evidence, high agreement*). {2.5.4, 2.5, 2.8}

The global wealthiest 10% contribute about 36–45% of global GHG emissions (*robust evidence, high agreement*). The global 10% wealthiest consumers live in all continents, with two-thirds in high-income regions and one-third in emerging economies (*robust evidence, medium agreement*). The lifestyle consumption emissions of the middle-income and poorest citizens in emerging economies are between 5 and 50 times below their counterparts in high-income countries (*medium evidence, medium agreement*). Increasing inequality within a country can exacerbate dilemmas of redistribution and social cohesion, and affect the willingness of rich and poor to accept lifestyle changes for mitigation and policies to protect the environment (*medium evidence, medium agreement*) {2.6.1, 2.6.2, Figure 2.25}

Estimates of future CO_2 emissions from existing fossil fuel infrastructures already exceed remaining cumulative net CO_2 emissions in pathways limiting warming to 1.5°C with no or limited overshoot (*high confidence*). Assuming variations in historical patterns of use and decommissioning, estimated future CO_2 emissions from existing fossil fuel infrastructure alone are 660 (460–890) $GtCO_2$ and from existing and currently planned infrastructure 850 (600–1100) $GtCO_2$. This compares to overall cumulative net CO_2 emissions until reaching net zero CO_2 of 510 (330–710) Gt in pathways that limit warming to 1.5°C with no or limited overshoot, and 890 (640–1160) Gt in pathways that limit warming to 2°C (<67%) (*high confidence*). While most future CO_2 emissions from existing and currently planned fossil fuel infrastructure are situated in the power sector, most remaining fossil fuel CO_2 emissions in pathways that limit warming to 2°C (<67%) and below are from non-electric energy – most importantly from the industry and transportation sectors (*high confidence*). Decommissioning and reduced utilisation of existing fossil fuel installations in the power sector as well as cancellation of new installations are required to align future CO_2 emissions from the power sector with projections in these pathways (*high confidence*). {2.7.2, 2.7.3, Figure 2.26, Table 2.6, Table 2.7}

A broad range of climate policies, including instruments like carbon pricing, play an increasing role in GHG emissions reductions. The literature is in broad agreement, but the magnitude of the reduction rate varies by the data and methodology used, country, and sector (*robust evidence, high agreement*). Countries with a lower carbon pricing gap (higher carbon price) tend to be less carbon intensive (*medium confidence*). {2.8.2, 2.8.3}

Climate-related policies have also contributed to decreasing GHG emissions. Policies such as taxes and subsidies for clean and public transportation, and renewable policies have reduced GHG emissions in some contexts (*robust evidence, high agreement*). Pollution control policies and legislations that go beyond end-of-pipe controls have also had climate co-benefits, particularly if complementarities with GHG emissions are considered in policy design (*medium evidence, medium agreement*). Policies on AFOLU and sector-related policies such as afforestation can have important impacts on GHG emissions (*medium evidence, medium agreement*). {2.8.4}

2

2.1   Introduction

As demonstrated by the contribution of Working Group I to the Sixth Assessment Report of the Intergovernmental Panel on Climate Change (AR6 WGI) (IPCC 2021a), greenhouse gas[4] (GHG) concentrations in the atmosphere and annual anthropogenic GHG emissions continue to grow and have reached a historic high, driven mainly by continued fossil fuels use (Jackson et al. 2019; Friedlingstein et al. 2020; Peters et al. 2020). Unsurprisingly, a large volume of new literature has emerged since AR5 on the trends and underlying drivers of anthropogenic GHG emissions. This chapter provides a structured assessment of this new literature and establishes the most important thematic links to other chapters in this report.

While AR5 has mostly assessed GHG emissions trends and drivers between 1970 and 2010, this assessment focuses on the period 1990–2019 with the main emphasis on changes since 2010. Compared to Chapter 5 in the contribution of WG III to AR5 (Blanco et al. 2014), the scope of the present chapter is broader. It presents the historical background of global progress in climate change mitigation for the rest of the report and serves as a starting point for the assessment of long-term as well as near- and medium-term mitigation pathways in Chapters 3 and 4, respectively. It also provides a systemic perspective on past emissions trends in different sectors of the economy (Chapters 6–12), and relates GHG emissions trends to past policies (Chapter 13) and observed technological development (Chapter 16). There is also a greater focus on the analysis of consumption-based sectoral emissions trends, empirical

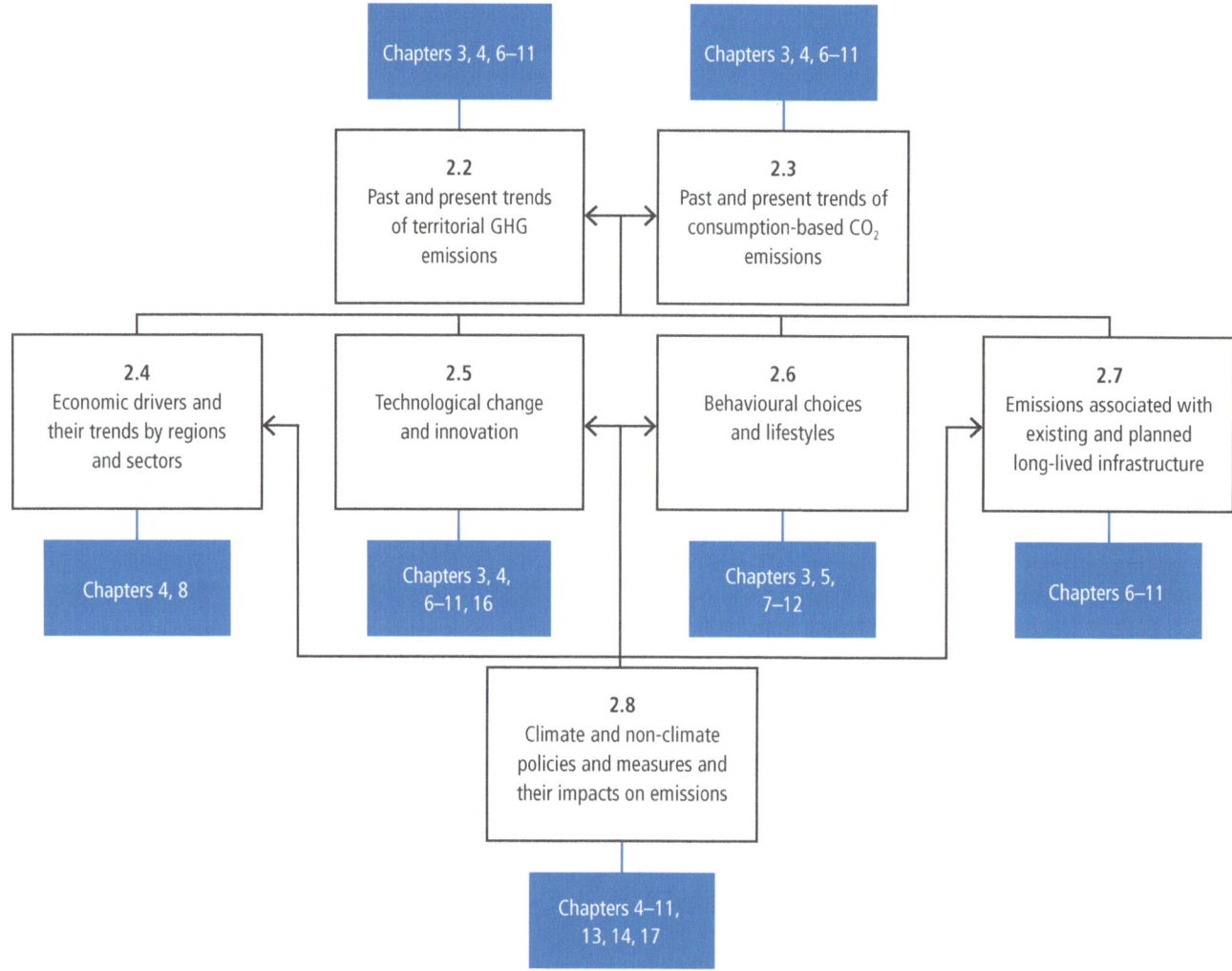

Figure 2.1 | Chapter 2 road map and linkages to other chapters. Black arrows show the causal chain driving emissions. Blue lines indicate key linkages to other chapters in this report.

---

4   Greenhouse gases are gaseous constituents of the atmosphere that absorb and emit radiation at specific wavelengths within the spectrum of radiation emitted by the Earth's surface, by the atmosphere itself, and by clouds. This property causes the greenhouse effect. Water vapour (H_2O), carbon dioxide (CO_2), nitrous oxide (N_2O), methane (CH_4), and ozone (O_3) are the primary GHGs in the Earth's atmosphere. Human-made GHGs include sulphur hexafluoride (SF_6), hydrofluorocarbons (HFCs), chlorofluorocarbons (CFCs), and perfluorocarbons (PFCs); see Annex I: Glossary.

evidence of emissions consequences of behavioural choices and lifestyles, and the social aspects of mitigation (Chapter 5). Finally, a completely new section discusses the mitigation implications of existing and planned long-lived infrastructure and carbon lock-in.

Figure 2.1 presents the road map of this chapter. It is a simplified illustration of the causal chain driving emissions along the black arrows. It also highlights the most important linkages to other chapters in this volume (blue lines). The logic of the figure is that the main topic of this chapter is GHG emissions trends (discussed only in this chapter at such level of detail), hence they are at the top of the figure in grey-outlined boxes. The secondary theme is the drivers behind these trends, depicted in the second line of grey-outlined boxes. Four categories of drivers highlight key issues and guide readers to chapters in which more details are presented. Finally, in addition to their own motivations and objectives, climate and non-climate policies and measures shape the aspirations and activities of actors in the main driver categories, as shown in the grey-outlined box below.

Accordingly, the grey-outlined boxes at the top of Figure 2.1 show that the first part of the chapter presents GHG emissions from two main perspectives: their geographical locations; and the places where goods are consumed and services are utilised. A complicated chain of drivers underlie these emissions. They are linked across time, space, and various segments of the economy and society in complex non-linear relationships. Sections shown in the second row of grey-outlined boxes assess the latest literature and improve the understanding of the relative importance of these drivers in mitigating GHG emissions. A huge mass of physical capital embodying immense financial assets and potentially operating over a long lifetime produces vast GHG emissions. This long-lived infrastructure can be a significant hindrance to fast and deep reductions of emissions; it is therefore also shown as an important driver. A large range of economic, social, environmental, and other policies has been shaping these drivers of GHG emissions in the past and are anticipated to influence them in the future, as indicated by the grey-outlined policies box and its manifold linkages. As noted, blue lines show linkages of sections to other chapters that discuss these drivers and their operating mechanisms in detail.

2.2 Past and Present Trends of Territorial GHG Emissions

Total anthropogenic greenhouse gas (GHG) emissions as discussed in this chapter comprise CO_2 emissions from fossil fuel combustion and industrial (FFI) processes,[5] net CO_2 emissions from land use, land-use change, and forestry (CO_2-LULUCF) (often named FOLU – forestry and other land-use – in previous IPCC reports), methane (CH_4), nitrous oxide (N_2O) and fluorinated gases (F-gases) comprising hydrofluorocarbons (HFCs), perfluorocarbons (PFCs), sulphur hexafluoride (SF_6) as well as nitrogen trifluoride (NF_3). There are other major sources of F-gas emissions that are regulated under the Montreal Protocol such as chlorofluorocarbons (CFCs) and hydrochlorofluorocarbons (HCFCs) that also have considerable warming impacts (Figure 2.4), however they are not considered

here. Other substances, including ozone and aerosols, that further contribute climate forcing are only treated very briefly, but a full chapter is devoted to this subject in the Working Group I contribution to AR6 (Szopa et al. 2021a; 2021b).

A growing number of global GHG emissions inventories have become available since AR5 (Minx et al. 2021). However, only a few are comprehensive in their coverage of sectors, countries and gases – namely EDGAR (Emissions Database for Global Atmospheric Research) (Crippa et al. 2021), PRIMAP (Potsdam Real-time Integrated Model for probabilistic Assessment of emissions Paths) (Gütschow et al. 2021a), CAIT (Climate Analysis Indicators Tool) (WRI 2019) and CEDS (A Community Emissions Data System for Historical Emissions) (Hoesly et al. 2018). None of these inventories presently cover CO_2-LULUCF, while CEDS excludes F-gases. For individual gases and sectors, additional GHG inventories are available, as shown in Figure 2.2, but each has varying system boundaries leading to important differences between their respective estimates (Section 2.2.1). Some inventories are compiled bottom-up, while others are produced synthetically and are dependent on other inventories. A more comprehensive list and discussion of different datasets is provided in the Chapter 2 Supplementary Material (2.SM.1) and in Minx et al. (2021).

Across this report, version 6 of EDGAR (Crippa et al. 2021) provided by the Joint Research Centre of the European Commission, is used for a consistent assessment of GHG emissions trends and drivers. It covers anthropogenic releases of CO_2-FFI, CH_4, N_2O, and F-gas (HFCs, PFCs, SF_6, NF_3) emissions by 228 countries and territories and across five sectors and 27 subsectors. EDGAR is chosen because it provides the most comprehensive global dataset in its coverage of sources, sectors and gases. For transparency, and as part of the uncertainty assessment, EDGAR is compared to other global datasets in Section 2.2.1 as well as in the Chapter 2 Supplementary Material (2.SM.1). For individual country estimates of GHG emissions, it may be more appropriate to use inventory data submitted to the United Nations Framework Convention on Climate Change (UNFCCC) under the common reporting format (CRF) (UNFCCC 2021). However, these inventories are only up to date for Annex I countries and cannot be used to estimate global or regional totals. As part of the regional analysis, a comparison of EDGAR and CRF estimates at the country-level is provided, where the latter is available (Figure 2.9).

Net CO_2-LULUCF estimates are added to the dataset as the average of estimates from three bookkeeping models of land-use emissions (Hansis et al. 2015; Houghton and Nassikas 2017; Gasser et al. 2020) following the Global Carbon Project (Friedlingstein et al. 2020). This is different to AR5, where land-based CO_2 emissions from forest fires, peat fires, and peat decay, were used as an approximation of the net-flux of CO_2-LULUCF (Blanco et al. 2014). Note that the definition of CO_2-LULUCF emissions by global carbon cycle models, as used here, differs from IPCC definitions (IPCC 2006) applied in national greenhouse gas inventories (NGHGI) for reporting under the climate convention (Grassi et al. 2018, 2021) and, similarly, from estimates by the Food and Agriculture Organization of the United Nations (FAO) for carbon fluxes on forest land (Tubiello et al. 2021). The conceptual

---

[5]   Industrial processes relate to CO_2 releases from fossil fuel oxidation and carbonate decomposition.

difference in approaches reflects different scopes. We use the global carbon cycle models' approach for consistency with Working Group I (Canadell et al. 2021) and to comprehensively distinguish natural from anthropogenic drivers, while NGHGI generally report as anthropogenic all CO_2 fluxes from lands considered managed (Section 7.2.2). Finally, note that the CO_2-LULUCF estimate from bookkeeping models as provided in this chapter is indistinguishable from the CO_2 from agriculture, forestry and other land use (AFOLU) as reported in Chapter 7, because the CO_2 emissions component from agriculture is negligible.

The resulting synthetic dataset used here has undergone additional peer review and is publicly available (Minx et al. 2021). Comprehensive information about the dataset as well as underlying uncertainties (including a comparison with other datasets) can be found in the Supplementary Material to this chapter and in Minx et al. (2021).

In this chapter and the report as a whole, different GHGs are frequently converted into common units of CO_2 equivalent (CO_2-eq) emissions using 100-year global warming potentials (GWP100) from AR6 WGI (Forster et al. 2021a). This reflects the dominant use in the scientific literature and is consistent with decisions made by Parties to the Paris Agreement for reporting and accounting of emissions and removals (UNFCCC 2019). Other GHG emissions metrics exist, all of which, like GWP100, are designed for specific purposes and have limitations and uncertainties. The appropriate choice of GHG emissions metrics depends on policy objective and context (Myhre et al. 2013; Kolstad et al. 2015). A discussion of GHG metrics is provided in a Cross-Chapter Box later in the chapter (Cross-Chapter Box 2) and at length in the Chapter 2 Supplementary Material. Throughout the chapter GHG emissions are reported (in GtCO$_2$-eq) at two significant digits to reflect prevailing uncertainties in emissions estimates. Estimates are subject to uncertainty, which we report for a 90% confidence interval.

2.2.1 Uncertainties in GHG Emissions

Estimates of historical GHG emissions – CO_2, CH_4, N_2O and F-gases – are uncertain to different degrees. Assessing and reporting uncertainties is crucial in order to understand whether available estimates are sufficiently robust to answer policy questions – for example, if GHG emissions are still rising, or if a country has achieved an emission reduction goal (Marland 2008). These uncertainties can be of scientific nature, such as when a process is not sufficiently understood. They also arise from incomplete or unknown parameter information (e.g., activity data, or emission factors), as well as estimation uncertainties from imperfect modelling techniques. There are at least three major ways to examine uncertainties in emission estimates (Marland et al. 2009): (i) by comparing estimates made by independent methods and observations (e.g., comparing atmospheric measurements with bottom-up emissions inventory estimates) (Saunois et al. 2020; Petrescu et al. 2020a and 2020b; Tian et al. 2020); (ii) by comparing estimates from multiple sources and understanding sources of variation (Macknick 2011; Andres et al. 2012; Andrew 2020; Ciais et al. 2021); and (iii) by evaluating estimates from a single source (Hoesly and Smith 2018), for instance via statistical sampling

across parameter values (e.g., Monni et al. 2007; Robert J. Andres et al. 2014; Tian et al. 2019; Solazzo et al. 2021).

Uncertainty estimates can be rather different depending on the method chosen. For example, the range of estimates from multiple sources is bounded by their interdependency; they can be lower than true structural plus parameter uncertainty, or than estimates made by independent methods. In particular, it is important to account for potential bias in estimates, which can result from using common methodological or parameter assumptions, or from missing sources (systemic bias). It is further crucial to account for differences in system boundaries – that is, which emissions sources are included in a dataset and which are not, otherwise direct comparisons can exaggerate uncertainties (Macknick 2011; Andrew 2020). Independent top-down observational constraints are, therefore, particularly useful to bound total emission estimates, but are not yet capable of verifying emission levels or trends (Petrescu et al. 2021a, 2021b). Similarly, uncertainties estimates are influenced by specific modelling choices. For example, uncertainty estimates from studies on the propagation of uncertainties associated with key input parameters (activity data, emissions factors) following the IPCC Guidelines (IPCC 2006) are strongly determined by assumptions on how these parameters are correlated between sectors, countries, and regions (Janssens-Maenhout et al. 2019; Solazzo et al. 2021). Assuming (full) covariance between source categories, and therefore dependence between them, increases uncertainty estimates. Estimates allowing for some covariance as in Sollazzo et al. (2021) also tend to yield higher estimates than the range of values from ensemble of dependent inventories (Saunois et al. 2016, 2020).

For this report, a comprehensive assessment of uncertainties is provided in the Supplementary Material (2.SM.2) to this chapter based on Minx et al. (2021). The uncertainties reported here combine statistical analysis, comparisons of global emissions inventories and an expert judgement of the likelihood of results lying outside a defined confidence interval, rooted in an understanding gained from the relevant literature. This literature has improved considerably since AR5, with a growing number of studies that assess uncertainties based on multiple lines of evidence (Saunois et al. 2016, 2020; Tian et al. 2020; Petrescu et al. 2021a, 2021b).

To report the uncertainties in GHG emissions estimates, a 90% confidence interval (5th–95th percentile) is adopted – that is, there is a 90% likelihood that the true value will be within the provided range if the errors have a Gaussian distribution, and no bias is assumed. This is in line with previous reporting in IPCC AR5 (Blanco et al. 2014; Ciais et al. 2014). Note that national emissions inventory submissions to the UNFCCC are requested to report uncertainty using a 95% confidence interval. The use of this broader uncertainty interval implies, however, a relatively high degree of knowledge about the uncertainty structure of the associated data, particularly regarding the distribution of uncertainty in the tails of the probability distributions. Such a high degree of knowledge is not present over all regions, emission sectors and species considered here.

Based on the assessment of relevant uncertainties above, a constant, relative, global uncertainty estimates for GHGs are applied at a 90%

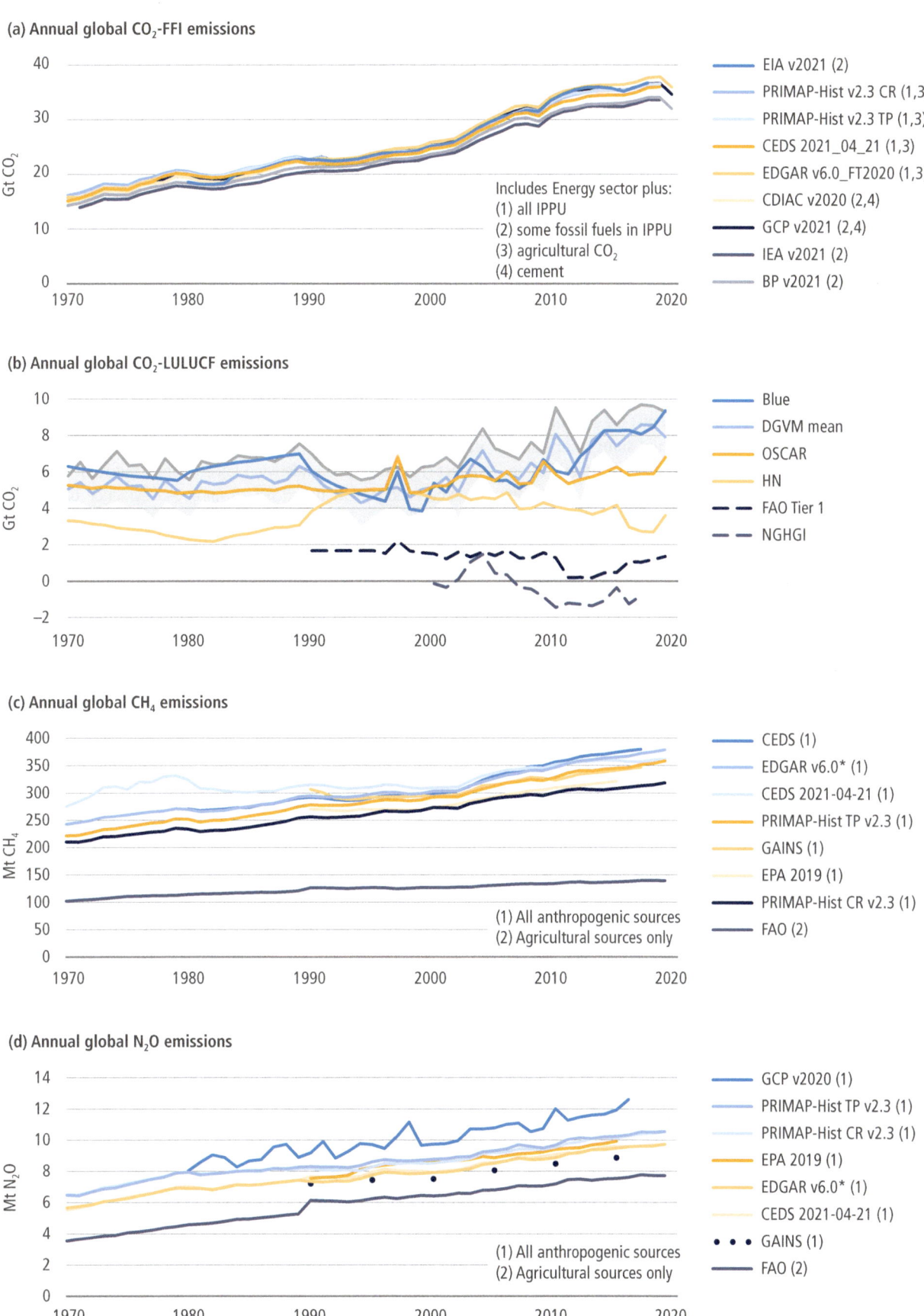

Figure 2.2 | Estimates of global anthropogenic greenhouse gas emissions from different data sources 1970–2019.

Figure 2.2 (continued): Estimates of global anthropogenic greenhouse gas emissions from different data sources 1970–2019. Panel (a): CO_2 FFI emissions from: EDGAR – Emissions Database for Global Atmospheric Research (this dataset) (Crippa et al. 2021); GCP – Global Carbon Project (Friedlingstein et al. 2020; Andrew and Peters 2021); CEDS – Community Emissions Data System (Hoesly et al. 2018; O'Rourke et al. 2021); CDIAC Global, Regional, and National Fossil-Fuel CO_2 Emissions (Gilfillan et al. 2020); PRIMAP-hist – Potsdam Real-time Integrated Model for probabilistic Assessment of emissions Paths (Gütschow et al. 2016, 2021b); EIA – Energy Information Administration International Energy Statistics (EIA 2021); BP – BP Statistical Review of World Energy (BP 2021); IEA – International Energy Agency (IEA 2021a, 2021b); IPPU refers to emissions from industrial processes and product use. **Panel (b):** Net anthropogenic CO_2-LULUCF emissions from: BLUE – Bookkeeping of land-use emissions (Hansis et al. 2015; Friedlingstein et al. 2020); DGVM-mean – multi-model mean of CO_2-LULUCF emissions from dynamic global vegetation models (Friedlingstein et al. 2020); OSCAR – an earth system compact model (Friedlingstein et al. 2020; Gasser et al. 2020); HN – Houghton and Nassikas Bookkeeping Model (Houghton and Nassikas 2017; Friedlingstein et al. 2020); for comparison, the net CO_2 flux from FAOSTAT (FAO Tier 1) is plotted, which comprises net emissions and removals on forest land and from net forest conversion (FAOSTAT 2021; Tubiello et al. 2021), emissions from drained organic soils under cropland/grassland (Conchedda and Tubiello 2020), and fires in organic soils (Prosperi et al. 2020), as well as a net CO_2 flux estimate from National Greenhouse Gas Inventories (NGHGI) based on country reports to the UNFCCC, which include land-use change, and fluxes in managed lands (Grassi et al. 2021). **Panel (c):** Anthropogenic CH_4 emissions from: EDGAR (above); CEDS (above); PRIMAP-hist (above); GAINS – The Greenhouse gas – Air pollution Interactions and Synergies Model (Höglund-Isaksson et al. 2020); EPA-2019: Greenhouse gas emission inventory (US-EPA, 2019); FAO –FAOSTAT inventory emissions (Tubiello et al. 2013; Tubiello 2018; FAOSTAT 2021); **Panel (d):** Anthropogenic N_2O emissions from: GCP – global nitrous oxide budget (Tian et al. 2020); CEDS (above); EDGAR (above); PRIMAP-hist (above); GAINS (Winiwarter et al. 2018); EPA-2019 (above); FAO (above). Differences in emissions across different versions of the EDGAR dataset are shown in the Supplementary Material (Figure 2.SM.2). Source: Minx et al. (2021).

confidence interval that range from relatively low values for CO_2-FFI (±8%), to intermediate values for CH_4 and F-gases (±30%), to higher values for N_2O (±60%) and CO_2-LULUCF (±70%). Uncertainties for aggregated total GHG emissions in terms of CO_2-eq emissions are calculated as the square root of the squared sums of absolute uncertainties for individual gases (taking F-gases together), using GWP100 to weight emissions of non-CO_2 gases but excluding uncertainties in the metric itself.

This assessment of uncertainties is broadly in line with AR5 WGIII (Blanco et al. 2014), but revises individual uncertainty judgements

in line with the more recent literature (Saunois et al. 2016, 2020; Janssens-Maenhout et al. 2019; Friedlingstein et al. 2020; Tian et al. 2020; Solazzo et al. 2021) as well as the underlying synthetic analysis provided here (e.g., Figures 2.2 and 2.3 in this chapter; and Minx et al. 2021). As such, reported changes in these estimates do not reflect changes in the underlying uncertainties, but rather a change in expert judgement based on an improved evidence base in the scientific literature. Uncertainty estimates for CO_2-FFI and N_2O remain unchanged compared to AR5. The change in the uncertainty estimates for CH_4 from 20% to 30% is justified by larger uncertainties reported for EDGAR emissions (Janssens-Maenhout et al. 2019; Solazzo et al.

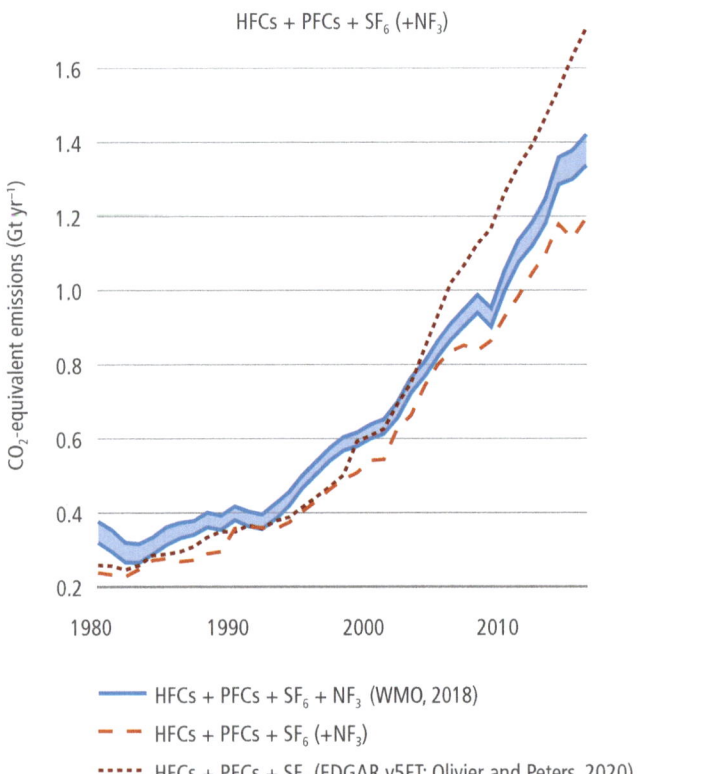

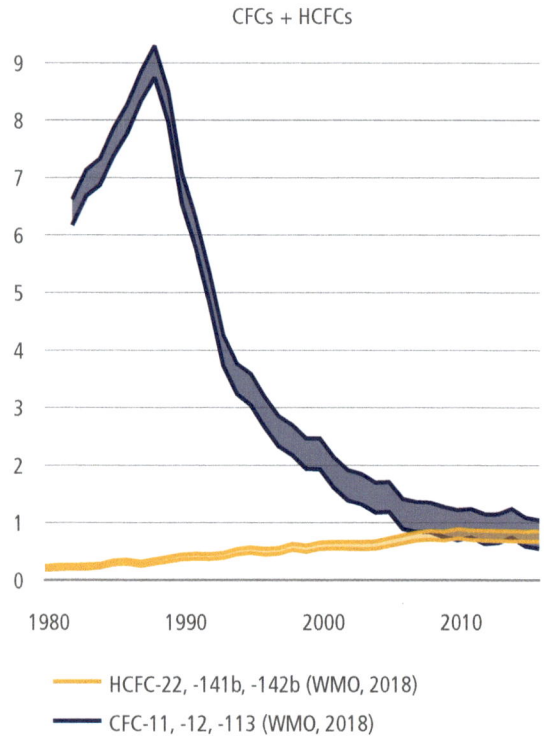

Figure 2.3 | Comparison between top-down estimates and bottom-up EDGAR inventory data on GHG emissions for 1980–2016. Left panel: Total GWP100-weighted emissions based on IPCC AR6 (Forster et al. 2021a) of F-gases in Olivier and Peters (2020) [EDGARv5FT] (dark-red dotted line, excluding C_4F_{10}, C_5F_{12}, C_6F_{14} and C_7F_{16}) and EDGARv6 (bright red dashed line) compared to top-down estimates based on AGAGE and NOAA data from WMO (2018) (blue lines; Engel and Rigby (2018); Montzka and Velders (2018)). **Right panel:** Top-down aggregated emissions for the three most abundant CFCs (–11, –12 and –113) and HCFCs (–22, –141b, –142b) not covered in bottom-up emissions inventories are shown in dark blue and yellow. For top-down estimates the shaded areas between two respective lines represent 1σ uncertainties. Source: Minx et al. (2021).

2021) as well as the wider literature (Kirschke et al. 2013; Tubiello et al. 2015; Saunois et al. 2016, 2020). As AR6 – in contrast to AR5 – uses CO_2-LULUCF data from global bookkeeping models, the respective uncertainty estimate is based on the reporting in the underlying literature (Friedlingstein et al. 2020) as well as Working Group I (Canadell et al. 2021). The 70% uncertainty value is at the higher end of the range considered in AR5 (Blanco et al. 2014).

Finally, for F-gas emissions top-down atmospheric measurements from the 2018 World Meteorological Organization's (WMO) Scientific Assessment of Ozone Depletion (Engel and Rigby 2018; Montzka and Velders 2018) are compared to the data used in this report (Crippa et al. 2021; Minx et al. 2021) as shown in Figure 2.3. Due to the general absence of natural F-gas fluxes, there is a sound understanding of global and regional F-gas emissions from top-down estimates of atmospheric measurements with small and well-understood measurement, lifetime and transport model uncertainties (Engel and Rigby 2018; Montzka and Velders 2018). However, when species are aggregated into total F-gas emissions, EDGARv6.0 emissions are around 10% lower than the WMO 2018 values throughout, with larger differences for individual F-gas species, and further discrepancies when comparing to older EDGAR versions. Based on this, the overall uncertainties for aggregate

F-gas emissions is judged conservatively at 30% − 10 percentage points higher than in AR5 (Blanco et al. 2014).

Aggregate uncertainty across all GHGs is approximately ±11% depending on the composition of gases in a particular year. AR5 applied a constant uncertainty estimates of ±10% for total GHG emissions. The upwards revision applied to the uncertainties of CO_2-LULUCF, CH_4 and F-gas emissions therefore has a limited overall effect on the assessment of GHG emissions.

GHG emissions metrics such as GWP100 have their own uncertainties, which has been largely neglected in the literature so far. Minx et al. (2021) report the uncertainty in GWP100 metric values as ±50% for methane and other short-lived climate forcers (SLCFs), and ±40% for non-CO_2 gases with longer atmospheric lifetimes (specifically, those with lifetimes longer than 20 years). If uncertainties in GHG metrics are considered, and are assumed independent (which may lead to an underestimate) the overall uncertainty of total GHG emissions in 2019 increases from ±11% to ±13%. Metric uncertainties are not further considered in this chapter, but are referred to in Cross-Chapter Box 2 in this chapter, and Chapter 2 Supplementary Material on GHG metrics (2.SM.3).

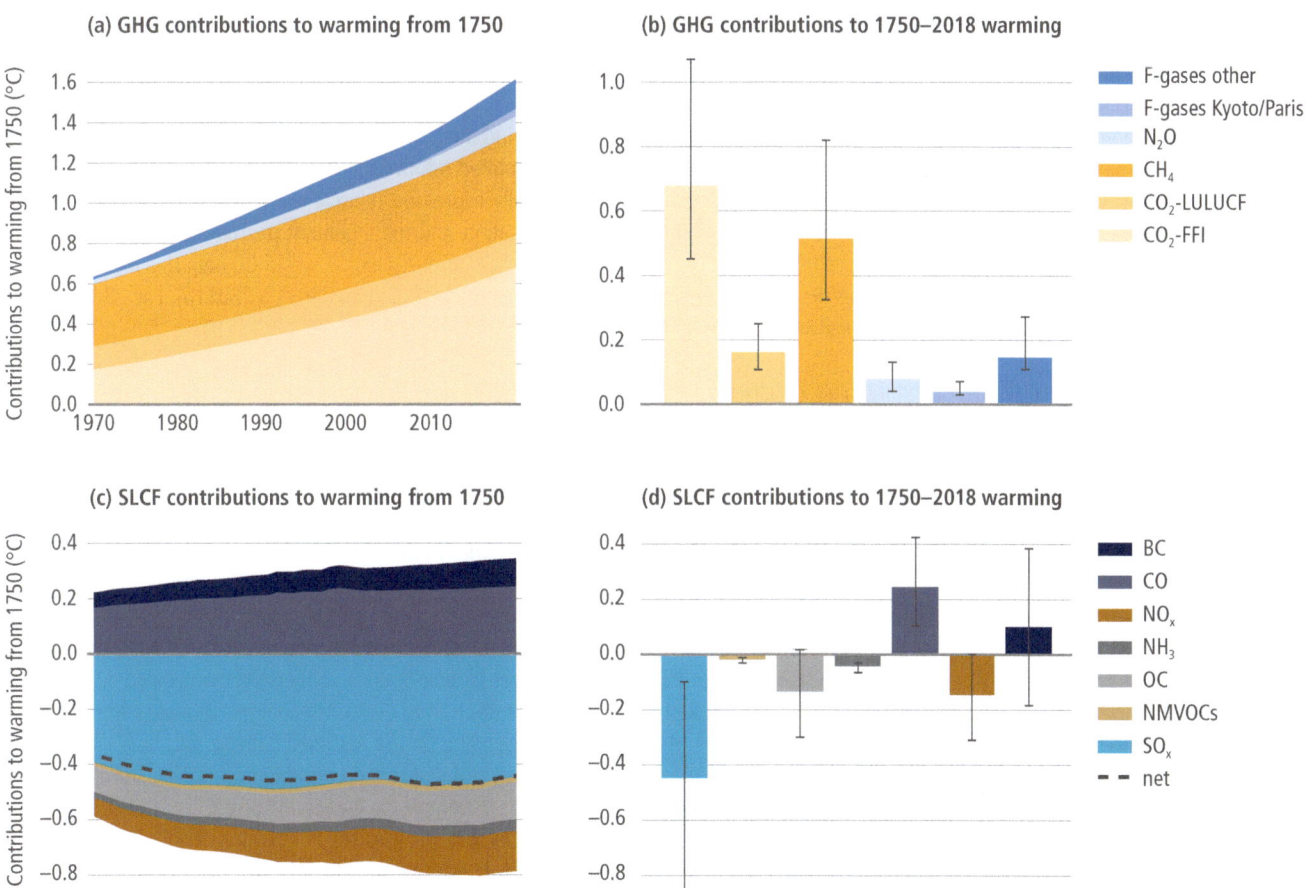

Figure 2.4 | Contribution of different GHGs to global warming over the period 1750 to 2018. Top row: contributions estimated with the FaIR reduced-complexity climate model. Major GHGs and aggregates of minor gases as a timeseries in **(a)** and as a total warming bar chart with 90% confidence interval added in **(b)**. Bottom row: contribution from short-lived climate forcers as a time series in **(c)** and as a total warming bar chart with 90% confidence interval added in **(d)**. The dotted line in (c) gives the net temperature change from short-lived climate forcers other than CH_4. F-Kyoto/Paris includes the gases covered by the Kyoto Protocol and Paris Agreement, while F-other includes the gases covered by the Montreal Protocol but excluding the HFCs. Source: Minx et al. (2021).

The most appropriate metric to aggregate GHG emissions depends on the objective (Cross-Chapter Box 2). One such objective can be to understand the contribution of emissions in any given year to warming, while another can be to understand the contribution of cumulative emissions over an extended time period to warming. In Figure 2.4 the modelled warming from emissions of each gas or group of gases is also shown – calculated using the reduced-complexity climate model Finite Amplitude Impulse Response (FaIR) model v1.6, which has been calibrated to match several aspects of the overall WGI assessment (Forster et al. 2021a; specifically Cross-Chapter Box 7 in Chapter 10 therein). Additionally, its temperature response to emissions with shorter atmospheric lifetimes such as aerosols, methane or ozone has been adjusted to broadly match those presented in Szopa et al. (2021a). There are some differences in actual warming compared to the GWP100 weighted emissions of each gas (Figure 2.4), in particular a greater contribution from CH_4 emissions to historical warming. This is consistent with warming from CH_4 being short-lived and hence having a more pronounced effect in the near-term during a period of rising emissions. Nonetheless, Figure 2.4 highlights that emissions weighted by GWP100 do not provide a fundamentally different information about the contribution of individual gases than modelled actual warming over the historical period, when emissions of most GHGs have been rising continuously, with CO_2 being the dominant and CH_4 being the second most important contributor to GHG-induced warming. Other metrics such as GWP* (or GWP star) (Cain et al. 2019) offer an even closer resemblance between cumulative CO_2-eq emissions and temperature change. Such a metric may be more appropriate when the key objective is to track temperature change when emissions are falling, as in mitigation scenarios.

Cross-Chapter Box 2 | GHG Emissions Metrics

Authors: Andy Reisinger (New Zealand), Alaa Al Khourdajie (United Kingdom/Syria), Kornelis Blok (the Netherlands), Harry Clark (New Zealand), Annette Cowie (Australia), Jan S. Fuglestvedt (Norway), Oliver Geden (Germany), Veronika Ginzburg (the Russian Federation), Céline Guivarch (France), Joanna I. House (United Kingdom), Jan Christoph Minx (Germany), Rachid Mrabet (Morocco), Gert-Jan Nabuurs (the Netherlands), Glen P. Peters (Norway/Australia), Keywan Riahi (Austria), Roberto Schaeffer (Brazil), Raphael Slade (United Kingdom), Anders Hammer Strømman (Norway), Detlef P. van Vuuren (the Netherlands)

Comprehensive mitigation policy relies on consideration of all anthropogenic forcing agents, which differ widely in their atmospheric lifetimes and impacts on the climate system. GHG emission metrics[6] provide simplified information about the effects that emissions of different GHGs have on global temperature or other aspects of climate, usually expressed relative to the effect of emitting CO_2 (see emission metrics in Annex I: Glossary). This information can inform prioritisation and management of trade-offs in mitigation policies and emission targets for non-CO_2 gases relative to CO_2, as well as for baskets of gases expressed in CO_2-eq. This assessment builds on the evaluation of GHG emission metrics from a physical science perspective by WGI (Forster et al. 2021b). For additional details and supporting references, see Chapter 2 Supplementary Material (2.SM.3) and Annex II.8.

The global warming potential (GWP) and the global temperature change potential (GTP) were the main metrics assessed in AR5 (Myhre et al. 2013; Kolstad et al. 2014). The GWP with a lifetime of 100 years (GWP100) continues to be the dominant metric used in the scientific literature on mitigation assessed by WGIII. The assessment by WGI (Forster et al. 2021) includes updated values for these metrics based on updated scientific understanding of the response of the climate system to emissions of different gases, including changing background concentrations. It also assesses new metrics published since AR5. Metric values in AR6 include climate-carbon cycle feedbacks by default; this provides an important update and clarification from AR5 which reported metric values both with and without such feedbacks.

The choice of metric, including time horizon, should reflect the policy objectives for which the metric is applied (Plattner et al. 2009). Recent studies confirm earlier findings that the GWP is consistent with a cost-benefit framework (Kolstad et al. 2014), which implies weighting each emission based on the economic damages that this emission will cause over time, or conversely, the avoided damages from avoiding that emission. The GWP time horizon can be linked to the discount rate used to evaluate economic damages from each emission. For methane, GWP100 implies a social discount rate of about 3–5% depending on the assumed damage function, whereas GWP20 implies a much higher discount rate, greater than 10% (*medium confidence*) (Mallapragada and Mignone 2019; Sarofim and Giordano 2018). The dynamic GTP is aligned with a cost-effectiveness framework, as it weights each emission based on its contribution to global warming in a specified future year (e.g., the expected year of peak warming for a given temperature goal). This implies a shrinking time horizon and increasing relative importance of SLCF emissions as the target year is approached (Johansson 2011; Aaheim and Mideksa 2017). The GTP with a static time horizon (e.g., GTP100) is not well-matched to either a cost-benefit or a cost-effectiveness framework, as the year for which the temperature outcome is evaluated would not match the year of peak warming, nor the overall damages caused by each emission (Edwards and Trancik 2014; Strefler et al. 2014; Mallapragada and Mignone 2017).

---

[6]　Emission metrics also exist for aerosols, but these are not commonly used in climate policy. This assessment focuses on GHG emission metrics only.

Cross-Chapter Box 2 (continued)

A number of studies since AR5 have evaluated the impact of various GHG emission metrics and time horizons on the global economic costs of limiting global average temperature change to a pre-determined level (e.g. Strefler et al. 2014; Harmsen et al. 2016; Tanaka et al. 2021) (see 2.SM.3 for additional detail). These studies indicate that, for mitigation pathways that limit warming to 2°C (<67%) above pre-industrial levels or lower, using GWP100 to inform cost-effective abatement choices between gases would achieve such long-term temperature goals at close to least global cost within a few percent (*high confidence*). Using the dynamic GTP instead of GWP100 could reduce global mitigation costs by a few percent in theory (*high confidence*), but the ability to realise those cost savings depends on the temperature limit, policy foresight and flexibility in abatement choices as the weighting of SLCF emissions increases over time (*medium confidence*) (van den Berg et al. 2015; Huntingford et al. 2015). Similar benefits as for the dynamic GTP might be obtained by regularly reviewing and potentially updating the time horizon used for GWP in light of actual emissions trends compared to climate goals (Tanaka et al. 2020).

The choice of metric and time horizon can affect the distribution of costs and the timing of abatement between countries and sectors in cost-effective mitigation strategies. Sector-specific lifecycle assessments find that different emission metrics and different time horizons can lead to divergent conclusions about the effectiveness of mitigation strategies that involve reductions of one gas but an increase of another gas with a different lifetime (e.g., Tanaka et al. 2019). Assessing the sensitivity of conclusions to different emission metrics and time horizons can support more robust decision-making (Levasseur et al. 2016; Balcombe et al. 2018) (see 2.SM.3 for details). Sectoral and national perspectives on GHG emission metrics may differ from a global least-cost perspective, depending on other policy objectives and equity considerations, but the literature does not provide a consistent framework for assessing GHG emission metrics based on equity principles.

Literature since AR5 has emphasised that the GWP100 is not well-suited to estimating the warming effect at specific points in time from sustained SLCF emissions (e.g., Allen et al. 2016; Cain et al. 2019; Collins et al. 2019). This is because the warming caused by an individual SLCF emission pulse diminishes over time and hence, unlike CO_2, the warming from SLCF emissions that are sustained over multiple decades to centuries depends mostly on their ongoing rate of emissions rather than their cumulative emissions. Treating all gases interchangeably based on GWP100 within a stated emissions target therefore creates ambiguity about actual global temperature outcomes (Fuglestvedt et al. 2018; Denison et al. 2019). Supplementing economy-wide emission targets with information about the expected contribution from individual gases to such targets would reduce the ambiguity in global temperature outcomes.

Recently developed step/pulse metrics such as the combined global temperature change potential (CGTP) (Collins et al. 2019) and GWP* (Allen et al. 2018; Cain et al. 2019) recognise that a sustained increase/decrease in the rate of SLCF emissions has a similar effect on global surface temperature over multiple decades as a one-off pulse emission/removal of CO_2. These metrics use this relationship to calculate the CO_2 emissions or removals that would result in roughly the same temperature change as a sustained change in the rate of SLCF emissions (CGTP) over a given time period, or as a varying time series of CH_4 emissions (GWP*). From a mitigation perspective, these metrics indicate greater climate benefits from rapid and sustained methane reductions over the next few decades than if such reductions are weighted by GWP100, while conversely, sustained methane increases have greater adverse climate impacts (Collins et al. 2019; Lynch et al. 2020). The ability of these metrics to relate changes in emission rates of short-lived gases to cumulative CO_2 emissions makes them well-suited, in principle, to estimating the effect on the remaining carbon budget from more, or less, ambitious SLCF mitigation over multiple decades compared to a given reference scenario (*high confidence*) (Collins et al. 2019; Forster et al. 2021).

The potential application of GWP* in wider climate policy (e.g., to inform equitable and ambitious emission targets or to support sector-specific mitigation policies) is contested, although relevant literature is still limited (Rogelj and Schleussner 2019, 2021; Schleussner et al. 2019; Allen et al. 2021; Cain et al. 2021). Whereas GWP and GTP describe the marginal effect of each emission relative to the absence of that emission, GWP* describes the equivalent CO_2 emissions that would give the same temperature change as an emissions trajectory of the gas considered, starting at a (user-determined) reference point. The warming based on those cumulative CO_2-equivalent emission at any point in time is relative to the warming caused by emissions of that gas before the reference point. Because of their different focus, GWP* and GWP100 can equate radically different CO_2 emissions to the same CH_4 emissions: rapidly declining CH_4 emissions have a negative CO_2-warming-equivalent value based on GWP* (rapidly declining SLCF emissions result in declining temperature, relative to the warming caused by past SLCF emissions at a previous point in time) but a positive CO_2-equivalent value based on GWP or GTP (each SLCF emission from any source results in increased future radiative forcing and global average temperature than without this emission, regardless of whether the rate of SLCF emissions is rising or declining). The different focus in these metrics can have important distributional consequences, depending on how they are used to inform emission targets (Lynch et al. 2021; Reisinger et al. 2021), but this has only begun to be explored in the scientific literature.

Cross-Chapter Box 2 (continued)

A key insight from WGI is that, for a given emissions scenario, different metric choices can alter the time at which net zero GHG emissions are calculated to be reached, or whether net zero GHG emissions are reached at all (2.SM.3). From a mitigation perspective, this implies that changing GHG emission metrics but retaining the same numerical CO_2-equivalent emissions targets would result in different climate outcomes. For example, achieving a balance of global anthropogenic GHG emissions and removals, as stated in Article 4.1 of the Paris Agreement could, depending on the GHG emission metric used, result in different peak temperatures and in either stable, or slowly or rapidly declining temperature after the peak (Allen et al. 2018; Fuglestvedt et al. 2018; Tanaka and O'Neill 2018; Schleussner et al. 2019). A fundamental change in GHG emission metrics used to monitor achievement of existing emission targets could therefore inadvertently change their intended climate outcomes or ambition, unless existing emission targets are re-evaluated at the same time (*very high confidence*).

The WGIII contribution to AR6 reports aggregate emissions and removals using updated GWP100 values from AR6 WGI unless stated otherwise. This choice was made on both scientific grounds (the alignment of GWP100 with a cost-benefit perspective under social discount rates and its performance from a global cost-effectiveness perspective) and for procedural reasons, including continuity with past IPCC reports and alignment with decisions under the Paris Agreement Rulebook (Annex II.8). A key constraint in the choice of metric is also that the literature assessed by WGIII predominantly uses GWP100 and often does not provide sufficient detail on emissions and abatement of individual gases to allow translation into different metrics. Presenting such information routinely in mitigation studies would enable the application of more diverse GHG emission metrics in future assessments to evaluate their contribution to different policy objectives.

All metrics have limitations and uncertainties, given that they simplify the complexity of the physical climate system and its response to past and future GHG emissions. No single metric is well-suited to all applications in climate policy. For this reason, the WGIII contribution to AR6 reports emissions and mitigation options for individual gases where possible; CO_2-equivalent emissions are reported in addition to individual gas emissions where this is judged to be policy-relevant. This approach aims to reduce the ambiguity regarding mitigation potentials for specific gases and actual climate outcomes over time arising from the use of any specific GHG emission metric.

2.2.2   Trends in the Global GHG Emissions Trajectories and Short-lived Climate Forcers

2.2.2.1   Anthropogenic Greenhouse Gas Emissions Trends

Global GHG emissions continued to rise since AR5, but the rate of emissions growth slowed (*high confidence*). GHG emissions reached 59 ± 6.6 GtCO$_2$-eq in 2019 (Table 2.1 and Figure 2.5). In 2019, CO_2 emissions from the FFI were 38 (±3.0) Gt, CO_2 from LULUCF 6.6 ± 4.6 Gt, CH$_4$ 11 ± 3.2 GtCO$_2$-eq, N$_2$O 2.7 ± 1.6 GtCO$_2$-eq and F-gases 1.4 ± 0.41 GtCO$_2$-eq. There is *high confidence* that average annual GHG emissions for the last decade (2010–2019) were the highest on record in terms of aggregate CO$_2$-eq emissions, but *low confidence* for annual emissions in 2019 as uncertainties are large considering the size and composition of observed increases in the most recent years (UNEP 2020a; Minx et al. 2021).

GHG emissions levels in 2019 were higher compared to 10 and 30 years earlier (*high confidence*): about 12% (6.5 GtCO$_2$-eq) higher than in 2010 (53 ± 5.7 GtCO$_2$-eq) (the last year of AR5 reporting) and about 54% (21 GtCO$_2$-eq) higher than in 1990 (38 ± 4.8 GtCO$_2$-eq) (the baseline year of the Kyoto Protocol and frequent nationally determined contribution (NDC) reference). GHG emissions growth slowed compared to the previous decade (*high confidence*): From 2010 to 2019, GHG emissions grew on average by about 1.3% per year compared to an average annual growth of

2.1% between 2000 and 2009. Nevertheless the absolute increase in average annual GHG emissions for 2010–2019 compared to 2000–2009 was 9.1 GtCO$_2$-eq and, as such, the largest observed in the data since 1970 (Table 2.1) – and most likely in human history (Friedlingstein et al. 2020; Gütschow et al. 2021b). Decade-by-decade growth in average annual GHG emissions was observed across all (groups of) gas as shown in Table 2.1, but for N$_2$O and CO$_2$-LULUCF emissions this is much more uncertain.

Reported total annual GHG emission estimates differ between the WGIII contributions in AR5 (Blanco et al. 2014) and AR6 (this chapter) mainly due to differing global warming potentials (*high confidence*). For the year 2010, total GHG emissions were estimated at 49 ± 4.9 GtCO$_2$-eq in AR5 (Blanco et al. 2014), while we report 53 ± 5.7 GtCO$_2$-eq here. However, in AR5 total GHG emissions were weighted based on GWP100 values from IPCC's Second Assessment Report. Applying those GWP values to the 2010 emissions from AR6 yields 50 GtCO$_2$-eq (Forster et al. 2021a). Hence, observed differences are mainly due to the use of most recent GWP values, which have higher warming potentials for methane (29% higher for biogenic and 42% higher for fugitive methane) and 12% lower values for nitrous oxide (Cross-Chapter Box 2 in this chapter).

Emissions growth has been persistent but varied in pace across gases. The average annual emission levels of the last decade (2010–2019) were higher than in any previous decade for each group of GHGs:

Table 2.1 | Total anthropogenic GHG emissions (GtCO$_2$-eq yr^{-1}) 1990–2019. CO$_2$ from fossil fuel combustion and industrial processes (FFI); CO$_2$ from Land Use, Land Use Change and Forestry (LULUCF); methane (CH$_4$); nitrous oxide (N$_2$O); fluorinated gases (F-gases: HFCs, PFCs, SF$_6$, NF$_3$). Aggregate GHG emissions trends by groups of gases reported in GtCO$_2$-eq converted based on global warming potentials with a 100-year time horizon (GWP100) from the IPCC Sixth Assessment Report (AR6). Uncertainties are reported for a 90% confidence interval. Source: Minx et al. (2021).

	Average annual emissions (GtCO$_2$-eq)					
	CO$_2$ FFI	CO$_2$ LULUCF	CH$_4$	N$_2$O	Fluorinated gases	GHG
2019	38 ± 3.0	6.6 ± 4.6	11 ± 3.2	2.7 ± 1.6	1.4 ± 0.41	59 ± 6.6
2010–2019	36 ± 2.9	5.7 ± 4.0	10 ± 3.0	2.6 ± 1.5	1.2 ± 0.35	56 ± 6.0
2000–2009	29 ± 2.4	5.3 ± 3.7	9.0 ± 2.7	2.3 ± 1.4	0.81 ± 0.24	47 ± 5.3
1990–1999	24 ± 1.9	5.0 ± 3.5	8.2 ± 2.5	2.1 ± 1.2	0.49 ± 0.15	40 ± 4.9
1990	23 ± 1.8	5.0 ± 3.5	8.2 ± 2.5	2.0 ± 1.2	0.38 ± 0.11	38 ± 4.8

CO$_2$, CH$_4$, N$_2$O, and F-gases (*high confidence*). Since 1990, CO$_2$-FFI have grown by 67% (15 GtCO$_2$-eq), CH$_4$ by 29% (2.4 GtCO$_2$-eq), and N$_2$O by 33% (0.65 GtCO$_2$-eq), respectively (Figure 2.5). Growth in fluorinated gases (F-gas) has been by far the highest with about 254% (1.0 GtCO$_2$-eq), but it occurred from low levels. In 2019, total F-gas levels were no longer negligible with a share of 2.3% of global GHG emissions. Note that the F-gases reported here do not include CFCs and HCFCs, which are groups of substances regulated under the Montreal Protocol. The aggregate CO$_2$-eq emissions of HFCs, HCFCs and CFCs were each approximately equal in 2016, with a smaller contribution from PFCs, SF$_6$, NF$_3$ and some more minor F-gases. Therefore, the GWP-weighted F-gas emissions reported here (HFCs, PFCs, SF$_6$, NF$_3$), which are dominated by the HFCs, represent less than half of the overall CO$_2$-eq F-gas emissions in 2016 (Figure 2.3).

Emissions of greenhouse gases have continued to increase since 1990, at varying rates

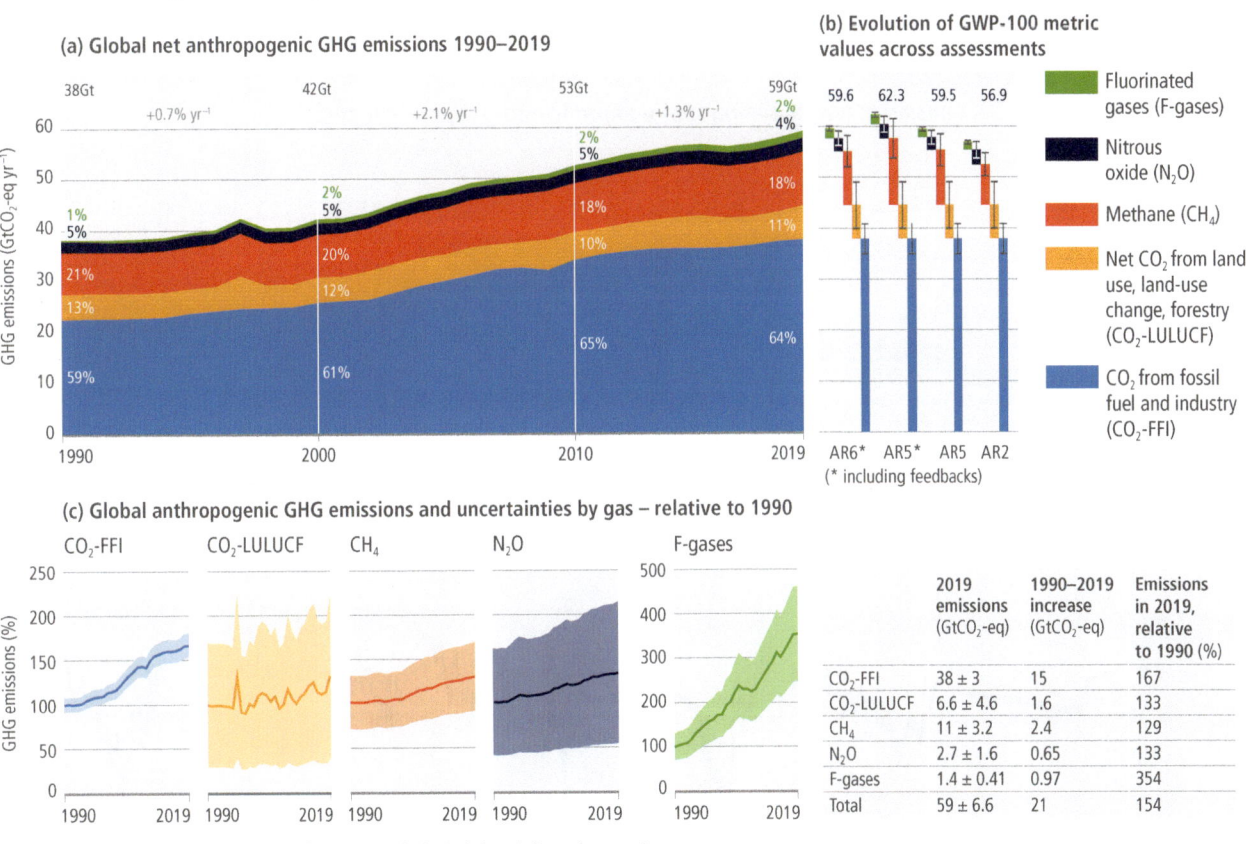

Figure 2.5 | Total anthropogenic GHG emissions (GtCO$_2$-eq yr^{-1}) 1990–2019. CO$_2$ from fossil fuel combustion and industrial processes (FFI); net CO$_2$ from land use, land use change and forestry (LULUCF); methane (CH$_4$); nitrous oxide (N$_2$O); fluorinated gases (F-gases: HFCs, PFCs, SF$_6$, NF$_3$). **Panel (a):** Aggregate GHG emissions trends by groups of gases reported in GtCO$_2$-eq converted based on global warming potentials with a 100-year time horizon (GWP100) from the IPCC Sixth Assessment Report. **Panel (b):** Waterfall diagrams juxtaposes GHG emissions for the most recent year (2019) in CO$_2$ equivalent units using GWP100 values from the IPCC's Second, Fifth, and Sixth Assessment Reports, respectively. Error bars show the associated uncertainties at a 90% confidence interval. **Panel (c):** individual trends in CO$_2$-FFI, CO$_2$-LULUCF, CH$_4$, N$_2$O and F-gas emissions for the period 1990–2019, normalised to 1 in 1990. Source: data from Minx et al. (2021).

The only exception to these patterns of GHG emissions growth is net anthropogenic CO_2-LULUCF emissions, where there is no statistically significant trend due to high uncertainties in estimates (Figures 2.2 and 2.5; Chapter 2 Supplementary Material). While the average estimate from the bookkeeping models report a slightly increasing trend in emissions, NGHGI and FAOSTAT estimates show a slightly decreasing trend, which diverges in recent years (Figure 2.2). Similarly, trends in CO_2-LULUCF estimates from individual bookkeeping models differ: while two models (BLUE and OSCAR) show a sustained increase in emissions levels since the mid-1990s, emissions from the third model (Houghton and Nassikas (HN)) declined (Figure 2.2 in this chapter; Friedlingstein et al. 2020). Differences in accounting approaches and their impacts CO_2 emissions estimates from land use is covered in Chapter 7 and in the Chapter 2 Supplementary Material (2.SM.2). Note that anthropogenic net emissions from bioenergy are covered by the CO_2-LULUCF estimates presented here.

The CO_2-FFI share in total CO_2-eq emissions has plateaued at about 65% in recent years and its growth has slowed considerably since AR5 (*high confidence*). The CO_2-FFI emissions grew at 1.1% during the 1990s and 2.5% during the 2000s. For the last decade (2010s) – not covered by AR5 – this rate dropped to 1.2%. This included a short period between 2014 and 2016 with little or no growth in CO_2-FFI emissions, mainly due to reduced emissions from coal combustion

(Jackson et al. 2016; Qi et al. 2016; Peters et al. 2017a; Canadell et al. 2021). Subsequently, CO_2-FFI emissions started to rise again (Peters et al. 2017b; Figueres et al. 2018; Peters et al. 2020).

Starting in the spring of 2020 a major break in global emissions trends was observed due to lockdown policies implemented in response to the COVID-19 pandemic (*high confidence*) (Forster et al. 2020; Le Quéré et al. 2020, 2021; Z. Liu et al. 2020b; Bertram et al. 2021). Overall, global CO_2-FFI emissions are estimated to have declined by 5.8% (5.1%–6.3%) in 2020, or about 2.2 (1.9–2.4) $GtCO_2$ in total (Friedlingstein et al. 2020; Z. Liu et al. 2020b; BP 2021; Crippa et al. 2021; IEA 2021a). This exceeds any previous global emissions decline since 1970, both in relative and absolute terms (Figure 2.6). Daily emissions, estimated based on activity and power-generation data, declined substantially compared to 2019 during periods of economic lockdown, particularly in April 2020 – as shown in Figure 2.6 – but rebounded by the end of 2020 (*medium confidence*) (Le Quéré et al. 2020, 2021; Z. Liu et al. 2020b). Impacts were differentiated by sector, with road transport and aviation particularly affected. Inventories estimate the total power sector CO_2 reduction from 2019 to 2020 at 3% (IEA 2021a) and 4.5% (Crippa et al. 2021). Approaches that predict near real-time estimates of the power sector reduction are more uncertain and estimates range more widely, between 1.8%

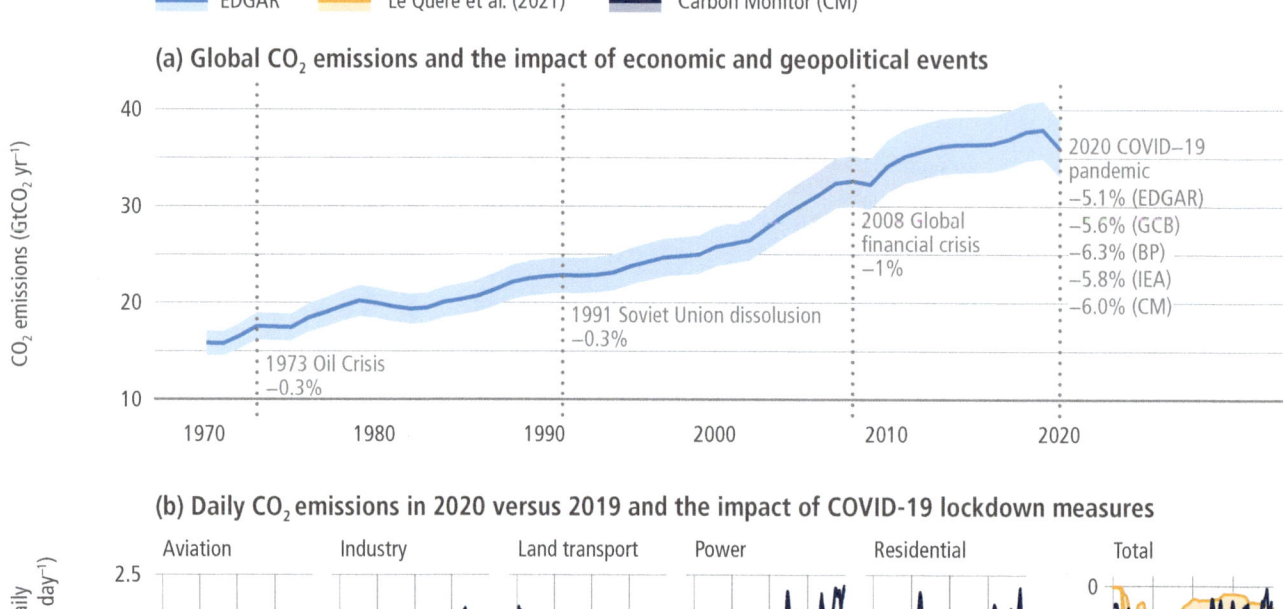

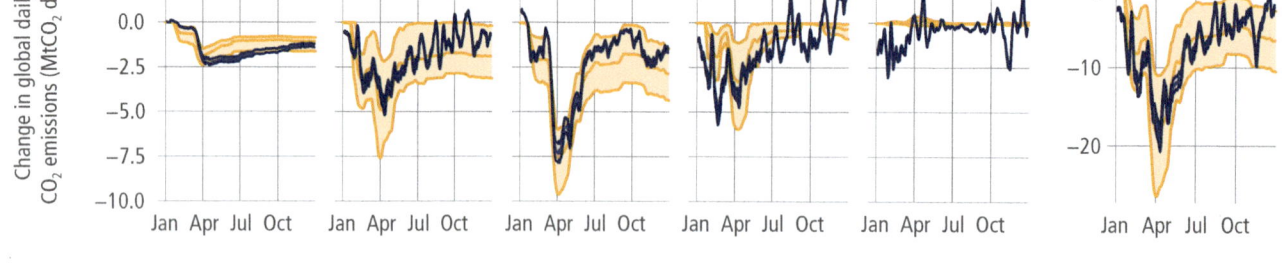

Figure 2.6 | Global CO_2 emissions from fossil fuel combustion and industry (FFI) in 2020 and the impact of COVID-19. Panel (a) depicts CO_2-FFI emissions over the past five decades ($GtCO_2$ yr^{-1}). The single year declines in emissions following major economic and geopolitical events are shown, as well as the decline recorded in five different datasets for emissions in 2020 (COVID-19) compared to 2019 (no COVID-19). **Panel (b)** depicts the change in global daily carbon emissions ($MtCO_2$ per day) in 2020 compared to 2019, showing the impact of COVID-19 lockdown policies. Source: Friedlingstein et al. (2020), Le Quéré et al. (2020), Carbon Monitor (Liu et al. 2020b), BP (2021), Crippa et al. (2021), IEA (2021a).

(Le Quéré et al. 2020, 2021), 4.1% (Z. Liu et al. 2020b) and 6.8% (Bertram et al. 2021); the latter taking into account the over-proportional reduction of coal generation due to low gas prices and merit order effects. Due to the very recent nature of this event, it remains unclear what the exact short- and long-term impacts on future global emissions trends will be.

From 1850 until around 1950, anthropogenic CO_2 emissions were mainly (>50%) from land use, land-use change and forestry (Figure 2.7). Over the past half-century CO_2 emissions from LULUCF have remained relatively constant around 5.1 ± 3.6 $GtCO_2$ but with a large spread across estimates (Le Quéré et al. 2018a; Friedlingstein et al. 2019, 2020). By contrast, global annual FFI-CO_2 emissions have continuously grown since 1850, and since the 1960s from a decadal average of 11 ± 0.9 $GtCO_2$ to 36 ± 2.9 $GtCO_2$ during 2010–2019 (Table 2.1).

Cumulative CO_2 emissions since 1850 reached 2400 ± 240 $GtCO_2$ in 2019 (*high confidence*).[7] More than half (62%) of total emissions from 1850 to 2019 occurred since 1970 (1500 ± 140 $GtCO_2$), about 42% since 1990 (1000 ± 90 $GtCO_2$) and about 17% since 2010 (410 ± 30 $GtCO_2$) (Friedlingstein et al. 2019; Friedlingstein et al. 2020; Canadell et al. 2021) (Figure 2.7). Emissions in the last decade are about the same size as the remaining carbon budget of 400 ± 220 (500, 650) $GtCO_2$ for limiting global warming to 1.5°C and between one-third and half the 1150 ± 220 (1350, 1700) $GtCO_2$ for limiting global warming below 2°C with a 67% (50%, 33%) probability, respectively (*medium confidence*) (Canadell et al. 2021).

At current (2019) levels of emissions, it would only take 8 (2–15) and 25 (18–35) years to emit the equivalent amount of CO_2 for a 67th percentile 1.5°C and 2°C remaining carbon budget, respectively. Related discussions of carbon budgets, short-term ambition in the context of Nationally Determined Contributions (NDCs), pathways to limiting warming to well below 2°C and carbon dioxide removals are mainly discussed in Chapters 3, 4, and 12, but also Section 2.7 of this chapter.

Even when taking uncertainties into account, historical emissions between 1850 and 2019 constitute a large share of total carbon budgets from 2020 onwards for limiting warming to 1.5°C with a 50% probability as well as for limiting warming to 2°C with a 67% probability. Based on central estimates only, historical cumulative net CO_2 emissions between 1850–2019 amount to about four fifths of the total carbon budget for a 50% probability of limiting global warming to 1.5°C (central estimate about 2900 $GtCO_2$), and to about two thirds of the total carbon budget for a 67% probability to limit global warming to 2°C (central estimate about 3550 $GtCO_2$). The carbon budget is the maximum amount of cumulative net global anthropogenic CO_2 emissions that would result in limiting global warming to a given level with a given likelihood, taking into account the effect of other anthropogenic climate forcers. This is referred to as the total carbon budget when expressed starting from the pre-industrial period, and as the remaining carbon budget when expressed from a recent specified date. The total carbon budgets reported here are the sum of historical emissions from 1850 to 2019 and the remaining carbon budgets from 2020 onwards, which extend

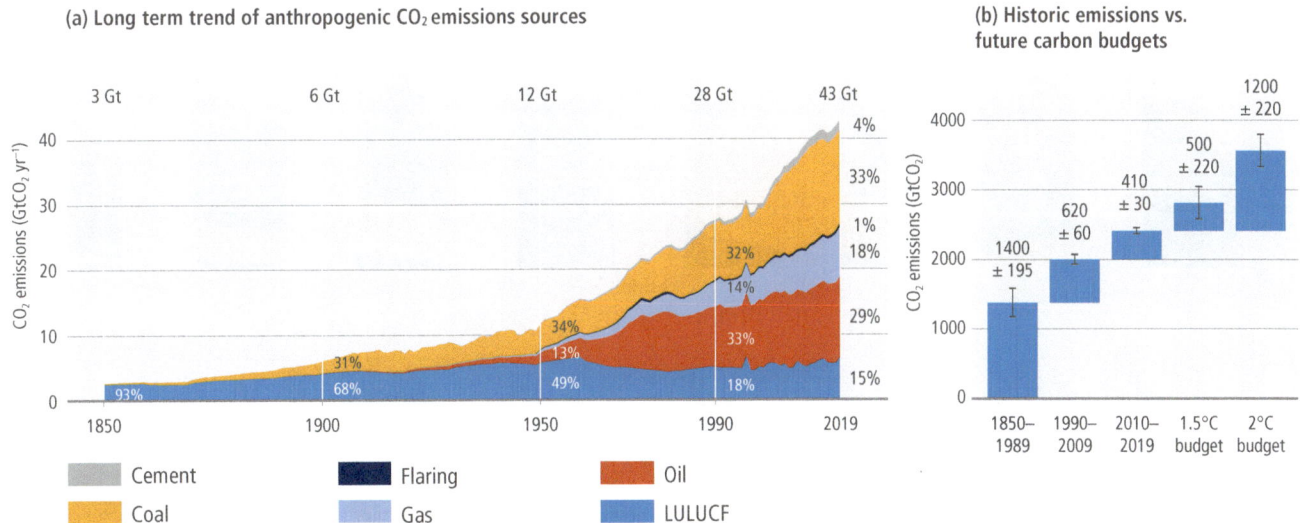

(a) Long term trend of anthropogenic CO_2 emissions sources

(b) Historic emissions vs. future carbon budgets

Figure 2.7 | Historic anthropogenic CO_2 emission and cumulative CO_2 emissions (1850–2019) as well as remaining carbon budgets for limiting warming to 1.5°C and 2°C. Panel (a) shows historic annual anthropogenic CO_2 emissions ($GtCO_2$ yr^{-1}) by fuel type and process. **Panel (b)** shows historic cumulative anthropogenic CO_2 emissions for the periods 1850–1989, 1990–2009, and 2010–2019 as well as remaining future carbon budgets as of 1 January 2020 to limit warming to 1.5°C and 2°C at the 67th percentile of the transient climate response to cumulative CO_2 emissions. The whiskers indicate a budget uncertainty of ± 220 $GtCO_2$-eq for each budget and the aggregate uncertainty range at one standard deviation for historical cumulative CO_2 emissions, consistent with Working Group 1. Sources: Friedlingstein et al. (2020) and Canadell et al. (2021).

---

[7]   For consistency with WGI, uncertainties in this paragraph are reported at a 68% confidence interval. This reflects the difficulty in the WGI context of characterising the uncertainty in the CO_2 fluxes between the atmosphere and the ocean and land reservoirs individually, particularly on an annual basis, as well as the difficulty of updating the emissions from land-use change.

until global net zero CO_2 emissions are reached. Uncertainties for total carbon budgets have not been assessed and could affect the specific calculated fractions (IPCC 2021 [Working Group 1 SPM], Canadell et al., 2021 [Working Group 1 Ch5]).

Comparisons between historic GHG emissions and baseline projections provide increased evidence that global emissions are not tracking high-end scenarios (Hausfather and Peters 2020), and rather followed 'middle-of-the-road' scenario narratives in the earlier series, and by combinations of 'global-sustainability' and 'middle-of-the-road' narratives in the most recent series (IPCC Special Report on Emissions Scenarios (SRES) and Shared Socioeconomic Pathways (SSP)-baselines) (Pedersen et al. 2020; Strandsbjerg Tristan Pedersen et al. 2021). As countries increasingly implement climate policies and technology costs continue to evolve, it is expected that emissions will continually shift away from scenarios that assume no climate policy but remain insufficient to limit warming to below 2°C (Vrontisi et al. 2018; Hausfather and Peters 2020; Roelfsema et al. 2020; UNEP 2020b).

The literature since AR5 suggests that compared to historical trends baseline scenarios might be biased towards higher levels of fossil fuel use compared to what is observed historically (Cross-Chapter Box 1 in Chapter 1; Ritchie and Dowlatabadi 2017, 2018; Ritchie 2019; Creutzig et al. 2021;). Ritchie and Dowlatabadi (2017) show that per-capita primary energy consumption in baseline scenarios

tends to increase at rates faster than those observed in the long-term historical evidence – particularly in terms of coal use. For example, SSP5 envisions a six-fold increase in per capita coal use by 2100 – against flat long-term historical observations – while the most optimistic baseline scenario SSP1-Sustainability is associated with coal consumption that is broadly in line with historical long-term trends (Ritchie and Dowlatabadi 2017). In contrast, models have struggled to reproduce historical upscaling of wind and solar and other granular energy technologies (Wilson et al. 2013; van Sluisveld et al. 2015; Creutzig et al. 2017; Shiraki and Sugiyama 2020; Sweerts et al. 2020; Wilson et al. 2020b).

2.2.2.2 Other Short-lived Climate Forcers (SLCFs)

There are other emissions with shorter atmospheric lifetimes that contribute to climate changes. Some of them (aerosols, sulphur emissions or organic carbon) reduce forcing, while others – such as black carbon, carbon monoxide or non-methane volatile organic compounds (NMVOC) – contribute to warming (Figure 2.4) as assessed in WGI (Forster et al. 2021c; Szopa et al. 2021a). Many of these other SLCFs are co-emitted during combustion processes in power plants, cars, trucks, airplanes, but also during wildfires and household activities such as traditional cooking with open biomass burning. As these co-emissions have implications for net warming, they are also considered in long-term emission reduction scenarios as covered in the literature (Harmsen et al. 2020; Rauner et al. 2020b;

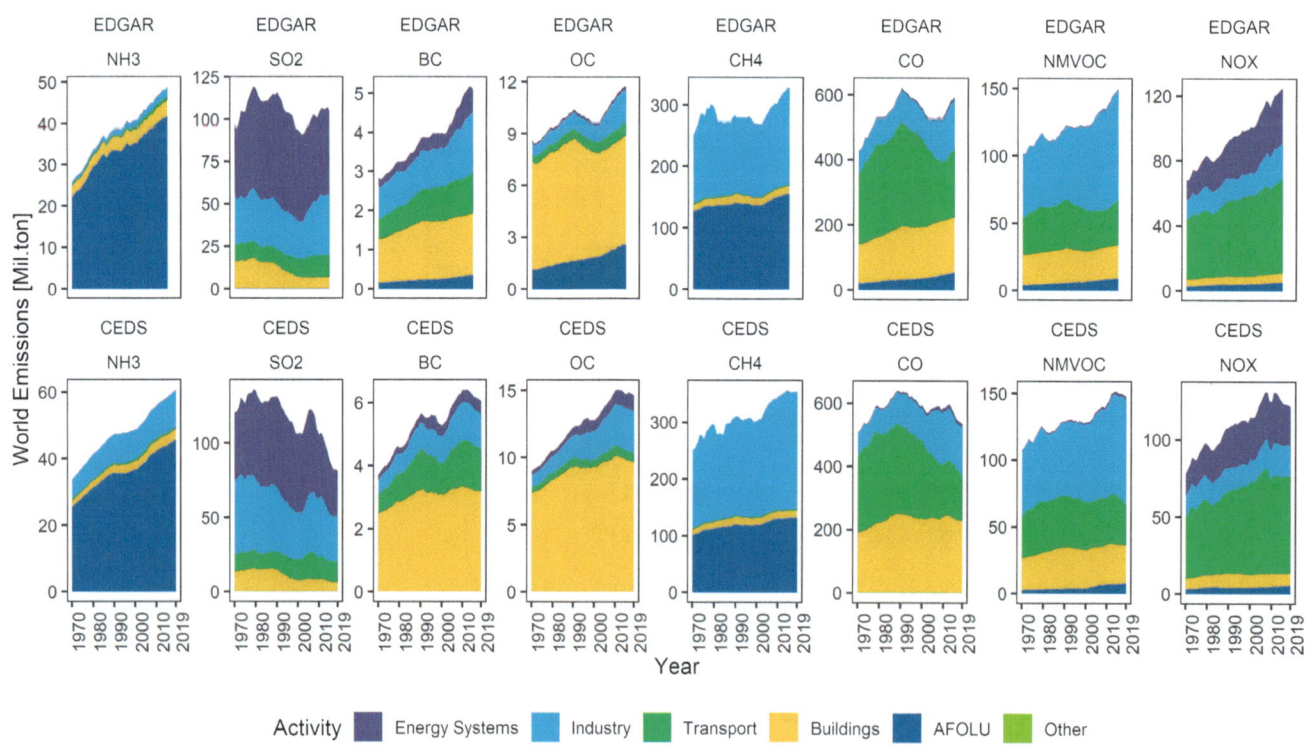

Figure 2.8 | Air pollution emissions by major sectors from CEDS (1970–2019) and EDGAR (1970–2015) inventories. Source: Crippa et al. (2019a, 2018); O'Rourke et al. (2020); McDuffie et al. (2020).

Smith et al. 2020; Vandyck et al. 2020) as well as Chapter 3 of this report. These air pollutants are also detrimental to human health (e.g., Lelieveld et al. 2015, 2018; Vohra et al. 2021). For example, Lelieveld et al. (2015) estimate a total of 3.3 (1.6–4.8) million premature deaths in 2010 from outdoor air pollution. Reducing air pollutants in the context of climate policies therefore leads to substantial co-benefits of mitigation efforts (Von Stechow et al. 2015; Rao et al. 2017; Lelieveld et al. 2019; Rauner et al. 2020a). Here we briefly outline the major trends in emissions of SLCFs.

Conventional air pollutants that are subject to significant emission controls in many countries include sulphur dioxide (SO_2), nitrogen oxides (NO_x), black carbon (BC) and carbon monoxide (CO). From 2015 to 2019, global SO_2 and NOx emissions declined, mainly due to reductions in energy systems (Figure 2.8). Reductions in BC and CO emissions appear to have occurred over the same period, but trends are less certain due to the large contribution of emissions from poorly quantified traditional biofuel use. Emissions of CH_4, OC and NMVOC have remained relatively stable in the past five years. OC and NMVOC may have plateaued, although there is additional uncertainty due to sources of NMVOCs that may be missing in current inventories (McDonald et al. 2018).

2.2.3 Regional GHG Emissions Trends

Regional contributions to global GHG emissions have shifted since the beginning of the international climate negotiations in the 1990s (*high confidence*). As shown in Figure 2.9, developed countries (North America, Europe, and Australia, Japan, New Zealand) as a group have not managed to reduce GHG emissions substantially, with fairly stable levels at about 15 GtCO$_2$-eq yr^{-1} between 1990 and 2010, while countries in Asia and Pacific (Eastern Asia, Southern Asia, and South-East Asia and Pacific) have rapidly increased their share of global GHG emissions – particularly since the 2000s (Jackson et al. 2019; Peters et al. 2020; UNEP 2020c; Crippa et al. 2021; IEA 2021b).

Most global GHG emission growth occurred in Asia and Pacific, which accounted for 77% of the net 21 GtCO$_2$-eq increase in GHG emissions since 1990, and 83% of the net 6.5 GtCO$_2$-eq increase since 2010.[8] Africa contributed 11% of GHG emissions growth since 1990 (2.3 GtCO$_2$-eq) and 10% (0.7 GtCO$_2$-eq) since 2010. The Middle East contributed 10% of GHG emissions growth since 1990 (2.1 GtCO$_2$-eq) and also 10% (0.7 GtCO$_2$-eq) since 2010. Latin America and the Caribbean contributed 11% of GHG emissions growth since 1990 (2.2 GtCO$_2$-eq), and 5% (0.3 GtCO$_2$-eq) since 2010. Two regions, Developed Countries, and Eastern Europe and West Central Asia, reduced emissions overall since 1990, by –1.6 GtCO$_2$-eq and –0.8 GtCO$_2$-eq, respectively. However, emissions in the latter started to grow again since 2010, contributing to 5% of the global GHG emissions change (0.3 GtCO$_2$-eq).

Average annual GHG emission growth across all regions slowed between 2010 and 2019 compared to 1990–2010, with the exception of Eastern Europe and West Central Asia. Global emissions changes tend to be driven by a limited number of countries, principally the G20 Group (Friedlingstein et al. 2020; UNEP 2020c; Xia et al. 2021). For instance, the slowing of global GHG emissions between 2010 and 2019, compared to the previous decade, was primarily triggered by substantial reductions in GHG emissions growth in China. Ten countries jointly contributed about 75% of the net 6.5 GtCO$_2$-eq yr^{-1} increase in GHG emissions during 2010–2019, of which two countries contributed more than 50% (Figure 2.9) (see also Minx et al., 2021; Crippa et al., 2021).

GHG and CO$_2$-FFI levels diverge starkly between countries and regions (*high confidence*) (Jackson et al. 2019; Friedlingstein et al. 2020; UNEP 2020c; Crippa et al. 2021). Developed Countries sustained high levels of per capita CO$_2$-FFI emissions at 9.5 tCO$_2$ per capita in 2019 (but with a wide range of 1.9–16 tCO$_2$ per capita). This is more than double that of three developing regions: 4.4 (0.3–12.8) tCO$_2$ per capita in Asia and Pacific; 1.2 (0.03–8.5) tCO$_2$ per capita in Africa; and 2.7 (0.3–24) tCO$_2$ per capita in Latin America.[9] Per capita CO$_2$-FFI emissions were 9.9 (0.89–15) tCO$_2$ per capita in Eastern Europe and West Central Asia, and 8.6 (0.36–38) tCO$_2$ per capita in the Middle East. CO$_2$-FFI emissions in the three developing regions together grew by 26% between 2010 and 2019, compared to 260% between 1990 and 2010, while in Developed Countries emissions contracted by 9.9% between 2010–2019 and by 9.6% between 1990–2010.

Least-Developed Countries and Small Island Developing States contributed only a negligible proportion of historic GHG emissions growth and have the lowest per capita emissions. As of 2019 Least Developed Countries contribute 3.3% of global GHG emissions, excluding LULUCF CO$_2$, despite making up 13% of the global population. Small Island Developing States contributed 0.6% of global GHG emissions in 2019, excluding LULUCF CO$_2$, with 0.9% of the global population. Since the start of the industrial revolution in 1850 up until 2019, Least Developed Countries contributed 0.4% of total cumulative CO$_2$ emissions, while Small Island Developing States contributed 0.5% (Figure 2.10). Conversely, Developed Countries have the highest share of historic cumulative emissions (Rocha et al. 2015; Gütschow et al. 2016; Matthews 2016), contributing approximately 57% (Figure 2.10), followed by Asia and Pacific (21%), Eastern Europe and West Central Asia (9%), Latin America and the Caribbean (4%), the Middle East (3%), and Africa (3%). Developed Countries still have the highest share of historic cumulative emissions (45%) when CO$_2$-LULUCF emissions are included, which typically account for a higher proportion of emissions in developing regions (Figure 2.10).

---

[8] Note that GHG emissions from international aviation and shipping could not be attributed to individual regions, while CO$_2$ emissions from AFOLU could not be attributed to individual countries. Change in GHG emissions that can be easily assigned to regions is 20.3 of 20.8 GtCO$_2$-eq for 1990–2019 and 6.3 of 6.5 GtCO$_2$-eq for 2010–2019.

[9] In all cases, constraining countries within the emissions range to those larger than 1 million population.

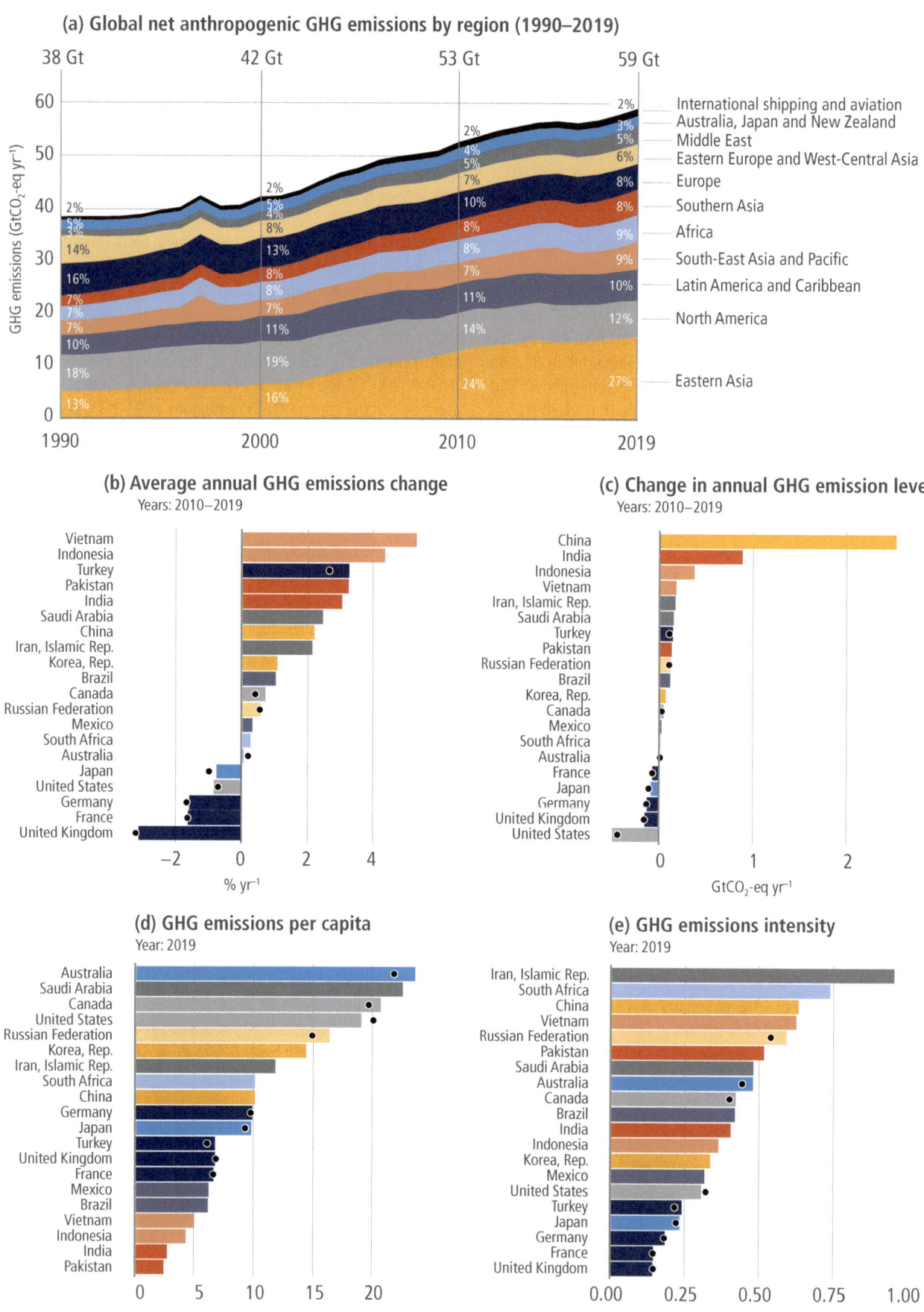

Figure 2.9 | Change in regional GHGs from multiple perspectives and their underlying drivers.

Figure 2.9 (continued): Change in regional GHGs from multiple perspectives and their underlying drivers. Panel (a): Regional GHG emissions trends (in $GtCO_2$-eq yr^{-1}) for the time period 1990–2019. GHG emissions from international aviation and shipping are not assigned to individual countries and shown separately. **Panels (b) and (c):** Changes in GHG emissions for the 20 largest emitters (as of 2019) for the post-AR5 reporting period 2010–2019 in relative (% annual change) and absolute terms ($GtCO_2$-eq). **Panels (d) and (e):** GHG emissions per capita and per GDP in 2019 for the 20 largest emitters (as of 2019). GDP estimated using constant international purchasing power parity (USD2017). Emissions are converted into CO_2-equivalents based on global warming potentials with a 100-year time horizon (GWP100) from the IPCC Sixth Assessment Report (Forster et al. 2021a). The black dots represent the emissions data from UNFCCC-CRFs (2021) that were accessed through Gütschow et al. (2021a). Net LULUCF CO_2 emissions are included in panel (a), based on the average of three bookkeeping models (Section 2.2), but are excluded in panels (b–e) due to a lack of country resolution.

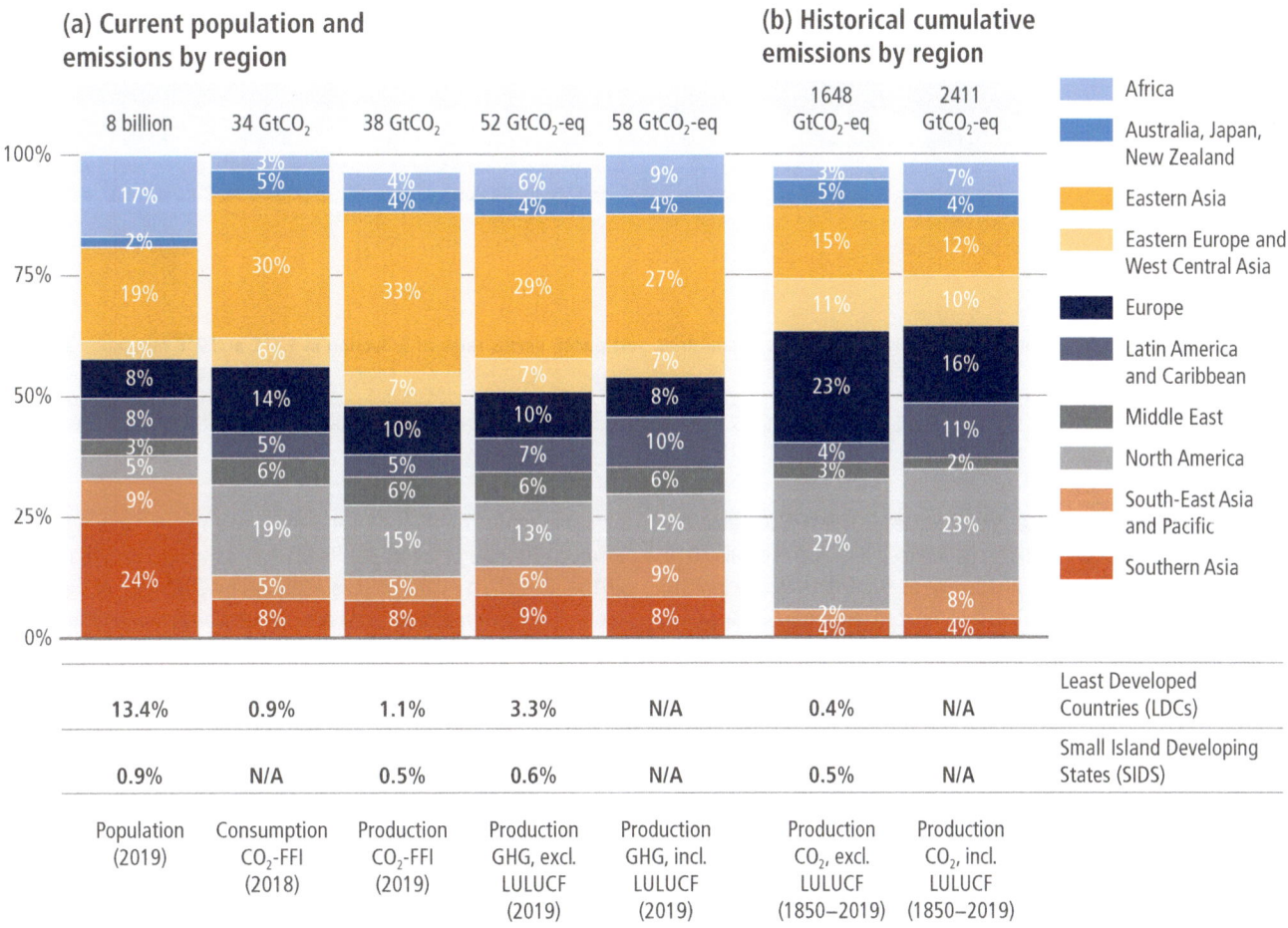

Figure 2.10 | Different perspectives on historic emissions and equity. Panel (a) shows the regional proportion (%) of total global population or emissions in 2018 or 2019, for five categories: population (persons); consumption-based CO_2-FFI emissions ($GtCO_2$); production-based CO_2-FFI emissions ($GtCO_2$); production-based GHG emissions excluding CO_2-LULUCF ($GtCO_2$-eq); and production-based GHG emissions including CO_2-LULUCF ($GtCO_2$-eq). **Panel (b)** shows the regional proportion (%) of total cumulative production-based CO_2 emissions from 1850 to 2019, including and excluding CO_2-LULUCF ($GtCO_2$). In the lower panels, the proportion of each population or emissions category attributable to Least-Developed Countries and Small Island Developing States (SIDS) are shown, where available (CO_2-LULUCF data is not available for these regions). GHG emissions are converted into CO_2-equivalents based on global warming potentials with a 100-year time horizon (GWP100) from the IPCC Sixth Assessment Report (Forster et al. 2021a). Source: data from Friedglinstein et al. (2020).

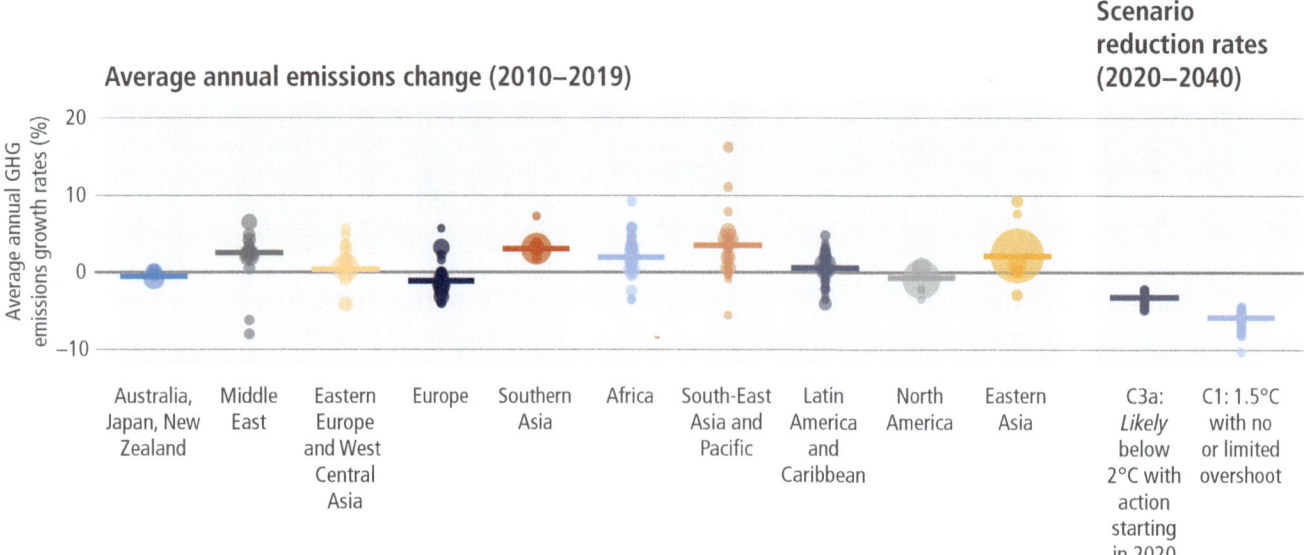

Figure 2.11 | Recent average annual GHG emissions changes of countries (left panel) versus rates of reduction in 1.5°C and 2°C mitigation scenarios. Scenario data is taken from Chapter 3 of this report with the scenario categories defined and summarised in Table 3.2 in Chapter 3. Emissions are converted into CO$_2$-equivalents based on global warming potentials with a 100-year time horizon (GWP100) from the IPCC Sixth Assessment Report (Forster et al. 2021a). Circles indicate countries (left panel) or individual scenarios (right panel), the former scaled by total emissions in 2019. Horizontal lines indicate the region average emissions change (left panel), or scenario category average emissions change (right panel). Source: data from Minx et al. (2021).

A growing number of countries have reduced CO$_2$ and GHG emissions for longer than 10 years (*high confidence*) (Le Quéré et al. 2019; Burck et al. 2021; Lamb et al. 2021a; Wu et al. 2021). Data up to 2018 indicates that about 24 countries have reduced territorial CO$_2$ and GHG emissions (excluding LULUCF CO$_2$), as well as consumption-based CO$_2$ emissions, for at least 10 years (Lamb et al. 2021a). Uncertainties in emissions levels and changes over time prevents a precise assessment of reductions in some cases. Of these 24 countries, 12 peaked emissions in the 2000s; six have sustained longer reductions since the 1970s; and six are former members of the Eastern Bloc, where emissions dropped rapidly in the 1990s and continued declining at a slower pace thereafter. Country emissions reductions have been driven by both climate and non-climate policies and factors, including structural changes. To date, most territorial emissions reductions were realised in the electricity and heat sector, followed by industry and buildings, while in many cases transport emissions have increased since countries reached their overall emissions peak (Climate Transparency 2021; Lamb et al. 2021a). One estimate of the total reduction in annual GHG emissions – from peak years to 2018 – sums to 3.2 GtCO$_2$-eq across all decarbonising countries (Lamb et al. 2021a). These reductions have therefore been far outweighed by recent emissions growth. However, climate policy related reductions may be even larger when compared against a counterfactual case of emissions growth across different sectors (Eskander and Fankhauser 2020) (Cross-Chapter Box 1 in Chapter 1; Section 2.8).

The recent (2010–2019) emissions changes of some countries are in line with pathways that limit warming to below 2°C (<67%) (e.g., –4% average annual reductions) (Figure 2.10). Overall, there are first country cases emerging that highlight the feasibility of sustained emission reductions outside of periods of economic disruption (Lamb et al. 2021a). However, such pathways will need to be taken by many more countries to keep the goals of the Paris Agreement in reach (Höhne et al. 2020; Roelfsema et al. 2020; Kriegler et al. 2018a; den Elzen et al. 2019) as analysed by Chapter 4 of this report. Moreover, observed reductions are not yet consistent and long-term, nor achieved across all sectors, nor fully aligned with country NDC targets (Le Quéré et al. 2019; Lamb et al. 2021a; den Elzen et al. 2019; Burck et al. 2021; Climate Transparency 2021).

2.2.4   Sectoral GHG Emissions Trends

In 2019, 34% (20 GtCO$_2$-eq) of the 59 GtCO$_2$-eq GHG emissions came from the energy sector, 24% (14 GtCO$_2$-eq) from industry, 22% (13 GtCO$_2$-eq) from AFOLU, 15% (8.7 GtCO$_2$-eq) from transport and 6% (3.3 GtCO$_2$-eq) from buildings (Figure 2.12). The relative size of each sector depends on the exact definition of sector boundaries (de la Rue du Can et al. 2015; Lamb et al. 2021b). The largest individual subsector contributing to global GHG emissions in 2019 was electricity and heat generation at 14 GtCO$_2$-eq. This subsector can be reallocated to consuming sectors as indirect (scope 2) emissions to emphasise the role of final energy demand and demand-side solutions in climate change mitigation (Creutzig et al. 2018) (Chapter 5). This increases the emission share of the industry sector to 34% and of the buildings sector to 16%.

Average annual GHG emissions growth has been fastest in the transport sector with about 1.8% for the most recent period 2010–2019, followed by direct emissions in the industry sector (1.4%) and the energy sector (1%) (Figure 2.13). This is different to growth patterns observed in the previous decade as reported in AR5 (IPCC 2014a; Blanco et al. 2014). Between 2000 and 2009 fastest GHG emissions growth was observed for industry with 3.4% followed by

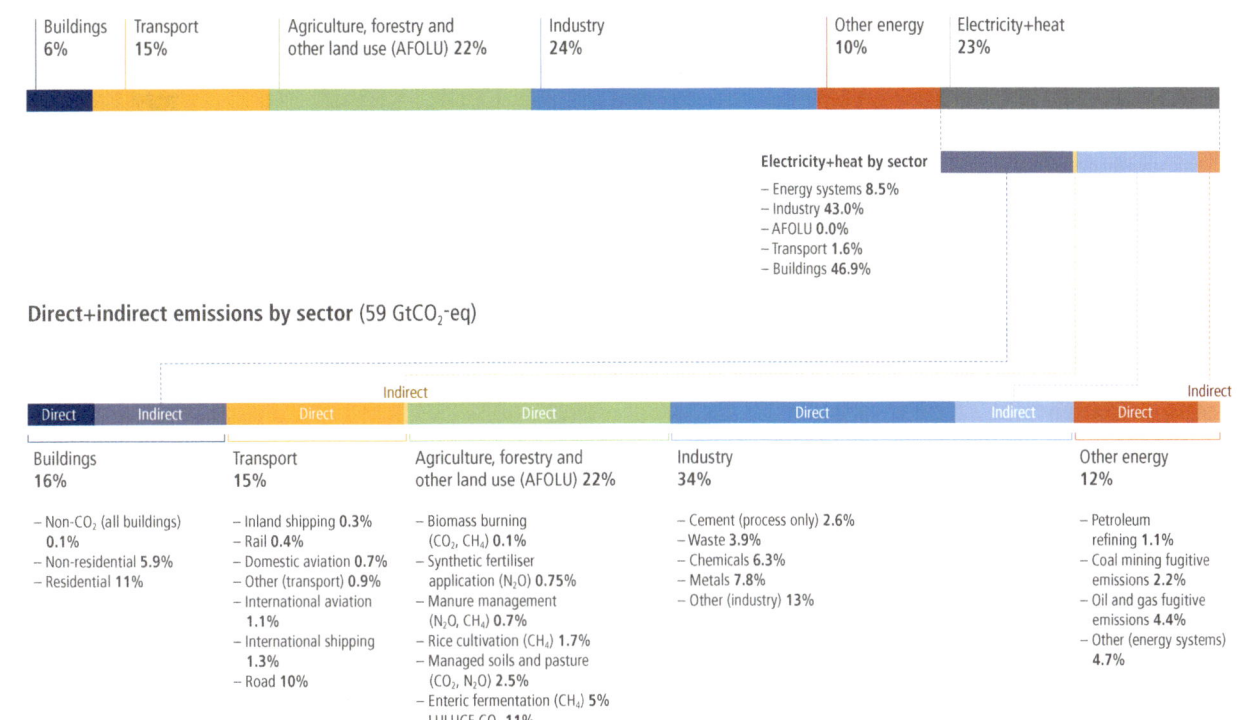

Figure 2.12 | Total anthropogenic direct and indirect GHG emissions for the year 2019 (in GtCO₂-eq) by sector and subsector. Direct emissions estimates assign emissions to the sector in which they arise (scope 1 reporting). Indirect emissions – as used here – refer to the reallocation of emissions from electricity and heat to the sector of final use (scope 2 reporting). Note that cement refers to process emissions only, as a lack of data prevents the full reallocation of indirect emissions to this sector. More comprehensive conceptualisations of indirect emissions including all products and services (scope 3 reporting) are discussed in Section 2.3 of this chapter. Emissions are converted into CO₂-equivalents based on global warming potentials with a 100-year time horizon (GWP100) from the IPCC Sixth Assessment Report. Percentages may not add up to 100 across categories due to rounding at the second significant digit. Source: based on Lamb et al. (2021b); data: Minx et al. (2021).

the energy sector with 2.3%. GHG emissions growth in the transport sector has been stable across both periods at about 1.8%, while direct building emissions growth averaged below 1% during 2010–2019. Ranking of high-emitting subsectors by direct emissions highlights the importance of CO₂ emissions from LULUCF (6.6 GtCO₂-eq; but with low confidence in magnitude and trend), road transport (6.1 GtCO₂-eq), metals (3.1 GtCO₂-eq), and other industry (4.4 GtCO₂-eq). Overall, some of the fastest growing sources of subsector emissions from 2010 to 2019 have been international aviation (+3.4%),[10] domestic aviation (+3.3%), inland shipping (+2.9%), metals (+2.3%), international shipping (+1.7%), and road transport (+1.7%).

---

[10]   Note that this does not include the additional warming impacts from aviation due to short-lived climate forcers, which are assessed in Chapter 10 (Section 10.5).

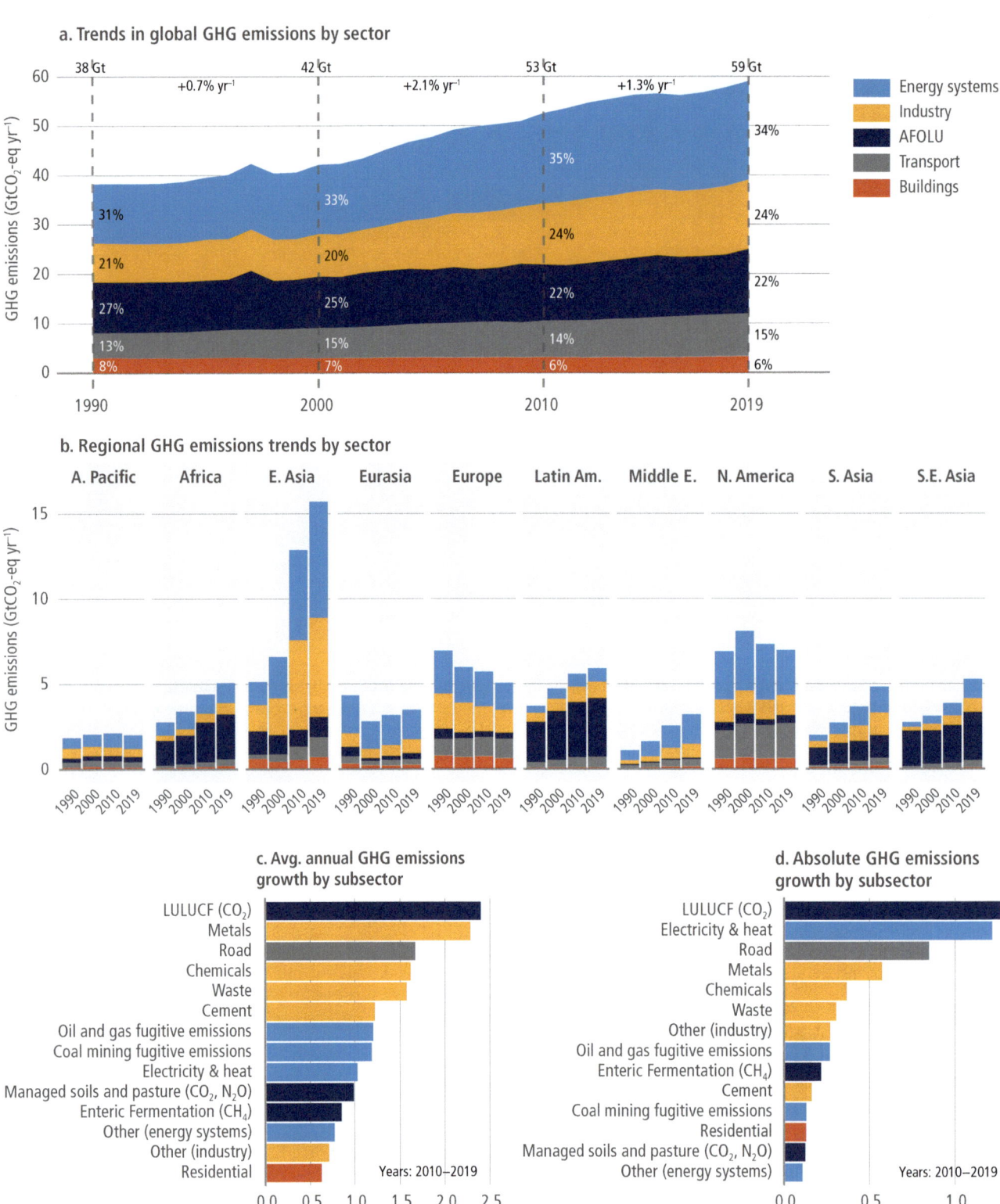

Figure 2.13 | Total annual anthropogenic GHG emissions by major economic sector and their underlying trends by region. Panel (a): Trends in total annual anthropogenic GHG emissions (in GtCO₂-eq yr⁻¹) by major economic sector. **Panel (b):** Trends in total annual anthropogenic GHG emissions (in GtCO₂-eq yr⁻¹) by major economic sector and region. Panels c and d: Largest subsectoral changes in GHG emissions for the reporting period 2010–2019 in relative (% annual change) and absolute terms (GtCO₂-eq yr⁻¹). Emissions are converted into CO₂-equivalents based on global warming potentials with a 100-year time horizon (GWP100) from the IPCC Sixth Assessment Report. Source: based on Lamb et al. (2021b); Data: Crippa et al. (2021); Minx et al. (2021).

2.3 Past and Present Trends of Consumption-based CO$_2$ Emissions (CBEs) and Emissions Embodied in Trade

2.3.1 Scope, Variability and Uncertainty of CBEs

Consumption is increasingly met by global supply chains often involving large geographical distances and causing emissions in producing countries (Hubacek et al. 2014, 2016; Wiedmann and Lenzen 2018). Therefore, accounting for emissions from production along the entire supply chain to fulfil final demand, – so-called consumption-based emissions (CBEs), – is necessary to understand why emissions occur and to what extent consumption choices and associated supply chains contribute to total emissions, and ultimately how to influence consumption to achieve climate mitigation targets and environmental justice (Vasconcellos 2020).

Production-based emissions (PBEs) and territorial emissions resulting from the production and consumption of goods and services within a region (for both domestic use and export) are often used by authorities to report carbon emissions (Peters 2008) (Section 2.2). PBEs also include emissions from international activities (e.g., international aviation/shipping and non-resident activities), which are excluded from territorial emissions (Karstensen et al. 2018; Shan et al. 2018). In contrast, CBEs refer to emissions along the entire supply chains induced by consumption, irrespective of the place of production (Liu et al. 2015b). This reflects a shared understanding that a wider system boundary going beyond territorial emissions is important to avoid outsourcing of pollution and to achieve global decarbonisation. CBEs allow for the identification of new policy levers through information on a country's trade balance of embodied emissions, households' carbon implications of their lifestyle choices, companies' upstream emissions as input for supply chain management, and cities' footprints outside their administrative boundaries (Davis and Caldeira 2010; Feng et al. 2013). Kander et al. (2015) proposed a technology-adjusted consumption-based emission accounting (TCBA) approach to address the issue of carbon intensity in exports. TCBA incorporates emissions embodied in trade but also adjusted for differences in carbon efficiency in exports of different countries. Unlike PBEs, there are no internationally agreed approaches to calculate CBEs, making it a major drawback for mainstreaming the use of this indicator in policymaking.

There are other proposed emission accounting approaches used in different circumstances. Historical cumulative emissions (HCEs) are used when analysing countries' historic contribution to emissions and responsibility for emission reduction. HCEs account for a country's cumulative past emissions, which may be different from the country's current annual emissions (Botzen et al. 2008; Ritchie 2019), but are sensitive to the choice of cut-off period. For example, the USA and EU-27 countries plus the UK contributed respectively 13.3% and 8.7% to global PBEs in 2019 (Crippa et al. 2020), however, they emitted around 25% and 22% of global historical PBEs since 1751 (Ritchie 2019). Extraction-based emissions (EBEs) accounting allocates all emissions from burning fossil fuels throughout the supply chains to the country where the fuels were extracted (Steininger and Schinko 2015). EBEs can be calculated by multiplying primary energy extraction of fossil fuels with their respective carbon content (Erickson and Lazarus 2013). Another approach for accounting emissions is income-based emission (IBE), which traces emissions throughout all supply chains and allocates emissions to primary inputs (e.g., capital and labour). In other words, IBEs investigate a country's direct and indirect downstream GHG emissions enabled by its primary inputs (Liang et al. 2017a). All these approaches provide complementary information and different angles to assigning responsibility for emissions reductions.

Box 2.1 | Policy Applications of Consumption-based Emissions

Consumption-based emissions provide additional or complementary information to production-based emissions that can be used for a variety of policy applications. These include:

- Complementary national-level emissions accounting and target or budget setting
- Raising awareness and increasing understanding of the GHG effects of consumption
- Accounting for and understanding of distributional and responsibility issues in GHG emissions mitigation, both nationally and internationally
- Incentives to change consumption patterns or reduce consumption (e.g., through taxation policies)
- Accounting for and understanding of carbon leakage and emissions embodied in trade*
- International emissions trading schemes or linked national schemes
- Trade policies addressing emissions embodied in trade and international supply chains (e.g., border tax adjustments and clean technology transfers, carbon offsetting or financing, etc.)
- Including embodied emissions in product performance standards and labelling
- Policies of public and private procurement
- Agreements with international suppliers
- Discussing the climate impacts of lifestyles and inequalities in consumption and associated emissions.

Box 2.1 (continued)

The points above are based on a synopsis of studies (Steininger et al. 2014; Afionis et al. 2017; Hubacek et al. 2017b; Wang and Zhou 2018; Bolea et al. 2020).

* Note, however, that comparing embodied emissions in trade between countries is further complicated by the fact that emission intensities differ across countries. Approaches to adjust for these differences and facilitate comparisons have been suggested (Kander et al. 2015; Baumert et al. 2019; Dietzenbacher et al. 2020; Jakob 2021). Many different approaches on how to share responsibility between producers and consumers have been proposed in designing effective integrated global climate policies (Liu and Fan 2017; Khajehpour et al. 2019; Jakob et al. 2021). Ultimately, assigning responsibility is normative.

Table 2.2 | Features of six global datasets for consumption-based emissions accounts.

Name of consumption-based account datasets (and references)	Years available	Number of countries/regions	Number of sectors
Eora (Lenzen et al. 2013); (https://worldmrio.com)	1990–2015	190	Varies from 25 to >500
EXIOBASE (Stadler et al. 2018); (https://www.exiobase.eu)	1995–2016	49	200 products and 163 industries
GTAP (Peters, et al. 2011b; Aguiar et al. 2019); (https://www.gtap.agecon.purdue.edu)	2004, 2007, 2011, 2014	140	57
OECD/ICIO (Yamano and Guilhoto, 2020); (http://oe.cd/io-co2)	1995–2015	67	36
WIOD (Dietzenbacher et al. 2013; Timmer et al. 2015); (http://wiod.org)	2000–2014	44	56
Global Carbon Budget (Friedlingstein et al. 2020)	1990–2018	118	N/A

The dominant method for calculating nations' CBEs is global multi-region input-output (GMRIO) analysis (Wiedmann and Lenzen 2018). Other frequently used approaches include analysing bilateral trade flows of products and their lifecycle emission factors (Sato 2014). Generally, the uncertainties associated with CBEs depends on the choice of the dataset/model used for calculation, which differs according to: (i) the national economic and trade data used; (ii) the emissions data used; (iii) the sector or product-level aggregation; (iv) the regional aggregation; (v) the conceptual scope (e.g., residential vs territorial accounting principle); and (vi) the model construction techniques, which include table-balancing algorithms and ways of dealing with missing or conflicting data (Moran and Wood 2014; Owen, 2017; Wieland et al. 2018; Wood et al. 2018, 2019). When excluding systematic error sources, research has shown that the stochastic relative standard deviation (RSD) of total national CBEs is not significantly different to that from PBEs accounts and in the region of 5–15% (Wood et al. 2018, 2019).

Six global accounts for consumption-based GHG emissions at the country level are widely used (Table 2.2). Each dataset has been constructed by different teams of researchers, covering different time periods and containing CBEs estimates for different sets of countries and regions (Owen 2017).

Wood et al. (2019) present a comprehensive and systematic model intercomparison and find a variation of 5–10% for both PBE and CBE accounts of major economies and country groups (e.g., EU-28, OECD). The estimates for the USA were the most closely aligned, with 3.7% RSD. For smaller countries, variability is in the order of 20–30% and can reach more than 40% in cases of very small, highly trade-exposed countries such as Singapore and Luxembourg

(Wood et al. 2019). It is recommended that CBEs results for such countries be interpreted with care.

Overall, production accounts showed a slightly higher convergence (8% average of RSD) than consumption-based accounts (12%). The variation across model results can be approximately halved, when normalising national totals to one common value for a selected base year. The difference between PBEs result variation (4% average RSD after normalisation) and CBEs results (7%) remains after normalisation.

In general, the largest contributors to uncertainty of CBEs results are – in descending order of priority – the total of territorial GHG emission accounts, the allocation of emissions to economic sectors, the total and composition of final demand, and lastly the structure of the economy. Harmonising territorial emissions across GMRIO datasets is the single most important factor that reduces uncertainty by about 50% (Tukker et al. 2020). More work is required to optimise or even institutionalise the compilation of multi-region input-output data and models to enhance the accuracy of consumption-based accounting (Tukker et al. 2018; Wood et al. 2018).

2.3.2   Trends in Global and Regional CBEs Trajectories

In comparison to territorial emissions discussed in Section 2.2, Figure 2.14 shows the trends of global and regional CBEs from 1990 to 2018. This section uses the PBEs and CBEs data from the Global Carbon Budget 2020 (Friedlingstein et al. 2020), which are slightly different from the PBEs used in Section 2.2. The Global Carbon Budget only includes CO_2 emissions from fossil fuels and cement production.

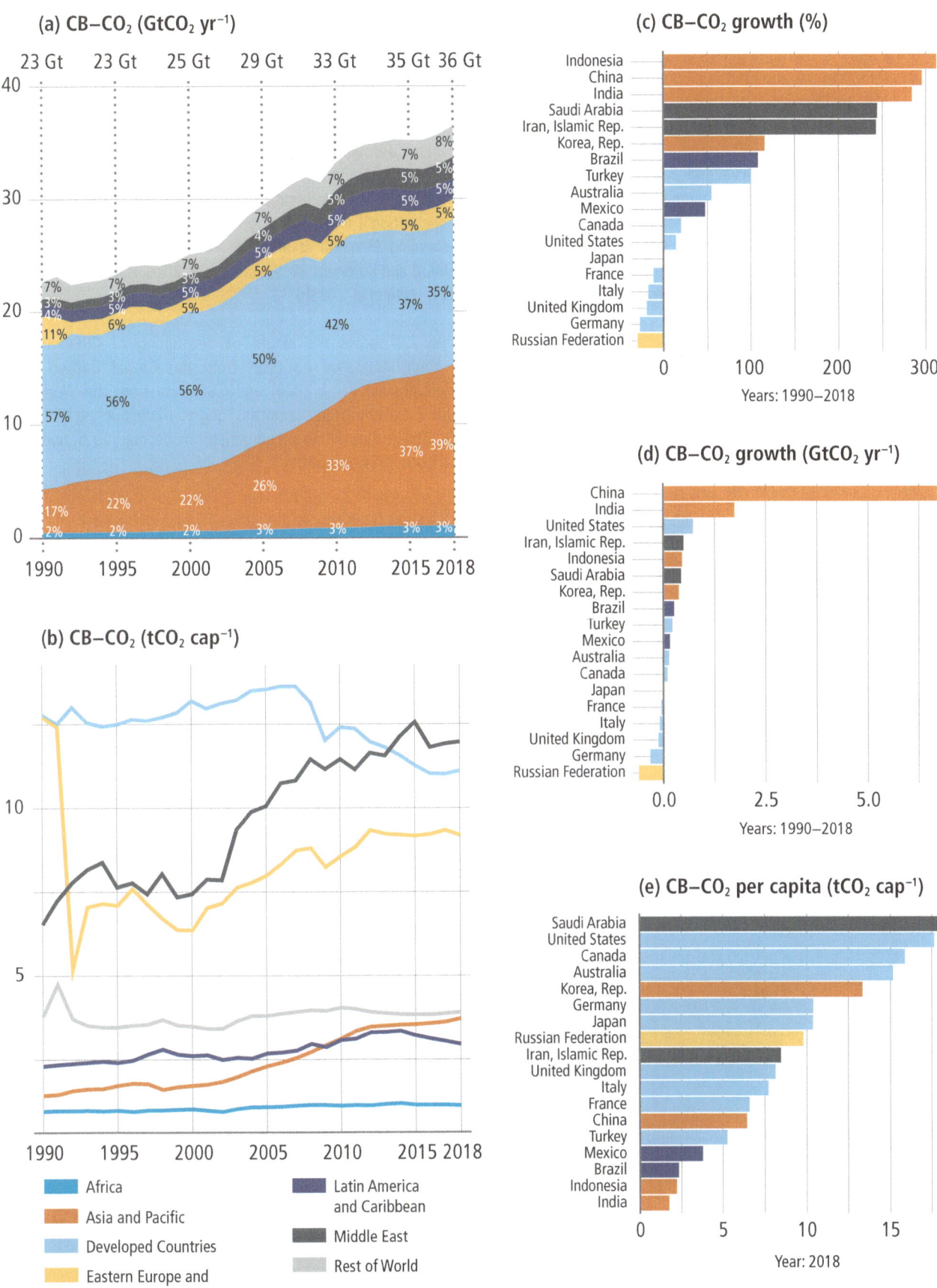

Figure 2.14 | Consumption-based CO₂ emissions trends for the period 1990–2018. The CBEs of countries are collected from the Global Carbon Budget 2020 (Friedlingstein et al. 2020). Source: this figure is modified based on Hubacek et al. (2021).

The two panels at left in Figure 2.14 show total and per capita CBEs for six regions. The three panels on the right show additional information for the 18 top-emitting countries with the highest CBEs in 2018. In Developed Countries, consumption-based CO_2 emissions peaked at 15 $GtCO_2$ in 2007 with a subsequent 16% decline until 2016 (to 12.7 $GtCO_2$) and a slight rebound of 1.6% until 2018 (to 12.9 $GtCO_2$). Asia and Pacific has been a major contributor to consumption-based CO_2 emissions growth since 2000 and exceeded Developed Countries as the global largest emissions source in 2015. From 1990 to 2018, the average growth rate of Asia and Pacific was 4.8% per year, while in other regions emissions declined by −1.1%–4.3% per year on average. In 2018, 35% of global consumption-based CO_2 emissions were from Developed Countries and 39% from Asia and Pacific, 5% from Latin American and Caribbean, 5% from Eastern Europe and West Central Asia, 5% from Middle East, and 3% from Africa (Hubacek et al. 2021). Global CBEs kept growing over the period with a short-lived decline in 2008 due to the global financial crisis. In 2020, lockdowns associated with COVID-19 significantly reduced global emissions (Section 2.2.2), including CBEs (Shan et al. 2021a).

2.3.3   Decoupling of Emissions from Economic Growth

There has been a long-standing discussion on whether environmental impacts such as carbon emissions and use of natural resources can be decoupled from economic growth. It is controversial whether absolute decoupling can be achieved at a global scale (Ward et al. 2016; Hickel and Kallis 2020; Haberl et al. 2020). However, a number of studies found that it is feasible to achieve decoupling at the national level, and they have explored the reasons for such decoupling (Schandl et al. 2016; Ward et al. 2016; Deutch 2017; Roinioti and Koroneos 2017; Vadén et al. 2020; Habimana Simbi et al. 2021; Shan et al. 2021b).

Table 2.3 shows the extent of decoupling of CBEs and GDP of countries based on CBEs from the Global Carbon Budget (Friedlingstein et al. 2020) and GDP data from the World Bank. Table 2.4 also presents countries' degree of decoupling of PBEs and GDP. These data allow a comparison of decoupling between GDP and both PBEs and CBEs.

Table 2.3 | Country groups with different degree of CBE–GDP decoupling from 2015 to 2018.

		Absolute decoupling	Relative decoupling	No decoupling	Economic recession
Number of countries		**23**	**67**	**19**	**6**
CBEs (gigatonnes)	Total	5.40	25.33	1.93	0.85
	Global share	16.1%	75.6%	5.8%	2.5%
PBEs (gigatonnes)	Total	4.84	25.73	2.16	0.84
	Global share	14.4%	76.6%	6.4%	2.5%
Population (million)	Total	625	5195	768	270
	Global share	9.1%	75.7%	11.2%	3.9%
GDP (billion)	Total	19,891	54,240	2300	2997
	Global share	25.0%	68.3%	2.9%	3.8%
Per capita GDP (1000 USD2010)	Average	31.45	16.29	6.57	17.78
	Median	23.55	8.03	2.56	13.12
	Max	110.70	79.23	63.93	33.11
	Min	1.31	0.49	0.52	5.80
Per capita CBEs (tonnes)	Average	10.27	5.30	4.47	12.55
	Median	8.87	4.13	1.67	11.33
	Max	37.95	17.65	25.35	23.21
	Min	0.64	0.09	0.18	2.33
CBE intensity (tonnes per 1000 USD2010)	Average	0.45	0.50	0.93	0.66
	Median	0.36	0.42	0.62	0.69
	Max	1.16	2.41	4.10	1.22
	Min	0.11	0.10	0.28	0.21
Per capita PBEs (tonnes)	Average	8.20	4.36	5.32	14.15
	Median	6.79	3.02	1.19	13.22
	Max	19.58	20.13	39.27	27.24
	Min	0.49	0.09	0.08	2.23
PBE intensity (tonnes per 1000 USD2010)	Average	0.42	0.40	0.94	0.75
	Median	0.28	0.31	0.58	0.68
	Max	1.57	1.47	4.83	1.80
	Min	0.10	0.05	0.16	0.20

Note: CBEs are obtained from the Global Carbon Budget 2020 (Friedlingstein et al. 2020), GDP and population are from the World Bank. One country (Venezuela) does not have GDP data after 2015, so the degree of decoupling was only calculated for 115 countries. This table is modified from Hubacek et al. (2021).

Absolute decoupling refers to a decline of emissions in absolute terms or as being stable while GDP grows (i.e., a decoupling index[11] greater than 1); relative decoupling refers to growth of emissions being lower than growth of GDP (a decoupling index between 0 and 1); and no decoupling, which refers to a situation where emissions grow to the same extent or faster than GDP (a decoupling index of less than 0) (Wu et al. 2018).

During the most recent three-year period from 2015 to 2018, 23 countries (or 20% of the 116 sample countries) have achieved absolute decoupling of CBEs and GDP, while 32 countries (or 28%) achieved absolute decoupling of PBEs and GDP: 14 of them (e.g., the UK, Japan,

and the Netherlands) also decoupled PBEs and GDP. Countries with absolute decoupling of CBEs tend to achieve decoupling at relatively high levels of economic development and high per capita emissions. Most of EU and North American countries are in this group. Decoupling was not only achieved by outsourcing carbon-intensive production, but also improvements in production efficiency and energy mix, leading to a decline of emissions. Structural Decomposition Analysis shows that the main driver for decoupling has been a reduction in carbon intensity (i.e., change in energy mix and energy efficiency) from both domestic production and imports (Hubacek et al. 2021). Similarly, Wood et al. (2020b) found that EU countries have reduced their overall consumption-based GHG emissions by 8% between 1995 and 2016,

Table 2.4 | Country groups with different degree of PBE–GDP decoupling from 2015 to 2018.

		Absolute decoupling	Relative decoupling	No decoupling	Economic recession
Number of countries		32	41	36	6
CBEs (gigatonnes)	Total	6.41	23.43	2.83	0.85
	Global share	19.1%	69.9%	8.4%	2.5%
PBEs (gigatonnes)	Total	5.33	24.36	3.04	0.84
	Global share	15.9%	72.6%	9.1%	2.5%
Population (million)	Total	857	4518	1213	270
	Global share	12.5%	65.9%	17.7%	3.9%
GDP (billion)	Total	27091	45255	4086	2997
	Global share	34.1%	57.0%	5.1%	3.8%
Per capita GDP (1000 USD2010)	Average	28.83	19.53	6.00	17.78
	Median	26.36	12.04	3.64	13.12
	Max	79.23	110.70	63.93	33.11
	Min	1.09	0.57	0.49	5.80
Per capita CBEs (tonnes)	Average	7.70	6.98	3.99	12.55
	Median	6.78	6.00	1.95	11.33
	Max	23.22	37.95	25.35	23.21
	Min	0.43	0.09	0.18	2.33
CBEs intensity (tonnes per 1000 USD2010)	Average	0.41	0.50	0.77	0.66
	Median	0.31	0.44	0.52	0.69
	Max	2.41	1.68	4.10	1.22
	Min	0.12	0.10	0.20	0.21
Per capita PBEs (tonnes)	Average	6.02	5.69	4.33	14.15
	Median	5.36	4.88	1.67	13.22
	Max	20.13	16.65	39.27	27.24
	Min	0.30	0.09	0.01	2.23
PBEs intensity (tonnes per 1000 USD2010)	Average	0.33	0.45	0.71	0.75
	Median	0.20	0.31	0.44	0.68
	Max	1.47	1.76	4.83	1.80
	Min	0.05	0.10	0.13	0.20

Note: CBEs are obtained from the Global Carbon Budget 2020 (Friedlingstein et al. 2020), GDP and population are from the World Bank. One country (Venezuela) does not have GDP data after 2015, so the degree of decoupling was only calculated for 115 countries. In order to be consistent with the results of CBEs, we calculate the decoupling of PBE until 2018.

---

[11] The decoupling index can be calculated based on changes of a country's GDP and CO_2 emissions (Akizu-Gardoki et al. 2018; Wu et al. 2018). See the equation below. *DI* refers to decoupling index; G_1 refers to the GDP of reporting year while G_0 refers to the base year; E_1 refers to emissions of the reporting year while E_0 refers to emissions of the base year.

$$DI = \frac{\Delta G\% - \Delta E\%}{\Delta G\%} = \left(\frac{G_1 - G_0}{G_0} - \frac{E_1 - E_0}{E_0} \right) \bigg/ \frac{G_1 - G_0}{G_0}$$

mainly due to the use of more efficient technology. The literature also shows that changes in the structure of economy with a shift to tertiary sectors of production may contribute to such decoupling (Kanitkar et al. 2015; Jiang et al. 2021).

A total of 67 (or 58%) countries, including China and India, have relatively decoupled GDP and CBEs between 2015 and 2018, reflecting a slower growth in emissions than GDP. It is worth noting that the USA shows relative decoupling of emissions (both CBEs and PBEs) and GDP over the most recent period, although it strongly decoupled economic growth from emissions between 2005 and 2015. Thus decoupling can be temporary and countries' emissions may again increase after a period of decoupling.

Another 19 (or 16%) countries, such as South Africa and Nepal, have experienced no decoupling between GDP and CBEs from 2015 to 2018, meaning the growth of their GDP is closely tied with the consumption of emission-intensive goods. As a result, a further increase of GDP in these countries will likely lead to higher emissions, if they follow the historical trend without substantive improvement in efficiency of production and energy use.

It is important to note that a country's degree of decoupling changes over time. For example, 32 countries achieved absolute decoupling from 2010 to 2015 but only 10 of them remained decoupled over the next three years. More importantly, although absolute decoupling has reduced annual emissions, the remaining emissions are still contributing to an increase in atmospheric carbon concentration. Absolute decoupling is not sufficient to avoid consuming the remaining CO_2 emission budget under the global warming limit of 1.5°C or 2°C and to avoid climate breakdown (Stoknes and Rockström 2018; Hickel and Kallis 2020). Even if all countries decouple in absolute terms this might still not be sufficient and thus can only serve as one of the indicators and steps toward fully decarbonising the economy and society.

2.3.4   Emissions Embodied in Trade (EET)

As global trade patterns have changed over recent decades, so have emissions embodied in trade (EET) (Jiang & Green 2017). EET refers to emissions associated with production of traded goods and services and is equal to the difference between PBEs and CBEs (Wiebe and Yamano 2016). EET includes two parts: emissions embodied in imports (EEI); and emissions embodied in exports (EEE). For a given country or region with CBEs higher than PBEs, it is a net importer with a higher EEI than EEE, and vice versa.

EET have been rising faster since the 1980s due to an increase in trade volume (Xu and Dietzenbacher 2014; Wood et al. 2018). CO_2 emissions from the production of internationally traded products peaked in 2006 at about 26% of global CO_2 emissions. Since then, international CO_2 emissions transfers declined but are likely to remain an important part of the climate policy agenda (Wood et al. 2020a). About 24% of global economic output and 25% of global CO_2 emissions are embodied in the international trade of goods and services as of 2014 (Hubacek et al. 2021).

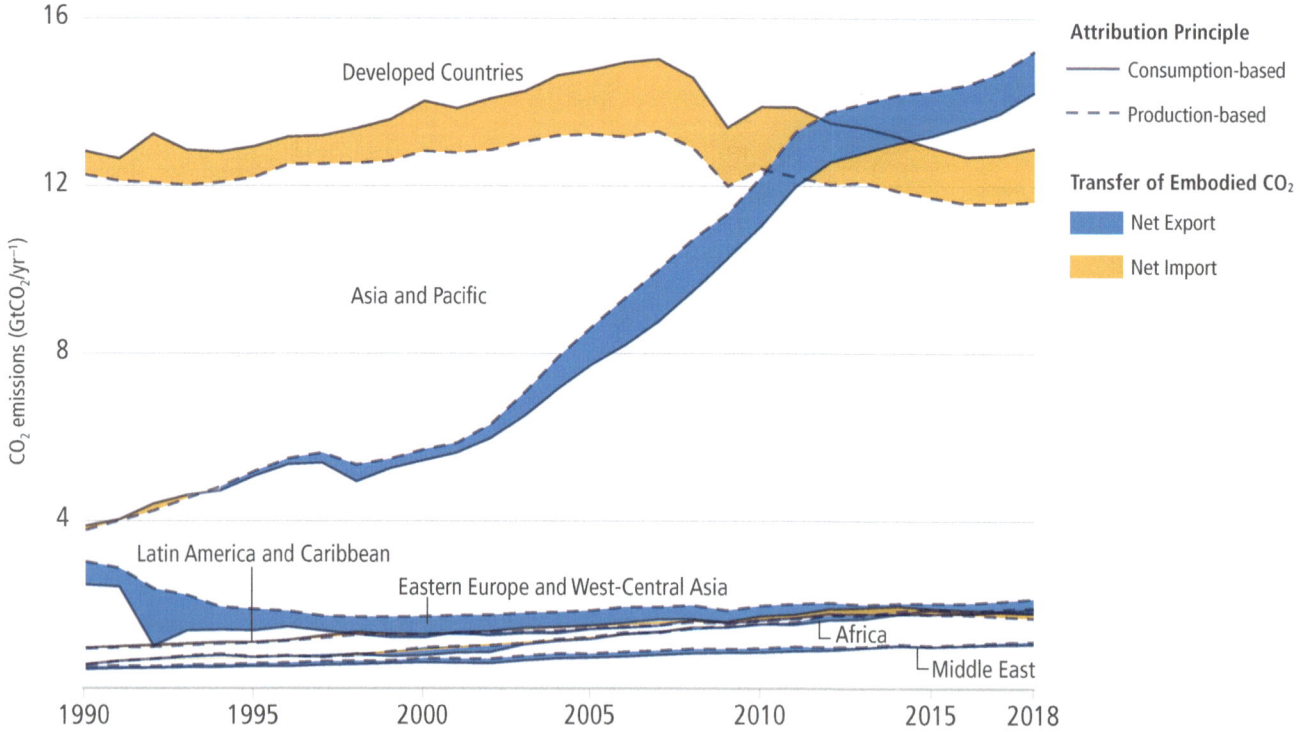

Figure 2.15 | Total annual CO_2 emissions for 116 countries by global region based on consumption- and production-based emissions. The shaded areas are the net CO_2 trade balances (differences) between each of the regions. Yellow shading indicates that the region is a net importer of embodied CO_2 emissions, leading to consumption-based emission estimates that are higher than traditional territorial emission estimates. Blue shading indicates the reverse. Production-based emissions are collected from EDGAR and consumption-based emissions from the Global Carbon Budget 2020 (Friedlingstein et al. 2020). Source: this figure is modified based on Hubacek et al. (2021).

2.3.4.1   Net Emission Transfers

Located downstream in global supply chains, developed countries (mostly in Western Europe and North America) tend to be net emission importers, that is, EEI are larger than EEE. For example, over 40% of national CO_2 footprints in France, Germany, Italy, and Spain are from imports (Fan et al. 2017). Developing countries tend to be net emission exporters with higher PBEs than their CBEs (Peters et al. 2011a), especially for Asia and Pacific (as shown in Figure 2.15). That is to say, there is a net emission transfer and outsourcing of carbon-intensive production from developed to developing economies via global trade (Jiang et al. 2018), mainly caused by cheap labour costs (Tate and Bals 2017) and cheap raw materials (Mukherjee 2018). Increasing openness to trade (Fernández-Amador et al. 2016) and less stringent environmental legislation (acting as so-called pollution havens) are also possible reasons (Hoekstra et al. 2016; Malik and Lan 2016; Banerjee and Murshed 2020).

Net emissions transferred between developing and developed countries peaked at 7.3% of global CO_2 emissions in 2006 and then subsequently declined (Wood et al. 2020a). The main reason for the decline was an improvement in the carbon intensity of traded products, rather than a decline in trade volume (Wood et al. 2020a). Despite continued improvements, developing economies tend to have higher emission intensity than developed economies due to less efficient technologies and a carbon-intensive fuel mix (Jiang and Guan 2017).

2.3.4.2   Geographical Shifts of Emissions Embodied in Trade

With the rapid growth of developing countries, the geographical centre of global trade as well as emissions embodies in trade is changing. The fast growth of Asian countries is shifting the global trade centre from Europe to Asia (Zhang et al. 2019). Asian exports in monetary units increased by 235% from 1996 to 2011, and its share in global exports increased from 25% to 46%, whereas Europe's share in global exports decreased from 51% in 1996 to 39% in 2011. After 2011, global trade has stalled, but Asia's share of global exports further increased to 42% in 2020 (UNCTAD 2021).

In addition to changes in trade volume, trading patterns have also been changing significantly in Asian countries. These countries are replacing traditional trading hubs (such as Russia and Germany) due to the fast growth in trade flows, especially with countries of the Global South (Zhang et al. 2019). The largest geographical shifts in trade-embodied emissions between 1995 and 2011 occurred in high-tech, electronics, and machinery (Malik and Lan 2016; Jiang et al. 2018). For example, China is shifting its exports to include more low-carbon and higher value-added goods and services. As a result, China's exported emissions declined by 20% from 2008 to 2015 (Mi et al. 2018).

Developing countries are increasingly playing an important role in global trade. EET between developing countries, so-called South-South trade, has more than doubled between 2004 (0.47 Gt) and 2011 (1.11 Gt), which is seen as a reflection of a new phase of globalisation (Meng et al. 2018). Developing countries, therefore, have gained importance as global suppliers of goods and services and have also become more relevant as global consumers as they grow their domestic demand (Fernández-Amador et al. 2016). Since 2014, CO_2 emission transfer between developing countries has plateaued and then slightly declined and seems to have stabilised at around the same level of transfers between non-OECD and OECD countries at around 2.4 $GtCO_2$ yr^{-1} (Wood et al. 2020a). In both cases, a decrease in carbon intensity of trade just about offset increased trade volumes (Wood et al. 2020a).

2.4   Economic Drivers and Their Trends by Regions and Sectors

This section provides a summary of the main economic drivers of GHG emissions (mostly territorial) by regions and sectors, including those that are more indirect drivers related to economic activity, such as inequality and rapid urbanisation. Trade as a driver of global GHG emissions is described in the Chapter 2 Supplementary Material. Socio-demographic drivers are described in Section 2.6. The Kaya decomposition presented in this section is based on the International Energy Agency (IEA) and Emissions Database for Global Atmospheric Research (EDGAR) v6 databases and tracks global, regional, and sectoral GHG emissions from 1990 to 2019 (Crippa et al. 2021; IEA 2021c; Lamb et al. 2021b; Minx et al. 2021). It shows main contributors to GHG emissions as independent factors, although these factors also interact with each other.

2.4.1   Economic Drivers at Global and Regional Levels

Economic growth (measured as GDP) and its main components – GDP per capita and population growth – remained the strongest drivers of GHG emissions in the last decade, following a long-term trend (*robust evidence, high agreement*) (Liddle 2015; Malik et al. 2016; Sanchez and Stern 2016; Chang et al. 2019; Dong et al. 2019; Liobikiene and Butkus 2019; Liu et al. 2019a; Mardani et al. 2019; Pan et al. 2019; Dong et al. 2020; Parker and Bhatti 2020; Xia et al. 2021). Globally, GDP per capita remained by far the strongest upward driver, increasing almost in tandem with energy consumption and CO_2 emissions up until 2015, after which some modest decoupling occurred (Deutch 2017; Wood et al. 2018) (Section 2.3.3). The main counteracting, yet insufficient, factor that led to emissions reductions was decreased energy use per unit of GDP in almost all regions ($-2.0%$ yr^{-1} between 2010 and 2019 globally) (see also Lamb et al. 2021b) (Figure 2.16) (*robust evidence, high agreement*). These reductions in energy intensity are a result of technological innovation, structural changes, regulation, fiscal support, and direct investment, as well as increased economic efficiency in underlying sectors (Yao et al. 2015; Sanchez and Stern 2016; Chang et al. 2019; Dong et al. 2019a; Mohmmed et al. 2019; Stern 2019; Azhgaliyeva et al. 2020; Goldemberg 2020; Gao et al. 2021; Liddle and Huntington 2021; Liu et al. 2019b; Xia et al. 2021).

The decades-long trend that efficiency gains were outpaced by an increase in worldwide GDP (or income) per capita continued unabated in the last 10 years (*robust evidence, high agreement*) (Wiedmann et al. 2020; Xia et al. 2021). In addition, the emissions-reducing effects of energy efficiency improvements are diminished by the energy rebound effect, which has been found in several studies to largely offset any energy savings (*robust evidence, high agreement*) (Rausch and Schwerin 2018; Colmenares et al. 2020; Stern 2020; Brockway et al. 2021; Bruns et al. 2021). The rebound effect is discussed extensively in Section 9.9.2.

A significant decarbonisation of the energy system was only noticeable in North America, Europe and Eurasia. Globally, the amount of CO_2 per unit of energy used has practically remained unchanged over the last three decades (Tavakoli 2018; Chang et al. 2019), although it is expected to decrease more consistently in the future (Xia et al. 2021). Population growth has also remained a strong and persistent upward driver in almost all regions (+1.2% yr^{-1} globally from 2010 to 2019) (Lamb et al. 2021) (Figure 2.16), although per capita emission levels are very uneven across world regions. Therefore, modest population increases in

(a) Total global GHG emission trends by sectors

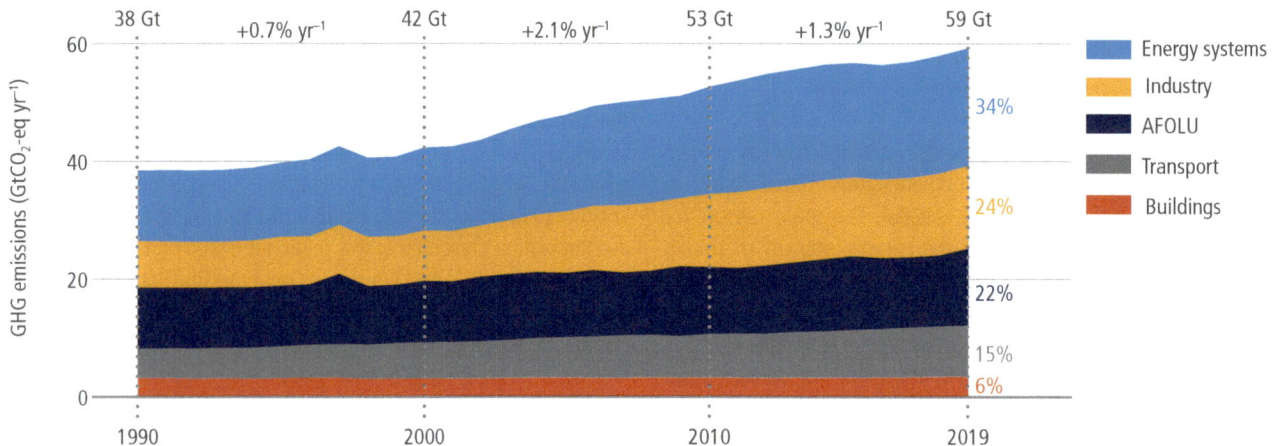

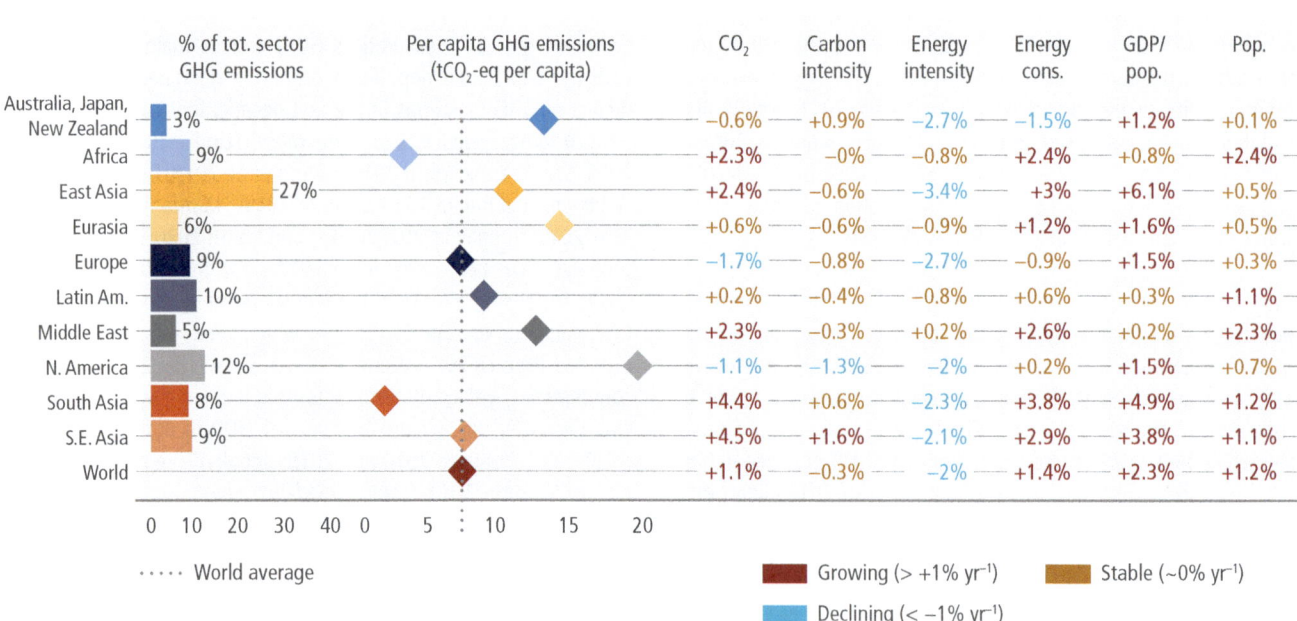

Figure 2.16 | Trends and drivers of global GHG emissions, including: (a) trends of GHG emissions by sectors 1990–2019; (b) share of total and per capita GHG emissions by world region in 2019; and (c) Kaya decomposition of CO_2 emissions drivers. The Kaya decomposition is based on the equation F = P(G/P)(E/G)(F/E), where F is CO_2 emissions, P is population, G/P is GDP per capita, E/G is the energy intensity of GDP and F/E is the carbon intensity of energy. The indicated annual growth rates are averaged across the years 2010–2019 (in panel (c), these are for fossil fuel CO_2 emissions only, in order to ensure compatibility with underlying energy data). Note that the energy consumption by itself (primary energy supply) is not part of the decomposition, but is listed here for comparison with the Kaya factors. Source: data from Crippa et al. (2021), IEA (2021c), Minx et al. (2021).

wealthy countries may have a similar impact on emissions as high population increases in regions with low per capita emission levels.

Developing countries remained major accelerators of global CO_2 emissions growth since 2010, mostly driven by increased consumption and production, in particular in East Asia (*robust evidence, high agreement*) (Jiborn et al. 2020). While energy intensity declined to a similar extent in countries of the Organisation for Economic Co-operation and Development (OECD) and non-OECD countries over the last 30 years, economic growth has been much stronger in non-OECD countries (González-Torres et al. 2021). This led to an average annual growth rate of 2.8% of CO_2 emissions in these countries, whereas they decreased by 0.3% yr^{-1} in OECD countries (UNEP 2019). The majority of developed economies reduced both production-based and consumption-based CO_2 emissions modestly (Jiborn et al. 2020; Xia et al. 2021). This was due to slower economic growth, increased energy efficiency (less energy per unit of GDP), fuel switching from coal to gas (mostly in North America) (Wang et al. 2020b), and the use of less and cleaner energy from renewables in Europe (Peters et al. 2017; Karstensen et al. 2018; Chang et al. 2019; Wood et al. 2019c).

Economic growth as the main driver of GHG emissions is particularly strong in China and India (*robust evidence, high agreement*) (Liu et al. 2019b; Ortega-Ruiz et al. 2020; Z. Wang et al. 2020b; Yang et al. 2020; Zheng et al. 2020; Xia et al. 2021), although both countries show signs of relative decoupling because of structural changes (Marin and Mazzanti 2019). A change in China's production structure (with relatively less heavy industry and lower-carbon manufacturing) and consumption patterns (i.e., the type of goods and services consumed) has become the main moderating factor of emissions after 2010, while economic growth, consumption levels, and investment remain the dominating factors driving up emissions (Wang and Jiang 2019; Jiborn et al. 2020; Zheng et al. 2020). In India, an expansion of production and trade as well as a higher energy intensity between 2010 and 2014 caused increased emissions (Kanitkar et al. 2015; Wang and Zhou 2020; Z. Wang et al. 2020b).

2.4.2   Sectoral Drivers

GHG emissions continued to rise since 2010 across all sectors and subsectors, most rapidly in electricity production, industry, and transport. Decarbonisation gains from improvements in energy efficiency across different sectors and worldwide have been largely wiped out by increases in demand for goods and services. Prevailing consumption patterns have also tended to aggravate energy use and emissions, with the long-term trend led by developed regions. Decarbonisation trends in some developed regions are limited in size and geographically. Globally, there are enormous unexploited mitigation potentials from adopting best available technologies.

The following subsections discuss main emissions drivers by sector. More detailed analyses of sectoral emissions and mitigation options are presented in Chapters 6–11.

2.4.2.1   Energy Systems

Global energy system emissions growth has slowed down in recent years, but global oil and gas use was still growing (Jackson et al. 2019) and the sector remained the single largest contributor to global GHG emissions in 2019 with 20 $GtCO_2$-eq (34%) (*high confidence*) (Figure 2.17). Most of the 14 $GtCO_2$-eq from electricity and heat generation (23% of global GHG emissions in 2019) were due to energy use in industry and in buildings, making these two sectors also prominent targets for mitigation (Davis et al. 2018; Crippa et al. 2019) (see subsections 2.4.2.2 and 2.4.2.3 below).

Growth in CO_2 emissions from energy systems has closely tracked rising GDP per capita globally (Lamb et al. 2021b), affirming the substantial literature describing the mutual relationship between economic growth and demand for energy and electricity (*robust evidence, high agreement*) (Khanna and Rao 2009; Stern, 2011). This relationship has played out strongly in developing regions, particularly in Asia, where a massive scale up of energy supply has accompanied economic growth – with average annual increases of energy demand between 3.8–4.3% in 2010–2019 (Figure 2.17). The key driver for slowing the growth of energy systems CO_2 emissions has been declining energy intensities in almost all regions. Annually, 1.9% less energy per unit of GDP was used globally between 2010 and 2019.

The carbon intensity of power generation varies widely between (and also within) regions (Chapter 6). In North America, a switch from coal to gas for power generation (Peters et al. 2017, 2020; Feng 2019; Mohlin et al. 2019) as well as an overall decline in the share of fossil fuels in electricity production (from 66% in 2010 to 59% in 2018) (Mohlin et al. 2019) has decreased carbon intensity and CO_2 emissions. Since 2007, Europe's carbon intensity improvements have been driven by the steady expansion of renewables in the share of electricity generation (*medium evidence, high agreement*) (Peters et al. 2017, 2020; Le Quéré et al. 2019; Rodrigues et al. 2020). Some studies attribute these effects to climate policies, such as the carbon floor price in the UK, the EU emissions trading scheme, and generous renewable energy subsidies across the continent (Dyrstad et al. 2019; H. Wang et al. 2020). South-East Asian developed countries and Australia, Japan and New Zealand stand out in contrast to other developed regions, with an increase of regional carbon intensity of 1.8 and 1.9% yr^{-1}, respectively (Figure 2.17). Generally, the use of natural gas for electricity production is growing strongly in most countries and gas has contributed to the largest increase in global fossil CO_2 emissions in recent years (Jackson et al. 2019; Peters et al. 2020). Furthermore, gas brings the risk of increased methane (CH_4) emissions from fugitive sources, as well as large cumulative emissions over the lifetime of new gas power plants that may erase early carbon intensity reductions (Shearer et al. 2020).

The growth of emissions from coal power slowed after 2010, and even declined between 2011 and 2019, primarily due to a slowdown of economic growth and fewer coal capacity additions in China (Friedlingstein et al. 2019; Peters et al. 2020). Discussions of a global 'peak coal', however, may be premature, as further growth was observed in 2019 (Friedlingstein et al. 2019; Peters et al. 2020). Large

(a) Total global GHG emission trends by sectors

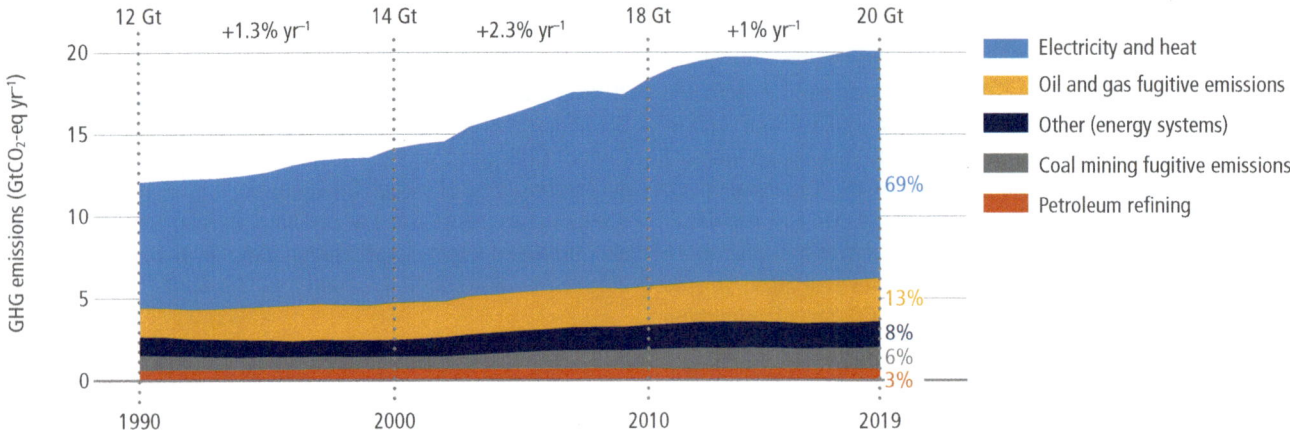

(b) Emissions by region in 2019
(all GHGs, incl. LULUCF CO$_2$, excl. indirect CO$_2$)

(c) Average annual change in Kaya factors 2010–2019
(CO$_2$ only, excl. LULUCF CO$_2$, excl. indirect CO$_2$)

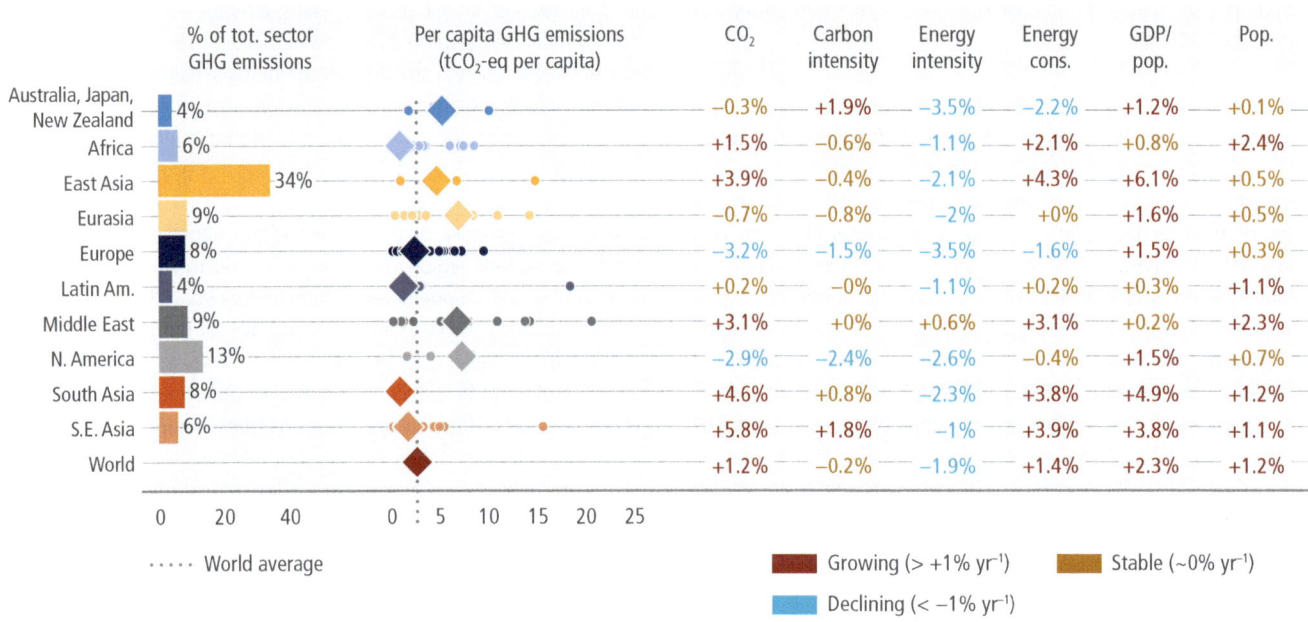

Figure 2.17 | Trends and drivers of global energy sector emissions (see Figure 2.16 caption for details) with energy measured as primary energy supply.

ongoing and planned capacity increases in India, Turkey, Indonesia, Vietnam, South Africa, and other countries has become a driver of thermal coal use after 2014 (UNEP 2017; Edenhofer et al. 2018; Steckel et al. 2019).

2.4.2.2   Industry Sector

When indirect emissions from electricity and heat production are included, industry becomes the single highest emitting sector of GHGs (20.0 GtCO$_2$-eq in 2019) (*high confidence*). Facilitated by globalisation, East Asia has been the main source and primary driver of global industry emissions growth since 2000 (*robust evidence, high agreement*) (Lamb et al. 2021). However, while East Asia has emitted 45% of the world's industry GHG emissions in 2019, a remarkable decrease of 5.0% yr^{-1} in energy intensity and 1.6% in

carbon intensity helped to stabilise direct industrial CO$_2$ emissions in this region (–0.3% yr^{-1} between 2010 and 2019; Figure 2.18). Direct industry CO$_2$ emissions have also declined in Latin America, Europe and Australia, Japan and New Zealand, and – to a smaller extent – in North America. In all other regions, they were growing – most rapidly in southern Asia (+4.3% annually for direct CO$_2$ emissions since 2010) (Figure 2.18).

The main global driver of industry emissions has been a massive rise in the demand for products that are indirectly used in production, such as cement, chemicals, steel, aluminium, wood, paper, plastics, lubricants, fertilisers, and so on. This demand was driven by economic growth, rising affluence, and consumption, as well as a rapid rise in urban populations and associated infrastructure development (*robust evidence, high agreement*) (Krausmann et al. 2018). There is

(a) Industry global GHG emission trends by subsectors

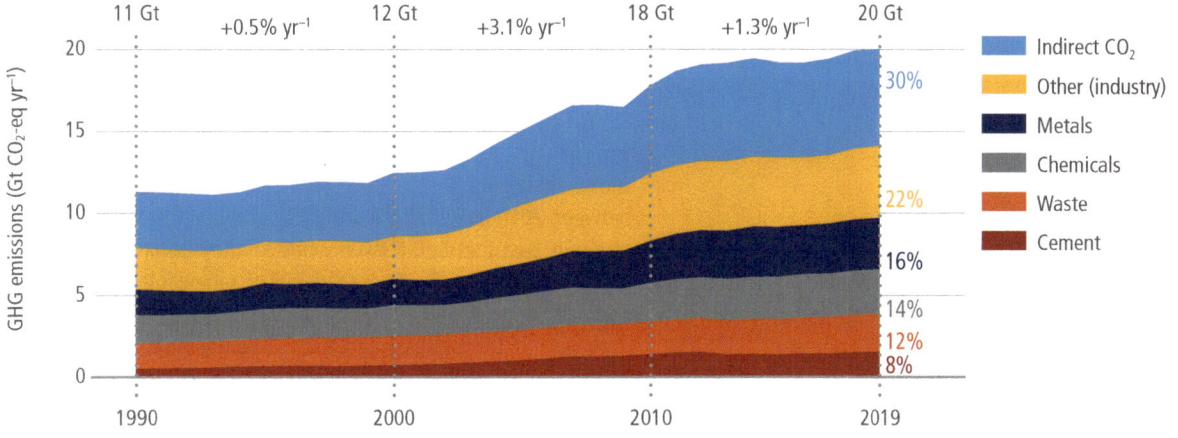

(b) Emissions by region in 2019
(all GHGs, incl. indirect CO₂)

(c) Average annual change in Kaya factors 2010–2019
(CO₂ only, excl. indirect CO₂)

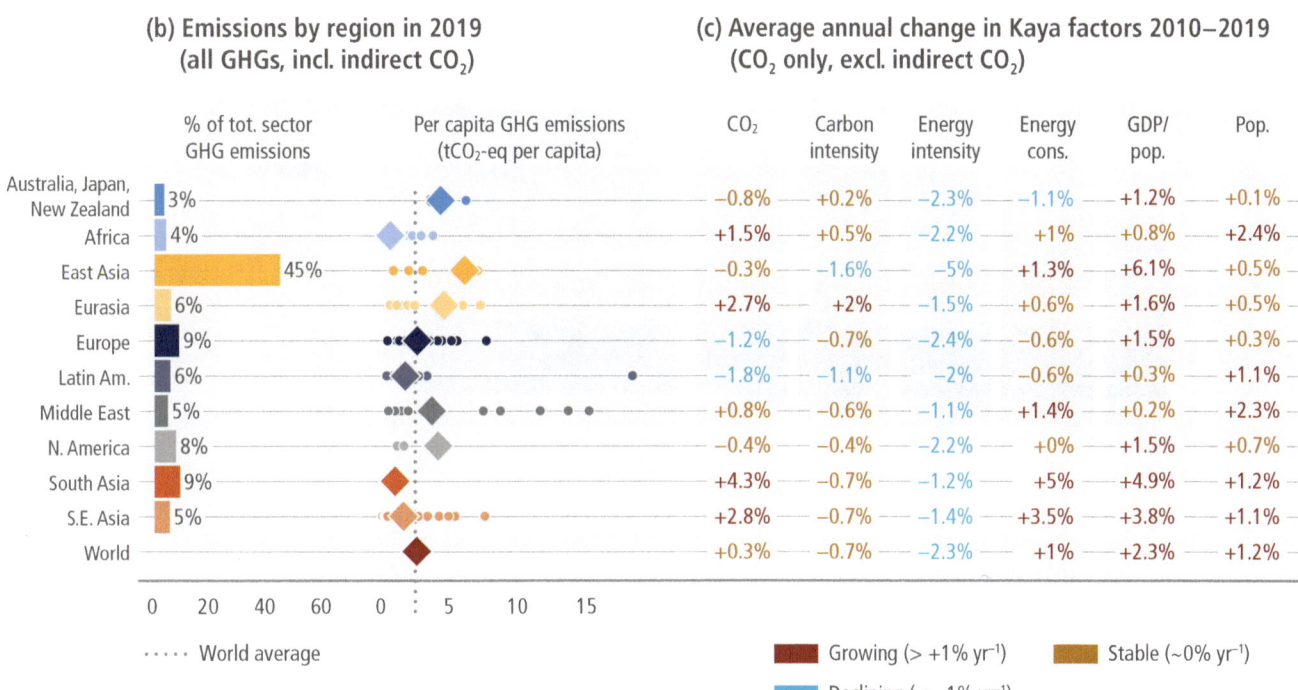

Figure 2.18 | Trends and drivers of global industry sector emissions (see Figure 2.16 caption for details) with energy measured as total final energy consumption.

strong evidence that the growing use of concrete, steel, and other construction materials is particularly tightly coupled to these drivers (Pauliuk et al. 2013; Cao et al. 2017; Krausmann et al. 2017; Plank et al. 2018; Haberl et al. 2020). Per capita stocks of cement and steel show a typical pattern of rapid take-off as countries urbanise and industrialise, before slowing down to low growth at high levels of GDP. Hence, in countries that have recently been industrialising and urbanising – that is Eastern, Southern and South-Eastern Asia – a particularly strong increase of emissions from these subsectors can be observed. Selected wealthy countries seem to stabilise at high per capita levels of stocks, although it is unclear if these stabilisations persist and if they result in significant absolute reductions of material use (Wiedenhofer et al. 2015; Cao et al. 2017; Krausmann et al. 2018). Opportunities for prolonging lifetimes and improving end of

life recycling in order to achieve absolute reductions in extraction activities are as yet unexploited (Krausmann et al. 2017; Zink and Geyer, 2017).

On the production side, improvements in the efficiency of material extraction, processing, and manufacturing have reduced industrial energy use per unit of output (J. Wang et al. 2019). These measures, alongside improved material substitution, lightweight designs, extended product and servicing lifetimes, improved service efficiency, and increased reuse and recycling will enable substantial emissions reductions in the future (Hertwich et al. 2019). In absence of these improvements in energy intensity, the growth of population and GDP per capita would have driven the industrial CO₂ emissions to rise by more than 100% by 2017 compared with 1990, instead of 56% (Lamb et al. 2021b). Nonetheless, many studies point to deep regional differences in efficiency levels and large globally unexploited potentials to improve industrial energy efficiency by adopting best available technologies and practices for metal, cement, and chemical production (Gutowski et al. 2013; Schulze et al. 2016; Hernandez et al. 2018; Talaei et al. 2018).

2.4.2.3   Buildings Sector

Global direct and indirect GHG emissions from the buildings sector reached 9.7 GtCO$_2$-eq in 2019, or 16% of global emissions). Most of these emissions (66%, or 6.4 GtCO$_2$-eq) were upstream emissions from power generation and commercial heat (Figure 2.19). The remaining 33% (3.3 GtCO$_2$-eq) of emissions were directly produced

in buildings, for instance by gas and coal boilers, and cooking and lighting devices that burn kerosene, biomass, and other fuels (Lamb et al. 2021). Residential buildings accounted for the majority of this sector's emissions (64%, 6.3 GtCO$_2$-eq, including both direct and indirect emissions), followed by non-residential buildings (35%, 3.5 GtCO$_2$-eq) (*high confidence*).

Global buildings sector GHG emissions increased by 0.7% yr^{-1} between 2010 and 2019 (Figure 2.19), growing the most in absolute terms in East and South Asia, whereas they declined the most in Europe, mostly due to the expansion of renewables in the energy sector and increased energy efficiency (Lamb et al. 2021). North America has the highest per capita GHG emissions from buildings and the second highest absolute level after East Asia (Figure 2.19).

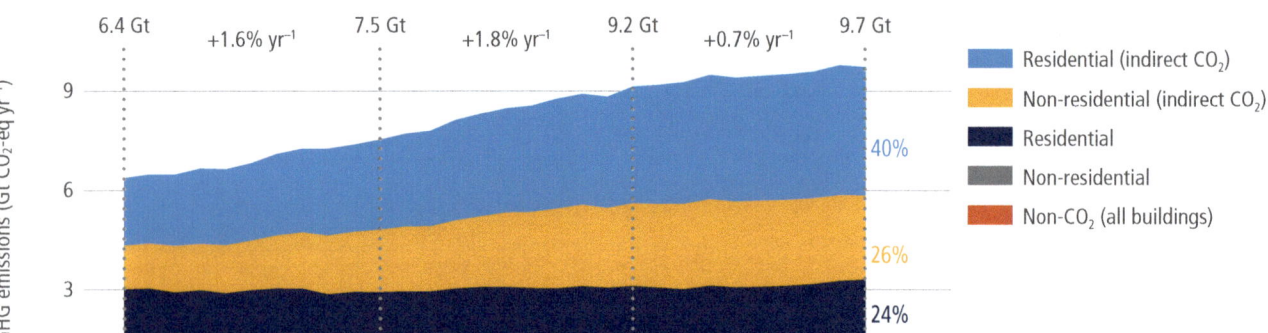

Figure 2.19 | Trends and drivers of global buildings sector emissions (see Figure 2.16 caption for details) with energy measured as total final energy consumption.

Rising wealth has been associated with more floor space being required to service growing demand in the retail, office, and hotel sectors (*medium evidence*, *high agreement*) (Daioglou et al. 2012; Deetman et al. 2020). In addition, demographic and social factors have driven a cross-national trend of increasing floor space per capita. As populations age and decrease in fertility, and as individuals seek greater privacy and autonomy, households declined in size, at least before the COVID-19 pandemic (Ellsworth-Krebs 2020). These factors led to increased floor space per capita, even as populations stabilise. This in turn is a key driver for building sector emissions, because building characteristics such as size and type, rather than occupant behaviour, tend to explain the majority of energy use within dwellings (Guerra Santin et al. 2009; Ürge-Vorsatz et al. 2015; Huebner and Shipworth 2017) (Chapter 9).

Energy activity levels further drive regional differences. In Eurasia, Europe and North America, thermal demands for space heating dominate building energy use, at 66%, 62% and 48% of residential energy demand, respectively (IEA 2020a). In contrast, cooking has a much higher share of building energy use in regions of the Global South, including China (Cao et al. 2016). And, despite temperatures being on average warmer in the Global South, electricity use for cooling is a more prominent factor in the Global North (Waite et al. 2017). This situation is changing, however, as rapid income growth and demographic changes in the Global South enable households to heat and cool their homes (Ürge-Vorsatz et al. 2015, 2020).

Steady improvements in building energy intensities across regions can be attributed to baseline improvements in building fabrics, appliance efficiencies, energy prices, and fuel shifts. Many countries have adopted a mix of relevant policies, such as energy labelling, building energy codes, and mandatory energy performance requirements (Nie and Kemp 2014; Nejat et al. 2015; Economidou et al. 2020). Efforts towards building refurbishments and retrofits have also been pursued in several nations, especially for historical buildings in Europe, but evidence suggests that the recent retrofit rates have not made a significant dent on emissions (Corrado and Ballarini 2016). The Chinese central government launched various policies, including command and control, economic incentives, and technology measures, but a big gap remains between the total rate of building green retrofit in the nation and the future retrofit potential (G. Liu et al. 2020a, 2020b). Still, one major global factor driving down energy intensities has been the global transition from inefficient coal and biomass use in buildings for heating and cooking, towards natural gas and electricity, in part led by concerted policy action in Asian countries (Ürge-Vorsatz et al. 2015; Kerimray et al. 2017; Thoday et al. 2018). As developing countries construct new buildings, there is sizable potential to reduce and use less carbon-intensive building materials and adopt building designs and standards that lower lifecycle buildings energy use and allow for passive comfort. Chapter 9 describes the mitigation options of the buildings sector.

2.4.2.4   Transport Sector

With a steady, average annual growth of +1.8% yr^{-1} between 2010 and 2019, global transport GHG emissions reached 8.9 $GtCO_2$-eq in 2019 and accounted for 15% of all direct and indirect emissions (Figure 2.20). Road transport passenger and freight emissions represented by far the largest component and source of this growth (6.1 $GtCO_2$-eq, 69% of all transport emissions in 2019) (*high confidence*). National plus international shipping and aviation emissions together accounted for 2.0 $GtCO_2$-eq or 22% of the sector's total in 2019. North America, Europe and Eastern Asia stand out as the main regional contributors to global transport emissions and together account for 50% of the sector's total.

The proportion of total final energy used in transport (28%) and its fast expansion over time weighs heavily on climate mitigation efforts, as 92% of transport energy comes from oil-based fuels (IEA 2020b). These trends situate transport as one of the most challenging sectors for climate change mitigation – no country has so far been able to realise significant emissions reductions in the sector. North America's absolute and per capita transport emissions are the highest amongst world regions, but those of South, South-East and East Asia are growing the fastest (*high confidence*) (between +4.6% and +5.2% yr^{-1} for CO_2 between 2010 and 2019) (Figure 2.20).

More so than any other sector, transport energy use has tracked GDP per capita growth (Figure 2.20), (Lamb et al. 2021). With the exception of road gasoline demand in OECD countries, the demand for all road fuels generally increases at least as fast as the rate at which GDP per capita increases (Liddle and Huntington 2020). Developments since 1990 continue a historical trend of increasing travel distances and a shift from low- to high-speed transport modes that goes along with GDP growth (Schäfer et al. 2009; Gota et al. 2019). Modest improvements in energy efficiency have been realised between 2010 and 2019, averaging –1.5% yr^{-1} in energy intensity globally, while carbon intensities of the transport sector have remained stable in all world regions (Figure 2.20). Overall, global increases in passenger and freight travel activity levels have outpaced energy efficiency and fuel economy improvements, continuing a long-term trend for the transport sector (*medium evidence*, *high agreement*) (Gucwa and Schäfer 2013; Grübler 2015; McKinnon 2016).

Despite some policy achievements, energy use in the global transport system remains to the present deeply rooted in fossil fuels (*robust evidence*, *high agreement*) (Figueroa et al. 2014; IEA 2019). In part this is due to the increasing adoption of larger, heavier combustion-based vehicles in some regions, which have tended to far outpace electric and hybrid vehicle sales (Chapter 10). Yet, stringent material efficiency and lightweight design of passenger vehicles alone would have the potential to cut cumulative global GHG emissions until 2060 by 16–39 $GtCO_2$-eq (Pauliuk et al. 2021).

While global passenger activity has expanded in all world regions, great disparities exist between low- and high-income regions, and within countries between urban and rural areas (ITF 2019). While private car use is dominant in OECD countries (EC 2019), the growth of passenger-km (the product of number of travellers and distance travelled) has considerably slowed there, down to an increase of just 1% yr^{-1} between 2000 and 2017 (SLoCaT 2018) (Chapter 10). Meanwhile, emerging economies in the Global South are becoming more car-dependent, with rapidly growing motorisation, on-demand private transport services, urban sprawl, and the emergence of local

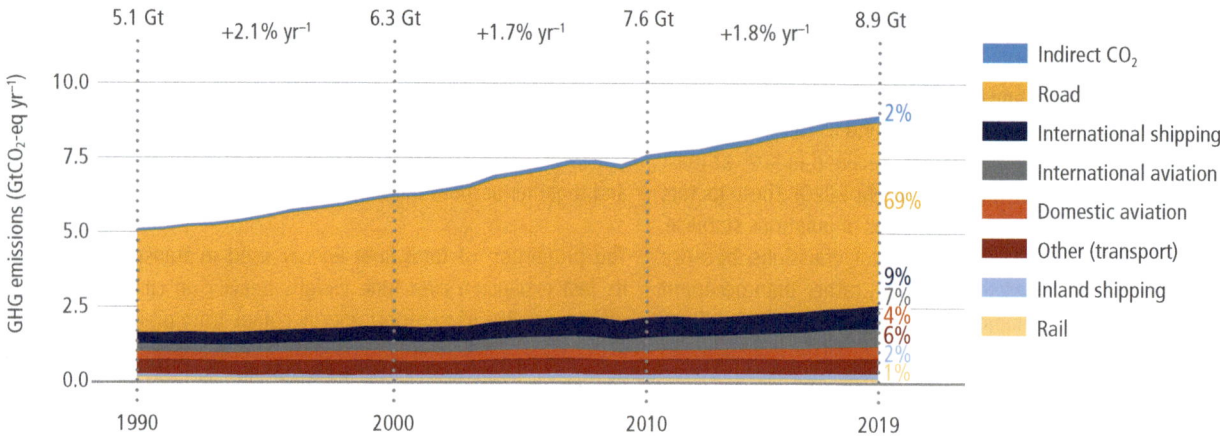

(a) Transport global GHG emission trends by subsectors

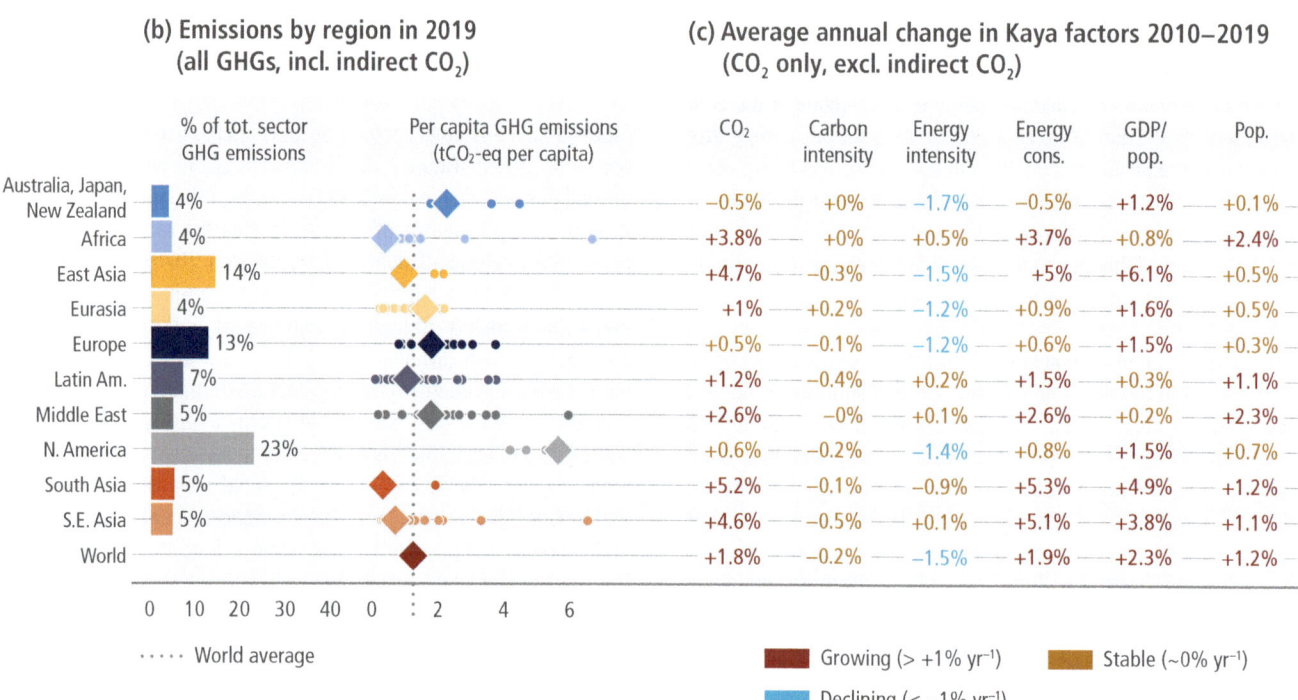

(b) Emissions by region in 2019
(all GHGs, incl. indirect CO$_2$)

(c) Average annual change in Kaya factors 2010–2019
(CO$_2$ only, excl. indirect CO$_2$)

Figure 2.20 | Trends and drivers of global transport sector emissions (see Figure 2.16 caption for details) with energy measured as total final energy consumption.

automotive production, while public transport struggles to provide adequate services (Dargay et al. 2007; Hansen and Nielsen 2017; Pojani and Stead 2017).

Freight travel activity grew across the globe by 68% in the last two decades, driven by global GDP increases, together with the proliferation of online commerce and rapid (i.e., same-day and next-day) delivery (SLoCaT 2018). Growth has been particularly rapid in heavy-duty road freight transport.

While accounting for a small share of total GHG emissions, domestic and international aviation have been growing faster than road transport emissions, with average annual growth rates of +3.3% and +3.4%, respectively, between 2010 and 2019 (Crippa et al. 2021;

Minx et al. 2021;). Energy efficiency improvements in aviation were considerably larger than in road transport, but were outpaced by even larger increases in activity levels (SLoCaT 2018; Lee et al. 2021) (Chapter 10).

2.4.2.5   AFOLU Sector

GHG emissions from agriculture, forestry and other land use (AFOLU) reached 13 GtCO$_2$-eq globally in 2019 (*medium confidence*) (Figure 2.21). AFOLU trends, particularly those for CO$_2$-LULUCF, are subject to a high degree of uncertainty (Section 2.2.1). Overall, the AFOLU sector accounts for 22% of total global GHG emissions, and in several regions – Africa, Latin America, and South-East Asia – it is the single largest emitting sector, which is also significantly affected itself by climate change (AR6 WGI Chapters 8, 11, and 12; and AR6 WGII Chapter 5). Latin America has the highest absolute and per capita AFOLU GHG emissions of any world region (Figure 2.21). CO_2 emissions from land-use change and CH_4 emissions from enteric fermentation together account for 74% of sector-wide GHGs. Note that CO_2-LULUCF estimates included in this chapter are not necessarily comparable with country GHG inventories, due to different approaches to estimating anthropogenic CO_2 sinks (Grassi et al. 2018) (Chapter 7).

Unlike all other sectors, AFOLU emissions are typically higher in developing compared to developed regions (*medium confidence*). In Africa, Latin America, and South-East Asia, CO_2 emissions associated with land-use change and management predominate, dwarfing other AFOLU and non-AFOLU sources and making AFOLU the single largest sector with more than 50% of emissions in these regions (Lamb et al. 2021b). Land-use and land-management emissions are associated with the expansion of agriculture into carbon-dense tropical forest areas (Vancutsem et al. 2021), where large quantities of CO_2 emissions result from the removal and burning of biomass and draining of carbon rich soils (Pearson et al. 2017;

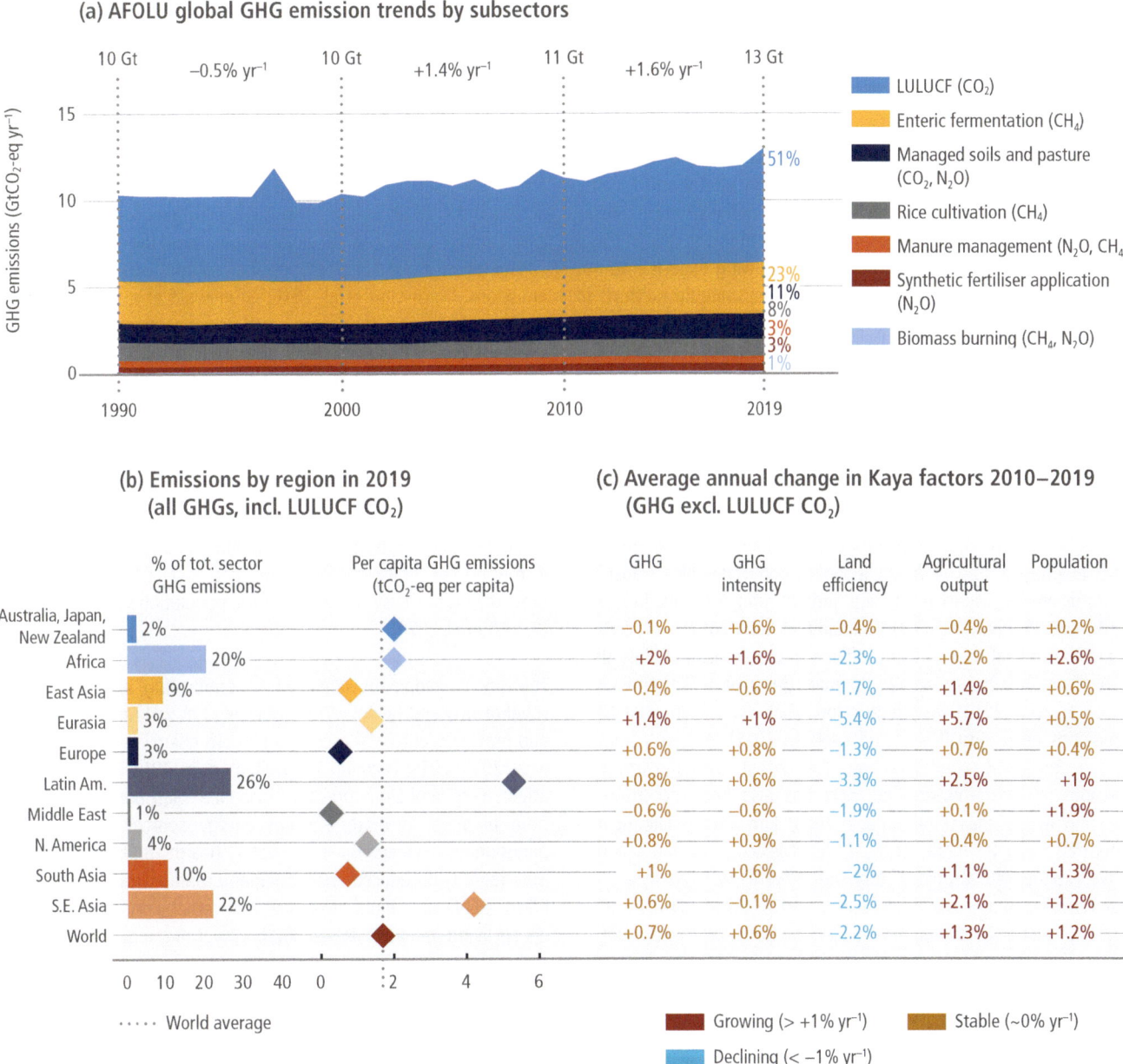

Figure 2.21 | Trends and drivers of global AFOLU sector emissions: (a) trends of GHG emissions by subsectors 1990–2019; (b) share of total sector and per capita GHG emissions by world region in 2019; and (c) Kaya decomposition of GHG emissions drivers. Based on the equation H=P(A/P)(L/A)(H/L), where P is population, A/P is agricultural output per capita, L/A is the land required per unit of agricultural output (land efficiency), and H/L is GHG emissions per unit of land (GHG intensity) (Hong et al. 2021). GHG emissions H comprise agricultural CH_4 and N_2O emissions from EDGAR v6.0. The indicated annual growth rates are averaged across the years 2010–2019 – LULUCF CO_2 emissions are excluded in panel (c). (Note: due to different datasets, the population breakdown for AFOLU emissions is slightly different than that in the other sector figures above).

IPCC 2018; Hong et al. 2021). Ruminant livestock rearing takes place on vast tracts of pasture land worldwide, contributing to large quantities of CH_4 emissions from enteric fermentation in Latin America (0.8 $GtCO_2$-eq in 2018), Southern Asia (0.6 $GtCO_2$-eq), and Africa (0.5 $GtCO_2$-eq), while also playing a sizable role in the total AFOLU emissions of most other regions (Lamb et al. 2021b).

In all regions, the amount of land required per unit of agricultural output has decreased significantly from 2010 to 2019, with a global average of –2.2% yr^{-1} (land efficiency metric in Figure 2.21). This reflects agricultural intensification and technological progress. However, in most regions this was mirrored by an increase in output per capita, meaning that absolute GHG emissions in most regions increased over the last decade. A significant increase in total AFOLU emissions occurred in Africa, driven by both increased GHG emissions per unit of land and increased populations (Figure 2.21).

The AFOLU sector and its emissions impacts are closely tied to global supply chains, with countries in Latin America and South-East Asia using large portions of their land for agricultural and forestry products exported to other countries (Chapter 7). The strong increases in production per capita and associated GHG emissions seen in these regions are at least partly attributable to growing exports and not national food system or dietary changes. At the same time, efforts to promote environmental sustainability in regions such as the EU and the USA (but also fast-growing emerging economies such as China) can take place at the cost of increasing land displacement elsewhere to meet their own demand (Meyfroidt et al. 2010; Yu et al. 2013; Creutzig et al. 2019).

Global diets are a key driver of production per capita, and thus land pressure and AFOLU emissions (Chapter 7). As per capita incomes rise and populations urbanise, traditional, low-calorie diets that emphasise starchy foods, legumes, and vegetables transition towards energy-intensive products such as refined sugars, fats, oils, and meat (Pradhan et al. 2013; Tilman and Clark 2014). At a certain point in national development, affluence and associated diets thus override population growth as the main driver of AFOLU emissions (Kastner et al. 2012). Very high calorie diets have high total GHG emissions per capita (Heller and Keoleian 2015) and are common in the developed world (Pradhan et al. 2013). Over the last few decades, a 'westernisation' of diets has also been occurring in developing countries (Pradhan et al. 2013). Low- and middle-income countries such as India, Brazil, Egypt, Mexico, and South Africa have experienced a rapid dietary shift towards western-style diets (De Carvalho et al. 2013; Pradhan et al. 2013; Popkin 2015). Another driver of higher food requirements per capita is food waste, which has increased more or less continuously since the 1960s in all regions but Europe (Porter and Reay 2016).

2.4.3   Poverty and Inequality

Increasing economic inequality globally has given rise to concern that unequal societies may be more likely to pollute and degrade their environments (Masud et al. 2018; Chancel 2020; Hailemariam et al. 2020; Millward-Hopkins and Oswald 2021). The nature of this

relationship has important implications for the design of income redistribution policies aiming to reduce inequalities (Section 2.6 presents evidence on how affluence and high consumption relate to emissions). Income inequality and carbon intensity of consumption differs across countries and individuals (Baležentis et al. 2020) (Section 2.3.3). Reduced income inequality between nations can reduce emissions intensity of global income growth, if energy intensity reductions from income growth in some nations offset increases in energy and emissions from higher growth in other nations (Rao and Min 2018). Increasing income inequality between individuals can translate into larger energy and emissions inequality if higher incomes are spent on more energy-intensive consumption and affluent lifestyles (Oswald et al. 2020; Wiedmann et al. 2020) (Section 2.6).

Literature shows that more equitable income distributions can improve environmental quality, but the nature of this relationship can vary by level of development (*low evidence, medium agreement*) (Knight et al. 2017; Chen et al. 2020; Hailemariam et al. 2020; Huang and Duan 2020; Liobikienė and Rimkuvienė 2020; Rojas-Vallejos and Lastuka 2020; Uddin et al. 2020). Differences in the energy and carbon intensities of consumption and the composition of consumption baskets across populations and nations matter for emissions. (Jorgenson et al. 2016; Grunewald et al. 2017). There is evidence to suggest that more equal societies place a higher value on environmental public goods (Baumgärtner et al. 2017; Drupp et al. 2018). Additional research shows that reducing top income inequality in OECD countries can reduce carbon emissions and improve environmental quality (Hailemariam et al. 2020) and that the effect of wealth inequality, measured as the wealth share of the top decile, on per capita emissions in high-income countries, is positive (Knight et al. 2017). Evidence from 40 sub-Saharan African countries suggests that a rise in income inequality contributed to increasing CO_2 emissions between 2010 and 2016, controlling for other drivers such as economic growth, population size, and inflation (Baloch et al. 2020).

The key development objective of eradicating extreme poverty (Chakravarty and Tavoni 2013; Hubacek et al. 2017a; Malerba 2020) and providing universal access to modern energy services (Pachauri et al. 2013, 2018; Pachauri 2014; Singh et al. 2017) only marginally affects GHG emissions (*medium evidence, high agreement*). Shifts from biomass to more efficient energy sources and collective provisioning systems for safe water, health, and education are associated with reduced energy demand (Baltruszewicz et al. 2021). Efforts to alleviate multi-dimensional poverty by providing minimum decent living standards universally, however, may require more energy and resources. Recent estimates of the additional energy needed are still within bounds of projections of energy demand under climate stabilisation scenarios (Hubacek et al. 2017a, 2017b; Rao et al. 2019; Pascale et al. 2020; Kikstra et al. 2021). Bottom-up estimates suggest that achieving decent living standards requires 13–40 GJ per capita annually, much less than the current world average energy consumption of 80 GJ per capita in 2020 (Millward-Hopkins et al. 2020) (*medium evidence, high agreement*). Aggregate top-down estimates suggest that achieving a high Human Development Index (HDI) score above 0.8 requires energy consumption between

30–100 GJ per capita yr^{-1} (Lamb and Rao 2015). There is some evidence, however, of a decoupling between energy consumption and HDI over time (Akizu-Gardoki et al. 2018). The emissions consequences of poverty alleviation and decent living also depend on whether improvements in well-being occur via energy- and carbon-intensive industrialisation or low-carbon development (Semieniuk and Yakovenko 2020; Fu et al. 2021; Huang and Tian 2021).

2.4.4 Rapid and Large-scale Urbanisation as a Driver of GHG Emissions

Economic growth and urbanisation go hand in hand and are both influencing GHG emissions. However, the exact role of urban development in driving emissions is multi-faceted and heterogeneous, depending on development status and other regional factors (*medium evidence, high agreement*) (Jorgenson et al. 2014; Lamb et al. 2014; Liddle and Lung 2014; Creutzig et al. 2015; Pincetl 2017; Azizalrahman and Hasyimi 2019; Muñoz et al. 2020). This calls for a differentiated assessment. This section assesses the process of rapid urban growth in developing countries and how emissions change over time when cities' urban populations and infrastructure expand at fast speed and at a massive scale (Seto et al. 2017; Elmqvist et al. 2021). To distinguish, Section 2.6 includes the carbon footprint of urban lifestyles and the difference in emissions profiles between already urbanised and less urbanised areas. Chapter 8 deals with urban strategies for climate change mitigation.

Urban development is most significant and rapid in developing and transition countries, accompanied by a substantial migration of rural populations to urban areas (Apergis and Li 2016; Azizalrahman and Hasyimi 2019; Z. Wang et al. 2019) and associated impacts on land use (Richardson et al. 2015). If the trend of developing countries following infrastructure stock patterns in industrialised nations continues until 2050, this could cause approximately 350 GtCO$_2$ from the production of materials (Müller et al. 2013). This would be equivalent to 70% of the 500 GtCO$_2$ estimated remaining carbon budget from the beginning of 2020 to limit global warming to 1.5°C with a likelihood of 50% (IPCC 2021b).

In many developing countries across the world, the process of urban expansion leads to higher per capita consumption-based GHG emissions (*medium evidence, high agreement*) (Jorgenson et al. 2014; Yao et al. 2015; Zhang et al. 2016; Wood et al. 2018a; Muñoz et al. 2020). The high disparity between rural and urban personal carbon footprints in these countries (Wiedenhofer et al. 2017) (Section 2.6) means that migration to urban areas increases overall emissions as levels of income and expenditure rise, leading to further economic growth and infrastructure development in urban areas (Müller et al. 2013; Li et al. 2015; Wang and Yang 2016; Zhang et al. 2016; Wiedenhofer et al. 2017; Cetin and Bakirtas 2019; Fan et al. 2019; Li and Zhou 2019; Xia et al. 2019; Sarkodie et al. 2020).

For total production-based emissions in general, urbanisation is thought to have a smaller effect than changes in population, GDP per capita, and energy and emissions intensities, which are all more influential (Lin et al. 2017). Another driver of urban emissions is rising

ambient air temperature caused by urban land expansion, which will likely drive a substantive increase in air conditioning use and cold storage for food (Huang et al. 2019). Specific emission drivers, however, depend on city- and place-specific circumstances such as income, household size, density, or local climate (Baiocchi et al. 2015; H. Wang et al. 2019). Geographical factors, urban form, and transport/fuel costs are dependent on each other, and, together with economic activity, have been found to explain 37% of urban direct energy use and 88% of urban transport energy use in a global sample of 274 cities (Creutzig et al. 2015).

2.5 Technological Change is Key to Reducing Emissions

Technological change for climate change mitigation involves improvement in and adoption of technologies, primarily those associated with energy production and use. Technological change has had a mitigating effect on emissions over the long term and is central to efforts to achieving climate goals (*high confidence*). Progress since AR5 shows that multiple low-carbon technologies are improving and falling in cost (*high confidence*); technology adoption is reaching substantial shares, and small-scale technologies are particularly promising on both (*medium confidence*). Faster adoption and continued technological progress can play a crucial role in accelerating the energy transition. However, the historical pace of technological change is still insufficient to catalyse a complete and timely transition to a low-carbon energy system: technological change needs to accelerate (*high confidence*). This section assesses the role of technological change in driving emissions reductions and the factors that drive technological change, with an emphasis on the speed of transitions. Incentives and support for technological change affect technology outcomes (Sivaram et al. 2018; Wilson et al. 2020a). Work since AR5 has focused on evaluating the effectiveness of policies: those that accelerate technological change by enhancing knowledge (technology push) and those that increase market opportunities for successful technologies (demand pull) (Nemet 2013); as well as the importance of tailoring support to country contexts (Barido et al. 2020; Rosenbloom et al. 2020), including the limits of carbon-pricing policies to date (Lilliestam et al. 2020). Section 2.8 and Chapter 13 describe how these polices affect emissions; Chapter 14 and Cross-Chapter Box 12 in Chapter 16 discuss transition dynamics; and Chapter 16 provides a more detailed assessment of the evolution and mitigation impacts of technology development, innovation, and transfer.

2.5.1 Technological Change Has Reduced Emissions

Technological change that facilitates efficient energy utilisation from production to its final conversion into end-use services is a critical driver of carbon emissions reductions (*high confidence*). Technological change can facilitate stringent mitigation, but it can also reduce these effects by changing consumer behaviour, such as through rebound effects (Section 2.6 and Chapter 16). AR6 includes an entire chapter on innovation, technology development, and transfer (Chapter 16). A focus gained in this section is the extent to which aligned, credible, and durable policies can accelerate technological change factors to put emissions reductions on a trajectory compatible with reaching United Nations Framework Convention on Climate Change (UNFCCC) goals.

Technological change has facilitated the provision of more diverse and efficient energy services (heating, cooling, lighting, and mobility) while generating fewer emissions per unit of service. As seen in Section 2.4, in Kaya identity terms (Lima et al. 2016) (see 'Kaya identity' in Glossary): population and economic growth are factors that have increased emissions, while technological change has reduced emissions (Peters et al. 2017). These Kaya statistics show that, while technological change can facilitate the transition to a low-carbon economy, it needs to proceed at a much faster pace than historical trends (Peters et al. 2017).

Multiple challenges exist in accelerating the past rate of technological change. First, an array of physical assets in the energy system are long-lived and thus involve substantial committed carbon (Section 2.7) (Knapp 1999; Cui et al. 2019). A process of 'exnovation', accelerating the phase-out of incumbent technology through intentional policy (such as by pricing carbon), provides a means to address long lifetimes (Davidson 2019; Rosenbloom and Rinscheid 2020). Second, countries may not have the capacity to absorb the flows of ideas and research results from international knowledge spillovers due to weak infrastructure, limited research capacity, lack of credit facilities (Chapter 15, Section 15.5), and other barriers to technology transfer (Adenle et al. 2015). In a developing country context, processes of innovation and diffusion need to include competence-building systems (Lema et al. 2015; Perrot and Sanni 2018; Stender et al. 2020). Third, public policy is central to stimulating technological change to reduce emissions; policy depends on creating credible expectations of future market opportunities (Alkemade and Suurs 2012), but the historical evidence shows that, despite recent progress, policies related to energy and climate over the long term have been inconsistent (Taylor 2012; Nemet et al. 2013; Koch et al. 2016). Bolstering the credibility and durability of policies related to low-carbon technology are crucial to accelerating technological change and inducing the private sector investment required (Helm et al. 2003; Habermacher et al. 2020).

2.5.2 A Low-carbon Energy Transition Needs to Occur Faster Than Previous Transitions

An illuminating debate on the possibility of faster transitions has emerged since AR5 – with diverging assumptions about future technological change at the core of the discourse (Bazilian et al. 2020; Lu and Nemet 2020). Table 2.5 summarises these arguments.

2.5.2.1 Energy Transitions Can Occur Faster Than in the Past

Recent studies have identified examples supporting fast energy transitions (Sovacool 2016; Bond et al. 2019; Reed et al. 2019). One describes five rapid national-scale transitions in end-use technologies, including lighting in Sweden, cook-stoves in China, liquefied petroleum gas stoves in Indonesia, ethanol vehicles in Brazil, and air conditioning in the USA (Sovacool 2016). Adoption of electric vehicles in Norway and in cities in China have also been rapid (Rietmann and Lieven 2019; Li et al. 2020; Fridstrøm 2021). Examples in energy supply, include electrification in Kuwait, natural gas in the Netherlands, nuclear electricity in France and Sweden, combined heat and power in Denmark, renewable energy in Uruguay, and coal retirements in Ontario, Canada (Qvist and Brook 2015). Reasons that these exemplars could be applied more broadly in the future include: growing urgency on climate change, shifting motivation from price response to proactive resource scarcity, and an increase in the likelihood of technological breakthroughs (*medium confidence*) (Sovacool 2016; Bazilian et al. 2020). The emergence of smaller unit scale, granular technologies (described below) also creates the potential for faster system change (Trancik 2006; Grubler et al. 2018; Wilson et al. 2020a). Energy service prices and government actions that affect demand are critical to the speed and extent of energy transitions (Kramer and Haigh 2009). Reasons scholars consider for expecting a fast transition include: intentional policy and alignment with goals; globalisation which diversifies sources and integrates supply chains; collective action via the Paris Agreement; as well as bottom-up grassroots movements and private sector initiatives (Kern and Rogge 2016). Political support for change can also speed transitions (Burke and Stephens 2017; Stokes and Breetz 2018), as can the credibility of transition-related targets (Li and Pye 2018; Rogge and Dütschke 2018).

Table 2.5 | Summary of reasons to expect a fast energy transition/slow transition.

	Fast transition	Slow transition
Evidentiary basis	Technology and country cases over 50 years	Historical global system over 200 years
Systems	Complementary technologies enable integration	Difficult integration with existing infrastructure
Economics	Falling costs of nascent technology	Mature incumbent technologies Upfront costs and capital constraints
Technology	Digitalisation and global supply chains More abundant innovation Granular technology	Long lifetimes of capital stock Difficult to decarbonise sectors
Actors	Proactive efforts for transition Bottom-up public concern Mobilised low-carbon interest groups	Risk-averse adopters Attributes do not appeal to consumers Rent-seeking by powerful incumbents
Governance	Leaders catalyse faster change	Collective action problems

The important role of leader countries is often missed when looking only at global aggregates (Meckling and Hughes 2018); leaders accumulate important knowledge, provide scaled market, and set positive examples for followers (*medium confidence*) (Schwerhoff 2016; Buchholz et al. 2019). In recent years, the conception of where leadership, climate-relevant innovation, and technology transfer originate has shifted to considering more meaningfully direct South-South and South-North forms of technology transfer, flows of capital, drivers for market access, origins of innovation, and other forms of cooperation (Urban 2018; Köhler et al. 2019). Recent evidence shows that South-South trade is enabling clean technology transfer (Gosens 2020). Leaders can initiate a process of 'catalytic cooperation' in which they overcome collective action problems and stimulate rapid change (Hale 2018). Similarly, 'sensitive intervention points' – targeted support of social movements, technologies, or policies themselves – can lead to rapid and self-sustaining change (Farmer et al. 2019), such as support for photovoltaics in Germany in the 2000s and student climate activism in Europe in 2019. The focus on leadership, catalysts, and intervention points reflects a systemic view of transitions that emphasises interactions and interdependence (Geels 2018; Meckling and Hughes 2018). Technological change has been at the core of transitions, but is best understood as part of a system in which social aspects are crucial (*medium confidence*) (Cherp et al. 2018; Köhler et al. 2019; Overland and Sovacool 2020).

2.5.2.2 Reasons Why Transitions Will Occur at Historical Rates of Change

Recent work has also reasserted previous claims that the speed of a low-carbon transition will follow historical patterns (*low confidence*). Broad transitions involve technological complexity, time-consuming technological development, risk-averse adopters, high upfront costs, and low immediate individual adoption benefits, attributes that are not all present in the examples of rapid change described above (Grubler et al. 2016). Additional factors that slow transitions include: the need for the transition to occur globally, thus requiring nations with unequal economic resources and development circumstances to engage in near-universal participation; slow progress in recent decades; intermittence of renewables, and the time involved in building supporting infrastructure (Smil 2016); difficulty in decarbonising transportation and industry (Rissman et al. 2020); and material resource constraints (Davidsson et al. 2014).

2.5.3 Improvements in Technologies Enable Faster Adoption

Since AR5, multiple low-carbon technologies have shown dramatic improvement, particularly solar photovoltaic (PV), wind, and batteries (*high confidence*). The observed pace of these changes and the likelihood of their continuation support the arguments in the previous section that future energy transitions are likely to occur more quickly than in the past (*medium confidence*).

2.5.3.1 Technological Change Has Produced Dramatic Cost Reductions

A wide array of technologies shows long-term improvements in performance, efficiency, and cost. Among the most notable are solar PV, wind power, and batteries (*high confidence*) (Chapters 6 and 16). The dynamics for PVs are the most impressive, having fallen in cost by a factor of 10,000 from the first commercial application on a satellite in 1958 (Maycock and Wakefield 1975) to power purchase agreements signed in 2019 (IRENA 2020). Wind has been on a nearly as steep trajectory (Wiser and Bolinger 2019) as are lithium-ion battery packs for electric vehicles (Nykvist and Nilsson 2015; Service 2019). The future potential for PV and batteries seems especially promising given that neither industry has yet begun to adopt alternative materials with attractive properties as the cost reductions and performance improvements associated with the current generation of each technology continue (*medium confidence*) (Kwade et al. 2018). A key challenge is improving access to finance, especially in developing country contexts, where the costs of financing are of crucial importance (Creutzig et al. 2017; Schmidt 2019).

2.5.3.2 Technological Change has Accelerated Since AR5

Figure 2.22 shows changes in the costs of four dynamic energy technologies. One can see rapid changes since AR5, cost data for which ended in 2010. Solar PV is by far the most dynamic technology, and its cost since AR5 has continued on its steep decline at about the same rate of change as before AR5, but now costs are well within the range of fossil fuels (*high confidence*) (Chapter 6). Very few concentrating solar power (CSP) plants had been built between the 1980s and 2012. Since AR5, 4GW have been built and costs have fallen by half. Onshore wind has continued its pace of cost reductions such that it is well within the range of fossil fuels. Offshore wind has changed the most since AR5. Whereas costs were increasing before AR5, they have decreased by 50% since. None of these technologies shows indications of reaching a limit in their cost reductions. Crucial to their impact will be extending these gains in the electricity and transportation sectors to the industrial sector (Davis et al. 2018).

2.5.3.3 Granular Technologies Improve Faster

The array of evidence of technology learning that has accumulated both before and since AR5 (Thomassen et al. 2020) has prompted investigations about the factors that enable rapid technology learning. From the wide variety of factors considered, unit size has generated the strongest and most robust results. Smaller unit sizes, sometimes referred to as 'granularity', tend to be associated with faster learning rates (*medium confidence*) (Sweerts et al. 2020; Wilson et al. 2020). Examples include solar PV, batteries, heat pumps, and to some extent wind power. The explanatory mechanisms for these observations are manifold and well established: more iterations are available with which to make improvements (Trancik 2006); mass production can be more powerful than economies of scale (Dahlgren et al. 2013); project management is simpler and less risky (Wilson et al. 2020); the ease of early retirement can enable risk-taking for innovative designs (Sweerts et al. 2020); and they tend to be less complicated (Malhotra and Schmidt 2020; Wilson

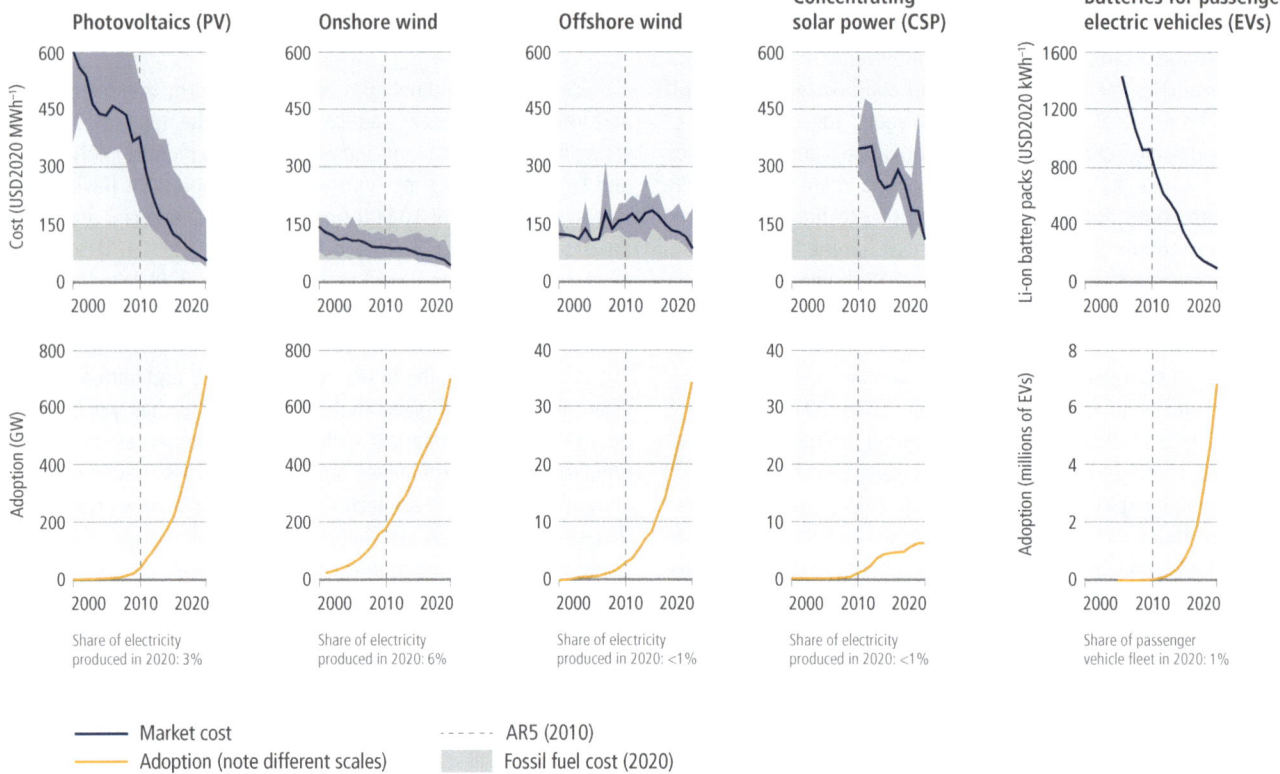

Figure 2.22 | Unit cost reductions and use in some rapidly changing mitigation technologies. The **top panel** shows global costs per unit of energy (USD per MWh) for some rapidly changing mitigation technologies. Solid blue lines indicate average unit cost in each year. Light blue shaded areas show the range between the 5th and 95th percentiles in each year. Grey shading indicates the range of unit costs for new fossil fuel (coal and gas) power in 2020 (corresponding to USD55–148 per MWh). In 2020, the levelised costs of energy (LCOE) of the four renewable energy technologies could compete with fossil fuels in many places. For batteries, costs shown are for 1 kWh of battery storage capacity; for the others, costs are LCOE, which includes installation, capital, operations, and maintenance costs per MWh of electricity produced. The literature uses LCOE because it allows consistent comparisons of cost trends across a diverse set of energy technologies to be made. However, it does not include the costs of grid integration or climate impacts. Further, LCOE does not take into account other environmental and social externalities that may modify the overall (monetary and non-monetary) costs of technologies and alter their deployment. The **bottom panel** shows cumulative global adoption for each technology, in GW of installed capacity for renewable energy and in millions of vehicles for battery-electric vehicles. A vertical dashed line is placed in 2010 to indicate the change since AR5. Shares of electricity produced and share of passenger vehicle fleet are indicated in text for 2020 based on provisional data, i.e., percentage of total electricity production (for PV, onshore wind, offshore wind, CSP) and of total stock of passenger vehicles (for EVs). The electricity production share reflects different capacity factors; for example, for the same amount of installed capacity, wind produces about twice as much electricity as solar PV. {2.5, 6.4} Renewable energy and battery technologies were selected as illustrative examples because they have recently shown rapid changes in costs and adoption, and because consistent data are available. Other mitigation options assessed in the report are not included as they do not meet these criteria.

et al. 2020). Small technologies often involve iterative production processes with many opportunities for learning by doing, and have much of the most advanced technology in the production equipment than in the product itself. In contrast, large unit scale technologies – such as full-scale nuclear power, carbon capture and storage (CCS), low-carbon steel making, and negative emissions technologies such as bioenergy with carbon capture and storage (BECCS) – are often primarily built on site and include thousands to millions of parts, such that complexity and system integration issues are paramount (Nemet 2019). Despite the accumulating evidence of the benefits of granularity, these studies are careful to acknowledge the role of other factors in explaining learning. In a study of 41 energy technologies (Figure 2.23), unit size explained 22% of the variation in learning rates (Sweerts et al. 2020) and a study of 31 low-carbon technologies showed that unit size explained 33% (Wilson et al. 2020). Attributing that amount of variation to a single factor is rare in studies of technological change. The large residual has motivated studies, which find that small-scale technologies provide

opportunities for rapid change, but they do not make rapid change inevitable; a supportive context, including supportive policy and complementary technologies, can stimulate more favourable technology outcomes (*high confidence*).

There is also evidence that small technologies not only learn but become adopted faster than large technologies (*medium confidence*) (Wilson et al. 2020b). Some of the mechanisms related to the adoption rate difference are associated with cost reductions; for example, smaller, less lumpy investments involve lower risk for adopters (Dahlgren et al. 2013; Wilson et al. 2020b). The shorter lifetimes of small technologies allow users to take advantage of new performance improvements (Knapp 1999) and access a large set of small adopters (Finger et al. 2019). Other mechanisms for faster adoption are distinctly related to markets: modular technologies can address a wide variety of niche markets (Geels 2018) with different willingness to pay (Nemet 2019) and strategically find protected niches while technology is maturing (Coles et al. 2018).

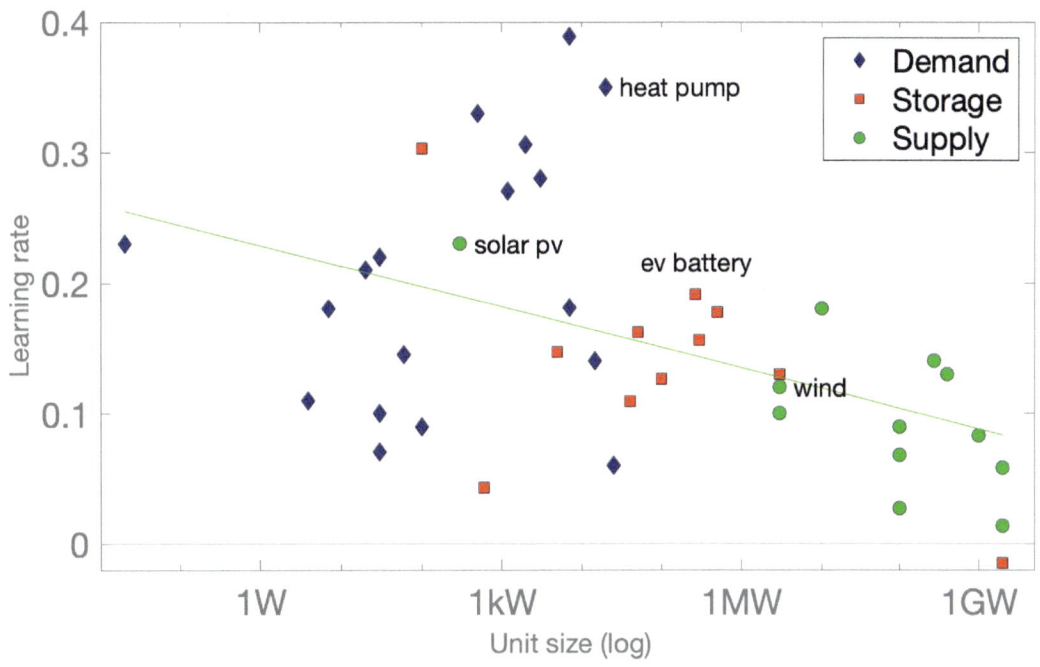

Figure 2.23 | Learning rates for 41 energy demand, supply, and storage technologies. Source: Sweerts et al. (2020).

2.5.4 Rapid Adoption Accelerates Energy Transitions

The transition to a more sustainable energy system depends not just on improvement in technologies, but also on their widespread adoption. Work since AR5 has also substantiated the bidirectional causal link between technology improvement and adoption. Cost reductions facilitate adoption, which generates opportunities for further cost reductions through a process of learning by doing (*medium confidence*). The rate of adoption is thus closely related to the speed at which an energy transition is possible.

Results of integrated assessment models (IAMs) show that scale-up needs are massive for 2°C scenarios. Using logistic growth rates of energy shares as in previous work (Wilson 2012; Cherp et al. 2021), most of these technologies include annual adoption growth rates of 20% in the 2020s and 2030s, and are in line with recent adoption of wind and solar. However, it is important to realise that IAMs include faster adoption rates for some mitigation technologies than for others (Peters et al. 2017). Growth rates in IAMs for large-scale CCS – biomass, coal, and gas – are between 15–30% (25th and 75th percentiles) (Figure 2.24). So few plants have been built that there is little historical data to analyse expected growth; with only two full-scale CCS power plants built and a 7% growth rate, if including industrial CCS. In contrast, IAMs indicate that they expect much lower rates of growth in future years for the technologies that have been growing fastest in recent years (wind and solar), without strong evidence for why this should occur.

The overall pattern shows that IAMs expect growth in small-scale renewables to fall to less than half of their recent pace, and large-scale CCS to more than double from the limited deployment assessed (*high confidence*). The emerging work since AR5 showing the rapid adoption and faster learning in small-scale technologies should prompt a keener focus on what technologies the world can depend on to scale up quickly (Grubb et al. 2021). The scenario results make it quite clear that climate stabilisation depends on rapid adoption of low-carbon technologies throughout the 2020–2040 period.

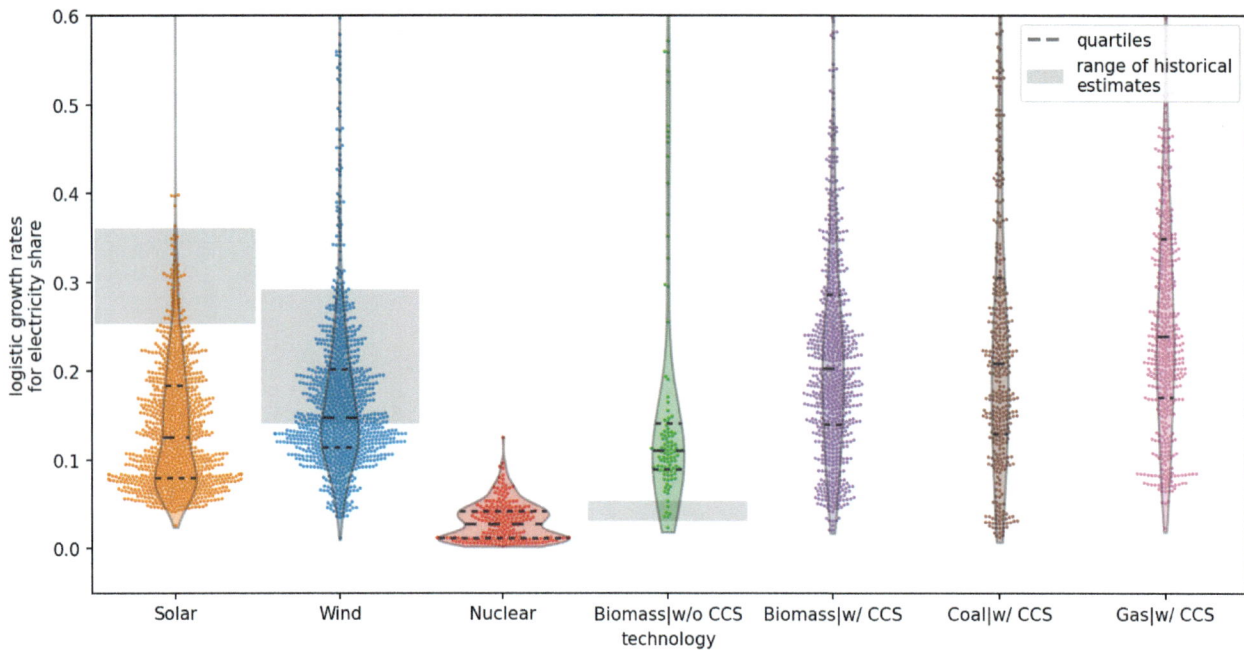

Figure 2.24 | Growth of key technologies (2020–2040) in Paris-consistent mitigation scenarios compared to historical growth. Comparisons of historical growth (grey bars) to growth in 2020–2040 mitigation scenarios (dots). Values on the vertical axis are logistic annual growth rates for share of each technology in electricity supply. Horizontal arrangement of dots within technology categories indicates the count of scenarios at each growth rate. Source: data on scenarios from Chapter 3; historical data from BP (2021).

2.6   Behavioural Choices and Lifestyles

2.6.1   Introduction

This section synthesises how behavioural choices, lifestyles, and consumption preferences affect energy use and emissions. Household consumption is the largest component of a country's gross domestic product (GDP) and the main contributor to greenhouse gas (GHG) emissions through direct energy consumption for heating and cooling or private transportation, and indirectly through carbon emitted during production of final consumption items. There is great variation in individual, group and household behaviour and consumption patterns within and between countries and over time. A number of factors affect people's consumption patterns and associated carbon emissions, such as: socio-demographics; socio-economic status; infrastructure and access to public services; the regulatory framework; availability, affordability and accessibility of more or less sustainable choices on markets; and individual values and preferences (Dietz et al. 2009).

Carbon footprints vary between and within countries and show an uneven distribution because of differences in development levels, economic structure, economic cycle, available public infrastructure, climate and residential lifestyles (Bruckner et al. 2021). Similar emission characteristics can also be found within a country – see, for China; Feng et al. (2013); for the USA: Pizer et al. (2010); Feng et al. (2013); Miehe et al. (2016); Hubacek et al. (2017b); Wang et al. (2018); for Brazil: Sanches-Pereira et al. (2016); and for Latin American countries: Zhong et al. (2020).

In western countries, the largest contribution to the household carbon footprint is from transportation, housing, and consumption of food (Druckman and Jackson 2015). The joint contribution of these three items varies in different countries, depending on consumption patterns, and account for 58.5%, on average, in EU25 countries (Tukker and Jansen 2006). However, different countries, and regions within countries, may have different emission patterns due to differences in income, lifestyle, geography, infrastructure, political and economic situation. For example, the main contributors to the average US household is private transport (19.6%), followed by electricity (14.8%) and meat (5.2%) (Jones and Kammen 2011), while UK households have 24.6% emissions on energy and housing, 13.7% emissions on food, and 12.2% emissions on consumables (Gough et al. 2011). A study of 49 Japanese cities found that energy (31%), food (27%), and accommodation (15%) were the largest sources of household emissions (Long et al. 2017). An investigation of Japan's household emissions found that energy, food, and utility are the three main emissions sources, but their shares are dependent on age (Shigetomi et al. 2014). See Section 12.4 (Chapter 12) and Box 5.4 (Chapter 5) for a more in-depth discussion on food systems and dietary shifts towards lower emission food.

In terms of rapidly growing economies, China is the most extensively researched country. China's household emissions were primarily derived from electricity and coal consumption, as well as residents' consumption of emission-intensive products, such as housing (33.4%), food (23.6%), private transportation and communication (14.8%) (Wang et al. 2018). Space heating was the largest contributor among various daily energy uses in northern cities (Yang and Liu 2017). In comparison, Indonesian rural households have a larger emission

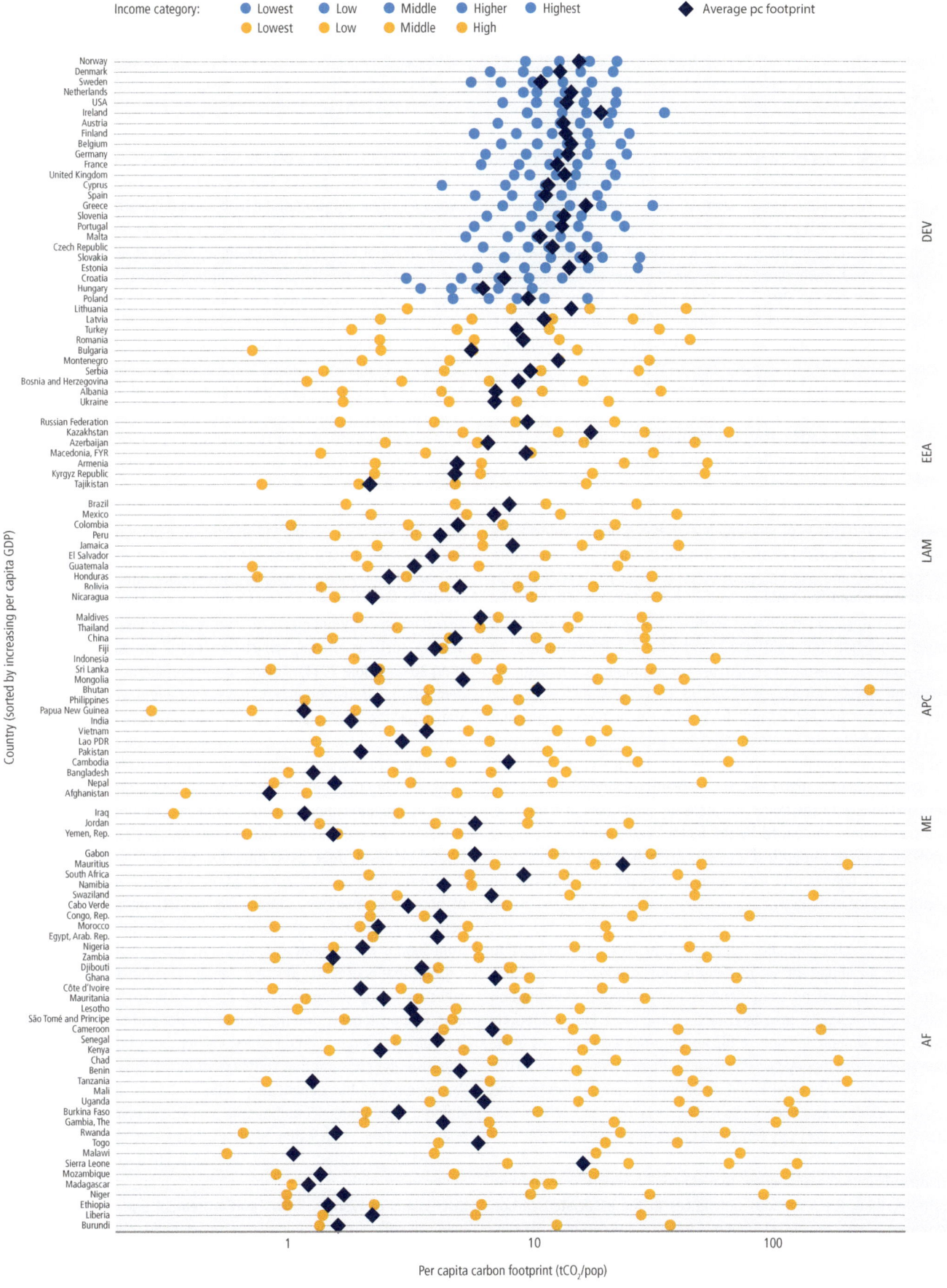

Figure 2.25 | Carbon footprints per capita income and expenditure category for 109 countries ranked by per capita income (consumption-based emissions).

Figure 2.25 (continued): Carbon footprints per capita income and expenditure category for 109 countries ranked by per capita income (consumption-based emissions). Notes: countries and income categories are dependent on data availability. Light blue dots represent income quintiles (lowest, low, middle, higher, and highest) of EU countries and the USA. Yellow dots are for the developing country group provided by the World Bank for four expenditure categories: lowest, low, middle and higher (Hubacek et al. 2017b). Dark blue diamonds represent average per capita carbon footprints. Countries are ranked from the lowest per capita income (bottom) to the highest income (top) within each country group. Countries are grouped using the IPCC's six high-level classification categories. Footprint values for higher income groups in the World Bank data are less reliable.

share on food and a much smaller share on services and recreation than urban households (Irfany and Klasen 2017). Urban Indonesian households have a much larger share of transport-related emissions (Irfany and Klasen 2017). Analysis from the Philippines shows that, on average, households in urban areas emit twice as much as rural ones because of much lower direct energy use in homes and for transport in rural areas (Serino 2017). In other emerging economies, such as India, Brazil, Turkey and South Africa, a high share of transport-related carbon emissions among urban middle- and high-income households is evident (Huang and Tian 2021).

2.6.2 Factors Affecting Household Consumption Patterns and Behavioural Choices

Households' carbon emissions are closely linked to activities and consumption patterns of individuals and as a group in households. Individual and group behaviour, in turn, is shaped by economic, technological, and psychological factors, social contexts (such as family ties, friends and peer pressure) and cultural contexts (social identity, status, and norms) as well as the natural environment (number of hot and cold days) and physical infrastructure, or geography (Jorgenson et al. 2019). For example, a city with an excellent bicycle infrastructure will make it safer and easier for citizens to become highly mobile by using their bikes; a city that has less density and is dominated by automobile infrastructure induces more people to travel by car (Chapters 8 and 10). As a consequence, many climate relevant consumption acts are not consciously decided on or deliberately made part of a lifestyle, but are strongly influenced by the factors listed above. Chapter 5 provides a more in-depth discussion on behavioural drivers and examples of behavioural interventions and policies that can be used to reduce emissions.

Demographic characteristics such as age, sex, and education constitute an important set of determinants influencing emissions patterns. People of different genders have different consumption patterns. For example, men tend to consume more food (especially meat) than women, leading to higher food-related emissions. Also, men spend more money on vehicles and driving (Wang et al. 2018). Similar evidence has been found in Germany, Greece, Norway, and Sweden, where men's energy use is 8%, 39%, 6%, and 22% higher than women's, respectively (Räty and Carlsson-Kanyama 2010).

Income. Due to the differences that shape individuals' consumption patterns, there are enormous differences in the associated carbon footprints – with income being one of the most important predictors. Globally, households with income in the top 10% – income higher than USD23.03 purchasing power parity (PPP) per capita per day – are responsible for 34–45% of GHG emissions, while those in the bottom 50% – income less than USD2.97 PPP per capita per day –

are responsible for only 13–15% of emissions, depending on the study (Chancel and Piketty 2015; Hubacek et al. 2017b) (Figure 2.25). The average carbon footprint of the high household incomes is more than an order of magnitudes larger than that of the lowest expenditure group (Feng et al. 2021). For example, Zhang et al. (2016) analysed the impact of household consumption across different income households on CO_2 emissions in China and concluded that the impact on CO_2 emissions generated by urban households' consumption is 1.8 times as much as that of rural ones. High-income households have higher emissions related to transport and entertainment – such as recreational expenditure, travel, and eating out – than low-income households. Low-income households tend to have a larger share on necessities such as fuel for heating and cooking (Kerkhof et al. 2009). Figure 2.25 shows the carbon footprint per capita ranked by per capita income.

Age. The effect of population ageing on emissions is contested in the literature. Ageing when accompanied by shrinking household size and more energy-intensive consumption and activity patterns results in increased emissions. However, an ageing labour force can also dampen economic growth and result in less energy-intensive activity such as driving, which decreases emissions (Liddle and Lung 2010; Liddle 2011). Ageing of the population characterises the demographic transition in both developed and developing countries. The implications of ageing for emissions depend on labour force participation of the elderly and differences in the consumption and investment patterns of different age groups (O'Neill et al. 2012). Analysis using panel macro data from OECD countries suggests that shifts in age and cohort composition have contributed to rising GHG emissions since the 1960s (Menz and Welsch 2012; Nassen 2014). Household-level data over time for the USA provides evidence that residential energy consumption increases over the lifetime of household members, largely due to accompanying changes in household size (Estiri and Zagheni 2019). Similar insights emerge from Japan, where analysis shows that those in their 70s or older, a group that is growing in size in Japan, have higher emissions than other age groups (Shigetomi et al. 2014, 2018, 2019). Recent analysis from China suggests that the shift to smaller and ageing households is resulting in higher carbon emissions because of the accompanying time-use and consumption shifts (Yu et al. 2018; Li and Zhou 2019). An increase in the dependency ratio – that is, the proportion of children aged under 15 and people over 65 relative to the working-age population – in other analyses, has been shown to lead to reduced CO_2 emissions in China (Wei et al. 2018; Li and Zhou 2019). Implications of the nature of this relationship are important to policy discussions of working hours and retirement age that are likely to have an influence on emissions. For example, children and youth tend to emit more education-related emissions than adults (Han et al. 2015). Older people tend to have higher emissions related to heating and cooling being more sensitive to temperature (Meier and Rehdanz 2010).

Household size. Per capita emissions tend to decrease with family size, as living together becomes more energy efficient (Qu et al. 2013). The household size in most countries is decreasing (Liu et al. 2011), but the degree differs across countries – for example, there is a higher decrease rate in China than in Canada and the UK (Maraseni et al. 2015). The evidence shows that shifts to smaller households are associated with larger per-capita footprints (Liddle and Lung 2014; Underwood and Zahran 2015; Ivanova et al. 2017; Wiedenhofer et al. 2018), at least in developed countries (Meangbua et al. 2019).

Urban living. The carbon footprint of individuals and households is also significantly influenced by urban-rural differences (Ivanova et al. 2018; Wiedenhofer et al. 2018). In some cases, the difference can be explained by the effect of locational and spatial configuration characteristics, such as levels of compactness/density, centrality, proximity and ease of access to services. In all these parameters, urban areas score higher compared with rural or peri-urban (outlying and suburban) areas, thus influencing household emissions in different ways. Urban households tend to have higher emissions than rural households (O'Neill et al. 2010; Liu et al. 2011), but with a different energy and consumption structures. For example, rural households have more diverse energy inputs, such as biomass, biogas, solar, wind, small hydro and geothermal in addition to coal (Maraseni et al. 2016).

In terms of indirect emissions, urban households have more service-related emissions – such as from education and entertainment – than rural households, while rural households tend to have higher emissions related to food consumption or transportation (Büchs and Schnepf 2013; Maraseni et al. 2016) but this is strongly dependent on the specific situation of the respective country, as in poorer regions, rural transport might be mainly based on public transport with lower carbon emissions per capita. Centrality and location also play a role on the level of urban household emissions. Studies on US households found that residents in the urban core have 20% lower household emissions than residents in suburbs, which show a large range of household emissions (from −50% to +60%) (Kahn 2000; Jones and Kammen 2014). Higher population density tends to be associated with lower per capita emissions (Liddle and Lung 2014; Liu et al. 2017).

Location choices are a significant contributor to household emissions. Suburbanites tend to own larger, spacious homes with larger heating and cooling requirements. Commuting distance and access to public transportation, recreation areas, city centres, public services, and shops are other important neighbourhood-specific determinants of carbon emissions (Baiocchi et al. 2010) (see more on this in Chapters 8 and 10).

Time use. A study on the emissions implications of time use (Wiedenhofer et al. 2018) found that the most carbon-intensive activities are personal care, eating and drinking and commuting. Indirect emissions are also high for repairs and gardening. In contrast, home-based activities, such as sleep and resting, cleaning and socialising at home, have low carbon intensities per hour of time use. The same study also found that households in cities and areas with higher incomes tend to substitute personal activities for contracted services, thus shifting away from households to

the service sector (Wiedenhofer et al. 2018). Improvements in the efficiency of time or resource use are diminished by rebound effects that have been shown to reduce emissions savings by 20–40% on average (Gillingham et al. 2015), while other authors argue that, potentially, the size of the rebound effect could be larger (Saunders 2015) (see more coverage of the rebound effect in Chapters 9 and 16). Lifestyle shifts brought about by using information technologies and socio-technological changes are inducing alterations in people's daily activities and time-use patterns.

The reduction of working hours is increasingly discussed as an approach to improve well-being and reduce emissions (Fitzgerald et al. 2015, 2018; Melo et al. 2018; Wiedenhofer et al. 2018; Smetschka et al. 2019). For instance, analysis of differences in working hours across the USA for the period 2007–2013 shows that there is a strong positive relationship between carbon emissions and working hours. This relationship holds, even after controlling for other differences in political, demographic and economic drivers of emissions (Fitzgerald et al. 2018). In other analyses, this relationship is seen to hold in both developed and developing countries (Fitzgerald et al. 2015). One recent study, however, finds evidence of nonlinear relationships between working time and environmental pressure in EU15 countries between 1970 and 2010, in cases where non-work time is spent instead in carbon-intensive leisure activities (Shao and Shen 2017).

Social norms. Evidence from experiments in the US shows that social norms cannot only help in reducing a household's absolute level of electricity use but also shift the time of use to periods when more renewable electricity is in the system (Horne and Kennedy, 2017). Analysis from Sweden shows that adoption of sustainable innovations like solar panels is influenced by perceived behaviour and expectations of others (Palm, 2017). Similar conclusions emerge from analysis in the Netherlands on the adoption of electric vehicles and smart energy systems (Noppers et al. 2019).

Broader contextual factors and cultural trends towards consumerism, individualisation and defining self-worth through conspicuous consumption can drive emissions up (Chancel and Piketty, 2015). However, cohort and generational shifts can drive emissions down. For instance, evidence, from millennials in the OECD shows that fewer younger people have driving licenses compared to older generations (Kuhnimhof et al. 2012). Similar, findings are evident from analysis for the US, where changing attitudes, decreased employment and rising virtual mobility explain decreased travel by Millennials (McDonald, 2015). Analysis for France shows that baby boomers are higher emitters than other generations (Chancel, 2014). A change in social norms is taking place with the spread of the sharing economy by which consumers share or borrow goods from other consumers. Sharing opportunities are more advanced within the mobility sector (Greenblatt and Shaheen, 2015). Successful car and bike sharing have rapidly expanded in countries such as China, Indonesia, Mexico, Brazil and Turkey. Technology and data advances are currently barriers to spreading of sharing in low- and lower middle-income cities but the potential offered by these technologies to allow poor countries to leapfrog to more integrated, efficient, multimodal transport systems is important (Yanocha et al. 2020). Despite this potential it is unclear how much shared mobility contributes to transport decarbonisation or to make it worse as it takes away riders from public transit (ITF, 2019). The evidence so far shows that the potential positive impacts of shared mobility with pooled rides in lowering travel costs, abating congestion, and reduced GHG emissions have not materialised to date (Merlin, 2019) (Chapter 5).

Education and environmental knowledge. A positive relationship was found between general and carbon-specific knowledge and the attitude towards carbon-specific behaviours in US consumers (Polonsky et al. 2012). One example, pertaining to students, found that the gain of environmental knowledge resulted in more environmentally favourable attitude among these high school students (Bradley et al. 1999). A comparison across states in the USA, for example, shows that environmental awareness can be a mitigating factor of territorial GHG emissions (Dietz et al. 2015). A 1% increase in 'environmentalism' – defined as the 'environmental voting record of the state's Congressional delegation' (Dietz et al. 2015) – leads to a 0.45% decrease in emissions.

Environmental knowledge is not always directly translating into decreased ecological footprint (Csutora 2012). While pro-environmental action is lagging behind, research shows that this is not caused by people undervaluing the environment, but rather by people structurally underestimating how much others care (Bouman and Steg 2019). Other evidence shows that there are multiple causal pathways through which a more educated population can effect emissions, some of which may be positive and others negative (Lutz et al. 2019). A more educated population is more productive and can drive higher economic growth and therefore emissions (Lenzen and Cummins 2013). Moreover, education that is designed to specifically inform decision makers of the impacts of their decisions and provide behavioural nudges can be a way to reduce emissions (Duarte et al. 2016).

Status competition. As part of a larger consumer society and consumer culture, based on consumer-oriented lifestyles, products frequently provide a source for identity and fulfilment (Stearns 2001; Baudrillard 2017; Jorgenson et al. 2019). People pursue cultural constructs such as status, comfort, convenience, hygiene, nutrition, and necessity. Consumption is, by and large, not an end in itself but a means to achieve some other end, and those ends are diverse and not necessarily connected to one another (Wilk 2010). This shows that consumption patterns cannot be sufficiently understood without also considering the context – for example, the cultural and social contexts leading to status competition and status-related consumption (Veblen 2009; Ehrhardt-Martinez, K. et al. 2015; Wilk 2017). Status seeking can work to reduce emissions when 'green products' such as an electric car or photovoltaics on the roof become a sign for high-status (Griskevicius et al. 2010). It also can work to increase emissions through visible and high-carbon intensive consumption items, such a larger homes, fuel-inefficient sport utility vehicles (SUVs), and long-distance vacations (Schor 1998), driven by a notion of having 'to keep up with the Joneses' (Hamilton 2011). This can lead to formation of new habits and needs, where products and services become normalised and are quickly perceived as needed, reinforced through social networks and advertisement, making it psychologically easy to convert a luxury item to a perceived necessity (Assadour 2012). For example, the share of adults who

consider a microwave a necessity was about one-third in 1996 but had increased to more than two-thirds in 2006, but retreated in importance during the recession years 2008–2009 (Morin and Taylor 2009). Similar ups and downs have been observed for television sets, air conditioning, dishwashers or clothes dryers. (Druckman and Jackson 2009). Basic needs and luxury items are subject to change over one's lifetime and in relation to others (Horowitz 1988). This shows that the boundaries of the public's luxury-versus-necessity perceptions are malleable (Morin and Taylor 2009).

Inequality. Global inequality within and between countries has shifted over the last decade's expanding consumption and consumer culture (Castilhos and Fonseca 2016; Alvaredo et al. 2018; Short and Martínez 2020). The rise of income of middle-class in countries, mostly in Asia – for example, China, India, Indonesia and Vietnam – and the stagnating incomes of the middle classes in developed economies reduced between countries' income differences; meanwhile, the population under extreme poverty (a threshold of USD1.9 per person per day) is now concentrated in Sub-Saharan Africa and South Asia (Milanović 2016). A major gap between top and bottom incomes occurred in parallel within countries. Since 1980, the top 1% richest individuals in the world captured twice as much growth as the bottom 50% individuals (Friedman and Savage 2017; Alvaredo et al. 2018). The influence of these dual inequality trends on lifestyles, new consumption patterns and carbon emissions at regional, local and global scale are large and have led to the fastest growth of global carbon emissions, in particular, for fast emerging economies (Sections 2.2. and 2.3). Emissions remain highly concentrated, with the top 10% per capita emitters contributing to between 35–45% of global emissions, while the bottom 50% emitters contribute to 13–15% of global emissions (Hubacek et al. 2017a). Furthermore, the top 1% of income earners by some estimates could have an average carbon footprint 175 times that of an average person in the bottom 10% (Otto et al. 2020). The top 10% high emitters live in all continents, and one-third of them live in emerging countries (Chancel and Piketty 2015; Hubacek et al. 2017a; Semieniuk and Yakovenko 2020). Mitigation pathways need to consider how to minimise the impacts of inequality on climate change and the different mechanisms and effects coming into play between the inequality of income and emissions (Baek and Gweisah 2013; Berthe and Elie 2015; Hao et al. 2016; Grunewald et al. 2017) (Section 2.4.3).

Inequality trends catalyse impact at a demand level, mobilising rapid lifestyles changes, symbolic consumption and ideals of material improvements and upward mobility (Castilhos et al. 2017) and emulation of high-carbon emissions intensive lifestyle of the wealthy (Gough 2017). Decoupling energy use and emissions from income growth and the decarbonisation of energy services have not counteracted these trends (Section 2.4.1). Alternative options to deal with carbon inequality, such as sharing global carbon emissions among high emitters (Chakravarty et al. 2009; Chakravarty and Tavoni 2013) or addressing the discourse of income distribution and the carbon intensity of high emitters lifestyles (Hubacek et al., 2017b; Gössling 2019; Otto et al. 2019) are met with caution that such alternatives may necessitate hard-to-implement institutional changes (Semieniuk and Yakovenko 2020). Growing inequality within countries may make recomposition of emission intensive consumption more difficult and, it may also exacerbate redistribution and social cohesion dilemmas (Gough 2017; Römpke et al. 2019). Climate mitigation action has different motivational departures in unequal context. An emerging global 'middle class' strengthens consumption at the margin as evidence by first-time purchases of white goods with likely impacts on energy demand (Wolfram et al. 2012), and with a warming climate, the increased use of air conditioning (Davis and Gertler 2015). Inequality may affect the willingness of rich and poor to pay for environmental goods or accept policies to protect the environment (Baumgärtner et al. 2017). Unequal departure for action is strongly manifested in cities of all sizes in developing countries with low-income urban residents hardest hit in lock-in situations such as lack of access to transportation and jobs (Altshuler 2013; Mattioli 2017), lack of green spaces (Joassart-Marcelli et al. 2011), poor access to waste collection (King and Gutberlet 2013) and to energy and clean water provision. The exacerbation of these conditions constrains the feasibility for achieving emissions reductions through lifestyle or behavioural changes alone (Baiocchi et al. 2010; Oxfam 2015). High inequality limits mitigation efforts and conversely, advancing mitigation should not contribute to deepen existing inequalities (Rao and Min 2018; Saheb et al. 2019). It is critically important to account for varying demands and affordability across heterogeneous household groups in access to quality energy, education, health, decent jobs and services, while recomposing consumption and balancing societal trade-offs via policies to boost the inclusion of low-income and energy-poor population groups (Pachauri et al. 2013). Further, there is a need to reduce inequalities and improve the capabilities people have to live the lives they value (Sen 1999; Gough et al. 2011; Gough, 2017; Aranoff et al. 2019).

2.7   Emissions Associated With Existing and Planned Long-lived Infrastructure

2.7.1   Introduction: Clarification of Concepts

Carbon lock-in can be understood as inertia in a system that limits the rate of transformation by a path-dependent process (Seto et al. 2016). For example, long lifetimes of infrastructures such as power plants, roads, buildings or industrial plants may influence the rate of transformation substantially and lock societies into carbon-intensive lifestyles and practices for many decades (Unruh 2000, 2002; Unruh and Carrillo-Hermosilla 2006; Grubler 2012; Seto et al. 2016; Sovacool 2016). Infrastructure stock evolution depends on technological and economic factors, but also on institutional and behavioural ones that are often mutually reinforcing. That is, physical infrastructure such as the built environment of urban areas can shape people's behaviour and practices, which in turn change the demand for such infrastructure and lock-in energy demand patterns (Banister et al. 1997; Makido et al. 2012; Creutzig et al. 2016; Seto et al. 2016; Shove and Trentmann 2018).

There is a broad literature on carbon lock-in related to infrastructure that has analysed different geographical scales and sectors, with a strong focus on the power sector (Fisch-Romito et al. 2020). Available quantifications differ in the time frames of analysis that can be classified as backward-looking, static for a given year, or forward-

looking using scenarios (Fisch-Romito et al. 2020). Quantifications also differ in the indicators used to describe carbon lock-in. Literature has assessed how delays in climate policy affect the evolution of fossil-fuel infrastructure stock in the short term (Bertram et al. 2015; Kefford et al. 2018; McGlade et al. 2018), overall mitigation costs (Riahi et al. 2015; Luderer et al. 2016), or the transition risks from premature retirements or underutilisation of existing assets (Iyer et al. 2015; Johnson et al. 2015; Lane et al. 2016; Luderer et al. 2016; Farfan and Breyer 2017; van Soest et al. 2017; Kefford et al. 2018; Cui et al. 2019; Fofrich et al. 2020; Malik et al. 2020; H. Wang et al. 2020; Pradhan et al. 2021). Only a few authors have relied on indicators related to institutional factors such as technology scale or employment (Erickson et al. 2015; Spencer et al. 2018). Complementary literature has explored how the sheer size of the world's fossil fuel reserves (and resources) and owners' financial interests could contribute to supply-side dynamics that sustain the use of fossil fuels (Jewell et al. 2013; Jakob and Hilaire 2015; McGlade and Ekins 2015; Bauer et al. 2016; Heede and Oreskes 2016; Welsby et al. 2021).

One way of quantifying potential carbon lock-in is to estimate the future CO_2 emissions from existing and planned infrastructure (Davis et al. 2010; Davis and Socolow 2014) based on historic patterns of use and decommissioning. Such estimates focus on CO_2 emissions from operating infrastructure and do not comprise any upstream or downstream emissions across the lifecycle, which are provided elsewhere in the literature (Müller et al. 2013; Creutzig et al. 2016; Krausmann et al. 2020; Fisch-Romito 2021). Estimates tend to focus on energy, while other areas, such as the agricultural sector are usually not covered. Another strand of literature quantifies lock-in by estimating fossil-fuel related CO_2 emissions that are hard to avoid in future scenarios using integrated assessment models (IAMs) (Kriegler et al. 2018b; Luderer et al. 2018). The remainder of this chapter will assess potential carbon lock-in through those two related strands of literature.

2.7.2   Estimates of Future CO_2 Emissions From Long-lived Infrastructures

Table 2.6 summarises studies that apply an accounting approach based on plant-level data to quantify future CO_2 emissions from long-lived fossil fuel infrastructure (Davis et al. 2010; Davis and Socolow 2014; Rozenberg et al. 2015; Edenhofer et al. 2018; Pfeiffer et al. 2018; Cui et al. 2019; Smith et al. 2019; Tong et al. 2019; Pradhan et al. 2021). Differences between studies arise in the scope of the infrastructure covered (including resolution), the inclusion of new infrastructure proposals, the exact estimation methodology applied as well as their assessments of uncertainties. Other studies provide analysis with a sectoral focus (Bullock et al. 2020; Vogl et al. 2021) or with a regional focus on the power sector (Shearer et al. 2017, 2020; González-Mahecha et al. 2019; Grubert 2020; Tao et al. 2020).

Assuming variations in historic patterns of use and decommissioning, comprehensive estimates of cumulative future CO_2 emissions from *current* fossil fuel infrastructures are 720 (550–910) $GtCO_2$ (Smith et al. 2019) and 660 (460–890) (*high confidence*) (Tong et al. 2019) (Table 2.6 and Figure 2.26). This is about the same size as the

Table 2.6 | Comparing cumulative future CO$_2$ emissions estimates from existing and proposed long-lived infrastructures by sector. Future CO$_2$ emissions estimates are reported from the 'year of dataset'. Note that, in some cases, the totals may not correspond to the sum of underlying sectors due to rounding (based on Tong et al. 2019). Initial estimates of future CO$_2$ emissions from fossil fuel infrastructures by Davis et al. (2010) are considerably lower than more recent estimates by Smith et al. (2019) and Tong et al. (2019) due to substantial growth in fossil energy infrastructure, as represented by more recent data. Estimates presented here are rounded to two significant digits.

		Davis et al. (2010)		Davis and Socolow (2014)		Rozenberg et al. (2015)		Edenhofer et al. (2018)		Pfeiffer et al. (2018)		Smith et al. (2019)		Tong et al. (2019)		Cui et al. (2019)	
		GtCO$_2$	Year of dataset	GtCO$_2$	Year of dataset	GtCO$_2$	Year of dataset	GtCO$_2$	Year of dataset	GtCO$_2$	Year of dataset	GtCO$_2$	Year of dataset	GtCO$_2$	Year of dataset	GtCO$_2$	Year of dataset
Existing	Electricity	220	2009	310	2012	–	–	–	–	310	2016	350 (260–450)	2009*	360 (240–490)	2018	–	–
	Coal		2009	210	2012	–	–	190	2016	220	2016	–	–	260 (180–360)	2018	340	2017
	Gas, oil, and other fuels		2009	100	2012	–	–	–	–	88	2016	–	–	98 (65–140)	2018	–	–
	Industry	100	2009			–	–	–	–	–	–	150 (120–190)	2009	160 (110–220)	2017	–	–
	Transport	120	2009			–	–	–	–	–	–	92 (73–110)	2017	64 (53–75)	2017	–	–
	Residential, commercial, and other energy	53	2009			–	–	–	–	–	–	120 (91–160)	2009*	74 (52–110)	2018	–	–
	All sectors	500 (280–700)				660 (370–890)	2013	–	–	–	–	720 (550–910)	–	660 (460–890)	–	–	–
Proposed	Electricity					–	–	–	–	270	2016	–	–	190 (140–230)	2018	–	–
	Coal					–	–	150	2016	210	2016	–	–	97 (74–120)	2018	180	2017
	Gas, oil, and other fuels					–	–	–	–	60	2016	–	–	91 (68–110)	2018	–	–
All sectors + proposed electricity														850 (600–1100)			

overall cumulative net CO_2 emissions until reaching net zero CO_2 of 510 (330–710) Gt in pathways that limit warming to 1.5°C with no or limited overshoot (Chapter 3). About 50% of cumulative future CO_2 emissions from *current* fossil fuel infrastructures come from the power sector and 70% of these (or about 40% of the total) are from coal plants only. Like global annual CO_2 emissions (Friedlingstein et al. 2020; Peters et al. 2020), future CO_2 emissions from fossil fuel infrastructures have increased over time – that is, future CO_2 emissions from fossil fuel infrastructure additions in a given year still outgrow 'savings' from infrastructure retirements (Davis and Socolow 2014; Tong et al. 2019). This could add further inertia to the system as it may require more and faster retirement of fossil-fuel based infrastructures later, and lead to higher costs for meeting climate goals (e.g., Bertram et al. 2015; Johnson et al. 2015).

Estimates of total cumulative future CO_2 commitments from *proposed infrastructure* focus only on the power sector due to data availability (Table 2.6 and Figure 2.26). Infrastructure proposals can be at various stages of development involving very different probabilities of implementation. About one-third of the currently proposed projects are more probable as they are already under construction (Cui et al. 2019). Pfeiffer et al. (2018) and Tong et al. (2019) assess the cumulated CO_2 emissions from proposed infrastructure in the entire power sector at 270 $GtCO_2$ and 190 $GtCO_2$ respectively. Estimates of CO_2 emissions implications for new coal power infrastructure plans are more frequent (Edenhofer et al. 2018; Pfeiffer et al. 2018; Cui et al. 2019; Tong et al. 2019) ranging between 100 and 210 $GtCO_2$. Differences across estimates of future CO_2 emissions from proposed power infrastructure mostly reflect substantial cancellations of coal infrastructure proposals in 2017 and 2018 (Tong et al. 2019).

The global estimate of future CO_2 emissions from *current and planned* fossil-fuel infrastructures is 850 (600–1100) $GtCO_2$ (Tong et al. 2019). This already exceeds total cumulative net CO_2 emissions in pathways that limit warming to 1.5°C with no or limited overshoot (see above). It is about the same size as the total cumulative net CO_2 emissions of 890 (640–1160) $GtCO_2$ from pathways that limit warming to 2°C (<67%) (Chapter 3). Hence, cumulative net CO_2 emissions to limit warming to 2°C (<67%) or lower could already be exhausted by current and planned fossil fuel infrastructure (*high confidence*) even though this estimate only covers a fraction of all infrastructure developments over the 21st century as present in mitigation pathways, does not cover all sectors (e.g., AFOLU) and does not include currently infrastructure development plans in transport, buildings, and industry due to a lack of data.

Hence, the Paris climate goals could move out of reach unless there are dedicated efforts for early decommissioning, and reduced utilisation of existing fossil fuel infrastructures, cancellation of plans for new fossil fuel infrastructures, or compensation efforts by removing some of the CO_2 emissions from the atmosphere (Cui et al. 2019; Smith et al. 2019; Tong et al. 2019; Pradhan et al. 2021). For example, Fofrich et al. (2020) suggest in a multi-model study that coal and gas power infrastructure would need to be retired 30 (19–34) and 24 (21–26) years earlier than the historical averages of 39 and 36 years when following 1.5°C pathways and 23 (11–33) and 19 (11–16) years earlier when following 2°C pathways. Cui et al. (2019) arrive at more conservative estimates for coal power plants, but only consider the existing and currently proposed capacity. Premature retirement of power plants pledged by members of the Powering Past Coal Alliance would cut emissions by 1.6 $GtCO_2$, which is 150 times less than future CO_2 emissions from existing coal power plants (Jewell et al. 2019).

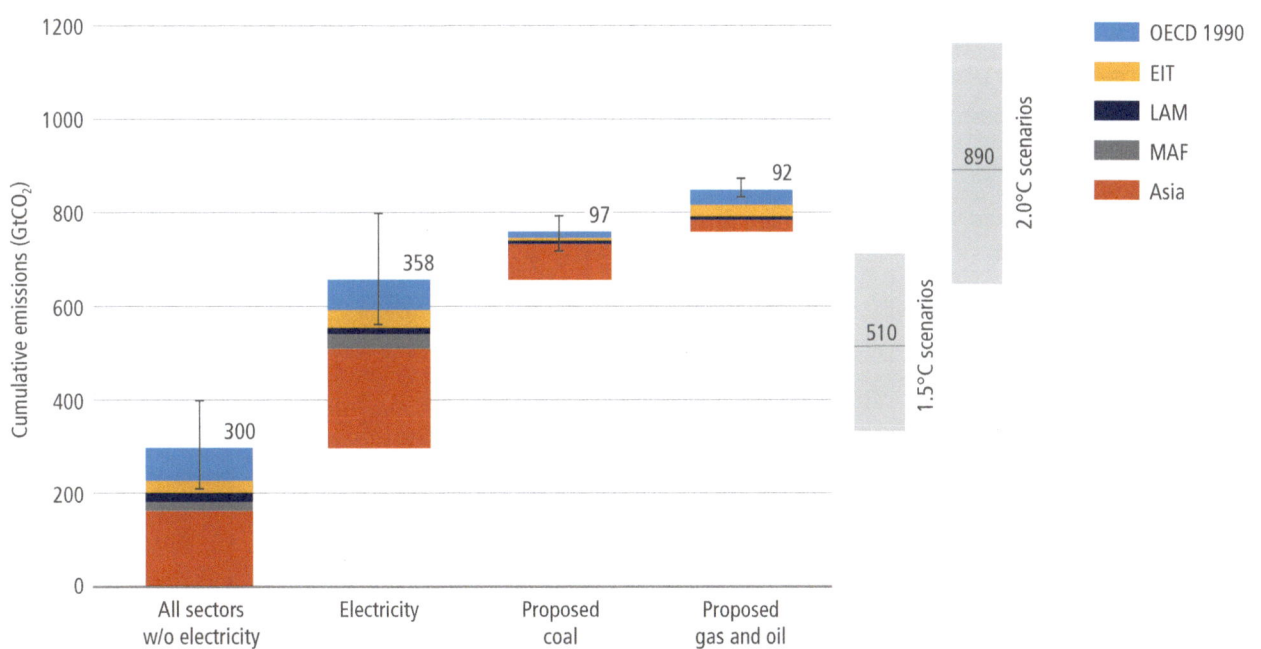

Figure 2.26 | Future CO_2 emissions from existing and currently planned fossil fuel infrastructure in the context of Paris carbon budgets in $GtCO_2$ based on historic patterns of infrastructure lifetimes and capacity utilisation. Future CO_2 emissions estimates of existing infrastructure for the electricity sector as well as all other sectors (industry, transport, buildings, other fossil fuel infrastructures) and of proposed infrastructures for coal power as well as gas and oil power. Grey bars on the right depict the range (5th–95th percentile) in overall cumulative net CO_2 emissions until reaching net zero CO_2 in pathways that limit warming to 1.5°C with no or limited overshoot (1.5°C scenarios), and in pathways that limit warming to 2°C (<67%) (2°C scenarios). Source: based on Edenhofer et al. (2018) and Tong et al. (2019).

Few quantifications of carbon lock-in from urban infrastructure, in particular urban form, have been attempted, in part because they also relate to behaviours that are closely tied to routines and norms that co-evolve with 'hard infrastructures' and technologies, as well as 'soft infrastructure' such as social networks and markets (Seto et al. 2016). There are some notable exceptions providing early attempts (Guivarch and Hallegatte 2011; Driscoll 2014; Seto et al.2014; Lucon et al. 2014; Erickson and Tempest 2015; Creutzig et al. 2016). Creutzig et al. (2016) attempt a synthesis of this literature and estimate the total cumulative future CO_2 emissions from existing urban infrastructure at 210 Gt, and from new infrastructures at 495 Gt for the period 2010–2030.

2.7.3   Synthesis – Comparison with Estimates of Residual Fossil Fuel CO_2 Emissions

A complementary strand of literature uses IAMs to assess the cumulative gross amount of unabated CO_2 emissions from fossil fuels across decarbonisation pathways that are not removed from the system, even under strong (short- and long-term) climate policy ambitions. Lower bound estimates for such a minimum amount of unabated residual CO_2 emissions across the 21st century that is not removed from the system, even under very ambitious climate policy assumptions, may be around 600–700 $GtCO_2$ (Kriegler et al. 2018b). This range increases to 650–1800 $GtCO_2$ (Table 2.7) as soon as a broader set of policy assumptions are considered, including delayed action in scenarios that limit warming to 1.5°C and 2°C respectively (Luderer et al. 2018).

Notably, the lower end of residual fossil fuel emissions in IAM scenarios (Luderer et al. 2018) is remarkably similar to global estimates from the accounting studies of the previous section, as shown in Table 2.6. Yet, there are important conceptual and interpretative differences that are also reflected in the very different distribution of reported future CO_2 emissions attached to current and future fossil fuel infrastructures (Table 2.7). Accounting studies start from granular, plant-based data for existing fossil fuel infrastructure and make statements about their future CO_2 emissions, assuming variations of historic patterns of use and decommissioning. Expansions to the future are limited to proposals for new infrastructures that we know of today. Scenario studies quantifying residual fossil fuel emissions start from aggregate infrastructure descriptions, but dynamically update those through new investment decisions in each time step across the 21st century based on the development of energy and energy service demands, as well as technology availability, guided by defined climate policy goals (or their absence).

In accounting studies, estimates of future CO_2 emissions from current fossil fuel infrastructures are dominated by the power sector with its large fossil fuel capacities. In contrast, scenario studies highlight residual emissions from non-electric energy – particularly in the transport and industry sectors. Fossil-fuel infrastructure in the power sector can be much more easily retired than in those sectors, where there are fewer and more costly alternatives. IAMs therefore account for continued investments into fossil-based energy technologies in areas with limited decarbonisation potential, such as some areas of

Table 2.7 | Residual (gross) fossil fuel emissions ($GtCO_2$) in climate change mitigation scenarios strengthening mitigation action after 2020 ('early strengthening'), compared to scenarios that keep Nationally Determined Contribution (NDC) ambition level until 2030 and only strengthen thereafter. Cumulative gross CO_2 emissions from fossil fuel and industry until reaching net zero CO_2 emissions are given in terms of the mean as well as minimum and maximum (in parentheses) across seven participating models: AIM/CGE, GCAM, IMAGE, MESSAGES, POLES, REMIND, WITCH. Scenario design prescribes a harmonised, global carbon price in line with long-term carbon budget. Delay scenarios follow the same price trajectory, but 10 years later. Carbon dioxide removal requirements represent ex-post calculations that subtract gross fossil fuel emissions from the carbon budget associated with the respective long-term warming limit. We take the carbon budget for limiting warming to 1.5°C with a 50% probability and to 2°C with a 67% probability (Canadell et al. 2021). Hence, carbon dioxide removal (CDR) requirements reflect a minimum amount of CDR for a given mitigation trajectory. Results are reported at two significant digits. Sources: Luderer et al. (2018); Tong et al. (2019).

Future CO_2 emissions from existing and planned fossil fuel infrastructure (accounting studies)				Residual fossil fuel emissions – cumulative gross CO_2 emissions from fossil fuel and industry until reaching net zero CO_2 emissions (in $GtCO_2$)					
		Tong et al. (2019)				Early strengthening from (2020)		Delayed strengthening from 2030	
		$GtCO_2$	Year			Well below 2°C	Below 1.5°C in 2100	Well below 2°C	Below 1.5°C in 2100
Existing and proposed	Electricity	550 (380–730)	2018	Existing AND future instalments	Electricity	180 (140–310)	130 (90–160)	250 (220–340)	200 (190–230)
	Non-electric supply				Non-electric supply	100 (42–130)	59 (27–83)	120 (55–150)	75 (40–100)
Existing	Industry	160 (110–220)	2017		Industry	260 (160–330)	140 (86–180)	290 (200–370)	200 (130–250)
	Transportation	64 (53–75)	2017		Transportation	310 (190–370)	170 (110–220)	310 (250–400)	200 (140–260)
	Buildings	74 (52–110)	2018		Buildings	110 (75–110)	58 (35–77)	120 (80–150)	73 (51–93)
	All sectors and proposed electricity	850 (600–1100)			All sectors (2021 – net zero CO_2)	960 (730–1100)	570 (400–640)	1100 (900–1200)	770 (590–860)
					All sectors (2021–2100)	1300 (970–1500)	850 (650–1100)	1400 (1200–1600)	1000 (860–1300)
					Implied minimum requirement for carbon dioxide removal until 2100	150 (0–350)	350 (150–600)	250 (50–450)	500 (360–800)

transportation (in particular aviation, shipping and road-based freight) or some industrial processes (such as cement production or feedstocks for chemicals). This explains the key discrepancies observable in Table 2.7. Therefore, our overall assessment of these available lines of evidence strongly emphasises the importance of decommissioning, reduced utilisation of existing power sector infrastructure, as well as continued cancellation of new power sector infrastructures in order to limit warming to well below 2°C (*high confidence*) (Kriegler et al. 2018b; Luderer et al. 2018; Chen et al. 2019; Cui et al. 2019; Fofrich et al. 2020). This is important as the power sector is comparatively easy to decarbonise (IPCC 2014a; Krey et al. 2014; Davis et al. 2018; Méjean et al. 2019) and it is crucial to make space for residual emissions from non-electric energy end uses that are more difficult to mitigate (*high confidence*). Any further delay in climate policy substantially increases carbon lock-in and mitigation challenges as well as a dependence on carbon dioxide removal technologies for meeting the Paris climate goals (Kriegler et al. 2018b; Luderer et al. 2018).

2.8 Climate and Non-Climate Policies and Measures and their Impacts on Emissions

2.8.1 Introduction

The key to achieving climate change mitigation targets includes crafting environmentally effective, economically efficient and socially equitable policies. For the purposes of this section, policies are defined broadly as actions to guide decisions to reach explicit goals and, accordingly, climate (mitigation) policies are the ones whose primary objective is to reduce GHG emissions. They include a range of domains from economic and institutional to research and development (R&D) and social policies, and are implemented by various instruments (e.g., market-based and regulatory in the economic domain) and measures (e.g., legal provisions and governance arrangements in the institutional domain) (Chapter 13, and see 'mitigation policies' in Glossary). Yet GHG emissions are also affected by policies enacted in various social, economic and environmental areas to pursue primarily non-climatic objectives. This section presents succinct assessments of the outcomes and effectiveness of a few selected policy instruments applied in the last two decades that target climate protection (Sections 2.8.2 and 2.8.3) and GHG emissions impacts of selected other policies primarily aimed at improvements in environmental quality and natural resource management (Section 2.8.4).[12]

It is rather difficult, though not impossible, to discern the genuine impacts of climate and non-climate policies on GHG emissions. Most current and past policies target only a small part of global emissions in a limited geographical area and/or from a small number of economic sectors. However, in addition to the targeted region or sector, policies and measures tend to affect GHG emissions in other parts of the world. Emissions leakage is the key channel by which such phenomena and complex interactions occur.[13] Uncertainties in impacts, synergies, and trade-offs between policies and measures also complicate the evaluation of emissions impacts. These make it challenging to identify the impacts of any specific policy or measure on emissions of any specific region or sector. Rigorous statistical analyses are necessary for building strong empirical evidence, but the experience with climate-related policy experiments to date is limited.

2.8.2 Comprehensive Multinational Assessments

Comprehensive multinational evaluations with wider regional and sectoral coverage enable the assessment of emissions impacts without distortions from emissions leakage. Among the wide range of climate policy instruments, pricing carbon – such as a carbon tax or an emissions trading system – has been one of the most widely used and effective options to reduce GHG emissions (*robust evidence, high agreement*). In a comparison of 142 countries with and without carbon pricing, countries with a carbon price show annual CO_2 emission growth rates of 2 percentage points lower than countries without such policies (Best et al. 2020). A more comprehensive evaluation of carbon prices shows that countries with a lower carbon pricing gap (a higher carbon price) tend to be more carbon-efficient, that is, they have a lower carbon intensity of GDP (OECD 2018).[14] An empirical analysis of the effects of environmental regulation and innovation on the carbon emissions of OECD countries during the period 1999–2014 indicates that a 1% increase in environmentally friendly patents reduced carbon emissions by 0.017%, and a 1% increase in environmental tax revenue per capita reduced carbon emissions by 0.03% (Hashmi and Alam 2019).

Domestic and international climate legislation have also contributed to the reduction of GHG emissions. An empirical analysis of legislative activity in 133 countries over the period 1999–2016 based on panel data indicates that each new law reduced annual CO_2 emissions per unit of GDP by 0.78% nationally in the first three years, and by 1.79% beyond three years. Additionally, climate laws as of 2016 were associated with an annual reduction in global CO_2 emissions of 5.9 $GtCO_2$ and 38 $GtCO_2$ cumulatively since 1999 (Eskander and Fankhauser 2020). It is notable that 36 countries that accepted legally binding targets under the Kyoto Protocol all complied (Shishlov et al. 2016). It is impossible to disentangle precisely the contribution of individual mitigation policies, but it is clear that the participating countries, especially those in the OECD, did make substantial policy efforts with material impact (Grubb 2016). An ex-post evaluation shows a significant impact of the Protocol on emissions reductions (Maamoun 2019).

---

[12]   This section only reviews the emission impacts of selected policy instruments. Other important aspects such as equity and cost-effectiveness are assessed in Chapter 13, presenting comprehensive evaluations of policies and measures.

[13]   Refer to Chapter 13 on policies and institutions for a detailed discussion of emissions leakages and complex interactions from policy mixes.

[14]   The OECD (2018) measures carbon prices using the *effective carbon rate* (ECR), which is the sum of three components: specific taxes on fossil fuels; carbon taxes; and prices of tradable emissions permits. The *carbon pricing gap* measures the difference between actual ECRs and benchmark rates. The carbon pricing gap indicates the extent to which polluters do not pay for the damage from carbon emissions.

Renewable energy policies, such as Renewable Portfolio Standards and Feed-in-Tariff, have played an essential role in the massive expansion of renewable energy capacities, another key driver of GHG emissions reductions (*robust evidence, high agreement*). Drivers of decreasing CO_2 emissions seen in a group of 18 developed economies that decarbonised over the period 2005–2015 are the displacement of fossil fuels by renewable energy and decreases in energy use (Le Quéré et al. 2019). Renewable energy policies both at the EU and member states level have played an essential role in abating GHG emissions (ICF International 2016).

2.8.3   National, Sectoral, and Cross-sectoral Policies

2.8.3.1   National and Regional Carbon Pricing

Carbon prices – such as carbon taxes and GHG emissions trading schemes (ETSs) – are among the most widely used climate policy instruments across the globe, together with technology support instruments (IRENA 2018). As of May 2020, there were 61 carbon pricing schemes in place or scheduled for implementation, consisting of 31 ETSs and 30 carbon tax regimes, covering 12 $GtCO_2$-eq or about 22% of annual global GHG emissions (World Bank 2020). The performance of carbon pricing in practice varies by countries and sectors, and depends on the policy environment (*robust evidence, high agreement*).

The European Union Emissions Trading Scheme (EU ETS), the longest-standing regional climate policy instrument to date, has reduced emissions, though the estimates of the amount vary by study, by country, and by sector; ranging from 3–28% (McGuinness and Ellerman 2008; Ellerman et al. 2010; Abrell et al. 2011; Anderson and Di Maria 2011; Egenhofer et al. 2011; Petrick and Wagner 2014; Arlinghaus 2015; Martin et al. 2016). The EU ETS avoided emitting about 1.2 $GtCO_2$ between 2008 and 2016 (3.8%), almost half of what EU governments promised to reduce under their Kyoto Protocol commitments (Bayer and Aklin 2020).

China's emission trading pilots have resulted in a decline in carbon intensity in the pilot provinces by adjusting the industrial structure (Zhou et al. 2019). The Regional Greenhouse Gas Initiative (RGGI) in the USA has induced leakage in emissions through increases in electricity generation in surrounding non-RGGI areas, but it has led to the reduction of emissions by way of changes in the fuel mix from coal to gas (Fell and Maniloff 2018). Actual emissions declined in six of the 10 ETSs for which data is available, although other factors, such as the 2009 recession, have had significant impacts on those emissions as well (Haites et al. 2018).

The evidence of environmental effectiveness of carbon taxes in Western European countries is varied depending on country and study (*robust evidence, high agreement*). A significant impact is found in Finland but insignificant impacts are found in Denmark and the Netherlands, and there are mixed results for Sweden (Lin and Li 2011; Brännlund et al. 2014). Only six of the 17 taxes, where data are available, have reduced actual emissions subject to the tax. Tax rates tend to be too low in many cases and the scale and frequency of the rate changes has not been sufficient to stimulate further emissions reductions (Haites et al. 2018).

2.8.3.2   Selected Sectoral Climate Policy Instruments

Many governments have implemented sector-specific policies, in addition to nationwide measures, to reduce GHG emissions (*high confidence*). Examples of sectoral climate policies include carbon taxes on transportation fuels, low-carbon fuel standards, and regulation of coal power generation.

The implementation of a carbon tax and value-added tax on gasoline and diesel in Sweden resulted in significant reductions of CO_2 emissions in the transportation sector (Shmelev and Speck 2018; Andersson 2019). An assessment of a variety of carbon tax schemes across various sectors in the EU shows a negative relationship between CO_2 emissions and a CO_2 tax (Hájek et al. 2019). In British Columbia (Canada), the carbon tax resulted in a decrease in demand for gasoline and a reduction in total GHG emissions (not exclusive to the transportation sector) estimated to be between 5–15% (Murray and Rivers 2015; Rivers and Schaufele 2015). The Low Carbon Fuel Standard in California has contributed to reducing carbon emissions in the transportation sector by approximately 9.85–13.28% during 1997–2014 (Huseynov and Palma 2018).

The power sector typically accounts for a large portion of countries' CO_2 emissions. Market-based regulation and government subsidies in China contributed to improving operational efficiency and reducing emissions (Zhao et al. 2015). In addition, the implementation of ultra-low emission standards has also resulted in a significant reduction in emissions from China's power plants (Tang et al. 2019). Mandatory climate and energy policies, including the California Global Warming Solutions Act, reduced CO_2 emissions by 2.7–25% of the average state-level annual emissions from the power sector over the period 1990–2014 in the USA. Mandatory GHG registry/reporting, electric decoupling and a public benefit fund have been effective in further decreasing power sector emissions in the USA (Martin and Saikawa 2017). In the UK electricity sector, a carbon price floor, combined with electricity market reform (competitive auctions for both firm capacity and renewable energy), displaced coal, whose share fell from 46% in 1995 to 7% in 2017, halving CO_2 emissions, while renewables grew from under 4% in 2008 to 22% by 2017 (Grubb and Newbery 2018). See Chapter 13 for more information.

An alternative approach to a carbon tax is an indirect emissions tax on fuels such as an excise tax, or on vehicles, based on the expected CO_2 intensity of new passenger vehicles. Vehicle purchase taxes can result in a reduction in GHG emissions through reducing the CO_2 emissions intensity of vehicles, while also discouraging new vehicle purchases (Aydin and Esen 2018). For example, a vehicle tax policy in Norway resulted in a reduction of average CO_2 intensity per kilometre of 7.5 gCO_2 km^{-1} (Ciccone 2018; Steinsland et al. 2018). Despite such evidence, studies of carbon pricing find that additional policies are often needed to stimulate sufficient emissions reductions in transportation (*medium confidence*) (Tvinnereim and Mehling 2018).

Electric vehicles (EVs) powered by clean electricity can reduce GHG emissions, and such policies are important for spurring adoption of such vehicles (Kumar and Alok 2020; Thiel et al. 2020). The extent to which EV deployment can decrease emissions by replacing internal combustion engine-based vehicles depends on the generation mix of the electric grid (Abdul-Manan 2015; Nichols et al. 2015; Canals Casals et al. 2016; Hofmann et al. 2016; Choi et al. 2018; Teixeira and Sodré 2018) although, even with current grids, EVs reduce emissions in almost all cases (Knobloch et al. 2020). Policy incentives for EV adoption can be an effective mechanism to increase EV sales (Langbroek et al. 2016) and may include discounts, purchase subsidies, regulations, and government leadership (*medium confidence*) (Bakker and Jacob Trip 2013; Silvia and Krause 2016; Teixeira and Sodré 2018; Qiu et al. 2019; Santos and Davies 2020). The presence of charging infrastructure and publicly available charging increases the adoption rate of EVs (Vergis and Chen 2015; Javid et al. 2019). A comparison of EV adoption rates across 30 countries shows a positive correlation between charging stations and EV market share (Sierzchula et al. 2014). A rollout of 80,000 DC fast chargers across the USA is estimated to have resulted in a 4% reduction in emissions compared to a baseline of no additional fast chargers (Levinson and West 2018). More recently, bans on internal combustion engine vehicles have provided a much more direct approach to stimulating the adoption of EVs and its supporting infrastructure; however, the efficacy of such measures depends on enforcement (Plötz et al. 2019).

Public transit can reduce vehicle travel and lower GHG emissions by reducing the number of trips taken by private vehicles and the length of those trips (*medium confidence*). Changes to the operation of public transportation systems (such as density of bus stops, distance from stops to households, duration and frequency of trip times, and lowering ridership costs) can result in a mode shift from private car trips to public transit trips (Cats et al. 2017; Choi 2018; Carroll et al. 2019). These changes in the public transit system operation and network optimisation have been shown to have reduced GHG emissions in cases such as San Francisco, where the cost optimisation of the transit network was estimated to decrease emissions by a factor of three (Cheng et al. 2018) and Barcelona, where the optimisation of the urban bus system was estimated to reduce GHG emissions by 50% (Griswold et al. 2017). For every 1% increase in investment in transit services and transit-oriented design, there is an estimated 0.16% reduction in private vehicle kilometres travelled per capita (McIntosh et al. 2014).

Bike- and car-sharing programmes can reduce GHG emissions (*medium confidence*). Albeit a study of eight cities in the USA with larger bike share systems and higher ridership found that their potential to reduce total emissions is limited to <0.1% of total GHG emissions from the transportation sectors of these cities (Kou et al. 2020). The emissions reductions effects of car-sharing programmes depends on the specifics of programmes: the mode shift from public transit to car-sharing services can outweigh the decreases in GHG emissions associated with a reduced number of cars on the road (Jung and Koo 2018), whereas car-sharing programmes with EV fleets may reduce GHG emissions (Luna et al. 2020).

2.8.4 Emission Impacts of Other Related Policies

Policies other than those intended directly to mitigate GHGs can also influence these emissions. Policies to protect the stratospheric ozone layer is a case in point. Implementing the Montreal Protocol and its amendments, emissions of controlled ozone-depleting substances (ODSs) (those covered by the protocol) declined to a very low level of about 1.4 GtCO$_2$-eq yr^{-1} by 2010, avoiding GHG emissions of an estimated 13.3–16.7 GtCO$_2$-eq yr^{-1} (9.7–12.5 GtCO$_2$-eq yr^{-1} when accounting for the ozone depletion and hydrofluorocarbons (HFCs) offsets) (Velders et al. 2007). Yet fluorinated gases (F-gases), the substances introduced to substitute ODSs are also potent GHGs. See Section 2.2 for emissions data, and Chapter 13 on current policies to mitigate HFCs and other F-gases. GHG implications of two other categories of non-climate policies are briefly assessed in this section.

2.8.4.1 Co-impacts of Air Quality, Sector-specific and Energy Policies on Climate Mitigation

Co-impacts of local or regional air pollution abatement policies for climate mitigation are widely studied in the literature. Cross-border externalities of air pollution have also made these a focus of several international agreements (Mitchell et al. 2020). Evaluating the effectiveness of such treaties and policies is difficult because deriving causal inferences and accurate attribution requires accounting for several confounding factors, and direct and indirect spillovers (Isaksen 2020). Nevertheless, several studies assess the effectiveness of such treaties and regulations (De Foy et al. 2016; Li et al. 2017a, 2017b; Morgenstern 2018; Mardones and Cornejo 2020). However, there is little ex-post empirical analysis and a greater focus on ex-ante studies in the literature.

At a local scale, air pollutants are often co-emitted with GHGs in combustion processes. Many air quality policies and regulations focus on local pollution from specific sources that can potentially either substitute or complement global GHG emissions in production and generation processes. Also, policies that reduce certain air pollutants, such as sulphur dioxide (SO$_2$), have a positive radiative forcing effect (Navarro et al. 2016). The evidence on individual air pollution control regulation and policies for GHG emissions is therefore mixed (*medium evidence, medium agreement*). Evidence from the USA suggests that increased stringency of local pollution regulation had no statistically detectable co-benefits or costs on GHG emissions (Brunel and Johnson 2019). Evidence from China suggests that the effectiveness of policies addressing local point sources differed from those of non-point sources and the co-benefits for climate are mixed, though policies addressing large industrial point sources have been easier to implement and have had significant impact (Huang and Wang 2016; Xu et al. 2016; van der A et al. 2017; Dang and Liao 2019; Fang et al. 2019; Yu et al. 2019). Legislation to reduce emissions of air pollutants in Europe have significantly improved air quality and health but have had an unintended warming effect on the climate (Turnock et al. 2016).

Often, the realisation of potential co-benefits depends on the type of pollutant addressed by the specific policy, and whether complementarities between local pollution and global GHG emissions are considered in policy design (*medium evidence, high agreement*) (Rafaj et al. 2014; Li et al. 2017a). Effective environmental regulations that also deliver co-benefits for climate mitigation require integrated policies (Schmale et al. 2014; Haines et al. 2017). Uncoordinated policies can have unintended consequences and even increase emissions (Holland et al. 2015). Many studies suggest that policies that target both local and global environmental benefits simultaneously may be more effective (*medium evidence, medium agreement*) (Klemun et al. 2020). Furthermore, air pollution policies aimed at inducing structural changes – for example, closure of polluting coal power plants or reducing motorised miles travelled – are more likely to have potential positive spillover effects for climate mitigation, as compared to policies incentivising end-of-pipe controls (Wang 2021).

Other policies that typically have potential co-benefits for climate mitigation include those specific to certain sectors and are discussed in Chapters 5–11. Examples of such policies include those that encourage active travel modes, which have been found to have ancillary benefits for local air quality, human health, and GHG emissions (Fujii et al. 2018). Policies to reduce energy use through greater efficiency have also been found to have benefits for air quality and the climate (*robust evidence, medium agreement*) (Tzeiranaki et al. 2019; Bertoldi and Mosconi 2020). Important air quality and climate co-benefits of renewable or nuclear energy policies have also been found (*medium evidence, medium agreement*) (Lee et al. 2017; Apergis et al. 2018; Sovacool and Monyei 2021).

Policies specific to other sectors, such as encouraging green building design, can also reduce GHG emissions (Eisenstein et al. 2017). Evidence from several countries also shows that replacing polluting solid biomass cooking with cleaner gas-burning or electric alternatives have strong co-benefits for health, air quality, and climate change (*robust evidence, high agreement*) (Anenberg et al. 2017; Singh et al. 2017; Tao et al. 2018).

2.8.4.2 Climate Impacts of Agricultural, Forestry, Land Use, and AFOLU-related Policies

Policies on agriculture, forestry, and other land use (AFOLU), and AFOLU sector-related policies have had a long history in many developing and developed countries. Co-impacts of these policies on the climate have been only marginally studied, although their impacts might be quite important because the AFOLU sector is responsible for 22% of total GHG emissions (*robust evidence, high agreement*). The results of afforestation policies around the world and the contribution to CCS are also important.

Private and governmental policies can have a major impact on the climate. Experience indicates that 'climate proofing' a policy is likely to require some stimulus, resources, and expertise from agencies or organisations from outside the country. Stimulus and support for adaptation and mitigation can come from the UN system and from international development institutions (FAO 2009). These findings are also valid for small/organic farmers vis-à-vis large-scale

agro-industry. For example, small/medium and environmentally concerned farmers in Europe are often asking for more policies and regulations, and see it as necessary from a climate perspective, and also to maintain competitiveness relative to large agro-industrial complexes. Therefore, the need for governmental support for small producers in regulations encompasses all AFOLU sectors.

Forestry case: zero deforestation

Forest is generally defined as land spanning more than 0.5 hectares with trees higher than 5 metres and a canopy cover of more than 10%, or trees able to reach these thresholds in situ (FAO 1998). Zero-deforestation (i.e., both gross and net zero deforestation) initiatives generate results at multiple levels (Meijer 2014). Efforts to achieve zero-deforestation (and consequently emissions) are announced by non-governmental organisations (NGOs), companies, governments, and other stakeholder groups. NGOs engage through their campaigning, but also propose tools and approaches for companies (Leijten et al. 2020). The extent to which companies can actually monitor actions conducive to zero-deforestation pledges depends on their position in the supply chain. Beyond the business practices of participating companies, achieving long-term positive societal impacts requires upscaling from supply chains towards landscapes, with engagement of all stakeholders, and in particular small producers. The various success indicators for zero deforestation mirror the multiple levels at which such initiatives develop: progress towards certification, improved traceability, and legality are apparent output measures, whereas direct-area monitoring and site selection approaches target the business practices themselves.

Such efforts have led to the development of the High Carbon Stock (HCS) approach that combines carbon stock values with the protection of HCS areas (including peatlands and riparian zones) and areas important for the livelihoods of local communities (Rosoman et al. 2017). Long-term positive impacts, however, will need to be assessed with hindsight and focus on national and global statistics. Successful initiatives targeting zero deforestation at jurisdictional level would also need to improve the enforcement of forest laws and regulations (EII 2015; Meyer and Miller 2015).

Large-scale agribusiness, banks, and consumer goods companies dominate supply chain-focused zero-deforestation initiatives, but only the producers, including local communities and smallholders, can change the production circumstances (TFD 2014). Producers shoulder much of the burden for meeting environmental requirements of pledges. And local communities and small producers are vulnerable to being cut out when supply chains reorient. The zero-deforestation pledges do not always devise programmes for introducing new sourcing strategies, and governments may have an important contribution to make, particularly in safeguarding the interests of small producers.

Other than in Brazil and Indonesia, beyond individual supply chains, there is still little evidence on positive results of zero-deforestation commitments, as information available for companies to judge their progress is scarce. Moreover, many zero-deforestation pledges set targets to be achieved by 2020 or 2030, and, consequently, many companies have not yet reported publicly on their progress. Similarly, only a few governments have yet shown progress in reducing deforestation, but the New York Declaration on Forests, the Sustainable Development Goals (SDGs) and the Paris Agreement were adopted relatively recently. The effectiveness of private-sector zero-deforestation pledges depends on the extent to which they can be supported by governmental action and foster a cooperative environment with the engagement of all stakeholders. Where the pledges are coordinated with regulation, multi-stakeholder dialogues, and technical and financial support, a true paradigm shift becomes possible. Many governments are still building the capacity to improve overall forest governance, but implementing ambitious international targets is likely to depend on technical and major financial support that has not yet been mobilised.

2.9   Knowledge Gaps

- Global GHG emissions estimates are published less frequently and with greater reporting lags than, for example, CO_2 from fossil fuel and industry. Data quality and reporting frequency remains an issue, particularly in developing countries where the statistical infrastructure is not well developed. Efforts to compile a global GHG emissions inventory by country, sector, and across time, that is annually updated based on the best-available inventory information, similar to ongoing activities for carbon dioxide (CO_2), methane (CH_4) or nitrous oxide (N_2O), could fill this gap. Uncertainties and their methodological treatment in GHG emissions estimates are still not comprehensively understood.

- There is a more fundamental data gap for F-gas emissions, where data quality in global inventories is poor due to considerable gaps in the underlying activity data – particularly in developing countries. Comprehensive tracking of fluorinated gases (F-gas) emissions would also imply the inclusion of other gases not covered under the Paris Agreement, such as chlorofluorocarbons, hydrochlorofluorocarbons and others.

- Currently, despite advances in terms of data availability, sectoral and spatial resolution, the results in consumption-based emission estimates are dependent on the database used, the level of sectoral aggregation and country resolution. More fine-grained data at spatial resolution as well as the product level would support exploring the mitigation options at the sub-national level, companies and households.

- Consumption-based emission accounts suffer from lack of quantification of uncertainties at the subnational level and especially in data-scarce environments, such as for developing countries. A better understanding of drivers that caused decoupling of emissions at the national and especially sub-national level are important to explore.

- Understanding how socio-economic drivers modulate emission mitigation is crucial. Technological improvements (e.g., improved energy or land-use intensity of the economy) have shown a persistent pattern over the last few decades, but gains have been outpaced by increases in affluence (GDP per capita) and population growth, leading to continued emissions growth. Therefore the key gap in knowledge is how these drivers of emissions can be mitigated by demand management, alternative economic models,

population control and rapid technological transition to different extents and in different settings. More research on decoupling and sustainability transformations would help to answer these questions. Key knowledge gaps also remain in the role of trade – in particular, how supporting low-carbon technologies in developing and exporting countries can counteract the upward-driving effect of trade, and how to achieve decoupling without outsourcing emissions to others and often to less developed regions.

- Understanding of how inequality affects emissions is in a nascent stage. Less is known about the causal mechanisms by which different dimensions of inequality – such as income, socio-economic, spatial, socio-cultural-gender and ethnicity – affect emissions. In particular, limited knowledge exists on the linkages between dimensions of inequality other than income or wealth and emissions arising from different service demands. Research gaps are apparent on how inequalities in living standards relate to emissions and how changes in inequalities between genders, social groups, and other marginalised communities impact emissions trends.

- Digitalisation of the economy is often quoted as providing new mitigation opportunities, but knowledge and evidences are yet limited – such as understanding of the role of smart apps and the potential and influence of disruptive technologies at the demand and supply side on GHG emissions.

- Despite growing evidence of technological progress across a variety of mitigation areas and the availability of increasingly precise datasets, knowledge gaps remain on technological change and innovation and evidence on speed of transitions to clarify what would make them fast or slow. Innovation is an inherently uncertain process and there will always be imperfect ex ante knowledge on technological outcomes and their effects on mitigation. The extent to which a low-carbon transition can proceed faster than historical examples is crucial to aid future mitigation. That depends on a better understanding of the speed of building, updating and replacing infrastructure. Additionally, how and whether financing for low-carbon technology investment in low- and middle-income countries can be delivered at low-cost and sustained over time are important questions. The emerging findings that small-scale technologies learn faster and are adopted more quickly need to be tested against a broader set of cases, and in particular against the large dispersion in data.

- Future CO_2 emissions from existing and planned infrastructure is not well understood and quantified outside the power sector. Further integration of bottom-up accounting and scenario approaches from integrated assessment seems promising. Comprehensive assessments of hard-to-abate residual fossil fuel emissions and their relationship to CO_2 removal activities are lacking, but will be important for informing net-zero emissions strategies.

- Empirical evidence of emission impacts from climate policies, including carbon pricing, is not sufficient for unambiguous attribution assessment, mainly due to the limited experience with climate-related policy experiments to date. More attention to the methodology for comprehensive evaluation of climate policies and measures, such as effective carbon rates is apparent. Key knowledge gaps also exist on ex-post evaluations of climate and non-climate policies and measures for their impact on emissions, particularly at the global scale, considering national circumstances and priorities.

Frequently Asked Questions (FAQs)

FAQ 2.1 | Are emissions still increasing or are they falling?

Global greenhouse gas (GHG) emissions continued to rise and reached 59 ± 6.6 $GtCO_2$-eq in 2019, although the rate of growth has fallen compared to the previous decade. However, emissions were higher than at any point in human history before. Emissions were around 12% and 54% higher than in 2010 and 1990, respectively. Average annual GHG emissions for 2009–2019 were higher compared to the periods 2000–2009 and 1990–1999, respectively. GHG emissions growth slowed since 2010: while average annual GHG emissions growth was 2.1% for 2000–2010, it was only 1.3% for 2010–2019. In order to stop the temperature increase, however, net emissions must be zero.

FAQ 2.2 | Are there countries that have reduced emissions and grown economically at the same time?

About 24 countries have reduced territorial CO_2 and GHG emissions for more than 10 years. Uncertainties in emission levels and changes over time prevent a precise assessment in some country cases. In the short observation period of 2010–2015, 43 out of 166 countries have achieved absolute decoupling of consumption-based CO_2 emissions from economic growth, which means that these countries experienced GDP growth while their emissions have stabilised or declined. A group of developed countries, such as some EU countries and the USA, and some developing countries, such as Cuba, have successfully achieved an absolute decoupling of consumption-based CO_2 emissions and GDP growth. Decoupling has been achieved at various levels of per capita income and per capita emissions. Overall, the absolute reduction in annual emissions achieved by some countries has been outweighed by growth in emissions elsewhere in the world.

FAQ 2.3 | How much time do we have to act to keep global warming below 1.5 degrees?

If global CO_2 emissions continue at current rates, the remaining carbon budget for keeping warming to 1.5°C will likely be exhausted before 2030. Between 1850 and 2019, total cumulative CO_2 emissions from the fossil fuel industry (FFI) and agriculture, forestry, and other land use (AFOLU) were 2400 ($\pm$240 $GtCO_2$). Of these, about 410 ± 30 $GtCO_2$ were added since 2010. This is about the same size as the remaining carbon budget for keeping global warming to 1.5°C and between one-third and one-half of the 1150 ± 220 (1350, 1700) $GtCO_2$ for limiting global warming below 2°C with a 67% (50%, 33%) probability, respectively (Canadell et al. 2021). At current (2019) rates of emissions, it would only take 8 (2–15) and 25 (18–35) years to emit the equivalent amount of CO_2 for a 67th percentile 1.5°C and 2°C remaining carbon budget, respectively. This highlights the dependence of 1.5°C pathways on the availability of substantial CO_2 removal capacities, as discussed in Chapters 3, 4, and 12, but also Section 2.7 of this chapter.

References

Aaheim, A. and T. Mideksa, 2017: Requirements to metrics of greenhouse gas emissions, given a cap on temperature. *Ecol. Econ.*, **131**, 460–467, doi:10.1016/j.ecolecon.2016.09.026.

Abdul-Manan, A.F.N., 2015: Uncertainty and differences in GHG emissions between electric and conventional gasoline vehicles with implications for transport policy making. *Energy Policy*, **87**, 1–7, doi:10.1016/j.enpol.2015.08.029.

Abrell, J., A. Ndoye Faye, and G. Zachmann, 2011: *Assessing the impact of the EU ETS using firm level data*. Bruegel, Brussels, Belgium, 23 pp.

Adenle, A.A., H. Azadi, and J. Arbiol, 2015: Global assessment of technological innovation in climate change adaptation and mitigation in developing world. *J. Environ. Manage.*, **161**, 261–275, doi:10.1016/j.jenvman.2015.05.040.

Afionis, S., M. Sakai, K. Scott, J. Barrett, and A. Gouldson, 2017: Consumption-based carbon accounting: does it have a future? *WIREs Clim. Change*, **8(1)**, e438, doi:10.1002/wcc.438.

Aguiar, A., M. Chepeliev, E.L. Corong, R. McDougall, and D. van der Mensbrugghe, 2019: The GTAP Data Base: Version 10. *J. Glob. Econ. Anal.*, **4(1)**, 1–27, doi:10.21642/JGEA.040101AF.

Akizu-Gardoki, O. et al., 2018: Decoupling between human development and energy consumption within footprint accounts. *J. Clean. Prod.*, **202**, 1145–1157, doi:10.1016/j.jclepro.2018.08.235.

Alkemade, F. and R.A.A. Suurs, 2012: Patterns of expectations for emerging sustainable technologies. *Technol. Forecast. Soc. Change*, **79(3)**, 448–456, doi:10.1016/j.techfore.2011.08.014.

Allen, M. et al., 2021: Ensuring that offsets and other internationally transferred mitigation outcomes contribute effectively to limiting global warming. *Environ. Res. Lett.*, **16(7)**, 074009, doi:10.1088/1748-9326/abfcf9.

Allen, M.R. et al., 2016: New use of global warming potentials to compare cumulative and short-lived climate pollutants. *Nat. Clim. Change.*, **6(8)**, 773–776, doi:10.1038/nclimate2998.

Allen, M.R. et al., 2018: A solution to the misrepresentations of CO_2-equivalent emissions of short-lived climate pollutants under ambitious mitigation. *npj Clim. Atmos. Sci.*, **1(1)**, 16, doi:10.1038/s41612-018-0026-8.

Altshuler, A., 2013: Equity as a Factor in Urban Transportation Politics. *Access*, **42**, 2–9.

Alvaredo, F., L. Chancel, T. Piketty, E. Saez, and G. Zucman, 2018: *World Inequality Report 2018*. Belknap Press of Harvard University Press, Cambridge, MA, USA, 344 pp.

Anderson, B. and C. Di Maria, 2011: Abatement and Allocation in the Pilot Phase of the EU ETS. *Environ. Resour. Econ.*, **48(1)**, 83–103, doi:10.1007/s10640-010-9399-9.

Andersson, J.J., 2019: Carbon Taxes and CO_2 Emissions: Sweden as a Case Study. *Am. Econ. J. Econ. Policy*, **11(4)**, 1–30, doi:10.1257/pol.20170144.

Andres, R.J. et al., 2012: A synthesis of carbon dioxide emissions from fossil-fuel combustion. *Biogeosciences*, **9(5)**, 1845–1871, doi:10.5194/bg-9-1845-2012.

Andres, R.J., T.A. Boden, and D. Higdon, 2014: A new evaluation of the uncertainty associated with CDIAC estimates of fossil fuel carbon dioxide emission. *Tellus B: Chem. Phys. Meteorol.*, **66(1)**, 23616, doi:10.3402/tellusb.v66.23616.

Andrew, R. and G. Peters, 2021: The Global Carbon Project's fossil CO_2 emissions dataset. doi:10.5281/zenodo.5569235.

Andrew, R.M., 2020: A comparison of estimates of global carbon dioxide emissions from fossil carbon sources. *Earth Syst. Sci. Data*, **12(2)**, 1437–1465, doi:10.5194/essd-12-1437-2020.

Anenberg, S.C. et al., 2017: Air pollution-related health and climate benefits of clean cookstove programs in Mozambique. *Environ. Res. Lett.*, **12(2)**, 025006, doi:10.1088/1748-9326/aa5557.

Apergis, N. and J. Li, 2016: Population and lifestyle trend changes in China: implications for environmental quality. *Appl. Econ.*, **48(54)**, 5246–5256, doi:10.1080/00036846.2016.1173184.

Apergis, N., M. Ben Jebli, and S. Ben Youssef, 2018: Does renewable energy consumption and health expenditures decrease carbon dioxide emissions? Evidence for sub-Saharan Africa countries. *Renew. Energy*, **127**, 1011–1016, doi:10.1016/j.renene.2018.05.043.

Aranoff, K., A. Battistonii, D. Aldana Cohen, and T. Riofrancos, 2019: *A Planet to Win: Why We Need a New Green Deal*. Verso, London UK and New York, NY, USA, 208 pp.

Arlinghaus, J., 2015: *Impacts of Carbon Prices on Indicators of Competitiveness: A Review of Empirical Findings*. OECD Environment Working Paper No. 87, OECD Publishing, Paris, France, 36 pp.

Assadour, E., 2012: The Path to Degrowth in Overdeveloped Countries. In: *State of the World 2012* [Starke, L., (ed.)], Island Press/Center for Resource Economics, Washington DC, USA, pp. 22–37.

Aydin, C. and Ö. Esen, 2018: Reducing CO_2 emissions in the EU member states: Do environmental taxes work? *J. Environ. Plan. Manag.*, **61(13)**, 2396–2420, doi:10.1080/09640568.2017.1395731.

Azhgaliyeva, D., Y. Liu, and B. Liddle, 2020: An empirical analysis of energy intensity and the role of policy instruments. *Energy Policy*, **145**, 111773, doi:10.1016/j.enpol.2020.111773.

Azizalrahman, H. and V. Hasyimi, 2019: A model for urban sector drivers of carbon emissions. *Sustain. Cities Soc.*, **44**, 46–55, doi:10.1016/j.scs.2018.09.035.

Baek, J. and G. Gweisah, 2013: Does income inequality harm the environment?: Empirical evidence from the United States. *Energy Policy*, **62**, 1434–1437, doi:10.1016/j.enpol.2013.07.097.

Baiocchi, G., J. Minx, and K. Hubacek, 2010: The Impact of Social Factors and Consumer Behavior on Carbon Dioxide Emissions in the United Kingdom. *J. Ind. Ecol.*, **14(1)**, 50–72, doi:10.1111/j.1530-9290.2009.00216.x.

Baiocchi, G., F. Creutzig, J. Minx, and P.-P. Pichler, 2015: A spatial typology of human settlements and their CO_2 emissions in England. *Glob. Environ. Change*, **34**, 13–21, doi:10.1016/j.gloenvcha.2015.06.001.

Bakker, S. and J. Jacob Trip, 2013: Policy options to support the adoption of electric vehicles in the urban environment. *Transp. Res. Part D Transp. Environ.*, **25**, 18–23, doi:10.1016/j.trd.2013.07.005.

Balcombe, P., J.F. Speirs, N.P. Brandon, and A.D. Hawkes, 2018: Methane emissions: choosing the right climate metric and time horizon. *Environ. Sci. Process. Impacts*, **20(10)**, 1323–1339, doi:10.1039/C8EM00414E.

Baležentis, T., G. Liobikienė, D. Štreimikienė, and K. Sun, 2020: The impact of income inequality on consumption-based greenhouse gas emissions at the global level: A partially linear approach. *J. Environ. Manage.*, **267**, 110635, doi:10.1016/j.jenvman.2020.110635.

Baloch, M.A., Danish, S.U.-D. Khan, Z.Ş. Ulucak, and A. Ahmad, 2020: Analyzing the relationship between poverty, income inequality, and CO_2 emission in Sub-Saharan African countries. *Sci. Total Environ.*, **740**, 139867, doi:10.1016/j.scitotenv.2020.139867.

Baltruszewicz, M. et al., 2021: Household final energy footprints in Nepal, Vietnam and Zambia: composition, inequality and links to well-being. *Environ. Res. Lett.*, **16(2)**, 025011, doi:10.1088/1748-9326/abd588.

Banerjee, S. and M. Murshed, 2020: Do emissions implied in net export validate the pollution haven conjecture? Analysis of G7 and BRICS countries. *Int. J. Sustain. Econ.*, **12(3)**, 297, doi:10.1504/IJSE.2020.111539.

Banister, D., S. Watson, and C. Wood, 1997: Sustainable cities: transport, energy, and urban form. *Environ. Plan. B Plan. Des.*, **24(1)**, 125–143, doi:10.1068/b240125.

Barido, D.P. de L., N. Avila, and D.M. Kammen, 2020: Exploring the Enabling Environments, Inherent Characteristics and Intrinsic Motivations Fostering Global Electricity Decarbonization. *Energy Res. Soc. Sci.*, **61**, 101343, doi:10.1016/j.erss.2019.101343.

Baudrillard, J., 2017: *The consumer society: Myths and structures.* SAGE Publications Ltd, Los Angeles, USA, 224 pp.

Bauer, N. et al., 2016: Global fossil energy markets and climate change mitigation – an analysis with REMIND. *Clim. Change*, **136(1)**, 69–82, doi:10.1007/s10584-013-0901-6.

Baumert, N., A. Kander, M. Jiborn, V. Kulionis, and T. Nielsen, 2019: Global outsourcing of carbon emissions 1995–2009: A reassessment. *Environ. Sci. Policy*, **92**, 228–236, doi:10.1016/j.envsci.2018.10.010.

Baumgärtner, S., M.A. Drupp, J.N. Meya, J.M. Munz, and M.F. Quaas, 2017: Income inequality and willingness to pay for environmental public goods. *J. Environ. Econ. Manage.*, **85**, 35–61, doi:10.1016/j.jeem.2017.04.005.

Bayer, P. and M. Aklin, 2020: The European Union Emissions Trading System reduced CO_2 emissions despite low prices. *Proc. Natl. Acad. Sci.*, **117(16)**, 8804–8812, doi:10.1073/pnas.1918128117.

Bazilian, M., M. Bradshaw, J. Gabriel, A. Goldthau, and K. Westphal, 2020: Four scenarios of the energy transition: Drivers, consequences, and implications for geopolitics. *WIREs Clim. Change*, **11(2)**, doi:10.1002/wcc.625.

Berthe, A. and L. Elie, 2015: Mechanisms explaining the impact of economic inequality on environmental deterioration. *Ecol. Econ.*, **116**, 191–200, doi:10.1016/j.ecolecon.2015.04.026.

Bertoldi, P. and R. Mosconi, 2020: Do energy efficiency policies save energy? A new approach based on energy policy indicators (in the EU Member States). *Energy Policy*, **139**(January), 111320, doi:10.1016/j.enpol.2020.111320.

Bertram, C. et al., 2015: Carbon lock-in through capital stock inertia associated with weak near-term climate policies. *Technol. Forecast. Soc. Change*, **90(PA)**, 62–72, doi:10.1016/j.techfore.2013.10.001.

Bertram, C. et al., 2021: COVID-19-induced low power demand and market forces starkly reduce CO_2 emissions. *Nat. Clim. Change*, **11(3)**, 193–196, doi:10.1038/s41558-021-00987-x.

Best, R., P.J. Burke, and F. Jotzo, 2020: Carbon Pricing Efficacy: Cross-Country Evidence. *Environ. Resour. Econ.*, **77(1)**, 69–94, doi:10.1007/s10640-020-00436-x.

Blanco G., R. Gerlagh, S. Suh, J. Barrett, H.C. de Coninck, C.F. Diaz Morejon, R. Mathur, N. Nakicenovic, A. Ofosu Ahenkora, J. Pan, H. Pathak, J. Rice, R. Richels, S.J. Smith, D.I. Stern, F.L. Toth, and P. Zhou, 2014: Drivers, Trends and Mitigation. In: *Climate Change 2014: Mitigation of Climate Change. Contribution of Working Group III to the Fifth Assessment Report of the Intergovernmental Panel on Climate Change* [Edenhofer, O., R. Pichs-Madruga, Y. Sokona, E. Farahani, S. Kadner, K. Seyboth, A. Adler, I. Baum, S. Brunner, P. Eickemeier, B. Kriemann, J. Savolainen, S. Schlömer, C. von Stechow, T. Zwickel and J.C. Minx (eds.)]. Cambridge University Press, Cambridge, UK and New York, NY, USA, pp. 351–411.

Bolea, L., R. Duarte, and J. Sánchez-Chóliz, 2020: Exploring carbon emissions and international inequality in a globalized world: A multiregional-multisectoral perspective. *Resour. Conserv. Recycl.*, **152**, 104516, doi:10.1016/j.resconrec.2019.104516.

Bond, K., A. McCrone, and J. Kortenhorst, 2019: *The Speed of the Energy Transition Gradual or Rapid Change.* World Economic Forum, Cologny/Geneva, Switzerland, 32 pp.

Botzen, W.J.W., J.M. Gowdy, and J.C.J.M. Van Den Bergh, 2008: Cumulative CO_2 emissions: shifting international responsibilities for climate debt. *Clim. Policy*, **8(6)**, 569–576, doi:10.3763/cpol.2008.0539.

Bouman, T. and L. Steg, 2019: Motivating Society-wide Pro-environmental Change. *One Earth*, **1(1)**, 27–30, doi:10.1016/j.oneear.2019.08.002.

BP, 2021: *Statistical Review of World Energy.* BP, London, UK, pp. 8–20.

Bradley, J.C., T.M. Waliczek, and J.M. Zajicek, 1999: Relationship Between Environmental Knowledge and Environmental Attitude of High School Students. *J. Environ. Educ.*, **30(3)**, 17–21, doi:10.1080/00958969909601873.

Brännlund, R., T. Lundgren, and P.-O. Marklund, 2014: Carbon intensity in production and the effects of climate policy – Evidence from Swedish industry. *Energy Policy*, **67**, 844–857, doi:10.1016/j.enpol.2013.12.012.

Brockway, P.E., S. Sorrell, G. Semieniuk, M.K. Heun, and V. Court, 2021: Energy efficiency and economy-wide rebound effects: A review of the evidence and its implications. *Renew. Sustain. Energy Rev.*, **141**, 110781, doi:10.1016/j.rser.2021.110781.

Bruckner, B., K. Hubacek, Y. Shan, H. Zhong, and K. Feng, 2021: Impacts of poverty alleviation on national and global carbon emissions. *Nat. Sustain.*, **5(4)**, 311–320, doi:10.1038/s41893-021-00842-z.

Brunel, C. and E.P. Johnson, 2019: Two birds, one stone? Local pollution regulation and greenhouse gas emissions. *Energy Econ.*, **78**, 1–12, doi:10.1016/j.eneco.2018.10.011.

Bruns, S.B., A. Moneta, and D.I. Stern, 2021: Estimating the economy-wide rebound effect using empirically identified structural vector autoregressions. *Energy Econ.*, **97**, 105158, doi:10.1016/j.eneco.2021.105158.

Buchholz, W., L. Dippl, and M. Eichenseer, 2019: Subsidizing renewables as part of taking leadership in international climate policy: The German case. *Energy Policy*, **129**, 765–773, doi:10.1016/j.enpol.2019.02.044.

Büchs, M. and S.V. Schnepf, 2013: Who emits most? Associations between socio-economic factors and UK households' home energy, transport, indirect and total CO_2 emissions. *Ecol. Econ.*, **90**, 114–123, doi:10.1016/j.ecolecon.2013.03.007.

Bullock, S., J. Mason, J. Broderick, and A. Larkin, 2020: Shipping and the Paris climate agreement: a focus on committed emissions. *BMC Energy*, **2(1)**, 5, doi:10.1186/s42500-020-00015-2.

Burck, J., U. Hagen, C. Bals, N. Höhne, and L. Nascimento, 2021: *Climate Change Performance Index 2021.* Germanwatch, New Climate Institute, Climate Action Network, Bonn, Germany, 13 pp. https://ccpi.org/download/the-climate-change-performance-index-2021/.

Burke, M.J. and J.C. Stephens, 2017: Energy democracy: Goals and policy instruments for sociotechnical transitions. *Energy Res. Soc. Sci.*, **33**, 35–48, doi:10.1016/j.erss.2017.09.024.

Cain, M. et al., 2019: Improved calculation of warming-equivalent emissions for short-lived climate pollutants. *Clim. Atmos. Sci.*, **2(1)**, 29, doi:10.1038/s41612-019-0086-4.

Cain, M. et al., 2021: Comment on 'Unintentional unfairness when applying new greenhouse gas emissions metrics at country level.' *Environ. Res. Lett.*, **16(6)**, 068001, doi:10.1088/1748-9326/ac02eb.

Canadell, J.G., P.M.S. Monteiro, M.H. Costa, L. Cotrim da Cunha, P.M. Cox, A.V. Eliseev, S. Henson, M. Ishii, S. Jaccard, C. Koven, A. Lohila, P.K. Patra, S. Piao, J. Rogelj, S. Syampungani, S. Zaehle, K. Zickfeld, 2021, Global Carbon and other Biogeochemical Cycles and Feedbacks. In: *Climate Change 2021: The Physical Science Basis. Contribution of Working Group I to the Sixth Assessment Report of the Intergovernmental Panel on Climate Change* [Masson-Delmotte, V., P. Zhai, A. Pirani, S.L. Connors, C. Péan, S. Berger, N. Caud, Y. Chen, L. Goldfarb, M.I. Gomis, M. Huang, K. Leitzell, E. Lonnoy, J.B.R. Matthews, T.K. Maycock, T. Waterfield, O. Yelekçi, R. Yu and B. Zhou (eds.)]. Cambridge University Press. In press.

Cao, X., X. Dai, and J. Liu, 2016: Building energy-consumption status worldwide and the state-of-the-art technologies for zero-energy buildings during the past decade. *Energy Build.*, **128**, 198–213, doi:10.1016/j.enbuild.2016.06.089.

Cao, Z., L. Shen, A.N. Løvik, D.B. Müller, and G. Liu, 2017: Elaborating the History of Our Cementing Societies: An In-Use Stock Perspective. *Environ. Sci. Technol.*, **51(19)**, 11468–11475, doi:10.1021/acs.est.7b03077.

Carroll, P., B. Caulfield, and A. Ahern, 2019: Measuring the potential emission reductions from a shift towards public transport. *Transp. Res. Part D Transp. Environ.*, **73**, 338–351, doi:10.1016/j.trd.2019.07.010.

Carvalho, A.M. de, C.L.G. César, R.M. Fisberg, and D.M.L. Marchioni, 2013: Excessive meat consumption in Brazil: diet quality and environmental impacts. *Public Health Nutr.*, **16(10)**, 1893–1899, doi:10.1017/S1368980012003916.

Casals, L.C., E. Martinez-Laserna, B. Amante García, and N. Nieto, 2016: Sustainability analysis of the electric vehicle use in Europe for CO_2 emissions reduction. *J. Clean. Prod.*, **127**, 425–437, doi:10.1016/j.jclepro.2016.03.120.

Castilhos, R.B. and M.J. Fonseca, 2016: Pursuing upward transformation: The construction of a progressing self among dominated consumers. *J. Bus. Res.*, **69(1)**, 6–17, doi:10.1016/j.jbusres.2015.07.015.

Castilhos, R.B., M.J. Fonseca, and V. Bavaresco, 2017: Consumption, crisis, and coping strategies of lower class families in Brazil: A sociological account. *Int. J. Consum. Studies*, **41(4)**, 379–388, doi:10.1111/ijcs.12341.

Cats, O., Y.O. Susilo, and T. Reimal, 2017: The prospects of fare-free public transport: evidence from Tallinn. *Transportation (Amst).*, **44(5)**, 1083–1104, doi:10.1007/s11116-016-9695-5.

Cetin, M.A. and I. Bakirtas, 2020: The long-run environmental impacts of economic growth, financial development, and energy consumption: Evidence from emerging markets. *Energy Environ.*, **31(4)**, 634–655, doi:10.1177/0958305X19882373.

Chakravarty, S. and M. Tavoni, 2013: Energy Poverty Alleviation and Climate Change Mitigation: Is There a Trade Off? *Energy Economics.*, 40, 67–73, doi:10.1016/j.eneco.2013.09.022

Chakravarty, S. et al., 2009: Sharing global CO_2 emission reductions among one billion high emitters. *Proc. Natl. Acad. Sci.*, **106(29)**, 11884–11888, doi:10.1073/pnas.0905232106.

Chancel, L., 2014: Are younger generations higher carbon emitters than their elders? *Ecol. Econ.*, **100**, 195–207, doi:10.1016/j.ecolecon.2014.02.009.

Chancel, L., 2020: 1 Economic Inequality as a Component of Unsustainability. In: *Unsustainable Inequalities*, Harvard University Press, Cambridge MA, USA and London, UK, pp. 11–35.

Chancel, L. and T. Piketty, 2015: *Carbon and inequality: from Kyoto to Paris*. Paris School of Economics, Paris, France, 48pp, doi:10.13140/RG.2.1.3536.0082.

Chang, C.-P., M. Dong, B. Sui, and Y. Chu, 2019: Driving forces of global carbon emissions: From time- and spatial-dynamic perspectives. *Econ. Model.*, **77**, 70–80, doi:10.1016/j.econmod.2019.01.021.

Chen, G. et al., 2019: Review on City-Level Carbon Accounting. *Environ. Sci. Technol.*, **53(10)**, 5545–5558, doi:10.1021/acs.est.8b07071.

Chen, J., Q. Xian, J. Zhou, and D. Li, 2020: Impact of income inequality on CO_2 emissions in G20 countries. *J. Environ. Manage.*, **271**, 110987, doi:10.1016/j.jenvman.2020.110987.

Cheng, H., C. Mao, S. Madanat, and A. Horvath, 2018: Minimizing the total costs of urban transit systems can reduce greenhouse gas emissions: The case of San Francisco. *Transp. Policy*, **66**(March), 40–48, doi:10.1016/j.tranpol.2018.02.009.

Cherp, A., V. Vinichenko, J. Jewell, E. Brutschin, and B. Sovacool, 2018: Integrating techno-economic, socio-technical and political perspectives on national energy transitions: A meta-theoretical framework. *Energy Res. Soc. Sci.*, **37**(January 2017), 175–190, doi:10.1016/j.erss.2017.09.015.

Cherp, A., V. Vinichenko, J. Tosun, J.A. Gordon, and J. Jewell, 2021: National growth dynamics of wind and solar power compared to the growth required for global climate targets. *Nat. Energy*, **6(7)**, 742–754, doi:10.1038/s41560-021-00863-0.

Choi, H., J. Shin, and J. Woo, 2018: Effect of electricity generation mix on battery electric vehicle adoption and its environmental impact. *Energy Policy*, **121**(October 2017), 13–24, doi:10.1016/j.enpol.2018.06.013.

Choi, K., 2018: The influence of the built environment on household vehicle travel by the urban typology in Calgary, Canada. *Cities*, **75**, 101–110, doi:10.1016/j.cities.2018.01.006.

Ciais, P., C. Sabine, G. Bala, L. Bopp, V. Brovkin, J. Canadell, A. Chhabra, R. DeFries, J. Galloway, M. Heimann, C. Jones, C. Le Quéré, R.B. Myneni, S. Piao and P. Thornton, 2013: Carbon and Other Biogeochemical Cycles. In: *Climate Change 2013: The Physical Science Basis. Contribution of Working Group I to the Fifth Assessment Report of the Intergovernmental Panel on Climate Change* [Stocker, T.F., D. Qin, G.-K. Plattner, M. Tignor, S.K. Allen, J. Boschung, A. Nauels, Y. Xia, V. Bex and P.M. Midgley (eds.)]. Cambridge University Press, Cambridge, UK, and New York, NY, USA, 465–570.

Ciais, P. et al., 2021: Empirical estimates of regional carbon budgets imply reduced global soil heterotrophic respiration. *Natl. Sci. Rev.*, **8(2)**, doi:10.1093/nsr/nwaa145.

Ciccone, A., 2018: Environmental effects of a vehicle tax reform: Empirical evidence from Norway. *Transp. Policy*, **69**(April 2017), 141–157, doi:10.1016/j.tranpol.2018.05.002.

Climate Transparency, 2021: *Climate Transparency Report*. 16 pp. https://www.climate-transparency.org/wp-content/uploads/2021/10/CT2021-Highlights-Report.pdf.

Clarke L., K. Jiang, K. Akimoto, M. Babiker, G. Blanford, K. Fisher-Vanden, J.-C. Hourcade, V. Krey, E. Kriegler, A. Löschel, D. McCollum, S. Paltsev, S. Rose, P.R. Shukla, M. Tavoni, B.C.C. van der Zwaan, and D.P. van Vuuren, 2014: Assessing Transformation Pathways. In: *Climate Change 2014: Mitigation of Climate Change. Contribution of Working Group III to the Fifth Assessment Report of the Intergovernmental Panel on Climate Change* [Edenhofer, O., R. Pichs-Madruga, Y. Sokona, E. Farahani, S. Kadner, K. Seyboth, A. Adler, I. Baum, S. Brunner, P. Eickemeier, B. Kriemann, J. Savolainen, S. Schlömer, C. von Stechow, T. Zwickel and J.C. Minx (eds.)]. Cambridge University Press, Cambridge, UK, and New York, NY, USA, pp 413–510.

Coles, A.-M., A. Piterou, and A. Sentić, 2018: Is small really beautiful? A review of the concept of niches in innovation. *Technol. Anal. Strateg. Manag.*, **30(8)**, 895–908, doi:10.1080/09537325.2017.1408907.

Collins, W.J., D.J. Frame, J.S. Fuglestvedt, and K.P. Shine, 2019: Stable climate metrics for emissions of short and long-lived species – combining steps and pulses. *Environ. Res. Lett.*, **15(2)**, 024018, doi:10.1088/1748-9326/ab6039.

Colmenares, G., A. Löschel, and R. Madlener, 2020: The rebound effect representation in climate and energy models. *Environ. Res. Lett.*, **15(12)**, 123010, doi:10.1088/1748-9326/abc214.

Conchedda, G. and F.N. Tubiello, 2020: Drainage of organic soils and GHG emissions: validation with country data. *Earth Syst. Sci. Data*, **12(4)**, 3113–3137, doi:10.5194/essd-12-3113-2020.

Corrado, V. and I. Ballarini, 2016: Refurbishment trends of the residential building stock: Analysis of a regional pilot case in Italy. *Energy Build.*, **132**(March 2013), 91–106, doi:10.1016/j.enbuild.2016.06.022.

Creutzig, F., G. Baiocchi, R. Bierkandt, P.-P. Pichler, and K.C. Seto, 2015: Global typology of urban energy use and potentials for an urbanization mitigation wedge. *Proc. Natl. Acad. Sci.*, **112(20)**, 6283–6288, doi:10.1073/pnas.1315545112.

Creutzig, F. et al., 2016: Urban infrastructure choices structure climate solutions. *Nat. Clim. Change*, **6(12)**, 1054–1056, doi:10.1038/nclimate3169.

Creutzig, F. et al., 2017: The underestimated potential of solar energy to mitigate climate change. *Nat. Energy*, **2(9)**, 17140, doi:10.1038/nenergy.2017.140.

Creutzig, F. et al., 2018: Towards demand-side solutions for mitigating climate change. *Nat. Clim. Change*, **8(4)**, 260–263, doi:10.1038/s41558-018-0121-1.

Creutzig, F. et al., 2019: Assessing human and environmental pressures of global land-use change 2000–2010. *Glob. Sustain.*, **2**(e1), e1, doi:10.1017/sus.2018.15.

Creutzig, F., J. Hilaire, G.F. Nemet, F. Müller-hansen, and J.C. Minx, 2021: Climate change mitigation easier than suggested by models 1. *Earth Sp. Sci. Open Arch.*, doi:10.1002/essoar.10506825.1.

Crippa, M. et al., 2018: Gridded emissions of air pollutants for the period 1970–2012 within EDGAR v4.3.2. *Earth Syst. Sci. Data*, **10(4)**, 1987–2013, doi:10.5194/essd-10-1987-2018.

Crippa, M. et al., 2019a: *Fossil CO_2 and GHG emissions of all world countries: 2019 report.* Publications Office of the European Union, Luxembourg, 251 pp.

Crippa, M., D. Guizzardi, M. Muntean, and E. Schaaf, 2019b: *EDGAR v5.0 Global Air Pollutant Emissions,* European Commission, JRC122516.

Crippa, M. et al., 2020: *Fossil CO_2 emissions of all world countries – 2020 Report.* European Commission Publications Office, Luxembourg, 244 pp.

Crippa, M. et al., 2021: *GHG emissions of all world countries – 2021 Report.* European Commission Publications Office, Luxembourg, 263 pp.

Csutora, M., 2012: One More Awareness Gap? The Behaviour–Impact Gap Problem. *J. Consum. Policy*, **35(1)**, 145–163, doi:10.1007/s10603-012-9187-8.

Cui, R.Y. et al., 2019: Quantifying operational lifetimes for coal power plants under the Paris goals. *Nat. Commun.*, **10(1)**, 4759, doi:10.1038/s41467-019-12618-3.

Dahlgren, E., C. Göçmen, K. Lackner, and G. van Ryzin, 2013: Small Modular Infrastructure. *Eng. Econ.*, **58(4)**, 231–264, doi:10.1080/0013791X.2013.825038.

Daioglou, V., B.J. van Ruijven, and D.P. van Vuuren, 2012: Model projections for household energy use in developing countries. *Energy*, **37(1)**, 601–615, doi:10.1016/j.energy.2011.10.044.

Dang, R. and H. Liao, 2019: Radiative Forcing and Health Impact of Aerosols and Ozone in China as the Consequence of Clean Air Actions over 2012–2017. *Geophys. Res. Lett.*, **46(21)**, 12511–12519, doi:10.1029/2019GL084605.

Dargay, J., D. Gately, and M. Sommer, 2007: Vehicle Ownership and Income Growth, Worldwide: 1960–2030. *Energy J.*, **28(4)**, 143–170, doi:10.5547/ISSN0195-6574-EJ-Vol28-No4-7.

Davidson, D.J., 2019: Exnovating for a renewable energy transition. *Nat. Energy*, **4(4)**, 254–256, doi:10.1038/s41560-019-0369-3.

Davidsson, S., L. Grandell, H. Wachtmeister, and M. Höök, 2014: Growth curves and sustained commissioning modelling of renewable energy: Investigating resource constraints for wind energy. *Energy Policy*, **73**, 767–776, doi:10.1016/j.enpol.2014.05.003.

Davis, L.W. and P.J. Gertler, 2015: Contribution of air conditioning adoption to future energy use under global warming. *Proc. Natl. Acad. Sci.*, **112(19)**, 5962–5967, doi:10.1073/pnas.1423558112.

Davis, S.J. and K. Caldeira, 2010: Consumption-based accounting of CO_2 emissions. *Proc. Natl. Acad. Sci.*, **107(12)**, 5687–5692, doi:10.1073/pnas.0906974107.

Davis, S.J. and R.H. Socolow, 2014: Commitment accounting of CO_2 emissions. *Environ. Res. Lett.*, **9(8)**, 084018, doi:10.1088/1748-9326/9/8/084018.

Davis, S.J., K. Caldeira, and H.D. Matthews, 2010: Future CO_2 Emissions and Climate Change from Existing Energy Infrastructure. *Science*, **329(5997)**, 1330–1333, doi:10.1126/science.1188566.

Davis, S.J. et al., 2018: Net-zero emissions energy systems. *Science*, **360(6396)**, doi:10.1126/science.aas9793.

de Foy, B., Z. Lu, and D.G. Streets, 2016: Satellite NO_2 retrievals suggest China has exceeded its NOx reduction goals from the twelfth Five-Year Plan. *Sci. Rep.*, **6(1)**, 35912, doi:10.1038/srep35912.

de la Rue du Can, S., L. Price, and T. Zwickel, 2015: Understanding the full climate change impact of energy consumption and mitigation at the end-use level: A proposed methodology for allocating indirect carbon dioxide emissions. *Appl. Energy*, **159**, 548–559, doi:10.1016/j.apenergy.2015.08.055.

Deetman, S. et al., 2020: Modelling global material stocks and flows for residential and service sector buildings towards 2050. *J. Clean. Prod.*, **245(118658)**, 118658, doi:10.1016/j.jclepro.2019.118658.

den Elzen, M. et al., 2019: Are the G20 economies making enough progress to meet their NDC targets? *Energy Policy*, **126**, 238–250, doi:10.1016/j.enpol.2018.11.027.

Denison, S., P.M. Forster, and C.J. Smith, 2019: Guidance on emissions metrics for nationally determined contributions under the Paris Agreement. *Environ. Res. Lett.*, **14(12)**, 124002, doi:10.1088/1748-9326/ab4df4.

Deutch, J., 2017: Decoupling Economic Growth and Carbon Emissions. *Joule*, **1(1)**, 3–5, doi:10.1016/j.joule.2017.08.011.

Dietz, T., G.T. Gardner, J. Gilligan, P.C. Stern, and M.P. Vandenbergh, 2009: Household actions can provide a behavioral wedge to rapidly reduce US carbon emissions. *Proc. Natl. Acad. Sci.*, **106(44)**, 18452–18456, doi:10.1073/pnas.0908738106.

Dietz, T., K.A. Frank, C.T. Whitley, J. Kelly, and R. Kelly, 2015: Political influences on greenhouse gas emissions from US states. *Proc. Natl. Acad. Sci.*, **112(27)**, 8254–8259, doi:10.1073/pnas.1417806112.

Dietzenbacher, E., B. Los, R. Stehrer, M. Timmer, and G. de Vries, 2013: The Construction of World Input–Output Tables in the WIOD Project. *Econ. Syst. Res.*, **25(1)**, 71–98, doi:10.1080/09535314.2012.761180.

Dietzenbacher, E., V. Kulionis, and F. Capurro, 2020: Measuring the effects of energy transition: A structural decomposition analysis of the change in renewable energy use between 2000 and 2014. *Appl. Energy*, **258**, 114040, doi:10.1016/j.apenergy.2019.114040.

Dong, K., X. Dong, and C. Dong, 2019a: Determinants of the global and regional CO_2 emissions: What causes what and where? *Appl. Econ.*, **51(46)**, 5031–5044, doi:10.1080/00036846.2019.1606410.

Dong, K., H. Jiang, R. Sun, and X. Dong, 2019b: Driving forces and mitigation potential of global CO_2 emissions from 1980 through 2030: Evidence from countries with different income levels. *Sci. Total Environ.*, **649**, 335–343, doi:10.1016/j.scitotenv.2018.08.326.

Dong, K., G. Hochman, and G.R. Timilsina, 2020: Do drivers of CO_2 emission growth alter overtime and by the stage of economic development? *Energy Policy*, **140**, 111420, doi:10.1016/j.enpol.2020.111420.

Driscoll, P.A., 2014: Breaking Carbon Lock-In: Path Dependencies in Large-Scale Transportation Infrastructure Projects. *Plan. Pract. Res.*, **29(3)**, 317–330, doi:10.1080/02697459.2014.929847.

Druckman, A. and T. Jackson, 2009: The carbon footprint of UK households 1990–2004: A socio-economically disaggregated, quasi-multi-regional input–output model. *Ecol. Econ.*, **68(7)**, 2066–2077, doi:10.1016/j.ecolecon.2009.01.013.

Druckman, A. and T. Jackson, 2016: Understanding Households as Drivers of Carbon Emissions. In: *Taking Stock of Industrial Ecology* [Clift, R. and A. Druckman, (eds.)], Springer International Publishing, Cham, Switzerland, pp. 181–203.

Drupp, M.A., J.N. Meya, S. Baumgärtner, and M.F. Quaas, 2018: Economic Inequality and the Value of Nature. *Ecol. Econ.*, **150**, 340–345, doi:10.1016/j.ecolecon.2018.03.029.

Duarte, R. et al., 2016: Modeling the carbon consequences of pro-environmental consumer behavior. *Appl. Energy*, **184**, 1207–1216, doi:10.1016/j.apenergy.2015.09.101.

Dyrstad, J.M., A. Skonhoft, M.Q. Christensen, and E.T. Ødegaard, 2019: Does economic growth eat up environmental improvements? Electricity production and fossil fuel emission in OECD countries 1980–2014. *Energy Policy*, **125**, 103–109, doi:10.1016/j.enpol.2018.10.051.

EC, 2019: *EU Transport in figures 2019*. Publications Office of the European Union, Luxembourg, 164 pp.

Economidou, M. et al., 2020: Review of 50 years of EU energy efficiency policies for buildings. *Energy Build.*, **225**, 110322, doi:10.1016/j.enbuild.2020.110322.

Edenhofer, O., J.C. Steckel, M. Jakob, and C. Bertram, 2018: Reports of coal's terminal decline may be exaggerated. *Environ. Res. Lett.*, **13(2)**, 024019, doi:10.1088/1748-9326/aaa3a2.

Edwards, M.R. and J.E. Trancik, 2014: Climate impacts of energy technologies depend on emissions timing. *Nat. Clim. Change*, **4(5)**, 347–352, doi:10.1038/nclimate2204.

Egenhofer, C., M. Alessi, A. Georgiev, and N. Fujiwara, 2011: *The EU Emissions Trading System and Climate Policy Towards 2050: Real incentives to reduce emissions and drive innovation? Special Report by CEPS*. Centre for European Policy Studies, Brussels, Belgium, 40 pp (Accessed May 2, 2021).

EIA, 2021: International Energy Statistics. https://www.eia.gov/beta/international/data/browser/ (Accessed July 8, 2019).

EII, 2015: *Territorial performance system.*, San Francisco, CA, USA. https://static1.squarespace.com/static/561fed9fe4b02e8febd96de0/t/564bafc0e4b06a249688ac05/1447800768039/EII_TPS_EN_2015.pdf (Accessed 10 May, 2021).

2

Eisenstein, W. et al., 2017: Climate co-benefits of green building standards: water, waste and transportation. *Build. Res. Inf.*, **45(8)**, 828–844, doi:10.1080/09613218.2016.1204519.

Ellerman, A.D., F.J. Conery, and C. de Perthuis, 2010: *Pricing Carbon: The European Union Emissions Trading Scheme*. Cambridge University Press, Cambridge, UK, 390 pp.

Ellsworth-Krebs, K., 2020: Implications of declining household sizes and expectations of home comfort for domestic energy demand. *Nat. Energy*, **5(1)**, 20–25, doi:10.1038/s41560-019-0512-1.

Elmqvist, T. et al., 2021: Urbanization in and for the Anthropocene. *npj Urban Sustain.*, **1(1)**, 6, doi:10.1038/s42949-021-00018-w.

Engel, A. et al., 2018: Chapter 1: Update on Ozone Depleting Substances (ODSs) and Other Gases of Interest to the Montreal Protocol. In: *Scientific Assessment of Ozone Depletion: 2018*, World Meterological Organization, Geneva, Switzerland, 91 pp.

Ehrhardt-Martinez, K., 2015: Consumption and climate change. In: *Climate change and society: Sociological perspectives* [Dunlap, R. and R. Brulle (eds.)], Oxford University Press, Oxford, UK, doi:10.1093/acprof:oso/9780199356102.001.0001.

Erickson, P. and M. Lazarus, 2013: *Accounting for Greenhouse Gas Emissions Associated with the Supply of Fossil Fuels*. Stockholm Environment Institute, Stockholm, Sweden, 1 pp.

Erickson, P. and K. Tempest, 2015: *Keeping cities green: Avoiding carbon lock-in due to urban development*. Stockholm Environment Institute, Seattle, USA, 28 pp.

Erickson, P., S. Kartha, M. Lazarus, and K. Tempest, 2015: Assessing carbon lock-in. *Environ. Res. Lett.*, **10(8)**, 084023, doi:10.1088/1748-9326/10/8/084023.

Eskander, S.M.S.U. and S. Fankhauser, 2020: Reduction in greenhouse gas emissions from national climate legislation. *Nat. Clim. Change*, **10(8)**, 750–756, doi:10.1038/s41558-020-0831-z.

Estiri, H. and E. Zagheni, 2019: Age matters: Ageing and household energy demand in the United States. *Energy Res. Soc. Sci.*, **55**, 62–70, doi:10.1016/j.erss.2019.05.006.

Fan, J.-L., Q. Wang, S. Yu, Y.-B. Hou, and Y.-M. Wei, 2017: The evolution of CO_2 emissions in international trade for major economies: a perspective from the global supply chain. *Mitig. Adapt. Strateg. Glob. Change*, **22(8)**, 1229–1248, doi:10.1007/s11027-016-9724-x.

Fan, Z., Y. Lei, and S. Wu, 2019: Research on the changing trend of the carbon footprint of residents' consumption in Beijing. *Environ. Sci. Pollut. Res.*, **26(4)**, 4078–4090, doi:10.1007/s11356-018-3931-9.

Fang, D. et al., 2019: Clean air for some: Unintended spillover effects of regional air pollution policies. *Sci. Adv.*, **5(4)**, doi:10.1126/sciadv.aav4707.

FAO, 1998: *Terms and Definitions. Forest Resources Assessment Programme Working Paper 1.*, FRA 2000, FAO, Rome.

FAO, 2009: *Climate Change and Agriculture Policies: How to mainstream climate change adaptation and mitigation into agriculture policies*. FAO, Rome, 76 pp.

FAOSTAT, 2021: Emissions Totals. http://www.fao.org/faostat/en/#data/GT/visualize (Accessed September 30, 2021).

Farfan, J. and C. Breyer, 2017: Structural changes of global power generation capacity towards sustainability and the risk of stranded investments supported by a sustainability indicator. *J. Clean. Prod.*, **141**, 370–384, doi:10.1016/j.jclepro.2016.09.068.

Farmer, J.D. et al., 2019: Sensitive intervention points in the post-carbon transition. *Science*, **364(6436)**, 132–134, doi:10.1126/science.aaw7287.

Fell, H. and P. Maniloff, 2018: Leakage in regional environmental policy: The case of the regional greenhouse gas initiative. *J. Environ. Econ. Manage.*, **87**, 1–23, doi:10.1016/j.jeem.2017.10.007.

Feng, K., 2019: Drivers of peak and decline. *Nat. Clim. Change*, **9(3)**, 188–189, doi:10.1038/s41558-019-0421-0.

Feng, K. et al., 2013: Outsourcing CO_2 within China. *Proc. Natl. Acad. Sci.*, **110(28)**, 11654–11659, doi:10.1073/pnas.1219918110.

Feng, K., K. Hubacek, and K. Song, 2021: Household carbon inequality in the U.S. *J. Clean. Prod.*, **278**, 123994, doi:10.1016/j.jclepro.2020.123994.

Fernández-Amador, O., J.F. Francois, and P. Tomberger, 2016: Carbon dioxide emissions and international trade at the turn of the millennium. *Ecol. Econ.*, **125**, 14–26, doi:10.1016/j.ecolecon.2016.01.005.

Figueres, C. et al., 2018: Emissions are still rising: ramp up the cuts. *Nature*, **564(7734)**, 27–30, doi:10.1038/d41586-018-07585-6.

Figueroa, M., O. Lah, L.M. Fulton, A. McKinnon, and G. Tiwari, 2014: Energy for Transport. *Annu. Rev. Environ. Resour.*, **39(1)**, 295–325, doi:10.1146/annurev-environ-031913-100450.

Finger, R., S.M. Swinton, N. El Benni, and A. Walter, 2019: Precision Farming at the Nexus of Agricultural Production and the Environment. *Annu. Rev. Resour. Econ.*, **11(1)**, 313–335, doi:10.1146/annurev-resource-100518-093929.

Fisch-Romito, V., 2021: Embodied carbon dioxide emissions to provide high access levels to basic infrastructure around the world. *Glob. Environ. Change*, **70**, 102362, doi:10.1016/j.gloenvcha.2021.102362.

Fisch-Romito, V., C. Guivarch, F. Creutzig, J.C. Minx, and M.W. Callaghan, 2021: Systematic map of the literature on carbon lock-in induced by long-lived capital. *Environ. Res. Lett.*, **16(5)**, 053004, doi:10.1088/1748-9326/aba660.

Fitzgerald, J.B., A.K. Jorgenson, and B. Clark, 2015: Energy consumption and working hours: a longitudinal study of developed and developing nations, 1990–2008. *Environ. Sociol.*, **1(3)**, 213–223, doi:10.1080/23251042.2015.1046584.

Fitzgerald, J.B., J.B. Schor, and A.K. Jorgenson, 2018: Working Hours and Carbon Dioxide Emissions in the United States, 2007–2013. *Soc. Forces*, **96(4)**, 1851–1874, doi:10.1093/sf/soy014.

Fofrich, R. et al., 2020: Early retirement of power plants in climate mitigation scenarios. *Environ. Res. Lett.*, **15(9)**, 094064, doi:10.1088/1748-9326/ab96d3.

Forster, P.M. et al., 2020: Current and future global climate impacts resulting from COVID-19. *Nat. Clim. Change*, **10(10)**, 913–919, doi:10.1038/s41558-020-0883-0.

Forster, P., T. Storelvmo, K. Armour, W. Collins, J.L. Dufresne, D. Frame, D.J. Lunt, T. Mauritsen, M.D. Palmer, M. Watanabe, M. Wild, H. Zhang, 2021, The Earth's Energy Budget, Climate Feedbacks, and Climate Sensitivity. In: *Climate Change 2021: The Physical Science Basis. Contribution of Working Group I to the Sixth Assessment Report of the Intergovernmental Panel on Climate Change* [Masson-Delmotte, V., P. Zhai, A. Pirani, S.L. Connors, C. Péan, S. Berger, N. Caud, Y. Chen, L. Goldfarb, M.I. Gomis, M. Huang, K. Leitzell, E. Lonnoy, J.B.R. Matthews, T.K. Maycock, T. Waterfield, O. Yelekçi, R. Yu and B. Zhou (eds.)]. Cambridge University Press, Cambridge, UK (in press).

Fridstrøm, L., 2021: The Norwegian Vehicle Electrification Policy and Its Implicit Price of Carbon. *Sustainability*, **13(3)**, 1346, doi:10.3390/su13031346.

Friedlingstein, P. et al., 2019: Global Carbon Budget 2019. *Earth Syst. Sci. Data*, **11(4)**, 1783–1838, doi:10.5194/essd-11-1783-2019.

Friedlingstein, P. et al., 2020: Global Carbon Budget 2020. *Earth Syst. Sci. Data*, **12(4)**, 3269–3340, doi:10.5194/essd-12-3269-2020.

Friedman, S. and Savage, M., 2017. The shifting politics of inequality and the class ceiling. *Renewal: A Journal of Labour Politics*, 25(2), 31 pp.

Fu, R., G. Jin, J. Chen, and Y. Ye, 2021: The effects of poverty alleviation investment on carbon emissions in China based on the multiregional input–output model. *Technol. Forecast. Soc. Change*, **162**, 120344, doi:10.1016/j.techfore.2020.120344.

Fuglestvedt, J. et al., 2018: Implications of possible interpretations of 'greenhouse gas balance' in the Paris Agreement. *Philos. Trans. R. Soc. A Math. Phys. Eng. Sci.*, **376(2119)**, 20160445, doi:10.1098/rsta.2016.0445.

Fujii, H., K. Iwata, A. Chapman, S. Kagawa, and S. Managi, 2018: An analysis of urban environmental Kuznets curve of CO_2 emissions: Empirical analysis of 276 global metropolitan areas. *Appl. Energy*, **228**, 1561–1568, doi:10.1016/j.apenergy.2018.06.158.

Gao, J., B. Peng, and R. Smyth, 2021: On income and price elasticities for energy demand: A panel data study. *Energy Econ.*, **96**, 105168, doi:10.1016/j.eneco.2021.105168.

2

Gasser, T. et al., 2020: Historical CO_2 emissions from land use and land cover change and their uncertainty. *Biogeosciences*, **17(15)**, 4075–4101, doi:10.5194/bg-17-4075-2020.

Geels, F.W., 2018: Disruption and low-carbon system transformation: Progress and new challenges in socio-technical transitions research and the Multi-Level Perspective. *Energy Res. Soc. Sci.*, **37**, 224–231, doi:10.1016/j.erss.2017.10.010.

Gilfillan, D., G. Marland, T. Boden, and R. Andres, 2020: Global, Regional, and National Fossil-Fuel CO_2 Emissions: 1751–2017. Zenodo, doi:10.5281/ZENODO.4281271.

Gillingham, K., D. Rapson, and G. Wagner, 2016: The Rebound Effect and Energy Efficiency Policy. *Rev. Environ. Econ. Policy*, **10(1)**, 68–88, doi:10.1093/reep/rev017.

Goldemberg, J., 2020: The evolution of the energy and carbon intensities of developing countries. *Energy Policy*, **137**, 111060, doi:10.1016/j.enpol.2019.111060.

González-Mahecha, E., O. Lecuyer, M. Hallack, M. Bazilian, and A. Vogt-Schilb, 2019: Committed emissions and the risk of stranded assets from power plants in Latin America and the Caribbean. *Environ. Res. Lett.*, **14(12)**, 124096, doi:10.1088/1748-9326/ab5476.

González-Torres, M., L. Pérez-Lombard, J.F. Coronel, and I.R. Maestre, 2021: Revisiting Kaya Identity to define an Emissions Indicators Pyramid. *J. Clean. Prod.*, **317**, 128328, doi:10.1016/j.jclepro.2021.128328.

Gosens, J., 2020: The greening of South-South trade: Levels, growth, and specialization of trade in clean energy technologies between countries in the global South. *Renew. Energy*, **160**, 931–943, doi:10.1016/j.renene.2020.06.014.

Gössling, S., 2019: Celebrities, air travel, and social norms. *Ann. Tour. Res.*, **79**, 102775, doi:10.1016/j.annals.2019.102775.

Gota, S., C. Huizenga, K. Peet, N. Medimorec, and S. Bakker, 2019: Decarbonising transport to achieve Paris Agreement targets. *Energy Effic.*, **12(2)**, 363–386, doi:10.1007/s12053-018-9671-3.

Gough, I., 2017: Decarbonising consumption: needs, necessities and eco-social policies. In: *Heat, greed and human need: climate change, capitalism and sustainable wellbeing*, Edward Elgar Publishing Ltd, Cheltenham, UK, pp. 146–170.

Gough, I., S. Abdallah, V. Johnson, J. Ryan, and C. Smith, 2011: *The distribution of total greenhouse gas emissions by households in the UK, and some implications for social policy*. Centre for Analysis of Social Exclusion, London, UK, 57 pp.

Grassi, G. et al., 2018: Reconciling global-model estimates and country reporting of anthropogenic forest CO_2 sinks. *Nat. Clim. Change*, **8(10)**, 914–920, doi:10.1038/s41558-018-0283-x.

Grassi, G. et al., 2021: Critical adjustment of land mitigation pathways for assessing countries' climate progress. *Nat. Clim. Change*, **11(5)**, 425–434, doi:10.1038/s41558-021-01033-6.

Greenblatt, J.B. and S. Shaheen, 2015: Automated Vehicles, On-Demand Mobility, and Environmental Impacts. *Curr. Sustain. Energy Reports*, **2(3)**, 74–81, doi:10.1007/s40518-015-0038-5.

Grimm, N.B. et al., 2008: Global Change and the Ecology of Cities. *Science*, **319(5864)**, 756–760, doi:10.1126/science.1150195.

Griskevicius, V., J.M. Tybur, and B. Van den Bergh, 2010: Going green to be seen: Status, reputation, and conspicuous conservation. *J. Pers. Soc. Psychol.*, **98(3)**, 392–404, doi:10.1037/a0017346.

Griswold, J.B., T. Sztainer, J. Lee, S. Madanat, and A. Horvath, 2017: Optimizing Urban Bus Transit Network Design Can Lead to Greenhouse Gas Emissions Reduction. *Front. Built Environ.*, **3**(February), 1–7, doi:10.3389/fbuil.2017.00005.

Grubb, M., 2016: Full legal compliance with the Kyoto Protocol's first commitment period – some lessons. *Clim. Policy*, **16(6)**, 673–681, doi:10.1080/14693062.2016.1194005.

Grubb, M. and D. Newbery, 2018: UK Electricity Market Reform and the Energy Transition: Emerging Lessons. *Energy J.*, **39(01)**, 1–25, doi:10.5547/01956574.39.6.mgru.

Grubb, M. et al., 2021: Induced innovation in energy technologies and systems: a review of evidence and potential implications for CO_2 mitigation. *Environ. Res. Lett.*, **16(4)**, 043007, doi:10.1088/1748-9326/abde07.

Grubert, E., 2020: Fossil electricity retirement deadlines for a just transition. *Science*, **370(6521)**, 1171–1173, doi:10.1126/science.abe0375.

Grübler, A., 1998: *Technology and Global Change*. Cambridge University Press, Cambridge, UK, 452 pp.

Grubler, A., 2012: Energy transitions research: Insights and cautionary tales. *Energy Policy*, **50**, 8–16, doi:10.1016/j.enpol.2012.02.070.

Grubler, A., C. Wilson, and G. Nemet, 2016: Apples, oranges, and consistent comparisons of the temporal dynamics of energy transitions. *Energy Res. Soc. Sci.*, **22**, 18–25, doi:10.1016/j.erss.2016.08.015.

Grubler, A. et al., 2018: A low energy demand scenario for meeting the 1.5°C target and sustainable development goals without negative emission technologies. *Nat. Energy*, **3(6)**, 515–527, doi:10.1038/s41560-018-0172-6.

Grunewald, N., S. Klasen, I. Martínez-Zarzoso, and C. Muris, 2017: The Trade-off Between Income Inequality and Carbon Dioxide Emissions. *Ecol. Econ.*, **142**, 249–256, doi:10.1016/j.ecolecon.2017.06.034.

Gucwa, M. and A. Schäfer, 2013: The impact of scale on energy intensity in freight transportation. *Transp. Res. Part D Transp. Environ.*, **23**, 41–49, doi:10.1016/j.trd.2013.03.008.

Guerra Santin, O., L. Itard, and H. Visscher, 2009: The effect of occupancy and building characteristics on energy use for space and water heating in Dutch residential stock. *Energy Build.*, **41(11)**, 1223–1232, doi:10.1016/j.enbuild.2009.07.002.

Guivarch, C. and S. Hallegatte, 2011: Existing infrastructure and the 2°C target. *Clim. Change*, **109(3–4)**, 801–805, doi:10.1007/s10584-011-0268-5.

Gutowski, T.G., J.M. Allwood, C. Herrmann, and S. Sahni, 2013: A Global Assessment of Manufacturing: Economic Development, Energy Use, Carbon Emissions, and the Potential for Energy Efficiency and Materials Recycling. *Annu. Rev. Environ. Resour.*, **38(1)**, 81–106, doi:10.1146/annurev-environ-041112-110510.

Gütschow, J. et al., 2016: The PRIMAP-hist national historical emissions time series. *Earth Syst. Sci. Data*, **8(2)**, 571–603, doi:10.5194/essd-8-571-2016.

Gütschow, J., A. Günther, and M. Pflüger, 2021a: The PRIMAP-hist national historical emissions time series (1750–2019) v2.3. *Earth Syst. Sci. Data*, **8**, 571-603, doi:10.5194/essd-8-571-2016.

Gütschow, J., M.L. Jeffery, and A. Günther, 2021b: PRIMAP-crf: UNFCCC CRF data in IPCC categories (PRIMAP-crf-2021-v1). **10**, 1427–1438, doi:10.5281/ZENODO.4723476.

Haberl, H. et al., 2020: A systematic review of the evidence on decoupling of GDP, resource use and GHG emissions, part II: synthesizing the insights. *Environ. Res. Lett.*, **15(6)**, 065003, doi:10.1088/1748-9326/ab842a.

Habermacher, F. and P. Lehmann, 2020: Commitment Versus Discretion in Climate and Energy Policy. *Environ. Resour. Econ.*, **76(1)**, 39–67, doi:10.1007/s10640-020-00414-3.

Habimana Simbi, C. et al., 2021: Decomposition and decoupling analysis of carbon dioxide emissions in African countries during 1984–2014. *J. Environ. Sci.*, **102**, 85–98, doi:10.1016/j.jes.2020.09.006.

Hailemariam, A., R. Dzhumashev, and M. Shahbaz, 2020: Carbon emissions, income inequality and economic development. *Empir. Econ.*, **59(3)**, 1139–1159, doi:10.1007/s00181-019-01664-x.

Haines, A. et al., 2017: Short-lived climate pollutant mitigation and the Sustainable Development Goals. *Nat. Clim. Change*, **7(12)**, 863–869, doi:10.1038/s41558-017-0012-x.

Haites, E. et al., 2018: Experience with Carbon Taxes and Greenhouse Gas Emissions Trading Systems. *SSRN Electron. J.*, **XXIX**, 109, doi:10.2139/ssrn.3119241.

Hájek, M., J. Zimmermannová, K. Helman, and L. Rozenský, 2019: Analysis of carbon tax efficiency in energy industries of selected EU countries. *Energy Policy*, **134**(June 2018), 110955, doi:10.1016/j.enpol.2019.110955.

Hale, T., 2020: Catalytic Cooperation. *Glob. Environ. Polit.*, **20(4)**, 73–98, doi:10.1162/glep_a_00561.

Hamilton, J., 2011: Keeping Up with the Joneses in the Great British Refurb: The Impacts and Limits of Social Learning in Eco-renovation. In: *Engaging the Public with Climate Change: Behaviour Change and Communication* [Whitmarsh, L., I. Lorenzoni, and S. O'Neill, (eds.)], Routledge, London, UK, pp. 20.

Han, L., X. Xu, and L. Han, 2015: Applying quantile regression and Shapley decomposition to analyzing the determinants of household embedded carbon emissions: evidence from urban China. *J. Clean. Prod.*, **103**, 219–230, doi:10.1016/j.jclepro.2014.08.078.

Hansen, A. and K.B. Nielsen, (eds.) 2017: *Cars, automobility and development in Asia: wheels of change*. Taylor & Francis, London UK and New York, USA, 202 pp.

Hansis, E., S.J. Davis, and J. Pongratz, 2015: Relevance of methodological choices for accounting of land use change carbon fluxes. *Global Biogeochem. Cycles*, **29(8)**, 1230–1246, doi:10.1002/2014GB004997.

Hao, Y., H. Chen, and Q. Zhang, 2016: Will income inequality affect environmental quality? Analysis based on China's provincial panel data. *Ecol. Indic.*, **67**, 533–542, doi:10.1016/j.ecolind.2016.03.025.

Harmsen, M. et al., 2020: The role of methane in future climate strategies: mitigation potentials and climate impacts. *Clim. Change*, **163(3)**, 1409–1425, doi:10.1007/s10584-019-02437-2.

Harmsen, M.J.H.M. et al., 2016: How climate metrics affect global mitigation strategies and costs: a multi-model study. *Clim. Change*, **136(2)**, 203–216, doi:10.1007/s10584-016-1603-7.

Hashmi, R. and K. Alam, 2019: Dynamic relationship among environmental regulation, innovation, CO_2 emissions, population, and economic growth in OECD countries: A panel investigation. *J. Clean. Prod.*, **231**, 1100–1109, doi:10.1016/j.jclepro.2019.05.325.

Hausfather, Z. and G.P. Peters, 2020: Emissions – the 'business as usual' story is misleading. *Nature*, **577(7792)**, 618–620, doi:10.1038/d41586-020-00177-3.

Heede, R. and N. Oreskes, 2016: Potential emissions of CO_2 and methane from proved reserves of fossil fuels: An alternative analysis. *Glob. Environ. Change*, **36**, 12–20, doi:10.1016/j.gloenvcha.2015.10.005.

Heller, M.C. and G.A. Keoleian, 2015: Greenhouse Gas Emission Estimates of U.S. Dietary Choices and Food Loss. *J. Ind. Ecol.*, **19(3)**, 391–401, doi:10.1111/jiec.12174.

Helm, D., C. Hepburn, and R. Mash, 2003: Credible carbon policy. *Oxford Rev. Econ. Policy*, **19(3)**, 438–450, doi:10.1093/oxrep/19.3.438.

Hernandez, A.G., S. Cooper-Searle, A.C.H. Skelton, and J. M. Cullen, 2018: Leveraging material efficiency as an energy and climate instrument for heavy industries in the EU. *Energy Policy*, **120**, 533–549, doi:10.1016/j.enpol.2018.05.055.

Hertwich, E.G. et al., 2019: Material efficiency strategies to reducing greenhouse gas emissions associated with buildings, vehicles, and electronics – a review. *Environ. Res. Lett.*, **14(4)**, 043004, doi:10.1088/1748-9326/ab0fe3.

Hickel, J. and G. Kallis, 2020: Is Green Growth Possible? *New Polit. Econ.*, **25(4)**, 469–486, doi:10.1080/13563467.2019.1598964.

Hoekstra, R., B. Michel, and S. Suh, 2016: The emission cost of international sourcing: using structural decomposition analysis to calculate the contribution of international sourcing to CO_2 emission growth. *Econ. Syst. Res.*, **28(2)**, 151–167, doi:10.1080/09535314.2016.1166099.

Hoesly, R.M. and S.J. Smith, 2018: Informing energy consumption uncertainty: an analysis of energy data revisions. *Environ. Res. Lett.*, **13(12)**, 124023, doi:10.1088/1748-9326/aaebc3.

Hoesly, R.M. et al., 2018: Historical **(1750–2014)** anthropogenic emissions of reactive gases and aerosols from the Community Emissions Data System (CEDS). *Geosci. Model Dev.*, **11(1)**, 369–408, doi:10.5194/gmd-11-369-2018.

Hofmann, J., D. Guan, K. Chalvatzis, and H. Huo, 2016: Assessment of electrical vehicles as a successful driver for reducing CO_2 emissions in China. *Appl. Energy*, **184**, 995–1003, doi:10.1016/j.apenergy.2016.06.042.

Höglund-Isaksson, L., A. Gómez-Sanabria, Z. Klimont, P. Rafaj, and W. Schöpp, 2020: Technical potentials and costs for reducing global anthropogenic methane emissions in the 2050 timeframe –results from the GAINS model. *Environ. Res. Commun.*, **2(2)**, 025004, doi:10.1088/2515-7620/ab7457.

Höhne, N. et al., 2020: Emissions: world has four times the work or one-third of the time. *Nature*, **579(7797)**, 25–28, doi:10.1038/d41586-020-00571-x.

Holland, S.P., J.E. Hughes, C.R. Knittel, and N.C. Parker, 2015: Unintended Consequences of Carbon Policies: Transportation Fuels, Land-Use, Emissions, and Innovation. *Energy J.*, **36(3)**, 35–74, doi:10.5547/01956574.36.3.shol.

Hong, C. et al., 2021: Global and regional drivers of land-use emissions in 1961–2017. *Nature*, **589(7843)**, 554–561, doi:10.1038/s41586-020-03138-y.

Horne, C. and E.H. Kennedy, 2017: The power of social norms for reducing and shifting electricity use. *Energy Policy*, **107**, 43–52, doi:10.1016/j.enpol.2017.04.029.

Horowitz, D., 1988: *The Morality of Spending*. Johns Hopkins University Press, Baltimore, Maryland, USA.

Houghton, R.A. and A.A. Nassikas, 2017: Global and regional fluxes of carbon from land use and land cover change 1850–2015. *Global Biogeochem. Cycles*, **31(3)**, 456–472, doi:10.1002/2016GB005546.

Huang, K., X. Li, X. Liu, and K.C. Seto, 2019: Projecting global urban land expansion and heat island intensification through 2050. *Environ. Res. Lett.*, **14(11)**, 114037, doi:10.1088/1748-9326/ab4b71.

Huang, M. and B. Wang, 2016: Factors influencing CO_2 emissions in China based on grey relational analysis. *Energy Sources, Part A Recover. Util. Environ. Eff.*, **38(4)**, 555–561, doi:10.1080/15567036.2013.802073.

Huang, R. and L. Tian, 2021: CO_2 emissions inequality through the lens of developing countries. *Appl. Energy*, **281**, 116043, doi:10.1016/j.apenergy.2020.116043.

Huang, Z. and H. Duan, 2020: Estimating the threshold interactions between income inequality and carbon emissions. *J. Environ. Manage.*, **263**, 110393, doi:10.1016/j.jenvman.2020.110393.

Hubacek, K., K. Feng, J.C. Minx, S. Pfister, and N. Zhou, 2014: Teleconnecting Consumption to Environmental Impacts at Multiple Spatial Scales. *J. Ind. Ecol.*, **18(1)**, 7–9, doi:10.1111/jiec.12082.

Hubacek, K., K. Feng, B. Chen, and S. Kagawa, 2016: Linking Local Consumption to Global Impacts. *J. Ind. Ecol.*, **20(3)**, 382–386, doi:10.1111/jiec.12463.

Hubacek, K., G. Baiocchi, K. Feng, and A. Patwardhan, 2017a: Poverty eradication in a carbon constrained world. *Nat. Commun.*, **8(1)**, 912, doi:10.1038/s41467-017-00919-4.

Hubacek, K. et al., 2017b: Global carbon inequality. *Energy, Ecol. Environ.*, **2(6)**, 361–369, doi:10.1007/s40974-017-0072-9.

Hubacek, K., X. Chen, K. Feng, T. Wiedmann, and Y. Shan, 2021: Evidence of decoupling consumption-based CO_2 emissions from economic growth. *Adv. Appl. Energy*, **4**, 100074, doi:10.1016/j.adapen.2021.100074.

Huebner, G.M. and D. Shipworth, 2017: All about size? – The potential of downsizing in reducing energy demand. *Appl. Energy*, **186**, 226–233, doi:10.1016/j.apenergy.2016.02.066.

Huntingford, C. et al., 2015: The implications of carbon dioxide and methane exchange for the heavy mitigation RCP2.6 scenario under two metrics. *Environ. Sci. Policy*, **51**, 77–87, doi:10.1016/j.envsci.2015.03.013.

Huseynov, S. and M.A. Palma, 2018: Does California's Low Carbon Fuel Standards reduce carbon dioxide emissions? *PLoS One*, **13(9)**, e0203167, doi:10.1371/journal.pone.0203167.

ICF International, 2016: *Decomposition analysis of the changes in GHG emissions in the EU and Member States*. Publication Office of the European Union, Luxembourg, 112 pp.

IEA, 2019: *Fuel Economy in Major Car Markets: Technology and Policy Drivers 2005–2017*. International Energy Agency, Paris, France, pp. 87–88.

IEA, 2020a: *World energy outlook 2020 – event*. International Energy Agency, Paris, France, 464 pp.

IEA, 2020b: *World Energy Balances*. International Energy Agency, Paris, France, 59 pp.

IEA, 2021a: *CO₂ emissions from fossil fuel combustion 2018*. International Energy Agency, Paris, France.

IEA, 2021b: *Global Energy Review 2021*. International Energy Agency, Paris, France, pp. 1–36.

IEA, 2021c: *World Energy Balances*. International Energy Agency, Paris, France.

IPCC 2006: *2006 IPCC Guidelines for National Greenhouse Gas Inventories*, Prepared by the National Greenhouse Gas Inventories Programme, Eggleston H.S., Buendia L., Miwa K., Ngara T. and Tanabe K. (eds). Published: IGES, Japan.

IPCC, 2018: Summary for Policymakers. In: *Global Warming of 1.5°C. An IPCC Special Report on the impacts of global warming of 1.5°C above pre-industrial levels and related global greenhouse gas emission pathways, in the context of strengthening the global response to the threat of climate change, sustainable development, and efforts to eradicate poverty* [Masson-Delmotte, V., P. Zhai, H.-O. Pörtner, D. Roberts, J. Skea, P.R. Shukla, A. Pirani, W. Moufouma-Okia, C. Péan, R. Pidcock, S. Connors, J.B.R. Matthews, Y. Chen, X. Zhou, M.I. Gomis, E. Lonnoy, T. Maycock, M. Tignor, and T. Waterfield (eds.)]. Cambridge University Press, Cambridge, UK and New York, NY, USA.

IPCC, 2021a: Climate Change 2021a: *The Physical Science Basis. Contribution of Working Group I to the Sixth Assessment Report of the Intergovernmental Panel on Climate Change* [Masson-Delmotte, V., P. Zhai, A. Pirani, S.L. Connors, C. Péan, S. Berger, N. Caud, Y. Chen, L. Goldfarb, M.I. Gomis, M. Huang, K. Leitzell, E. Lonnoy, J.B.R. Matthews, T.K. Maycock, T. Waterfield, O. Yelekçi, R. Yu, and B. Zhou (eds.)]. Cambridge University Press, Cambridge, UK and New York, NY, USA.

IPCC, 2021b: Summary for Policymakers. In: *Climate Change 2021: The Physical Science Basis. Contribution of Working Group I to the Sixth Assessment Report of the Intergovernmental Panel on Climate Change* [MassonDelmotte, V., P. Zhai, A. Pirani, S.L. Connors, C. Péan, S. Berger, N. Caud, Y. Chen, L. Goldfarb, M.I. Gomis, M. Huang, K. Leitzell, E. Lonnoy, J.B.R. Matthews, T.K. Maycock, T. Waterfield, O. Yelekçi, R. Yu, and B. Zhou (eds.)]. Cambridge University Press, Cambridge, UK and New York, NY, USA.

IRENA, 2020: *Renewable Capacity Statistics 2020*. IRENA, Abu Dhabi, United Arab Emirates, 66 pp.

IRENA, IEA, and REN21, 2018: *Renewable Energy Policies in a Time of Transition*. IRENA, REN21, IEA, 112 pp.

Irfany, M.I. and S. Klasen, 2017: Affluence and emission tradeoffs: evidence from Indonesian households' carbon footprint. *Environ. Dev. Econ.*, **22(5)**, 546–570, doi:10.1017/S1355770X17000262.

Isaksen, E.T., 2020: Have international pollution protocols made a difference? *J. Environ. Econ. Manage.*, **103**, 102358, doi:10.1016/j.jeem.2020.102358.

ITF, 2019: *ITF Transport Outlook 2019*. OECD Publishing, Paris, France, 200 pp.

Ivanova, D. et al., 2017: Mapping the carbon footprint of EU regions. *Environ. Res. Lett.*, **12(5)**, 054013, doi:10.1088/1748-9326/aa6da9.

Ivanova, D. et al., 2018: Carbon mitigation in domains of high consumer lock-in. *Glob. Environ. Change*, **52**, 117–130, doi:10.1016/j.gloenvcha.2018.06.006.

Iyer, G.C. et al., 2015: The contribution of Paris to limit global warming to 2°C. *Environ. Res. Lett.*, **10(12)**, 125002, doi:10.1088/1748-9326/10/12/125002.

Jackson, R.B. et al., 2016: Reaching peak emissions. *Nat. Clim. Change*, **6(1)**, 7–10, doi:10.1038/nclimate2892.

Jackson, R.B. et al., 2019: Persistent fossil fuel growth threatens the Paris Agreement and planetary health. *Environ. Res. Lett.*, **14(12)**, 121001, doi:10.1088/1748-9326/ab57b3.

Jakob, M., 2021: Climate policy and international trade – A critical appraisal of the literature. *Energy Policy*, **156**, 112399, doi:10.1016/j.enpol.2021.112399 Jakob, M. and J. Hilaire, 2015: Unburnable fossil-fuel reserves. *Nature*, **517(7533)**, 150–151, doi:10.1038/517150a.

Jakob, M., H. Ward, and J.C. Steckel, 2021: Sharing responsibility for trade-related emissions based on economic benefits. *Glob. Environ. Change*, **66**, 102207, doi:10.1016/j.gloenvcha.2020.102207.

Janssens-Maenhout, G. et al., 2019: EDGAR v4.3.2 Global Atlas of the three major greenhouse gas emissions for the period 1970–2012. *Earth Syst. Sci. Data*, **11(3)**, 959–1002, doi:10.5194/essd-11-959-2019.

Javid, R.J., M. Salari, and R. Jahanbakhsh Javid, 2019: Environmental and economic impacts of expanding electric vehicle public charging infrastructure in California's counties. *Transp. Res. Part D Transp. Environ.*, **77**(November), 320–334, doi:10.1016/j.trd.2019.10.017.

Jewell, J. et al., 2013: Energy Security of China, India, the E.U. and the U.S. Under Long-Term Scenarios: Results FROM Six IAMs. *Clim. Change Econ.*, **04(04)**, 1340011, doi:10.1142/S2010007813400113.

Jewell, J., V. Vinichenko, L. Nacke, and A. Cherp, 2019: Prospects for powering past coal. *Nat. Clim. Change*, **9(8)**, 592–597, doi:10.1038/s41558-019-0509-6.

Jiang, M. H. An X. Gao N. Jia S. Liu and H. Zheng, 2021: Structural decomposition analysis of global carbon emissions: The contributions of domestic and international input changes. *J. Environ. Manage.*, **294**, 112942, doi: 10.1016/j.jenvman.2021.112942.

Jiang, X. and C. Green, 2017: The Impact on Global Greenhouse Gas Emissions of Geographic Shifts in Global Supply Chains. *Ecol. Econ.*, **139**, 102–114, doi:10.1016/j.ecolecon.2017.04.027.

Jiang, X. and D. Guan, 2017: The global CO₂ emissions growth after international crisis and the role of international trade. *Energy Policy*, **109**, 734–746, doi:10.1016/j.enpol.2017.07.058.

Jiang, K., C. He, H. Dai, J. Liu, and X. Xu, 2018: Emission scenario analysis for China under the global 1.5°C target. *Carbon Manag.*, **9(5)**, 481–491, doi:10.1080/17583004.2018.1477835.

Jiang, X., D. Guan, and L.A. López, 2018: The global CO₂ emission cost of geographic shifts in international sourcing. *Energy Econ.*, **73**, 122–134, doi:10.1016/j.eneco.2018.05.015.

Jiborn, M., V. Kulionis, and A. Kander, 2020: Consumption versus Technology: Drivers of Global Carbon Emissions 2000–2014. *Energies*, **13(2)**, 339, doi:10.3390/en13020339.

Joassart-Marcelli, P., J. Wolch, and Z. Salim, 2011: Building the Healthy City: The Role of Nonprofits in Creating Active Urban Parks. *Urban Geogr.*, **32(5)**, 682–711, doi:10.2747/0272-3638.32.5.682.

Johansson, D.J.A., 2012: Economics- and physical-based metrics for comparing greenhouse gases. *Clim. Change*, **110(1–2)**, 123–141, doi:10.1007/s10584-011-0072-2.

Johnson, N. et al., 2015: Stranded on a low-carbon planet: Implications of climate policy for the phase-out of coal-based power plants. *Technol. Forecast. Soc. Change*, **90**(PA), 89–102, doi:10.1016/j.techfore.2014.02.028.

Jones, C. and D.M. Kammen, 2014: Spatial Distribution of U.S. Household Carbon Footprints Reveals Suburbanization Undermines Greenhouse Gas Benefits of Urban Population Density. *Environ. Sci. Technol.*, **48(2)**, 895–902, doi:10.1021/es4034364.

Jones, C.M. and D.M. Kammen, 2011: Quantifying Carbon Footprint Reduction Opportunities for U.S. Households and Communities. *Environ. Sci. Technol.*, **45(9)**, 4088–4095, doi:10.1021/es102221h.

Jorgenson, A.K., D. Auerbach, and B. Clark, 2014: The (De-) carbonization of urbanization, 1960–2010. *Clim. Change*, **127(3–4)**, 561–575, doi:10.1007/s10584-014-1267-0.

Jorgenson, A.K., J.B. Schor, K.W. Knight, and X. Huang, 2016: Domestic Inequality and Carbon Emissions in Comparative Perspective. *Sociol. Forum*, **31**(September), 770–786, doi:10.1111/socf.12272.

Jorgenson, A.K. et al., 2019: Social science perspectives on drivers of and responses to global climate change. *WIREs Clim. Change*, **10(1)**, 1–17, doi:10.1002/wcc.554.

Jung, J. and Y. Koo, 2018: Analyzing the Effects of Car Sharing Services on the Reduction of Greenhouse Gas (GHG) Emissions. *Sustainability*, **10(2)**, 539, doi:10.3390/su10020539.

Kahn, M.E., 2000: The environmental impact of suburbanization. *J. Policy Anal. Manag.*, **19(4)**, 569–586, doi:10.1002/1520-6688(200023)19:4<569::AID-PAM3>3.0.CO;2-P.

Kander, A., M. Jiborn, D.D. Moran, and T.O. Wiedmann, 2015: National greenhouse-gas accounting for effective climate policy on international trade. *Nat. Clim. Change*, **5(5)**, 431–435, doi:10.1038/nclimate2555.

Kanitkar, T., R. Banerjee, and T. Jayaraman, 2015: Impact of economic structure on mitigation targets for developing countries. *Energy Sustain. Dev.*, **26**, 56–61, doi:10.1016/j.esd.2015.03.003.

Karstensen, J., G.P. Peters, and R.M. Andrew, 2018: Trends of the EU's territorial and consumption-based emissions from 1990 to 2016. *Clim. Change*, **151(2)**, 131–142, doi:10.1007/s10584-018-2296-x.

Kastner, T., M.J.I. Rivas, W. Koch, and S. Nonhebel, 2012: Global changes in diets and the consequences for land requirements for food. *Proc. Natl. Acad. Sci.*, **109(18)**, 6868–6872, doi:10.1073/pnas.1117054109.

Kefford, B.M., B. Ballinger, D.R. Schmeda-Lopez, C. Greig, and S. Smart, 2018: The early retirement challenge for fossil fuel power plants in deep decarbonisation scenarios. *Energy Policy*, **119**, 294–306, doi:10.1016/j.enpol.2018.04.018.

Kerimray, A., L. Rojas-Solórzano, M. Amouei Torkmahalleh, P.K. Hopke, and B.P. Ó Gallachóir, 2017: Coal use for residential heating: Patterns, health implications and lessons learned. *Energy Sustain. Dev.*, **40**, 19–30, doi:10.1016/j.esd.2017.05.005.

Kerkhof, A.C., R.M.J. Benders, and H.C. Moll, 2009: Determinants of variation in household CO_2 emissions between and within countries. *Energy Policy*, **37(4)**, 1509–1517, doi:10.1016/j.enpol.2008.12.013.

Kern, F. and K.S. Rogge, 2016: The pace of governed energy transitions: Agency, international dynamics and the global Paris agreement accelerating decarbonisation processes? *Energy Res. Soc. Sci.*, **22**, 13–17, doi:10.1016/j.erss.2016.08.016.

Khajehpour, H., Y. Saboohi, and G. Tsatsaronis, 2019: Exergy-Based Responsibility Allocation of Climate Change. In: *University Initiatives in Climate Change Mitigation and Adaptation* [Leal Filho, W. and R. Leal-Arcas, (eds.)], Springer International Publishing, Cham, Switzerland, pp. 291–315.

Khanna, M. and N.D. Rao, 2009: Supply and Demand of Electricity in the Developing World. *Annu. Rev. Resour. Econ.*, **1(1)**, 567–596, doi:10.1146/annurev.resource.050708.144230.

Kikstra, J.S., A. Mastrucci, J. Min, K. Riahi, and N.D. Rao, 2021: Decent living gaps and energy needs around the world. *Environ. Res. Lett.*, **16(9)**, 095006, doi:10.1088/1748-9326/ac1c27.

King, M.F. and J. Gutberlet, 2013: Contribution of cooperative sector recycling to greenhouse gas emissions reduction: A case study of Ribeirão Pires, Brazil. *Waste Manag.*, **33(12)**, 2771–2780, doi:10.1016/j.wasman.2013.07.031.

Kirschke, S. et al., 2013: Three decades of global methane sources and sinks. *Nat. Geosci.*, **6(10)**, 813–823, doi:10.1038/ngeo1955.

Klemun, M.M., M.R. Edwards, and J.E. Trancik, 2020: Research priorities for supporting subnational climate policies. *WIREs Clim. Change*, **11**, 1–9, doi:10.1002/wcc.646.

Knapp, K.E., 1999: Exploring Energy Technology Substitution for Reducing Atmospheric Carbon Emissions. *Energy J.*, **20(2)**, 121–143, doi:10.5547/ISSN0195-6574-EJ-Vol20-No2-5.

Knight, K.W., J.B. Schor, and A.K. Jorgenson, 2017: Wealth Inequality and Carbon Emissions in High-income Countries. *Soc. Curr.*, **4(5)**, 403–412, doi:10.1177/2329496517704872.

Knobloch, F. et al., 2020: Net emission reductions from electric cars and heat pumps in 59 world regions over time. *Nat. Sustain.*, **3(6)**, 437–447, doi:10.1038/s41893-020-0488-7.

Koch, N., G. Grosjean, S. Fuss, and O. Edenhofer, 2016: Politics matters: Regulatory events as catalysts for price formation under cap-and-trade. *J. Environ. Econ. Manage.*, **78**, 121–139, doi:10.1016/j.jeem.2016.03.004.

Köhler, J. et al., 2019: An agenda for sustainability transitions research: State of the art and future directions. *Environ. Innov. Soc. Transitions*, **31**(January), 1–32, doi:10.1016/j.eist.2019.01.004.

Kolstad C., K. Urama, J. Broome, A. Bruvoll, M. Cariño Olvera, D. Fullerton, C. Gollier, W.M. Hanemann, R. Hassan, F. Jotzo, M.R. Khan, L. Meyer, and L. Mundaca, 2014: Social, Economic and Ethical Concepts and Methods. In: *Climate Change 2014: Mitigation of Climate Change. Contribution of Working Group III to the Fifth Assessment Report of the Intergovernmental Panel on Climate Change* [Edenhofer, O., R. Pichs-Madruga, Y. Sokona, E. Farahani, S. Kadner, K. Seyboth, A. Adler, I. Baum, S. Brunner, P. Eickemeier, B. Kriemann, J. Savolainen, S. Schlömer, C. von Stechow, T. Zwickel and J.C. Minx (eds.)]. Cambridge University Press, Cambridge, UK and New York, NY, USA.

Kou, Z.-S. pd., X. Wang, S.F. (Anthony) Chiu, and H. Cai, 2020: Quantifying greenhouse gas emissions reduction from bike share systems: a model considering real-world trips and transportation mode choice patterns. *Resour. Conserv. Recycl.*, **153**(October 2019), 104534, doi:10.1016/j.resconrec.2019.104534.

Kramer, G.J. and M. Haigh, 2009: No quick switch to low-carbon energy. *Nature*, **462(7273)**, 568–569, doi:10.1038/462568a.

Krausmann, F. et al., 2017: Global socioeconomic material stocks rise 23-fold over the 20th century and require half of annual resource use. *Proc. Natl. Acad. Sci.*, **114(8)**, 1880–1885, doi:10.1073/pnas.1613773114.

Krausmann, F., C. Lauk, W. Haas, and D. Wiedenhofer, 2018: From resource extraction to outflows of wastes and emissions: The socioeconomic metabolism of the global economy, 1900–2015. *Glob. Environ. Change*, **52**, 131–140, doi:10.1016/j.gloenvcha.2018.07.003.

Krausmann, F., D. Wiedenhofer, and H. Haberl, 2020: Growing stocks of buildings, infrastructures and machinery as key challenge for compliance with climate targets. *Glob. Environ. Change*, **61**, 102034, doi:10.1016/j.gloenvcha.2020.102034.

Krey, V., G. Luderer, L. Clarke, and E. Kriegler, 2014: Getting from here to there – energy technology transformation pathways in the EMF27 scenarios. *Clim. Change*, **123(3–4)**, 369–382, doi:10.1007/s10584-013-0947-5.

Kriegler, E. et al., 2018a: Short term policies to keep the door open for Paris climate goals. *Environ. Res. Lett.*, **13(7)**, 074022, doi:10.1088/1748-9326/aac4f1.

Kriegler, E. et al., 2018b: Pathways limiting warming to 1.5°C: a tale of turning around in no time? *Philos. Trans. R. Soc. A Math. Phys. Eng. Sci.*, **376(2119)**, 20160457, doi:10.1098/rsta.2016.0457.

Kuhnimhof, T. et al., 2012: Men Shape a Downward Trend in Car Use among Young Adults – Evidence from Six Industrialized Countries. *Transp. Rev.*, **32(6)**, 761–779, doi:10.1080/01441647.2012.736426.

Kumar, R.R. and K. Alok, 2020: Adoption of electric vehicle: A literature review and prospects for sustainability. *J. Clean. Prod.*, **253**, 119911, doi:10.1016/j.jclepro.2019.119911.

Kwade, A. et al., 2018: Current status and challenges for automotive battery production technologies. *Nat. Energy*, **3(4)**, 290–300, doi:10.1038/s41560-018-0130-3.

Lamb, W.F. and N.D. Rao, 2015: Human development in a climate-constrained world: What the past says about the future. *Glob. Environ. Change*, **33**, 14–22, doi:10.1016/j.gloenvcha.2015.03.010.

Lamb, W.F. et al., 2014: Transitions in pathways of human development and carbon emissions. *Environ. Res. Lett.*, **9(1)**, 014011, doi:10.1088/1748-9326/9/1/014011.

Lamb, W.F. et al., 2021a: A review of trends and drivers of greenhouse gas emissions by sector from 1990 to 2018. *Environ. Res. Lett.*, **16(7)**, 073005, doi:10.1088/1748-9326/abee4e.

Lamb, W.F., M. Grubb, F. Diluiso, and J.C. Minx, 2021b: Countries with sustained greenhouse gas emissions reductions: an analysis of trends and progress by sector. *Clim. Policy*, **22(1)**, 1–17, doi:10.1080/14693062.2021.1990831.

Lane, J.L. et al., 2016: Understanding constraints to the transformation rate of global energy infrastructure. *WIREs Energy Environ.*, **5(1)**, 33–48, doi:10.1002/wene.177.

Langbroek, J.H.M., J.P. Franklin, and Y.O. Susilo, 2016: The effect of policy incentives on electric vehicle adoption. *Energy Policy*, **94**, 94–103, doi:10.1016/j.enpol.2016.03.050.

Le Quéré, C. et al., 2018: Global Carbon Budget 2018. *Earth Syst. Sci. Data*, **10(4)**, 2141–2194, doi:10.5194/essd-10-2141-2018.

Le Quéré, C. et al., 2019: Drivers of declining CO_2 emissions in 18 developed economies. *Nat. Clim. Change*, **9(3)**, 213–217, doi:10.1038/s41558-019-0419-7.

Le Quéré, C. et al., 2020: Temporary reduction in daily global CO_2 emissions during the COVID-19 forced confinement. *Nat. Clim. Change*, **10(7)**, 647–653, doi:10.1038/s41558-020-0797-x.

Le Quéré, C. et al., 2021: Fossil CO_2 emissions in the post-COVID-19 era. *Nat. Clim. Change*, **11(3)**, 197–199, doi:10.1038/s41558-021-01001-0.

Lee, D.S. et al., 2021: The contribution of global aviation to anthropogenic climate forcing for 2000 to 2018. *Atmos. Environ.*, **244**, 117834, doi:10.1016/j.atmosenv.2020.117834.

Lee, S., M. Kim, and J. Lee, 2017: Analyzing the Impact of Nuclear Power on CO_2 Emissions. *Sustainability*, **9(8)**, 1428, doi:10.3390/su9081428.

Leijten, F., S. Sim, H. King, and P.H. Verburg, 2020: Which forests could be protected by corporate zero deforestation commitments? A spatial assessment. *Environ. Res. Lett.*, **15(6)**, 064021, doi:10.1088/1748-9326/ab8158.

Lelieveld, J., J.S. Evans, M. Fnais, D. Giannadaki, and A. Pozzer, 2015: The contribution of outdoor air pollution sources to premature mortality on a global scale. *Nature*, **525(7569)**, 367–371, doi:10.1038/nature15371.

Lelieveld, J., A. Haines, and A. Pozzer, 2018: Age-dependent health risk from ambient air pollution: a modelling and data analysis of childhood mortality in middle-income and low-income countries. *Lancet Planet. Heal.*, **2(7)**, e292–e300, doi:10.1016/S2542-5196(18)30147-5.

Lelieveld, J. et al., 2019: Effects of fossil fuel and total anthropogenic emission removal on public health and climate. *Proc. Natl. Acad. Sci.*, **116(15)**, 7192–7197, doi:10.1073/pnas.1819989116.

Lema, R., M. Iizuka, and R. Walz, 2015: Introduction to low-carbon innovation and development: insights and future challenges for research. *Innov. Dev.*, **5(2)**, 173–187, doi:10.1080/2157930X.2015.1065096.

Lenzen, M. and R. Cummins, 2013: Happiness versus the Environment – A Case Study of Australian Lifestyles. *Challenges*, **4(1)**, 56–74, doi:10.3390/challe4010056.

Lenzen, M., R. Wood, and T. Wiedmann, 2010: Uncertainty Analysis for Multi-Region Input–Output Models – A Case Study of the UK'S Carbon Footprint. *Econ. Syst. Res.*, **22(1)**, 43–63, doi:10.1080/09535311003661226.

Lenzen, M., D. Moran, K. Kanemoto, and A. Geschke, 2013: Building EORA: A Global Multi-Region Input–Output Database at High Country and Sector Resolution. *Econ. Syst. Res.*, **25(1)**, 20–49, doi:10.1080/09535314.2013.769938.

Levasseur, A. et al., 2016: Enhancing life cycle impact assessment from climate science: Review of recent findings and recommendations for application to LCA. *Ecol. Indic.*, **71**, 163–174, doi:10.1016/j.ecolind.2016.06.049.

Levinson, R.S. and T.H. West, 2018: Impact of public electric vehicle charging infrastructure. *Transp. Res. Part D Transp. Environ.*, **64**(October 2017), 158–177, doi:10.1016/j.trd.2017.10.006.

Li, F.G.N. and S. Pye, 2018: Uncertainty, politics, and technology: Expert perceptions on energy transitions in the United Kingdom. *Energy Res. Soc. Sci.*, **37**, 122–132, doi:10.1016/j.erss.2017.10.003.

Li, H., J. Strauss, and L. Lu, 2019: The impact of high-speed rail on civil aviation in China. *Transp. Policy*, **74**, 187–200, doi:10.1016/j.tranpol.2018.11.015.

Li, M., H. Ye, X. Liao, J. Ji, and X. Ma, 2020: How Shenzhen, China pioneered the widespread adoption of electric vehicles in a major city: Implications for global implementation. *WIREs Energy Environ.*, **9(4)**, doi:10.1002/wene.373.

Li, S. and C. Zhou, 2019: What are the impacts of demographic structure on CO_2 emissions? A regional analysis in China via heterogeneous panel estimates. *Sci. Total Environ.*, **650**, 2021–2031, doi:10.1016/j.scitotenv.2018.09.304.

Li, X., Y. Qiao, and L. Shi, 2017a: The aggregate effect of air pollution regulation on CO_2 mitigation in China's manufacturing industry: an econometric analysis. *J. Clean. Prod.*, **142**, 976–984, doi:10.1016/j.jclepro.2016.03.015.

Li, X., Y. Qiao, J. Zhu, L. Shi, and Y. Wang, 2017b: The "APEC blue" endeavor: Causal effects of air pollution regulation on air quality in China. *J. Clean. Prod.*, **168**, 1381–1388, doi:10.1016/j.jclepro.2017.08.164.

Li, Y., R. Zhao, T. Liu, and J. Zhao, 2015: Does urbanization lead to more direct and indirect household carbon dioxide emissions? Evidence from China during 1996–2012. *J. Clean. Prod.*, **102**, 103–114, doi:10.1016/j.jclepro.2015.04.037.

Liang, S., S. Qu, Z. Zhu, D. Guan, and M. Xu, 2017: Income-Based Greenhouse Gas Emissions of Nations. *Environ. Sci. Technol.*, **51(1)**, 346–355, doi:10.1021/acs.est.6b02510.

Liddle, B., 2011: Consumption-Driven Environmental Impact and Age Structure Change in OECD Countries. *Demogr. Res.*, **24**, 749–770, doi:10.4054/DemRes.2011.24.30.

Liddle, B., 2013: Urban density and climate change: a STIRPAT analysis using city-level data. *J. Transp. Geogr.*, **28**, 22–29, doi:10.1016/j.jtrangeo.2012.10.010.

Liddle, B., 2015: What are the carbon emissions elasticities for income and population? Bridging STIRPAT and EKC via robust heterogeneous panel estimates. *Glob. Environ. Change*, **31**, 62–73, doi:10.1016/j.gloenvcha.2014.10.016.

Liddle, B. and S. Lung, 2010: Age-structure, urbanization, and climate change in developed countries: Revisiting STIRPAT for disaggregated population and consumption-related environmental impacts. *Popul. Environ.*, **31(5)**, 317–343, doi:10.1007/s11111-010-0101-5.

Liddle, B. and S. Lung, 2014: Might electricity consumption cause urbanization instead? Evidence from heterogeneous panel long-run causality tests. *Glob. Environ. Change*, **24**, 42–51, doi:10.1016/j.gloenvcha.2013.11.013.

Liddle, B. and H. Huntington, 2020: 'On the Road Again': A 118 country panel analysis of gasoline and diesel demand. *Transp. Res. Part A Policy Pract.*, **142**, 151–167, doi:10.1016/j.tra.2020.10.015.

Liddle, B. and H. Huntington, 2021: There's Technology Improvement, but is there Economy-wide Energy Leapfrogging? A Country Panel Analysis. *World Dev.*, **140**, 105259, doi:10.1016/j.worlddev.2020.105259.

Lilliestam, J., A. Patt, and G. Bersalli, 2021: The effect of carbon pricing on technological change for full energy decarbonization: A review of empirical ex-post evidence. *WIREs Clim. Change*, **12(1)**, doi:10.1002/wcc.681.

Lima, F., M.L. Nunes, J. Cunha, and A.F.P. Lucena, 2016: A cross-country assessment of energy-related CO_2 emissions: An extended Kaya Index Decomposition Approach. *Energy*, **115**, 1361–1374, doi:10.1016/j.energy.2016.05.037.

Lin, B. and X. Li, 2011: The effect of carbon tax on per capita CO_2 emissions. *Energy Policy*, **39(9)**, 5137–5146, doi:10.1016/j.enpol.2011.05.050.

Lin, S., S. Wang, D. Marinova, D. Zhao, and J. Hong, 2017: Impacts of urbanization and real economic development on CO_2 emissions in non-high income countries: Empirical research based on the extended STIRPAT model. *J. Clean. Prod.*, **166**, 952–966, doi:10.1016/j.jclepro.2017.08.107.

Liobikienė, G. and M. Butkus, 2019: Scale, composition, and technique effects through which the economic growth, foreign direct investment, urbanization, and trade affect greenhouse gas emissions. *Renew. Energy*, **132**, 1310–1322, doi:10.1016/j.renene.2018.09.032.

Liobikienė, G. and D. Rimkuvienė, 2020: The role of income inequality on consumption-based greenhouse gas emissions under different stages of economic development. *Environ. Sci. Pollut. Res.*, **27(34)**, 43067–43076, doi:10.1007/s11356-020-10244-x.

Liu, D., X. Guo, and B. Xiao, 2019a: What causes growth of global greenhouse gas emissions? Evidence from 40 countries. *Sci. Total Environ.*, **661**, 750–766, doi:10.1016/j.scitotenv.2019.01.197.

Liu, G., C.E. Bangs, and D.B. Müller, 2013: Stock dynamics and emission pathways of the global aluminium cycle. *Nat. Clim. Change*, **3(4)**, 338–342, doi:10.1038/nclimate1698.

Liu, G., Y. Tan, and X. Li, 2020a: China's policies of building green retrofit: A state-of-the-art overview. *Build. Environ.*, **169**(September 2019), 106554, doi:10.1016/j.buildenv.2019.106554.

Liu, G., X. Li, Y. Tan, and G. Zhang, 2020b: Building green retrofit in China: Policies, barriers and recommendations. *Energy Policy*, **139**(May 2019), 111356, doi:10.1016/j.enpol.2020.111356.

Liu, H. and X. Fan, 2017: Value-Added-Based Accounting of CO_2 Emissions: A Multi-Regional Input-Output Approach. *Sustainability*, **9(12)**, 2220, doi:10.3390/su9122220.

Liu, H., W. Liu, X. Fan, and W. Zou, 2015: Carbon emissions embodied in demand–supply chains in China. *Energy Econ.*, **50**, 294–305, doi:10.1016/j.eneco.2015.06.006.

Liu, L.-C., G. Wu, J.-N. Wang, and Y.-M. Wei, 2011: China's carbon emissions from urban and rural households during 1992–2007. *J. Clean. Prod.*, **19(15)**, 1754–1762, doi:10.1016/j.jclepro.2011.06.011.

Liu, X. et al., 2019b: Low-carbon developments in Northeast China: Evidence from cities. *Appl. Energy*, **236**, 1019–1033, doi:10.1016/j.apenergy.2018.12.060.

Liu, Y., S. Chen, B. Chen, and W. Yang, 2017: Analysis of CO_2 emissions embodied in China's bilateral trade: a non-competitive import input–output approach. *J. Clean. Prod.*, **163**, S410–S419, doi:10.1016/j.jclepro.2016.02.085.

Liu, Z. et al., 2015: Four system boundaries for carbon accounts. *Ecol. Modell.*, **318**, 118–125, doi:10.1016/j.ecolmodel.2015.02.001.

Liu, Z. et al., 2020a Carbon Monitor, a near-real-time daily dataset of global CO_2 emission from fossil fuel and cement production. *Sci. Data*, **7(1)**, 392, doi:10.1038/s41597-020-00708-7.

Liu, Z. et al., 2020b: Near-real-time monitoring of global CO_2 emissions reveals the effects of the COVID-19 pandemic. *Nat. Commun.*, **11(1)**, 5172, doi:10.1038/s41467-020-18922-7.Liu 209.

Long, Y., Y. Yoshida, and L. Dong, 2017: Exploring the indirect household carbon emissions by source: Analysis on 49 Japanese cities. *J. Clean. Prod.*, **167**, 571–581, doi:10.1016/j.jclepro.2017.08.159.

Lu, J. and G.F. Nemet, 2020: Evidence map: topics, trends, and policy in the energy transitions literature. *Environ. Res. Lett.*, **15(12)**, 123003, doi:10.1088/1748-9326/abc195.

Lucon O., D. Ürge-Vorsatz, A. Zain Ahmed, H. Akbari, P. Bertoldi, L.F. Cabeza, N. Eyre, A. Gadgil, L.D.D. Harvey, Y. Jiang, E. Liphoto, S. Mirasgedis, S. Murakami, J. Parikh, C. Pyke, and M.V. Vilariño, 2014: Buildings. In: *Climate Change 2014: Mitigation of Climate Change. Contribution of Working Group III to the Fifth Assessment Report of the Intergovernmental Panel on Climate Change* [Edenhofer, O., R. Pichs-Madruga, Y. Sokona, E. Farahani, S. Kadner, K. Seyboth, A. Adler, I. Baum, S. Brunner, P. Eickemeier, B. Kriemann, J. Savolainen, S. Schlömer, C. von Stechow, T. Zwickel and J.C. Minx (eds.)]. Cambridge University Press, Cambridge, UK and New York, NY, USA.

Luderer, G., C. Bertram, K. Calvin, E. De Cian, and E. Kriegler, 2016: Implications of weak near-term climate policies on long-term mitigation pathways. *Clim. Change*, **136(1)**, 127–140, doi:10.1007/s10584-013-0899-9.

Luderer, G. et al., 2018: Residual fossil CO_2 emissions in 1.5–2°C pathways. *Nat. Clim. Change*, **8(7)**, 626–633, doi:10.1038/s41558-018-0198-6.

Luna, T.F., M. Uriona-Maldonado, M.E. Silva, and C.R. Vaz, 2020: The influence of e-carsharing schemes on electric vehicle adoption and carbon emissions: An emerging economy study. *Transp. Res. Part D Transp. Environ.*, **79**(July 2019), 102226, doi:10.1016/j.trd.2020.102226.

Lutz, W. et al., 2019: Education rather than age structure brings demographic dividend. *Proc. Natl. Acad. Sci.*, **116(26)**, 12798–12803, doi:10.1073/pnas.1820362116.

Lynch, J., M. Cain, R. Pierrehumbert, and M. Allen, 2020: Demonstrating GWP: a means of reporting warming-equivalent emissions that captures the contrasting impacts of short- and long-lived climate pollutants. *Environ. Res. Lett.*, **15(4)**, 044023, doi:10.1088/1748-9326/ab6d7e.

Lynch, J., M. Cain, D. Frame, and R. Pierrehumbert, 2021: Agriculture's Contribution to Climate Change and Role in Mitigation Is Distinct From Predominantly Fossil CO_2-Emitting Sectors. *Front. Sustain. Food Syst.*, **4**, 1–9, doi:10.3389/fsufs.2020.518039.

Maamoun, N., 2019: The Kyoto protocol: Empirical evidence of a hidden success. *J. Environ. Econ. Manage.*, **95**, 227–256, doi:10.1016/j.jeem.2019.04.001.

Macknick, J., 2011: Energy and CO_2 emission data uncertainties. *Carbon Manag.*, **2(2)**, 189–205, doi:10.4155/cmt.11.10.

Makido, Y., S. Dhakal, and Y. Yamagata, 2012: Relationship between urban form and CO_2 emissions: Evidence from fifty Japanese cities. *Urban Clim.*, **2**, 55–67, doi:10.1016/j.uclim.2012.10.006.

Malerba, D., 2020: The Trade-off Between Poverty Reduction and Carbon Emissions, and the Role of Economic Growth and Inequality: An Empirical Cross-Country Analysis Using a Novel Indicator. *Soc. Indic. Res.*, **150(2)**, 587–615, doi:10.1007/s11205-020-02332-9.

Malhotra, A. and T.S. Schmidt, 2020: Accelerating Low-Carbon Innovation. *Joule*, **4(11)**, 2259–2267, doi:10.1016/j.joule.2020.09.004.

Malik, A. and J. Lan, 2016: The role of outsourcing in driving global carbon emissions. *Econ. Syst. Res.*, **28(2)**, 168–182, doi:10.1080/09535314.2016.1172475.

Malik, A., J. Lan, and M. Lenzen, 2016: Trends in Global Greenhouse Gas Emissions from 1990 to 2010. *Environ. Sci. Technol.*, **50(9)**, 4722–4730, doi:10.1021/acs.est.5b06162.

Malik, A. et al., 2020: Reducing stranded assets through early action in the Indian power sector. *Environ. Res. Lett.*, **15(9)**, 094091, doi:10.1088/1748-9326/ab8033.

Mallapragada, D. and B.K. Mignone, 2017: A consistent conceptual framework for applying climate metrics in technology life cycle assessment. *Environ. Res. Lett.*, **12(7)**, 074022, doi:10.1088/1748-9326/aa7397.

Mallapragada, D.S. and B.K. Mignone, 2020: A theoretical basis for the equivalence between physical and economic climate metrics and implications for the choice of Global Warming Potential time horizon. *Clim. Change*, **158(2)**, 107–124, doi:10.1007/s10584-019-02486-7.

Maraseni, T.N., J. Qu, and J. Zeng, 2015: A comparison of trends and magnitudes of household carbon emissions between China, Canada and UK. *Environ. Dev.*, **15**, 103–119, doi:10.1016/j.envdev.2015.04.001.

Maraseni, T.N., J. Qu, B. Yue, J. Zeng, and J. Maroulis, 2016: Dynamism of household carbon emissions (HCEs) from rural and urban regions of northern and southern China. *Environ. Sci. Pollut. Res.*, **23(20)**, 20553–20566, doi:10.1007/s11356-016-7237-5.

Mardani, A., D. Streimikiene, F. Cavallaro, N. Loganathan, and M. Khoshnoudi, 2019: Carbon dioxide (CO_2) emissions and economic growth: A systematic review of two decades of research from 1995 to 2017. *Sci. Total Environ.*, **649**, 31–49, doi:10.1016/j.scitotenv.2018.08.229.

Mardones, C. and N. Cornejo, 2020: Ex - post evaluation of a program to reduce critical episodes due to air pollution in southern Chile. *Environ. Impact Assess. Rev.*, **80**, 106334, doi:10.1016/j.eiar.2019.106334.

Marin, G. and M. Mazzanti, 2019: Structural Change and the Environment. In: *New Perspectives on Structural Change: Causes and Consequences of Structural Change in the Global Economy* [Alcorta, L., N. Foster-McGregor, B. Verspagen, and A. Szirmai, (eds.)], Oxford University Press, Oxford, UK, pp. 622–647.

Marland, G., 2008: Uncertainties in Accounting for CO_2 From Fossil Fuels. *J. Ind. Ecol.*, **12(2)**, 136–139, doi:10.1111/j.1530-9290.2008.00014.x.

Marland, G., K. Hamal, and M. Jonas, 2009: How Uncertain Are Estimates of CO_2 Emissions? *J. Ind. Ecol.*, **13(1)**, 4–7, doi:10.1111/j.1530-9290.2009.00108.x.

Martin, G. and E. Saikawa, 2017: Effectiveness of state climate and energy policies in reducing power-sector CO_2 emissions. *Nat. Clim. Change*, **7(12)**, 912–919, doi:10.1038/s41558-017-0001-0.

2

Martin, R., M. Muûls, and U.J. Wagner, 2016: The Impact of the European Union Emissions Trading Scheme on Regulated Firms: What Is the Evidence after Ten Years? *Rev. Environ. Econ. Policy*, **10(1)**, 129–148, doi:10.1093/reep/rev016.

Masud, M.M., F.B. Kari, H. Banna, and M.K. Saifullah, 2018: Does income inequality affect environmental sustainability? Evidence from the ASEAN-5. *J. Asia Pacific Econ.*, **23(2)**, 213–228, doi:10.1080/13547860.2018.1442146.

Matthews, H.D., 2016: Quantifying historical carbon and climate debts among nations. *Nat. Clim. Change*, **6(1)**, 60–64, doi:10.1038/nclimate2774.

Mattioli, G., 2017: 'Forced Car Ownership' in the UK and Germany: Socio-Spatial Patterns and Potential Economic Stress Impacts. *Soc. Incl.*, **5(4)**, 147–160, doi:10.17645/si.v5i4.1081.

Maycock, P.D. and G.F. Wakefield, 1975: Business Analysis of Solar Photovoltaic Energy Conversion. In: *Photovoltaic Specialists Conference, 11th, Scottsdale, Ariz., May 6–8, 1975, Conference Record.* (A76-14727 04-44) Institute of Electrical and Electronics Engineers, Inc., New York, NY, USA, pp. 252–255.

McDonald, B.C. et al., 2018: Volatile chemical products emerging as largest petrochemical source of urban organic emissions. *Science*, **359(6377)**, 760–764, doi:10.1126/science.aaq0524.

McDonald, N.C., 2015: Are Millennials Really the "Go-Nowhere" Generation? *J. Am. Plan. Assoc.*, **81(2)**, 90–103, doi:10.1080/01944363.2015.1057196.

McDuffie, E.E. et al., 2020: A global anthropogenic emission inventory of atmospheric pollutants from sector- and fuel-specific sources **(1970–2017)**: an application of the Community Emissions Data System (CEDS). *Earth Syst. Sci. Data*, **12(4)**, 3413–3442, doi:10.5194/essd-12-3413-2020.

McGlade, C. and P. Ekins, 2015: The geographical distribution of fossil fuels unused when limiting global warming to 2°C. *Nature*, **517(7533)**, 187–190, doi:10.1038/nature14016.

McGlade, C., S. Pye, P. Ekins, M. Bradshaw, and J. Watson, 2018: The future role of natural gas in the UK: A bridge to nowhere? *Energy Policy*, **113**, 454–465, doi:10.1016/j.enpol.2017.11.022.

McGuinness, M. and A.D. Ellerman, 2008: CO₂ Abatement in the UK Power Sector: Evidence from the EU ETS Trial Period. *Vasa*, (**September**), 16.

McIntosh, J., R. Trubka, J. Kenworthy, and P. Newman, 2014: The role of urban form and transit in city car dependence: Analysis of 26 global cities from 1960 to 2000. *Transp. Res. Part D Transp. Environ.*, **33**, 95–110, doi:10.1016/j.trd.2014.08.013.

McKinnon, A.C., 2016: Freight Transport Deceleration: Its Possible Contribution to the Decarbonisation of Logistics. *Transp. Rev.*, **36(4)**, 418–436, doi:10.1080/01441647.2015.1137992.

Meangbua, O., S. Dhakal, and J.K.M. Kuwornu, 2019: Factors influencing energy requirements and CO₂ emissions of households in Thailand: A panel data analysis. *Energy Policy*, **129**, 521–531, doi:10.1016/j.enpol.2019.02.050.

Meckling, J. and L. Hughes, 2018: Global interdependence in clean energy transitions. *Bus. Polit.*, **20(4)**, 467–491, doi:10.1017/bap.2018.25.

Meier, H. and K. Rehdanz, 2010: Determinants of residential space heating expenditures in Great Britain. *Energy Econ.*, **32(5)**, 949–959, doi:10.1016/j.eneco.2009.11.008.

Meijer, K., 2014: *Can supply chain initiatives reduce deforestation? A comparative analysis of cases from Brazil and Indonesia.* German Development Institute, Bonn, Germany, 39 pp.

Méjean, A., C. Guivarch, J. Lefèvre, and M. Hamdi-Cherif, 2019: The transition in energy demand sectors to limit global warming to 1.5°C. *Energy Effic.*, **12(2)**, 441–462, doi:10.1007/s12053-018-9682-0.

Melo, P.C., J. Ge, T. Craig, M.J. Brewer, and I. Thronicker, 2018: Does Work-life Balance Affect Pro-environmental Behaviour? Evidence for the UK Using Longitudinal Microdata. *Ecol. Econ.*, **145**, 170–181, doi:10.1016/j.ecolecon.2017.09.006.

Meng, J. et al., 2018: The rise of South–South trade and its effect on global CO₂ emissions. *Nat. Commun.*, **9(1)**, 1871, doi:10.1038/s41467-018-04337-y.

Menz, T. and H. Welsch, 2012: Population aging and carbon emissions in OECD countries: Accounting for life-cycle and cohort effects. *Energy Econ.*, **34(3)**, 842–849, doi:10.1016/j.eneco.2011.07.016.

Merlin, L. A., 2019: Transportation Sustainability Follows From More People in Fewer Vehicles, Not Necessarily Automation. *J. Am. Plan. Assoc.*, **85(4)**, 501–510, doi:10.1080/01944363.2019.1637770.

Meyer, C. and D. Miller, 2015: Zero Deforestation Zones: The Case for Linking Deforestation-Free Supply Chain Initiatives and Jurisdictional REDD+. *J. Sustain. For.*, **34(6–7)**, 559–580, doi:10.1080/10549811.2015.1036886.

Meyfroidt, P., T.K. Rudel, and E.F. Lambin, 2010: Forest transitions, trade, and the global displacement of land use. *Proc. Natl. Acad. Sci.*, **107(49)**, 20917–20922, doi:10.1073/pnas.1014773107.

Mi, Z., J. Meng, F. Green, D.M. Coffman, and D. Guan, 2018: China's "Exported Carbon" Peak: Patterns, Drivers, and Implications. *Geophys. Res. Lett.*, **45(9)**, 4309–4318, doi:10.1029/2018GL077915.

Miehe, R., R. Scheumann, C.M. Jones, D.M. Kammen, and M. Finkbeiner, 2016: Regional carbon footprints of households: a German case study. *Environ. Dev. Sustain.*, **18(2)**, 577–591, doi:10.1007/s10668-015-9649-7.

Milanović, B., 2016: *Global inequality: a new approach for the age of globalization.* The Belknap Press of Harvard University Press, Cambridge, Massachusetts, USA, 299 pp.

Millward-Hopkins, J. and Y. Oswald, 2021: 'Fair' inequality, consumption and climate mitigation. *Environ. Res. Lett.*, **16(3)**, 034007, doi:10.1088/1748-9326/abe14f.

Millward-Hopkins, J., J.K. Steinberger, N.D. Rao, and Y. Oswald, 2020: Providing decent living with minimum energy: A global scenario. *Glob. Environ. Change*, **65**, 102168, doi:10.1016/j.gloenvcha.2020.102168.

Minx, J.C. et al., 2021: A comprehensive and synthetic dataset for global, regional, and national greenhouse gas emissions by sector 1970–2018 with an extension to 2019. *Earth Syst. Sci. Data*, **13(11)**, 5213–5252, doi:10.5194/essd-13-5213-2021.

Mitchell, R.B. et al., 2020: What We Know (and Could Know) About International Environmental Agreements. *Glob. Environ. Polit.*, **20(1)**, 103–121, doi:10.1162/glep_a_00544.

Mohlin, K., A. Bi, S. Brooks, J. Camuzeaux, and T. Stoerk, 2019: Turning the corner on US power sector CO₂ emissions – a 1990–2015 state level analysis. *Environ. Res. Lett.*, **14(8)**, 084049, doi:10.1088/1748-9326/ab3080.

Mohmmed, A. et al., 2019: Driving factors of CO₂ emissions and nexus with economic growth, development and human health in the Top Ten emitting countries. *Resour. Conserv. Recycl.*, **148**, 157–169, doi:10.1016/j.resconrec.2019.03.048.

Monni, S., P. Perälä, and K. Regina, 2007: Uncertainty in Agricultural CH₄ AND N₂O Emissions from Finland – Possibilities to Increase Accuracy in Emission Estimates. *Mitig. Adapt. Strateg. Glob. Change*, **12(4)**, 545–571, doi:10.1007/s11027-006-4584-4.

Montzka, S.A. and G.J.M. Velders, 2018: Chapter 2: Hydrofluorocarbons (HFCs). In: *Scientific Assessment of Ozone Depletion: 2018*, World Meterological Organization, Geneva, Switzerland.

Moran, D. and R. Wood, 2014: Convergence Between the EORA, WIOD, EXIOBASE, and OPENEU'S Consumption-Based Carbon Accounts. *Econ. Syst. Res.*, **26(3)**, 245–261, doi:10.1080/09535314.2014.935298.

Moran, D. et al., 2018: Carbon footprints of 13 000 cities. *Environ. Res. Lett.*, **13(6)**, 064041, doi:10.1088/1748-9326/aac72a.

Morgenstern, R., 2018: Retrospective Analysis of U.S. Federal Environmental Regulation. *J. Benefit-Cost Anal.*, **9(2)**, 285–304, doi:10.1017/bca.2017.17.

Morin, R. and P. Taylor, 2009: *Luxury or Necessity? The Public Makes a U-Turn,* Pew Research Centre, Washington, DC, USA, 21 pp.

Mukherjee, S., 2018: Services Outsourcing and Productivity Growth. *South Asia Econ. J.*, **19(2)**, 192–209, doi:10.1177/1391561418794693.

Müller, D.B. et al., 2013: Carbon Emissions of Infrastructure Development. *Environ. Sci. Technol.*, **47(20)**, 11739–11746, doi:10.1021/es402618m.

Muñoz, P., S. Zwick, and A. Mirzabaev, 2020: The impact of urbanization on Austria's carbon footprint. *J. Clean. Prod.*, **263**, 121326, doi:10.1016/j.jclepro.2020.121326.

Myhre, G., D. Shindell, F.-M. Bréon, W. Collins, J. Fuglestvedt, J. Huang, D. Koch, J.-F. Lamarque, D. Lee, B. Mendoza, T. Nakajima, A. Robock, G. Stephens, T. Takemura and H. Zhang, 2013: Anthropogenic and Natural Radiative Forcing. In: *Climate Change 2013: The Physical Science Basis*. *Contribution of Working Group I to the Fifth Assessment Report of the Intergovernmental Panel on Climate Change* [Stocker, T.F., D. Qin, G.-K. Plattner, M. Tignor, S.K. Allen, J. Boschung, A. Nauels, Y. Xia, V. Bex and P.M. Midgley (eds.)]. Cambridge University Press, Cambridge, UK and New York, NY, USA.

Murray, B. and N. Rivers, 2015: British Columbia's revenue-neutral carbon tax: A review of the latest "grand experiment" in environmental policy. *Energy Policy*, **86**, 674–683, doi:10.1016/j.enpol.2015.08.011.

Nässén, J., 2014: Determinants of greenhouse gas emissions from Swedish private consumption: Time-series and cross-sectional analyses. *Energy*, **66**, 98–106, doi:10.1016/j.energy.2014.01.019.

Navarro, J.C.A. et al., 2016: Amplification of Arctic warming by past air pollution reductions in Europe. *Nat. Geosci.*, **9(4)**, 277–281, doi:10.1038/ngeo2673.

Nejat, P., F. Jomehzadeh, M.M. Taheri, M. Gohari, and M.Z. Abd. Majid, 2015: A global review of energy consumption, CO_2 emissions and policy in the residential sector (with an overview of the top ten CO_2 emitting countries). *Renew. Sustain. Energy Rev.*, **43**, 843–862, doi:10.1016/j.rser.2014.11.066.

Nemet, G., 2013: Technological change and climate change policy. In: *Encyclopedia of Energy, Natural Resource and Environmental Economics* [Shogren, J., (ed.)], Elsevier, Amsterdam, Netherlands, pp. 107–116.

Nemet, G.F., P. Braden, and F. Cubero, 2013: *Credibility, ambition, and discretion in long-term U.S. energy policy targets from 1973 to 2011*. University of Wisconsin-Madison La Follette School of Public Affairs, Working Paper 2013-007, Madison, WI, USA, 30 pp.

Nemet, G.G.F., 2019: *How solar became cheap: A model for low-carbon innovation*. Earthscan Routledge, New York City, NY, USA, 223 pp.

Nichols, B.G., K.M. Kockelman, and M. Reiter, 2015: Air quality impacts of electric vehicle adoption in Texas. *Transp. Res. Part D Transp. Environ.*, **34**, 208–218, doi:10.1016/j.trd.2014.10.016.

Nie, H. and R. Kemp, 2014: Index decomposition analysis of residential energy consumption in China: 2002–2010. *Appl. Energy*, **121**, 10–19, doi:10.1016/j.apenergy.2014.01.070.

Noppers, E., K. Keizer, M. Milovanovic, and L. Steg, 2019: The role of adoption norms and perceived product attributes in the adoption of Dutch electric vehicles and smart energy systems. *Energy Res. Soc. Sci.*, **57**(October 2018), 101237, doi:10.1016/j.erss.2019.101237.

Nykvist, B. and M. Nilsson, 2015: Rapidly falling costs of battery packs for electric vehicles. *Nat. Clim. Change*, **5(4)**, 329–332, doi:10.1038/nclimate2564.

O'Neill, B.C. et al., 2010: Global demographic trends and future carbon emissions. *Proc. Natl. Acad. Sci.*, **107(41)**, 17521–17526, doi:10.1073/pnas.1004581107.

O'Neill, B.C. et al., 2012: Demographic change and carbon dioxide emissions. *Lancet*, **380(9837)**, 157–164, doi:10.1016/S0140-6736(12)60958-1.

O'Rourke, P.R. et al., 2020: CEDS v-2020-09-11 Pre-Release Emission Data 1975–2019. Zenodo, doi:10.5281/zenodo.4025316.

O'Rourke, P.R. and S.J. Smith et al., 2021: CEDS v_2021_04_21 Release Emission Data. Zenodo, doi:10.5281/ZENODO.4741285.

OECD, 2021: *Effective Carbon Rates 2021: Pricing Carbon Emissions through Taxes and Emissions Trading*. OECD Publishing, Paris, France, 40 pp.

Ortega-Ruiz, G., A. Mena-Nieto, and J.E. García-Ramos, 2020: Is India on the right pathway to reduce CO_2 emissions? Decomposing an enlarged Kaya identity using the LMDI method for the period 1990–2016. *Sci. Total Environ.*, **737**, 139638, doi:10.1016/j.scitotenv.2020.139638.

Oswald, Y., A. Owen, and J.K. Steinberger, 2020: Large inequality in international and intranational energy footprints between income groups and across consumption categories. *Nat. Energy*, **5(3)**, 231–239, doi:10.1038/s41560-020-0579-8.

Otto, I.M., K.M. Kim, N. Dubrovsky, and W. Lucht, 2019: Shift the focus from the super-poor to the super-rich. *Nat. Clim. Change*, **9(2)**, 82–84, doi:10.1038/s41558-019-0402-3.

Overland, I. and B.K. Sovacool, 2020: The misallocation of climate research funding. *Energy Res. Soc. Sci.*, **62**, 101349, doi:10.1016/j.erss.2019.101349.

Owen, A., 2017: *Techniques for Evaluating the Differences in Multiregional Input-Output Databases: A Comparative Evaluation of CO_2 Consumption-Based Accounts Calculated Using Eora, GTAP and WIOD*. Springer International Publishing, Cham, Switzerland, 217 pp.

Oxfam, 2015: *Extreme Carbon Inequality: Why the Paris climate deal must put the poorest, lowest emitting and most vulnerable people first*. Oxfam International, London, UK, 14 pp. https://oxfamilibrary.openrepository.com/handle/10546/582545.

Pachauri, S., 2014: Household electricity access a trivial contributor to CO_2 emissions growth in India. *Nat. Clim. Change*, **4(12)**, 1073–1076, doi:10.1038/nclimate2414.

Pachauri, S. et al., 2013: Pathways to achieve universal household access to modern energy by 2030. *Environ. Res. Lett.*, **8(2)**, 024015, doi:10.1088/1748-9326/8/2/024015.

Pachauri, S., N.D. Rao, and C. Cameron, 2018: Outlook for modern cooking energy access in Central America. *PLoS One*, **13(6)**, e0197974, doi:10.1371/journal.pone.0197974.

Palm, A., 2017: Peer effects in residential solar photovoltaics adoption – A mixed methods study of Swedish users. *Energy Res. Soc. Sci.*, **26**, 1–10, doi:10.1016/j.erss.2017.01.008.

Pan, X., M.K. Uddin, B. Ai, X. Pan, and U. Saima, 2019: Influential factors of carbon emissions intensity in OECD countries: Evidence from symbolic regression. *J. Clean. Prod.*, **220**, 1194–1201, doi:10.1016/j.jclepro.2019.02.195.

Parker, S. and M.I. Bhatti, 2020: Dynamics and drivers of per capita CO_2 emissions in Asia. *Energy Econ.*, **89**, 104798, doi:10.1016/j.eneco.2020.104798.

Pascale, A., S. Chakravarty, P. Lant, S. Smart, and C. Greig, 2020: The rise of (sub) nations? Sub-national human development, climate targets, and carbon dioxide emissions in 163 countries. *Energy Res. Soc. Sci.*, **68**, 101546, doi:10.1016/j.erss.2020.101546.

Pathak, H., N. Jain, A. Bhatia, J. Patel, and P.K. Aggarwal, 2010: Carbon footprints of Indian food items. *Agric. Ecosyst. Environ.*, **139(1–2)**, 66–73, doi:10.1016/j.agee.2010.07.002.

Pauliuk, S., T. Wang, and D.B. Müller, 2013: Steel all over the world: Estimating in-use stocks of iron for 200 countries. *Resour. Conserv. Recycl.*, **71**, 22–30, doi:10.1016/j.resconrec.2012.11.008.

Pauliuk, S. et al., 2021: Global scenarios of resource and emission savings from material efficiency in residential in buildings and cars. *Nat. Commun.*, **12(1)**, 5097, doi:10.1038/s41467-021-25300-4.

Pearson, T.R.H., S. Brown, L. Murray, and G. Sidman, 2017: Greenhouse gas emissions from tropical forest degradation: an underestimated source. *Carbon Balance Manag.*, **12(1)**, 3, doi:10.1186/s13021-017-0072-2.

Pedersen, J.S.T. et al., 2020: Variability in historical emissions trends suggests a need for a wide range of global scenarios and regional analyses. *Commun. Earth Environ.*, **1(1)**, 41, doi:10.1038/s43247-020-00045-y.

Pedersen, J.S.T. et al., 2021: An assessment of the performance of scenarios against historical global emissions for IPCC reports. *Glob. Environ. Change*, **66**, 102199, doi:10.1016/j.gloenvcha.2020.102199.

Perrot, R. and M. Sanni, 2018: Building low-carbon energy innovation systems in Africa. *African J. Sci. Technol. Innov. Dev.*, **10(5)**, 519–524, doi:10.1080/20421338.2018.1523033.

Peters, G.P., 2008: From production-based to consumption-based national emission inventories. *Ecol. Econ.*, **65(1)**, 13–23, doi:10.1016/j.ecolecon.2007.10.014.

2

Peters, G.P., R. Andrew, and J. Lennox, 2011b: Constructing an Environmentally-Extended Multi-Regional Input–Output Table Using the GTAP Database. *Econ. Syst. Res.*, **23(2)**, 131–152, doi:10.1080/09535314.2011.563234.

Peters, G.P., J.C. Minx, C.L. Weber, and O. Edenhofer, 2011a: Growth in emission transfers via international trade from 1990 to 2008. *Proc. Natl. Acad. Sci.*, **108(21)**, 8903–8908, doi:10.1073/pnas.1006388108.

Peters, G.P. et al., 2017a: Towards real-time verification of CO_2 emissions. *Nat. Clim. Change*, **7(12)**, 848–850, doi:10.1038/s41558-017-0013-9.

Peters, G.P. et al., 2017b: Key indicators to track current progress and future ambition of the Paris Agreement. *Nat. Clim. Change*, **7(2)**, 118–122, doi:10.1038/nclimate3202.

Peters, G.P. et al., 2020: Carbon dioxide emissions continue to grow amidst slowly emerging climate policies. *Nat. Clim. Change*, **10(1)**, 3–6, doi:10.1038/s41558-019-0659-6.

Petrescu, A.M.R. et al., 2020: European anthropogenic AFOLU greenhouse gas emissions: a review and benchmark data. *Earth Syst. Sci. Data*, **12(2)**, 961–1001, doi:10.5194/essd-12-961-2020.

Petrescu, A.M.R. et al., 2021a: The consolidated European synthesis of CO_2 emissions and removals for the European Union and United Kingdom: 1990–2018. *Earth Syst. Sci. Data*, **13(5)**, 2363–2406, doi:10.5194/essd-13-2363-2021.

Petrescu, A.M.R. et al., 2021b: The consolidated European synthesis of CH_4 and N_2O emissions for the European Union and United Kingdom: 1990–2017. *Earth Syst. Sci. Data*, **13(5)**, 2307–2362, doi:10.5194/essd-13-2307-2021.

Petrick, S. et al., 2014: *The Impact of Carbon Trading on Industry: Evidence from German Manufacturing Firms*. Kiel Institute for the World Economy, Kiel, Germany, pp. 1–52.

Pfeiffer, A., C. Hepburn, A. Vogt-Schilb, and B. Caldecott, 2018: Committed emissions from existing and planned power plants and asset stranding required to meet the Paris Agreement. *Environ. Res. Lett.*, **13(5)**, 054019, doi:10.1088/1748-9326/aabc5f.

Pincetl, S., 2017: Cities in the age of the Anthropocene: Climate change agents and the potential for mitigation. *Anthropocene*, **20**, 74–82, doi:10.1016/j.ancene.2017.08.001.

Pizer, W., J.N. Sanchirico, and M. Batz, 2010: Regional patterns of U.S. household carbon emissions. *Clim. Change*, **99(1–2)**, 47–63, doi:10.1007/s10584-009-9637-8.

Plank, B., N. Eisenmenger, A. Schaffartzik, and D. Wiedenhofer, 2018: International Trade Drives Global Resource Use: A Structural Decomposition Analysis of Raw Material Consumption from 1990–2010. *Environ. Sci. Technol.*, **52(7)**, 4190–4198, doi:10.1021/acs.est.7b06133.

Plattner, G.-K., T.F. Stocker, P. Midgley, and M. Tignor, (eds.) 2009: *Meeting Report of the IPCC Expert Meeting on the Science of Alternative Metrics*. IPCC WGI Technical Support Unit, Bern, Switzerland, 82 pp.

Plötz, P., J. Axsen, S.A. Funke, and T. Gnann, 2019: Designing car bans for sustainable transportation. *Nat. Sustain.*, **2(7)**, 534–536, doi:10.1038/s41893-019-0328-9.

Pojani, D. and D. Stead, 2017: *The urban transport crisis in emerging economies*. Springer Nature, Cham, Switzerland, 301 pp.

Polonsky, M.J., A. Vocino, S.L. Grau, R. Garma, and A.S. Ferdous, 2012: The impact of general and carbon-related environmental knowledge on attitudes and behaviour of US consumers. *J. Mark. Manag.*, **28(3–4)**, 238–263, doi:10.1080/0267257X.2012.659279.

Popkin, B.M., 2015: Nutrition Transition and the Global Diabetes Epidemic. *Curr. Diab. Rep.*, **15(9)**, 64, doi:10.1007/s11892-015-0631-4.

Porter, S.D. and D.S. Reay, 2016: Addressing food supply chain and consumption inefficiencies: potential for climate change mitigation. *Reg. Environ. Change*, **16(8)**, 2279–2290, doi:10.1007/s10113-015-0783-4.

Pradhan, P., D.E. Reusser, and J.P. Kropp, 2013: Embodied Greenhouse Gas Emissions in Diets. *PLoS One*, **8(5)**, e62228, doi:10.1371/journal.pone.0062228.

Pradhan, S. et al., 2021: Effects of Direct Air Capture Technology Availability on Stranded Assets and Committed Emissions in the Power Sector. *Front. Clim.*, **3**, 1–12, doi:10.3389/fclim.2021.660787.

Prosperi, P. et al., 2020: New estimates of greenhouse gas emissions from biomass burning and peat fires using MODIS Collection 6 burned areas. *Clim. Change*, **161(3)**, 415–432, doi:10.1007/s10584-020-02654-0.

Qi, Y., N. Stern, T. Wu, J. Lu, and F. Green, 2016: China's post-coal growth. *Nat. Geosci.*, **9(8)**, 564–566, doi:10.1038/ngeo2777.

Qiu, Y.Q., P. Zhou, and H.C. Sun, 2019: Assessing the effectiveness of city-level electric vehicle policies in China. *Energy Policy*, **130**, 22–31, doi:10.1016/j.enpol.2019.03.052.

Qu, J. et al., 2013: Household carbon dioxide emissions from peasants and herdsmen in northwestern arid-alpine regions, China. *Energy Policy*, **57**, 133–140, doi:10.1016/j.enpol.2012.12.065.

Qvist, S.A. and B.W. Brook, 2015: Potential for Worldwide Displacement of Fossil-Fuel Electricity by Nuclear Energy in Three Decades Based on Extrapolation of Regional Deployment Data. *PLoS One*, **10(5)**, e0124074, doi:10.1371/journal.pone.0124074.

Rafaj, P., M. Amann, J. Siri, and H. Wuester, 2014: Changes in European greenhouse gas and air pollutant emissions 1960–2010: decomposition of determining factors. *Clim. Change*, **124(3)**, 477–504, doi:10.1007/s10584-013-0826-0.

Rao, N.D. and J. Min, 2018: Less global inequality can improve climate outcomes. *WIREs Clim. Change*, **9(2)**, doi:10.1002/wcc.513.

Rao, N.D., J. Min, and A. Mastrucci, 2019: Energy requirements for decent living in India, Brazil and South Africa. *Nat. Energy*, **4(12)**, 1025–1032, doi:10.1038/s41560-019-0497-9.

Rao, S. et al., 2017: Future air pollution in the Shared Socio-economic Pathways. *Glob. Environ. Change*, **42**, 346–358, doi:10.1016/j.gloenvcha.2016.05.012.

Räty, R. and A. Carlsson-Kanyama, 2010: Energy consumption by gender in some European countries. *Energy Policy*, **38(1)**, 646–649, doi:10.1016/j.enpol.2009.08.010.

Rauner, S. et al., 2020a: Coal-exit health and environmental damage reductions outweigh economic impacts. *Nat. Clim. Change*, **10(4)**, 308–312, doi:10.1038/s41558-020-0728-x.

Rauner, S., J. Hilaire, D. Klein, J. Strefler, and G. Luderer, 2020b: Air quality co-benefits of ratcheting up the NDCs. *Clim. Change*, **163(3)**, 1481–1500, doi:10.1007/s10584-020-02699-1.

Rausch, S. and H. Schwerin, 2018: *Does Higher Energy Efficiency Lower Economy-Wide Energy Use?* CER-ETH – Center of Economic Research at ETH Zurich, Zurich, Switzerland.

Reed, A. et al., 2019: Interrogating uncertainty in energy forecasts: the case of the shale gas boom. *Energy Transitions*, **3(1–2)**, 1–11, doi:10.1007/s41825-019-00015-9.

Reisinger, A. et al., 2021: How necessary and feasible are reductions of methane emissions from livestock to support stringent temperature goals? *Philos. Trans. R. Soc. A Math. Phys. Eng. Sci.*, **379(2210)**, 20200452, doi:10.1098/rsta.2020.0452.

Riahi, K. et al., 2015: Locked into Copenhagen pledges – Implications of short-term emission targets for the cost and feasibility of long-term climate goals. *Technol. Forecast. Soc. Change*, **90**, 8–23, doi:10.1016/j.techfore.2013.09.016.

Richardson, R.B., L.S. Olabisi, N. Sakana, K. Waldman, and P. Grabowski, 2015: *The impact of sustainable intensification on landscapes and livelihoods (SILL) in Zambia*. International Institute of Tropical Agriculture, Ibadan, Nigeria, 76 pp.

Rietmann, N. and T. Lieven, 2019: How policy measures succeeded to promote electric mobility – Worldwide review and outlook. *J. Clean. Prod.*, **206**, 66–75, doi:10.1016/j.jclepro.2018.09.121.

Rissman, J. et al., 2020: Technologies and policies to decarbonize global industry: Review and assessment of mitigation drivers through 2070. *Appl. Energy*, **266**, 114848, doi:10.1016/j.apenergy.2020.114848.

2

Ritchie, H., 2019: Who has contributed most to global CO_2 emissions? Our World in Data, https://ourworldindata.org/contributed-most-global-co2#:~:text=The%20USA%20has%20emitted%20most,over%20the%20last%20266%20years.

Ritchie, J. and H. Dowlatabadi, 2017: Why do climate change scenarios return to coal? *Energy*, **140**, 1276–1291, doi:10.1016/j.energy.2017.08.083.

Ritchie, J. and H. Dowlatabadi, 2018: Defining climate change scenario characteristics with a phase space of cumulative primary energy and carbon intensity. *Environ. Res. Lett.*, **13(2)**, 024012, doi:10.1088/1748-9326/aaa494.

Rivers, N. and B. Schaufele, 2015: Salience of carbon taxes in the gasoline market. *J. Environ. Econ. Manage.*, **74**, 23–36, doi:10.1016/j.jeem.2015.07.002.

Rocha, M. et al., 2015: *Historical Responsibility for Climate Change – from countries emissions to contribution to temperature increase*. Climate Analytics and Potsdam Institute for Climate Impact Research, 51 pp.

Rodrigues, J.F.D., J. Wang, P. Behrens, and P. de Boer, 2020: Drivers of CO_2 emissions from electricity generation in the European Union 2000–2015. *Renew. Sustain. Energy Rev.*, **133**, 110104, doi:10.1016/j.rser.2020.110104.

Roelfsema, M. et al., 2020: Taking stock of national climate policies to evaluate implementation of the Paris Agreement. *Nat. Commun.*, **11(1)**, 2096, doi:10.1038/s41467-020-15414-6.

Rogelj, J. and C.-F. Schleussner, 2019: Unintentional unfairness when applying new greenhouse gas emissions metrics at country level. *Environ. Res. Lett.*, **14(11)**, 114039, doi:10.1088/1748-9326/ab4928.

Rogelj, J. and C.-F. Schleussner, 2021: Reply to Comment on 'Unintentional unfairness when applying new greenhouse gas emissions metrics at country level.' *Environ. Res. Lett.*, **16(6)**, 068002, doi:10.1088/1748-9326/ac02ec.

Rogge, K.S. and E. Dütschke, 2018: What makes them believe in the low-carbon energy transition? Exploring corporate perceptions of the credibility of climate policy mixes. *Environ. Sci. Policy*, **87**, 74–84, doi:10.1016/j.envsci.2018.05.009.

Roinioti, A. and C. Koroneos, 2017: The decomposition of CO_2 emissions from energy use in Greece before and during the economic crisis and their decoupling from economic growth. *Renew. Sustain. Energy Rev.*, **76**, 448–459, doi:10.1016/j.rser.2017.03.026.

Rojas-Vallejos, J. and A. Lastuka, 2020: The income inequality and carbon emissions trade-off revisited. *Energy Policy*, **139**, 111302, doi:10.1016/j.enpol.2020.111302.

Römpke, A.-K., I. Fritsche, and G. Reese, 2019: Get together, feel together, act together: International personal contact increases identification with humanity and global collective action. *J. Theor. Soc. Psychol.*, **3(1)**, 35–48, doi:10.1002/jts5.34.

Rosenbloom, D. and A. Rinscheid, 2020: Deliberate decline: An emerging frontier for the study and practice of decarbonization. *WIREs Clim. Change*, **11(6)**, doi:10.1002/wcc.669.

Rosenbloom, D., J. Markard, F.W. Geels, and L. Fuenfschilling, 2020: Why carbon pricing is not sufficient to mitigate climate change – and how "sustainability transition policy" can help. *Proc. Natl. Acad. Sci.*, **117(16)**, 8664–8668, doi:10.1073/pnas.2004093117.

Rosoman, G., S.S. Sheun, C. Opal, P. Anderson, and R. Trapshah, (eds.) 2017: The HCS Approach – Putting no deforestation into practice. *HCS Approach Toolkit Version 2.0*, (August). HSCA Foundation, Kuala Lumpur, Malaysia.

Rozenberg, J., S.J. Davis, U. Narloch, and S. Hallegatte, 2015: Climate constraints on the carbon intensity of economic growth. *Environ. Res. Lett.*, **10(9)**, 095006, doi:10.1088/1748-9326/10/9/095006.

Saheb, Y. et al., 2019: *The European Energy Poverty Index (EEPI)*. OpenExp, 29 pp. https://www.openexp.eu/sites/default/files/publication/files/european_energy_poverty_index-eepi_en.pdf.

Sanches-Pereira, A., L.G. Tudeschini, and S.T. Coelho, 2016: Evolution of the Brazilian residential carbon footprint based on direct energy consumption. *Renew. Sustain. Energy Rev.*, **54**, 184–201, doi:10.1016/j.rser.2015.09.024.

Sanchez, L.F. and D.I. Stern, 2016: Drivers of industrial and non-industrial greenhouse gas emissions. *Ecol. Econ.*, **124**, 17–24, doi:10.1016/j.ecolecon.2016.01.008.

Santos, G. and H. Davies, 2020: Incentives for quick penetration of electric vehicles in five European countries: Perceptions from experts and stakeholders. *Transp. Res. Part A Policy Pract.*, **137**, 326–342, doi:10.1016/j.tra.2018.10.034.

Sarkodie, S.A., P.A. Owusu, and T. Leirvik, 2020: Global effect of urban sprawl, industrialization, trade and economic development on carbon dioxide emissions. *Environ. Res. Lett.*, **15(3)**, 034049, doi:10.1088/1748-9326/ab7640.

Sarofim, M.C. and M.R. Giordano, 2018: A quantitative approach to evaluating the GWP timescale through implicit discount rates. *Earth Syst. Dyn.*, **9(3)**, 1013–1024, doi:10.5194/esd-9-1013-2018.

Sato, M., 2014: Product level embodied carbon flows in bilateral trade. *Ecol. Econ.*, **105**, 106–117, doi:10.1016/j.ecolecon.2014.05.006.

Saunders, H.D., 2015: Recent Evidence for Large Rebound: Elucidating the Drivers and their Implications for Climate Change Models. *Energy J.*, **36(1)**, 23–48, doi:10.5547/01956574.36.1.2.

Saunois, M. et al., 2016: The global methane budget 2000–2012. *Earth Syst. Sci. Data*, **8(2)**, 697–751, doi:10.5194/essd-8-697-2016.

Saunois, M. et al., 2020: The Global Methane Budget 2000–2017. *Earth Syst. Sci. Data*, **12(3)**, 1561–1623, doi:10.5194/essd-12-1561-2020.

Schäfer, A., J.B. Heywood, H.D. Jacoby, and I.A. Waitz, 2009: *Transportation in a Climate-Constrained World*. The MIT Press, Cambridge, Massachusetts, USA, 357 pp.

Schandl, H. et al., 2016: Decoupling global environmental pressure and economic growth: scenarios for energy use, materials use and carbon emissions. *J. Clean. Prod.*, **132**, 45–56, doi:10.1016/j.jclepro.2015.06.100.

Schleussner, C.-F., A. Nauels, M. Schaeffer, W. Hare, and J. Rogelj, 2019: Inconsistencies when applying novel metrics for emissions accounting to the Paris agreement. *Environ. Res. Lett.*, **14(12)**, 124055, doi:10.1088/1748-9326/ab56e7.

Schmale, J., D. Shindell, E. von Schneidemesser, I. Chabay, and M. Lawrence, 2014: Air pollution: Clean up our skies. *Nature*, **515(7527)**, 335–337, doi:10.1038/515335a.

Schmidt, T.S., 2019: Making electrification models more realistic by incorporating differences in institutional quality and financing cost. *Prog. Energy*, **2(1)**, 013001, doi:10.1088/2516-1083/ab43a3.

Schor, J.B., 1998: *The Overspent American*. Basic Books, New York, NY, USA, pp 272.

Schulze, M., H. Nehler, M. Ottosson, and P. Thollander, 2016: Energy management in industry – a systematic review of previous findings and an integrative conceptual framework. *J. Clean. Prod.*, **112**, 3692–3708, doi:10.1016/j.jclepro.2015.06.060.

Schwerhoff, G., 2016: The economics of leadership in climate change mitigation. *Clim. Policy*, **16(2)**, 196–214, doi:10.1080/14693062.2014.992297.

Semieniuk, G. and V.M. Yakovenko, 2020: Historical evolution of global inequality in carbon emissions and footprints versus redistributive scenarios. *J. Clean. Prod.*, **264**, 121420, doi:10.1016/j.jclepro.2020.121420.

Sen, A., 1999: *Development as freedom*. Oxford University Press, Oxford, UK, 84 pp.

Seriño, M.N.V., 2017: Is Decoupling Possible? Association between Affluence and Household Carbon Emissions in the Philippines. *Asian Econ. J.*, **31(2)**, 165–185, doi:10.1111/asej.12119.

Service, R.F., 2019: Solar plus batteries is now cheaper than fossil power. *Science*, **365(6449)**, 108–108, doi:10.1126/science.365.6449.108.

Seto K.C., S. Dhakal, A. Bigio, H. Blanco, G.C. Delgado, D. Dewar, L. Huang, A. Inaba, A. Kansal, S. Lwasa, J.E. McMahon, D.B. Müller, J. Murakami, H. Nagendra, and A. Ramaswami, 2014: Human Settlements, Infrastructure and Spatial Planning. In: *Climate Change 2014: Mitigation of Climate Change. Contribution of Working Group III to the Fifth Assessment Report of the Intergovernmental Panel on Climate Change* [Edenhofer, O., R. Pichs-Madruga, Y. Sokona, E. Farahani, S. Kadner, K. Seyboth, A. Adler, I. Baum, S. Brunner, P. Eickemeier, B. Kriemann, J. Savolainen, S. Schlömer, C. von Stechow, T. Zwickel and J.C. Minx (eds.)]. Cambridge University Press, Cambridge, UK and New York, NY, USA.

Seto, K.C. et al., 2016: Carbon Lock-In: Types, Causes, and Policy Implications. *Annu. Rev. Environ. Resour.*, **41(1)**, 425–452, doi:10.1146/annurev-environ-110615-085934.

Seto, K.C., J.S. Golden, M. Alberti, and B.L. Turner, 2017: Sustainability in an urbanizing planet. *Proc. Natl. Acad. Sci.*, **114(34)**, 8935–8938, doi:10.1073/pnas.1606037114.

Shan, Y. et al., 2018: China CO_2 emission accounts 1997–2015. *Sci. Data*, **5(1)**, 170201, doi:10.1038/sdata.2017.201.

Shan, Y. et al. 2021a: Impacts of COVID-19 and fiscal stimuli on global emissions and the Paris Agreement. Nat. Clim. Chang, 11, 200–206. doi:10.1038/s41558-020-00977-5.

Shan, Y. et al., 2021b: Chinese cities exhibit varying degrees of decoupling of economic growth and CO_2 emissions between 2005 and 2015. *One Earth*, **4(1)**, 124–134, doi:10.1016/j.oneear.2020.12.004.

Shao, Q. and S. Shen, 2017: When reduced working time harms the environment: A panel threshold analysis for EU-15, 1970–2010. *J. Clean. Prod.*, **147**, 319–329, doi:10.1016/j.jclepro.2017.01.115.

Shearer, C., R. Fofrich, and S.J. Davis, 2017: Future CO_2 emissions and electricity generation from proposed coal-fired power plants in India. *Earth's Futur.*, **5(4)**, 408–416, doi:10.1002/2017EF000542.

Shearer, C., D. Tong, R. Fofrich, and S.J. Davis, 2020: Committed Emissions of the U.S. Power Sector, 2000–2018. *AGU Adv.*, **1(3)**, doi:10.1029/2020AV000162.

Shigetomi, Y., K. Nansai, S. Kagawa, and S. Tohno, 2014: Changes in the Carbon Footprint of Japanese Households in an Aging Society. *Environ. Sci. Technol.*, **48(11)**, 6069–6080, doi:10.1021/es404939d.

Shigetomi, Y. et al., 2018: Driving forces underlying sub-national carbon dioxide emissions within the household sector and implications for the Paris Agreement targets in Japan. *Appl. Energy*, **228**, 2321–2332, doi:10.1016/j.apenergy.2018.07.057.

Shigetomi, Y. et al., 2019: Clarifying Demographic Impacts on Embodied and Materially Retained Carbon toward Climate Change Mitigation. *Environ. Sci. Technol.*, **53(24)**, 14123–14133, doi:10.1021/acs.est.9b02603.

Shiraki, H. and M. Sugiyama, 2020: Back to the basic: toward improvement of technoeconomic representation in integrated assessment models. *Clim. Change*, **162(1)**, 13–24, doi:10.1007/s10584-020-02731-4.

Shishlov, I., R. Morel, and V. Bellassen, 2016: Compliance of the Parties to the Kyoto Protocol in the first commitment period. *Clim. Policy*, **16(6)**, 768–782, doi:10.1080/14693062.2016.1164658.

Shmelev, S.E. and S.U. Speck, 2018: Green fiscal reform in Sweden: Econometric assessment of the carbon and energy taxation scheme. *Renew. Sustain. Energy Rev.*, **90**, 969–981, doi:10.1016/j.rser.2018.03.032.

Short, J.R. and L. Martínez, 2020: The urban effects of the emerging middle class in the global south. *Geogr. Compass*, **14(4)**, doi:10.1111/gec3.12484.

Shove, E. and F. Trentmann, (eds.) 2018: *Infrastructures in Practice: The Dynamics of Demand in Networked Societies*. Routledge, Abingdon, Oxon; New York, NY, USA, 236 pp.

Sierzchula, W., S. Bakker, K. Maat, and B. van Wee, 2014: The influence of financial incentives and other socio-economic factors on electric vehicle adoption. *Energy Policy*, **68(0)**, 183–194, doi:10.1016/j.enpol.2014.01.043.

Silvia, C. and R.M. Krause, 2016: Assessing the impact of policy interventions on the adoption of plug-in electric vehicles: An agent-based model. *Energy Policy*, **96**, 105–118, doi:10.1016/j.enpol.2016.05.039.

Singh, D., S. Pachauri, and H. Zerriffi, 2017: Environmental payoffs of LPG cooking in India. *Environ. Res. Lett.*, **12(11)**, 115003, doi:10.1088/1748-9326/aa909d.

Sivaram, V., J.O. Dabiri, and D.M. Hart, 2018: The Need for Continued Innovation in Solar, Wind, and Energy Storage. *Joule*, **2(9)**, 1639–1642, doi:10.1016/j.joule.2018.07.025.

SLoCaT, 2018: *Transport and Climate Change: Global Status Report 2018*. SLoCaT, 184 pp. http://slocat.net/tcc-gsr.

Smetschka, B. et al., 2019: Time Matters: The Carbon Footprint of Everyday Activities in Austria. *Ecol. Econ.*, **164**, 106357, doi:10.1016/j.ecolecon.2019.106357.

Smil, V., 2016: Examining energy transitions: A dozen insights based on performance. *Energy Res. Soc. Sci.*, **22**, 194–197, doi:10.1016/j.erss.2016.08.017.

Smith, C.J. et al., 2019: Current fossil fuel infrastructure does not yet commit us to 1.5°C warming. *Nat. Commun.*, **10(1)**, 101, doi:10.1038/s41467-018-07999-w.

Smith, S.J. et al., 2020: The Energy Modeling Forum (EMF)-30 study on short-lived climate forcers: introduction and overview. *Clim. Change*, **163(3)**, 1399–1408, doi:10.1007/s10584-020-02938-5.

Solazzo, E. et al., 2021: Uncertainties in the Emissions Database for Global Atmospheric Research (EDGAR) emission inventory of greenhouse gases. *Atmos. Chem. Phys.*, **21(7)**, 5655–5683, doi:10.5194/acp-21-5655-2021.

Sovacool, B.K., 2016: How long will it take? Conceptualizing the temporal dynamics of energy transitions. *Energy Res. Soc. Sci.*, **13**, 202–215, doi:10.1016/j.erss.2015.12.020.

Sovacool, B.K. and C.G. Monyei, 2021: Positive Externalities of Decarbonization: Quantifying the Full Potential of Avoided Deaths and Displaced Carbon Emissions from Renewable Energy and Nuclear Power. *Environ. Sci. Technol.*, **55(8)**, 5258–5271, doi:10.1021/acs.est.1c00140.

Spencer, T. et al., 2018: The 1.5°C target and coal sector transition: at the limits of societal feasibility. *Clim. Policy*, **18(3)**, 335–351, doi:10.1080/14693062.2017.1386540.

Stadler, K. et al., 2018: EXIOBASE 3: Developing a Time Series of Detailed Environmentally Extended Multi-Regional Input-Output Tables. *J. Ind. Ecol.*, **22(3)**, 502–515, doi:10.1111/jiec.12715.

Stearns, P., 2001: *Consumerism in World History: The Global Transformation of Desire*. Routledge, New York, USA, 180 pp.

Steckel, J.C., J. Hilaire, M. Jakob, and O. Edenhofer, 2020: Coal and carbonization in sub-Saharan Africa. *Nat. Clim. Change*, **10(1)**, 83–88, doi:10.1038/s41558-019-0649-8.

Steininger, K. et al., 2014: Justice and cost effectiveness of consumption-based versus production-based approaches in the case of unilateral climate policies. *Glob. Environ. Change*, **24**, 75–87, doi:10.1016/j.gloenvcha.2013.10.005.

Steininger, K.W. and T. Schinko, 2015: Environmental Policy in an Open Economy: Refocusing Climate Policy to Address International Trade Spillovers. In: *Dynamic Approaches to Global Economic Challenges*, Springer International Publishing, Cham, Switzerland, pp. 171–190.

Steinsland, C., L. Fridstrøm, A. Madslien, and H. Minken, 2018: The climate, economic and equity effects of fuel tax, road toll and commuter tax credit. *Transp. Policy*, **72**(April), 225–241, doi:10.1016/j.tranpol.2018.04.019.

Stender, F., U. Moslener, and W.P. Pauw, 2020: More than money: does climate finance support capacity building? *Appl. Econ. Lett.*, **27(15)**, 1247–1251, doi:10.1080/13504851.2019.1676384.

Stern, D.I., 2011: The role of energy in economic growth. *Ann. N. Y. Acad. Sci.*, **1219(1)**, 26–51, doi:10.1111/j.1749-6632.2010.05921.x.

Stern, D.I., 2019: Energy and economic growth. In: *Routledge Handbook of Energy Economics* [Soytaş, U. and R. Sarı, (eds.)], Routledge, London, UK, pp. 28–46.

Stern, D.I., 2020: How large is the economy-wide rebound effect? *Energy Policy*, **147**, 111870, doi:10.1016/j.enpol.2020.111870.

Stokes, L.C. and H.L. Breetz, 2018: Politics in the U.S. energy transition: Case studies of solar, wind, biofuels and electric vehicles policy. *Energy Policy*, **113**, 76–86, doi:10.1016/j.enpol.2017.10.057.

Stoknes, P.E. and J. Rockström, 2018: Redefining green growth within planetary boundaries. *Energy Res. Soc. Sci.*, **44**, 41–49, doi:10.1016/j.erss.2018.04.030.

Strefler, J., G. Luderer, T. Aboumahboub, and E. Kriegler, 2014: Economic impacts of alternative greenhouse gas emission metrics: a model-based assessment. *Clim. Change*, **125(3–4)**, 319–331, doi:10.1007/s10584-014-1188-y.

Su, B. and B.W. Ang, 2016: Multi-region comparisons of emission performance: The structural decomposition analysis approach. *Ecol. Indic.*, **67**, 78–87, doi:10.1016/j.ecolind.2016.02.020.

Sweerts, B., R.J. Detz, and B. van der Zwaan, 2020: Evaluating the Role of Unit Size in Learning-by-Doing of Energy Technologies. *Joule*, **4(5)**, 967–970, doi:10.1016/j.joule.2020.03.010.

Szopa, S., V. Naik, B. Adhikary, P. Artaxo, T. Berntsen, W.D. Collins, S. Fuzzi, L. Gallardo, A. Kiendler-Scharr, Z. Klimont, H. Liao, N. Unger, and P. Zanis, 2021a: Short-Lived Climate Forcers. In *Climate Change 2021: The Physical Science Basis. Contribution of Working Group I to the Sixth Assessment Report of the Intergovernmental Panel on Climate Change* [Masson-Delmotte, V., P. Zhai, A. Pirani, S.L. Connors, C. Péan, S. Berger, N. Caud, Y. Chen, L. Goldfarb, M.I. Gomis, M. Huang, K. Leitzell, E. Lonnoy, J.B.R. Matthews, T.K. Maycock, T. Waterfield, O. Yelekçi, R. Yu, and B. Zhou (eds.)]. Cambridge University Press, Cambridge, United Kingdom and New York, NY, USA, pp. 817–922, doi:10.1017/9781009157896.008.

Szopa, S., V. Naik, B. Adhikary, P. Artaxo, T. Berntsen, W.D. Collins, S. Fuzzi, L. Gallardo, A. Kiendler-Scharr, Z. Klimont, H. Liao, N. Unger, and P. Zanis, 2021b: Short-Lived Climate Forcers Supplementary Material. In *Climate Change 2021: The Physical Science Basis. Contribution of Working Group I to the Sixth Assessment Report of the Intergovernmental Panel on Climate Change* [Masson-Delmotte, V., P. Zhai, A. Pirani, S.L. Connors, C. Péan, S. Berger, N. Caud, Y. Chen, L. Goldfarb, M.I. Gomis, M. Huang, K. Leitzell, E. Lonnoy, J.B.R. Matthews, T.K. Maycock, T. Waterfield, O. Yelekçi, R. Yu, and B. Zhou (eds.)]. Available from https://www.ipcc.ch/.

Talaei, A., M. Ahiduzzaman, and A. Kumar, 2018: Assessment of long-term energy efficiency improvement and greenhouse gas emissions mitigation potentials in the chemical sector. *Energy*, **153**, 231–247, doi:10.1016/j.energy.2018.04.032.

Tanaka, K. and B.C. O'Neill, 2018: The Paris Agreement zero-emissions goal is not always consistent with the 1.5°C and 2°C temperature targets. *Nat. Clim. Change*, 8, 319-324, doi:10.1038/s41558-018-0097-x.

Tanaka, K., O. Cavalett, W.J. Collins, and F. Cherubini, 2019: Asserting the climate benefits of the coal-to-gas shift across temporal and spatial scales. *Nat. Clim. Change*, **9(5)**, 389–396, doi:10.1038/s41558-019-0457-1.

Tanaka, K., O. Boucher, P. Ciais, and D.J.A. Johansson, 2020: Cost-effective implementation of the Paris Agreement using flexible greenhouse gas metrics. *Nat. Commun.* (in press).

Tang, L. et al., 2019: Substantial emission reductions from Chinese power plants after the introduction of ultra-low emissions standards. *Nat. Energy*, **4(11)**, doi:10.1038/s41560-019-0468-1.

Tao, S. et al., 2018: Quantifying the rural residential energy transition in China from 1992 to 2012 through a representative national survey. *Nat. Energy*, **3(7)**, 567–573, doi:10.1038/s41560-018-0158-4.

Tao, Y., H. Liang, and M.A. Celia, 2020: Electric power development associated with the Belt and Road Initiative and its carbon emissions implications. *Appl. Energy*, **267**, 114784, doi:10.1016/j.apenergy.2020.114784.

Tate, W.L. and L. Bals, 2017: Outsourcing/offshoring insights: going beyond reshoring to rightshoring. *Int. J. Phys. Distrib. Logist. Manag.*, **47(2/3)**, 106–113, doi:10.1108/IJPDLM-11-2016-0314.

Tavakoli, A., 2018: A journey among top ten emitter country, decomposition of "Kaya Identity." *Sustain. Cities Soc.*, **38**, 254–264, doi:10.1016/j.scs.2017.12.040.

Taylor, M.R., 2012: Innovation under cap-and-trade programs. *Proc. Natl. Acad. Sci.*, **109(13)**, 4804–4809, doi:10.1073/pnas.1113462109.

Teixeira, A.C.R. and J.R. Sodré, 2018: Impacts of replacement of engine powered vehicles by electric vehicles on energy consumption and CO_2 emissions. *Transp. Res. Part D Transp. Environ.*, **59**(February), 375–384, doi:10.1016/j.trd.2018.01.004.

TFD, 2014: *Scoping dialogue on understanding deforestation-free (UDF).*, New Haven, Connecticut, USA, 14 pp.

Thiel, C., A. Tsakalidis, and A. Jäger-Waldau, 2020: Will Electric Vehicles Be Killed (again) or Are They the Next Mobility Killer App? *Energies*, **13(7)**, 1828, doi:10.3390/en13071828.

Thoday, K., P. Benjamin, M. Gan, and E. Puzzolo, 2018: The Mega Conversion Program from kerosene to LPG in Indonesia: Lessons learned and recommendations for future clean cooking energy expansion. *Energy Sustain. Dev.*, **46**, 71–81, doi:10.1016/j.esd.2018.05.011.

Thomassen, G., S. Van Passel, and J. Dewulf, 2020: A review on learning effects in prospective technology assessment. *Renew. Sustain. Energy Rev.*, **130**, 109937, doi:10.1016/j.rser.2020.109937.

Tian, H. et al., 2019: Global soil nitrous oxide emissions since the preindustrial era estimated by an ensemble of terrestrial biosphere models: Magnitude, attribution, and uncertainty. *Glob. Change Biol.*, **25(2)**, 640–659, doi:10.1111/gcb.14514.

Tilman, D. and M. Clark, 2014: Global diets link environmental sustainability and human health. *Nature*, **515(7528)**, 518–522, doi:10.1038/nature13959.

Timmer, M.P., E. Dietzenbacher, B. Los, R. Stehrer, and G.J. de Vries, 2015: An Illustrated User Guide to the World Input-Output Database: the Case of Global Automotive Production. *Rev. Int. Econ.*, **23(3)**, 575–605, doi:10.1111/roie.12178.

Tong, D. et al., 2019: Committed emissions from existing energy infrastructure jeopardize 1.5°C climate target. *Nature*, **572(7769)**, 373–377, doi:10.1038/s41586-019-1364-3.

Trancik, J.E., 2006: Scale and innovation in the energy sector: a focus on photovoltaics and nuclear fission. *Environ. Res. Lett.*, **1(1)**, 014009, doi:10.1088/1748-9326/1/1/014009.

Tubiello, F.N., 2019: Greenhouse Gas Emissions Due to Agriculture. In: *Encyclopedia of Food Security and Sustainability*, Elsevier, New York, NY, USA, pp. 196–205.

Tubiello, F.N. et al., 2013: The FAOSTAT database of greenhouse gas emissions from agriculture. *Environ. Res. Lett.*, **8(1)**, 015009, doi:10.1088/1748-9326/8/1/015009.

Tubiello, F.N. et al., 2015: The Contribution of Agriculture, Forestry and other Land Use Activities to Global Warming, 1990-2012. *Glob. Change Biol.*, **21(7)**, 2655–2660, doi:10.1111/gcb.12865.

Tubiello, F.N. et al., 2021: Carbon emissions and removals from forests: new estimates, 1990–2020. *Earth Syst. Sci. Data*, **13(4)**, 1681–1691, doi:10.5194/essd-13-1681-2021.

Tukker, A. and B. Jansen, 2006: Environmental Impacts of Products: A Detailed Review of Studies. *J. Ind. Ecol.*, **10(3)**, 159–182, doi:10.1162/jiec.2006.10.3.159.

Tukker, A. et al., 2018: Towards Robust, Authoritative Assessments of Environmental Impacts Embodied in Trade: Current State and Recommendations. *J. Ind. Ecol.*, **22(3)**, 585–598, doi:10.1111/jiec.12716.

Tukker, A., R. Wood, and S. Schmidt, 2020: Towards accepted procedures for calculating international consumption-based carbon accounts. *Clim. Policy*, **20(sup1)**, S90–S106, doi:10.1080/14693062.2020.1722605.

Turnock, S.T. et al., 2016: The impact of European legislative and technology measures to reduce air pollutants on air quality, human health and climate. *Environ. Res. Lett.*, **11(2)**, 024010, doi:10.1088/1748-9326/11/2/024010.

Tvinnereim, E. and M. Mehling, 2018: Carbon pricing and deep decarbonisation. *Energy Policy*, **121**, 185–189, doi:10.1016/j.enpol.2018.06.020.

Tzeiranaki, S.T. et al., 2019: Analysis of the EU Residential Energy Consumption: Trends and Determinants. *Energies*, **12(6)**, 1065, doi:10.3390/en12061065.

Uddin, M.M., V. Mishra, and R. Smyth, 2020: Income inequality and CO_2 emissions in the G7, 1870–2014: Evidence from non-parametric modelling. *Energy Econ.*, **88**, 104780, doi:10.1016/j.eneco.2020.104780.

UNCTAD, 2021: Merchandise: Total trade and share, annual. https://unctadstat.unctad.org/EN/BulkDownload.html.

Underwood, A. and S. Zahran, 2015: The carbon implications of declining household scale economies. *Ecol. Econ.*, **116**, 182–190, doi:10.1016/j.ecolecon.2015.04.028.

UNEP, 2017: *The Emissions Gap Report 2017*. United Nations Environment Programme, Nairobi, Kenya, 116 pp.

UNEP, 2019: *Emissions Gap Report 2019. Executive summary*. United Nations Environment Programme, Nairobi, Kenya, pp. XIV–XXV.

UNEP, 2020a: *Emissions Gap Report 2020*. United Nations Environment Programme, Nairobi, Kenya, 128 pp.

UNEP, 2020b: Global emissions trends and G20 status and outlook. In: *Emissions Gap Report 2020*, United Nations Environment Programme, Nairobi, Kenya, pp. 3–24.

UNFCCC, 2019: *Report of the Conference of the Parties serving as the meeting of the Parties to the Paris Agreement on the third part of its first session, held in Katowice from 2 to 15 December 2018. Addendum, Part 2: Action taken by the Conference of the Parties*. UNFCCC, Bonn, Germany, 37 pp.

UNFCCC, 2021: National Inventory Submissions 2021. https://unfccc.int/ghg-inventories-annex-i-parties/2021 (Accessed September 30, 2021).

Unruh, G.C., 2000: Understanding carbon lock-in. *Energy Policy*, **28(12)**, 817–830, doi:10.1016/S0301-4215(00)00070-7.

Unruh, G.C., 2002: Escaping carbon lock-in. *Energy Policy*, **30(4)**, 317–325, doi:10.1016/S0301-4215(01)00098-2.

Unruh, G.C. and J. Carrillo-Hermosilla, 2006: Globalizing carbon lock-in. *Energy Policy*, **34(10)**, 1185–1197, doi:10.1016/j.enpol.2004.10.013.

Urban, F., 2018: China's rise: Challenging the North-South technology transfer paradigm for climate change mitigation and low carbon energy. *Energy Policy*, **113**, 320–330, doi:10.1016/j.enpol.2017.11.007.

Ürge-Vorsatz, D., L.F. Cabeza, S. Serrano, C. Barreneche, and K. Petrichenko, 2015: Heating and cooling energy trends and drivers in buildings. *Renew. Sustain. Energy Rev.*, **41**, 85–98, doi:10.1016/j.rser.2014.08.039.

Ürge-Vorsatz, D. et al., 2020: Advances Toward a Net-Zero Global Building Sector. *Annu. Rev. Environ. Resour.*, **45(1)**, 227–269, doi:10.1146/annurev-environ-012420-045843.

US-EPA, 2019: *Global Non-CO$_2$ Greenhouse Gas Emission Projections & Mitigation.*, Washington D.C., USA, 84 pp. https://www.epa.gov/global-mitigation-non-co2-greenhouse-gases.

Vadén, T. et al., 2020: Decoupling for ecological sustainability: A categorisation and review of research literature. *Environ. Sci. Policy*, **112**, 236–244, doi:10.1016/j.envsci.2020.06.016.

van den Berg, M., A.F. Hof, J. van Vliet, and D.P. van Vuuren, 2015: Impact of the choice of emission metric on greenhouse gas abatement and costs. *Environ. Res. Lett.*, **10(2)**, 024001, doi:10.1088/1748-9326/10/2/024001.

van der A, R.J. et al., 2017: Cleaning up the air: effectiveness of air quality policy for SO$_2$ and NOx emissions in China. *Atmos. Chem. Phys.*, **17(3)**, 1775–1789, doi:10.5194/acp-17-1775-2017.

van Sluisveld, M.A.E. et al., 2015: Comparing future patterns of energy system change in 2°C scenarios with historically observed rates of change. *Glob. Environ. Change*, **35**, 436–449, doi:10.1016/j.gloenvcha.2015.09.019.

van Soest, H.L. et al., 2017: Early action on Paris Agreement allows for more time to change energy systems. *Clim. Change*, **144(2)**, 165–179, doi:10.1007/s10584-017-2027-8.

Vancutsem, C. et al., 2021: Long-term **(1990–2019)** monitoring of forest cover changes in the humid tropics. *Sci. Adv.*, **7(10)**, eabe1603–eabe1603, doi:10.1126/sciadv.abe1603.

Vandyck, T., K. Keramidas, S. Tchung-Ming, M. Weitzel, and R. Van Dingenen, 2020: Quantifying air quality co-benefits of climate policy across sectors and regions. *Clim. Change*, **163(3)**, 1501–1517, doi:10.1007/s10584-020-02685-7.

Vasconcellos Oliveira, R., 2020: A Methodological Framework for Developing More Just Footprints: The Contribution of Footprints to Environmental Policies and Justice. *Sci. Eng. Ethics*, **26(1)**, 405–429, doi:10.1007/s11948-019-00100-8.

Veblen, T., 2009: *The Theory of the Leisure Class*. Oxford University Press, Oxford, UK, 300 pp.

Velders, G.J.M., S.O. Andersen, J.S. Daniel, D.W. Fahey, and M. McFarland, 2007: The importance of the Montreal Protocol in protecting climate. *Proc. Natl. Acad. Sci.*, **104(12)**, 4814–4819, doi:10.1073/pnas.0610328104.

Vergis, S. and B. Chen, 2015: Comparison of plug-in electric vehicle adoption in the United States: A state by state approach. *Res. Transp. Econ.*, **52**(December 2010), 56–64, doi:10.1016/j.retrec.2015.10.003.

Vermeulen, S.J., B.M. Campbell, and J.S.I. Ingram, 2012: Climate Change and Food Systems. *Annu. Rev. Environ. Resour.*, **37(1)**, 195–222, doi:10.1146/annurev-environ-020411-130608.

Vogl, V., O. Olsson, and B. Nykvist, 2021: Phasing out the blast furnace to meet global climate targets. *Joule*, **5(10)**, 2646–2662, doi:10.1016/j.joule.2021.09.007.

Vohra, K. et al., 2021: Global mortality from outdoor fine particle pollution generated by fossil fuel combustion: Results from GEOS-Chem. *Environ. Res.*, **195**, 110754, doi:10.1016/j.envres.2021.110754.

von Stechow, C. et al., 2015: Integrating Global Climate Change Mitigation Goals with Other Sustainability Objectives: A Synthesis. *Annu. Rev. Environ. Resour.*, **40(1)**, 363–394, doi:10.1146/annurev-environ-021113-095626.

Vrontisi, Z. et al., 2018: Enhancing global climate policy ambition towards a 1.5°C stabilization: a short-term multi-model assessment. *Environ. Res. Lett.*, **13(4)**, 044039, doi:10.1088/1748-9326/aab53e.

Waite, M. et al., 2017: Global trends in urban electricity demands for cooling and heating. *Energy*, **127**, 786–802, doi:10.1016/j.energy.2017.03.095.

Wang, H. and P. Zhou, 2018: Assessing Global CO$_2$ Emission Inequality From Consumption Perspective: An Index Decomposition Analysis. *Ecol. Econ.*, **154**, 257–271, doi:10.1016/j.ecolecon.2018.08.008.

Wang, H. et al., 2019: China's CO$_2$ peak before 2030 implied from characteristics and growth of cities. *Nat. Sustain.*, **2(8)**, 748–754, doi:10.1038/s41893-019-0339-6.

Wang, H. et al., 2020: Early transformation of the Chinese power sector to avoid additional coal lock-in. *Environ. Res. Lett.*, **15(2)**, 024007, doi:10.1088/1748-9326/ab5d99.

Wang, J., J.F.D. Rodrigues, M. Hu, P. Behrens, and A. Tukker, 2019: The evolution of Chinese industrial CO$_2$ emissions 2000–2050: A review and meta-analysis of historical drivers, projections and policy goals. *Renew. Sustain. Energy Rev.*, **116**, 109433, doi:10.1016/j.rser.2019.109433.

Wang, P., 2021: China's air pollution policies: Progress and challenges. *Curr. Opin. Environ. Sci. Heal.*, **19**, 100227, doi:10.1016/j.coesh.2020.100227.

Wang, Q. and R. Jiang, 2019: Is China's economic growth decoupled from carbon emissions? *J. Clean. Prod.*, **225**, 1194–1208, doi:10.1016/j.jclepro.2019.03.301.

Wang, Q. and Y. Zhou, 2020a: Evolution and drivers of production-based carbon emissions in China and India: Differences and similarities. *J. Clean. Prod.*, **277**, 123958, doi:10.1016/j.jclepro.2020.123958.

Wang, Q., S. Li, and Z. Pisarenko, 2020b: Heterogeneous effects of energy efficiency, oil price, environmental pressure, R&D investment, and policy on renewable energy – evidence from the G20 countries. *Energy*, **209**, 118322, doi:10.1016/j.energy.2020.118322.

Wang, Y., G. Yang, Y. Dong, Y. Cheng, and P. Shang, 2018: The Scale, Structure and Influencing Factors of Total Carbon Emissions from Households in 30 Provinces of China – Based on the Extended STIRPAT Model. *Energies*, **11(5)**, 1125, doi:10.3390/en11051125.

Wang, Z. and Y. Yang, 2016: Features and influencing factors of carbon emissions indicators in the perspective of residential consumption: Evidence from Beijing, China. *Ecol. Indic.*, **61**, 634–645, doi:10.1016/j.ecolind.2015.10.015.

Wang, Z., C. Cui, and S. Peng, 2019: How do urbanization and consumption patterns affect carbon emissions in China? A decomposition analysis. *J. Clean. Prod.*, **211**, 1201–1208, doi:10.1016/j.jclepro.2018.11.272.

Wang, Z., Q. Jiang, K. Dong, M.S. Mubarik, and X. Dong, 2020a: Decomposition of the US CO$_2$ emissions and its mitigation potential: An aggregate and sectoral analysis. *Energy Policy*, **147**, 111925, doi:10.1016/j.enpol.2020.111925.

Wang, Z., J. Meng, and D. Guan, 2020b: Dynamic Driving Forces of India's Emissions From Production and Consumption Perspectives. *Earth's Futur.*, **8(8)**, e2020EF001485, doi:10.1029/2020EF001485.

Ward, J.D. et al., 2016: Is Decoupling GDP Growth from Environmental Impact Possible? *PLoS One*, **11(10)**, e0164733, doi:10.1371/journal.pone.0164733.

2

Wei, T., Q. Zhu, and S. Glomsrød, 2018: How Will Demographic Characteristics of the Labor Force Matter for the Global Economy and Carbon Dioxide Emissions? *Ecol. Econ.*, **147**, 197–207, doi:10.1016/j.ecolecon.2018.01.017.

Welsby, D., J. Price, S. Pye, and P. Ekins, 2021: Unextractable fossil fuels in a 1.5°C world. *Nature*, **597(7875)**, 230–234, doi:10.1038/s41586-021-03821-8.

Wiebe, K.S. and N. Yamano, 2016: Estimating CO_2 Emissions Embodied in Final Demand and Trade Using the OECD ICIO 2015: Methodology and Results. *OECD Sci. Technol. Ind. Work. Pap. No. 2016/05*, doi:10.1787/5jlrcm216xkl-en.

Wiedenhofer, D., J.K. Steinberger, N. Eisenmenger, and W. Haas, 2015: Maintenance and Expansion: Modeling Material Stocks and Flows for Residential Buildings and Transportation Networks in the EU25. *J. Ind. Ecol.*, **19(4)**, 538–551, doi:10.1111/jiec.12216.

Wiedenhofer, D. et al., 2017: Unequal household carbon footprints in China. *Nat. Clim. Change*, **7(1)**, 75–80, doi:10.1038/nclimate3165.

Wiedenhofer, D., B. Smetschka, L. Akenji, M. Jalas, and H. Haberl, 2018: Household time use, carbon footprints, and urban form: a review of the potential contributions of everyday living to the 1.5°C climate target. *Curr. Opin. Environ. Sustain.*, **30**, 7–17, doi:10.1016/j.cosust.2018.02.007.

Wiedmann, T. and M. Lenzen, 2018: Environmental and social footprints of international trade. *Nat. Geosci.*, **11(5)**, 314–321, doi:10.1038/s41561-018-0113-9.

Wiedmann, T., M. Lenzen, L.T. Keyßer, and J.K. Steinberger, 2020: Scientists' warning on affluence. *Nat. Commun.*, **11(1)**, 3107, doi:10.1038/s41467-020-16941-y.

Wieland, H., S. Giljum, M. Bruckner, A. Owen, and R. Wood, 2018: Structural production layer decomposition: a new method to measure differences between MRIO databases for footprint assessments. *Econ. Syst. Res.*, **30(1)**, 61–84, doi:10.1080/09535314.2017.1350831.

Wilk, R., 2010: Consumption embedded in culture and language: implications for finding sustainability. *Sustain. Sci. Pract. Policy*, **6(2)**, 38–48, doi:10.1080/15487733.2010.11908048.

Wilk, R., 2017: Without Consumer Culture, There is No Environmental Crisis. In: *Panel contribution to the Population-Environment Research Network Cyberseminar*, Population-Environment Research Network, p. 4.

Wilson, C., 2012: Up-scaling, formative phases, and learning in the historical diffusion of energy technologies. *Energy Policy*, **50**, 81–94, doi:10.1016/j.enpol.2012.04.077.

Wilson, C., A. Grubler, N. Bauer, V. Krey, and K. Riahi, 2013: Future capacity growth of energy technologies: are scenarios consistent with historical evidence? *Clim. Change*, **118(2)**, 381–395, doi:10.1007/s10584-012-0618-y.

Wilson, C. et al., 2020a: Granular technologies to accelerate decarbonization. *Science*, **368(6486)**, 36–39, doi:10.1126/science.aaz8060.

Wilson, C., L. Kerr, F. Sprei, E. Vrain, and M. Wilson, 2020b: Potential Climate Benefits of Digital Consumer Innovations. *Annu. Rev. Environ. Resour.*, **45(1)**, 113–144, doi:10.1146/annurev-environ-012320-082424.

Winiwarter, W., L. Höglund-Isaksson, Z. Klimont, W. Schöpp, and M. Amann, 2018: Technical opportunities to reduce global anthropogenic emissions of nitrous oxide. *Environ. Res. Lett.*, **13(1)**, 014011, doi:10.1088/1748-9326/aa9ec9.

Wiser, R.H. and M. Bolinger, 2019: 2018 Wind Technologies Market Report. In: *Wind Power Market and Economic Trends*, Nova Science Publishers, Inc., Hauppauge, NY, USA, pp. 199–261.

WMO, 2018: *Scientific Assessment of Ozone Depletion: 2018*. Global Ozo. World Meterological Organization, Geneva, Switzerland.

Wolfram, C., O. Shelef, and P. Gertler, 2012: How Will Energy Demand Develop in the Developing World? *J. Econ. Perspect.*, **26(1)**, 119–138, doi:10.1257/jep.26.1.119.

Wood, R. et al., 2018: Growth in Environmental Footprints and Environmental Impacts Embodied in Trade: Resource Efficiency Indicators from EXIOBASE3. *J. Ind. Ecol.*, **22(3)**, 553–564, doi:10.1111/jiec.12735.

Wood, R., D.D. Moran, J.F.D. Rodrigues, and K. Stadler, 2019: Variation in trends of consumption based carbon accounts. *Sci. Data*, **6(1)**, 99, doi:10.1038/s41597-019-0102-x.

Wood, R. et al., 2020a: Beyond peak emission transfers: historical impacts of globalization and future impacts of climate policies on international emission transfers. *Clim. Policy*, **20(sup1)**, S14–S27, doi:10.1080/14693062.2019.1619507.

Wood, R. et al., 2020b: The structure, drivers and policy implications of the European carbon footprint. *Clim. Policy*, **20(sup1)**, S39–S57, doi:10.1080/14693062.2019.1639489.

World Bank, 2020: *State and Trends of Carbon Pricing 2020*. The World Bank, Wasgington DC, USA, 109 pp.

WRI, 2019: CAIT – Country Greenhouse Gas Emissions Data. https://www.wri.org/resources/data-sets/cait-country-greenhouse-gas-emissions-data (Accessed July 8, 2019).

Wu, R., J. Wang, S. Wang, and K. Feng, 2021: The drivers of declining CO_2 emissions trends in developed nations using an extended STIRPAT model: A historical and prospective analysis. *Renew. Sustain. Energy Rev.*, **149**, 111328, doi:10.1016/j.rser.2021.111328.

Wu, Y., Q. Zhu, and B. Zhu, 2018: Comparisons of decoupling trends of global economic growth and energy consumption between developed and developing countries. *Energy Policy*, **116**, 30–38, doi:10.1016/j.enpol.2018.01.047.

Xia, Q., H. Wang, X. Liu, and X. Pan, 2021: Drivers of global and national CO_2 emissions changes 2000–2017. *Clim. Policy*, **21(5)**, 604–615, doi:10.1080/14693062.2020.1864267.

Xia, Y., H. Wang, and W. Liu, 2019: The indirect carbon emission from household consumption in China between 1995–2009 and 2010–2030: A decomposition and prediction analysis. *Comput. Ind. Eng.*, **128**, 264–276, doi:10.1016/j.cie.2018.12.031.

Xu, S.-C., Z.-X. He, R.-Y. Long, and H. Chen, 2016: Factors that influence carbon emissions due to energy consumption based on different stages and sectors in China. *J. Clean. Prod.*, **115**, 139–148, doi:10.1016/j.jclepro.2015.11.050.

Xu, X.Y. and B.W. Ang, 2013: Index decomposition analysis applied to CO_2 emission studies. *Ecol. Econ.*, **93**, 313–329, doi:10.1016/j.ecolecon.2013.06.007.

Xu, Y. and E. Dietzenbacher, 2014: A structural decomposition analysis of the emissions embodied in trade. *Ecol. Econ.*, **101**, 10–20, doi:10.1016/j.ecolecon.2014.02.015.

Yamano, N. and J. Guilhoto, 2020: *CO_2 emissions embodied in international trade and domestic final demand – Methodology and results using the OECD Inter-Country Input-Output Database*. OECD Publishing, Paris, France, 57 pp.

Yang, J. et al., 2020: Driving forces of China's CO_2 emissions from energy consumption based on Kaya-LMDI methods. *Sci. Total Environ.*, **711**, 134569, doi:10.1016/j.scitotenv.2019.134569.

Yang, T. and W. Liu, 2017: Inequality of household carbon emissions and its influencing factors: Case study of urban China. *Habitat Int.*, **70**, 61–71, doi:10.1016/j.habitatint.2017.10.004.

Yang, W., Z. Wang, J. Cui, Z. Zhu, and X. Zhao, 2015: Comparative study of the thermal performance of the novel green (planting) roofs against other existing roofs. *Sustain. Cities Soc.*, **16**(C), 1–12, doi:10.1016/j.scs.2015.01.002.

Yanocha, D., J. Mason, and J. Hagen, 2020: Using data and technology to integrate mobility modes in low-income cities. *Transp. Rev.*, **41(3)**, 262–284, doi:10.1080/01441647.2020.1834006.

Yao, C., K. Feng, and K. Hubacek, 2015: Driving forces of CO_2 emissions in the G20 countries: An index decomposition analysis from 1971 to 2010. *Ecol. Inform.*, **26**, 93–100, doi:10.1016/j.ecoinf.2014.02.003.

Yu, B., Y.-M. Wei, G. Kei, and Y. Matsuoka, 2018: Future scenarios for energy consumption and carbon emissions due to demographic transitions in Chinese households. *Nat. Energy*, **3(2)**, 109–118, doi:10.1038/s41560-017-0053-4.

Yu, M. et al., 2019: Effects of air pollution control measures on air quality improvement in Guangzhou, China. *J. Environ. Manage.*, **244**, 127–137, doi:10.1016/j.jenvman.2019.05.046.

Yu, Y., K. Feng, and K. Hubacek, 2013: Tele-connecting local consumption to global land use. *Glob. Environ. Change*, **23(5)**, 1178–1186, doi:10.1016/j.gloenvcha.2013.04.006.

Zhang, C., X. Cao, and A. Ramaswami, 2016: A novel analysis of consumption-based carbon footprints in China: Unpacking the effects of urban settlement and rural-to-urban migration. *Glob. Environ. Change*, **39**, 285–293, doi:10.1016/j.gloenvcha.2016.06.003.

Zhang, Y., Y. Li, K. Hubacek, X. Tian, and Z. Lu, 2019: Analysis of CO_2 transfer processes involved in global trade based on ecological network analysis. *Appl. Energy*, **233–234**, 576–583, doi:10.1016/j.apenergy.2018.10.051.

Zhao, X., H. Yin, and Y. Zhao, 2015: Impact of environmental regulations on the efficiency and CO_2 emissions of power plants in China. *Appl. Energy*, **149**, 238–247, doi:10.1016/j.apenergy.2015.03.112.

Zhao, Y., T. Ercan, and O. Tatari, 2016: Life cycle based multi-criteria optimization for optimal allocation of commercial delivery truck fleet in the United States. *Sustain. Prod. Consum.*, **8**, 18–31, doi:10.1016/j.spc.2016.04.003.

Zheng, X. et al., 2020: Drivers of change in China's energy-related CO_2 emissions. *Proc. Natl. Acad. Sci.*, **117(1)**, 29–36, doi:10.1073/pnas.1908513117.

Zhong, H., K. Feng, L. Sun, L. Cheng, and K. Hubacek, 2020: Household carbon and energy inequality in Latin American and Caribbean countries. *J. Environ. Manage.*, **273**, 110979, doi:10.1016/j.jenvman.2020.110979.

Zhong, X.Y., J.X. Gao, H. Ren, and W.G. Cai, 2018: EKC Analysis and Decomposition of Influencing Factors in Building Energy Consumption of Three Municipalities in China. *IOP Conf. Ser. Earth Environ. Sci.*, **143**, 012011, doi:10.1088/1755-1315/143/1/012011.

Zhou, B., C. Zhang, H. Song, and Q. Wang, 2019: How does emission trading reduce China's carbon intensity? An exploration using a decomposition and difference-in-differences approach. *Sci. Total Environ.*, **676**, 514–523, doi:10.1016/j.scitotenv.2019.04.303.

Zhu, K., J. Zhang, S. Niu, C. Chu, and Y. Luo, 2018: Limits to growth of forest biomass carbon sink under climate change. *Nat. Commun.*, **9(1)**, 2709, doi:10.1038/s41467-018-05132-5.

Zink, T. and R. Geyer, 2017: Circular Economy Rebound. *J. Ind. Ecol.*, **21(3)**, 593–602, doi:10.1111/jiec.12545.

Mitigation Pathways Compatible with Long-term Goals

3

Coordinating Lead Authors:

Keywan Riahi (Austria), Roberto Schaeffer (Brazil)

Lead Authors:

Jacobo Arango (Colombia), Katherine Calvin (the United States of America), Céline Guivarch (France), Tomoko Hasegawa, (Japan), Kejun Jiang (China), Elmar Kriegler (Germany), Robert Matthews (United Kingdom), Glen P. Peters (Norway/Australia), Anand Rao (India), Simon Robertson (Australia), Adam Mohammed Sebbit (Uganda), Julia Steinberger (Switzerland/United Kingdom), Massimo Tavoni (Italy), Detlef P. van Vuuren (the Netherlands)

Contributing Authors:

Alaa Al Khourdajie (United Kingdom/Syria), Christoph Bertram (Germany), Valentina Bosetti (Italy), Elina Brutschin (Austria), Edward Byers (Austria/Ireland), Tamma Carleton (the United States of America), Leon Clarke (the United States of America), Annette Cowie (Australia), Delavane Diaz (the United States of America), Laurent Drouet (Italy/France), Navroz K. Dubash (India), James Edmonds (the United States of America) Jan S. Fuglestvedt (Norway), Shinichiro Fujimori (Japan), Oliver Geden (Germany), Giacomo Grassi (Italy/European Union), Michael Grubb (United Kingdom), Anders Hammer Strømman (Norway), Frank Jotzo (Australia), Jarmo Kikstra (Austria/the Netherlands), Zbigniew Klimont (Austria/Poland), Alexandre Köberle (Brazil/United Kingdom), Robin Lamboll (United Kingdom/the United States of America), Franck Lecocq (France), Jared Lewis (Australia/New Zealand), Yun Seng Lim (Malaysia), Giacomo Marangoni (Italy), Eric Masanet (the United States of America), Toshihiko Masui (Japan), David McCollum (the United States of America), Malte Meinshausen (Australia/Germany), Aurélie Méjean (France), Joel Millward-Hopkins (United Kingdom), Catherine Mitchell (United Kingdom), Gert-Jan Nabuurs (the Netherlands), Zebedee Nicholls (Australia), Brian O'Neill (the United States of America), Anthony Patt (Switzerland), Franziska Piontek (Germany), Andy Reisinger (New Zealand), Joeri Rogelj (Belgium/United Kingdom), Steven Rose (the United States of America), Bastiaan van Ruijven (the Netherlands), Yamina Saheb (France/Algeria), Marit Sandstad (Norway), Jim Skea (United Kingdom), Chris Smith (Austria/United Kingdom), Björn Soergel (Germany), Florian Tirana (France), Kaj-Ivar van der Wijst (the Netherlands), Harald Winkler (South Africa)

Review Editors:

Vaibhav Chaturvedi (India), Wenying Chen (China), Julio Torres Martínez (Cuba)

Chapter Scientists:

Edward Byers (Austria/Ireland), Eduardo Müller-Casseres (Brazil)

This chapter should be cited as:

Riahi, K., R. Schaeffer, J. Arango, K. Calvin, C. Guivarch, T. Hasegawa, K. Jiang, E. Kriegler, R. Matthews, G.P. Peters, A. Rao, S. Robertson, A.M. Sebbit, J. Steinberger, M. Tavoni, D.P. van Vuuren, 2022: Mitigation pathways compatible with long-term goals. In IPCC, 2022: *Climate Change 2022: Mitigation of Climate Change. Contribution of Working Group III to the Sixth Assessment Report of the Intergovernmental Panel on Climate Change* [P.R. Shukla, J. Skea, R. Slade, A. Al Khourdajie, R. van Diemen, D. McCollum, M. Pathak, S. Some, P. Vyas, R. Fradera, M. Belkacemi, A. Hasija, G. Lisboa, S. Luz, J. Malley, (eds.)]. Cambridge University Press, Cambridge, UK and New York, NY, USA. doi: 10.1017/9781009157926.005

Table of Contents

3

Executive Summary

Chapter 3 assesses the emissions pathways literature in order to identify their key characteristics (both in commonalities and differences) and to understand how societal choices may steer the system into a particular direction (*high confidence*). More than 2000 quantitative emissions pathways were submitted to the IPCC's Sixth Assessment Report AR6 scenarios database, out of which 1202 scenarios included sufficient information for assessing the associated warming consistent with WGI. Five Illustrative Mitigation Pathways (IMPs) were selected, each emphasising a different scenario element as its defining feature: heavy reliance on renewables (IMP-Ren), strong emphasis on energy demand reductions (IMP-LD), extensive use of carbon dioxide removal (CDR) in the energy and the industry sectors to achieve net negative emissions (IMP-Neg), mitigation in the context of broader sustainable development (IMP-SP), and the implications of a less rapid and gradual strengthening of near-term mitigation actions (IMP-GS). {3.2, 3.3}

Pathways consistent with the implementation and extrapolation of countries' implemented policies until the end of 2020 see greenhouse gas (GHG) emissions reaching 54–61 GtCO$_2$-eq yr^{-1} by 2030 and to 47–67 GtCO$_2$-eq yr^{-1} by 2050, leading to a median global warming of 2.2°C to 3.5°C by 2100 (*medium confidence*). These pathways consider policies at the time that they were developed. The Shared Socio-economic Pathways (SSPs) permit a more systematic assessment of future GHG emissions and their uncertainties than was possible in AR5. The main emissions drivers include growth in population, reaching 8.5–9.7 billion by 2050, and an increase in global GDP of 2.7–4.1% per year between 2015 and 2050. Final energy demand in the absence of any new climate policies is projected to grow to around 480–750 EJ yr^{-1} in 2050 (compared to around 390 EJ in 2015) (*medium confidence*). The highest emissions scenarios in the literature result in global warming of >5°C by 2100, based on assumptions of rapid economic growth and pervasive climate policy failures (*high confidence*). {3.3}

Many pathways in the literature show how to limit global warming compared to pre-industrial times to 2°C (>67%) with no overshoot or to limit warming to 1.5°C (>50%) with no or limited overshoot. The likelihood of limiting warming to 1.5°C with no or limited overshoot has dropped in AR6 compared to the *Special Report on Global Warming of 1.5°C* (SR1.5) because global GHG emissions have risen since the time SR1.5 was published, leading to higher near-term emissions (2030) and higher cumulative CO$_2$ emissions until the time of net zero (*medium confidence*). Only a small number of published pathways limit global warming to 1.5°C without overshoot over the course of the 21st century. {3.3, Annex III.II.3}

Cost-effective mitigation pathways assuming immediate action[1] to limit warming to 2°C (>67%) are associated with net global GHG emissions of 30–49 GtCO$_2$-eq yr^{-1} by 2030 and 14–26 GtCO$_2$-eq yr^{-1} by 2050 (*medium confidence*). This corresponds to reductions, relative to 2019 levels, of 13–45% by 2030 and 52–76% by 2050. Pathways that limit global warming to below 1.5°C with no or limited overshoot require a further acceleration in the pace of the transformation, with net GHG emissions typically around 21–36 GtCO$_2$-eq yr^{-1} by 2030 and 1–15 GtCO$_2$-eq yr^{-1} by 2050; thus, reductions of 34–60% by 2030 and 73–98% by 2050 relative to 2019 levels. {3.3}

Pathways following Nationally Determined Contributions (NDCs) announced prior to COP26[2] until 2030 reach annual emissions of 47–57 GtCO$_2$-eq by 2030, thereby making it impossible to limit warming to 1.5°C with no or limited overshoot and strongly increasing the challenge to limit warming to 2°C (>67%) (*high confidence*). A high overshoot of 1.5°C increases the risks from climate impacts and increases the dependence on large-scale carbon dioxide removal from the atmosphere. A future consistent with NDCs announced prior to COP26 implies higher fossil fuel deployment and lower reliance on low-carbon alternatives until 2030, compared to mitigation pathways with immediate action to limit warming to 2°C (>67%) or lower. To limit warming to 2°C (>67%) after following the NDCs to 2030, the pace of global GHG emission reductions would need to accelerate rapidly from 2030 onward: to an average of 1.4–2.0 GtCO$_2$-eq yr^{-1} between 2030 and 2050, which is around two-thirds of the global CO$_2$ emission reductions in 2020 due to the COVID-19 pandemic, and around 70% faster than in immediate action pathways that limit warming to 2°C (>67%). Accelerating emission reductions after following an NDC pathway to 2030 would be particularly challenging because of the continued buildup of fossil fuel infrastructure that would be expected to take place between now and 2030. {3.5, 4.2}

Pathways accelerating actions compared to NDCs announced prior to COP26 that reduce annual GHG emissions to 48 (38–52) GtCO$_2$-eq by 2030, or 2–9 GtCO$_2$-eq below projected emissions from fully implementing NDCs announced prior to COP26, reduce the mitigation challenge for limiting warming to 2°C (>67%) after 2030 (*medium confidence*). The accelerated action pathways are characterised by a global, but regionally differentiated, roll out of regulatory and pricing policies. Compared to NDCs, they see less fossil fuels and more low-carbon fuels until 2030, and narrow, but do not close the gap to pathways assuming immediate global action using all available least-cost abatement options. All delayed or accelerated action pathways that limit warming to 2°C (>67%) converge to a global mitigation regime at some point after 2030 by putting a significant value on reducing carbon and other GHG emissions in all sectors and regions. {3.5}

---

[1]   Immediate action in modelled global pathways refers to the adoption between 2020 and at latest before 2025 of climate policies intended to limit global warming to a given level. Modelled pathways that limit warming to 2°C (>67%) based on immediate action are summarised in category C3a in Table SPM.2. All assessed modelled global pathways that limit warming to 1.5°C (>50%) with no or limited overshoot assume immediate action as defined here (Category C1 in Table SPM.2).

[2]   NDCs announced prior to COP26 refer to the most recent nationally determined contributions submitted to the UNFCCC up to the literature cut-off date of this report, 11 October 2021, and revised NDCs announced by China, Japan and the Republic of Korea prior to October 2021 but only submitted thereafter.

Mitigation pathways limiting warming to 1.5°C (>50%) with no or limited overshoot reach 50% reductions of CO$_2$ in the 2030s, relative to 2019, then reduce emissions further to reach net zero CO$_2$ emissions in the 2050s. Pathways limiting warming to 2°C (>67%) reach 50% reductions in the 2040s and net zero CO$_2$ by 2070s (*medium confidence*). {3.3, Cross-Chapter Box 3 in this chapter}

Peak warming in mitigation pathways is determined by the cumulative net CO$_2$ emissions until the time of net zero CO$_2$ and the warming contribution of other GHGs and climate forcers at that time (*high confidence*). Cumulative net CO$_2$ emissions from 2020 to the time of net zero CO$_2$ are 510 (330–710) GtCO$_2$ in pathways that limit warming to 1.5°C (>50%) with no or limited overshoot and 890 (640–1160) GtCO$_2$ in pathways limiting warming to 2°C (>67%). These estimates are consistent with the assessment of remaining carbon budgets by WGI after adjusting for differences in peak warming levels. {3.3, Box 3.4}

Rapid reductions in non-CO$_2$ GHGs, particularly methane, would lower the level of peak warming (*high confidence*). Residual non-CO$_2$ emissions at the time of reaching net zero CO$_2$ range between 5 and 11 GtCO$_2$-eq yr^{-1} in pathways limiting warming to 2°C (>67%) or lower. Methane (CH$_4$) is reduced by around 19% (4–46%) in 2030 and 45% (29–64%) in 2050, relative to 2019. Methane emission reductions in pathways limiting warming to 1.5°C (>50%) with no or limited overshoot are substantially higher by 2030, 34% (21–57%), but only moderately so by 2050, 51% (35–70%). Methane emissions reductions are thus attainable at relatively lower GHG prices but are at the same time limited in scope in most 1.5°C–2°C pathways. Deeper methane emissions reductions by 2050 could further constrain the peak warming. N$_2$O emissions are reduced too, but similar to CH$_4$, emission reductions saturate for more stringent climate goals. In the mitigation pathways, the emissions of cooling aerosols are reduced due to reduced use of fossil fuels. The overall impact on non-CO$_2$-related warming combines these factors. {3.3}

Net zero GHG emissions imply net negative CO$_2$ emissions at a level compensating residual non-CO$_2$ emissions. Only 30% of the pathways limiting warming to 2°C (>67%) or lower reach net zero GHG emissions in the 21st century (*high confidence*). In those pathways reaching net zero GHGs, it is achieved around 10 to 40 years later than for net zero CO$_2$ (*medium confidence*). The reported quantity of residual non-CO$_2$ emissions depends on accounting: the choice of GHG metric. Reaching and sustaining global net zero GHG emissions, measured in terms of GWP-100, results in a gradual decline of temperature (*high confidence*). {Cross-Chapter Box 2 in Chapter 2, 3.3, Cross-Chapter Box 3 in this chapter}

Pathways limiting warming to 2°C (>67%) or lower exhibit substantial reductions in emissions from all sectors (*high confidence*). Projected CO$_2$ emissions reductions between 2019 and 2050 in 1.5°C (>50%) pathways with no or limited overshoot are around 77% (31–96%) for energy demand, 115% (90–167%) for energy supply, and 148% (94–387%) for agriculture, forestry and other land use (AFOLU). In pathways limiting warming to 2°C

(>67%), projected CO$_2$ emissions are reduced between 2019 and 2050 by around 49% for energy demand, 97% for energy supply, and 136% for AFOLU (*medium confidence*). {3.4}

Delaying or sacrificing emissions reductions in one sector or region involves compensating reductions in other sectors or regions if warming is to be limited (*high confidence*). Mitigation pathways show differences in the timing of decarbonisation and when net zero CO$_2$ emissions are achieved across sectors and regions. At the time of global net zero CO$_2$ emissions, emissions in some sectors and regions are positive while others are negative; the ordering depends on the mitigation options available, the cost of those options, and the policies implemented. In cost-effective mitigation pathways, the energy-supply sector typically reaches net zero CO$_2$ before the economy as a whole, while the demand sectors reach net zero CO$_2$ later, if ever (*high confidence*). {3.4}

Pathways limiting warming to 2°C (>67%) or lower involve substantial reductions in fossil fuel consumption and a near elimination of the use of coal without carbon capture and storage (CCS) (*high confidence*). These pathways show an increase in low-carbon energy, with 88% (69–97%) of primary energy coming from these sources by 2100. {3.4}

Stringent emissions reductions at the level required for 2°C (>67%) or lower are achieved through increased direct electrification of buildings, transport, and industry, resulting in increased electricity generation in all pathways (*high confidence*). Nearly all electricity in pathways limiting warming to 2°C (>67%) or lower is from low- or no-carbon technologies, with different shares of nuclear, biomass, non-biomass renewables, and fossil CCS across pathways. {3.4}

The measures required to limit warming to 2°C (>67%) or lower can result in large-scale transformation of the land surface (*high confidence*). Pathways limiting warming to 2°C (>67%) or lower are projected to reach net zero CO$_2$ emissions in the AFOLU sector between the 2020s and 2070, with an increase of forest cover of about 322 million ha (–67 to 890 million ha) in 2050 in pathways limiting warming to 1.5°C (>50%) with no or limited overshoot. Cropland area to supply biomass for bioenergy (including bioenergy with carbon capture and storage – BECCS) is around 199 (56–482) million ha in 2050 in pathways limiting warming to 1.5°C (>50%) with no or limited overshoot. The use of bioenergy can lead to either increased or reduced emissions, depending on the scale of deployment, conversion technology, fuel displaced, and how/where the biomass is produced (*high confidence*). {3.4}

Anthropogenic land CO$_2$ emissions and removals in Integrated Assessment Model (IAM) pathways cannot be directly compared with those reported in national GHG inventories (*high confidence*). Methodologies enabling a more like-for-like comparison between models' and countries' approaches would support more accurate assessment of the collective progress achieved under the Paris Agreement. {3.4, 7.2.2.5}

Pathways that limit warming to 2°C (>67%) or lower involve some amount of CDR to compensate for residual GHG emissions remaining after substantial direct emissions reductions in all sectors and regions (*high confidence*). CDR deployment in pathways serves multiple purposes: accelerating the pace of emissions reductions, offsetting residual emissions, and creating the option for net negative CO_2 emissions in case temperature reductions need to be achieved in the long term (*high confidence*). CDR options in the pathways are mostly limited to BECCS, afforestation and direct air carbon capture and storage (DACCS). CDR through some measures in AFOLU can be maintained for decades but not in the very long term because these sinks will ultimately saturate (*high confidence*). {3.4}

Mitigation pathways show reductions in energy demand relative to reference scenarios, through a diverse set of demand-side interventions (*high confidence*). Bottom-up and non-IAM studies show significant potential for demand-side mitigation. A stronger emphasis on demand-side mitigation implies less dependence on CDR and, consequently, reduced pressure on land and biodiversity. {3.4, 3.7}

Limiting warming requires shifting energy investments away from fossil fuels and towards low-carbon technologies (*high confidence*). The bulk of investments are needed in medium- and low-income regions. Investment needs in the electricity sector are on average 2.3 trillion USD2015 yr^{-1} over 2023 to 2052 for pathways that limit warming to 1.5°C (>50%) with no or limited overshoot, and 1.7 trillion USD2015 yr^{-1} for pathways that limit warming to 2°C (>67%). {3.6.1}

Pathways limiting warming to 2°C (>67%) require more rapid near-term transformations and are associated with higher upfront transition costs, but meanwhile bring long-term gains for the economy as well as earlier benefits in avoided climate change impacts (*high confidence*). This conclusion is independent of the discount rate applied, though the modelled cost-optimal balance of mitigation action over time does depend on the discount rate. Lower discount rates favour earlier mitigation, reducing reliance on CDR and temperature overshoot. {3.6.1, 3.8}

Mitigation pathways that limit warming to 2°C (>67%) entail losses in global GDP with respect to reference scenarios of between 1.3% and 2.7% in 2050; and in pathways that limit warming to 1.5°C (>50%) with no or limited overshoot, losses are between 2.6% and 4.2%. Yet, these estimates do not account for the economic benefits of avoided climate change impacts (*medium confidence*). In mitigation pathways that limit warming to 2°C (>67%), marginal abatement costs of carbon are about 90 (60–120) USD2015 tCO$_2$ in 2030 and about 210 (140–340) USD2015 tCO$_2$ in 2050; in pathways that limit warming to 1.5°C (>50%) with no or limited overshoot, they are about 220 (170–290) USD2015 tCO$_2$ in 2030 and about 630 (430–990) USD2015 tCO$_2$ in 2050.[3] {3.6.1}

The global benefits of pathways limiting warming to 2°C (>67%) outweigh global mitigation costs over the 21st century, if aggregated economic impacts of climate change are at the moderate to high end of the assessed range, and a weight consistent with economic theory is given to economic impacts over the long term. This holds true even without accounting for benefits in other sustainable development dimensions or non-market damages from climate change (*medium confidence*). The aggregate global economic repercussions of mitigation pathways include the macroeconomic impacts of investments in low-carbon solutions and structural changes away from emitting activities, co-benefits and adverse side effects of mitigation, (avoided) climate change impacts, and (reduced) adaptation costs. Existing quantifications of global aggregate economic impacts show a strong dependence on socio-economic development conditions, as these shape exposure and vulnerability and adaptation opportunities and responses. (Avoided) impacts for poorer households and poorer countries represent a smaller share in aggregate economic quantifications expressed in GDP or monetary terms, whereas their well-being and welfare effects are comparatively larger. When aggregate economic benefits from avoided climate change impacts are accounted for, mitigation is a welfare-enhancing strategy (*high confidence*). {3.6.2}

The economic benefits on human health from air quality improvement arising from mitigation action can be of the same order of magnitude as mitigation costs, and potentially even larger (*medium confidence*). {3.6.3}

Differences between aggregate employment in mitigation pathways compared to reference scenarios are relatively small, although there may be substantial reallocations across sectors, with job creation in some sectors and job losses in others (*medium confidence*). The net employment effect (and its sign) depends on scenario assumptions, modelling framework, and modelled policy design. Mitigation has implications for employment through multiple channels, each of which impacts geographies, sectors and skill categories differently (*medium confidence*). {3.6.4}

The economic repercussions of mitigation vary widely across regions and households, depending on policy design and level of international cooperation (*high confidence*). Delayed global cooperation increases policy costs across regions, especially in those that are relatively carbon intensive at present (*high confidence*). Pathways with uniform carbon values show higher mitigation costs in more carbon-intensive regions, in fossil fuel exporting regions and in poorer regions (*high confidence*). Aggregate quantifications expressed in GDP or monetary terms undervalue the economic effects on households in poorer countries; the actual effects on welfare and well-being are comparatively larger (*high confidence*). Mitigation at the speed and scale required to limit warming to 2°C (>67%) or lower implies deep economic and structural changes, thereby raising multiple types of distributional concerns across regions, income classes and sectors (*high confidence*). {3.6.1, 3.6.4}

---

[3]   Numbers in parenthesis represent the interquartile range of the scenario samples.

The timing of mitigation actions and their effectiveness will have significant consequences for broader sustainable development outcomes in the longer term (*high confidence*). Ambitious mitigation can be considered a precondition for achieving the Sustainable Development Goals (SDGs), especially for vulnerable populations and ecosystems with little capacity to adapt to climate impacts. Dimensions with anticipated co-benefits include health, especially regarding air pollution, clean energy access and water availability. Dimensions with potential trade-offs include food, employment, water stress, and biodiversity, which come under pressure from large-scale CDR deployment, energy affordability/ access, and mineral-resource extraction (*high confidence*). {3.7}

Many of the potential trade-offs of mitigation measures for other sustainable development outcomes depend on policy design and can thus be compensated or avoided with additional policies and investments or through policies that integrate mitigation with other SDGs (*high confidence*). Targeted SDG policies and investments, for example in the areas of healthy nutrition, sustainable consumption and production, and international collaboration, can support climate change mitigation policies and resolve or alleviate trade-offs. Trade-offs can be addressed by complementary policies and investments, as well as through the design of cross-sectoral policies integrating mitigation with the Sustainable Development Goals of health, nutrition, sustainable consumption and production, equity and biodiversity. {3.7}

Decent living standards, which encompass many SDG dimensions, are achievable at lower energy use than previously thought (*high confidence*). Mitigation strategies that focus on lower demands for energy and land-based resources exhibit reduced trade-offs and negative consequences for sustainable development relative to pathways involving either high emissions and climate impacts or those with high consumption and emissions that are ultimately compensated by large quantities of BECCS. {3.7}

Different mitigation pathways are associated with different feasibility challenges, though appropriate enabling conditions can reduce these challenges (*high confidence*). Feasibility challenges are transient and concentrated in the next two to three decades (*high confidence*). They are multidimensional, context-dependent and malleable to policy, technological and societal trends. {3.8}

Mitigation pathways are associated with significant institutional and economic feasibility challenges rather than technological and geophysical feasibility challenges (*medium confidence*). The rapid pace of technological development and deployment in mitigation pathways is not incompatible with historical records. Institutional capacity is rather a key limiting factor for a successful transition. Emerging economies appear to have the highest feasibility challenges in the short to medium term. {3.8}

Pathways relying on a broad portfolio of mitigation strategies are more robust and resilient (*high confidence*). Portfolios of technological solutions reduce the feasibility risks associated with the low-carbon transition. {3.8}

3

3.1   Introduction

3.1.1   Assessment of Mitigation Pathways and Their Compatibility With Long-term Goals

Chapter 3 takes a long-term perspective on climate change mitigation pathways. Its focus is on the implications of long-term targets for the required short- and medium-term system changes and associated greenhouse gas (GHG) emissions. This focus dictates a more global view and on issues related to path-dependency and up-scaling of mitigation options necessary to achieve different emissions trajectories, including particularly deep mitigation pathways that require rapid and fundamental changes.

Stabilising global average-temperature change requires reducing CO_2 emissions to net zero. Thus, a central cross-cutting topic within the chapter is the timing of reaching net zero CO_2 emissions and how a 'balance between anthropogenic emissions by sources and removals by sinks' could be achieved across time and space. This includes particularly the increasing body of literature since the *IPCC Special Report on Global Warming of 1.5°C* (SR1.5) which focuses on net zero CO_2 emissions pathways that avoid temperature overshoot and hence do not rely on net negative CO_2 emissions. The chapter conducts a systematic assessment of the associated economic costs as well as the benefits of mitigation for other societal objectives, such as the Sustainable Development Goals (SDGs). In addition, the chapter builds on SR1.5 and introduces a new conceptual framing for the assessment of possible social, economic, technical, political, and geophysical 'feasibility' concerns of alternative pathways, including the enabling conditions that would need to fall into place so that stringent climate goals become attainable.

The structure of the chapter is as follows: Section 3.2 introduces different types of mitigation pathways as well as the available modelling. Section 3.3 explores different emissions trajectories given socio-economic uncertainties and consistent with different long-term climate outcomes. A central element in this section is the systematic categorisation of the scenario space according to key characteristics of the mitigation pathways (including e.g., global average-temperature change, socio-economic development, technology assumptions, etc.). In addition, the section introduces selected Illustrative Mitigation Pathways (IMPs) that are used across the whole report. Section 3.4 conducts a sectoral analysis of the mitigation pathways, assessing the pace and direction of systems changes across sectors. Among others, this section aims at the integration of the sectoral information across AR6 WGIII chapters through a comparative assessment of the sectoral dynamics in economy-wide systems models compared to the insights from bottom-up sectoral models (from Chapters 6 to 11). Section 3.5 focuses on the required timing of mitigation actions, and the implication of near-term choices for the attainability of a range of long-term climate goals. After having explored the underlying systems transitions and the required timing of the mitigation actions, Section 3.6 assesses the economic implications, mitigation costs and benefits; and Section 3.7 assesses related co-benefits, synergies, and possible trade-offs for sustainable development and other societal (non-climate) objectives. Section 3.8 assumes a central role in the chapter and introduces a multidimensional feasibility metric

that permits the evaluation of mitigation pathways across a range of feasibility concerns. Finally, methods of the assessment and knowledge gaps are discussed in Section 3.9, followed by Frequently Asked Questions (FAQs).

3.1.2   Linkages to Other Chapters in the Report

Chapter 3 is linked to many other chapters in the report. The most important connections exist with Chapter 4 on mitigation and development pathways in the near to mid-term; with the sectoral chapters (Chapters 6–11); with the chapters dealing with cross-cutting issues (Chapters 12 and 17, e.g., feasibility); and finally also with AR6 WGI and WGII.

Within the overall framing of the AR6 report, Chapter 3 and Chapter 4 provide important complementary views of the required systems transitions across different temporal and spatial scales. While Chapter 3 focuses on the questions concerning the implications of the long-term objectives for the medium-to-near-term transformations, Chapter 4 comes from the other direction, and focuses on current near-term trends and policies (such as the Nationally Determined Contributions – NDCs) and their consequences with regards to GHG emissions. The latter chapter naturally focuses much more on the regional and national dimensions, and the heterogeneity of current and planned policies. Bringing together the information from these two chapters enables the assessment of whether current and planned actions are consistent with the required systems changes for the long-term objectives of the Paris Agreement.

Important other linkages comprise the collaboration with the 'sectoral' Chapters 6 to 11 to provide an integrated cross-sectoral perspective. This information (including information also from the sectoral chapters) is taken up ultimately also by Chapter 5 on demand/services and Chapter 12 for a further assessment of sectoral potential and costs.

Linkages to other chapters exist also on the topic of feasibility, which are informed by the policy, the sectoral and the demand chapters, the technology and finance chapters, as well as Chapter 4 on national circumstances.

Close collaboration with WGI permitted the use of AR6-calibrated emulators, which assure full consistency across the different working groups. Linkages to WGII concern the assessment of macroeconomic benefits of avoided impacts that are put into the context of mitigation costs as well as co-benefits and trade-offs for sustainable development.

3.1.3   Complementary Use of Large Scenario Ensembles and a Limited Set of Illustrative Mitigation Pathways (IMPs)

The assessment of mitigation pathways explores a wide scenario space from the literature within which seven Illustrative Pathways (IPs) are explored. The overall process is indicated in Figure 3.5a.

For a comprehensive assessment, a large ensemble of scenarios is collected and made available through an interactive AR6 Scenarios Database[4]. The collected information is shared across the chapters of AR6 and includes more than 3000 different pathways from a diverse set of studies. After an initial screening and quality control, scenarios were further vetted to assess if they sufficiently represented historical trends (Annex III.II.3.1). Subsequently, the climate consequences of each scenario were assessed using the climate emulator (leading to further classification). The assessment in Chapter 3 is, however, not limited to the scenarios from the database, and wherever necessary other literature sources are also assessed in order to bring together multiple lines of evidence.

In parallel, based on the overall AR6 assessment, seven illustrative pathways (IP) were defined representing critical mitigation strategies discussed in the assessment. The seven pathways are composed of two sets: (i) one set of five Illustrative Mitigation Pathways (IMPs) and (ii) one set of two reference pathways illustrative for high emissions. The IMPs are on the one hand representative of the scenario spac but also help to communicate archetypes of distinctly different systems transformations and related policy choices. Subsequently, seven scenarios were selected from the full database that fitted these storylines of each IP best. For these scenarios more strict vetting criteria were applied. The selection was done by first applying specific filters based on the storyline followed by a final selection (Box 3.1 and Figure 3.5a).

3.2 Which Mitigation Pathways are Compatible With Long-term Goals?

3.2.1 Scenario and Emission Pathways

Scenario and emission pathways are used to explore possible long-term trajectories, the effectiveness of possible mitigation strategies, and to help understand key uncertainties about the future. A **scenario** is an integrated description of a possible future of the human–environment system (Clarke et al. 2014), and could be a qualitative narrative, quantitative projection, or both. Scenarios typically capture interactions and processes that change key driving forces such as population, GDP, technology, lifestyles, and policy, and the consequences on energy use, land use, and emissions. Scenarios are not predictions or forecasts. An emission pathway is a modelled trajectory of anthropogenic emissions (Rogelj et al. 2018a) and, therefore, a part of a scenario.

There is no unique or preferred method to develop scenarios, and future pathways can be developed from diverse methods, depending on user needs and research questions (Turnheim et al. 2015; Trutnevyte et al. 2019a; Hirt et al. 2020). The most comprehensive scenarios in the literature are qualitative narratives that are translated into quantitative pathways using models (Clarke et al. 2014; Rogelj et al. 2018a). Schematic or illustrative pathways can also be used to communicate specific features of more complex scenarios (Allen et al. 2018). Simplified models can be used to explain the mechanisms operating in more complex models (e.g., Emmerling et al. 2019). Ultimately, a diversity of scenario and modelling approaches can lead to more robust findings (Schinko et al. 2017; Gambhir et al. 2019).

3.2.1.1 Reference Scenarios

It is common to define a reference scenario (also called a baseline scenario). Depending on the research question, a reference scenario could be defined in different ways (Grant et al. 2020): (i) a hypothetical world with no climate policies or climate impacts (Kriegler et al. 2014b), (ii) assuming current policies or pledged policies are implemented (Roelfsema et al. 2020), or (iii) a mitigation scenario to compare sensitivity with other mitigation scenarios (Kriegler et al. 2014a; Sognnaes et al. 2021).

No-climate-policy reference scenarios have often been compared with mitigation scenarios (Clarke et al. 2014). A no-climate-policy scenario assumes that no future climate policies are implemented, beyond what is in the model calibration, effectively implying that the carbon price is zero. No-climate-policy reference scenarios have a broad range depending on socio-economic assumptions and model characteristics, and consequently are important when assessing mitigation costs (Riahi et al. 2017; Rogelj et al. 2018b). As

---

Box 3.1 | Illustrative Mitigation Pathways (IMPs)

The literature shows a wide range of possible emissions trajectories, depicting developments in the absence of new climate policies or showing pathways consistent with the Paris Agreement. From the literature, a set of five Illustrative Mitigation Pathways (IMPs) was selected to denote implications of choices on socio-economic development and climate policies, and the associated transformations of the main GHG-emitting sectors (Figure 3.5b). The IMPs include a set of transformative pathways that illustrate how choices may lead to distinctly different transformations that may keep temperature increase to below 2°C (>67%) or 1.5°C. These pathways illustrate the implications of a focus on renewable energy such as solar and wind; reduced energy demand; extensive use of CDR in the energy and the industry sectors to achieve net negative emissions and reliance on other supply-side measures; strategies that avoid net negative carbon emissions, and gradual strengthening. In addition, one IMP explores how climate policies consistent with keeping limit warming to 1.5C (>50%) can be combined with a broader shift towards sustainable development. These IMPs are used in various chapters, exploring for instance their implications for different sectors, regions, and innovation characteristics (Figure 3.5b).

---

4   Available at: https://doi.org/10.5281/zenodo.5886911. All figures and tables in this chapter source data from the AR6 Scenarios Database, unless otherwise stated.

countries move forward with climate policies of varying stringency, no-climate-policy baselines are becoming increasingly hypothetical (Hausfather and Peters 2020). Studies clearly show current policies are having an effect, particularly when combined with the declining costs of low-carbon technologies (IEA 2020a; Roelfsema et al. 2020; Sognnaes et al. 2021; UNEP 2020), and, consequently, realised trajectories begin to differ from earlier no-climate-policy scenarios (Burgess et al. 2020). High-end emission scenarios, such as RCP8.5 and SSP5-8.5, are becoming less likely with climate policy and technology change (Box 3.3), but high-end concentration and warming levels may still be reached with the inclusion of strong carbon or climate feedbacks (Hausfather and Peters 2020; Pedersen et al. 2020).

3.2.1.2   Mitigation Scenarios

Mitigation scenarios explore different strategies to meet climate goals and are typically derived from reference scenarios by adding climate or other policies. Mitigation pathways are often developed to meet a predefined level of climate change, often referred to as a backcast. There are relatively few IAMs that include an endogenous climate model or emulator due to the added computational complexity, though exceptions do exist. In practice, models implement climate constraints by either iterating carbon-price assumptions (Strefler et al. 2021b) or by adopting an associated carbon budget (Riahi et al. 2021). In both cases, other GHGs are typically controlled by CO_2-equivalent pricing. A large part of the AR5 literature has focused on forcing pathways towards a target at the end of the century (van Vuuren et al. 2007, 2011; Clarke et al. 2009; Blanford et al. 2014; Riahi et al. 2017), featuring a temporary overshoot of the warming and forcing levels (Geden and Löschel 2017). In comparison, many recent studies explore mitigation strategies that limit overshoot (Johansson et al. 2020; Riahi et al. 2021). An increasing number of IAM studies also explore climate pathways that limit adverse side effects with respect to other societal objectives, such as food security (van Vuuren et al. 2019; Riahi et al. 2021) or larger sets of sustainability objectives (Soergel et al. 2021a).

3.2.2   The Utility of Integrated Assessment Models

Integrated Assessment Models (IAMs) are critical for understanding the implications of long-term climate objectives for the required near-term transition. For doing so, an integrated systems perspective including the representation of all sectors and GHGs is necessary. IAMs are used to explore the response of complex systems in a formal and consistent framework. They cover a broad range of modelling frameworks (Keppo et al. 2021). Given the complexity of the systems under investigation, IAMs necessarily make simplifying assumptions and therefore results need to be interpreted in the context of these assumptions. IAMs can range from economic models that consider only carbon dioxide emissions through to detailed process-based representations of the global energy system, covering separate regions and sectors (such as energy, transport, and land use), all GHG emissions and air pollutants, interactions with land and water, and a reduced representation of the climate system. IAMs are generally driven by economics and can have a variety of characteristics such as partial-, general- or non-equilibrium; myopic or perfect foresight; be

based on optimisation or simulation; have exogenous or endogenous technological change amongst many other characteristics. IAMs take as input socio-economic and technical variables and parameters to represent various systems. There is no unique way to integrate this knowledge into a model, and due to their complexity, various simplifications and omissions are made for tractability. IAMs therefore have various advantages and disadvantages which need to be weighed up when interpreting IAM outcomes. Annex III.I contains an overview of the different types of models and their key characteristics.

Most IAMs are necessarily broad as they capture long-term dynamics. IAMs are strong in showing the key characteristics of emission pathways and are most suited to questions related to short- versus long-term trade-offs, key interactions with non-climate objectives, long-term energy and land-use characteristics, and implications of different overarching technological and policy choices (Clarke et al. 2014; Rogelj et al. 2018a). While some IAMs have a high level of regional and sectoral detail, for questions that require higher levels of granularity (e.g., local policy implementation) specific region and sector models may be better suited. Utility of the IAM pathways increases when the quantitative results are contextualized through qualitative narratives or other additional types of knowledge to provide deeper insights (Geels et al. 2016a; Weyant 2017; Gambhir et al. 2019).

IAMs have a long history in addressing environmental problems, particularly in the IPCC assessment process (van Beek et al. 2020). Many policy discussions have been guided by IAM-based quantifications, such as the required emission reduction rates, net zero years, or technology deployment rates required to meet certain climate outcomes. This has led to the discussion about whether IAM scenarios have become performative, meaning that they act upon, transform or bring into being the scenarios they describe (Beck and Mahony 2017, 2018). Transparency of underlying data and methods is critical for scenario users to understand what drives different scenario results (Robertson 2020). A number of community activities have thus focused on the provision of transparent and publicly accessible databases of both input and output data (Riahi et al. 2012; Huppmann et al. 2018; Krey et al. 2019; Daioglou et al. 2020), as well as the provision of open-source code, and increased documentation (Annex III.I.9). Transparency is needed to reveal conditionality of results on specific choices in terms of assumptions (e.g., discount rates) and model architecture. More detailed explanations of underlying model dynamics would be critical to increase the understanding of what drives results (Bistline et al. 2020; Butnar et al. 2020; Robertson 2020).

Mitigation scenarios developed for a long-term climate constraint typically focus on cost-effective mitigation action towards a long-term climate goal. Results from IAM as well as sectoral models depend on model structure (Mercure et al. 2019), economic assumptions (Emmerling et al. 2019), technology assumptions (Pye et al. 2018), climate/emissions target formulation (Johansson et al. 2020), and the extent to which pre-existing market distortions are considered (Guivarch et al. 2011). The vast majority of IAM pathways do not consider climate impacts (Schultes et al. 2021). Equity hinges upon ethical and normative choices. As most IAM pathways follow the cost-effectiveness approach, they do not make any additional equity assumptions. Notable exceptions include Tavoni et al. (2015), Pan et al. (2017), van den Berg et al. (2020), and Bauer et al. (2020). Regional IAM results therefore need to be assessed with care, considering that emissions reductions are happening where it is most cost-effective, which needs to be separated from who is ultimately paying for the mitigation costs. Cost-effective pathways can provide a useful benchmark, but may not reflect real-world developments (Calvin et al. 2014a; Trutnevyte 2016). Different modelling frameworks may lead to different outcomes (Mercure et al. 2019). Recent studies have shown that other desirable outcomes can evolve with only minor deviations from cost-effective pathways (Bauer et al. 2020; Neumann and Brown 2021). IAM and sectoral models represent social, political, and institutional factors only in a rudimentary way. This assessment is thus relying on new methods for the *ex post* assessment of feasibility concerns (Jewell and Cherp 2020; Brutschin et al. 2021). A literature is emerging that recognises and reflects on the diversity and strengths/weaknesses of model-based scenario analysis (Keppo et al. 2021).

The climate constraint implementation can have a meaningful impact on model results. The literature so far includes many temperature overshoot scenarios with heavy reliance on long-term CDR and net negative CO_2 emissions to bring back temperatures after the peak (Rogelj et al. 2019b; Johansson et al. 2020). New approaches have been developed to avoid temperature overshoot. The new generation of scenarios show that CDR is important beyond its ability to reduce temperature, but is essential also for offsetting residual emissions to reach net zero CO_2 emissions (Rogelj et al. 2019b; Johansson et al. 2020; Riahi et al. 2021; Strefler et al. 2021b).

Many factors influence the deployment of technologies in the IAMs. Since AR5, there has been fervent debate on the large-scale deployment of bioenergy with carbon capture and storage (BECCS) in scenarios (Fuss et al. 2014; Geden 2015; Anderson and Peters 2016; Smith et al. 2016; van Vuuren et al. 2017; Galik 2020; Köberle 2019). Hence, many recent studies explore mitigation pathways with limited BECCS deployment (Grubler et al. 2018; van Vuuren et al. 2019; Riahi et al. 2021; Soergel et al. 2021a). While some have argued that technology diffusion in IAMs occurs too rapidly (Gambhir et al. 2019), others argued that most models prefer large-scale solutions resulting in a relatively slow phase-out of fossil fuels (Carton 2019). While IAMs are particularly strong on supply-side representation, demand-side measures still lag in detail of representation despite progress since AR5 (Grubler et al. 2018; Lovins et al. 2019; van den Berg et al. 2019; O'Neill et al. 2020b; Hickel et al. 2021; Keyßer and Lenzen 2021). The discount rate has a significant impact on the balance between near-term and long-term mitigation. Lower discount rates <4% (than used in IAMs) may lead to more near-term emissions reductions – depending on the stringency of the target (Emmerling et al. 2019; Riahi et al. 2021). Models often use simplified policy assumptions (O'Neill et al. 2020b) which can affect the deployment of technologies (Sognnaes et al. 2021). Uncertainty in technologies can lead to more or less short-term mitigation (Grant et al. 2021; Bednar et al. 2021). There is also a recognition to put more emphasis on what drives the results of different IAMs (Gambhir et al. 2019) and suggestions to focus more on what is driving differences in result across IAMs (Nikas et al. 2021). As noted by Weyant (2017, p. 131),

'IAms can provide very useful information, but this information needs to be carefully interpreted and integrated with other quantitative and qualitative inputs in the decision-making process.'

3.2.3   The Scenario Literature and Scenario Databases

IPCC reports have often used voluntary submissions to a scenario database in its assessments. The database is an ensemble of opportunity, as there is not a well-designed statistical sampling of the hypothetical model or scenario space: the literature is unlikely to cover all possible models and scenarios, and not all scenarios in the literature are submitted to the database. Model intercomparisons are often the core of scenario databases assessed by the IPCC (Cointe et al. 2019; Nikas et al. 2021). Single-model studies may allow more detailed sensitivity analyses or address specific research questions. The scenarios that are organised within the scientific community are more likely to enter the assessment process via the scenario database (Cointe et al. 2019), while scenarios from different communities, in the emerging literature, or not structurally consistent with the database may be overlooked. Scenarios in the grey literature may not be assessed even though they may have greater weight in a policy context.

One notable development since AR5 is the Shared Socio-economic Pathways (SSPs), conceptually outlined in Moss et al. (2010) and subsequently developed to support integrated climate research across the IPCC Working Groups (O'Neill et al. 2014). Initially, a set of SSP narratives were developed, describing worlds with different challenges to mitigation and adaptation (O'Neill et al. 2017a): SSP1 (sustainability), SSP2 (middle of the road), SSP3 (regional rivalry), SSP4 (inequality) and SSP5 (rapid growth). The SSPs have now been quantified in terms of energy, land-use, and emission pathways (Riahi et al. 2017), for both no-climate-policy reference scenarios and mitigation scenarios that follow similar radiative-forcing pathways as the Representative Concentration Pathways (RCPs) assessed in AR5 WGI. Since then the SSPs have been successfully applied in thousands of studies (O'Neill et al. 2020b) including some critiques on the use and application of the SSP framework (Pielke and Ritchie 2021; Rosen 2021). A selection of the quantified SSPs are used prominently in AR6 WGI as they were the basis for most climate modelling since AR5 (O'Neill et al. 2016). Since 2014, when the first set of SSP data was made available, there has been a divergence between scenario and historic trends (Burgess et al. 2020). As a result, the SSPs require updating (O'Neill et al. 2020b). Most of the scenarios in the AR6 database are SSP-based and consider various updates compared to the first release (Riahi et al. 2017).

3.2.4   The AR6 Scenario Database

To facilitate this assessment, a large ensemble of scenarios has been collected and made available through an interactive AR6 WGIII scenario database. The collection of the scenario outputs is coordinated by Chapter 3 and expands upon the IPCC SR1.5 scenario explorer (Huppmann et al. 2018; Rogelj et al. 2018a). A complementary database for national pathways has been established by Chapter 4. Annex III.II.3 contains full details on how the scenario database was compiled.

Number of scenarios from each model family

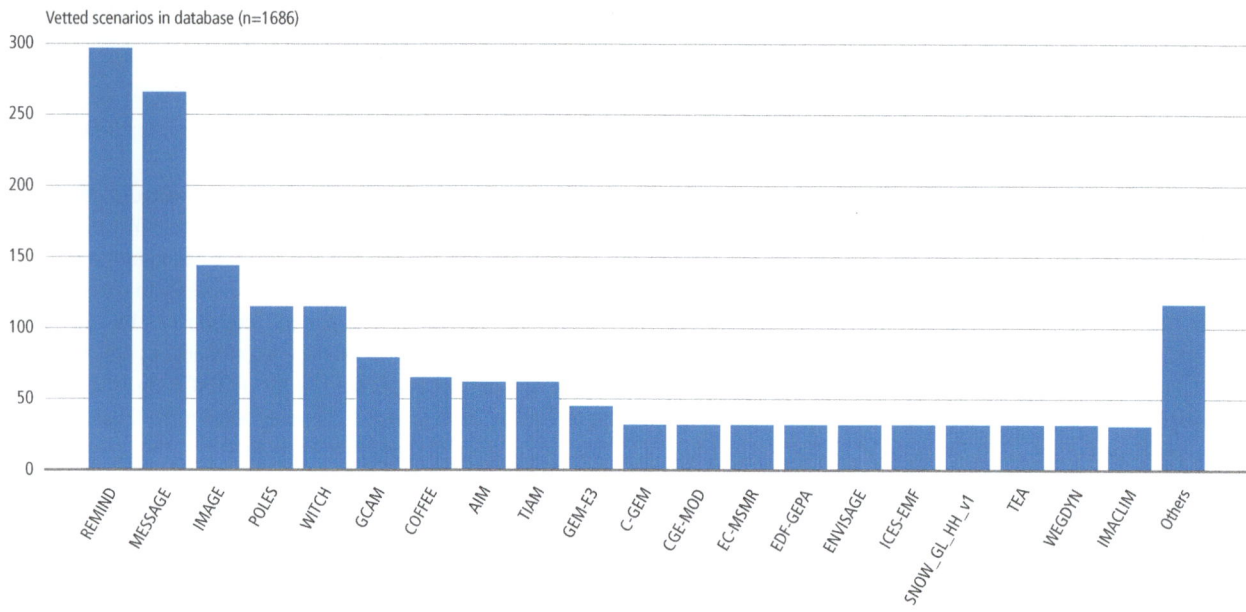

Figure 3.1 | Scenario counts from each model family defined as all versions under the same model's name.

Number of scenarios from each project

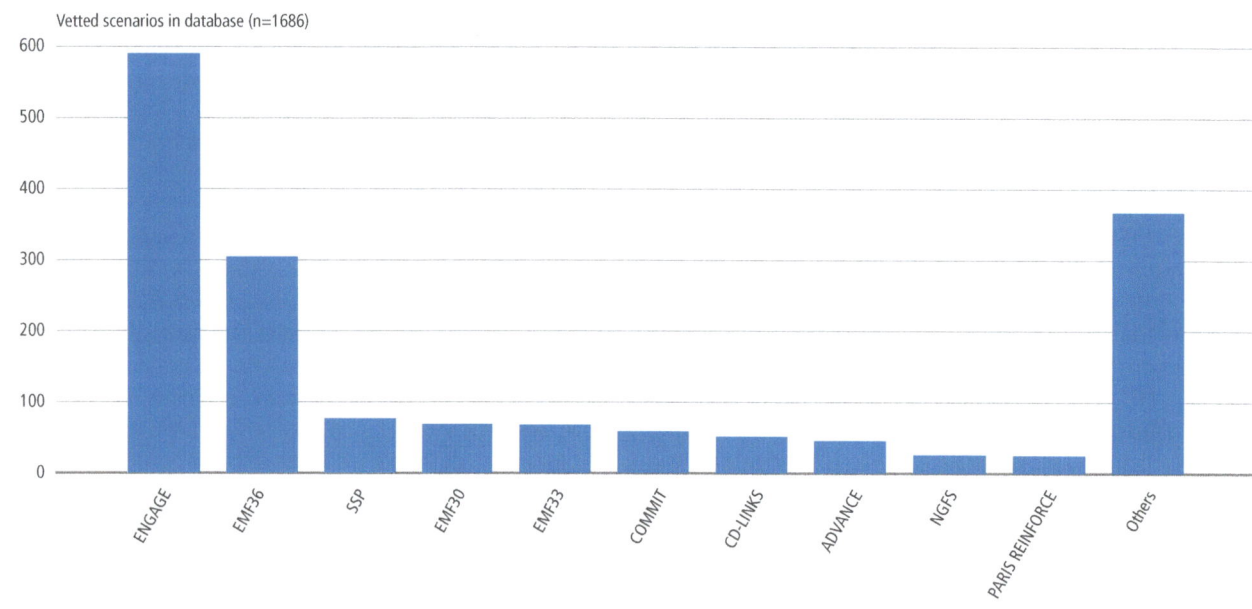

Figure 3.2 | Scenario counts from each named project.

The AR6 scenario database contains 3131 scenarios (Figure 3.5a). After an initial screening and quality control, scenarios were further vetted to assess if they sufficiently represented historical trends (Annex III.II.3.1). Of the initial 2266 scenarios with global scope, 1686 scenarios passed the vetting process and are assessed in this chapter. The scenarios that did not pass the vetting are still available in the database. The vetted scenarios were from over 50 different model families, or over 100 when considering all versions of the same family (Figure 3.1). The scenarios originated from over 15 different model

intercomparison projects, with around one-fifth originating from individual studies (Figure 3.2). Because of the uneven distribution of scenarios from different models and projects, uncorrected statistics from the database can be misleading.

Each scenario with sufficient data is given a temperature classification using climate model emulators. Three emulators were used in the assessment: FAIR (Smith et al. 2018), CICERO-SCM (Skeie et al. 2021), MAGICC (Meinshausen et al. 2020). Only the

Table 3.1 | Classification of emissions scenarios into warming levels using MAGICC

Category	Description	WGI SSP	WGIII IP/IMP	Scenarios
C1: Limit warming to 1.5°C (>50%) with no or limited overshoot	Reach or exceed 1.5°C during the 21st century with a likelihood of ≤67%, and limit warming to 1.5°C in 2100 with a likelihood >50%. Limited overshoot refers to exceeding 1.5°C by up to about 0.1°C and for up to several decades.	SSP1-1.9	IMP-SP, IMP-LD, IMP-Ren	97
C2: Return warming to 1.5°C (>50%) after a high overshoot	Exceed warming of 1.5°C during the 21st century with a likelihood of >67%, and limit warming to 1.5°C in 2100 with a likelihood of >50%. High overshoot refers to temporarily exceeding 1.5°C global warming by 0.1°C–0.3°C for up to several decades.		IMP-Neg[a]	133
C3: *Limit warming to 2°C (>67%)*	Limit peak warming to 2°C throughout the 21st century with a likelihood of >67%.	SSP1-2.6	IMP-GS	311
C4: Limit warming to 2°C (>50%)	Limit peak warming to 2°C throughout the 21st century with a likelihood of >50%.			159
C5: Limit warming to 2.5°C (>50%)	Limit peak warming to 2.5°C throughout the 21st century with a likelihood of >50%.			212
C6: Limit warming to 3°C (>50%)	Limit peak warming to 3°C throughout the 21st century with a likelihood of >50%.	SSP2-4.5	ModAct	97
C7: Limit warming to 4°C (>50%)	Limit peak warming to 4°C throughout the 21st century with a likelihood of >50%.	SSP3-7.0	CurPol	164
C8: Exceed warming of 4°C (≥50%)	Exceed warming of 4°C during the 21st century with a likelihood of ≥50%.	SSP5-8.5		29
C1, C2, C3: limit warming to 2°C (>67%) or lower	All scenarios in Categories C1, C2 and C3			541

[a]   The Illustrative Mitigation Pathway 'Neg' has extensive use of carbon dioxide removal (CDR) in the AFOLU, energy and the industry sectors to achieve net negative emissions. Warming peaks around 2060 and declines to below 1.5°C (50% likelihood) shortly after 2100. Whilst technically classified as C3, it strongly exhibits the characteristics of C2 high-overshoot pathways, hence it has been placed in the C2 category. See Box SPM.1 for an introduction of the IPs and IMPs.

Number of scenarios in each climate category

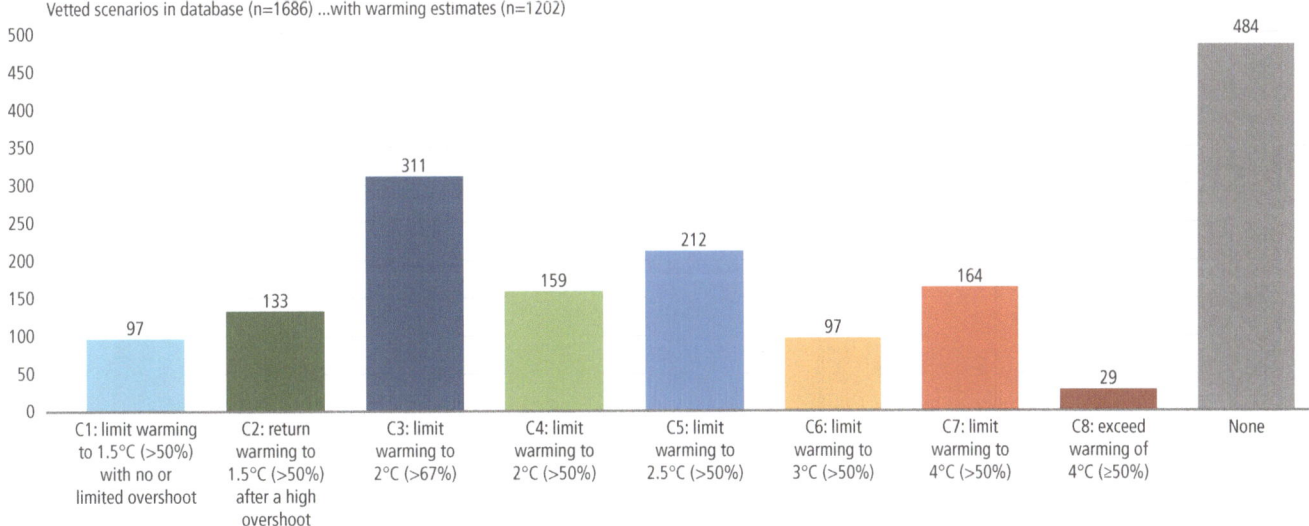

Figure 3.3 | Of the 1686 scenarios that passed vetting, 1202 had sufficient data available to be classified according to temperature, with an uneven distribution across warming levels.

results of MAGICC are shown in this chapter as it adequately covers the range of outcomes. The emulators are calibrated against the behaviour of complex climate models and observation data, consistent with the outcomes of AR6 WGI (Cross-Chapter Box 7.1). The climate assessment is a three-step process of harmonisation, infilling and a probabilistic climate model emulator run (Annex III.II.2.5). Warming projections until the year 2100 were derived for 1574 scenarios, of which 1202 passed vetting, with the remaining scenarios having insufficient information (Figure 3.3 and Table 3.1). For scenarios that limit warming to 2°C or lower, the SR1.5 classification was adopted in AR6, with more disaggregation provided for higher warming levels (Table 3.1).

These choices can be compared with the selection of common global warming levels (GWLs) of 1.5°C, 2°C, 3°C and 4°C to classify climate change impacts in the WGII assessment.

In addition to the temperature classification, each scenario is assigned to one of the following policy categories: (P0) diagnostic scenarios – 99 of 1686 vetted scenarios; (P1) scenarios with no globally coordinated policy (500) and (P1a) no climate mitigation efforts – 124, (P1b) current national mitigation efforts – 59, (P1c) Nationally Determined Contributions (NDCs) – 160, or (P1d) other non-standard assumptions – 153; (P2) globally coordinated climate policies with immediate

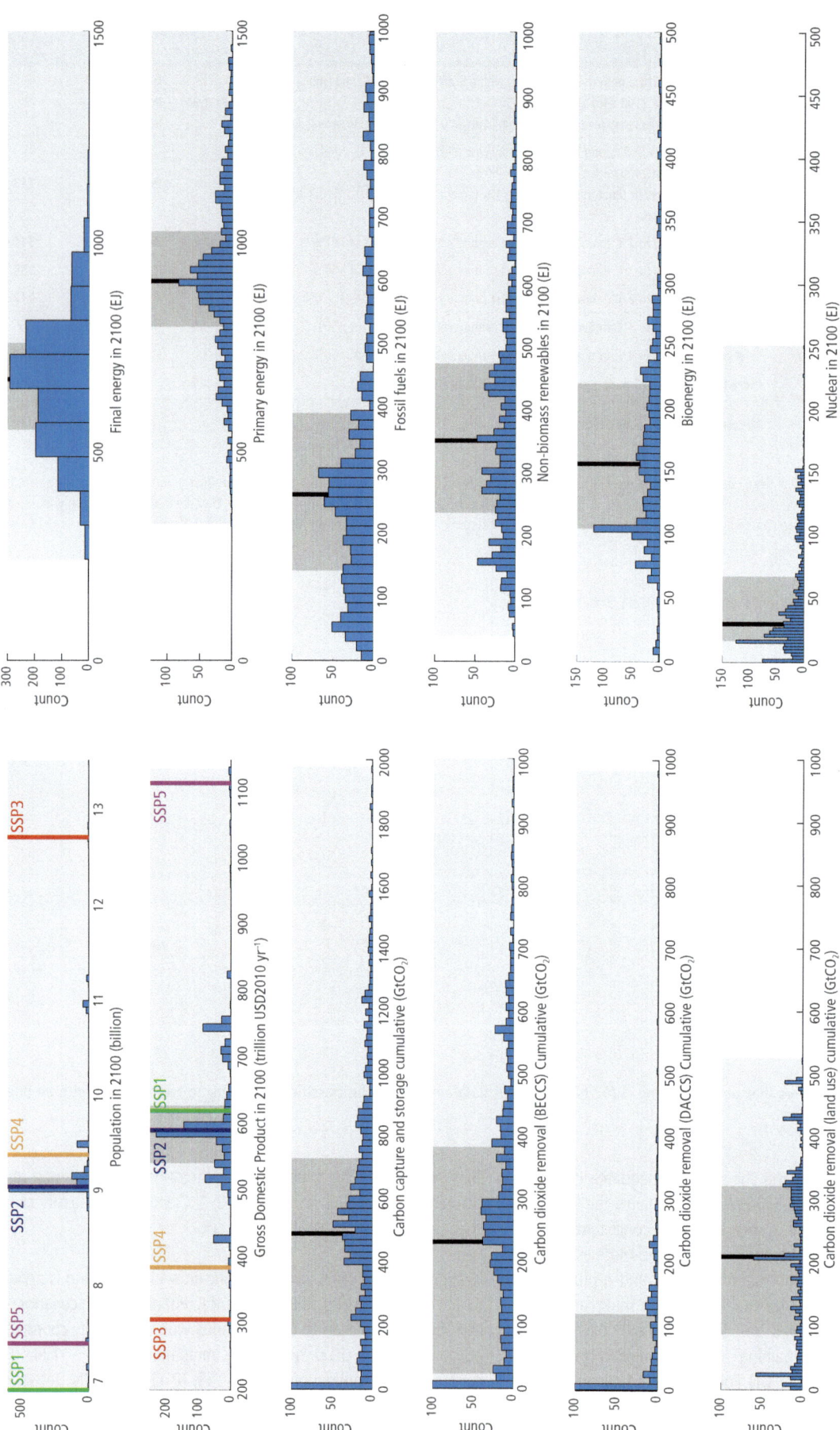

Figure 3.4 | Histograms for key categories in the AR6 scenario database. Only scenarios that passed vetting are shown. For population and GDP, the SSP input data are also shown. The grey shading represents the 0–100% range (light grey), 25–75% range (dark grey), and the median is a black line. The figures with white areas are outside of the scenario range, but the axis limits are retained to allow comparability with other categories. Each sub-figure potentially has different x- and y-axis limits. Each figure also potentially contains different numbers of scenarios, depending on what was submitted to the database. Source: AR6 scenarios database.

action (634) and (P2a) without any transfer of emission permits – 435, (P2b) with transfers – 70; or (P2c) with additional policy assumptions – 55; (P3) globally coordinated climate policies with delayed (i.e., from 2030 onwards or after 2030) action (451), preceded by (P3a) no mitigation commitment or current national policies – 7, (P3b) NDCs – 426, (P3c) NDCs and additional policies – 18; (P4) cost-benefit analysis (CBA) – 2. The policy categories were identified using text pattern matching on the scenario metadata and calibrated on the best-known scenarios from model intercomparisons, with further validation against the related literature, reported emission and carbon price trajectories, and exchanges with modellers. If the information available is enough to qualify a policy category number but not sufficient for a subcategory, then only the number is retained (e.g., P2 instead of P2a/b/c). A suffix added after P0 further qualifies a diagnostic scenario as one of the other policy categories. To demonstrate the diversity of the scenarios, the vetted scenarios were classified into different categories along the dimensions of population, GDP, energy, and cumulative emissions (Figure 3.4). The number of scenarios in each category provides some insight into the current literature, but this does not indicate a higher probability of that category occurring in reality. For population, the majority of scenarios are consistent with the SSP2 'middle of the road' category, with very few scenarios exploring the outer extremes. GDP has a slightly larger variation, but overall most scenarios are around the SSP2 socio-economic assumptions. The level of CCS and CDR is expected to change depending on the extent of mitigation, but there remains extensive use of both CDR and CCS in scenarios. CDR is dominated by bioenergy with CCS (BECCS) and sequestration on land, with relatively few scenarios using direct air capture with carbon storage (DACCS) and even less with enhanced weathering (EW) and other technologies (not shown). In terms of energy consumption, final energy has a much smaller range than primary energy as conversion losses are not included in final energy. Both mitigation and reference scenarios are shown, so there is a broad spread in different energy carriers represented in the database. Bioenergy has a number of scenarios at around 100 EJ, representing a constraint used in many model intercomparisons.

3.2.5   Illustrative Mitigation Pathways

Successive IPCC Assessment Reports (ARs) have used scenarios to illustrate key characteristics of possible climate (policy) futures. In AR5 four RCPs made the basis of climate modelling in WGI and WGII, with WGIII assessing over 1000 scenarios spanning those RCPs (Clarke et al. 2014). Of the over 400 scenarios assessed in SR1.5, four scenarios were selected to highlight the trade-off between short-term emission reductions and long-term deployment of BECCS (Rogelj et al. 2018a), referred to as 'Illustrative Pathways' (IPs). AR6 WGI and WGII rely on the scenarios selected for CMIP6, called ScenarioMIP (O'Neill et al. 2016), to assess warming levels. In addition to the full set of scenarios, AR6 WGIII also uses selected Illustrative Mitigation Pathways (IMPs).

In WGIII, IMPs were selected to denote the implications of different societal choices for the development of future emissions and associated transformations of main GHG-emitting sectors (Figure 3.5a and Box 3.1). The most important function of the IMPs is to illustrate key themes that form a common thread in the report, both with a storyline and a quantitative illustration. The storyline describes the

key characteristics that define an IMP. The quantitative versions of the IMPs provide numerical values that are internally consistent and comparable across chapters of the report. The quantitative IMPs have been selected from the AR6 scenario database. No assessment of the likelihood of each IMP has been made.

The selected scenarios (IPs) are divided into two sets (Figures 3.5 and 3.6): two reference pathways illustrative of high emissions and five Illustrative Mitigation Pathways (IMPs). The narratives are explained in full in Annex III.II.2.4. The two reference pathways explore the consequences of current policies and pledges: Current Policies (*CurPol*) and Moderate Action (*ModAct*). The *CurPol* pathway explores the consequences of continuing along the path of implemented climate policies in 2020 and only a gradual strengthening after that. The scenario illustrates the outcomes of many scenarios in the literature that project the trend from implemented policies until the end of 2020. The *ModAct* pathway explores the impact of implementing the Nationally Determined Contributions (NDCs) as formulated in 2020 and some further strengthening after that. In line with current literature, these two reference pathways lead to an increase in global mean temperature of more than 2°C (Section 3.3).

The Illustrative Mitigation Pathways (IMPs) properly explore different pathways consistent with meeting the long-term temperature goals of the Paris Agreement. They represent five different pathways that emerge from the overall assessment. The IMPs differ in terms of their focus, for example, placing greater emphasis on renewables (IMP-Ren), deployment of carbon dioxide removal that results in net negative global GHG emissions (IMP-Neg), and efficient resource use and shifts in consumption patterns, leading to low demand for resources, while ensuring a high level of services (IMP-LD). Other IMPs illustrate the implications of a less rapid introduction of mitigation measures followed by a subsequent gradual strengthening (IMP-GS), and how shifting global pathways towards sustainable development, including by reducing inequality, can lead to mitigation (IMP-SP) In the IMP framework, *IMP-GS* is consistent with limiting warming to 2°C (>67%) (C3), *IMP-Neg* shows a strategy that also limits warming to 2°C (>67%) but returns to nearly 1.5°C (>50%) by the end of the century (hence indicated as C2*). The other variants that can limit warming to 1.5°C (>50%) (C1) were selected. In addition to these IMPs, sensitivity cases that explore alternative warming levels (C3) for *IMP-Neg* and *IMP-Ren* are assessed (*IMP-Neg-2.0* and *IMP-Ren-2.0*).

The IMPs are selected to have different mitigation strategies, which can be illustrated looking at the energy system and emission pathways (Figure 3.7 and Figure 3.8). The mitigation strategies show the different options in emission reduction (Figure 3.7). Each panel shows the key characteristics leading to total GHG emissions, consisting of residual (gross) emissions (fossil CO_2 emissions, CO_2 emissions from industrial processes, and non-CO_2 emissions) and removals (net land-use change, bioenergy with carbon capture and storage – BECCS, and direct air carbon capture and storage – DACCS), in addition to avoided emissions through the use of carbon capture and storage on fossil fuels. The *IMP-Neg* and *IMP-GS* scenarios were shown to illustrate scenarios with a significant role of CDR. The energy supply (Figure 3.8) shows the phase-out of fossil fuels in the *IMP-LD*, *IMP-Ren* and *IMP-SP* cases, but a less substantial decrease in the *IMP-Neg* case. The *IMP-GS* case

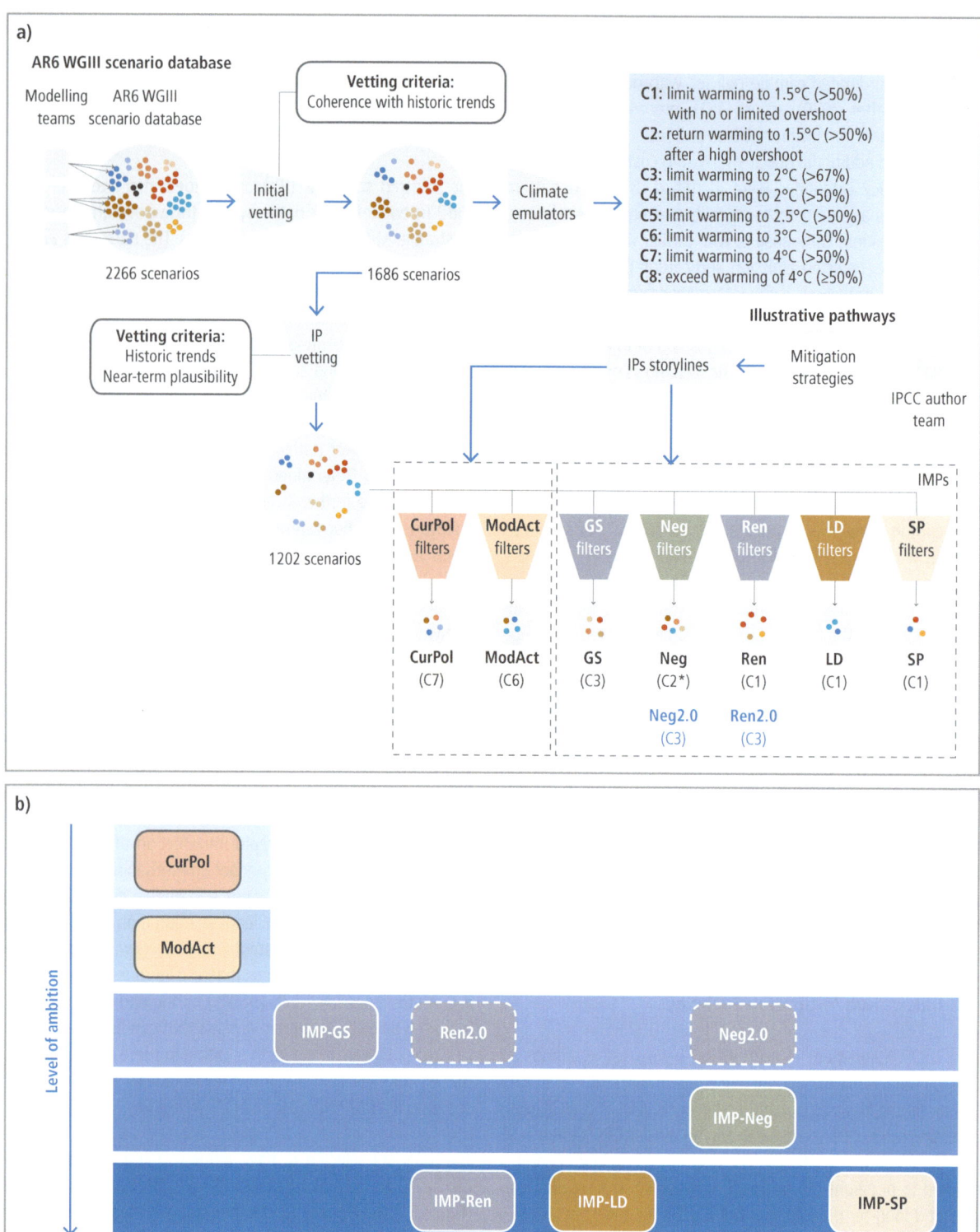

Figure 3.5 | (a) Process for creating the AR6 scenario database and selecting the illustrative (mitigation) pathways. The compiled scenarios in the AR6 scenarios database were vetted for consistency with historical statistics and subsequently a temperature classification was added using climate model emulators. The illustrative (mitigation) pathways were selected from the full set of pathways based on storylines of critical mitigation strategies that emerged from the assessment. **(b)** An overview of the Illustrative Pathways selected for use in IPCC AR6 WGIII, consisting of pathways illustrative of higher emissions, Current Policies (*CurPol*) and Moderate Action (*ModAct*), and Illustrative Mitigation Pathways (IMPs): gradual strengthening of current policies (*IMP-GS*), extensive use of net negative emissions (*IMP-Neg*), renewables (*IMP-Ren*), low demand (*IMP-LD*), and shifting pathways (*IMP-SP*). The Ren2.0 and Neg2.0 scenarios are alternative scenarios to the IMPs. These pathways are based on renewables and extensive use of negative emissions, respectively, but leading to temperature levels comparable to the C3 category and have sometimes been used for comparison.

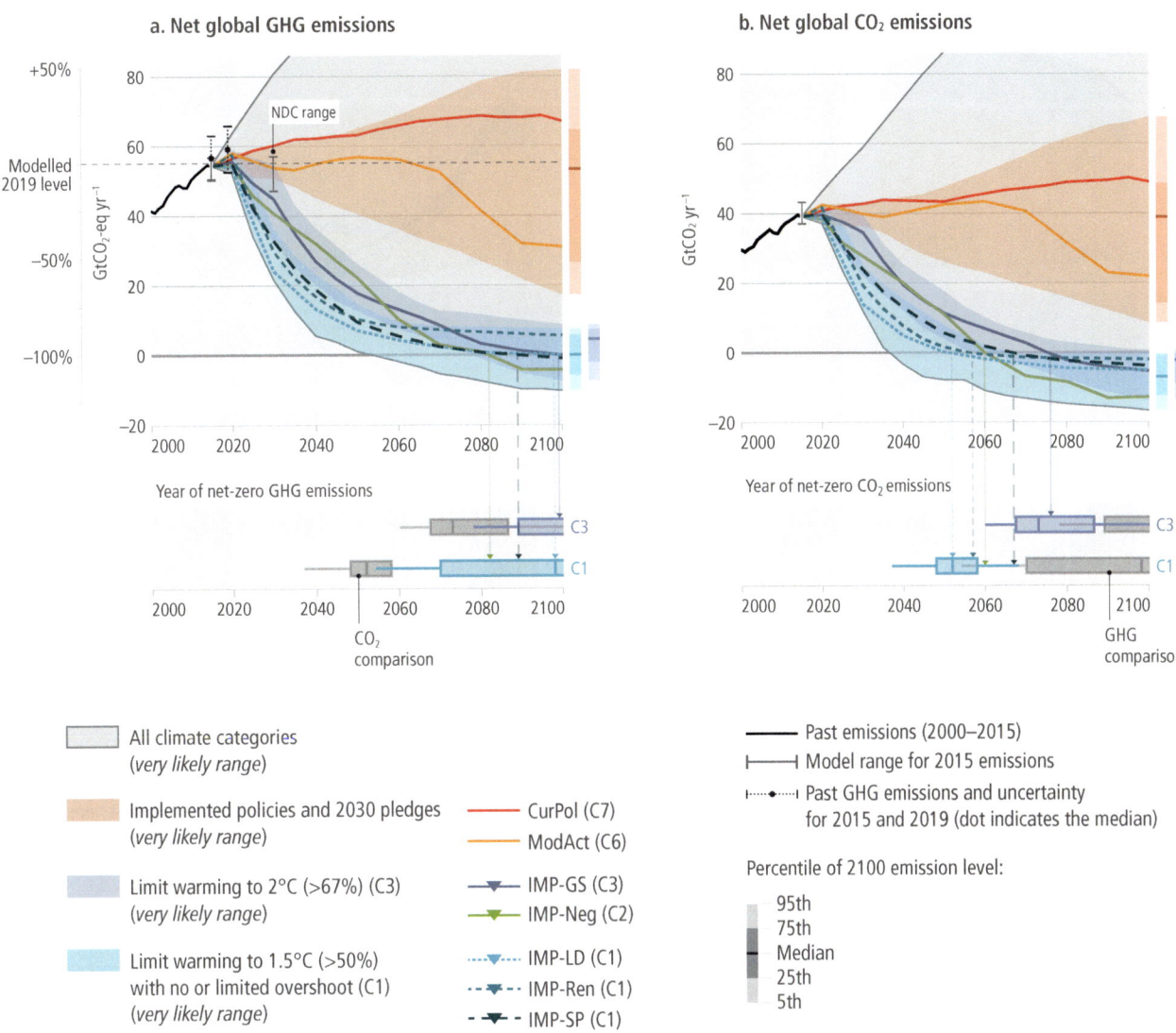

Figure 3.6 | Overview of the net CO₂ emissions and Kyoto greenhouse gas (GHG) emissions for each Illustrative Mitigation Pathway (IMP).

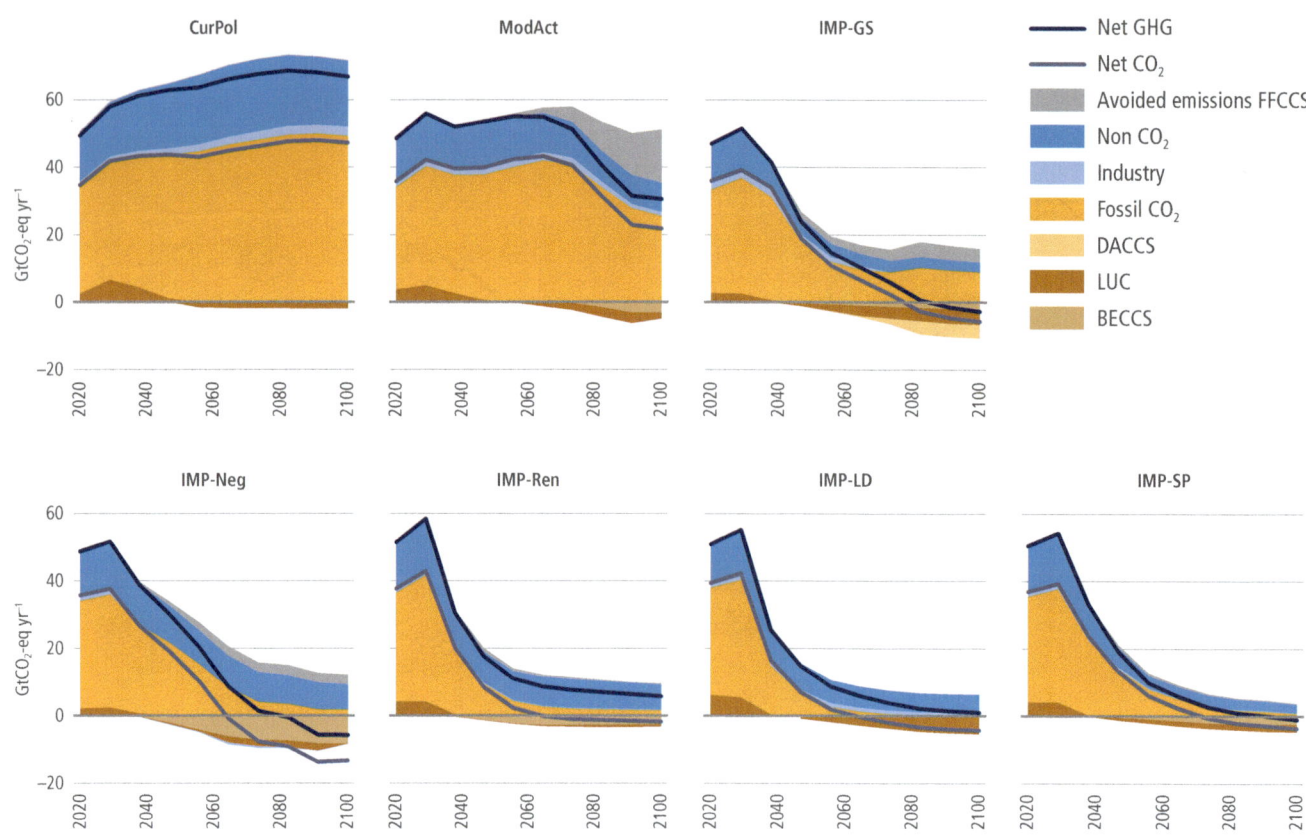

Figure 3.7 | The residual fossil fuel and industry emissions, carbon dioxide removal (CDR) {LUC, DACCS, BECCS}, and non-CO$_2$ emissions (using AR6 GWP-100) for each of the seven illustrative pathways (IPs). Fossil CCS is also shown, though this does not lead to emissions to the atmosphere (Section 3.2.5).

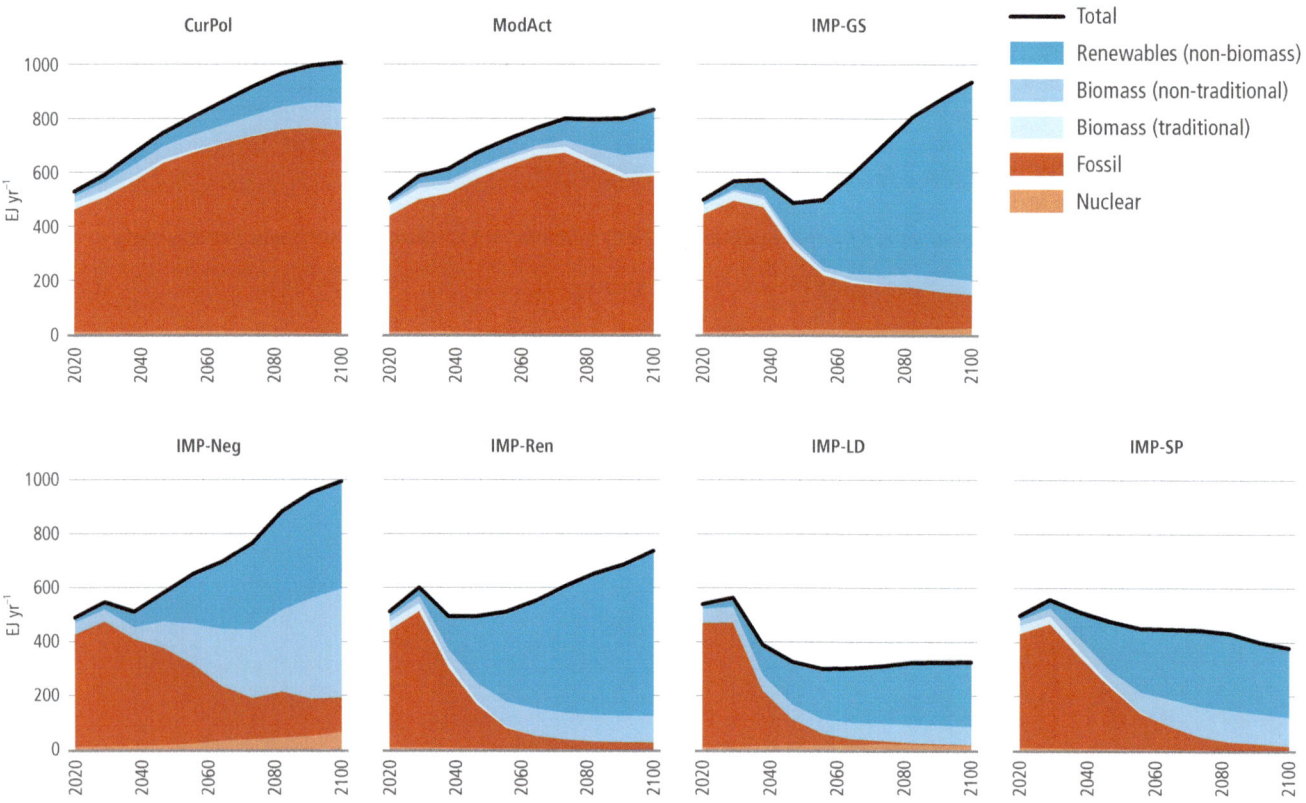

Figure 3.8 | The energy system in each of the illustrative pathways (IPs).

needs to make up its slow start by (i) rapid reductions mid-century and (ii) massive reliance on net negative emissions by the end of the century. The *CurPol* and *ModAct* cases both result in relatively high emissions, showing a slight increase and stabilisation compared to current emissions, respectively.

3.3 Emission Pathways, Including Socio-economic, Carbon Budget and Climate Responses Uncertainties

3.3.1 Socio-economic Drivers of Emissions Scenarios

Greenhouse gas (GHG) emissions mainly originate from the use and transformation of energy, agriculture, land use (change) and industrial activities. The future development of these sources is influenced by trends in socio-economic development, including population, economic activity, technology, politics, lifestyles, and climate policy. Trends for these factors are not independent, and scenarios provide a consistent outlook for these factors together (Section 3.2). Marangoni et al. (2017) show that in projections, assumptions influencing energy intensity (e.g., structural change, lifestyle and efficiency) and economic growth are the most important determinants of future CO_2 emissions from energy combustion. Other critical factors include technology assumptions, preferences, resource assumptions and policy (van Vuuren et al. 2008). As many of the factors are represented differently in specific models, the model itself is also an important factor – providing a reason for the importance of model diversity (Sognnaes et al. 2021). For land use, Stehfest et al. (2019) show that assumptions on population growth are more dominant given that variations in per capita consumption of food are smaller than for energy. Here, we only provide a brief overview of some key drivers. We focus first on so-called reference scenarios (without stringent climate policy) and look at mitigation scenarios in detail later. We use the SSPs to discuss trends in more detail. The SSPs were published in 2017, and by now, some elements will have to be updated (O'Neill et al. 2020b). Still, the ranges represent the full literature relatively well.

Historically, population and GDP have been growing over time. Scenario studies agree that further global population growth is likely up to 2050, leading to a range of possible outcomes of around 8.5–11 billion people (Figure 3.9a). After 2050, projections show a much wider range. If fertility drops below replacement levels, a decline in the global population is possible (as illustrated by SSP1 and SSP5). This typically includes scenarios with rapid development and investment in education. However, median projections mostly show a stabilisation of the world population (e.g., SSP2), while high-end projections show a continued growth (e.g., SSP3). The UN Population Prospects include considerably higher values for both the medium projection and the high end of the range than the SSP scenarios (KC and Lutz 2017; UN 2019). The most recent median UN projection reaches almost 11 billion people in 2100. The key differences are in Africa and China: here, the population projections are strongly influenced by the rate of fertility change (faster drop in SSPs). Underlying these differences, the UN approach is more based on current demographic trends while the SSPs assume a broader range of factors (including education) driving future fertility.

Economic growth is even more uncertain than the population projections (Figure 3.9c). The average growth rate of GDP was about 2.8% per year (constant USD) in the 1990–2019 period (The World Bank 2021). In 2020, the COVID-19 crisis resulted in a considerable drop in GDP (estimated around 4–5%) (IMF 2021). After a recovery period, most economic projections assume growth rates to converge back to previous projections, although at a lower level (IMF 2021; OECD 2021) (see also Box 3.2). In the long term, assumptions on future growth relate to political stability, the role of the progress of the technology frontier and the degree to which countries can catch up (Johansson et al. 2013). The SSP scenarios cover an extensive range, with low per-capita growth in SSP3 and SSP4 (mostly in developing countries) and rapid growth in SSP1 and SSP5. At the same, however, also scenarios outside the range have some plausibility – including the option of economic decline (Kallis et al. 2012) or much faster economic development (Christensen et al. 2018). The OECD long-term projection is at the global level reasonably consistent with SSP2. Equally important economic parameters include income distribution (inequity) and the type of growth (structural change, i.e., services vs manufacturing industries). Some projections (like SSP1) show a considerable convergence of income levels within and across countries, while in other projections, this does not occur (e.g., SSP3). Most scenarios reflect the suggested inverse relationship between the assumed growth rate for income and population growth (Figure 3.9e). SSP1 and SSP5 represent examples of scenarios with relatively low population increase and relatively high-income increase over the century. SSP3 represents an example of the opposite – while SSP2 and SSP4 are placed more in the middle. Nearly all scenarios assessed here do not account for climate impacts on growth (mostly for methodological reasons). As discussed in Section 3.5 these impacts can be considerable. An emerging area of literature emphasises the possibility of stabilisation (or even decline) of income levels in developed countries, arguing that such a trend would be preferred or even needed for environmental reasons (Anderson and Larkin 2013; Hickel and Kallis 2020; Kallis et al. 2020; Hickel et al. 2021; Keyßer and Lenzen 2021) (see also Chapter 5). Such scenarios are not common among IAM outcomes, that are more commonly based on the idea that decarbonisation can be combined with economic growth by a combination of technology, lifestyle and structural economic changes. Still, such scenarios could result in a dramatic reduction of energy and resource consumption.

Scenarios show a range of possible energy projections. In the absence of climate policy, most scenarios project the final energy demand to continue to grow to around 650–800 EJ yr^{-1} in 2100 (based on the AR6 Scenarios Database, Figure 3.9b). Some projections show a very high energy demand up to 1000 EJ yr^{-1} (comparable to SSP5). The scenario of the IEA lies within the SSP range but near the SSP1 projection. However, it should be noted that the IEA scenario includes current policies (most reference scenarios do not) and many scenarios published before 2021 did not account for the COVID-19 crisis. Several researchers discuss the possibility of decoupling material and energy demand from economic growth in the literature, mainly in developed countries (Kemp-Benedict 2018) (decoupling here refers to either a much slower increase in demand or even a decrease). In the scenario literature, this is reflected by scenarios with very low demand for final energy based on increased energy efficiency and less energy-intensive lifestyles (e.g., SSP1 and the LED scenario) (Grubler et al. 2018; van Vuuren et al. 2018). While these studies show the feasibility of such

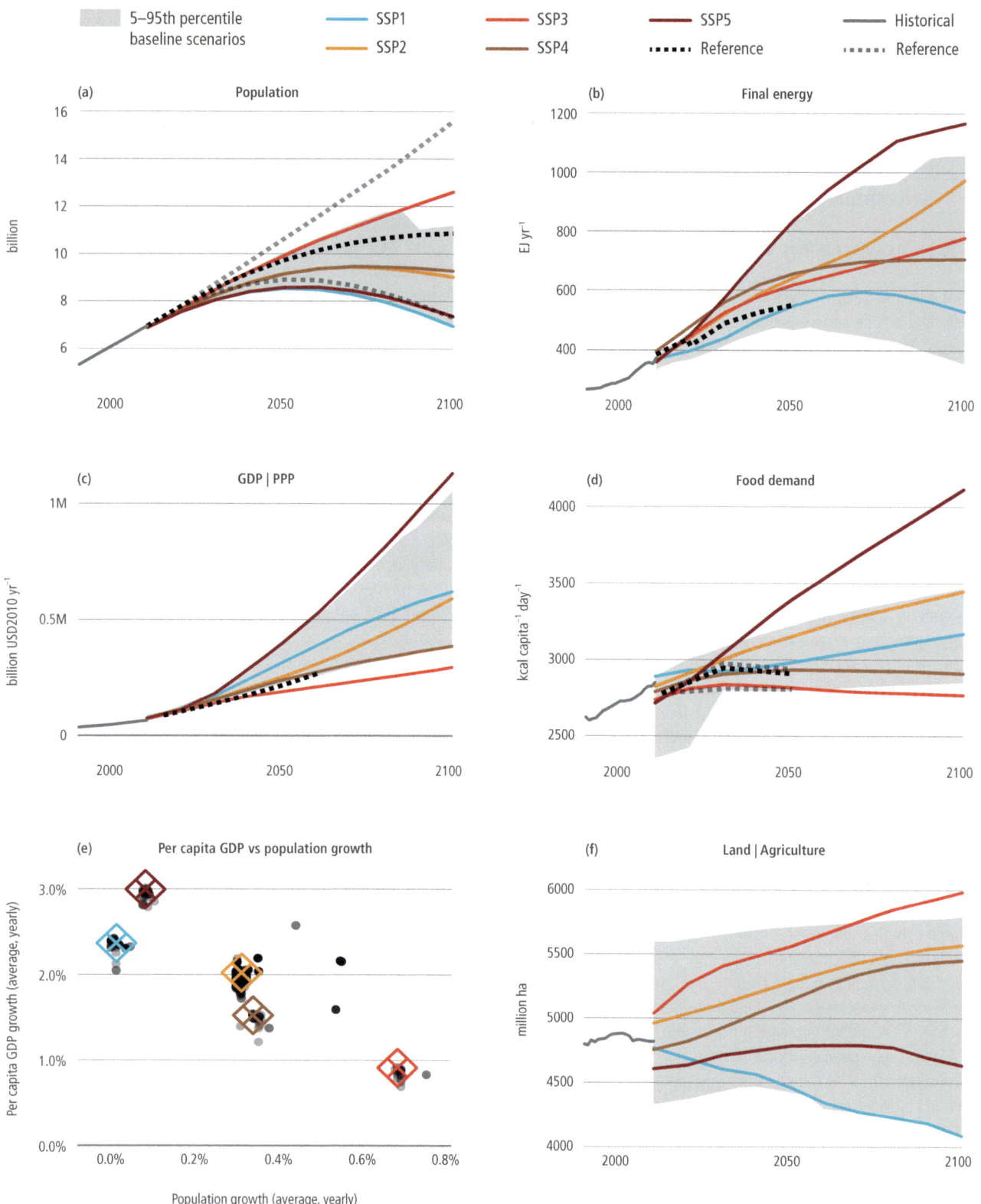

Figure 3.9 | Trends in key scenario characteristics and driving forces as included in the SSP scenarios (showing 5–95th percentiles of the reference scenarios as included in the database in grey shading). Reference (dotted lines) refers to the UN low-, medium- and high-population scenarios (UN 2019), the OECD long-term economic growth scenario (OECD 2021), the scenarios from the IEA's World Energy Outlook (IEA 2019), and the scenarios in the FAO assessment (FAO 2018).

pathways, their energy efficiency improvement rates are considerably above the historic range of around 2% (Gütschow et al. 2018; Jeffery et al. 2018; Vrontisi et al. 2018; Haberl et al. 2020; Roelfsema et al. 2020; Giarola et al. 2021; Höhne et al. 2021; IEA 2021a; Höhne et al. 2021; Sognnaes et al. 2021). These scenarios also show clear differences in food consumption and the amount of land used for agriculture. Food demand in terms of per-capita caloric intake is projected to increase in most scenarios (Figure 3.9d). However, it should be noted that there are large differences in dietary composition across the scenarios (from more meat-intensive in scenarios such as SSP5 to a decrease in meat consumptions in other scenarios such as SSP1). Land-use projections also depend on assumed changes in yield and the population scenarios (Figure 3.9f). Typically, changes in land use are less drastic than some other parameters (in fact, the 5–95th percentile database range is almost stable). Agriculture land is projected to increase in SSP3,

SSP2, and SSP4 – it is more-or-less stable in SSP5 and is projected to decline in SSP1.

3.3.2 Emission Pathways and Temperature Outcomes

3.3.2.1 Overall Mitigation Profiles and Temperature Consequences

Figure 3.10 shows the GHG and CO_2 emission trajectories for different temperature categories as defined in Section 3.2 (the temperature levels are calculated using simple climate models, consistent with the outcomes of the recent WGI assessment, Cross-Chapter Box 7.1). It should be noted that most scenarios currently in the literature do not account for the impact of COVID-19 (Box 3.2).

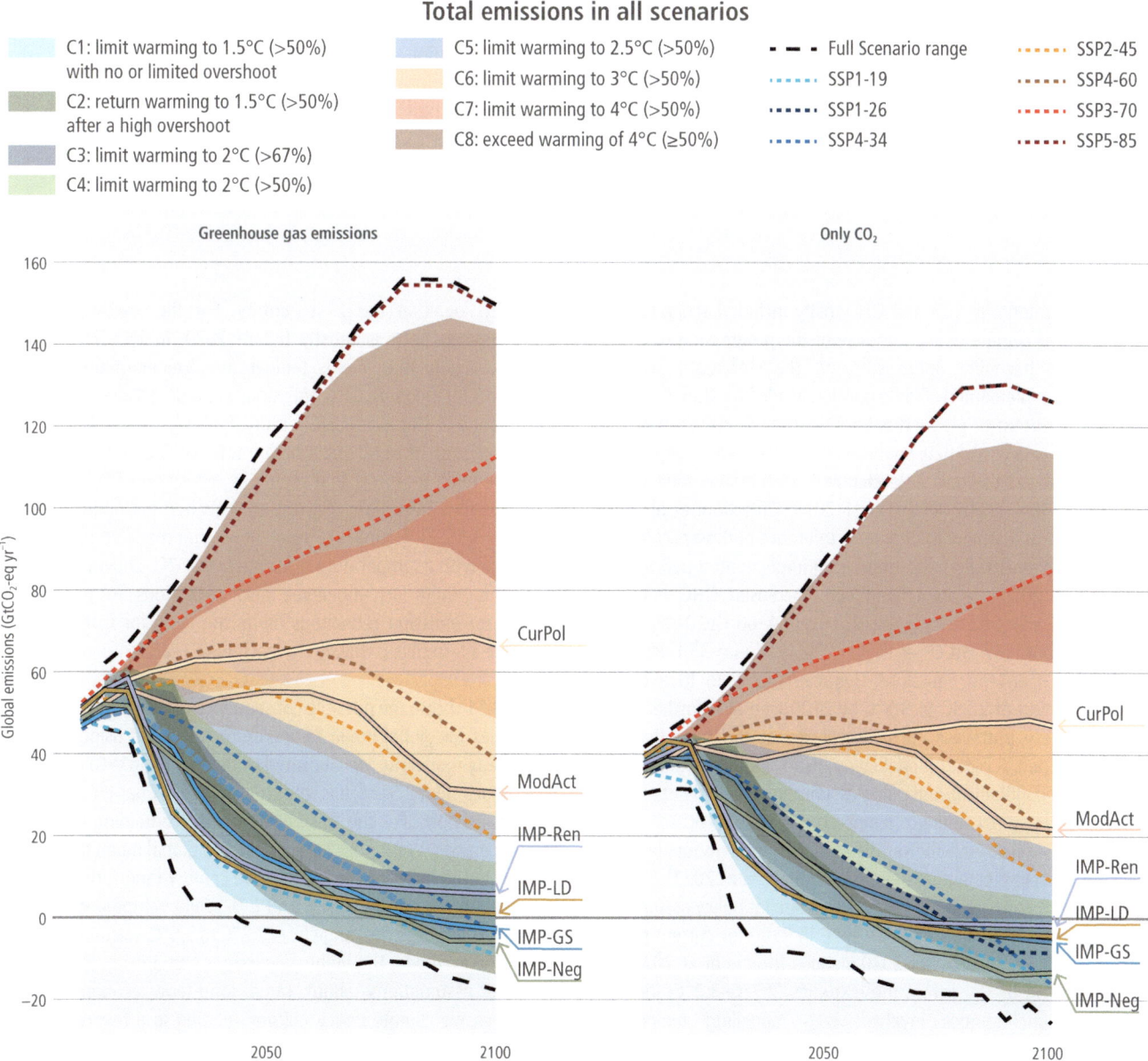

Figure 3.10 | Total emissions profiles in the scenarios based on climate category for GHGs (AR6 GWP-100) and CO$_2$. The Illustrative mitigation pathways (IMPs) are also indicated.

Box 3.2 | Impact of COVID-19 on Long-term Emissions

The reduction in CO_2 emissions of the COVID-19 pandemic in 2020 was estimated to be about 6% (Section 4.2.2.4 and Table 4.SM.2) lower than 2019 levels (Forster et al. 2020; Friedlingstein et al. 2020; Liu et al. 2020c; BP 2021; Crippa et al. 2021; IEA 2021; Le Quéré et al. 2021). Near-real-time monitoring estimates show a rebound in emissions levels, meaning 2021 emissions levels are expected to be higher than 2020 (Le Quéré et al. 2021). The longer-term effects are uncertain but so far do not indicate a clear structural change for climate policy related to the pandemic. The increase in renewable shares in 2020 could stimulate a further transition, but slow economic growth can also slow down (renewable) energy investments. Also, lifestyle changes during the crisis can still develop in different directions (working from home, but maybe also living further away from work). Without a major intervention, most long-term scenarios project that emissions will start to follow a similar pathway as earlier projections (although at a reduced level) (IEA 2020b; Kikstra et al. 2021a; Rochedo et al. 2021). If emissions reductions are limited to only a short time, the adjustment of pathways will lead to negligible outcomes in the order of 0.01K (Forster et al. 2020; Jones et al. 2021). At the same time, however, the large amount of investments pledged in the recovery packages could provide a unique opportunity to determine the long-term development of infrastructure, energy systems and land use (Andrijevic et al. 2020b; Hepburn et al. 2020; Pianta et al. 2021). Near-term alternative recovery pathways have been shown to have the potential to influence carbon-price pathways, and energy investments and electrification requirements under stringent mitigation targets (Bertram et al. 2021; Kikstra et al. 2021a; Pollitt et al. 2021; Rochedo et al. 2021; Shan et al. 202). Most studies suggest a noticeable reduction in 2030 emissions. However, much further reductions would be needed to reach the emission levels consistent with mitigation scenarios that limit warming to 2°C (>67%) or lower (see Chapter 4). At the moment, the share of investments in greenhouse gas reduction is relatively small in most recovery packages, and no structural shifts for climate policies are observed linked to the pandemic. Finally, most of the scenarios analysed in this Chapter do not include the 2020 emissions reduction related to the COVID-19 pandemic. The effect of the pandemic on the pathways will likely be very small. The assessment of climate mitigation pathways in this chapter should be interpreted as being almost exclusively based on the assumption of a fast recovery with limited persistent effects on emissions or structural changes.

The higher categories (C6 and C7) mostly included scenarios with no or modest climate policy. Because of the progression of climate policy, it is becoming more common that reference scenarios incorporate implemented climate policies. Modelling studies typically implement current or pledged policies up until 2030 (Vrontisi et al. 2018; Roelfsema et al. 2020; Sognnaes et al. 2021) with some studies focusing also on the policy development in the long term (Höhne et al. 2021; IEA 2021a; Jeffery et al. 2018; Gütschow et al. 2018). Based on the assessment in Chapter 4, reference pathways consistent with the implementation and trend from implemented policies until the end of 2020 are associated with increased GHG emissions from 59 (53–65) $GtCO_2$-eq yr^{-1} in 2019 to 54–60 $GtCO_2$-eq yr^{-1} by 2030 and to 47–67 $GtCO_2$-eq yr^{-1} by 2050 (Figure 3.6). Pathways with these near-term emissions characteristics lead to a median global warming of 2.2°C to 3.5°C by 2100 (see also further in this section). These pathways consider policies at the time that they were developed. A recent model comparison that harmonised socio-economic, technological, and policy assumptions (Giarola et al. 2021) found a 2.2°C–2.9°C median temperature rise in 2100 for current and stated policies, with the results sensitive to the model used and the method of implementing policies (Sognnaes et al. 2021). Scenario inference and construction methods using similar policy assumptions lead to a median range of 2.9°C–3.2°C in 2100 for current policies and 2.4°C–2.9°C in 2100 for 2030 pledges (Höhne et al. 2021). The median spread of 1°C across these studies (2.2°C–3.2°C) indicates the deep uncertainties involved with modelling temperature outcomes of 2030 policies through to 2100 (Höhne et al. 2021).

The lower categories include increasingly stringent assumed climate policies. For all scenario categories, except the highest category, emissions peak in the 21st century. For the lowest categories, the emissions peak is mostly before 2030. In fact, for scenarios in the category that avoids temperature overshoot for the 1.5°C scenario (C1 category), GHG emissions are reduced already to almost zero around the middle of the century. Typically, CO_2 emissions reach net zero about 10 to 40 years before total GHG emissions reach net zero. The main reason is that scenarios reduce non-CO_2 greenhouse gas emissions less than CO_2 due to a limited mitigation potential (Section 3.3.2.2). Figure 3.10 also shows that many scenarios in the literature with a temperature outcome below 2°C show net negative emissions. There are, however, also exceptions in which more immediate emission reductions limits the need for CDR. The IMPs illustrate alternative pathways to reach the C1–C3 temperature levels.

Figure 3.11 shows the possible consequences of the different scenario categories for global mean temperature calculated using a reduced complexity model (RCM) calibrated to the IPCC AR6 WGI assessment (see Annex III.II.2.5 of this report and Cross-Chapter Box 7.1 in AR6 WGI report). For the C5–C7 categories (containing most of the reference and current policy scenarios), the global mean temperature is expected to increase throughout the century (and further increase will happen after 2100 for C6 and C7). While warming would *more likely than not* be in the range from 2.2°C to 3.5°C, warming up to 5°C cannot be excluded. The highest emissions scenarios in the literature combine assumptions about rapid long-term economic growth and pervasive climate policy failures, leading to a reversal of some recent trends (Box 3.3). For the categories C1–C4, a peak in global mean temperature is reached mid-century for most scenarios in the database, followed by a small (C3/C4) or more considerable decline (C1/C2). There is a clear distinction between the scenarios with no or

Box 3.3 | The Likelihood of High-end Emissions Scenarios

At the time the Representative Concentration Pathways (RCPs) were published, they included three scenarios that could represent emission developments in the absence of climate policy: RCP4.5, RCP6 and RCP8.5, described as, respectively, low, medium and high-end scenarios in the absence of strong climate policy (van Vuuren et al. 2011). RCP8.5 was described as representative of the top 5% scenarios in the literature. The SSPs-based set of scenarios covered the RCP forcing levels, adding a new low scenario (at 1.9 W m^{-2}). Hausfather and Peters (2020) pointed out that since 2011, the rapid development of renewable energy technologies and emerging climate policy have made it considerably less likely that emissions could end up as high as RCP8.5. Still, emission trends in developing countries track RCP8.5 Pedersen et al. (2020), and high land-use emissions could imply that emissions would continue to do so in the future, even at the global scale (Schwalm et al. 2020). Other factors resulting in high emissions include higher population or economic growth as included in the SSPs (Section 3.3.1) or rapid development of new energy services. Climate projections of RCP8.5 can also result from strong feedbacks of climate change on (natural) emission sources and high climate sensitivity (AR6 WGI Chapter 7), and therefore their median climate impacts might also materialise while following a lower emission path (e.g., Hausfather and Betts 2020). The discussion also relates to a more fundamental discussion on assigning likelihoods to scenarios, which is extremely difficult given the deep uncertainty and direct relationship with human choice. However, it would help to appreciate certain projections (e.g., Ho et al. 2019). All in all, this means that high-end scenarios have become considerably less likely since AR5 but cannot be ruled out. It is important to realise that RCP8.5 and SSP5-8.5 do not represent a typical 'business-as-usual' projection but are only useful as high-end, high-risk scenarios. Reference emission scenarios (without additional climate policy) typically end up in the C5–C7 categories included in this assessment.

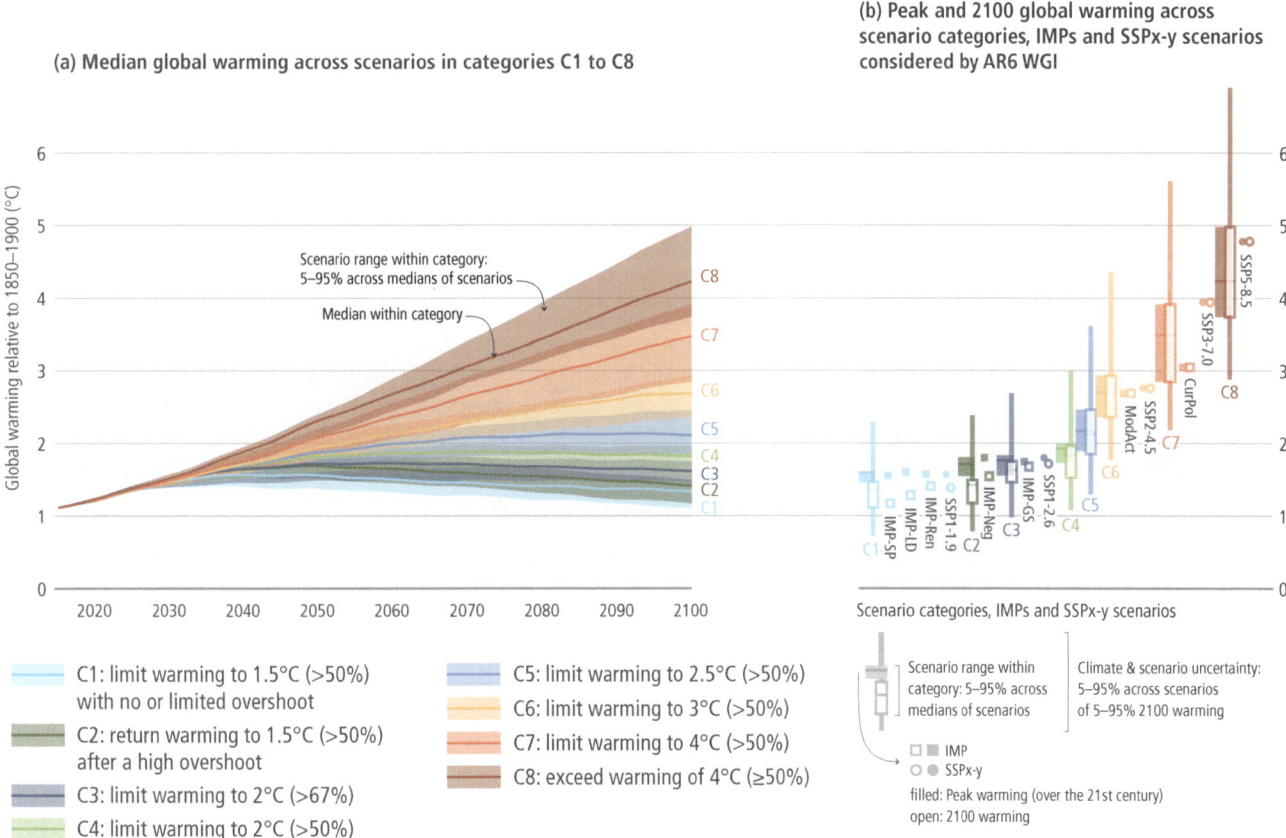

(a) Median global warming across scenarios in categories C1 to C8

(b) Peak and 2100 global warming across scenario categories, IMPs and SSPx-y scenarios considered by AR6 WGI

Figure 3.11 | Global mean temperature outcome of the ensemble of scenarios included in the climate categories C1–C8 (based on a reduced complexity model – RCM – calibrated to the WGI assessment, both in terms of future and historic warming). The left panel shows the ranges of scenario uncertainty (shaded area) with the P50 RCM probability (line). The right panel shows the P5 to P95 range of combined RCM climate uncertainty (C1–C8 is explained in Table 3.1) and scenario uncertainty, and the P50 (line).

limited overshoot (typically <0.1°C, C1) compared to those with high overshoot (C2): in emissions, the C1 category is characterised by steep early reductions and a relatively small contribution of net negative emissions (like *IMP-LD* and *IMP-Ren*) (Figure 3.10). In addition to the temperature caused by the range of scenarios in each category (main panel), climate uncertainties also contribute to a range of temperature outcomes (including uncertainties regarding the carbon cycle, climate sensitivity, and the rate of change, see AR6 WGI). The bars on the right of Figure 3.11 show the uncertainty range for each category (combining scenario and climate uncertainty). While the C1 category *more likely than not* limits warming to 1.5°C (>50%) by the end of the century, even with such a scenario, warming above 2°C cannot be excluded (95th percentile). The uncertainty range for the highest emission categories (C7) implies that these scenarios could lead to a warming above 6°C.

3.3.2.2 The Role of Carbon Dioxide and Other Greenhouse Gases

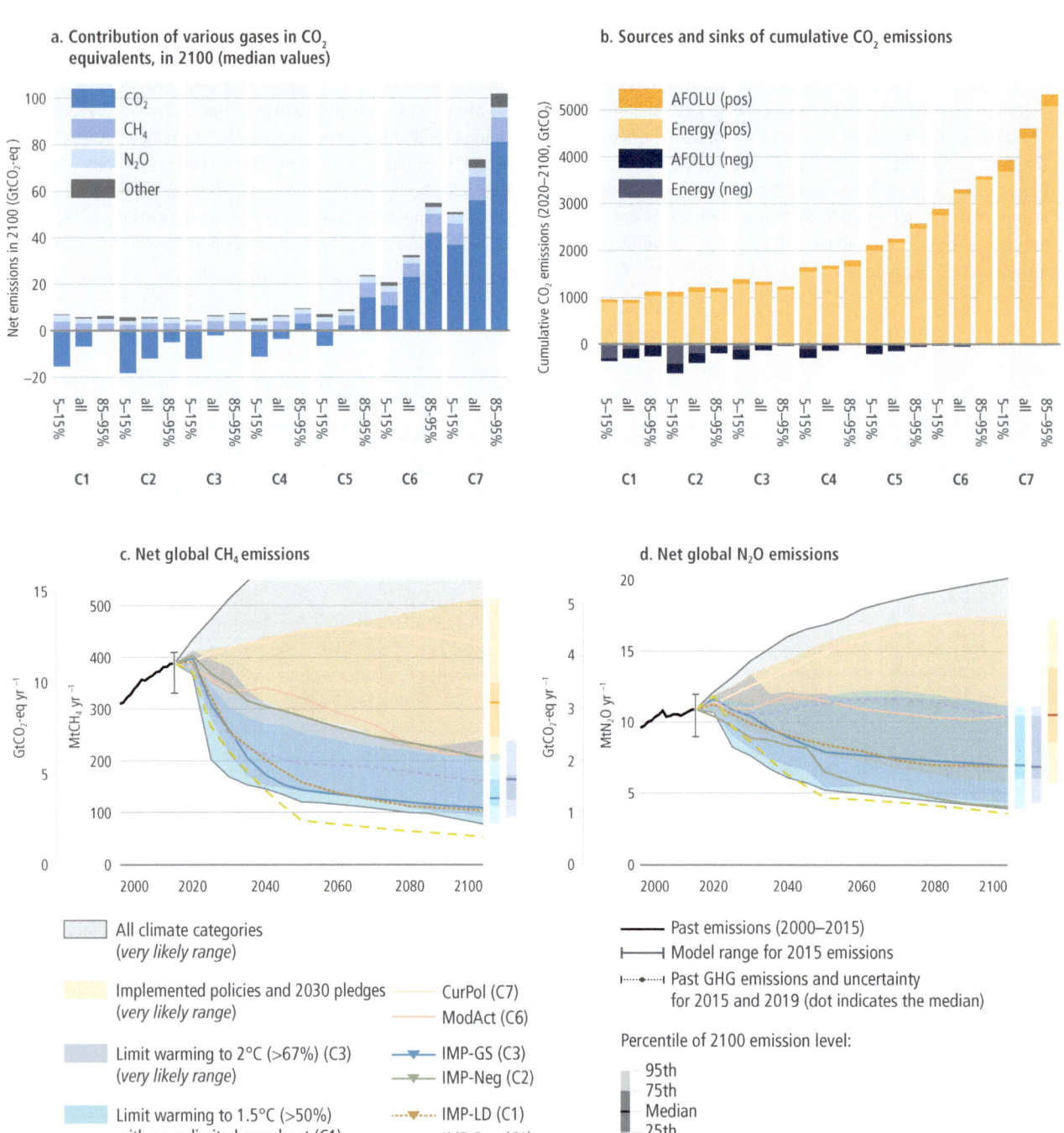

Figure 3.12 | (a) The role of CO₂ and other greenhouse gases. Emission in CO₂-eq in 2100 (using AR6 GWP-100) (other = halogenated gases) and **(b)** cumulative CO₂ emissions in the 2020–2100 period. Panels **(c)** and **(d)** show the development of CH₄ and N₂O emissions over time. Energy emissions include the contribution of BECCS. For both energy and AFOLU sectors, the positive and negative values represent the cumulated annual balances. In both panels, the three bars per scenario category represent the lowest 5–15th percentile, the average value and the highest 5–15th percentile. These illustrate the range of scenarios in each category. The definition of C1–C7 can be found in Table 3.1.

The trajectory of future CO_2 emissions plays a critical role in mitigation, given CO_2 long-term impact and dominance in total greenhouse gas forcing. As shown in Figure 3.12, CO_2 dominates total greenhouse gas emissions in the high-emissions scenarios but is also reduced most, going from scenarios in the highest to lower categories. In C4 and below, most scenarios exhibit net negative CO_2 emissions in the second half of the century compensating for some of the residual emissions of non-CO_2 gases as well as reducing overall warming from an intermediate peak. Still, early emission reductions and further reductions in non-CO_2 emissions can also lead to scenarios without net negative emissions in 2100, even in C1 and C3 (shown for the 85–95th percentile). In C1, avoidance of significant overshoot implies that immediate gross reductions are more relevant than long-term net negative emissions (explaining the lower number than in C2) but carbon dioxide removal (CDR) is still playing a role in compensating for remaining positive emissions in hard-to-abate sectors.

CH_4 and N_2O emissions are also reduced from C7 to C1, but this mostly occurs between C7 and C5. The main reason is the characteristics of abatement potential: technical measures can significantly reduce CH_4 and N_2O emissions at relatively low costs to about 50% of the current levels (e.g., by reducing CH_4 leaks from fossil fuel production and transport, reducing landfill emissions gazing, land management and introducing measures related to manure management, see also Chapter 7 and 11). However, technical potential estimates become exhausted even if the stringency of mitigation is increased (Harmsen et al. 2019a,b; Höglund-Isaksson et al. 2020). Therefore, further reduction may come from changes in activity levels, such as switching to a less meat-intensive diet, therefore reducing livestock (Stehfest et al. 2009; Willett et al. 2019; Ivanova et al. 2020) (Chapter 7). Other non-CO_2 GHG emissions (halogenated gases) are reduced to low levels for scenarios below 2.5°C.

Short-lived climate forcers (SLCFs) also play an important role in climate change, certainly for short-term changes (AR6 WGI, Figure SPM.2) (Shindell et al. 2012). These forcers consist of (i) substances contributing to warming, such as methane, black carbon and tropospheric ozone, and (ii) substances contributing to cooling (other aerosols, such as related to sulphur emissions). Most SLCFs are also air pollutants, and reducing their emissions provides additional co-benefits (Shindell et al. 2017a,b; Hanaoka and Masui 2020). In the case of the first group, emission reduction thus leads to both air pollution and climate benefits. For the second, group there is a possible trade-off (Shindell and Smith 2019; Lund et al. 2020). As aerosol emissions are mostly associated with fossil fuel combustion, the benefits of reducing CO_2 could, in the short term, be reduced as a result of lower aerosol cooling. There has been an active discussion on the exact climate contribution of SLCF-focused policies in the literature. This discussion partly emerged from different assumptions on possible reductions in the absence of ambitious climate policy and the uncertain global climate benefit from aerosol (black carbon) (Rogelj et al. 2014). The latter is now assessed to be smaller than originally thought (Takemura and Suzuki 2019; Smith et al. 2020b) (see also AR6 WGI Section 6.4). Reducing SLCF emissions is critical to meet long-term climate goals and might help reduce the rate of climate change in the short term. Deep SLCF emission reductions also increase the remaining carbon budget for a specific temperature goal (Rogelj et al. 2015a; Reisinger et al. 2021) (Box 3.4). A more detailed discussion can be found in AR6 WGI Chapters 5 and 6.

For accounting of emissions and the substitution of different gases as part of a mitigation strategy, typically, emission metrics are used to compare the climate impact of different gases. Most policies currently use Global Warming Potentials (GWPs) with a 100-year time horizon as this is also mandated for emissions reporting in the Paris Rulebook (for a wider discussion of GHG metrics, see Box 2.1 in Chapter 2 of this report, and AR6 WGI, Chapter 7, Section 7.6). Alternative metrics have also been proposed, such as those using a shorter or longer time horizon, or those that focus directly on the consequences of reaching a certain temperature target (Global Temperature Change Potential – GTP), allowing a more direct comparison with cumulative CO_2 emissions (Allen et al. 2016; Lynch et al. 2020) or focusing on damages (Global Damage Potential) (an overview is given in Chapter 2, and Cross-Chapter Box 3 in Chapter 3). Depending on the metric, the value attributed to reducing short-lived forcers such as methane can be lower in the near term (e.g., in the case of GTP) or higher (GWP with a short reference period). For most metrics, however, the impact on mitigation strategies is relatively small, among others, due to the marginal abatement cost curve of methane (low costs for low-to-medium mitigation levels; expensive for high levels). The timing of reductions across different gases impacts warming and the co-benefits (Harmsen et al. 2016; Cain et al. 2019). Nearly all scenarios in the literature use GWP-100 in cost-optimisation, reflecting the existing policy approach; the use of GWP-100 deviates from cost-optimal mitigation pathways by at most a few percent for temperature goals that limit warming to 2°C (>67%) or lower (Box 2.1).

Cumulative CO_2 emissions and temperature goals

The dominating role of CO_2 and its long lifetime in the atmosphere and some critical characteristics of the Earth System implies that there is a strong relationship between cumulative CO_2 emissions and temperature outcomes (Allen et al. 2009; Matthews et al. 2009; Meinshausen et al. 2009; MacDougall and Friedlingstein 2015). This is illustrated in Figure 3.13, which plots the cumulative CO_2 emissions against the projected outcome for global mean temperature, both until peak temperature and through to end of century (or 2100). The deviations from a linear relationship in Figure 3.13 are mostly caused by different non-CO_2 emission and forcing levels (see also Rogelj et al. 2015b). This means that reducing non-CO_2 emissions can play an important role in limiting peak warming: the smaller the residual non-CO_2 warming, the larger the carbon budget. This impact on carbon budgets can be substantial for stringent warming limits. For 1.5°C pathways, variations in non-CO_2 warming across different emission scenarios have been found to vary the remaining carbon budget by approximately 220 $GtCO_2$ (AR6 WGI Chapter 5, Section 5.5.2.2). In addition to reaching net zero CO_2 emissions, a strong reduction in methane emissions is the most critical component in non-CO_2 mitigation to keep the Paris climate goals in reach (Collins et al. 2018; van Vuuren et al. 2018) (see also AR6 WGI, Chapters 5, 6 and 7). It should be noted that the temperature categories (C1–C7) generally aligned with the horizontal axis, except for the end-of-century values for C1 and C2 that coincide.

Box 3.4 | Consistency of Remaining Carbon Budgets in the WGI Assessment and Cumulative CO_2 Emissions in WGIII Mitigation Pathways

Introduction

The WGI assessment has shown that the increase in global mean temperature has a near-linear relationship with cumulative CO_2 emissions (Chapter 5, Section 5.5, Box 5.3 of AR6 WGI report). Consistently, WGI has confirmed that net zero CO_2 emissions are required to halt CO_2-induced warming. This permits the estimation of carbon budgets consistent with specific temperature goals. In Chapter 3, we present the temperature outcomes and cumulative CO_2 emissions associated with different warming levels for around 1200 scenarios published in the literature and which were classified according to different warming levels (Section 3.2 and Annex III. II.3.2). In this box, we discuss the consistency of the assessments presented here and in IPCC AR6 WGI. The box summarises how the remaining carbon budgets assessed by AR6 WGI relate to the remaining cumulative CO_2 emissions until the time of net zero CO_2 emissions in mitigation pathways (Tables 3.2 and SPM.1) assessed by AR6 WGIII.

In its assessment, AR6 WGI uses a framework in which the various components of the remaining carbon budget are informed by various lines of evidence and assessed climate system characteristics. The AR6 WGIII, instead, uses around 1200 emission scenarios with estimated warming levels that cover the scenario range presented in AR6 WGI but also contain many more intermediate projections with varying emission profiles and a combination of CO_2 emissions and other greenhouse gases. In order to assess their climate outcomes, climate model emulators are used. The emulators are reduced complexity climate models that are provided by AR6 WGI, and which are calibrated to the AR6 WGI assessment of future warming for various purposes (a detailed description of the use of climate model emulators in the AR6 WGI and WGIII assessments can be found in Cross-Chapter Box 7.1 in the AR6 WGI report, with the connection of WGI and WGIII discussed in Annex III.2.5.1).

Remaining carbon budgets estimated by AR6 WGI

The AR6 WGI estimated the remaining carbon budgets from their assessment of (i) the transient climate response to cumulative emissions of carbon dioxide (TCRE), and estimates of (ii) the historical human-induced warming, (iii) the temperature change after reaching net zero CO_2 emissions, (iv) the contribution of future non-CO_2 warming (derived from the emissions scenarios assessed in the Special Report on 1.5°C Warming using WGI-calibrated emulators), and (v) the Earth System feedbacks (AR6 WGI Chapter 5.5, Box 5.2). For a given warming level, AR6 WGI assessed the remaining carbon budget from the beginning of 2020 onwards. These are 650/500/400 $GtCO_2$ for limiting warming to 1.5°C with 33%/50%/ 67% chance and 1350/1150 $GtCO_2$ for limiting warming to 2°C with 50%/67% chance. The estimates are subject to considerable uncertainty related to historical warming, future non-CO_2 forcing, and poorly quantified climate feedbacks. For instance, variation in non-CO_2 emissions across scenarios are estimated to either increase or decrease the remaining carbon budget estimates by 220 $GtCO_2$. The estimates of the remaining carbon budget assume that non-CO_2 emissions are reduced consistently with the tight temperature targets for which the budgets are estimated.

Cumulative CO_2 emissions until net zero estimated by AR6 WGIII

The AR6 WGIII provides estimates of cumulative net CO_2 emissions (from 2020 inclusive) until the time of reaching net zero CO_2 emissions (henceforth called 'peak cumulative CO_2 emissions') and until the end of the century for eight temperature classes that span a range of warming levels. The numbers can be found in Table 3.2 (330–710 $GtCO_2$ for C1; 530–930 for C2; and 640–1160 for C3).

Comparing the AR6 WGI remaining carbon budgets and remaining cumulative CO_2 emissions of the AR6 WGIII scenarios

A comparison between AR6 WGI and WGIII findings requires recognising that, unlike in WGI, cumulative emissions in WGIII are not provided for a specific peak-warming threshold or level but are instead provided for a set of scenarios in a category, representing a specific range of peak-temperature outcomes (for instance the C4 category contains scenarios with a median peak warming anywhere between approximately 1.8°C and up to 2°C). When accounting for this difference, the AR6 WGI and WGIII findings are very consistent for temperature levels below 2°C. Figure 1 compares the peak temperatures and associated cumulative CO_2 emissions (i.e., peak cumulative CO_2 emissions) for the WGIII scenarios to the remaining carbon budgets assessed by WGI. This shows only minor differences between the WGI and WGIII approaches.

After correcting for the categorisation, some (small) differences between the AR6 WGI and WGIII numbers arise from remaining differences between the outcomes of the climate emulators and their set-up (IPCC AR6 WGI Cross-Chapter Box 7.1) and the differences in the underlying scenarios. Moreover, the WGI assessment estimated the non-CO_2 warming at the time of net zero CO_2 emissions based on a relationship derived from the SR1.5 scenario database with historical emission estimates as in Meinshausen et al. (2020) (AR6 WGI Chapter 5). The WGIII assessment uses the same climate emulator with improved historical emissions estimates (Nicholls et al. 2021) (AR6 WGI Cross-Chapter Box 7.1). Annex III.II.2.5.1 further explores the effects of these factors on the relationship between non-CO_2 warming at peak cumulative CO_2 and peak surface temperature.

Box 3.4 (continued)

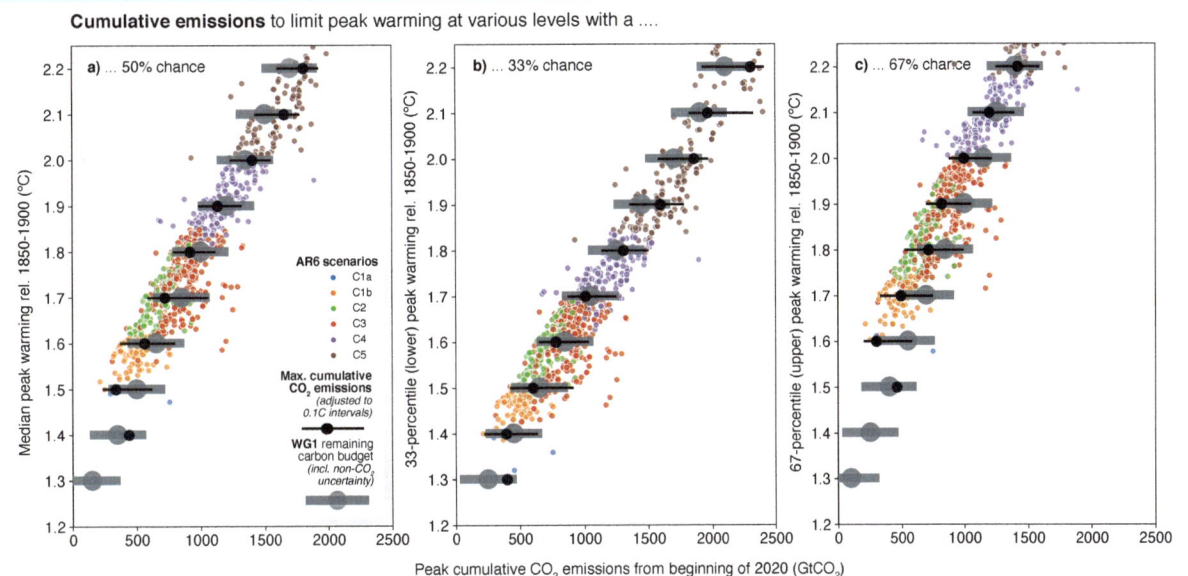

Box 3.4, Figure 1 | Cumulative CO$_2$ emissions from AR6 scenario categories (coloured dots), adjusted for distinct 0.1°C warming levels (black bars) in comparison to the WGI remaining carbon budgets (grey bars). The cumulative carbon emissions for the AR6 scenarios are shown for the median peak warming **(a)**, the 33rd-percentile peak warming **(b)** and the upper 67th-percentile peak warming **(c)** calculated with the WGI-calibrated emulator MAGICC7 (IPCC AR6 WGI, Cross-Chapter Box 7.1). The adjustment to the nearest 0.1°C intervals is made using AR6 WGI TCRE (at the relevant percentile, e.g., the 67th-percentile TCRE is used to adjust the 67th-percentile peak warming), with the 5–95% range of adjusted scenarios provided by the black bar. The AR6 WGI remaining carbon budget is shown, including the WGI estimate of at least a ±220 GtCO$_2$ uncertainty due to non-CO$_2$ emissions variations across scenarios (grey bars). For median peak warming (panel a) projections below 2°C relative to 1850–1900, the AR6 WGIII assessment of cumulative carbon emissions tends to be slightly smaller than the remaining carbon budgets provided by WGI but well within the uncertainties. Note that only a few scenarios in WGIII limit warming to below 1.5°C with a 50% chance, thus statistics for that specific threshold have low confidence.

Estimates of the remaining carbon budgets thus vary with the assumed level of non-CO$_2$ emissions, which are a function of policies and technology development. The linear relationship used in the AR6 WGI assessment between peak temperature and the warming as a result of non-CO$_2$ emissions (based on the SR1.5 data) is shown in the right panel of Figure 2 (dashed line). In the AR6 WGIII approach, the non-CO$_2$ warming for each single scenario is based on the individual scenario characteristics. This is shown in the same figure by plotting the outcomes of scenario outcomes of a range of models (dots). The lines show the fitted data for individual models, emphasising the clear differences across models and the relationship with peak warming (policy level). In some scenarios, stringent non-CO$_2$ emission reductions provide an option to reach more stringent climate goals with the same carbon budget. This is especially the case for scenarios with a very low non-CO$_2$ warming, for instance, as a result of methane reductions through diet change. The left panel shows how these differences impact estimates of the remaining carbon budget. While the AR6 scenarios database includes a broad range of non-CO$_2$ emission projections the overall range is still very consistent with the WGI relationship and the estimated uncertainty with a ±220 GtCO$_2$ range (see also Figure 5 in Annex III.II.2.5.1).

Overall, the slight differences between the cumulative emissions in AR6 WGIII and the carbon budget in AR6 WGI are because the non-CO$_2$ warming in the WGIII scenarios is slightly lower than in the SR1.5 scenarios that are used for the budget estimates in WGI (Annex III.2.5.1). In addition, improved consistency with Cross-Chapter Box 7.1 in Chapter 7, AR6 WGI results in a non-CO$_2$-induced temperature difference of about about 0.05K between the assessments. Recalculating the remaining carbon budget using the WGI methodology combined with the full AR6 WGIII scenario database results in a reduction of the estimated remaining 1.5°C carbon budget by about 100 GtCO$_2$ (–20%), and a reduction of about 40 GtCO$_2$ (–3%) for 2°C. Accounting also for the categorisation effect, the difference between the WGI and WGIII estimates is found to be small and well within the uncertainty range (Figure 1). This means that the cumulative CO$_2$ emissions presented in WGIII and the WGI carbon budgets are highly consistent.

A detailed comparison of the impact of different assessment steps (i.e., the new emulators, scenarios, and harmonisation methods), has been made and is presented in Figure 6 in Annex III.II.3.2 .

Box 3.4 (continued)

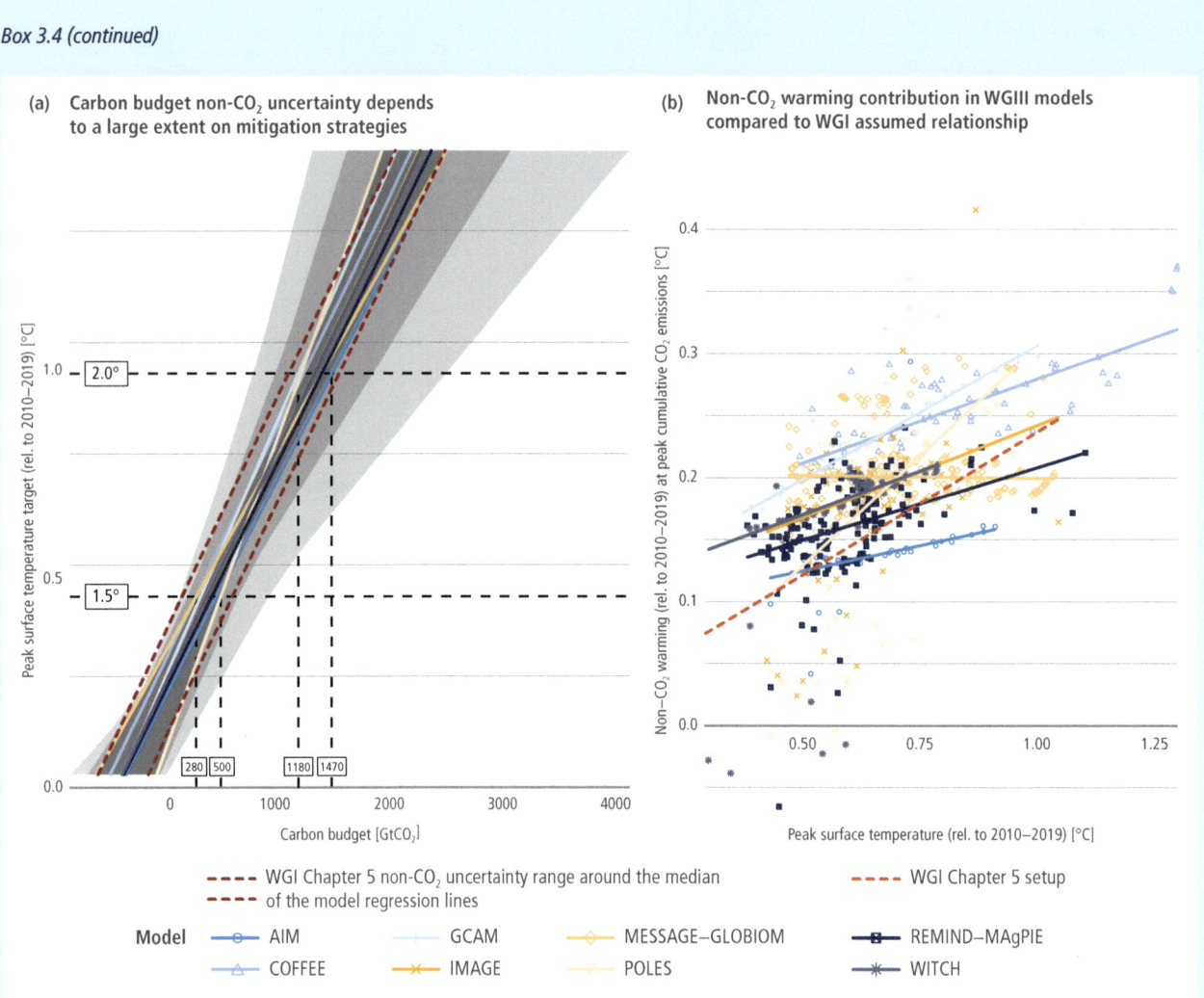

Box 3.4, Figure 2 | (a) Differences in regressions of the relationship between peak surface temperature and associated cumulative CO₂ emissions from 2020 derived from scenarios of eight integrated assessment model frameworks. The coloured lines show the regression at median for scenarios of the eight modelling frameworks, each with more than 20 scenarios in the database and a detailed land-use representation. The red dotted lines indicate the non-CO₂ uncertainty range of AR6 WGI Chapter 5 (±220 GtCO₂), here visualised around the median of the eight model framework lines. Carbon budgets from 2020 until 1.5°C (0.43K above 2010–2019 levels) and 2.0°C (0.93K above 2010–2019 levels) are shown for minimum and maximum model estimates at the median, rounded to the nearest 10 GtCO₂. Panel **(b)** shows the relationship between the estimated non-CO₂ warming in mitigation scenarios that reach net zero and the associated peak surface temperature outcomes. The coloured lines show the regression at median for scenarios of the eight modelling frameworks with more than 20 scenarios in the database and a detailed land-use representation. The black dashed line indicates the non-CO₂ relationship based on the scenarios and climate emulator setup as was assessed in AR6 WGI Chapter 5.

Policy implications

The concept of a finite carbon budget means that the world needs to get to net zero CO₂, no matter whether global warming is limited to 1.5°C or well below 2°C (or any other level). Moreover, exceeding the remaining carbon budget will have consequences by overshooting temperature levels. Still, the relationship between the timing of net zero and temperature targets is a flexible one, as discussed further in Cross-Chapter Box 3 in this chapter. It should be noted that the national-level inventory as used by UNFCCC for the land use, land-use change and forestry sector is different from the overall concept of anthropogenic emissions employed by IPCC AR6 WGI. For emissions estimates based on these inventories, the remaining carbon budgets must be correspondingly reduced by approximately 15%, depending on the scenarios (Grassi et al., 2021) (Chapter 7).

One of the uncertainties of the remaining carbon budget is the level of non-CO₂ emissions which is a function of policies and technology development. This represents a point of leverage for policies rather than an inherent geophysical uncertainty. Stringent non-CO₂ emission reductions hence can provide – to some degree – an option to reach more stringent climate goals with the same carbon budget.

The near-linear relationship implies that cumulative CO_2 emissions are critically important for climate outcomes (Collins et al. 2013). The maximum temperature increase is a direct function of the cumulative emissions until net zero CO_2 emissions is reached (the emission budget) (Figure 3.13, left side). The end-of-century temperature correlates well with cumulative emissions across the century (right panel). For long-term climate goals, positive emissions in the first half of the century can be offset by net removal of CO_2 from the atmosphere (net negative emissions) at the cost of a temporary overshoot of the target (Tokarska et al. 2019). The bottom panels of Figure 3.13 show the contribution of net negative CO_2 emissions.

Focusing on cumulative emissions, the right-hand panel of Figure 3.12b shows that for high-end scenarios (C6–C7), most emissions originate from fossil fuels, with a smaller contribution from net deforestation. For C5 and lower, there is also a negative contribution to emissions from both AFOLU emissions and energy systems. For the energy systems, these negative emissions originate from bioenergy with carbon capture and storage (BECCS), while for AFOLU, they originate from reforestation and afforestation. For C3–C5, reforestation has a larger CDR contribution than BECCS, mostly due to considerably lower costs (Rochedo et al. 2018). For C1 and C2, the tight carbon budgets imply in many scenarios more CDR use (Riahi et al. 2021). Please note that net negative emissions are not so relevant for peak-temperature targets, and thus the C1 category, but CDR can still be used to offset the remaining positive emissions (Riahi et al. 2021). While positive CO_2 emissions from fossil fuels are significantly reduced, inertia and hard-to-abate sectors imply that in many C1–C3 scenarios, around 800–1000 $GtCO_2$ of net positive cumulative CO_2 emissions remain. This is consistent with literature estimates that current infrastructure is associated with 650 $GtCO_2$ (best estimate) if operated until the end of its lifetime (Tong et al. 2019). These numbers are considerably above the estimated carbon budgets for 1.5°C estimated in AR6 WGI, hence explaining CDR reliance (either to offset emissions immediately or later in time).

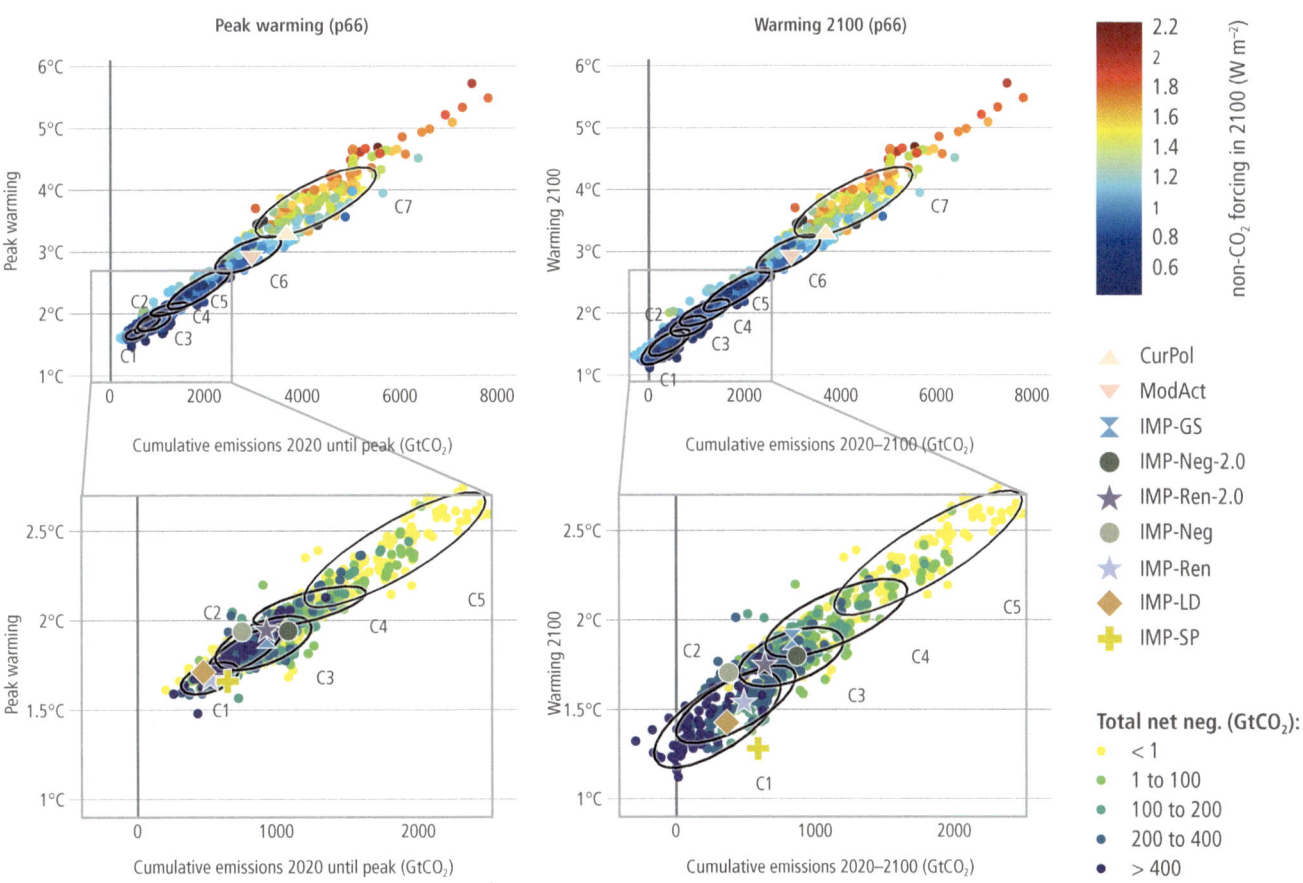

Figure 3.13 | The near-linear relationship between cumulative CO_2 emissions and temperature. The left panel shows cumulative emissions until net zero emission is reached. The right panel shows cumulative emissions until the end of the century, plotted against peak and end-of-century temperature, respectively. Both are shown as a function of non-CO_2 forcing and cumulative net negative CO_2 emissions. Position temperature categories (circles) and IPs are also indicated, including two 2°C sensitivity cases for *Neg* (Neg-2.0) and *Ren* (Ren-2.0).

Creating net negative emissions can thus be an important part of a mitigation strategy to offset remaining emissions or compensate for emissions earlier in time. As indicated above, there are different ways to potentially achieve this, including reforestation and afforestation and BECCS (as often covered in IAMs) but also soil carbon enhancement, direct air carbon capture and storage (DACCS) and ocean alkalinisation (Chapter 12). Except for reforestation, these options have not been tested at large scale and often require more R&D. Moreover, the reliance on CDR in scenarios has been discussed given possible consequences of land use related to biodiversity loss and food security (BECCS and afforestation), the reliance on uncertain storage potentials (BECCS and DACCS), water use (BECCS), energy use (DACCS), the risks of possible temperature overshoot and the consequences for meeting Sustainable Development Goals (SDGs) (Anderson and Peters 2016; Smith et al. 2016; Venton 2016; Peters and Geden 2017; van Vuuren et al. 2017; Honegger et al. 2021). In the case of BECCS, it should be noted that bioenergy typically is associated with early-on positive CO_2 emissions and net negative effects are only achieved in time (carbon debt), and its potential is limited (Cherubini et al. 2013; Hanssen et al. 2020); most IAMs have only a very limited representation of these time dynamics. Several scenarios have therefore explored how reliance on net negative CO_2 emissions can be reduced or even avoided by alternative emission strategies (Grubler et al. 2018; van Vuuren et al. 2018) or early reductions by more stringent emission reduction in the short term (Rogelj et al. 2019b; Riahi et al. 2021). A more in-depth discussion of land-based mitigation options can be found in Chapter 7. It needs to be emphasised that even in strategies with net negative CO_2 emissions, the emission reduction via more conventional mitigation measures (efficiency improvement, decarbonisation of energy supply) is much larger than the CDR contribution (Tsutsui et al. 2020).

3.3.2.3 The Timing of Net Zero Emissions

In addition to the constraints on change in global mean temperature, the Paris Agreement also calls for reaching a balance of sources and sinks of GHG emissions (Art. 4). Different interpretations of the concept related to balance have been published (Rogelj et al. 2015c; Fuglestvedt et al. 2018). Key concepts include that of net zero CO_2 emissions (anthropogenic CO_2 sources and sinks equal zero) and net zero greenhouse gas emissions (see Annex I: Glossary, and Box 3.3). The same notion can be used for all GHG emissions, but here ranges also depend on the use of equivalence metrics (Box 2.1). Moreover, it should be noted that while reaching net zero CO_2 emissions typically coincides with the peak in temperature increase; net zero GHG emissions (based on GWP-100) imply a decrease in global temperature (Riahi et al. 2021) and net zero GHG emissions typically require negative CO_2 emissions to compensate for the remaining emissions from other GHGs. Many countries have started to formulate climate policy in the year that net zero emissions (either CO_2 or all greenhouse gases) are reached – although, at the moment, formulations are often still vague (Rogelj et al. 2021). There has been increased attention on the timing of net zero emissions in the scientific literature and ways to achieve it.

Figure 3.14 shows that there is a relationship between the temperature target, the cumulative CO_2 emissions budget, and the net zero year for CO_2 emissions (panel a) and the sum of greenhouse gases (panel b) for the scenarios published in the literature. In other words, the temperature targets from the Paris Agreement can, to some degree, be translated into a net-zero emission year (Tanaka and O'Neill 2018). There is, however, a considerable spread. In addition to the factors influencing the emission budget (AR6 WGI and Section 3.3.2.2), this is influenced by the emission trajectory until net zero is reached, decisions related to temperature overshoot and non-CO_2 emissions (especially for the moment CO_2 reaches net zero emissions). Scenarios with limited or no net negative emissions and rapid near-term emission reductions can allow small positive emissions (e.g., in hard-to-abate-sectors). They may therefore have a later year that net zero CO_2 emissions are achieved. High emissions in the short term, in contrast, require an early net zero year.

For the scenarios in the C1 category (limit warming to 1.5°C (>50% with no or limited overshoot, the net zero year for CO_2 emissions is typically around 2035–2070. For scenarios in C3 (limiting warming to 2°C (>67%)), CO_2 emissions reach net zero around after 2050. Similarly, also the years for net zero GHG emissions can be calculated (see Fig 3.14b. The GHG net zero emissions year is typically around 10–40 years later than the carbon neutrality. Residual non-CO_2 emissions at the time of reaching net zero CO_2 range between 5–11 $GtCO_2$-eq in pathways that limit warming to 2°C (>67%) or lower. In pathways limiting warming to 2°C (>67%), methane is reduced by around 19% (3–46%) in 2030 and 46% (29–64%) in 2050, and in pathways limiting warming to 1.5°C (>50%) with no or limited overshoot by around 34% (21–57%) in 2030 and a similar 51% (35–70%) in 2050. Emissions-reduction potentials assumed in the pathways become largely exhausted when limiting warming to 2°C (>50%). N_2O emissions are reduced too, but similar to CH_4, emission reductions saturate for stringent climate goals. In the mitigation pathways, the emissions of cooling aerosols are reduced due to reduced use of fossil fuels. The overall impact on non-CO_2-related warming combines these factors.

In cost-optimal scenarios, regions will mostly achieve net zero emissions as a function of options for emission reduction, CDR, and expected baseline emission growth (van Soest et al. 2021b). This typically implies relatively early net zero emission years in scenarios for the Latin America region and relatively late net zero years for Asia and Africa (and average values for OECD countries). However, an allocation based on equity principles (such as responsibility, capability and equality) might result in different net zero years, based on the principles applied – with often earlier net zero years for the OECD (Fyson et al. 2020; van Soest et al. 2021b). Therefore, the emission trajectory until net zero emissions is a critical determinant of future warming (Section 3.5). The more CO_2 is emitted until 2030, the less CO_2 can be emitted after that to stay below a warming limit (Riahi et al. 2015). As discussed before, also non-CO_2 forcing plays a key role in the short term.

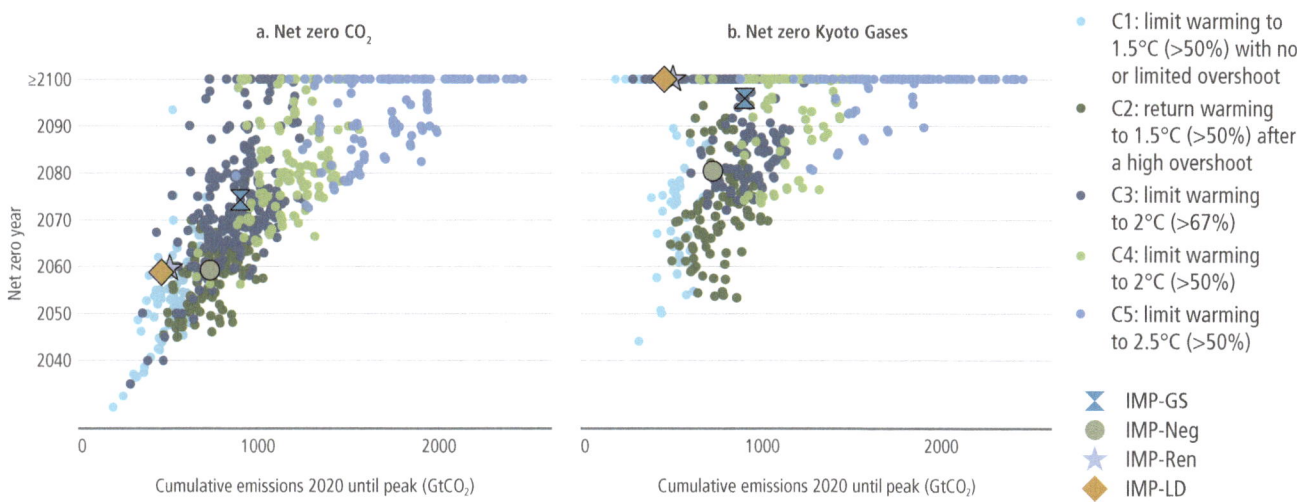

Figure 3.14 | Net zero year for CO₂ and all GHGs (based on AR6 GWP100) as a function of remaining carbon budget and temperature outcomes (note that scenarios that stabilise (near) zero are also included in determining the net zero year).

Cross-Chapter Box 3 | Understanding Net Zero CO₂ and Net Zero GHG Emissions

Authors: Elmar Kriegler (Germany), Alaa Al Khourdajie (United Kingdom/Syria), Edward Byers (Austria/Ireland), Katherine Calvin (the United States of America), Leon Clarke (the United States of America), Annette Cowie (Australia), Navroz Dubash (India), Jae Edmonds (the United States of America), Jan S. Fuglestvedt (Norway), Oliver Geden (Germany), Giacomo Grassi (Italy/European Union), Anders Hammer Strømman (Norway), Frank Jotzo (Australia), Alexandre Köberle (Brazil/United Kingdom), Franck Lecocq (France), Yun Seng Lim (Malaysia), Eric Masanet (the United States of America), Toshihiko Masui (Japan), Catherine Mitchell (United Kingdom), Gert-Jan Nabuurs (the Netherlands), Anthony Patt (the United States of America/Switzerland), Glen P. Peters (Norway/Australia), Andy Reisinger (New Zealand), Keywan Riahi (Austria), Joeri Rogelj (United Kingdom/Belgium), Yamina Saheb (France/Algeria), Jim Skea (United Kingdom), Detlef P. van Vuuren (the Netherlands), Harald Winkler (Republic of South Africa)

This Cross-Chapter Box surveys scientific, technical and policy aspects of net zero carbon dioxide (CO₂) and net zero greenhouse gas (GHG) emissions, with a focus on timing, the relationship with warming levels, and sectoral and regional characteristics of net zero emissions. Assessment of net zero GHG emissions additionally requires consideration of non-CO₂ gases and choice of GHG emission metrics used to aggregate emissions and removals of different GHGs (Cross-Chapter Box 2 in Chapter 2 and Cross-Chapter Box 7 in Chapter 10). The following considers net zero CO₂ and GHG emissions globally, followed by regional and sectoral dimensions.

Net zero CO₂ emissions

Reaching net zero CO₂ emissions globally is necessary for limiting global warming to any level. At the point of net zero CO₂, the amount of CO₂ human activity is putting into the atmosphere equals the amount of CO₂ human activity is removing from the atmosphere (see Annex I: Glossary). Reaching and sustaining net zero CO₂ emissions globally stabilizes CO₂-induced warming. Reaching net zero CO₂ emissions and then moving to net negative CO₂ emissions globally leads to a peak and decline in CO₂-induced warming (AR6 WGI Sections 5.5 and 5.6).

Limiting warming to 1.5°C (>50%) or to 2°C (>67%) requires deep, rapid, and sustained reductions of other greenhouse gases including methane alongside rapid reductions of CO₂ emissions to net zero. This ensures that the warming contributions from non-CO₂ forcing agents as well as from CO₂ emissions are both limited at low levels. The AR6 WGI estimated remaining carbon budgets until the time of reaching net zero CO₂ emissions for a range of warming limits, taking into account historical CO₂ emissions and projections of the warming from non-CO₂ forcing agents (Box 3.4 in Section 3.3, AR6 WGI Section 5.5).

The earlier global net zero CO₂ emissions are reached, the lower the cumulative net amount of CO₂ emissions and human-induced global warming, all else being equal (Figure 1a in this Cross-Chapter Box). For a given net zero date, a variation in the shape of the CO₂ emissions profile can lead to a variation in the cumulative net amount of CO₂ emissions until the time of net zero CO₂ and as a result to different peak-warming levels. For example, cumulative net CO₂ emissions until the time of reaching net zero CO₂ will be smaller, and peak warming lower, if emissions are reduced steeply and then more slowly compared to reducing emissions slowly and then more steeply (Figure 1b in this Cross-Chapter Box).

Cross-Chapter Box 3 (continued)

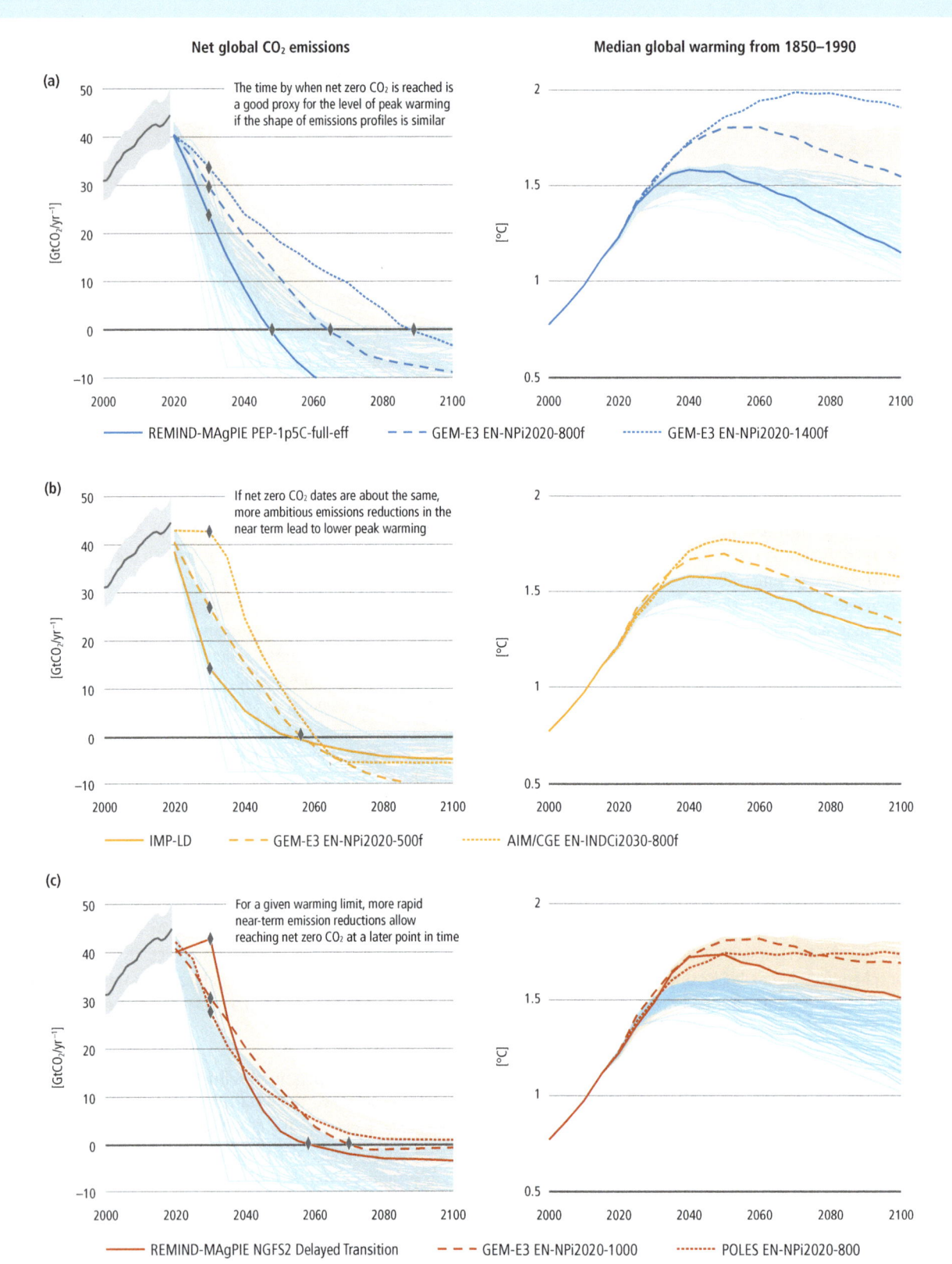

Cross-Chapter Box 3, Figure 1 | Selected global CO$_2$ emissions trajectories with similar shape and different net zero CO$_2$ date (a), different shape and similar net zero CO$_2$ date (b), and similar peak warming, but varying shapes and net zero CO$_2$ dates (c). Funnels show pathways limiting warming to 1.5°C (>50%) with no or limited overshoot (light blue) and limiting warming to 2°C (>67%) (beige). Historic CO$_2$ emissions from Section 2.2 (EDGAR v6).

Cross-Chapter Box 3 (continued)

Net zero CO_2 emissions are reached between 2050–2055 (2035–2070) in global emissions pathways limiting warming to 1.5°C (>50%) with no or limited overshoot, and between 2070–2075 (2055–…) in pathways limiting warming to 2°C (>67%) as reported in the AR6 scenarios database (median five-year interval and 5–95th percentile ranges).[5] The variation of non-CO_2 emissions in 1.5°C–2°C pathways varies the available remaining carbon budget which can move the time of reaching net zero CO_2 in these pathways forward or backward.[6] The shape of the CO_2 emissions reduction profile also affects the time of reaching net zero CO_2 (Figure 1c in this Cross-Chapter Box). Global emission pathways that more than halve CO_2 emissions from 2020 to 2030 can follow this rapid reduction by a more gradual decline towards net zero CO_2 and still limit warming to 1.5°C with no or limited overshoot, reaching the point of net zero after 2050. The literature since SR1.5 included a larger fraction of such pathways than were available at the time of SR1.5. This is the primary reason for the small backward shift in the median estimate of reaching global net zero CO_2 emissions in 1.5°C pathways collected in the AR6 scenario database compared to SR1.5. This does not mean that the world is assessed to have more time to rapidly reduce current emissions levels compared to SR1.5. The assessment of emissions reductions by 2030 and 2040 in pathways limiting warming to 1.5°C (>50%) with no or limited overshoot has not changed substantially. It only means that the exact timing of reaching net zero CO_2 after a steep decline of CO_2 emissions until 2030 and 2040 can show some variation, and the SR1.5 median value of 2050 is still close to the middle of the current range (Figure 1c in this Cross-Chapter Box).

Pathways following emissions levels projected from the implementation of Nationally Determined Contributions (NDCs) announced prior to COP26 until 2030 would result in substantially (>0.1°C) exceeding 1.5°C. They would have to reach net zero CO_2 around 5–10 years later[7] than in pathways with no or limited overshoot in order to reach the net negative emissions that would then be required to return warming to 1.5°C (>50%) after a high overshoot by 2100. Those high overshoot pathways have higher transient warming and higher reliance on net negative CO_2 emissions towards the end of the 21st century. As they need to reach net zero CO_2 emissions in only limited amount of time but from much higher 2030 emissions levels, their post-2030 CO_2 emissions reduction rates are substantially higher (by around 30%) than in pathways limiting warming to 1.5°C with no or limited overshoot. (Section 3.5).

Pathways following emissions levels projected from the implementation of NDCs announced prior to COP26 until 2030 would have to reach net zero CO_2 around 5 years earlier[8] than cost-effective pathways that limit warming to 2°C (>67%). While cost-effective pathways take around 50–55 years to reach net zero CO_2 emissions, those pathways would only have 35–40 years left for transitioning to net zero CO_2 from 2030 onwards, close to the transition times that 1.5°C pathways are faced with today. Current CO_2 emissions and 2030 emission levels projected under the NDCs announced prior to COP26 are in a similar range (Sections 3.5 and 4.2).

Net zero greenhouse gas (GHG) emissions
The amount of CO_2-equivalent emissions and the point when net zero GHG emissions are reached in multi-GHG emissions pathways depends on the choice of GHG emissions metric. Various GHG emission metrics are available for this purpose.[9] GWP-100 is the most commonly used metric for reporting CO_2-equivalent emissions and is required for emissions reporting under the Rulebook of the Paris Agreement. (Cross-Chapter Box 2 in Chapter 2, Annex I and Annex II.9)

---

[5]   A small fraction of pathways in the AR6 scenarios database that limit warming to 2°C (7% for C3 and 14% for C4) do not reach net zero CO_2 emissions during the 21st century. This is not inconsistent with the fundamental scientific requirement to reach net zero CO_2 emissions for a stable climate, but reflects that in some pathways, concurrent reductions in non-CO_2 emissions temporarily compensate for ongoing warming from CO_2 emissions. These would have to reach net zero CO_2 emissions eventually after 2100 to maintain these warming limits. For the two classes of pathways, the 95th percentile cannot be deduced from the scenario database as more than 5% of them do not reach net zero CO_2 by 2100.

[6]   The AR6 WGI Section 5.5 estimates a variation of the remaining carbon budget by ±220 $GtCO_2$ due to variations of the non-CO_2 warming contribution in 1.5°C–2°C pathways. This translates to a shift of the timing of net zero CO_2 by about ±10 years, assuming global CO_2 emissions decrease linearly from current levels of around 40 $GtCO_2$ to net zero.

[7]   Pathways following emissions levels of NDCs announced prior to COP26 to 2030 and then returning warming to 1.5°C (>50%) after high overshoot by 2100 reach net zero during 2055–2060 (2045–2070) (median five-year interval and 5–95th percentile range).

[8]   Pathways that follow emission levels projected from the implementation of NDCs announced prior to COP26 until 2030 and that still limit warming to 2°C (>67%) reach net zero CO_2 emissions during 2065–2070 (2055–2090) compared with 2070–2075 (2055–…) in cost-effective pathways acting immediately to *likely* limit warming to 2°C (median five-year interval and 5–95th percentile range). See Footnote 5 for the lack of 95th percentile (Section 3.3 and Table 3.2).

[9]   Defining net zero GHG emissions for a basket of greenhouse gases (GHGs) relies on a metric to convert GHG emissions including methane (CH_4), nitrous oxide (N_2O), fluorinated gases (F-gases), and potentially other gases, to CO_2-equivalent emissions. The choice of metric ranges from global warming potentials (GWPs) and global temperature change potentials (GTP) to economically oriented metrics. All metrics have advantages and disadvantages depending on the context in which they are used (Cross-Chapter Box 2 in Chapter 2).

For most choices of GHG emissions metric, reaching net zero GHG emissions requires net negative CO$_2$ emissions in order to balance residual CH$_4$, N$_2$O and F-gas emissions. Under foreseen technology developments, some CH$_4$, N$_2$O and F-gas emissions from, for example, agriculture and industry, will remain over the course of this century. Net negative CO$_2$ emissions will therefore be needed to balance these remaining non-CO$_2$ GHG emissions to obtain net zero GHG emissions at a point in time after net zero CO$_2$ has been reached in emissions pathways. Both the amount of net negative CO$_2$ emissions and the time lag to reaching net zero GHG depend on the choice of GHG emission metric.

Reaching net zero GHG emissions globally in terms of GWP-100 leads to a reduction in global warming from an earlier peak. This is due to net negative CO$_2$ emissions balancing the GWP-100-equivalent emissions of short-lived GHG emissions, which by themselves do not contribute to further warming if sufficiently declining (Fuglestvedt et al. 2018; Rogelj et al. 2021). Hence, 1.5°C–2°C emissions pathways in the AR6 scenario database that reach global net zero GHG emissions in the second half of the century show warming being halted at some peak value followed by a gradual decline towards the end of the century (AR6 WGI Chapter 1, Box 1.4).

Global net zero GHG emissions measured in terms of GWP-100 are reached between 2095 and 2100 (2050–…)[10] in emission pathways limiting warming to 1.5°C (>50%) with no or limited overshoot (median and 5–95th percentile). Around 50% of pathways limiting warming to 1.5°C (>50%) with no or limited overshoot and 70% of pathways limiting warming to 2°C (>67%) do not reach net zero GHG emissions in terms of GWP-100 before 2100. These pathways tend to show less reduction in warming after the peak than pathways that reach net zero GHG emissions. For the subset of pathways that reach net zero GHG emissions before 2100, including around 90% of pathways that return warming to 1.5°C after a high overshoot (>0.1°C) by 2100, the time lag between reaching net zero CO$_2$ and net zero GHG is 12–14 (7–39) years and the amount of net negative CO$_2$ emissions deployed to balance non-CO$_2$ emissions at the time of net zero GHG is around -7 (–10 to –4) GtCO$_2$ (range of medians and lowest 5th to highest 95 percentile across the four scenario classes that limit median warming to 2°C or lower) (Section 3.3 and Table 3.2).

Sectoral and regional aspects of net zero

The timing of net zero CO$_2$ or GHG emissions may differ across regions and sectors. Achieving net zero emissions globally implies that some sectors and regions must reach net zero CO$_2$ or GHG ahead of the time of global net zero CO$_2$ or GHG if others reach it later. Similarly, some sectors and regions would need to achieve net negative CO$_2$ or GHG emissions to compensate for continued emissions by other sectors and regions after the global net zero year. Differences in the timing to reach net zero emissions between sectors and regions depend on multiple factors, including the potential of countries and sectors to reduce GHG emissions and undertake carbon dioxide removal (CDR), the associated costs, and the availability of policy mechanisms to balance emissions and removals between sectors and countries (Fyson et al. 2020; Strefler et al. 2021a; van Soest et al. 2021b). A lack of such mechanisms could lead to higher global costs to reach net zero emissions globally, but less interdependencies and institutional needs (Fajardy and Mac Dowell 2020). Sectors will reach net zero CO$_2$ and GHG emissions at different times if they are aiming for such targets with sector-specific policies or as part of an economy-wide net zero emissions strategy integrating emissions reductions and removals across sectors. In the latter case, sectors with large potential for achieving net negative emissions would go beyond net zero to balance residual emissions from sectors with low potential, which in turn would take more time compared to the case of sector-specific action. Global pathways project global AFOLU emissions to reach global net zero CO$_2$ the earliest, around 2030 to 2035 in pathways to limit warming to 2°C (>67%) or lower, by rapid reduction of deforestation and enhancing carbon sinks on land, although net zero GHG emissions from global AFOLU are typically reached 30 years later, if at all. The ability of global AFOLU CO$_2$ emissions to reach net zero as early as in the 2030s in modelled pathways hinges on optimistic assumptions about the ability to establish global cost-effective mechanisms to balance emissions reductions and removals across regions and sectors. These assumptions have been challenged in the literature and the *Special Report on Climate Change and Land* (IPCC SRCCL).

The adoption and implementation of net zero CO$_2$ or GHG emission targets by countries and regions also depends on equity and capacity criteria. The Paris Agreement recognises that peaking of emissions will occur later in developing countries (Art. 4.1). Just transitions to net zero CO$_2$ or GHG could be expected to follow multiple pathways, in different contexts. Regions may decide about net zero pathways based on their consideration of potential for rapid transition to low-carbon development pathways, the capacity to design and implement those changes, and perceptions of equity within and across countries. Cost-effective pathways from global models have been shown to distribute the mitigation effort unevenly and inequitably in the absence of financial support mechanisms and capacity building (Budolfson et al. 2021), and hence would require additional measures to become aligned with

---

[10] The 95th percentile cannot be deduced from the scenario database as more than 5% of pathways do not reach net zero GHG by 2100 (Section 3.3 and Table 3.2.), hence denoted by -….

equity considerations (Fyson et al. 2020; van Soest et al. 2021b). Formulation of net zero pathways by countries will benefit from clarity on scope, roadmaps and fairness (Rogelj et al. 2021; Smith 2021). Achieving net zero emission targets relies on policies, institutions and milestones against which to track progress. Milestones can include emissions levels, as well as markers of technological diffusion.

The accounting of anthropogenic carbon dioxide removal on land matters for the evaluation of net zero CO_2 and net zero GHG strategies. Due to the use of different approaches between national inventories and global models, the current net CO_2 emissions are lower by 5.5 $GtCO_2$, and cumulative net CO_2 emissions in modelled 1.5°C–2°C pathways would be lower by 104–170 $GtCO_2$, if carbon dioxide removals on land are accounted based on national GHG inventories. National GHG inventories typically consider a much larger area of managed forest than global models, and on this area additionally consider the fluxes due to human-induced global environmental change (indirect effects) to be anthropogenic, while global models consider these fluxes to be natural. Both approaches capture the same land fluxes, only the accounting of anthropogenic vs natural emissions is different. Methods to convert estimates from global models to the accounting scheme of national GHG inventories will improve the use of emission pathways from global models as benchmarks against which collective progress is assessed. (Section 7.2.2.5).

Net zero CO_2 and carbon neutrality have different meanings in this assessment, as is the case for net zero GHG and GHG neutrality. They apply to different boundaries in the emissions and removals being considered. Net zero (GHG or CO_2) refers to emissions and removals under the direct control or territorial responsibility of the reporting entity. In contrast, (GHG or carbon) neutrality includes anthropogenic emissions and anthropogenic removals within and also those beyond the direct control or territorial responsibility of the reporting entity. At the global scale, net zero CO_2 and carbon neutrality are equivalent, as is the case for net zero GHG and GHG neutrality. The term 'climate neutrality' is not used in this assessment because the concept of climate neutrality is diffuse, used differently by different communities, and not readily quantified.

Table 3.2 summarises the key characteristics for all temperature categories in terms of cumulative CO_2 emissions, near-term emission reductions, and the years of peak emission and net zero CO_2 and GHG emissions. The table shows again that many pathways in the literature limit global warming to 2°C (>67%) or limit warming to 1.5°C (>50%) with no or limited overshoot compared to pre-industrial levels. Cumulative net CO_2 emissions from the year 2020 until the time of net zero CO_2 in pathways that limit warming to 1.5°C (>50%) with no or limited overshoot are 510 (330–710) $GtCO_2$ and in pathways that limit warming to 2°C (>67%), 890 (640–1160) $GtCO_2$ (see also Cross-Chapter Box 3 in this chapter). Mitigation pathways that limit warming to 2°C (>67%) compared to pre-industrial levels are associated with net global GHG emissions of 44 (32–55) $GtCO_2$-eq yr^{-1} by 2030 and 20 (13–26) $GtCO_2$-eq yr^{-1} in 2050. These correspond to GHG emissions reductions of 21% (1–42%) by 2030, and 64% (53–77%) by 2050 relative to 2019 emission levels. Pathways that limit global warming to 1.5°C (>50%) with no or limited overshoot require a further acceleration in the pace of the transformation, with GHG emissions reductions of 43% (34–60%) by 2030 and 84% (73–98%) in 2050 relative to modelled 2019 emission levels. The likelihood of limiting warming to below 1.5°C (>50%) with no or limited overshoot of the most stringent mitigation pathways in the literature (C1) has declined since SR1.5. This is because emissions have risen since 2010 by about 9 $GtCO_2$ yr^{-1}, resulting in relatively higher near-term emissions of the AR6 pathways by 2030 and slightly later dates for reaching net zero CO_2 emissions compared to SR1.5.

Given the larger contribution of scenarios in the literature that aim to reduce net negative emissions, emission reductions are somewhat larger in the short term compared to similar categories in the IPCC SR1.5. At the same time, the year of net zero emissions is somewhat later (but only if these rapid, short-term emission reductions are achieved). The scenarios in the literature in C1–C3 show a peak in global emissions before 2025. Not achieving this requires a more rapid reduction after 2025 to still meet the Paris goals (Section 3.5).

Table 3.2 | GHG, CO₂ emissions and warming characteristics of different mitigation pathways submitted to the AR6 scenarios database and as categorised in the climate assessment.

Category [# pathways]	Category/subset label	WG I SSP & WG III IPs/IMPs alignment	GHG emissions Gt CO₂-eq/yr 2030	2040	2050	GHG reductions from 2019 % 2030	2040	2050	Peak CO₂ emissions (% before 2100)	Peak GHG emissions (% peak before 2100)	Net-zero CO₂ (% net-zero pathways)	Net-zero GHGs (% net-zero pathways)	Cumulative CO₂ 2020 to net-zero CO₂	Cumulative CO₂ 2020–2100	Net-negative CO₂, Year of net-zero CO₂ to 2100	Temp at peak warming °C	Temp 2100 °C	<1.5°C	<2°C	<3°C	1.5°C	2°C	3°C
C1 [97]	limit warming to 1.5°C (>50%) with no or limited overshoot		31 [21–36]	17 [6–23]	9 [1–15]	43 [34–60]	69 [58–90]	84 [73–98]	2020–2025 (100%) [2020–2025]		2050–2055 (100%) [2035–2070]	2095–2100 (52%) [2050–...]	510 [330–710]	320 [–210–570]	–220 [–660––20]	1.6 [1.4–1.6]	1.3 [1.1–1.5]	38 [33–58]	90 [86–97]	100 [99–100]	2030–2035 (91%) [2030–...]	...–... (0%) [...–...]	...–... (0%) [...–...]
C1a [50]	...with net-zero GHGs	SSP1-1.9, IMP-SP, IMP-LD	33 [22–37]	18 [6–24]	8 [0–15]	41 [31–59]	66 [58–89]	85 [72–100]				2070–2075 (100%) [2050–2090]	550 [340–760]	160 [–220–620]	–360 [–680––140]	1.6 [1.4–1.6]	1.2 [1.1–1.4]	38 [34–60]	90 [85–98]	100 [99–100]	2030–2035 (90%) [2030–...]	...–... (0%) [...–...]	...–... (0%) [...–...]
C1b [47]	...without net-zero GHGs	IMP-Ren	29 [21–36]	16 [7–21]	9 [4–13]	48 [35–61]	70 [62–87]	84 [76–93]				...–... (0%) [...–...]	460 [320–590]	360 [10–540]	–60 [–440–0]	1.6 [1.5–1.6]	1.4 [1.3–1.5]	37 [33–56]	89 [87–96]	100 [99–100]	2030–2035 (91%) [2030–...]	...–... (0%) [...–...]	...–... (0%) [...–...]
C2 [133]	return warming to 1.5°C (<50%) after a high overshoot	IMP-Neg	42 [31–55]	25 [17–34]	14 [5–21]	23 [0–44]	55 [40–71]	75 [62–91]	2020–2030 [2020–2025]	2020–2025 (100%) [2020–2025]	2055–2060 (100%) [2045–2070]	2070–2075 (87%) [2055–...]	720 [530–930]	400 [–90–620]	–360 [–680––60]	1.7 [1.5–1.8]	1.4 [1.2–1.5]	24 [15–42]	82 [71–93]	100 [99–100]	2030–2035 (100%) [...–...]	...–... (0%) [...–...]	...–... (0%) [...–...]
C3 [311]	limit warming to 2°C (>67%)		44 [32–55]	29 [20–36]	20 [13–26]	21 [1–42]	46 [34–63]	64 [53–77]	2020–2030 [2020–2030]	2020–2025 (100%) [2020–2025]	2070–2075 (93%) [2055–...]	...–... (30%) [2075–...]	890 [640–1160]	800 [510–1140]	–40 [–290–0]	1.7 [1.6–1.8]	1.6 [1.5–1.8]	20 [13–41]	76 [68–91]	99 [98–100]	2030–2035 (100%) [...–...]	...–... (0%) [...–...]	...–... (0%) [...–...]
C3a [204]	...with action starting in 2020	SSP1-2.6	40 [30–49]	29 [21–36]	20 [14–27]	27 [13–45]	47 [35–63]	63 [52–76]	2020–2025 [2020–2025]	2020–2025 (100%) [2020–2025]	2070–2075 (91%) [2055–...]	...–... (24%) [2080–...]	860 [640–1180]	790 [480–1150]	–30 [–280–0]	1.7 [1.6–1.8]	1.6 [1.5–1.8]	21 [14–42]	78 [69–91]	100 [98–100]	2030–2035 (100%) [2030–2040]	...–... (0%) [...–...]	...–... (0%) [...–...]

Column description notes:

- **p50 [p5–p95]**: Modelled global emissions pathways categorised by projected global warming levels (GWL). Detailed likelihood definitions are provided in SPM Box1. The five illustrative scenarios (SSPx-yy) considered by AR6 WGI and the Illustrative (Mitigation) Pathways assessed in WGIII are aligned with the temperature categories and are indicated in a separate column. Global emission pathways contain regionally differentiated information. This assessment focuses on their global characteristics.

- **GHG emissions Gt CO₂-eq/yr**: Projected median GHG emissions in the scenarios, with the 5th–95th percentile in brackets. Modelled GHG emissions in 2019: 55 [53–58] Gt CO₂-eq.

- **GHG emissions reductions from 2019 %**: Projected median GHG emissions reductions of pathways in the year across the scenarios compared to modelled 2019, with the 5th–95th percentile in brackets. Negative numbers indicate increase in emissions compared to 2019.

- **Emissions milestones**: Median 5-year intervals at which projected CO₂ & GHG emissions peak, with the 5th–95th percentile interval in square brackets. Percentage of peaking pathways is denoted in round brackets. Three dots (...) denotes emissions peak in 2100 or beyond for that percentile. Median 5-year intervals at which projected CO₂ & GHG emissions of pathways in this category reach net-zero, with the 5th–95th percentile interval in square brackets. Percentage of net zero pathways is denoted in round brackets. Three dots (...) denotes net zero not reached for that percentile.

- **Cumulative CO₂ emissions Gt CO₂**: Median cumulative net CO₂ emissions across the projected scenarios in this category until reaching net-zero or until 2100, with the 5th–95th percentile interval in square brackets.

- **Cumulative net-negative CO₂ emissions Gt CO₂**: Median cumulative net-negative CO₂ emissions between the year of net-zero CO₂ and 2100. More net-negative results in greater temperature declines after peak.

- **Global mean temperature changes 50% probability °C**: Projected temperature change of pathways in this category across the range of climate uncertainties), relative to 1850–1900, at peak warming and in 2100, for the median value across the scenarios and the 5th–95th percentile interval in square brackets.

- **Likelihood of peak global warming staying below (%)**: Median likelihood that the projected pathways in this category stay below a given global warming level, with the 5th–95th percentile interval in square brackets.

- **Time when specific global warming levels are reached (with a 50% probability)**: Median 5-year intervals at which specific global warming levels are reached (50% probability), with the 5th–95th percentile interval in square brackets. Percentage of pathways is denoted in round brackets. Three dots (...) denotes temperature does not exceed the GWL by 2100 for that percentile.

Table 3.2 (continued):

Modelled global emissions pathways categorised by projected global warming levels (GWL). Detailed likelihood definitions are provided in SPM Box1.

The five illustrative scenarios (SSPx-yy) considered by AR6 WGI and the Illustrative (Mitigation) Pathways assessed in WGIII are aligned with the temperature categories and are indicated in a separate column. Global emission pathways contain regionally differentiated information. This assessment focuses on their global characteristics.

Column descriptions:

- **GHG emissions Gt CO_2-eq/yr [g]:** Projected median annual GHG emissions in the year across the scenarios, with the 5th–95th percentile in brackets. Modelled GHG emissions in 2019: 55 [53–58] Gt CO_2-eq.
- **GHG emissions reductions from 2019 % [h]:** Projected median GHG emissions reductions of pathways in the year across the scenarios compared to modelled 2019, with the 5th–95th percentile in brackets. Negative numbers indicate increase in emissions compared to 2019.
- **Emissions milestones — Peak CO2 & GHG emissions (% peak before 2100):** Median 5-year intervals at which projected CO_2 & GHG emissions peak, with the 5th–95th percentile interval in square brackets. Percentage of peaking pathways is denoted in round brackets. Three dots (…) denotes emissions peak in 2100 or beyond for that percentile.
- **Net-zero CO2 & GHGs [k,l] (% net-zero pathways):** Median 5-year intervals at which projected CO_2 & GHG emissions in this category reach net-zero, with the 5th–95th percentile interval in square brackets. Percentage of net zero pathways is denoted in round brackets. Three dots (…) denotes net zero not reached for that percentile.
- **Cumulative CO2 emissions Gt CO2 [m]:** Median cumulative net CO_2 emissions across the projected scenarios in this category until reaching net-zero or until 2100, with the 5th–95th percentile interval in square brackets.
- **Cumulative net-negative CO2 emissions Gt CO2:** Median cumulative net-negative CO_2 emissions between the year of net-zero CO_2 and 2100. More net-negative results in greater temperature declines after peak.
- **Global mean temperature changes 50% probability [n] °C:** Projected temperature change of pathways in this category (50% probability across the range of climate uncertainties), relative to 1850–1900, at peak warming and in 2100, for the median value across the scenarios and the 5th–95th percentile interval in square brackets.
- **Likelihood of peak global warming staying below (%) [o]:** Median likelihood that the projected pathways stay below a given global warming level, with the 5th–95th percentile interval in square brackets.
- **Time when specific global warming levels are reached (with a 50% probability):** Median 5-year intervals at which specific global warming levels are reached (50% probability), with the 5th–95th percentile interval in square brackets. Percentage of pathways is denoted in round brackets. Three dots (…) denotes temperature does not exceed the GWL by 2100 for that percentile.

Category [b,c,d] [# pathways]	Category/subset label	WGI SSP & WGIII IPs/IMPs alignment [e,f]	GHG 2030	GHG 2040	GHG 2050	Red. 2030	Red. 2040	Red. 2050	Peak CO_2 (% peak before 2100)	Peak GHG (% peak before 2100)	Net-zero CO_2 (% net-zero pathways)	Net-zero GHGs [k,l] (% net-zero pathways)	Cum. 2020 to net-zero CO_2	Cum. 2020–2100	Net-neg. Year of net-zero CO_2 to 2100	Temp. at peak warming	Temp. 2100	<1.5°C	<2°C	<3°C	Time 1.5°C	Time 2°C	Time 3°C
C3b [97]	…NDCs until 2030	IMP-GS	52 [47–56]	29 [20–36]	18 [10–25]	5 [0–14]	46 [34–63]	68 [56–82]			2065–2070 (97%) [2055–2090]	…–… (41%) [2075–…]	910 [720–1150]	800 [560–1050]	−60 [−300–0]	1.8 [1.6–1.8]	1.6 [1.5–1.7]	17 [12–35]	73 [67–87]	99 [98–99]	2030–2035 (100%) [2030–2035]	…–… (0%) […–…]	…–… (0%) […–…]
C4 [159]	limit warming to 2°C (>50%)	Mod-Act	50 [41–56]	38 [28–44]	28 [19–35]	10 [0–27]	31 [20–50]	49 [35–65]	2020–2025 (100%) [2020–2030]	2020–2025 (100%) [2020–2030]	2080–2085 (86%) [2065–…]	…–… (31%) [2075–…]	1210 [970–1490]	1160 [700–1490]	−30 [−390–0]	1.9 [1.7–2.0]	1.8 [1.5–2.0]	11 [7–22]	59 [50–77]	98 [95–99]	2030–2035 (100%) [2030–2035]	2060–2065 (99%) [2050–2095]	…–… (0%) […–…]
C5 [212]	limit warming to 2.5°C (>50%)		52 [46–56]	45 [37–53]	39 [30–49]	6 [−1–18]	18 [4–33]	29 [11–48]			…–… (41%) [2080–…]	…–… (12%) [2090–…]	1780 [1140–2360]	1780 [1260–2360]	0 [−160–0]	2.2 [1.9–2.5]	2.1 [1.9–2.5]	4 [0–10]	37 [18–59]	91 [83–98]	2030–2035 (100%) [2030–2035]	2050–2055 (100%) [2050–2095]	…–… (0%) […–…]
C6 [97]	limit warming to 3°C (>50%)	SSP2-4.5 / Mod-Act	54 [50–62]	53 [48–61]	52 [45–57]	2 [−10–11]	3 [−14–14]	5 [−2–18]	2030–2035 (96%) [2020–2090]	2020–2025 (97%) [2020–2090]	no net-zero	no net-zero	no net-zero	2790 [2440–3520]		temperature does not peak by 2100	2.7 [2.4–2.9]	0 [0–0]	8 [2–18]	71 [53–88]	2030–2035 (100%) [2030–2035]	2050–2055 (100%) [2045–2060]	2080–2085 (100%) [2070–2100]
C7 [164]	limit warming to 4°C (>50%)	SSP3-7.0 / Cur-Pol	62 [53–69]	67 [56–76]	70 [58–83]	−11 [−18–3]	−19 [−31–1]	−24 [−41–2]	2085–2090 (57%) [2040–…]	2090–2095 (56%) [2070–…]	no net-zero	no net-zero	no net-zero	4220 [3160–5000]		temperature does not peak by 2100	3.5 [2.8–3.9]	0 [0–0]	0 [0–2]	22 [7–60]	2030–2035 (100%) [2030–2035]	2045–2050 (100%) [2040–2055]	2080–2085 (100%) [2070–2100]
C8 [29]	exceed warming of 4°C (≥50%)	SSP5-8.5	71 [69–81]	80 [78–96]	88 [82–112]	−20 [−34–−17]	−35 [−65–−29]	−46 [−92–−36]	2080–2085 (90%) [2070–…]		no net-zero	no net-zero	no net-zero	5600 [4910–7450]		temperature does not peak by 2100	4.2 [3.7–5.0]	0 [0–0]	0 [0–0]	4 [0–11]	2030–2035 (100%) [2030–2035]	2040–2045 (100%) [2040–2050]	2065–2070 (100%) [2060–2075]

Table 3.2 (continued):

[a] Values in the table refer to the 50th and [5th–95th] percentile values across the pathways falling within a given category as defined in Box SPM.1. For emissions-related columns these values relate to the distribution of all the pathways in that category. Harmonised emissions values are given for consistency with projected global warming outcomes using climate emulators. Based on the assessment of climate emulators in AR6 WGI (WG1 Chapter 7, Box 7.1), two climate emulators are used for the probabilistic assessment of the resulting warming of the pathways. For the 'Temperature change' and 'Likelihood' columns, the single upper-row values represent the 50th percentile across the pathways in that category and the median [50th percentile] across the warming estimates of the probabilistic MAGICC climate model emulator. For the bracketed ranges, the median warming for every pathway in that category is calculated for each of the two climate model emulators (MAGICC and FaIR). Subsequently, the 5th and 95th percentile values across all pathways for each emulator are calculated. The coolest and warmest outcomes (i.e., the lowest p5 of two emulators, and the highest p95, respectively) are shown in square brackets. These ranges therefore cover both the uncertainty of the emissions pathways as well as the climate emulators' uncertainty.

[b] For a description of pathways categories see Box SPM.1 and Table 3.1.

[c] All global warming levels are relative to 1850–1900. (See footnote n below and Box SPM.1[45] for more details.)

[d] C3 pathways are sub-categorised according to the timing of policy action to match the emissions pathways in Figure SPM.4. Two pathways derived from a cost-benefit analysis have been added to C3a, whilst 10 pathways with specifically designed near-term action until 2030, whose emissions fall below those implied by NDCs announced prior to COP26, are not included in either of the two subsets.

[e] Alignment with the categories of the illustrative SSP scenarios considered in AR6 WGI, and the Illustrative (Mitigation) Pathways (IPs/IMPs) of WGIII. The IMPs have common features such as deep and rapid emissions reductions, but also different combinations of sectoral mitigation strategies. See Box SPM.1 for an introduction of the IPs and IMPs, and Chapter 3 for full descriptions. {3.2, 3.3, Annex III.II.2.4}

[f] The Illustrative Mitigation Pathway 'Neg' has extensive use of carbon dioxide removal (CDR) in the AFOLU, energy and the industry sectors to achieve net negative emissions. Warming peaks around 2060 and declines to below 1.5°C (50% likelihood) shortly after 2100. Whilst technically classified as C3, it strongly exhibits the characteristics of C2 high-overshoot pathways, hence it has been placed in the C2 category. See Box SPM.1 for an introduction of the IPs and IMPs.

[g] The 2019 range of harmonised GHG emissions across the pathways [53–58 GtCO$_2$-eq] is within the uncertainty ranges of 2019 emissions assessed in Chapter 2 [53–66 GtCO$_2$-eq].[49] (Figure SPM.1, Figure SPM.2, Box SPM.1)

[h] Rates of global emission reduction in mitigation pathways are reported on a pathway-by-pathway basis relative to harmonised modelled global emissions in 2019 rather than the global emissions reported in SPM Section B and Chapter 2; this ensures internal consistency in assumptions about emission sources and activities, as well as consistency with temperature projections based on the physical climate science assessment by WGI.[49] {Annex III.II.2.5}. Negative values (e.g., in C7, C8) represent an increase in emissions.

[i] Emissions milestones are provided for five-year intervals in order to be consistent with the underlying five-year time-step data of the modelled pathways. Peak emissions (CO$_2$ and GHGs) are assessed for five-year reporting intervals starting in 2020. The interval 2020–2025 signifies that projected emissions peak as soon as possible between 2020 and at latest before 2025. The upper five-year interval refers to the median interval within which the emissions peak or reach net zero. Ranges in square brackets underneath refer to the range across the pathways, comprising the lower bound of the 5th percentile five-year interval and the upper bound of the 95th percentile five-year interval. Numbers in round brackets signify the fraction of pathways that reach specific milestones.

[j] Percentiles reported across all pathways in that category include those that do not reach net zero before 2100 (fraction of pathways reaching net zero is given in round brackets). If the fraction of pathways that reach net zero before 2100 is lower than the fraction of pathways covered by a percentile (e.g., 0.95 for the 95th percentile), the percentile is not defined and denoted with '…'. The fraction of pathways reaching net zero includes all with reported non-harmonised, and/or harmonised emissions profiles that reach net zero. Pathways were counted when at least one of the two profiles fell below 100 MtCO$_2$ yr^{-1} until 2100.

[k] The timing of net zero is further discussed in SPM C2.4 and Cross-Chapter Box 3 in Chapter 3 on net zero CO$_2$ and net zero GHG emissions.

[l] For cases where models do not report all GHGs, missing GHG species are infilled and aggregated into a Kyoto basket of GHG emissions in CO$_2$-eq defined by the 100-year global warming potential. For each pathway, reporting of CO$_2$, CH$_4$, and N$_2$O emissions was the minimum required for the assessment of the climate response and the assignment to a climate category. Emissions pathways without climate assessment are not included in the ranges presented here. {See Annex III.II.2.5 }

[m] Cumulative emissions are calculated from the start of 2020 to the time of net zero and 2100, respectively. They are based on harmonised net CO$_2$ emissions, ensuring consistency with the WGI assessment of the remaining carbon budget.[50] {Box 3.4}

[n] Global mean temperature change for category (at peak, if peak temperature occurs before 2100, and in 2100) relative to 1850–1900, based on the median global warming for each pathway assessed using the probabilistic climate model emulators calibrated to the AR6 WGI assessment.[12] (See also Box SPM.1) {Annex III.II.2.5; WGI Cross-Chapter Box 7.1}

[o] Probability of staying below the temperature thresholds for the pathways in each category, taking into consideration the range of uncertainty from the climate model emulators consistent with the AR6 WGI assessment. The probabilities refer to the probability at peak temperature. Note that in the case of temperature overshoot (e.g., category C2 and some pathways in C1), the probabilities of staying below at the end of the century are higher than the probabilities at peak temperature.

3.3.2.4   Mitigation Strategies

Detailed sectoral implications are discussed in Section 3.4 and Chapters 5–11 (see also Table 3.3). The stringency of climate policy has clear implications for mitigation action (Figure 3.15). There are a number of important commonalities of pathways limiting warming to 2°C (>67%) or lower: for instance, they all rely on significant improvement of energy efficiency, rapid decarbonisation of supply and, many of them, CDR (in energy supply or AFOLU), either in terms of net negative emissions or to compensate residual emissions. Still, there are also important differences and the (IMPs) show how different choices can steer the system into alternative directions with different combinations of response options. For decarbonisation of energy supply many options exist, including CCS, nuclear power, and renewables (Chapter 6). In the majority of the scenarios reaching low GHG targets, a considerable amount of CCS is applied (Figure 3.15d).

The share of renewables is around 30–70% in the scenarios that limit warming to 2°C (>67%) and clearly above 40% for scenarios that limit warming 1.5°C (>50%) (panel c). Scenarios have been published with 100% renewable energy systems even at a global scale, partly reflecting the rapid progress made for these technologies in the last decade (Creutzig et al. 2017; Jacobson et al. 2018; Breyer and Jefferson 2020). These scenarios do not show in the graph due to a lack of information from non-energy sources. There is a debate in the literature on whether it is possible to achieve a 100% renewable energy system by 2050 (Brook et al. 2018). This critically depends on assumptions made on future system integration, system flexibility, storage options, consequences for material demand and the ability to supply high-temperature functions and specific mobility functions with renewable energy. The range of studies published showing 100% renewable energy systems show that it is possible to design such systems in the context of energy system models (Hong et al.

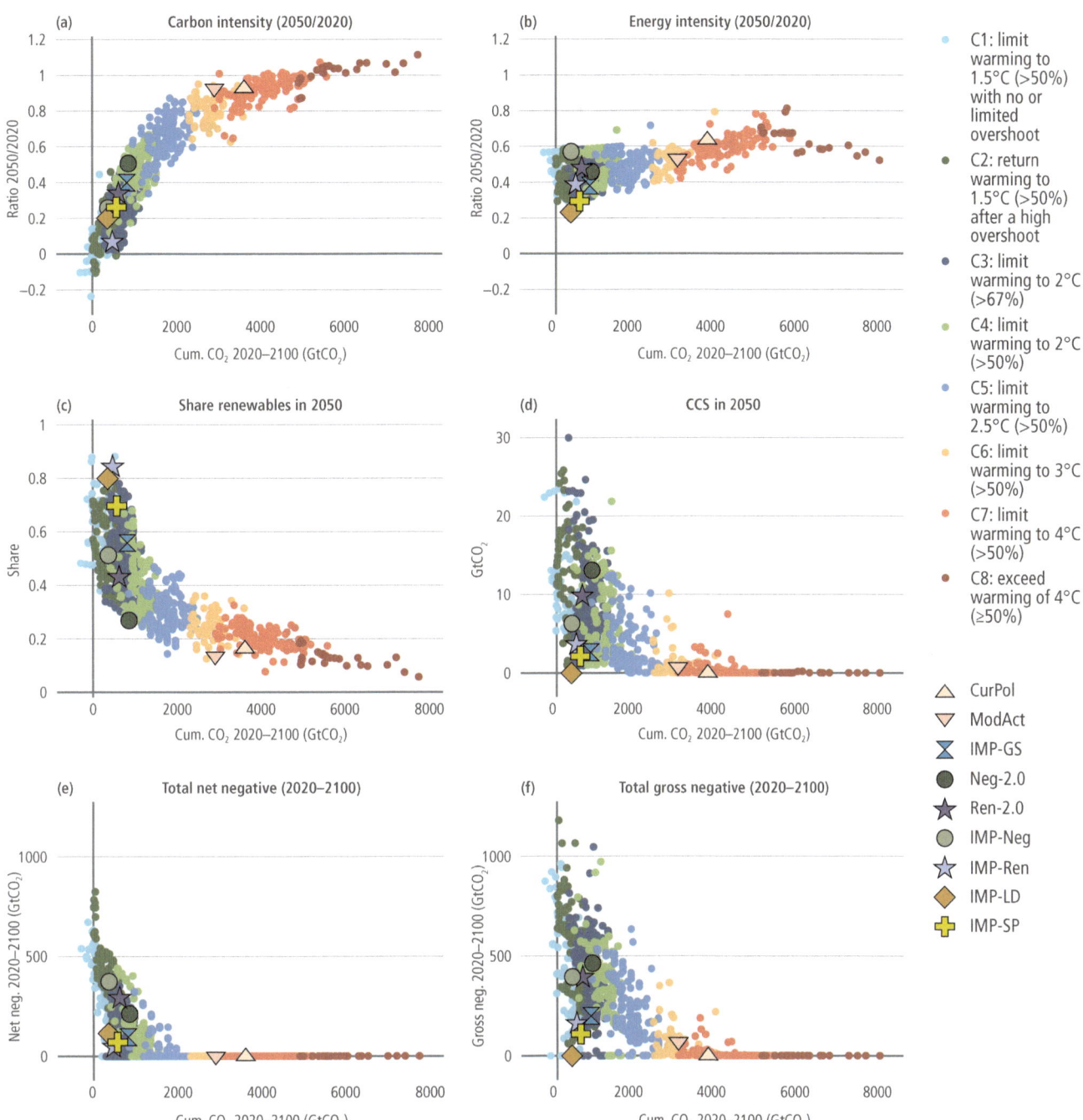

Figure 3.15 | Characteristics of scenarios as a function of the remaining carbon budget (mean decarbonisation rate is shown as the average reduction in the period 2010–2050 divided by 2010 emissions). The categories C1–C7 are explained in Table 3.1.

2014a,b; Lehtveer and Hedenus 2015a,b; Pfenninger and Keirstead 2015; Sepulveda et al. 2018; Zappa et al. 2019; IEA 2021b) (see also Box 6.6 on 100% renewables in net zero CO_2 systems). Panels e and f, finally, show the contribution of CDR – both in terms of net negative emissions and gross CDR. The contribution of total CDR obviously exceeds the net negative emissions. It should be noted that while a majority of scenarios rely on net negative emissions to reach stringent mitigation goals – this is not the case for all of them.

The spread shown in Figure 3.15 implies different mitigation strategies that could all lead to emissions levels consistent with the Paris Agreement (and reach zero emissions). The IMPs illustrate some

options for different decarbonisation pathways with heavy reliance on renewables (*IMP-Ren*), strong emphasis on energy-demand reductions (*IMP-LD*), widespread deployment of CDR methods coupled with CCS (BECCS and DACCS) (*IMP-Neg*), mitigation in the context of sustainable development (*IMP-SP*) (Figure 3.16). For example, in some scenarios, a small part of the energy system is still based on fossil fuels in 2100 (*IMP-Neg*), while in others, fossil fuels are almost or completely phased out (*IMP-Ren*). Nevertheless, in all scenarios, fossil fuel use is greatly reduced and unabated coal use is completely phased out by 2050. Also, nuclear power can be part of a mitigation strategy (however, the literature only includes some scenarios with high-nuclear contributions, such as Berger et al. 2017).

a. IMP characteristics: primary energy

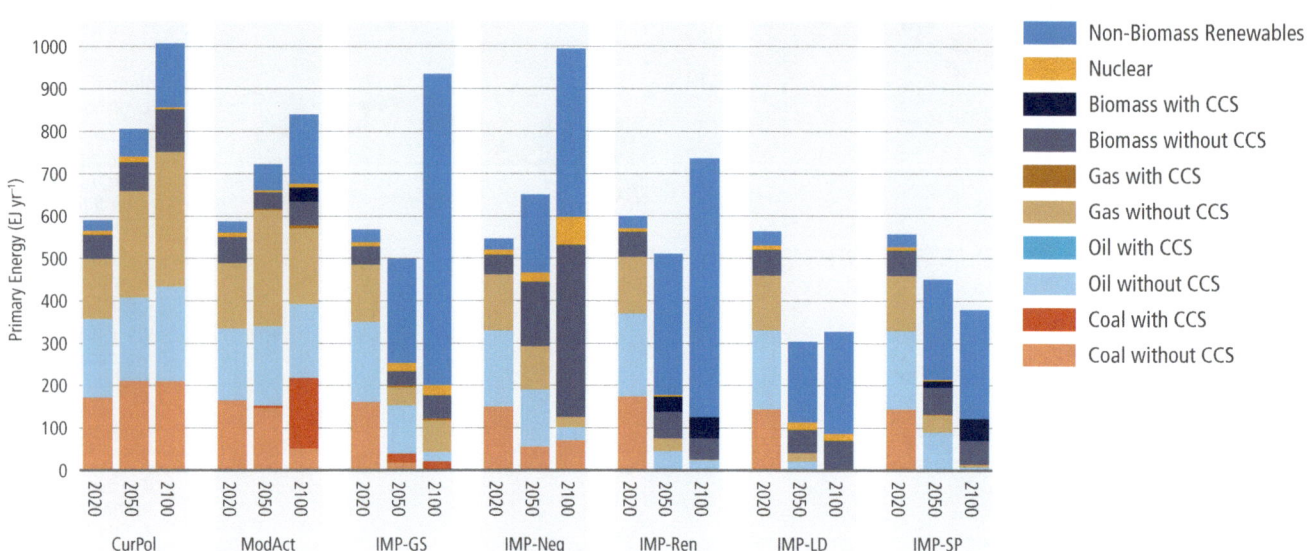

Non-Biomass Renewables
Nuclear
Biomass with CCS
Biomass without CCS
Gas with CCS
Gas without CCS
Oil with CCS
Oil without CCS
Coal with CCS
Coal without CCS

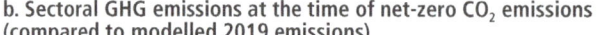

b. Sectoral GHG emissions at the time of net-zero CO$_2$ emissions
(compared to modelled 2019 emissions)

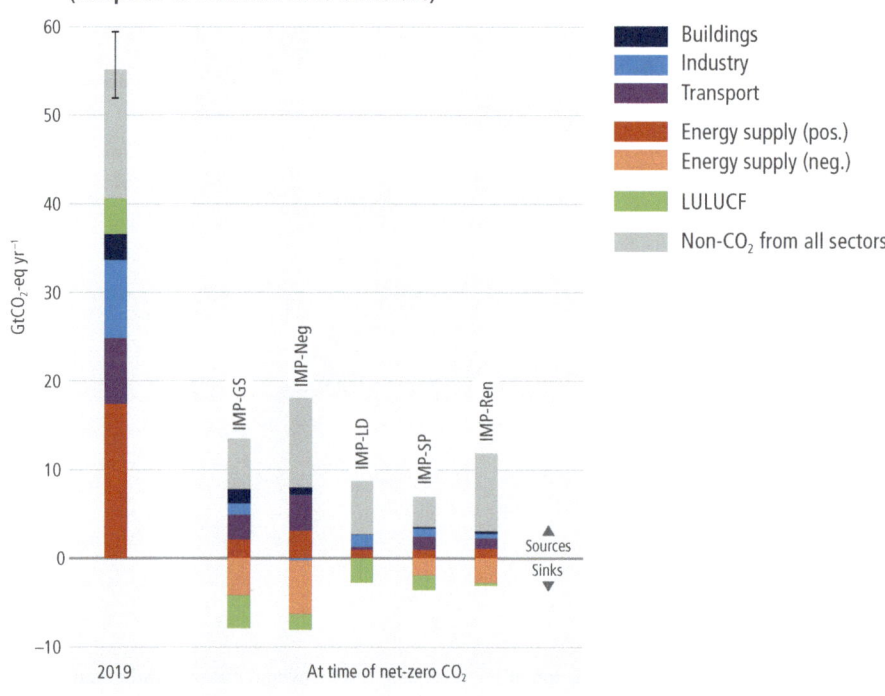

Buildings
Industry
Transport
Energy supply (pos.)
Energy supply (neg.)
LULUCF
Non-CO$_2$ from all sectors

Figure 3.16 | Primary energy use and net emissions at net zero year for the different IMPS. Source: AR6 Scenarios Database.

This is explored further in Section 3.5. The different strategies are also clearly apparent in the way they scenarios reach net zero emissions. While *IMP-GS* and *IMP-Neg* rely significantly on BECCS and DACCS, their use is far more restricted in the other IMPs. Consistently, in these IMPs residual emissions are also significantly lower.

Mitigation pathways also have a regional dimension. In 2010, about 40% of emissions originated from the Developed Countries and Eastern Europe and West Central Asia regions. According to the projections shown in Figure 3.17, the share of the latter regions will further increase to about 70% by 2050. In the scenarios in the literature, emissions are typically almost equally reduced across the regions.

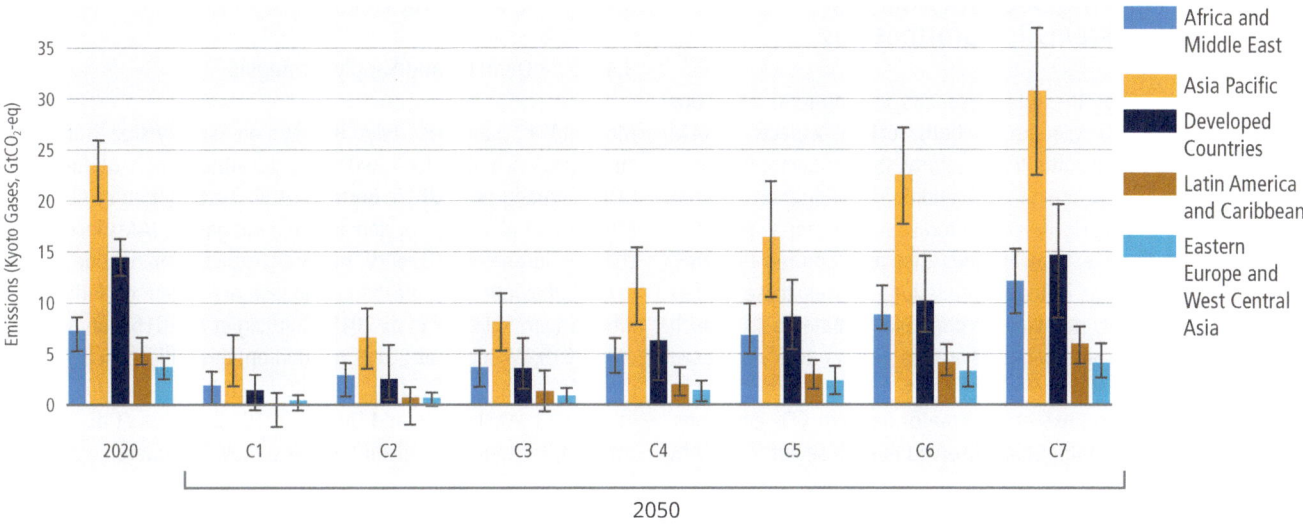

Figure 3.17[11] | Emissions by region (including 5–95th percentile range). Source: AR6 Scenarios Database.

3.3.3   Climate Impacts on Mitigation Potential

At the moment, climate change impact on mitigation potential is hardly considered in model-based scenarios. While a detailed overview of climate impacts is provided in IPCC AR6 WGII and Section 3.6 discusses the economic consequences, here we concentrate on the implications for mitigation potential. Climate change directly impacts the carbon budget via all kinds of feedbacks – which is included in the ranges provided for the carbon budget (e.g., 300–900 GtCO$_2$ for 17th–83rd percentile for not exceeding 1.5°C; see AR6 WGI Chapter 5, 2021). Climate change, however, alters the production and consumption of energy (Section 6.5). An overview of the literature is provided by Yalew et al. (2020). In terms of supply, impacts could influence the cooling capacity of thermal plants, the potential and predictability of renewable energy, and energy infrastructure (van Vliet et al. 2016; Turner et al. 2017; Cronin et al. 2018a; Lucena et al. 2018; Yalew et al. 2020; Gernaat et al. 2021). Although the outcomes of these studies differ, they seem to suggest that although impacts might be relatively small at the global scale, they could be substantial at the regional scale (increasing or decreasing potential). Climate change can also impact energy demand, with rising temperatures resulting in decreases in heating demand and increases in cooling demand (Isaac and van Vuuren 2009; Zhou et al. 2014; Labriet et al. 2015; McFarland et al. 2015; Auffhammer et al. 2017; Clarke et al. 2018; van Ruijven et al. 2019; Yalew et al. 2020). As expected, the increase in cooling demand dominates the impact in warm regions and decreases in heating demand in cold regions (Isaac and van Vuuren 2009; Zhou et al. 2014; Clarke et al. 2018). Globally, most studies show a net increase in energy demand at the end of the century due to climate impacts (Isaac and van Vuuren 2009; Clarke et al. 2018; van Ruijven et al. 2019); however, one study shows a net decrease (Labriet et al. 2015). Only a few studies quantify the combined impacts of climate change on energy supply and energy demand (McFarland et al. 2015; Mima and Criqui 2015; Emodi et al. 2019;

Steinberg et al. 2020). These studies show increases in electricity generation in the USA (McFarland et al. 2015; Steinberg et al. 2020) and increases in CO$_2$ emissions in Australia (Emodi et al. 2019) or the USA (McFarland et al. 2015).

Climate change can impact the potential for AFOLU mitigation action by altering terrestrial carbon uptake, crop yields and bioenergy potential (Chapter 7). Carbon sequestration in forests may be positively or adversely affected by climate change and CO$_2$ fertilisation. On the one hand, elevated CO$_2$ levels and higher temperatures could enhance tree growth rates, carbon sequestration, and timber and biomass production (Beach et al. 2015; Kim et al. 2017; Anderegg et al. 2020). On the other hand, climate change could lead to greater frequency and intensity of disturbance events in forests, such as fires, prolonged droughts, storms, pests and diseases (Kim et al. 2017; Anderegg et al. 2020). The impact of climate change on crop yields could also indirectly impact the availability of land for mitigation and AFOLU emissions (Calvin et al. 2013; Bajželj and Richards 2014; Kyle et al. 2014; Beach et al. 2015; Meijl et al. 2018). The impact is, however, uncertain, as discussed in AR6 WGII Chapter 5. A few studies estimate the effect of climate impacts on AFOLU on mitigation, finding increases in carbon prices or mitigation costs by 1–6% in most scenarios (Calvin et al. 2013; Kyle et al. 2014).

In summary, a limited number of studies quantify the impact of climate on emissions pathways. The most important impact in energy systems might be through the impact on demand, although climate change could also impact renewable mitigation potential – certainly at the local and regional scale. Climate change might be more important for land-use related mitigation measures, including afforestation, bioenergy and nature-based solutions. The net effect of changes in climate and CO$_2$ fertilisation are uncertain but could be substantial (Chapter 7).

---

[11]   The countries and areas classification in this figure deviate from the standard classification scheme adopted by AR6 WGIII as set out in Annex II.I.1.

3.4 Integrating Sectoral Analysis Into Systems Transformations

This section describes the role of sectors in long-term emissions pathways (Table 3.3). We discuss both sectoral aspects of IAM pathways and some insights from sectoral studies. Sectoral studies typically include more detail and additional mitigation options compared to IAMs. However, sectoral studies miss potential feedbacks and cross-sectoral linkages that are captured by IAMs. Additionally, since IAMs include all emissions sources, these models can be used to identify pathways to particular climate goals. In such pathways, emissions are balanced across sectors typically based on relative marginal abatement costs; as a result, some sectors are sources and some are sinks at the time of net zero CO_2 emissions. For these reasons, the mitigation observed in each sector in an IAM may differ from the potential in sectoral studies. Given the strengths and limitations of each type of model, IAMs and sectoral models are complementary, providing different perspectives.

Table 3.3 | Section 3.4 structure, definitions, and relevant chapters.

Section	Sector	What is included	Relevant chapter(s)
3.4.1	Cross-sector	Supply and demand, bioenergy, timing of net zero CO_2, other interactions among sectors	Chapters 5, 12
3.4.2	Energy supply	Energy resources, transformation (e.g., electricity generation, refineries, etc.)	Chapter 6
3.4.3	Buildings[a]	Residential and commercial buildings, other non-specified[b]	Chapter 9
3.4.4	Transportation[a]	Road, rail, aviation, and shipping	Chapter 10
3.4.5	Industry[a]	Industrial energy use and industrial processes	Chapter 11
3.4.6	AFOLU	Agriculture, forestry, and other land use	Chapter 7
3.4.7	Other CDR	CDR options not included in individual sectors (e.g., direct air carbon capture and sequestration, enhanced weathering)	Chapter 12

[a] Direct energy use and direct emissions only; emissions do not include those associated with energy production.
[b] Other non-specified fuel use, including military. Some models report this category in the buildings sector, while others report it in the 'Other' sector.

3.4.1 Cross-sector Linkages

3.4.1.1 Demand and Supply Strategies

Most IAM pathways rely heavily on supply-side mitigation strategies, including fuel switching, decarbonisation of fuels, and CDR (Creutzig et al. 2016; Bertram et al. 2018; Rogelj et al. 2018b; Mundaca et al. 2019). For demand-side mitigation, IAMs incorporate changes in energy efficiency, but many other demand-side options (e.g., behaviour and lifestyle changes) are often excluded from models (van Sluisveld et al. 2015; Creutzig et al. 2016; van den Berg et al. 2019; Wilson et al. 2019). In addition, this mitigation is typically price-driven and limited in magnitude (Yeh et al. 2017; Luderer et al. 2018; Wachsmuth and Duscha 2019; Sharmina et al. 2020). In contrast, bottom-up modelling studies show considerable potential for demand-side mitigation (Creutzig et al. 2016; Yeh et al. 2017; Mundaca et al. 2019; Wachsmuth and Duscha 2019) (Chapter 5), which can slow emissions growth and/or reduce emissions (Creutzig et al. 2016; Samadi et al. 2017).

A small number of mitigation pathways include stringent demand-side mitigation, including changes in thermostat set points (van Sluisveld et al. 2016; van Vuuren et al. 2018), more efficient or smarter appliances (van Sluisveld et al. 2016; Grubler et al. 2018; Napp et al. 2019), increased recycling or reduced industrial goods (Liu et al. 2018; van Sluisveld et al. 2016; Grubler et al. 2018; van de Ven et al. 2018; Napp et al. 2019), telework and travel avoidance (Grubler et al. 2018; van de Ven et al. 2018), shifts to public transit (van Sluisveld et al. 2016; Grubler et al. 2018; van Vuuren et al. 2018), reductions in food waste (van de Ven et al. 2018) and less meat-intensive diets (Liu et al. 2018; van de Ven et al. 2018; van Vuuren et al. 2018). These pathways show reduced dependence on CDR and reduced pressure on land (Grubler et al. 2018; Rogelj et al. 2018a; van de Ven et al. 2018; van Vuuren et al. 2018) (Section 5.3.3). However, the representation of these demand-side mitigation options in IAMs is limited, with most models excluding the costs of such changes (van Sluisveld et al. 2016), using stylised assumptions to represent them (van den Berg et al. 2019), and excluding rebound effects (Krey et al. 2019; Brockway et al. 2021). Furthermore, there are questions about the achievability of such pathways, including whether the behavioural changes included are feasible (Azevedo et al. 2021) and the extent to which development and demand can be decoupled (Steckel et al. 2013; Brockway et al. 2021; Keyßer and Lenzen 2021; Semieniuk et al. 2021).

Figure 3.18 shows indicators of supply- and demand-side mitigation in the IMPs, as well as the range across the database. Two of these IMPs (*IMP-SP*, *IMP-LD*) show strong reductions in energy demand, resulting in less reliance on bioenergy and limited CDR from energy supply. In contrast, *IMP-Neg* has higher energy demand, depending more on bioenergy and net negative CO_2 emissions from energy supply.

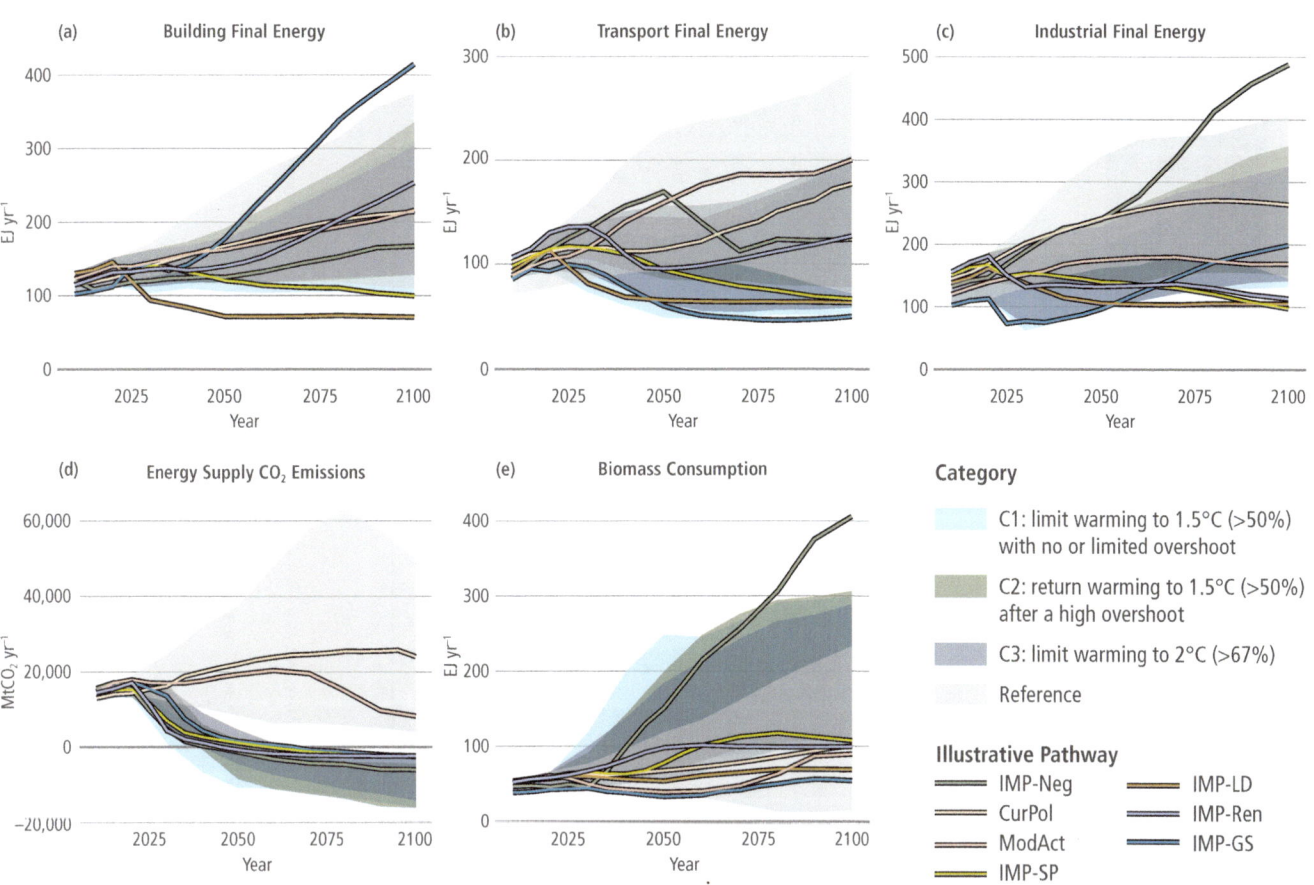

Figure 3.18 | Indicators of demand and supply-side mitigation in the Illustrative Pathways (lines) and the 5–95% range of Reference, 1.5°C and 2°C scenarios (shaded areas).

3.4.1.2   Sectoral Emissions Strategies and the Timing of Net Zero

Mitigation pathways show differences in the timing of decarbonisation (Figure 3.20) and the timing of net zero (Figure 3.19) across sectors and regions (*high confidence*); the timing in a given sector depends on the cost of abatement in it, the availability of CDR options, the scenario design, near-term emissions levels, and the amount of non-CO_2 abatement (Yeh et al. 2017; Emmerling et al. 2019; Rogelj et al. 2019a,b; Johansson et al. 2020; Azevedo et al. 2021; Ou et al. 2021; van Soest et al. 2021b) (Cross-Chapter Box 3 in this chapter). However, delaying emissions reductions, or more limited emissions reductions in one sector or region, involves compensating reductions in other sectors or regions if warming is to be limited (*high confidence*) (Price and Keppo 2017; Grubler et al. 2018; Rochedo et al. 2018; van Soest et al. 2021b).

At the time of net zero global CO_2 emissions, emissions in some sectors are positive and some negative. In cost-effective mitigation pathways, the energy supply sector typically reaches net zero CO_2 before the economy as a whole, while the demand sectors reach net zero CO_2 later, if at all (Pietzcker et al. 2014; Price and Keppo 2017; Luderer et al. 2018; Rogelj et al. 2018a,b; Méjean et al. 2019; Azevedo

et al. 2021) (Section 6.7). CO_2 emissions from transport, industry, and buildings are positive, and non-CO_2 GHG emissions are also positive at the time of global net zero CO_2 emissions (Figure 3.20).

So, while pathways indicate some flexibility in emissions reductions across sectors, all pathways involve substantial CO_2 emissions reductions in all sectors and regions (*high confidence*) (Luderer et al. 2018; Rogelj et al. 2018a,b; Méjean et al. 2019; Azevedo et al. 2021). Projected CO_2 emissions reductions between 2019 and 2050 in 1.5°C (>50%) pathways with no or limited overshoot are around 77% for energy demand, with a 5–95% range of 31–96%,[12] 115% for energy supply (90–167%), and 148% for AFOLU (94–387%). In pathways that limit warming to 2°C (>67%), projected CO_2 emissions are reduced between 2019 and 2050 by around 49% for energy demand, 97% for energy supply, and 136% for AFOLU (Sections 3.4.2–3.4.6). Almost 75% of GHG reductions at the time of net zero GHG are from the energy system, 13% are from AFOLU CO_2, and 13% from non-CO_2 (Figure 3.21). These reductions are achieved through a variety of sectoral strategies, illustrated in Figure 3.21 (Figure 3.21b), and described in Sections 3.4.2 to 3.4.7; the primary strategies include declines in fossil energy, increases in low-carbon energy use, and CDR to address residual emissions.

---

[12]   Unless otherwise specified, the values in parentheses in Section 3.4 from this point forward indicate the 5–95th percentile range.

Table 3.4 | Energy and emissions characteristics of the pathways by climate category for 2030, 2050, 2100. Source: AR6 scenarios database.

Category [# pathways] [b,c]	Global Mean Surface Air Temperature change	WG1 SSP & IPs alignment	Category/ subset	Low-carbon share of Primary Energy [d,e] [%] 2020 = 16 (12–18) 2030	2050	2100	Energy & Industrial Processes Index 2020 = 100 2030	2050	2100	Final energy demand [EJ/yr] 2020 = 419 (367–458) 2030	2050	2100	Final energy intensity of GDP Index 2020 = 100 2030	2050	2100	Electricity share in final energy [%] 2020 = 20 (18–25) 2030	2050	2100	CO2 intensity of electricity [Mt CO2/TWh] 2020 = 469 (419–538) 2030	2050	2100	Non-energy GHG emissions [Gt CO2-eq] 2020 = 18 (15–21) 2030	2050	2100	Fossil CCS (2100) [Gt CO2] 2020 = 0 (0–0) 2030	2050	2100	2020–2100
C1 [97]	limit warming to 1.5°C (>50%) with no or limited overshoot	IMP-SD, IMP-LD, IMP-Ren, SSP1-1.9		32 (17–48)	68 (25–86)	75 (19–98)	65 (49–75)	8 (−8–24)	−3 (−20–8)	399 (293–447)	410 (325–540)	612 (321–818)	71 (59–81)	46 (34–60)	26 (14–45)	27 (23–35)	52 (40–64)	66 (50–78)	99 (4–215)	−5 (−66–11)	−4 (−104–1)	10 (5–13)	5 (1–9)	2 (−2–9)	1 (0–5)	2 (0–13)	3 (0–16)	196 (3–882)
C2 [133]	return warming to 1.5°C (>50%) after a high overshoot	IMP-Neg		24 (11–35)	57 (19–77)	86 (25–97)	79 (66–94)	18 (2–37)	−14 (−25–0)	458 (372–504)	442 (345–561)	675 (415–819)	76 (64–88)	44 (35–63)	23 (15–45)	25 (20–29)	45 (34–56)	61 (49–73)	218 (99–353)	0 (−75–16)	−1 (−118–3)	13 (10–19)	6 (2–9)	1 (−7–7)	0 (0–4)	3 (0–13)	1 (0–16)	280 (7–831)
C3 [311]	limit warming to 2°C (>67%)			24 (16–32)	51 (29–75)	73 (34–94)	84 (70–95)	31 (9–47)	−1 (−19–8)	446 (356–491)	448 (344–540)	625 (421–788)	77 (65–88)	50 (36–62)	26 (18–41)	24 (20–29)	42 (30–54)	60 (43–72)	248 (93–375)	5 (−72–51)	−8 (−105–5)	12 (6–18)	7 (3–12)	5 (−1–8)	0 (0–3)	3 (0–12)	5 (0–15)	266 (7–773)
C3a [204]	...with action starting in 2020	SSP2-2.6		21 (14–24)	39 (24–63)	71 (34–91)	92 (80–100)	45 (26–64)	−3 (−21–9)	459 (379–497)	489 (362–601)	641 (450–796)	76 (71–87)	45 (39–65)	22 (19–41)	23 (19–28)	35 (23–44)	56 (44–69)	322 (227–381)	24 (−48–112)	−14 (−117–7)	13 (8–19)	9 (3–12)	2 (−1–9)	0 (0–2)	2 (0–9)	6 (0–16)	279 (7–684)
C3b [97]	...NDCs until 2030	IMP-GS		21 (12–24)	31 (22–44)	67 (42–84)	92 (84–102)	66 (50–84)	9 (−13–32)	466 (389–499)	519 (435–585)	680 (383–812)	77 (74–88)	51 (45–66)	23 (18–40)	23 (19–28)	32 (19–41)	53 (40–65)	341 (257–418)	107 (14–208)	−3 (−73–34)	15 (10–19)	10 (5–15)	4 (−1–11)	0 (0–1)	1 (0–7)	5 (0–15)	200 (5–730)
C4 [159]	limit warming to 2°C (>50%)			20 (11–23)	25 (14–36)	47 (28–65)	94 (87–101)	82 (67–92)	47 (21–78)	467 (410–508)	551 (471–632)	701 (432–910)	79 (75–89)	55 (50–70)	26 (20–42)	23 (19–28)	29 (19–38)	48 (30–56)	354 (257–469)	216 (69–317)	28 (−20–166)	17 (11–20)	13 (9–17)	8 (2–12)	0 (0–0)	0 (0–4)	4 (0–16)	47 (0–536)
C5 [212]	limit warming to 2.5°C (>50%)			17 (11–21)	19 (8–29)	29 (8–51)	98 (91–101)	94 (80–101)	73 (56–106)	492 (434–540)	599 (513–701)	804 (557–983)	85 (76–91)	64 (54–76)	33 (27–48)	24 (20–28)	29 (23–35)	41 (29–50)	414 (311–538)	311 (130–499)	185 (12–461)	19 (13–24)	19 (14–25)	16 (9–26)	0 (0–0)	0 (0–2)	0 (0–8)	0 (0–221)
C6 [97]	limit warming to 3°C (>50%)	SSP2-4.5 Mod-Act		13 (11–17)	13 (9–20)	29 (14–45)	102 (99–103)	106 (104–109)	91 (87–95)	540 (413–574)	696 (504–856)	941 (692–1136)	89 (88–92)	73 (64–79)	47 (25–51)	26 (22–30)	31 (28–35)	43 (35–50)	463 (372–514)	425 (352–484)	189 (142–441)	20 (19–25)	21 (20–29)	20 (13–31)	0 (0–0)	0 (0–0)	0 (0–2)	0 (0–38)
C7 [164]	limit warming to 4°C (>50%)	SSP3-7.0 Cur-Pol		32 (17–48)	68 (25–86)	75 (19–98)	65 (49–75)	8 (−8–24)	−3 (−20–8)	399 (293–447)	410 (325–540)	612 (321–818)	71 (59–81)	46 (34–60)	26 (14–45)	27 (23–35)	52 (40–64)	66 (50–78)	99 (4–215)	−5 (−66–11)	−4 (−104–1)	10 (5–13)	5 (1–9)	2 (−2–9)	1 (0–5)	2 (0–13)	3 (0–16)	196 (3–882)
C8 [29]	exceed warming of 4°C (≥50%)	SSP5-8.5		24 (11–35)	57 (19–77)	86 (25–97)	79 (66–94)	18 (2–37)	−14 (−25–0)	458 (372–504)	442 (345–561)	675 (415–819)	76 (64–88)	44 (35–63)	23 (15–45)	25 (20–29)	45 (34–56)	61 (49–73)	218 (99–353)	0 (−75–16)	−1 (−118–3)	13 (10–19)	6 (2–9)	1 (−7–7)	0 (0–4)	3 (0–13)	1 (0–16)	280 (7–831)

a Values in the table refer to the 50th and (5–95th) percentile values.

b See category descriptions in Table 3.1.

c The warming profile of *IMP-Neg* peaks around 2060 and declines thereafter to below 1.5°C (50% likelihood) shortly after 2100. Whilst technically classified as a C3, it strongly exhibits the characteristics of C2 high-overshoot scenarios.

d Primary Energy as calculated in 'Direct Equivalent' terms according to IPCC reporting conventions.

e Low-carbon energy here defined to include: renewables (including biomass, solar, wind, hydro, geothermal, ocean); fossil fuels when used with CCS; and, nuclear power.

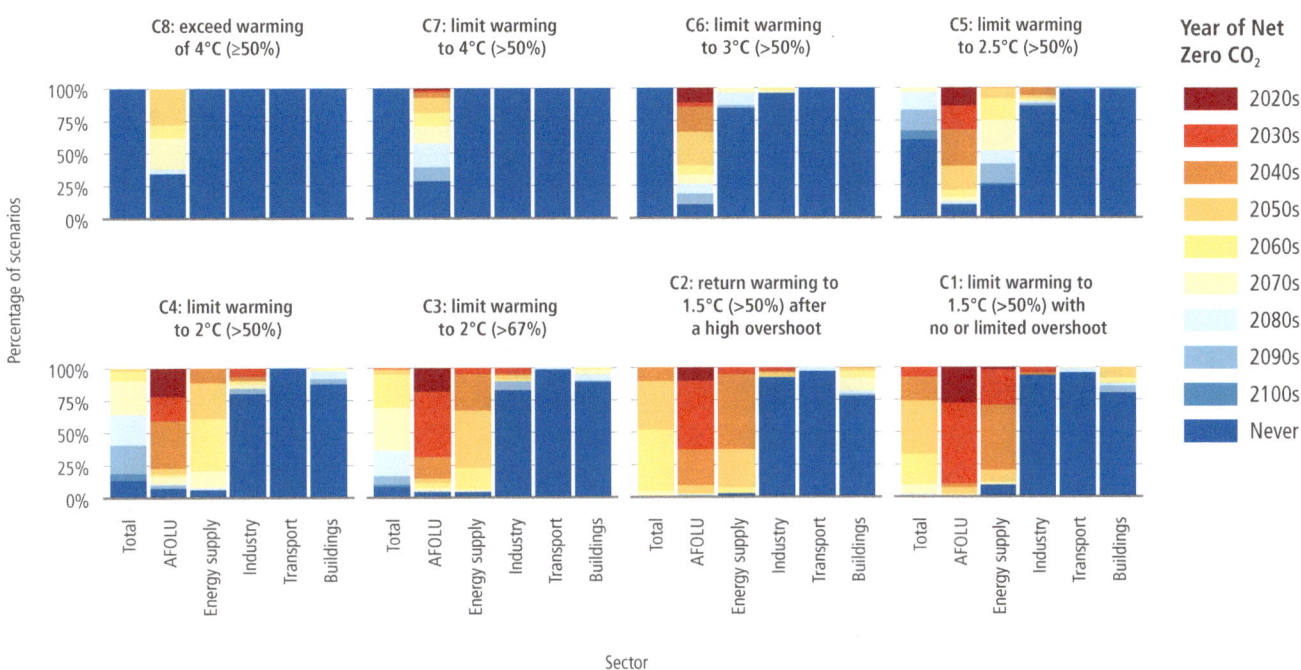

Figure 3.19 | Decade in which sectoral CO₂ emissions first reach net negative values. Each panel is a different temperature level. The colours indicate the decade in which CO₂ emissions go negative; the y-axis indicates the share of scenarios achieving net zero in that decade. Only scenarios that pass the vetting criteria are included (Section 3.2). Scenarios achieving net zero prior to 2020 are excluded.

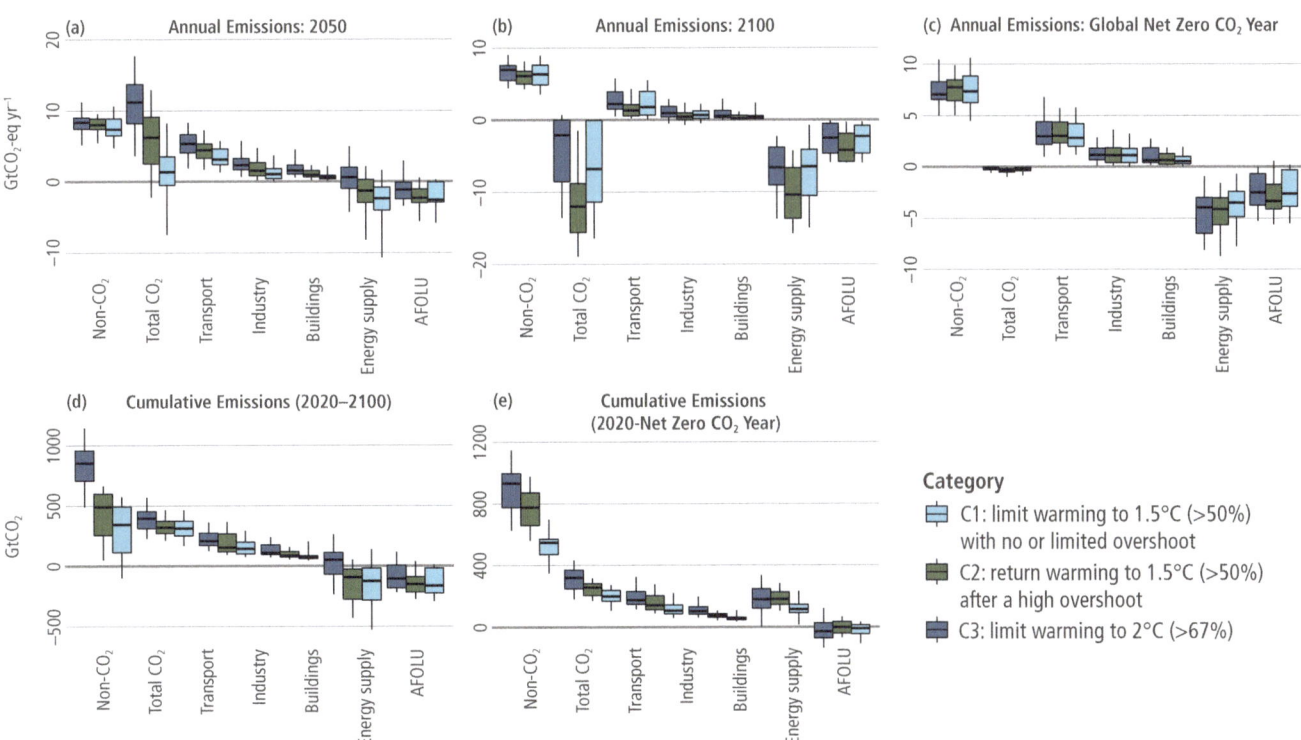

Figure 3.20 | Greenhouse gas (GHG) emissions, including CO₂ emissions by sector and total non-CO₂ GHGs in 2050 (top left), 2100 (top middle), year of global net zero CO₂ (top right), cumulative CO₂ emissions from 2020–2100 (bottom left), and cumulative CO₂ emissions from 2020 until the year of net zero CO₂ for scenarios that limit warming to below 2°C. Scenarios are grouped by their temperature category. 'Industry' includes CO₂ emissions associated with industrial energy use only; sectors shown in this figure do not necessarily sum to total CO₂. In this, and other figures in Section 3.4, unless stated otherwise, only scenarios that pass the vetting criteria are included (Section 3.2). Boxes indicate the interquartile range, the median is shown with a horizontal black line, while vertical lines show the 5–95% interval.

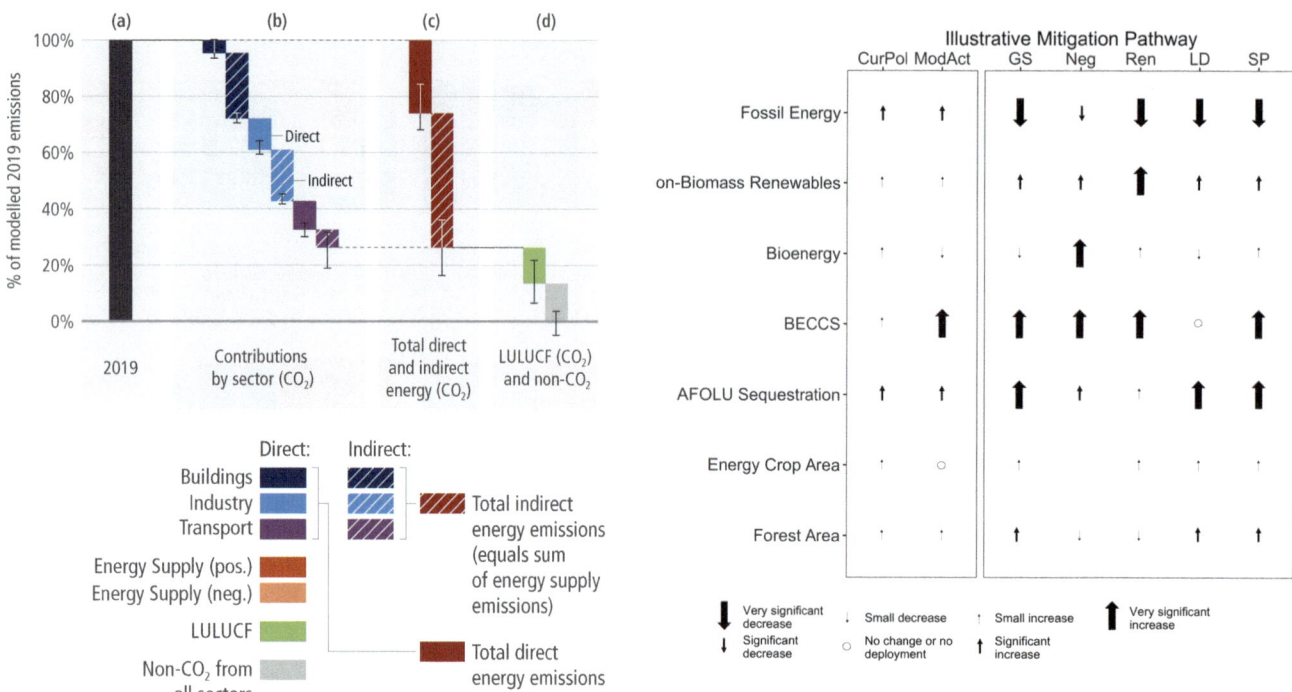

Figure 3.21 | Left panel: Greenhouse gas (GHG) emissions reductions from 2019 by sector at the year of net zero GHG for all scenarios that reach net zero GHG. Emissions reductions by sector for direct (demand) and indirect (upstream supply) are shown as the percent of total GHG reductions. **Right panel:** key indicators in 2050 for the IMPs. Definitions of significant and very significant are defined relative to 2019 and vary between indicators, as follows: fossil energy (significant >10%, very significant >50%), renewables (>150 EJ yr^{-1}, >200 EJ yr^{-1}), bioenergy (>100%, >200%), BECCS (>2.0 GtCO$_2$ yr^{-1}, >3.5 GtCO$_2$ yr^{-1}), AFOLU (>100% decline, >130% decline), energy crops (>150 million ha, >400 million ha), forest (>5% increase, >15% increase). Source: AR6 Scenarios Database.

In the context of mitigation pathways, only a few studies have examined solar radiation modification (SRM), typically focusing on Stratospheric Aerosol Injection (Arinoa et al. 2016; Emmerling and Tavoni 2018a,b; Heutel et al. 2018; Helwegen et al. 2019; Rickels et al. 2020; Belaia et al. 2021). These studies find that substantial mitigation is required to limit warming to a given level, even if SRM is available (Moreno-Cruz and Smulders 2017; Emmerling and Tavoni 2018b; Belaia et al. 2021). SRM may reduce some climate impacts, reduce peak temperatures, lower mitigation costs, and extend the time available to achieve mitigation; however, SRM does not address ocean acidification and may involve risks to crop yields, economies, human health, or ecosystems (AR6 WGII Chapter 16; AR6 WGI TS and Chapter 5; SR1.5 SPM; and Cross-Working Group Box 4 in Chapter 14 of this report). There are also significant uncertainties surrounding SRM, including uncertainties on the costs and risks, which can substantially alter the amount of SRM used in modelled pathways (Tavoni et al. 2017; Heutel et al. 2018; IPCC 2018; Helwegen et al. 2019; NASEM 2021). Furthermore, the degree of international cooperation can influence the amount of SRM deployed in scenarios, with uncoordinated action resulting in larger SRM deployment and consequently larger risks/impacts from SRM (Emmerling and Tavoni 2018a). Bridging research and governance involves consideration of the full range of societal choices and ramifications (Sugiyama et al. 2018). More information on SRM, including the caveats, risks, uncertainties, and governance issues is found in AR6 WGI Chapter 4; AR6 WGIII Chapter 14; and Cross-Working Group Box 4 in Chapter 14 of this report.

3.4.1.3   Linkages Among Sectors

Mitigation in one sector can be dependent upon mitigation in another sector, or may involve trade-offs between sectors. Mitigation in energy demand often includes electrification (Pietzcker et al. 2014; Luderer et al. 2018; Sharmina et al. 2020; DeAngelo et al. 2021), however such pathways only result in reduced emissions *if* the electricity sector is decarbonised (Zhang and Fujimori 2020) (Chapter 12). Relatedly, the mitigation potential of some sectors (e.g., transportation) depends on the decarbonisation of liquid fuels, for example, through biofuels (Pietzcker et al. 2014; Wise et al. 2017; Sharmina et al. 2020) (Chapter 12). In other cases, mitigation in one sector results in reduced emissions in another sector. For example, increased recycling can reduce primary resource extraction; planting trees or green roofs in urban areas can reduce the energy demand associated with space cooling (Chapter 12).

Mitigation in one sector can also result in additional emissions in another. One example is electrification of end use which can result in increased emissions from energy supply. However, one comparitively well-researched example of this linkage is bioenergy. An increase in demand for bioenergy within the energy system has the potential to influence emissions in the AFOLU sector through the intensification of land and forest management and/or via land-use change (Daioglou et al. 2019; Smith et al. 2019; Smith et al. 2020a; IPCC 2019a). The effect of bioenergy and BECCS on mitigation depends on a variety of factors in modelled pathways. In the energy system, the emissions mitigation depends on the scale of deployment, the conversion technology, and the fuel displaced (Calvin et al. 2021).

Limiting or excluding bioenergy and/or BECCS increases mitigation cost and may limit the ability of a model to reach a low warming level (Edmonds et al. 2013; Calvin et al. 2014b; Luderer et al. 2018; Muratori et al. 2020). In AFOLU, bioenergy can increase or decrease terrestrial carbon stocks and carbon sequestration, depending on the scale, biomass feedstock, land management practices, and prior land use (Calvin et al. 2014c; Wise et al. 2015; IPCC 2019a; Smith et al. 2019, 2020a; Calvin et al. 2021).

Pathways with very high biomass production for energy use typically include very high carbon prices in the energy system (Popp et al. 2017; Rogelj et al. 2018b), little or no land policy (Calvin et al. 2014b), a high discount rate (Emmerling et al. 2019), and limited non-BECCS CDR options (e.g., afforestation, DACCS) (Chen and Tavoni 2013; Calvin et al. 2014b; Marcucci et al. 2017; Realmonte et al. 2019; Fuhrman et al. 2020). Higher levels of bioenergy consumption are likely to involve trade-offs with mitigation in other sectors, notably in construction (i.e., wood for material and structural products) and AFOLU (carbon stocks and future carbon sequestration), as well as trade-offs with sustainability (Section 3.7) and feasibility concerns (Section 3.8). Not all of these trade-offs are fully represented in all IAMs. Based on sectoral studies, the technical potential for bioenergy, when constraints for food security and environmental considerations are included, are 5–50 EJ yr^{-1} and 50–250 EJ yr^{-1} in 2050 for residues and dedicated biomass production systems, respectively (Chapter 7). Bioenergy deployment in IAMs is within the range of these potentials,

with between 75 and 248 EJ yr^{-1} in 2050 in pathways that limit warming to 1.5°C with no or limited overshoot. Finally, IAMs do not include all potential feedstock and management practices, and have limited representation of institutions, governance, and local context (Brown et al. 2019; Butnar et al. 2020; Calvin et al. 2021).

The inclusion of CDR options, like BECCS, can affect the timing of emissions mitigation in IAM scenarios, that is, delays in mitigations actions are compensated by net negative emissions in the second half of the century. However, studies with limited net negative emissions in the long term require very rapid declines in emissions in the near term (van Vuuren et al. 2017). Especially in forest-based systems, increased harvesting of forests can perturb the carbon balance of forestry systems, increasing emissions for some period; the duration of this period of increased emissions, preceding net emissions reductions, can be very variable (Mitchell et al. 2012; Lamers and Junginger 2013; Röder et al. 2019; Hanssen et al. 2020; Cowie et al. 2021). However, the factors contributing to differences in recovery time are known (Mitchell et al. 2012; Zanchi et al. 2012; Lamers and Junginger 2013; Laganière et al. 2017; Röder et al. 2019). Some studies that consider market-mediated effects find that an increased demand for biomass from forests can provide incentives to maintain existing forests and potentially to expand forest areas, providing additional carbon sequestration as well as additional biomass (Dwivedi et al. 2014; Kim et al. 2018; Baker et al. 2019; Favero et al. 2020). However, these responses are uncertain and likely to vary geographically.

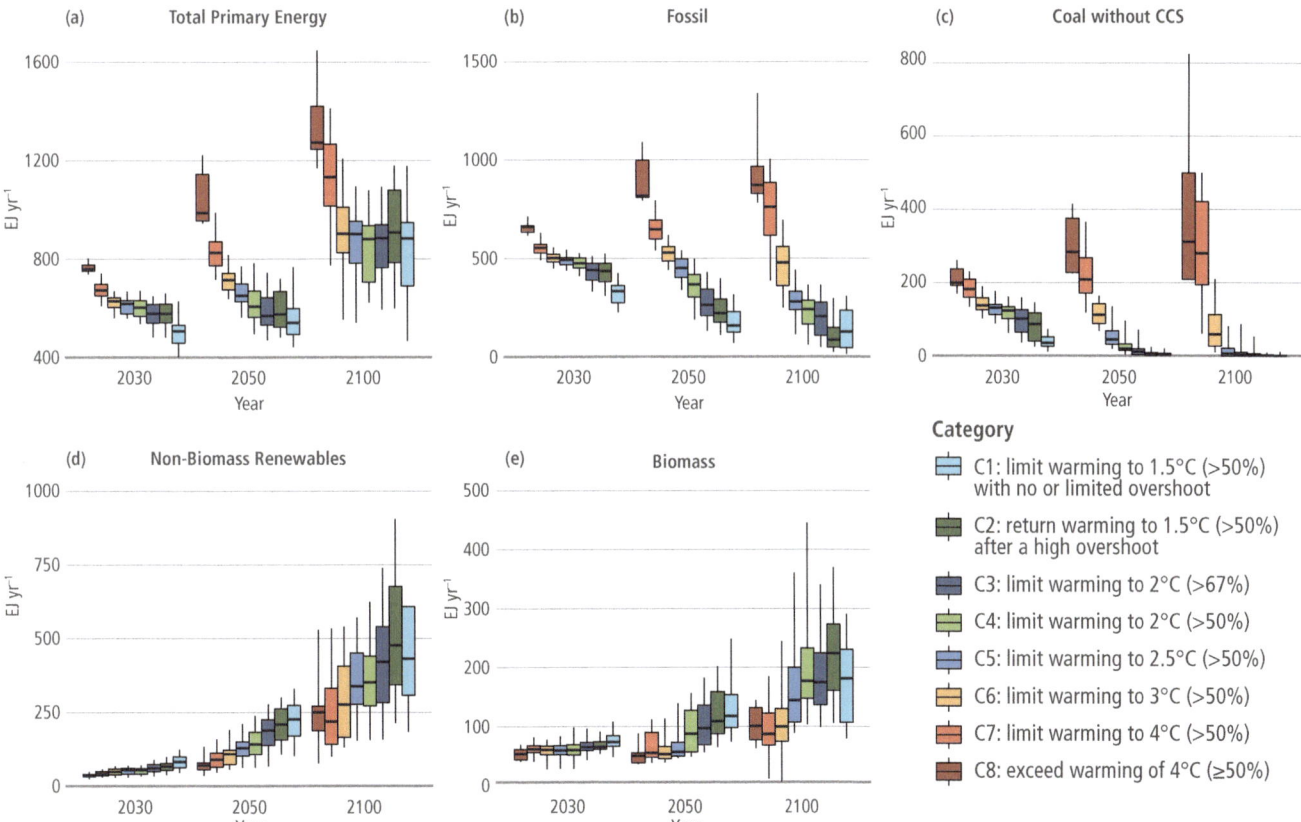

Figure 3.22 | Primary energy consumption across scenarios: total primary energy (a), fossil fuels (b), coal without CCS (c), non-biomass renewables (d), and biomass (e). Scenarios are grouped by their temperature category. Primary energy is reported in direct equivalent, where one unit of nuclear or non-biomass renewable energy output is reported as one unit of primary energy. Not all subcategories of primary energy are shown.

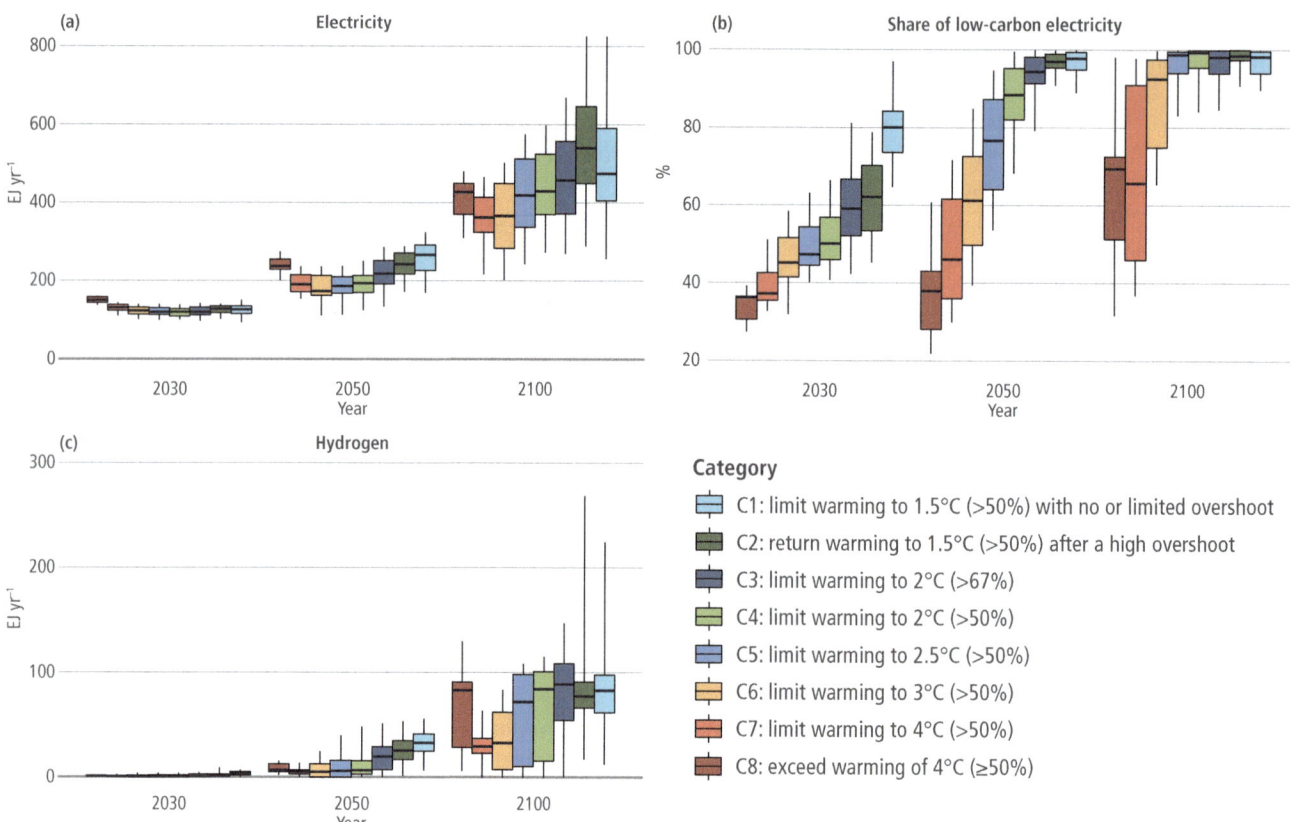

Figure 3.23 | Electricity (top left), share of low-carbon electricity (top right), and hydrogen (bottom left) production across all scenarios, grouped by the categories introduced in Section 3.2. Low carbon includes non-biomass renewables, biomass, nuclear, and CCS.

3.4.2   Energy Supply

Without mitigation, energy consumption and supply emissions continue to rise (*high confidence*) (Kriegler et al. 2016; Bauer et al. 2017; Riahi et al. 2017; Mcjeon et al. 2021) (Section 6.7). While the share of renewable energy continues to grow in reference scenarios, fossil fuel accounts for the largest share of primary energy (Bauer et al. 2017; Price and Keppo 2017; Riahi et al. 2017). In scenarios that limit warming to 2°C or lower, transition of the energy-supply sector to a low- or no-carbon system is rapid (Rogelj et al. 2016, 2018b; Grubler et al. 2018; Luderer et al. 2018; van Vuuren et al. 2018). CO_2 emissions from energy supply reach net zero around 2041 (2033–2057) in pathways limiting warming to 1.5°C (>50%) with no or limited overshoot and around 2053 (2040–2066) in pathways that limit warming to 2°C (>67%). Emissions reductions continue, with emissions reaching −7.1 $GtCO_2$ yr^{-1} (−15 to −2.3 $GtCO_2$ yr^{-1}) in 2100 in all pathways that limit warming to 2°C (>67%) or lower.

All pathways that limit warming to 2°C (>67%) or lower show substantial reductions in fossil fuel consumption and a near elimination of the use of coal without CCS (*high confidence*) (Bauer et al. 2017; van Vuuren et al. 2018; Grubler et al. 2018; Luderer et al. 2018; Rogelj et al. 2018a,b; Azevedo et al. 2021; Mcjeon et al. 2021; Welsby et al. 2021) (Figure 3.22). In these pathways, the use of coal, gas and oil is reduced by 90%, 25%, and 41%, respectively, between 2019 and 2050 and 91%, 39%, and 78% between 2019 and 2100; coal without CCS is

further reduced to 99% below its 2019 levels in 2100. These pathways show an increase in low-carbon energy, with 88% (69–97%) of primary energy from low-carbon sources in 2100, with different combinations of low-carbon fuels (e.g., non-biomass renewables, biomass, nuclear, and CCS) (Rogelj et al. 2018a,b; van Vuuren et al. 2018) (Sections 3.4.1 and 6.7). Across all pathways that limit warming to 2°C and below, non-biomass renewables account for 52% (24–77%) of primary energy in 2100 (Creutzig et al. 2017; Pietzcker et al. 2017; Rogelj et al. 2018b) (Chapter 6 and Figure 3.22). There are some studies analysing the potential for 100% renewable energy systems (Hansen et al. 2019); however, there are a range of issues around such systems (Box 6.6).

Stringent emissions reductions at the level required to limit warming to 2°C (>67%) or 1.5°C are achieved through increased electrification of end use, resulting in increased electricity generation in all pathways (*high confidence*) (Rogelj et al. 2018a; Azevedo et al. 2021) (Figure 3.23). Nearly all electricity in pathways *likely* to limit warming to 2°C and below is from low- or no-carbon fuels (Rogelj et al. 2018a; Azevedo et al. 2021), with different shares of nuclear, biomass, non-biomass renewables, and fossil CCS across pathways. Low-emissions scenarios also show increases in hydrogen use (Figure 3.23).

3.4.3   Buildings

Global final energy use in the building sector increases in all pathways as a result of population growth and increasing affluence

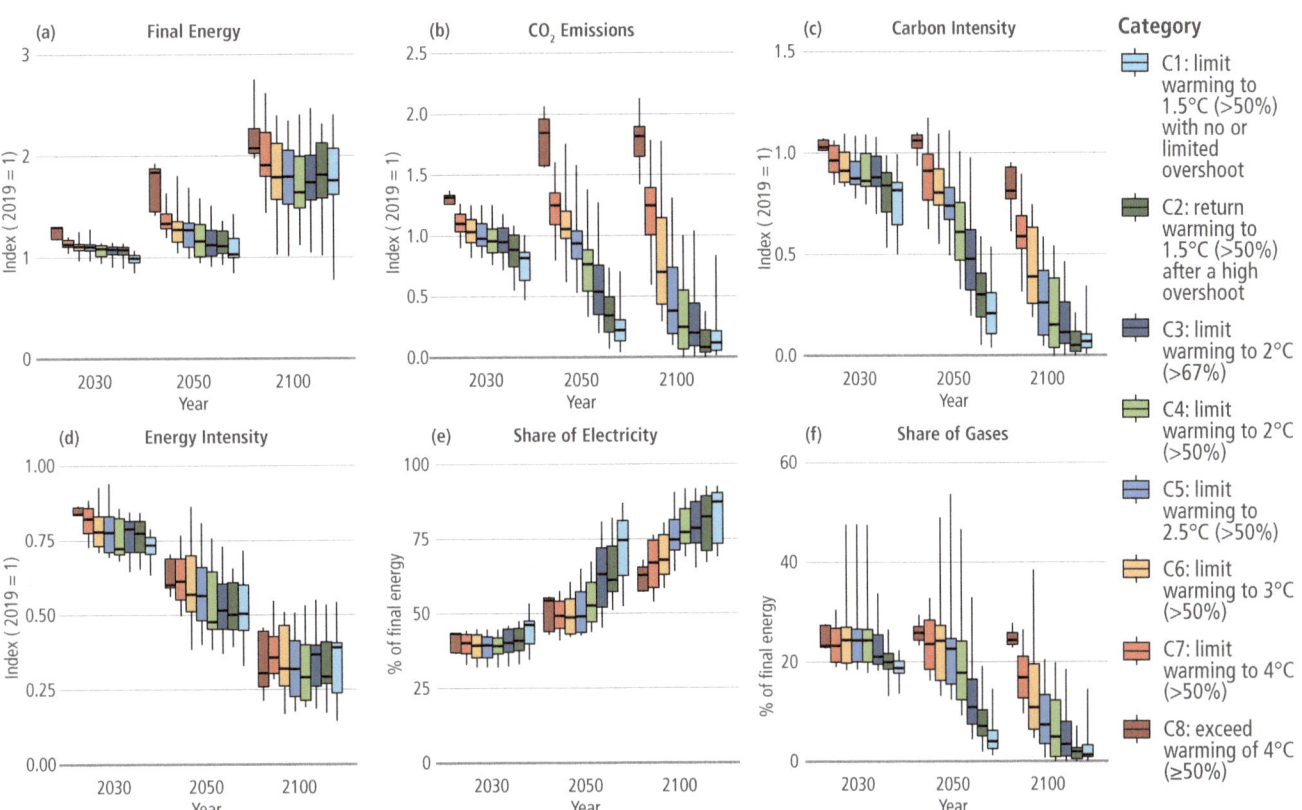

Figure 3.24 | Buildings final energy (a), CO₂ emissions (b), carbon intensity (c), energy intensity (d), share of final energy from electricity (e), and share of final energy from gases (f). Energy intensity is final energy per unit of GDP. Carbon intensity is CO_2 emissions per EJ of final energy. The first four indicators are indexed to 2019,[12] where values less than 1 indicate a reduction.

(Figure 3.24). There is very little difference in final energy intensity for the buildings sector across scenarios. Direct CO_2 emissions from the buildings sector vary more widely across temperature stabilisation levels than energy consumption. In 2100, scenarios above 3°C [C7–C8] still show an increase of CO_2 emissions from buildings around 29% above 2019, while all scenarios *likely* to limit warming to 2°C and below have emission reductions of around 85% (8–100%). Carbon intensity declines in all scenarios, but much more sharply as the warming level is reduced.

In all scenarios, the share of electricity in final energy use increases, a trend that is accelerated by 2050 for the scenarios *likely* to limit warming to 2°C and below (Figure 3.23). By 2100, the low-warming scenarios show large shares of electricity in final energy consumption for buildings. The opposite is observed for gases.

While several global IAM models have developed their buildings modules considerably over the past decade (Daioglou et al. 2012; Knobloch et al. 2017; Clarke et al. 2018; Edelenbosch et al. 2021; Mastrucci et al. 2021), the extremely limited availability of key sectoral variables in the AR6 scenarios database (such as floor space and energy use for individual services) prohibit a detailed analysis of sectoral dynamics. Individual studies in the literature often focus on single aspects of the buildings sector, though collectively providing a more comprehensive overview (Edelenbosch et al.

2020; Ürge-Vorsatz et al. 2020). For example, energy demand is driven by economic development that fulfills basic needs (Mastrucci et al. 2019; Rao et al. 2019a), but also drives up floor space in general (Daioglou et al. 2012; Levesque et al. 2018; Mastrucci et al. 2021) and ownership of energy-intensive appliances such as air conditioners (Isaac and van Vuuren 2009; Colelli and Cian 2020; Poblete-Cazenave et al. 2021). These dynamics are heterogeneous and lead to differences in energy demand and emission mitigation potential across urban/rural buildings and income levels (Krey et al. 2012; Poblete-Cazenave et al. 2021). Mitigation scenarios rely on fuel switching and technology (Knobloch et al. 2017; Dagnachew et al. 2020), efficiency improvement in building envelopes (Levesque et al. 2018; Edelenbosch et al. 2021) and behavioural changes (van Sluisveld et al. 2016; Niamir et al. 2018, 2020). The in-depth dynamics of mitigation in the building sector are explored in Chapter 9.

3.4.4 Transport

Reference scenarios show growth in transport demand, particularly in aviation and freight (Yeh et al. 2017; Sharmina et al. 2020; Müller-Casseres et al. 2021b). Energy consumption continues to be dominated by fossil fuels in reference scenarios, with some increases in electrification (Yeh et al. 2017; Edelenbosch et al. 2020; Yeh et al.

---

[13]   2019 values are from model results and interpolated from other years when not directly reported.

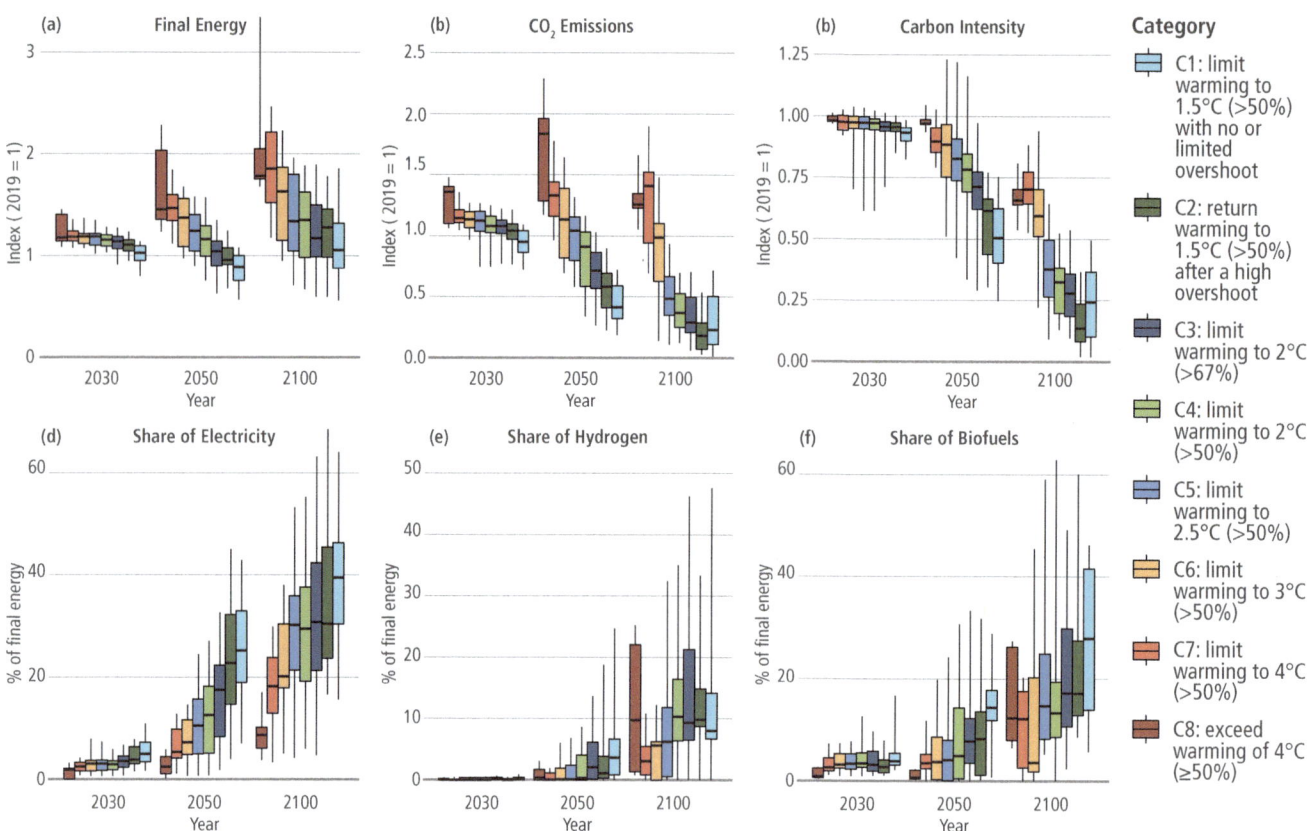

Figure 3.25 | Transport final energy (a), CO₂ emissions (b), carbon intensity (cand share of final energy from electricity (d), hydrogen (e), and biofuels (f). See Chapter 10 for a discussion of energy intensity. Carbon intensity is CO₂ emissions per EJ of final energy. The first three indicators are indexed to 2019,[13] where values less than 1 indicate a reduction.

2017). CO_2 emissions from transport increase for most models in reference scenarios (Yeh et al. 2017; Edelenbosch et al. 2020).

The relative contribution of demand-side reduction, energy- efficiency improvements, fuel switching, and decarbonisation of fuels, varyies by model, level of mitigation, mitigation options available, and underlying socio-economic pathway (Longden 2014; Wise et al. 2017; Yeh et al. 2017; Luderer et al. 2018; Yeh et al. 2017; Edelenbosch et al. 2020; Müller-Casseres et al. 2021a,b). IAMs typically rely on technology-focused measures like energy- efficiency improvements and fuel switching to reduce carbon emissions (Pietzcker et al. 2014; Edelenbosch et al. 2017a; Yeh et al. 2017; Zhang et al. 2018a,b; Rogelj et al. 2018b; Zhang et al. 2018a,b; Sharmina et al. 2020). Many mitigation pathways show electrification of the transport system (Luderer et al. 2018; Pietzcker et al. 2014; Longden 2014; Luderer et al. 2018; Zhang et al. 2018a); however, without decarboniszation of the electricity system, transport electrification can increase total energy system emissions (Zhang and Fujimori 2020). A small number of pathways include demand-side mitigation measures in the transport sector; these studies show reduced carbon prices and reduced dependence on CDR (Grubler et al. 2018; Méjean et al. 2019; van de Ven et al. 2018; Zhang et al. 2018c; Méjean et al. 2019) (Section 3.4.1).

Across all IAM scenarios assessed, final energy demand for transport continues to grow, including in many stringent mitigation pathways (Figure 3.25). The carbon intensity of energy declines substantially by 2100 in *likely* 2°C (>67%) and below scenarios, leading to substantial declines in transport sector CO_2 emissions with increased electrification of the transport system (Figure 3.23).

The transport sector has more detail than other sectors in many IAMs (Edelenbosch et al. 2020); however, there is considerable variation across models. Some models (e.g., GCAM, IMAGE, MESSAGE-GLOBIOM) represent different transport modes with endogenous shifts across modes as a function of income, price, and modal speed (Edelenbosch et al. 2020).[15] However, IAMs, including those with detailed transport, exclude several supply-side (e.g., synthetic fuels) and demand-side (e.g., behaviour change, reduced shipping, telework and automation) mitigation options (Pietzcker et al. 2014; Creutzig et al. 2016; Mittal et al. 2017; Davis et al. 2018; Köhler et al. 2020; Mittal et al. 2017; Gota et al. 2019; Wilson et al. 2019; Creutzig et al. 2016; Köhler et al. 2020; Sharmina et al. 2020; Pietzcker et al. 2014; Lefèvre et al. 2021; Müller-Casseres et al. 2021a,b).

---

[14] 2019 values are from model results and interpolated from other years when not directly reported.

[15] Some of these models are treated as global transport energy sectoral models (GTEMs) in Chapter 10.

As a result of these missing options and differences in how mitigation is implemented, IAMs tend to show less mitigation than the potential from national transport/energy models (Wachsmuth and Duscha 2019; Gota et al. 2019; Yeh et al. 2017; Gota et al. 2019; Wachsmuth and Duscha 2019; Edelenbosch et al. 2020). For the transport sector as a whole, studies suggest a mitigation potential of 4–-5 GtCO$_2$ per year in 2030 (Edelenbosch et al. 2020) with complete decarbonization decarbonisation possible by 2050 (Gota et al. 2019; Wachsmuth and Duscha 2019). However, in the scenarios assessed in this chapter that limit warming to below 1.5°C (>50%) with no or limited overshoot, transport sector CO$_2$ emissions are reduced by only 59% (28–% to 81%) in 2050 compared to 2015. IAM pathways also show less electrification than the potential from other studies; pathways that limit warming to 1.5°C with no or limited overshoot show a median of 25% (7– to 43%) of final energy from electricity in 2050, while the IEA NZE scenario includes 45% (IEA 2021a).

3.4.5 Industry

Reference scenarios show declines in energy intensity, but increases in final energy use in the industrial sector (Edelenbosch et al. 2017b). These scenarios show increases in CO$_2$ emissions both for the total industrial sector (Edelenbosch et al. 2017b, 2020; Luderer et al. 2018) and individual subsectors such as cement and iron and steel (van Ruijven et al. 2016; van Sluisveld et al. 2021) or chemicals (Daioglou et al. 2014; van Sluisveld et al. 2021).

In mitigation pathways, CO$_2$ emissions reductions are achieved through a combination of energy savings (via energy-efficiency improvements and energy conservation), structural change, fuel switching, and decarbonisation of fuels (Edelenbosch et al. 2017b, 2020; Grubler et al. 2018; Luderer et al. 2018). Mitigation pathways show reductions in final energy for industry compared to the baseline (Edelenbosch et al. 2017b; Luderer et al. 2018; Edelenbosch et al. 2020) and reductions in the carbon intensity of the industrial sector through both fuel switching and the use of CCS (van Ruijven et al. 2016; Edelenbosch et al. 2017b, 2020; Luderer et al. 2018; Paltsev et al. 2021; van Sluisveld et al. 2021). The mitigation potential differs depending on the industrial subsector and the availability of CCS, with larger potential reductions in the steel sector (van Ruijven et al. 2016) and cement industry (Sanjuán et al. 2020) than in the

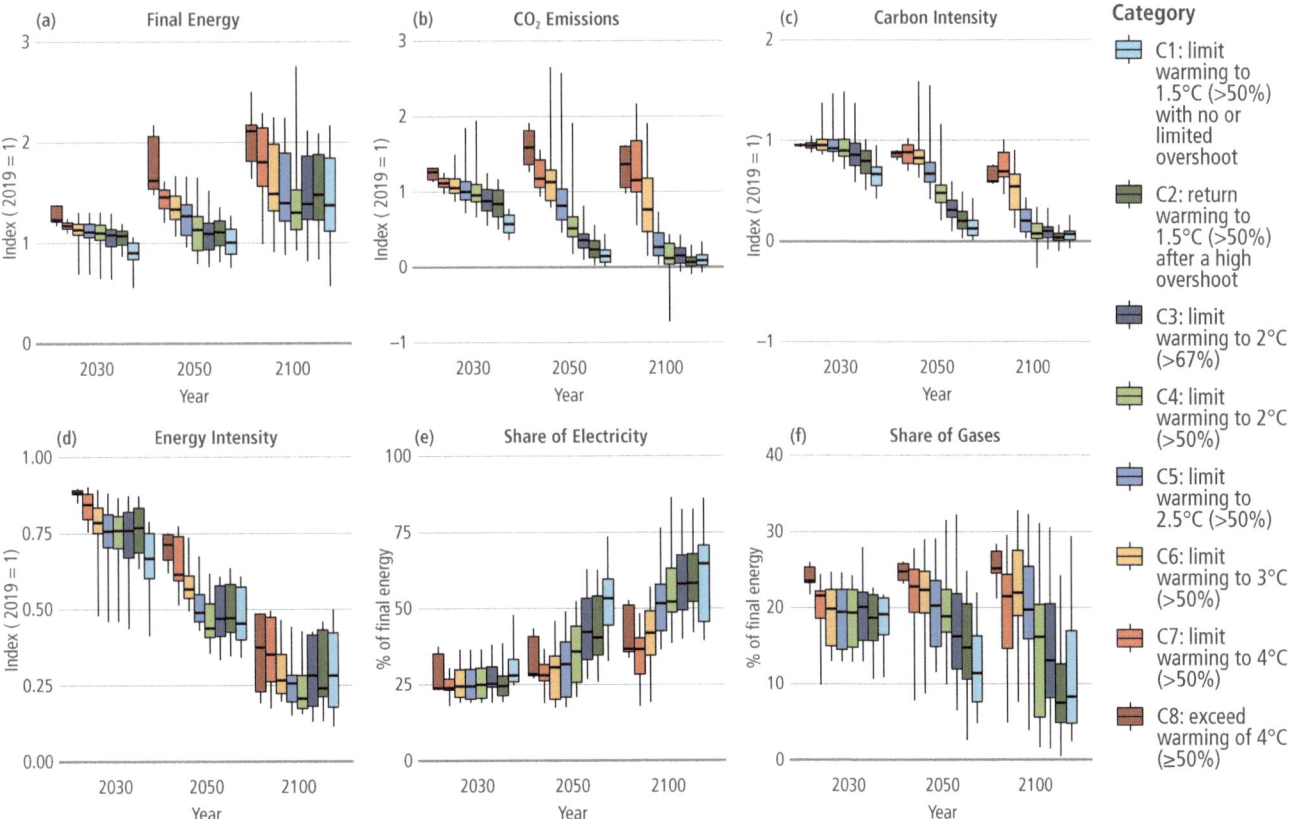

Figure 3.26 | Industrial final energy, including feedstocks (a), CO$_2$ emissions (b), carbon intensity (c), energy intensity (d), share of final energy from electricity (e), and share of final energy from gases (f). Energy intensity is final energy per unit of GDP. Carbon intensity is CO$_2$ emissions per EJ of final energy. The first four indicators are indexed to 2019,[15] where values less than 1 indicate a reduction. Industrial sector CO$_2$ emissions include fuel combustion emissions only.

---

[16] 2019 values are from model results and interpolated from other years when not directly reported.

chemicals sector (Daioglou et al. 2014). Many scenarios, including stringent mitigation scenarios, show continued growth in final energy; however, the carbon intensity of energy declines in all mitigation scenarios (Figure 3.26).

The representation of the industry sector is very aggregated in most IAMs, with only a small subset of models disaggregating key sectors such as cement, fertiliser, chemicals, and iron and steel (Daioglou et al. 2014; Edelenbosch et al. 2017b; Pauliuk et al. 2017; Napp et al. 2019; van Sluisveld et al. 2021). IAMs often account for both energy combustion and feedstocks (Edelenbosch et al. 2017b), but IAMs typically ignore material flows and miss linkages between sectors (Pauliuk et al. 2017; Kermeli et al. 2019). By excluding these processes, IAMs misrepresent the mitigation potential of the industry sector, for example by overlooking mitigation from material efficiency and circular economies (Sharmina et al. 2020), which can have substantial mitigation potential (Sections 5.3.4 and 11.3).

Sectoral studies indicate a large mitigation potential in the industrial sector by 2050, including the potential for net zero CO_2 emissions for steel, plastics, ammonia, and cement (Section 11.4.1). Detailed industry sector pathways show emissions reductions between 39% and 94% by mid-century compared to the present day[17] (Section 11.4.2) and a substantial increase in direct electrification (IEA 2021a). IAMs show comparable mitigation potential to sectoral

studies with median reductions in CO_2 emissions between 2019 and 2050 of 70% in scenarios *likely* to limit warming to 2°C (>67%) and below and a maximum reduction of 96% (Figure 3.26). Some differences between IAMs and sectoral models can be attributed to differences in technology availability, with IAMs sometimes including more technologies (van Ruijven et al. 2016) and sometimes less (Sharmina et al. 2020).

3.4.6 Agriculture, Forestry and Other Land Use (AFOLU)

Mitigation pathways show substantial reductions in CO_2 emissions, but more modest reductions in AFOLU CH_4 and N_2O emissions (*high confidence*) (Popp et al. 2017; Roe et al. 2019; Reisinger et al. 2021) (Figure 3.27). Pathways limiting warming to *likely* 2°C or lower are projected to reach net zero CO_2 emissions in the AFOLU sector around 2033 (2024–2060); however, AFOLU CH_4 and N_2O emissions remain positive in all pathways (Figure 3.27). While IAMs include many land-based mitigation options, these models exclude several options with large mitigation potential, such as biochar, agroforestry, restoration/avoided conversion of coastal wetlands, and restoration/avoided conversion of peatland (IPCC 2019a; Smith et al. 2019) (Chapter 7 and Section 3.4). Sectoral studies show higher mitigation potential than IAM pathways, as

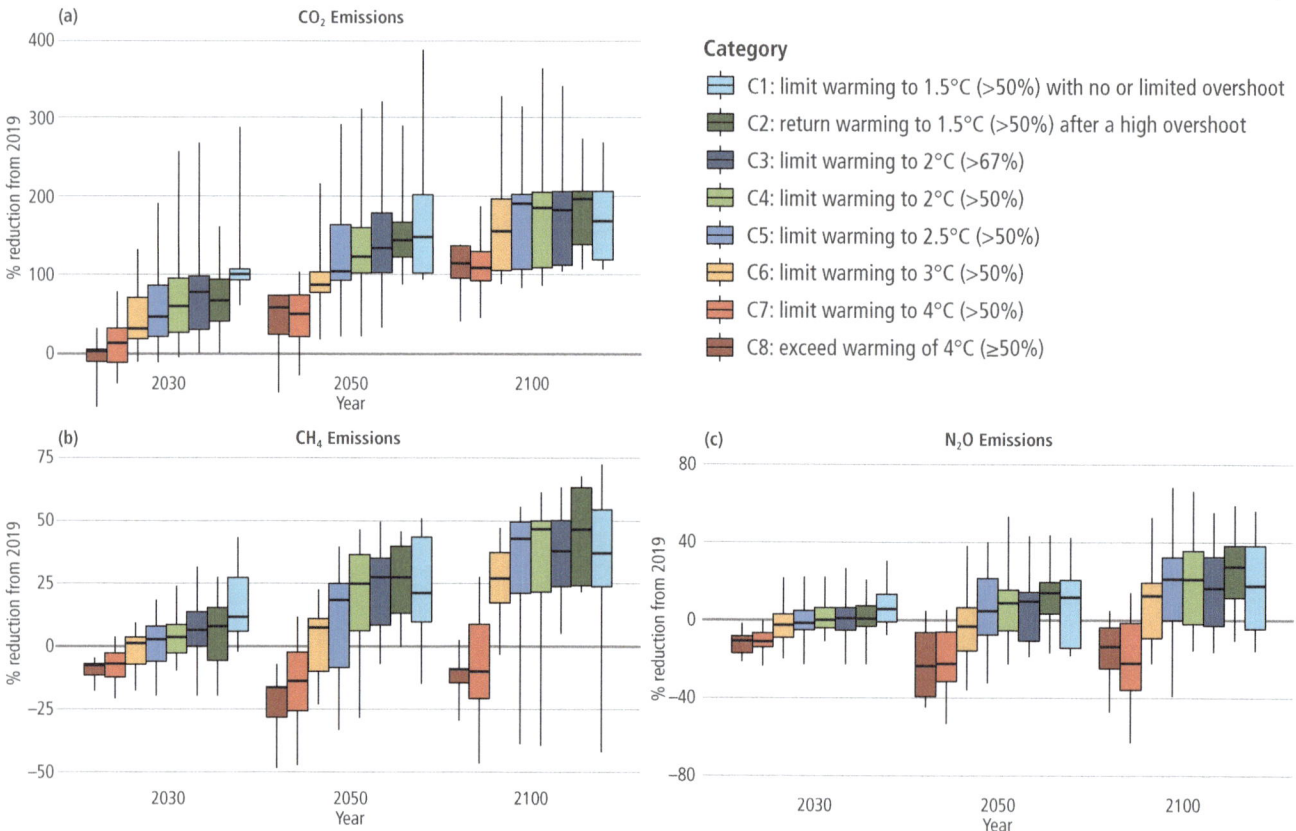

Figure 3.27 | Reduction in AFOLU GHG emissions from 2019. The AFOLU CO_2 estimates in this figure are not necessarily comparable with country GHG inventories (see Chapter 7).

---

17   Some studies calculate emissions reductions in 2050 compared to 2014, while others note emissions reductions in 2060 relative to 2018.

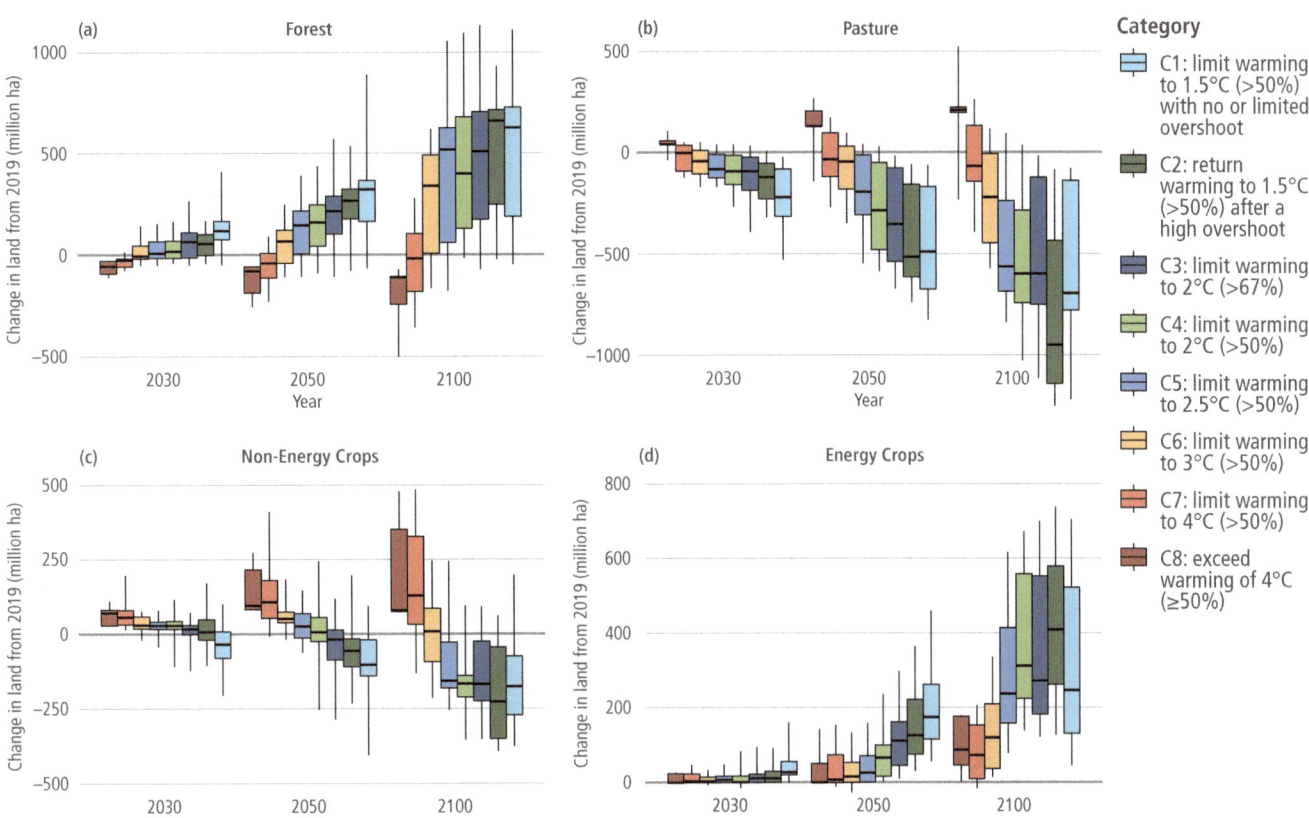

Figure 3.28 | Change in land cover from 2019 in million hectares. Positive values indicate an increase in area.

these studies include more mitigation options than IAMs (*medium confidence*) (Chapter 7).

Limiting warming to *likely* 2°C (>67%) or lower can result in large-scale transformation of the land surface (*high confidence*) (Popp et al. 2017; Rogelj et al. 2018a,b; Brown et al. 2019; Roe et al. 2019). The scale of land transformation depends, *inter alia*, on the temperature goal and the mitigation options included (Popp et al. 2017; Rogelj et al. 2018a; IPCC 2019a). Pathways with more demand-side mitigation options show less land transformation than those with more limited options (Grubler et al. 2018; van Vuuren et al. 2018; IPCC 2019a). Most of these pathways show increases in forest cover, with an increase of 322 million ha (−67 to 890 million ha) in 2050 in pathways that limit warming to 1.5°C (>50%) with no or limited overshoot, whereas bottom-up models portray an economic potential of 300–500 million ha of additional forest (Chapter 7). Many IAM pathways also include large amounts of energy cropland area, to supply biomass for bioenergy and BECCS, with 199 (56–482) million ha in 2050 in pathways that limit warming to 1.5°C (>50%) with no or limited overshoot. Large land transformations, such as afforestation/reforestation and widespread planting of energy crops, can have implications for biodiversity and sustainable development (Sections 3.7, 7.7.4 and 12.5).

Delayed mitigation has implications for land-use transitions (Hasegawa et al. 2021a). Delaying mitigation action can result in a temporary overshoot of temperature and large-scale deployment of CDR in the second half of the century to reduce temperatures from

their peak to a given level (Smith et al. 2019; Hasegawa et al. 2021a). IAM pathways rely on afforestation and BECCS as CDR measures, so delayed mitigation action results in substantial land-use change in the second half of the century with implications for sustainable development (Hasegawa et al. 2021a) (Section 3.7). Shifting to earlier mitigation action reduces the amount of land required for this, though at the cost of larger land-use transitions earlier in the century (Hasegawa et al. 2021a). Earlier action could also reduce climate impacts on agriculture and land-based mitigation options (Smith et al. 2019).

Some AFOLU mitigation options can enhance vegetation and soil carbon stocks such as reforestation, restoration of degraded ecosystems, protection of ecosystems with high carbon stocks and changes to agricultural land management to increase soil carbon (*high confidence*) (Griscom et al. 2017; de Coninck et al. 2018; Fuss et al. 2018; Smith et al. 2019) (AR6 WGIII Chapter 7). The time scales associated with these options indicate that carbon sinks in terrestrial vegetation and soil systems can be maintained or enhanced so as to contribute towards long-term mitigation (*high confidence*); however, many AFOLU mitigation options do not continue to sequester carbon indefinitely (Fuss et al. 2018; de Coninck et al. 2018; IPCC 2019a) (AR6 WGIII Chapter 7). In the very long term (the latter part of the century and beyond), it will become more challenging to continue to enhance vegetation and soil carbon stocks, so that the associated carbon sinks could diminish or even become sources (*high confidence*) (de Coninck et al. 2018; IPCC 2019a) (AR6 WGI Chapter 5). Sustainable forest management, including harvest and forest regeneration, can help to remediate and slow any decline in the forest carbon sink, for example by restoring degraded forest areas, and so go some way towards addressing the issue of sink saturation (IPCC 2019) (AR6 WGI Chapter 5; and Chapter 7 in this report). The accumulated carbon resulting from mitigation options that enhance carbon sequestration (e.g., reforestation, soil carbon sequestration) is also at risk of future loss due to disturbances (e.g., fire, pests) (Boysen et al. 2017; de Coninck et al. 2018; Fuss et al. 2018; Smith et al. 2019; IPCC 2019a; Anderegg et al. 2020) (AR6 WGI Chapter 5). Maintaining the resultant high vegetation and soil carbon stocks could limit future land-use options, as maintaining these carbon stocks would require retaining the land use and land-cover configuration implemented to achieve the increased stocks.

Anthropogenic land CO_2 emissions and removals in IAM pathways cannot be directly compared with those reported in national GHG inventories (*high confidence*) (Grassi et al. 2018, 2021) (Section 7.2). Due to differences in definitions for the area of managed forests and which emissions and removals are considered anthropogenic, the reported anthropogenic land CO_2 emissions and removals differ by about 5.5 GtCO$_2$ yr^{-1} between IAMs, which rely on bookkeeping approaches (e.g., Houghton and Nassikas 2017), and national GHG inventories (Grassi et al. 2021). Such differences in definitions can alter the reported time at which anthropogenic net zero CO_2 emissions are reached for a given emission scenario. Using national inventories would lead to an earlier reported time of net zero (van Soest et al. 2021b) or to lower calculated cumulative emissions until the time of net zero (Grassi et al. 2021) as compared to IAM pathways. The numerical differences are purely due to differences in the conventions applied for reporting the anthropogenic emissions and do not have any implications for the underlying land-use changes or mitigation measures in the pathways. Grassi et al. (Grassi et al. 2021) offer a methodology for adjusting to reconcile these differences and enable a more accurate assessment of the collective progress achieved under the Paris Agreement (Chapter 7 and Cross-Chapter Box 6 in Chapter 7).

(DACCS), enhanced weathering (EW), and ocean-based approaches, focusing on the role of these options in long-term mitigation pathways, using both IAMs (Chen and Tavoni 2013; Marcucci et al. 2017; Rickels et al. 2018; Fuhrman et al. 2019, 2020, 2021; Realmonte et al. 2019; Akimoto et al. 2021; Strefler et al. 2021a) and non-IAMs (Fuss et al. 2013; González and Ilyina 2016; Bednar et al. 2021; Shayegh et al. 2021). There are other options discussed in the literature, such as methane capture (Jackson et al. 2019), however, the role of these options in long-term mitigation pathways has not been quantified and is thus excluded here. Chapter 12 includes a more detailed description of the individual technologies, including their costs, potentials, financing, risks, impacts, maturity and upscaling.

Very few studies and pathways include other CDR options (Table 3.5). Pathways with DACCS include potentially large removal from DACCS (up to 37 GtCO$_2$ yr^{-1} in 2100) in the second half of the century (Chen and Tavoni 2013; Marcucci et al. 2017; Realmonte et al. 2019; Fuhrman et al. 2020, 2021; Shayegh et al. 2021; Akimoto et al. 2021) and reduced cost of mitigation (Bistline and Blanford 2021; Strefler et al. 2021a). At large scales, the use of DACCS has substantial implications for energy use, emissions, land, and water; substituting DACCS for BECCS results in increased energy usage, but reduced land-use change and water withdrawals (Fuhrman et al., 2020, 2021) (Chapter 12.3.2; AR6 WGI Chapter 5). The level of deployment of DACCS is sensitive to the rate at which it can be scaled up, the climate goal or carbon budget, the underlying socio-economic scenario, the availability of other decarbonisation options, the cost of DACCS and other mitigation options, and the strength of carbon-cycle feedbacks (Chen and Tavoni 2013; Fuss et al. 2013; Honegger and Reiner 2018; Realmonte et al. 2019; Fuhrman et al. 2020; Bistline and Blanford 2021; Fuhrman et al. 2021; Strefler et al. 2021a) (AR6 WGI Chapter 5). Since DACCS consumes energy, its effectiveness depends on the type of energy used; the use of fossil fuels would reduce its sequestration efficiency (Creutzig et al. 2019; NASEM 2019; Babacan et al. 2020). Studies with additional CDR options in addition to DACCS (e.g., enhanced weathering, BECCS, afforestation, biochar, and soil carbon sequestration) find that CO_2 removal is spread across

Table 3.5 | Carbon dioxide removal in assessed pathways. Scenarios are grouped by temperature categories, as defined in Section 3.2.4. Quantity indicates the median and 5–95th percentile range of cumulative sequestration from 2020 to 2100 in GtCO$_2$. Count indicates the number of scenarios with positive values for that option. Source: AR6 Scenarios Database.

CDR option	C1: Limit warming to 1.5°C (>50%) with no or limited overshoot		C2: Return warming to 1.5°C (>50%) after a high overshoot		C3: Limit warming to 2°C (>67%)	
	Quantity	Count	Quantity	Count	Quantity	Count
CO_2 removal on managed land including Afforestation/Reforestation[1]	262 (17–397)	64	330 (28–439)	82	209 (20–415)	196
BECCS	334 (32–780)	91	464 (226–842)	122	291 (174–653)	294
Enhanced weathering	0 (0–47)	2	0 (0–0)	1	0 (0–0)	1
DACCS	30 (0–308)	31	109 (0 – 539)	24	19 (0–253)	91

[1] Cumulative CDR from AFOLU cannot be quantified precisely because models use different reporting methodologies that in some cases combine gross emissions and removals, and use different baselines.

3.4.7   Other Carbon Dioxide Removal Options

This subsection includes other CDR options not discussed in the previous subsections, including direct air carbon capture and storage

available options (Holz et al. 2018; Strefler et al. 2021a). Similar to DACCS, the deployment of deep-ocean storage depends on cost and the strength of carbon-cycle feedbacks (Rickels et al. 2018).

3.5 Interaction Between Near-, Medium- and Long-term Action in Mitigation Pathways

This section assesses the relationship between long-term climate goals and short- to medium-term emissions reduction strategies based on the mitigation pathway literature. After an overview of this relationship (Section 3.5.1), it provides an assessment of what currently planned near-term action implies for limiting warming to 1.5°C–2°C (Section 3.5.2), and to what extent pathways with accelerated action beyond current NDCs can improve the ability to keep long-term targets in reach (Section 3.5.3).

The assessment in this section shows that if mitigation ambitions in NDCs announced prior to COP26[2,18] are followed until 2030, leading to estimated emissions of 47–57 $GtCO_2$-eq in 2030[19] (Section 4.2.2), it is no longer possible to limit warming to 1.5°C (>50%) with no or limited overshoot (*high confidence*). Instead, it would entail high overshoot (typically >0.1°C) and reliance on net negative CO_2 emissions with uncertain potential to return warming to 1.5°C (>50%) by the end of the century. It would also strongly increase mitigation challenges to limit warming to 2°C (>67%) (*high confidence*). GHG emissions reductions would need to abruptly increase after 2030 to an annual average rate of 1.4–2.0 $GtCO_2$-eq during the period 2030–2050, around 70% higher than in mitigation pathways assuming immediate action[1] to limit warming to 2°C (>67%). The higher post-2030 reduction rates would have to be obtained in an environment of continued buildup of fossil fuel infrastructure and less development of low-carbon alternatives until 2030. A lock-in to fossil fuel-intensive production systems (carbon lock-in) will increase the societal, economic and political strain of a rapid low-carbon transition after 2030 (*high confidence*).

The section builds on previous assessments in the IPCC's *Fifth Assessment Report* (Clarke et al. 2014) and the *IPCC Special Report on 1.5°C Warming* (Rogelj et al. 2018a). The literature assessed in these two reports has focused on delayed action until 2030 in the context of limiting warming to 2°C (den Elzen et al. 2010; van Vuuren and Riahi 2011; Luderer et al. 2013, 2016; Rogelj et al. 2013a; Kriegler et al. 2015; Riahi et al. 2015) and 1.5°C (Rogelj et al. 2013b; Luderer et al. 2018; Strefler et al. 2018). Here we provide an update of these assessments drawing on the most recent literature on global mitigation pathways. New studies have focused, *inter alia*, on constraining near-term developments by peak warming limits (Rogelj et al. 2019b; Riahi et al. 2021; Strefler et al. 2021b) and updating assumptions about near- and medium-term emissions developments based on national plans and long-term strategies (Roelfsema et al. 2020) (Section 4.2). Several studies have explored new types of pathways with accelerated action bridging between current policy plans and the goal of limiting warming below 2°C (Kriegler et al. 2018a; van Soest et al. 2021a) and looked at hybrid international policy regimes to phase in global collective action (Bauer et al. 2020).

3.5.1 Relationship Between Long-term Climate Goals and Near- to Medium-term Emissions Reductions

The close link between cumulative CO_2 emissions and warming has strong implications for the relationship between near-, medium-, and long-term climate action to limit global warming. The AR6 WGI Assessment has estimated a remaining carbon budget of 500 (400) $GtCO_2$ from the beginning of 2020 onwards for staying below 1.5°C with 50% (67%) likelihood, subject to additional uncertainties about historic warming and the climate response, and variations in warming from non-CO_2 climate forcers (Canadell and Monteiro 2019) (AR6 WGI Chapter 5, Section 5.5). For comparison, if current CO_2 emissions of more than 40 $GtCO_2$ are keeping up until 2030, more than 400 $GtCO_2$ will be emitted during 2021–2030, already exhausting the remaining carbon budget for 1.5°C by 2030.

The relationship between warming limits and near-term action is illustrated in Figure 3.29, using a set of 1.5°C–2°C scenarios with different levels of near-term action, overshoot and non-CO_2 warming contribution from a recent study (Riahi et al. 2021). In general, the more CO_2 is emitted until 2030, the less CO_2 can be emitted thereafter to stay within a remaining carbon budget and below a warming limit. Scenarios with immediate action to observe the warming limit give the longest time to exhaust the associated remaining carbon budget and reach net zero CO_2 emissions (see light blue lines in Figure 3.29 and Cross-Chapter Box 3 in this chapter). In comparison, following projected NDC emissions until 2030 would imply a more pronounced drop in emissions from 2030 levels to net zero to make up for the additional near-term emissions (see orange lines in Figure 3.29). If such a drop does not occur, the remaining carbon budget is exceeded and net negative CO_2 emissions are required to return global mean temperature below the warming limit (see black lines in Figure 3.29) (Clarke et al. 2014; Fuss et al. 2014; Rogelj et al. 2018a).

The relationship between warming limits and near-term action is also affected by the warming contribution of non-CO_2 greenhouse gases and other short-lived climate forcers (Section 3.3; AR6 WGI Section 6.7). The estimated budget values for limiting warming to 1.5°C–2°C already assume stringent reductions in non-CO_2 greenhouse gases and non-CO_2 climate forcing as found in 1.5°C–2°C pathways (Section 3.3 and Cross-Working Group Box 1 in this chapter; AR6 WGI Section 5.5 and Box 5.2 in Chapter 5). Further variations in non-CO_2 warming observed across 1.5°C–2°C pathways can vary the median estimate for the remaining carbon budget by 220 $GtCO_2$ (AR6 WGI Section 5.5). In 1.5°C–2°C pathways, the non-CO_2 warming contribution differs strongly between the near, medium and long term. Changes to the atmospheric composition of short-lived climate forcers (SLCFs) dominate the warming response in the near term (AR6 WGI Section 6.7). CO_2 reductions are combined with strong reductions in air pollutant emissions due to rapid reduction in fossil fuel combustion and in some cases the assumption of stringent air quality policies (Rao et al. 2017b; Smith et al. 2020c). As air pollutants exert a net-cooling effect,

---

[18]   Original NDCs refer to those submitted to the UNFCCC in 2015 and 2016. See Section 4.2.

[19]   In this section, the emissions range associated with NDCs announced prior to COP26 (or original NDCs) refer to the combined emissions ranges from the two cases of implementing only the unconditional elements of NDCs announced prior to COP26 (50–57 $GtCO_2$-eq) and implementing both unconditional and conditional elements of NDCs announced prior to COP26 (47–55 $GtCO_2$-eq), if not specified otherwise.

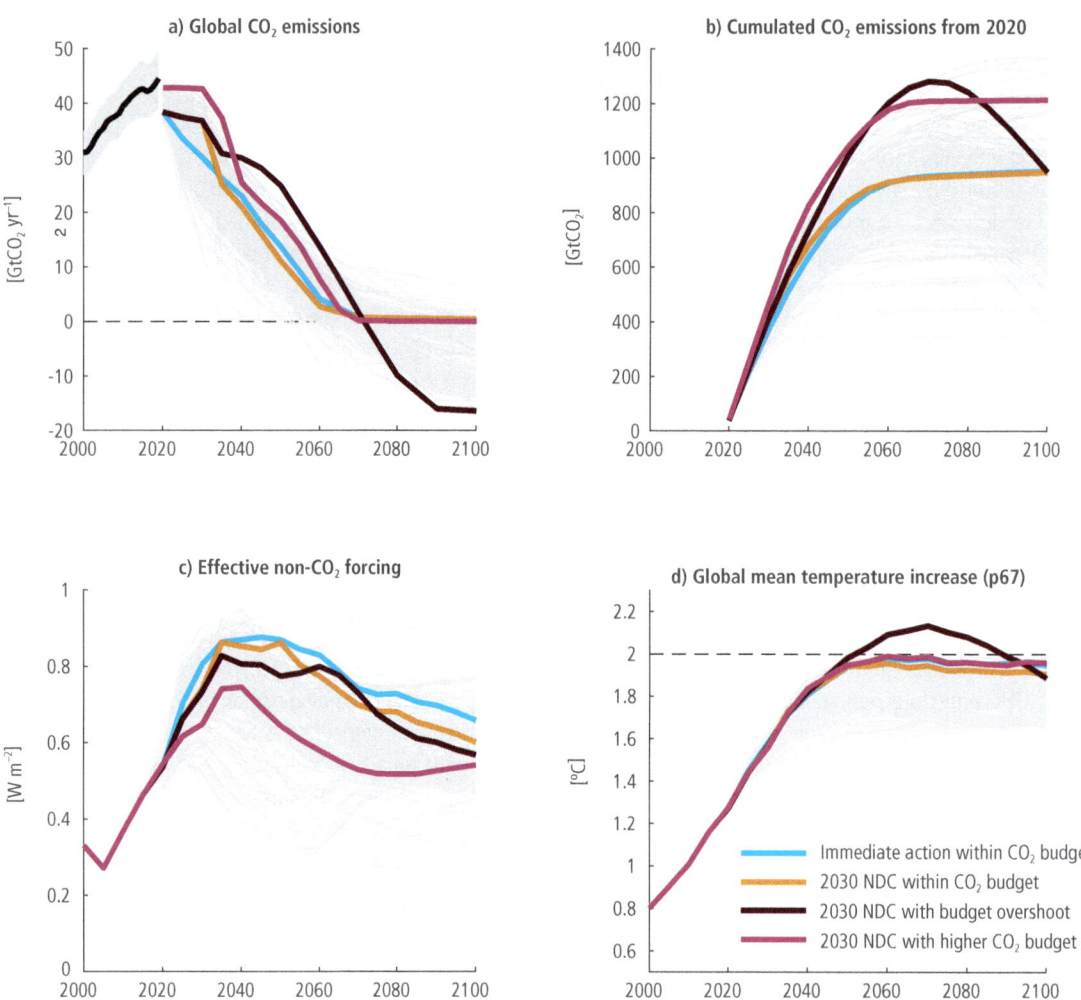

Figure 3.29 | Illustration of emissions and climate response in four mitigation pathways with different assumptions about near-term policy developments, global warming limit and non-CO₂ warming contribution drawn from Riahi et al. (2021). Shown are **(a)** CO₂ emissions trajectories, **(b)** cumulative CO₂ emissions, **(c)** effective non-CO₂ radiative forcing, and **(d)** the resulting estimate of the 67th percentile of global mean temperature response relative to 1850–1900. Light blue lines show a scenario that acts immediately on a remaining carbon budget of 900 GtCO₂ from 2020 without allowing net negative CO₂ emissions (i.e., temporary budget overshoot) (COFFEE 1.1, Scenario EN_NPi2020_900). Orange and black lines show scenarios drawn from the same model that follow the NDCs until 2030 and thereafter introduce action to stay within the same budget – in one case excluding net negative CO₂ emissions like before (orange lines; COFFEE 1.1., Scenario EN-INDCi2030_900) and in the other allowing for a temporary overshoot of the carbon budget until 2100 (black lines; COFFEE 1.1., Scenario EN-INDCi2030_900f). Light blue lines describe a scenario following the NDCs until 2030, and then aiming for a higher budget of 2300 GtCO₂ without overshoot (AIM/CGE 2.2, Scenario EN-INDCi2030_1200). It is drawn from another model which projects a lower anthropogenic non-CO₂ forcing contribution and therefore achieves about the same temperature outcome as the other two non-overshoot scenarios despite the higher CO₂ budget. Grey funnels include the trajectories from all scenarios that limit warming to 2°C (>67%) (category C3). Historical CO₂ emissions until 2019 are from Chapter SM.2.1 EDGAR v6.0.

their reduction drives up non-CO₂ warming in the near term, which can be attenuated by the simultaneous reduction of methane and black carbon (Shindell and Smith 2019; Smith et al. 2020b) (AR6 WGI Section 6.7). After 2030, the reduction in methane concentrations and associated reductions in tropospheric ozone levels tend to dominate so that a peak and decline in non-CO₂ forcing and non-CO₂-induced warming can occur before net zero CO₂ is reached (Figure 3.29) (Rogelj et al. 2018a). The more stringent the reductions in methane and other short-lived warming agents such as black carbon, the lower this peak and the earlier the decline of non-CO₂ warming, leading to a reduction of warming rates and overall warming in the near to medium term (Harmsen et al. 2020; Smith et al. 2020b). This is important for keeping warming below a tight warming limit that is already reached around mid-century as is the case in 1.5°C pathways (Xu and Ramanathan

2017). Early and deep reductions of methane emissions, and other short-lived warming agents such as black carbon, provide space for residual CO₂-induced warming until the point of net zero CO₂ emissions is reached (see purple lines in Figure 3.29). Such emissions reductions have also been advocated due to co-benefits for, for example, reducing air pollution (Rao et al. 2016; Shindell et al. 2017a, 2018; Shindell and Smith 2019; Rauner et al. 2020a; Vandyck et al. 2020).

The relationship between long-term climate goals and near-term action is further constrained by social, technological, economic and political factors (Cherp et al. 2018; van Sluisveld et al. 2018b; Aghion et al. 2019; Mercure et al. 2019; Trutnevyte et al. 2019b; Jewell and Cherp 2020). These factors influence path dependency and transition speed (Pahle et al. 2018; Vogt-Schilb et al. 2018). While detailed integrated assessment modelling of global mitigation pathways accounts for technology inertia (Bertram et al. 2015a; Mercure et al. 2018) and technology innovation and diffusion (Wilson et al. 2013; van Sluisveld et al. 2018a; Luderer et al. 2021), there are limitations in capturing socio-technical and political drivers of innovation, diffusion and transition processes (Gambhir et al. 2019; Köhler et al. 2019; Hirt et al. 2020; Keppo et al. 2021). Mitigation pathways show a wide range of transition speeds that have been interrogated in the context of socio-technical inertia (Gambhir et al. 2017; Kefford et al. 2018; Kriegler et al. 2018a; Brutschin et al. 2021) vs accelerating technological change and self-enforcing socio-economic developments (Creutzig et al. 2017; Zenghelis 2019) (Section 3.8). Diagnostic analysis of detailed IAMs found a lag of 8–20 years between the convergence of emissions pricing and the convergence of emissions response after a period of differentiated emission prices (Harmsen et al. 2021). This provides a measure of the inertia to changing policy signals in the model response. It is about half the time scale of 20–40 years observed for major energy transitions (Grubb et al. 2021). Hence, the mitigation pathways assessed here capture socio-technical inertia in reducing emissions, but the limited modelling of socio-political factors may alter the extent and persistence of this inertia.

3.5.2 Implications of Near-term Emission Levels for Keeping Long-term Climate Goals Within Reach

The implications of near-term climate action for long-term climate outcomes can be explored by comparing mitigation pathways with different near-term emissions developments aiming for the same climate target (Riahi et al. 2015; Vrontisi et al. 2018; Roelfsema et al. 2020). A particular example is the comparison of cost-effective pathways with immediate action to limit warming to 1.5°C–2°C with mitigation pathways pursuing more moderate mitigation action until 2030. After the adoption of the Paris Agreement, near-term action was often modelled to reflect conditional and unconditional elements of originally submitted NDCs (2015–2019) (Fawcett et al. 2015; Fujimori et al. 2016a; Kriegler et al. 2018a; Vrontisi et al. 2018; Roelfsema et al. 2020). The most recent modelling studies also include submission of updated NDCs or announcements of planned updates in the first half of 2021 (Network for Greening the Financial System 2021; Riahi et al. 2021). Emissions levels under NDCs announced prior to COP26 are assessed to range between 47–57 GtCO$_2$-eq in 2030 (Section 4.2.2). This assessed range corresponds well to 2030 emissions levels in 2°C mitigation pathways in the literature that are designed to follow the original or updated NDCs until 2030.[20] For the 139 scenarios of this kind that are collected in the AR6 scenario database and that still limit warming to 2°C (>67%), the 2030 emissions range is 53 (45–58) GtCO$_2$-eq (based on native model reporting) and 52.5 (47–56.5) GtCO$_2$-eq, respectively (based on harmonised emissions data for climate assessment (Annex III.2.5.1); median and 5–95th percentile). This close match allows a robust assessment of the implications of implementing NDCs announced prior to COP26 for

post-2030 mitigation efforts and warming outcomes based on the literature and the AR6 scenarios database.

Without a strengthening of policies beyond those that are implemented by the end of 2020, GHG emissions are projected to rise beyond 2025, leading to a median global warming of 3.2 [2.2 to 3.5] °C by 2100. Modelled pathways that are consistent with NDCs announced prior to COP26 until 2030 and assume no increase in ambition thereafter have lower emissions, leading to a median global warming of 2.8°C [2.1–3.4°C] by 2100.

The assessed emission ranges from implementing the unconditional (unconditional and conditional) elements of NDCs announced prior to COP26 implies an emissions gap to cost-effective mitigation pathways of 19–26 (16–23) GtCO$_2$-eq in 2030 for limiting warming to 1.5°C (>50%) with no or limited overshoot and 10–16 (6–14) GtCO$_2$-eq in 2030 for limiting warming to 2°C (>67%) (Cross-Chapter Box 4 in Chapter 4). The emissions gap gives rise to a number of mitigation challenges (Kriegler et al. 2013a, 2018a,b; Luderer et al. 2013, 2018; Rogelj et al. 2013a; Fawcett et al. 2015; Riahi et al. 2015; Fujimori et al. 2016b; Strefler et al. 2018; Winning et al. 2019; SEI et al. 2020; UNEP 2020): (i) larger transitional challenges post-2030 to still remain under the warming limit, in particular higher CO$_2$ emissions reduction rates and technology transition rates required during 2030–2050; (ii) larger lock-in into carbon-intensive infrastructure and increased risk of stranded fossil fuel assets (Section 3.5.2.2); and (iii) larger reliance on CDR to reach net zero CO$_2$ more rapidly and compensate excess emissions in the second half of the century (Section 3.5.2.1). All these factors exacerbate the socio-economic strain of implementing the transition, leading to an increased risk of overshooting the warming and a higher risk of climate change impacts (Drouet et al. 2021).

The challenges are illustrated in Table 3.6 and Figure 3.30, surveying global mitigation pathways in the literature that were collected in the AR6 scenarios database. There is a clear trend of increasing peak warming with increasing 2030 GHG emission levels (Figure 3.30a,b). In particular, there is no mitigation pathway designed to follow the NDCs until 2030 that can limit warming to 1.5°C (>50%) with no or limited overshoot. Our assessment confirms the finding of the *IPCC Special Report on Global Warming of 1.5°C* (Rogelj et al. 2018) for the case of NDCs announced prior to COP26 that pathways following the NDCs until 2030 'would not limit global warming to 1.5°C, even if supplemented by very challenging increases in the scale and ambition of emissions reductions after 2030' (SR1.5 SPM). This assessment is now more robust than in SR1.5 as it is based on a larger set of 1.5°C–2°C pathways with better representation of current trends and plans covering a wider range of post-2030 emissions developments. In particular, a recent multi-model study limiting peak cumulative CO$_2$ emissions for a wide range of carbon budgets and immediate vs NDC-type action until 2030 established a feasibility frontier for the existence of such pathways across participating models (Riahi et al. 2021).

---

[20] The intended design of mitigation pathways in the literature can be deduced from underlying publications and study protocols. This information was collected as part of this assessment to establish a categorisation of policy assumptions underpinning the mitigation pathways collected in the AR6 scenario database (Section 3.2 and Annex III.II.3.2.2).

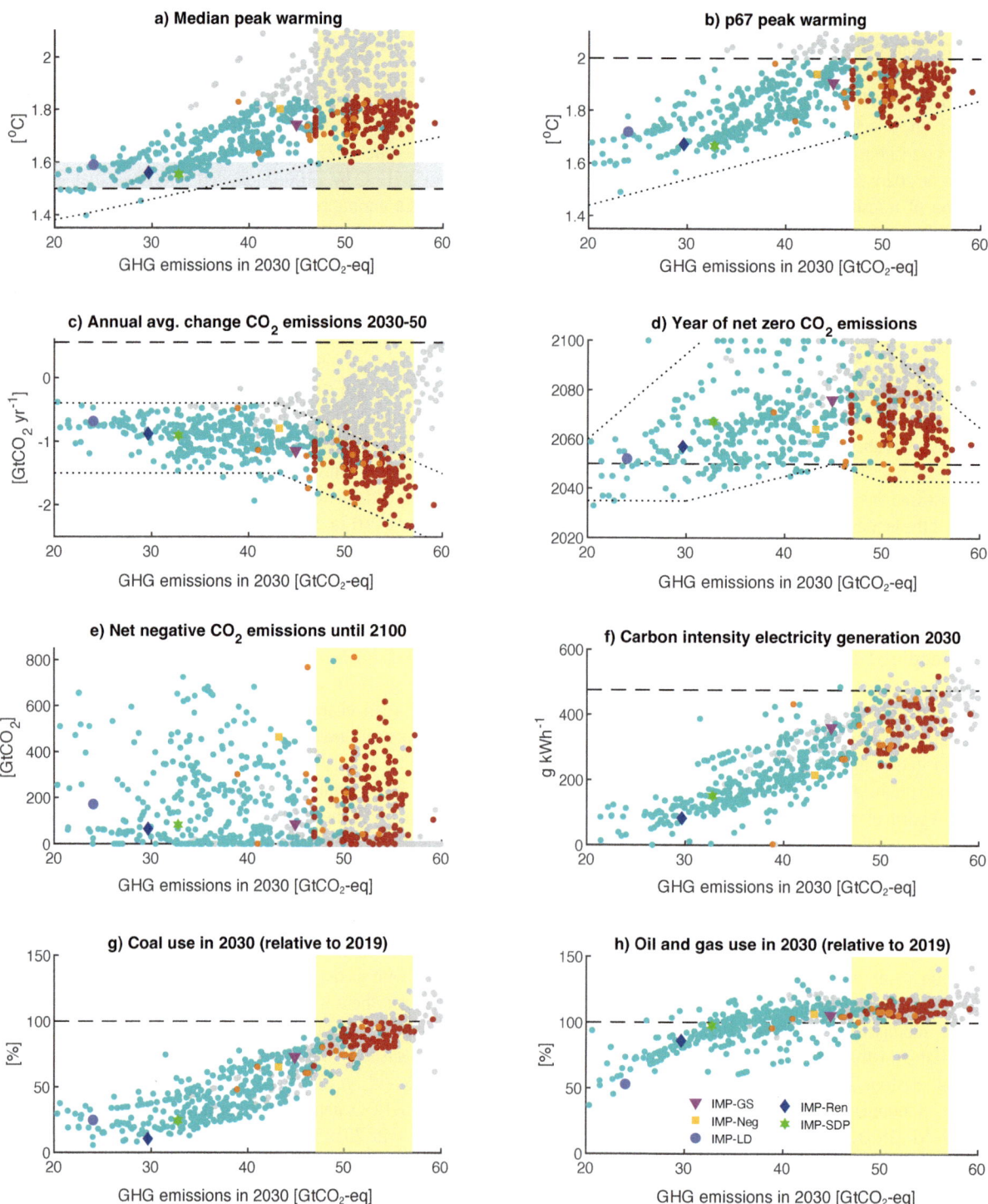

Figure 3.30 | Relationship between level of global GHG emissions in 2030 and selected indicators as listed in the panel titles for scenarios collected in the AR6 scenario database. Emissions data based on harmonised emissions used for the climate assessment. All scenarios that limit warming to 2°C (>67%) or lower are coloured blue or red (see p67 peak warming in panel (b)). The large majority of blue-coloured scenarios act immediately on the temperature target, while red-coloured scenarios depict all those that were designed to follow the NDCs or lesser action until 2030 and orange-coloured scenarios comprise a small set of pathways with additional regulatory action beyond NDCs (Section 3.5.3). Grey-coloured scenarios do not limit warming to 2°C (>67%) due to temporary overshoot or towards the end of the century. Large markers denote the five Illustrative Mitigation Pathways (IMPs) (legend in Panel (h); Section 3.2). Shaded yellow areas depict the estimated range of 2030 emissions from NDCs announced prior to COP26 (Section 4.2.2). Dotted lines are inserted in some panels to highlight trends in the dependency of selected output variables on 2030 GHG emissions levels (Section 3.5.2).

Table 3.6 | Comparison of key scenario characteristics for five scenario classes (see Table 3.2): (i) immediate action to limit warming to 1.5°C (>50%) with no or limited overshoot, (ii) near team action following the NDCs until 2030 and returning warming to below 1.5°C (>50%) by 2100 after a high overshoot, (iii) immediate action to limit warming to 2°C (>67%), (iv) near term action following the NDCs until 2030 followed by post-2030 action to limit warming to 2°C (>67%). Also shown are the characteristics for (v) the combined class of all scenarios that limit warming to 2°C (>67%). The classes (ii) and (iv) comprise the large majority of scenarios indicated by red dots, and the classes (i) and (iii) comprise the scenarios depicted by blue dots in Figure 3.30. Shown are median and interquartile ranges (in brackets) for selected global indicators. Emissions ranges are based on harmonized emissions data for the climate assessment with the exception of land use CO_2 emissions for which uncertainty in historic estimates is large. Numbers are rounded to the nearest 5, with the exception of cumulative CCS, BECCS, and net negative CO_2 emissions rounded to the nearest 10.

Global indicators	1.5°C	1.5°C (>50%) by 2100	2°C (>67%)		
	Immediate action, with no or limited overshoot (C1, 97 scenarios)	NDCs until 2030, with overshoot before 2100 (subset of 42 scenarios in C2)	Immediate action (C3a, 204 scenarios)	NDCs until 2030 (C3b; 97 scenarios)	All (C3; 311 scenarios)
Change in GHG emissions in 2030 (% rel to 2019)	−45 (−50,−40)	−5 (−5,0)	−25 (−35,−20)	−5 (−10,0)	−20 (−30,−10)
in 2050 (% rel to 2019)	−85 (−90,−80)	−75 (−85,−70)	−65 (−70,−60)	−70 (−70,−60)	−65 (−70,−60)
Change in CO_2 emissions in 2030 (% rel to 2019)	−50 (−60,−40)	−5 (−5,0)	−25 (−35,−20)	−5 (−5,0)	−20 (−30,−5)
in 2050 (% rel to 2019)	−100 (−105,−95)	−85 (−95,−80)	−70 (−80,−65)	−75 (−80,−65)	−75 (−80,−65)
Change in net land use CO_2 emissions in 2030 (% rel to 2019)	−100 (−105,−95)	−30 (−60,−20)	−90 (−105,−75)	−20 (−80,−20)	−80 (−100,−30)
in 2050 (% rel to 2019)	−150 (−200,−100)	−135 (−165,−120)	−135 (−185,−100)	−130 (−145,−115)	−135 (−180,−100)
Change in CH_4 emissions in 2030 (% rel to 2019)	−35 (−40,−30)	−5 (−5,0)	−25 (−35,−20)	−10 (−15,−5)	−20 (−25,−10)
in 2050 (% rel to 2019)	−50 (−60,−45)	−50 (−60,−45)	−45 (−50,−40)	−50 (−65,−45)	−45 (−55,−40)
Cumulative CCS until 2100 (GtCO_2)	670 (520,900)	670 (540,860)	610 (490,900)	530 (440,720)	590 (480,820)
of which BECCS (GtCO_2)	330 (250,560)	370 (280,590)	350 (240,450)	270 (240,400)	290 (240,430)
Cumulative net negative CO_2 emissions until 2100 (GtCO_2)	*220 (70,430)*	*380 (300,470)*	*30 (0,130)*	*60 (20,210)*	*40 (10, 180)*
Change in primary energy from coal in 2030 (% rel to 2019)	−75 (−80,−65)	−10 (−20,−5)	−50 (−65,−35)	−15 (−20,−10)	−35 (−55,−20)
in 2050 (% rel to 2019)	−95 (−100,−80)	−90 (−100,−85)	−85 (−100,−65)	−80 (−90,−70)	−85 (−95,−65)
Change in primary energy from coal without CCS in 2030 (% rel to 2019)	−75 (−80,−65)	−10 (−20,−10)	−50 (−65,−35)	−15 (−20,−10)	−35 (−55,−20)
in 2050 (% rel to 2019)	−100 (−100,−95)	−95 (−100,−95)	−95 (−100,−90)	−90 (−95,−85)	−95 (−100,−90)
Change in primary energy from oil in 2030 (% rel to 2019)	−10 (−25,0)	5 (5,10)	0 (−10,10)	10 (5,10)	5 (0,10)
in 2050 (% rel to 2019)	−60 (−75,−40)	−50 (−65,−35)	−30 (−45,−15)	−40 (−55,−20)	−30 (−50,−15)
Change in primary energy from oil without CCS in 2030 (% rel to 2019)	−5 (−20,0)	5 (5,10)	0 (−10,10)	10 (5,10)	5 (−5,10)
in 2050 (% rel to 2019)	−60 (−75,−45)	−50 (−65,−30)	−30 (−45,−15)	−40 (−55,−20)	−35 (−50,−15)
Change in primary energy from gas in 2030 (% rel to 2019)	−10 (−30,0)	15 (10,25)	10 (0,15)	15 (10,15)	10 (0,15)
in 2050 (% rel to 2019)	−45 (−60,−20)	−45 (−55,−30)	−10 (−35,15)	−30 (−45,−5)	−15 (−40,10)
Change in primary energy from gas without CCS in 2030 (% rel to 2019)	−20 (−30,−5)	15 (10,25)	5 (−5,10)	15 (10,15)	10 (0,15)
in 2050 (% rel to 2019)	−70 (−80,−60)	−60 (−70,−50)	−35 (−50,−20)	−40 (−60,−35)	−40 (−55,−20)
Change in primary energy from nuclear in 2030 (% rel to 2019)	40 (10,70)	10 (0,25)	35 (5,50)	10 (0,30)	25 (0,45)
in 2050 (% rel to 2019)	90 (15,295)	100 (45,130)	85 (30,200)	75 (30,120)	80 (30,140)
Change in primary energy from modern biomass in 2030 (% rel to 2019)	75 (55,130)	45 (20,75)	60 (35,105)	45 (20,80)	55 (35,105)
in 2050 (% rel to 2019)	290 (215,430)	230 (170,420)	240 (130,355)	260 (95,435)	250 (115,405)
Change in primary energy from non–biomass renewables in 2030 (% rel to 2019)	225 (155,270)	100 (85,145)	150 (115,190)	115 (85,130)	130 (90,170)
in 2050 (% rel to 2019)	725 (545,950)	665 (535,925)	565 (415,765)	625 (545,700)	605 (470,735)
Change in carbon intensity of electricity in 2030 (% rel to 2019)	−75 (−80,−70)	−30 (−40,−30)	−60 (−70,−50)	−35 (−40,−30)	−50 (−65,−35)
in 2050 (% rel to 2019)	−100 (−100,−100)	−100 (−100,−100)	−95 (−100,−95)	−100 (−100,−95)	−95 (−100,−95)
Change in carbon intensity of non–electric final energy consumption in 2030 (% rel to 2019)	−15 (−15,−10)	0 (−5,0)	−10 (−10,−5)	0 (−5,5)	−5 (−10,0)
in 2050 (% rel to 2019)	−50 (−55,−40)	−35 (−40,−30)	−30 (−35,−25)	−30 (−40,−20)	−30 (−35,−20)

3

The 2030 emissions levels in the NDCS announced prior to COP26 also tighten the remaining space to limit warming to 2°C (>67%). As shown in Figure 3.30b, the 67th percentile of peak warming reaches values above 1.7°C in pathways with 2030 emissions levels in this range. To still limit warming to 2°C (>67%), the global post-2030 GHG emission reduction rates would need to be abruptly raised in 2030 from 0–0.7 $GtCO_2$-eq yr^{-1} to an average of 1.4–2.0 $GtCO_2$-eq yr^{-1} during the period 2030–2050 (Figure 3.30c), around 70% higher than in immediate mitigation pathways confirming findings in the literature (Winning et al. 2019). Their average reduction rate of 0.6–1.4 $GtCO_2$ yr^{-1} would already be unprecedented at the global scale and, with a few exceptions, national scale for an extended period of time (Riahi et al. 2015). For comparison, the impact of COVID-19 on the global economy is projected to have lead to a decline of around 2.5–3 $GtCO_2$ of global CO_2 emissions from fossil fuels and industry in 2020 (Friedlingstein et al. 2020) (Section 2.2).

The increased post-2030 transition challenge in mitigation pathways with moderate near-term action is also reflected in the timing of reaching net zero CO_2 emissions (Figure 3.30d and Cross-Chapter Box 3 in this chapter). As 2030 emission levels and the cumulated CO_2 emissions until 2030 increase, the remaining time for dropping to net zero CO_2 and staying within the remaining carbon budget shortens (Figure 3.29). This gives rise to an inverted v-shape of the lower bound on the year of reaching net zero as a function of 2030 emissions levels. Reaching low emissions in 2030 facilitates reaching net zero early (left leg of the inverted v), but staying high until 2030 also requires reaching net zero CO_2 faster to compensate for higher emissions early on (right leg of the inverted v). Overall, there is a considerable spread of the timing of net zero CO_2 for any 2030 emissions level due to variation in the timing of spending the remaining carbon budget and the non-CO_2 warming contribution (Cross-Chapter Box 3 in this chapter).

There is also a profound impact on the underlying transition of energy and land use (Figure 3.30f–h and Table 3.6). Scenarios following NDCs until 2030 show a much smaller reduction in fossil fuel use, a slower growth in renewable energy use, and a smaller reduction in CO_2 and CH_4 land-use emissions in 2030 compared to immediate action scenarios. This is then followed by a much faster reduction of land-use emissions and fossil fuels, and a larger increase of nuclear energy, bioenergy and non-biomass renewable energy during the medium term in order to get close to the levels of the immediate action pathways in 2050. This is combined with a larger amount of net negative CO_2 emissions that are used to compensate the additional emissions before 2030. The faster transition during 2030–2050 is taking place from a greater investment in fossil fuel infrastructure and lower deployment of low-carbon alternatives in 2030, adding to the socio-economic challenges to realise the higher transition rates (Section 3.5.2.2). Therefore, these pathways also show higher mitigation costs, particularly during the period 2030–2050, than immediate action scenarios (Section 3.6.1 and Figure 3.34d) (Liu et al. 2016; Kriegler et al. 2018a; Vrontisi et al. 2018). Given these circumstances and the fact the modelling of socio-political and institutional constraints is limited in Integrated Assessment Models (IAMs) (Gambhir et al. 2019; Köhler et al. 2019; Hirt et al. 2020; Keppo et al. 2021), the feasibility of realising these scenarios is assessed to

be lower (Gambhir et al. 2017; Napp et al. 2017; Brutschin et al. 2021) (cf. Section 3.8), increasing the risk of an overshoot of climate goals.

3.5.2.1   Overshoot and Net Negative CO_2 Emissions

If near- to medium-term emissions developments deplete the remaining carbon budget, the associated warming limit will be overshot. Some pathways that return warming to 1.5°C (>50%) by the end of the century show mid-century overshoots of up to 1.8°C median warming. The overshoot tends to be higher, the higher the 2030 emissions. Mitigation pathways with 2030 emissions levels in the NDCS announced prior to COP26 consistently overshoot 1.5°C by 0.15°C–0.3°C. This leads to higher risks from climate change impacts during the time of overshoot compared to pathways that limit warming to 1.5°C (>50%) with no or limited overshoot (Schleussner et al. 2016a; Mengel et al. 2018; Hofmann et al. 2019; Lenton et al. 2019; Tachiiri et al. 2019; Drouet et al. 2021). Furthermore, even if warming is reversed by net negative emissions, other climate changes such as sea level rise would continue in their current direction for decades to millennia (AR6 WGI Sections 4.6 and 5.6).

Returning warming to lower levels requires net negative CO_2 emissions in the second half of the century (Clarke et al. 2014; Fuss et al. 2014; Rogelj et al. 2018a). The amount of net negative CO_2 emissions in pathways limiting warming to 1.5°C–2°C climate goals varies widely, with some pathways not deploying net negative CO_2 emissions at all and others deploying up to –600 to –800 $GtCO_2$. The amount of net negative CO_2 emissions tends to increase with 2030 emissions levels (Figure 3.30e and Table 3.6). Studies confirmed the ability of net negative CO_2 emissions to reduce warming, but pointed to path dependencies in the storage of carbon and heat in the Earth System and the need for further research particularly for cases of high overshoot (Zickfeld et al. 2016, 2021; Keller et al. 2018a,b; Tokarska et al. 2019). The AR6 WGI assessed the reduction in global surface temperature to be approximately linearly related to cumulative CO_2 removal and, with lower confidence, that the amount of cooling per unit CO_2 removed is approximately independent of the rate and amount of removal (AR6 WGI TS.3.3.2). Still there remains large uncertainty about a potential asymmetry between the warming response to CO_2 emissions and the cooling response to net negative CO_2 emissions (Zickfeld et al. 2021). It was also shown that warming can adversely affect the efficacy of carbon dioxide removal measures and hence the ability to achieve net negative CO_2 emissions (Boysen et al. 2016).

Obtaining net negative CO_2 emissions requires massive deployment of carbon dioxide removal (CDR) in the second half of the century, on the order of 220 (160–370) $GtCO_2$ for each 0.1°C degree of cooling (based on the assessment of the *likely* range of the transient response to cumulative CO_2 emissions in AR6 WGI Section 5.5 in Chapter 5, not taking into account potential asymmetries in the temperature response to CO_2 emissions and removals). CDR is assessed in detail in Section 12.3 of this report (see also Cross-Chapter Box 8 in Chapter 12). Here we only point to the finding that CDR ramp-up rates and absolute deployment levels are tightly limited by techno-economic, social, political, institutional and sustainability constraints (Smith et al. 2016; Boysen et al. 2017; Fuss et al. 2018, 2020; Nemet et al. 2018; Hilaire et al. 2019; Jia et al. 2019) (Section 12.3). CDR therefore cannot be deployed arbitrarily to compensate any degree of overshoot. A fraction of models was not able to compute pathways that would follow the mitigation ambition in unconditional and conditional NDCs until 2030 and return warming to below 1.5°C by 2100 (Luderer et al. 2018; Roelfsema et al. 2020; Riahi et al. 2021). There exists a three-way trade-off between near-term emissions developments until 2030, transitional challenges during 2030–50, and long-term CDR deployment post-2050 (Sanderson et al. 2016; Holz et al. 2018; Strefler et al. 2018). For example, Strefler et al. (2018) find that if CO_2 emission levels stay at around 40 $GtCO_2$ until 2030, within the range of what is projected for NDCs announced prior to COP26, rather than being halved to 20 $GtCO_2$ until 2030, CDR deployment in the second half of the century would have to increase by 50–100%, depending on whether the 2030–2050 CO_2 emissions reduction rate is doubled from 6% to 12% or kept at 6% yr^{-1}. This three-way trade-off has also been identified at the national level (Pan et al. 2020).

In addition to enabling a temporary budget overshoot by net negative CO_2 emissions in the second half of the century, CDR can also be used to compensate – on an annual basis – residual CO_2 emissions from sources that are difficult to eliminate and to reach net zero CO_2 emissions more rapidly if deployed before this point (Kriegler et al. 2013b; Rogelj et al. 2018a). This explains its continued deployment in pathways that exclude overshoot and net negative CO_2 emissions (Riahi et al. 2021). However, given the time scales that would likely be needed to ramp-up CDR to gigatonne scale (Nemet et al. 2018), it can be expected to only make a limited contribution to reaching net zero CO_2 as fast as possible. In the vast majority (95%) of 1.5°C–2°C mitigation pathways assessed in this report, cumulative CDR deployment did not exceed 100 $GtCO_2$ until mid-century. This adds to the risk of excessively relying on CDR to compensate for weak mitigation action until 2030 by either facilitating massive net CO_2 emissions reduction rates during 2030–2050 or allowing a high temporary overshoot of 1.5°C until the end of the century. If international burden-sharing considerations are taken into account, the CDR penalty for weak action could increase further, in particular for developed countries (Fyson et al. 2020). Further assessment of CDR deployment in 1.5°C–2°C mitigation pathways is found in Section 3.4.7.

3.5.2.2 Carbon Lock-in and Stranded Assets

There already exists a substantial and growing carbon lock-in today, as measured by committed emissions associated with existing long-lived infrastructure (Section 2.7 and Figure 2.31). If existing fossil fuel infrastructure would continue to be operated as historically, it would entail CO_2 emissions exceeding the carbon budget for 1.5°C (Section 2.7.2 and Figure 2.32). However, owner-operators and societies may choose to retire existing infrastructure earlier than in the past, and committed emissions are thus contingent on the competitiveness of non-emitting alternative technologies and climate policy ambition. Therefore, in mitigation pathways, some infrastructure may become stranded assets. Stranded assets have been defined as 'assets that have suffered from unanticipated or

premature write-downs, devaluations or conversion to liabilities' (Caldecott 2017).

A systematic map of the literature on carbon lock-in has synthesized quantification of stranded assets in the mitigation pathways literature, and showed that (i) coal power plants are the most exposed to risk of becoming stranded, (ii) delayed mitigation action increases stranded assets, and (iii) sectoral distribution and the amount of stranded assets differ between countries (Fisch-Romito et al. 2021). There is high agreement that existing fossil fuel infrastructure would need to be retired earlier than historically, used less, or retrofitted with CCS, to stay within the remaining carbon budgets of limiting warming to 1.5°C or 2°C (Johnson et al. 2016; Kefford et al. 2018; Pfeiffer et al. 2018; Cui et al. 2019; Fofrich et al. 2020; Rogelj et al. 2018a). Studies estimate that cumulative early retired power plant capacities by 2060 can be up to 600 GW for gas and 1700 GW for coal (Iyer et al. 2015a; Kefford et al. 2018), that only 42% of the total capital stock of both operating and planned coal-fired powers plants can be utilised to be compatible with the 2°C target (Pfeiffer et al. 2018), and that coal-fired power plants in scenarios consistent with keeping global warming below 2°C or 1.5°C retire one to three decades earlier than historically has been the case (Cui et al. 2019; Fofrich et al. 2020). After coal, electricity production based on gas is also projected to be phased out, with some capacity remaining as back-up (van Soest et al. 2017a). Kefford et al. (2018) find USD541 billion worth of stranded fossil fuel power plants could be created by 2060, with China and India the most exposed.

Some publications have suggested that stranded long-lived assets may be even more important outside of the power sector. While stranded power sector assets by 2050 could reach up to USD1.8 trillion in scenarios consistent with a 2°C target, Saygin et al. (2019) found a range of USD5–11 trillion in the buildings sector. Muldoon-Smith and Greenhalgh (2019) have even estimated a potential value at risk for global real estate assets up to USD21 trillion. More broadly, the set of economic activities that are potentially affected by a low-carbon transition is wide and includes also energy-intensive industries, transport and housing, as reflected in the concept of climate policy relevant sectors introduced in Battiston et al. (2017). The sectoral distribution and amount of stranded assets differ across countries (Fisch-Romito et al. 2021). Capital for fossil fuel production and distribution represents a larger share of potentially stranded assets in fossil fuel-producing countries such as the United States and Russia. Electricity generation would be a larger share of total stranded assets in emerging countries because this capital is relatively new compared to its operational lifetime. Conversely, buildings could represent a larger part of stranded capital in more developed countries and regions such as the USA, EU or even Russia because of high market value and low turnover rate.

Many quantitative estimates of stranded assets along mitigation pathways have focused on fossil fuel power plants in pathways characterised by mitigation ambition until 2030 corresponding to the NDCs followed by strengthened action afterwards to limit warming to 2°C (>67%) or lower (Bertram et al. 2015a; Iyer et al. 2015b; Lane et al. 2016; Farfan and Breyer 2017; van Soest et al. 2017a; Kriegler et al. 2018a; Luderer et al. 2018; Cui et al. 2019; Saygin et al.

2019; SEI et al. 2020). Pathways following NDCs announced prior to COP26 until 2030 do not show a significant reduction of coal, oil and gas use (Figure 3.30f–h and Table 3.6) compared to immediate action pathways. Stranded coal power assets are evaluated to be higher by a factor of two to three if action is strengthened after 2030 rather than now (Iyer et al. 2015b; Cui et al. 2019). There is high agreement that the later climate policies are implemented, the higher the expected stranded assets and the societal, economic and political strain of strengthening action. Associated price increases for carbon-intensive goods and transitional macro-economic costs have been found to scale with the emissions gap in 2030 (Kriegler et al. 2013a). At the aggregate level of the whole global economy, Rozenberg et al. (2015) showed that each year of delaying the start of mitigation decreases the required CO_2 intensity of new production by 20–50 gCO_2 per USD. Carbon lock-in can have a long-lasting effect on future emissions trajectories after 2030. Luderer et al. (2018) compared cost-effective pathways with immediate action to limit warming to 1.5°C–2°C with pathways following the NDCs until 2030 and adopting the pricing policy of the cost-effective pathways thereafter, and found that the majority of additional CO_2 emissions from carbon lock-in occur after 2030, reaching a cumulative amount of 290 (160–330) $GtCO_2$ by 2100 (Section 2.7.2). Early action and avoidance of investments in new carbon-intensive assets can minimise these risks.

The risk of stranded assets has implications for workers depending on those assets, asset owners, assets portfolio managers, financial institutions and the stability of the financial system. Chapter 6 assesses the risks and implications of stranded assets for energy systems (Section 6.7.3 and Box 6.11) and fossil fuels (Section 6.7.4). The implications of stranded assets for inequality and Just Transition are assessed in Chapter 17 (Section 17.3.2.3). Chapter 15 assesses the literature on those implications for the financial system as well as on coping options (Sections 15.5.2 and 15.6.1).

On the other hand, mitigation, by limiting climate change, reduces the risk of destroyed or stranded assets from the physical impacts of climate change on natural and human systems, from more frequent, intense or extended extreme events and from sea level rise (O'Neill et al. 2020a). The literature on mitigation pathways rarely includes an evaluation of stranded assets from climate change impacts. Unruh (2019) suggest that these are the real stranded assets of carbon lock-in and could prove much more costly.

3.5.3 Global Accelerated Action Towards Long-term Climate Goals

A growing literature explores long-term mitigation pathways with accelerated near-term action going beyond the NDCs (Graichen et al. 2017; Jiang et al. 2017; Kriegler et al. 2018a; Roelfsema et al. 2018; Fekete et al. 2021; van Soest et al. 2021a). Global accelerated action pathways are designed to transition more gradually from implemented policies and planned implementation of NDCs onto a 1.5°C–2°C pathway and at the same time alleviate the abrupt transition in 2030 that would be caused by following the NDCs until 2030 and strengthening towards limiting warming to 2°C thereafter (Section 3.5.2). Therefore, they have sometimes been called bridging

scenarios/pathways in the literature (IEA 2011; Spencer et al. 2015; van Soest et al. 2021a). They rely on regionally differentiated regulatory and pricing policies to gradually strengthening regional and sectoral action beyond the mitigation ambition in the NDCs. There are limitations to this approach. The tighter the warming limit, the more likely it is that disruptive action becomes inevitable to achieve the speed of transition that would be required (Kriegler et al. 2018a). Cost-effective pathways already have abrupt shifts in deployments, investments and prices at the time a stringent warming limit is imposed, reflecting the fact that the overall response to climate change has so far been misaligned with long-term climate goals (Fawcett et al. 2015; Rogelj et al. 2016; Schleussner et al. 2016b; Geiges et al. 2020). Disruptive action can help to break lock-ins and enable transformative change (Vogt-Schilb et al. 2018).

The large literature on accelerating climate action was assessed in the *IPCC Special Report on Global Warming of 1.5°C* (de Coninck et al. 2018) and is taken up in this report primarily in Chapters 4, 13, and 14. Accelerating climate action and facilitating transformational change requires a perspective on socio-technical transitions (Geels et al. 2016a; Geels et al. 2016b; Geels 2020), a portfolio of policy instruments to manage technological and environmental change (Fischer and Newell 2008; Goulder and Parry 2008; Acemoglu et al. 2012, 2016), a notion of path dependency and policy sequencing (Pierson 2000; Meckling et al. 2017; Pahle et al. 2018) and the evolvement of polycentric governance layers of institutions and norms in support of the transformation (Dietz et al. 2003; Leach et al. 2007; Messner 2015). This subsection is focused on an assessment of the emerging quantitative literature on global accelerated action pathways towards 1.5°C–2°C, which to a large extent abstracts from the underlying processes and uses a number of stylised approaches to generate these pathways. A representative of accelerated action pathways has been identified as one of the Illustrative Mitigation Pathways (IMPs) in this assessment (*IMP-GS*, Figure 3.31).

One approach relies on augmenting initially moderate emissions-pricing policies with robust anticipation of ratcheting up climate action in the future (Spencer et al. 2015). If announcements of strong future climate policies are perceived to be credible, they can help to prevent carbon lock-in as investors anticipating high future costs of GHG emissions would reduce investment into fossil fuel infrastructure, such as coal power plants (Bauer et al. 2018b). However, the effectiveness of such announcements strongly hinges on their credibility. If investors believe that policymakers could drop them if anticipatory action did not occur, they may not undertake such action.

Another approach relies on international cooperation to strengthen near-term climate action. These studies build on international climate policy architectures that could incentivise a coalition of like-minded countries to raise their mitigation ambition beyond what is stated in their NDC (Graichen et al. 2017). Examples are the idea of climate clubs characterised by harmonised carbon and technology markets (Nordhaus 2015; Keohane et al. 2017; Paroussos et al. 2019; Pihl 2020) and the Powering Past Coal Alliance (PPCA) (Jewell et al. 2019). Paroussos et al. (2019) find economic benefits of joining a climate club despite the associated higher mitigation effort, in particular due

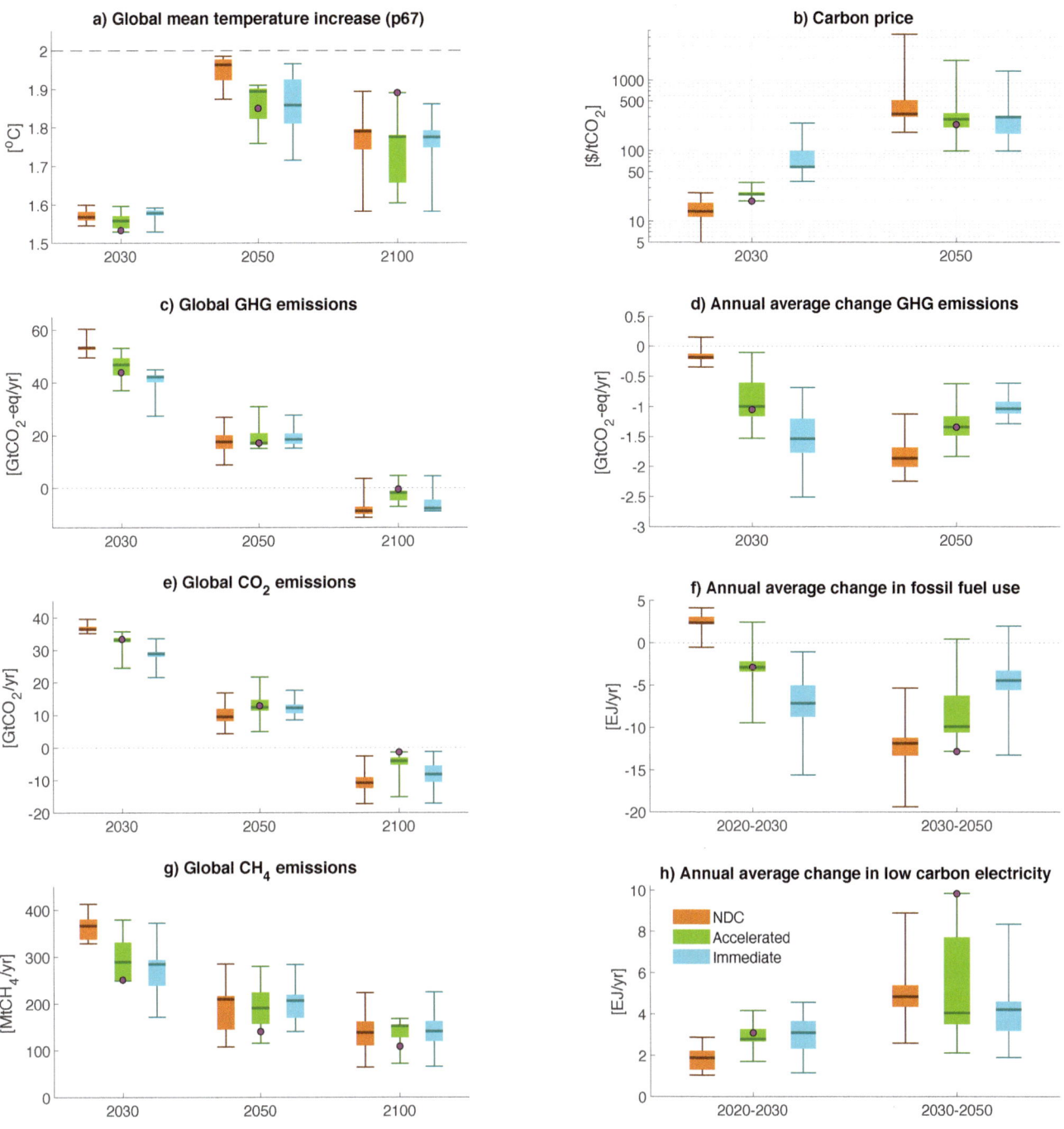

Figure 3.31 | Comparison of (i) pathways with immediate action to limit warming to 2°C (>67%) (Immediate, light blue), (ii) pathways following the NDCs until 2030 and limiting warming to 2°C (>67%) thereafter (NDC; orange), and (iii) pathways accelerating near-term action until 2030 beyond NDC ambition levels and limiting warming to 2°C (>67%) thereafter (accelerated) for selected indicators as listed in the panel titles, based on pathways from van Soest et al. (2021a). Low-carbon electricity comprises renewable and nuclear power. Indicator ranges are shown as box plots (full range, interquartile range, and median) for the years 2030, 2050 and 2100 (absolute values) and for the periods 2020–2030, 2030–2050 (change indicators). Ranges are based on nine models participating in van Soest et al. (2021a) with only seven models reporting emissions and climate results and eight models reporting carbon prices. The purple dot denotes the Illustrative Mitigation Pathway *GS* that was part of the study by van Soest et al.

to access to technology and climate finance. Graichen et al. (2017) find an additional reduction of 5–11 GtCO$_2$-eq compared to the mitigation ambition in the NDCs from the successful implementation of international climate initiatives. Other studies assess benefits from international transfers of mitigation outcomes (Stua 2017; Edmonds et al. 2021). Edmonds et al. (2021) find economic gains from sharing NDC emissions-reduction commitments compared to purely domestic implementation of NDCs. If reinvested in mitigation efforts, the study projects an additional reduction of 9 billion tonnes of CO$_2$ in 2030.

The most common approach relies on strengthening regulatory policies beyond current policy trends, also motivated by the finding that such policies have so far been employed more often than comprehensive carbon pricing (Kriegler et al. 2018a; Roelfsema et al. 2018; Fekete et al. 2021; IEA 2021a; van Soest et al. 2021a). Some studies have focused on generic regulatory policies such as low-carbon support policies, fossil fuel-sunset policies, and resource-efficiency policies (Bertram et al. 2015b; Hatfield-Dodds et al. 2017). Bertram et al. (2015b) found that a moderate carbon price combined with a coal moratorium and ambitious low-carbon support policies can limit efficiency losses until 2030 if emissions pricing is raised thereafter to limit warming to 2°C. They also showed that all three components are needed to achieve this outcome. Hatfield-Dodds et al. (2017) found that resource efficiency can lower 2050 emissions by an additional 15–20% while boosting near-term economic growth. The International Energy Agency (IEA 2021a) developed a detailed net zero scenario for the global energy sector characterised by a rapid phase-out of fossil fuels, a massive clean energy and electrification push, and the stabilisation of energy demand, leading to 10 GtCO$_2$ lower emissions from energy use in 2030 than in a scenario following the announced pledges.

The Paris Agreement has spurred the formulation of NDCs for 2030 and mid-century strategies around the world (cf. Chapter 4). This is giving researchers a rich empirical basis to formulate accelerated policy packages taking national decarbonisation pathways as a starting point (Graichen et al. 2017; Jiang et al. 2017; van Soest et al. 2017b; Waisman et al. 2019). The concept is to identify good practice policies that had demonstrable impact on pushing low-carbon options or reducing emissions in a country or region and then consider a wider roll out of these policies taking into account regional specificities (den Elzen et al. 2015; Fekete et al. 2015, 2021; Kriegler et al. 2018a; Kuramochi et al. 2018; Roelfsema et al. 2018). A challenge for this approach is to account for the fact that policy effectiveness varies with different political environments in different geographies. As a result, a global roll out of good practice policies to close the emissions gap will still be an idealised benchmark, but it is useful to understand how much could be gained from it.

Accelerated action pathways derived with this approach show considerable scope for narrowing the emissions gap between pathways reflecting the ambition level of the NDCs and cost-effective mitigation pathways in 2030. Kriegler et al. (2018a) find around 10 GtCO$_2$-eq lower emissions compared to original NDCs from a global roll out of good practice plus net zero policies and a moderate increase in regionally differentiated carbon pricing. Fekete et al. (2021) show that global replication of sector progress in five major economies would reduce GHG emissions in 2030 by about 20% compared to a current policy scenario. These findings were found in good agreement with a recent model comparison study based on results from nine integrated assessment models (IAMs) (van Soest et al. 2021a). Based on these three studies, implementing accelerated action in terms of a global roll out of regulatory and moderate pricing policies is assessed to lead to global GHG emissions of 48 (38–52) GtCO$_2$-eq in 2030 (median and 5–95th percentile based on 10 distinct modelled pathways). This closes the implementation gap for the NDCs, and in addition falls below the emissions range implied by implementing unconditional and conditional elements of NDCs by 2–9 GtCO$_2$-eq. However, it does not close the emissions gap to immediate action pathways that limit warming to 2°C (>67%), and, based on our assessment in Section 3.5.2, emission levels above 40 GtCO$_2$-eq in 2030 still have a very low prospect for limiting warming to 1.5°C (>50%) with no or limited overshoot.

Figure 3.31 shows the intermediate position of accelerated action pathways derived by van Soest et al. (2021a) between pathways that follow the NDCs until 2030 and immediate action pathways limiting warming to 2°C (>67%). Accelerated action is able to reduce the abrupt shifts in emissions, fossil fuel use and low-carbon power generation in 2030 and also limits peak warming more effectively than NDC pathways. But primarily due to the moderate carbon price assumptions (Figure 3.31b), the reductions in emissions and particular fossil fuel use are markedly smaller than what would be obtained in the case of immediate action. The assessment shows that accelerated action until 2030 can have significant benefits in terms of reducing the mitigation challenges from following the NDCs until 2030. But putting a significant value on GHG emissions reductions globally remains a key element of moving onto 1.5°C–2°C pathways. The vast majority of pathways that limit warming to 2°C (>67%) or lower, independently of their differences in near-term emission developments, converge to a global mitigation regime putting a significant value on GHG emission reductions in all regions and sectors.

3.6 Economics of Long-term Mitigation and Development Pathways, Including Mitigation Costs and Benefits

A complete appraisal of economic effects and welfare effects at different temperature levels would include the macroeconomic impacts of investments in low-carbon solutions and structural change away from emitting activities, co-benefits and adverse side effects of mitigation, (avoided) climate damages, as well as (reduced) adaptation costs, with high temporal, spatial and social heterogeneity using a harmonised framework. If no such complete appraisal in a harmonised framework exists, key elements are emerging from the literature, and assessed in the following subsections: on aggregated economy-wide global mitigation costs (Section 3.6.1), on the economic benefits of avoiding climate impacts (Section 3.6.2), on economic benefits and costs associated with mitigation co-benefits and co-harms (Section 3.6.3) and on the distribution of economic implications between economic sectors and actors (Section 3.6.4).

3.6.1   Economy-wide Implications of Mitigation

3.6.1.1   Global Economic Effects of Mitigation and Carbon
                Values in Mitigation Pathways

Box 3.5 | Concepts and Modelling Frameworks Used for Quantifying Macroeconomic Effects of Mitigation

Most studies that have developed mitigation pathways have used a cost-effectiveness analysis (CEA) framework, which aim to compare the costs of different mitigation strategies designed to meet a given climate change mitigation goal (e.g., an emission-reduction target or a temperature stabilisation target) but does not represent economic impacts from climate change itself, nor the associated economic benefits of avoided impacts. Other studies use modelling frameworks that represent the feedback of damages from climate change on the economy in a cost-benefit analysis (CBA) approach, which balances mitigation costs and benefits. This second type of study is represented in Section 3.6.2.

The marginal abatement cost of carbon, also called carbon price, is determined by the mitigation target under consideration: it describes the cost of reducing the last unit of emissions to reach the target at a given point in time. Total macroeconomic mitigation costs (or gains) aggregate the economy-wide impacts of investments in low-carbon solutions and structural changes away from emitting activities. The total macroeconomic effects of mitigation pathways are reported in terms of variations in economic output or consumption levels, measured against a reference scenario, also called baseline, at various points in time or discounted over a given time period. Depending on the study, the reference scenario reflects specific assumptions about patterns of socio-economic development and assumes either no-climate policies or the climate policies in place or planned at the time the study was carried out. When available in the AR6 scenarios database, this second type of reference scenario, with trends from implemented policies until the end of 2020, has been chosen for computation of mitigation costs. In the vast majority of studies that have produced the body of work on the cost of mitigation assessed here, and in particular in all studies that have submitted global scenarios to the AR6 scenarios database except (Schultes et al. 2021), the feedbacks of climate change impacts on the economic development pathways are not accounted for. This omission of climate impacts leads to overly optimistic economic projections in the reference scenarios, in particular in reference scenarios with no or limited mitigation action where the extent of global warming is the greatest. Mitigation cost estimates computed against no or limited policy reference scenarios therefore omit economic benefits brought by avoided climate change impact along mitigation pathways, and should be interpreted with care (Grant et al. 2020). When aggregate economic benefits from avoided climate change impacts are accounted for, mitigation is a welfare-enhancing strategy (Section 3.6.2).

If GDP or consumption in mitigation pathways are below the reference scenario levels, they are reported as losses or macroeconomic costs. Such cost estimates give an indication of how economic activity slows relative to the reference scenario; they do not necessarily describe, in absolute terms, a reduction of economic output or consumption levels relative to previous years along the pathway. Aggregate mitigation costs depend strongly on the modelling framework used and the assumptions about the reference scenario against which mitigation costs are measured, in particular whether the reference scenario is, or not, on the efficiency frontier of the economy. If the economy is assumed to be at the efficiency frontier in the reference scenario, mitigation inevitably leads to actual costs, at least in the short-run until the production frontier evolves with technical and structural change. Starting from a reference scenario that is not on the efficiency frontier opens the possibility to simultaneously reduce emissions and obtain macroeconomic gains, depending on the design and implementation of mitigation policies. A number of factors can result in reference scenarios below the efficiency frontier, for instance distorting labour taxes and/or fossil fuel subsidies, misallocation or under-utilisation of production factors such as involuntary unemployment, imperfect information or non-rational behaviours. Although these factors are pervasive, the modelling frameworks used to construct mitigation pathways are often limited in their ability to represent them (Köberle et al. 2021).

The absolute level of economic activity and welfare also strongly depends on the socio-economic pathway assumptions regarding, *inter alia*, evolutions in demography, productivity, education levels, inequality, and technical change and innovation. The GDP or consumption indicators reported in the database of scenarios, and synthesized below, represent the absolute level of aggregate economic activity or consumption but do not reflect welfare and well-being (Roberts et al. 2020), that notably depend on human-needs satisfaction, distribution within society and inequality (Section 3.6.4).

Chapter 1 and Annex III.I give further details of the economic concepts and modelling frameworks, including their limitations, used in this report, respectively.

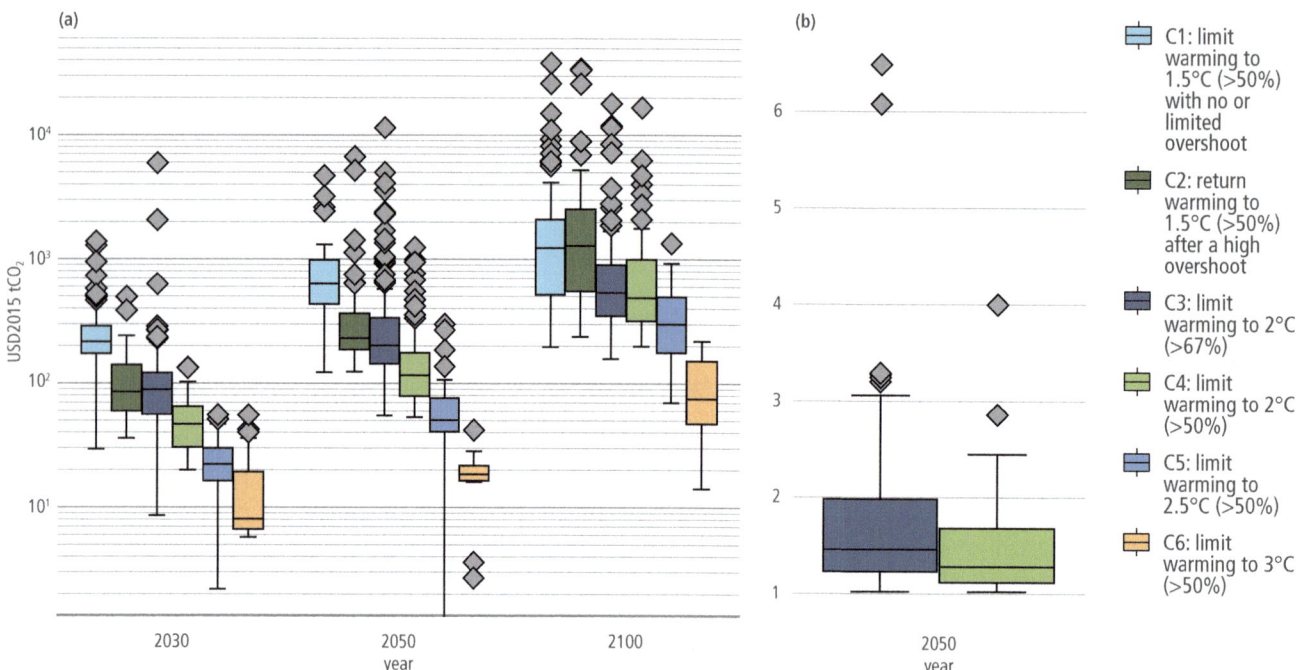

Figure 3.32 | Marginal abatement cost of carbon in 2030, 2050 and 2100 for mitigation pathways with immediate global mitigation action (a), and ratio in 2050 between pathways that correspond to NDCs announced prior to COP26 in 2030 and strengthen action after 2030 and pathways with immediate global mitigation action, for C3 and C4 temperature categories (b).

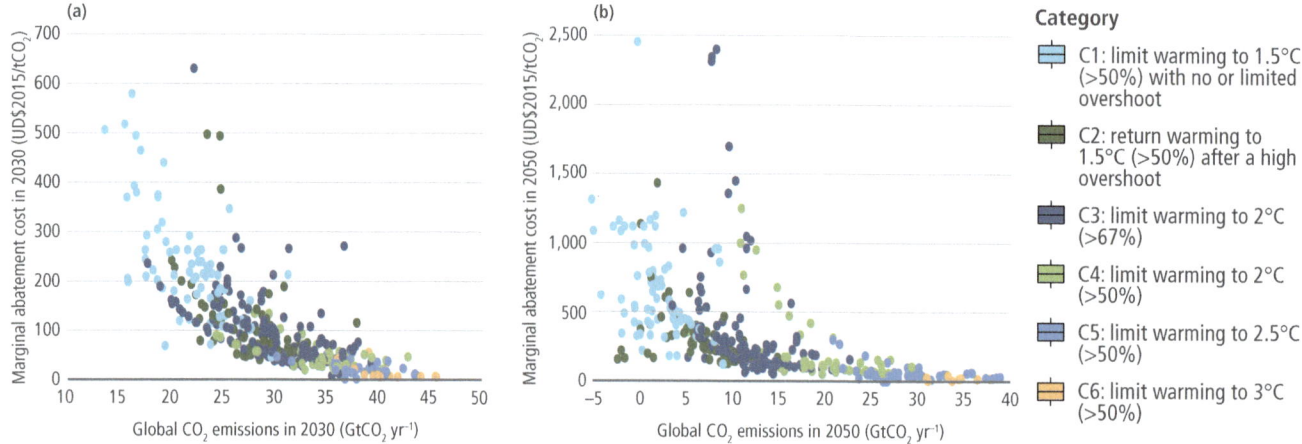

Figure 3.33 | Marginal abatement cost of carbon with respect to CO_2 emissions for mitigation pathways with immediate global mitigation action, in 2030 (a) and 2050 (b).

Estimates for the marginal abatement cost of carbon in mitigation pathways vary widely, depending on the modelling framework used and socio-economic, technological and policy assumptions. However, it is robust across modelling frameworks that the marginal abatement cost of carbon increases for lower temperature categories, with a higher increase in the short term than in the longer term (Figure 3.32, left panel) (*high confidence*). The marginal abatement cost of carbon increases non-linearly with the decrease of CO_2 emissions level, but the uncertainty in the range of estimates also increases (Figure 3.33). Mitigation pathways with low-energy consumption patterns exhibit lower carbon values (Méjean et al. 2019; Meyer et al. 2021). In the context of the COVID-19 pandemic recovery, Kikstra et al. (2021a) also show that a low-energy-demand recovery scenario reduces carbon prices for a 1.5°C-consistent pathway by 19% compared to a scenario with energy demand trends restored to pre-pandemic levels.

For optimisation modelling frameworks, the time profile of marginal abatement costs of carbon depends on the discount rate, with lower discount rates implying higher carbon values in the short term but lower values in the long term (Emmerling et al. 2019) (see also 'Discounting' in Annex I: Glossary, and Annex III.I.2). In that case, the discount rate also influences the shape of the emissions trajectory, with low discount rates implying more emissions reduction in the short term and, for low-temperature categories, limiting CDR and temperature overshoot.

Pathways that correspond to NDCs announced prior to COP26 in 2030 and strengthen action after 2030 imply higher marginal abatement costs of carbon in the longer run than pathways with stronger immediate global mitigation action (Figure 3.32b) (*high confidence*).

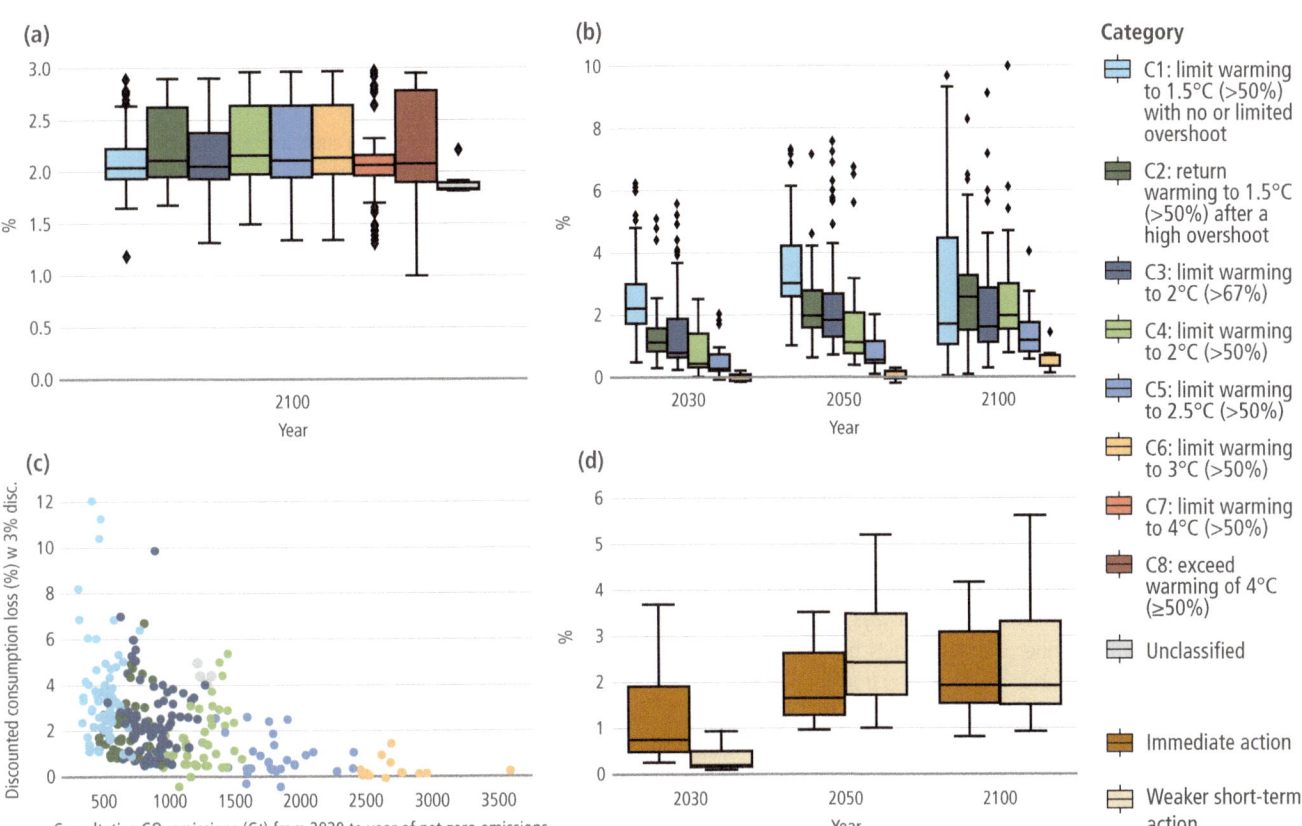

Figure 3.34 | (a) Mean annual global consumption growth rate over 2020–2100 for the mitigation pathways in the AR6 scenarios database. (b) Global GDP loss compared to baselines (not accounting for climate change damages) in 2030, 2050 and 2100 for mitigation pathways with immediate global action. **(c)** Total discounted consumption loss (with a 3% discount rate) in mitigation scenarios with respect to their corresponding baseline (not accounting for climate change damages) as a function of cumulative CO_2 emissions until date of net zero CO_2. **(d)** Comparison of GDP losses compared to baselines (not accounting for climate change damages) in 2030, 2050 and 2100 for pairs of scenarios depicting immediate action pathways and delayed action pathways. Source: AR6 Scenarios Database.

Aggregate economic activity and consumption levels in mitigation pathways are primarily determined by socio-economic development pathways but are also influenced by the stringency of the mitigation goal and the policy choices to reach the goal (*high confidence*). Mitigation pathways in temperature categories C1 and C2 entail losses in global consumption with respect to their baselines – not including benefits of avoided climate change impacts nor co-benefits or co-harms of mitigation action – that correspond to an annualised reduction of consumption growth by 0.04 (median value) (interquartile range [0.02–0.06]) percentage points over the century. For pathways in temperature categories C3 and C4 this reduction in global consumption growth is 0.03 (median value) (interquartile range [0.01–0.05]) percentage points over the century. In the majority of studies that focus on the economic effects of mitigation without accounting for climate damages, global economic growth and consumption growth is reduced compared to baseline scenarios (that omit damages from climate change), but mitigation pathways do not represent an absolute decrease of economic activity level (Figure 3.34b,c).

However, the possibility for increased economic activity following mitigation action, and conversely the risk of large negative economic effects, are not excluded. Some studies find that mitigation increases the speed of economic growth compared to baseline scenarios (Pollitt and Mercure 2018; Mercure et al. 2019). These studies are based on a macroeconomic modelling framework that represent baselines

below the efficiency frontier, based on non-equilibrium economic theory, and assume that mitigation is undertaken in such a way that green investments do not crowd out investment in other parts of the economy – and therefore offers an economic stimulus. In the context of the recovery from the COVID-19 crisis, it is estimated that a green investment push would initially boost the economy while also reducing GHG emissions (IMF 2020; Pollitt et al. 2021). Conversely, several studies find that only a GDP non-growth/degrowth or post-growth approach enable reaching climate stabilisation below 2°C (Hardt and O'Neill 2017; D'Alessandro et al. 2020; Hickel and Kallis 2020; Nieto et al. 2020), or to minimise the risks of reliance on high energy-GDP decoupling, large-scale CDR and large-scale renewable energy deployment (Keyßer and Lenzen 2021). Similarly, feedbacks of financial system risk amplifying shocks induced by mitigation policy and lead to a higher impact on economic activity (Stolbova et al. 2018).

Mitigation costs increase with the stringency of mitigation (Hof et al. 2017; Vrontisi et al. 2018) (Figure 3.34b,c), but are reduced when energy demand is moderated through energy efficiency and lifestyle changes (Fujimori et al. 2014; Bibas et al. 2015; Liu et al. 2018; Méjean et al. 2019), when sustainable transport policies are implemented (Zhang et al. 2018c), and when international technology cooperation is fostered (Schultes et al. 2018; Paroussos et al. 2019). Mitigation costs also depend on assumptions on availability and costs of technologies (Clarke et al. 2014; Bosetti et al. 2015; Dessens et al. 2016; Creutzig et al.

2018; Napp et al. 2019; Giannousakis et al. 2021), on the representation of innovation dynamics in modelling frameworks (Hoekstra et al. 2017; Rengs et al. 2020) (Chapter 16), as well as the representation of investment dynamics and financing mechanisms (Iyer et al. 2015c; Mercure et al. 2019; Battiston et al. 2021). In particular, endogenous and induced innovation reduce technology costs over time, create path dependencies and reduce the macroeconomic cost of reaching a mitigation target (Section 1.7.1.2). Mitigation costs also depend on socio-economic assumptions (Hof et al. 2017; van Vuuren et al. 2020).

Mitigation pathways with early emissions reductions represent higher mitigation costs in the short-run but bring long-term gains for the economy compared to delayed transition pathways (*high confidence*). Pathways with earlier mitigation action bring higher long-term GDP than pathways reaching the same end-of-century temperature with weaker early action (Figure 3.34d). Comparing counterfactual history scenarios, Sanderson and O'Neill (2020) also find that delayed mitigation action leads to higher peak costs. Rogelj et al. (2019b) and Riahi et al. (2021) also show that pathways with earlier timing of net zero CO_2 lead to higher transition costs but lower long-term mitigation costs, due to dynamic effects arising from lock-in avoidance and learning effects. For example, Riahi et al.(2021) find that for a 2°C target, the GDP losses (compared to a reference scenario without impacts from climate change) in 2100 are 5–70% lower in pathways that avoid net negative CO_2 emissions and temperature overshoot than in pathways with overshoot. Accounting also for climate change damage, van der Wijst et al. (2021a) show that avoiding net negative emissions leads to a small increase in total discounted mitigation costs over 2020–2100, between 5% and 14% in their medium assumptions, but does not increase mitigation costs when damages are high and when using a low discount rate, and becomes economically attractive if damages are not fully reversible. The modelled cost-optimal balance of mitigation action over time strongly depends on the discount rate used to compute or evaluate mitigation pathways: lower discount rates favour earlier mitigation, reducing both temperature overshoot and reliance on net negative carbon emissions (Emmerling et al.

2019; Riahi et al. 2021). Mitigation pathways with weak early action corresponding to NDCs announced prior to COP26 in 2030 and strengthening action after 2030 to reach end-of-century temperature targets imply limited mitigation costs in 2030, compared to immediate global action pathways, but faster increase in costs post-2030, with implications for intergenerational equity (Aldy et al. 2016; Liu et al. 2016; Vrontisi et al. 2018). Emissions trading policies reduce global aggregate mitigation costs, in particular in the context of achieving NDCs (Fujimori et al. 2015, 2016a; Böhringer et al. 2021; Edmonds et al. 2021), and change the distribution of mitigation costs between regions and countries (Section 3.6.1.2).

3.6.1.2   Regional Mitigation Costs and Effort-sharing Regimes

The economic repercussions of mitigation policies vary across countries (Aldy et al. 2016; Hof et al. 2017): regional variations exist in institutions, economic and technological development, and mitigation opportunities. For a globally uniform carbon price, carbon-intensive and energy-exporting countries bear the highest economic costs because of a deeper transformation of their economies and of trade losses in the fossil markets (Stern et al. 2012; Tavoni et al. 2015; Böhringer et al. 2021). This finding is confirmed in Figure 3.35. Since carbon-intensive countries are often poorer, uniform global carbon prices raise equity concerns (Tavoni et al. 2015). On the other hand, the climate economic benefits of mitigating climate change will be larger in poorer countries (Cross-Working Group Box 1 in this chapter). This reduces policy regressivity but does not eliminate it (Taconet et al. 2020; Gazzotti et al. 2021). Together with co-benefits, such as health benefits of improved air quality, the economic benefits of mitigating climate change are likely to outweigh mitigation costs in many regions (Li et al. 2018, 2019; Scovronick et al. 2021).

Regional policy costs depend on the evaluation framework (Budolfson et al. 2021), policy design, including revenue recycling, and on international coordination, especially among trade partners. By fostering technological change and finance, climate cooperation can

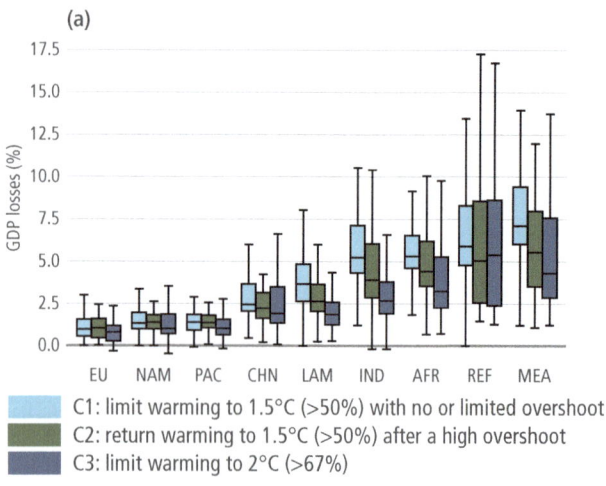
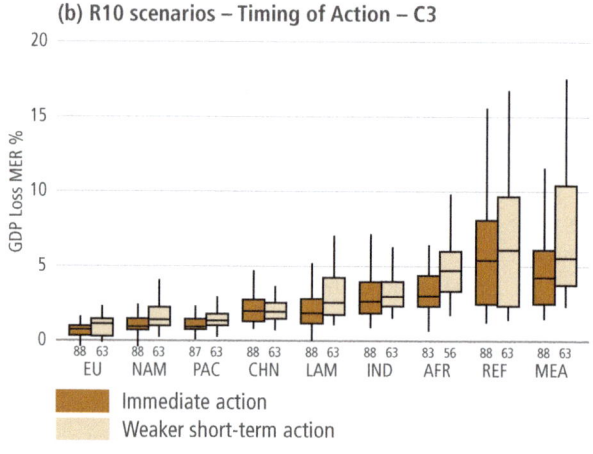

Figure 3.35 | a: regional mitigation costs in the year 2050 (expressed as GDP losses between mitigation scenarios and corresponding baselines, not accounting for climate change damages), under the assumption of immediate global action with uniform global carbon pricing and no international transfers, by climate categories for the 2°C (>67%) and 1.5°C (>50%) (with and without overshoot) categories. Right panel: policy costs in 2050 (as in panel a) for 2°C (>67%) climate category C3 for scenario pairs that represent either immediate global action ('immediate') or delayed global action ('delayed') with weaker action in the short term, strengthening to reach the same end-of-century temperature target.

generate economic benefits, both in large developing economies such as China and India (Paroussos et al. 2019) and industrialised regions such as Europe (Vrontisi et al. 2020). International coordination is a major driver of regional policy costs. Delayed participation in global mitigation efforts raises participation costs, especially in carbon-intensive economies (Figure 3.35a. Trading systems and transfers can deliver cost savings and improve equity (Rose et al. 2017a). On the other hand, measures that reduce imports of energy-intensive goods such as carbon-border tax adjustment may imply costs outside of the policy jurisdiction and have international equity repercussions, depending on how they are designed (Böhringer et al. 2012, 2017; Cosbey et al. 2019) (Section 13.6.6).

An equitable global emission-trading scheme would require very large international financial transfers, in the order of several hundred billion USD per year (Tavoni et al. 2015; Bauer et al. 2020; van den Berg et al. 2020). The magnitude of transfers depends on the stringency of the climate goals and on the burden-sharing principle. Some interpretations of equitable burden sharing compliant with the Paris Agreement leads to negative carbon allowances for developed countries and some developing countries by mid-century (van den Berg et al. 2020), more stringent than cost-optimal pathways. International transfers also depend on the underlying socio-economic development (Leimbach and Giannousakis 2019), as these drive the mitigation costs of meeting the Paris Agreement

(Rogelj et al. 2018b). By contrast, achieving equity without international markets would result in a large discrepancy in regional carbon prices, up to a factor of 100 (Bauer et al. 2020). The efficiency-sovereignty trade-off can be partly resolved by allowing for limited differentiation of regional carbon prices: moderate financial transfers substantially reduce inefficiencies by narrowing the carbon price spread (Bauer et al. 2020).

3.6.1.3   Investments in Mitigation Pathways

Figures 3.36 and 3.37 show increased investment needs in the energy sector in lower temperature categories, and a major shift away from fossil fuel generation and extraction towards electricity, including for system enhancements for electricity transmission, distribution and storage, and low-carbon technologies. Investment needs in the electricity sector are 2.3 trillion USD2015 yr^{-1} over 2023–2050 on average for C1 pathways, 2 trillion USD for C2 pathways, 1.7 trillion USD for C3, 1.2 trillion USD for C4 and 0.9–1.1 billion USD for C5/C6/C7 (mean values for pathways in each temperature category). The regional pattern of power sector investments broadly mirrors the global picture. However, the bulk of investment requirements are in medium- and low-income regions. These results from the AR6 scenarios database corroborate the findings from McCollum et al. (2018a), Zhou et al. (2019) and Bertram et al. (2021).

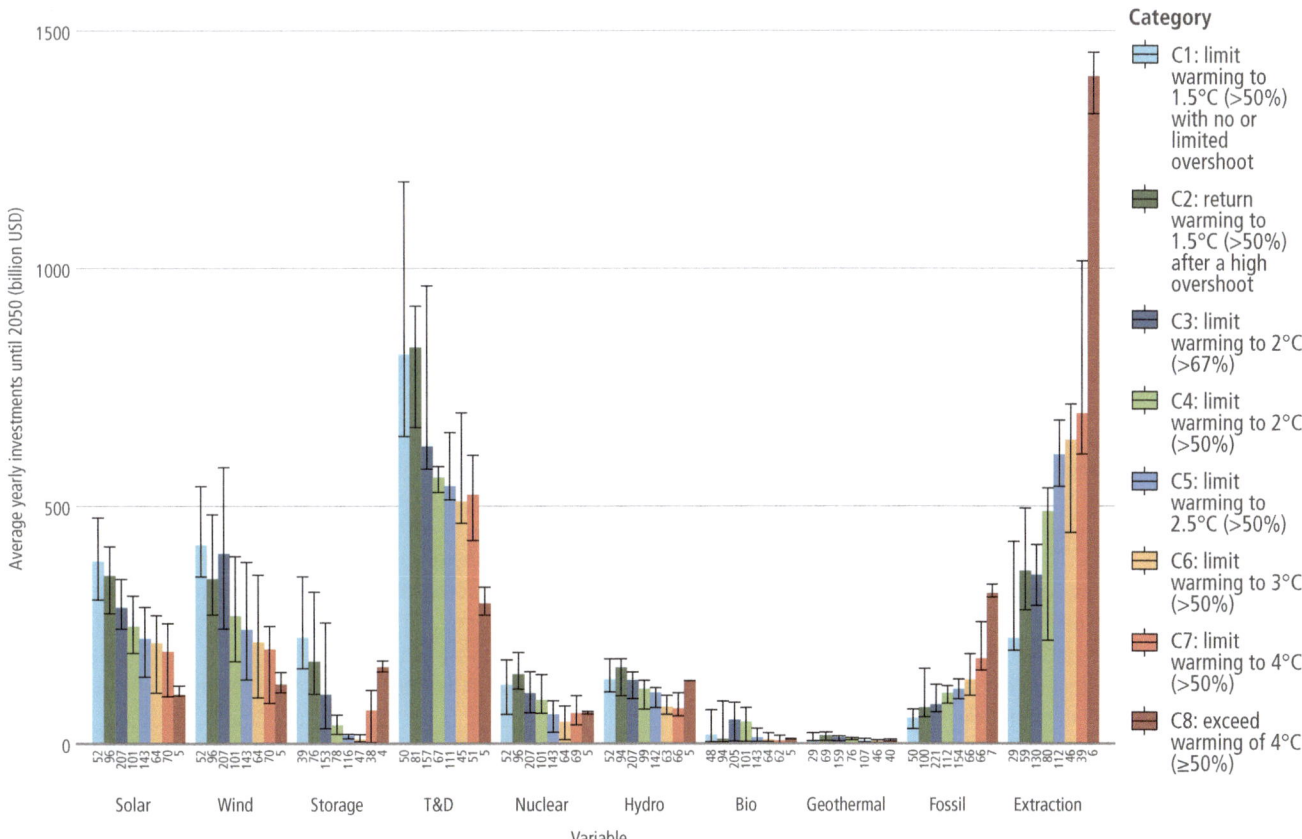

Figure 3.36 | Global average yearly investments from 2023–2052 for nine electricity supply subcomponents and for extraction of fossil fuels (in billion USD2015), in pathways by temperature categories. T&D: transmission and distribution of electricity. Bars show the median values (number of pathways at the bottom), and whiskers show the interquartile ranges.

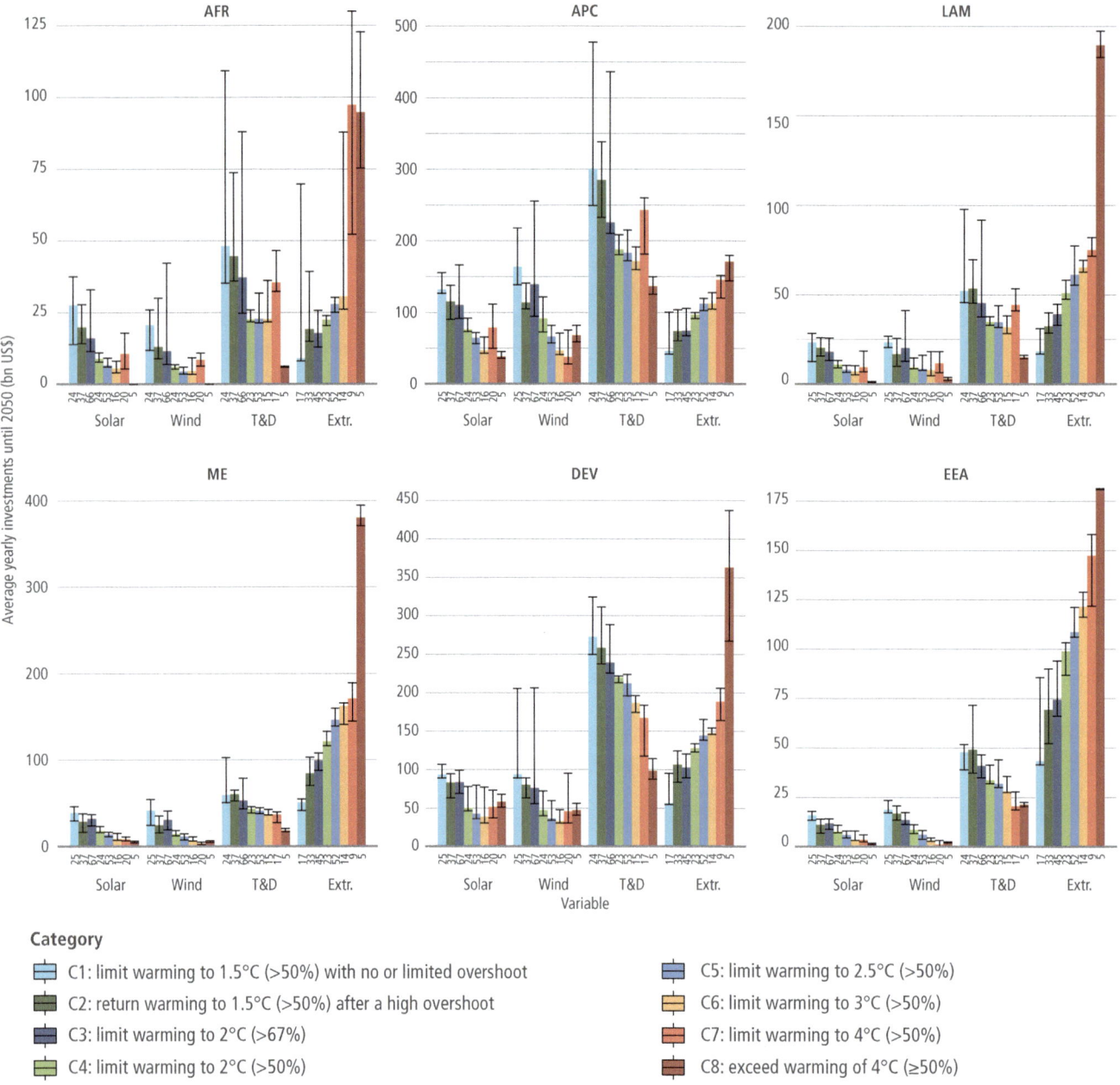

Category

- C1: limit warming to 1.5°C (>50%) with no or limited overshoot
- C2: return warming to 1.5°C (>50%) after a high overshoot
- C3: limit warming to 2°C (>67%)
- C4: limit warming to 2°C (>50%)
- C5: limit warming to 2.5°C (>50%)
- C6: limit warming to 3°C (>50%)
- C7: limit warming to 4°C (>50%)
- C8: exceed warming of 4°C (≥50%)

Figure 3.37 | Average yearly investments from 2023–2052 for the four subcomponents of the energy system representing the larger amounts (in billion USD2015), by aggregate regions, in pathways by temperature categories. T&D: transmissions and distribution of electricity. Extr.: extraction of fossil fuels. Bars show the median values (number of pathways at the bottom), and whiskers show the interquartile ranges. For definition of regional classifications used see Annex II Table 1.

In the context of the COVID-19 pandemic recovery, Kikstra et al. (2021a) show that a low-energy-demand recovery scenario reduces energy investments required until 2030 for a 1.5°C consistent pathway by 9% (corresponding to reducing total required energy investment by USD1.8 trillion) compared to a scenario with energy demand trends restored to pre-pandemic levels.

Few studies extend the scope of the investment needs quantification beyond the energy sector. Fisch-Romito and Guivarch (2019) and Ó Broin and Guivarch (2017) assess investment needs for transportation infrastructures and find lower investment needs in low-carbon pathways, due to a reduction in transport activity and a shift towards less road construction, compared to high-carbon

pathways. Rozenberg and Fay (2019) estimate the funding needs to close the service gaps in water and sanitation, transportation, electricity, irrigation, and flood protection in thousands of scenarios, showing that infrastructure investment paths compatible with full decarbonisation in the second half of the century need not cost more than more-polluting alternatives. Investment needs are estimated between 2% to 8% of GDP, depending on the quality and quantity of services targeted, the timing of investments, construction costs, and complementary policies.

Chapter 15 also reports investment requirements in global mitigation pathways in the near term, compares them to recent investment trends, and assesses financing issues.

3.6.2   Economic Benefits of Avoiding Climate Change Impacts

Cross-Working Group Box 1 | Economic Benefits from Avoided Climate Impacts Along Long-term Mitigation Pathways

Authors: Céline Guivarch (France), Steven Rose (the United States of America), Alaa Al Khourdajie (United Kingdom/Syria), Valentina Bosetti (Italy), Edward Byers (Austria/Ireland), Katherine Calvin (the United States of America), Tamma Carleton (the United States of America), Delavane Diaz (the United States of America), Laurent Drouet (France/Italy), Michael Grubb (United Kingdom), Tomoko Hasegawa (Japan), Alexandre C. Köberle (Brazil/United Kingdom), Elmar Kriegler (Germany), David McCollum (the United States of America), Aurélie Méjean (France), Brian O'Neill (the United States of America), Franziska Piontek (Germany), Julia Steinberger (United Kingdom/Switzerland), Massimo Tavoni (Italy)

Mitigation reduces the extent of climate change and its impacts on ecosystems, infrastructure, and livelihoods. This box summarises elements from the AR6 WGII report on aggregate climate change impacts and risks, putting them into the context of mitigation pathways. AR6 WGII provides an assessment of current lines of evidence regarding potential climate risks with future climate change, and therefore, the avoided risks from mitigating climate change. Regional and sectoral climate risks to physical and social systems are assessed (AR6 WGII Chapters 2–15). Over 100 of these are identified as Key Risks (KRs) and further synthesised by WGII Chapter 16 into eight overarching Representative Key Risks (RKRs) relating to low-lying coastal systems; terrestrial and ocean ecosystems; critical physical infrastructure, networks and services; living standards; human health; food security; water security; and peace and mobility (AR6 WGII Section 16.5.2). The RKR assessment finds that risks increase with global warming level, and also depend on socio-economic development conditions, which shape exposure and vulnerability, and adaptation opportunities and responses. 'Reasons For Concern', another WGII aggregate climate-impacts risk framing, are also assessed to increase with climate change, with increasing risk for unique and threatened systems, extreme weather events, distribution of impacts, global aggregate impacts, and large-scale singular events (AR6 WGII Chapter 16). For human systems, in general, the poor and disadvantaged are found to have greater exposure level and vulnerability for a given hazard. With some increase in global average warming from today expected regardless of mitigation efforts, human and natural systems will be exposed to new conditions and additional adaptation will be needed (AR6 WGII Chapter 18). The range of dates for when a specific warming level could be reached depends on future global emissions, with significant overlap of ranges across emissions scenarios due to climate system response uncertainties (AR6 WGI Tables 4.2 and 4.5). The speed at which the climate changes is relevant to adaptation timing, possibilities, and net impacts.

The AR6 WGII also assesses the growing literature estimating the global aggregate economic impacts of climate change and the social cost of carbon dioxide and other greenhouse gases (AR6 WGII Cross-Working Box ECONOMIC: Estimating Global Economic Impacts from Climate Change and the Social Cost of Carbon in AR6 WGII Chapter 16). The former represents aggregate estimates that inform assessment of the economic benefits of mitigation. This literature is characterised by significant variation in the estimates, including for today's level of global warming, due primarily to fundamental differences in methods, but also differences in impacts included, representation of socio-economic exposure, consideration of adaptation, aggregation approach, and assumed persistence of damages. The AR6 WGII's assessment identifies different approaches to quantification of aggregated economic impacts of climate change, including: physical modelling of impact processes, such as projected mortality rates from climate risks such as heat, vector- or waterborne diseases that are then monetised; structural economic modelling of impacts on production, consumption, and markets for economic sectors and regional economies; and statistical estimation of impacts based on observed historical responses to weather and climate. The AR6 WGII finds that variation in estimated global economic impacts increases with warming in all methodologies, indicating higher risk in terms of economic impacts at higher temperatures (*high confidence*). Many estimates are non-linear with marginal economic impacts increasing with temperature, although some show declining marginal economic impacts with temperature, and functional forms cannot be determined for all studies. The AR6 WGII's assessment finds that the lack of comparability between methodologies does not allow for identification of robust ranges of global economic impact estimates (*high confidence*). Further, AR6 WGII identifies evaluating and reconciling differences in methodologies as a research priority for facilitating use of the different lines of evidence (*high confidence*). However, there are estimates that are higher than AR5, indicating that global aggregate economic impacts could be higher than previously estimated (*low confidence* due to the lack of comparability across methodologies and lack of robustness of estimates) (AR6 WGII Cross-Working Box ECONOMIC).

Conceptually, the difference in aggregate economic impacts from climate change between two given temperature levels represents the aggregate economic benefits arising from avoided climate change impacts due to mitigation action. A subset of the studies whose estimates were evaluated by AR6 WGII (5 of 15) are used to derive illustrative estimates of aggregate economic benefits in 2100 arising

Cross-Working Group Box 1 (continued)

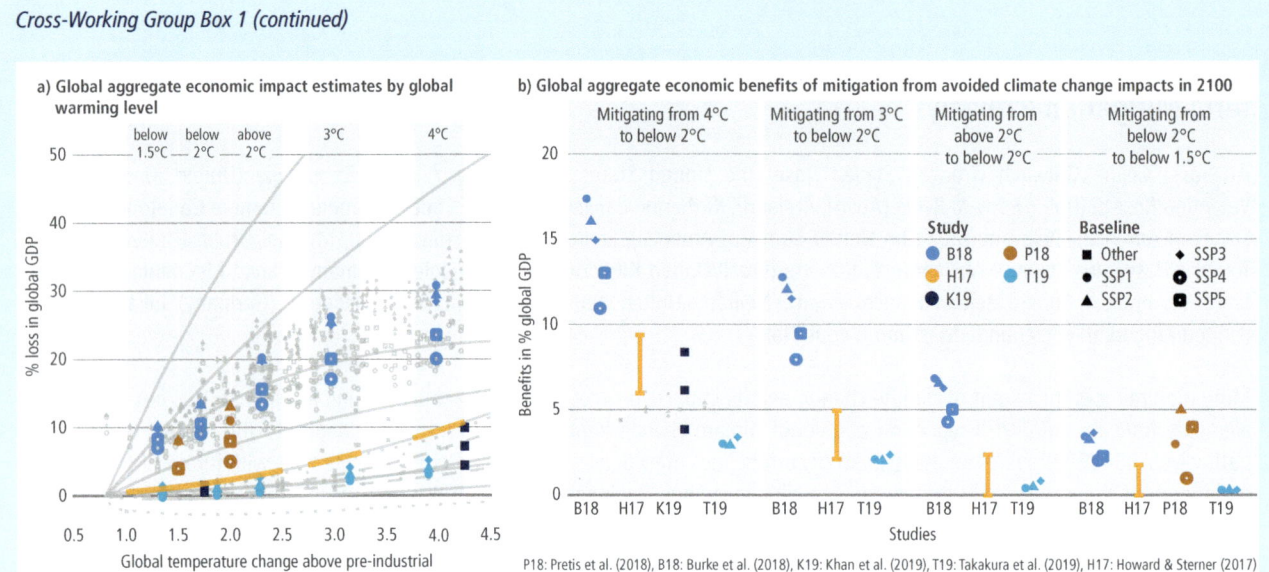

Cross-Working Group Box 1, Figure 1 | Global aggregate economic benefits of mitigation from avoided climate change impacts in 2100 corresponding to shifting from a higher temperature category (4°C (3.75°C–4.25°C), 3°C (2.75°C–3.25°C), or above 2°C (2°C–2.5°C), to below 2°C (1.5°C–2°C), as well as from below 2°C to below 1.5°C (1°C–1.5°C)), from the five studies discussed in the text. Panel (a) is adapted from AR6 WGII Cross-Working Group Box ECONOMIC, Figure 1, showing global aggregate economic impact estimates (% global GDP loss relative to GDP without additional climate change) by temperature change level. All estimates are shown in grey. Estimates used for the computation of estimated benefits in 2100 in panel (b) are coloured for the selected studies, which provide results for different temperature change levels. See the AR6 WGII AR6 WGII Cross-Working Group Box ECONOMIC for discussion and assessment of the estimates in panel (a) and the differences in methodologies. For B18 and T19, median estimates in the cluster are considered. Shape distinguishes the baseline scenarios. Temperature ranges are highlighted. HS17 estimates are based on their preferred model –50th percentile of non-catastrophic damage. Panel **(b)** shows the implied aggregate economic benefits in 2100 of a lower temperature increase. Economic benefits for point estimates are computed as a difference, while economic benefits from the curve HS17 are computed as ranges from the segment differences.

from avoided climate change (Howard and Sterner 2017; Burke et al. 2018; Pretis et al. 2018; Kahn et al. 2019; Takakura et al. 2019). Burke et al. (2018), Pretis et al. (2018) and Kahn et al. (2019) are examples of statistical estimations of historical relationships between temperature and economic growth, whereas Takakura et al. (2019) is an example of structural modelling, which evaluates selected impact channels (impacts on agriculture productivity, undernourishment, heat-related mortality, labour productivity, cooling/heating demand, hydro-electric and thermal power generation capacity and fluvial flooding) with a general equilibrium model. Howard and Sterner (2017) and Rose et al. (2017b) estimate damage functions that can be used to compute the economic benefits of mitigation from avoiding a given temperature level for a lower one. Howard and Sterner (2017) estimate a damage function from a meta-analysis of aggregate economic impact studies, while Rose et al. (2017b) derive global functions by temperature and socio-economic drivers from stylised aggregate cost-benefit-analysis (CBA) integrated assessment models (IAMs) using diagnostic experiments. Cross-Working Group Box 1, Figure 1 summarises the global aggregate economic benefits in 2100 of avoided climate change impacts from individual studies corresponding to shifting from a higher temperature category (above 3°C, below 3°C or below 2.5°C) to below 2°C, as well as from below 2°C to below 1.5°C. Benefits are positive and increase with the temperature gap for any given study, and this result is robust across socio-economic scenarios. The Figure provides evidence of a wide range of quantifications, and illustrates the important differences associated with methods. Panel a puts the studies used to calculate aggregate economic benefits arising from avoided impacts into the context of the broader set of studies assessed in WGII (Section 16.6.2 of this report, AR6 WGII Cross-Working Group Box ECONOMIC,). However, economic benefits in 2100 arising from avoided impacts cannot be directly computed from damage estimates across this broader set of studies, due to inconsistencies – different socio-economic assumptions, scenario designs, and counterfactual reference scenarios across studies. Furthermore, these types of estimates cannot be readily compared to mitigation cost estimates. The comparison would require a framework that ensures consistency in assumptions and dynamics and allows for consideration of benefits and costs along the entire pathway.

Aggregate benefits from avoided impacts expressed in GDP terms, as in Figure 1, do not encompass all avoided climate risks, adaptation possibilities, and do not represent their influence on well-being and welfare (AR6 WGII Cross-Working Group Box ECONOMIC). Methodological challenges for economic impact estimates include representing uncertainty and variability, capturing interactions and spillovers, considering distributional effects, representing micro- and macro-adaptation processes, specifying non-gradual damages and non-linearities, and improving understanding of potential long-run growth effects. In addition, the economic benefits aggregated

Cross-Working Group Box 1 (continued)

at the global scale provide limited insights into regional heterogeneity. Global economic impact studies with regional estimates find large differences across regions in absolute and percentage terms, with developing and transitional economies typically more vulnerable. Furthermore, (avoided) impacts for poorer households and poorer countries can represent a smaller share in aggregate quantifications expressed in GDP terms or monetary terms, compared to their influence on well-being and welfare (Hallegatte et al. 2020; Markhvida et al. 2020). Finally, as noted by AR6 WGII, other lines of evidence regarding climate risks, beyond monetary estimates, should be considered in decision-making, including Key Risks and Reasons for Concern.

Cost-benefit analyses (CBA) aim to balance all costs and benefits in a unified framework (Nordhaus, 2008). Estimates of economic benefits from avoided climate change impacts depend on the types of damages accounted for, the assumed exposure and vulnerability to these damages as well as the adaptation capacity, which in turn are based on the development pathway assumed (Cross-Working Group Box 1 in this chapter). CBA IAMs raised criticism, in particular for omitting elements of dynamic realism, such as inertia, induced innovation and path dependence, in their representation of mitigation (Grubb et al. 2021), and for underestimating damages from climate change, missing non-monetary damages, the uncertain and heterogeneous nature of damages and the risk of catastrophic damages (Stern 2013, 2016; Diaz and Moore 2017; NASEM 2017; Pindyck 2017; Stoerk et al. 2018; Stern and Stiglitz 2021). Emerging literature has started to address those gaps, and integrated into cost-benefit frameworks the account of heterogeneity of climate damage and inequality (Dennig et al. 2015; Budolfson et al. 2017; Fleurbaey et al. 2019; Kornek et al. 2021), damages with higher persistence, including damages on capital and growth (Moyer et al. 2014; Dietz and Stern 2015; Moore and Diaz 2015; Guivarch and Pottier 2018; Ricke et al. 2018; Piontek et al. 2019), risks of tipping points (Cai et al. 2015, 2016; Lontzek et al. 2015; Lemoine and Traeger 2016; van der Ploeg and de Zeeuw 2018; Cai and Lontzek 2019; Nordhaus 2019; Yumashev et al. 2019; Taconet et al. 2021) and damages to natural capital and non-market goods (Tol 1994; Sterner and Persson 2008; Bastien-Olvera and Moore 2020; Drupp and Hänsel 2021).

Each of these factors, when accounted for in a CBA framework, tends to increase the welfare benefit of mitigation, thus leading to stabilisation at a lower temperature in optimal mitigation pathways. The limitations in CBA modelling frameworks remain significant, their ability to represent all damages incomplete, and the uncertainty in estimates remains large. However, emerging evidence suggests that, even without accounting for co-benefits of mitigation on other sustainable development dimensions (see Section 3.6.3 for further details about on co-benefits), global benefits of pathways that limit warming to 2°C outweigh global mitigation costs over the 21st century: depending on the study, the reason for this result lies in assumptions of economic damages from climate change in the higher end of available estimates (Moore and Diaz 2015; Ueckerdt et al. 2019; Brown and Saunders 2020; Glanemann et al. 2020), in the introduction of risks of tipping points (Cai and

Lontzek 2019), in the consideration of damages to natural capital and non-market goods (Bastien-Olvera and Moore 2020) or in the combination of updated representations of carbon cycle and climate modules, updated damage estimates and/or updated representations of economic and mitigation dynamics (Dietz and Stern 2015; Hänsel et al. 2020; Wei et al. 2020; van der Wijst et al. 2021b). In the studies cited above that perform a sensitivity analysis, this result is found to be robust to a wide range of assumptions on social preferences (in particular, on inequality aversion and pure rate-of-time preference) and holds except if assumptions of economic damages from climate change are in the lower end of available estimates and the pure rate-of-time preference is in the higher range of values usually considered (typically above 1.5%). However, although such pathways bring net benefits over time (in terms of aggregate discounted present value), they involve distributional consequences and transition costs (Brown et al. 2020; Brown and Saunders 2020) (Sections 3.6.1.2 and 3.6.4).

The standard discounted utilitarian framework dominates CBA, thus often limiting the analysis to the question of discounting. CBA can be expanded to accommodate a wider variety of ethical values to assess mitigation pathways (Fleurbaey et al. 2019). The role of ethical values with regard to inequality and the situation of the worse off (Adler et al. 2017), risk (van den Bergh and Botzen 2014; Drouet et al. 2015), and population size (Scovronick et al. 2017; Méjean et al. 2020) has been explored. In most of these studies, the optimal climate policy is found to be more stringent than the one obtained using a standard discounted utilitarian criterion.

Comparing economic costs and benefits of mitigation raises a number of methodological and fundamental difficulties. Monetising the full range of climate change impacts is extremely hard, if not impossible (AR6 WGII Chapter 16), as is aggregating costs and benefits over time and across individuals when values are heterogeneous (Chapter 1; AR5 WGIII Chapter 3). Other approaches should thus be considered in supplement for decision-making (Chapter 1 and Section 1.7), in particular cost-effectiveness approaches that analyse how to achieve a defined mitigation objective at least cost or while also reaching other societal goals (Koomey 2013; Kaufman et al. 2020; Köberle et al. 2021; Stern and Stiglitz 2021). In cost-effectiveness studies too, incorporating benefits from avoided climate damages influences the results and leads to more stringent mitigation in the short term (Drouet et al. 2021; Schultes et al. 2021).

3.6.3 Aggregate Economic Implication of Mitigation Co-benefits and Trade-offs

Mitigation actions have co-benefits and trade-offs with other sustainable development dimensions (Section 3.7) beyond climate change, which imply welfare effects and economic effects, as well as other implications beyond the economic dimension. The majority of quantifications of mitigation costs and benefits synthesized in Sections 3.6.1 and 3.6.2 do not account for these economic benefits and costs associated with co-benefits and trade-offs along mitigation pathways.

Systematic reviews of the literature on co-benefits and trade-offs from mitigation actions have shown that only a small portion of articles provide economic quantifications (Deng et al. 2017; Karlsson et al. 2020). Most economic quantifications use monetary valuation approaches. Improved air quality, and associated health effects, are the co-benefit category dominating the literature (Markandya et al. 2018; Vandyck et al. 2018; Scovronick et al. 2019; Howard et al. 2020; Karlsson et al. 2020b; Rauner et al. 2020a,b), but some studies cover other categories, including health effects from diet change (Springmann et al. 2016b) and biodiversity impacts (Rauner et al. 2020a). Regarding health effects from air quality improvement and from diet change, co-benefits are shown to be of the same order of magnitude as mitigation costs (Thompson et al. 2014; Springmann et al. 2016a,b; Markandya et al. 2018; Scovronick et al. 2019b; Howard et al. 2020; Rauner et al. 2020a,b; Liu et al. 2021; Yang et al. 2021). Co-benefits from improved air quality are concentrated sooner in time than economic benefits from avoided climate change impacts (Karlsson et al. 2020), such that when accounting both for positive health impacts from reduced air pollution and for the negative climate effect of reduced cooling aerosols, optimal GHG mitigation pathways exhibit immediate and continual net economic benefits (Scovronick et al. 2019a). However, AR6 WGI Chapter 6 (Section 6.7.3) shows a delay in air pollution reduction benefits when they come from climate change mitigation policies compared with air pollution reduction policies.

Achieving co-benefits is not automatic but results from coordinated policies and implementation strategies (Clarke et al. 2014; McCollum et al. 2018a). Similarly, avoiding trade-offs requires targeted policies (van Vuuren et al. 2015; Bertram et al. 2018). There is limited evidence of such pathways, but the evidence shows that mitigation pathways designed to reach multiple Sustainable Development Goals instead of focusing exclusively on emissions reductions, result in limited additional costs compared to the increased benefits (Cameron et al. 2016; McCollum et al. 2018b; Fujimori et al. 2020a; Sognnaes et al. 2021).

3.6.4 Structural Change, Employment and Distributional Issues Along Mitigation Pathways

Beyond aggregate effects at the economy-wide level, mitigation pathways have heterogeneous economic implications for different sectors and different actors. Climate-related factors are only one driver of the future structure of the economy, of the future of employment, and of future inequality trends, as overarching trends in demographics, technological change (innovation, automation, etc.), education and institutions will be prominent drivers. For instance, Rao et al. (2019b) and Benveniste et al. (2021) have shown that income inequality projections for the 21st century vary significantly, depending on socio-economic assumptions related to demography, education levels, social public spending and migrations. However, the sections below focus on climate-related factors, both climate-mitigation actions themselves and the climate change impacts avoided along mitigation pathways, effects on structural change, including employment, and distributional effects.

3.6.4.1 Economic Structural Change and Employment in Long-term Mitigation Pathways

Mitigation pathways entail transformation of the energy sector, with structural change away from fossil energy and towards low-carbon energy (Section 3.3), as well as broader economic structural change, including industrial restructuring and reductions in carbon-intensive activities in parallel to extensions in low-carbon activities.

Mitigation affects work through multiple channels, which impacts geographies, sectors and skill categories differently (Fankhaeser et al. 2008; Bowen et al. 2018; Malerba and Wiebe 2021). Aggregate employment impacts of mitigation pathways mainly depend on the aggregate macroeconomic effect of mitigation (Sections 3.6.1 and 3.6.2) and of mitigation policy design and implementation (Freire-González 2018) (Section 4.2.6.3). Most studies that quantify overall employment implications of mitigation policies are conducted at the national or regional scales (Section 4.2.6.3), or sectoral scales (e.g., see Chapter 6 for energy sector jobs). The evidence is limited at the multinational or global scale, but studies generally find small differences in aggregate employment in mitigation pathways compared to baselines: the sign of the difference depends on the assumptions and modelling frameworks used and the policy design tested, with some studies or policy design cases leading to small increases in employment (Chateau and Saint-Martin 2013; Pollitt et al. 2015; Barker et al. 2016; Garcia-Casals et al. 2019; Fujimori et al. 2020a; Vrontisi et al. 2020; Malerba and Wiebe 2021) and other studies or policy design cases leading to small decreases (Chateau and Saint-Martin 2013; Vandyck et al. 2016). The small variations in aggregate employment hide substantial reallocation of jobs across sectors, with jobs creation in some sectors and jobs destruction in others. Mitigation action through thermal renovation of buildings, installation and maintenance of low-carbon generation, and the expansion of public transit lead to job creation, while jobs are lost in fossil fuel extraction, energy supply and energy-intensive sectors in mitigation pathways (von Stechow et al. 2015, 2016; Barker et al. 2016; Fuso Nerini et al. 2018; Perrier and Quirion 2018; Pollitt and Mercure 2018; Dominish et al. 2019; Garcia-Casals et al. 2019). In the energy sector, job losses in the fossil fuel sector are found to be compensated by gains in wind and solar jobs, leading to a net increase in energy sector jobs in 2050 in a mitigation pathway compatible with stabilisation of the temperature increase below 2°C (Pai et al. 2021). Employment effects also differ by geographies, with energy-importing regions benefiting from net job creations but energy-exporting regions experiencing very small gains or suffering from net job destruction (Barker et al. 2016; Pollitt and Mercure 2018; Garcia-Casals et al. 2019; Malerba and Wiebe 2021). Coal phase-out raises acute issues of just transition for the coal-dependent countries (Spencer et al. 2018; Jakob et al. 2020) (Section 4.5 and Box 6.2).

Mitigation action also affects employment through avoided climate change impacts. Mitigation reduces the risks to human health and associated impacts on labour and helps protect workers from the occupational health and safety hazards imposed by climate change (Kjellstrom et al. 2016, 2018, 2019; Levi et al. 2018; Day et al. 2019) (AR6 WGII Chapter 16).

3.6.4.2 Distributional Implications of Long-term Mitigation Pathways

Mitigation policies can have important distributive effects between and within countries, either reducing or increasing economic inequality and poverty, depending on policy instruments' design and implementation (see Section 3.6.1.2 for an assessment of the distribution of mitigation costs across regions in mitigation pathways; Sections 3.7 and 4.2.2.6, and Box 3.6 for an assessment of the fairness and ambition of NDCs; and Section 4.5 for an assessment of national mitigation pathways along the criteria of equity, including Just Transition, as well as Section 17.4.5 for equity in a Just Transition). For instance, emissions taxation has important distributive effects, both between and within income groups (Cronin et al. 2018b; Klenert et al. 2018; Pizer and Sexton 2019; Douenne 2020; Steckel et al. 2021). These effects are more significant in some sectors, such as transport, and depend on country-specific consumption structures (Dorband et al. 2019; Fullerton and Muehlegger 2019; Ohlendorf et al. 2021). However, revenues from emissions taxation can be used to lessen their regressive distributional impacts or even turn the policy into a progressive policy reducing inequality and/or leading to gains for lower-income households (Cameron et al. 2016; Jakob and Steckel 2016; Fremstad and Paul 2019; Fujimori et al. 2020b; Böhringer et al. 2021; Budolfson et al. 2021; Soergel et al. 2021b; Steckel et al. 2021). Mitigation policies may affect the poorest through effects on energy and food prices (Hasegawa et al. 2015; Fujimori et al. 2019). Markkanen and Anger-Kraavi (2019) and Lamb et al. (2020) synthesize evidence from the existing literature on social co-impacts of climate change mitigation policy and their implications for inequality. They show that most policies can compound or lessen inequalities depending on contextual factors, policy design and policy implementation, but that negative inequality impacts of climate policies can be mitigated (and possibly even prevented), when distributive and procedural justice are taken into consideration in all stages of policymaking, including policy planning, development and implementation, and when focusing on the carbon intensity of lifestyles, sufficiency and equity, well-being and decent living standards for all (Section 13.6).

Mitigation pathways also affect economic inequalities between and within countries, and poverty, through the reduction of climate change impacts that fall more heavily on low-income countries, communities and households, and exacerbate poverty (AR6 WGII Chapters 8 and 16). Higher levels of warming are projected to generate higher inequality between countries as well as within them

(AR6 WGII Chapter 16). Through avoiding impacts, mitigation thus reduces economic inequalities and poverty (*high confidence*).

A few studies consider both mitigation policies' distributional impacts and avoided climate change impacts on inequalities along mitigation pathways. Rezai et al. (2018) find that unmitigated climate change impacts increase inequality, whereas mitigation has the potential to reverse this effect. Considering uncertainty in socio-economic assumptions, emission pathways, mitigation costs, temperature response, and climate damage, Taconet et al. (2020) show that the uncertainties associated with socio-economic assumptions and damage estimates are the main drivers of future inequalities between countries and that in most cases mitigation policies reduce future inequalities between countries. Gazzotti et al. (2021) show that inequality persists in 2°C-consistent pathways due to regressivity of residual climate damages. However, the evidence on mitigation pathways' implications for global inequality and poverty remains limited, and the modelling frameworks used have limited ability to fully represent the different dimensions of inequality and poverty and all the mechanisms by which mitigation affects inequality and poverty (Rao et al. 2017a; Emmerling and Tavoni 2021; Jafino et al. 2021).

3.7 Sustainable Development, Mitigation and Avoided Impacts

3.7.1 Synthesis Findings on Mitigation and Sustainable Development

Rapid and effective climate mitigation is a necessary part of sustainable development (*high confidence*) (Cross-Chapter Box 5 in Chapter 4), but the latter can only be realised if climate mitigation becomes integrated with sustainable development policies (*high confidence*). Targeted policy areas must include healthy nutrition, sustainable consumption and production, inequality and poverty alleviation, air quality and international collaboration (*high confidence*). Lower energy demand enables synergies between mitigation and sustainability, with lower reliance on CDR (*high confidence*).

This section covers the long-term interconnection of sustainable development and mitigation, taking forward the holistic vision of sustainable development described in the SDGs (Brandi 2015; Leal Filho et al. 2018). Recent studies have explored the aggregated impact of mitigation for multiple sustainable-development dimensions (Hasegawa et al. 2014; Bertram et al. 2018; Fuso Nerini et al. 2018; Grubler et al. 2018; McCollum et al. 2018b; Soergel et al. 2021a; van Vuuren et al. 2019). For instance, Figure 3.38 shows selected mitigation co-benefits and trade-offs based on a subset of models and scenarios, since so far many IAMs do not have a comprehensive coverage of SDGs (Rao et al. 2017a; van Soest et al. 2019). Figure 3.38 shows that mitigation *likely* leads to increased forest cover (SDG 15 – life on land) and reduced mortality from ambient PM2.5 pollution (SDG 3 – good health and well-being) compared to reference scenarios. However, mitigation policies can also cause higher food prices and an increased population at risk of hunger (SDG 2 – zero hunger) and relying on solid fuels (SDG 3 – good health and well-being; and SDG 7 – affordable and clean energy) as side effects. These trade-offs can be compensated through targeted support measures and/or additional sustainable development policies (Cameron et al. 2016; Bertram et al. 2018; Fujimori et al. 2019; Soergel et al. 2021a).

The synthesis of the interplay between climate mitigation and sustainable development is shown in Figure 3.39. Panel a shows the reduction in population affected by climate impacts at 1.5°C compared to 3°C according to sustainability domains (Byers et al. 2018). Reducing warming reduces the population impacted by all impact categories shown (*high confidence*). The left panel does not take into account any side effects of mitigation efforts or policies to reduce warming: only reductions in climate impacts. This underscores that mitigation is an integral basis for comprehensive sustainable development (Watts et al. 2015).

Panels b and c of Figure 3.39 show the effects of 1.5°C mitigation policies compared to current national policies: narrow

mitigation policies (averaged over several models, middle panel), and policies integrating sustainability considerations (right panel of Figure 3.39, based on the Illustrative Mitigation Pathway 'Shifting Pathways' (*IMP-SP*) (Soergel et al. 2021a)). Note that neither middle nor right panels include climate impacts.

Areas of co-benefits include human health, ambient air pollution and other specific kinds of pollution, while areas of trade-off include food access, habitat loss and mineral resources (*medium confidence*). For example, action consistent with 1.5°C in the absence of energy-demand reduction measures require large quantities of CDR, which, depending on the type used, are likely to negatively impact both food availability and areas for biodiversity (Fujimori et al. 2018; Ohashi et al. 2019; Roelfsema et al. 2020).

Mitigation to 1.5°C reduces climate impacts on sustainability (left). Policies integrating sustainability and mitigation (right) have far fewer trade-offs than narrow mitigation policies (middle).

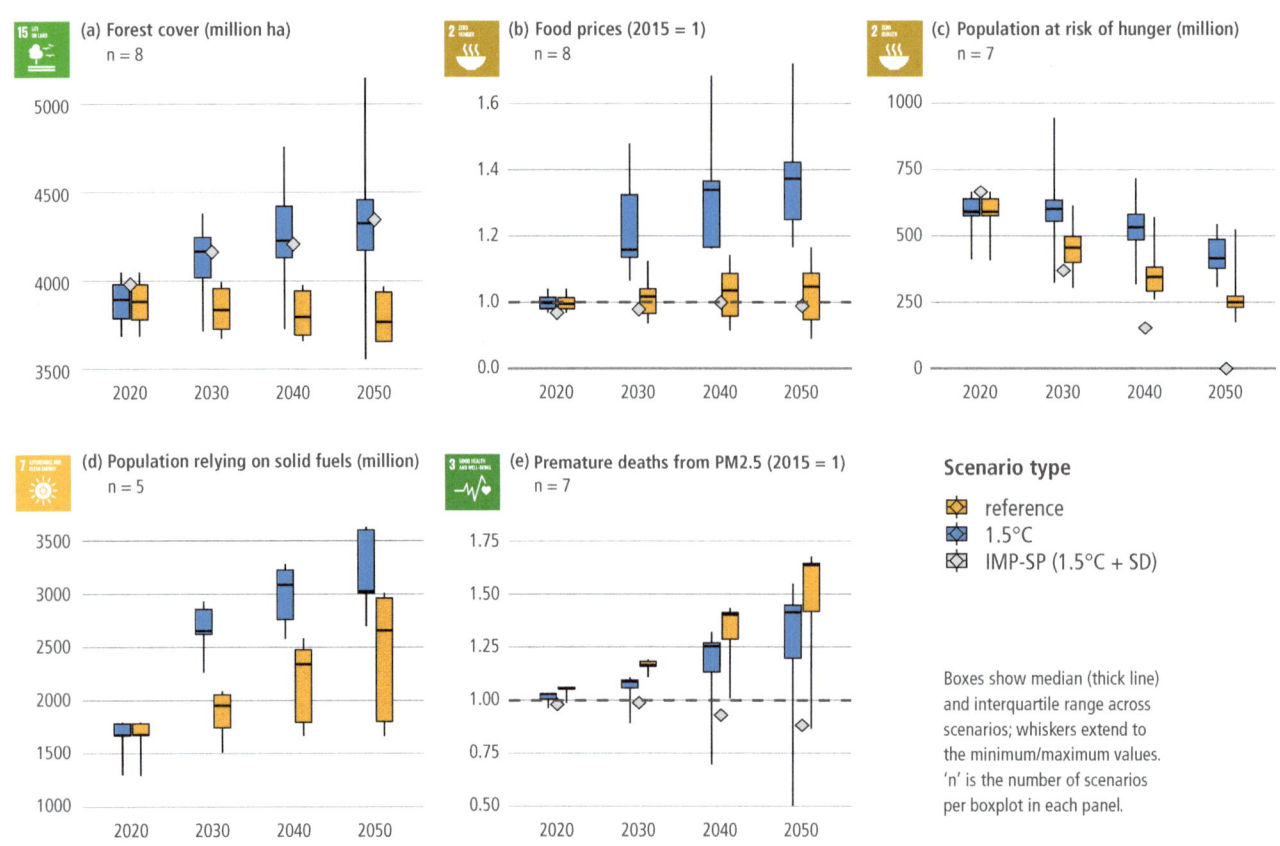

Figure 3.38 | Effect of climate change mitigation on different dimensions of sustainable development: shown are mitigation scenarios compatible with the 1.5°C target (blue) and reference scenarios (yellow). Blue box plots contain scenarios that include narrow mitigation policies from different studies (see below). This is compared to a sustainable development scenario (*SP*, Soergel et al. 2021a, grey diamonds) integrating mitigation and SD policies (e.g., zero hunger in 2050 by assumption). Scenario sources for box plots: single scenarios from: (i) Fujimori et al. (2020a); (ii) Soergel et al. (2021a); multi-model scenario set from CD-LINKS (McCollum et al. 2018b; Fujimori et al. 2019; Roelfsema et al. 2020). For associated methods, see also Cameron et al. (2016) and Rafaj et al. (2021). The reference scenario for Fujimori et al. (2020a) is no-policy baseline; for all other studies, it includes current climate policies. In the 'Food prices' and 'Risk of hunger' panels, scenarios from CD-LINKS include a price cap of USD200 tCO_2-eq for land-use emissions (Fujimori et al. 2019). For the other indicators, CD-LINKS scenarios without price cap (Roelfsema et al. 2020) are used due to SDG indicator availability. In the 'Premature deaths' panel, a well-below 2°C scenario from Fujimori et al. (2020a) is used in place of a 1.5°C scenario due to data availability, and all scenarios are indexed to their 2015 values due to a spread in reported levels between models. SDG icons were created by the United Nations.

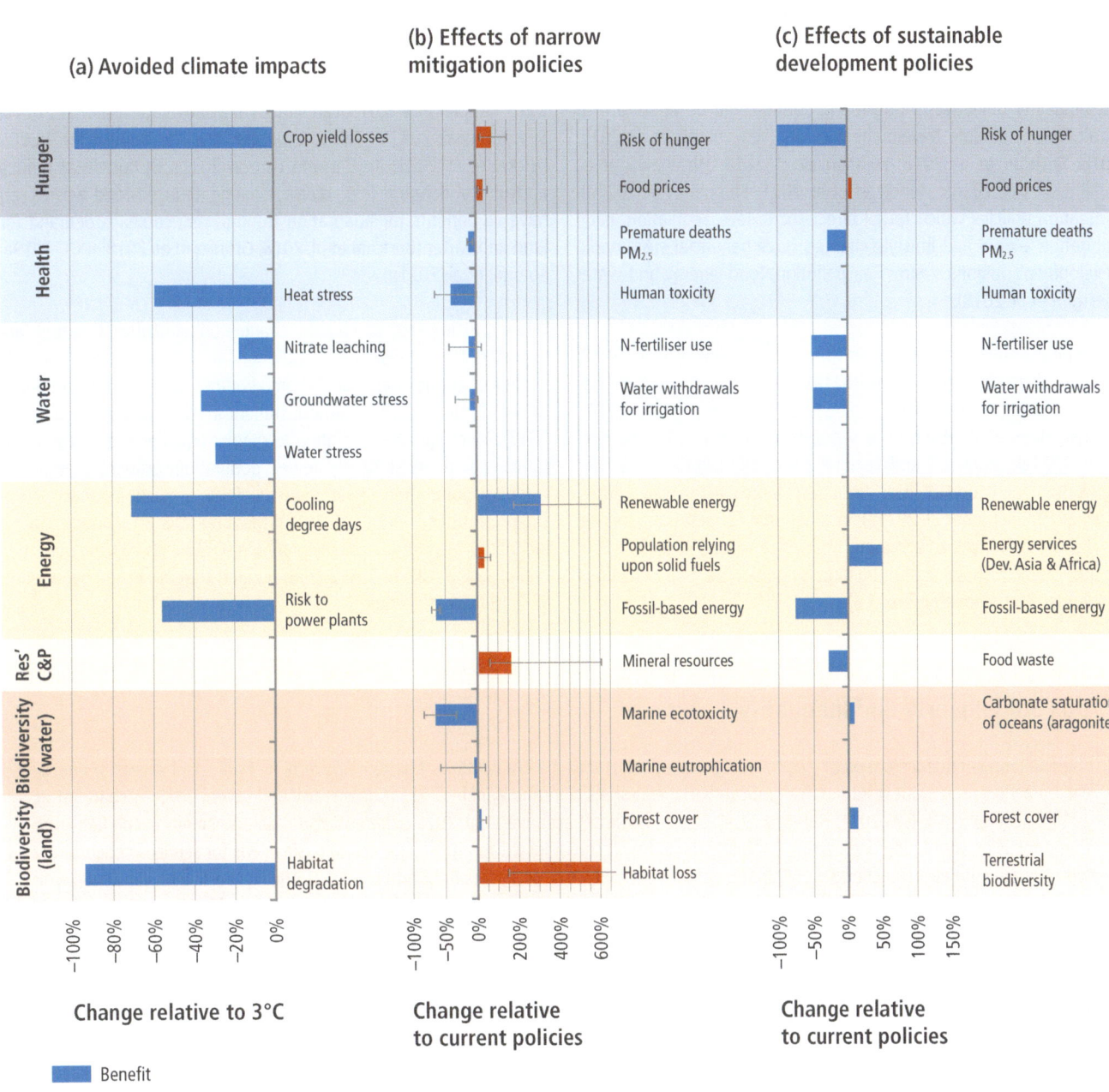

Figure 3.39 | Sustainable development effects of mitigation to 1.5°C. Panel (a): benefits of mitigation from avoided impacts. **Panel (b):** sustainability co-benefits and trade-offs of narrow mitigation policies (averaged over multiple models). **Panel (c):** sustainability co-benefits and trade-offs of mitigation policies integrating Sustainable Development Goals. Scale: 0% means no change compared to 3°C (left) or current policies (middle and right). Blue values correspond to proportional improvements, red values to proportional worsening. Note: only the left panel considers climate impacts on sustainable development; the middle and right panels do not. 'Res' C&P' stands for Responsible Consumption and Production (SDG 12). Data are from Byers et al. (2018) (left), *SP*/Soergel et al. (2021a) (right). Methods used in middle panel: for biodiversity, Ohashi et al. (2019); for ecotoxicity and eutrophication, Arvesen et al. (2018) and Pehl et al. (2017); for energy access, Cameron et al. (2016). 'Energy services' on the right is a measure of useful energy in buildings and transport. 'Food prices' and 'Risk of hunger' in the middle panel are the same as in Figure 3.38.

3.7.1.1 Policies Combining Mitigation and Sustainable Development

These findings indicate that holistic policymaking integrating sustainability objectives alongside mitigation will be important in attaining Sustainable Development Goals (van Vuuren et al. 2015, 2018; Bertram et al. 2018; Fujimori et al. 2018; Hasegawa et al. 2018; Liu et al. 2020a; Honegger et al. 2021; Soergel et al. 2021a). Mitigation policies which target direct sector-level regulation, early mitigation action, and lifestyle changes have beneficial sustainable development outcomes across air pollution, food, energy and water (Bertram et al. 2018).

These policies include ones around stringent air quality (Kinney 2018; Rafaj et al. 2018; Soergel et al. 2021a); efficient and safe demand-side technologies, especially cook stoves (Cameron et al. 2016); lifestyle changes (Bertram et al. 2018; Grubler et al. 2018; Soergel et al. 2021a); industrial and sectoral policy (Bertram et al. 2018); agricultural and food policies (including food waste) (van Vuuren et al. 2019; Soergel et al. 2021a); international cooperation (Soergel et al. 2021a); as well as economic policies described in Section 3.6. Recent research shows that mitigation is compatible with reductions in inequality and poverty (Box 3.6).

Lower demand – for example, for energy and land-intensive consumption such as meat – represents a synergistic strategy for achieving ambitious climate mitigation without compromising Sustainable Development Goals (*high confidence*) (Bertram et al. 2018; Grubler et al. 2018; van Vuuren et al. 2018; Kikstra et al. 2021b; Soergel et al. 2021a). This is especially true for reliance on BECCS (Hickel et al. 2021; Keyßer and Lenzen 2021). Options that reduce agricultural demand (e.g., dietary change, reduced food waste) can have co-benefits for adaptation through reductions in demand for land and water (Bertram et al. 2018; Grubler et al. 2018; IPCC 2019a; Soergel et al. 2021a).

While the impacts of climate change on agricultural output are expected to increase the population at risk of hunger, there is evidence suggesting population growth will be the dominant driver of hunger and undernourishment in Africa in 2050 (Hall et al. 2017). Meeting SDG 5, relating to gender equality and reproductive rights, could substantially lower population growth, leading to a global population lower than the 95% prediction range of the UN projections (Abel et al. 2016). Meeting SDG 5 (gender equality, including via voluntary family planning (O'Sullivan 2018)) could thus minimise the risks to SDG 2 (zero hunger) that are posed by meeting SDG 13 (climate action).

Box 3.6 | Poverty and Inequality

There is high confidence (*medium evidence*, *high agreement*) that the eradication of extreme poverty and universal access to energy can be achieved without resulting in significant GHG emissions (Tait and Winkler 2012; Chakravarty and Tavoni 2013; Pachauri et al. 2013; Pachauri 2014; Rao 2014; Hubacek et al. 2017b; Poblete-Cazenave et al. 2021). There is also high agreement in the literature that a focus on well-being and decent living standards for all can reduce disparities in access to basic needs for services concurrently with climate mitigation (Section 5.2). Mitigation pathways in which national redistribution of carbon-pricing revenues is combined with international climate finance, achieve poverty reduction globally (Fujimori et al. 2020b; Soergel et al. 2021b). Carbon-pricing revenues in mitigation pathways consistent with limiting temperature increase to 2°C could also contribute to finance investment needs for basic infrastructure (Jakob et al. 2016) and the achievement of the SDGs (Franks et al. 2018).

Several studies conclude that reaching higher income levels globally, beyond exiting extreme poverty, and achieving more qualitative social objectives and well-being, are associated with higher emissions (Ribas et al. 2017, 2019; Hubacek et al. 2017b; Fischetti 2018; Scherer et al. 2018). Studies give divergent results on the effect of economic inequality reduction on emissions, with either an increase or a decrease in emissions (Berthe and Elie 2015; Lamb and Rao 2015; Grunewald et al. 2017; Hubacek et al. 2017a,b; Jorgenson et al. 2017; Knight et al. 2017; Mader 2018; Rao and Min 2018; Liu et al. 2019; Sager 2019; Baležentis et al. 2020; Liobikienė 2020; Liobikienė and Rimkuvienė 2020; Liu et al. 2020b; Millward-Hopkins and Oswald 2021). However, the absolute effect of economic inequality reduction on emissions remains moderate, under the assumptions tested. For instance, Sager (2019) finds that a full redistribution of income leading to equality among US households in a counterfactual scenario for 2009 would raise emissions by 2.3%; and Rao and Min (2018) limit to 8% the maximum plausible increase in emissions that would accompany the reduction of the global Gini coefficient from its current level of 0.55 to a level of 0.3 by 2050. Similarly, reduced income inequality would lead to a global energy-demand increase of 7% (Oswald et al. 2021). Reconciling mitigation and inequality reduction objectives requires policies that take into account both objectives at all stages of policymaking (Markkanen and Anger-Kraavi 2019), including focusing on the carbon intensity of lifestyles (Scherer et al. 2018), attention to sufficiency and equity (Fischetti 2018), and targeting the consumption of the richest and highest-emitting households (Otto et al. 2019).

In modelled mitigation pathways, inequality in per-capita emissions between regions are generally reduced over time, and the reduction is generally more pronounced in lower-temperature pathways (Box 3.6, Figure 1). Already in 2030, if NDCs from the Paris Agreement, announced prior to COP26, are fully achieved, inequalities in per-capita GHG emissions between countries would be reduced (Benveniste et al. 2018).

Box 3.6 (continued)

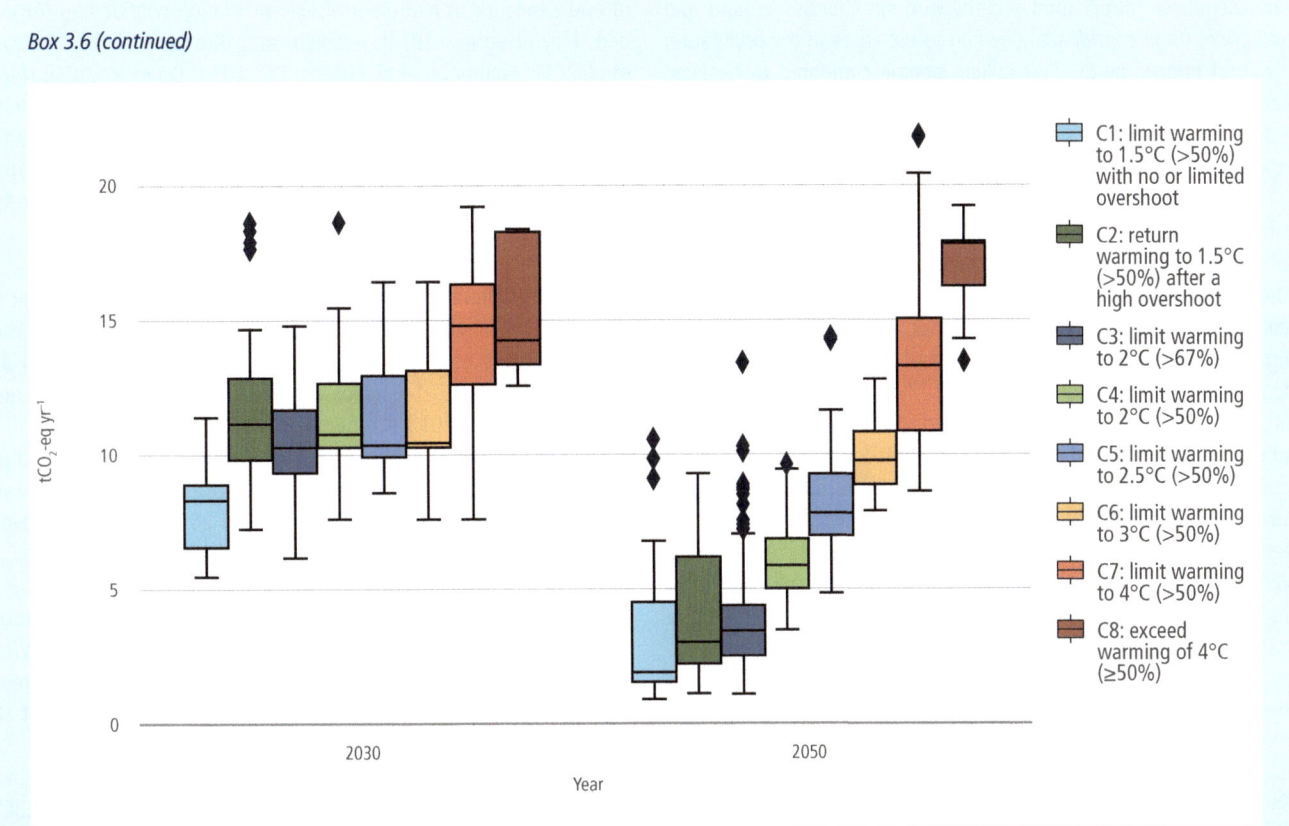

Box 3.6, Figure 1 | Difference in per-capita emissions of Kyoto gases between the highest emitting and the lowest emitting of the 10 regions, in 2030 and 2050, by temperature category of pathways.

Through avoiding impacts of climate change, which fall more heavily on low-income countries, communities and households, and exacerbate poverty, mitigation reduces inequalities and poverty (Section 3.6.4.2).

The remainder of this section covers specific domains of sustainable development: food (Section 3.7.2), water (Section 3.7.3), energy (Section 3.7.4), health (Section 3.7.5), biodiversity (Section 3.7.6) and multi-sector – cities, infrastructure, industry, production and consumption (Section 3.7.7). These represent the areas with the strongest research connecting mitigation to sustainable development. The links to individual SDGs are given within these sections. Each domain covers the benefits of avoided climate impacts and the implications (synergies and trade-offs) of mitigation efforts.

3.7.2 Food

The goal of SDG 2 is to achieve 'zero-hunger' by 2030. According to the UN (2015), over 25% of the global population currently experience food insecurity and nearly 40% of these experience severe food insecurity, a situation worsened by the COVID-19 pandemic (Paslakis et al. 2021).

3.7.2.1 Benefits of Avoided Climate Impacts Along Mitigation Pathways

Climate change will reduce crop yields, increase food insecurity, and negatively influence nutrition and mortality (*high confidence*) (AR6 WGII Chapter 5). Climate mitigation will thus reduce these impacts, and hence reduce food insecurity (*high confidence*). The yield reduction of global food production will increase food insecurity and influence nutrition and mortality (Hasegawa et al. 2014; Springmann et al. 2016a). For instance, Springmann et al. (2016a) estimate that climate change could lead to 315,000–736,000 additional deaths by 2050, though these could mostly be averted by stringent mitigation efforts. Reducing warming reduces the impacts of climate change, including extreme climates, on food production and risk of hunger (Hasegawa et al. 2014, 2021b).

3.7.2.2 Implications of Mitigation Efforts Along Pathways

Recent studies explore the effect of climate change mitigation on agricultural markets and food security (Havlík et al. 2014; Hasegawa et al. 2018; Doelman et al. 2019; Fujimori et al. 2019). Mitigation policies aimed at achieving 1.5°C–2°C, if not managed properly, could negatively affect food security through changes in land and food prices (*high confidence*), leading to increases in the population at risk of hunger by 80–280 million people compared to baseline scenarios. These studies assume uniform carbon prices on AFOLU sectors (with some sectoral caps) and do not account for climate impacts on food production.

Mitigating climate change while ensuring that food security is not adversely affected requires a range of different strategies and interventions (*high confidence*). Fujimori et al. (2018) explore possible economic solutions to these unintended impacts of mitigation (e.g., agricultural subsidies, food aid, and domestic reallocation of income) with an additional small (<0.1%) change in global GDP. Targeted food-security support is needed to shield impoverished and vulnerable people from the risk of hunger that could be caused by the economic effects of policies narrowly focussed on climate objectives. Introducing more biofuels and careful selection of bioenergy feedstocks could also reduce negative impacts (FAO, IFAD, UNICEF, WFP and WHO, 2017). Reconciling bioenergy demands with food and biodiversity, as well as competition for land and water, will require changes in food systems – agricultural intensification, open trade, less consumption of animal products and reduced food losses – and advanced biotechnologies (Henry et al. 2018; Xu et al. 2019).

There are many other synergistic measures for climate mitigation and food security. Agricultural technological innovation can improve the efficiency of land use and food systems, thus reducing the pressure on land from increasing food demand (Foley et al. 2011; Popp et al. 2014; Obersteiner et al. 2016; Humpenöder et al. 2018; Doelman et al. 2019). Furthermore, decreasing consumption of animal products could contribute to SDG 3.4 by reducing the risk of non-communicable diseases (Garnett 2016).

Taken together, climate changes will reduce crop yields, increase food insecurity and influence nutrition and mortality (*high confidence*) (see 3.7.2.1). However, if measures are not properly designed, mitigating climate change will also negatively impact on food consumption and security. Additional solutions to negative impacts associated with climate mitigation on food production and consumption include a transition to a sustainable agriculture and food system that is less resource intensive, more resilient to a changing climate, and in line with biodiversity and social targets (Kayal et al. 2019).

3.7.3   Water

Water is relevant to SDG 6 (clean water and sanitation), SDG 15 (life on land), and SDG Targets 12.4 and 3.9 (water pollution and health). This section discusses water quantity, water quality, and water-related extremes. See Section 3.7.5 for water-related health effects.

3.7.3.1   Benefits of Avoided Climate Impacts Along Mitigation Pathways

Global precipitation, evapotranspiration, runoff and water availability increase with warming (Hanasaki et al. 2013; Greve et al. 2018) (AR6 WGII Chapter 4). Climate change also affects the occurrence

of and exposure to hydrological extremes (*high confidence*) (Arnell and Lloyd-Hughes 2014; Asadieh and Krakauer 2017; Dottori et al. 2018; Naumann et al. 2018; IPCC 2019a; Do et al. 2020) (AR6 WGII Chapter 4). Climate models project increases in precipitation intensity (*high confidence*), local flooding (*medium confidence*), and drought risk (*very high confidence*) (Arnell and Lloyd-Hughes 2014; Asadieh and Krakauer 2017; Dottori et al. 2018; IPCC 2019a) (AR6 WGII Chapter 4).

The effect of climate change on water availability and hydrological extremes varies by region (*high confidence*) due to differences in the spatial patterns of projected precipitation changes (Hanasaki et al. 2013; Schewe et al. 2014; Schlosser et al. 2014; Asadieh and Krakauer 2017; Dottori et al. 2018; Naumann et al. 2018; Koutroulis et al. 2019) (AR6 WGII Chapter 4). Global exposure to water stress is projected to increase with increased warming, but increases will not occur in all regions (Hanasaki et al. 2013; Schewe et al. 2014; Arnell and Lloyd-Hughes 2014; Gosling and Arnell 2016; IPCC 2019a).

Limiting warming could reduce water-related risks (*high confidence*) (O'Neill et al. 2017b; Byers et al. 2018; Hurlbert et al. 2019) (AR6 WGII Chapter 4) and the population exposed to increased water stress (Hanasaki et al. 2013; Arnell and Lloyd-Hughes 2014; Schewe et al. 2014; Gosling and Arnell 2016; IPCC 2019a).

The effect of climate change on water depends on the climate model, the hydrological model, and the metric (*high confidence*) stress Hanasaki et al. (2013); Arnell and Lloyd-Hughes (2014); Schewe et al. (2014); Schlosser et al. (2014); Gosling and Arnell (2016); IPCC (2019a).

However, the effect of socio-economic development could be larger than the effect of climate change (*high confidence*) (Arnell and Lloyd-Hughes 2014; Schlosser et al. 2014; Graham et al. 2020).

Climate change can also affect water quality (both thermal and chemical) (Liu et al. 2017), leading to increases in stream temperature and nitrogen loading in rivers (Ballard et al. 2019).

3.7.3.2   Implications of Mitigation Efforts Along Pathways

The effects of mitigation on water demand depends on the mitigation technologies deployed (*high confidence*) (Chaturvedi et al. 2013a,b; Hanasaki et al. 2013; Kyle et al. 2013; Hejazi et al. 2014; Bonsch et al. 2016; Jakob and Steckel 2016; Mouratiadou et al. 2016; Fujimori et al. 2017; Maïzi et al. 2017; Bijl et al. 2018; Cui et al. 2018; Graham et al. 2018; Parkinson et al. 2019). Some mitigation options could increase water consumption (volume removed and not returned) while decreasing withdrawals (total volume of water removed, some of which may be returned) (Kyle et al. 2013; Fricko et al. 2016; Mouratiadou et al. 2016; Parkinson et al. 2019). Bioenergy and BECCS can increase water withdrawals and water consumption (*high confidence*) (Chaturvedi et al. 2013a; Kyle et al. 2013; Hejazi et al. 2014; Bonsch et al. 2016; Jakob and Steckel 2016; Mouratiadou et al. 2016; Fujimori et al. 2017; Maïzi et al. 2017; Séférian et al. 2018; Yamagata et al. 2018; Parkinson et al. 2019) (AR6 WGII Chapter 4). DACCS (Fuhrman et al. 2020) and CCS (Kyle et al. 2013; Fujimori et al. 2017) could increase water demand; however, the implications of CCS depend on the cooling technology and when capture occurs (Magneschi et al. 2017; Maïzi et al. 2017; Giannaris et al. 2020). Demand-side mitigation (e.g., dietary change, reduced food waste, reduced energy demand) can reduce water demand (Bajželj et al. 2014; Aleksandrowicz et al. 2016; Green et al. 2018; Springmann et al. 2018). Introducing specific measures (e.g., environmental flow requirements, improved efficiency, priority rules) can reduce water withdrawals (Bertram et al. 2018; Bijl et al. 2018; Parkinson et al. 2019).

The effect of mitigation on water quality depends on the mitigation option, its implementation, and the aspect of quality considered (*high confidence*) (Ng et al. 2010; Flörke et al. 2019; Sinha et al. 2019; Smith et al. 2019; Fuhrman et al. 2020; Karlsson et al. 2020; McElwee et al. 2020).

3.7.4 Energy

Energy is relevant to SDG 7 (affordable and clean energy). Access to sufficient levels of reliable, affordable and renewable energy is essential for sustainable development. Currently, over 1 billion people still lack access to electricity (Ribas et al. 2019).

3.7.4.1 Benefits of Avoided Climate Impacts Along Mitigation Pathways

Climate change alters the production of energy through changes in temperature (hydropower, fossil fuel, nuclear, solar, bioenergy, transmission and pipelines), precipitation (hydropower, fossil fuel, nuclear and bioenergy), windiness (wind and wave), and cloudiness (solar) (*high confidence*). Increases in temperature reduce efficiencies of thermal power plants (e.g., fossil fuel and nuclear plants) with air-cooled condensers by 0.4–0.7% per °C increase in ambient temperature (Cronin et al. 2018a; Simioni and Schaeffer 2019; Yalew, S.G. et al. 2020). Potentials and costs for renewable energy technologies are also affected by climate change, though with considerable regional variation and uncertainty (Gernaat et al. 2021). Biofuel yields could increase or decrease depending on the level of warming, changes in precipitation, and the effect of CO_2 fertilisation (Calvin et al. 2013; Kyle et al. 2014; Gernaat et al. 2021). Coastal energy facilities could potentially be impacted by sea level rise (Brown et al. 2014).

The energy sector uses large volumes of water (Fricko et al. 2016), making it highly vulnerable to climate change (Tan and Zhi 2016) (*high confidence*). Thermoelectric and hydropower sources are the most vulnerable to water stress (van Vliet et al. 2016). Restricted water supply to these power sources can affect grid security and affordable energy access (Koch et al. 2014; Ranzani et al. 2018; Zhang et al. 2018d). The hydropower facilities from high mountain areas of Central Europe, Iceland, Western USA/Canada, and Latin America (Hock et al. 2019), as well as Africa and China (Bartos and Chester 2015; Gaupp et al. 2015; Tarroja et al. 2016; Conway et al. 2017; Byers et al. 2018; Eyer and Wichman 2018; Ranzani et al. 2018; Savelsberg et al. 2018; Zhang et al. 2018d; Zhou et al. 2018; Wang et al. 2019) have experienced changes in seasonality and availability.

3.7.4.2 Implications of Mitigation Efforts Along Pathways

Extending energy access to all in line with SDG7 is compatible with strong mitigation consistent with the Paris Agreement (*high confidence*). The Low Energy Demand (LED) scenario projects that these twin goals can be achieved by relying heavily on energy efficiency and rapid social transformations (Grubler et al. 2018). The IEA's Sustainable Development Scenario (IEA 2020a) achieves development outcomes but with higher average energy use, and bottom-up modelling suggests that decent living standards could be provided to all in 2040–2050 with roughly 150 EJ, or 40% of current final energy use (Millward-Hopkins et al. 2020; Kikstra et al. 2021b). The trade-offs between climate mitigation and increasing energy consumption of the world's poorest are negligible (Rao and Min 2018; Scherer et al. 2018).

The additional energy demand to meet the basic cooling requirement in the Global South is estimated to be much larger than the electricity needed to provide basic residential energy services universally via clean and affordable energy, as defined by SDG 7 (IEA 2019; Mastrucci et al. 2019) (*high confidence*). If conventional air-conditioning systems are widely deployed to provide cooling, energy use could rise significantly (van Ruijven et al. 2019; Bezerra et al. 2021; Falchetta and Mistry 2021), thus creating a positive feedback further increasing cooling demand. However, the overall emissions are barely altered by the changing energy demand composition with reductions in heating demand occurring simultaneously (Isaac and van Vuuren 2009; Labriet et al. 2015; McFarland et al. 2015; Clarke et al. 2018). Some mitigation scenarios show price increases of clean cooking fuels, slowing the transition to clean cooking fuels (SDG 7.1) and leaving a billion people in 2050 still reliant on solid fuels in South Asia (Cameron et al. 2016).

In contrast, future energy infrastructure could improve reliability, thus lowering dependence on high-carbon, high-air pollution back-up diesel generators (Farquharson et al. 2018) that are often used to cope with unreliable power in developing countries (Maruyama Rentschler et al. 2019). There can be significant reliability issues where mini-grids are used to electrify rural areas (Numminen and Lund 2019). A stable, sustainable energy transition policy that considers national sustainable development in the short and long term is critical in driving a transition to an energy future that addresses the trilemma of energy security, equity, and sustainability (La Viña et al. 2018).

3.7.5 Health

SDG 3 (good health and well-being) aims to ensure healthy lives and promote well-being for all at all ages. Climate change is increasingly causing injuries, illnesses, malnutrition, threats to mental health and well-being, and deaths (AR6 WGII Chapter 7). Mitigation policies and technologies to reduce GHG emissions are often beneficial for human health on a shorter time scale than benefits in terms of slowing climate change (Limaye et al. 2020). The financial value of health benefits from improved air quality alone is projected to exceed the costs of meeting the goals of the Paris Agreement (Markandya et al. 2018).

3.7.5.1 Benefits of Avoided Climate Impacts Along Mitigation Pathways

The human health chapter of the WGII contribution to the AR6 concluded that climate change is increasingly affecting a growing number of health outcomes, with negative net impacts at the global scale and positive impacts only in a few limited situations. There are few estimates of economic costs of increases in climate-sensitive health outcomes. In the USA in 2012, the financial burden in terms of deaths, hospitalisations, and emergency department visits for ten climate-sensitive events across 11 states were estimated to be 10 (2.7–24.6) billion USD2018 (Limaye et al. 2019).

3.7.5.2 Implications of Mitigation Efforts Along Pathways

Transitioning toward equitable, low-carbon societies has multiple co-benefits for health and well-being (AR6 WGII Chapter 7). Health benefits can be gained from improvements in air quality through transitioning to renewable energy and active transport (e.g., walking and cycling); shifting to affordable low-meat, plant-rich diets; and green buildings and nature-based solutions, such as green-and-blue urban infrastructure, as shown in Figure 3.40 (Iacobucci 2016).

The avoided health impacts associated with climate change mitigation can substantially offset mitigation costs at the societal level (Ščasný et al. 2015; Schucht et al. 2015; Chang et al. 2017; Markandya et al. 2018). Models of health co-benefits show that a 1.5°C pathway could result in 152 million ± 43 million fewer premature deaths worldwide between 2020 and 2100 in comparison to a business-as-usual scenario, particularly due to reductions in exposure to PM2.5 (Shindell et al. 2018; Rauner et al. 2020a; Rafaj et al. 2021). Some of the most substantial health, well-being, and equity benefits associated with climate action derive from investing in basic infrastructure: sanitation, clean drinking water, clean energy, affordable healthy diets, clean public transport, and improved air quality from transformative solutions across economic sectors including agriculture, energy, transport and buildings (Chang et al. 2017).

The health co-benefits of the NDCs for 2040 were compared for two scenarios, one consistent with the goal of the Paris Agreement and the SDGs and the other also placing health as a central focus of the policies (i.e., health in all climate policies scenario) (Hamilton et al. 2021), for Brazil, China, Germany, India, Indonesia, Nigeria, South Africa, the UK, and the USA. Modelling of the energy, food and agriculture, and transport sectors, and associated risk factors

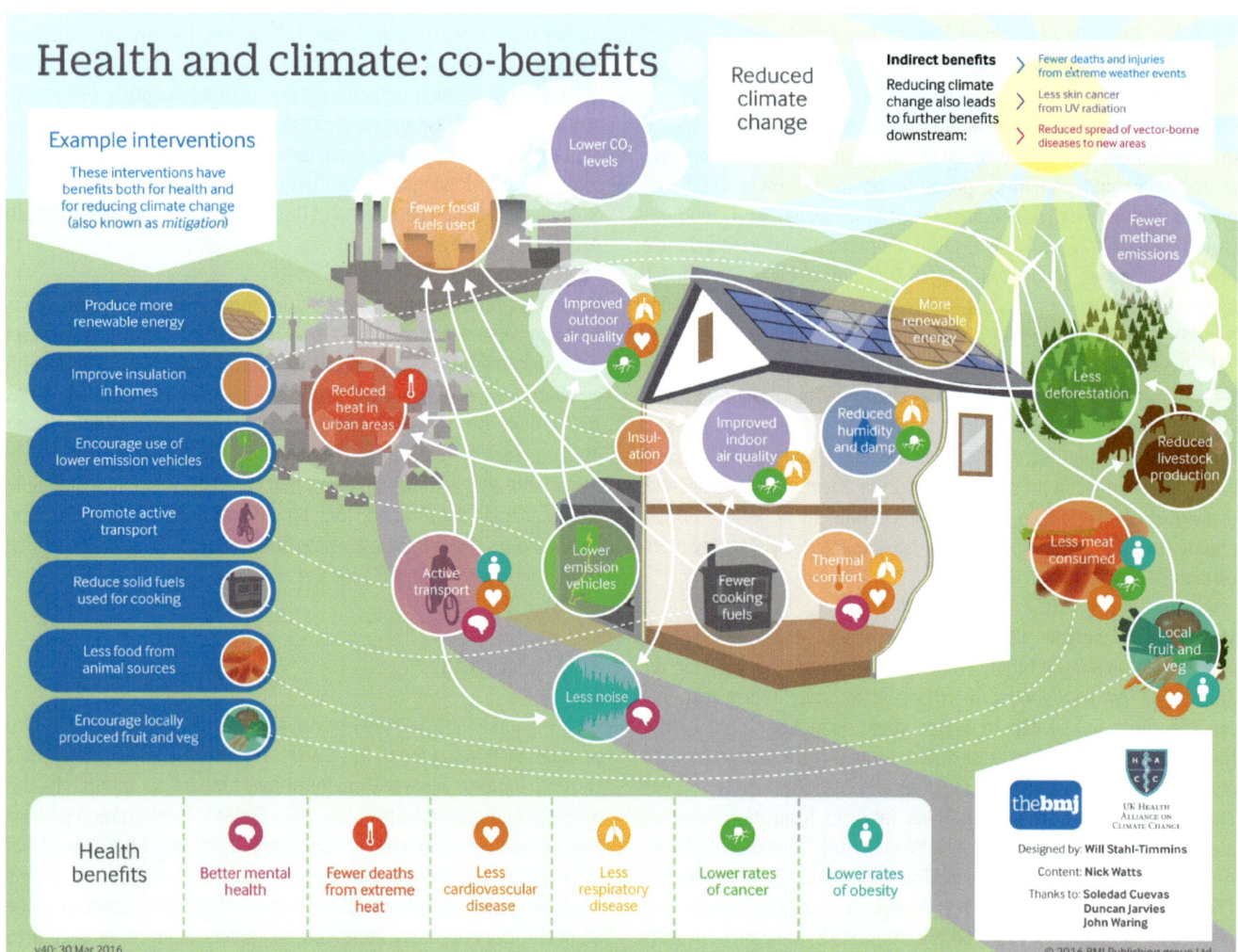

Figure 3.40 | Diagram showing the co-benefits between health and mitigation. Source: with permission from Iacobucci 2016.

related to mortality, suggested the sustainable pathways scenario could result in annual reductions of 1.18 million air pollution-related deaths, 5.86 million diet-related deaths, and 1.15 million deaths due to physical inactivity. Adopting the more ambitious health in all climate policies scenario could result in further reductions of 462,000 annual deaths attributable to air pollution, 572,000 annual deaths attributable to diet, and 943,000 annual deaths attributable to physical inactivity. These benefits were attributable to the mitigation of direct GHG emissions and the commensurate actions that reduce exposure to harmful pollutants, as well as improved diets and safe physical activity.

Cost-benefit analyses for climate mitigation in urban settings that do not account for health may underestimate the potential cost savings and benefits (Hess et al. 2020). The net health benefits of controlling air pollution as part of climate mitigation efforts could reach trillions of dollars annually, depending on the air quality policies adopted globally (Markandya et al. 2018; Scovronick et al. 2019b). Air pollution reductions resulting from meeting the Paris Agreement targets were estimated to provide health co-benefits-to-mitigation ratios of between 1.4 and 2.5 (Markandya et al. 2018). In Asia, the benefit of air pollution reduction through mitigation measures was estimated to reduce premature mortality by 0.79 million, with an associated health benefit of USD2.8 trillion versus mitigation costs of USD840 billion, equating to 6% and 2% of GDP, respectively (Xie et al. 2018). Similarly, stabilising radiative forcing to 3.4 W m^{-2} in South Korea could cost USD1.3–8.5 billion in 2050 and could lead to a USD23.5 billion cost reduction from the combined benefits of avoided premature mortality, health expenditures, and lost work hours (Kim et al. 2020). The health co-benefits related to physical exercise and reduced air pollution largely offset the costs of implementing low-CO_2-emitting urban mobility strategies in three Austrian cities (Wolkinger et al. 2018).

Just in the USA, over the next 50 years, a 2°C pathway could prevent roughly 4.5 million premature deaths, about 3.5 million hospitalisations and emergency room visits, and approximately 300 million lost workdays (Shindell 2020). The estimated yearly benefits of USD700 billion were more than the estimated cost of the energy transition.

3.7.6   Biodiversity (Land and Water)

Biodiversity covers life below water (SDG 14) and life on land (SDG 15). Ecosystem services are relevant to the goals of zero hunger (SDG 2), good health and well-being (SDG 3), clean water and sanitation (SDG 6) and responsible consumption and production (SDG 12), as well as being essential to human existence (IPBES 2019).

3.7.6.1   Benefits of Avoided Climate Impacts Along Mitigation Pathways

Terrestrial and freshwater aquatic ecosystems

Climate change is a major driver of species extinction and terrestrial and freshwater ecosystems destruction (*high confidence*) (AR6 WGII Chapter 2). Analysis shows that approximately half of all species with long-term records have shifted their ranges in elevation and about

two thirds have advanced their timing of spring events (Parmesan and Hanley 2015). Under 3.2°C warming, 49% of insects, 44% of plants and 26% of vertebrates are projected to be at risk of extinction. At 2°C, this falls to 18% of insects, 16% of plants and 8% of vertebrates and at 1.5°C, to 6% of insects, 8% of plants and 4% of vertebrates (Warren et al. 2018). Incidents of migration of invasive species, including pests and diseases, are also attributable to climate change, with negative impacts on food security and vector-borne diseases. Moreover, if climate change reduces crop yields, cropland may expand – a primary driver of biodiversity loss – in order to meet food demand (Molotoks et al. 2020). Land restoration and halting land degradation under all mitigation scenarios has the potential for synergy between mitigation and adaptation.

Marine and coastal ecosystems

Marine ecosystems are being affected by climate change and growing non-climate pressures including temperature change, acidification, land-sourced pollution, sedimentation, resource extraction and habitat destruction (*high confidence*) (Bindoff et al. 2019; IPCC 2019b). The impacts of climate drivers and their combinations vary across taxa (AR6 WGII Chapter 3). The danger or warming and acidification to coral reefs, rocky shores and kelp forests is well established (*high confidence*) (AR6 WGII Chapter 3). Migration towards optimal thermal and chemical conditions (Burrows et al. 2019) contributes to large-scale redistribution of fish and invertebrate populations, and major impacts on global marine biomass production and maximum sustainable yield (Bindoff et al. 2019).

3.7.6.2   Implications of Mitigation Efforts Along Pathways

Mitigation measures have the potential to reduce the progress of negative impacts on ecosystems, although it is *unlikely* that all impacts can be mitigated (*high confidence*) (Ohashi et al. 2019). The specifics of mitigation achievement are crucial, since large-scale deployment of some climate mitigation and land-based CDR measures could have deleterious impacts on biodiversity (Santangeli et al. 2016; Hof et al. 2018).

Climate change mitigation actions to reduce or slow negative impacts on ecosystems are *likely* to support the achievement of SDGs 2, 3, 6, 12, 14 and 15. Some studies show that stringent and constant GHG mitigation practices bring a net benefit to global biodiversity even if land-based mitigation measures are also adopted (Ohashi et al. 2019), as opposed to delayed action which would require much more widespread use of BECCS. Scenarios based on demand reductions of energy and land-based production are expected to avoid many such consequences, due to their minimised reliance on BECCS (Conijn et al. 2018; Grubler et al. 2018; Bowles et al. 2019; Soergel et al. 2021a). Stringent mitigation that includes reductions in demand for animal-based foods and food waste could also relieve pressures on land use and biodiversity (*high confidence*), both directly by reducing agricultural land requirements (Leclère et al. 2020) and indirectly by reducing the need for land-based CDR (van Vuuren et al. 2018).

As environmental conservation and sustainable use of the Earth's terrestrial species and ecosystems are strongly related, recent studies have evaluated interconnections among key aspects of land and show a pathway to the global sustainable future of land (Popp et al. 2014; Erb et al. 2016; Obersteiner et al. 2016; Humpenöder et al. 2018). Most studies agree that many biophysical options exist to achieve global climate mitigation and sustainable land use in future. Conserving local biodiversity requires careful policy design in conjunction with land-use regulations and societal transformation in order to minimise the conversion of natural habitats.

3.7.7 Cities and Infrastructure

This subsection focuses upon SDG 9 (industry, innovation and infrastructure) and SDG 11 (sustainable cities and communities).

3.7.7.1 Benefits of Avoided Climate Impacts Along Mitigation Pathways

By 2100, urban population will be almost double and more urban areas will be built (Jiang and O'Neill 2017), although COVID-19 may modify these trends (Kii 2021). Urbanisation will amplify projected air temperature changes in cities, including amplifying heatwaves (AR6 WGI Chapter 10, Box 10.3). Benefits of climate mitigation in urban areas include reducing heat, air pollution and flooding. Industrial infrastructure and production-consumption supply networks also benefit from avoided impacts.

3.7.7.2 Implications of Mitigation Efforts Along Pathways

Many co-benefits to urban mitigation actions (Chapter 8, Section 8.2.1) improve the liveability of cities and contribute to achieving SDG 11. In particular, compact urban form, efficient technologies and infrastructure can play a valuable role in mitigation by reducing energy demand (Creutzig et al. 2016; Güneralp et al. 2017), thus averting carbon lock-in, while reducing land sprawl and hence increasing carbon storage and biodiversity (D'Amour et al. 2017). Benefits of mitigation include air quality improvements from decreased traffic and congestion when private vehicles are displaced by other modes; health benefits from increases in active travel; and lowered urban heat island effects from green-blue infrastructures (Section 8.2.1).

However, increasing urban density or enlarging urban green spaces can increase property prices and reduce affordability (Section 8.2.1). Raising living conditions for slum dwellers and people living in informal settlements will require significant materials and energy; however, regeneration can be conducted in ways that avoid carbon-intense infrastructure lock-in (Chapters 8 and 9). Cities affect other regions through supply chains (Marinova et al. 2020).

Sustainable production, consumption and management of natural resources are consistent with, and necessary for, mitigation (Chapters 5 and 11). Demand-side measures can lower requirements for upstream material and energy use (Chapter 5). In terms of industrial production, transformational changes across sectors will be necessary for mitigation (Sections 11.3 and 11.4).

Addressing multiple SDG arenas requires new systemic thinking in the areas of governance and policy, such as those proposed by Sachs et al. (2019).

3.8 Feasibility of Socio/Techno/Economic Transitions

The objective of this section is to discuss concepts of feasibility in the context of the low-carbon transition and pathways. We aim to identify drivers of low-carbon scenarios feasibility and to highlight enabling conditions which can ameliorate feasibility concerns.

3.8.1 Feasibility Frameworks for the Low-carbon Transition and Scenarios

Effectively responding to climate change and achieving sustainable development requires overcoming a series of challenges to transition away from fossil-based economies. Feasibility can be defined in many ways (Chapter 1). The political science literature (Majone 1975a,b; Gilabert and Lawford-Smith 2012) distinguishes the feasibility of 'what' (i.e., emission reduction strategies), 'when and where' (i.e., in the year 2050, globally) and 'whom' (i.e., cities). It distinguishes desirability from political feasibility (von Stechow et al. 2015): the former represents a normative assessment of the compatibility with societal goals (i.e., SDGs), while the latter evaluates the plausibility of what can be attained given the prevailing context of transformation (Nielsen et al. 2020). Feasibility concerns are context and time dependent and malleable: enabling conditions can help overcome them. For example, public support for carbon taxes has been hard to secure but appropriate policy design and household rebates can help dissipate opposition (Murray and Rivers 2015; Carattini et al. 2019).

Regarding scenarios, the feasibility 'what' question is the one most commonly dealt with in the literature, though most of the studies have focused on expanding low-carbon system, and yet political constraints might arise mostly from phasing out fossil fuel-based ones (Spencer et al. 2018; Fattouh et al. 2019). The 'when and where' dimension can also be related to the scenario assessment, but only insofar that the models generating them can differentiate time and geographical contextual factors. Distinguishing mitigation potential by regional institutional capacity has a significant influence on the costs of stabilising climate (Iyer et al. 2015c). The 'whom' question is the most difficult to capture by scenarios, given the multitude of actors involved as well as their complex interactions. The focus of socio-technical transition sciences on the co-evolutionary processes can shed light on the dynamics of feasibility (Nielsen et al. 2020).

The when-where-whom distinction allows depicting a feasibility frontier beyond which implementation challenges prevent mitigation action (Jewell and Cherp 2020). Even if the current feasibility frontier appears restraining in some jurisdictions, it is context-dependent and dynamic as innovation proceeds and institutional capacity builds up (Nielsen et al. 2020). The question is whether the feasibility frontier can move faster than the pace at which the carbon budget is being exhausted. Jewell et al. (2019) show that the emission savings from the pledges of premature retirement of coal plants is 150 times less than globally committed emissions from existing coal power plants. The pledges come from countries with high institutional capacity and relatively low shares of coal in electricity. Other factors currently limiting the capacity to steer transitions at the necessary speed include the electoral-market orientation of politicians (Willis 2017), the status-quo orientation of senior public officials (Geden 2016), path dependencies created by 'instrument constituencies' (Béland and Howlett 2016), or the impacts of deliberate inconsistencies between talk, decisions and actions in climate policy (Rickards et al. 2014). All in all, a number of different delay mechanisms in both science and policy have been identified to potentially impede climate goal achievement (Karlsson and Gilek 2020) (Chapter 13).

In addition to its contextual and dynamic nature, feasibility is a multi-dimensional concept. The IPCC SR1.5 distinguishes six dimensions of feasibility: geophysical, environmental-ecological, technological, economic, socio-cultural and institutional. At the individual option level, different mitigation strategies face various barriers as well as enablers (see Chapter 6 for the option-level assessment). However, a systemic transformation involves interconnections of a wide range of indicators. Model-based assessments are meant to capture the integrative elements of the transition and of associated feasibility challenges. However, the translation of model-generated pathways into feasibility concerns (Rogelj et al. 2018b) has developed only recently. Furthermore, multiple forms of knowledge can be mobilised to support strategic decision-making and complement scenario analysis (Turnheim and Nykvist 2019). We discuss both approaches next.

3.8.2 Feasibility Appraisal of Low-carbon Scenarios

Evaluating the feasibility of low-carbon pathways can take different forms. In the narrowest sense, there is feasibility pertaining the reporting of model-generated scenarios: here an infeasible scenario is one which cannot meet the constraints embedded implicitly or explicitly in the models which attempted to generate it. Second, there is a feasibility that relates to specific elements or overall structure characterising the low-carbon transition compared to some specified benchmark.

3.8.2.1 Model Solvability

In order to be generated, scenarios must be coherent with the constraints and assumptions embedded in the models (i.e., deployment potential of given technologies, physical and geological limits) and in the scenario design (i.e., carbon budget). Sometimes, models cannot solve specific scenarios. This provides a first, coarse indication of feasibility concerns. Specific vetting criteria can be imposed, such as carbon-price values above which scenarios should not be reported, as in Clarke et al. (2009). However, model solvability raises issues of aggregation in model ensembles. Since model solving is not a random process, but a function of the characteristics of the models, analysing only reported outcomes leads to statistical biases (Tavoni and Tol 2010).

Although model-feasibility differs distinctly from feasibility in the real world, it can indicate the relative challenges of low-carbon scenarios – primarily when performed in a model ensemble of sufficient size. Riahi et al. (2015) interpreted infeasibility across a large number of models as an indication of increased risk that the transformation may not be attainable due to technical or economic concerns. All models involved in a model comparison of 1.5°C targets (Rogelj et al. 2018b) (Table S1) were able to solve under favourable underlying socio-economic assumptions (SSP1), but none for the more challenging SSP3. This interpretation of feasibility was used to highlight the importance of socio-economic drivers for attaining climate stabilisation. Gambhir et al. (2017) constrained the models to historically observed rates of change and found that it would no longer allow to solve for 2°C, highlighting the need for rapid technological change.

3.8.2.2 Scenario Feasibility

Evaluating the feasibility of scenarios involves several steps (Figure 3.41). First, one needs to identify which dimensions of feasibility to focus on. Then, for each dimension, one needs to select relevant indicators for which sufficient empirical basis exists and which are an output of models (or at least of a sufficient number of them). Then, thresholds marking different levels of feasibility concerns are defined based on available literature, expert elicitations and empirical analysis based on appropriately chosen historical precedents. Finally, scenario feasibility scores are obtained for each indicator, and where needed aggregated up in time or dimensions, as a way to provide an overall appraisal of feasibility trade-offs, depending on the timing, disruptiveness and scale of transformation.

Most of the existing literature has focused on the technological dimensions, given the technology focus of models and the ease of comparison. The literature points to varied findings. Some suggest that scenarios envision technological progress consistent with historical benchmarks (Wilson et al. 2013; Loftus et al. 2015). Others that scenarios exceed historically observed rates of low-carbon technology deployment and of energy demand transformation globally (van der Zwaan et al. 2013; Napp et al. 2017; Cherp et al. 2021; Semieniuk et al. 2021), but not for all countries (Cherp et al. 2021). The reason for these discrepancies depends on the unit of analysis and the indicators used. Comparing different kinds of historical indicators, (van Sluisveld et al. 2015) find that indicators that look into the absolute change of energy systems remain within the range of historical growth frontiers for the next decade, but increase to unprecedented levels before mid-century. Expert assessments provide another way of benchmarking scenarios, though they have shown to be systematically biased (Wiser et al. 2021) and to underperform empirical methods (Meng et al. 2021). van Sluisveld et al. (2018a) find that scenarios and experts align for baseline scenarios but differ for low-carbon ones. Scenarios rely more on conventional technologies based on existing infrastructure (such as nuclear and CCS) than what is forecasted by experts. Overall, the technology assessment of the feasibility space highlights that Paris-compliant transformations would have few precedents, but not zero (Cherp et al. 2021).

Step 1 Feasibility dimensions	Step 2 Indicators	Step 3 Thresholds	Step 4 Aggregation (geometric mean)	
geophysical technological economic institutional socio-cultural	For each dimension, selection of relevant indicators measuring decadal changes (among indicators available or computable based on scenario set)	Categorisation of level of feasibility concern for each indicator in each decade based on thresholds defined based on the literature and available empirical data – 3 high – 2 medium – 1 low	Aggregation within each dimension	allows assessing **tradeoffs** among feasibility dimensions
			Aggregation across dimensions at different points in time	allows assessing the **timing** and **disruptiveness** of the transformation
			Aggregation across dimensions and across time	allows assessing the **scale** of the transformation

Figure 3.41 | Steps involved in evaluating the feasibility of scenarios. Source: adapted with permission from Brutschin et al. 2021.

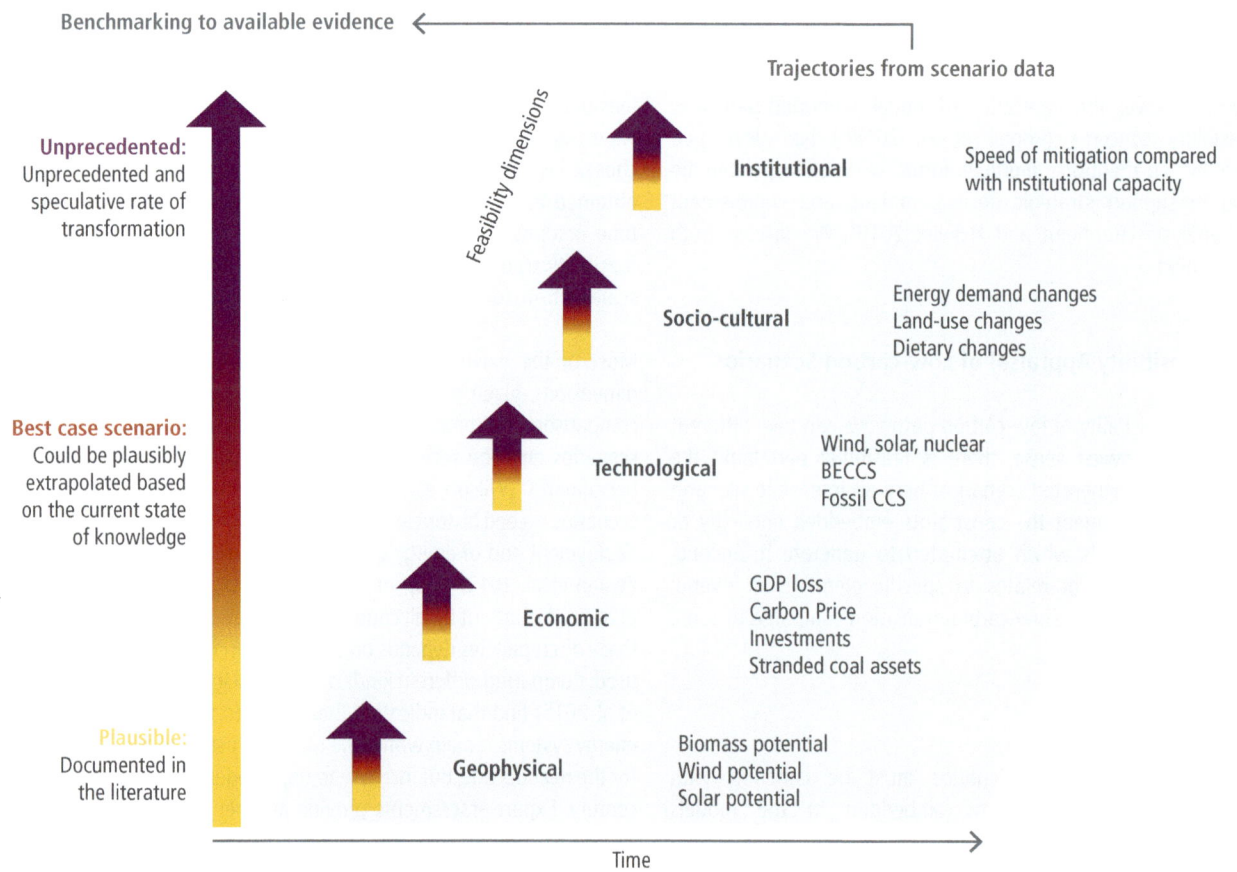

Figure 3.42 | Example of multi-dimensional feasibility analysis and indicators used in the IPCC AR6 scenarios. The approach defines relevant indicators characterising the key dimensions of feasibility. Indicators capture the timing, scale and disruptiveness challenges. Low-, medium- and high-feasibility concerns are defined based on historical trends and available literature. Details about indicator and threshold values can be found in Annex III.II.2.3.

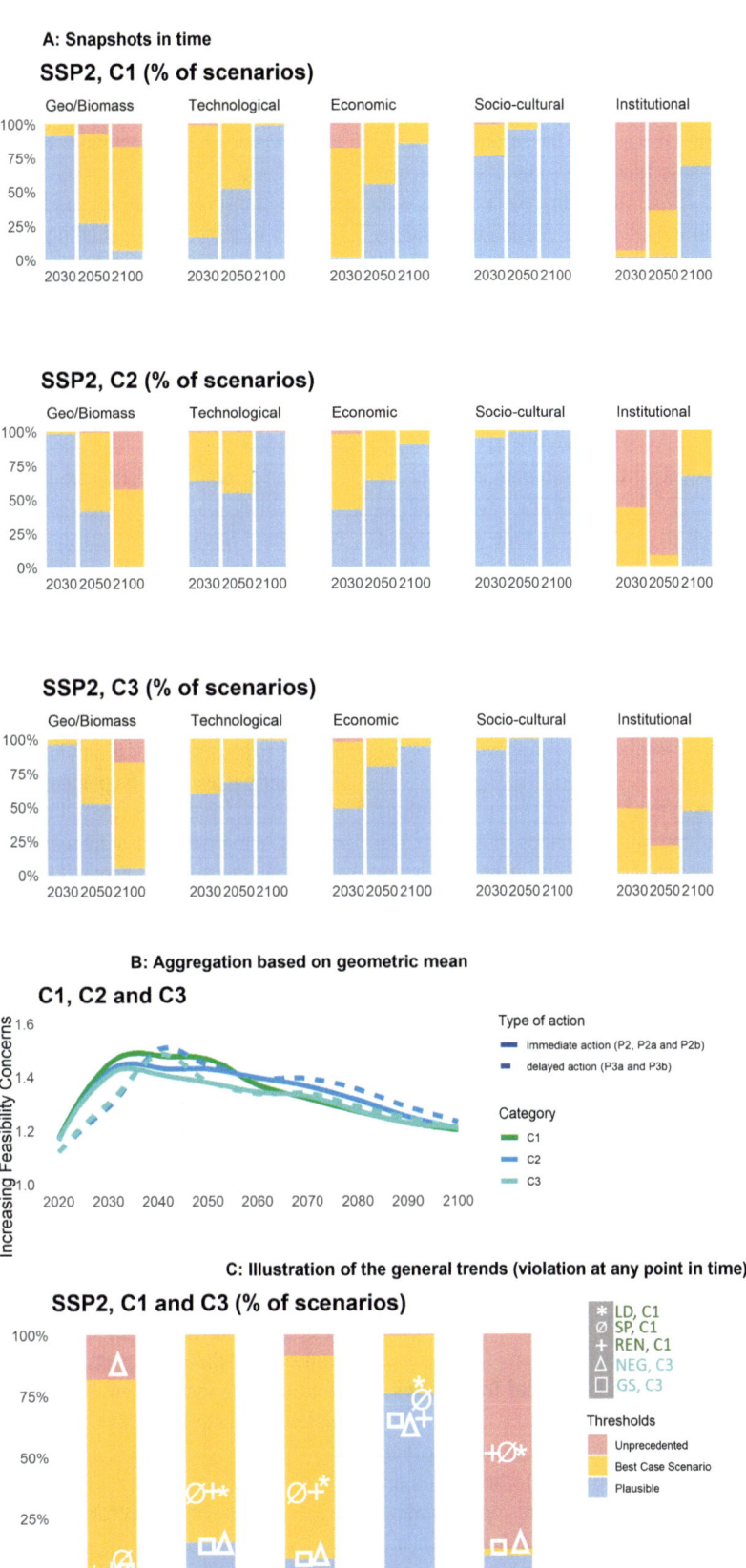

Figure 3.43 | Feasibility characteristics of the Paris-consistent scenarios in the AR6 scenarios database : Feasibility corridors for the AR6 scenarios database, applying the methodology by (Brutschin et al. 2021). (a) The fraction of scenarios falling within three categories of feasibility concerns (plausible, best case, unprecedented), for different times (2030, 2050, 2100), different climate categories consistent with the Paris Agreement and five dimensions. **(b)** Composite feasibility score (obtained by geometric mean of underlying indicators) over time for scenarios with immediate and delayed global mitigation efforts, for different climate categories (C1, C2, C3. Note: no C1 scenario has delayed participation). **(c)** The fraction of scenarios which in any point in time over the century exceed the feasibility concerns, for C1 and C3 climate categories. Overlayed are the Illustrative Mitigation Pathways (*IMP-LP*, *IMP-SP*, *IMP-Ren*: C1 category; *IMP-Neg*, *IMP-GS*: C3 category).

Recent approaches have addressed multiple dimensions of feasibility, an important advancement since social and institutional aspects are as, if not more, important than technology ones (Jewell and Cherp 2020). Feasibility corridors of scenarios based on their scale, rate of change and disruptiveness have been identified (Kriegler et al. 2018b; Warszawski et al. 2021). The reality check shows that many 1.5°C-compatible scenarios violate the feasibility corridors. The ones that didn't are associated with a greater coverage of the available mitigation levers (Warszawski et al. 2021).

Brutschin et al. (2021) proposed an operational framework covering all six dimensions of feasibility. They developed a set of multi-dimensional metrics capturing the timing, disruptiveness and the scale of the transformative change within each dimension (as in Kriegler et al. 2018b). Thresholds of feasibility risks of different intensity are obtained through the review of the relevant literature and empirical analysis of historical data. Novel indicators include governance levels (Andrijevic et al. 2020a). The 17 bottom-up indicators are then aggregated up across time and dimension, as a way to highlight feasibility trade-offs. Aggregation is done via compensatory approaches such as the geometric mean. This is employed, for instance, for the Human Development Index. A conceptual example of this approach as applied to the IPCC AR6 scenarios database is shown in Figure 3.42 and further described in the Annex III.II.2.3.

In Figure 3.43, we show the results of applying the methodology of Brutschin et al. (2021) to the AR6 scenarios database. The charts highlight the dynamic nature of feasibility risks, which are mostly concentrated in the decades before mid-century except for geophysical risks driven by CO_2 removals later in the century. Different dimensions pose differentiated challenges: for example, institutional feasibility challenges appear to be the most relevant, in line with the qualitative literature. Thus, feasibility concerns might be particularly relevant in countries with weaker institutional capacity. Figure 3.43 also highlights the key roles of policy and technology as enabling factors. In particular (panel b), internationally coordinated and immediate emission reductions allow to smooth out feasibility concerns and reduce long-term challenges compared to delayed policy action, as a result of a more gradual transition and lower requirements of CO_2 removals. For the same climate objective, different Illustrative Mitigation Pathways entail somewhat different degrees and distributions of implementation challenges (panel c).

3.8.3   Feasibility in Light of Socio-technical Transitions

The limitations associated with quantitative low-carbon transition pathways stem from a predominant reliance on techno-economic considerations with a simplified or non-existent representation of the socio-political and institutional agreement. Accompanying the required deployment of low-carbon technologies will be the formation of new socio-technical systems (Bergek et al. 2008). With a socio-technical system being defined as a cluster of elements comprising of technology, regulation, user practices and markets, cultural meaning, infrastructure, maintenance networks, and supply networks (Hofman et al. 2004; Geels and Geels 2005); the inter-relationship between technological systems and social systems must

be comprehensively understood. It is of vital importance that the process of technical change must be considered in its institutional and social context so as to ascertain potential transition barriers which in turn provide an indication of pathway feasibility. In order to address the multitudinous challenges associated with low-carbon transition feasibility and governance, it has been opined that the robustness of evaluating pathways may be improved by the bridging of differing quantitative-qualitative analytical approaches (Haxeltine et al. 2008; Foxon et al. 2010; Hughes 2013; Wangel et al. 2013; Li et al. 2015; Turnheim et al. 2015; Geels et al. 2016a,b, 2020; Moallemi et al. 2017; De Cian et al. 2020; Li and Strachan 2019). The rationale for such analytical bridging is to rectify the issue that in isolation each disciplinary approach can only generate a fragmented comprehension of the transition pathway with the consequence being an incomplete identification of associated challenges in terms of feasibility. Concerning low-carbon transition pathways generated by IAMs, it has been argued that a comprehensive analysis should include social scientific enquiry (Geels et al. 2016a, 2020; van Sluisveld et al. 2018b). The normative analysis of IAM pathways assists in the generation of a vision or the formulation of a general plan with this being complemented by socio-technical transition theory (Geels et al. 2016a). Such an approach thereby allowing for the socio-political feasibility and the social acceptance and legitimacy of low-carbon options to be considered. Combining computer models and the multi-level perspective can help identify 'transition bottlenecks' (Geels et al. 2020). Similarly, increased resolution of integrated assessment models' actors has led to more realistic narratives of transition in terms of granularity and behaviour (McCollum et al. 2017; van Sluisveld et al. 2018b). Increased data availability of actual behaviour from smart technology lowers the barriers to representing behavioural change in computer simulations, and thus better represents crucial demand-side transformations (Creutzig et al. 2018). Increasing the model resolution is a meaningful way forward. However, integrating a much broader combination of real-life aspects and dynamics into models could lead to an increased complexity that could restrict them to smaller fields of applications (De Cian et al. 2020).

Other elements of feasibility relate to social justice, which could be essential to enhance the political and public acceptability of the low-carbon transition. Reviewing the literature, one study finds that employing social justice as an orienting principle can increase the political feasibility of low-carbon policies (Patterson et al. 2018). Three elements are identified as key: (i) protecting vulnerable people from climate change impacts, (ii) protecting people from disruptions of transformation, (iii) enhancing the process of envisioning and implementing an equitable post-carbon society.

3.8.4   Enabling Factors

There is strong agreement that the climate policy institutional framework as well as technological progress have a profound impact on the attainability of low-carbon pathways. Delaying international cooperation reduces the available carbon budget and locks into carbon-intensive infrastructure exacerbating implementation challenges (Keppo and Rao 2007; Bosetti et al. 2009; Boucher et al. 2009; Clarke et al. 2009; Krey and Riahi 2009; van Vliet et al. 2009;

Knopf et al. 2011; Jakob et al. 2012; Luderer et al. 2013; Rogelj et al. 2013a; Aboumahboub et al. 2014; Kriegler et al. 2014a; Popp et al. 2014; Riahi et al. 2015; Gambhir et al. 2017; Bertram et al. 2021). Similarly, technological availability influences the feasibility of climate stabilisation, though differently for different technologies (Kriegler et al. 2014a; Iyer et al. 2015a; Riahi et al. 2015).

One of the most relevant factors affecting mitigation pathways and their feasibility is the rate and kind of socio-economic development. For example, certain socio-economic trends and assumptions about policy effectiveness preclude achieving stringent mitigation futures (Rogelj et al. 2018b). The risk of failure increases markedly in high-growth, unequal and/or energy-intensive worlds such as those characterised by the shared socio-economic pathways SSP3, SSP4 and SSP5. On the other hand, socio-economic development conducive to mitigation relieves the energy sector transformation from relying on large-scale technology development: for example, the amount of biomass with CCS in SSP1 is one third of that in SSP5. The reason why socio-economic trends matter so much is that they both affect the CO_2 emissions in counterfactual scenarios as well as the mitigation capacity (Riahi et al. 2017; Rogelj et al. 2018b). Economic growth assumptions are the most important determinant of scenario emissions (Marangoni et al. 2017). Degrowth and post-growth scenarios have been suggested as valuable alternatives to be considered (Hickel et al. 2021; Keyßer and Lenzen 2021), though substantial challenges remain regarding political feasibility (Keyßer and Lenzen 2021).

The type of policy instrument assumed to drive the decarbonisation process also plays a vital role for determining feasibility. The majority of scenarios exploring climate stabilisation pathways in the past have focused on uniform carbon pricing as the most efficient instrument to regulate emissions. However, carbon taxation raises political challenges (Beiser-McGrath and Bernauer 2019) (Chapters 13 and 14). Carbon pricing will transfer economic surplus from consumers and producers to the government. Losses for producers will be highly concentrated in those industries possessing fixed or durable assets with 'high asset specificity' (Murphy 2002; Dolphin et al. 2020). These sectors have opposed climate jurisdictions (Jenkins 2014). Citizens are sensitive to rising energy prices, though revenue recycling can be used to increase support (Carattini et al. 2019). A recent model comparison project confirms findings from the extant literature: using revenues to reduce pre-existing capital or, to a lesser extent, labour taxes, reduces policy costs and eases distributional concerns (Barron et al. 2018; Mcfarland et al. 2018).

Nonetheless, winning support will require a mix of policies which go beyond carbon pricing, and include subsidies, mandates and feebates (Jenkins 2014; Rozenberg et al. 2018). More recent scenarios take into account a more comprehensive range of policies and regional heterogeneity in the near to medium term (Roelfsema et al. 2020). Regulatory policies complementing carbon prices could reduce the implementation challenges by increasing short-term emission reduction, though they could eventually reduce economic efficiency (Bertram et al. 2015b; Kriegler et al. 2018a). Innovation policies such as subsidies to R&D have been shown to be desirable due to

innovation market failures, and also address the dynamic nature of political feasibility (Bosetti et al. 2011).

3.9   Methods of Assessment and Gaps in Knowledge and Data

3.9.1   AR6 Mitigation Pathways

The analysis in this chapter relies on the available literature as well as an assessment of the scenarios contained in the AR6 scenarios database. Scenarios were submitted by research and other institutions following an open call (Annex III.II.3.1). The scenarios included in the AR6 scenarios database are an unstructured ensemble, as they are from multiple underlying studies and depend on which institutions chose to submit scenarios to the database. As noted in Section 3.2, they do not represent the full scenario literature or the complete set of possible scenarios. For example, scenarios that include climate change impacts or economic degrowth are not fully represented, as these scenarios, with a few exceptions, were not submitted to the database. Additionally, sensitivity studies, which could help elucidate model behaviour and drivers of change, are mostly absent from the database – though examples exist in the literature (Marangoni et al. 2017).

The AR6 scenarios database contains 3131 scenarios of which 2425 with global scope were considered by this chapter, generated by almost 100 different model versions, from more than 50 model families. Of the 1686 vetted scenarios, 1202 provided sufficient information for a climate categorisation. Around 46% of the pathways are consistent with an end-of-century temperature of at least *likely* limiting warming to below 2°C (>67%). There are many ways of constructing scenarios that limit warming to a particular level and the choice of scenario construction has implications for the timing of both net zero CO_2 and GHG emissions and the deployment of CDR (Emmerling et al. 2019; Rogelj et al. 2019b; Johansson et al. 2020). The AR6 scenarios database includes scenarios where temperature is temporarily exceeded (40% of all scenarios in the database have median temperature in 2100 that is 0.1°C lower than median peak temperature). Climate stabilisation scenarios are typically implemented by assuming a carbon price rising at a particular rate per year, though that rate varies across model, scenario, and time period. Standard scenarios assume a global single carbon price to minimise policy costs. Cost-minimising pathways can be reconciled with equity considerations through posterior international transfers. Many scenarios extrapolate current policies and include non-market, regulatory instruments such as technology mandates.

Scenarios are not independent of each other and not representative of all possible outcomes, nor of the underlying scenario generation process; thus, the statistical power of the database is limited. Dependencies in the data-generation process originate from various sources. Certain model groups, and types, are over-represented. For example, eight model teams contributed 90% of scenarios. Second, not all models can generate all scenarios, and these differences are not random, thereby creating selection bias (Tavoni and Tol 2010).

Third, there are strong model dependencies: the modelling scientific community shares code and data, and several IAMs are open-source.

3.9.2   Models Assessed in This Chapter

The models assessed in this chapter differ in their sectoral coverage and the level of complexity in each sector. Models tend to have more detail in their representation of energy supply and transportation, than they do for industry (Section 3.4 and Annex III.I). Some models include detailed land-use models, while others exclude land models entirely and use supply curves to represent bioenergy potential (Bauer et al. 2018a). IAMs do not include all mitigation options available in the literature (Rogelj et al. 2018b; Smith et al. 2019). For example, most IAM pathways exclude many granular demand-side mitigation options and land-based mitigation options found in more detailed sectoral models; additionally, only a few pathways include CDR options beyond afforestation/reforestation and BECCS. Section 3.4 and Chapter 12 include some results and comparisons to non-IAM models (e.g., bottom-up studies and detailed sectoral models). These sectoral studies often include a more complete set of mitigation options but exclude feedbacks and linkages across sectors which may alter the mitigation potential of a given sector. There is an increasing focus in IAM studies on SDGs (Section 3.7), with some studies reporting the implications of mitigation pathways on SDGs (e.g., Bennich et al. 2020) and others using achieving SDGs as a constraint on the scenario itself (van Vuuren et al. 2015; Soergel et al. 2021a). However, IAMs are still limited in the SDGs they represent, often focusing on energy, water, air pollution and land. On the economic side, the majority of the models report information on marginal costs (i.e., carbon price). Only a subset provides full economic implications measured by either economic activity or welfare. Also often missing, is detail about economic inequality within countries or large aggregate regions.

For further details about the models and scenarios, see Annex III.

FAQ 3.1 | Is it possible to stabilise warming without net negative CO_2 and GHG emissions?

Yes. Achieving net zero CO_2 emissions and sustaining them into the future is sufficient to stabilise the CO_2-induced warming signal which scales with the cumulative net amount of CO_2 emissions. At the same time, the warming signal of non-CO_2 GHGs can be stabilised or reduced by declining emissions that lead to stable or slightly declining concentrations in the atmosphere. For short-lived GHGs with atmospheric lifetimes of less than 20 years, this is achieved when residual emissions are reduced to levels that are lower than the natural removal of these gases in the atmosphere. Taken together, mitigation pathways that bring CO_2 emissions to net zero and sustain it, while strongly reducing non-CO_2 GHGs to levels that stabilise or decline their aggregate warming contribution, will stabilise warming without using net negative CO_2 emissions and with positive overall GHG emissions when aggregated using GWP-100. A considerable fraction of pathways that limit warming to 1.5°C (>50%) with no or limited overshoot and limit warming to 2°C (>67%), respectively, do not or only marginally (<10 $GtCO_2$ cumulative until 2100) deploy net negative CO_2 emissions (26% and 46%, respectively) and do not reach net zero GHG emissions by the end of the century (48% and 70%, respectively). This is no longer the case in pathways that return warming to 1.5°C (>50%) after a high overshoot (typically >0.1°C). All of these pathways deploy net negative emissions on the order of 360 (60–680) $GtCO_2$ (median and 5–95th percentile) and 87% achieve net negative GHGs emissions in AR6 GWP-100 before the end of the century. Hence, global net negative CO_2 emissions, and net zero or net negative GHG emissions, are only needed to decline, not to stabilise global warming. The deployment of carbon dioxide removal (CDR) is distinct from the deployment of net negative CO_2 emissions, because it is also used to neutralise residual CO_2 emissions to achieve and sustain net zero CO_2 emissions. CDR deployment can be considerable in pathways without net negative emissions and all pathways limiting warming to 1.5°C use it to some extent.

FAQ 3.2 | How can net zero emissions be achieved and what are the implications of net zero emissions for the climate?

Halting global warming in the long term requires, at a minimum, that no additional CO_2 emissions from human activities are added to the atmosphere (i.e., CO_2 emissions must reach 'net' zero). Given that CO_2 emissions constitute the dominant human influence on global climate, global net zero CO_2 emissions are a prerequisite for stabilising warming at any level. However, CO_2 is not the only greenhouse gas that contributes to global warming and reducing emissions of other greenhouse gases (GHGs) alongside CO_2 towards net zero emissions of all GHGs would lower the level at which global temperature would peak. The temperature implications of net zero GHG emissions depend on the bundle of gases that is being considered, and the emissions metric used to calculate aggregated GHG emissions and removals. If reached and sustained, global net zero GHG emissions using the 100-year Global Warming Potential (GWP-100) will lead to gradually declining global temperature.

Not all emissions can be avoided. Achieving net zero CO_2 emissions globally therefore requires deep emissions cuts across all sectors and regions, along with active removal of CO_2 from the atmosphere to balance remaining emissions that may be too difficult, too costly, or impossible to abate at that time. Achieving global net zero GHG emissions would require, in addition, deep reductions of non-CO_2 emissions and additional CO_2 removals to balance remaining non-CO_2 emissions.

Not all regions and sectors must reach net zero CO_2 or GHG emissions individually to achieve global net zero CO_2 or GHG emissions, respectively; instead, positive emissions in one sector or region can be compensated by net negative emissions from another sector or region. The time each sector or region reaches net zero CO_2 or GHG emissions depends on the mitigation options available, the cost of those options, and the policies implemented (including any consideration of equity or fairness). Most modelled pathways that *likely* limit warming to 2°C (>67%) above pre-industrial levels and below use land-based CO_2 removal such as afforestation/reforestation and BECCS to achieve net zero CO_2 and net zero GHG emissions even while some CO_2 and non-CO_2 emissions continue to occur. Pathways with more demand-side interventions that limit the amount of energy we use, or where the diet that we consume is changed, can achieve net zero CO_2, or net zero GHG emissions with less carbon dioxide removal (CDR). All available studies require at least some kind of carbon dioxide removal to reach net zero; that is, there are no studies where absolute zero GHG or even CO_2 emissions are reached by deep emissions reductions alone.

Total GHG emissions are greater than emissions of CO_2 only; reaching net zero CO_2 emissions therefore occurs earlier, by up to several decades, than net zero GHG emissions in all modelled pathways. In most modelled pathways that *likely* limit warming to 2°C (>67%) above pre-industrial levels and below in the most cost-effective way, the agriculture, forestry and other land-use (AFOLU) and energy supply sectors reach net zero CO_2 emissions several decades earlier than other sectors; however, many pathways show much reduced, but still positive, net GHG emissions in the AFOLU sector in 2100.

FAQ 3.3 | How plausible are high emissions scenarios, and how do they inform policy?

IAMs are used to develop a wide range of scenarios describing future trajectories for greenhouse gas emissions based on a wide set of assumptions regarding socio-economic development, technological changes, political development and climate policy. Typically, the IAM-based scenarios can be divided into (i) reference scenarios (describing possible trajectories in the absence of new stringent climate policies) and (ii) mitigation scenarios (describing the impact of various climate policy assumptions). Reference scenarios typically result in high emissions and, subsequently, high levels of climate change (in the order of 2.5°C–4°C during the 21st century). The purpose of such reference scenarios is to explore the consequences of climate change and act as a reference for mitigation scenarios. The possible emission levels for reference scenarios diverge from stabilising and even slowly declining emissions (e.g., for current policy scenarios or SSP1) to very high emission levels (e.g., SSP5 and RCP8.5). The latter leads to nearly 5°C of warming by the end of the century for medium climate sensitivity. Hausfather and Peters (2020) pointed out that since 2011, the rapid development of renewable energy technologies and emerging climate policy have made it considerably less likely that emissions could end up as high as RCP8.5. This means that reaching emissions levels as high as RCP8.5 has become less likely. Still, high emissions cannot be ruled out for many reasons, including political factors and, for instance, higher than anticipated population and economic growth. Climate projections of RCP8.5 can also result from strong feedbacks of climate change on (natural) emission sources and high climate sensitivity (AR6 WGI Chapter 7). Therefore, their median climate impacts might also materialise while following a lower emission path (e.g., Hausfather and Betts 2020). All in all, this means that high-end scenarios have become considerably less likely since AR5 but cannot be ruled out. High-end scenarios (like RCP8.5) can be very useful to explore high-end risks of climate change but are not typical 'business-as-usual' projections and should therefore not be presented as such.

References

Abel, G.J., B. Barakat, K.C. Samir, and W. Lutz, 2016: Meeting the Sustainable Development Goals leads to lower world population growth. *Proc. Natl. Acad. Sci.*, **113(50)**, 14294 LP – 14299, doi:10.1073/pnas.1611386113.

Aboumahboub, T. et al., 2014: On the regional distribution of climate mitigation costs: the impact of delayed cooperative action. *Clim. Change Econ.*, **5(1)**, 1–27, doi:10.1142/S2010007814400028.

Acemoglu, D., P. Aghion, L. Bursztyn, and D. Hemous, 2012: The Environment and Directed Technical Change. *Am Econ Rev*, **102(1)**, 131–166, doi:10.1257/aer.102.1.131.

Acemoglu, D., U. Akcigit, D. Hanley, and W. Kerr, 2016: Transition to clean technology. *J. Polit. Econ.*, **124(1)**, 52–104, doi:10.1086/684511.

Adler, M. et al., 2017: Priority for the worse-off and the social cost of carbon. *Nat. Clim. Change*, **7(6)**, 443–449, doi:10.1038/nclimate3298.

Aghion, P., C. Hepburn, A. Teytelboym, and D. Zenghelis, 2019: Path dependence, innovation and the economics of climate change. In: *Handbook on Green Growth* [R. Fouquet (ed.)]. Edward Elgar Publishing, Cheltenham, UK, pp. 67–83.

Akimoto, K., F. Sano, J. Oda, H. Kanaboshi, and Y. Nakano, 2021: Climate change mitigation measures for global net-zero emissions and the roles of CO_2 capture and utilization and direct air capture. *Energy Clim. Change*, **2**, 100057, doi:https://doi.org/10.1016/j.egycc.2021.100057.

Aldy, J. et al., 2016: Economic tools to promote transparency and comparability in the Paris Agreement. *Nat. Clim. Change*, **6(11)**, 1000–1004, doi:10.1038/nclimate3106.

Aleksandrowicz, L., R. Green, E.J.M. Joy, P. Smith, and A. Haines, 2016: The Impacts of Dietary Change on Greenhouse Gas Emissions, Land Use, Water Use, and Health: A Systematic Review. *PLoS One*, **11(11)**, e0165797.

Allen, M.R. et al., 2009: Warming caused by cumulative carbon emissions towards the trillionth tonne. *Nature*, **458(7242)**, 1163–1166, doi:10.1038/nature08019.

Allen, M.R. et al., 2016: New use of global warming potentials to compare cumulative and short-lived climate pollutants. *Nat. Clim. Change*, **6(8)**, 773–776, doi:10.1038/nclimate2998.

Allen, M.R., O.P. Dube, W. Solecki, F. Aragón-Durand, W. Cramer, S. Humphreys, M. Kainuma, J. Kala, N. Mahowald, Y. Mulugetta, R. Perez, M. Wairiu, and K. Zickfeld, 2018: Framing and Context. In: *Global Warming of 1.5°C. An IPCC Special Report on the impacts of global warming of 1.5°C above pre-industrial levels and related global greenhouse gas emission pathways, in the context of strengthening the global response to the threat of climate change, sustainable development, and efforts to eradicate poverty* [Masson-Delmotte, V., P. Zhai, H.-O. Pörtner, D. Roberts, J. Skea, P.R. Shukla, A. Pirani, W. Moufouma-Okia, C. Péan, R. Pidcock, S. Connors, J.B.R. Matthews, Y. Chen, X. Zhou, M.I. Gomis, E. Lonnoy, T. Maycock, M. Tignor, and T. Waterfield (eds.)]. Cambridge University Press, Cambridge, UK, and New York, NY, USA, pp. 49–91.

Anderegg, W.R.L. et al., 2020: Climate-driven risks to the climate mitigation potential of forests. *Science*, **368(6497)**, eaaz7005, doi:10.1126/science.aaz7005.

Anderson, K. and A. Larkin, 2013: *Avoiding dangerous climate change demands de-growth strategies from wealthier nations.* https://kevinanderson.info/blog/avoiding-dangerous-climate-change-demands-de-growth-strategies-from-wealthier-nations/.

Anderson, K. and G. Peters, 2016: The trouble with negative emissions. *Science*, **354(6309)**, 182–183, doi:10.1126/science.aah4567.

Andrijevic, M., J. Crespo Cuaresma, R. Muttarak, and C.-F. Schleussner, 2020a: Governance in socioeconomic pathways and its role for future adaptive capacity. *Nat. Sustain.*, **3(1)**, 35–41, doi:10.1038/s41893-019-0405-0.

Andrijevic, M., C.-F. Schleussner, M.J. Gidden, D.L. McCollum, and J. Rogelj, 2020b: COVID-19 recovery funds dwarf clean energy investment needs. *Science*, **370(6514)**, 298–300, doi:10.1126/science.abc9697.

Arinoa, Y. et al., 2016: Estimating option values of solar radiation management assuming that climate sensitivity is uncertain. *Proc. Natl. Acad. Sci.*, **113(21)**, 5886–5891, doi:10.1073/pnas.1520795113.

Arnell, N.W. and B. Lloyd-Hughes, 2014: The global-scale impacts of climate change on water resources and flooding under new climate and socio-economic scenarios. *Clim. Change*, **122(1–2)**, 127–140, doi:10.1007/s10584-013-0948-4.

Arvesen, A., G. Luderer, M. Pehl, B.L. Bodirsky, and E.G. Hertwich, 2018: Deriving life cycle assessment coefficients for application in integrated assessment modelling. *Environ. Model. Softw.*, **99**, 111–125, doi:https://doi.org/10.1016/j.envsoft.2017.09.010.

Asadieh, B., and N.Y. Krakauer, 2017: Global change in streamflow extremes under climate change over the 21st century. *Hydrol. Earth Syst. Sci.*, **21(11)**, 5863–5874, doi:10.5194/hess-21-5863-2017.

Auffhammer, M., P. Baylis, and C.H. Hausman, 2017: Climate change is projected to have severe impacts on the frequency and intensity of peak electricity demand across the United States. *Proc. Natl. Acad. Sci.*, **114(8)**, 1886–1891, doi:10.1073/pnas.1613193114.

Azevedo, I., C. Bataille, J. Bistline, L. Clarke, and S. Davis, 2021: Net-Zero Emissions Energy Systems: What We Know and Do Not Know. *Energy Clim. Change*, **2**, 100049, doi: 10.1016/j.egycc.2021.100049.

Babacan, O. et al., 2020: Assessing the feasibility of carbon dioxide mitigation options in terms of energy usage. *Nat. Energy*, **5(9)**, 720–728, doi:10.1038/s41560-020-0646-1.

Bajželj, B. and K.S. Richards, 2014: The positive feedback loop between the impacts of climate change and agricultural expansion and relocation. *Land*, **3(3)**, 898–916, doi:10.3390/land3030898.

Bajželj, B. et al., 2014: Importance of food-demand management for climate mitigation. *Nat. Clim. Change*, **4(10)**, 924–929, doi:10.1038/nclimate2353.

Baker, J.S., C.M. Wade, B.L. Sohngen, S. Ohrel, and A.A. Fawcett, 2019: Potential complementarity between forest carbon sequestration incentives and biomass energy expansion. *Energy Policy*, **126** (August 2018), 391–401, doi:10.1016/j.enpol.2018.10.009.

Baležentis, T., G. Liobikienė, D. Štreimikienė, and K. Sun, 2020: The impact of income inequality on consumption-based greenhouse gas emissions at the global level: {A} partially linear approach. *J. Environ. Manage.*, **267**, 110635, doi:10.1016/j.jenvman.2020.110635.

Ballard, T.C., E. Sinha, and A.M. Michalak, 2019: Long-Term Changes in Precipitation and Temperature Have Already Impacted Nitrogen Loading. *Environ. Sci. Technol.*, **53(9)**, 5080–5090, doi:10.1021/acs.est.8b06898.

Barker, T., E. Alexandri, J.F. Mercure, Y. Ogawa, and H. Pollitt, 2016: GDP and employment effects of policies to close the 2020 emissions gap. *Clim. Policy*, **16(4)**, 393–414, doi:10.1080/14693062.2014.1003774.

Barron, A.R., A.A. Fawcett, M.A.C. Hafstead, J.R. Mcfarland, and A.C. Morris, 2018: Policy Insights From the EMF 32 Study on U.S. Carbon Tax Scenarios. *Clim. Change Econ.*, **09(01)**, 1840003, doi:10.1142/S2010007818400031.

Bartos, M.D. and M.V. Chester, 2015: Impacts of climate change on electric power supply in the Western United States. *Nat. Clim. Change*, **5(8)**, 748–752, doi:10.1038/nclimate2648.

Bastien-Olvera, B.A. and F.C. Moore, 2020: Use and non-use value of nature and the social cost of carbon. *Nat. Sustain.*, **4**, 101–108, doi:10.1038/s41893-020-00615-0.

Battiston, S., A. Mandel, I. Monasterolo, F. Schütze, and G. Visentin, 2017: A climate stress-test of the financial system. *Nat. Clim. Change*, **7(4)**, 283–288, doi:10.1038/nclimate3255.

Battiston, S., I. Monasterolo, K. Riahi, and B.J. van Ruijven, 2021: Accounting for finance is key for climate mitigation pathways. *Science*, **372(6545)**, 918–920, doi:10.1126/science.abf3877.

3

Bauer, N. et al., 2017: Shared Socio-Economic Pathways of the Energy Sector – Quantifying the Narratives. *Glob. Environ. Change*, **42**, 316–330, doi:10.1016/j.gloenvcha.2016.07.006.

Bauer, N. et al., 2018a: Global energy sector emission reductions and bioenergy use: overview of the bioenergy demand phase of the EMF-33 model comparison. *Clim. Change*, **163**, 1553–1568, doi:10.1007/s10584-018-2226-y.

Bauer, N., C. McGlade, J. Hilaire, and P. Ekins, 2018b: Divestment prevails over the green paradox when anticipating strong future climate policies. *Nat. Clim. Change*, **8(2)**, 130–134, doi:10.1038/s41558-017-0053-1.

Bauer, N. et al., 2020: Quantification of an efficiency–sovereignty trade-off in climate policy. *Nature*, **588(7837)**, 261–266, doi:10.1038/s41586-020-2982-5.

Beach, R.H. et al., 2015: Climate change impacts on US agriculture and forestry: Benefits of global climate stabilization. *Environ. Res. Lett.*, **10(9)**, doi:10.1088/1748-9326/10/9/095004.

Beck, S. and M. Mahony, 2017: The IPCC and the politics of anticipation. *Nat. Clim. Change*, **7(5)**, 311–313, doi:10.1038/nclimate3264.

Beck, S. and M. Mahony, 2018: The politics of anticipation: The IPCC and the negative emissions technologies experience. *Glob. Sustain.*, **1**, 1–8, doi:10.1017/sus.2018.7.

Bednar, J. et al., 2021: Operationalizing the net-negative carbon economy. *Nature*, **596**, 377–383, doi:10.1038/s41586-021-03723-9.

Beiser-McGrath, L.F. and T. Bernauer, 2019: Could revenue recycling make effective carbon taxation politically feasible? *Sci. Adv.*, **5(9)**, eaax3323, doi:10.1126/sciadv.aax3323.

Belaia, M., J.B. Moreno-Cruz, and D.W. Keith, 2021: Optimal Climate Policy in 3D: Mitigation, Carbon Removal and Solar Geoengineering. *Clim. Change Econ.*, **12(3)**, 2150008, doi:10.1142/S2010007821500081.

Béland, D. and M. Howlett, 2016: How Solutions Chase Problems: Instrument Constituencies in the Policy Process. *Governance*, **29(3)**, 393–409, doi:https://doi.org/10.1111/gove.12179.

Bennich, T., N. Weitz, and H. Carlsen, 2020: Deciphering the scientific literature on SDG interactions: A review and reading guide. *Sci. Total Environ.*, **728**, 138405, doi:10.1016/j.scitotenv.2020.138405.

Benveniste, H., O. Boucher, C. Guivarch, H. Le Treut, and P. Criqui, 2018: Impacts of nationally determined contributions on 2030 global greenhouse gas emissions: uncertainty analysis and distribution of emissions. *Environ. Res. Lett.*, **13(1)**, 14022, doi:10.1088/1748-9326/aaa0b9.

Benveniste, H., J. C. Cuaresma, M. Gidden, and R. Muttarak, 2021: Tracing international migration in projections of income and inequality across the Shared Socioeconomic Pathways. *Clim. Change*, **166(3)**, 39, doi:10.1007/s10584-021-03133-w.

Bergek, A., S. Jacobsson, and B.A. Sandén, 2008: 'Legitimation' and 'development of positive externalities': two key processes in the formation phase of technological innovation systems. *Technol. Anal. Strateg. Manag.*, **20(5)**, 575–592, doi:10.1080/09537320802292768.

Berger, A. et al., 2017: How much can nuclear energy do about global warming? *Int. J. Glob. Energy Issues*, **40(1/2)**, doi:10.1504/IJGEI.2017.080766.

Berthe, A. and L. Elie, 2015: Mechanisms explaining the impact of economic inequality on environmental deterioration. *Ecol. Econ.*, **116**, 191–200, doi:10.1016/j.ecolecon.2015.04.026.

Bertram, C. et al., 2015a: Carbon lock-in through capital stock inertia associated with weak near-term climate policies. *Technol. Forecast. Soc. Change*, **90(PA)**, 62–72, doi:10.1016/j.techfore.2013.10.001.

Bertram, C. et al., 2015b: Complementing carbon prices with technology policies to keep climate targets within reach. *Nat. Clim. Change*, **5(3)**, 235–239, doi:10.1038/nclimate2514.

Bertram, C. et al., 2018: Targeted policies can compensate most of the increased sustainability risks in 1.5°C mitigation scenarios. *Environ. Res. Lett.*, **13(6)**, doi:10.1088/1748-9326/aac3ec.

Bertram, C. et al., 2021: Energy system developments and investments in the decisive decade for the Paris Agreement goals. *Environ. Res. Lett.*, **16(7)**, 74020, doi:10.1088/1748-9326/ac09ae.

Bezerra, P. et al., 2021: Impacts of a warmer world on space cooling demand in Brazilian households. *Energy Build.*, **234**, 110696, doi:https://doi.org/10.1016/j.enbuild.2020.110696.

Bibas, R., A. Méjean, and M. Hamdi-Cherif, 2015: Energy efficiency policies and the timing of action: An assessment of climate mitigation costs. *Technol. Forecast. Soc. Change*, **90(PA)**, 137–152, doi:10.1016/j.techfore.2014.05.003.

Bijl, D.L. et al., 2018: A Global Analysis of Future Water Deficit Based On Different Allocation Mechanisms. *Water Resour. Res.*, **54(8)**, 5803–5824, doi:10.1029/2017WR021688.

Bindoff, N.L., W.W.L. Cheung, J.G. Kairo, J. Arístegui, V.A. Guinder, R. Hallberg, N. Hilmi, N. Jiao, M.S. Karim, L. Levin, S. O'Donoghue, S.R. Purca Cuicapusa, B. Rinkevich, T. Suga, A. Tagliabue, and P. Williamson, 2019: Changing Ocean, Marine Ecosystems, and Dependent Communities. In: *IPCC Special Report on the Ocean and Cryosphere in a Changing Climate* [H.-O. Pörtner, D.C. Roberts, V. Masson-Delmotte, P. Zhai, M. Tignor, E. Poloczanska, K. Mintenbeck, A. Alegría, M. Nicolai, A. Okem, J. Petzold, B. Rama, N.M. Weyer (eds.)]. Cambridge University Press, Cambridge, UK and New York, NY, USA, pp. 447–587. https://doi.org/10.1017/9781009157964.007.

Bistline, J., M. Budolfson, and B. Francis, 2020: Deepening transparency about value-laden assumptions in energy and environmental modelling: improving best practices for both modellers and non-modellers. *Clim. Policy*, **21(1)**, 1–15, doi:10.1080/14693062.2020.1781048.

Bistline, J.E.T. and G.J. Blanford, 2021: Impact of carbon dioxide removal technologies on deep decarbonization of the electric power sector. *Nat. Commun.*, **12(1)**, 3732, doi:10.1038/s41467-021-23554-6.

Blanford, G.J., E. Kriegler, and M. Tavoni, 2014: Harmonization vs. fragmentation: Overview of climate policy scenarios in EMF27. *Clim. Change*, **123(3–4)**, 383–396, doi:10.1007/s10584-013-0951-9.

Böhringer, C., E.J. Balistreri, and T.F. Rutherford, 2012: The role of border carbon adjustment in unilateral climate policy: Overview of an Energy Modeling Forum study (EMF 29). *Energy Econ.*, **34**, S97–S110, doi: 10.1016/j.eneco.2012.10.003.

Böhringer, C., K.E. Rosendahl, and H.B. Storrøsten, 2017: Robust policies to mitigate carbon leakage. *J. Public Econ.*, **149**, 35–46, doi.org/10.1016/j.jpubeco.2017.03.006.

Böhringer, C., S. Peterson, T.F. Rutherford, J. Schneider, and M. Winkler, 2021: Climate policies after Paris: Pledge, Trade and Recycle: Insights from the 36th Energy Modeling Forum Study (EMF36). *Energy Econ.*, **103**, 105471, doi.org/10.1016/j.eneco.2021.105471.

Bonsch, M. et al., 2016: Trade-offs between land and water requirements for large-scale bioenergy production. *GCB Bioenergy*, **8(1)**, 11–24, doi:10.1111/gcbb.12226.

Bosetti, V., C. Carraro, and M. Tavoni, 2009: Climate change mitigation strategies in fast-growing countries: The benefits of early action. *Energy Econ.*, **31(sup2)**, S144–S151, doi:10.1016/j.eneco.2009.06.011.

Bosetti, V., C. Carraro, R. Duval, and M. Tavoni, 2011: What should we expect from innovation? A model-based assessment of the environmental and mitigation cost implications of climate-related R&D. *Energy Econ.*, **33(6)**, 1313–1320, doi:10.1016/j.eneco.2011.02.010.

Bosetti, V. et al., 2015: Sensitivity to energy technology costs: A multi-model comparison analysis. *Energy Policy*, **80**, 244–263, doi.org/10.1016/j.enpol.2014.12.012.

Boucher, O., J.A. Lowe, and C.D. Jones, 2009: Implications of delayed actions in addressing carbon dioxide emission reduction in the context of geo-engineering. *Clim. Change*, **92(3–4)**, 261–273, doi:10.1007/s10584-008-9489-7.

Bowen, A., K. Kuralbayeva, and E.L. Tipoe, 2018: Characterising green employment: {The} impacts of 'greening' on workforce composition. *Energy Econ.*, **72**, 263–275, doi:10.1016/j.eneco.2018.03.015.

3

Bowles, N., S. Alexander, and M. Hadjikakou, 2019: The livestock sector and planetary boundaries: A 'limits to growth' perspective with dietary implications. *Ecol. Econ.*, **160** (January), 128–136, doi:10.1016/j.ecolecon.2019.01.033.

Boysen, L.R., W. Lucht, D. Gerten, and V. Heck, 2016: Impacts devalue the potential of large-scale terrestrial CO2 removal through biomass plantations. *Environ. Res. Lett.*, **11(9)**, 1–10, doi:10.1088/1748-9326/11/9/095010.

Boysen, L.R. et al., 2017: The limits to global-warming mitigation by terrestrial carbon removal. *Earth's Future*, **5(5)**, 463–474, doi:10.1002/2016EF000469.

BP, 2021: *Statistical Review of World Energy 2021.* Statistical Review of World Energy, London, UK, 70pp. https://www.bp.com/content/dam/bp/business-sites/en/global/corporate/pdfs/energy-economics/statistical-review/bp-stats-review-2021-full-report.pdf.

Brandi, C., 2015: Safeguarding the earth system as a priority for sustainable development and global ethics: The need for an earth system SDG. *J. Glob. Ethics*, **11(1)**, 32–36, doi:10.1080/17449626.2015.1006791.

Breyer, C. and M. Jefferson, 2020: Use and Abuse of Energy and Climate Scenarios—A Week of Controversy on Scenarios. *Econ. Energy Environ. Policy*, **9**, doi:10.5547/2160-5890.9.1.mjef.

Brockway, P.E., S. Sorrell, G. Semieniuk, M.K. Heun, and V. Court, 2021: Energy efficiency and economy-wide rebound effects: A review of the evidence and its implications. *Renew. Sustain. Energy Rev.*, **141** (December 2020), 110781, doi:10.1016/j.rser.2021.110781.

Brook, B.W., T. Blees, T.M.L. Wigley, and S. Hong, 2018: Silver Buckshot or Bullet: Is a Future 'Energy Mix' Necessary? *Sustainability*, **10(2)**, doi:10.3390/su10020302.

Brown, C., P. Alexander, A. Arneth, I. Holman, and M. Rounsevell, 2019: Achievement of Paris climate goals unlikely due to time lags in the land system. *Nat. Clim. Change*, **9(3)**, 203–208, doi:10.1038/s41558-019-0400-5.

Brown, P.T. and H. Saunders, 2020: Approximate calculations of the net economic impact of global warming mitigation targets under heightened damage estimates. *PLoS One*, **15(10)**, e0239520, doi:10.1371/journal.pone.0239520.

Brown, P.T., J. Moreno-Cruz, and K. Caldeira, 2020: Break-even year: a concept for understanding intergenerational trade-offs in climate change mitigation policy. *Environ. Res. Commun.*, **2(9)**, 95002, doi:10.1088/2515-7620/abb413.

Brown, S., S. Hanson, and R. Nicholls, 2014: Implications of sea-level rise and extreme events around Europe: A review of coastal energy infrastructure. *Clim. Change*, **122**, doi:10.1007/s10584-013-0996-9.

Brutschin, E. et al., 2021: A multidimensional feasibility evaluation of low-carbon scenarios. *Environ. Res. Lett.*, **16(6)**, 64069, doi:10.1088/1748-9326/abf0ce.

Budolfson, M., F. Dennig, M. Fleurbaey, A. Siebert, and R.H. Socolow, 2017: The comparative importance for optimal climate policy of discounting, inequalities and catastrophes. *Clim. Change*, **145(3–4)**, 481–494, doi:10.1007/s10584-017-2094-x.

Budolfson, M.B. et al., 2021: Utilitarian benchmarks for emissions and pledges promote equity, climate and development. *Nat. Clim. Change*, **11(10)**, 827–833, doi:10.1038/s41558-021-01130-6.

Burgess, M.G., J. Ritchie, J. Shapland, and R. Pielke, 2020: IPCC baseline scenarios have over-projected CO2 emissions and economic growth. *Environ. Res. Lett.*, **16(1)**, doi:10.1088/1748-9326/abcdd2.

Burke, M., W.M. Davis, and N.S. Diffenbaugh, 2018: Large potential reduction in economic damages under UN mitigation targets. *Nature*, **557(7706)**, 549–553, doi:10.1038/s41586-018-0071-9.

Burrows, M.T. et al., 2019: Ocean community warming responses explained by thermal affinities and temperature gradients. *Nat. Clim. Change*, **9(12)**, 959–963, doi:10.1038/s41558-019-0631-5.

Butnar, I. et al., 2020: A deep dive into the modelling assumptions for biomass with carbon capture and storage (BECCS): A transparency exercise. *Environ. Res. Lett.*, **15(8)**, doi:10.1088/1748-9326/ab5c3e.

Byers, E. et al., 2018: Global exposure and vulnerability to multi-sector development and climate change hotspots. *Environ. Res. Lett.*, **13(5)**, 055012, doi:10.1088/1748-9326/aabf45.

Cai, Y. and T.S. Lontzek, 2019: The Social Cost of Carbon with Economic and Climate Risks. *J. Polit. Econ.*, **127(6)**, 2684–2734, doi:10.1086/701890.

Cai, Y., K.L. Judd, T.M. Lenton, T.S. Lontzek, and D. Narita, 2015: Environmental tipping points significantly affect the cost-benefit assessment of climate policies. *Proc. Natl. Acad. Sci.*, **112(15)**, 4606–4611, doi:10.1073/pnas.1503890112.

Cai, Y., T.M. Lenton, and T.S. Lontzek, 2016: Risk of multiple interacting tipping points should encourage rapid CO$_2$ emission reduction. *Nat. Clim. Change*, **6(5)**, 520–525, doi:10.1038/nclimate2964.

Cain, M. et al., 2019: Improved calculation of warming-equivalent emissions for short-lived climate pollutants. *npj Clim. Atmos. Sci.*, **2(1)**, doi:10.1038/s41612-019-0086-4.

Caldecott, B., 2017: Introduction to special issue: stranded assets and the environment. *J. Sustain. Financ. Invest.*, **7(1)**, 1–13, doi:10.1080/20430795.2016.1266747.

Calvin, K. et al., 2013: Implications of simultaneously mitigating and adapting to climate change: Initial experiments using GCAM. *Clim. Change*, **117(3)**, 545–560, doi:10.1007/s10584-012-0650-y.

Calvin, K. et al., 2014a: EU 20-20-20 energy policy as a model for global climate mitigation. *Clim. Policy*, **14(5)**, 581–598, doi:10.1080/14693062.2013.879794.

Calvin, K. et al., 2014b: Trade-offs of different land and bioenergy policies on the path to achieving climate targets. *Clim. Change*, **123(3–4)**, 691–704, doi:10.1007/s10584-013-0897-y.

Calvin, K. et al., 2021: Bioenergy for climate change mitigation: Scale and sustainability. *GCB Bioenergy*, **13(9)**, 1346–1371, doi.org/10.1111/gcbb.12863.

Calvin, K.V., R. Beach, A. Gurgel, M. Labriet, and A.M. Loboguerrero Rodriguez, 2014c: Agriculture, forestry, and other land-use emissions in Latin America. *Energy Econ.*, **56**, 615–624, doi:10.1016/j.eneco.2015.03.020.

Cameron, C. et al., 2016: Policy trade-offs between climate mitigation and clean cook-stove access in South Asia. *Nat. Energy*, **1(1)**, 1–5, doi:10.1038/nenergy.2015.10.

Canadell, J.G. and P.M.S. Monteiro, 2019: Global Carbon and other Biogeochemical Cycles and Feedbacks. In *Climate Change 2021: The Physical Science Basis. Contribution of Working Group I to the Sixth Assessment Report of the Intergovernmental Panel on Climate Change* [Masson-Delmotte, V., P. Zhai, A. Pirani, S.L. Connors, C. Péan, S. Berger, N. Caud, Y. Chen, L. Goldfarb, M.I. Gomis, M. Huang, K. Leitzell, E. Lonnoy, J.B.R. Matthews, T.K. Maycock, T. Waterfield, O. Yelekçi, R. Yu, and B. Zhou (eds.)]. Cambridge University Press, Cambridge, United Kingdom and New York, NY, USA (in press).

Carattini, S., S. Kallbekken, and A. Orlov, 2019: How to win public support for a global carbon tax. *Nature*, **565**, 289–291, doi: 10.1038/d41586-019-00124-x.

Carton, W., 2019: Carbon Unicorns and Fossil Futures: Whose Emissions Reduction Pathways Is the IPCC Performing? In: *Has It Come to This? The Promises and Perils of Geoengineering on the Brink?* [J.P. Sapinski, Buck, H.J., and Malm A. (eds.)]. Rutgers University Press, Ithaca, NY, pp. 34–49, doi: 10.36019/9781978809390-003.

Chakravarty, S. and M. Tavoni, 2013: Energy poverty alleviation and climate change mitigation: Is there a trade off? *Energy Econ.*, **40**, S67–S73, doi:10.1016/j.eneco.2013.09.022.

Chang, K.M. et al., 2017: Ancillary health effects of climate mitigation scenarios as drivers of policy uptake: a review of air quality, transportation and diet co-benefits modeling studies. *Environ. Res. Lett.*, **12(11)**, 113001, doi:10.1088/1748-9326/aa8f7b.

Chateau, J. and A. Saint-Martin, 2013: Economic and employment impacts of climate change mitigation policies in {OECD}: {A} general-

3

equilibrium perspective. *Int. Econ.*, **135–136**, 79–103, doi:10.1016/j.inteco.2013.08.001.

Chaturvedi, V. et al., 2013a: *Climate Policy Implications for Agricultural Water Demand*. Pacific Northwest National Laboratory (PNNL), 16 pp. Available at: http://www.globalchange.umd.edu/wp-content/uploads/projects/PNNL-22356.pdf.

Chaturvedi, V. et al., 2013b: Climate mitigation policy implications for global irrigation water demand. *Mitig. Adapt. Strateg. Glob. Change*, **20(3)**, 389–407, doi:10.1007/s11027-013-9497-4.

Chen, C. and M. Tavoni, 2013: Direct air capture of CO_2 and climate stabilization: A model based assessment. *Clim. Change*, **118(1)**, 59–72, doi:10.1007/s10584-013-0714-7.

Cherp, A., V. Vinichenko, J. Jewell, E. Brutschin, and B. Sovacool, 2018: Integrating techno-economic, socio-technical and political perspectives on national energy transitions: A meta-theoretical framework. *Energy Res. Soc. Sci.*, **37** (January 2017), 175–190, doi:10.1016/j.erss.2017.09.015.

Cherp, A., V. Vinichenko, J. Tosun, J.A. Gordon, and J. Jewell, 2021: National growth dynamics of wind and solar power compared to the growth required for global climate targets. *Nat. Energy*, **6(7)**, 742–754, doi:10.1038/s41560-021-00863-0.

Cherubini, F., R.M. Bright, and A.H. Strømman, 2013: Erratum: Global climate impacts of forest bioenergy: What, when and how to measure? *Environ. Res. Lett.*, **8(2)**, doi:10.1088/1748-9326/8/2/029503.

Christensen, P., K. Gillingham, and W. Nordhaus, 2018: Uncertainty in forecasts of long-run economic growth. *Proc. Natl. Acad. Sci.*, **115(21)**, 5409–5414, doi:10.1073/pnas.1713628115.

Clarke, L. et al., 2009: International climate policy architectures: Overview of the EMF 22 International Scenarios. *Energy Econ.*, **31(Sup2)**, S64–S81, doi:10.1016/j.eneco.2009.10.013.

Clarke, L. et al., 2018: Effects of long-term climate change on global building energy expenditures. *Energy Econ.*, **72**, 667–677, doi:10.1016/j.eneco.2018.01.003.

Clarke L., K. Jiang, K. Akimoto, M. Babiker, G. Blanford, K. Fisher-Vanden, J.-C. Hourcade, V. Krey, E. Kriegler, A. Löschel, D. McCollum, S. Paltsev, S. Rose, P.R. Shukla, M. Tavoni, B.C.C. van der Zwaan, and D.P. van Vuuren, 2014: Assessing Transformation Pathways. In *Climate Change 2014: Mitigation of Climate Change. Contribution of Working Group III to the Fifth Assessment Report of the Intergovernmental Panel on Climate Change* [Edenhofer, O., R. Pichs-Madruga, Y. Sokona, E. Farahani, S. Kadner, K. Seyboth, A. Adler, I. Baum, S. Brunner, P. Eickemeier, B. Kriemann, J. Savolainen, S. Schlömer, C. von Stechow, T. Zwickel and J.C. Minx (eds.)]. Cambridge University Press, Cambridge, UK, and New York, NY, USA, pp. 413–510.

Cointe, B., C. Cassen, and A. Nadaï, 2019: Organising policy-relevant knowledge for climate action: Integrated assessment modelling, the IPCC, and the emergence of a collective expertise on socioeconomic emission scenarios. *Sci. Technol. Stud.*, **32(4)**, 36–57, doi:10.23987/sts.65031.

Colelli, F. Pietro, and E. De Cian, 2020: Cooling demand in integrated assessment models: a methodological review. *Environ. Res. Lett.*, **15(11)**, 113005, doi:10.1088/1748-9326/abb90a.

Collins, M., R. Knutti, J. Arblaster, J.-L. Dufresne, T. Fichefet, P. Friedlingstein, X. Gao, W.J. Gutowski, T. Johns, G. Krinner, M. Shongwe, C. Tebaldi, A.J. Weaver and M. Wehner, 2013: Long-term Climate Change: Projections, Commitments and Irreversibility. *In Climate Change 2013: The Physical Science Basis. Contribution of Working Group I to the Fifth Assessment Report of the Intergovernmental Panel on Climate Change* [Stocker, T.F., D. Qin, G.-K. Plattner, M. Tignor, S.K. Allen, J. Boschung, A. Nauels, Y. Xia, V. Bex and P.M. Midgley (eds.)]. Cambridge University Press, Cambridge, UK, and New York, NY, USA, pp. 1029–1136.

Collins, W.J. et al., 2018: Increased importance of methane reduction for a 1.5 degree target. *Environ. Res. Lett.*, **13(5)**, 54003, doi:10.1088/1748-9326/aab89c.

Conijn, J.G., P.S. Bindraban, J.J. Schröder, and R.E.E. Jongschaap, 2018: Can our global food system meet food demand within planetary boundaries? *Agric. Ecosyst. Environ.*, **251** (December 2016), 244–256, doi:10.1016/j.agee.2017.06.001.

Conway, D., C. Dalin, W.A. Landman, and T.J. Osborn, 2017: Hydropower plans in eastern and southern Africa increase risk of concurrent climate-related electricity supply disruption. *Nat. Energy*, **2(12)**, 946–953, doi:10.1038/s41560-017-0037-4.

Cosbey, A., S. Droege, C. Fischer, and C. Munnings, 2019: Developing Guidance for Implementing Border Carbon Adjustments: Lessons, Cautions, and Research Needs from the Literature. *Rev. Environ. Econ. Policy*, **13(1)**, 3–22, doi:10.1093/reep/rey020.

Cowie, A.L. et al., 2021: Applying a science-based systems perspective to dispel misconceptions about climate effects of forest bioenergy. *GCB Bioenergy*, **13(8)**, 1210–1231, doi:10.1111/gcbb.12844.

Crippa, M., E. et al., 2021: *GHG emissions of all world countries - 2021 Report*, Publications Office of the European Union, Luxembourg, doi:10.2760/173513.

Creutzig, F. et al., 2016: Beyond Technology: Demand-Side Solutions for Climate Change Mitigation. *Annu. Rev. Environ. Resour.*, **41(1)**, 173–198, doi:10.1146/annurev-environ-110615-085428.

Creutzig, F. et al., 2017: The underestimated potential of solar energy to mitigate climate change. *Nature Energy*, **2**, 17140, doi: 10.1038/nenergy.2017.140.

Creutzig, F. et al., 2018: Towards demand-side solutions for mitigating climate change. *Nat. Clim. Change*, **8(4)**, 268–271, doi:10.1038/s41558-018-0121-1.

Creutzig, F. et al., 2019: The mutual dependence of negative emission technologies and energy systems. *Energy Environ. Sci.*, **12(6)**, 1805–1817, doi:10.1039/c8ee03682a.

Cronin, J., G. Anandarajah, and O. Dessens, 2018a: Climate change impacts on the energy system: a review of trends and gaps. *Clim. Change*, **151(2)**, 79–93, doi:10.1007/s10584-018-2265-4.

Cronin, J.A., D. Fullerton, and S. Sexton, 2018b: Vertical and Horizontal Redistributions from a Carbon Tax and Rebate. *J. Assoc. Environ. Resour. Econ.*, **6(Sup1)**, S169–S208, doi:10.1086/701191.

Cui, R.Y. et al., 2018: Regional responses to future, demand-driven water scarcity. *Environ. Res. Lett.*, **13(9)**, 94006, doi:10.1088/1748-9326/aad8f7.

Cui, R.Y. et al., 2019: Quantifying operational lifetimes for coal power plants under the Paris goals. *Nat. Commun.*, **10(1)**, doi:10.1038/s41467-019-12618-3.

D'Alessandro, S., A. Cieplinski, T. Distefano, and K. Dittmer, 2020: Feasible alternatives to green growth. *Nat. Sustain.*, **3**, 329–335, doi:10.1038/s41893-020-0484-y.

D'Amour, C.B. et al., 2017: Future urban land expansion and implications for global croplands. *Proc. Natl. Acad. Sci.*, **114(34)**, 8939–8944, doi:10.1073/pnas.1606036114.

Dagnachew, A.G. et al., 2020: Integrating energy access, efficiency and renewable energy policies in Sub-Saharan Africa: a model-based analysis. *Environ. Res. Lett.*, **15(12)**, doi:10.1088/1748-9326/abcbb9.

Daioglou, V., B.J. van Ruijven, and D.P. van Vuuren, 2012: Model projections for household energy use in developing countries. *Energy*, **37(1)**, 601–615, doi:10.1016/j.energy.2011.10.044.

Daioglou, V. et al., 2014: Energy demand and emissions of the non-energy sector. *Energy Environ. Sci.*, **7(2)**, 482–498, doi:10.1039/c3ee42667j.

Daioglou, V., J.C. Doelman, B. Wicke, A. Faaij, and D.P. van Vuuren, 2019: Integrated assessment of biomass supply and demand in climate change mitigation scenarios. *Glob. Environ. Change*, **54**, 88–101, doi:10.1016/j.gloenvcha.2018.11.012.

Daioglou, V. et al., 2020: Bioenergy technologies in long-run climate change mitigation: results from the EMF-33 study. *Clim. Change*, **163(3)**, 1603–1620, doi:10.1007/s10584-020-02799-y.

Davis, S.J. et al., 2018: Net-zero emissions energy systems. *Science*, **360(6396)**, doi:10.1126/science.aas9793.

Day, E., S. Fankhauser, N. Kingsmill, H. Costa, and A. Mavrogianni, 2019: Upholding labour productivity under climate change: an assessment of adaptation options. *Clim. Policy*, **19(3)**, 367–385, doi:10.1080/14693062.2018.1517640.

De Cian, E. et al., 2020: Actors, decision-making, and institutions in quantitative system modelling. *Technol. Forecast. Soc. Change*,), **151** 1–10, doi:10.1016/j.techfore.2018.10.004.

de Coninck, H. et al., 2018: Strengthening and Implementing the Global Response Supplementary Material. In: *Global Warming of 1.5°C. An IPCC Special Report on the impacts of global warming of 1.5°C above pre-industrial levels and related global greenhouse gas emission pathways, in the context of strengthening the global response to the threat of climate change, sustainable development and efforts to eradicate poverty* [Masson-Delmotte, V., P. Zhai, H.-O. Pörtner, D. Roberts, J. Skea, P.R. Shukla, A. Pirani, W. Moufouma-Okia, C. Péan, R. Pidcock, S. Connors, J.B.R. Matthews, Y. Chen, X. Zhou, M.I. Gomis, E. Lonnoy, T. Maycock, M. Tignor, and T. Waterfield (eds.)]. Cambridge University Press, Cambridge, United Kingdom and New York, NY, USA, pp. 313–443.

DeAngelo, J. et al., 2021: Energy systems in scenarios at net-zero CO_2 emissions. *Nat. Commun.*, **12(1)**, 6096, doi:10.1038/s41467-021-26356-y.

den Elzen, M.G.J., D.P. van Vuuren, and J. van Vliet, 2010: Postponing emission reductions from 2020 to 2030 increases climate risks and long-term costs. *Clim. Change*, **99(1)**, 313–320, doi:10.1007/s10584-010-9798-5.

den Elzen, M.G.J. et al., 2015: *Enhanced policy scenarios for major emitting countries. Analysis of current and planned policies, and selected enhanced mitigation measures*. PBL Netherlands Environmental Assessment Agency, NewClimate Institute, International Institute for Applied Systems Analysis and Ecofys, Bilthoven, the Netherlands.

Deng, H.-M., Q.-M. Liang, L.-J. Liu, and L.D. Anadon, 2017: Co-benefits of greenhouse gas mitigation: a review and classification by type, mitigation sector, and geography. *Environ. Res. Lett.*, **12(12)**, 123001, doi:10.1088/1748-9326/aa98d2.

Dennig, F., M.B. Budolfson, M. Fleurbaey, A. Siebert, and R.H. Socolow, 2015: Inequality, climate impacts on the future poor, and carbon prices. *Proc. Natl. Acad. Sci.*, **112 (52)**, 15827–32, doi:10.1073/pnas.1513967112.

Dessens, O., G. Anandarajah, and A. Gambhir, 2016: Limiting global warming to 2°C: What do the latest mitigation studies tell us about costs, technologies and other impacts? *Energy Strateg. Rev.*, **13–14**, 67–76, doi:https://doi.org/10.1016/j.esr.2016.08.004.

Diaz, D., and F. Moore, 2017: Quantifying the economic risks of climate change. *Nat. Clim. Change*, **7(11)**, 774–782, doi:10.1038/nclimate3411.

Dietz, S. and N. Stern, 2015: Endogenous Growth, Convexity of Damage and Climate Risk: How Nordhaus' Framework Supports Deep Cuts in Carbon Emissions. *Econ. J.*, **125(583)**, 574–620, doi:10.1111/ecoj.12188.

Dietz, T., E. Ostrom, and P.C. Stern, 2003: The Struggle to Govern the Commons. *Science*, **302(5652)**, 1907–1912, doi:10.1126/science.1091015.

Do, H.X. et al., 2020: Historical and future changes in global flood magnitude - evidence from a model-observation investigation. *Hydrol. Earth Syst. Sci.*, **24(3)**, 1543–1564, doi:10.5194/hess-24-1543-2020.

Doelman, J.C., E. Stehfest, A. Tabeau, and H. van Meijl, 2019: Making the Paris agreement climate targets consistent with food security objectives. *Glob. Food Sec.*, **23**, 93–103, doi:https://doi.org/10.1016/j.gfs.2019.04.003.

Dolphin, G., M.G. Pollitt, and D.M. Newbery, 2020: The political economy of carbon pricing: a panel analysis. *Oxf. Econ. Pap.*, **72(2)**, 472–500.

Dominish, E., C. Briggs, S. Teske, and F. Mey, 2019: Just transition: Employment projections for the 2.0°C and 1.5°C scenarios. In: *Achieving the Paris Climate Agreement Goals: Global and Regional 100% Renewable Energy Scenarios with Non-Energy GHG Pathways for +1.5°C and +2°C* [Sven T. Springer International Publishing, Cham, pp. 413–435, doi: 10.1007/978-3-030-05843-2_10.

Dorband, I.I., M. Jakob, M. Kalkuhl, and J.C. Steckel, 2019: Poverty and distributional effects of carbon pricing in low- and middle-income countries – A global comparative analysis. *World Dev.*, **115**, 246–257, doi:10.1016/j.worlddev.2018.11.015.

Dottori, F. et al., 2018: Increased human and economic losses from river flooding with anthropogenic warming. *Nat. Clim. Change*, **8(9)**, 781–786, doi:10.1038/s41558-018-0257-z.

Douenne, T., 2020: The Vertical and Horizontal Distributive Effects of Energy Taxes: A Case Study of a French Policy. *Energy J.*, **41(3)**, 231–254, doi:10.5547/01956574.41.3.tdou.

Drouet, L., V. Bosetti, and M. Tavoni, 2015: Selection of climate policies under the uncertainties in the Fifth Assessment Report of the IPCC. *Nat. Clim. Change*, **5(10)**, 937–943, doi:10.1038/nclimate2721.

Drouet, L. et al., 2021: Net zero emission pathways reduce the physical and economic risks of climate change. *Nat. Clim. Change*, **11**, 1070–1076, doi:10.1038/s41558-021-01218-z.

Drupp, M.A. and M.C. Hänsel, 2021: Relative Prices and Climate Policy: How the Scarcity of Nonmarket Goods Drives Policy Evaluation. *Am. Econ. J. Econ. Policy*, **13(1)**, 168–201, doi:10.1257/pol.20180760.

Dwivedi, P., M. Khanna, R. Bailis, and A. Ghilardi, 2014: Potential greenhouse gas benefits of transatlantic wood pellet trade. *Environ. Res. Lett.*, **9(2)**, 24007, doi:10.1088/1748-9326/9/2/024007.

Edelenbosch, O., D. Rovelli, A. Levesque, and E. Al., 2021: Long term, cross country effects of buildings insulation policies. *Technological Forecasting and Social Change*, **170**, 120887, doi: 10.1016/j.techfore.2021.120887.

Edelenbosch, O.Y., D.P. van Vuuren, K. Blok, K. Calvin, and S. Fujimori, 2020: Mitigating energy demand sector emissions: The integrated modelling perspective. *Appl. Energy*, **261** (December 2019), 114347, doi:10.1016/j.apenergy.2019.114347.

Edelenbosch, O.Y. et al., 2017a: Decomposing passenger transport futures: Comparing results of global integrated assessment models. *Transp. Res. Part D Transp. Environ.*, **55**, 281–293, doi:10.1016/j.trd.2016.07.003.

Edelenbosch, O.Y. et al., 2017b: Comparing projections of industrial energy demand and greenhouse gas emissions in long-term energy models. *Energy*, **122**, 701–710, doi.org/10.1016/j.energy.2017.01.017.

Edmonds, J. et al., 2013: Can radiative forcing be limited to 2.6 W m^{-2} without negative emissions from bioenergy and CO_2 capture and storage? *Clim. Change*, **118(1)**, 29–43, doi:10.1007/s10584-012-0678-z.

Edmonds, J. et al., 2021: How Much Could Article 6 Enhance Nationally Determined Contribution Ambition Toward Paris Agreement Goals Through Economic Efficiency? *Clim. Change Econ.*, **12(02)**, 2150007, doi:10.1142/S201000782150007X.

Emmerling, J. and M. Tavoni, 2018a: Exploration of the interactions between mitigation and solar radiation management in cooperative and non-cooperative international governance settings. *Glob. Environ. Change*, **53**, 244–251, doi:10.1016/j.gloenvcha.2018.10.006.

Emmerling, J. and M. Tavoni, 2018b: Climate Engineering and Abatement: A 'flat' Relationship Under Uncertainty. *Environ. Resour. Econ.*, **69(2)**, 395–415, doi:10.1007/s10640-016-0104-5.

Emmerling, J. and M. Tavoni, 2021: Representing inequalities in integrated assessment modeling of climate change. *One Earth*, **4(2)**, 177–180, doi.org/10.1016/j.oneear.2021.01.013.

Emmerling, J. et al., 2019: The role of the discount rate for emission pathways and negative emissions. *Environ. Res. Lett.*, **14(10)**, 104008, doi:10.1088/1748-9326/ab3cc9.

Emodi, N.V., T. Chaiechi, and A.B.M. R. Alam Beg, 2019: A techno-economic and environmental assessment of long-term energy policies and climate variability impact on the energy system. *Energy Policy*, **128** (June 2018), 329–346, doi:10.1016/j.enpol.2019.01.011.

Erb, K.-H. et al., 2016: Exploring the biophysical option space for feeding the world without deforestation. *Nat. Commun.*, **7(1)**, 11382, doi:10.1038/ncomms11382.

Eyer, J. and C.J. Wichman, 2018: Does water scarcity shift the electricity generation mix toward fossil fuels? Empirical evidence from the United States. *J. Environ. Econ. Manage.*, **87**, 224–241, doi:10.1016/j.jeem.2017.07.002.

3

Fajardy, M. and N. Mac Dowell, 2020: Recognizing the Value of Collaboration in Delivering Carbon Dioxide Removal. *One Earth*, **3(2)**, 214–225, doi.org/10.1016/j.oneear.2020.07.014.

Falchetta, G. and M.N. Mistry, 2021: The role of residential air circulation and cooling demand for electrification planning: Implications of climate change in sub-Saharan Africa. *Energy Econ.*, **99**, 105307, doi.org/10.1016/j.eneco.2021.105307.

Fankhaeser, S., F. Sehlleier, and N. Stern, 2008: Climate change, innovation and jobs. *Clim. Policy*, **8(4)**, 421–429, doi: 10.3763/cpol.2008.0513.

FAO, 2018: *The future of food and agriculture – Alternative pathways to 2050*. Global Perspectives Studies. Food and Agriculture Organization of the United Nations (FAO), Rome, Italy, 224 pp. http://www.fao.org/global-perspectives-studies/resources/detail/en/c/1157082/.

FAO, IFAD, UNICEF, WFP and WHO, 2017: *The State of Food Security and Nutrition in the World 2017 Builiding Resilience for Peace and Food Security*. Food and Agriculture Organization of the United Nations (FAO), Rome, Italy, 132 pp.

Farfan, J. and C. Breyer, 2017: Structural changes of global power generation capacity towards sustainability and the risk of stranded investments supported by a sustainability indicator. *J. Clean. Prod.*, **141**, 370–384, doi:10.1016/j.jclepro.2016.09.068.

Farquharson, D., P. Jaramillo, and C. Samaras, 2018: Sustainability implications of electricity outages in sub-Saharan Africa. *Nat. Sustain.*, **1(10)**, 589–597, doi:10.1038/s41893-018-0151-8.

Fattouh, B., R. Poudineh, and R. West, 2019: The rise of renewables and energy transition: what adaptation strategy exists for oil companies and oil-exporting countries? *Energy Transitions*, **3(1)**, 45–58, doi:10.1007/s41825-019-00013-x.

Favero, A., A. Daigneault, and B. Sohngen, 2020: Forests: Carbon sequestration, biomass energy, or both? *Sci. Adv.*, **6(13)**, eaay6792, doi:10.1126/sciadv.aay6792.

Fawcett, A.A. et al., 2015: Can Paris pledges avert severe climate change? *Science*, **350(6265)**, 1168–1169, doi:10.1126/science.aad5761.

Fekete, H. et al., 2015: *Impacts of good practice policies on regional and global greenhouse gas emissions*. NewClimate Institute, PBL Netherlands Environmental Assessment Agency and International Institute for Applied Systems Analysis, Cologne, Germany, 81 pp. https://newclimate.org/wp-content/uploads/2015/07/task2c_goodpracticeanalysis_july_2015.pdf.

Fekete, H. et al., 2021: A review of successful climate change mitigation policies in major emitting economies and the potential of global replication. *Renew. Sustain. Energy Rev.*, **137**, 110602, doi.org/10.1016/j.rser.2020.110602.

Fisch-Romito, V. and C. Guivarch, 2019: Transportation infrastructures in a low carbon world: An evaluation of investment needs and their determinants. *Transp. Res. Part D Transp. Environ.*, **72** (May), 203–219, doi:10.1016/j.trd.2019.04.014.

Fisch-Romito, V., C. Guivarch, F. Creutzig, J.C. Minx, and M.W. Callaghan, 2021: Systematic map of the literature on carbon lock-in induced by long-lived capital. *Environ. Res. Lett.*, **16(5)** , doi:10.1088/1748-9326/aba660.

Fischer, C. and R.G. Newell, 2008: Environmental and technology policies for climate mitigation. *J. Environ. Econ. Manage.*, **55(2)**, 142–162, doi:10.1016/j.jeem.2007.11.001.

Fischetti, M., 2018: A Good Life for All. *Sci. Am.*, **318(6)**, 84, doi:10.1038/scientificamerican0618-84.

Fleurbaey, M. et al., 2019: The Social Cost of Carbon: Valuing Inequality, Risk, and Population for Climate Policy. *Monist*, **102(1)**, 84–109, doi:10.1093/monist/ony023.

Flörke, M., I. Bärlund, M.T. van Vliet, A.F. Bouwman, and Y. Wada, 2019: Analysing trade-offs between SDGs related to water quality using salinity as a marker. *Curr. Opin. Environ. Sustain.*, **36**, 96–104, doi:10.1016/j.cosust.2018.10.005.

Fofrich, R. et al., 2020: Early retirement of power plants in climate mitigation scenarios. *Environ. Res. Lett.*, **15(9)**, 94064, doi:10.1088/1748-9326/ab96d3.

Foley, J.A. et al., 2011: Solutions for a cultivated planet. *Nature*, **478(7369)**, 337–342, doi:10.1038/nature10452.

Forster, P.M. et al., 2020: Current and future global climate impacts resulting from COVID-19. *Nat. Clim. Change*, **10(10)**, 913–919, doi:10.1038/s41558-020-0883-0.

Foxon, T.J., G.P. Hammond, and P.J.G. Pearson, 2010: Developing transition pathways for a low carbon electricity system in the UK. *Technol. Forecast. Soc. Change*, **77(8)**, 1203–1213, doi:10.1016/j.techfore.2010.04.002.

Franks, M., K. Lessmann, M. Jakob, J.C. Steckel, and O. Edenhofer, 2018: Mobilizing domestic resources for the Agenda 2030 via carbon pricing. *Nat. Sustain.*, **1(7)**, 350–357, doi:10.1038/s41893-018-0083-3.

Freire-González, J., 2018: Environmental taxation and the double dividend hypothesis in CGE modelling literature: A critical review. *J. Policy Model.*, **40(1)**, 194–223, doi:10.1016/j.jpolmod.2017.11.002.

Fremstad, A. and M. Paul, 2019: The Impact of a Carbon Tax on Inequality. *Ecol. Econ.*, **163**, 88–97, doi:10.1016/j.ecolecon.2019.04.016.

Fricko, O. et al., 2016: Energy sector water use implications of a 2°C climate policy. *Environ. Res. Lett.*, **11(3)**, 34011, doi:10.1088/1748-9326/11/3/034011.

Friedlingstein, P. et al., 2020: Global Carbon Budget 2020. *Earth Syst. Sci. Data Discuss.*, **12(4)**, 1–3, doi:10.5194/essd-2020-286.

Fuglestvedt, J. et al., 2018: Implications of possible interpretations of 'greenhouse gas balance' in the Paris Agreement. *Philos. Trans. R. Soc. A Math. Phys. Eng. Sci.*, **376(2119)**, 20160445, doi:10.1098/rsta.2016.0445.

Fuhrman, J., H. McJeon, S.C. Doney, W. Shobe, and A.F. Clarens, 2019: From Zero to Hero?: Why Integrated Assessment Modeling of Negative Emissions Technologies Is Hard and How We Can Do Better. *Front. Clim.*, **1** (December), doi:10.3389/fclim.2019.00011.

Fuhrman, J. et al., 2020: Food–energy–water implications of negative emissions technologies in a +1.5°C future. *Nat. Clim. Change*, **10(10)**, 920–927, doi:10.1038/s41558-020-0876-z.

Fuhrman, J. et al., 2021: The Role of Direct Air Capture and Negative Emissions Technologies in the Shared Socioeconomic Pathways towards +1.5°C and +2°C Futures. *Environ. Res. Lett*, **16(11)**.

Fujimori, S., M. Kainuma, T. Masui, T. Hasegawa, and H. Dai, 2014: The effectiveness of energy service demand reduction: A scenario analysis of global climate change mitigation. *Energy Policy*, **75**, 379–391, doi:10.1016/j.enpol.2014.09.015.

Fujimori, S., T. Masui, and Y. Matsuoka, 2015: Gains from emission trading under multiple stabilization targets and technological constraints. *Energy Econ.*, **48**, 306–315, doi:10.1016/j.eneco.2014.12.011.

Fujimori, S. et al., 2016a: Will international emissions trading help achieve the objectives of the Paris Agreement? *Environ. Res. Lett.*, **11(10)**, 104001, doi:10.1088/1748-9326/11/10/104001.

Fujimori, S. et al., 2016b: Implication of Paris Agreement in the context of long-term climate mitigation goals. *Springerplus*, **5(1)**, 1620, doi:10.1186/s40064-016-3235-9.

Fujimori, S., N. Hanasaki, and T. Masui, 2017: Projections of industrial water withdrawal under shared socioeconomic pathways and climate mitigation scenarios. *Sustain. Sci.*, **12(2)**, 275–292, doi:10.1007/s11625-016-0392-2.

Fujimori, S. et al., 2018: Inclusive climate change mitigation and food security policy under 1.5°C climate goal. *Environ. Res. Lett.*, **13(7)**, 74033, doi:10.1088/1748-9326/aad0f7.

Fujimori, S. et al., 2019: A multi-model assessment of food security implications of climate change mitigation. *Nat. Sustain.*, **2(5)**, 386–396, doi:10.1038/s41893-019-0286-2.

Fujimori, S. et al., 2020a: Measuring the sustainable development implications of climate change mitigation. *Environ. Res. Lett.*, **15(8)**, 85004, doi:10.1088/1748-9326/ab9966.

Fujimori, S., T. Hasegawa, and K. Oshiro, 2020b: An assessment of the potential of using carbon tax revenue to tackle poverty. *Environ. Res. Lett.*, **15(11)**, 114063, doi:10.1088/1748-9326/abb55d.

Fullerton, D. and E. Muehlegger, 2019: Who Bears the Economic Burdens of Environmental Regulations? *Rev. Environ. Econ. Policy*, **13(1)**, 62–82, doi:10.1093/reep/rey023.

Fuso Nerini, F. et al., 2018: Mapping synergies and trade-offs between energy and the Sustainable Development Goals. *Nat. Energy*, **3(1)**, 10–15, doi:10.1038/s41560-017-0036-5.

Fuss, S., W.H. Reuter, J. Szolgayová, and M. Obersteiner, 2013: Optimal mitigation strategies with negative emission technologies and carbon sinks under uncertainty. *Clim. Change*, **118(1)**, 73–87, doi:10.1007/s10584-012-0676-1.

Fuss, S. et al., 2014: Betting on negative emissions. *Nat. Clim. Change*, **4(10)**, 850–853, doi:10.1038/nclimate2392.

Fuss, S. et al., 2018: Negative emissions – Part 2: Costs, potentials and side effects. *Environ. Res. Lett.*, **13**, 2–4, doi.org/10.1088/1748-9326/aabf9f.

Fuss, S. et al., 2020: Moving toward Net-Zero Emissions Requires New Alliances for Carbon Dioxide Removal. *One Earth*, **3(2)**, 145–149, doi:10.1016/j.oneear.2020.08.002.

Fyson, C.L., S. Baur, M. Gidden, and C.F. Schleussner, 2020: Fair-share carbon dioxide removal increases major emitter responsibility. *Nat. Clim. Change*, **10(9)**, 836–841, doi:10.1038/s41558-020-0857-2.

Galik, C.S., 2020: A continuing need to revisit BECCS and its potential. *Nat. Clim. Change*, **10(1)**, 2–3, doi:10.1038/s41558-019-0650-2.

Gambhir, A. et al., 2017: Assessing the feasibility of global long-term mitigation scenarios. *Energies*, **10(1)**, doi:10.3390/en10010089.

Gambhir, A., I. Butnar, P.H. Li, P. Smith, and N. Strachan, 2019: A review of criticisms of integrated assessment models and proposed approaches to address these, through the lens of BECCs. *Energies*, **12(9)**, doi:10.3390/en12091747.

Garcia-Casals, X., R. Ferroukhi, and B. Parajuli, 2019: Measuring the socio-economic footprint of the energy transition. *Energy Transitions*, **3(1–2)**, 105–118, doi:10.1007/s41825-019-00018-6.

Garnett, T., 2016: Plating up solutions. *Science*, **353(6305)**, 1202–1204, doi:10.1126/science.aah4765.

Gaupp, F., J. Hall, and S. Dadson, 2015: The role of storage capacity in coping with intra- and inter-annual water variability in large river basins. *Environ. Res. Lett.*, **10(12)**, doi:10.1088/1748-9326/10/12/125001.

Gazzotti, P. et al., 2021: Persistent inequality in economically optimal climate policies. *Nat. Commun.*, **12(1)**, 3421, doi:10.1038/s41467-021-23613-y.

Geden, O., 2015: Policy: Climate advisers must maintain integrity. *Nature*, **521(7550)**, 27–28, doi:10.1038/521027a.

Geden, O., 2016: The Paris Agreement and the inherent inconsistency of climate policymaking. *WIREs Clim. Change*, **7(6)**, 790–797, doi.org/10.1002/wcc.427.

Geden, O. and A. Löschel, 2017: Define limits for temperature overshoot targets. *Nat. Geosciences*, **10(12)**, 881–882, doi:10.1038/s41561-017-0026-z.

Geels, D.I.F. W., and I.F.W. Geels, 2005: The dynamics of transitions in socio-technical systems: A multi-level analysis of the transition pathway from horse-drawn carriages to automobiles (1860–1930). *Technol. Anal. Strateg. Manag.*, **17(4)**, 445–476, doi:10.1080/09537320500357319.

Geels, F.W., 2018: Disruption and low-carbon system transformation: Progress and new challenges in socio-technical transitions research and the Multi-Level Perspective. *Energy Res. Soc. Sci.*, **37** (October), 224–231, doi:10.1016/j.erss.2017.10.010.

Geels, F.W., F. Berkhout, and D.P. Van Vuuren, 2016a: Bridging analytical approaches for low-carbon transitions. *Nat. Clim. Change*, **6(6)**, 576–583, doi:10.1038/nclimate2980.

Geels, F.W. et al., 2016b: The enactment of socio-technical transition pathways: A reformulated typology and a comparative multi-level analysis of the German and UK low-carbon electricity transitions (1990–2014). *Res. Policy*, **45(4)**, 896–913, doi:10.1016/j.respol.2016.01.015.

Geels, F.W., A. McMeekin, and B. Pfluger, 2020: Socio-technical scenarios as a methodological tool to explore social and political feasibility in low-carbon transitions: Bridging computer models and the multi-level

perspective in UK electricity generation (2010–2050). *Technol. Forecast. Soc. Change*, **151**, doi:10.1016/j.techfore.2018.04.001.

Geiges, A. et al., 2020: Incremental improvements of 2030 targets insufficient to achieve the Paris Agreement goals. *Earth Syst. Dyn. Discuss.*, 1–18, doi:10.5194/esd-2019-54.

Gernaat, D.E.H. J. et al., 2021: Climate change impacts on renewable energy supply. *Nat. Clim. Change*, **11(2)**, 119–125, doi:10.1038/s41558-020-00949-9.

Giannaris, S., C. Bruce, B. Jacobs, W. Srisang, and D. Janowczyk, 2020: Implementing a second generation CCS facility on a coal fired power station – results of a feasibility study to retrofit SaskPower's Shand power station with CCS. *Greenh. Gases Sci. Technol.*, **10(3)**, 506–518, doi.org/10.1002/ghg.1989.

Giannousakis, A. et al., 2021: How uncertainty in technology costs and carbon dioxide removal availability affect climate mitigation pathways. *Energy*, **216**, 119253, doi.org/10.1016/j.energy.2020.119253.

Giarola, S. et al., 2021: Challenges in the harmonisation of global integrated assessment models: A comprehensive methodology to reduce model response heterogeneity. *Sci. Total Environ.*, **783**, 146861, doi.org/10.1016/j.scitotenv.2021.146861.

Gilabert, P., and H. Lawford-Smith, 2012: Political Feasibility: A Conceptual Exploration. *Polit. Stud.*, **60(4)**, 809–825, doi:10.1111/j.1467-9248.2011.00936.x.

Glanemann, N., S.N. Willner, and A. Levermann, 2020: Paris Climate Agreement passes the cost-benefit test. *Nat. Commun.*, **11(1)**, 110, doi:10.1038/s41467-019-13961-1.

González, M.F. and T. Ilyina, 2016: Impacts of artificial ocean alkalinization on the carbon cycle and climate in Earth system simulations. *Geophys. Res. Lett.*, **43(12)**, 6493–6502, doi:10.1002/2016GL068576.

Gosling, S.N., and N.W. Arnell, 2016: A global assessment of the impact of climate change on water scarcity. *Clim. Change*, **134(3)**, 371–385, doi:10.1007/s10584-013-0853-x.

Gota, S., C. Huizenga, K. Peet, N. Medimorec, and S. Bakker, 2019: Decarbonising transport to achieve Paris Agreement targets. *Energy Effic.*, **12(2)**, 363–386, doi:10.1007/s12053-018-9671-3.

Goulder, L.H., and I.W.H. Parry, 2008: Instrument choice in environmental policy. *Rev. Environ. Econ. Policy*, **2(2)**, 152–174, doi: 10.1093/reep/ren005.

Graham, N.T. et al., 2018: Water Sector Assumptions for the Shared Socioeconomic Pathways in an Integrated Modeling Framework. *Water Resour. Res.*, **54(9)**, 6423–6440, doi:10.1029/2018WR023452.

Graham, N.T. et al., 2020: Humans drive future water scarcity changes across all Shared Socioeconomic Pathways. *Environ. Res. Lett.*, **15(1)**, doi:10.1088/1748-9326/ab639b.

Graichen, J., S. Healy, A. Siemons, N. Höhne, and T. Kuramochi, 2017: International Climate Initiatives – A way forward to close the emissions gap? Dessau-Roßlau , ISSN 1862-4359, **28**. https://inis.iaea.org/collection/NCLCollectionStore/_Public/49/072/49072173.pdf.

Grant, N., A. Hawkes, T. Napp, and A. Gambhir, 2020: The appropriate use of reference scenarios in mitigation analysis. *Nat. Clim. Change*, **10(7)**, 605–610, doi:10.1038/s41558-020-0826-9.

Grant, N., A. Hawkes, S. Mittal, and A. Gambhir, 2021: The policy implications of an uncertain carbon dioxide removal potential. *Joule*, **5**, doi:10.1016/j.joule.2021.09.004.

Grassi, G. et al., 2018: Reconciling global-model estimates and country reporting of anthropogenic forest CO_2 sinks. *Nat. Clim. Change*, **8(10)**, 914–920, doi:10.1038/s41558-018-0283-x.

Grassi, G. et al., 2021: Critical adjustment of land mitigation pathways for assessing countries' climate progress. *Nat. Clim. Change*, **11(5)**, 425–434, doi:10.1038/s41558-021-01033-6.

Green, R.F. et al., 2018: Greenhouse gas emissions and water footprints of typical dietary patterns in India. *Sci. Total Environ.*, **643**, 1411–1418, doi.org/10.1016/j.scitotenv.2018.06.258.

3

Greve, P. et al., 2018: Global assessment of water challenges under uncertainty in water scarcity projections. *Nat. Sustain.*, **1(9)**, 486–494, doi:10.1038/s41893-018-0134-9.

Griscom, B.W. et al., 2017: Natural climate solutions. *Proc. Natl. Acad. Sci.*, **(6)**, 1–6, doi:10.1073/pnas.1710465114.

Grubb, M., C. Wieners, and P. Yang, 2021: Modeling myths: On DICE and dynamic realism in integrated assessment models of climate change mitigation. *WIREs Clim. Change*, **12(3)**, e698, doi.org/10.1002/wcc.698.

Grubler, A. et al., 2018: A low energy demand scenario for meeting the 1.5°C target and sustainable development goals without negative emission technologies. *Nat. Energy*, **3(6)**, 515–527, doi:10.1038/s41560-018-0172-6.

Grunewald, N., S. Klasen, I. Martínez-Zarzoso, and C. Muris, 2017: The Trade-off Between Income Inequality and Carbon Dioxide Emissions. *Ecol. Econ.*, **142**, 249–256, doi:10.1016/j.ecolecon.2017.06.034.

Guivarch, C. and A. Pottier, 2018: Climate Damage on Production or on Growth: What Impact on the Social Cost of Carbon? *Environ. Model. Assess.*, **23(2)**, 117–130, doi:10.1007/s10666-017-9572-4.

Guivarch, C., R. Crassous, O. Sassi, and S. Hallegatte, 2011: The costs of climate policies in a second-best world with labour market imperfections. *Clim. Policy*, **11(1)**, 768–788, doi:10.3763/cpol.2009.0012.

Güneralp, B. et al., 2017: Global scenarios of urban density and its impacts on building energy use through 2050. *Proc. Natl. Acad. Sci.*, **114(34)**, 8945 LP–8950, doi:10.1073/pnas.1606035114.

Gütschow, J., M.L. Jeffery, M. Schaeffer, and B. Hare, 2018: Extending Near-Term Emissions Scenarios to Assess Warming Implications of Paris Agreement NDCs. *Earth's Future*, **6(9)**, 1242–1259, doi.org/10.1002/2017EF000781.

Haberl, H. et al., 2020: A systematic review of the evidence on decoupling of GDP, resource use and GHG emissions, part II: synthesizing the insights. *Environ. Res. Lett.*, **15(6)**, 65003, doi:10.1088/1748-9326/ab842a.

Hall, C., T.P. Dawson, J.I. Macdiarmid, R.B. Matthews, and P. Smith, 2017: The impact of population growth and climate change on food security in Africa: looking ahead to 2050. *Int. J. Agric. Sustain.*, **15(2)**, 124–135, doi:10.1080/14735903.2017.1293929.

Hallegatte, S., A. Vogt-Schilb, J. Rozenberg, M. Bangalore, and C. Beaudet, 2020: From Poverty to Disaster and Back: a Review of the Literature. *Econ. Disasters Clim. Change*, **4**, 223–247, 1–25, doi: 10.1007/s41885-020-00060-5.

Hamilton, I. et al., 2021: The public health implications of the Paris Agreement: a modelling study. *Lancet Planet. Heal.*, **5(2)**, e74–e83, doi:10.1016/S2542-5196(20)30249-7.

Hanaoka, T. and T. Masui, 2020: Exploring effective short-lived climate pollutant mitigation scenarios by considering synergies and trade-offs of combinations of air pollutant measures and low carbon measures towards the level of the 2°C target in Asia. *Environ. Pollut.*, **261**, 113650, doi:10.1016/j.envpol.2019.113650.

Hanasaki, N. et al., 2013: A global water scarcity assessment under Shared Socio-economic Pathways – Part 2: Water availability and scarcity. *Hydrol. Earth Syst. Sci.*, **17(7)**, 2375–2391, doi:10.5194/hess-17-2393-2013.

Hänsel, M.C. et al., 2020: Climate economics support for the UN climate targets. *Nat. Clim. Change* **10**, , 781–789, doi:10.1038/s41558-020-0833-x.

Hansen, K., C. Breyer, and H. Lund, 2019: Status and perspectives on 100% renewable energy systems. *Energy*, **175**, 471–480, doi.org/10.1016/j.energy.2019.03.092.

Hanssen, S.V. et al., 2020: The climate change mitigation potential of bioenergy with carbon capture and storage. *Nat. Clim. Change*, **10(11)**, 1023–1029, doi:10.1038/s41558-020-0885-y.

Hardt, L. and D.W. O'Neill, 2017: Ecological Macroeconomic Models: Assessing Current Developments. *Ecol. Econ.*, **134**, 198–211, doi:10.1016/j.ecolecon.2016.12.027.

Harmsen, J.H.M. et al., 2019a: Long-term marginal abatement cost curves of non-CO$_2$ greenhouse gases. *Environ. Sci. Policy*, **99** (March), 136–149, doi:10.1016/j.envsci.2019.05.013.

Harmsen, M. et al., 2019b: The role of methane in future climate strategies: mitigation potentials and climate impacts. *Clim. Change*, **163**, 1409–1425, doi:10.1007/s10584-019-02437-2.

Harmsen, M. et al., 2020: Taking some heat off the NDCs? The limited potential of additional short-lived climate forcers' mitigation. *Clim. Change*, **163(3)**, 1443–1461, doi:10.1007/s10584-019-02436-3.

Harmsen, M. et al., 2021: Integrated assessment model diagnostics: key indicators and model evolution. *Environ. Res. Lett.*, **16(5)**, 54046, doi:10.1088/1748-9326/abf964.

Harmsen, M.J.H.M. et al., 2016: How climate metrics affect global mitigation strategies and costs: a multi-model study. *Clim. Change*, **136(2)**, 203–216, doi:10.1007/s10584-016-1603-7.

Hasegawa, T. et al., 2014: Climate change impact and adaptation assessment on food consumption utilizing a new scenario framework. *Environ. Sci. Technol.*, **48(1)**, 438–445, doi:10.1021/es4034149.

Hasegawa, T. et al., 2015: Consequence of Climate Mitigation on the Risk of Hunger. *Environ. Sci. Technol.*, **49(12)**, 7245–7253, doi:10.1021/es5051748.

Hasegawa, T. et al., 2018: Risk of increased food insecurity under stringent global climate change mitigation policy. *Nat. Clim. Change*, **8(8)**, 699–703, doi:10.1038/s41558-018-0230-x.

Hasegawa, T. et al., 2021a: Land-based implications of early climate actions without global net-negative emissions. *Nat. Sustain.*, 4, 1052–1059, doi:10.1038/s41893-021-00772-w.

Hasegawa, T. et al., 2021b: Extreme climate events increase risk of global food insecurity and adaptation needs. *Nat. Food*, **2(8)**, 587–595, doi:10.1038/s43016-021-00335-4.

Hatfield-Dodds, S. et al., 2017: Assessing global resource use and greenhouse emissions to 2050, with ambitious resource efficiency and climate mitigation policies. *J. Clean. Prod.*, **144**, 403–414, doi:10.1016/j.jclepro.2016.12.170.

Hausfather, Z. and G.P. Peters, 2020: Emissions – the 'business as usual' story is misleading. *Nature*, **577(7792)**, 618–620, doi:10.1038/d41586-020-00177-3.

Havlík, P. et al., 2014: Climate change mitigation through livestock system transitions. *Proc. Natl. Acad. Sci.*, **111(10)**, 3709–3714, doi:10.1073/pnas.1308044111.

Haxeltine, A. et al., 2008: A Conceptual Framework for transition modelling. *Int. J. Innov. Sustain. Dev.*, **3(1/2)**, 93, doi:10.1504/IJISD.2008.018195.

Hejazi, M. et al., 2014: Long-term global water projections using six socioeconomic scenarios in an integrated assessment modeling framework. *Technol. Forecast. Soc. Change*, **81**, 205–226, doi: 10.1016/j.techfore.2013.05.006.

Helwegen, K.G., C.E. Wieners, J.E. Frank, and H.A. Dijkstra, 2019: Complementing CO$_2$ emission reduction by solar radiation management might strongly enhance future welfare. *Earth Syst. Dynam.*, **10(3)**, 453–472, doi:10.5194/esd-10-453-2019.

Henry, R.C. et al., 2018: Food supply and bioenergy production within the global cropland planetary boundary. *PLoS One*, **13(3)**, e0194695, doi: 10.1371/journal.pone.0194695.

Hepburn, C., B. O'Callaghan, N. Stern, J. Stiglitz, and D. Zenghelis, 2020: *Will COVID-19 fiscal recovery packages accelerate or retard progress on climate change?* Oxford Review of Economic Policy, **36(1)**, S359–S381, doi: 10.1093/oxrep/graa015.

Hess, J.J. et al., 2020: Guidelines for Modeling and Reporting Health Effects of Climate Change Mitigation Actions. *Environ. Health Perspect.*, **128(11)**, 115001, doi:10.1289/EHP6745.

Heutel, G., J. Moreno-Cruz, and S. Shayegh, 2018: Solar geoengineering, uncertainty, and the price of carbon. *J. Environ. Econ. Manage.*, **87**, 24–41, doi.org/10.1016/j.jeem.2017.11.002.

Hickel, J. and G. Kallis, 2020: Is Green Growth Possible? *New Polit. Econ.*, **25(4)**, 469–486, doi:10.1080/13563467.2019.1598964.

Hickel, J. et al., 2021: Urgent need for post-growth climate mitigation scenarios. *Nat. Energy*, **6(8)**, 766–768, doi:10.1038/s41560-021-00884-9.

Hilaire, J. et al., 2019: Negative emissions and international climate goals—learning from and about mitigation scenarios. *Clim. Change*, **157(2)**, 189–219, doi:10.1007/s10584-019-02516-4.

Hirt, L.F., G. Schell, M. Sahakian, and E. Trutnevyte, 2020: A review of linking models and socio-technical transitions theories for energy and climate solutions. *Environ. Innov. Soc. Transitions*, **35**, 162–179, doi:10.1016/j.eist.2020.03.002.

Hock, R., G. Rasul, C. Adler, B. Cáceres, S. Gruber, Y. Hirabayashi, M. Jackson, A. Kääb, S. Kang, S. Kutuzov, Al. Milner, U. Molau, S. Morin, B. Orlove, and H. Steltzer, 2019: High Mountain Areas. In *IPCC Special Report on the Ocean and Cryosphere in a Changing Climate* [H.-O. Pörtner, D.C. Roberts, V. Masson-Delmotte, P. Zhai, M. Tignor, E. Poloczanska, K. Mintenbeck, A. Alegría, M. Nicolai, A. Okem, J. Petzold, B. Rama, N.M. Weyer (eds.)]. Cambridge University Press, Cambridge, UK and New York, NY, USA, pp. 131–202.

Hoekstra, A., M. Steinbuch, and G. Verbong, 2017: Creating Agent-Based Energy Transition Management Models That Can Uncover Profitable Pathways to Climate Change Mitigation. *Complexity*, **2017**, 1967645, doi:10.1155/2017/1967645.

Hof, A.F. et al., 2017: Global and regional abatement costs of Nationally Determined Contributions (NDCs) and of enhanced action to levels well below 2°C and 1.5°C. *Environ. Sci. Policy*, **71**, 30–40, doi:10.1016/j.envsci.2017.02.008.

Hof, C. et al., 2018: Bioenergy cropland expansion may offset positive effects of climate change mitigation for global vertebrate diversity. *Proc. Natl. Acad. Sci.*, **115(52)**, 13294 LP–13299, doi:10.1073/pnas.1807745115.

Hofman, P., B. Elzen, and F.W. Geels, 2004: Sociotechnical scenarios as a new policy tool to explore system innovations: Co-evolution of technology and society in the Netherland's electricity domain. *Innov. Manag. Policy Pract.*, **6(2)**, 344–360, doi:10.5172/impp.2004.6.2.344.

Hofmann, M., S. Mathesius, E. Kriegler, D.P. va. van Vuuren, and H.J. Schellnhuber, 2019: Strong time dependence of ocean acidification mitigation by atmospheric carbon dioxide removal. *Nat. Commun.*, **10(1)**, 5592, doi:10.1038/s41467-019-13586-4.

Höglund-Isaksson, L., A. Gómez-Sanabria, Z. Klimont, P. Rafaj, and W. Schöpp, 2020: Technical potentials and costs for reducing global anthropogenic methane emissions in the 2050 timeframe –results from the GAINS model. *Environ. Res. Commun.*, **2(2)**, 25004, doi:10.1088/2515-7620/ab7457.

Höhne, N. et al., 2021: Wave of net zero emission targets opens window to meeting the Paris Agreement. *Nat. Clim. Change*, **11(10)**, 820–822, doi:10.1038/s41558-021-01142-2.

Holz, C., L.S. Siegel, E. Johnston, A.P. Jones, and J. Sterman, 2018: Ratcheting ambition to limit warming to 1.5°C trade-offs between emission reductions and carbon dioxide removal. *Environ. Res. Lett.*, **13(6)**, doi:10.1088/1748-9326/aac0c1.

Honegger, M. and D. Reiner, 2018: The political economy of negative emissions technologies: consequences for international policy design. *Clim. Policy*, **18(3)**, 306–321, doi:10.1080/14693062.2017.1413322.

Honegger, M., A. Michaelowa, and J. Roy, 2021: Potential implications of carbon dioxide removal for the sustainable development goals. *Clim. Policy*, **21(5)**, 678–698, doi:10.1080/14693062.2020.1843388.

Hong, S., C.J.A. Bradshaw, and B.W. Brook, 2014a: South Korean energy scenarios show how nuclear power can reduce future energy and environmental costs. *Energy Policy*, **74**, 569–578, doi.org/10.1016/j.enpol.2014.05.054.

Hong, S., C.J.A. Bradshaw, and B.W. Brook, 2014b: Nuclear power can reduce emissions and maintain a strong economy: Rating Australia's optimal future electricity-generation mix by technologies and policies. *Appl. Energy*, **136**, 712–725, doi:10.1016/j.apenergy.2014.09.062.

Houghton, R.A. and A.A. Nassikas, 2017: Global and regional fluxes of carbon from land use and land cover change 1850–2015. *Global Biogeochem. Cycles*, **31**, 456–472, doi: 10.1002/2016GB005546.

Howard, D.B., R. Soria, J. Thé, R. Schaeffer, and J.-D. Saphores, 2020: The energy-climate-health nexus in energy planning: A case study in Brazil. *Renew. Sustain. Energy Rev.*, **132**, 110016, doi.org/10.1016/j.rser.2020.110016.

Howard, P.H. and T. Sterner, 2017: Few and Not So Far Between: A Meta-analysis of Climate Damage Estimates. *Environ. Resour. Econ.*, **68**, 197–225, doi:10.1007/s10640-017-0166-z.

Hubacek, K. et al., 2017a: Global carbon inequality. *Energy, Ecol. Environ.*, **2(6)**, 361–369, doi:10.1007/s40974-017-0072-9.

Hubacek, K., G. Baiocchi, K. Feng, and A. Patwardhan, 2017b: Poverty eradication in a carbon constrained world. *Nat. Commun.*, **8(1)**, 1–8, doi:10.1038/s41467-017-00919-4.

Hughes, N., 2013: Towards improving the relevance of scenarios for public policy questions: A proposed methodological framework for policy relevant low carbon scenarios. *Technol. Forecast. Soc. Change*, **80(4)**, 687–698, doi:10.1016/j.techfore.2012.07.009.

Humpenöder, F. et al., 2018: Large-scale bioenergy production: How to resolve sustainability trade-offs? *Environ. Res. Lett.*, **13(2)**, doi:10.1088/1748-9326/aa9e3b.

Huppmann, D., J. Rogelj, E. Kriegler, V. Krey, and K. Riahi, 2018: A new scenario resource for integrated 1.5 °C research. *Nat. Clim. Change*, **8(12)**, 1027–1030, doi:10.1038/s41558-018-0317-4.

Hurlbert, M., J. Krishnaswamy, E. Davin, F.X. Johnson, C.F. Mena, J. Morton, S. Myeong, D. Viner, K. Warner, A. Wreford, S. Zakieldeen, Z. Zommers, 2019: Risk Management and Decision making in Relation to Sustainable Development. In: *Climate Change and Land: an IPCC special report on climate change, desertification, land degradation, sustainable land management, food security, and greenhouse gas fluxes in terrestrial ecosystems* [P.R. Shukla, J. Skea, E. Calvo Buendia, V. Masson-Delmotte, H.-O. Pörtner, D.C. Roberts, P. Zhai, R. Slade, S. Connors, R. van Diemen, M. Ferrat, E. Haughey, S. Luz, S. Neogi, M. Pathak, J. Petzold, J. Portugal Pereira, P. Vyas, E. Huntley, K. Kissick, M. Belkacemi, J. Malley, (eds.)]. Cambridge University Press, Cambridge, UK and New York, NY, USA.

Iacobucci, G., 2016: NHS is unprepared for risks posed by climate change, warn leading UK health bodies. *BMJ*, **352**, i1781, doi:10.1136/bmj.i1781.

IEA, 2011: *Climate change*. International Energy Agency (IEA), Paris, France, 267–268 pp.

IEA, 2019: *World Energy Outlook 2019*. International Energy Agency (IEA), Paris, France, 810 pp. https://www.iea.org/reports/world-energy-outlook-2019.

IEA, 2020a: *World Energy Outlook 2020*. International Energy Agency (IEA), Paris, France 464 pp. https://www.iea.org/reports/world-energy-outlook-2020.

IEA, 2020b: *Global Energy Review 2020*. International Energy Agency (IEA), Paris, France, 55pp. https://www.iea.org/reports/global-energy-review-2020.

IEA, 2021a: *Net Zero by 2050. A Roadmap for the Global Energy Sector*. International Energy Agency (IEA), Paris, France, 224 pp. https://www.iea.org/reports/net-zero-by-2050.

IEA, 2021b: *Conditions and requirements for the technical feasibility of a power system with a high share of renewables in France towards 2050*. International Energy Agency (IEA), Paris, France, 186 pp. https://www.iea.org/reports/conditions-and-requirements-for-the-technical-feasibility-of-a-power-system-with-a-high-share-of-renewables-in-france-towards-2050.

IEA, 2021: *CO₂ Emissions from Fossil Fuel Combustion 2021*. International Energy Agency (IEA), Paris, France. https://www.iea.org/reports/global-energy-review-co2-emissions-in-2021-2.

IMF, 2020: *World Economic Outlook, October 2020: a long and difficult ascent*. https://www.imf.org/en/Publications/WEO/Issues/2020/09/30/world-economic-outlook-october-2020#Full Report and Executive Summary.

3

IMF, 2021: *World Economic Outlook, October 2021: Recovery during a Pandemic—Health Concerns, Supply Disruptions, Price Pressures.* https://www.imf.org/en/Publications/WEO/Issues/2021/10/12/world-economic-outlook-october-2021.

IPBES, 2019: Summary for policymakers of the global assessment report on biodiversity and ecosystem services of the Intergovernmental Science-Policy Platform on Biodiversity and Ecosystem Services [S. Díaz, J. Settele, E. S. Brondízio, H. T. Ngo, M. Guèze et al.(eds.)]. IPBES secretariat, Bonn, Germany. 56 pp.

IPCC, 2018: Summary for Policymakers. In: *Global Warming of 1.5°C. An IPCC Special Report on the impacts of global warming of 1.5°C above pre-industrial levels and related global greenhouse gas emission pathways, in the context of strengthening the global response to the threat of climate change, sustainable development and efforts to eradicate poverty* [Masson-Delmotte, V., P. Zhai, H.-O. Pörtner, D. Roberts, J. Skea, P.R. Shukla, A. Pirani, W. Moufouma-Okia, C. Péan, R. Pidcock, S. Connors, J.B.R. Matthews, Y. Chen, X. Zhou, M.I. Gomis, E. Lonnoy, T. Maycock, M. Tignor, and T. Waterfield (eds.)]. Cambridge University Press, Cambridge, United Kingdom and New York, NY, USA.

IPCC, 2019a: Summary for Policymakers. In: *Climate Change and Land: an IPCC special report on climate change, desertification, land degradation, sustainable land management, food security, and greenhouse gas fluxes in terrestrial ecosystems* [P.R. Shukla, J. Skea, E. Calvo Buendia, V. Masson-Delmotte, H.-O. Pörtner, D.C. Roberts, P. Zhai, R. Slade, S. Connors, R. van Diemen, M. Ferrat, E. Haughey, S. Luz, S. Neogi, M. Pathak, J. Petzold, J. Portugal Pereira, P. Vyas, E. Huntley, K. Kissick, M. Belkacemi, J. Malley, (eds.)]. Cambridge University Press, Cambridge, United Kingdom and New York, NY, USA.

IPCC, 2019b: IPCC *Special Report on the Ocean and Cryosphere in a Changing Climate* [H.-O. Pörtner, D.C. Roberts, V. Masson-Delmotte, P. Zhai, M. Tignor, E. Poloczanska, K. Mintenbeck, A. Alegría, M. Nicolai, A. Okem, J. Petzold, B. Rama, N.M. Weyer (eds.)]. Cambridge University Press, Cambridge, United Kingdom and New York, NY, USA.

Isaac, M. and D.P. van Vuuren, 2009: Modeling global residential sector energy demand for heating and air conditioning in the context of climate change. *Energy Policy*, **37(2)**, 507–521, doi:10.1016/j.enpol.2008.09.051.

Ivanova, D. et al., 2020: Quantifying the potential for climate change mitigation of consumption options. *Environ. Res. Lett.*, **15(9)**, 93001, doi:10.1088/1748-9326/ab8589.

Iyer, G. et al., 2015a: Diffusion of low-carbon technologies and the feasibility of long-term climate targets. *Technol. Forecast. Soc. Change*, **90(PA)**, 103–118, doi:10.1016/j.techfore.2013.08.025.

Iyer, G.C. et al., 2015b: The contribution of Paris to limit global warming to 2°C. *Environ. Res. Lett.*, **10(12)**, doi:10.1088/1748-9326/10/12/125002.

Iyer, G.C. et al., 2015c: Improved representation of investment decisions in assessments of CO_2 mitigation. *Nat. Clim. Change*, **5(5)**, 436–440, doi:10.1038/nclimate2553.

Jackson, R.B., E.I. Solomon, J.G. Canadell, M. Cargnello, and C.B. Field, 2019: Methane removal and atmospheric restoration. *Nat. Sustain.*, **2(6)**, 436–438, doi:10.1038/s41893-019-0299-x.

Jacobson, M.Z., M.A. Delucchi, M.A. Cameron, and B. V Mathiesen, 2018: Matching demand with supply at low cost in 139 countries among 20 world regions with 100% intermittent wind, water, and sunlight (WWS) for all purposes. *Renew. Energy*, **123**, 236–248, doi.org/10.1016/j.renene.2018.02.009.

Jafino, B.A., J.H. Kwakkel, and B. Taebi, 2021: Enabling assessment of distributive justice through models for climate change planning: A review of recent advances and a research agenda. *WIREs Clim. Change*, **12(4)**, e721, doi.org/10.1002/wcc.721.

Jakob, M. and J.C. Steckel, 2016: Implications of climate change mitigation for sustainable development. *Environ. Res. Lett.*, **11(10)**, doi:10.1088/1748-9326/11/10/104010.

Jakob, M., G. Luderer, J. Steckel, M. Tavoni, and S. Monjon, 2012: Time to act now? Assessing the costs of delaying climate measures and benefits of early action. *Clim. Change*, **114**, 79–99, doi: 10.1007/s10584-011-0128-3.

Jakob, M. et al., 2016: Carbon Pricing Revenues Could Close Infrastructure Access Gaps. *World Dev.*, **84**, 254–265, doi:10.1016/j.worlddev.2016.03.001.

Jakob, M. et al., 2020: The future of coal in a carbon-constrained climate. *Nat. Clim. Change*, **10**, 704–707, doi:10.1038/s41558-020-0866-1.

Jeffery, M.L., J. Gütschow, M.R. Rocha, and R. Gieseke, 2018: Measuring Success: Improving Assessments of Aggregate Greenhouse Gas Emissions Reduction Goals. *Earth's Future*, **6(9)**, 1260–1274, doi:10.1029/2018EF000865.

Jenkins, J.D., 2014: Political economy constraints on carbon pricing policies: What are the implications for economic efficiency, environmental efficacy, and climate policy design? *Energy Policy*, **69**, 467–477, doi:10.1016/j.enpol.2014.02.003.

Jewell, J. and A. Cherp, 2020: On the political feasibility of climate change mitigation pathways: Is it too late to keep warming below 1.5°C? *Wiley Interdiscip. Rev. Clim. Change*, **11(1)**, 1–12, doi:10.1002/wcc.621.

Jewell, J., V. Vinichenko, L. Nacke, and A. Cherp, 2019: Prospects for powering past coal. *Nat. Clim. Change*, **9(8)**, 592–597, doi:10.1038/s41558-019-0509-6.

Jia, G., E. Shevliakova, P. Artaxo, N. De Noblet-Ducoudré, R. Houghton, J. House, K. Kitajima, C. Lennard, A. Popp, A. Sirin, R. Sukumar, L. Verchot, 2019: Land–climate interactions. In: *Climate Change and Land: an IPCC Special Report on climate change, desertification, land degradation, sustainable land management, food security, and greenhouse gas fluxes in terrestrial ecosystems* [P.R. Shukla, J. Skea, E. Calvo Buendia, V. Masson-Delmotte, H.-O. Pörtner, D.C. Roberts, P. Zhai, R. Slade, S. Connors, R. van Diemen, M. Ferrat, E. Haughey, S. Luz, S. Neogi, M. Pathak, J. Petzold, J. Portugal Pereira, P. Vyas, E. Huntley, K. Kissick, M. Belkacemi, J. Malley, (eds.)]. Cambridge University Press, Cambridge, UK, and New York, NY, USA, pp. 131–247.

Jiang, K.J., K. Tamura, and T. Hanaoka, 2017: Can we go beyond INDCs: Analysis of a future mitigation possibility in China, Japan, EU and the U.S. *Adv. Clim. Change Res.*, **8(2)**, 117–122, doi:10.1016/j.accre.2017.05.005.

Jiang, L. and B.C. O'Neill, 2017: Global urbanization projections for the Shared Socioeconomic Pathways. *Glob. Environ. Change*, **42**, 193–199, doi.org/10.1016/j.gloenvcha.2015.03.008.

Johansson, Å. et al., 2013: *Long-term growth scenarios*. OECD Economics Department Working Papers No. 1000, 90 pp. https://www.oecd-ilibrary.org/economics/long-term-growth-scenarios_5k4ddxpr2fmr-en.

Johansson, D.J.A., C. Azar, M. Lehtveer, and G.P. Peters, 2020: The role of negative carbon emissions in reaching the Paris climate targets: The impact of target formulation in integrated assessment models. *Environ. Res. Lett*, (in press), doi:10.1088/1748-9326/abc3f0.

Johnson, V.C.A., F. Sherry-Brennan, and P.J.G. Pearson, 2016: Alternative liquid fuels in the UK in the inter-war period (1918–1938): Insights from a failed energy transition. *Environ. Innov. Soc. Transitions*, **20**, 33–47, doi:10.1016/j.eist.2015.12.001.

Jones, C.D. et al., 2021: The Climate Response to Emissions Reductions Due to COVID-19: Initial Results From CovidMIP. *Geophys. Res. Lett.*, **48(8)**, e2020GL091883, doi.org/10.1029/2020GL091883.

Jorgenson, A., J. Schor, and X. Huang, 2017: Income Inequality and Carbon Emissions in the United States: A State-level Analysis, 1997–2012. *Ecol. Econ.*, **134**, 40–48, doi:10.1016/j.ecolecon.2016.12.016.

Kahn, M.E. et al., 2019: *Long-Term Macroeconomic Effects of Climate Change: A Cross-Country Analysis*. IMF Working Papers, Working Paper No. 19/215, 59 pp. https://www.imf.org/en/Publications/WP/Issues/2019/10/11/Long-Term-Macroeconomic-Effects-of-Climate-Change-A-Cross-Country-Analysis-48691.

Kallis, G., C. Kerschner, and J. Martinez-Alier, 2012: The economics of degrowth. *Ecol. Econ.*, **84**, 172–180, doi:10.1016/j.ecolecon.2012.08.017.

3

Kallis, G., S. Paulson, G. D'Alisa, and F. Demaria, 2020: *The case for degrowth.* John Wiley & Sons, Hoboken, NJ, USA, 140 pp.

Karlsson, M. and M. Gilek, 2020: Mind the gap: Coping with delay in environmental governance. *Ambio*, **49(5)**, 1067–1075, doi:10.1007/s13280-019-01265-z.

Karlsson, M., E. Alfredsson, and N. Westling, 2020: Climate policy co-benefits: a review. *Clim. Policy*, **20(3)**, 292–316, doi:10.1080/14693062.2020.1724070.

Kaufman, N., A.R. Barron, W. Krawczyk, P. Marsters, and H. McJeon, 2020: A near-term to net zero alternative to the social cost of carbon for setting carbon prices. *Nat. Clim. Change*, **10(11)**, 1010–1014, doi:10.1038/s41558-020-0880-3.

Kayal, M., H. Lewis, J. Ballard, and E. Kayal, 2019: Humanity and the 21st century's resource gauntlet: a commentary on Ripple et al.'s article "World scientists' warning to humanity: a second notice". *Rethink. Ecol.*, **4**, 21–30, doi: 10.3897/rethinkingecology.4.32116.

KC, S. and W. Lutz, 2017: The human core of the shared socioeconomic pathways: Population scenarios by age, sex and level of education for all countries to 2100. *Glob. Environ. Change*, **42**, 181–192, doi:10.1016/j.gloenvcha.2014.06.004.

Kefford, B.M., B. Ballinger, D.R. Schmeda-Lopez, C. Greig, and S. Smart, 2018: The early retirement challenge for fossil fuel power plants in deep decarbonisation scenarios. *Energy Policy*, **119**, 294–306, doi:10.1016/j.enpol.2018.04.018.

Keller, D.P. et al., 2018a: The Carbon Dioxide Removal Model Intercomparison Project (CDRMIP): Rationale and experimental protocol for CMIP6. *Geosci. Model Dev.*, **11(3)**, 1133–1160, doi:10.5194/gmd-11-1133-2018.

Keller, D.P. et al., 2018b: The Effects of Carbon Dioxide Removal on the Carbon Cycle. *Curr. Clim. Change Reports*, **4(3)**, 250–265, doi:10.1007/s40641-018-0104-3.

Kemp-Benedict, E., 2018: Dematerialization, Decoupling, and Productivity Change. *Ecol. Econ.*, **150** (April), 204–216, doi:10.1016/j.ecolecon.2018.04.020.

Keohane, N., A. Petsonk, and A. Hanafi, 2017: Toward a club of carbon markets. *Clim. Change*, **144(1)**, 81–95, doi:10.1007/s10584-015-1506-z.

Keppo, I. and S. Rao, 2007: International climate regimes: Effects of delayed participation. *Technol. Forecast. Soc. Change*, **74(7)**, 962–979, doi:10.1016/j.techfore.2006.05.025.

Keppo, I. et al., 2021: Exploring the possibility space: Taking stock of the diverse capabilities and gaps in integrated assessment models. *Environ. Res. Lett.*, **16**, 053006, doi: 10.1088/1748-9326/abe5d8.

Kermeli, K. et al., 2019: The scope for better industry representation in long-term energy models: Modeling the cement industry. *Appl. Energy*, **240** (February), 964–985, doi:10.1016/j.apenergy.2019.01.252.

Keyßer, L.T. and M. Lenzen, 2021: 1.5°C degrowth scenarios suggest the need for new mitigation pathways. *Nat. Commun.*, **12(1)**, 2676, doi:10.1038/s41467-021-22884-9.

Kii, M., 2021: Projecting future populations of urban agglomerations around the world and through the 21st century. *npj Urban Sustain.*, **1(1)**, 10, doi:10.1038/s42949-020-00007-5.

Kikstra, J.S. et al., 2021a: Climate mitigation scenarios with persistent COVID-19-related energy demand changes. *Nat. Energy*, **6**, 1114–1123 doi:10.1038/s41560-021-00904-8.

Kikstra, J.S., A. Mastrucci, J. Min, K. Riahi, and N.D. Rao, 2021b: Decent living gaps and energy needs around the world. *Environ. Res. Lett.*, **16(9)**, 95006, doi:10.1088/1748-9326/ac1c27.

Kim, J.B. et al., 2017: Assessing climate change impacts, benefits of mitigation, and uncertainties on major global forest regions under multiple socioeconomic and emissions scenarios. *Environ. Res. Lett.*, **12(4)**, doi:10.1088/1748-9326/aa63fc.

Kim, S.E. et al., 2020: Air quality co-benefits from climate mitigation for human health in South Korea. *Environ. Int.*, **136**, 105507, doi.org/10.1016/j.envint.2020.105507.

Kim, S. J., J.S. Baker, B.L. Sohngen, and M. Shell, 2018: Cumulative global forest carbon implications of regional bioenergy expansion policies. *Resour. Energy Econ.*, **53**, 198–219, doi.org/10.1016/j.reseneeco.2018.04.003.

Kinney, P.L., 2018: Interactions of Climate Change, Air Pollution, and Human Health. *Curr. Environ. Heal. Reports*, **5(1)**, 179–186, doi:10.1007/s40572-018-0188-x.

Kjellstrom, T. et al., 2016: Heat, Human Performance, and Occupational Health: A Key Issue for the Assessment of Global Climate Change Impacts. *Annu. Rev. Public Health*, **37(1)**, 97–112, doi:10.1146/annurev-publhealth-032315-021740.

Kjellstrom, T., C. Freyberg, B. Lemke, M. Otto, and D. Briggs, 2018: Estimating population heat exposure and impacts on working people in conjunction with climate change. *Int. J. Biometeorol.*, **62(3)**, 291–306, doi:10.1007/s00484-017-1407-0.

Klenert, D. et al., 2018: Making carbon pricing work for citizens. *Nat. Clim. Change*, **8(8)**, 669–677, doi:10.1038/s41558-018-0201-2.

Knight, K.W., J.B. Schor, and A.K. Jorgenson, 2017: Wealth Inequality and Carbon Emissions in High-income Countries: *Soc. Curr.*, **4(5)**, 403–412, doi:10.1177/2329496517704872.

Knobloch, F., H. Pollitt, U. Chewpreecha, V. Daioglou, and J.F. Mercure, 2017: Simulating the deep decarbonisation of residential heating for limiting global warming to 1.5°C. *arXiv*, **12**, 521–550, doi: 10.1007/s12053-018-9710-0.

Knopf, B., G. Luderer, and O. Edenhofer, 2011: Exploring the feasibility of low stabilization targets. *Wiley Interdiscip. Rev. Clim. Change*, **2(4)**, 617–626, doi:10.1002/wcc.124.

Köberle, A.C., 2019: The Value of BECCS in IAMs: a Review. *Curr. Sustain. Energy Reports*, **6(4)**, 107–115, doi:10.1007/s40518-019-00142-3.

Köberle, A. et al., 2021: The Cost of Mitigation Revisited. *Nat. Clim. Change* (in press).

Koch, H., S. Vögele, F. Hattermann, and S. Huang, 2014: Hydro-climatic conditions and thermoelectric electricity generation – Part II: Model application to 17 nuclear power plants in Germany. *Energy*, **69**, 700–707, doi:10.1016/j.energy.2014.03.071.

Köhler, J. et al., 2019: An agenda for sustainability transitions research: State of the art and future directions. *Environ. Innov. Soc. Transitions*, **31**, 1–32, doi.org/10.1016/j.eist.2019.01.004.

Köhler, J., B. Turnheim, and M. Hodson, 2020: Low carbon transitions pathways in mobility: Applying the MLP in a combined case study and simulation bridging analysis of passenger transport in the Netherlands. *Technol. Forecast. Soc. Change*, **151**, doi:10.1016/j.techfore.2018.06.003.

Koomey, J., 2013: Moving beyond benefit–cost analysis of climate change. *Environ. Res. Lett.*, **8(4)**, 41005, doi:10.1088/1748-9326/8/4/041005.

Kornek, U., D. Klenert, O. Edenhofer, and M. Fleurbaey, 2021: The social cost of carbon and inequality: When local redistribution shapes global carbon prices. *J. Environ. Econ. Manage.*, **107**, 102450, doi.org/10.1016/j.jeem.2021.102450.

Koutroulis, A.G. et al., 2019: Global water availability under high-end climate change: A vulnerability based assessment. *Glob. Planet. Change*, **175** (August 2018), 52–63, doi:10.1016/j.gloplacha.2019.01.013.

Krey, V. and K. Riahi, 2009: Implications of delayed participation and technology failure for the feasibility, costs, and likelihood of staying below temperature targets—Greenhouse gas mitigation scenarios for the 21st century. *Energy Econ.*, **31**, S94–S106, doi: 10.1016/j.eneco.2009.07.001.

Krey, V. et al., 2012: Urban and rural energy use and carbon dioxide emissions in Asia. *Energy Econ.*, **34(sup3)**, S272–S283, doi:10.1016/j.eneco.2012.04.013.

Krey, V. et al., 2019: Looking under the hood: A comparison of techno-economic assumptions across national and global integrated assessment models. *Energy*, **172**, 1254–1267, doi:10.1016/j.energy.2018.12.131.

Kriegler, E. et al., 2013a: What does the 2°C target imply for a global climate agreement in 2020? The LIMITS study on Durban Platform scenarios. *Clim. Change Econ.*, **4(4)**, 1340008, doi:10.1142/S2010007813400083.

3

Kriegler, E., O. Edenhofer, L. Reuster, G. Luderer, and D. Klein, 2013b: Is atmospheric carbon dioxide removal a game changer for climate change mitigation? *Clim. Change*, **118(1)**, 45–57, doi:10.1007/s10584-012-0681-4.

Kriegler, E. et al., 2014a: The role of technology for achieving climate policy objectives: Overview of the EMF 27 study on global technology and climate policy strategies. *Clim. Change*, **123(3–4)**, 353–367, doi:10.1007/s10584-013-0953-7.

Kriegler, E. et al., 2014b: A new scenario framework for climate change research: The concept of shared climate policy assumptions. *Clim. Change*, **122(3)**, 401–414, doi:10.1007/s10584-013-0971-5.

Kriegler, E. et al., 2015: Making or breaking climate targets: The AMPERE study on staged accession scenarios for climate policy. *Technol. Forecast. Soc. Change*, **90(PA)**, 24–44, doi:10.1016/j.techfore.2013.09.021.

Kriegler, E. et al., 2016: Will economic growth and fossil fuel scarcity help or hinder climate stabilization?: Overview of the RoSE multi-model study. *Clim. Change*, **136(1)**, 7–22, doi:10.1007/s10584-016-1668-3.

Kriegler, E. et al., 2018a: Short term policies to keep the door open for Paris climate goals. *Environ. Res. Lett.*, **13(7)**, 74022, doi:10.1088/1748-9326/aac4f1.

Kriegler, E. et al., 2018b: Pathways limiting warming to 1.5°C: A tale of turning around in no time? *Philos. Trans. R. Soc. A Math. Phys. Eng. Sci.*, **376(2119)**, 20160457, doi:10.1098/rsta.2016.0457.

Kuramochi, T. et al., 2018: Ten key short-term sectoral benchmarks to limit warming to 1.5°C. *Clim. Policy*, **18(3)**, 287–305, doi:10.1080/14693062.2017.1397495.

Kyle, P. et al., 2013: Influence of climate change mitigation technology on global demands of water for electricity generation. *Int. J. Greenh. Gas Control*, **13**, 112–123, doi:10.1016/j.ijggc.2012.12.006.

Kyle, P., C. Müller, K. Calvin, and A. Thomson, 2014: Meeting the radiative forcing targets of the representative concentration pathways in a world with agricultural climate impacts. *Earth's Future*, **2(2)**, 83–98, doi:10.1002/2013ef000199.

La Viña, A.G., J.M. Tan, T.I.M. Guanzon, M.J. Caleda, and L. Ang, 2018: Navigating a trilemma: Energy security, equity, and sustainability in the Philippines' low-carbon transition. *Energy Res. Soc. Sci.*, **35** (October), 37–47, doi:10.1016/j.erss.2017.10.039.

Labriet, M. et al., 2015: Worldwide impacts of climate change on energy for heating and cooling. *Mitig. Adapt. Strateg. Glob. Change*, **20(7)**, 1111–1136, doi:10.1007/s11027-013-9522-7.

Laganière, J., D. Paré, E. Thiffault, and P.Y. Bernier, 2017: Range and uncertainties in estimating delays in greenhouse gas mitigation potential of forest bioenergy sourced from Canadian forests. *GCB Bioenergy*, **9(2)**, 358–369, doi.org/10.1111/gcbb.12327.

Lamb, W.F. and N.D. Rao, 2015: Human development in a climate-constrained world: What the past says about the future. *Glob. Environ. Change*, **33**, 14–22, doi:10.1016/j.gloenvcha.2015.03.010.

Lamb, W.F. et al., 2020: What are the social outcomes of climate policies? A systematic map and review of the ex-post literature. *Environ. Res. Lett.*, **15(11)**, doi:10.1088/1748-9326/abc11f.

Lamers, P. and M. Junginger, 2013: The 'debt' is in the detail: a synthesis of recent temporal forest carbon analyses on woody biomass forenergy. *Biofuels, Bioprod. Biorefining*, **7(4)**, 373–384, doi:10.1002/bbb.1407.

Lane, J.L. et al., 2016: Understanding constraints to the transformation rate of global energy infrastructure. *Wiley Interdiscip. Rev. Energy Environ.*, **5(1)**, 33–48, doi:10.1002/wene.177.

Le Quéré, C. et al., 2021: Fossil CO_2 emissions in the post-COVID-19 era. *Nat. Clim. Change*, **11(3)**, 197–199, doi:10.1038/s41558-021-01001-0.

Leach, M. et al., 2007: *Understanding governance: Pathways to sustainability*. STEPS Working Paper 2, Brighton: STEPS Centre.

Leal Filho, W. et al., 2018: Reinvigorating the sustainable development research agenda: the role of the sustainable development goals (SDG). *Int. J. Sustain. Dev. World Ecol.*, **25(2)**, 131–142, doi:10.1080/13504509.2017.1342103.

Leclère, D. et al., 2020: Bending the curve of terrestrial biodiversity needs an integrated strategy. *Nature*, **585(7826)**, 551–556, doi:10.1038/s41586-020-2705-y.

Lefèvre, J. et al., 2021: A pathway design framework for sectoral deep decarbonization: the case of passenger transportation. *Clim. Policy*, **21(1)**, 93–106, doi:10.1080/14693062.2020.1804817.

Lehtveer, M. and F. Hedenus, 2015a: Nuclear power as a climate mitigation strategy – technology and proliferation risk. *J. Risk Res.*, **18(3)**, 273–290, doi:10.1080/13669877.2014.889194.

Lehtveer, M. and F. Hedenus, 2015b: How much can nuclear power reduce climate mitigation cost? – Critical parameters and sensitivity. *Energy Strateg. Rev.*, **6**, 12–19, doi.org/10.1016/j.esr.2014.11.003.

Leimbach, M. and A. Giannousakis, 2019: Burden sharing of climate change mitigation: global and regional challenges under shared socio-economic pathways. *Clim. Change*, **155(2)**, 273–291, doi:10.1007/s10584-019-02469-8.

Lemoine, D. and C.P. Traeger, 2016: Economics of tipping the climate dominoes. *Nat. Clim. Change*, **6(5)**, 514–519, doi:10.1038/nclimate2902.

Lenton, T.M. et al., 2019: Climate tipping points – too risky to bet against. *Nature*, **575**, 592–595, doi: 10.1038/d41586-019-03595-0.

Levesque, A. et al., 2018: How much energy will buildings consume in 2100? A global perspective within a scenario framework. *Energy*, **148**, 514–527, doi:10.1016/j.energy.2018.01.139.

Levi, M., T. Kjellstrom, and A. Baldasseroni, 2018: Impact of climate change on occupational health and productivity: a systematic literature review focusing on workplace heat. *Med. Lav.*, **109(3)**, 163–179, doi:10.23749/mdl.v109i3.6851.

Li, F.G.N. and N. Strachan, 2019: Take me to your leader: Using socio-technical energy transitions (STET) modelling to explore the role of actors in decarbonisation pathways. *Energy Res. Soc. Sci.*, **51**, 67–81, doi:10.1016/j.erss.2018.12.010.

Li, F.G.N., E. Trutnevyte, and N. Strachan, 2015: A review of socio-technical energy transition (STET) models. *Technol. Forecast. Soc. Change*, **100(C)**, 290–305, doi: 10.1016/j.techfore.2015.07.017.

Li, M. et al., 2018: Air quality co-benefits of carbon pricing in China. *Nat. Clim. Change*, **8(5)**, 398–403, doi:10.1038/s41558-018-0139-4.

Li, N. et al., 2019: Air Quality Improvement Co-benefits of Low-Carbon Pathways toward Well Below the 2°C Climate Target in China. *Environ. Sci. Technol.*, **53(10)**, 5576–5584, doi:10.1021/acs.est.8b06948.

Limaye, V.S., W. Max, J. Constible, and K. Knowlton, 2019: Estimating the Health-Related Costs of 10 Climate-Sensitive U.S. Events During 2012. *GeoHealth*, **3(9)**, 245–265, doi.org/10.1029/2019GH000202.

Limaye, V.S., W. Max, J. Constible, and K. Knowlton, 2020: Estimating The Costs Of Inaction And The Economic Benefits Of Addressing The Health Harms Of Climate Change. *Health Aff.*, **39(12)**, 2098–2104, doi:10.1377/hlthaff.2020.01109.

Liobikienė, G., 2020: The revised approaches to income inequality impact on production-based and consumption-based carbon dioxide emissions: literature review. *Environ. Sci. Pollut. Res.*, **27(9)**, 8980–8990, doi:10.1007/s11356-020-08005-x.

Liobikienė, G., and D. Rimkuvienė, 2020: The role of income inequality on consumption-based greenhouse gas emissions under different stages of economic development. *Environ. Sci. Pollut. Res.*, **27**, 43067–43076, doi:10.1007/s11356-020-10244-x.

Liu, C., Y. Jiang, and R. Xie, 2019: Does income inequality facilitate carbon emission reduction in the US? *J. Clean. Prod.*, **217**, 380–387, doi:10.1016/j.jclepro.2019.01.242.

Liu, J.-Y. et al., 2020a: The importance of socioeconomic conditions in mitigating climate change impacts and achieving Sustainable Development Goals. *Environ. Res. Lett.*, **16(1)**, 14010, doi:10.1088/1748-9326/abcac4.

Liu, J. et al., 2017: Water scarcity assessments in the past, present, and future. *Earth's Future*, **5(6)**, 545–559, doi:10.1002/2016EF000518.

Liu, J.Y., S. Fujimori, and T. Masui, 2016: Temporal and spatial distribution of global mitigation cost: INDCs and equity. *Environ. Res. Lett.*, **11(11)**, doi:10.1088/1748-9326/11/11/114004.

Liu, J.Y. et al., 2018: Socioeconomic factors and future challenges of the goal of limiting the increase in global average temperature to 1.5°C. *Carbon Manag.*, **9(5)**, 447–457, doi:10.1080/17583004.2018.1477374.

Liu, S. et al., 2021: Health Benefits of Emission Reduction under 1.5°C Pathways Far Outweigh Climate-Related Variations in China. *Environ. Sci. Technol.*, **55(16)**, 10957–10966, doi:10.1021/acs.est.1c01583.

Liu, Y., M. Zhang, and R. Liu, 2020b: The Impact of Income Inequality on Carbon Emissions in China: A Household-Level Analysis. *Sustainability*, **12(7)**, 2715, doi:10.3390/su12072715.

Liu, Z. et al., 2020c: Near-real-time monitoring of global CO_2 emissions reveals the effects of the COVID-19 pandemic. *Nat. Commun.*, **11(1)**, 5172, doi:10.1038/s41467-020-18922-7.

Loftus, P.J., A.M. Cohen, J.C.S. Long, and J.D. Jenkins, 2015: A critical review of global decarbonization scenarios: what do they tell us about feasibility? *Wiley Interdiscip. Rev. Clim. Change*, **6(1)**, 93–112, doi: 10.1002/wcc.324.

Longden, T., 2014: Travel intensity and climate policy: The influence of different mobility futures on the diffusion of battery integrated vehicles. *Energy Policy*, **72(2014)**, 219–234, doi:10.1016/j.enpol.2014.04.034.

Lontzek, T.S., Y. Cai, K.L. Judd, and T.M. Lenton, 2015: Stochastic integrated assessment of climate tipping points indicates the need for strict climate policy. *Nat. Clim. Change*, **5(5)**, 441–444, doi:10.1038/nclimate2570.

Lovins, A.B., D. Ürge-Vorsatz, L. Mundaca, D.M. Kammen, and J.W. Glassman, 2019: Recalibrating climate prospects. *Environ. Res. Lett.*, **14(12)**, 120201, doi:10.1088/1748-9326/ab55ab.

Lucena, A.F.P. et al., 2018: Interactions between climate change mitigation and adaptation: The case of hydropower in Brazil. *Energy*, **164**, 1161–1177, doi:10.1016/j.energy.2018.09.005.

Luderer, G. et al., 2013: Economic mitigation challenges: How further delay closes the door for achieving climate targets. *Environ. Res. Lett.*, **8(3)**, 034033, doi:10.1088/1748-9326/8/3/034033.

Luderer, G., C. Bertram, K. Calvin, E. De Cian, and E. Kriegler, 2016: Implications of weak near-term climate policies on long-term mitigation pathways. *Clim. Change*, **136(1)**, 127–140, doi:10.1007/s10584-013-0899-9.

Luderer, G. et al., 2018: Residual fossil CO_2 emissions in 1.5–2°C pathways. *Nat. Clim. Change*, **8(7)**, 626–633, doi:10.1038/s41558-018-0198-6.

Luderer, G. et al., 2022: Impact of declining renewable energy costs on electrification in low-emission scenarios. *Nat. Energy*, **7**, 32–42, doi:10.1038/s41560-021-00937-z.

Lund, M.T. et al., 2020: A continued role of short-lived climate forcers under the Shared Socioeconomic Pathways. *Earth Syst. Dyn.*, **11(4)**, 977–993, doi:10.5194/esd-11-977-2020.

Lynch, J., M. Cain, R. Pierrehumbert, and M. Allen, 2020: Demonstrating GWP*: a means of reporting warming-equivalent emissions that captures the contrasting impacts of short- and long-lived climate pollutants. *Environ. Res. Lett.*, **15(4)**, 44023, doi:10.1088/1748-9326/ab6d7e.

MacDougall, A.H. and P. Friedlingstein, 2015: The Origin and Limits of the Near Proportionality between Climate Warming and Cumulative CO_2 Emissions. *J. Clim.*, **28(10)**, 4217–4230, doi:10.1175/jcli-d-14-00036.1.

Mader, S., 2018: The nexus between social inequality and CO_2 emissions revisited: Challenging its empirical validity. *Environ. Sci. Policy*, **89**, 322–329, doi:10.1016/j.envsci.2018.08.009.

Magneschi, G., T. Zhang, and R. Munson, 2017: The Impact of CO_2 Capture on Water Requirements of Power Plants. *Energy Procedia*, **114** (November 2016), 6337–6347, doi:10.1016/j.egypro.2017.03.1770.

Maïzi, N., S. Bouckaert, and E. Assoumou, 2017: Long-Term Water and Energy Issues in European Power Systems. *Compet. Water Resour. Exp. Manag. Approaches US Eur.*, 233–251, doi:10.1016/B978-0-12-803237-4.00013-6.

Majone, G., 1975a: The feasibility of social policies. *Policy Sci.*, **6(1)**, 49–69, doi:10.1007/BF00186755.

Majone, G., 1975b: On the Notion of Political Feasibility*. *Eur. J. Polit. Res.*, **3(3)**, 259–274, doi:10.1111/j.1475-6765.1975.tb00780.x.

Malerba, D. and K.S. Wiebe, 2021: Analysing the effect of climate policies on poverty through employment channels. *Environ. Res. Lett.*, **16(3)**, 35013, doi:10.1088/1748-9326/abd3d3.

Marangoni, G. et al., 2017: Sensitivity of projected long-term CO_2 emissions across the Shared Socioeconomic Pathways. *Nat. Clim. Change*, **7(2)**, 113–117, doi:10.1038/nclimate3199.

Marcucci, A., S. Kypreos, and E. Panos, 2017: The road to achieving the long-term Paris targets: energy transition and the role of direct air capture. *Clim. Change*, **144(2)**, 181–193, doi:10.1007/s10584-017-2051-8.

Marinova, S., S. Deetman, E. van der Voet, and V. Daioglou, 2020: Global construction materials database and stock analysis of residential buildings between 1970–2050. *J. Clean. Prod.*, **247**, 119146, doi.org/10.1016/j.jclepro.2019.119146.

Markandya, A. et al., 2018: Health co-benefits from air pollution and mitigation costs of the Paris Agreement: a modelling study. *Lancet Planet. Heal.*, **2(3)**, e126–e133, doi:10.1016/S2542-5196(18)30029-9.

Markhvida, M., B. Walsh, S. Hallegatte, and J. Baker, 2020: Quantification of disaster impacts through household well-being losses. *Nat. Sustain.*, **3**, 538–547, doi:10.1038/s41893-020-0508-7.

Markkanen, S. and A. Anger-Kraavi, 2019: Social impacts of climate change mitigation policies and their implications for inequality. *Clim. Policy*, **19(7)**, 827–844, doi:10.1080/14693062.2019.1596873.

Maruyama Rentschler, J.E., M.G.M. Kornejew, S. Hallegatte, J.M. Braese, and M.A.B. Obolensky, 2019: Underutilized potential: The business costs of unreliable infrastructure in developing countries. World Bank Group, Climate Change Group, Global Facility for Disaster Reduction and Recovery, World Bank policy research working paper 8899.

Mastrucci, A., E. Byers, S. Pachauri, and N.D. Rao, 2019: Improving the SDG energy poverty targets: Residential cooling needs in the Global South. *Energy Build.*, **186**, 405–415, doi:10.1016/j.enbuild.2019.01.015.

Mastrucci, A., B. van Ruijven, E. Byers, M. Poblete-Cazenave, and S. Pachauri, 2021: Global scenarios of residential heating and cooling energy demand and CO_2 emissions. *Clim. Change*, **168(3)**, 14, doi:10.1007/s10584-021-03229-3.

Matthews, H.D., N.P. Gillett, P.A. Stott, and K. Zickfeld, 2009: The proportionality of global warming to cumulative carbon emissions. *Nature*, **459(7248)**, 829–832, doi:10.1038/nature08047.

McCollum, D.L. et al., 2017: Improving the behavioral realism of global integrated assessment models: An application to consumers' vehicle choices. *Transp. Res. Part D Transp. Environ.*, **55**, 322–342, doi:10.1016/j.trd.2016.04.003.

McCollum, D.L. et al., 2018a: Energy investment needs for fulfilling the Paris Agreement and achieving the Sustainable Development Goals. *Nat. Energy*, **3(7)**, 589, doi:10.1038/s41560-018-0179-z.

McCollum, D.L. et al., 2018b: Connecting the sustainable development goals by their energy inter-linkages. *Environ. Res. Lett.*, **13(3)**, doi:10.1088/1748-9326/aaafe3.

McElwee, P. et al., 2020: The impact of interventions in the global land and agri-food sectors on Nature's Contributions to People and the UN Sustainable Development Goals. *Glob. Chang. Biol.*, **26(9)**, 4691–4721, doi:10.1111/gcb.15219.

McFarland, J. et al., 2015: Impacts of rising air temperatures and emissions mitigation on electricity demand and supply in the United States: a multi-model comparison. *Clim. Change*, **131(1)**, 111–125, doi:10.1007/s10584-015-1380-8.

Mcfarland, J.R., A.A. Fawcett, A.C. Morris, J.M. Reilly, and P.J. Wilcoxen, 2018: Overview of the EMF 32 study on U.S. carbon tax scenarios. *Clim. Change Econ.*, **09(01)**, 1840002, doi:10.1142/S201000781840002X.

Mcjeon, H. et al., 2021: Fossil energy deployment through midcentury consistent with 2°C climate stabilization. *Energy Clim. Change*, **2** (April), 100034, doi:10.1016/j.egycc.2021.100034.

3

Meckling, J., T. Sterner, and G. Wagner, 2017: Policy sequencing toward decarbonization. *Nat. Energy*, **2(12)**, 918–922, doi:10.1038/s41560-017-0025-8.

Meijl, H. Van et al., 2018: Comparing impacts of climate change and mitigation on global agriculture by 2050. *Environ. Res. Lett.*, **13 (6)**, doi: 10.1088/1748-9326/aabdc4.

Meinshausen, M. et al., 2009: Greenhouse-gas emission targets for limiting global warming to 2°C. *Nature*, **458(7242)**, 1158–1162, doi:10.1038/nature08017.

Meinshausen, M. et al., 2020: The shared socio-economic pathway (SSP) greenhouse gas concentrations and their extensions to 2500. *Geosci. Model Dev.*, **13(8)**, 3571–3605, doi:10.5194/gmd-13-3571-2020.

Méjean, A., C. Guivarch, J. Lefèvre, and M. Hamdi-Cherif, 2019: The transition in energy demand sectors to limit global warming to 1.5 °C. *Energy Effic.*, **12(2)**, 441–462, doi:10.1007/s12053-018-9682-0.

Méjean, A., A. Pottier, M. Fleurbaey, and S. Zuber, 2020: Catastrophic climate change, population ethics and intergenerational equity. *Clim. Change*, **163(2)**, 873–890, doi:10.1007/s10584-020-02899-9.

Meng, J., R. Way, E. Verdolini, and L. Diaz Anadon, 2021: Comparing expert elicitation and model-based probabilistic technology cost forecasts for the energy transition. *Proc. Natl. Acad. Sci.*, **118(27)**, e1917165118, doi:10.1073/pnas.1917165118.

Mengel, M., A. Nauels, J. Rogelj, and C.F. Schleussner, 2018: Committed sea-level rise under the Paris Agreement and the legacy of delayed mitigation action. *Nat. Commun.*, **9(1)**, 601, doi:10.1038/s41467-018-02985-8.

Mercure, J.F. et al., 2018: Macroeconomic impact of stranded fossil fuel assets. *Nat. Clim. Change*, **8(7)**, 588–593, doi:10.1038/s41558-018-0182-1.

Mercure, J.F. et al., 2019: Modelling innovation and the macroeconomics of low-carbon transitions: theory, perspectives and practical use. *Clim. Policy*, **19(8)**, 1019–1037, doi:10.1080/14693062.2019.1617665.

Messner, D., 2015: A social contract for low carbon and sustainable development. Reflections on non-linear dynamics of social realignments and technological innovations in transformation processes. *Technol. Forecast. Soc. Change*, **98**, 260–270, doi:10.1016/j.techfore.2015.05.013.

Meyer, M., A. Löschel, and C. Lutz, 2021: Carbon price dynamics in ambitious climate mitigation scenarios: an analysis based on the IAMC 1.5°C scenario explorer. *Environ. Res. Commun.*, **3(8)**, 81007, doi:10.1088/2515-7620/ac02ad.

Millward-Hopkins, J. and Y. Oswald, 2021: 'Fair' inequality, consumption and climate mitigation. *Environ. Res. Lett.*, **16(3)**, 34007, doi:10.1088/1748-9326/abe14f.

Millward-Hopkins, J., J.K. Steinberger, N.D. Rao, and Y. Oswald, 2020: Providing decent living with minimum energy: A global scenario. *Glob. Environ. Change*, **65**, 102168, doi.org/10.1016/j.gloenvcha.2020.102168.

Mima, S. and P. Criqui, 2015: The Costs of Climate Change for the European Energy System, an Assessment with the POLES Model. *Environ. Model. Assess.*, **20(4)**, 303–319, doi:10.1007/s10666-015-9449-3.

Mitchell, S.R., M.E. Harmon, and K.E.B. O'Connell, 2012: Carbon debt and carbon sequestration parity in forest bioenergy production. *GCB Bioenergy*, **4**, 818–827, doi:10.1111/j.1757-1707.2012.01173.x.

Mittal, S., H. Dai, S. Fujimori, T. Hanaoka, and R. Zhang, 2017: Key factors influencing the global passenger transport dynamics using the AIM/transport model. *Transp. Res. Part D Transp. Environ.*, **55**, 373–388, doi:10.1016/j.trd.2016.10.006.

Moallemi, E.A., L. Aye, F.J. de Haan, and J.M. Webb, 2017: A dual narrative-modelling approach for evaluating socio-technical transitions in electricity sectors. *J. Clean. Prod.*, **162**, 1210–1224, doi:10.1016/j.jclepro.2017.06.118.

Molotoks, A. et al., 2020: Comparing the impact of future cropland expansion on global biodiversity and carbon storage across models and scenarios. *Philos. Trans. R. Soc. B Biol. Sci.*, **375(1794)**, 20190189, doi:10.1098/rstb.2019.0189.

Moore, F.C. and D.B. Diaz, 2015: Temperature impacts on economic growth warrant stringent mitigation policy. *Nat. Clim. Change*, **5(2)**, 127–131, doi:10.1038/nclimate2481.

Moreno-Cruz, J.B. and S. Smulders, 2017: Revisiting the economics of climate change: the role of geoengineering. *Res. Econ.*, **71(2)**, 212–224, doi:10.1016/j.rie.2016.12.001.

Moss, R.H. et al., 2010: The next generation of scenarios for climate change research and assessment. *Nature*, **463(7282)**, 747–756, doi:10.1038/nature08823.

Mouratiadou, I. et al., 2016: The impact of climate change mitigation on water demand for energy and food: An integrated analysis based on the Shared Socioeconomic Pathways. *Environ. Sci. Policy*, **64**, 48–58, doi:10.1016/J.ENVSCI.2016.06.007.

Moyer, E.J., M.D. Woolley, N.J. Matteson, M.J. Glotter, and D.A. Weisbach, 2014: Climate impacts on economic growth as drivers of uncertainty in the social cost of carbon. *J. Legal Stud.*, **43(2)**, 401–425, doi:10.1086/678140.

Muldoon-Smith, K. and P. Greenhalgh, 2019: Suspect foundations: Developing an understanding of climate-related stranded assets in the global real estate sector. *Energy Res. Soc. Sci.*, **54**, 60–67, doi:10.1016/j.erss.2019.03.013.

Müller-Casseres, E. et al., 2021a: Production of alternative marine fuels in Brazil: An integrated assessment perspective. *Energy*, **219**, 119444, doi.org/10.1016/j.energy.2020.119444.

Müller-Casseres, E., O.Y. Edelenbosch, A. Szklo, R. Schaeffer, and D.P. van Vuuren, 2021b: Global futures of trade impacting the challenge to decarbonize the international shipping sector. *Energy*, **237**, 121547, doi:10.1016/j.energy.2021.121547.

Mundaca, L., D. Ürge-Vorsatz, and C. Wilson, 2019: Demand-side approaches for limiting global warming to 1.5 °C. *Energy Effic.*, **12(2)**, 343–362, doi:10.1007/s12053-018-9722-9.

Muratori, M. et al., 2020: EMF-33 insights on bioenergy with carbon capture and storage (BECCS). *Clim. Change*,, doi:10.1007/s10584-020-02784-5.

Murphy, K.J., 2002: Explaining executive compensation: Managerial power versus the perceived cost of stock options. *Univ. Chicago Law Rev.*, **69(3)**, 847–869, doi:10.2307/1600633.

Murray, B. and N. Rivers, 2015: British Columbia's revenue-neutral carbon tax: A review of the latest 'grand experiment' in environmental policy. *Energy Policy*, **86**, 674–683, doi.org/10.1016/j.enpol.2015.08.011.

Napp, T. et al., 2017: Exploring the feasibility of low-carbon scenarios using historical energy transitions analysis. *Energies*, **10(1)**, doi:10.3390/en10010116.

Napp, T.A. et al., 2019: The role of advanced demand-sector technologies and energy demand reduction in achieving ambitious carbon budgets. *Appl. Energy*, **238** (January), 351–367, doi:10.1016/j.apenergy.2019.01.033.

NASEM, 2017: *Valuing climate damages: updating estimation of the social cost of carbon dioxide*. National Academies of Sciences, Engineering, and Medicine, National Academies Press, Washington, DC, 280 pp.

NASEM, 2019: *Negative Emissions Technologies and Reliable Sequestration: A Research Agenda*. National Academies of Sciences, Engineering, and Medicine, National Academies Press, Washington D.C, USA, 510 pp.

NASEM, 2021: *Reflecting Sunlight: Recommendations for Solar Geoengineering Research and Research Governance*. National Academies of Sciences, Engineering, and Medicine, National Academies Press, Washington D.C, USA, 328 pp.

Naumann, G. et al., 2018: Global Changes in Drought Conditions Under Different Levels of Warming. *Geophys. Res. Lett.*, **45(7)**, 3285–3296, doi:10.1002/2017GL076521.

Nemet, G.F. et al., 2018: Negative emissions – Part 3: Innovation and upscaling. *Environ. Res. Lett.*, **13(6)**, 063003, doi:10.1088/1748-9326/aabff4.

Network for Greening the Financial System, 2021: NGFS Climate Scenarios for central banks and supervisors. https://www.ngfs.net/ngfs-scenarios-portal/.

Neumann, F. and T. Brown, 2021: The near-optimal feasible space of a renewable power system model. *Electr. Power Syst. Res.*, **190**, 106690, doi:10.1016/j.epsr.2020.106690.

Ng, T.L., J.W. Eheart, X. Cai, and F. Miguez, 2010: Modeling miscanthus in the Soil and Water Assessment Tool (SWAT) to simulate its water quality effects as a bioenergy crop. *Environ. Sci. Technol.*, **44(18)**, 7138–7144, doi:10.1021/es9039677.

Niamir, L., T. Filatova, A. Voinov, and H. Bressers, 2018: Transition to low-carbon economy: Assessing cumulative impacts of individual behavioral changes. *Energy Policy*, **118**, 325–345, doi:10.1016/j.enpol.2018.03.045.

Niamir, L. et al., 2020: Assessing the macroeconomic impacts of individual behavioral changes on carbon emissions. *Clim. Change*, **158(2)**, 141–160, doi:10.1007/s10584-019-02566-8.

Nicholls, Z. et al., 2021: Reduced Complexity Model Intercomparison Project Phase 2: Synthesizing Earth System Knowledge for Probabilistic Climate Projections. *Earth's Future*, **9(6)**, e2020EF001900, doi.org/10.1029/2020EF001900.

Nielsen, K.S. et al., 2020: Improving Climate Change Mitigation Analysis: A Framework for Examining Feasibility. *One Earth*, **3(3)**, 325–336, doi:10.1016/j.oneear.2020.08.007.

Nieto, J., Ó. Carpintero, L.J. Miguel, and I. de Blas, 2020: Macroeconomic modelling under energy constraints: {Global} low carbon transition scenarios. *Energy Policy*, **137**, 111090, doi:10.1016/j.enpol.2019.111090.

Nikas, A. et al., 2021: Perspective of comprehensive and comprehensible multi-model energy and climate science in Europe. *Energy*, **215**, 119153, doi:10.1016/j.energy.2020.119153.

Nordhaus, W., 2015: Climate clubs: Overcoming free-riding in international climate policy. *Am. Econ. Rev.*, **105(4)**, 1339–1370, doi:10.1257/aer.15000001.

Nordhaus, W., 2019: Economics of the disintegration of the Greenland ice sheet. *Proc. Natl. Acad. Sci.*, **116(25)**, 12261 LP–12269, doi:10.1073/pnas.1814990116.

Numminen, S. and P. Lund, 2019: Evaluation of the reliability of solar micro-grids in emerging markets – Issues and solutions. *Energy Sustain. Dev.*, **48**, 34–42, doi:10.1016/j.esd.2018.10.006.

O'Neill, B.C. et al., 2014: A new scenario framework for climate change research: The concept of shared socioeconomic pathways. *Clim. Change*, **122(3)**, 387–400, doi:10.1007/s10584-013-0905-2.

O'Neill, B.C. et al., 2016: The Scenario Model Intercomparison Project (ScenarioMIP) for CMIP6. *Geosci. Model Dev.*, **9(9)**, 3461–3482, doi:10.5194/gmd-9-3461-2016.

O'Neill, B.C. et al., 2017a: The roads ahead: Narratives for shared socioeconomic pathways describing world futures in the 21st century. *Glob. Environ. Change*, **42**, 169–180, doi:10.1016/j.gloenvcha.2015.01.004.

O'Neill, B.C. et al., 2017b: IPCC reasons for concern regarding climate change risks. *Nat. Clim. Change*, **7(1)**, 28–37, doi:10.1038/nclimate3179.

O'Neill, B., M. van Aalst, Z. Zaiton Ibrahim, L. Berrang Ford, S. Bhadwal, H. Buhaug, D. Diaz, K. Frieler, M. Garschagen, A. Magnan, G. Midgley, A. Mirzabaev, A. Thomas, and R. Warren, 2022: Key Risks Across Sectors and Regions. In: *Climate Change 2022: Impacts, Adaptation, and Vulnerability. Contribution of Working Group II to the Sixth Assessment Report of the Intergovernmental Panel on Climate Change* [H.-O. Pörtner, D.C. Roberts, M. Tignor, E.S. Poloczanska, K. Mintenbeck, A. Alegría, M. Craig, S. Langsdorf, S. Löschke, V. Möller, A. Okem, B. Rama (eds.)]. Cambridge University Press, Cambridge, United Kingdom and New York, NY, USA (in press).

O'Neill, B.C. et al., 2020b: Achievements and needs for the climate change scenario framework. *Nat. Clim. Change*, **10(12)**, 1074–1084, doi:10.1038/s41558-020-00952-0.

O'Sullivan, J.N., 2018: Synergy between Population Policy, Climate Adaptation and Mitigation BT – Pathways to a Sustainable Economy: Bridging the Gap between Paris Climate Change Commitments and Net Zero Emissions. [Hossain, M., R. Hales, and T. Sarker, (eds.)], Springer International Publishing, Cham, Switzerland, pp. 103–125.

Ó Broin, E. and C. Guivarch, 2017: Transport infrastructure costs in low-carbon pathways. *Transp. Res. Part D Transp. Environ.*, **55**, 389–403, doi:10.1016/j.trd.2016.11.002.

Obersteiner, M. et al., 2016: Assessing the land resource–food price nexus of the Sustainable Development Goals. *Sci. Adv.*, **2(9)**, e1501499, doi:10.1126/sciadv.1501499.

OECD, 2021: Real GDP long-term forecast (indicator). *OECD Data*, doi:10.1787/d927bc18-en.

Ohashi, H. et al., 2019: Biodiversity can benefit from climate stabilization despite adverse side effects of land-based mitigation. *Nat. Commun.*, **10(1)**, 5240, doi:10.1038/s41467-019-13241-y.

Ohlendorf, N., M. Jakob, J.C. Minx, C. Schröder, and J.C. Steckel, 2021: Distributional Impacts of Carbon Pricing: A Meta-Analysis. *Environ. Resour. Econ.*, **78(1)**, 1–42, doi:10.1007/s10640-020-00521-1.

Oswald, Y., J.K. Steinberger, D. Ivanova, and J. Millward-Hopkins, 2021: Global redistribution of income and household energy footprints: a computational thought experiment. *Glob. Sustain.*, **4**, e4, doi: 10.1017/sus.2021.1.

Otto, I.M., K.M. Kim, N. Dubrovsky, and W. Lucht, 2019: Shift the focus from the super-poor to the super-rich. *Nat. Clim. Change*, **9(2)**, 82–84, doi:10.1038/s41558-019-0402-3.

Ou, Y. et al., 2021: Deep Mitigation of CO_2 and non-CO_2 Greenhouse Gases towards 1.5°C and 2°C Futures. *Nat. Commun.*, **12**, 6245, doi; 10.1038/s41467-021-26509-z.

Pachauri, S., 2014: Household electricity access a trivial contributor to CO_2 emissions growth in India. *Nat. Clim. Change*, **4(12)**, 1073–1076, doi:10.1038/nclimate2414.

Pachauri, S. et al., 2013: Pathways to achieve universal household access to modern energy by 2030. *Environ. Res. Lett.*, **8(2)**, doi:10.1088/1748-9326/8/2/024015.

Pahle, M. et al., 2018: Sequencing to ratchet up climate policy stringency. *Nat. Clim. Change*, **8(10)**, 861–867, doi:10.1038/s41558-018-0287-6.

Pai, S., J. Emmerling, L. Drouet, H. Zerriffi, and J. Jewell, 2021: Meeting well-below 2°C target would increase energy sector jobs globally. *One Earth*, **4(7)**, 1026–1036, doi.org/10.1016/j.oneear.2021.06.005.

Paltsev, S., J. Morris, H. Kheshgi, and H. Herzog, 2021: Hard-to-Abate Sectors: The role of industrial carbon capture and storage (CCS) in emission mitigation. *Appl. Energy*, **300** (June), doi:10.1016/j.apenergy.2021.117322.

Pan, X., M. den Elzen, N. Höhne, F. Teng, and L. Wang, 2017: Exploring fair and ambitious mitigation contributions under the Paris Agreement goals. *Environ. Sci. Policy*, **74**, 49–56, doi:10.1016/j.envsci.2017.04.020.

Pan, X. et al., 2020: Implications of near-term mitigation on China's long-term energy transitions for aligning with the Paris goals. *Energy Econ.*, **90**, 104865, doi:10.1016/j.eneco.2020.104865.

Parkinson, S. et al., 2019: Balancing clean water-climate change mitigation trade-offs. *Environ. Res. Lett.*, **14(1)**, 014009, doi:10.1088/1748-9326/aaf2a3.

Parmesan, C. and M.E. Hanley, 2015: Plants and climate change: Complexities and surprises. *Ann. Bot.*, **116(6)**, 849–864, doi:10.1093/aob/mcv169.

Paroussos, L. et al., 2019: Climate clubs and the macro-economic benefits of international cooperation on climate policy. *Nat. Clim. Change*, **9(7)**, 542–546, doi:10.1038/s41558-019-0501-1.

Paslakis, G., G. Dimitropoulos, and D.K. Katzman, 2021: A call to action to address COVID-19–induced global food insecurity to prevent hunger, malnutrition, and eating pathology. *Nutr. Rev.*, **79(1)**, 114–116, doi:10.1093/nutrit/nuaa069.

Patterson, J.J. et al., 2018: Political feasibility of 1.5°C societal transformations: the role of social justice. *Curr. Opin. Environ. Sustain.*, **31**, 1–9, doi:10.1016/j.cosust.2017.11.002.

Pauliuk, S., A. Arvesen, K. Stadler, and E.G. Hertwich, 2017: Industrial ecology in integrated assessment models. *Nat. Clim. Change*, **7(1)**, 13–20, doi:10.1038/nclimate3148.

3

Pedersen, J.S.T. et al., 2020: Variability in historical emissions trends suggests a need for a wide range of global scenarios and regional analyses. *Commun. Earth Environ.*, **1(1)**, 1–7, doi:10.1038/s43247-020-00045-y.

Pehl, M. et al., 2017: Understanding future emissions from low-carbon power systems by integration of life-cycle assessment and integrated energy modelling. *Nat. Energy*, **2(12)**, 939–945, doi:10.1038/s41560-017-0032-9.

Perrier, Q. and P. Quirion, 2018: How shifting investment towards low-carbon sectors impacts employment: Three determinants under scrutiny. *Energy Econ.*, **75**, 464–483, doi:10.1016/j.eneco.2018.08.023.

Peters, G.P. and O. Geden, 2017: Catalysing a political shift from low to negative carbon. *Nat. Clim. Change*, **7(9)**, 619–621, doi:10.1038/nclimate3369.

Pfeiffer, A., C. Hepburn, A. Vogt-Schilb, and B. Caldecott, 2018: Committed emissions from existing and planned power plants and asset stranding required to meet the Paris Agreement. *Environ. Res. Lett.*, **13(5)**, doi:10.1088/1748-9326/aabc5f.

Pfenninger, S. and J. Keirstead, 2015: Renewables, nuclear, or fossil fuels? Scenarios for Great Britain's power system considering costs, emissions and energy security. *Appl. Energy*, **152**, 83–93, doi.org/10.1016/j.apenergy.2015.04.102.

Pianta, S., E. Brutschin, B. van Ruijven, and V. Bosetti, 2021: Faster or slower decarbonization? Policymaker and stakeholder expectations on the effect of the COVID-19 pandemic on the global energy transition. *Energy Res. Soc. Sci.*, **76**, 102025, doi.org/10.1016/j.erss.2021.102025.

Pielke, R. and J. Ritchie, 2021: Distorting the view of our climate future: The misuse and abuse of climate pathways and scenarios. *Energy Res. Soc. Sci.*, **72**, 101890, doi.org/10.1016/j.erss.2020.101890.

Pierson, P., 2000: Increasing Returns, Path Dependence, and the Study of Politics. *Am. Polit. Sci. Rev.*, **94(2)**, 251–267, doi:10.2307/2586011.

Pietzcker, R.C. et al., 2014: Long-term transport energy demand and climate policy: Alternative visions on transport decarbonization in energy-economy models. *Energy*, **64**, 95–108, doi:10.1016/j.energy.2013.08.059.

Pietzcker, R.C. et al., 2017: System integration of wind and solar power in integrated assessment models: A cross-model evaluation of new approaches. *Energy Econ.*, **64**, 583–599, doi.org/10.1016/j.eneco.2016.11.018.

Pihl, H., 2020: A Climate Club as a complementary design to the UN Paris agreement. *Policy Des. Pract.*, **3(1)**, 45–57, doi:10.1080/25741292.2019.1710911.

Pindyck, R.S., 2017: The use and misuse of models for climate policy. *Rev. Environ. Econ. Policy*, **11(1)**, 100–114, doi:10.1093/reep/rew012.

Piontek, F. et al., 2019: Economic Growth Effects of Alternative Climate Change Impact Channels in Economic Modeling. *Environ. Resour. Econ.*, **73(4)**, 1357–1385, doi:10.1007/s10640-018-00306-7.

Pizer, W.A. and S. Sexton, 2019: The Distributional Impacts of Energy Taxes. *Rev. Environ. Econ. Policy*, **13(1)**, 104–123, doi:10.1093/reep/rey021.

Poblete-Cazenave, M., S. Pachauri, E. Byers, A. Mastrucci, and B. van Ruijven, 2021: Global scenarios of household access to modern energy services under climate mitigation policy. *Nat. Energy*, **6(8)**, 824–833, doi:10.1038/s41560-021-00871-0.

Pollitt, H. and J.F. Mercure, 2018: The role of money and the financial sector in energy-economy models used for assessing climate and energy policy. *Clim. Policy*, **18(2)**, 184–197, doi:10.1080/14693062.2016.1277685.

Pollitt, H., E. Alexandri, U. Chewpreecha, and G. Klaassen, 2015: Macroeconomic analysis of the employment impacts of future EU climate policies. *Clim. Policy*, **15(5)**, 604–625, doi:10.1080/14693062.2014.953907.

Pollitt, H., R. Lewney, B. Kiss-Dobronyi, and X. Lin, 2021: Modelling the economic effects of COVID-19 and possible green recovery plans: a post-Keynesian approach. *Clim. Policy*, **21 (10)**, 1257–1271, doi:10.1080/14693062.2021.1965525.

Popp, A. et al., 2014: Land-use transition for bioenergy and climate stabilization: Model comparison of drivers, impacts and interactions with other land use based mitigation options. *Clim. Change*, **123(3–4)**, 495–509, doi:10.1007/s10584-013-0926-x.

Popp, A. et al., 2017: Land-use futures in the shared socio-economic pathways. *Glob. Environ. Change*, **42**, 331–345, doi:10.1016/j.gloenvcha.2016.10.002.

Pretis, F., M. Schwarz, K. Tang, K. Haustein, and M.R. Allen, 2018: Uncertain impacts on economic growth when stabilizing global temperatures at 1.5°C or 2°C warming. *Phil. Trans. R. Soc. A*, **376(2119)**, 20160460, doi:10.1098/rsta.2016.0460.

Price, J., and I. Keppo, 2017: Modelling to generate alternatives: A technique to explore uncertainty in energy-environment-economy models. *Appl. Energy*, **195**, 356–369, doi:10.1016/j.apenergy.2017.03.065.

Pye, S. et al., 2018: Assessing qualitative and quantitative dimensions of uncertainty in energy modelling for policy support in the United Kingdom. *Energy Res. Soc. Sci.*, **46**, 332–344, doi.org/10.1016/j.erss.2018.07.028.

Rafaj, P. et al., 2018: Outlook for clean air in the context of sustainable development goals. *Glob. Environ. Change*, **53**, 1–11, doi.org/10.1016/j.gloenvcha.2018.08.008.

Rafaj, P. et al., 2021: Air quality and health implications of 1.5°C–2°C climate pathways under considerations of ageing population: a multi-model scenario analysis. *Environ. Res. Lett.*, **16(4)**, 45005, doi:10.1088/1748-9326/abdf0b.

Ranzani, A., M. Bonato, E.R. Patro, L. Gaudard, and C. De Michele, 2018: Hydropower future: Between climate change, renewable deployment, carbon and fuel prices. *Water (Switzerland)*, **10(9)**, 1–17, doi:10.3390/w10091197.

Rao, N.D., 2014: International and intranational equity in sharing climate change mitigation burdens. *Int. Environ. Agreements Polit. Law Econ.*, **14(2)**, 129–146, doi:10.1007/s10784-013-9212-7.

Rao, N.D. and J. Min, 2018: Less global inequality can improve climate outcomes. *Wiley Interdiscip. Rev. Clim. Change*, **9(2)**, 1–6, doi:10.1002/wcc.513.

Rao, N.D., B.J. Van Ruijven, K. Riahi, and V. Bosetti, 2017a: Improving poverty and inequality modelling in climate research. *Nat. Clim. Change*, **7(12)**, 857–862, doi:10.1038/s41558-017-0004-x.

Rao, N.D., J. Min, and A. Mastrucci, 2019a: Energy requirements for decent living in India, Brazil and South Africa. *Nat. Energy*, **4(12)**, 1025–1032, doi:10.1038/s41560-019-0497-9.

Rao, N.D., P. Sauer, M. Gidden, and K. Riahi, 2019b: Income inequality projections for the Shared Socioeconomic Pathways (SSPs). *Futures*, **105**, 27–39, doi.org/10.1016/j.futures.2018.07.001.

Rao, S. et al., 2016: A multi-model assessment of the co-benefits of climate mitigation for global air quality. *Environ. Res. Lett.*, **11(12)**, doi:10.1088/1748-9326/11/12/124013.

Rao, S. et al., 2017b: Future air pollution in the Shared Socio-economic Pathways. *Glob. Environ. Chang.*, **42**, 346–358, doi:10.1016/j.gloenvcha.2016.05.012.

Rauner, S. et al., 2020a: Coal-exit health and environmental damage reductions outweigh economic impacts. *Nat. Clim. Change*, **10**, 308–312, doi:10.1038/s41558-020-0728-x.

Rauner, S., J. Hilaire, D. Klein, J. Strefler, and G. Luderer, 2020b: Air quality co-benefits of ratcheting up the NDCs. *Clim. Change*, **163**, 1481–1500, doi:10.1007/s10584-020-02699-1.

Realmonte, G. et al., 2019: An inter-model assessment of the role of direct air capture in deep mitigation pathways. *Nat. Commun.*, **10(1)**, 1–12, doi:10.1038/s41467-019-10842-5.

Reisinger, A. et al., 2021: How necessary and feasible are reductions of methane emissions from livestock to support stringent temperature goals? *Philos. Trans. R. Soc. A*, **379(20200452)**. http://doi.org/10.1098/rsta.2020.0452.

Rengs, B., M. Scholz-Wäckerle, and J. van den Bergh, 2020: Evolutionary macroeconomic assessment of employment and innovation impacts of climate policy packages. *J. Econ. Behav. Organ.*, **169**, 332–368, doi.org/10.1016/j.jebo.2019.11.025.

Rezai, A., L. Taylor, and D. Foley, 2018: Economic Growth, Income Distribution, and Climate Change. *Ecol. Econ.*, **146**, 164–172, doi:10.1016/j.ecolecon.2017.10.020.

Riahi, K. et al., 2012: Chapter 17 – Energy Pathways for Sustainable Development. In: *Global Energy Assessment – Toward a Sustainable Future*. Cambridge University Press, Cambridge, UK and New York, NY, USA and the International Institute for Applied Systems Analysis, Laxenburg, Austria, pp. 1203–1306.

Riahi, K. et al., 2015: Locked into Copenhagen pledges – Implications of short-term emission targets for the cost and feasibility of long-term climate goals. *Technol. Forecast. Soc. Change*, **90(A)**, 8–23, doi:10.1016/j.techfore.2013.09.016.

Riahi, K. et al., 2017: The Shared Socioeconomic Pathways and their energy, land use, and greenhouse gas emissions implications: An overview. *Glob. Environ. Change*, **42**, 153–168, doi:10.1016/j.gloenvcha.2016.05.009.

Riahi, K. et al., 2021: Long-term economic benefits of stabilizing warming without overshoot – the ENGAGE model intercomparison. *Nat. Clim. Change* (in press), doi: 10.1038/s41558-021-01215-2.

Ribas, A., A.F.P. Lucena, and R. Schaeffer, 2017: Bridging the energy divide and securing higher collective well-being in a climate-constrained world. *Energy Policy*, **108**, 435–450, doi:10.1016/j.enpol.2017.06.017.

Ribas, A., A.F.P. Lucena, and R. Schaeffer, 2019: Closing the energy divide in a climate-constrained world: A focus on the buildings sector. *Energy Build.*, **199**, 264–274, doi:10.1016/j.enbuild.2019.06.053.

Rickards, L., J. Wiseman, and Y. Kashima, 2014: Barriers to effective climate change mitigation: the case of senior government and business decision makers. *WIREs Clim. Change*, **5(6)**, 753–773, doi.org/10.1002/wcc.305.

Ricke, K., L. Drouet, K. Caldeira, and M. Tavoni, 2018: Country-level social cost of carbon. *Nat. Clim. Change*, **8(10)**, 895–900, doi:10.1038/s41558-018-0282-y.

Rickels, W., F. Reith, D. Keller, A. Oschlies, and M.F. Quaas, 2018: Integrated Assessment of Carbon Dioxide Removal. *Earth's Future*, **6(3)**, 565–582, doi:10.1002/2017EF000724.

Rickels, W. et al., 2020: Who turns the global thermostat and by how much? *Energy Econ.*, **91**, 104852, doi.org/10.1016/j.eneco.2020.104852.

Roberts, J.T. et al., 2020: Four agendas for research and policy on emissions mitigation and well-being. *Glob. Sustain.*, **3**, doi:10.1017/sus.2019.25.

Robertson, S., 2020: Transparency, trust, and integrated assessment models: An ethical consideration for the Intergovernmental Panel on Climate Change. *Wiley Interdiscip. Rev. Clim. Change*, e679, doi:10.1002/wcc.679.

Rochedo, P.R.R. et al., 2018: The threat of political bargaining to climate mitigation in Brazil. *Nat. Clim. Change*, **8(8)**, 695–698, doi:10.1038/s41558-018-0213-y.

Rochedo, P.R.R. et al., 2021: Is Green Recovery Enough? Analysing the Impacts of Post-COVID-19 Economic Packages. *Energies*, **14**(17), doi:10.3390/en14175567.

Röder, M. et al., 2019: Understanding the timing and variation of greenhouse gas emissions of forest bioenergy systems. *Biomass and Bioenergy*, **121**, 99–114, doi.org/10.1016/j.biombioe.2018.12.019.

Roe, S. et al., 2019: Contribution of the land sector to a 1.5°C world. *Nat. Clim. Change*, **9**(11), 817–828, doi:10.1038/s41558-019-0591-9.

Roelfsema, M. et al., 2018: Reducing global GHG emissions by replicating successful sector examples: the 'good practice policies' scenario. *Clim. Policy*, **18(9)**, 1103–1113, doi:10.1080/14693062.2018.1481356.

Roelfsema, M. et al., 2020: Taking stock of national climate policies to evaluate implementation of the Paris Agreement. *Nat. Commun.*, **11(1)**, 2096, doi:10.1038/s41467-020-15414-6.

Rogelj, J., D.L. Mccollum, B.C. O'Neill, and K. Riahi, 2013a: 2020 emissions levels required to limit warming to below 2°C. *Nat. Clim. Change*, **3(4)**, 405–412, doi:10.1038/nclimate1758.

Rogelj, J., D.L. McCollum, A. Reisinger, M. Meinshausen, and K. Riahi, 2013b: Probabilistic cost estimates for climate change mitigation. *Nature*, **493(7430)**, 79–83, doi:10.1038/nature11787.

Rogelj, J. et al., 2014: Disentangling the effects of CO_2 and short-lived climate forcer mitigation. *Proc. Natl. Acad. Sci.*, **111(46)**, 16325 LP–16330, doi:10.1073/pnas.1415631111.

Rogelj, J., M. Meinshausen, M. Schaeffer, R. Knutti, and K. Riahi, 2015a: Impact of short-lived non-CO_2 mitigation on carbon budgets for stabilizing global warming. *Environ. Res. Lett.*, **10(7)**, 075001, doi:10.1088/1748-9326/10/7/075001.

Rogelj, J. et al., 2015b: Mitigation choices impact carbon budget size compatible with low temperature goals. *Environ. Res. Lett.*, **10(7)**, 75003, doi:10.1088/1748-9326/10/7/075003.

Rogelj, J. et al., 2015c: Zero emission targets as long-term global goals for climate protection. *Environ. Res. Lett.*, **10(10)**, 105007, doi:10.1088/1748-9326/10/10/105007.

Rogelj, J. et al., 2016: Paris Agreement climate proposals need a boost to keep warming well below 2°C. *Nature*, **534(7609)**, 631–639, doi:10.1038/nature18307.

Rogelj, J., D. Shindell, K. Jiang, S. Fifita, P. Forster, V. Ginzburg, C. Handa, H. Kheshgi, S. Kobayashi, E. Kriegler, L. Mundaca, R. Séférian, and M.V. Vilariño, 2018: Mitigation pathways compatible with 1.5°C in the context of sustainable development. In: *Global warming of 1.5°C. An IPCC Special Report on the impacts of global warming of 1.5°C above pre-industrial levels and related global greenhouse gas emission pathways, in the context of strengthening the global response to the threat of climate change* [Masson-Delmotte, V., P. Zhai, H.-O. Pörtner, D. Roberts, J. Skea, P.R. Shukla, A. Pirani, W. Moufouma-Okia, C. Péan, R. Pidcock, S. Connors, J.B.R. Matthews, Y. Chen, X. Zhou, M.I. Gomis, E. Lonnoy, T. Maycock, M. Tignor, and T. Waterfield (eds.)]. Cambridge University Press, Cambridge, United Kingdom and New York, NY, USA.

Rogelj, J. et al., 2018b: Scenarios towards limiting global mean temperature increase below 1.5 °c. *Nat. Clim. Change*, **8(4)**, 325–332, doi:10.1038/s41558-018-0091-3.

Rogelj, J., P.M. Forster, E. Kriegler, C.J. Smith, and R. Séférian, 2019a: Estimating and tracking the remaining carbon budget for stringent climate targets. *Nature*, **571(7765)**, 335–342, doi:10.1038/s41586-019-1368-z.

Rogelj, J. et al., 2019b: A new scenario logic for the Paris Agreement long-term temperature goal. *Nature*, **573(7774)**, 357–363, doi:10.1038/s41586-019-1541-4.

Rogelj, J., O. Geden, A. Cowie, and A. Reisinger, 2021: Net-zero emissions targets are vague: three ways to fix. *Nature*, **591**, 365–368, doi.org/10.1038/d41586-021-00662-3.

Rose, A., D. Wei, N. Miller, and T. Vandyck, 2017a: Equity, Emissions Allowance Trading and the Paris Agreement on Climate Change. *Econ. Disasters Clim. Change*, **1(3)**, 203–232, doi:10.1007/s41885-017-0012-3.

Rose, S.K., D.B. Diaz, and G.J. Blanford, 2017b: Understanding the social cost of carbon: a model diagnostic and inter-comparison study. *Clim. Change Econ.*, **08(02)**, 1750009, doi:10.1142/S2010007817500099.

Rosen, R.A., 2021: Why the shared socioeconomic pathway framework has not been useful for improving climate change mitigation policy analysis. *Technol. Forecast. Soc. Change*, **166**, 120611, doi.org/10.1016/j.techfore.2021.120611.

Rozenberg, J. and M. Fay, 2019: Making Infrastructure Needs Assessments Useful and Relevant. In: *Beyond the Gap: How Countries Can Afford the Infrastructure They Need while Protecting the Planet*, Sustainable Infrastructure Series, The World Bank, Washington, DC, pp. 29–46. https://openknowledge.worldbank.org/handle/10986/31291. (Accesssed December 1, 2021).

Rozenberg, J., S.J. Davis, U. Narloch, and S. Hallegatte, 2015: Climate constraints on the carbon intensity of economic growth. *Environ. Res. Lett.*, **10(9)**, 95006, doi:10.1088/1748-9326/10/9/095006.

Rozenberg, J., A. Vogt-Schilb, and S. Hallegatte, 2018: Instrument choice and stranded assets in the transition to clean capital. *J. Environ. Econ. Manage.*, **100**, 102183, doi:10.1016/j.jeem.2018.10.005.

3

Sachs, J.D. et al., 2019: Six Transformations to achieve the Sustainable Development Goals. *Nat. Sustain.*, **2(9)**, 805–814, doi:10.1038/s41893-019-0352-9.

Sager, L., 2019: Income inequality and carbon consumption: Evidence from Environmental Engel curves. *Energy Econ.*, **84**, 104507, doi:10.1016/j.eneco.2019.104507.

Samadi, S. et al., 2017: Sufficiency in energy scenario studies: Taking the potential benefits of lifestyle changes into account. *Technol. Forecast. Soc. Change*, **124**, 126–134, doi:10.1016/j.techfore.2016.09.013.

Sanderson, B.M. and B.C. O'Neill, 2020: Assessing the costs of historical inaction on climate change. *Sci. Rep.*, **10(1)**, 1–12, doi:10.1038/s41598-020-66275-4.

Sanderson, B.M., B.C. O'Neill, and C. Tebaldi, 2016: What would it take to achieve the Paris temperature targets? *Geophys. Res. Lett.*, **43(13)**, 7133–7142, doi:10.1002/2016GL069563.

Sanjuán, M.A., C. Argiz, P. Mora, and A. Zaragoza, 2020: Carbon Dioxide Uptake in the Roadmap 2050 of the Spanish Cement Industry. *Energies*, **13(13)**, doi:10.3390/en13133452.

Santangeli, A. et al., 2016: Global change synergies and trade-offs between renewable energy and biodiversity. *GCB Bioenergy*, **8(5)**, 941–951, doi.org/10.1111/gcbb.12299.

Savelsberg, J., M. Schillinger, I. Schlecht, and H. Weigt, 2018: The impact of climate change on Swiss hydropower. *Sustainability*, **10(7)**, doi:10.3390/su10072541.

Saygin, D., J. Rigter, B. Caldecott, N. Wagner, and D. Gielen, 2019: Power sector asset stranding effects of climate policies. *Energy Sources, Part B Econ. Plan. Policy*, **14(4)**, 99–124, doi:10.1080/15567249.2019.1618421.

Ščasný, M., E. Massetti, J. Melichar, and S. Carrara, 2015: Quantifying the Ancillary Benefits of the Representative Concentration Pathways on Air Quality in Europe. *Environ. Resour. Econ.*, **62(2)**, 383–415, doi:10.1007/s10640-015-9969-y.

Scherer, L. et al., 2018: Trade-offs between social and environmental Sustainable Development Goals. *Environ. Sci. Policy*, **90**, 65–72, doi:10.1016/j.envsci.2018.10.002.

Schewe, J. et al., 2014: Multimodel assessment of water scarcity under climate change. *Proc. Natl. Acad. Sci.*, **111(9)**, 3245–3250, doi:10.1073/pnas.1222460110.

Schinko, T., G. Bachner, S.P. Schleicher, and K.W. Steininger, 2017: Modeling for insights not numbers: The long-term low-carbon transformation. *Atmósfera*, **30(2)**, 137–161, doi.org/10.20937/ATM.2017.30.02.05.

Schleussner, C.F. et al., 2016a: Differential climate impacts for policy-relevant limits to global warming: The case of 1.5°C and 2°C. *Earth Syst. Dyn.*, **7(2)**, 327–351, doi:10.5194/esd-7-327-2016.

Schleussner, C.F. et al., 2016b: Science and policy characteristics of the Paris Agreement temperature goal. *Nat. Clim. Change*, **6**(9), 827–835, doi:10.1038/nclimate3096.

Schlosser, C.A. et al., 2014: The future of global water stress: An integrated assessment. *Earth's Future*, **2(8)**, 341–361, doi:10.1002/2014ef000238.

Schucht, S. et al., 2015: Moving towards ambitious climate policies: Monetised health benefits from improved air quality could offset mitigation costs in Europe. *Environ. Sci. Policy*, **50**, 252–269, doi.org/10.1016/j.envsci.2015.03.001.

Schultes, A. et al., 2018: Optimal international technology cooperation for the low-carbon transformation. *Clim. Policy*, **18(9)**, 1165–1176, doi:10.1080/14693062.2017.1409190.

Schultes, A. et al., 2021: Economic damages from on-going climate change imply deeper near-term emission cuts. *Environ. Res. Lett.*, **16**, 104053, doi:10.1088/1748-9326/ac27ce.

Scovronick, N. et al., 2017: Impact of population growth and population ethics on climate change mitigation policy. *Proc. Natl. Acad. Sci.*, **114(46)**, 12338 LP–12343, doi:10.1073/pnas.1618308114.

Scovronick, N. et al., 2019a: The impact of human health co-benefits on evaluations of global climate policy. *Nat. Commun.*, **10(1)**, 1–12, doi:10.1038/s41467-019-09499-x.

Scovronick, N. et al., 2019b: Human Health and the Social Cost of Carbon: A Primer and Call to Action. *Epidemiology*, **30(5)**, 642–647, doi: 10.1097/EDE.0000000000001057.

Scovronick, N. et al., 2021: The importance of health co-benefits under different climate policy cooperation frameworks. *Environ. Res. Lett.*, **16(5)**, 55027, doi:10.1088/1748-9326/abf2e7.

Séférian, R., M. Rocher, C. Guivarch, and J. Colin, 2018: Constraints on biomass energy deployment in mitigation pathways: The case of water scarcity. *Environ. Res. Lett.*, **13(5)**, doi:10.1088/1748-9326/aabcd7.

SEI, IISD, ODI, E3G, and UNEP, 2020: *The Production Gap Report: 2020 Special Report*. http://productiongap.org/2020report.

Semieniuk, G., L. Taylor, A. Rezai, and D.K. Foley, 2021: Plausible energy demand patterns in a growing global economy with climate policy. *Nat. Clim. Change*, **11(4)**, 313–318, doi:10.1038/s41558-020-00975-7.

Sepulveda, N.A., J.D. Jenkins, F.J. de Sisternes, and R.K. Lester, 2018: The Role of Firm Low-Carbon Electricity Resources in Deep Decarbonization of Power Generation. *Joule*, **2(11)**, 2403–2420, doi.org/10.1016/j.joule.2018.08.006.

Shan, Y. et al., 2021: Impacts of COVID-19 and fiscal stimuli on global emissions and the Paris Agreement. *Nat. Clim. Change*, **11(3)**, 200–206, doi:10.1038/s41558-020-00977-5.

Sharmina, M. et al., 2020: Decarbonising the critical sectors of aviation, shipping, road freight and industry to limit warming to 1.5–2°C. *Clim. Policy*, **0(0)**, 1–20, doi:10.1080/14693062.2020.1831430.

Shayegh, S., V. Bosetti, and M. Tavoni, 2021: Future Prospects of Direct Air Capture Technologies: Insights From an Expert Elicitation Survey. **3** (May), 1–14, doi:10.3389/fclim.2021.630893.

Shindell, D., 2020: Health and Economic Benefits of a 2°C Climate Policy. Testimony to the House Committee on Oversight and Reform. Hearing on 'The Devastating Impacts of Climate Change on Health'. https://nicholas.duke.edu/sites/default/files/documents/Shindell_Testimony_July2020_final.pdf.

Shindell, D. and C.J. Smith, 2019: Climate and air-quality benefits of a realistic phase-out of fossil fuels. *Nature*, **573(7774)**, 408–411, doi:10.1038/s41586-019-1554-z.

Shindell, D. et al., 2012: Simultaneously Mitigating Near-Term Climate Change and Improving Human Health and Food Security. *Science*, **335(6065)**, 183–189, doi:10.1126/science.1210026.

Shindell, D. et al., 2017a: A climate policy pathway for near- and long-term benefits. *Science*, **356(6337)**, 493–494, doi:10.1126/science.aak9521.

Shindell, D., G. Faluvegi, K. Seltzer, and C. Shindell, 2018: Quantified, localized health benefits of accelerated carbon dioxide emissions reductions. *Nat. Clim. Change*, **8(4)**, 291–295, doi:10.1038/s41558-018-0108-y.

Shindell, D.T., J.S. Fuglestvedt, and W.J. Collins, 2017b: The social cost of methane: theory and applications. *Faraday Discuss.*, **200(0)**, 429–451, doi:10.1039/C7FD00009J.

Simioni, T. and R. Schaeffer, 2019: Georeferenced operating-efficiency solar potential maps with local weather conditions – An application to Brazil. *Sol. Energy*, **184** (October 2018), 345–355, doi:10.1016/j.solener.2019.04.006.

Sinha, E., A.M. Michalak, K.V. Calvin, and P.J. Lawrence, 2019: Societal decisions about climate mitigation will have dramatic impacts on eutrophication in the 21st century. *Nat. Commun.*, **10(1)**, 939, doi:10.1038/s41467-019-08884-w.

Skeie, R.B., G.P. Peters, J. Fuglestvedt, and R. Andrew, 2021: A future perspective on historical contributions to climate change. *Clim. Change*, **164(1)**, 24, doi:10.1007/s10584-021-02982-9.

Smith, C.J. et al., 2018: FAIR v1.3: A simple emissions-based impulse response and carbon cycle model. *Geosci. Model Dev.*, **11(6)**, 2273–2297, doi:10.5194/gmd-11-2273-2018.

3

Smith, P. et al., 2016: Biophysical and economic limits to negative CO_2 emissions. *Nat. Clim. Change*, **6(1)**, 42–50, doi:10.1038/nclimate2870.

Smith, P., J. Nkem, K. Calvin, D. Campbell, F. Cherubini, G. Grassi, V. Korotkov, A.L. Hoang, S. Lwasa, P. McElwee, E. Nkonya, N. Saigusa, J.-F. Soussana, M.A. Taboada, 2019: Interlinkages Between Desertification, Land Degradation, Food Security and Greenhouse Gas Fluxes: Synergies, Trade-offs and Integrated Response Options. In: *Climate Change and Land: an IPCC special report on climate change, desertification, land degradation, sustainable land management, food security, and greenhouse gas fluxes in terrestrial ecosystems* [P.R. Shukla, J. Skea, E. Calvo Buendia, V. Masson-Delmotte, H.-O. Portner, D.C. Roberts, P. Zhai, R. Slade, S. Connors, R. van Diemen, M. Ferrat, E. Haughey, S. Luz, S. Neogi, M. Pathak, J. Petzold, J. Portugal Pereira, P. Vyas, E. Huntley, K. Kissick, M. Belkacemi, J. Malley, (eds.)]. Cambridge University Press, Cambridge, UK and New York, NY, USA, pp. 551–672.

Smith, P. et al., 2020a: Which practices co-deliver food security, climate change mitigation and adaptation, and combat land degradation and desertification? *Glob. Change Biol.*, **26(3)**, 1532–1575, doi:10.1111/gcb.14878.

Smith, S.J. et al., 2020b: Impact of methane and black carbon mitigation on forcing and temperature: a multi-model scenario analysis. *Clim. Change*, **163**, 1427–1442,, doi:10.1007/s10584-020-02794-3.

Smith, S.J. et al., 2020c: The Energy Modeling Forum (EMF)-30 study on short-lived climate forcers: introduction and overview. *Clim. Change*, **163(3)**, 1399–1408, doi:10.1007/s10584-020-02938-5.

Smith, S.M., 2021: A case for transparent net-zero carbon targets. *Commun. Earth Environ.*, **2(1)**, 24, doi:10.1038/s43247-021-00095-w.

Soergel, B. et al., 2021a: A sustainable development pathway for climate action within the UN 2030 Agenda. *Nat. Clim. Change*, **11(8)**, 656–664, doi:10.1038/s41558-021-01098-3.

Soergel, B. et al., 2021b: Combining ambitious climate policies with efforts to eradicate poverty. *Nat. Commun.*, **12(1)**, 2342, doi:10.1038/s41467-021-22315-9.

Sognnaes, I. et al., 2021: A multi-model analysis of long-term emissions and temperature implications of current mitigation efforts. *Nat. Clim. Change* (in press), doi:10.1038/s41558-021-01206-3.

Spencer, T. et al., 2015: Beyond the Numbers: Understanding the Transformation Induced by INDCs. IDDRI, ISSN 2258-7071. https://www.iddri.org/sites/default/files/import/publications/miles-report.pdf.

Spencer, T. et al., 2018: The 1.5°C target and coal sector transition: at the limits of societal feasibility. *Clim. Policy*, **18(3)**, 335–351, doi:10.1080/14693062.2017.1386540.

Springmann, M. et al., 2016a: Global and regional health effects of future food production under climate change: A modelling study. *Lancet*, **387(10031)**, 1937–1946, doi:10.1016/S0140-6736(15)01156-3.

Springmann, M., H.C.J. Godfray, M. Rayner, and P. Scarborough, 2016b: Analysis and valuation of the health and climate change cobenefits of dietary change. *Proc. Natl. Acad. Sci.*, **113(15)**, 4146–4151, doi:10.1073/pnas.1523119113.

Springmann, M. et al., 2018: Health and nutritional aspects of sustainable diet strategies and their association with environmental impacts: a global modelling analysis with country-level detail. *Lancet Planet. Heal.*, **2(10)**, e451–e461, doi.org/10.1016/S2542-5196(18)30206-7.

Steckel, J.C., R.J. Brecha, M. Jakob, J. Strefler, and G. Luderer, 2013: Development without energy? Assessing future scenarios of energy consumption in developing countries. *Ecol. Econ.*, **90**, 53–67, doi.org/10.1016/j.ecolecon.2013.02.006.

Steckel, J.C. et al., 2021: Distributional impacts of carbon pricing in developing Asia. *Nat. Sustain.*, **4**, 1005–1014, doi:10.1038/s41893-021-00758-8.

Stehfest, E. et al., 2009: Climate benefits of changing diet. *Clim. Change*, **95(1)**, 83–102, doi:10.1007/s10584-008-9534-6.

Stehfest, E. et al., 2019: Key determinants of global land-use projections. *Nat. Commun.*, **10(1)**, 1–10, doi:10.1038/s41467-019-09945-w.

Steinberg, D.C. et al., 2020: Correction to: Decomposing supply-side and demand-side impacts of climate change on the US electricity system through 2050 *Clim. Change*, **158**, 125–139, doi:10.1007/s10584-020-02660-2.

Stern, D.I., J.C.V. Pezzey, and N.R. Lambie, 2012: Where in the world is it cheapest to cut carbon emissions? *Aust. J. Agric. Resour. Econ.*, **56(3)**, 315–331, doi:10.1111/j.1467-8489.2011.00576.x.

Stern, N., 2013: The Structure of Economic Modeling of the Potential Impacts of Climate Change: Grafting Gross Underestimation of Risk onto Already Narrow Science Models. *J. Econ. Lit.*, **51(3)**, 838–859, doi:10.1257/jel.51.3.838.

Stern, N., 2016: Economics: Current climate models are grossly misleading. *Nature*, **530(7591)**, 407–409, doi:10.1038/530407a.

Stern, N., and J. Stiglitz, 2021: The economics of immense risk, urgent action and radical change: towards new approaches to the economics of climate change. *J. Econ. Methodol.* (in press).

Sterner, T. and U.M. Persson, 2008: An Even Sterner Review: Introducing Relative Prices into the Discounting Debate. *Rev. Environ. Econ. Policy*, **2(1)**, 61–76, doi:10.1093/reep/rem024.

Stoerk, T., G. Wagner, and R.E.T. Ward, 2018: Policy Brief – Recommendations for Improving the Treatment of Risk and Uncertainty in Economic Estimates of Climate Impacts in the Sixth Intergovernmental Panel on Climate Change Assessment Report. *Rev. Environ. Econ. Policy*, **12(2)**, 371–376, doi:10.1093/reep/rey005.

Stolbova, V., I. Monasterolo, and S. Battiston, 2018: A Financial Macro-Network Approach to Climate Policy Evaluation. *Ecol. Econ.*, **149**, 239–253, doi:10.1016/j.ecolecon.2018.03.013.

Strefler, J. et al., 2018: Between Scylla and Charybdis: Delayed mitigation narrows the passage between large-scale CDR and high costs. *Environ. Res. Lett.*, **13(4)**, 044015, doi:10.1088/1748-9326/aab2ba.

Strefler, J. et al., 2021a: Carbon dioxide removal technologies are not born equal. *Environ. Res. Lett.*, **16(7)**, 74021, doi:10.1088/1748-9326/ac0a11.

Strefler, J. et al., 2021b: Alternative carbon price trajectories can avoid excessive carbon removal. *Nat. Commun.*, **12**, 2264, doi.org/10.1038/s41467-021-22211-2.

Stua, M., 2017: Article 6 of the Paris agreement as foundation for the mitigation alliance. In: *From the Paris Agreement to a Low-Carbon Bretton Woods: Rationale for the Establishment of a Mitigation Alliance* [Stua, M., (ed.)], Springer, Cham., Switzerland, pp. 49–66.

Sugiyama, M., Y. Arino, T. Kosugi, A. Kurosawa, and S. Watanabe, 2018: Next steps in geoengineering scenario research: limited deployment scenarios and beyond. *Clim. Policy*, **18(6)**, 681–689, doi:10.1080/14693062.2017.1323721.

Tachiiri, K., D. Silva Herran, X. Su, and M. Kawamiya, 2019: Effect on the Earth system of realizing a 1.5°C warming climate target after overshooting to the 2°C level. *Environ. Res. Lett.*, **14(12)**, 124063, doi:10.1088/1748-9326/ab5199.

Taconet, N., A. Méjean, and C. Guivarch, 2020: Influence of climate change impacts and mitigation costs on inequality between countries. *Clim. Change*, **160(1)**, 15–34, doi:10.1007/s10584-019-02637-w.

Taconet, N., C. Guivarch, and A. Pottier, 2021: Social Cost of Carbon Under Stochastic Tipping Points. *Environ. Resour. Econ.*, **78(4)**, 709–737, doi:10.1007/s10640-021-00549-x.

Tait, L. and H. Winkler, 2012: Estimating greenhouse gas emissions associated with achieving universal access to electricity for all households in South Africa. *J. Energy South. Africa*, **23(4)**, 8–17, doi:10.17159/2413-3051/2012/v23i4a3174.

Takakura, J. et al., 2019: Dependence of economic impacts of climate change on anthropogenically directed pathways. *Nat. Clim. Change*, **9(10)**, 737–741, doi:10.1038/s41558-019-0578-6.

Takemura, T. and K. Suzuki, 2019: Weak global warming mitigation by reducing black carbon emissions. *Sci. Rep.*, **9(1)**, 4419, doi:10.1038/s41598-019-41181-6.

3

Tan, C. and Q. Zhi, 2016: The energy-water nexus: A literature review of the dependence of energy on water. *Energy Procedia*, **88**, 277–284, doi:10.1016/j.egypro.2016.06.154.

Tanaka, K, and B.C. O'Neill, 2018: The Paris Agreement zero-emissions goal is not always consistent with the 1.5°C and 2°C temperature targets. *Nat. Clim. Change*, **8(4)**, 319–324, doi:10.1038/s41558-018-0097-x.

Tarroja, B., A. AghaKouchak, and S. Samuelsen, 2016: Quantifying climate change impacts on hydropower generation and implications on electric grid greenhouse gas emissions and operation. *Energy*, **111**, 295–305, doi:10.1016/j.energy.2016.05.131.

Tavoni, M. and R.S.J. Tol, 2010: Counting only the hits? The risk of underestimating the costs of stringent climate policy: A letter. *Clim. Change*, **100(3)**, 769–778, doi:10.1007/s10584-010-9867-9.

Tavoni, M. et al., 2015: Post-2020 climate agreements in the major economies assessed in the light of global models. *Nat. Clim. Change*, **5(2)**, 119–126, doi:10.1038/nclimate2475.

Tavoni, M. et al., 2017: Challenges and Opportunities for Integrated Modeling of Climate Engineering. *FEEM Work. Pap.*, **38**, doi:10.2139/ssrn.3035166.

The World Bank, 2021: World Development Indicators. *DataBank*. https://databank.worldbank.org/source/world-development-indicators.

Thompson, T.M., S. Rausch, R.K. Saari, and N.E. Selin, 2014: A systems approach to evaluating the air quality co-benefits of US carbon policies. *Nat. Clim. Chang.*, **4**(10), 917–923, doi:10.1038/nclimate2342.

Tokarska, K.B., K. Zickfeld, and J. Rogelj, 2019: Path Independence of Carbon Budgets When Meeting a Stringent Global Mean Temperature Target After an Overshoot. *Earth's Future*, **7(12)**, 1283–1295, doi:10.1029/2019EF001312.

Tol, R.S.J., 1994: The damage costs of climate change: a note on tangibles and intangibles, applied to DICE. *Energy Policy*, **22(5)**, 436–438, doi.org/10.1016/0301-4215(94)90173-2.

Tong, D. et al., 2019: Committed emissions from existing energy infrastructure jeopardize 1.5°C climate target. *Nature*, **3** (May), doi:10.1038/s41586-019-1364-3.

Trutnevyte, E., 2016: Does cost optimization approximate the real-world energy transition? *Energy*, **106**, 182–193, doi:10.1016/j.energy.2016.03.038.

Trutnevyte, E. et al., 2019a: Societal Transformations in Models for Energy and Climate Policy: The Ambitious Next Step. *One Earth*, **1(4)**, 423–433, doi:10.1016/j.oneear.2019.12.002.

Trutnevyte, E. et al., 2019b: Societal Transformations in Models for Energy and Climate Policy: The Ambitious Next Step. *One Earth*, **1(4)**, 423–433, doi:10.1016/j.oneear.2019.12.002.

Tsutsui, J., H. Yamamoto, S. Sakamoto, and M. Sugiyama, 2020: The role of advanced end-use technologies in long-term climate change mitigation: the interlinkage between primary bioenergy and energy end-use. *Clim. Change*, **163(3)**, 1659–1673, doi:10.1007/s10584-020-02839-7.

Turner, S.W.D., M. Hejazi, S.H. Kim, L. Clarke, and J. Edmonds, 2017: Climate impacts on hydropower and consequences for global electricity supply investment needs. *Energy*, **141**, 2081–2090, doi:10.1016/j.energy.2017.11.089.

Turnheim, B. and B. Nykvist, 2019: Opening up the feasibility of sustainability transitions pathways (STPs): Representations, potentials, and conditions. *Res. Policy*, **48(3)**, 775–788, doi:10.1016/j.respol.2018.12.002.

Turnheim, B. et al., 2015: Evaluating sustainability transitions pathways: Bridging analytical approaches to address governance challenges. *Glob. Environ. Change*, **35**(2015), 239–253, doi:10.1016/j.gloenvcha.2015.08.010.

Ueckerdt, F. et al., 2019: The economically optimal warming limit of the planet. *Earth Syst. Dyn.*, **10(4)**, doi: 10.5194/esd-10-741-2019.

UN, 2019: *World Population Prospects 2019: Highlights (ST/ESA/SER.A/423)*. New York, USA, 1–39 pp. https://population.un.org/wpp/Publications/Files/WPP2019_Highlights.pdf.

UNEP, 2019: Bridging the Gap – Enhancing Mitigation Ambition and Action at G20 Level and Globally: Pre-release version of a chapter in the forthcoming UNEP Emissions Gap Report 2019. *Emiss. Gap Rep. 2019*, 62 pp. https://wedocs.unep.org/bitstream/handle/20.500.11822/30012/EGRgap.pdf?sequence=1&isAllowed=y.

UNEP, 2020: *Emissions Gap Report 2020*. UN Environment Programme, Nairobi, Kenya. https://www.unep.org/emissions-gap-report-2020, 128 pp.

Unruh, G.C., 2019: The Real Stranded Assets of Carbon Lock-In. *One Earth*, **1(4)**, 399–401, doi:10.1016/j.oneear.2019.11.012.

Ürge-Vorsatz, D. et al., 2020: Advances Toward a Net-Zero Global Building Sector. *Annu. Rev. Environ. Resour.*, **45(1)**, 227–269, doi:10.1146/annurev-environ-012420-045843.

van Beek, L., M. Hajer, P. Pelzer, D. van Vuuren, and C. Cassen, 2020: Anticipating futures through models: the rise of Integrated Assessment Modelling in the climate science-policy interface since 1970. *Glob. Environ. Change*, **65** (October), 102191, doi:10.1016/j.gloenvcha.2020.102191.

van de Ven, D.J., M. González-Eguino, and I. Arto, 2018: The potential of behavioural change for climate change mitigation: a case study for the European Union. *Mitig. Adapt. Strateg. Glob. Change*, **23(6)**, 853–886, doi:10.1007/s11027-017-9763-y.

van den Berg, N.J. et al., 2019: Improved modelling of lifestyle changes in Integrated Assessment Models: Cross-disciplinary insights from methodologies and theories. *Energy Strateg. Rev.*, **26**, 100420, doi:10.1016/j.esr.2019.100420.

van den Berg, N.J. et al., 2020: Implications of various effort-sharing approaches for national carbon budgets and emission pathways. *Clim. Change*, **162(4)**, 1805–1822, doi:10.1007/s10584-019-02368-y.

van den Bergh, J.C.J.M., and W.J.W. Botzen, 2014: A lower bound to the social cost of CO_2 emissions. *Nat. Clim. Change*, **4(4)**, 253–258, doi:10.1038/nclimate2135.

van der Ploeg, F. and A. de Zeeuw, 2018: Climate tipping and economic growth: Precautionary capital and the price of carbon. *J. Eur. Econ. Assoc.*, **16(5)**, 1577–1617, doi:10.1093/jeea/jvx036.

van der Wijst, K.-I., A.F. Hof, and D.P. van Vuuren, 2021a: Costs of avoiding net negative emissions under a carbon budget. *Environ. Res. Lett.*, **16(6)**, 64071, doi:10.1088/1748-9326/ac03d9.

van der Wijst, K.-I., A.F. Hof, and D.P. van Vuuren, 2021b: On the optimality of 2°C targets and a decomposition of uncertainty. *Nat. Commun.*, **12(1)**, 2575, doi:10.1038/s41467-021-22826-5.

van der Zwaan, B.C.C. et al., 2013: A Cross-Model Comparison of Global Long-Term Technology Diffusion Under a 2°C Climate Change Control Target. *Clim. Change Econ.*, **4(4)**, 1–25, doi:10.1142/S2010007813400137.

van Ruijven, B.J. et al., 2016: Long-term model-based projections of energy use and CO_2 emissions from the global steel and cement industries. *Resour. Conserv. Recycl.*, **112**, 15–36, doi:10.1016/j.resconrec.2016.04.016.

van Ruijven, B.J., E. De Cian, and I. Sue Wing, 2019: Amplification of future energy demand growth due to climate change. *Nat. Commun.*, **10(1)**, 1–12, doi:10.1038/s41467-019-10399-3.

van Sluisveld, M.A.E., S.H. Martínez, V. Daioglou, and D.P. van Vuuren, 2016: Exploring the implications of lifestyle change in 2°C mitigation scenarios using the IMAGE integrated assessment model. *Technol. Forecast. Soc. Change*, **102**, 309–319, doi:10.1016/j.techfore.2015.08.013.

van Sluisveld, M.A.E. et al., 2018a: Comparing future patterns of energy system change in 2°C scenarios to expert projections. *Glob. Environ. Change*, **50** (March), 201–211, doi:10.1016/j.gloenvcha.2018.03.009.

van Sluisveld, M.A.E. et al., 2018b: Aligning integrated assessment modelling with socio-technical transition insights: An application to low-carbon energy scenario analysis in Europe. *Technol. Forecast. Soc. Change*, 151, 119177, doi:10.1016/j.techfore.2017.10.024.

van Sluisveld, M.A.E., H.S. De Boer, V. Daioglou, A.F. Hof, and D.P. Van Vuuren, 2021: A race to zero – Assessing the position of heavy industry in a global net-zero CO_2 emissions context. *Energy Clim. Change*, **2** (July), doi:10.1016/j.egycc.2021.100051.

van Sluisveld, M.A.E. et al., 2015: Comparing future patterns of energy system change in 2°C scenarios with historically observed rates of change. *Glob. Environ. Change*, 35, 436–449, doi:10.1016/j.gloenvcha.2015.09.019.

3

van Soest, H.L. et al., 2017a: Early action on Paris Agreement allows for more time to change energy systems. *Clim. Change*, **144(2)**, 165–179, doi:10.1007/s10584-017-2027-8.

van Soest, H.L. et al., 2017b: Low-emission pathways in 11 major economies: Comparison of cost-optimal pathways and Paris climate proposals. *Clim. Change*, **142(3–4)**, 491–504, doi:10.1007/s10584-017-1964-6.

van Soest, H.L. et al., 2019: Analysing interactions among Sustainable Development Goals with Integrated Assessment Models. *Glob. Transitions*, **1**, 210–225, doi:10.1016/j.glt.2019.10.004.

van Soest, H.L. et al., 2021a: A Global Roll-out of Nationally Relevant Policies can Bridge the Emissions Gap. *Nat. Commun.* (in press), doi:10.1038/s41467-021-26595-z.

van Soest, H.L., M.G.J. den Elzen, and D.P. van Vuuren, 2021b: Net-zero emission targets for major emitting countries consistent with the Paris Agreement. *Nat. Commun.*, **12(1)**, 1–9, doi:10.1038/s41467-021-22294-x.

van Vliet, J., M.G.J. den Elzen, and D.P. van Vuuren, 2009: Meeting radiative forcing targets under delayed participation. *Energy Econ.*, **31(sup2)**, S152–S162, doi:10.1016/j.eneco.2009.06.010.

van Vliet, M.T.H., D. Wiberg, S. Leduc, and K. Riahi, 2016: Power-generation system vulnerability and adaptation to changes in climate and water resources. *Nat. Clim. Change*, **6(4)**, 375–380, doi:10.1038/nclimate2903.

van Vuuren, D.P. and K. Riahi, 2011: The relationship between short-term emissions and long-term concentration targets. *Clim. Change*, **104(3–4)**, 793–801, doi:10.1007/s10584-010-0004-6.

van Vuuren, D.P. et al., 2007: Stabilizing greenhouse gas concentrations at low levels: an assessment of reduction strategies and costs. *Clim. Change*, **81(2)**, 119–159, doi:10.1007/s10584-006-9172-9.

van Vuuren, D.P., B. de Vries, A. Beusen, and P.S.C. Heuberger, 2008: Conditional probabilistic estimates of 21st century greenhouse gas emissions based on the storylines of the IPCC-SRES scenarios. *Glob. Environ. Change*, **18(4)**, 635–654, doi:10.1016/j.gloenvcha.2008.06.001.

van Vuuren, D.P. et al., 2011: The representative concentration pathways: An overview. *Clim. Change*, **109(1)**, 5–31, doi:10.1007/s10584-011-0148-z.

van Vuuren, D.P. et al., 2015: Pathways to achieve a set of ambitious global sustainability objectives by 2050: Explorations using the IMAGE integrated assessment model. *Technol. Forecast. Soc. Change*, **98**, 303–323, doi:10.1016/J.TECHFORE.2015.03.005.

van Vuuren, D.P., A.F. Hof, M.A.E. van Sluisveld, and K. Riahi, 2017: Open discussion of negative emissions is urgently needed. *Nat. Energy*, **2(12)**, 902–904, doi:10.1038/s41560-017-0055-2.

van Vuuren, D.P. et al., 2018: Alternative pathways to the 1.5°C target reduce the need for negative emission technologies. *Nat. Clim. Change*, **8(5)**, 391–397, doi:10.1038/s41558-018-0119-8.

van Vuuren, D.P. et al., 2019: Integrated scenarios to support analysis of the food–energy–water nexus. *Nat. Sustain.*, **2(12)**, 1132–1141, doi:10.1038/s41893-019-0418-8.

van Vuuren, D.P. et al., 2020: The costs of achieving climate targets and the sources of uncertainty. *Nat. Clim. Change*, 10, 329–334, doi:10.1038/s41558-020-0732-1.

Vandyck, T., K. Keramidas, B. Saveyn, A. Kitous, and Z. Vrontisi, 2016: A global stocktake of the Paris pledges: Implications for energy systems and economy. *Glob. Environ. Change*, **41**, 46–63, doi:10.1016/j.gloenvcha.2016.08.006.

Vandyck, T. et al., 2018: Air quality co-benefits for human health and agriculture counterbalance costs to meet Paris Agreement pledges. *Nat. Commun.*, **9(1)**, 1–11, doi:10.1038/s41467-018-06885-9.

Vandyck, T., K. Keramidas, S. Tchung-Ming, M. Weitzel, and R. Van Dingenen, 2020: Quantifying air quality co-benefits of climate policy across sectors and regions. *Clim. Change*, **163(3)**, 1501–1517, doi:10.1007/s10584-020-02685-7.

Venton, D., 2016: Core Concept: Can bioenergy with carbon capture and storage make an impact? *Proc. Natl. Acad. Sci.*, **113(47)**, 13260 LP–13262, doi:10.1073/pnas.1617583113.

Vogt-Schilb, A., G. Meunier, and S. Hallegatte, 2018: When starting with the most expensive option makes sense: Optimal timing, cost and sectoral allocation of abatement investment. *J. Environ. Econ. Manage.*, **88**, 210–233, doi:10.1016/j.jeem.2017.12.001.

von Stechow, C. et al., 2015: Integrating Global Climate Change Mitigation Goals with Other Sustainability Objectives: A Synthesis. *Annu. Rev. Environ. Resour.*, **40(1)**, 363–394, doi:10.1146/annurev-environ-021113-095626.

von Stechow, C. et al., 2016: 2°C and SDGs: United they stand, divided they fall? *Environ. Res. Lett.*, **11(3)**, doi:10.1088/1748-9326/11/3/034022.

Vrontisi, Z. et al., 2018: Enhancing global climate policy ambition towards a 1.5°C stabilization: a short-term multi-model assessment. *Environ. Res. Lett.*, **13(4)**, 44039, doi:10.1088/1748-9326/aab53e.

Vrontisi, Z., K. Fragkiadakis, M. Kannavou, and P. Capros, 2020: Energy system transition and macroeconomic impacts of a European decarbonization action towards a below 2°C climate stabilization. *Clim. Change*, 162, 1857–1875, doi: 10.1007/s10584-019-02440-7.

Wachsmuth, J. and V. Duscha, 2019: Achievability of the Paris targets in the EU – the role of demand-side-driven mitigation in different types of scenarios. *Energy Effic.*, **12(2)**, 403–421, doi:10.1007/s12053-018-9670-4.

Waisman, H. et al., 2019: A pathway design framework for national low greenhouse gas emission development strategies. *Nat. Clim. Change*, **9(4)**, 261–268, doi:10.1038/s41558-019-0442-8.

Wang, Y. et al., 2019: Vulnerability of existing and planned coal-fired power plants in Developing Asia to changes in climate and water resources. *Energy Environ. Sci.*, **12(10)**, 3164–3181, doi:10.1039/c9ee02058f.

Wangel, J., S. Gustafsson, and Ö. Svane, 2013: Goal-based socio-technical scenarios: Greening the mobility practices in the Stockholm City District of Bromma, Sweden. *Futures*, **47**, 79–92, doi:10.1016/j.futures.2013.01.005.

Warren, R., J. Price, E. Graham, N. Forstenhaeusler, and J. VanDerWal, 2018: The projected effect on insects, vertebrates, and plants of limiting global warming to 1.5°C rather than 2°C. *Science*, **360(6390)**, 791 LP–795, doi:10.1126/science.aar3646.

Warszawski, L. et al., 2021: All options, not silver bullets, needed to limit global warming to 1.5°C: a scenario appraisal. *Environ. Res. Lett.*, **16(6)**, 64037, doi:10.1088/1748-9326/abfeec.

Watts, N., W.N. Adger, and P. Agnolucci, 2015: Health and climate change: Policy responses to protect public health. *Environnement, Risques et Sante*, **14(6)**, 466–468, doi:10.1016/S0140-6736(15)60854-6.

Wei, Y.-M. et al., 2020: Self-preservation strategy for approaching global warming targets in the post-Paris Agreement era. *Nat. Commun.*, **11(1)**, 1624, doi:10.1038/s41467-020-15453-z.

Welsby, D., J. Price, S. Pye, and P. Ekins, 2021: Unextractable fossil fuels in a 1.5°C world. *Nature*, **597(7875)**, 230–234, doi:10.1038/s41586-021-03821-8.

Weyant, J., 2017: Some Contributions of Integrated Assessment Models of Global Climate Change. *Rev. Environ. Econ. Policy*, **11(1)**, 115–137, doi:10.1093/reep/rew018.

Willett, W. et al., 2019: Food in the Anthropocene: the EAT–Lancet Commission on healthy diets from sustainable food systems. *Lancet*, **393(10170)**, 447–492, doi:10.1016/S0140-6736(18)31788-4.

Willis, R., 2017: How Members of Parliament understand and respond to climate change. *Sociol. Rev.*, **66(3)**, 475–491, doi:10.1177/0038026117731658.

Wilson, C., A. Grubler, N. Bauer, V. Krey, and K. Riahi, 2013: Future capacity growth of energy technologies: are scenarios consistent with historical evidence? *Clim. Change*, **118(2)**, 381–395, doi:10.1007/s10584-012-0618-y.

Wilson, C., H. Pettifor, E. Cassar, L. Kerr, and M. Wilson, 2019: The potential contribution of disruptive low-carbon innovations to 1.5°C climate mitigation. *Energy Effic.*, **12(2)**, 423–440, doi:10.1007/s12053-018-9679-8.

Winning, M. et al., 2019: Nationally Determined Contributions under the Paris Agreement and the costs of delayed action. *Clim. Policy*, **19(8)**, 947–958, doi:10.1080/14693062.2019.1615858.

Wise, M. et al., 2015: An approach to computing marginal land use change carbon intensities for bioenergy in policy applications. *Energy Econ.*, **50**, 337–347, doi:10.1016/j.eneco.2015.05.009.

Wise, M., M. Muratori, and P. Kyle, 2017: Biojet fuels and emissions mitigation in aviation: An integrated assessment modeling analysis. *Transp. Res. Part D Transp. Environ.*, **52**, 244–253, doi:10.1016/j.trd.2017.03.006.

Wiser, R. et al., 2021: Expert elicitation survey predicts 37% to 49% declines in wind energy costs by 2050. *Nat. Energy*, **6(5)**, 555–565, doi:10.1038/s41560-021-00810-z.

Wolkinger, B. et al., 2018: Evaluating Health Co-Benefits of Climate Change Mitigation in Urban Mobility. *Int. J. Environ. Res. Public Health*, **15(5)**, doi:10.3390/ijerph15050880.

Xie, Y. et al., 2018: Co-benefits of climate mitigation on air quality and human health in Asian countries. *Environ. Int.*, **119**, 309–318, doi.org/10.1016/j.envint.2018.07.008.

Xu, H., M. Wu, and M. Ha, 2019: A county-level estimation of renewable surface water and groundwater availability associated with potential large-scale bioenergy feedstock production scenarios in the United States. *GCB Bioenergy*, **11(4)**, 606–622, doi.org/10.1111/gcbb.12576.

Xu, Y. and V. Ramanathan, 2017: Well below 2°C: Mitigation strategies for avoiding dangerous to catastrophic climate changes. *Proc. Natl. Acad. Sci.*, **114(39)**, 10315–10323, doi:10.1073/pnas.1618481114.

Yalew, S.G. et al., 2020: Impacts of climate change on energy systems in global and regional scenarios. *Nat. Energy*, **5(10)**, 794–802, doi:10.1038/s41560-020-0664-z.

Yamagata, Y. et al., 2018: Estimating water–food–ecosystem trade-offs for the global negative emission scenario (IPCC-RCP2.6). *Sustain. Sci.*, **13(2)**, 301–313, doi:10.1007/s11625-017-0522-5.

Yang, X., J. Pang, F. Teng, R. Gong, and C. Springer, 2021: The environmental co-benefit and economic impact of China's low-carbon pathways: Evidence from linking bottom-up and top-down models. *Renew. Sustain. Energy Rev.*, **136**, 110438, doi.org/10.1016/j.rser.2020.110438.

Yeh, S. et al., 2017: Detailed assessment of global transport-energy models' structures and projections. *Transp. Res. Part D Transp. Environ.*, **55**, 294–309, doi:10.1016/j.trd.2016.11.001.

Yumashev, D. et al., 2019: Climate policy implications of nonlinear decline of Arctic land permafrost and other cryosphere elements. *Nat. Commun.*, **10(1)**, 1900, doi:10.1038/s41467-019-09863-x.

Zanchi, G., N. Pena, and N. Bird, 2012: Is woody bioenergy carbon neutral? A comparative assessment of emissions from consumption of woody bioenergy and fossil fuel. *GCB Bioenergy*, **4(6)**, 761–772, doi.org/10.1111/j.1757-1707.2011.01149.x.

Zappa, W., M. Junginger, and M. van den Broek, 2019: Is a 100% renewable European power system feasible by 2050? *Appl. Energy*, **233–234**, 1027–1050, doi.org/10.1016/j.apenergy.2018.08.109.

Zenghelis, D., 2019: Securing Decarbonisation and Growth. *Natl. Inst. Econ. Rev.*, **250(1)**, R54–R60, doi:10.1177/002795011925000118.

Zhang, R. and S. Fujimori, 2020: The role of transport electrification in global climate change mitigation scenarios. *Environ. Res. Lett.*, **15(3)**, doi:10.1088/1748-9326/ab6658.

Zhang, R., S. Fujimori, H. Dai, and T. Hanaoka, 2018a: Contribution of the transport sector to climate change mitigation: Insights from a global passenger transport model coupled with a computable general equilibrium model. *Appl. Energy*, **211** (November 2017), 76–88, doi:10.1016/j.apenergy.2017.10.103.

Zhang, R., S. Fujimori, and T. Hanaoka, 2018b: The contribution of transport policies to the mitigation potential and cost of 2°C and 1.5°C goals. *Environ. Res. Lett.*, **13(5)**, 54008, doi:10.1088/1748-9326/aabb0d.

Zhang, X. et al., 2018d: Impacts of climate change, policy and Water-Energy-Food nexus on hydropower development. *Renew. Energy*, **116**, 827–834, doi:10.1016/j.renene.2017.10.030.

Zhou, T., N. Voisin, and T. Fu, 2018: Non-stationary hydropower generation projections constrained by environmental and electricity grid operations over the western United States. *Environ. Res. Lett.*, **13(7)**, doi:10.1088/1748-9326/aad19f.

Zhou, W. et al., 2019: A comparison of low carbon investment needs between China and Europe in stringent climate policy scenarios. *Environ. Res. Lett.*, **14(5)**, 054017, doi:10.1088/1748-9326/ab0dd8.

Zhou, Y. et al., 2014: Modeling the effect of climate change on U.S. state-level buildings energy demands in an integrated assessment framework. *Appl. Energy*, **113**, 1077–1088, doi:10.1016/j.apenergy.2013.08.034.

Zickfeld, K., A.H. MacDougall, and H. Damon Matthews, 2016: On the proportionality between global temperature change and cumulative CO_2 emissions during periods of net negative CO_2 emissions. *Environ. Res. Lett.*, **11(5)**, 055006, doi:10.1088/1748-9326/11/5/055006.

Zickfeld, K., D. Azevedo, S. Mathesius, and H.D. Matthews, 2021: Asymmetry in the climate–carbon cycle response to positive and negative CO_2 emissions. *Nat. Clim. Change*, **11(7)**, 613–617, doi:10.1038/s41558-021-01061-2.

4

Mitigation and Development Pathways in the Near to Mid-term

Coordinating Lead Authors:
Franck Lecocq (France), Harald Winkler (South Africa)

Lead Authors:
Julius Partson Daka (Zambia), Sha Fu (China), James S. Gerber (the United States of America), Sivan Kartha (the United States of America), Volker Krey (Germany/Austria), Hans Lofgren (Sweden/the United States of America), Toshihiko Masui (Japan), Ritu Mathur (India), Joana Portugal-Pereira (Brazil), Benjamin K. Sovacool (Denmark/United Kingdom), Maria Virginia Vilariño (Argentina), Nan Zhou (the United States of America)

Contributing Authors:
Michel den Elzen (the Netherlands), Reuben Dlamini (eSwatini), Noel Healy (the United States of America), Niklas Höhne (Germany), Angel Hsu (the United States of America/Singapore), Nina Khanna (the United States of America), Claire Lepault (France), Carlisle Ford Runge (the United States of America), Dimakatso Sebothoma (South Africa)

Review Editors:
Marzio Domenico Galeotti (Italy), Roque Pedace (Argentina)

Chapter Scientist:
Kaleem Anwar Mir (Pakistan)

This chapter should be cited as:
Lecocq, F., H. Winkler, J.P. Daka, S. Fu, J.S. Gerber, S. Kartha, V. Krey, H. Lofgren, T. Masui, R. Mathur, J. Portugal-Pereira, B. K. Sovacool, M. V. Vilariño, N. Zhou, 2022: Mitigation and development pathways in the near- to mid-term. In IPCC, 2022: *Climate Change 2022: Mitigation of Climate Change. Contribution of Working Group III to the Sixth Assessment Report of the Intergovernmental Panel on Climate Change* [P.R. Shukla, J. Skea, R. Slade, A. Al Khourdajie, R. van Diemen, D. McCollum, M. Pathak, S. Some, P. Vyas, R. Fradera, M. Belkacemi, A. Hasija, G. Lisboa, S. Luz, J. Malley, (eds.)]. Cambridge University Press, Cambridge, UK and New York, NY, USA. doi: 10.1017/9781009157926.006

Table of Contents

4

Executive Summary

This chapter focuses on accelerating mitigation and on shifting development pathways to increased sustainability, based on literature particularly at national scale. While previous WGIII assessments have discussed mitigation pathways, focus on development pathways is more recent. The timeframe is the near term (now up to 2030) to mid-term (2030 to 2050), complementing Chapter 3 on the long term (from 2050 onward).

An emissions gap persists, exacerbated by an implementation gap, despite mitigation efforts including those in near-universal nationally determined contributions (NDCs). The 'emissions gap' is understood as the difference between the emissions with NDCs in 2030, and mitigation pathways consistent with the temperature goals. In general, the term 'implementation gap' refers to the difference between goals on paper and how they are achieved in practice. In this report, the term refers to the gap between mitigation pledges contained in national determined contributions, and the expected outcome of existing policies. There is considerable literature on country-level mitigation pathways, including but not limited to NDCs. Country distribution of this literature is very unequal (*robust evidence, high agreement*). Current policies lead to median global greenhouse gas (GHG) emissions of 57 $GtCO_2$-eq with a full range of 52–60 by 2030. NDCs with unconditional and conditional elements[1] lead to 53 (50–57) and 50 (47–55) $GtCO_2$-eq, respectively (*medium evidence, medium agreement*) (Table 4.3). This leaves estimated **emissions gaps** in 2030 between projected outcomes of unconditional elements of NDCs and emissions in scenarios that limit warming to 1.5°C (>50%) with no or limited overshoot of 19–26 $GtCO_2$-eq, and 10–16 $GtCO_2$-eq for scenarios that limit warming to 2°C (>67%) with immediate action. When conditional elements of NDCs are included, these gaps narrow to 16–23 $GtCO_2$-eq and 6–14 $GtCO_2$-eq, respectively. {Cross-Chapter Box 4, Figure 1}

Studies evaluating up to 105 updated NDCs submitted by October 2021 indicate that emissions in conditional NDCs have been reduced by 4.5 (2.7–6.3) $GtCO_2$-eq, but only closes the emission gaps by about one-third to 2°C and about 20% to 1.5°C compared to the original NDCs submitted in 2015/16 (*medium evidence, medium agreement*). The magnitude of these emission gaps calls into question whether current development pathways and efforts to accelerate mitigation are adequate to achieve the Paris mitigation objectives. In addition, an **implementation gap** exists between the projected emissions of 'current policies' and the projected emissions resulting from the implementation of the unconditional and conditional elements of NDCs, and is estimated to be around and 7 $GtCO_2$-eq in 2030, respectively (*medium evidence, medium agreement*), with many countries requiring additional policies and associated climate action to meet their autonomously determined mitigation targets as specified under the first NDCs (*limited evidence*). There is, furthermore, a potential difference between mitigation targets set in NDCs *ex ante* and what is achieved *ex post*. A limited number of studies assess the implementation gaps of conditional NDCs in terms of finance, technology and capacity building support. The disruptions triggered by the COVID-19 epidemic increase uncertainty over range of projections relative to pre-COVID-19 literature. As indicated by a growing number of studies at the national and global level, how large near- to mid-term emissions implications of the COVID-19 pandemic are, to a large degree depends on how stimulus or recovery packages are designed. {4.2, 4.2.2.5, Cross-Chapter Box 4}

Given the gaps, there is a need to explore accelerated mitigation (relative to NDCs and current policies). There is increasing understanding of the technical content of accelerated mitigation pathways, differentiated by national circumstances, with considerable though uneven literature at country-level (*medium evidence, high agreement*). Transformative technological and institutional changes for the near term include demand reductions through efficiency and reduced activity, rapid decarbonisation of the electricity sector and low-carbon electrification of buildings, industry and transport (*robust evidence, medium agreement*). A focus on energy use and supply is essential, but not sufficient on its own – the land sector and food systems deserve attention. The literature does not adequately include demand-side options and systems analysis, and captures the impact from non-CO_2 GHGs with medium confidence. Countries and regions will have different starting points for transition pathways. Some factors include climate conditions resulting in different heating and cooling needs, endowments with different energy resources, patterns of spatial development, and political and economic conditions. {4.2.5}

Accelerated mitigation alone may run into obstacles. If such obstacles are rooted in underlying structural features of society, then transforming such structures helps remove obstacles, which amounts to shifting development pathways. Various actors have developed an increasing number of mitigation strategies up to 2050 (mid-term). A growing number of such strategies aim at net zero GHG or CO_2 emissions, but it is not yet possible to draw global implications due to the limited size of sample (*medium evidence, low agreement*). Non-state actors are also engaging in a wide range of mitigation initiatives. When adding up emission reduction potentials, sub-national and non-state international cooperative initiatives could reduce up to about 20 $GtCO_2$-eq in 2030 (*limited evidence, medium agreement*). Yet perceived or real conflicts between mitigation and other Sustainable Development Goals (SDGs) can impede such action. If undertaken without precaution, accelerated mitigation is found to have significant implications for development objectives and macroeconomic costs at country level. For example, most country-level mitigation modelling studies in which GDP is an endogenous variable report negative impacts of mitigation on GDP in 2030 and 2050, relative to the reference. In all reviewed studies, however, GDP continues to grow even with mitigation (*robust evidence, high agreement*). The literature finds that employment effect of mitigation policies tends to be limited on aggregate, but can be significant at sectoral level (*limited evidence, medium agreement*). Detailed design of mitigation policies is critical for distributional impacts and avoiding lock-in (*robust evidence, high agreement*), though further research is needed in that direction. {4.2.3, 4.2.4, 4.2.6}

---

[1] See Section 4.2.1 for description of 'unconditional' and 'conditional' elements of NDCs.

Shifting development pathways towards sustainability offers ways to (i) broaden the range of levers and enablers that a society can use to provide enabling conditions and accelerate mitigation; and (ii) increase the chances of advancing at the same time towards mitigation and towards other development goals. The way countries develop determines their capacity to accelerate mitigation and achieve other sustainable development objectives simultaneously (*medium-robust evidence, medium agreement*). Yet meeting ambitious mitigation and development goals cannot be achieved through incremental change, hence the focus on shifting development pathways (*robust evidence, medium agreement*). Though development pathways result from the actions of a wide range of actors, it is possible to shift development pathways through policies and enhancing enabling conditions (*limited evidence, medium agreement*). For example, policies such as those listed in Table 4.12 are typically associated with broader objectives than greenhouse gas mitigation. They are generally conceived and implemented in the pursuit of overall societal development objectives, such as job creation, macroeconomic stability, economic growth, and public health and welfare. In some countries, such policies are framed as part of a just transition. However, they can have major influence on mitigative capacity, and hence can be seen as tools to broaden mitigation options, as illustrated by the Illustrative Mitigation Pathway 'Shifting Pathways' (*medium evidence, medium agreement*). There are practical options to shift development pathways in ways that advance mitigation and other sustainable development objectives, supporting political feasibility, increase resources to meet multiple goals, and reduce emissions (*limited evidence, high agreement*). Concrete examples assessed in this chapter include high employment and low emissions structural change, fiscal reforms for mitigation and social contract, combining housing policies to deliver both housing and transport mitigation, and change economic, social and spatial patterns of development of the agriculture sector provide the basis for sustained reductions in emissions from deforestation. These examples differ by context. Examples in other chapters include transformations in energy, urban, building, industrial, transport, and land-based systems, changes in behaviour and social practices, as well as transformational changes across whole economies and societies. Coordinated policy mixes would need to coordinate multiple actors – individuals, groups and collectives, corporate actors, institutions and infrastructure actors – to deepen decarbonisation and shift pathways towards sustainability. Shifts in one country may spill over to other countries. Shifting development pathways can jointly support mitigation and adaptation. Some studies explore the risks of high complexity and potential delay attached to shifting development pathways. {4.3, 4.3.1, 4.3.2, 4.4.2, 4.4.3, 4.4.1.7–4.4.1.10, Figure 4.7, Cross-Chapter Box 5, 5.8, Box 6.2, 8.2, 8.3.1, 8.4, 9.8.1, 9.8.2, 10.4.1, Cross-Chapter Box 5, Cross-Chapter Box 7, Cross-Chapter Box 12}

The literature identifies a broad set of enabling conditions that can both foster shifting development pathways and accelerated mitigation, along five categories (*medium evidence, high agreement*). Policy integration is a necessary component of shifting development pathways, addressing multiple objectives. To this aim, mobilising a range of policies is preferable to single policy instruments (*robust evidence, high agreement*). Governance for climate mitigation and shifting development pathways is enhanced when tailored to national and local contexts. Improved institutions and governance enable ambitious climate action and help bridge implementation gaps (*medium evidence, high agreement*). Given that strengthening institutions may be a long term endeavour, it needs attention in the near term. Accelerated mitigation and shifting development pathways necessitates both redirecting existing financial flows from high- to low-emissions technologies and systems and to provide additional resources to overcome current financial barriers (*robust evidence, high agreement*). Opportunities exist in the near term to close the finance gap. At the national level, public finance for actions promoting the SDG agenda helps broaden the scope of mitigation (*medium evidence, medium agreement*). Changes in behaviour and lifestyles are important to move beyond mitigation as incremental change, and when supporting shifts to more sustainable development pathways will broadening the scope of mitigation (*medium evidence, medium agreement*). The direction of innovation matters (*robust evidence, high agreement*). The necessary transformational changes are likely to be more acceptable if rooted in the development aspirations of the economy and society within which they take place. {4.4.1, 4.4.1.2, 4.4.1.3, 4.4.1.4, 4.4.1.5, 4.4.1.6, Figure 4.8, 15.2.2}

Equity can be an important enabler of deeper ambition for accelerated mitigation, dealing with the distribution of costs and benefits and how these are shared as per social contracts, national policy and international agreements. Transition pathways have distributional consequences such as large changes in employment and economic structure (*robust evidence, high agreement*). In that regard, the just transition concept has become an international focal point tying together social movements, trade unions, and other key stakeholders to ensure equity is better accounted for in low-carbon transitions. Effectiveness of cooperative action and the perception of fairness of such arrangements are closely related, in that pathways that prioritise equity and allow broad stakeholders participation can enable broader consensus for the transformational change implied by deeper mitigation efforts (*robust evidence, medium agreement*). Hence, equity is a concept that is instrumentally important. {4.5, Figure 4.9}

In sum, this chapter suggests that the immediate tasks are to broaden and deepen mitigation in the near term if the global community is to deliver emission reductions at the scale required to keep temperature well below 2°C and pursue efforts at 1.5°C. Deepening mitigation means more rapid decarbonisation. Shifting development pathways to increased sustainability (SDPS) broadens the scope of mitigation. Putting the enabling conditions above in place supports both. Depending on context, some enabling conditions such as shifting behaviour may take time to establish, underscoring the importance of early action. Other enabling conditions, such as improved access to financing, can be put in place in a relatively short time frame, and can yield results rapidly.

Accelerating mitigation: The literature points to well-understood policy measures and technologies for accelerating mitigation, though the balance depends on country specificities: (i) decarbonising electricity supply to produce net zero CO_2, including renewable energy, (ii) radically more efficient use of energy than today; (iii) electrification of end-uses including transport; (iv) dramatically lower use of fossil fuels than today; (v) converting other uses to low- or zero-carbon fuels (e.g., hydrogen, bioenergy, ammonia) in hard-to-decarbonise sectors; (vi) promote bioenergy, demand reduction, dietary changes, and policies, incentives, and rules for mitigation in the land sector; and (vii) setting and meeting ambitious targets to reduce methane and other short-lived climate forcers. Charting just transitions to net zero may provide a vision, which policy measures can help achieve. Though there is increasing experience with pricing carbon directly or indirectly, decision-makers might consider a broader toolbox of enablers and levers that is available in domains that have not traditionally been considered climate policy. {4.5, Annex II.IV.11}

Broadening opportunities by focusing on development pathways and considering how to shift them: Some of the policy measures may yield rapid results, whereas other, larger transformations may take longer. If we are to overcome obstacles, a near-term priority is to put in place the enabling conditions to shifting development pathways to increased sustainability. Learning from the examples above, focusing on SDPS also provides a broader set of tools to accelerating mitigation and achieve other sustainable development goals. Consider climate whenever you make choices about development, and vice versa. {4.4.1}

4.1   Introduction

The recent IPCC Report on Global Warming of 1.5°C (SR1.5) made clear that the next three decades are critical if we are to achieve the long-term mitigation goal of the Paris Agreement (IPCC 2018a). The present chapter assesses the literature on mitigation and development pathways over that timeframe, in the near (up to 2030) and mid-term (up to 2050).

It considers three questions: (i) Where are we heading now? That is, what is the current state of affairs with respect to climate mitigation and how did we get here? (ii) Where do we want to go? For example, what state of affairs would meet the objectives of the Paris Agreement and achieving the Sustainable Development Goals (SDGs)? and (iii) How do we bring about this shift? In other words, what interventions are at societies' disposal to bring about the necessary change in an equitable manner?

Where are we heading now? Despite the drop in emissions due to the COVID-19 crisis, the gap between projected emissions based on Nationally Determined Contributions (NDCs) in 2030 and emissions pathways compatible with the long term temperature goal set in the Paris Agreement remains large (Section 4.2.2). In addition to this persistent emissions gap, we face an implementation gap, as current policies are insufficient to achieve mitigation targets in NDCs, and sufficient international support is not yet available to developing countries who have requested and quantified support needs. Continuing along a development pathway characterised by the same underlying drivers, structural obstacles and insufficient enabling conditions that led to high emissions will not address the problem (*robust evidence, high agreement*).

The analysis of the gap is conducted together with Chapter 3 (Cross-Chapter Box 4 in this chapter). Chapter 3 is working backward, assessing mitigation in the long term (beyond 2050 up to 2100) to draw the near- and mid-term implications of long-term temperature and mitigations goals. Chapter 4, on the other hand, works forward from current and planned mitigation (including NDCs) (Sections 4.2.1 and 4.2.2) and from current development paths to assess the implications for near- and mid-term greenhouse gases (GHG) emissions and development goals. Some countries, regions, cities, communities and non-state actors are taking leadership in implementing more ambitious action (Section 4.2.3). This chapter also assesses national low emission development strategies (Section 4.2.4).

Where do we want to go? Technical alternatives and policy options exist to bridge the emissions and implementation gaps, and the literature illustrates these with a wide range of accelerated techno-economic pathways that deepen decarbonisation closer to the pace and scale required (Section 4.2.5), and examines their impacts on other development objectives (Section 4.2.6). In practice, however, scaling up at the broader, deeper, and faster level required to meet climate goals while advancing other development objectives regularly faces prohibitive obstacles (Section 4.2.7). Mitigation policies grafted on to existing development pathways are unlikely to achieve rapid and deep emission reductions.

Secondly, even if carefully designed, climate policies to accelerate mitigation may have adverse consequences for other development objectives. As a complement to mitigation action, taking action to shift development pathways towards sustainability broadens the range of mitigation options, while increasing the possibility to meet other development priorities at the same time (*medium evidence, high agreement*).

Development pathways and shifting them to increased sustainability are introduced in Chapter 1, and constitute a thread throughout the report (see 'development pathways' in Annex I: Glossary). The AR6 WGII Report highlights the related concept of *climate resilient development pathways* (AR6 WGII, Chapter 18). Cross-Chapter Box 5 in this chapter − on shifting sustainable pathway towards sustainability − elaborates on the concept. The influence of development pathways on emissions and mitigative capacity is discussed in Chapter 2. Chapter 3 assesses modelling of shifts in development pathways, illustrated by the illustrative mitigation pathway called 'shifting pathways'. The importance of behavioural change as societies make decisions that intentionally shift their future development pathway is emphasised in Chapter 5. The systems Chapters (6–12) take sectoral perspectives, while pathways that are sustainable are the specific focus of Chapter 17.

How can one shift development pathway and accelerate mitigation? The literature does not provide a complete handbook for shifting development pathways and accelerating mitigation. The literature does, however, shed light on some of the underlying dynamics. Shifting development pathways can be necessitated by the existence of pervasive obstacles that prove prohibitive to reaching mitigation and other development objectives (Section 4.2.7). Deliberate measures taken to facilitate the shifting of development pathways and accelerated mitigation involve putting in place key enabling conditions that help overcome those obstacles (Figure 4.6) − improving governance and institutional capacity, fostering behavioural change and technological innovation, designing and implementing adequate policy, and finance. Just transitions, while they will differ by context, are critical to identifying and avoiding or addressing inequitable distributive consequences (*robust evidence, high agreement*).

Enabling conditions necessary to accelerate mitigation and shift development pathways are discussed in depth in Chapters 5, 13, 14, 15 and 16. In addition, Chapters 13 and 14 detail the policy instruments that could help shift development pathways and accelerate the scale and pace of mitigation, while Chapter 4 describes those in broad strategies terms. Chapter 13 adds more texture on institutional and governance machinery; policy choice, design and implementation; as well as policy formulation processes, actors and structure across scales.

Since development pathways and mitigation options depend to large extent on national objectives and circumstances, this chapter is primarily concerned with literature at national level (or in the case of the European Union, at regional level), while Chapter 3 is primarily concerned with literature at global scale. The national scale selected in this chapter requires attention as national mitigation pathways cannot be linked directly to global mitigation goals (Box 4.2). This chapter is also concerned mostly with economy-wide development and mitigation pathways, as distinct from detailed sectoral work that is assessed in the systems Chapters 6 to 12. The present chapter also assesses literature on non-state action.

Chapter 4 draws on five major strands of literature: (i) an emerging literature on development pathways – conceptual, empirical, and model-based, including at the national and sub-national scales; (ii) a rapidly expanding, model-based, literature on mitigation pathways in the near- and mid-term (Lepault and Lecocq 2021); (iii) studies of NDCs and mid-century strategies; (iv) a broader literature on transformation and shifts in development pathways, including from non-climate literatures; and (v) a significant literature on equity, including just transitions. This is supported by a database of country-level mitigation scenarios at country level assembled for the preparation of this chapter (Annex III, Table I.10 and I.11).

The chapter builds on past IPCC reports. In AR5, all mitigation pathways were assessed in a single chapter (Clarke et al. 2014), which focused mostly on the long term. IPCC Special Report on Global Warming of 1.5°C (SR1.5) included a chapter on mitigation pathways compatible with the temperature goal in the Paris Agreement (Rogelj et al. 2018a), mostly at the global level. It also considered strengthening mitigation (de Coninck et al. 2018) in the context of poverty, inequality and sustainable development (Roy et al. 2018). Development pathways have also been explored, albeit less frequently, in past IPCC reports starting with the Special Report on Emissions Scenarios (Nakicenovic et al. 2000). Some early framing of development pathways was included in the Third Assessment Report (Banuri et al. 2001), further developed in the Fourth Assessment Report (Sathaye et al. 2007). An extended discussion of climate change and equity was conducted in AR5 (Fleurbaey et al. 2014).

Chapter 4 examines mitigation within the broader context of development pathways, and examines how shifting development pathways can have a major impact on mitigative capacity and broadening mitigation options. It is organised as follows.

Section 4.2 demonstrates that collective mitigation actions fall short of pathways that keep in reach the Paris temperature goals in the long term. Section 4.3 introduces development pathways (given its relative novelty in IPCC assessments), considers the implications of mitigation for development and vice versa, and articulates an approach on *both* accelerating mitigation *and* shifting development pathways.

Section 4.4 discusses how to shift development pathway and accelerate the scale and pace of mitigation, what levers are available to policymakers, and how policies may intersect with adaptation goals. It points out that development pathways also drive adaptation and adaptative capacity, and discusses various risks associated with shifting development pathways and accelerated mitigation strategies.

Finally, equity and just transitions are recurring themes in the chapter, specifically in relation to accelerating mitigation and shifting development pathways toward sustainability. In Section 4.2.2.7, equity is discussed in the context of Parties' assertions regarding the fairness of their NDCs, alongside reflections from academic

scholarship on the ethical underpinnings of these assertions and of various quantitative analyses of equitable effort-sharing. Section 4.2.6 discusses certain distributional implications of domestic mitigation efforts, such as shifts in employment. Sections 4.2.7 and 4.3 note the relevance of potential distributional impacts as an obstacle to climate action, as well as the inequitable distribution of decision-making authority. Finally, Section 4.5 recognises the structural relationship between equity and climate, explores just transitions as an international focal point tying together social movements, trade unions, and other stakeholders, and thus an instrumental role in establishing consensus.

4.2 Accelerating Mitigation Actions Across Scales

4.2.1 Mitigation Targets and Measures in Nationally Determined Contributions

A central instrument of the Paris Agreement is the NDCs, submitted by each country, and reflecting national efforts to reduce GHG emissions and build resilience to the impacts of climate change. Every five years, collective progress will be compared against long-term goals of the Paris Agreement. Considering the outcome of a global stocktake, countries will prepare subsequent NDCs, showing progression in their ambition and enhancing international cooperation (UNFCCC 2015a).

Prior to COP21, in 2015, most countries submitted their Intended Nationally Determined Contributions (INDCs), which included mitigation targets for 2025 or 2030. INDCs become first NDCs on ratification and/or after national governments' revision, and by 11 October 2021, the official NDC registry contained 194 first NDCs with 105 new and updated NDCs from 132 Parties to the Paris Agreement, covering 53% of the total global emissions in 2019 of 52.4 $GtCO_2$-eq without land use, land-use change and forestry (LULUCF), and 13 second NDCs. Most of the Parties that submitted new or updated NDCs have demonstrated increased ambition in addressing climate change. Moreover, though some countries have not submitted their updated NDCs yet, they have already announced their updated NDC goals somewhere. Countries will take the first stock in 2023 based on their progression towards achieving the objectives of Paris Agreement (UNFCCC 2015a, 2018a; SB Chairs 2021) (Section 14.3.2.5).

Submitted NDCs vary in content, scope and background assumptions. First NDCs contain mitigation targets, and in many cases also provisions about adaptation. The mitigation targets range from economy-wide absolute emission reduction targets to strategies, plans and actions for low-emission development. Baseline years vary from 1990 to 2015 and in almost all NDCs the targeted time frame is 2030, with a few specified periods of until 2025, 2035, 2040 or 2050. Around 43% of the mitigation targets in first NDCs are expressed in terms of deviation below business-as-usual by a specified target year, either for the whole economy or for specific sectors, while around 35% include fixed-level targets (either reductions or limitations compared to base years), and another 22% refer to intensity targets (in terms of GHG, CO_2 or energy) or policies and measures, with an increasing number of Parties moving to absolute emission reduction targets in their new or updated NDCs (UNFCCC 2016a, 2021). Some developing countries' NDCs include unconditional elements, while others include conditional ones, the latter with higher ambition if finance, technology and capacity building support from developed countries is provided (UNFCCC 2016a).[2] In some NDCs, the additional mitigation is quantified, in others not (Figure 14.2).

Most first NDCs cover all specific sectors, including LULUCF, and communicate specific targets for individual sub-sectors to support their overall mitigation targets. Concrete actions and priority areas are more detailed in the energy sector, with increased share of renewable energies and energy efficiency being highlighted in the majority of NDCs. Given the uncertainty behind LULUCF emission and removal accounting (Grassi et al. 2017; Jian et al. 2019), several countries state that their accounting framework will only be defined in later NDCs. The GHG included and the global warming potentials (GWPs) used to aggregate emissions also vary across NDCs. Most countries only refer to carbon dioxide, methane and nitrous oxide emissions aggregated based on IPCC AR2 or AR4 metrics, while few NDCs also include fluorinated gases and use IPCC AR5 GWPs. The shares of Parties that indicate possible use of at least one type of voluntary cooperation and set qualitative limits on their use have both nearly doubled in new or updated NDCs.

There is considerable literature on country-level mitigation pathways, including but not limited to NDCs. Country distribution of this literature is very unequal (*robust evidence, high agreement*). In particular, there is a growing literature on (I)NDCs, with a wide scope which includes estimate of emissions levels of NDCs (Section 4.2.2.2); alignment with sustainable development goals (Caetano et al. 2020; Campagnolo and Davide 2019; Fuso Nerini et al. 2019; Antwi-Agyei et al. 2018); ambition (Höhne et al. 2018; Vogt-Schilb and Hallegatte 2017; Hermwille et al. 2019); energy development (Scott et al. 2018); and the legality of downgrading NDCs (Rajamani and Brunnée 2017). Other studies note that many NDCs contain single-year mitigation targets, and suggest that a multi-year trajectory is important for more rigorous monitoring (Elliott et al. 2017; Dagnet et al. 2017).

The literature also points out that beyond the 'headline numbers', information in (I)NDCs is difficult to analyse (Pauw et al. 2018). Information for 'clarity, transparency and understanding' is to be communicated with NDCs, although initial guidance was not specific (UNFCCC 2014). While the adoption of the Paris rule-book provided some greater specificity (UNFCCC 2018b,c), the information included in the NDCs remains uneven. Many NDCs omit important mitigation sectors and do not adequately provide details on costs and financing of implementation (Pauw et al. 2018). Countries are also invited to explain how their NDCs are fair and ambitious, though the way this has been done so far has been criticised as insufficiently rigorous (Winkler et al. 2018).

4.2.2 Aggregate Effects of NDCs and Other Mitigation Efforts Relative to Long-term Mitigation Pathways

4.2.2.1 Introduction

Near-term mitigation targets submitted as part of NDCs to the UNFCCC, as well as currently implemented policies, provide a basis for assessing potential emissions levels up to 2030 at the national, regional and global level. The following sections present an evaluation of the methods used for assessing projected emissions under NDCs and current policies (Section 4.2.2.2), and the results of these assessments at global, regional and national level assessing a broad available literature based on first NDC submissions from 2015/16 and pre-COVID economic projections (Section 4.2.2.3). The impacts of the COVID-19 pandemic and related government responses on emissions projections are then discussed in Section 4.2.2.4 and the implications of updated NDCs submitted in 2020/21 on emissions follow in Section 4.2.2.5. Section 4.2.2.6 presents an assessment of the so-called 'implementation gap' between what currently implemented policies are expected to deliver and what the ambitions laid out under the full implementation of the NDCs are projected to achieve. Finally, a comparison of ambitions across different countries or regions (Section 4.2.2.7) is presented and the uncertainties of projected emissions associated with NDCs and current policies are estimated, including a discussion of measures to reduce uncertainties in the specification of NDCs (Section 4.2.2.8).

The literature reviewed in this section includes globally comprehensive assessments of NDCs and current policies, both peer-reviewed and non-peer-reviewed (but not unpublished model results) as well as synthesis reports by the UNFCCC Secretariat, government reports and national studies.

The aggregate effects of NDCs provide information on where emissions might be in 2025/2030, working forward from their recent levels. Chapter 3 of this report works backwards from temperature goals, defining a range of long-term global pathways consistent with 1.5°C, 2°C and higher temperature levels. By considering the two together, it is possible to assess whether NDCs are collectively consistent with 1.5°C, 2°C and other temperature pathways (Cross-Chapter Box 4 in this chapter).

4.2.2.2 Methods to Project Emissions Under NDCs and Current Policies

A variety of different methods are used to assess emissions implications of NDCs and current policies over the time horizon to 2025 or 2030. Some of these projections were explicitly submitted as part of an official communication to UNFCCC (e.g., Biennial Report, Biennial Update Reports or National Communications) while the majority is from independent studies.

---

[2] 'Unconditional' NDCs refer to abatement efforts pledged without any conditions (this terminology is used by the literature, not by the Paris Agreement). They are based mainly on domestic abatement actions, although countries can use international cooperation to meet their targets. 'Conditional' NDCs require international cooperation, for example bilateral agreements under article 6, financing or monetary and/or technological transfers (14.3.2).

Methods that are used in independent studies (but that can also underlie the official communications) can broadly be separated into two groups:

1. system modelling studies which analyse policies and targets in a comprehensive modelling framework such an integrated assessment, energy systems or integrated land-use model to project emissions (or other indicators) of mitigation targets in NDCs and current policies, either at the national or global scale (noting some differences in the systems); and
2. hybrid approaches that typically start out with emissions pathways as assessed by other published studies (e.g., the IEA World Energy Outlook, national emissions pathways such as those specified in some NDCs) and use these directly or apply additional modifications to them.

System modelling studies are conducted at global, regional and national scales. Global models provide an overview, are necessary for assessment of global phenomena (e.g., temperature change), can integrate climate models and trade effects. National models typically include more details on sectors, technology, behaviour and intersectoral linkages, but often use simplifying assumptions for international trade (e.g., the Armington elasticity approach). Critically, they can also better reflect local socio-economic and political conditions and their evolution (i.e., national development pathways). A variety of modelling paradigms are found, including optimisation and simulation models, myopic and with foresight, monolithic and modular (Annex III: Scenarios and Modelling Methods).

Among the hybrid approaches, three broader categories can be distinguished, (i) direct use of official emission projection as part of submitted NDC or other communication to UNFCCC, (ii) historical trend extrapolation of emissions based on inventory data, possibly disaggregated by sector and emission species, and (iii) use of Reference/Business-As-Usual pathways from an independent published study (e.g., IEA WEO). In all cases, the reductions are then estimated on top of the resulting emission trajectory. Note that globally comprehensive studies may vary the approach used depending on the country.

Beyond the method applied, studies also differ in a number of dimensions, including (i) their spatial resolution and coverage, (ii) their sectoral resolution and coverage, (iii) the GHGs that are included in the assessment, the GWPs (or other metrics) to aggregate them, the emissions inventory (official vs independent inventory data) and related accounting approaches used as a starting point for the projections, (iv) the set of scenarios analysed (Reference/Business-As-Usual, Current Policies, NDCs, etc.), and (v) the degree to which individual policies and their impact on emissions are explicitly represented (Table 4.1).

First, the studies are relevant to different spatial levels, ranging from macro-scale regions with globally comprehensive coverage to national level (Section 4.2.2.3) and sub-national and company level in a few cases (Section 4.2.3). It is important to recognise that globally comprehensive studies typically resolve a limited number of countries individually, in particular those that contribute a high share to global emissions, but have poor resolution of remaining countries or regions, which are assessed in aggregate terms. Conversely, studies with high resolution of a particular country tend to treat interactions with the global scale in a limited way. The recent literature includes attempts to provide a composite global picture from detailed national studies (Bataille et al. 2016a; Deep Decarbonization Pathways Project 2015; Roelfsema et al. 2020).

A second dimension in which the studies are different is their comprehensiveness of covering different emitting sectors. Some studies focus on the contribution of a single sector, for example the agriculture, forestry and other land use (AFOLU) sector (Fyson and Jeffery 2019; Grassi et al. 2017) or the energy system (including both energy supply and demand sectors), to emission reductions as specified in the NDC. Such studies give an indication of the importance of a given sector to achieving the NDC target of a country and can be used as a benchmark to compare to comprehensive studies, but adding sectoral contributions up represents a methodological challenge.

Third, GHG coverage is different across studies. Some focus on CO_2 only, while others take into account the full suite of Kyoto gases (CO_2, CH_4, N_2O, HFCs, PFCs and SF_6). For the latter, different metrics for aggregating GHGs to a CO_2-equivalent metric are being used, typically GWP 100 from different IPCC assessments (Table 4.1).

Fourth, studies typically cover a set of scenarios, though how these scenarios are defined varies widely. The literature reporting IAM results often includes *Nationally Determined Contribution* (NDC), which are officially communicated, and *Current Policies* (CP) as interpreted by modellers. Studies based on national modelling, by contrast, tend to define scenarios reflecting very different national contexts. In both cases, modellers typically include so-called *No Policy Baseline* scenarios (alternatively referred to as *Reference* or *Business-as-Usual scenarios*) which do not necessarily reflect currently implemented policies and thus are not assessed as reference pathways (Section 4.2.6.1). There are also various approaches to considering more ambitious action compared to the CP or NDC projections that are covered in addition.

Fifth, studies differ in the way they represent policies (current or envisioned in NDCs), depending on their internal structure. For example, a subsidy to energy efficiency in buildings may be explicitly modelled (e.g., in a sectoral model that represents household decisions relative to building insulation), represented by a proxy (e.g., by an exogenous decrease in the discount rate households use to make choices), or captured by its estimated outcome (e.g., by an exogenous decrease in the household demand for energy, say in an energy system model or in a compact CGE). Detailed representations (such as the former example) do not necessarily yield more accurate results than compact ones (the latter example), but the set of assumptions that are necessary to represent the same policy will be very different.

Finally, policy coverage strongly varies across studies with some just implementing high level targets specified in policy documents and NDCs while others represent the policies with the largest impact on emissions and some looking at very detailed measures and

4

policies at sub-national level. In addition, in countries with rapidly evolving policy environments, slightly different cut-off dates for the policies considered in an emission projection can make a significant difference for the results (Dubash et al. 2018).

The challenges described above are dealt with in the assessment of quantitative results in Section 4.2.2.3 by (i) comparing national studies with country-level results from global studies to understand systematic biases; (ii) comparing economy-wide emissions (including AFOLU) as well as energy-related emissions; (iii) using different emission metrics including CO_2 and Kyoto GHG emissions where the latter have been harmonised to using AR6 GWP100 metrics; and (iv) tracking cut-off dates of implemented policies and NDCs used in different references (Table 4.SM.1). The most notable differences in quantitative emission estimates related to current policies and NDCs relate to the COVID-19 pandemic and its implications and to the updated NDCs mostly submitted since early 2020 which are separately dealt with in Sections 4.2.2.4 and 4.2.2.5, respectively.

In addition to assessing the emissions outcomes of NDCs, some studies report development indicators, by which they mean a wide diversity of socio-economic indicators (Jiang et al. 2013; Chai and Xu 2014; Delgado et al. 2014; La Rovere et al. 2014a; Zevallos et al. 2014; Benavides et al. 2015; Altieri et al. 2016; Bataille et al. 2016a; Zou et al. 2016; Paladugula et al. 2018; Parikh et al. 2018; Yang et al. 2021), share of low-carbon energy (Bertram et al. 2015; Riahi et al. 2015), renewable energy deployment (Roelfsema et al. 2018), production of fossil fuels (SEI et al. 2020) or investments into low-carbon mitigation measures (McCollum et al. 2018) to track progress towards long-term temperature goals.

4.2.2.3   Projected Emissions Under NDCs and Current Policies by 2025/2030

The emissions projections presented in this section relate to the first NDCs, as communicated in 2015 and 2016, and on which an extensive literature exists. New and updated NDCs, mostly submitted since the beginning of 2020, are dealt with in Section 4.2.2.5. Similarly, the implications of COVID-19 and the related government responses on emissions projections is specifically dealt with in Section 4.2.2.4.

Table 4.1 presents the evidence base for the assessment of projected emissions of original NDCs and current policies until 2030. It covers 31 countries and regions responsible for about 82% of global GHG emission (excluding FOLU CO_2 emissions) and draws quantitative estimates from more than 40 studies (Table 4.SM.1 in the Supplementary Material to this chapter). The table allows comparing emission projections from national and globally comprehensive studies as well as official communications by countries to the UNFCCC at the national/regional level. The global aggregates presented in Table 4.1 derive from globally comprehensive studies only and are not the result of aggregating country projections up

to the global level. As different studies report different emission indicators, the table includes four different indicators: CO_2 and GHG emissions, including or excluding AFOLU emissions. Where possible, multiple indicators are included per study.

Globally comprehensive studies

The UNFCCC Secretariat has assessed the aggregate effect of NDCs multiple times. The first report considered the intended NDCs in relation to 2°C (UNFCCC 2015b), whereas the second considered NDCs also in relation to 1.5°C (UNFCCC 2016b). New submissions and updates of NDCs in 2020/21 are assessed in Section 4.2.2.5. A number of globally comprehensive studies (den Elzen et al. 2016; Luderer et al. 2016; Rogelj et al. 2016, 2017; Vandyck et al. 2016; Rose et al. 2017; Baumstark et al. 2021) which estimate aggregate emissions outcomes of NDCs and current policies have previously been assessed in Cross-Chapter-Box 11 of IPCC SR1.5.

According to the assessment in this report, studies projecting emissions of current policies based on pre-COVID assumptions lead to median global GHG emissions of 60 $GtCO_2$-eq with a full range of 54–68 by 2030 and original unconditional and conditional NDCs submitted in 2015/16 to 57 (49–63) and 54 (50–60) $GtCO_2$-eq, respectively (*robust evidence, medium agreement*) (Table 4.1). Globally comprehensive and national-level studies project emissions of current policies and NDCs to 2025 and 2030 and, in general, are in good agreement about projected emissions at the country level.

These estimates are close to the ones provided by the IPCC SR1.5, Cross-Chapter-Box 11, and the UNEP emissions gap report (UNEP 2020a).[3]

National studies

A large body of literature on national and regional emissions projections, including official communications of as part of the NDC submissions and independent studies exist. A subset of this literature provides quantitative estimates for the 2030 timeframe. As highlighted in Section 4.2.1, the number of independent studies varies considerably across countries with an emphasis on the largest emitting countries. This is reflected in Table 4.1 (see also Table 4.SM.1). Despite smaller differences between globally comprehensive and national studies for a few countries, there is generally good agreement between the different types of studies, providing evidence that these quantitative estimates are fairly robust.

Sectoral studies

Sectoral studies are essential to understand the contributions of concrete measures of NDCs and current policies. For example, approximately 98% of NDCs include the energy sector in their mitigation contributions, of which nearly 50% include a specific

---

[3]   Note that the statistical metrics reported are slightly different across the reports. For example, IPCC SR1.5 reported the 25th to 75th percentile range while the UNEP Emissions Gap Report uses median and 10th to 90th percentile ranges. In addition, this report applies 100-year GWPs from AR6 to aggregate across different GHG emission species, whereas 100-year GWPs from AR4 were applied in IPCC SR1.5 and UNEP 2020a. The application of AR6 GWPs on average leads to increase of estimates by about 1.3% and ranges are wider due to the difference in statistical error metrics.

Table 4.1 | Assessment of projected 2030 emissions of current policies based on pre-COVID assumptions and original NDCs submitted in 2015/16 for 28 individual countries/regions and the world. The table compares projected emissions from globally comprehensive studies, national studies and, when available, official communications to UNFCCC using different emission sources (fossil fuels, AFOLU sector) and different emission metrics (CO_2, Kyoto GHGs). The comparison allows identifying potential biases across the ranges and median estimates projected by the different sets of studies.

Region[a]	GHG share [%][b]	Type[c]	# estimates[d]	Current Policies 2030 emissions			NDC 2030 emissions (conditional/unconditional)		
				CO_2 only [$GtCO_2$] median (min–max)[f]		Kyoto GHGs[e] [$GtCO_2$-eq] median (min–max)[f]	CO_2 only [$GtCO_2$] median (min–max)[f]		Kyoto GHGs[e] [$GtCO_2$-eq] median (min–max)[f]
				incl. AFOLU[g]	fossil fuels	incl. AFOLU[g]	incl. AFOLU[g]	fossil fuels	incl. AFOLU[g]
World	100	global	93	43 (38–51)	37 (33–45)	60 (54–68)	40 (35–45)/ 37 (35–39)	32 (26–39)/ 31 (27–37)	54 (50–60)/ 57 (49–63)
CHN	27	global	76	12 (9.7–15)	11 (8.4–14)	15 (12–18)	– /11 (9.8–13)	– /8.8 (6.9–13)	– /14 (13–16)
		national	13	12 (12–12)	11 (9.2–13)	15 (13–15)	– /12 (11–12)	– /11 (10–11)	– /15 (13–16)
USA[h]	12	global	71	4.9 (4.4–6.6)	4.6 (3.5–6.5)	5.9 (4.9–6.6)	– /3.8 (3.3–4.1)	– /3.9 (3.1–5.3)	– /4.6 (4–5.1)
		national	5	4.1	4.5 (4.1–4.9)	5.9 (5.2–6.7)	– /3.4	– /3.5	– /4.3
EU[i]	8.1	global	24	2.7 (2.1–3.5)	2.6 (2.1–3.3)	3.4 (2.6–4.7)	– /2.6 (2.1–2.8)	– /2.4 (2.1–2.7)	– /3.2 (2.6–3.7)
		national	3	3.1	2.6		– /2.5		
		official	3			3.2 (2.8–3.7)			
IND	7.1	global	79	3.7 (3–4.5)	3.2 (2.5–4.5)	4.7 (4.1–6.4)	3.3 (3.1–4.4)/4	3.3 (2.4–5.6)/3.8 (2.9–5.6)	5 (4.2–6.4)/5.8 (4.9–6.1)
		national	9	3.4 (3.3–4)	3.4 (2.9–3.9)	5.5 (5–5.7)	3.4 (3.2–3.6)/3.2	3.4 (3.2–3.5)/2.9	5.1/4.9
RUS	4.5	global	66	1.7 (0.84–2)	1.6 (1.5–2)	2.3 (1.6–3.3)	– /1.7 (0.85–1.9)	– /1.6 (1.2–1.9)	– /2.6 (1.9–3.1)
		national	6		1.5 (1.5–1.5)	2.6		– /1.5 (1.5–1.5)	– /2.5
		official	2			2.1			– /2.7
BRA	2.5	global	69	1.1 (0.79–1.7)	0.5 (0.28–1.1)	1.8 (1.4–2.7)	– /0.94 (0.52–1.5)	– /0.38 (0.097–0.86)	– /1.3 (1.2–2.5)
		national	4	0.59	0.47	1.8	– /0.51	– /0.47	– /1.2
		official	1						– /1.2
JPN	2.4	global	66	1.2 (0.94–1.3)	1.1 (0.67–1.3)	1.2 (0.95–1.3)	– /1 (0.9–1.2)	– /0.83 (0.65–1.2)	– /1 (0.95–1.2)
		national	16	1.1 (1.1–1.6)	1.1 (1.1–1.5)	1.3 (1.2–1.7)	– /0.93 (0.91–1.2)	– /0.93 (0.87–1.1)	– /1 (1–1.3)
		official	1						– /1
IDN	2.2	global	25	1.1 (0.79–2)	0.62 (0.51–0.89)	1.7 (1.4–2.4)	0.93 (0.76–1.4)/0.99	0.53 (0.45–0.66)/0.68 (0.6–0.77)	1.8 (1.3–2.1)/2.1 (1.5–2.2)
		official	2						1.9 (1.8–1.9)/2.2
CAN	1.5	global	67	0.58 (0.4–0.8)	0.43 (0.38–0.72)	0.68 (0.51–1)	– /0.43 (0.34–0.67)	– /0.43 (0.31–0.64)	– /0.53 (0.49–0.82)
		national	2	0.54		0.71	– /0.41		– /0.54
		official	2			0.67			
MEX	1.5	global	31	0.61 (0.54–1.3)	0.48 (0.3–0.56)	0.82 (0.72–1.7)	0.54 (0.48–1)/0.46	0.43 (0.27–0.54)/0.33 (0.26–0.42)	0.65 (0.62–1.4)/0.73 (0.63–0.79)
		official	2						0.62/0.76
SAU	1.5	global	6	0.7 (0.57–0.82)	0.61 (0.48–0.74)	1 (0.7–1.1)	0.7 (0.58–0.82)/–	0.62 (0.49–0.74)/–	0.83 (0.7–0.96)/–
KOR	1.4	global	64	0.69 (0.55–0.76)	0.67 (0.42–0.91)	0.72 (0.68–0.81)	– /0.57 (0.5–0.65)	– /0.4 (0.26–0.61)	– /0.57 (0.5–0.69)
		national	4	0.78 (0.75–0.81)	0.73 (0.7–0.76)	0.86 (0.83–0.89)	– /0.62 (0.51–0.72)	– /0.58 (0.49–0.67)	– /0.68 (0.56–0.8)
		official	1						
AUS	1.1	global	16	0.42 (0.34–0.49)	0.34 (0.28–0.46)	0.54 (0.46–0.69)	– /0.36 (0.28–0.43)	– /0.3 (0.24–0.41)	– /0.44 (0.39–0.52)
		national	3			0.55			
		official	2			0.52 (0.51–0.52)			
TUR	1.1	global	18	0.44 (0.44–0.49)	0.4 (0.34–0.43)	0.6 (0.51–0.83)	– /0.44 (0.44–0.49)	– /0.4 (0.27–0.43)	– /0.94 (0.55–1)
		official	1						– /0.93

4

Region[a]	GHG share [%][b]	Type[c]	# estimates[d]	Current Policies 2030 emissions			NDC 2030 emissions (conditional/unconditional)		
				CO_2 only [GtCO_2] median (min–max)[f]		Kyoto GHGs[e] [GtCO_2-eq] median (min–max)[f]	CO_2 only [GtCO_2] median (min–max)[f]		Kyoto GHGs[e] [GtCO_2-eq] median (min–max)[f]
				incl. AFOLU[g]	fossil fuels	incl. AFOLU[g]	incl. AFOLU[g]	fossil fuels	incl. AFOLU[g]
ZAF	1.1	global	26	0.49 (0.35–0.62)	0.36 (0.23–0.56)	0.64 (0.45–0.85)	– /0.4 (0.27–0.55)	– /0.35 (0.21–0.44)	0.41/0.58 (0.39–0.65)
		official	1						– /0.52 (0.41–0.64)
VNM	0.92	global	2						0.61/0.77
		national	4	0.36	0.28		0.32 (0.28–0.36)/0.36	0.26 (0.24–0.28)/0.28	
GBR	0.86	global	4	0.37	0.33 (0.3–0.37)		– /0.37	– /0.33 (0.3–0.37)	
FRA	0.85	global	4	0.22	0.32 (0.24–0.4)		– /0.22	– /0.32 (0.24–0.4)	
THA	0.84	global	5			0.41 (0.41–0.41)			0.44/0.47
		national	3	0.43	0.4	0.58	0.35/0.36	0.32/0.34	0.43/0.46
ARG	0.76	global	22	0.33 (0.17–0.52)	0.2 (0.15–0.35)	0.51 (0.33–0.75)	0.25 (0.17–0.46)/0.25	0.21 (0.18–0.23)/0.15 (0.14–0.16)	0.39 (0.32–0.69)/0.51 (0.33–0.52)
		national	2			0.42 (0.41–0.43)		– /0.19	
		official	2						0.4/0.52
KAZ	0.71	global	3			0.45			0.28/0.32
UKR	0.52	global	2			0.42 (0.42–0.42)			– /0.54
PHL	0.48	global	3			0.24			0.082/ –
COL	0.4	global	5			0.23 (0.23–0.23)			0.26 (0.26–0.26)/0.29 (0.29–0.29)
ETH	0.31	global	5		0.022	0.23 (0.19–0.27)		– /0.023	0.16 (0.15–0.16)/ –
MAR	0.21	global	5			0.11 (0.087–0.13)			0.13 (0.1–0.15)/0.13 (0.1–0.15)
KEN	0.18	global	5		0.022	0.13 (0.11–0.14)		– /0.023	0.11 (0.11–0.11)/ –
SWE	0.13	global	4	–0.012	0.03 (0.029–0.031)		– /–0.012	– /0.03 (0.028–0.032)	
PRT	0.12	global	2	0.045	0.036		– /0.045	– /0.036	
		national	1					– /0.023	
CHE	0.094	global	1						– /0.026
		national	1	0.027	0.025				
MDG	0.065	global	1						0.033/ –
		national	3	0.071	0.0059		0.07 (0.068–0.071)/ –	0.0043 (0.0026–0.0059)/ –	

Notes: [a] Countries are abbreviated by their ISO 3166-1 alpha-3 letter codes. EU denotes the European Union. [b] 2018 Share of global Kyoto GHG emissions, excluding FOLU emissions, based on 2019 GHG emissions from Chapter 2 (Minx et al. 2021; Crippa et al. 2021). [c] Type distinguishes between independent globally comprehensive studies (that also provide information at the country/region level), independent national studies and official communications via Biennial Reports, Biennial Update Reports or National Communications. [d] Different estimates from one study (e.g., data from multiple models or minimum and maximum estimates) are counted individually, if available. [e] GHG emissions expressed in CO_2-eq emission using AR6 100-year GWPs (see Section 2.2.2 for a discussion of implications for historical emissions). GHG emissions from scenario data is recalculated from individual emission species using AR6 100-year GWPs. GHG emissions from studies that do provide aggregate GHG emissions using other GWPs are rescaled using 2019 GHG emissions from Chapter 2 (Minx et al. 2021; Crippa et al. 2021). [f] If more than one value is available, a median is provided and the full range of estimates (in parenthesis). To avoid a bias due to multiple estimates provided by the same model, only one estimate per model, typically the most recent update, is included in the median estimate. In the full range, multiple estimates from the same model might be included, in case these reflect specific sensitivity analyses of the 'central estimate' (e.g., Baumstark et al. 2021; Rogelj et al. 2017). [g] Note that AFOLU emissions from national GHG inventories and global/national land use models are generally different due to different approaches to estimate the anthropogenic CO_2 sink (Grassi et al. 2018, 2021) (Section 7.2.3 and Cross-Chapter Box 6 in Chapter 7). [h] The estimates for USA are based on the first NDC submitted prior to the withdrawal from the Paris Agreement, but not including the updated NDC submitted following its re-entry. [i] The EU estimates are based on the 28 member states up until 31 January 2020, i.e., including UK.

target for the share of renewables, and about 5% aim at increasing nuclear energy production (Stephan et al. 2016). Transport is covered explicitly in 75% of NDCs, although specific targets for the sector exist in only 21% of NDCs (PPMC and SLoCaT 2016). Measures or targets for buildings are referred to explicitly in 27% of NDCs (GIZ 2017). Additionally, 36% of NDCs include targets or actions that are specific to the agriculture sector (FAO 2016). LULUCF (mitigation) is included in 80% of all submitted NDCs, while 59% include adaptation and 29% refer to REDD+.

Greater sectoral expertise and involvement will be critical to accomplishing development and climate goals due to enhanced availability of information and expertise on specific sectoral options, greater ease of aligning the NDCs with sectoral strategies, and greater awareness among sector-level decision-makers and stakeholders (Fekete et al. 2015; NDC Partnership 2017). Sector-specific studies are assessed in the sectoral Chapters (6 to 11) of this report.

4.2.2.4 Estimated Impact of COVID-19 and Governmental Responses on Emissions Projections

The impacts of COVID-19 and national governments' economic recovery measures on current (Section 2.2.2) and projected emissions of individual countries and globally under current policies scenarios until 2030 may be significant, although estimates are highly uncertain and vary across the few available studies. The analyses published to date (October 2021) are based on limited information about how COVID-19 has affected the economy and hence GHG emissions across countries so far in 2020, and also based on assumptions about COVID-19's longer term impact. Moreover, the comparison of pre- and post-COVID-19 projections captures the impact of COVID-19 as well as other factors such as the consideration of recently adopted policies not related to COVID-19, and methodological changes.

Across different studies (Kikstra et al. 2021; IEA 2020; Dafnomilis et al. 2021; Pollitt et al. 2021; UNEP 2020a; Climate Action Tracker 2020; Keramidas et al. 2021; Dafnomilis et al. 2020), the impact of the general slowdown of the economy due to the COVID-19 pandemic and its associated policy responses would lead to a reduced estimate of global GHG emissions in 2030 of about 1 to 5 $GtCO_2$-eq, equivalent to 1.5–8.5%, compared to the pre-COVID-19 estimates

(Table 4.SM.2). Nascimento et al. (2021) analyse the impacts of COVID-19 on current policy emission projections for 26 countries and regions and find a large range of emission reduction – between –1% and –21% – across these.

As indicated by a growing number of studies at the national and global level, how large near- to mid-term emissions implications of the COVID-19 pandemic are to a large degree depends on how stimulus or recovery packages are designed (Forster et al. 2020; Gillingham et al. 2020; IEA 2020; Le Quéré et al. 2020; Malliet et al. 2020; Wang et al. 2020; Obergassel et al. 2021; Pollitt et al. 2021; UNEP 2020a).

Four studies (Climate Action Tracker 2021; den Elzen et al. 2021; JRC 2021; Riahi et al. 2021) provide an update of the current policies assessment presented in Section 4.2.2.3 by taking into account the effects of COVID-19 as well as potential updates of policies. The resulting GHG emissions in 2030 are estimated to be 57 $GtCO_2$-eq with a full range of 52 to 60 $GtCO_2$-eq (Table 4.2). This is a reduction of about 3 $GtCO_2$-eq or 5% compared to the pre-COVID estimates from Section 4.2.2.3.

4.2.2.5 Estimated Impact of New and Updated NDCs on Emissions Projections

The number of studies estimating the emissions implications of new and updated NDCs and announced mitigation pledges that can be used for the quantitative assessment is limited to four (Table 4.3) (Climate Action Tracker 2021; den Elzen et al. 2021; Meinshausen et al. 2021; JRC 2021). One other study includes a limited number of NDC updates (Riahi et al. 2021) and another (UNFCCC 2021) excludes LULUCF emissions. They are therefore not directly comparable to the other two. In addition, the UNEP Emissions Gap Report 2021 (UNEP 2021) in itself is assessment of almost the same studies included here. The evidence base for the updated NDC assessment is thus considerably smaller compared to that of the assessment of emissions implications of original NDCs presented in Section 4.2.2.3. However, it is worthwhile to note that the earlier versions of the studies summarised in Table 4.2 and Table 4.3 are broadly representative for the emissions range implied by the pre-COVID-19 current policies and original NDCs of the full set of studies shown in Table 4.1, therefore building confidence in estimates.

Table 4.2 | Projected global GHG emissions of current policies by 2030.

Study	Cut-off date	Kyoto GHGs[a] [$GtCO_2$-eq] median (min–max)[b]	References
Climate Action Tracker	8/2020	54 (52–56)	Climate Action Tracker (2021)
PBL	11/2020	58	den Elzen et al. (2021); Nascimento et al. (2021)
JRC – GECO	12/2019	57	JRC (2021)
ENGAGE[c]	7/2019	57 (52–60)	Riahi et al. (2021)
Total[d]		57 (52–60)	

Notes: [a] GHG emissions expressed in CO_2-eq emission using AR6 100-year GWPs. GHG emissions from studies that provide aggregate GHG emissions using other GWPs are rescaled using 2019 GHG emissions from Chapter 2 (Minx et al. 2021; Crippa et al. 2021). [b] If a range is available from a study, a median is provided in addition to the range. [c] Range includes estimates from four models: GEM-E3, MESSAGEix-GLOBIOM, POLES, REMIND-MAgPIE, based on sensitivity analysis. [d] To avoid a bias due to multiple estimates provided by the same model, only one estimate per model, typically the most recent update, is included in the median estimate for the total.

Table 4.3 | Projected global GHG emissions of new and updated NDCs by 2030.

Study	Cut-off date	Kyoto GHGs[a] [GtCO$_2$-eq]				References
		Historical		Median (min–max)[b] 2030		
		2015	2019	Unconditional NDCs	Conditional NDCs	
Climate Action Tracker[c]	5/2021	51	52	50	47	Climate Action Tracker (2021)
PBL[d]	9/2021	52	54	53 (51–55)	52 (49–53)	den Elzen et al. (2021); Nascimento et al. (2021)
JRC – GECO[e]	10/2021	51			48	JRC (2021)
Meinshausen et al.[f]	10/2021	54	56	55 (54–57)	53 (52–55)	Meinshausen et al. (2021)
Total[g]				53 (50–57)	50 (47–55)	
Other studies for comparison						
UNEP EGR[h]	9/2021			53 (50–55)	50 (47–53)	UNEP (2017a)
UNFCCC Secretariat[i]	7/2021			57 (55–58)	54 (52–56)	UNFCCC (2021)
ENGAGE[j]	3/2021				51 (49–53)	Riahi et al. (2021)

Notes: [a] GHG emissions expressed in CO$_2$-eq emission using AR6 100-year GWPs. GHG emissions from studies that provide aggregate GHG emissions using other GWPs are rescaled using 2019 GHG emissions from Chapter 2 (Minx et al. 2021; Crippa et al. 2021). Note that due to slightly different system boundaries across historical emission datasets as well as data uncertainties (Chapter 2, SM2.2) relative change compared to historical emissions should be calculated vis-à-vis the historical emissions data used by a particular study. [b] If a range is available from a study, a median is provided in addition to the range. [c] Announced mitigation pledges on global 2030 emissions of China and Japan included. [d] Announced mitigation pledges of China, Japan, Republic of Korea included. [e] Announced mitigation pledge of Korea not included. [f] Announced mitigation pledges of China and Republic of Korea not included, emissions from international aviation and shipping not included. [g] Ranges across four studies are calculated using the median and the full range including the minimum and maximum of studies if available. [h] UNEP EGR 2021 estimate listed for comparison, but since largely relying on the same studies not included in range estimate. [i] NDCs submitted until 30 July included, announcements not included, excluding LULUCF emissions. [j] NDC updates of Brazil, EU and announcement of China included as a sensitivity analysis compared to original NDCs.

An additional challenge lies in the fact that these studies do not all apply the same cut-off date for NDC updates, potentially leading to larger systematic deviations in the resulting emission estimates. Another complication is the fact that publicly announced mitigation pledges on global 2030 emissions that have not been officially submitted to the UNFCCC NDC registry yet, have been included in several of the studies to anticipate their impact on emission levels (see notes to Table 4.3). In addition to the updates of NDC targets, most of the new studies also include impacts of COVID-19 on future emission levels (as discussed in Section 4.2.2.4) which may have led to considerable downward revisions of emission trends unrelated to NDCs. Table 4.3 presents the emission estimates of the four studies that form the basis of the quantitative assessment presented here and three other studies to compare with.

Comparing the emission levels implied by the new and updated NDCs as shown in Table 4.3 with those estimated by the original NDCs from the same studies (as included in Table 4.1), a downward revision of 3.8 (3.0–5.3) GtCO$_2$-eq of the central unconditional NDC estimates and of 4.5 (2.7–6.3) GtCO$_2$-eq of the central conditional NDC estimate emerges (*medium evidence, medium agreement*). The emissions gaps between temperature limits and new and updated NDCs are assessed in Cross-Chapter Box 4 below. New and updated unconditional NDCs reduce the median gap with emissions pathways that limit warming to 2°C (>67%) in 2030 by slightly more than 20%, from a median gap of 17 GtCO$_2$-eq (9–23) to 13 (10–16). New and updated conditional NDCs reduce the median gap with emissions pathways that limt warming to 2°C (>67%) in 2030 by about one third, from 14 GtCO$_2$-eq (10–20) to 9 (6–14). New and updated unconditional NDCs reduce the median gap with emissions pathways that limit warming to 1.5°C (>50%) with no or limited overshoot in 2030 by about 15%, from a median gap of 27 GtCO$_2$-eq (19–32) to

22 GtCO$_2$-eq (19–26). New and updated conditional NDCs reduce the median gap with emissions pathways that limit warming to 1.5°C (>50%) with no or limited overshoot in 2030 by about 20%, from a median gap of 24 GtCO$_2$-eq (20–29) to 19 GtCO$_2$-eq (16–23). Box 4.1 discusses the adaptation gap.

Globally, the implementation gap between projected emissions of current policies and the unconditional and conditional new and updated NDCs is estimated to be around 4 and 7 GtCO$_2$-eq in 2030, respectively (*medium evidence, medium agreement*) (Tables 4.2 and 4.3), with many countries requiring additional policies and associated climate action to meet their mitigation targets as specified under the NDCs (*limited evidence*) (Section 4.2.2.6). It should be noted that the implementation gap varies considerably across countries, with some having policies in place estimated to be sufficient to achieve the emission targets their NDCs, some where additional policies may be required to be sufficient, as well as differences between the policies in place and action on the ground.

4.2.2.6   Tracking Progress in Implementing and Achieving NDCs

Under the Enhanced Transparency Framework, countries will transition from reporting biennial reports (BRs) and biennial update reports (BURs) to reporting biennial transparency reports (BTRs) starting, at the latest, by December 2024. Each Party will be required to report information necessary to track progress made in implementing and achieving its NDC under the Paris Agreement (UNFCCC 2018b). Thus, no official data exists yet on tracking progress of individual NDCs.

Meanwhile, there is some literature at global and national level that aims at assessing whether countries are on track or progressing towards implementing their NDCs and to which degree the NDCs collectively are sufficient to reach the temperature targets of the Paris agreement (Rogelj et al. 2016; Quéré et al. 2018; Höhne et al. 2018; Roelfsema et al. 2020; den Elzen et al. 2019; Höhne et al. 2020). Most of these studies focus on major emitters such as G20 countries and with the aim to inform countries to strengthen their ambition regularly, for example, through progress of NDCs and as part of the global stocktake (Höhne et al. 2018; Peters et al. 2017). However, a limited number of studies assess the implementation gaps of conditional NDCs in terms of finance, technology and capacity building support. Some authors conclude that finance needed to fulfil conditional NDCs exceeds available resources or the current long-term goal for finance (USD100 billion yr^{-1}) (Pauw et al. 2019); others assess financial resources needed for forest-related activities (Kissinger et al. 2019) (Section 15.4.2). The literature suggests that consistent and harmonised approach to track progress of countries towards their NDCs would be helpful (Peters et al. 2017; Höhne et al. 2018; den Elzen et al. 2019), and negotiations on a common tabular format are expected to conclude during COP26 in November 2021.

With an implementation gap in 2030 of 4 to 7 GtCO$_2$-eq (Section 4.2.2.5), many countries will need to implement additional policies to meet their self-determined mitigation targets as specified under the NDCs. Studies that assess the level of projected emissions under current policies indicate that new policies (that have been implemented since the first assessment of the NDCs in 2015 and are thus covered in more recent projections) have reduced projections, by about two GtCO$_2$-eq since the adoption of the Paris Agreement in 2015 to 2019 (Climate Action Tracker 2019; UNEP 2020a; den Elzen et al. 2019).

4.2.2.7   Literature on Fairness and Ambition of NDCs

Most countries provided information on how they consider their NDCs to be fair and ambitious in the NDCs submitted to UNFCCC and many of these NDCs refer to specific national circumstances such as social, economic and geographical factors when outlining why they are fair and ambitious. Further, several Parties provided information on specific criteria for evaluating fairness and ambition, including criteria relating to: responsibility and capability; share of emissions; development and/or technological capacity; mitigation potential; cost of mitigation actions; the degree of progression or stretching beyond the current level of effort; and the link to objectives and global goals (UNFCCC 2016a).

According to its Article 2.2, the Paris Agreement will be implemented to reflect equity and the principle of common but differentiated responsibilities and respective capabilities, in the light of different national circumstances, the latter clause being new, added to the UNFCCC principle (Voigt and Ferreira 2016; Rajamani 2017). Possible different interpretations of equity principles lead to different assessment frameworks (Lahn and Sundqvist 2017; Lahn 2018).

Various assessment frameworks have been proposed to analyse fair share ranges for NDCs. The literature on equity frameworks including quantification of national emissions allocation is assessed in section 4.5 (Sections 13.4.2, 14.3.2 and 14.5.3). Recent literature

has assessed equity, analysing how fairness is expressed in NDCs in a bottom-up manner (Mbeva and Pauw 2016; Cunliffe et al. 2019; Winkler et al. 2018). Some studies compare NDC ambition level with different effort sharing regimes and which principles are applied to various countries and regions (Peters et al. 2015; Pan et al. 2017; Robiou Du Pont et al. 2017; Holz et al. 2018; Robiou du Pont and Meinshausen 2018; van den Berg et al. 2019). Others propose multi-dimensional evaluation schemes for NDCs that combine a range of indicators, including the NDC targets, cost-effectiveness compared to global models, recent trends and policy implementation into consideration (Aldy et al. 2017; Höhne et al. 2018). Yet other literature evaluates NDC ambition against factors such as technological progress of energy efficiency and low-carbon technologies (Jiang et al. 2017; Kuramochi et al. 2017; Wakiyama and Kuramochi 2017), synergies with adaptation plans (Fridahl and Johansson 2017), the obligations to deploy carbon dioxide removal technologies like bioenergy with carbon capture and storage (BECCS) in the future implied by their near-term emission reductions where they are not reflected on in the first NDCs (Peters and Geden 2017; Fyson et al. 2020; Pozo et al. 2020; Mace et al. 2021). Others identify possible risks of unfairness when applying GWP* as emissions metric at national scale (Rogelj and Schleussner 2019). A recent study on national fair shares draws on principles of international environmental law, excludes approaches based on cost and grandfathering, thus narrowing the range of national fair shares previously assessed, and apply this to the quantification of national fair share emissions targets (Rajamani et al. 2021).

4.2.2.8   Uncertainty in Estimates

There are many factors that influence the global aggregated effects of NDCs. There is limited literature on systematically analysing the impact of uncertainties on the NDC projections with some exception (Rogelj et al. 2017; Benveniste et al. 2018). The UNEP Gap Report (UNEP 2017a) discusses uncertainties of NDC estimates in some detail. The main factors include variations in overall socio-economic development; uncertainties in GHG inventories; conditionality; targets with ranges or for single years; accounting of biomass; and different GHG aggregation metrics (e.g., GWP values from different IPCC assessments). In addition, when mitigation effort in NDCs is described as measures that do only indirectly translate into emission reductions, assumptions necessary for the translation come into play (Doelle 2019). For a more elaborate discussion of uncertainties in NDCs (Section 14.3.2).

Some studies assume successful implementation of all of the NDCs' proposed measures, sometimes including varying assumptions to account for some of the NDC features which are subject to assumed conditions related to finance and technology transfer. Countries 'shall pursue domestic mitigation measures' under Article 4.2 of the Paris Agreement (UNFCCC 2015a), but they are not legally bound to the result of reducing emissions (Winkler 2017a). Some authors consider this to be a lack of a strong guarantee that mitigation targets in NDCs will be implemented (Nemet et al. 2017). Others point to growing extent of national legislation to provide a legal basis for action (Iacobuta et al. 2018) (Section 13.2). These factors together with incomplete information in NDCs mean there is uncertainty about the estimates of anticipated 2030 emission levels.

The aggregation of targets results in large uncertainty (Rogelj et al. 2017; Benveniste et al. 2018). In particular, clarity on the contributions from the land use sector to NDCs is needed 'to prevent high LULUCF uncertainties from undermining the strength and clarity of mitigation in other sectors' (Fyson and Jeffery 2019). Methodological differences in the accounting of the LULUCF anthropogenic CO_2 sink between scientific studies and national GHG inventories (as submitted to UNFCCC) further complicate the comparison and aggregation of emissions of NDC implementation (Grassi et al. 2018, 2021) (Section 7.2.3 and Cross-Chapter Box 6 in Chapter 7). This uncertainty could be reduced with clearer guidelines for compiling future NDCs, in particular when it comes to mitigation efforts not expressed as absolute economy-wide targets (Doelle 2019), and explicit specification of technical details, including energy accounting methods, harmonised emission inventories (Rogelj et al. 2017) and finally, increased transparency and comparability (Pauw et al. 2018).

Cross-Chapter Box 4 | Comparison of NDCs and current policies with the 2030 GHG Emissions from Long-term Temperature Pathways

Authors: Edward Byers (Austria/Ireland), Michel den Elzen (the Netherlands), Céline Guivarch (France), Volker Krey (Germany/Austria), Elmar Kriegler (Germany), Franck Lecocq (France), Keywan Riahi (Austria), Harald Winkler (South Africa)

Introduction

The Paris Agreement (PA) sets a long-term goal of holding the increase of global average temperature to 'well below 2°C above pre-industrial levels' and pursuing efforts to limit the temperature increase to 1.5°C above pre-industrial levels. This is underpinned by the 'aim to reach global peaking of greenhouse gas emissions as soon as possible' and 'achieve a balance between anthropogenic emissions by sources and removals by sinks of GHG in the second half of this century' (UNFCCC 2015a). The PA adopts a bottom-up approach in which countries determine their contribution to reach the PA's long-term goal. These national targets, plans and measures are called 'nationally determined contributions' or NDCs.

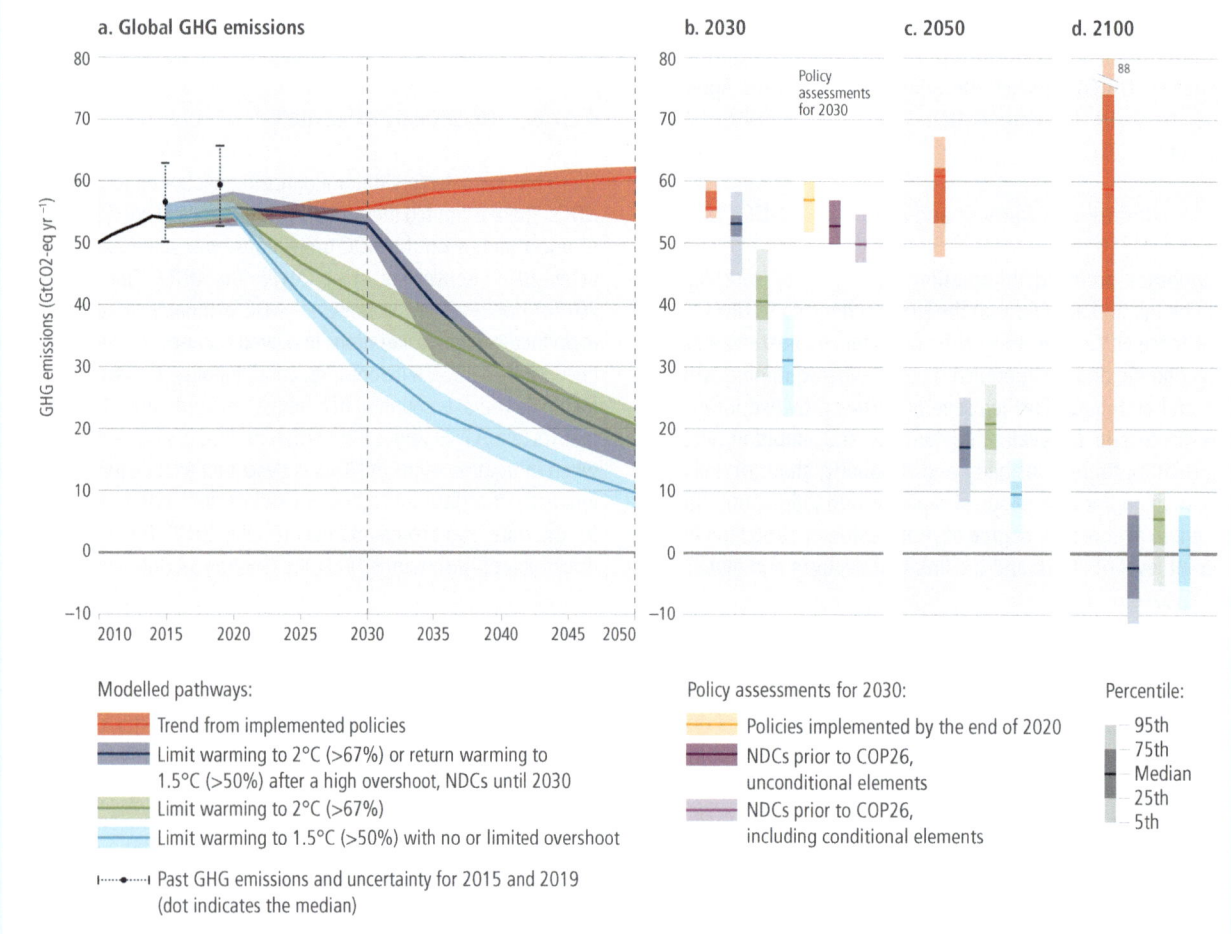

Cross-Chapter Box 4, Figure 1 | Global GHG emissions of modelled pathways (funnels in Panel a, and associated bars in Panels b, c, d) and projected emission outcomes from near-term policy assessments for 2030 (Panel b).

Cross-Chapter Box 4 (continued)

Cross-Chapter Box 4, Figure 1 (continued): Global GHG emissions of modelled pathways (funnels in Panel a, and associated bars in Panels b, c, d) and projected emission outcomes from near-term policy assessments for 2030 (Panel b).

Panel a shows global GHG emissions over 2015–2050 for four types of assessed modelled global pathways:

– Trend from implemented policies: Pathways with projected near-term GHG emissions in line with policies implemented until the end of 2020 and extended with comparable ambition levels beyond 2030 (29 scenarios across categories C5–C7, Table SPM.2).

– Limit to 2°C (>67%) or return warming to 1.5°C (>50%) after a high overshoot, NDCs until 2030: Pathways with GHG emissions until 2030 associated with the implementation of NDCs announced prior to COP26, followed by accelerated emissions reductions likely to limit warming to 2°C (C3b, Table SPM.2) or to return warming to 1.5°C with a probability of 50% or greater after high overshoot (subset of 42 scenarios from C2, Table SPM.2).

– Limit to 2°C (>67%) with immediate action: Pathways that limit warming to 2°C (>67%) with immediate action after 2020 (C3a, Table SPM.2).

– Limit to 1.5°C (>50%) with no or limited overshoot: Pathways limiting warming to 1.5°C with no or limited overshoot (C1, Table SPM.2 C1). All these pathways assume immediate action after 2020.

Past GHG emissions for 2010–2015 used to project global warming outcomes of the modelled pathways are shown by a black line[4] and past global GHG emissions in 2015 and 2019 as assessed in Chapter 2 are shown by whiskers.

Panels b, c and d show snapshots of the GHG emission ranges of the modelled pathways in 2030, 2050, and 2100, respectively. Panel b also shows projected emissions outcomes from near-term policy assessments in 2030 from Chapter 4.2 (Tables 4.2 and 4.3; median and full range). GHG emissions are in CO_2-equivalent using GWP100 from AR6 WGI. {3.5, 4.2, Table 4.2, Table 4.3, Cross-Chapter Box 4 in Chapter 4}

The NDCs are a central instrument of the PA to achieve its long-term goal. It thus combines a global goal with a country-driven (bottom-up) instrument to a hybrid climate policy architecture to strengthen the global response to climate change. All signatory countries committed to communicating nationally determined contributions including mitigation targets, every five years. While the NDCs mostly state targets, countries are also obliged to pursue domestic mitigation measures to achieve the objectives. The literature examines the emissions outcome of the range of policies implemented to reach these targets.

Emissions gap

A comparison between the projected emission outcomes of current policies, the NDCs (which include unconditional and conditional elements, Section 4.2.1) and mitigation pathways acting immediately, i.e. from 2020 onwards, on reaching different temperature goals in the long-term (Section 3.3.3) allows identifying different 'emission gaps' in 2030 (Cross-Chapter Box 4, Figure 1). First, the implementation gap between 'current policies' and unconditional and conditional NDCs is estimated to be around 4 and 7 GtCO$_2$-eq in 2030, respectively (Section 4.2.2 and Tables 4.2 and 4.3). Second, the comparison of unconditional (conditional) NDCs and long-term mitigation pathways that limit warming to 2°C (>67%) or lower gives rise to a 2030 median emissions gap of 19–26 GtCO$_2$-eq (16–23 GtCO$_2$-eq) for limiting end-of-century warming to 1.5°C (>50%) with no or limited overshoot and 10–16 GtCO$_2$-eq (6–14 GtCO$_2$-eq) for limiting warming to 2°C (>67%).[5] GHG emissions of NDCs are broadly consistent with 2030 emission levels of cost-effective long-term pathways staying below 2.5°C (scenarios category C5, Table 3.2, Chapter 3).

Other 'gap indicators'

Beyond the quantification of different GHG emissions gaps, there is an emerging literature that identifies gaps between current policies, NDCs and long-term temperature in terms of other indicators, including for example the deployment of low-carbon energy sources, energy efficiency improvements, fossil fuel production levels or investments into mitigation measures (Roelfsema et al. 2020; McCollum et al. 2018; SEI et al. 2020).

A 2030 gap in the contribution of low-carbon energy sources to the energy mix in 2030 between current policies and cost-effective long-term temperature pathways is calculated to be around 7percentage-points (2°C) and 13percentage-points (1.5°C) by Roelfsema et al. (Roelfsema et al. 2020). The same authors estimate an energy intensity improvement gap 10% and 18% for 2030 between current policies pathways and 2°C and 1.5°C pathways, respectively. SEI et al. (2020) estimates the 'fossil fuel production gap', by which they mean 'the level of countries' planned fossil fuel production expressed in their carbon content to be 120% and 50% higher compared to the fossil fuel production consistent with 1.5°C and 2°C pathways, respectively, as assessed in IPCC SR1.5 (Rogelj et al. 2018a).

---

[4] See Box SPM.1 for a description of the approach to project global warming outcomes of modelled pathways and its consistency with the climate assessment in AR6 WGI.

[5] The emission gap ranges provided here is calculated as the difference between minimum and maximum emissions estimates of NDCs and the median of the 1.5°C and 2°C pathways.

The methodology used for this estimation is very similar to how emissions gaps are derived (SEI et al. 2019). The gap of global annual average investments in low-carbon energy and energy efficiency in 2030 between following current policy on the one hand and achieving the NDCs, the 2°C and 1.5°C targets on the other hand, is estimated to be approximately USD 130, 320, or 480 billion per year (McCollum et al. 2018).

It is important to note that such comparisons are less straight forward as the link between long-term temperature goals and these indicators is less pronounced compared to the emission levels themselves; they are therefore associated with greater uncertainty compared to the emissions gap.

Box 4.1 | Adaptation gap and NDCs

NDCs have been an important driver of national adaptation planning, with cascading effects on sectors and sub-national action, especially in developing countries. Yet, only 40 developing countries have quantifiable adaptation targets in their current NDCs; 49 countries include quantifiable targets in their national legislation (UNEP 2018a).

Working Group II contribution to this Assessment finds that the overall extent of adaptation-related responses in human systems is low (*high confidence*) and that there is limited evidence on the extent to which adaptation-related responses in human systems are reducing climate risk (O'Neill et al. 2020). Thus there is an adaptation gap (UNEP 2018a), and bridging that gap requires enablers including institutional capacity, planning and investment (UNEP 2016). Estimates of adaptation costs vary greatly across studies. Recent studies based on climate change under RCP8.5 report adaptation costs for developing countries of up to 400 billion (300 billion in RCP2.6) USD2005 in 2030 (New et al. 2020). Of the NDCs submitted in 2015, 50 countries estimated adaptation costs of USD39 billion annually. Both public and private finance for adaptation is increasing, but remains insufficient and constitutes a small fraction (4–8%) of total climate finance which is mostly aimed at mitigation. The pledge of developed countries of mobilising finance for developing countries to address adaptation needs globally as part of the Paris Agreement are insufficient. By 2030 the adaptation needs are expected to be three to six times larger than what is pledged, further increasing towards 2050 (UNEP 2016; New et al. 2020).

4.2.3   Mitigation Efforts in Sub-national and Non-state Action Plans and Policies

The decision adopting the Paris Agreement stresses the importance of 'stronger and more ambitious climate action' by non-government and sub-national stakeholders, 'including civil society, the private sector, financial institutions, cities and other sub-national authorities, local communities and indigenous peoples' (UNFCCC 2015a). The Marrakech Partnership for Global Action, launched in the 2016 UNFCCC Conference of Parties by two 'high-level champions,' further formalised the contributions of non-government and sub-national actors taking action through seven thematic areas (e.g., energy, human settlements, industry, land-use, etc.) and one cross-cutting area (resilience). Since then, non-state actors, for example, companies and civil society, and sub-national actors, such as cities and regions, have emerged to undertake a range of largely voluntary carbon mitigation actions (Hsu et al. 2018, 2019) both as individual non-state actors (NSAs in the following) and through national and international cooperative initiatives, or ICIs (Hsu et al. 2018). ICIs take a variety of forms, ranging from those that focus solely on non-state actors to those that engage national and even local governments. They can also range in commitment level, from primarily membership-based initiatives that do not require specific actions to those that require

members to tackle emissions reductions in specific sectors or aim for transformational change.

Quantification of the (potential) impact of these actions is still limited. Almost all studies estimate the potential impact of the implementation of actions by NSAs and ICIs, but do not factor in that they may not reach their targets. The main reason for this is that there is very limited data currently available from individual actors (e.g., annual GHG inventory reports) and initiatives to assess their progress towards their targets. A few studies have attempted to assess progress of initiatives by looking into the initiatives' production of relevant outputs (Chan et al. 2018). Quantification does not yet cover all commitments and only a selected number of ICIs are analysed in the existing literature. Most of these studies exclude commitments that are not (self-)identified as related to climate change mitigation, those that are not connected to international networks, or those that are communicating in languages other than English.

Non state action could make significant contributions to achieving the Paris climate goals (*limited evidence, high agreement*). However, efforts to measure the extent to which non-state and sub-national actors go beyond national policy are still nascent (Hsu et al. 2019; Kuramochi et al. 2020) and we do not fully understand the extent

Table 4.4 | Emissions reduction potential for sub-national and non-state international cooperative initiatives by 2030.

Sector	Leading actor	Name	Scale	Target(s)	2030 emissions reduction potential compared to no policy, current policies or NDC baseline ($GtCO_2$-eq yr^{-1})		Membership assumptions
					Min	Max	
Energy efficiency	Intergovernmental (UNEP)	United for Efficiency (U4E)	Global (focus on developing countries)	Members to adopt policies for energy-efficient appliances and equipment	0.6	1.25	Current membership
Energy efficiency	Intergovernmental	Super-efficient Equipment and Appliance Deployment (SEAD) Initiative	Global	Members to adopt current policy best practices for energy efficiency product standards	0.5	1.7 (excl. China)	Current membership
Buildings	Business	Architecture 2030	Global (focus on North America)	New buildings and major renovations shall be designed to meet an energy consumption performance standard of 70% below the regional (or country) average/median for that building type and to go carbon-neutral in 2030	0.2	0.2	Current membership
Transport	Business (aviation sector)	Collaborative Climate Action Across the Air Transport World (CAATW)	Global	Two key objectives: (i) 2% annual fuel efficiency improvement through 2050, (ii) stabilise net carbon emissions from 2020	0.3	0.6	Current membership
Transport	Business	Lean and Green	Europe	Member companies to reduce CO_2 emissions from logistics and freight activity by at least 25% over a five-year period	0.02	0.02	Current membership
Transport	Hybrid	Global Fuel Economy Initiative (GFEI)	Global	Halve the fuel consumption of the LDV fleet in 2050 compared to 2005	0.5	1.0	Current membership
Transport	Business	Below50 LCTPi [a]	Global	Replace 10% of global transportation fossil fuel use with low-carbon transport fuels by 2030	0.5	0.5	Scaled-up global potential
Renewable energy	Business	European Technology & Innovation Platform Photovoltaic (ETIP PV)	Europe	Supply 20% of electricity from solar Photovoltaic PV technologies by 2030	0.2	0.5	Current membership
Renewable energy	Intergovernmental (African Union)	Africa Renewable Energy Initiative (AREI)	Africa	Produce 300 gigawatt (GW) of electricity for Africa by 2030 from clean, affordable and appropriate forms of energy	0.3	0.8	Current membership
Renewable energy	Hybrid	Global Geothermal Alliance (GGA)	Global	Achieve a five-fold growth in the installed capacity for geothermal power generation and a more than two-fold growth in geothermal heating by 2030	0.2	0.5	Targeted capacity
Renewable energy	Business	REscale LCTPi [a]	Global	Support deployment of 1.5 TW of additional renewable energy capacity by 2025 in line with the IEA's 2°C scenario	5	5	Scaled-up global potential
Renewable energy	Business	RE100 initiative	Global	2,000 companies commit to source 100% of their electricity from renewable sources by 2030	1.9	4	Targeted membership
Forestry	Hybrid	Bonn Challenge/Governors' Climate and Forests Task Force (GCFTF)/New York Declaration on Forests (NYDF)	Global	End forest loss by 2030 in member countries and restore 150 million hectares of deforested and degraded lands by 2020 and an additional 200 million hectares by 2030	3.8	8.8	Scaled-up global potential
Non-CO2 emissions	Government	Climate & Clean Air Coalition (CCAC)	Global	Members to implement policies that will deliver substantial short-lived climate pollutants (SLCP) reductions in the near to medium-term (i.e., by 2030) for HFCs and methane	1.4	3.8	Current membership

4

Sector	Leading actor	Name	Scale	Target(s)	2030 emissions reduction potential compared to no policy, current policies or NDC baseline (GtCO$_2$-eq yr^{-1})		Membership assumptions
					Min	Max	
Non-CO$_2$ emissions	Intergovernmental (World Bank)	Zero Routine Flaring	Global	Eliminate routine flaring no later than 2030	0.4	0.4	Current membership
Multisectoral	Cities and regions	Under2 Coalition	Global	Local governments (220 members) aim to limit their GHG emissions by 80 to 95% below 1990 levels by 2050	4.6	5	Current membership
Multisectoral	Cities and regions	Global Covenant of Mayors for Climate & Energy (GCoM)	Global	Member cities have a variety of targets (+9,000 members)	1.4	1.4	Current membership
Multisectoral	Cities and regions	C40 Cities Climate Leadership Group (C40)	Global	94 member cities have a variety of targets, aiming for 1.5°C compatibility by 2050. The network carries two explicit goals: (i) to have every C40 city develop a climate action plan before the end of 2020 (Deadline 2020), which is to 'deliver action consistent with the objectives of the Paris Agreement' and (ii) to have cities achieve emissions neutrality by 2050	1.5	3	Current membership
Agriculture	Business	Climate Smart Agriculture (CSA) LCTPi [a]	Global	Reducing agricultural and land-use change emissions from agriculture by at least 50% by 2030 and 65% by 2050. 24 companies and 15 partners	3.7	3.7	Scaled-up global potential
Multisectoral	Business	Science Based Targets initiative (SBTi)	Global	By 2030, 2000 companies have adopted a science-based target in line with a 2°C temperature goal	2.7	2.7	Targeted membership

Source: Hsu et al. (2020). Note [a] As of December 2020 most of the Low Carbon Technology Partnerships (LCTPi) initiatives are defunct, except the Climate Smart Agriculture programme.

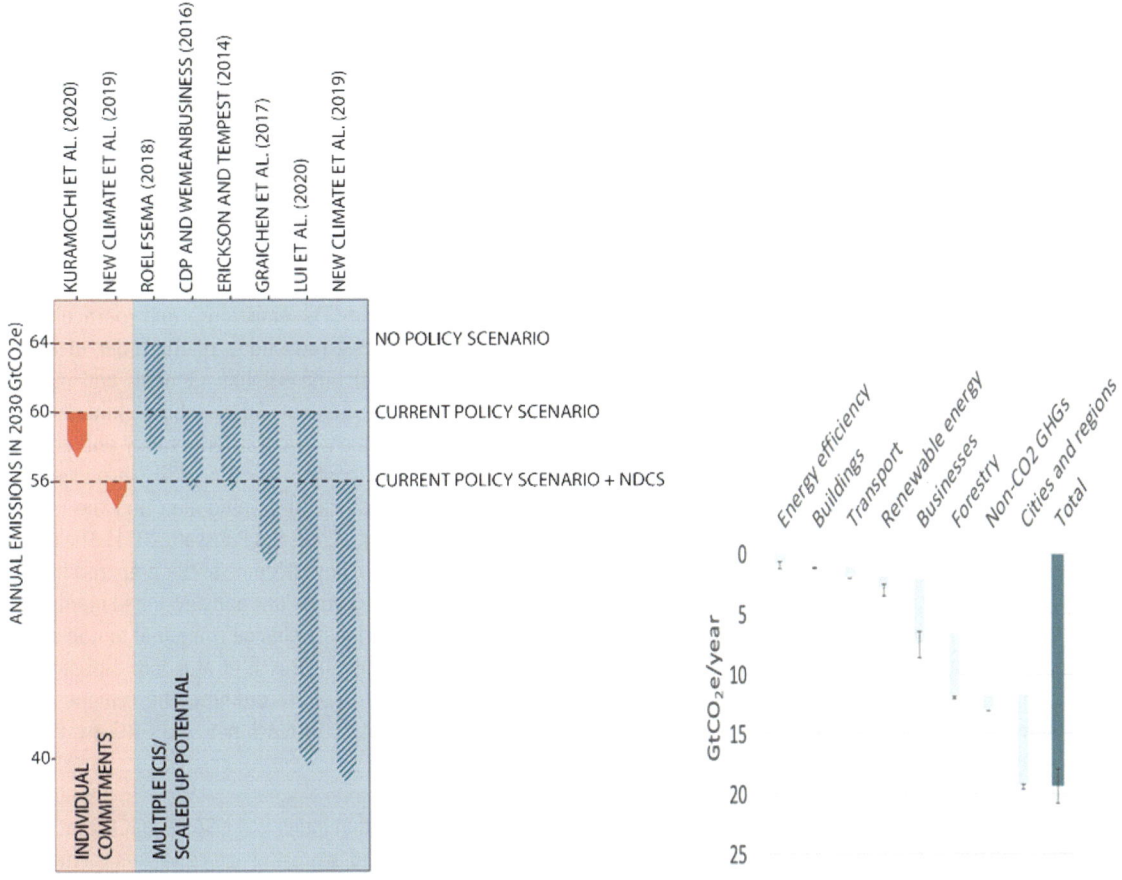

Figure 4.1 | Emissions reduction potential for non-state and sub-national actors by 2030. Source: data in left panel from Hsu et al. (2020), right panel from Lui et al. (2020).

to which ambitious action by non-state actors is additional to what national governments intend to do. Sub-national and non-state climate action may also have benefits in reinforcing, implementing, or piloting national policy, in place of or in addition to achieving additional emissions reductions (Broekhoff et al. 2015; Heidrich et al. 2016; Hsu et al. 2017).

Quantification of commitments by individual NSAs are limited to date. Attempts to quantify aggregate effects in 2030 of commitments by individual non-state and sub-national actors are reported by (Hsu et al. 2019; Kuramochi et al. 2020). Kuramochi et al. (2020) estimate potential mitigation by more than 1,600 companies, around 6,000 cities and many regions (cities assessed have a collective population of 579 million, and regions 514 million). Individual commitments by these sub-national regions, cities and companies could reduce GHG emissions in 2030 by 1.2 to 2.0 $GtCO_2$-eq yr^{-1} compared to current national policies scenario projections, reducing projected emissions by 3.8–5.5% in 2030, if commitments are fully implemented and do not lead to weaker mitigation actions by others (Figure 4.1 left). In several countries, NSA commitments could potentially help meet or exceed national mitigation targets.

Quantification of potential emission reductions from international cooperative initiatives have been assessed in several studies, and recently synthesised (Hsu et al. 2020; Lui et al. 2021), with some

initiatives reporting high potential. In Table 4.4 and Figure 4.1, we report estimates of the emissions reductions from 19 distinct sub-national and non-state initiatives to mitigate climate change. The table shows wide ranges of potential mitigation based on current, target or potential membership, as well as a wide diversity of actors and membership assumptions. Current membership reflects the number of non-state or sub-national actors that are presently committed to a particular initiative; while targeted or potential membership represents a membership goal (e.g., increasing from 100 to 200 members) that an initiative may seek to achieve (Kuramochi et al. 2020). When adding up emission reduction potentials, sub-national and non-state international cooperative initiatives could reduce up to about 20 Gt of CO_2-eq in 2030 (*limited evidence, medium agreement*). Chapter 8 also presents data on the savings potential of cities and it suggests that these could reach 2.3 $GtCO_2$-eq annually by 2030 and 4.2 $GtCO_2$-eq annually for 2050.

Non-state action may be broader than assessed in the literature so far, though subject to uncertainty. The examples in Table 4.4 and Figure 4.1 do not include initiatives that target the emissions from religious organisations, colleges and universities, civic and cultural groups, and, to some extent, households, and in this sense may underestimate sub-national potential for mitigating emissions, rather than overestimate it. That said, the estimates are contingent on assumptions that sub-national and non-state actors achieve commitments – both with respect to mitigation and in some cases membership – and that these actions are not accounted for in nor lead to weakening of national actions.

Care is to be taken not to depict these efforts as additional to action within national NDCs, unless this is clearly established (Broekhoff et al. 2015). There are potential overlaps between individual NSAs and ICIs, and across ICIs. Kuramochi et al. (2020) propose partial and conservative partial effect methods to avoid double counting when comparing ambition, a matter that merits further attention. As the diversity of actions increased, the potential to count the same reductions multiple times increases.

Equally important to note here is that none of the studies reviewed in Figure 4.1 quantified the potential impact of financial sector actions, for example, divestment from emission intensive activities (Section 15.3 has a more detailed discussion of how financial actors and instruments are addressing climate change). Moreover, only a limited number of studies on the impact of actions by diverse actors go beyond 2050 (Table 4.4), which may reflect analysts' recognition of the increasing uncertainties of longer time horizons. Accurate accounting methods can help to avoiding counting finance multiple times, and methods across mitigation and finance would consider counting carbon market flows and the tons reduced. As Table 4.4 and Figure 4.1 indicate, activities by businesses have potential to significantly contribute to global mitigation efforts. For example, the SBTi (Science Based Targets initiative) encourages companies to pledge to reduce their emissions at rates which according to SBTi would be compatible with global pathways to well below 2°C or 1.5°C, with various methodologies being proposed (Andersen et al. 2021; Faria and Labutong 2019). Readers may note, however, that the link between emissions by individual actors and long-term temperature goals cannot be inferred without additional assumptions (Box 4.2). In the energy sector, some voluntary initiatives are also emerging to stop methane emissions associated with oil and gas supply chains. The Oil and Gas Methane Partnership (OGMP) is a voluntary initiative lead by the Climate and Clean Air Coalition, which has recently published a comprehensive framework for methane detection, measurement and reporting (UNEP 2020b).

Initiatives made up of cities and sub-national regions have an especially large potential to reduce emissions, due to their inclusion of many actors, across a range of different geographic regions, with ambitious emissions reduction targets, and these actors' coverage of a large share of emissions (Kuramochi et al. 2020). Hsu et al. (2019) find largest potential in that area. Several sub-national regions like California and Scotland have set zero emission targets (Höhne et al. 2019), supported by short- and medium-term interim goals (Scottish Government 2020b; State of California 2018). Sharing of effort across global and sub-global scales has not been quantified, though one study suggests that non-state actors have increasingly adopted more diverse framings, including vulnerability, human rights and transformational framings of justice (Shawoo and McDermott 2020). Initiatives focused on forestry have high emissions reduction potential due to the current high deforestation rates, and due to the ambitious targets of many of these forestry initiatives, such as the New York Declaration on Forests' goal to end deforestation by 2030 (Höhne et al. 2019; Lui et al. 2021), although the Initiative acknowledges

that insufficient progress has to-date been made towards this goal (NYDF Assessment Partners 2020). On the other hand, uncertainties in global forest carbon emissions (and therefore potential reductions) are high and despite a multitude of initiatives in the sector, actually measured deforestation rates have not declined since the initiative was announced in 2014 (Sections 7.2 and 7.3.1). Moreover, not all initiatives are transparent about how they plan to reach their goals and may also rely on offsets.

Initiatives focused on non-CO_2 emissions, and particularly on methane, can achieve sizable reductions, in the order of multiple $GtCO_2$-eq yr^{-1} (Table 4.4). The Global Cement and Concrete Association (formerly the Cement Sustainability Initiative), has contributed to the development of consistent energy and emissions reporting from member companies. The CSI also suggested possible approaches to balance GHG mitigation and the issues of competitiveness and leakage (Cook and Ponssard 2011). The member companies of the GCCA (CSI) have become better prepared for future legislation on managing GHG emissions and developed management competence to respond to climate change compared to non-member companies in the cement sector (Busch et al. 2008; Global Cement and Concrete Association 2020). Accordingly, the cement industry has developed some roadmaps to reach net zero GHG around 2050 (Sanjuán et al. 2020).

It is also important to note that individual NSAs and ICIs that commit to GHG mitigation activities are often scarce in many crucial and 'hard-to-abate' sectors, such as iron and steel, cement and freight transport (Chapters 10 and 11). Sub-national and non-state action efforts could help these sectors meet an urgent need to accelerate the commercialisation and uptake of technical options to achieve low zero emissions (Bataille 2020).

4.2.4   Mid-century Low-emission Strategies at the National Level

An increasing amount of literature describes mitigation pathways for the mid-term (up to 2050). We assess literature reflecting on the UNFCCC process (Section 4.2.4.1), other official plans and strategies (Section 4.2.4.2) and academic literature on mid-century low-emission pathways at the national level (Section 4.2.4.3). After the Paris Agreement and the IPCC SR1.5 Report, the number of academic papers analysing domestic emission pathways compatible with the 1.5°C limit has been increasing. Governments have developed an increasing number of mitigation strategies up to 2050. Several among these strategies aim at net zero CO_2 or net zero GHG, but it is not yet possible to draw global implications due to the limited size of sample (*limited evidence, limited agreement*).

Box 4.2 | Direct Links Between an Individual Actor's Mitigation Efforts in the Near Term and Global Temperature Goals in the Long Term Cannot be Inferred: Making direct links requires clear distinctions of spatial and temporal scales (Robertson 2021; Rogelj et al. 2021) and explicit treatment of ethical judgements made (Klinsky et al. 2017a; Holz et al. 2018; Klinsky and Winkler 2018; Rajamani et al. 2021)

The literature frequently refers to *national* mitigation pathways up to 2030 or 2050 using long-term temperature limits in the Paris Agreement (i.e., '2°C' or '1.5°C scenario'). Without additional information, such denomination is incorrect. Working Group I reaffirmed 'with high confidence the AR5 finding that there is a near-linear relationship between cumulative anthropogenic CO_2 emissions and the global warming they cause' (WGI SPM AR6). It is not the function of any single country's mitigation efforts, nor any individual actor's. Emission pathways of *individual* countries or sectors in the near to mid-term can only be linked to a long-term temperature with additional assumptions specifying (i) the GHG emissions and removals of other countries up the mid-term; and (ii) the GHG emissions and removals of all countries beyond the near and mid-term. For example, a national mitigation pathway can be labelled '2°C compatible' if it derives from a global mitigation pathway consistent with 2°C via an explicit effort sharing scheme across countries (Sections 4.2.2.6 and 4.5).

4.2.4.1 GHG Mitigation Target Under UNFCCC and Paris Agreement

The Paris Agreement requests that Parties should strive to formulate and communicate long-term low GHG development strategies by 2020. (Note that by 'long-term', the UNFCCC means 2050, which is the end point of the 'mid-term' horizon range in the present report.)

As of August 25, 2021, 31 countries and the European Union had submitted low-emissions development strategies (LEDS) (Table 4.5).

By 2018, most long-term strategies targeted 80% emissions reduction in 2050 relative to a reference (1990, 2000 or 2005). After IPCC SR1.5 was published, the number of the countries aiming at net zero CO_2 or GHG emissions has been increasing.[6]

Table 4.5 | Countries having submitted long-term low-GHG emission development strategy (as of 25 August 2021).

Country	Date submitted	GHG reduction target
USA	Nov. 16, 2016	80% reduction of GHG in 2050 compared to 2005 level
Mexico	Nov. 16, 2016	50% reduction of GHG in 2050 compared to 2000 level
Canada	Nov. 17, 2016	80% reduction of GHG in 2050 compared to 2005 level
Germany	Nov. 17, 2016 Rev. Apr. 26, 2017 Rev. May 4, 2017	GHG neutrality by 2050 (Old target: 80–95% reduction of GHG in 2050 compared to 1990 level)
France	Dec. 28, 2016 Rev. Apr. 18, 2017 Rev. Feb. 8, 2021	Achieving net zero GHG emissions by 2050 (Old target: 75% reduction of GHG in 2050 compared to 1990 level)
Benin	Dec. 12, 2016	Resilient to climate change and low-carbon intensity by 2025
Czech Republic	Jan. 15, 2018	80% reduction of GHG in 2050 compared to 1990 level
UK	April 17, 2018	80% reduction of GHG in 2050 compared to 1990 level
Ukraine	July 30, 2018	66–69% reduction of GHG in 2050 compared to 1990 level
Republic of the Marshall Islands	Sept. 25, 2018	Net zero GHG emissions by 2050
Fiji	Feb. 25, 2019	Net zero carbon by 2050 as central goal, and net negative emissions in 2041 under a Very High Ambition scenario
Japan	June 26, 2019	80% reduction of GHG in 2050, and decarbonised society as early as possible in the 2nd half of 21st century
Portugal	Sept. 20, 2019	Carbon neutrality by 2050
Costa Rica	Dec. 12, 2019	Decarbonised economy with net zero emissions by 2050
European Union	March 6, 2020	Net zero GHG emissions by 2050
Slovakia	March 30, 2020	Climate neutrality by 2050, with decarbonisation targets implying reduction of at least 90% compared to 1990 (not taking into account removals)
Singapore	March 31, 2020	Halving emissions from its peak to 33 $MtCO_2$-eq by 2050, with a view to achieving net zero emissions as soon as viable in the second half of the century

---

[6] Specifying gases aids clarity, see Cross-Chapter Boxes 2 and 3 in chapters 2 and 3, respectively. Some countries refer to net zero GHG emissions as 'climate neutrality' or 'carbon neutrality'; the more precise terms are used where supported by the information assessed in this report.

Country	Date submitted	GHG reduction target
South Africa	Sep. 23, 2020	Net zero carbon economy by 2050
Finland	Oct. 5, 2020	Carbon neutrality by 2035; 87.5–90% reduction of GHG in 2050 to 1990 level (excluding land use sector)
Norway	Nov. 25, 2020	Being a low-emission society by 2050
Latvia	Dec. 9, 2020	Climate neutrality by 2050 (non-reducible GHG emissions are compensated by removals in the LULUCF sector)
Spain	Dec. 10, 2020	Climate neutrality by 2050
Belgium	Dec. 10, 2020	Carbon neutrality by 2050 (Walloon Region); Full climate neutrality (Flemish Region), and the European target of carbon neutrality by 2050 (Brussels-Capital Region)
Austria	Dec. 11, 2020	Climate-neutral by no later than 2050
Netherlands	Dec. 11, 2020	Reduction of GHG emissions by 95% by 2050 compared to 1990 level.
Sweden	Dec. 11, 2020	Zero net emissions of GHG into the atmosphere latest by 2045
Denmark	Dec. 30, 2020	Climate neutrality by 2050
Republic of Korea	Dec. 30, 2020	Carbon neutrality by 2050
Switzerland	Jan. 28, 2021	2050 net zero GHG
Guatemala	July 6, 2021	59% reduction of projected emissions by 2050
Indonesia	July 22, 2021	540 MtCO$_2$-eq by 2050, and with further exploring opportunity to rapidly progress towards net zero emission in 2060 or sooner
Slovenia	Aug. 23, 2021	Net zero emissions or climate neutrality by 2050

'rev.' = 'date revised'

4.2.4.2   Other National Emission Pathways to Mid-century

At the 2019 Climate Action Summit, 77 countries indicated their aim to reach net zero CO$_2$ emissions by 2050, more the number of countries having submitted LEDS to the UNFCCC. Table 4.6 lists the countries that have a national net zero by 2050 target in laws, strategies or other documents (The Energy and Climate Intelligence Unit 2019). Bhutan and Suriname already have achieved net negative emissions. France second 'low-carbon national strategy' adopted in 2020 has an objective of GHG neutrality by 2050. Net zero is also the basis of the recent revision of the official notional price of carbon for public investment in France (Quinet et al. 2019). The Committee on Climate Change of the UK analyses sectoral options and concludes that delivering net zero GHG by 2050 is technically feasible but highly challenging (Committee on Climate Change 2019). For Germany, three steps to climate neutrality by 2050 are introduced: first, a 65% reduction of emissions by 2030; second, a complete switch to climate-neutral technologies, leading to a 95% cut in emissions, all relative to 1990 levels by 2050; and third balancing of residual emissions through carbon capture and storage (Prognos et al. 2020). In addition to the countries in Table 4.6, EU reported the net zero GHG emission pathways by 2050 under Green Deal (European Commission 2019). China and South Korea, have made announcements of carbon neutrality before 2060 and net zero GHG emission by 2050, respectively (UN 2020a,b). In the case of Japan, the new target to net zero GHG emission by 2050 was announced in 2020 (UN 2020c). As of August 25, 2021, a total 121 countries participate in the 'Climate Ambition Alliance: Net Zero 2050', together with businesses, cities and regions.

Table 4.6 | Countries with a national net zero CO$_2$ or GHG target by 2050 (as of 25 August 2021).

Country	Target year	Target status	Source
Suriname		Achieved	Suriname INDC
Bhutan		Achieved	Royal Government of Bhutan National Environment Commission
Germany	2045	In Law	KSG
Sweden	2045	In Law	Climate Policy Framework
European Union	2050	In Law	European Climate Law
Japan	2050	In Law	Japan enshrines PM Suga's 2050 carbon neutrality promise into law
United Kingdom	2050	In Law	The Climate Change Act
France	2050	In Law	Energy and Climate Law
Canada	2050	In Law	Canadian Net Zero Emissions Accountability Act
Spain	2050	In Law	New Law
Denmark	2050	In Law	The Climate Act
New Zealand	2050	In Law	Zero Carbon Act
Hungary	2050	In Law	Climate Ambition Alliance: Net Zero 2050
Luxembourg	2050	In Law	Climate Ambition Alliance: Net Zero 2050
South Korea	2050	Proposed Legislation	Speeches and Statements by the President
Ireland	2050	Proposed Legislation	Climate Action and Low Carbon Development (Amendment) Bill 2021
Chile	2050	Proposed Legislation	Chile charts path to greener, fairer future
Fiji	2050	Proposed Legislation	Draft Climate Law

Note: In addition to the above list, the numbers of 'In Policy Document' and 'Target Under discussion' as Target status are 37 countries and 79 countries, respectively.

4.2.4.3 Mid-century Low Emission Strategies at the National Level in the Academic Literature

Since the 2000s, an increasing number of studies have quantified the emission pathways to mid-century by using national scale models. In the early stages, the national emission pathways were mainly assessed in the developed countries such as Germany, UK, France, the Netherlands, Japan, Canada, and USA. For example, the Enquete Commission in Germany identified robust and sustainable 80% emission reduction pathways (Deutscher Bundestag 2002). In Japan, 2050 Japan Low-Carbon Society scenario team (2008) assessed the 70% reduction scenarios in Japan, and summarised the necessary measures to 'Dozen Actions towards Low-Carbon Societies'.

Among developing countries, China, India, South Africa assessed their national emission pathways. For example, detailed analysis was undertaken to analyse pathways to China's goal for carbon neutrality (EFC 2020). In South Africa, a Scenario Building Team (2007) quantified the Long Term Mitigation Scenarios for South Africa.

Prior to COP21, most of the literature on mid-century mitigation pathways at the national level was dedicated to pathways compatible with a 2°C limit (see Box 4.2 for a discussion on the relationship between national mitigation pathways and global, long-term targets). After COP21 and the IPCC SR1.5, literature increasingly explored just transition to net zero emissions around 2050. This literature reflects on low-emissions development strategies (cognate with SDPS, Section 4.3.1) and policies to get to net zero CO_2 or GHG emissions (Garg and Waisman 2021) (Cross-Chapter Box 5 in this chapter).

Figure 4.2 provides a snapshot of this literature. For a selected set of countries, it shows the mid-century emission pathways at national scale that have been registered in the International Institute for Applied Systems Analysis (IIASA) national mitigation scenario database built for the purpose of this Report (Annex III.3.3). Overall, the database contains scenarios for 50 countries. Total GHG emission are the most comprehensive information to assess the pathways on climate mitigation actions, but energy-related CO_2 emissions are the most widely populated data in the scenarios. As a result, Figure 4.2 shows energy-related CO_2 emission trajectories. Scenarios for EU countries show reduction trends even in the reference scenario, whereas developing countries and non-European developed countries such as Japan and USA show emissions increase in the reference. In most countries plotted on Figure 4.2, studies have found that reaching net zero energy related CO_2 emissions by 2050 is feasible, although the number of such pathways is limited.

The literature underlines the differences induced by the shift from '2°C scenarios' (typically assumed to imply mitigation in 2050 around 80% relative to 1990) to '1.5°C scenarios' (typically assumed to imply net zero CO_2 or GHG emissions in 2050) (Box 4.2). For Japan, Oshiro et al. (2018) shows the difference between the implications of a 2°C scenario (80% reduction of CO_2 in 2050) and a 1.5°C scenario (net zero CO_2 emission in 2050), suggesting that for a net zero CO_2 emission scenario, BECCS is a key technology. Their sectoral analysis aims in 2050 at negative CO_2 emissions in the energy sector, and near-zero emissions in the buildings and transport sectors, requiring energy efficiency improvement and electrification. To do so, drastic mitigation is introduced immediately, and, as a result, the mitigation

Table 4.7 | Examples of research projects on country-level mitigation pathways in the near to medium-term under the multi-national analyses.

Project name	Features
DDPP (Deep Decarbonisation Pathways Project)	16 countries participated and estimated the deep decarbonisation pathways from the viewpoint of each country's perspective using their own models (Waisman et al. 2019).
COMMIT (Climate Policy assessment and Mitigation Modelling to Integrate national and global Transition pathways)	This research project assessed the country contributions to the target of the Paris Agreement (COMMIT 2019).
MAPS (Mitigation Action Plans and Scenarios)	The mitigation potential and socio-economic implications in Brazil, Chile, Colombia and Peru were assessed (Delgado et al. 2014; Zevallos et al. 2014; Benavides et al. 2015; La Rovere et al. 2018). The experiences of the MAPS programme suggests that co-production of knowledge by researchers and stakeholders strengthens the impact of research findings, and in depth studies of stakeholder engagement provide lessons (Boulle et al. 2015; Raubenheimer et al. 2015; Kane and Boulle 2018), which can assist building capacity for long-term planning in other contexts (Calfucoy et al. 2019).
CD-LINKS (Linking Climate and Development Policies – Leveraging International Networks and Knowledge Sharing)	The complex interplay between climate action and development at both the global scale and some national perspectives were explored. The climate policies for G20 countries up to 2015 and some levels of the carbon budget are assessed for short-term and long-term, respectively (Rogelj et al. 2017).
APEC Energy Demand and Supply Outlook	Total 21 APEC countries assessed a 2°C scenario scenario which follows the carbon emissions reduction pathway included in the IEA Energy Technology Perspectives (IEA 2017) by using the common framework (APERC 2019).
Low-Carbon Asia Research Project	The low-carbon emission scenarios for several countries and cities in Asia were assessed by using the same framework (Matsuoka et al. 2013). The mitigation activities were summarised into 10 actions toward Low Carbon Asia to show a guideline to plan and implement the strategies for an LCS in Asia (Low-Carbon Asia Research Project 2012).
CLIMACAP–LAMP	This is an inter-model comparison exercise that focused on energy and climate change mitigation in Latin America (Clarke et al. 2016).
DDPP-LAC (Latin American Deep Decarbonisation Pathways project)	Six countries in Latin America analysed the activities in agriculture, forestry and other land use (AFOLU) commonly (Bataille et al. 2020).
MILES (Modelling and Informing Low-Emission Strategies)	This is an international research project which covers five countries and one region in order to build capacity and knowledge on low-emissions development strategies both at a national and global level, by investigating the concrete implications of INDCs for the low-carbon transformation by and beyond 2030 (Spencer et al. 2015).

4

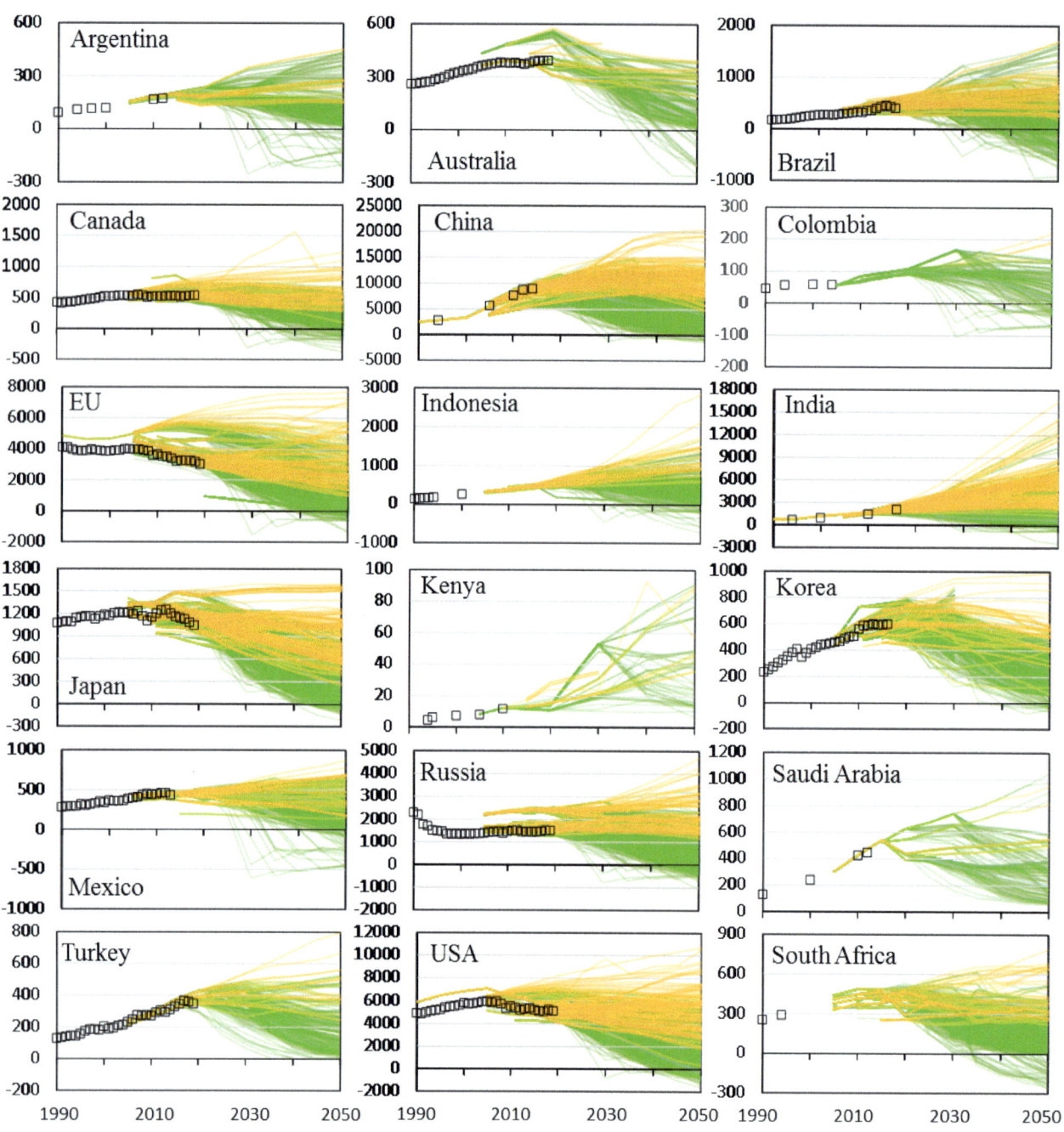

Note: Unit: MtCO₂

□: Historical emissions from Greenhouse Gas Inventory Data of UNFCCC

▬ Emissions of Baseline and current policy

▬ Emissions of mitigation scenarios including NDC

Figure 4.2 | Energy related CO₂ emission pathways to mid-century from existing studies. Source of the historical data: Greenhouse Gas Inventory Data of UNFCCC
(https://di.unfccc.int/detailed_data_by_party)

target of Japan's current NDC is considered not sufficient to achieve a 1.5°C scenario. Jiang et al. (2018) also show the possibility of net negative emissions in the power sector in China by 2050, indicating that biomass energy with carbon capture and storage (CCS) must be adopted on a large scale by 2040. Samadi et al. (2018) indicate the widespread use of electricity-derived synthetic fuels in end-use sectors as well as behavioural change for the 1.5°C scenario in Germany.

In addition to those analyses, Vishwanathan et al. (2018b), Chunark and Limmeechokchai (2018) and Pradhan et al. (2018b) build national scenarios in India, Thailand and Nepal, respectively, compatible with a global 1.5°C. Unlike the studies mentioned in the previous paragraph, they translate the 1.5°C goal by introducing in their model a carbon price trajectory estimated by global models as sufficient to achieve the 1.5°C target. Because of the high economic growth and

4

increase of GHG emissions in the reference case, CO_2 emissions in 2050 do not reach zero. Finally, the literature also underlines that to achieve a 1.5°C target, mitigation measures relative to non-CO_2 emissions become important, especially in developing countries where the share of non-CO_2 emissions is relatively high. (La Rovere et al. 2018) treat mitigation actions in AFOLU sector.

Chapter 3 reported on multi-model analyses, comparison of results using different models, of global emissions in the long term. At the national scale, multi-model analyses are still limited, though such analyses are growing as shown in Table 4.7. By comparing the results among different models and different scenarios in a country, the uncertainties on the emission pathways including the mitigation measures to achieve a given emission target can be assessed.

Another type of multi-model analysis is international, in other words, different countries join the same project and use their own national models to assess a pre-agreed joint mitigation scenario. By comparing the results of various national models, such projects help highlight specific features of each country. More robust mitigation measures can be proposed if different types of models participate. These activities can also contribute to capacity building in developing countries.

4.2.5   What Is to Be Done to Accelerate Mitigation?

4.2.5.1   Overview of Accelerated Mitigation Pathways

The literature reports an increasing number of accelerated mitigation pathways that are beyond NDCs in different regions and countries. There is increasing understanding of the technical content of such pathways, though the literature remains limited on some dimensions, such as demand-side options, systems analysis, or mitigation of AFOLU non-CO_2 GHGs. The present section describes insights from this literature.

Overall, the literature shows that pathways considered consistent with below 2°C (>67%) or 1.5°C (Box 4.2) – including inter alia 80% reduction of GHG emissions in 2050 relative to 1990 or 100% renewable electricity scenarios – are technically feasible (Lund and Mathiesen 2009; Mathiesen et al. 2011; Esteban and Portugal-Pereira 2014; Young and Brans 2017; Esteban et al. 2018; Child et al. 2019; Hansen et al. 2019). They entail increased end-use energy efficiency, significant increases in low-carbon energy, electrification, other new and transformative technologies in demand sectors, adoption of carbon capture and sequestration (CCS) to reduce gross emissions, and contribution to net negative emissions through carbon dioxide removal (CDR) and carbon sinks. For these pathways to be realised, the literature assumes higher carbon prices, combined in policy packages with a range of other policy measures.

The most recent literature also reflects on accelerated mitigation pathways aiming at reaching net zero CO_2 emissions or net zero GHG emissions by 2050 (Section 4.2.4 and Table 4.6; see Glossary entries on 'net zero CO_2 emissions' and 'net zero GHG emissions').

Specific policies, measures and technologies are needed to reach such targets. These include, broadly, decarbonising electricity supply, including through low-carbon energy, radically more efficient use of energy than today; electrification of end-uses (including transport/electric vehicles); dramatically lower use of fossil fuels than today; converting other uses to low- or zero-carbon fuels (e.g., hydrogen, bioenergy, ammonia) in hard-to-decarbonise sectors; and setting ambitious targets to reduce methane and other short-lived climate forcers (SLCFs).

Accelerated mitigation pathways differ by countries, depending inter alia on sources of emissions, mitigation opportunities and economic context. In China, India, Japan and other Southeast Asian countries, more aggressive action related to climate change is also motivated by regional concerns over health and air quality related to air pollutants and SLCFs (Ashina et al. 2012; Aggarwal 2017; Kuramochi et al. 2017; Xunzhang et al. 2017; Dhar et al. 2018; Jiang et al. 2018; Oshiro et al. 2018; China National Renewable Energy Centre 2019; Energy Transitions Commission and Rocky Mountain Institute 2019; Khanna et al. 2019). Studies of accelerated mitigation pathways in North America tend to focus on power sector and imported fuel decarbonisation in the US , and on electrification and demand-side reductions in Canada (Vaillancourt et al. 2017; Hodson et al. 2018; Victor et al. 2018; Bahn and Vaillancourt 2020; Hammond et al. 2020; Jayadev et al. 2020). In Latin America, many pathways emphasise supply-side mitigation measures, finding that replacing thermal power generation and developing bioenergy (where resources are available) utilisation offers the greatest mitigation opportunities (Herreras Martínez et al. 2015; Nogueira de Oliveira et al. 2016; Arango-Aramburo et al. 2019; Delgado et al. 2020; Lap et al. 2020). The European Union member states (EU-28) recently announced 2050 climate neutrality goal is explored by pathways that emphasise complete substitution of fossil fuels with electricity generated by low-carbon sources, particularly renewables; demand reductions through efficiency and conservation, and novel fuels and end-use technologies (Prognos et al. 2020). The limited literature so far on Africa's future pathways suggest those could be shaped by increasing energy access and mitigating the air pollution and health effects of relying on traditional biomass use, as well as cleaner expansion of power supply alongside end-use efficiency improvements (Hamilton and Kelly 2017; Oyewo et al. 2019, 2020; Ven et al. 2019; Wright et al. 2019; Forouli et al. 2020).

Though they differ across countries, accelerated mitigation pathways share common characteristics as follows. First, energy efficiency, conservation, and reducing energy use in all energy demand sectors (buildings, transport, and industry) are included in nearly all literature that addresses future demand growth (Ashina et al. 2012; Saveyn et al. 2012; Schmid and Knopf 2012; Chiodi et al. 2013; Deetman et al. 2013; Jiang et al. 2013; Thepkhun et al. 2013; Schiffer 2015; Altieri et al. 2016; Jiang et al. 2016; McNeil et al. 2016; Nogueira de Oliveira et al. 2016; Chilvers et al. 2017; Elizondo et al. 2017; Fragkos et al. 2017; Jacobson et al. 2017, 2019; Kuramochi et al. 2017; Oshiro et al. 2017a; Ouedraogo 2017; Shahiduzzaman and Layton 2017; Vaillancourt et al. 2017; Hanaoka and Masui 2018; Hodson et al. 2018; Lee et al. 2018; Lefèvre et al. Oshiro et al. 2018; Capros et al. 2019; Dioha et al. 2019; Duscha et al. 2019;

Khanna et al. 2019; Kato and Kurosawa 2019; Nieves et al. 2019; Sugiyama et al. 2019; Zhou et al. 2019; Dioha and Kumar 2020).

Similarly, electrification of industrial processes (up to 50% for EU and China) and transport (e.g., 30–60% for trucks in Canada), buildings, and district heating and cooling are commonplace (Ashina et al. 2012; Massetti 2012; Saveyn et al. 2012; Chiodi et al. 2013; Deetman et al. 2013; Fragkos et al. 2017; Oshiro et al. 2017b; Vaillancourt et al. 2017; Xunzhang et al. 2017; Jiang et al. 2018; Mittal et al. 2018; Oshiro et al. 2018; Capros et al. 2019; Zhou et al. 2019; Hammond et al. 2020).

Third, lower emissions sources of energy, such as nuclear, renewables, and some biofuels, are seen as necessary in all pathways. However, the extent of deployment depends on resource availability. Some countries have set targets of up to 100% renewable electricity, while others such as Brazil rely on increasing biomass up to 40–45% of total or industry energy consumption by 2050.

Fourth, CCS and CDR are part of many of the national studies reviewed (Ashina et al. 2012; Massetti 2012; Jiang et al. 2013; Thepkhun et al. 2013; Herreras Martínez et al. 2015; van der Zwaan et al. 2016; Chilvers et al. 2017; Solano Rodriguez et al. 2017; Xunzhang et al. 2017; Kuramochi et al. 2018; Mittal et al. 2018; Oshiro et al. 2018; Roberts et al. 2018b; Vishwanathan et al. 2018b; Kato and Kurosawa 2019). CCS helps reduce gross emissions but does not remove CO_2 from the atmosphere, unless combined with bioenergy (BECCS). CO_2 removal from sources with no identified mitigation measures is considered necessary to help achieve economy-wide net negative emissions (Massetti 2012; Deetman et al. 2013; Solano Rodriguez et al. 2017).

Each option is assessed in more detail in the following sections.

4.2.5.2 Accelerated Decarbonisation of Electricity Through Renewable Energy

Power generation could decarbonise much faster with scaled up deployment of renewable energy and storage. Both technologies are mature, available, and fast decreasing in costs, more than for many other mitigation options. Models continuously underestimate the speed at which renewables and storage expand. Higher penetration of renewable energy in the power sector is a common theme in scenarios. Some studies provide cost optimal electricity mix under emission constraints, while others explicitly explore a 100% renewables or 100% emission free electricity sector (Box 4.3).

Figure 4.3 shows an increasing share of renewable electricity in most countries historically, with further increases projected in many decarbonisation pathways. Targets for very high shares of renewable electricity generation – up to 100% – are shown for a number of countries, with the global share projected to range from 60% to 70% for 1.5°C with no overshoot (C0) to below 2°C (C4) scenarios. Countries and states that have set 100% renewables targets include Scotland for 2020 (Scottish Government 2021), Austria (2030), Denmark (2035) and California (2045) (Figure 4.3).

While 100% renewable electricity generation by 2050 is found to be feasible, it is not without issues. For example, (Jacobson et al. 2017, 2019) find it feasible for 143 countries with only a 9% average increase in economic costs (considering all social costs) if annual electricity demand can be reduced by 57%. Others state that challenges exist with speed of expansion, ensuring sufficient supply at all times or higher costs compared to other alternatives (Clack et al. 2017). In-depth discussion of net zero electricity systems can be found in Section 6.6.

Box 4.3 | Examples of High-renewable Accelerated Mitigation Pathways

Many accelerated mitigation pathways include high shares of renewable energy, with national variations. In Europe, some argue that the EU 2050 net zero GHG emissions goal can be met with 100% renewable power generation, including use of renewable electricity to produce hydrogen, biofuels (including imports), and synthetic hydrocarbons, but will require significant increases in transmission capacity (Duscha et al. 2019; Zappa et al. 2019). Capros et al. (2019) explore a 1.5°C compatible pathway that includes 85% renewable generation, with battery, pumped hydro, and chemical storage for variable renewables. High-renewable scenarios also exist for individual Member States. In France, for example, Krakowski et al. (2016) propose a 100% renewable power generation scenario that relies primarily on wind (62%), solar PV (26%) and oceans (12%). To reach this aim, integration into the European grid is of vital importance (Brown et al. 2018). While debated, incremental costs could be limited regardless of specific assumptions of future costs of individual technologies (Shirizadeh et al. 2020). In Germany, similarly, 100% renewable electricity systems are found feasible by numerous studies (Oei et al. 2020; Thomas Klaus et al. 2010; Wuppertal-Institut 2021; Hansen et al. 2019).

In South Africa, it is found that long-term mitigation goals could be achieved with accelerated adoption of solar PV and wind generation, if the electricity sector decarbonises by phasing-out coal entirely by 2050, even if CCS is not feasible before 2025 (Altieri et al. 2015; Beck et al. 2013). Abundant solar PV and wind potential, coupled with land availability suggest that more than 75% of power generation could ultimately originate from solar PV and wind (Oyewo et al. 2019; Wright et al. 2019).

For the US, share of renewables in power generation in 2050 in accelerated mitigation scenarios vary widely, 40% in (Hodson et al. 2018; Jayadev et al. 2020), more than half renewable and nuclear in (Victor et al. 2018) to 100% in Jacobson et al. (2017, 2019).

4

Box 4.3 (continued)

Under cost optimisation scenarios for Brazil, electricity generation, which is currently dominated by hydropower, could reach 100% by adding biomass (Köberle et al. 2020). Other studies find that renewable energy, including biomass, could account for more than 30% of total electricity generation (Nogueira de Oliveira et al. 2016; Portugal-Pereira et al. 2016).

In Colombia, where hydropower resources are abundant and potential also exist for solar and wind, a deep decarbonisation pathway would require 57% renewable power generation by 2050 (Arango-Aramburo et al. 2019) while others find 80% would be possible (Delgado et al. 2020).

In Asia, Japan could have up to 50% variable renewable electricity supply to reduce CO_2 emissions by 80% by 2050 in some of its deep mitigation scenarios (Kato and Kurosawa 2019; Sugiyama et al. 2019; Ju et al. 2021; Shiraki et al. 2021; Silva Herran and Fujimori 2021). One view of China's 1.5°C pathway includes 59% renewable power generation by 2050 (Jiang et al. 2018). One view of India's 1.5°C pathway also includes 52% renewable power generation, and would require storage needs for 35% of generation (Parikh et al. 2018).

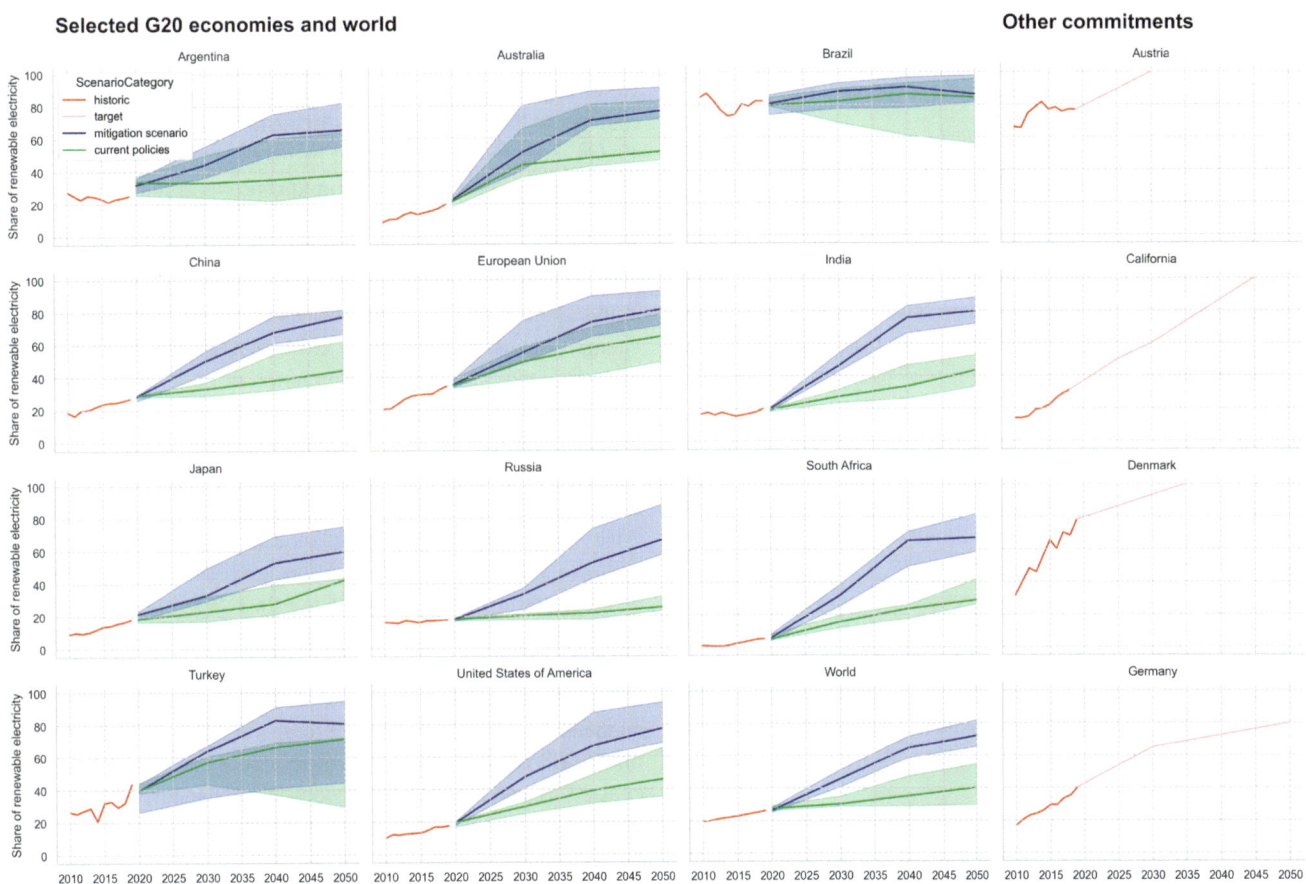

Figure 4.3 | Historical and projected levels and targets for the share of renewables in electricity generation. Sources: IEA energy balances for past trends, IPCC AR6 scenario dataset including national model and regional versions in global models (10th to 90th percentile of 1.5°C with no overshoot (C0) to below 2°C (C4) scenarios), national/regional sources.

4.2.5.3 Bioenergy Plays Significant Role in Resource Abundant Countries in Latin America and Parts of Europe

Bioenergy could account for up to 40% of Brazil's total final energy consumption, and a 60% share of fuel for light-duty vehicles by 2030 (Lefèvre et al. 2018), and is considered most cost-effective in transport and industrial applications (Lap et al. 2020). BECCS in the power sector is also considered cost-effective option for supply-side mitigation (Borba et al. 2012; Herreras Martínez et al. 2015; Lucena et al. 2016).

Bioenergy also plays a prominent role in some EU countries' deep decarbonisation strategies. Domestic biomass alone can help Germany meet its 95% CO_2 reduction by 2050 goal, and biomass and CCS together are needed to reduce CO_2 by 80% by 2050 in the Netherlands (Mikova et al. 2019). Studies suggest that mitigation efforts in France include biofuels and significant increases in biomass use, including up to 45% of industry energy by 2050 for its net GHG neutrality goal (Doumax-Tagliavini and Sarasa 2018; Capros et al. 2019). Increased imports may be needed to meet significant increases in EU's bioenergy use, which could affect energy security and the sustainability of bioenergy production outside of the EU (Mandley et al. 2020; Daioglou et al. 2020).

While BECCS is needed in multiple accelerated mitigation pathways, large-scale land-based biological CDR may not prove as effective as expected, and its large-scale deployment may result in ecological and social impacts, suggesting it may not be a viable carbon removal strategy in the next 10–20 years (Vaughan and Gough 2016; Boysen et al. 2017; Dooley and Kartha 2018). The effectiveness of BECCS could depend on local contexts, choice of biomass, fate of initial aboveground biomass and fossil-fuel emissions offsets – carbon removed through BECCS could be offset by losses due to land-use change (Harper et al. 2018; Butnar et al. 2020; Calvin et al. 2021). Large-scale BECCS may push planetary boundaries for freshwater use, exacerbate land-system change, significantly alter biosphere integrity and biogeochemical flows (Heck et al. 2018; Fuhrman et al. 2020; Stenzel et al. 2021; Ai et al. 2021). (Sections 7.4 and 12.5)

4.2.5.4 CCS May Be Needed to Mitigate Emissions From the Remaining Fossil Fuels That Cannot Be Decarbonised, but the Economic Feasibility of Deployment Is Not Yet Clear

CCS is present in many accelerated mitigation scenarios in the literature. In Brazil, (Nogueira de Oliveira et al. 2016) consider BECCS and CCS in hydrogen generation more feasible than CCS in thermal power plants, with costs ranging from USD70–100 per tCO_2. Overall, (van der Zwaan et al. 2016) estimate that 33–50% of total electricity generation in Latin America could be ultimately covered by CCS. In Japan, CCS and increased bioenergy adoption plus waste-to-energy and hydrogen-reforming from fossil fuel are all considered necessary in the power sector in existing studies, with potential up to 200 $MtCO_2$ yr^{-1} (Ashina et al. 2012; Oshiro et al. 2017a; Kato and Kurosawa 2019; Sugiyama et al. 2021). In parts of the EU, after 2030, CCS could become profitable with rising CO_2 prices (Schiffer 2015). CDR is seen as necessary in some net GHG neutrality

pathways (Capros et al. 2019) but evidence on cost-effectiveness is scarce and uncertain (European Commission 2013). For France and Sweden, (Millot et al. 2020) include CCS and BECCS to meet net zero GHG emissions by 2050. For Italy, (Massetti 2012) propose a zero-emission electricity scenario with a combination of renewable and coal, natural gas, and BECCS.

In China, an analysis concluded that CCS is necessary for remaining coal and natural gas generation out to 2050 (Jiang et al. 2018; Energy Transitions Commission and Rocky Mountain Institute 2019). Seven to 10 CCS projects with installed capacity of 15 GW by 2020 and total CCS investment of 105 billion RMB (2010 RMB) are projected to be needed by 2050 under a 2°C compatible pathway according to (Jiang et al. 2013, 2016; Lee et al. 2018). Under 1.5°C pathway, an analysis found China would need full CCS coverage of the remaining 12% of power generation from coal and gas power and 250 GW of BECCS (Jiang et al. 2018). Combined with expanded renewable and nuclear development, total estimated investment in this study is 5% of China's total GDP in 2020, 1.3% in 2030, and 0.6% in 2050 (Jiang et al. 2016).

Views regarding feasibility of CCS can vary greatly for the same country. In the case of India's electricity sector for instance, some studies indicate that CCS would be necessary (Vishwanathan et al. 2018a), while others do not – citing concerns around its feasibility due to limited potential sites and issues related to socio-political acceptance – and rather point to very ambitious increase in renewable energy, which in turn could pose significant challenges in systematically integrating renewable energy into the current energy systems (Viebahn et al. 2014; Mathur and Shekhar 2020). Some limitations of CCS, including uncertain costs, lifecycle and net emissions, other biophysical resource needs, and social acceptance are acknowledged in existing studies (Viebahn et al. 2014; Jacobson 2019; Mathur and Shekhar 2020; Sekera and Lichtenberger 2020).

While national mitigation portfolios aiming at net zero emissions or lower will need to include some level of CDR, the choice of methods and the scale and timing of their deployment will depend on the ambition for gross emission reductions, how sustainability and feasibility constraints are managed, and how political preferences and social acceptability evolve (Cross-Chapter Box 8). Furthermore, mitigation deterrence may create further uncertainty, as anticipated future CDR could dilute incentives to reduce emissions now (Grant et al. 2021), and the political economy of net negative emissions has implications for equity (Mohan et al. 2021).

4.2.5.5 Nuclear Power Is Considered Strategic for Some Countries, While Others Plan to Reach Their Mitigation Targets Without Additional Nuclear Power

Nuclear power generation is developed in many countries, though larger-scale national nuclear generation does not tend to associate with significantly lower carbon emissions (Sovacool et al. 2020). Unlike other energy sources such as wind and PV solar, levelised costs of nuclear power has been rising in the last decades (Grubler 2010; Gilbert et al. 2017; Portugal-Pereira et al. 2018). This is mainly due to overrun of overnight construction costs related to delays in project approvals and construction, and more stringent passive safety measures, which increases the complexity of systems. After the Fukushima Daiichi accident in Japan, nuclear programs in several countries have been phased out or cancelled (Carrara 2020; Huenteler et al. 2012; Kharecha and Sato 2019; Hoffman and Durlak 2018). Also the compatibility of conventional prresurised water reactors and boiling water reactors with large proportion of renewable energy in the grid it is yet to be fully understood.

Accelerated mitigation scenarios offer contrasting views on the share of nuclear in power generation. In the USA, (Victor et al. 2018) build a scenario in which nuclear contributes 23% of CO_2 emission reductions needed to reduce GHG emissions by 80% from 2005 levels by 2050. Deep power sector decarbonisation pathways could require a two-folded increase in nuclear capacity according to (Jayadev et al. 2020) for the USA, and nearly a ten-fold increase for Canada, but may be difficult to implement (Vaillancourt et al. 2017). For China to meet a 1.5°C pathway or achieve carbon neutrality by 2050, nuclear may represent 14–28% of power generation in 2050 according to (Jiang et al. 2018; China National Renewable Energy Centre 2019; Energy Transitions Commission and Rocky Mountain Institute 2019). For South Korea, Hong et al. (2014) and Hong and Brook (2018) find that increasing nuclear power can help complement renewables in decarbonising the grid. Similarly, India has put in place a three-stage nuclear programme which aims to enhance nuclear power capacity from the current level of 6 GW to 63 GW by 2032, if fuel supply is ensured (GoI 2015). Nuclear energy is also considered necessary as part of accelerated mitigation pathways in Brazil, although it is not expected to increase significantly by 2050 even under stringent low-carbon scenarios (Lucena et al. 2016). France developed its nuclear strategy in response to energy security concerns after the 1970s oil crisis, but has committed to reducing nuclear's share of power generation to 50% by 2035 (Millot et al. 2020). Conversely, some analysis find deep mitigation pathways, including net zero GHG emissions and 80–90% reduction from 2013 levels, feasible without additional nuclear power in EU-28 and Japan respectively, but assuming a combination of bio- and novel fuels and CCS or land-use based carbon sinks (Kato and Kurosawa 2019; Duscha et al. 2019).

Radically more efficient use of energy than today, including electricity, is a complementary set of measures, explored in the following.

4.2.5.6   Efficient Cooling, SLCFs and Co-benefits

In warmer climate regions undergoing economic transitions, improving the energy efficiency of cooling and refrigeration equipment is often important for managing peak electricity demand and can have co-benefits for climate mitigation as well as SLCF reduction, as expected in India, Africa, and Southeast Asia in the future.

Air conditioner adoption is rising significantly in low- and middle-income countries as incomes rise and average temperatures increase, including in Southeast Asian countries such as Thailand, Indonesia, Vietnam, and the Philippines, as well as Brazil, Pakistan, Bangladesh, and Nigeria (Biardeau et al. 2020). Cooling appliances are expected to increase from 3.6 billion to 9.5 billion by 2050, though up to 14 billion could be required to provide adequate cooling for all

(Birmingham Energy Institute 2018). Current technology pathways are not sufficient to deliver universal access to cooling or meet the 2030 targets under the SDGs, but energy efficiency, including in equipment efficiency like air conditioners, can reduce this demand and help limit additional emissions that would further exacerbate climate change (Biardeau et al. 2020; Dreyfus et al. 2020; UNEP and IEA 2020). Some countries (India, South Africa) have started to recognise the need for more efficient equipment in their mitigation strategies (Altieri et al. 2016; Ouedraogo 2017; Paladugula et al. 2018).

One possible synergy between SLCF and climate change mitigation is the simultaneous improvement in energy efficiency in refrigeration and air-conditioning equipment during the hydrofluorocarbon (HFC) phase-down, as recognised in the Kigali Amendment to the Montreal Protocol. The Kigali Amendment and related national and regional regulations are projected to reduce future radiative forcing from HFCs by about half in 2050 compared to a scenario without any HFC controls, and to reduce future global average warming in 2100 from a baseline of 0.3°C–0.5°C to less than 0.1°C, according to a recent scientific assessment of a wide literature (World Meteorological Organization 2018). If ratified by signatories, the rapid phase-down of HFCs under the Kigali Amendment is possible because of extensive replacement of high-global warming potential (GWP) HFCs with commercially available low-GWP alternatives in refrigeration and air-conditioning equipment. Each country's choices of alternative refrigerants will likely be determined by energy efficiency, costs, and refrigerant toxicity and flammability. National and regional regulations will be needed to drive technological innovation and development (Polonara et al. 2017).

4.2.5.7   Efficient Buildings, Cooler in Summer, Warmer in Winter, Towards Net Zero Energy

Most accelerated mitigation pathway scenarios include significant increase in building energy efficiency. Countries in cold regions, in particular, often focus more on building sector GHG emissions mitigation measures such as improving building envelopes and home appliances, and electrifying space heating and water heating.

For example, scenarios for Japan project continued electrification of residential and commercial buildings to 65% and 79% respectively by 2050 to reach 70–90% CO_2 reduction from 2013 levels (Kato and Kurosawa 2019). Similarly, a mitigation pathway for China compatible with 1.5°C would require 58% to 70% electrification of buildings according to (Jiang et al. 2018; China National Renewable Energy Centre 2019E; nergy Transitions Commission and Rocky Mountain Institute 2019). For the EU-28 to reach net carbon neutrality, complete substitution of fossil fuels with electricity (up to 65% share), district heating, and direct use of solar and ambient heat are projected to be needed for buildings, along with increased use of solar thermal and heat pumps for heating (Duscha et al. 2019). In the UK and Canada, improved insulation to reduce energy demand and efficient building appliances and heating systems are important building strategies needed to reduce emissions to zero by 2050 (Vaillancourt et al. 2017; Chilvers et al. 2017; Roberts et al. 2018a). In Ireland, achieving 80–95% emissions reduction below 1990 levels by 2050 also requires changes in building energy

Table 4.8 | Targets by countries, regions, cities and businesses on decarbonising the building sector.

	Countries	Sub-national Regions	Cities	Businesses
Shift to 100% (near-)zero energy buildings for new buildings	3	6	>28	>44
Fully decarbonise the building sector	1	6	>28	>44
Phase out fossil fuels (for example, gas) for residential heating	1	–	>3	
Increase the rate of zero-energy renovations	1 (public buildings)			

Source: Höhne et al. (2020), supplementary information. https://newclimate.org/ambitiousactions.

technology and efficiency, including improving building envelopes, fuel switching for residential buildings, and replacing service-sector coal use with gas and renewables according to (Chiodi et al. 2013). In South Africa, improving industry and building energy efficiency is also considered a key part of mitigation strategies (Altieri et al. 2016; Ouedraogo 2017).

In addition, an increasing number of countries have set up net zero energy building targets (Table 4.8) (Höhne et al. 2020). Twenty-seven countries have developed roadmap documents for NZEBs, mostly in developed countries in Europe, North America, and Asia-Pacific, focusing on energy efficiency and improved insulation and design, renewable and smart technologies (Mata et al. 2020). The EU, Japan and the USA (the latter for public buildings only) have set targets for shifting new buildings to 100% near-zero energy buildings by 2030, with earlier targets for public buildings. Scotland has a similar target for 2050 (Höhne et al. 2020). Technologies identified as needed for achieving near-zero energy buildings vary by region, but include energy-efficient envelope components, natural ventilation, passive cooling and heating, high performance building systems, air heat recovery, smart and information and communication technologies, and changing future heating and cooling supply fuel mixes towards solar, geothermal, and biomass (Mata et al. 2020). Sub-national regions in Spain, USA, Germany, and Mexico have set local commitments to achieving net zero carbon new buildings by 2050, with California having the most ambitious aspirational target of zero net energy buildings for all new buildings by 2030 (Höhne et al. 2020). The EU is also targeting the retrofitting of 3% of existing public buildings to zero-energy, with emphasis on greater thermal insulation of building envelopes (Höhne et al. 2020; Mata et al. 2020). China's roadmaps have emphasised insulation of building envelope, heat recovery systems in combination with renewable energy, including solar, shallow geothermal, and air source heat pumps (Mata et al. 2020).

4.2.5.8   Electrifying Transport

Electrification of transport in tandem with power sector decarbonisation is expected to be a key strategy for deep CO_2 mitigation in many countries. Passenger transport and light duty freight can already be electrified, but electrifying heavy-duty road transport and fuel switching in aviation and shipping are much more difficult and have not been addressed in most of the recent research.

In Germany, widespread electrification of private vehicles is expected by 2030 (Schmid and Knopf 2012) while for the EU-28, 50% overall transport electrification (excluding feedstock) and 75% electrification of road transport is needed to reach net carbon neutrality according to (Duscha et al. 2019). In addition, novel fuels such as hydrogen, synthetic hydrocarbons and sustainable biogenic fuels are needed to decarbonise aviation and water transport to achieve net carbon neutrality (Duscha et al. 2019).

In India, electrification, hydrogen, and biofuels are key to decarbonising the transport sector (Dhar et al. 2018; Mittal et al. 2018; Vishwanathan et al. 2018b; Mathur and Shekhar 2020). Under a 1.5°C scenario, nearly half of the light-duty passenger vehicle stock needs to be electrified according to (Parikh et al. 2018). In China, a 1.5°C-compatible pathway would require electrification of two-fifths of transport (Jiang et al. 2018; China National Renewable Energy Centre 2019).

Similarly, in Canada, electrification of 59% of light-duty trucks and 23% of heavy-duty trucks are needed as part of overall strategy to reduce CO_2 emissions by 80% by 2050. In addition, hydrogen is expected to play a major role by accounting for nearly one-third of light-duty trucks, 68% of heavy-duty trucks, and 33% of rail by 2050 according to Hammond et al. (2020).

4.2.5.9   Urban Form Meets Information Technology

Beyond technological measures, some densely populated countries including Germany, Japan, and India are exploring using information technology/internet of things (IOT) to support mode-shifting and reduce mobility demand through broader behaviour and lifestyle changes (Ashina et al. 2012; Canzler and Wittowsky 2016; Aggarwal 2017; Dhar et al. 2018; Vishwanathan et al. 2018b). In Japan, accelerated mitigation pathways consider the use of information technology and internet of things (IoT) to transform human behaviour and transition to a sharing economy (Ashina et al. 2012; Oshiro et al. 2017a, 2018). In Germany, one study points to including electromobility information and communication technologies in the transport sector as key (Canzler and Wittowsky 2016) while another emphasise shifting from road to rail transport, and reduced distances travelled as other possible transport strategies (Schmid and Knopf 2012). India's transport sector strategies also include use of information technology and the internet, a transition to a sharing economy, and increasing infrastructure investment (Dhar et al. 2018; Vishwanathan et al. 2018b). Behaviour and lifestyle change along with stakeholder integration in decision-making are considered key to implementing new transport policies (Aggarwal 2017; Dhar et al. 2018).

4.2.5.10   Industrial Energy Efficiency

Industrial energy efficiency improvements are considered in nearly all countries but for countries where industry is expected to continue to be a key sector, new and emerging technologies that require significant R&D investment, such as hydrogen and CCS, make ambitious targets achievable.

In China, for example, non-conventional electrical and renewable technologies, including low-grade renewable heat, biomass use for high-temperature heat in steel and cement sectors, and additional electrification in glass, food and beverage, and paper and pulp industries, are part of scenarios that achieve 60% reduction in national CO_2 emission by 2050 (Khanna et al. 2019; Zhou et al. 2019), in addition to increased recycled steel for electric arc furnaces and direct electrolysis or hydrogen-based direct reduction of iron and CCS utilisation in clinker and steel-making (Jiang et al. 2018; China National Renewable Energy Centre 2019). Similarly, in India, (Vishwanathan and Garg 2020) point to the need for renewable energy and CCS to decarbonise the industrial sector. In EU-28, net CO_2 neutrality can only be reached with 92% reduction in industrial emissions relative to 1990, through electrification, efficiency improvement and new technologies such as hydrogen-based direct reduction of steel, low-carbon cement and recycling (Duscha et al. 2019). Both China and EU see 50% of industry electrification by 2050 as needed to meet 1.5°C and net carbon neutrality pathways (Jiang et al. 2018; Capros et al. 2019).

Aggressive adoption of technology solutions for power sector decarbonisation coupled with end-use efficiency improvements and low-carbon electrification of buildings, industry and transport provides a pathway for accelerated mitigation in many key countries, but will still be insufficient to meet zero emission/1.5°C goals for all countries. Although not included in a majority of the studies related to pathways and national modelling analysis, energy demand reduction through deeper efficiency and other measures such as lifestyle changes and system solutions that go beyond components, as well as the co-benefits of the reduction of short-lived pollutants, needs to be evaluated for inclusion in future zero emission/1.5°C pathways.

4.2.5.11   Lowering Demand, Downscaling Economies

Studies have identified socio-technological pathways to help achieve net zero CO_2 and GHG targets at national scale, that in aggregate are crucial to keeping global temperature below agreed limits. However, most of the literature focuses on supply-side options, including carbon dioxide removal mechanisms (BECCS, afforestation, and others) that are not fully commercialised (Cross-Chapter Box 8 in Chapter 12). Costs to research, deploy, and scale up these technologies are often high. Recent studies have addressed lowering demand through energy conversion efficiency improvements, but few studies have considered demand reduction through efficiency (Grubler et al. 2018) and the related supply implications and mitigation measures.

Five main drivers of long-term energy demand reduction that can meet the 1.5°C target include quality of life, urbanisation, novel energy services, diversification of end-user roles, and information innovation (Grubler et al. 2018). A Low Energy Demand scenario requires fundamental societal and institutional transformation from current patterns of consumption, including: decentralised services and increased granularity (small-scale, low-cost technologies to provide decentralised services), increased use value from services (multi-use vs single use), sharing economies, digitalisation, and rapid transformation driven by end-user demand. This approach to transformation differs from the status quo and current climate change policies in emphasising energy end-use and services first, with downstream effects driving intermediate and upstream structural change.

Radical low-carbon innovation involves systemic, cultural, and policy changes and acceptance of uncertainty in the beginning stages. However, the current dominant analytical perspectives are grounded in neoclassical economics and social psychology, and focus primarily on marginal changes rather than radical transformations (Geels et al. 2018). Some literature is beginning to focus on mitigation through behaviour and lifestyle changes, but specific policy measures for supporting such changes and their contribution to emission reductions remain unclear (Section 4.4.2 and Chapter 5).

4.2.5.12   Ambitious Targets to Reduce Short-lived Climate Forcers, Including Methane

Recent research shows that temperature increases are likely to exceed 1.5°C during the 2030s and 2°C by mid-century unless both CO_2 and short-lived climate forcers (SLCFs) are reduced (Shindell et al. 2017; Rogelj et al. 2018a). Because of their short lifetimes (days to a decade and a half), SLCFs can provide fast mitigation, potentially avoiding warming of up to 0.6°C at 2050 and up to 1.2°C at 2100 (Ramanathan and Xu 2010; Xu and Ramanathan 2017). In Asia especially, co-benefits of drastic CO_2 and air pollution mitigation measures reduce emissions of methane, black carbon, sulphur dioxide, nitrogen oxide, and fine particulate matter by approximately 23%, 63%, 73%, 27%, and 65% respectively in 2050 as compared to 2010 levels. Including the co-benefits of reduction of climate forcing adds significantly to the benefits reducing air pollutants (Hanaoka and Masui 2018).

To achieve net zero GHG emissions implies consideration of targets for non-CO_2 gases. While methane emissions have grown less rapidly than CO_2 and F-gases since 1990 (Chapter 2), the literature urges action to bring methane back to a pathway more in line with the Paris goals (Nisbet et al. 2020). Measures to reduce methane emissions from anthropogenic sources are considered intractable – where they sustain livelihoods – but also becoming more feasible, as studies report the options for mitigation in agriculture without undermining food security (Wollenberg et al. 2016; Frank et al. 2017; Nisbet et al. 2020). The choice of emission metrics has implications for SLCF (Cain et al. 2019) (Cross-Chapter Box 2 in Chapter 2). Ambitious reductions of methane are complementary to, rather than substitutes for, reductions in CO_2 (Nisbet et al. 2020).

Rapid SLCF reductions, specifically of methane, black carbon, and tropospheric ozone have immediate co-benefits including meeting sustainable development goals for reducing health burdens of household air pollution and reversing health- and crop-damaging tropospheric ozone (Jacobson 2002, 2010). SLCF mitigation measures can have regional impacts, including avoiding premature deaths in Asia and Africa and warming in central and northern Asia, southern Africa, and the Mediterranean (Shindell et al. 2012). Reducing outdoor air pollution could avoid 2.4 million premature deaths and 52 million tonnes of crop losses for four major staples (Haines et al. 2017). Existing research emphasises climate and agriculture benefits of methane mitigation measures with relatively small human health benefits (Shindell et al. 2012). Research also predicts that black carbon mitigation could substantially benefit global climate and human health, but there is more uncertainty about these outcomes than about some other predictions (Shindell et al. 2012). Other benefits to SLCF reduction include reducing warming in the critical near term, which will slow amplifying feedbacks, reduce the risk of non-linear changes, and reduce long-term cumulative climate impacts – like sea-level rise – and mitigation costs (Hu et al. 2017; UNEP and WMO 2011; Rogelj et al. 2018a; Xu and Ramanathan 2017; Shindell et al. 2012).

4.2.5.13 System Analysis Solutions Are Only Beginning to Be Recognised in Current Literature on Accelerated Mitigation Pathways, and Rarely Included in Existing National Policies or Strategies

Most models and studies fail to address system impacts of widespread new technology deployment, for example: (i) material and resources needed for hydrogen production or additional emissions and energy required to transport hydrogen; or (ii) materials, resources, grid integration, and generation capacity expansion limits of a largely decarbonised power sector and electrified transport sector. These impacts could limit regional and national scale-ups.

Systemic solutions are also not being sufficiently discussed, such as low-carbon materials; light-weighting of buildings, transport, and industrial equipment; promoting circular economy, recyclability and reusability, and addressing the food-energy-water nexus. These solutions reduce demand in multiple sectors, improve overall supply chain efficiency, and require cross-sector policies. Using fewer building materials could reduce the need for cement, steel, and other materials and thus the need for production and freight transport. Concrete can also be produced from low-carbon cement, or designed to absorb CO_2 from the atmosphere. Few regions have developed comprehensive policies or strategies for a circular economy, with the exception of the EU and China, and policies in the EU have only emerged within the last decade. While China's circular economy policies emphasises industrial production, water, pollution and scaling-up in response to rapid economic growth and industrialisation, EU's strategy is focused more narrowly on waste and resources and overall resource efficiency to increase economic competitiveness (McDowall et al. 2017).

Increased bioenergy consumption is considered in many 1.5°C and 2°C scenarios. System thinking is needed to evaluate bioenergy's viability because increased demand could affect land and water availability, food prices, and trade (Sharmina et al. 2016). To adequately address the water-energy-food nexus, policies and models must consider interconnections, synergies, and trade-offs among and within sectors, which is currently not the norm (Section 12.4).

A systems approach is also needed to support technological innovation. This includes recognising unintended consequences of political support mechanisms for technology adoption and restructuring current incentives to realise multi-sector benefits. It also entails assimilating knowledge from multiple sources as a basis for policy and decision-making (Hoolohan et al. 2019).

Current literature does not explicitly consider systematic, physical drivers of inertia, such as capital and infrastructure needed to support accelerated mitigation (Pfeiffer et al. 2018). This makes it difficult to understand what is needed to successfully shift from current limited mitigation actions to significant transformations needed to rapidly achieve deep mitigation.

4.2.6 Implications of Accelerated Mitigation for National Development Objectives

4.2.6.1 Introduction

This section examines how accelerated mitigation may impact the realisation of development objectives in the near- and mid-term. It focuses on three objectives discussed in the literature, sustaining economic growth (Section 4.2.6.2), providing employment (Section 4.2.6.3), and alleviating poverty and ensuring equity (Section 4.2.6.4). It complements similar review performed at global level in Section 3.6. For a comprehensive survey of research on the impact of mitigation in other areas (including air quality, health, and biodiversity), see Karlsson et al. (2020).

4.2.6.2 Mitigation and Economic Growth in the Near- and Mid-term

A significant part of the literature assesses the impacts of mitigation on GDP, consistent with policymakers' interest in this variable. It must be noted upfront that computable equilibrium models, on which our assessments are mostly based, capture the impact of mitigation on GDP and other core economic variables while typically overlooking other effects that may matter (like improvements in air quality). Second, even though GDP (or better, GDP per capita) is not an indicator of welfare (Fleurbaey and Blanchet 2013), changes in GDP per capita across countries and over time are highly correlated with changes in welfare indicators in the areas of poverty, health, and education (Gable et al. 2015). The mechanisms linking mitigation to GDP outlined below would remain valid even with alternative indicators of well-being (Section 5.2.1). Third, another stream of literature criticises the pursuit of economic growth as a goal, instead advocating a range of alternatives and suggesting modelling of post-growth approaches to achieve rapid mitigation while improving social outcomes (Hickel et al. 2021). In the language of the present chapter, these alternatives constitute alternative development pathways.

Most country-level mitigation modelling studies in which GDP is an endogenous variable report negative impacts of mitigation on GDP

Figure 4.4 | GDP against emissions in country-level modelling studies, in variations relative to reference.

in 2030 and 2050, relative to the reference (*robust evidence*, *high agreement*), for example (Nong et al. 2017) for Australia, (Chen et al. 2013) for Brazil, (Dai et al. 2016; Li et al. 2017; Dong et al. 2018; Mu et al. 2018a; Zhao et al. 2018; Cui et al. 2019) for China, (Álvarez-Espinosa et al. 2018) for Colombia, (Fragkos et al. 2017) for the EU, (Mittal et al. 2018) for India, (Fujimori et al. 2019) for Japan, (Veysey et al. 2014) for Mexico, (Pereira et al. 2016) for Portugal, (Alton et al. 2014; van Heerden et al. 2016) for South Africa, (Chunark et al. 2017) for Thailand, (Acar and Yeldan 2016) for Turkey, (Roberts et al. 2018b) for the UK, (Zhang et al. 2017; Chen and Hafstead 2019) for USA, (Nong 2018) for Vietnam (Figure 4.4). The downward relationship between mitigation effort and emissions is strong in studies up to

2030, much weaker for studies looking farther ahead. In all reviewed studies, however, GDP continues to grow even with mitigation. It may be noted that none of the studies assessed above integrates the benefits of mitigation in terms of reduced impacts of climate change or lower adaptation costs. This is not surprising since these studies are at national or regional scale and do not extend beyond 2050, whereas the benefits depend on global emissions and primarily occur after 2050. Discussion on reduced impacts is provided in Section 3.6.2 and Cross-Working Group Box 1 in Chapter 3.

Two major mechanisms interplay to explain the impact of mitigation on GDP. First, the carbon constraint imposes reduced

Table 4.9 | Examples of country-level modelling studies finding positive short-term outcome of mitigation on GDP relative to baseline.

Reference	Country/region	Explanation for positive outcome of mitigation on GDP
Antimiani et al. (2016)	European Union	GDP increases relative to reference only in the scenario with global cooperation on mitigation.
Willenbockel et al. (2017)	Kenya	The mitigation scenario introduces cheaper (geothermal) power generation units than in BAU (in which thermal increases). Electricity prices actually decrease.
Siagian et al. (2017)	Indonesia	Coal sector with low productivity is forced into BAU. Mitigation redirects investment towards sectors with higher productivity.
Blazquez et al. (2017)	Saudi Arabia	Renewable energy penetration assumed to free oil that would have been sold at publicly subsidised price on the domestic market to be sold internationally at market price.
Wei et al. (2019)	China	Analyse impacts of feed-in tariffs to renewables, find positive short-run impacts on GDP; public spending boost activity in the RE sector. New capital being built at faster rate than in reference increases activity more than activity decreases due to lower public spending elsewhere.
Gupta et al. (2019)	India	Savings adjust to investment and fixed unemployment is considered target of public policy, thereby limiting impact of mitigation on GDP relative to other economic variables (consumption, terms of trade).
Huang et al. (2019)	China	Power generation plan in the baseline is assumed not cost minimising.

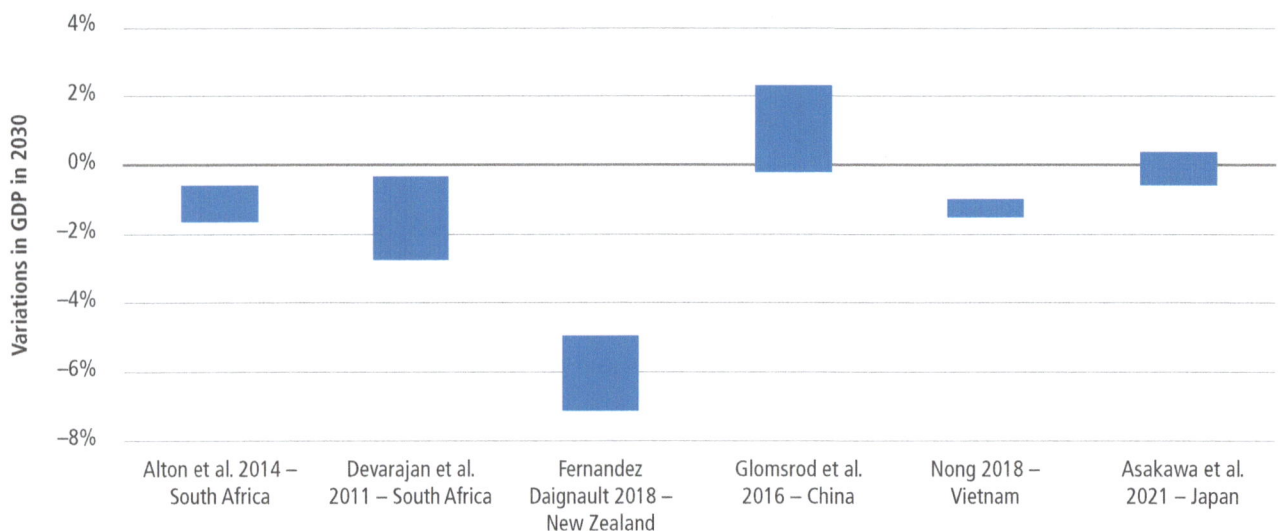

Figure 4.5 | Illustrative ranges of variations in GDP relative to reference in 2030 associated with introduction of carbon constraint, depending on modality of policy implementation. Source: based on Alton et al. (2014); Devarajan et al. (2011); Fernandez and Daigneault (2018); Glomsrød et al. (2016); Nong (2018); Asakawa et al. (2021). Stringency of carbon constraint is not comparable across the studies.

use of a production factor (fossil energy), thus reducing GDP. In the simulations, the mechanism at work is that firms and households reduce their use of GHG-intensive goods and services in response to higher prices due to reduced fossil energy use. Second, additional investment required for mitigation partially crowds out productive investment elsewhere (Fujimori et al. 2019), except in Keynesian models in which increased public investment actually boosts GDP (Pollitt et al. 2015; Landa Rivera et al. 2016; Bulavskaya and Reynès 2018). Magnitude and duration of GDP loss depend on the stringency of the carbon constraint, the degree of substitutability with less-GHG-intensive goods and services, assumptions about costs of low-carbon technologies and their evolution over time (e.g., Duan et al. 2018; van Meijl et al. 2018; Cui et al. 2019) and decisions by trading partners, which influence competitiveness impacts for firms (Alton et al. 2014; Fragkos et al. 2017) (*high evidence, high agreement*).

In the near term, presence of long-lived emissions intensive capital stock, and rigidities in the labour market (Devarajan et al. 2011) and other areas may increase impacts of mitigation on GDP. In the mid-term, on the other hand, physical and human capital, technology, institutions, skills or location of households and activities are more flexible. The development of renewable energy may help create more employment and demands for new skills, particularly in the high-skill labour market (Helgenberger, S. et al., 2019). In addition, cumulative mechanisms such as induced technical change or learning by doing on low-emissions technologies and process may reduce the impacts of mitigation on GDP.

Country-level studies find that the negative impacts of mitigation on GDP can be reduced if pre-existing economic or institutional obstacles are removed in complement to the imposition of the carbon constraint (*robust evidence, high agreement*). For example, if the carbon constraint takes the form of a carbon tax or of permits that are auctioned, the way the proceeds from the tax (or the revenues from the sales of permits) are used is critical for the overall macroeconomic impacts (Chen et al. 2013). (For a detailed discussion

of different carbon pricing instruments, including the auctioning of permits, see Section 13.6.3).

Figure 4.5 shows that depending on the choice of how to implement a carbon constraint, the same level of carbon constraint can yield very different outcomes for GDP. The potential for mitigating GDP implications of mitigation through fiscal reform is discussed in Section 4.4.1.8.

More generally, mitigation costs can be reduced by proper policy design if the economy initially is not on the efficiency frontier (Grubb 2014), defined as the set of configurations within which the quality of the environment and economic activity cannot be simultaneously improved given current technologies – such improvements in policy design may include reductions in distortionary taxes. Most of the studies which find that GDP increases with mitigation in the near term precisely assume that the economy is initially not on the frontier. Making the economy more efficient – in other words, lifting the constraints that maintain the economy in an interior position – creates opportunities to simultaneously improve economic activity and reduce emissions. Table 4.9 describes the underlying assumptions in a selection of studies.

Finally, *marginal* costs of mitigation are not always reported in studies of national mitigation pathways. Comparing numbers across countries is not straightforward due to exchange rate fluctuations, differing assumptions by modellers in individual country studies, etc. The database of national mitigation pathways assembled for this Report – which covers only a fraction of available national mitigation studies in the literature – shows that marginal costs of mitigation are positive, with a median value of 101 USD2010 tCO$_2$$^{-1}$ in 2030, 244 in 2040 and 733 in 2050 for median mitigation efforts of 21%, 46% and 76% relative to business-as-usual respectively. Marginal costs increase over time along accelerated mitigation pathways, as constraints become tighter, with a non-linearity as mitigation reaches 80% of reference emissions or more. Dispersion across and within countries is high, even in the near term but increases notably in the mid-term (*medium evidence*, *medium agreement*).

4.2.6.3 Mitigation and Employment in the Short- and Medium-term

Numerous studies have analysed the potential impact of carbon pricing on labour markets. Chateau et al. (2018) and OECD (2017a) find that the implementation of green policies globally (defined broadly as policies that internalise environmental externalities through taxes and other tools, shifting profitability from polluting to green sectors) need not harm total employment, and that the broad skill composition (low-, high- and medium-skilled jobs) of emerging and contracting sectors is very similar, with the largest shares of job creation and destruction at the lowest skill level. To smoothen the labour market transition, they conclude that it may be important to reduce labour taxes, to compensate vulnerable households, and to provide education and training programs, the latter making it easier for labour to move to new jobs. Consistent with this, other studies that simulate the impact of scenarios with more or less ambitious mitigation policies (including 100% reliance on renewable energy by 2050) find relatively small (positive or negative) impacts on aggregate global employment that are more positive if labour taxes are reduced but encompass substantial losses for sectors and regions that today are heavily dependent on fossil fuels (Arndt et al. 2013; Huang et al. 2019; Vandyck et al. 2016; Jacobson et al. 2019). Among worker categories, low-skilled workers tend to suffer wage losses as they are more likely to have to reallocate, something that can come at a cost in the form of a wage cut (assuming that workers who relocate are initially less productive than those who already work in the sector). The results for alternative carbon revenue recycling schemes point to trade-offs: a reduction in labour taxes often leads to the most positive employment outcomes while lump-sum (uniform per-capita) transfers to households irrespective of income yield a more egalitarian outcome.

The results from country-level studies using CGE models tend be similar to those at global level. Aggregate employment impacts are small and may be positive especially if labour taxes are cut, see for example, Telaye et al. (2019) for Ethiopia,(Kolsuz and Yeldan (2017) for Turkey, Fragkos et al. (2017) for the EU, and Mu et al. (2018b) for China. On the other hand, sectoral reallocations away from fossil-dependent sectors may be substantial, see for example, Alton et al. (2014) for South Africa or Huang et al. (2019) for China. Targeting of investment to labour-intensive green sectors may generate the strongest employment gains, see, for example, Perrier and Quirion (2018) for France, van Meijl et al. (2018) for the Netherlands, and Patrizio et al. 2(018) for the USA. Changes in skill requirements between emerging and declining sectors appear to be quite similar, involving smaller transitions than during the IT revolution (Bowen et al. 2018).

In sum, the literature suggests that the employment impact of mitigation policies tends to be limited on aggregate, but can be significant at the sectoral level (*medium evidence*, *medium agreement*) and that cutting labour taxes may limit adverse effects on employment (*limited evidence*, *medium agreement*). Labour market impacts, including job losses in certain sectors, can be mitigated by equipping workers for job changes via education and training,

and by reducing labour taxes to boost overall labour demand (Stiglitz et al. 2017) (Section 4.5).

Like most of the literature on climate change, the above studies do not address gender aspects. These may be significant since the employment shares for men and women vary across sectors and countries.

4.2.6.4 Mitigation and Equity in the Near and Mid-term

Climate mitigation may exacerbate socio-economic pressures on poorer households (Jakob et al. 2014). First, the price increase in energy-intensive goods and services – including food (Hasegawa et al. 2018) – associated with mitigation may affect poorer households disproportionally (Bento 2013), and increase the number of energy-poor (Berry 2019). Second, the mitigation may disproportionally affect low-skilled workers (see previous section). Distributional issues have been identified not only with explicit price measures (carbon tax, emission permits system, subsidy removal), but also with subsidies for renewables (Borenstein and Davis 2016), and efficiency and emissions standards (Davis and Knittel 2019; Bruegge et al. 2019; Levinson 2019; Fullerton and Muehlegger 2019).

Distributional implications, however, are context specific, depending on consumption patterns (initially and ease of adjusting them in response to price changes) and asset ownership (see for example analysis of energy prices in Indonesia by Renner et al. 2019). In an analysis of the distributional impact of carbon pricing based on household expenditure data for 87 low- and middle-income countries, Dorband et al. (2019) find that, in countries with a per-capita income of up to USD15,000 per capita (purchasing power parity (PPP) adjusted), carbon pricing has a progressive impact on income distribution and that there may be an inversely U-shaped relationship between energy expenditure shares and per-capita income, rendering carbon pricing regressive in high-income countries, in other words, in countries where the capacity to pursue compensatory policies tends to be relatively strong.

The literature finds that the detailed design of mitigation policies is critical for their distributional impacts (*robust evidence*, *high agreement*). For example, Vogt-Schilb et al. (2019) suggest to turn to cash transfer programs, established as some of the most efficient tools for poverty reduction in developing countries. In an analysis of Latin America and the Caribbean, they find that allocation of 30% of carbon revenues would suffice to compensate poor and vulnerable households on average, leaving the rest for other uses. This policy tool is not only available in countries with relatively high per-capita incomes: in Sub-Saharan Africa, where per-capita incomes are relatively low, cash transfer programs have been implemented in almost all countries (Beegle et al. 2018, p. 57), and are found central to the success of energy subsidy reforms (Rentschler and Bazilian 2017). In the same vein, Böhringer et al. (2021) finds that recycling of revenues from emissions pricing in equal amounts to every household appeals as an attractive strategy to mitigate regressive effects and thereby make stringent climate policy more acceptable on societal fairness grounds. However, distributional gains from such recycling may come at the opportunity cost of not reaping efficiency

4

gains from reductions in the taxes that are most distortionary (Goulder et al. 2019).

Distributional concerns related to climate mitigation are also prevalent in developed countries, as demonstrated, for instance, by France's recent yellow-vest movement, which was ignited by an increase in carbon taxes. It exemplifies the fact that, when analysing the distributional effects of carbon pricing, it is not sufficient to consider vertical redistribution (i.e., redistribution between households at different incomes levels but also horizontal redistribution (i.e., redistribution between households at similar incomes which is due to differences in terms of spending shares and elasticities for fuel consumption). Compared to vertical redistribution, it is more difficult to devise policies that effectively address horizontal redistribution (Cronin et al. 2019; Pizer and Sexton 2019; Douenne 2020). However, it has been shown ex post that transfer schemes considering income levels and location could have protected or even improved the purchasing power of the bottom half of the population (Bureau et al. 2019). Investments in public transportation may reduce horizontal redistribution if it makes it easier for households to reduce fossil fuel consumption when prices increase (see Sections 4.4.1.5 and 4.4.1.9). Similarly, in relation to energy use in housing, policies that encourage investments that raise energy efficiency for low-income households may complement or be an alternative to taxes and subsidies as a means of simultaneously mitigating and reducing fuel poverty (Charlier et al. 2019). From a different angle, public acceptance of the French increase in the carbon tax could also have been enhanced via a public information campaign could have raised public acceptance of the carbon tax increase (Douenne and Fabre 2020). (See Section 4.4.1.8 for a discussion of this and other factors that influence public support for carbon taxation.)

4.2.7 Obstacles to Accelerated Mitigation and How Overcoming Them Amounts to Shifts in Development Pathways

As outlined in Sections 4.2.3, 4.2.4, 4.2.5 and 4.2.6 there is improved understanding since AR5 of what accelerated mitigation would entail in the coming decades. A major finding is that accelerated mitigation pathways in the near to mid-term appear technically and economically feasible in most contexts. Chapter 4, however, cannot stop here. Section 4.2.2 has documented an important policy gap

for current climate pledges, and Cross-Chapter Box 4 in this chapter shows an even larger ambition gap between current pledges and what would be needed in the near term to be on pathways consistent with below 2°C, let alone 1.5°C. In other words, while the implementation of mitigation policies to achieve updated NDC almost doubles the mitigation efforts, and notwithstanding the widespread availability of the necessary technologies, this doubling of effort merely narrows the gap to pathways consistent with 2°C by at most 20%.

Obstacles to the implementation of accelerated mitigation pathways can be grouped in four main categories (Table 4.10). The first set of arguments can be understood through the lens of cost-benefit analysis of decision-makers, as they revolve around the following question: Are costs too high relative to benefits? More precisely, are the opportunity costs – in economics terms, what is being forfeited by allocating scarce resources to mitigation – justified by the benefits for the decision-maker (whether individual, firm, or nation)? This first set of obstacles is particularly relevant because accelerated mitigation pathways imply significant effort in the short-run, while benefits in terms of limited warming accrue later and almost wholly to other actors. However, as discussed in Sections 3.6 and 4.2.6, mitigation costs for a given mitigation target are not carved in stone. They strongly depend on numerous factors, including the way mitigation policies have been designed, selected, and implemented, the processes through which markets have been shaped by market actors and institutions, and nature of socially- and culturally-determined influences on consumer preferences. Hence, mitigation choices that might be expressed straightforwardly as techno-economic decisions are, at a deeper level, strongly conditioned by underlying structures of society.

A second set of likely obstacles in the short-term to accelerated mitigation revolves around undesirable distributional consequences, within and across countries. As discussed in Section 4.2.6.3, the distributional implications of climate policies depend strongly on their design, the way they are implemented, and on the context into which they are inserted. Distributional implications of climate policies have both ethics and equity dimensions, to determine what is desirable/acceptable by a given society in a given context, notably the relative power of different winners and losers to have their interests taken into account, or not, in the relevant decision-making processes. Like costs, distributional implications of accelerated mitigation are rooted in the underlying socio-political-institutional structures of a society.

Table 4.10 | Objections to accelerated mitigation and where they are assessed in the WG3 report.

Category	Main dimensions	Location in AR6 WGIII report where objection is assessed and solutions are discussed
Costs of mitigation	Marginal, sectoral or macroeconomic costs of mitigation too high; scarce resources could/should be used for other development priorities; mitigation benefits are not worth the costs (or even non-existent); lack of financing	Sections 3.6, 4.2.6, 12.2; Chapter 15, Chapter 17
Distributional implications	Risk of job losses; diminished competitiveness; inappropriate impact on poor/vulnerable people; negative impact on vested interests	Section 4.5; Chapter 5, Chapter 13, Chapter 14
Lack of technology	Lack of suitable technologies; lack of technology transfer; unfavourable socio-political environment	Section 4.2.5, Chapter 16
Unsuitable 'structures'	Inertia of installed capital stock; inertia of socio-technical systems; inertia to behaviour change; unsuitable institutions	Section 3.5; Chapter 5, Chapter 13

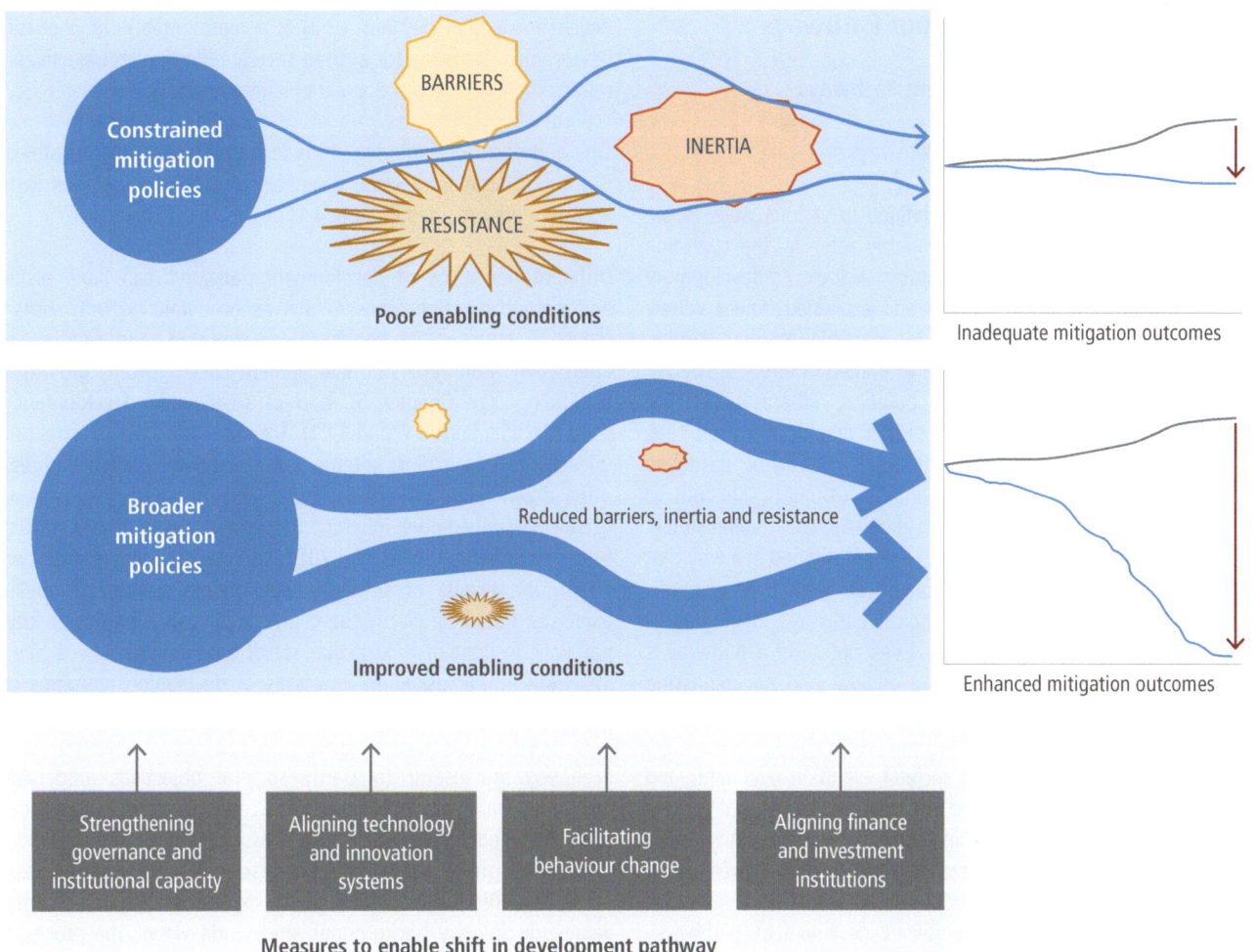

BARRIERS

Constrained
mitigation
policies

INERTIA

RESISTANCE

Poor enabling conditions

Inadequate mitigation outcomes

Broader
mitigation
policies

Reduced barriers, inertia and resistance

Improved enabling conditions

Enhanced mitigation outcomes

| Strengthening governance and institutional capacity | Aligning technology and innovation systems | Facilitating behaviour change | Aligning finance and investment institutions |

Measures to enable shift in development pathway

Figure 4.6 | Obstacles to mitigation (top panel) and measures to remove these obstacles and enable shift in development pathways (lower panel).

A third set of obstacles are about technology availability and adoption. Lack of access even to existing cost-effective mitigation technologies remains an important issue, particularly for many developing countries, and even in the short-term. Though it relates most directly to techno-economic costs, technology availability raises broader issues related to the socio-technical systems within which innovation and adoption are embedded, and issues of technology availability are inherently issues of systemic failure (Section 16.3). The underlying legal, economic and social structures of the economy are central to the different stages of socio-transition processes (Cross-Chapter Box 12 in Chapter 16).

The last set of obstacles revolves around the unsuitability of existing structures to accelerated mitigation. We include here all forms of established structures, material (e.g., physical capital) or not (institutions, social norms, patterns of individual behaviour), that are potentially long-lived and limit the implementation of accelerated mitigation pathways. Typically, such structures exist for reasons other than climate change and climate mitigation, including the distribution of power among various actors. Modifying them in the name of accelerated climate mitigation thus requires to deal with other non-climate issues as well. For example, resolving the landlord-tenant dilemma, an institutional barrier to the deployment of energy

efficiency in building, opens fundamental questions on private property in buildings.

A common thread in the discussion above is that the obstacles to accelerated mitigation are to a large degree rooted in the underlying structural features of societies. As a result, transforming those underlying structures can help to remove those obstacles, and thus facilitate the acceleration of mitigation. This remark is all the more important that accelerated mitigation pathways, while very different across countries, all share three characteristics: speed of implementation, breadth of action across all sectors of the economy, and depth of emission reduction achieving more ambitious targets. Transforming those underlying structures amounts to shifting a society's development pathway (Figure 4.6). In the following Sections 3 and 4, we argue that it is thus necessary to recast accelerated mitigation in the broader context of shifting development pathways, and that doing so opens up additional opportunities to (i) overcome the obstacles outlined above, and also (ii) combine climate mitigation with other development objectives.

4.3   Shifting Development Pathways

4.3.1   Framing of Development Pathways

4.3.1.1   What are Development Pathways?

The term development pathway is defined in various ways in the literature, and these definitions invariably refer to the evolution over time of a society's defining features. A society's development pathway can be described, analysed, and explained from a variety of perspectives, capturing a range of possible features, trends, processes, and mechanisms. It can be examined in terms of specific quantitative indicators, such as population, urbanisation level, life expectancy, literacy rate, GDP, carbon dioxide emission rate, average surface temperature, etc. Alternately, it can be described with reference to trends and shifts in broad socio-political or cultural features, such as democratisation, liberalisation, colonisation, globalisation, consumerism, etc. Or, it can be described in a way that highlights and details a particular domain of interest; for example, as an 'economic pathway', 'technological pathway', 'demographic pathway', or others. Any such focused description of a pathway is more limited, by definition, than the general and encompassing notion of a development pathway.

Development pathways represent societal evolution over time, and can be assessed retrospectively and interpreted in a historical light, or explored prospectively by anticipating and assessing alternative future pathways. Development pathways, and prospective development pathways in particular, can reflect societal objectives, as in 'low-emission development pathways', 'climate-resilient development pathways', 'sustainable development pathways', 'inclusive development pathway', and as such can embed normative assumptions or preferences, or can reflect potential dystopian futures to be avoided. A national

development plan (Section 4.3.2) is a representation of a possible development pathway for a given society reflecting its objectives, as refracted through its development planning process.

One approach for exploring shifts in future development pathways is through scenarios. Some examples of scenario exercises in the literature are provided in Table 4.11.

Different narratives of development pathways can have distinct and even competing focuses such as economic growth, shifts in industrial structure, technological determinism, and can embody alternative framings of development itself (from growth to well-being, see Chapter 5), and of sustainable development in particular (Sections 1.6 and 17.1). Scenario exercises are structured undertakings to explore alternative future development pathways, often drawing on stakeholder input and accepting the deep and irreducible uncertainty inherent in societal development into the future (Schweizer and Kriegler 2012; Kahane 2012; Raskin and Swart 2020). The results of scenario explorations, including modelling exercises, thus help clarify the characteristics of a particular future pathway, in light of a particular set of assumptions and choice of indicators for assessment. Processes of developing scenarios can inform choices by decision makers of various kinds.

Scenarios are useful to clarify societal objectives, understand constraints, and explore future shifts. Scenario exercises are effective when they enable multi-dimensional assessment, and accommodate divergent normative viewpoints (Kowarsch et al. 2017). Such processes might take into account participants' explicit and implicit priorities, values, disciplinary backgrounds, and world views. The process of defining and describing a society's development pathway contributes to the ongoing process of understanding, explaining and defining the historical and contemporary meaning and significance of a society.

Table 4.11 | Prospective development pathways at global, national and local scale.

Scale	Process and publication	Description of development pathways
Global	IPCC Special Report on Emission Scenarios (Nakicenovic et al. 2000)	Four different narrative storylines describing relationships between driving forces and the evolution of emission scenarios over the 21st century.
Global	Shared Socio-economic Pathways (SSPs) (Riahi et al. 2017; O'Neill et al. 2017)	Five narratives describing alternative socio-economic developments, including sustainable development, regional rivalry, inequality, fossil-fuelled development, and middle-of-the-road development, using alternative long-term projections of demographics, human development, economy and lifestyle, policies and institutions, technology, and environment and natural resources.
Global	Income inequality projections for SSPs (Rao et al. 2019)	Alternative development pathways that explore several drivers of rising or falling inequality.
Global	Futures of Work (World Economic Forum 2018)	Eight possible visions of the future of work in the year 2030, based on different combinations of three core variables: the rate of technological change and its impact on business models, the evolution of learning among the current and future workforce, and the magnitude of labour mobility across geographies – all of which are likely to strongly influence the nature of work in the future.
National	Mont Fleur Scenarios (Galer 2004)	Four socio-political scenarios intended to explore possible futures of a newly post-apartheid South Africa, which included three dark prophecies and one bright vision which reportedly influenced the new leadership.
National	Mitigation Action Plans and Scenarios (MAPS) (Winkler et al. 2017; Raubenheimer et al. 2015)	Mitigation and development-focused scenarios for Brazil, Chile, Peru, and Colombia, entailing linked sectoral and economy modelling including socio-economic implications, combined with intensive stakeholder engagement.
National	Deep Decarbonisation Pathways (Bataille et al. 2016a; Waisman et al. 2019)	Mitigation-focused scenarios for sixteen countries from each country's perspective, carried out by local institutes using national models. The common method is a tool for decision-makers in each context to debate differing concrete visions for deep decarbonisation, seek consensus on near-term policy packages, with aim to contribute to long-term global decarbonisation.
Local	New Lenses on Future Cities (Shell Global 2014)	Six city archetypes used to create scenarios to help understand how cities could evolve through more sustainable urbanisation processes and become more efficient, while coping with major development challenges in the past.

The imagination of facilitated stakeholder process combined with the rigour of modelling helps improve understanding of constraints, trade-offs, and choices. 'Scenario analysis offers a structured approach for illuminating the vast range of possibilities. A scenario is a story, told in words and numbers, describing the way events might unfold. If constructed with rigor and imagination, scenarios help us to explore where we might be headed, but more, offering guidance on how to act now to direct the flow of events toward a desirable future' (Raskin et al. 2002). Scenario processes are valuable for the quantitative and qualitative insights they can provide, and also for the role they can play in providing a forum and process by which diverse institutions and even antagonistic stakeholders can come together, build trust, improve understanding, and ultimately converge in their objectives (Kane and Boulle 2018; Dubash 2021).

4.3.1.2   Shifting Development Pathways

Development pathways evolve as the result of the countless decisions and actions at all levels of societal structure, as well due to the emergent dynamics within and between institutions, cultural norms, socio-technological systems, and the biogeophysical environment. Society can choose to make decisions and take actions with the shared intention of influencing the future development pathway toward specific agreed objectives.

The SDGs provide a lens on diverse national and local development objectives. Humankind currently faces multiple sustainability challenges that together present global society with the challenge of assessing, deliberating, and attempting to bring about a viable, positive future development pathway. Ecological sustainability challenges include reducing GHG emissions, protecting the ozone layer, controlling pollutants such as aerosols and persistent organics, managing nitrogen and phosphorous cycles, etc. (Steffen et al. 2015), which are necessary to address the rising risks to biodiversity and ecosystem services on which humanity depends (IPBES 2019a). Socio-economic sustainability challenges include conflict, persistent poverty and deprivation, various forms of pervasive and systemic discrimination and deprivation, and socially corrosive inequality.

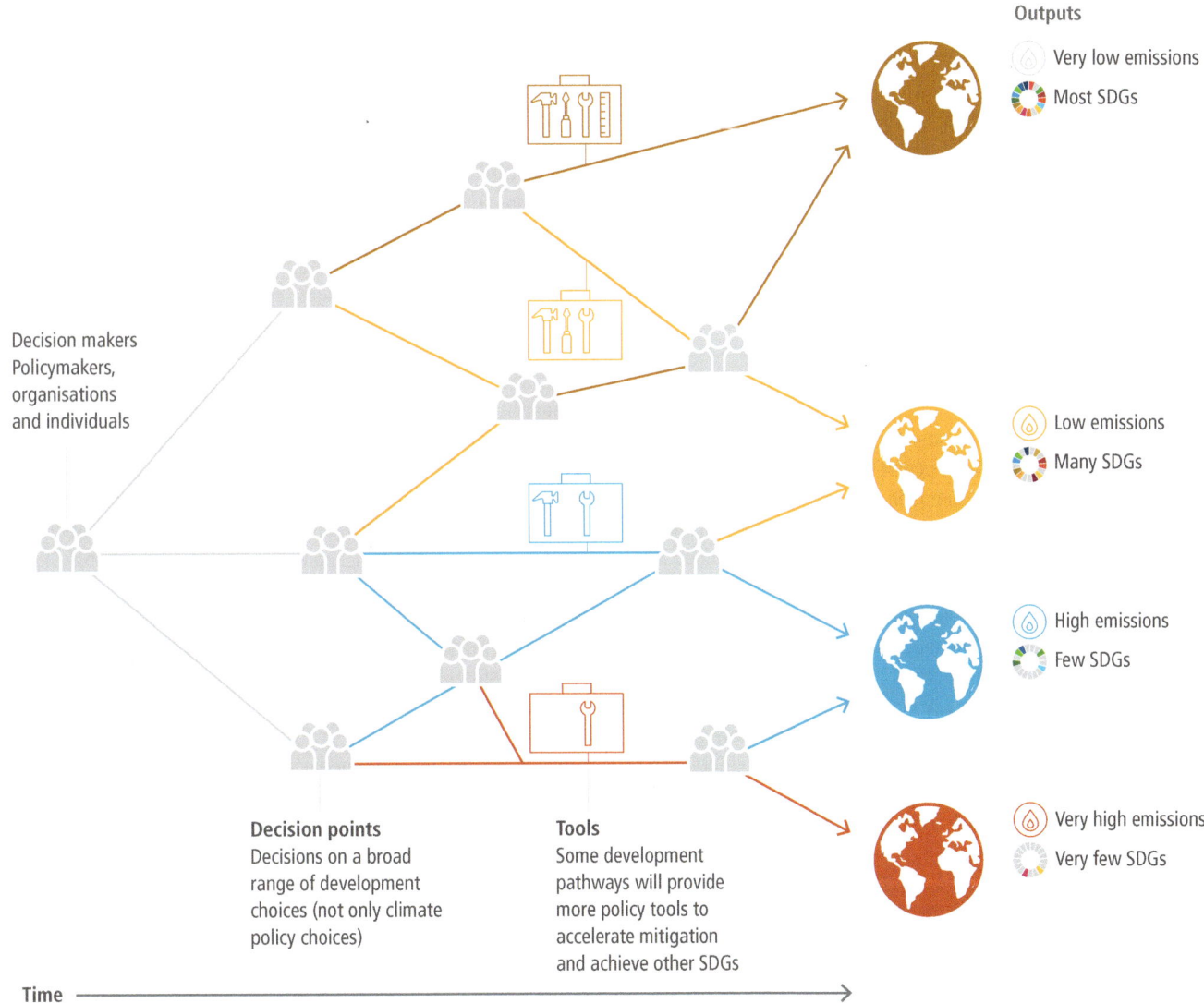

Figure 4.7 | Shifting development pathways to increased sustainability: choices by a wide range of actors at key decision points on development pathways can reduce barriers and provide more tools to accelerate mitigation and achieve other Sustainable Development Goals.

The global adoption of the SDGs and their underlying indicators (UN 2017, 2018 and 2019) reflect a negotiated prioritisation of these common challenges.

Figure 4.7 illustrates the process of shifting development pathways. The lines illustrate different possible development pathways through time, some of which (shown here toward the top of the figure) remove obstacles to the adoption and effective implementation of sustainable development policies, and thus give access to a rich policy toolbox for accelerating mitigation and achieving SDGs. Other development pathways (shown here toward the bottom of the figure) do not overcome, or even reinforce the obstacles to adopting and effectively implementing sustainable development policies, and thus leave decision-makers with more limited policy toolbox (Section 4.2.7 and Figure 4.6). A richer tool box enables faster, deeper and broader mitigation.

The development pathways branch and branch again, signifying how a diversity of decision-makers (policymakers, organisations, investors, voters, consumers, etc.) are continuously making choices that influence which of many potential development pathways society follows. Some of these choices fall clearly within the domain of mitigation policy. For example, what level carbon price, if any, should be imposed? Should fossil fuel subsidies be removed? Most decisions, of course, fall outside the direct domain of mitigation policy. *Shifting development pathways toward sustainability* involves this broader realm of choices beyond mitigation policy *per se*, and requires identifying those choices that are important determinants of the existing obstacles to accelerating mitigation and meeting other SDGs. Addressing these choices coherently shifts the development pathway away from a continuation of existing trends.

4.3.1.3   Expanding the Range of Policies and Other Mitigative Options

Shifting development pathways aims to influence the ultimate drivers of emissions (and development generally), such as the systemic and cultural determinants of consumption patterns, the political systems and power structures that govern decision-making, the institutions and incentives that guide and constrain socio-technical innovation, and the norms and information platforms that shape knowledge and discourse, and culture, values and needs (Raskin et al. 2002). These ultimate drivers determine the mitigative capacity of a society.

Decision-makers might usefully consider a broader palette of policies and measures as part of an overall strategy to meet climate goals and other sustainable development goals (Section 4.3.2 and Table 4.12). This is consistent with the fact that mitigation is increasingly understood to be inseparable from broader developmental goals, which can be facilitated by policy coherence and integration with broader objectives and policies sectorally and societally. This is supported by other observations that mitigation measures based on conventional climate policy instruments, such as emissions taxes or permits, price incentives such as feed-in tariffs for low-carbon electricity generation, and fuel economy standards, and building codes, which aim to influence the proximate drivers of emissions

alone will not achieve the long-term goals of the Paris Agreement (Méjean et al. 2015; Rogelj et al. 2016; IPCC 2018a; UNEP 2018). An approach of shifting development pathways to increased sustainability (SDPS) broadens the scope for mitigation.

4.3.1.4   An Approach of SDPS Helps Manage Trade-offs Between Mitigation and Other SDGs

Beyond removing structural obstacles to accelerated mitigation, broadening the approach to policies that facilitate shifts in development pathways also helps manage the potential trade-offs between mitigation and other development objectives discussed in Section 4.2.7.

Systematic studies of the 17 SDGs have found the interactions among them to be manifold and complex (Nilsson et al. 2016; Pradhan et al. 2017; Weitz et al. 2018; Fuso Nerini et al. 2019). Addressing them calls for interventions affecting fundamental, interconnected, structural features of global society (International Panel on Social Progress 2018; TWI2050 – The World in 2050 2018), such as to our physical infrastructure (e.g., energy, water, industrial, urban infrastructure) (Waage et al. 2015; Adshead et al. 2019; Chester 2019; Mansell et al. 2019; Thacker et al. 2019;), our societal institutions (e.g., educational, public health, economic, innovation, and political institutions) (Ostrom 2010; Kläy et al. 2015; Messner 2015; Sachs et al. 2019), and behavioural and cultural tendencies (e.g., consumption patterns, conventional biases, discriminatory interpersonal and intergroup dynamics, and inequitable power structures) (Esquivel 2016; Sachs et al. 2019). These observations imply that attempt to address each SDG in isolation, or as independent technical challenges, would be insufficient, as would incremental, marginal changes. In contrast, effectively addressing the SDGs is likely to mean significant disruption of long-standing trends and transformative progress to shift development pathways to meet al. the SDGs, including climate action, beyond incremental changes targeted at addressing mitigation objectives in isolation. In other words, mitigation conceived as incremental change is not enough. Transformational change has implications for equity in its multiple dimensions (Steffen and Stafford Smith 2013; Klinsky et al. 2017a; Leach et al. 2018) including just transitions (Section 4.5).

Working Group II examines climate resilient development pathways (CRDP) – continuous processes that imply deep societal changes and/or transformation, so as to strengthen sustainable development, efforts to eradicate poverty and reduce inequalities while promoting fair and cross-scalar capacities for adaptation to global warming and reduction of GHG emissions in the atmosphere. Transformative action in the context of CRDP specifically concerns leveraging change in the five dimensions of development (people, prosperity, partnership, peace, planet) (AR6 WGII, Chapter 18).

Section 4.3.2 provides more details on the way development pathways influence emissions and mitigative capacity. Section 4.3.3 provides examples of shifts in development pathways, as well as of policies that might facilitate those. Cross-Chapter Box 5 in this chapter details the links between SDPS and sustainability.

4.3.2 Implications of Development Pathways for Mitigation and Mitigative Capacity

4.3.2.1 Countries Have Different Development Priorities

At the global level, the SDGs adopted by all the United Nations Member States in 2015 are delineated with a view to end poverty, protect the planet and ensure that all people enjoy peace and prosperity by 2030. The 17 SDGs are integrated and imply that development must balance social, economic and environmental sustainability.

While all countries share the totality of the SDGs, development priorities differ across countries and over time. These priorities are strongly linked to local contexts, and depend on which dimensions of improvements in the well-being of people are considered the most urgent.

Development priorities are reflected in the decisions that actors within societies make, such as policy choices by governments and parliaments at all levels, votes over competing policy platforms by citizens, or selection of issues that non-state actors push for. Multiple objectives range from poverty eradication to providing energy access, addressing concerns of inequality, providing education, improving health, cleaning air and water, improving connectivity, sustaining growth and providing jobs, among others. For example, eradicating poverty and reducing inequality is a key development priority across many countries, such as Brazil (Grottera et al. 2017), Indonesia (Irfany and Klasen 2017), India (GoI 2015), South Africa (Winkler 2018) and other low- and middle-income countries (Dorband et al. 2019). Reducing inequality relates not only to income, but also to other dimensions such as in access to energy services (Tait 2017), gender, education, racial and ethnic profiles (Andrijevic et al. 2020), and thereby assumes relevance in both developing and developed countries. The development priorities of many poor countries and communities with low capacities to adapt, has been focused more on reducing poverty, providing basic infrastructure, education and improving health, rather than on mitigation (Chimhowu et al. 2019).

4.3.2.2 The Nature of National Development Plans Is Changing

Governments are increasingly resorting to the development of national plans to build institutions, resources, and risk/shock management capabilities to guide national development. The number of countries with a national development plan has more than doubled, from about 62 in 2006 (World Bank 2007) to 134 plans published between 2012 and 2018 (Chimhowu et al. 2019). The comeback of planning may be linked to increased consideration given to sustainability, which is by construction forward-looking and far ranging, and therefore requires state and civil society to prepare and implement plans at all levels of governance. Governments are increasingly engaging in the development and formulation of national plans in an organised, conscious and continual attempt to select the best available alternatives to achieve specific goals.

A systematic assessment of 107 national development plans and 10 country case studies provides useful insights regarding the type and content of the plans (Chimhowu et al. 2019). development plans are increasingly focusing on mobilising action across multiple actors and multiple dimensions to enhance resilience and improve the ability to undertake stronger mitigation actions. Various initiatives such as the World Summit for Children in 1990; the Heavily Indebted Poor Country initiative that started offering debt relief in exchange for commitments by beneficiary states to invest in health, education, nutrition and poverty reduction in 1996; and push towards Comprehensive Development Frameworks seem to have catalysed the development of national actions plans across countries to estimate, measure and track investments and progress towards SDGs.

The most recent development plans also tend to differ from the earlier ones in terms of their approach. Complexity science has over the years argued for new forms of planning based on contingency, behaviour change, adaptation and constant learning (Colander and Kupers 2016; Ramalingam, 2013), and new plans have increasingly focused on increasing resilience of individuals, organisations and systems (Hummelbrunner and Jones, 2013). Finally, alongside short-term (typically five year) plans with operational purpose, countries have also expressed visions of their development pathways over longer time horizons, via, for example, Voluntary National Reviews submitted in the context of the UN High Level Political Forum on Sustainable Development.

National development plans are also increasingly more holistic in their approach, linking closely with SDGs and incorporating climate action in their agendas. For instance, the Low Carbon Development Initiative (LCDI), launched in 2017 by the Government of Indonesia, seeks to identify the development policies that can help Indonesia achieve multiple (social, economic, and environmental) goals simultaneously along with preserving and improving the country's natural resources (Bappenas 2019). Likewise, Nepal's Fifteenth Plan (five-year) recognises the need for climate mitigation and adaptation and corresponding access to international finance and technologies. The plan suggests mobilisation of foreign aid in the climate change domain in line with Nepal's priorities and its inclusion in the country's climate-friendly development programs as the key opportunities in this regard (Nepal 2020).

China's development plans have evolved over time from being largely growth oriented, and geared largely towards the objectives of addressing poverty, improving health, education and public well-being to also including modernisation of agriculture, industry and infrastructure, new forms of urbanisation and a clear intent of focusing on innovation and new drivers of development (Central Compilation & Translation Press 2016). China's 14th Five Year Plan not only seeks to promote high quality development in all aspects and focus on strengthening the economy in the global industrial chain, but also includes a vision of an 'ecological civilisation', which had been developed (CPC-CC 2015) and analysed earlier (He 2016; Xiao and Zhao 2017). It seeks to enhance China's climate pledge to peak CO_2 emissions by 2030 and achieve carbon neutrality by 2060 through more vigorous policies and measures. Development plans tie in multiple development priorities that evolve and broaden over time as societies develop, as exemplified inter alia by the history of development plans in India (Box 4.4).

Box 4.4 | India's National Development Plan

India's initial national development plans focused on improving the living standards of its people, increasing national income and food self-sufficiency. Accordingly, there was a thrust towards enhancing productivity of the agricultural and industrial sectors. While the main focus was on maintaining high economic growth and industrial productivity, poverty eradication, employment and inclusive growth remained important priorities. The National Action Plan on Climate Change with eight National Missions focusing on mitigation as well as adaptation was launched in 2008 integrating climate change considerations in planning and decision-making (MoEF 2008). The 12th Five-Year Plan (2012–2017) also brought in a focus on sustainability and mentioned the need for faster, sustainable and inclusive growth. The National Institution for Transforming India (NITI Aayog) was set up in 2017 replacing the erstwhile Planning Commission, with a renewed focus towards bringing innovation, technology, enterprise and efficient management together at the core of policy formulation and implementation. However, while India has moved away from its Five-Year Plans, decision-making is more dynamic, with a number of sector-specific initiatives and targets focused on integrating sustainability dimensions through a series of policies and measures supporting resource efficiency, improved energy access, infrastructure development, low-carbon options and building resilient communities, among other objectives (MoEFCC 2018, 2021). India's overall development pathway currently has a strong focus on achieving robust and inclusive growth to ensure balanced development across all regions and states and across sectors. There is a thrust on embracing new technologies while fostering innovation and upskilling, modernisation of agriculture, improving regional and interpersonal equity, bridging the gap between public and private sector performance, by focusing on efficient delivery of public services, rooting out corruption and black economy, formalising the economy and expanding the tax base, improving the ease of doing business, nursing the stressed commercial banking sector back to a healthy state, and stopping leakages through direct benefit transfers, among other measures (GoI 2015, 2018; MoEFCC 2021).

4.3.2.3 Development Pathways Shape Emissions and Capacities to Mitigate

Analysis in the mitigation literature often frames mitigation policy as having development co-benefits, the main objective being climate stabilisation. This misses the point that development drives emissions, and not vice versa, and it is the overall development approach and policies that determine mitigation pathways (Munasinghe 2007). A large body of literature supports the fact that development pathways have direct and, just as importantly, indirect implications for GHG emissions (Nakicenovic et al. 2000; Winkler 2017b), through multiple channels, such as the nature of economic activity, spatial patterns of development, degree of inequality, and population growth.

Economic structure: Chapter 2 notes that overall, affluence (GDP per capita), economic growth and population growth have remained the main upward drivers of CO_2 emissions from fossil-fuel combustion in the past decade, with energy efficiency the main countervailing force (Lin and Liu 2015; Wang and Feng 2017) (Section 2.4). A major component of the development pathway of a country is precisely the nature of the economic activities on which the country relies (e.g., agriculture and mining, heavy industry, services, high-tech products, etc.) as well as the way it articulates its economy with the rest of the World (e.g., export-led growth vs import substitution strategies). Hence, the development pathway ultimately drives the underlying structure of the economy, and to a large degree the relationship between activity and GHG emissions.

At country level, however, the picture is more nuanced. Both India and China show signs of relative decoupling between GDP and emissions because of structural change (Chen et al. 2018a). Sumabat et al. (2016) indicate that economic growth had a negative impact on CO_2 emissions in Philippines. Baek and Gweisah (2013) find that CO_2 emissions tend to drop monotonously as incomes increased. Lantz and Feng (2006) also indicate that per capita GDP is not related to CO_2 emissions in Canada. Other studies point to an emerging consensus that the relationship between CO_2 emissions and economic indicators depends on the level of development of countries (Nguyen and Kakinaka 2019; Sharma 2011). While some literature indicates that absolute decoupling of economic growth and GHG emissions has occurred in some countries (Le Quéré et al. 2019), a larger systematic review found limited evidence of this (Haberl et al. 2020).

Looking ahead, choices about the nature of economic activities are expected to have significant implications for emissions. For example, a development pathway that focuses on enhancing economic growth based on manufacturing is likely to lead to very different challenges for mitigation compared to one that focuses on services-led growth. (Quéré et al. 2018) find that choices about whether or not to export offshore oil in Brazil will have significant implications for the country's GHG emissions. Similarly, in China, transforming industrial structure towards tertiary sectors (Kwok et al. 2018) and restructuring exports towards higher value-added products (Wu et al. 2019) are expected to have significant implications for GHG emissions.

Spatial patterns of development: Chapter 2 notes that rapid urbanisation in developing and transition countries leads to increased CO_2 emissions, the substantial migration of rural populations to urban areas in these countries being the main factor leading to increased levels of income and expenditure of new urban dwellers which in turn leads to increased personal carbon footprints and overall emissions (Section 2.4). Urbanisation, and more broadly spatial patterns of development, are in turned driven to a large part by development choices, such as, inter alia, spatial provision of infrastructure and services, choices regarding the agriculture and forestry sector, land-use policies, support to regional/local development, among others (World Bank 2009). For example, Dorin (2017) points out that if agriculture sectors in Africa and India follow the same development path that developed countries have followed in the past, namely increased labour productivity through enlargement and robotisation of farms, then unprecedented emigrations of rural workers towards cities or foreign countries will ensue, with large-scale social, economic and environmental consequences. Looking ahead, a development pathway that encourages concentrated influx of people to large urban centres will lead to very different energy and infrastructure consumption patterns than a pathway that prioritises the development of smaller, self-contained towns and cities.

Degree of inequality: Chapter 2 notes that while eradicating extreme poverty and providing universal access to modern energy services to poor populations across the globe has negligible implications for emissions growth, existing studies on the role of poverty and inequality as drivers of GHG emissions provide limited evidence that under certain contexts greater inequality can lead to a deterioration in environmental quality and may be associated with higher GHG emissions (Section 2.4). In fact, factors affecting household consumption-based emissions include household size, age, education attainment, employment status, urban vs rural location and housing stock (Druckman and Jackson 2015). There is evidence to indicate that at the household level, the increase in emissions from additional consumption of the lower income households could be larger than the reduction in emissions from the drop in consumption from the high income households (Sager 2019). Accordingly, as countries seek to fulfil the objective of reducing inequality, there are possibilities of higher increase in emissions (Sager 2019).

Since reducing inequality, as noted above, is globally one of the main development priorities, a large body of literature focuses on the compatibility of climate change mitigation and reduction in economic inequality (Baek and Gweisah 2013; Auffhammer and Wolfram 2014; Berthe and Elie 2015; Hao et al. 2016; Grunewald et al. 2017; Wiedenhofer et al. 2017). However, the use of narrow approaches or simple methods of studying the relationships of income inequality and emissions by looking at correlations, may miss important linkages. For example, the influence of inequality on social values such as status and civic mindedness and non-political interests that shape environmental policy can influence overall consumption and its environmental impacts (Berthe and Elie 2015). Moreover, inequalities may also be reflected in gender, education, racial and

ethnic profiles and could accordingly be associated with the level of emissions and mitigation prospects (Andrijevic et al. 2020).

The Illustrative Mitigation Pathways (IMP) developed for this Report (Box 3.1 and Section 3.2.5) provide another example of how development pathways influence mitigative capacity. Precisely, IMP1.5-SP (Shifting Pathways) and 1.5-Ren (Renewables) lead to the same long-term temperature, but differ in underlying socio-economic conditions. The former is based on Shared Socio-economic Pathway (SSP) 1 (sustainable development), whereas the latter is based on SSP2 (middle of the road). Comparing 1.5-Ren to 1.5-SP can thus be interpreted as a numerical translation of trying the reach the same long-term temperature goal without and with shifting development pathways towards sustainability. Data shows that the global price of carbon necessary to remain on target is 40–50% lower in the latter relative to the former, thus indicating that mitigation is cheaper with a shift in development pathway towards sustainability. Other cost indicators (e.g. consumption loss or GDP loss) tell the same story. Since both IMPs were computed using the same underlying model, the comparison is even more robust.

In sum, development pathways can lead to different emission levels and different capacities and opportunities to mitigate (*medium evidence*, *high agreement*). Thus, focusing on shifting development pathways can lead to larger systemic sustainability benefits.

4.3.2.4   Integrating Mitigation Considerations Requires Non-marginal Shifts in Development Pathways

Concerns about mitigation are already being introduced in national development plans, as there is evidence that development strategies and pathways can be carefully designed so as to align towards multiple priorities and achieve greater synergistic benefits. For example, India's solar programme is a key element in its NDC that can in the long run, not only provide energy security and contribute to mitigation, but can simultaneously contribute to economic growth, improved energy access and additional employment opportunities, if appropriate policies and measures are carefully planned and implemented. However, the environmental implications of the transition need to be carefully examined with regard to the socio-economic implications in light of the potential of other alternatives like green hydrogen, nuclear or carbon capture, use and storage (CCUS). Similarly, South Africa National Development Plan (2011) also integrates transition to low-carbon as part of the country development objectives (Box 4.5).

Box 4.5 | South Africa's National Development Plan

South Africa adopted its first National Development Plan (NDP) in 2011 (NPC 2011), the same year in which the country adopted climate policy (RSA 2011) and hosted COP17 in Durban. Chapter 5 of the NDP addresses environmental sustainability in the context of development planning, and specifically 'an equitable transition to a low-carbon economy' (NPC 2011). The chapter refers explicitly to the need for a just transition, protecting the poor from impacts and any transitional costs from emissions-intensive to low-carbon. The plan proposes several mitigation measures, including a carbon budgeting approach, reference to Treasury's carbon tax, use of various low-carbon options while maintaining energy security, and the integrated resource plan for electricity. The NDP refers to coal in several chapters, in some places suggesting additional investment (including new rail lines to transport coal and coal to liquids),

Box 4.5 (continued)

in others decommissioning coal-fired power 'procuring at least 20,000 MW of renewable electricity by 2030, importing electricity from the region, decommissioning 11,000 MW of ageing coal-fired power stations and stepping up investments in energy-efficiency' (NPC 2011: p. 46). Reference to environmental sustainability is not limited to Chapter 5 – the introductory vision statement includes acknowledgement 'that each and every one of us is intimately and inextricably of this earth with its beauty and life-giving sources; that our lives on earth are both enriched and complicated by what we have contributed to its condition' (NPC 2011: p. 21); and the overview of the plan includes a section on climate change, addressing both mitigation and adaptation.

Looking ahead, given that different development pathways can lead to different levels of GHG emissions and to different capacities and opportunities to mitigate, there is increasing research on how to make development pathways more sustainable. Literature is also focusing on the need for a 'new normal' as a system capable of achieving higher quality growth while addressing multiple development objectives by focusing on 'innovative development pathways'.

Literature suggests that if development pathways are to be changed to address the climate change problem, choices that would need to be made about development pathways would not be marginal (Stern 2009), and would require a new social contract to address a complex set of inter-linkages across sectors, classes and the whole economy (Winkler 2017b). Shifting development pathways necessitates planning in a holistic manner, rather than thinking about discrete and isolated activities and actions to undertake mitigation. Further, the necessary transformational changes can be positive if they are rooted in the development aspirations of the economy and society in which they take place (Dubash 2012; Jones et al. 2013), but they can also lead to carbon colonialism if the transformations are imposed by Northern donors or perceived as such.

Accordingly, influencing a societies' development pathways draws upon a broader range of policies and other efforts than narrowly influencing mitigation pathways, to be able to achieve the multiple objectives of reducing poverty, inequality and GHG emissions. The implications for employment, education, mobility, housing and many other development aspects must be integrated and new ways of looking at development pathways which are low carbon must be considered (Bataille et al. 2016b; Waisman et al. 2019). For instance, job creation and education are important elements that could play a key role in reducing inequality and poverty in countries like South Africa and India (Winkler et al. 2015; Rao and Min 2018) while these also open up broader opportunities for mitigation.

4.3.2.5   New Tools Are Needed to Pave and Assess Development Pathways

Relative to the literature on mitigation pathways described in 4.2.5 and in 4.3.3, the literature on development pathways is limited. The climate research community has developed the Shared Socio-economic Pathways (SSPs) that link several socio-economic drivers including equity in relation to welfare, resources, institutions, governance and climate mitigation policies in order to reflect many of the key development directions (O'Neill et al. 2014). In most modelling exercises however, development remains treated as an exogenous input. In addition, models may capture only some dimensions of development that are relevant for mitigation options, thereby not capturing distributional aspects and not allowing consistency checks with broader developmental goals (Valadkhani et al. 2016). Quantitative tools for assessing mitigation pathways could be more helpful if they could provide information on a broader range of development indicators, and could model substantively different alternative development paths, thereby providing information on which levers might shift development in a more sustainable direction.

Doing so requires new ways of thinking with interdisciplinary research and use of alternative frameworks and methods suited to deeper understanding of change agents, determinants of change and adaptive management among other issues (Winkler 2018). This includes, inter alia, being able to examine enabling conditions for shifting development pathways (Section 4.4.1); re-evaluating the neo-classical assumptions within most models, both on the functioning of markets and on the behaviour of agents, to better address obstacles on the demand side, obstacles on the supply side and market distortions (Ekholm et al. 2013; Staub-Kaminski et al. 2014; Grubb et al. 2015) improving representation of issues related with uncertainty, innovation, inertia and irreversibility within the larger development contexts, including energy access and security; improving the representation of social and human capital, and of social, technological and governance innovations (Pedde et al. 2019).

Tools have been developed in that direction, for example in the Mitigation Action Plans and Scenarios (MAPS) community (La Rovere et al. 2014b), but need to be further mainstreamed in the analysis. Back-casting is often a preferred modelling approach for assessment aiming to align national development goals with global climate goals like CO_2 stabilisation. Back-casting is a normative approach where modellers construct desirable futures and specify upfront targets and then find out possible pathways to attain these targets (IPCC et al. 2001). Use of approaches like back-casting are useful not only in incorporating the long term national development objectives in the models, but also evaluating conflicts and synergies more effectively (van der Voorn et al. 2020). In back casting, the long-term national development objectives remain the key benchmarks guiding the model dynamics and the global climate goal is interfaced to realise the co-benefits. The models then delineate the roadmap of national actions such that the national goals are achieved with a comprehensive understanding of the full costs and benefits of low-carbon development (often including the costs of adaptation and impacts from residual climate change). Back-casting modelling exercises show that aligning development and climate actions could result in much lower 'social cost of carbon' (Shukla et al. 2008). Back-casting does not aim to produce blueprints. Rather, it indicates the relative feasibility and the social, environmental, and political implications of different development and climate futures on the assumption of a clear relationship between goal setting and policy planning (Dreborg 1996). Accordingly, back-casting exercises are well suited for preparing local specific roadmaps like for cities (Gomi et al. 2010, 2011).

4.3.3   Examples of Shifts in Development Pathways and of Supporting Policies

As noted in Section 4.3.1, policy approaches that include a broader range of instruments and initiatives would impact more fundamentally on the actors, institutions and structures of societies and the dynamics among them, aiming to alter the underlying drivers of emissions, opening up a wider range of mitigation opportunities and potential in the process of achieving societal development goals. While the evolution of these drivers is subject to varied influences and complex interactions, there are policy measures by which decision-makers might influence them. Table 4.12 provides some examples of policy measures that can affect key drivers (shown in the row headings).

Table 4.12 | Examples of policies that can help shift development pathways.

Drivers	Examples of policy measures
Behaviour	– Progressive taxation – Ecological tax reform – Regulation of advertisement – Investment in public transit – Eco-labelling
Governance and institutions	– Campaign finance laws – Regulatory transparency – Commitment to multilateral environmental governance – Public investment in education and R&D – Public-service information initiatives – Public sector commitment to science-based decision-making – Anti-corruption policies
Innovation	– Investment in public education – Public sector R&D support – Fiscal incentives for private investments in public goods – International technology development and transfer initiatives
Finance and investment	– International investment treaties support common objectives – Litigation and liability regulations – Reform of subsidies and other incentives not aligned with – Insurance sector and pension regulation – Green quantitative easing – Risk disclosure

Policies such as those listed in Table 4.12 are typically associated with broader objectives than GHG mitigation. They are generally conceived and implemented in the pursuit of overall societal development objectives, such as job creation, macroeconomic stability, economic growth, and public health and welfare. However, they can have major influence on mitigative capacity, and hence can be seen as necessary tools if mitigation options are to be significantly broadened and accelerated (*medium evidence*, *medium agreement*). The example of the UK shows how accelerated mitigation through dietary changes require a wide set of efforts to shift underlying drivers of behaviour. In this case, multiple forces have interacted to lead to reduced meat consumption, including health attitudes, animal welfare concerns, and an increasing focus on climate and other environmental impacts of livestock production, along with corporate investment in market opportunities, and technological developments in meat alternatives (Box 5.5).

Other historic cases that are unrelated to recent mitigation efforts might be more appropriate examples of major socio-technical shifts that were largely driven by intentional, coherent intentional policy initiatives across numerous domains to meet multiple objectives. The modernisation of agriculture in various national contexts fits such a mold. In the USA, for example, major government investments in agricultural innovation through the creation of agricultural universities and support for research provided advances in the technological basis for modernisation. A network of agricultural extension services accelerated the popularization and uptake of modern methods. Infrastructure investments in irrigation and drainage made production more viable, and investment in roadways and rail for transport supported market formation. Agricultural development banks made credit available, and government subsidies improved the profitability for farmers and agricultural corporations. Public campaigns were launched to modify food habits (Ferleger 2000).

Further examples of SDPS across many different systems and sectors are elaborated across this report. Concrete examples assessed in this chapter include high employment and low emissions structural change, fiscal reforms for mitigation and social contract, combining housing policies to deliver both housing and transport mitigation, and change economic, social and spatial patterns of development of the agriculture sector provide the basis for sustained reductions in emissions from deforestation (Sections 4.4.1.7–4.4.1.10). These examples differ by context. Examples in other chapters include transformations in energy, urban, building, industrial, transport, and land-based systems, changes in behaviour and social practices, as well as transformational changes across whole economies and societies (Cross-Chapter Box 5 in this chapter, Section 5.8, Box 6.2, Sections 8.2, 8.3.1, 8.4, 9.8.1, 9.8.2 and 10.4.1, and Cross-Chapter Box 12 in Chapter 16). These examples and others can be understood in the context of an explanation of the concept of SDPS, and how to shifting development pathways (Cross-Chapter Box 5 in this chapter).

4

Cross-Chapter Box 5 | Shifting Development Pathways to Increase Sustainability and Broaden Mitigation Options

Authors: Franck Lecocq (France), Harald Winkler (Republic of South Africa), Mustafa Babiker (Sudan/Saudi Arabia), Brett Cohen (Republic of South Africa), Heleen de Coninck (the Netherlands), Dipak Dasgupta (India), Navroz K. Dubash (India), María Josefina Figueroa Meza (Venezuela/Denmark), Michael Grubb (United Kingdom), Kirsten Halsnæs (Denmark), Şiir Kılkış (Turkey), William Lamb (Germany/United Kingdom), Sebastian Mirasgedis (Greece), Sudarmanto Budi Nugroho (Indonesia), Chukwumerije Okereke (Nigeria/United Kingdom), Minal Pathak (India), Joyashree Roy (India/Thailand), Ambuj Sagar (India), Yamina Saheb (France/Algeria), Priyadarshi Shukla (India), Jim Skea (United Kingdom), Youba Sokona (Mali), Julia Steinberger (United Kingdom/Switzerland), Mariama Williams (Jamaica/the United States of America)

1. What do we mean by development pathways?

In the present report, development pathways refer to patterns of development resulting from multiple decisions and choices made by many actors in the national and global contexts. Each society whether in the Global North or the Global South follows its own pattern of development (Figure 1.6). Development pathways can also be described at smaller scales (e.g., for regions or cities). By extension, the concept can also be applied to sectors and systems (e.g., the development pathway of the agricultural sector or of industrial systems).

2. Why do development pathways matter in a report about mitigation?

2a. Past development pathways determine both today's GHG emissions and the set of opportunities to reduce emissions
Development pathways drive GHG emissions for a large part (Sections 2.4, 2.5 and 2.6). For example, different social choices and policy packages with regard to land use and associated rents will result in human settlements with different spatial patterns, different types of housing markets and cultures, and different degrees of inclusiveness, and thus different demand for transport services and associated GHG emissions (Sections 8.3.1 and 10.2.1).

There is compelling evidence to show that continuing along existing development pathways is unlikely to achieve rapid and deep emission reductions (*robust evidence, medium agreement*). For example, investments in long-lived infrastructure, including energy supply systems, could lock-in high emissions pathways and risk making deep decarbonisation and sustainable policies more difficult and expensive.

Development pathways also determine the set of tools available to mitigate climate change (Figure 4.7). For example, the capacity of households to move closer to their workplace, in response to, for example, a price signal on carbon and thus on gasoline, depends on rents, which themselves depend on the spatial patterns of development of human settlements (Section 8.3.1). Said differently, mitigation costs depend on past development choices. Similarly, development pathways determine the enablers and levers available for adaptation (AR6 WGII, Chapter 18) and for achieving other SDGs.

In the absence of shifts in development pathways, conventional mitigation policy instruments (e.g., carbon tax, emission quotas, technological norms, etc.) may not be able to limit emissions to a degree sufficient for deep decarbonisation or only at very high economic and social costs.

Policies to shift development pathways, on the contrary, make mitigation policies more effective. For example, policies that prioritise non-car transit, or limit rents close to work places would make it easier for households to relocate in response to a price signal on transport, and thus makes the same degree of mitigation achievable at lower economic and social cost.

2b. Shifting development pathways broadens the scope for synergies between development objectives and mitigation
Second, societies pursue a variety of development objectives, of which protecting the Earth's climate is part. The SDGs provide a global mapping of these goals. Absent climate mitigation, our collective ability to achieve the SDGs in 2030 and to sustain them beyond 2030 is likely to be compromised, even if adaptation measures are put in place (AR6 WGII).

There are many instances in which reducing GHG emissions and moving towards the achievement of other development objectives can go hand in hand, in the near-, mid- and long-term (Sections 3.7, 6.7.7, 7.6.5, 8.2, 9.8, 10.1.1, 11.5.3 and 17.3, and Figures 3.40 and 12.1). For example, transitions from coal-based power to lower-emissions electricity generation technologies and from internal combustion engine to lower-carbon transport has large mitigation potential and direct benefits for health through reduction in local air pollution (Box 6.2 and Section 10.4.1). Energy efficiency in buildings and energy poverty alleviation through improved access to clean fuels also delivers significant health benefits (Sections 9.8.1 and 9.8.2).

Cross-Chapter Box 5 (continued)

Careful design of mitigation policies is critical to achieving these synergies (Section 13.8). Integrated policies can support the creation of synergies between climate change goals and other SDGs. For example, when measures promoting walkable urban areas are combined with electrification and clean renewable energy, there are several co-benefits to be attained (Figure SPM.8 and Section 5.2). These include reduced pressures on agricultural land from reduced urban growth, health co-benefits from cleaner air and benefits from enhanced mobility (Sections 8.2, 8.4 and 4.4.1.9).

Policy design can also manage trade-offs, for example through policy measures as part of just transitions (Section 17.4). However, even with good policy design, decisions about mitigation actions, and the timing and scale thereof, may entail trade-offs with the achievement of other national development objectives in the near-, mid- and long term. In the near term, for example, regulations may ban vehicles from city centres to reduce congestion and local air pollution, but reduce mobility and choice. Increasing green spaces within cities without caps on housing prices may involve trade-offs with affordable housing and push low income residents outside the city (Section 8.2.2). In the mid- and long-term, large-scale deployment of biomass energy raises concerns about food security and biodiversity conservation (Sections 3.7.1, 3.7.5, 7.4.4, 9.8.1, 12.5.2 and 12.5.3). Conflicts between mitigation and other development objectives can act as an impediment to climate action (Section 13.8). Climate change is the result of decades of unsustainable energy production, land-use, production and consumption patterns, as well as governance arrangements and political economic institutions that lock in resource-intensive development patterns (*robust evidence, high agreement*). Reframing development objectives and shifting development pathways towards sustainability can help transform these patterns and practices, allowing space for transitions transforming unsustainable systems (*medium evidence, high agreement*) (Chapter 17, Executive Summary).

Prioritising is one way to manage trade-offs, addressing some national development objectives earlier than others. Another way is to adopt policy packages aimed at shifting development pathways towards sustainability as they expand the range of tools available to simultaneously achieve multiple development objectives, including mitigation. In the city example of Section 2a, a carbon tax alone would run counter to other development objectives if it made suburban households locked into high emissions transport modes poorer or if it restricted mobility choices, in particular for low- and middle-income households. Policy packages combining affordable housing and provision of safe low-carbon mobility could both facilitate equitable access to housing (a major development objective in many countries) and make it easier to mitigate by shifting the urban development pathway.

Similarly, a fundamental shift in the service provision that helps reduce energy demand (Chapter 5), driven by targeted policies, investment and enabling socio-cultural and behavioural change, would reduce pressure on supply side mitigation need, hence limiting pressure on water and food and the achievement of associated SDGs. Some studies assume Western European lifestyle as a reference for the Global North and an improvement in the living standard for the Global South to reduce energy demand and emissions (Grubler et al. 2018), while others explore a transformative change in the Global North to achieve a decent living standard for all (Bertram et al. 2018; Millward-Hopkins et al. 2020) (Section 3.7.8). For example, in the UK, interaction between multiple behavioural, socio-cultural, and corporate drivers including NGO campaigns, social movements and product innovations resulted in an observed decline in meat consumption (Sections 5.4 and 5.6.4).

3. What does shifting development pathways towards sustainability entail?

Shifting development pathways towards sustainability implies making transformative changes that disrupt existing developmental trends. Such choices would not be marginal (Stern 2009), but include technology adoption, infrastructure availability and use, and socio-behavioural factors (Chapter 5).

These include creating new infrastructure, sustainable supply chains, institutional capacities for evidence-based and integrated decision-making, financial alignment towards low-carbon socially responsible investments, just transitions and shifts in behaviour and norms to support shifts away from fossil-fuel consumption (Green and Denniss 2018). Adopting multi-level governance modes, tackling corruption where it inhibits shifts to sustainability, and improving social and political trust are also key for aligning and supporting long-term environmentally just policies and processes.

Shifting development pathways entails fundamental changes in energy, urban, building, industrial, transport, and land-based systems. It also requires changes in behaviour and social practices. Overcoming inertia and locked-in practices may face considerable opposition (Geels et al. 2017) (Section 5.4.5). The durability of carbon intensive transport modes and electricity generating infrastructures increase the risk of lock-in to high emissions pathways, as these comprise not just consumer practices, but sunk costs in infrastructure, supporting institutions and rules (Seto et al. 2016; Mattioli et al. 2020). Shifting investments towards low-GHG solutions requires a combination of conducive public policies, attractive investment opportunities, as well as the availability of financing to enable such a transition (Section 15.3).

4

4. How to shift development pathways?

Shifting development paths is complex. If history is any guide, practices that can easily supplant existing systems and are clearly profitable move fastest (Griliches 1957). Changes that involve 'dissimilar, unfamiliar and more complex science-based components' take more time, acceptance and legitimation and involve complex social learning (Conley and Udry 2010), even when they promise large gains (Pezzoni et al. 2019).

Yet despite the complexities of the interactions that result in patterns of development, history also shows that societies can influence the direction of development pathways based on choices made by decision-makers, citizens, the private sector and social stakeholders. For example, fundamentally different responses to the first oil shock shifted then-comparable economies on to different energy sector development and economic pathways in the 1970s and 80s (Sathaye et al. 2009). More recent examples have shown evidence of voluntary transitions for example, advanced lighting in Sweden, improved cook-stoves in China, liquefied petroleum gas stoves in Indonesia or ethanol vehicles in Brazil (Sovacool 2016).

There is no one-size-fits-all recipe for shifting development pathways. However, the following insights can be drawn from past experience and scenarios of possible future development pathways (Section 4.4.1). For example, policies making inner-urban neighbourhoods more accessible and affordable reduce transport costs for low- and middle-income households, and also reduce transport emissions (Section 4.4.1.9). Shifts in development pathways result from both sustained political interventions and bottom-up changes in public opinion. No single sector or policy action is enough to achieve this. Coordinated policy mixes would need to coordinate multiple actors – in other words, individuals, groups and collectives, corporate actors, institutions and infrastructure actors – to deepen decarbonisation and shift pathways towards sustainability (Pettifor 2020). One example was the liquefied petroleum gas (LPG) Subsidy ('Zero Kero') Program in Indonesia which harnessed creative policy design to shift to cleaner energy by overcoming existing private interests. The objective of decreasing fiscal expenditures on domestic kerosene subsidies by replacing it with LPG was achieved by harnessing distribution networks of existing providers supported by government subsidised provision of equipment and subsidised pricing (Cross-Chapter Box 9 in Chapter 13).

Shifts in one country may spill over to other countries. Collective action by individuals as part of formal social movements or informal lifestyle changes underpins system change (Sections 5.2.3, 5.4.1, 5.4.5.3 and 13.5).

Sectoral transitions that aspire to shift development pathways often have multiple objectives, and deploy a diverse mix or package of policies and institutional measures (Figure 13.6). Context specific governance conditions can significantly enable or disable sectoral transitions, and play a determinative role in whether a sectoral transition leads to a shift in development pathway. For example, if implemented policies to tackle fuel poverty target the most socially vulnerable households, this can help address barriers poor households face in undertaking building retrofits. In the EU-28, it has been shown that accelerated energy efficiency policies coupled with strong social policies targeting the most vulnerable households, can help reduce the energy demand in residential sector, and deliver additional co-benefits of avoided premature deaths and reduced health impacts (Section 9.8.2).

Literature suggests that through equitable resource distribution, high levels of human development can be provided at moderate energy and carbon levels by changing consumption patterns and redirecting systems in the direction of more sustainable resource use, suggesting that a special effort can be made in the near term for those on higher incomes who account for a disproportionate fraction of global emissions (Millward-Hopkins et al. 2020; Hickel et al. 2021) (Section 5.2.2 and Figure 5.14).

The necessary transformational changes are likely to be more acceptable if rooted in the development aspirations of the economy and society within which they take place (Dubash 2012; Jones et al. 2013) and may enable a new social contract to address a complex set of inter-linkages across sectors, classes and the whole economy (Fleurbaey et al. 2018).

Taking advantage of windows of opportunity and disruptions to mindsets and socio-technical systems could advance deeper transformations. These might include the globally declining costs of renewables (Figure 1.7, Section 2.2.5 and Box 16.2), emerging social norms for climate mitigation (Green and Denniss 2018), or the COVID-19 pandemic, all of which might be harnessed to centre political action on protecting human and planetary health (Büchs et al. 2020), but if not handled carefully could also risk undermining the support for transformation.

Cross-Chapter Box 5 (continued)

5. How can shifts in development pathways be implemented by actors in different contexts?
Shifting development pathways to increased sustainability is a shared aspiration. Yet since countries differ in starting points (e.g., social, economic, cultural, political) and history, they have different urgent needs in terms of facilitating the economic, social, and environmental dimensions of sustainable development and, therefore, give different priorities (Sections 4.3.2 and 17.4). The appropriate set of policies to shift development pathways thus depends on national circumstances and capacities.

In some developed countries and communities, affluence leads to high levels of consumption and emissions across sectors (Mazur and Rosa 1974; Wiedmann et al. 2020). For some countries, reducing consumption can reduce emissions without compromising on wellbeing. However, some developing countries still face the challenge of escaping 'middle-income traps' (Agénor and Canuto 2015), as labour-saving technological change and globalisation have limited options to develop via the manufacturing sector (Altenburg and Rodrik 2017). In least developed countries, infrastructure, industry, and public services are still being established, posing both a challenge to financial support to deploy technologies, and large opportunities to support accelerating low-to-zero carbon options – especially in terms of efficient and sufficient provision (Millward-Hopkins et al. 2020). Availability of capital, or lack thereof, is a critical discriminant across countries and requires international cooperation (Section 15.2.2).

Shifting development pathways towards sustainability needs to be supported by global partnerships to strengthen suitable capacity, technological innovation (Section 16.6), and financial flows (Sections 14.4.1, 15.2.4). The international community can play a particularly key role by helping ensure the necessary broad participation in climate-mitigation efforts, including by countries at different development levels, through sustained support for policies and partnerships that support shifting development pathways towards sustainability while promoting equity and being mindful of different transition capacities (Sections 4.3.2, 16.5, 16.6, 14.4 and 17.4).

In sum, development pathways unfold over time in response to complex dynamics among various drivers and diverse actors with varying interests and motivations (*high agreement, robust evidence*). The way countries develop determines the nature and degree of the obstacles to accelerating mitigation and achieving other sustainable development objectives (*medium-robust evidence, medium agreement*). Meeting ambitious mitigation and development goals cannot be achieved through incremental change (*robust evidence, medium agreement*). Shifting development pathways thus involves designing and implementing policies where possible to intentionally enhance enabling conditions and reduce obstacles to desired outcomes (*medium evidence, medium agreement*).

Section 4.4 elaborates mechanisms through which societies can develop and implement policies to substantially shift development pathways toward securing shared societal objectives. Such policies entail overcoming obstacles (Section 4.2.7) by means of favourable enabling conditions: governance and institutions, behaviour, innovation, policy and finance. These enabling conditions are amenable to intentional change – to greater or lesser degrees and over longer or shorter time scales – based on a range of possible measures and processes (Section 4.4).

4.4 How to Shift Development Pathways and Accelerate the Pace and Scale of Mitigation

4.4.1 Approaches, Enabling Conditions and Examples

4.4.1.1 Framing the Problem

What have we learned so far? As highlighted above, despite 30 years of UNFCCC and growing contributions by non-state actors, the emissions gap keeps growing (Sections 4.2.2 and 4.2.3). Mitigation conceived as incremental change is not enough. Meeting ambitious mitigation goals entails rapid, non-marginal changes in production and consumption patterns (Sections 4.2.4 and 4.2.5). Taking another approach, we have seen in Section 4.3 that shifting development pathways broadens the scope for mitigation (Sections 4.3.1 and 4.3.2) and offers more opportunities than mitigation alone to combine mitigation with the realisation of other SDGs (Section 4.3.1 and Cross-Chapter Box 5 in this chapter).

A practical way forward is to combine shifting development pathways and accelerating mitigation (*medium evidence, high agreement*). This means introducing multi-objective policy packages and sequences with climate and development components that both target mitigation directly and create the conditions for shifts in development pathways that will help accelerate further mitigation down the line, and meet other development objectives. Since development pathways result from myriad decisions from multiple actors (Section 4.3.1), coordination across countries and with non-state actors is essential.

The literature does not provide a handbook on how to accomplish the above. However, analysis of past experience as well as understanding of how societies function yield insights that the present section aims at presenting. Human history has seen multiple transformation of economies due to path-breaking innovations (Michaelowa et al. 2018), like the transformation of the energy system from traditional biomass to fossil fuels or from steam to electricity (Fouquet 2010, 2016a; Sovacool 2016). Fouquet (2016b) and Smil (2016) argue that even the most rapid global transformations have taken several decades. Enabling transformational change implies to create now the conditions that lead to that transformation (Díaz et al. 2019). The starting point is that there is no single factor determining such a transformation. Rather a range of enabling conditions can combine in a co-evolutionary process. Amongst the conditions that have been cited in the literature are higher levels of innovation, multilevel governance, transformative policy regimes or profound behavioural transformation (Rockström et al. 2017; IPCC 2018a; Geels et al. 2018; Kriegler et al. 2018). It might be possible to put in place some of the above conditions rapidly, while others may take longer, thereby requiring an early start.

The present chapter uses the set of enabling conditions identified in the IPCC SR1.5 report, namely policy, governance and institutional capacity, finance, behaviour and lifestyles and innovation and technology (de Coninck et al. 2018). As Figure 4.8 illustrates, *public policies* are required to foster both accelerating mitigation and shifting development pathways. They are also vital to guide and provide the other enabling conditions (compare Table 4.12). Improved governance and enhanced institutional capacity facilitate the adoption of policies that accelerate mitigation and shift development pathways, with the potential to achieve multiple mitigation and development objectives. Finance is required both to accelerate mitigation and to shift development pathways. Chapter 15

argues that near term actions to shift the financial system over the next decade (2021–2030) are critically important and feasible, and that the immediate post-COVID recovery opens up opportunities to scale up financing from billions to trillions (Mawdsley 2018) (Section 15.6.7). As discussed in Section 4.2.5, accelerated mitigation pathways encompass both rapid deployment of new technologies such as CCS or electric vehicles, as well as changes in consumption patterns: rapid deployment of mitigation *technology* and *behaviour change* are thus two enabling conditions to accelerated mitigation. Dynamics of deployment of technologies are relatively well known, pointing to specific, short-term action to accelerate innovation and deployment (Cross-Chapter Box 12 in Chapter 16), whereas dynamics of collective behaviour change is less well understood. Arguably, the latter also facilitates shifting development pathways.

Individual enabling conditions are discussed at length in Chapter 5 (behaviour change), 13 (policies, governance and institutional capacity), 15 (finance) and 16 (innovation). The purpose of the discussion below is to draw operational implications from these chapters for action, taking into account the focus of the present Chapter on action at the national level in the near- and mid-term, and its special emphasis on shifting development pathways in addition to accelerated mitigation.

The rest of the Section is organised as follows. Policy packages that combine climate and development policies are first discussed (Section 4.4.1.2). The next sections are dedicated to the conditions that facilitate shifts in development pathways and accelerated mitigation: governance and institutions (Section 4.4.1.3), financial resources (Section 4.4.1.4), behaviour change (Section 4.4.1.5) and innovation (Section 4.4.1.6). Four examples of how climate and development policies can be combined to shift pathways and accelerate mitigation are then presented

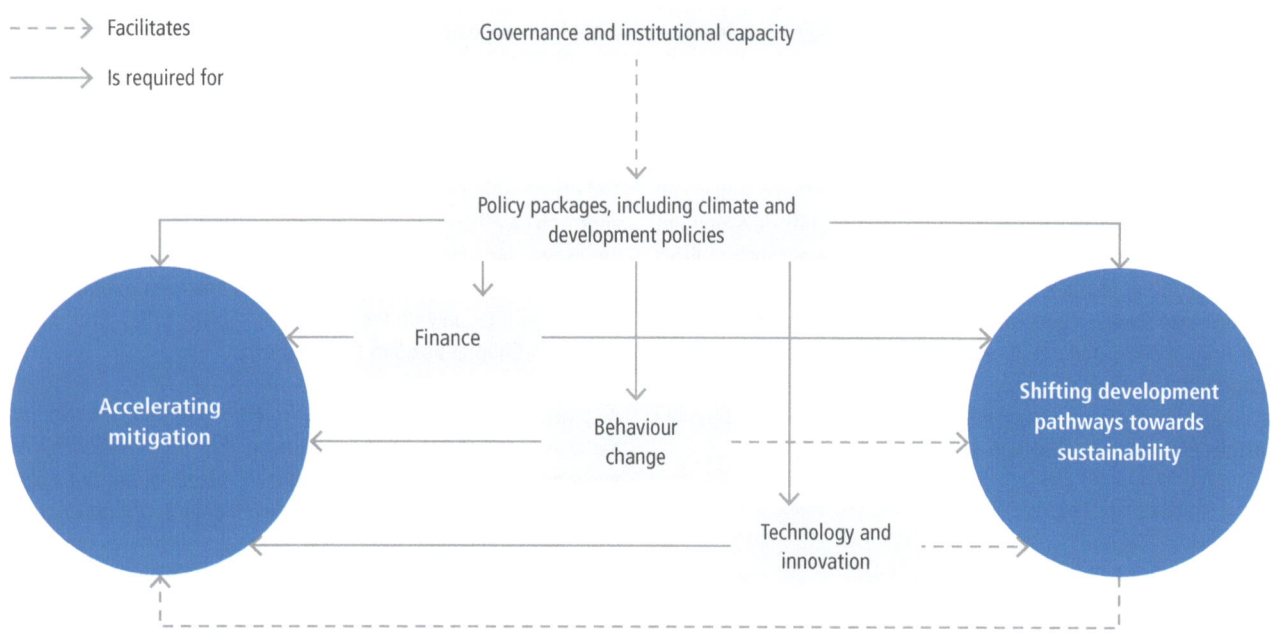

Figure 4.8 | Enabling conditions for accelerating mitigation and shifting development pathways towards sustainability.

(Sections 4.4.1.7, 4.4.1.8, 4.4.1.9 and 4.4.1.10). Section 4.4.2 focuses specifically on how shifts in development pathways can deliver both mitigation and adaptation. Finally, Section 4.4.3 discusses risks and uncertainties associated with combining shifting development pathways and accelerating mitigation.

4.4.1.2   Policy Packages That Include Climate and Development Policies

Although many transformations in the past have been driven by the emergence and diffusion of an innovative technology, policy intervention was frequent, especially in the more rapid ones (Michaelowa et al. 2018; Grubb et al. 2021). Likewise, it is not expected that spontaneous behaviour change or market evolution alone yield the type of transformations outlined in the accelerated mitigation pathways described in Section 4.2.5, or in the shifts in development pathways described in Section 4.3.3. On the contrary, stringent temperature targets imply bold policies in the short term (Rockström et al. 2017; Kriegler et al. 2018) to enforce effective existing policy instruments and regulations, as well as to reform or remove harmful existing policies and subsidies (Díaz et al. 2019).

Policy integration, addressing multiple objectives, is an essential component of shifting development pathways and accelerating mitigation (*robust evidence, high agreement*). A shift in development pathways that fosters accelerated mitigation may best be achieved through integrated actions that comprise policies in support of the broader SDG agenda, based on country-specific priorities (Sections 4.3.2, 13.8 and 13.9). These may include for example, fiscal policies, or integrating industrial (Nilsson et al. 2021) and energy policies (Fragkos et al. 2021) with climate policies. Similarly, sectoral transitions that aspire to shifting development pathways towards sustainability often have multiple objectives, and deploy a diverse mix or package of policies and institutional measures (Cross-Chapter Box 5).

Because low-carbon transitions are political processes, analyses are needed *of* policy as well as *for* policy (Section 13.6). Political scientists have developed a number of theoretical models that both *explain* policy-making processes and provide useful insights for *influencing* those processes. Case studies of successes and failures in sustainable development and mitigation offer equally important insights. Both theoretical and empirical analysis reinforce the argument that single policy instruments are not sufficient (*robust evidence, high agreement*). Policymakers might rather mobilise a range of policies, such as financial instruments (taxes, subsidies, grants, loans), regulatory instruments (standards, laws, performance targets) and processual instruments (demonstration projects, network management, public debates, consultations, foresight exercises, roadmaps) (Voß et al. 2007). Policies can be designed to focus on limiting or phasing out high-carbon technology. The appropriate mix is likely to vary between countries and domains, depending on political cultures and stakeholder configurations (Rogge and Reichardt 2016), but is likely to include a combination of: (i) standards, nudges and information to encourage low-carbon technology adoption and behavioural change; (ii) economic incentives to reward low-carbon investments; (iii) supply-side policy instruments including for fossil

fuel production (to complement demand-side climate policies) and (iv) innovation support and strategic investment to encourage systemic change (Grubb 2014). These approaches can be mutually reinforcing. For example, carbon pricing can incentivise low-carbon innovation, while targeted support for emerging niche technologies can make them more competitive encourage their diffusion and ultimately facilitate a higher level of carbon pricing. Similarly, the success of feed-in tariffs in Germany only worked as well as it did because it formed part of a broader policy mix including 'supply-push' mechanisms such as subsidies for research and 'systemic measures' such as collaborative research projects and systems of knowledge exchange (Rogge et al. 2015).

4.4.1.3   Governance and Institutional Capacity

Governance for climate mitigation and shifting development pathways is enhanced when tailored to national and local contexts. Improved institutions and governance enable ambitious climate action and help bridge implementation gaps (*medium evidence, high agreement*). Improving institutions involve a broad range of stakeholders and multiple regional and temporal scales. It necessitates a credible and trusted process for reconciling perspectives and balancing potential side-effects, managing winners and losers and adopting compensatory measures to ensure an inclusive and just transition (Newell and Mulvaney 2013; Miller and Richter 2014; Gambhir et al. 2018; Diffenbaugh and Burke 2019), managing the risk of inequitable or non-representative power dynamics and avoiding regulatory capture by special interests (Helsinki Design Lab 2011; Boulle et al. 2015; Kahane 2012).

Long experience of political management of change demonstrates that managing such risks is not easy, and requires sufficiently strong and competent institutions (Stiglitz 1998). For example, shift away from fossil fuel-based energy economy could significantly disrupt the status quo, leading to a stranding of financial and capital assets and shifting of political-economic power. Ensuring the decision-making process is not unduly influenced by actors with much to lose is key to managing a transformation. Effective governance, as noted in Chapter 13, requires establishing strategic direction, coordination of policy responses, and mediation among divergent interests. Among varieties of climate governance, which institutions emerge is path-dependent, based on the interplay of national political institutions, international drivers, and bureaucratic structures (Dubash 2021). Focused national climate institutions to address these challenges are more likely to emerge, persist and be effective when they are consistent with a framing of climate change that has broad national political support (*medium evidence, medium agreement*) (Sections 4.5, 13.2 and 13.5).

Innovative governance approaches can help meet these challenges (Clark et al. 2018; Díaz et al. 2019). *Enabling multilevel governance* – i.e., better alignment across governance scales – and coordination of international organisations and national governments can help accelerate a transition to sustainable development and deep decarbonisation (Tait and Euston-Brown 2017; Michaelowa and Michaelowa 2017; Ringel 2017; Revi 2017; Cheshmehzangi 2016; IPCC 2018a). *Participatory and inclusive governance* – partnerships

4

between state and non-state actors, and concerted effort across different stakeholders are crucial in supporting acceleration (Burch et al. 2014; Hering et al. 2014; Roberts 2016; Figueres et al. 2017; Clark et al. 2018; Leal Filho et al. 2018; Lee et al. 2018). So do *partnerships through transnational climate governance initiatives*, which coordinate nation states and non-state actors on an international scale (Hsu et al. 2018). Although they are unlikely to close the gap of the insufficient mitigation effort of national governments (Michaelowa and Michaelowa 2017) (Section 4.2.3), they help building confidence in governments concerning climate policy and push for more ambitious national goals (UNEP 2018b).

Meeting these challenges also requires enhanced institutional capacity and enhanced institutional mechanisms to strengthen the coordination between multiple actors, improve complementarities and synergies between multiple objectives (Rasul 2016; Ringel 2017; Liu et al. 2018) and pursue climate action and other development objectives in an integrated and coherent way (Von Stechow et al. 2016; McCollum et al. 2018; Rogelj et al. 2018b; Roy et al. 2018; Fuso Nerini et al. 2019), particularly in developing countries (Adenle et al. 2017; Rosenbloom 2017). Institutional capacities to be strengthened include vertical collaboration and interaction within nation states and horizontal collaboration (e.g., transnational city networks) for the development and implementation of plans, regulations and policies. More specifically capacities include: capacity for knowledge harnessing and integration (from multiple perspectives); for integrated policy design and implementation (Scott 2017); for long-term planning (Lecocq et al. 2021) for monitoring and review process; for coordinating multi-actor processes to create synergies and avoid trade-offs. As a result, institutions that enable and improve human capacities and capabilities are a major driver of transformation. To this extent, promoting education, health care and social safety, also are instrumental to undertake climate change mitigation and cope with environmental problems (Winkler et al. 2007; Sachs et al. 2019). Given that strengthening institutions may be a long-term endeavour, it needs attention in the near term.

4.4.1.4   Channelling Financial Resources

Accelerated mitigation and shifting development pathways necessitate both redirecting existing financial flows from high- to low-emissions technologies and systems and providing additional resources (*robust evidence*, *high agreement*). An example is changes in investments from fossil fuels to renewable energy, with pressures to disinvest in the former while increasing levels of 'green finance' (Sections 6.7.4 and 15.5). While some lower-carbon technologies have become competitive (Sections 1.4.3 and 2.5), support remains needed for the low-emissions options have higher costs per unit of service provided than high-emission ones. Lack of financial resources is identified as a major barrier to the implementation of accelerated mitigation and of shifts in development pathways. Overcoming this obstacle has two major components. One relates to private capital. The other to public finance.

There is substantial amount of research on the redirection of private financial flows towards low-carbon investment and the role of

financial regulators and central banks, as detailed in Chapter 15. Financial systems are an indispensable element of a systemic transition (Fankhauser et al. 2016; Naidoo 2020). Policy frameworks can redirect financial resources towards low-emission assets and services (UNEP 2015), mainstreaming climate finance within financial and banking system regulation, and reducing transaction costs for bankable mitigation technology projects (Mundaca et al. 2013; Brunner and Enting 2014; Yeo 2019). Shifts in the financial system to finance climate mitigation and other SDGs can be achieved by aligning incentives and investments with multiple objectives (UNEP Inquiry 2016).

Different approaches have been explored to improve such alignment (Section 15.6), from national credit policies to directly green mainstream financial regulations (e.g., through modifications in the Basel rules for banks). For all approaches, an essential precondition is to assess and monitor the contribution of financial flows to climate and sustainability goals, with better metrics that clearly link with financial activity (Chenet et al. 2019). Enabling the alignment of investment decision-making with achieving climate and broader sustainability goals includes acknowledgment and disclosure of climate-change related risk and of risks associated with mitigation in financial portfolios. Current disclosures remain far from the scale the markets need to channel investment to sustainable and resilient solutions (UNEP - Finance Initiative 2020; Clark et al. 2018; Task Force on Climate-Related Financial Disclosures 2019; IPCC 2018b). Disclosure, however, is not enough (Ameli et al. 2020). In addition, climate targets can be translated into investment roadmaps and financing needs for financial institutions, both at national and international level. Financing needs are usable for financial institutions, to inform portfolio allocation decisions and financing priorities (Chenet et al. 2019). At the international level, for example, technology roadmaps for key sectors can be translated into investment roadmaps and financing needs, as shown by existing experiences in energy and industrial sectors (IEA 2015; IEA and WBSCD 2018; Chenet et al. 2019).

The transition from traditional public climate finance interventions to the market-based support of climate mitigation (Bodnar et al. 2018) demands innovative forms of financial cooperation and innovative financing mechanisms to help de-risk low-emission investments and support new business models. These financial innovations may involve sub-national actors like cities and regional governments in raising finance to achieve their commitments (Cartwright 2015; CCFLA 2017). Moreover, public-private partnerships have proved to be an important vehicle for financing investments to meet the SDGs, including economic instruments for financing conservation (Sovacool 2013; Díaz et al. 2019).

Overall, early action is needed to overcome barriers and to adjust the existing incentive system to align national development strategies with climate and sustainable development goals in the medium-term. Steckel et al. (2017) conclude that climate finance could become a central pillar of sustainable development by reconciling the global goal of cost-efficient mitigation with national policy priorities. Without a more rapid, scaled redeployment of financing, in development trajectories that hinder the realisation of the global goals will be locked in (Zadek and Robins 2016). Investment might be designed to avoid trading off the Paris goals against other SDGs, as well as those that simultaneously reduce poverty, inequality, and emissions (Fuso Nerini et al. 2019).

At the national level, it is also essential to create public fiscal space for actions promoting the SDG agenda and thereby broadening the scope of mitigation (*medium evidence, medium agreement*). To do so, pricing carbon – either through tax payments based on the level of emissions or cap-and-trade systems that limit total allowable emissions – is an efficient means of discouraging carbon emissions throughout an economy (both in consumption and production) while simultaneously encouraging a switch to non-carbon energy sources and generating revenues for prioritised actions (Section 13.6.3). Regarding to levels, the High-Level Commission on Carbon Prices concluded that 'carbon-price level consistent with achieving the Paris temperature target is at least USD40–80 tCO_2^{-1} by 2020 and USD50–100 tCO_2^{-1} by 2030, provided a supportive policy environment is in place' (CPLC 2017; Wall Street Journal 2019). National level models yield median carbon values of carbon values of USD733 tCO_2^{-1} in 2050 along accelerated mitigation pathways (Section 4.2.6), while global models find a median value of USD578 tCO_2^{-1} for pathways that reach net zero CO_2 between 2045 and 2055 [interquartile range USD405–708] (Section 3.6.1).

Carbon pricing, however, is designed to reduce its fiscal base. Fiscal space may therefore also need to stem from other sources, although fiscal reforms are complex endeavours (Section 4.4.1.8). For countries at lower income levels, foreign aid can make an important contribution to the same agenda (Kharas and McArthur 2019). It may also be noted that, according to estimates at the global level, military spending amounted to USD1.748 trillion in 2012 (the last year with data), a figure that corresponded to 2.3% of GDP, 55% of government spending in education, and was 13 times the level of net ODA (World Bank 2020; SIPRI 2020). Given this, moderate reductions in military spending (which may involve conflict resolution and cross-country agreements on arms limitations) could free up considerable resources for the SDG agenda, both in the countries that reduce spending and in the form of ODA. The resolution of conflicts within and between countries before they become violent would also reduce the need for public and private spending repairing human and physical damage. The fact that civil wars are common in the countries that face the severest SDG challenges underscores the importance of this issue (Collier 2007, pp.17–37).

4.4.1.5 Changing Behaviour and Lifestyles

Changes in behaviour and lifestyles are important to accelerated mitigation. Most global mitigation pathways that limit warming to 2°C (>67%) or lower assume substantial behavioural and societal change and low-carbon lifestyles (de Coninck et al. 2018; IPCC 2018a; Luderer et al. 2018a) (see also Section 3.3.1 in this report; and Table 4.9 and Figure 4.3 in IPCC SR1.5). Chapter 5 concludes that behavioural changes within transition pathways offer Gigaton-scale CO_2 savings potential at the global level, an often overlooked strategy in traditional mitigation scenarios.

Individual motivation and capacity are impacted by different factors that go beyond traditional social, demographic and economic predictors. However, it is unclear to what extent behavioural factors (i.e., cognitive, motivational and contextual aspects) are taken into account in policy design (Dubois et al. 2019; Mundaca et al. 2019). In fact, while economic policies play a significant role in influencing people's decisions and behaviour, many drivers of human behaviour and values work largely outside the market system (Winkler et al. 2015; Díaz et al. 2019) as actors in society, particularly individuals, do not respond in an economically 'rational' manner based on perfect-information cost-benefit analyses (Runge 1984; Shiller 2019). Rather, compelling narratives can drive individuals to adopt new norms and policies. And norms can be more quickly and more robustly shifted by proposing and framing policies designed with awareness of how framings interact with individual cognitive tendencies (van der Linden et al. 2015). Transformative policies are thus much more likely to be successfully adopted and lead to long-term behavioural change if designed in accordance with principles of cognitive psychology (van der Linden et al. 2015), and with the deep understanding of decision-making offered by behavioural science (UNEP 2017b). Similarly, given that present bias – being motivated by costs and benefits that take effect immediately than those delivered later – significantly shapes behaviour, schemes that bring forward distant costs into the present or that upfront incentives have proved to be more effective (Zauberman et al. 2009; van den Broek et al. 2017; Safarzyńska 2018). Overall, transformational strategies that align mitigation with subjective life satisfaction, and build societal support by positive discourses about economic, social, and cultural benefits of low-carbon innovations, promises far more success than targeting mitigation alone (WBGU 2011; Asensio and Delmas 2016; Geels et al. 2017).

Climate actions are related to knowledge but even strongly to motivational factors (Hornsey et al. 2016; Bolderdijk et al. 2013; Boomsma and Steg 2014), which explains the gap between awareness and action (Ünal et al. 2018). Social influences, particularly from peers, affect people's engagement in climate action (Schelly 2014). Role models appear to have a solid basis in people's everyday preferences (WBGU 2011). Social norms can reinforce individuals' underlying motivations and be effective in encouraging sustainable consumption patterns, as many examples offered by behavioural science illustrate. Social networks also influence and spread behaviours (Service et al. 2014; Clayton et al. 2015; Farrow et al. 2017; Shah et al. 2019). These social influences can be harnessed by climate policy.

Collective action by individuals as part of formal social movements or informal lifestyle movements underpins system change (*robust evidence, high agreement*) (Sections 5.4 and 5.5). Organisations are comprised of individuals, but also become actors in their own right. Recent literature has considered the role of coalitions and social movements in energy democracy and energy transitions towards sustainability (Hess 2018). Other scholars have examined the role of women in redistributing power, both in the sense of energy transition and in terms of gender relations (Allen et al. 2019; Routledge et al. 2018). Mitigation and broader sustainable development policies that facilitate active participation by stakeholders can build trust, forge new social contracts, and contribute to a positive cycle building climate governance capacity (Section 5.2.3).

However, behavioural change not embedded in structural change will contribute little to climate change mitigation, suggesting that behavioural change is not only a function of individual agency but also depends on other enabling factors, such as the provision of infrastructure and institutions (Section 5.4). Successful shifts towards public transport, for example, involve technologies (buses, trams), infrastructure (light rail, dedicated bus lanes), regulations (operational licenses, performance contracts), institutions (new organisations, responsibilities, oversight), and high-enough density, which in turn depends on such choices as housing or planning policies (Section 4.4.1.9).

4.4.1.6   Fostering Technological Innovation

As outlined in Section 4.2.5, rapid, large-scale deployment of improved low-carbon technology is a critical component of accelerated mitigation pathways. As part of its key role in technological change, R&D can make a crucial contribution to accelerated mitigation up to 2030 and beyond, among other things by focusing on closing technology gaps that stand in the way of decarbonising today's high emitting sectors. Such sectors include shipping, trucking, aviation and heavy industries like steel, cement and chemicals. More broadly, it is increasingly clear that digital changes are becoming a key driving force in societal transformation (Tegmark 2017). Digitalisation is not only an 'instrument' for resolving sustainability challenges, it is also a fundamental driver of disruptive, multiscalar change (Sachs et al. 2019) that amounts to a shift in development pathway. Information and communication technologies, artificial intelligence, the internet of things, nanotechnologies, biotechnologies, robotics, are not usually categorised as climate technologies, but have a potential impact on GHG emissions (OECD 2017b) (Cross-Chapter Box 11 in Chapter 16).

The direction of innovation matters (*robust evidence, high agreement*). The research community has called for more 'responsible innovation' (Pandza and Ellwood 2013), 'open innovation' (Rauter et al. 2019), 'mission-oriented' innovation (Mazzucato and Semieniuk 2017), 'holistic innovation' (Chen et al. 2018b), 'next-generation innovation policy' (Kuhlmann and Rip 2018) or 'transformative innovation' (Schot and Steinmueller 2018) so that innovation patterns and processes are commensurate to our growing sustainability challenges. There is a growing recognition that new forms of innovation can be harnessed and coupled to climate objectives (Fagerberg et al. 2016; Wang et al. 2018). As such, innovation and socio-technical change can be channelled to intensify mitigation via 'deliberate acceleration' (Roberts et al. 2018a) and 'coalition building' (Hess 2018).

Innovation goes beyond technology. For example, decarbonisation in sectors with long lived capital stock (such as heavy industry, buildings, transport infrastructure) entail technology, policy and financing innovations (Bataille 2020). Similarly, expanding the deployment of photovoltaics can draw upon policies that support specific technical innovations (e.g., to improve photovoltaics efficiency), or innovations in regulatory and market regimes (e.g., net-metering), to innovations in social organisation (e.g., community-ownership). System innovation is a core focus of the transitions literature (Grin et al. 2010; Markard et al. 2012; Geels et al. 2017). Accelerating low-

carbon transitions not only involves a shift of system elements but also underlying routines and rules, and hence transitions shift the directionality of innovation. They hence concern the development of a new paradigm or regime that is more focused on solving sustainability challenges that cannot be solved within the dominant regime they substitute (Cross-Chapter Box 12 in Chapter 16).

Several studies have pointed at the important possible contributions of grassroots innovators for the start-up of sustainability transitions (Seyfang and Smith 2007; Seyfang et al. 2014; Smith et al. 2016). In particular, a range of studies have shown that users can play a variety of roles in promoting system innovation: shielding, nurturing (including learning, networking and visioning) and empowering the niches in relation to the dominant system and regime (Schot et al. 2016; Randelli and Rocchi 2017; Meelen et al. 2019). More fundamentally, innovation regimes can be led and guided by markets driven by monetisable profits (as much of private sector led technological innovation of patentable intellectual property), or prioritise social returns (e.g., innovation structures such as innovation prizes, public sector innovation, investments in human capital, and socially-beneficial intellectual property regimes). In both cases, public policies can play a key role by providing resources and favourable incentives (IEA 2020). Chapter 16 provides more details on ways to foster innovation.

4.4.1.7   Example: Structural Change Provides a Way to Keep Jobs and Mitigate

Developing countries have experienced a period of rapid economic growth in the past two decades. Patterns of growth have differed markedly across regions, with newly emerging East Asian economies building on transition to manufacturing – as China has done in the past – while Latin American countries tend to transition directly from primary sector to services (Rodrik 2016), and African countries tend to rely on productivity improvements in the primary sectors (Diao et al. 2019). Yet many countries still face the challenge of getting out of the 'middle-income trap' (Agénor and Canuto 2015), as labour-saving technological change and globalisation have limited options to develop via the manufacturing sector (Altenburg and Rodrik 2017).

Looking ahead, several studies have illustrated how structural change towards sustainability could lead to reduced emissions intensity and higher mitigative capacity. In China, for example, the shift away from heavy industry (to light industry and services) has already been identified as the most important force limiting emissions growth (Guan et al. 2018), and as a major factor for future emissions (Kwok et al. 2018).

Overall, Altenburg et al. (2017) argue that reallocation of capital and labour from low- to high-productivity sectors – in other words, structural change – remains a necessity, and that it is possible to combine it with reduced environmental footprint (including, but not limited to, mitigation). They argue that this dual challenge calls for structural transformation policies different from those implemented in the past, most importantly through a 'systematic steering of investment behaviour in a socially agreed direction' and encompassing policy coordination (*limited evidence, medium agreement*).

In order to permit progress on their SDG agendas, it is essential that countries develop visions of their future decarbonised sectoral production structure, including its ability to generate growth in incomes, employment and foreign exchange earnings. as well as the related spatial distribution of production, employment, and housing. To this extent, governance and institutional capacity matter, such as availability of tools to support long-term planning. A sectoral structure that permits strong growth is essential given strong associations between growth in per-capita incomes and progress on most SDGs (including those related to poverty; health; education; and access to water, sanitation, electricity, and roads; but not income equality), in part due to the fact that higher incomes provide both households and governments with resources that at least in part would be used to promote SDGs (Gable et al. 2015).

The future viability of sectors will depend on the extent to which they can remain profitable while relying on lower-carbon energy. The challenge to identify alternative sectors of growth is particularly acute for countries that today depend on oil and natural gas for most of their foreign exchange and government revenues (Mirzoev et al. 2020). Changes in economic structure will also have gender implications since the roles of men and women vary across sectors. For example, in many developing countries, sectors in which women play a relatively important role, including agriculture and unpaid household services like collection of water and fuel wood, may be negatively affected by climate change (Roy 2018). It may thus be important to take complementary actions to address the gender implications of changes in economic structure.

Given strong complementarities between policies discussed above, an integrated policy approach is crucial. For example, as suggested, the actions that influence the pace at which GHG emissions can be cut with political support may depend on taxation (including carbon taxes), investments in infrastructure, spending on R&D, changes in income distribution (influenced by transfers), and communication. In this light, it is important to consider the demands that alternative policy packages put on government policy-making efficiency and credibility as well as the roles of other enabling conditions. In fact, plans to undertake major reforms may provide governments with impetus to accelerate the enhancement of their capacities as part of the preparations (Karapin 2016; Withana 2016; Jakob et al. 2019).

4.4.1.8   Example: Embedding Carbon Finance in Broader Fiscal Reforms Offers a Way to Mitigate and Rethink the Social Contract

In many countries, fiscal systems are currently under stress to provide resources for the implementation of development priorities, such as, for example, providing universal health coverage and other social services (Meheus and McIntyre 2017) or sustainably funding pension systems in the context of aging populations (Asher and Bali 2017; Cruz-Martinez 2018). Overall, Baum et al. (2017) argue that low-income countries are likely not to have the fiscal space to undertake the investment entailed in reaching the SDGs. To create additional fiscal space, major options include improving tax recovery, reducing subsidies and levying additional taxes.

Mitigation offers an opportunity to create additional fiscal space, and thus to serve the objectives outlined above, by creating a new source of revenue for the government via carbon taxation or emissions permit auctioning and by reducing existing expenditures via reduction in subsidies to fossil-fuel. The 1991 tax reform in Sweden is an early example in which environmental taxation (including, but not limited to, fossil fuel taxation) was introduced as part of a package primarily aimed at lowering the marginal tax rates (more than 80% at the time), at reducing other taxes, while keeping most of the welfare state. To do so, the tax base was broadened, including through environmental and carbon taxation (Sterner 2007). Once in place, the carbon tax rate was substantially ramped up over time, and its base broadened (Criqui et al. 2019).

The future potential for using carbon taxation as a way to provide space for fiscal reform has been highlighted in the so-called 'green fiscal reform' literature (Vogt-Schilb et al. 2019). The potential is large, since only 13% of global GHG emissions were covered by carbon pricing schemes in 2019 (Watts et al. 2019) and since many countries price carbon negatively by subsidising fossil fuel use, thus generating effects that are the opposite of those that positive carbon prices hope to promote. In 2018, the global subsidy value amounted to USD427 billion, some 10 times the payment for carbon use (Watts et al. 2019). However, the size of the potential for creating fiscal space varies strongly across countries given differences in terms of current carbon prices and fuel subsidies.

The limited adoption of and political support for carbon pricing may be explained by the fact that most of the gains occur in the future and depend on actions across the globe, making them seem abstract and unpredictable, whereas the costs in the form of higher carbon prices are immediate (Karapin 2016). Furthermore, the links between carbon pricing and emissions may not be clear to the public who, in addition, may not trust that the government will use budgetary savings according to stated plans. The latter may be due to various factors, including a history of limited government commitment and corruption (Withana 2016; Chadwick 2017; Maestre-Andrés et al. 2019).

The literature reports limited systematic evidence based on ex post analysis of the performance of carbon pricing – carbon taxes and greenhouse gas (GHG) emissions trading systems (ETSs) (Haites 2018). Performance assessment is complicated by the effect of other policies and exogenous factors. Haites (2018) suggests that since 2008, other policies have probably contributed more to emission reductions than carbon taxes, and most tax rates are too low to achieve mitigation objectives. Emissions under ETSs have declined, with the exception of four systems without emissions caps (ibid). Every jurisdiction with an ETS and/or carbon tax also has other policies that affect its GHG emissions.

To help policymakers overcome obstacles, research has reviewed the international experience from carbon pricing reforms. Elimination of fossil fuel subsidies, equivalent to the elimination of negative carbon prices, have been more successful when they have included complementary and transparent measures that enjoy popular support, accompanied by a strong communications component that explains the measures and stresses their benefits (Withana 2016; Rentschler and Bazilian 2017; Maestre-Andrés et al. 2019).

Part of the losses (and related calls for compensation or exemptions) due to carbon pricing are related to the fact that it hurts the competitiveness of sectors that face imports from countries with lower carbon prices, leading to 'carbon leakage' if carbon-intensive production (and related jobs) migrates from countries with relatively high carbon prices. Some research suggests that evidence that a border carbon tax (or adjustment), set on the basis of the carbon content of the import, including a downward adjustment on the basis of any carbon payments (taxes or other) already made before entry, could reduce carbon leakage while also raising additional revenue and encouraging carbon pricing in the exporting country (Withana 2016; Cosbey et al. 2019).

The timing of carbon pricing reforms is also important: they are more likely to succeed if they exploit windows of opportunity provided by events that raise awareness of the costs of carbon emissions (like bouts of elevated local air pollution or reports about the role of emissions in causing global warming), as well as momentum from climate actions by other countries and international climate agreements (Karapin 2016; Jakob et al.2019). It is also important to consider the level of international prices of carbon energy: when they are low, consumer resistance would be smaller since prices will remain relatively low, though the tax may become more visible when energy prices increase again. As part of ongoing efforts to accelerate mitigation, such tax hikes may be crucial to avoid a slow down in the shift to renewable energy sources (Withana 2016; Rentschler and Bazilian 2017). In countries that export carbon energy, carbon taxation may run into additional resistance from producers.

There is also considerable literature providing insights on the political and social acceptability of carbon taxes, suggesting for example that political support may be boosted if the revenue is recycled to the tax payers or earmarked for areas with positive environmental effects (e.g., Bachus et al. (2019) for Belgium, and Beiser-McGrath and Bernauer (2019) for Germany and the USA), as well as on the difficulties associated with political vagaries (and economic consequences thereof) associated with the introduction of such instruments (Pereira et al. 2016). Similarly, 'best practices' have been drawn from past experience on fossil-fuel subsidy reforms (Rentschler and Bazilian 2017; Sovacool 2017). Specific policies, however, depend on societal objectives, endowments, structure of production, employment, and trade, and institutional structure (including the functioning of markets and government capacity) (Kettner et al. 2019). As noted in Section 4.2.6, macroeconomic analysis finds that the overall economic implications of carbon pricing differ markedly depending on the way the proceeds from carbon pricing are used, and thus on the way the fiscal system is reformed, with potential for double dividend if the proceeds from the tax are used to repeal the most distortive taxes in the economy.

In the context of this section on development pathways, it is worth emphasising that potential revenues drawn from the climate mitigation component of the fiscal reform varies strongly with the context, and may not be sufficient to address the other objectives pursued. Even if the carbon price is high, the revenue it generates may be moderate as a share of GDP and eventually it will be zero if emissions are eliminated. For example, Jakob et al. (2016) find that the carbon pricing revenues that most countries in Sub-Saharan Africa could expect to generate only would meet a small part of their infrastructure spending needs. In Sweden, the country with the highest carbon tax rate in the world, the tax has not been a significant part of total tax revenues. Moreover, emissions from sectors covered by the tax have shrunk and, as a result, the revenues from the tax, as a share of GDP, have also declined, from a peak of 0.93% in 2004, when the rate was USD109 per metric tonne of CO_2, to 0.48% in 2018, when the rate had reached USD132 (Jonsson et al. 2020; Statistics Sweden 2020). This means that governments that want to avoid a decline in the GDP share for total tax revenues over time would have to raise the intake from other taxes. However, it is here important to note that domestic tax hikes are likely to involve trade-offs since, at the same time as the spending they fund may provide various benefits, they may also reduce the capacity of households and the private sector to consume and invest, something that may reduce growth over time and reduced resources for spending in support of human development (Lofgren et al. 2013). It is also worth emphasising that restructuring of the fiscal system amount to changes in the social contract of the society (Combet and Hourcade 2017 and 2014), and thus represents a major economic and social decision.

4.4.1.9 Example: Combining Housing Policies With Carbon Taxation Can Deliver Both Housing and Mitigation in the Transport Sector

The spatial distribution of households and firms across urban and rural areas is a central characteristic of development pathways. Patterns of urbanisation, territorial development, and regional integration have wide-ranging implications for economic, social and environmental objectives (World Bank 2009). Notably, choices regarding spatial forms of development have large-scale implications for demand for transportation and associated GHG emissions.

Exclusionary mechanisms such as decreasing accessibility and affordability of inner-urban neighbourhoods is a major cause of suburbanisation of low- to middle-income households (e.g., Hochstenbach and Musterd 2018). Suburbanisation, in turn, is associated with higher transportation demand (Bento et al. 2005) and higher carbon footprints for households (Jones and Kammen 2014). Similarly, other studies find a significant positive link between housing prices and energy demand (Lampin et al. 2013).

Reducing emissions from transport in cities through traditional climate policy instruments (e.g., through a carbon tax) is more difficult when inner-urban neighbourhoods are less accessible and less affordable, because exclusionary mechanisms act as a countervailing force to the rising transportation costs induced by the climate policy, pushing households outwards rather than inwards. Said differently, the costs of mitigating intra-city transportation emissions are higher when inner-urban housing prices are higher (Lampin et al. 2013).

This suggests that policies making inner-urban neighbourhoods more accessible and more affordable can open up broader opportunities for suburban households to relocate in the face of increasing transportation costs. This is particularly important for low- and middle-income households, who spend a greater portion of their income on housing and transportation, and are more likely to be locked into locations that are distant from their jobs. Making inner-urban neighbourhoods more accessible and more affordable has the potential to reduce both the social costs (e.g., households feeling helpless in front of rising fuel prices) and the economic costs of mitigation policies – as a lower price of carbon is likely to achieve the same amount of emission reductions since households have more capacities to adjust.

Making inner-cities neighbourhoods more accessible and more affordable is a complex endeavour (Benner and Karner 2016). At the same time, it is already a policy objective in its own right in many countries, independent of the climate mitigation motivation, for a range of social, health and economic reasons. Revenues derived from climate policies could provide additional resources to support such programs, as some climate policy already have provisions to use their revenues towards low-income groups (Karner and Marcantonio 2018). The mitigation benefits of keeping inner-cities more accessible and affordable for low- and middle-income households often remains out of, or is only emerging in the debates surrounding the planning of fast-developing cities in many developing countries (IADB 2012; Grant 2015; Khosla and Bhardwaj 2019). Finally, from a political economy perspective, it is also interesting to note that (Bergquist et al. 2020) find higher support for climate policy packages in the USA when affordable housing programs are included.

In addition, investment in infrastructure is critical to the development of decarbonised economic structures that generate growth, employment, and universal access to a wide range of services that are central to the SDG agenda: transportation, water, sanitation, electricity, flood protection, and irrigation. For low- and middle-income countries, annual costs of reaching these goals by 2030 and putting their economies on a path toward decarbonisation may range between 2% and 8% of GDP, with the level depending on spending efficiency. Notably, these costs need not exceed those of more polluting alternatives (Rozenberg and Fay 2019). For transportation, this involves a shift toward more public transportation (rail and bus), and decarbonised electricity for vehicles, combined with land-use policies that densify cities and reduce distances between homes and jobs. By influencing the spatial distribution of households and firms and the organisation of transportation, infrastructure has a strong bearing on GHG emissions and the costs of providing services to different populations. Depending on country context, the private sector may play a particularly important role in the financing of infrastructure (World Bank 2009; Klein 2015).

Many investments in infrastructure and sectoral capital stocks have long lifetimes. Given this, it may be important to make sure that today's investments be fully decarbonised at the start or that they later can be converted to zero carbon. Today's investments in electric vehicles in settings where electricity is produced with fossil fuels is an example of convertible investments – they will be decarbonised once electricity production has switched to renewable energies. For capital stocks that cannot be decarbonised, countries may face costs of decommissioning well before the end of their useful lifetimes, especially when it is needed to respect country commitments to future full decarbonisation.

4.4.1.10 Example: Changing Economic, Social and Spatial Patterns of Development of the Agriculture Sector Provide the Basis for Sustained Reductions in Emissions From Deforestation

A growing literature assesses co-benefits of sectoral policies that lead to decarbonisation and simultaneously promote economic development, improve living standards, reduce inequality, and create job opportunities (Maroun and Schaeffer 2012; Bataille et al. 2016b; Pye et al. 2016; Bataille et al. 2018; La Rovere et al. 2018; Richter et al. 2018; Waisman et al. 2019). While this may be particularly challenging in developing countries, given large populations still lacking basic needs, previous development paths show that finding synergies in development and climate objectives in the AFOLU sector is possible. One example is Brazil, which has arguably shifted its development pathway to reduce emissions and make progress towards several SDGs, though progress is not linear. Over the past two decades, Brazil had made remarkable progress in implementing a sequence of policies across multiple sectors. This policy package simultaneously increased minimum wages of low income families, achieved universal energy access, and raised the quality of life and well-being for the large majority of the population (Da Silveira Bezerra et al. 2017; Grottera et al. 2017, 2018; La Rovere et al. 2018). This led to significant social benefits, reduction of income inequality and poverty eradication (Da Silveira Bezerra et al. 2017; Grottera et al. 2017), reflected in a decrease of the Gini coefficient and a rise in the human development index (La Rovere 2017).

Regulatory instruments were used to limit deforestation rates, together with implemented economic instruments that provided benefits to those protecting local ecosystems and enhancing land-based carbon sinks (Nunes et al. 2017; Bustamante et al. 2018; Soterroni et al. 2018, 2019). In parallel, public policies reinforced environmental regulation and command-and-control instruments to limit deforestation rates and implemented market-based mechanisms to provide benefits to those protecting local ecosystems and enhancing land-based carbon sinks (Sunderlin et al. 2014; Nunes et al. 2017; Hein et al. 2018; Simonet et al. 2019). The private sector, aligned with public policies and civil society, implemented the Amazon Soy Moratorium, a voluntary agreement that bans trading of soybeans from cropland associated with cleared Amazon rainforest and blacklists farmers using slave labour. This was achieved without undermining production of soybean commodities (Soterroni et al. 2019). As a result, between 2005 and 2012, the country halved its GHG emissions and reduced the rate of deforestation by 78% (INPE 2019a,b). This example shows that development delivering well-being can be accompanied by significant mitigation. A long-term and strategic vision was important in guiding enabling policies and mechanisms.

4

In more recent years, some of these shifts in Brazil's development pathways were undone. Political changes have redefined development priorities, with higher priority being given to agricultural development than climate change mitigation. The current administration has reduced the power of environmental agencies and forestry protection laws (including the forest code), while allowing the expansion of cropland to protected Amazon rainforest areas (Ferrante and Fearnside 2019; Rochedo et al. 2018). As a result, in 2020, deforestation exceeded 11,000 km^2, and reached the highest rate in the last 12 years (INPE 2020). The literature cautions that, if current policies and trends continue, the Amazon may reach an irreversible tipping point beyond which it will be impossible to remediate lost ecosystems and restore carbon sinks and indigenous people knowledge (Lovejoy and Nobre 2018; INPE 2019a; Nobre 2019). In addition, fossil fuel subsidies and other fiscal support of increased exploitation of oil resources may create carbon lock-ins that further inhibit low-carbon investments (Lefèvre et al. 2018).

Brazil's progress in mitigation depended significantly on reduced deforestation in the past. If deforestation rates keep on rising, mitigation efforts would need to shift to the energy sector. However, according to Rochedo et al. (2018), mitigation costs in the energy sector in Brazil are three times the costs of reducing deforestation and increasing land-based carbon sinks. Further mitigation strategies may depend on CCS in Brazil as elsewhere (Herreras Martínez et al. 2015; Nogueira de Oliveira et al. 2016), though the economic feasibility of deployment is not yet clear (Section 4.2.5.4).

4.4.2 Adaptation, Development Pathways and Mitigation

Mitigation actions are strongly linked to adaptation. These connections come about because mitigation actions can be adaptive (e.g., some agroforestry projects) but also through policy choices (e.g., climate finance is allocated among adaptation or mitigation projects) and even biophysical links (e.g., climate trajectories, themselves determined by mitigation, can influence the viability of adaptation projects). As development pathways shape the levers and enablers available to a society (Section 4.3.1, Figure 4.7), a broader set of enabling conditions also helps with adaptation (*medium evidence, high agreement*).

Previous assessments have consistently recognised this linkage. The Paris Agreement includes mitigation and adaptation as key areas of action, through NDCs and communicating adaptation actions and plans. The Agreement explicitly recognises that mitigation co-benefits resulting from adaptation can count towards NDC targets. The IPCC Fifth Assessment Report (IPCC 2014) emphasised that sustainable development is helpful in going beyond a narrow focus on separate mitigation and adaptation options and their specific co-benefits. The IPCC Special Report on climate change and land addresses GHG emissions from land-based ecosystems with a focus on the vulnerability of land-based systems to climate change. The report identifies the potential of changes to land use and land management practices to mitigate and adapt to climate change, and to generate co-benefits that help meet other SDGs (Jian et al. 2019).

A substantial literature detailing trade-offs and synergies between mitigation and adaptation exists and is summarised in the IPCC SR1.5 including energy system transitions; land and ecosystem transitions (including addressing food system efficiency, sustainable agricultural intensification, ecosystem restoration); urban and infrastructure system transitions (including land use planning, transport systems, and improved infrastructure for delivering and using power); industrial system transitions (including energy efficiency, bio-based and circularity, electrification and hydrogen, and industrial carbon capture, utilisation and storage (CCUS); and carbon dioxide removal (including bioenergy with CCS, afforestation and reforestation, soil carbon sequestration, and enhanced weathering) (IPCC 2018: Table 4.SM.5.1). Careful design of policies to shift development pathways towards sustainability can increase synergies and manage trade-offs between mitigation and adaptation (*robust evidence, medium agreement*).

This section examines how development pathways can build greater adaptive and mitigative capacity, and then turns to several examples of mitigation actions with implications for adaptation where there is a notable link to development pathways and policy choices. These examples are in the areas of agriculture, blue carbon and terrestrial ecosystem restoration.

4.4.2.1 Development Pathways can Build Greater Capacity for Both Adaptation and Mitigation

Previous IPCC assessments have reflected on making development more sustainable (IPCC et al. 2001; Sathaye et al. 2007; Fleurbaey et al. 2014). Other assessments have highlighted how ecosystem functions can support sustainable development and are critical to meeting the goals of the Paris Agreement (IPBES 2019b). IPCC SR1.5 found that sustainable development pathways to 1.5°C broadly support and often enable transformations and that 'sustainable development has the potential to significantly reduce systemic vulnerability, enhance adaptive capacity, and promote livelihood security for poor and disadvantaged populations (*high confidence*)' (IPCC 2018b: Section 5.3.1). With careful management, shifting development pathways can build greater adaptive and mitigative capacity, as further confirmed in recent literature (Schramski et al. 2018; Harvey et al. 2014; Ebi et al. 2014; Rosenbloom et al. 2018; Antwi-Agyei et al. 2015; Singh 2018; IPBES 2019b). The literature points to the challenge of design of specific policies and shifts in development pathways to achieve both mitigation and adaptation goals.

Governance and institutional capacity

Governance and institutional capacity necessary for mitigation actions also enables effective adaptation actions. Implementation of mitigation and adaptation actions can, however, encounter different sets of challenges. Mitigation actions requiring a shift away from established sectors and resources (e.g., fossil fuels) entail governance challenges to overcome vested interests (Piggot et al. 2020; SEI et al. 2020). Mitigation-focused initiatives from non-state actors tend to attain greater completion than adaptation-focused initiatives (NewClimate Institute et al. 2019).

4

Behaviour and lifestyles

On the level of individual entities, adaptation is reactive to current or anticipated environmental changes but mitigation is undertaken deliberately. Chapter 5 considers behavioural change, including the reconsideration of values and what is meant by well-being, and reflecting on a range of actors addressing both adaptation and mitigation. Shifting development pathways may be disruptive (Cross-Chapter Box 5), and there may be limits to propensity to change. Some studies report that climate change deniers and sceptics can be induced to undertake pro-environmental action if those actions are framed in terms of societal welfare, not climate change (Bain et al. 2012; Hornsey et al. 2016). Concrete initiatives to change behaviour and lifestyles include the Transition Town movement, which seeks to implement a just transition – both in relation to adaptation and mitigation – in specific localities (Roy et al. 2018).

Finance

Finance and investment of mitigation actions must be examined in conjunction with funding of adaptation actions, due to biophysical linkages and policy trade-offs (Box 15.1). Most climate funding supports mitigation efforts, not adaptation efforts (Buchner et al. 2019) (Halimanjaya and Papyrakis 2012). Mitigation projects are often more attractive to private capital (Abadie et al. 2013; Buchner et al. 2019). Efforts to integrate adaptation and mitigation in climate change finance are limited (Kongsager et al. 2016; Locatelli et al. 2016) There is a perception that integration of mitigation and adaptation projects would lead to competition for limited finance available for adaptation (Locatelli et al. 2016). Long-standing debates (Ayers and Huq 2009; Smith et al. 2011) whether development finance counts as adaptation funding remain unresolved. See Chapter 15 for more in-depth discussion relating investment in funding mitigation and adaptation actions.

Innovation and technologies

Systems transitions that address both adaptation and mitigation include the widespread adoption of new and possibly disruptive technologies and practices and enhanced climate-driven innovation (IPCC 2018a). See Chapter 16 for an in-depth discussion of innovation and technology transfer. The literature points to trade-offs that developing countries face in investing limited resources in research and development, though finding synergies in relation to agriculture (Adenle et al. 2015). Other studies point to difference in technology transfers for adaptation and mitigation (Biagini et al. 2014). Adaptation projects tend to use existing technologies whereas mitigation climate actions are more likely to rely on novel technologies. Innovations for mitigation are typically technology transfers from developed to less-developed countries (Biagini et al. 2014), however this so-called North-South technology transfer pathway is not exclusive (Biagini et al. 2014), and is increasingly challenged by China's global role in implementing mitigation actions (Chen 2018; Urban 2018). Indigenous knowledge can be a unique source for techniques for adaptation (Nyong et al. 2007) and may be favoured over externally generated knowledge (Tume et al. 2019).

Policy

Adaptation-focused pathways might reduce inequality, if adequate support is available and well-distributed (Pelling and Garschagen 2019). Some studies suggest that cities might plan for possible synergies in adaptation and mitigation strategies, currently done independently (Grafakos et al. 2019). The literature suggests that cities might identify both mitigation and adaptation as co-benefits of interventions targeted at developmental goals (Dulal 2017).

4.4.2.2   Specific Links Between Mitigation and Adaptation

Mitigation actions can be adaptive and vice-versa. In particular, many nature-based solutions (NBS) for climate mitigation are adaptive (*medium evidence*, *medium agreement*). Multiple NBS are being pursued under current development pathways (Chapter 7), but shifting to sustainable development pathways may enable a wider set of nature-based mitigation solutions with adaptation benefits. An example of this would be a shift to more sustainable diets through guidelines, carbon taxes, or investment in R&D of animal product substitutes (Figure 13.2) which could reduce pressure on land and allow for implementation of multiple NBS. Many of these solutions are consistent with meeting other societal goals, including biodiversity conservation and other sustainable development goals (Griscom et al. 2017; Fargione et al. 2018; Tallis et al. 2018). However, there can be synergies and trade-offs in meeting a complex set of sustainability goals (e.g., biodiversity, Section 7.6.5 and 3.1.5).

Development is a key factor leading to land degradation in many parts of the world (IPBES 2019b). Shifting development pathways to sustainability can include restoration and protection of ecosystems, which can enhance capacity for both mitigation and adaptation actions (IPBES 2019b).

In this section, we explore mitigation actions related to sustainable agriculture, coastal ecosystems ('blue carbon'), and restoration and protection of some terrestrial ecosystems. These mitigation actions are exemplary of trade-offs and synergies with adaptation, sensitivity to biophysical coupling, and linkages to development pathways. Other specific examples can be found in Chapters 6 to 11.

Farming system approaches can benefit mitigation and adaptation

Farming system approaches can be a significant contributor to mitigation pathways. These practices (which are not mutually exclusive) include agroecology, conservation agriculture, integrated production systems and organic farming (Box 7.5). Such methods have potential to sequester significant amounts of soil carbon (Section 7.4.3.1) as well as reduce emissions from on-field practices such as rice cultivation, fertilizer management, and manure management (Section 7.4.3) with total mitigation potential of 3.9 ± 0.2 GtCO$_2$-eq yr^{-1} (Chapter 7). Critically, these approaches may have significant benefits in terms of adaptation and other development goals.

Farming system approaches to agricultural mitigation have a wide variety of co-benefits and trade-offs. Indeed, there are conceptual formulations for these practices in which the co-benefits are more of a focus, such as climate-smart agriculture (CSA) which ties mitigation to adaptation through its three pillars of increased productivity, mitigation, and adaptation (Lipper et al. 2014). The '4 per 1000' goal to increase soil carbon by 0.4% per year (Soussana et al. 2019) is compatible with the three pillars of CSA. Sustainable intensification, a framework which centers around a need for increased agricultural production within environmental constraints also complements CSA (Campbell et al. 2014). The literature reports examples of mitigation co-benefits of adaptation actions, with evidence from various regions (Thornton and Herrero 2015; Thornton et al. 2018) (Chapter 7).

Conservation agriculture, promoted for improving agricultural soils and crop diversity (Powlson et al. 2016) can help build adaptive capacity (Smith et al. 2017; Pradhan et al. 2018a) and yield mitigation co-benefits through improved fertiliser use or efficient use of machinery and fossil fuels (Harvey et al. 2014; Cui et al. 2018; Pradhan et al. 2018a).

There is a complex set of barriers to implementation of farming-system approaches for climate mitigation (Section 7.6.4), suggesting a need for deliberate shifts in development pathways to achieve significant progress in this sector. The link between NDCs and mitigation in the land use sector can provide impetus for such policies. For example, there are multiple agricultural mitigation options that southeast Asian countries could use to meet NDCs that would have an important adaptive impact (Amjath-Babu et al. 2019).

Some agricultural practices considered sustainable have trade-offs, and their implementation can have negative effects on adaptation or other ecosystem services. Fast-growing tree monocultures or biofuel crops may enhance carbon stocks but reduce downstream water availability and decrease availability of agricultural land (Windham-Myers et al. 2018; Kuwae and Hori 2019). In some dry environments similarly, agroforestry can increase competition with crops and pastures, decreasing productivity, and reduce catchment water yield (Schrobback et al. 2011).

Agricultural practices can adapt to climate change while decreasing CO_2 emissions on the farm field. However, if such a practice leads to lower yields, interconnections of the global agricultural system can lead to land use change elsewhere and a net increase in GHG emissions (Erb et al. 2016). Implementation of sustainable agriculture can increase or decrease yields depending on context (Pretty et al. 2006).

Blue carbon and mitigation co-benefits of adaptation actions

The Paris Agreement recognises that mitigation co-benefits resulting from Parties' adaptation actions and/or economic diversification plans can contribute to mitigation outcomes (UNFCCC 2015a: Article 4.7). Blue carbon refers to biologically-driven carbon flux or storage in coastal ecosystems such as seagrasses, salt marshes, and mangroves (Wylie et al. 2016; Fennessy et al. 2019; Fourqurean et al.

2012; Tokoro et al. 2014) (see Cross-Chapter Box 8 on blue carbon as a storage medium and removal process).

Restoring or protecting coastal ecosystems is a mitigation action with synergies with adaptation and development. Such restoration has been described as a 'no regrets' mitigation option in the Special Report on the Ocean and Cryosphere in a Changing Climate (Bindoff et al. 2019) and advocated as a climate solution at national scales (Bindoff et al. 2019; Taillardat et al. 2018; Fargione et al. 2018) and global scales (Howard et al. 2017). On a per-area basis, carbon stocks in coastal ecosystems can be higher than in terrestrial forests (Howard et al. 2017), with below-ground carbon storage up to 1000 $tC\ ha^{-1}$ (McLeod et al. 2011; Crooks et al. 2018; Bindoff et al. 2019). Overall, coastal vegetated systems have a mitigation potential of around 0.5% of current global emissions, with an upper limit of less than 2% (Bindoff et al. 2019).

Restoration or protection of coastal ecosystems is an important adaptation action with multiple benefits, with bounded global mitigation benefits (Gattuso et al. 2018; Bindoff et al. 2019). Such restoration/preservation reduces coastal erosion and protects from storm surges, and otherwise mitigates impacts of sea level rise and extreme weather along the coast line (Siikamäki et al. 2012; Romañach et al. 2018; Alongi 2008). Restoration of tidal flow to coastal wetlands inhibits methane emissions which occur in fresh and brackish water (Kroeger et al. 2017) (Section 7.4.2.8 describes a more inclusive set of ecosystem services provided by coastal wetlands). Coastal habitat restoration projects can also provide significant social benefits in the form of job creation (through tourism and recreation opportunities), as well as ecological benefits through habitat preservation (Edwards et al. 2013; Sutton-Grier et al. 2015; Sutton-Grier and Moore 2016; Wylie et al. 2016; Kairo et al. 2018; Bindoff et al. 2019).

Coastal ecosystem-based mitigation can be cost-effective, but interventions should be designed with care. One concern is to assure that actions remain effective at higher levels of climate change (Alongi 2015; Bindoff et al. 2019). Also, methane emissions from ecosystems may partially reduce the benefit of the carbon sequestration (Rosentreter et al. 2018) depending on the salinity (Poffenbarger et al. 2011; Kroeger et al. 2017). As the main driver of mangrove forest loss is aquaculture/agriculture (Thomas et al. 2017), there may be entrenched interests opposing restoration and protection actions.

Restoration and protection of terrestrial ecosystems

Restoration of terrestrial landscapes can be a direct outcome of development pathways, and can be critical to achieving a variety of SDGs (especially 1, 2, 6, 8, 13, 15) (Vergara et al. 2016; Lapola et al. 2018) although it also presents risks and can have trade-offs with other SDGs (Cao et al. 2010; Dooley and Kartha 2018). Landscape restoration is nearly always a mitigation action, and can also provide adaptive capacity. While policy in Brazil has tended to focus on the Amazon as a carbon sink, the mitigation co-benefits of ecosystem-based adaptation actions have been highlighted in the literature (Locatelli et al. 2011; Di Gregorio et al. 2016). A study of potential

4

restoration of degraded lands in Latin America (Vergara et al. 2016) indicates that substantial benefits for mitigation, adaptation, and economic development accrue after several years, underscoring a reliance on deliberate development choices. In agricultural contexts, restoration is a development choice that can enhance adaptive and mitigative capacity via impact on farmer livelihoods.

Preventing degradation of landscapes can support both mitigation and adaptation (IPCC 2019). Restoration of ecosystems is associated with improved water filtration, groundwater recharge and flood control and multiple other ecosystem services (Ouyang et al. 2016).

Restoration projects must be designed with care. There can be trade-offs in addition to the synergies noted above (Section 7.6.4.3). Restorations may be unsuccessful if not considered in their socio-economic context (Lengefeld et al. 2020; Iftekhar et al. 2017; Jellinek et al. 2019). Restoration projects for mitigation purposes can be more effective if done with adaptation in mind (Gray et al. 2011) as a changing climate may render some mitigation actions biophysically infeasible (Arneth et al. 2021). Landscape restoration projects intended for CDR may underperform due to future release of stored carbon, or deferral of storage until after irreversible climate change effects (e.g. extinctions) (Dooley and Kartha 2018).

Afforestation plans have received substantial attention as a climate mitigation action, with ongoing unresolved debate on the feasibility and trade-offs of such plans. Such afforestation programs can fail for biophysical reasons (Fleischman et al. 2020) (Section 7.4.2.2) but also lack of consideration of socioeconomic and development contexts (Fleischman et al. 2020).

4.4.3   Risks and Uncertainties

Shifting development pathways and accelerating mitigation are complex endeavours that carry risks. Some of these risks can be easily captured by quantitative models. Others are better understood via qualitative approaches, such as qualitative narrative storylines (told in words) and methods mixing qualitative and quantitative models (Kemp-Benedict 2012; Hanger-Kopp et al. 2019). The following outline key risks and relevant hedging strategies identified in the literature.

4.4.3.1   Actions by Others Not Consistent With Domestic efforts

The international context is a major source of uncertainty for national-level planning, especially for small- or medium-sized open economies, because the outcome of domestic choices may significantly depend on decisions made by other countries and actor, over which national governments have limited or no control (Lachapelle and Paterson 2013). Availability of foreign financial resources in countries with limited domestic savings (Baum et al. 2017) and availability of technology transfers (Glachant and Dechezleprêtre 2017) are some examples. Other external decisions with significant bearing on domestic action include mitigation policies in other countries (Dai

et al. 2017), and especially in major trading partners, the lack of which can result in competitive disadvantage for sectors exposed to international competition (Alton et al. 2014). The international prices of the key commodities (notably energy), goods and services are important, notably when shifting development pathway is based on structural change (e.g., Willenbockel et al. 2017 for Ghana and Kenya).

Remedies include first devising policy packages that are, to the extent possible, robust to uncertainty regarding external decisions. For example, mitigation in the building sector is considered less problematic for competitiveness since the construction sector is less exposed to international competition. Remedies also include securing international cooperation to reduce the uncertainty that domestic decision-makers face about the international context. Shifting investments towards low-GHG solutions requires a combination of conducive public policies, attractive investment opportunities and financing of transitions (Section 15.6), which can enable shifting development pathways. Cooperation can generate positive spill overs through technology diffusion (Section 13.6.6). Third, cooperation is not limited to governments. As discussed in Section 4.2.3, international cooperative initiatives among non-state actors (cities, economic branches, etc.) can also provide know-how, resources and stable cooperative frameworks that reduce uncertainty for individual actors (Section 14.5.5).

4.4.3.2   Parts of Complex Policy Packages Fail

As outlined in the examples in Section 4.4.1 above, shifting development pathways and accelerating mitigation are complex endeavours, on which there is limited experience and know-how from the past. An uncertainty is that parts of these policy packages may fail, in other words, under-deliver relative to the amount of mitigation and of transformations initially expected. For example, France has failed to meet its 2015–2018 carbon budget as housing retrofitting programs, in particular, have failed to deliver the expected amount of emission reductions (Haut Conseil pour le Climat 2019). There are two main options to tackle this risk. The first is to build in redundancy. The second is to anticipate that some parts of the policies will inevitably fail, and build-in monitoring and corrective mechanisms in a sequential decision-making process. To this regard, building institutions that can properly monitor, learn from and improve over time is critical (Nair and Howlett 2017).

4.4.3.3   New Information Becomes Available

The science on climate change, its impacts and the opportunities to mitigate is continuously being updated. Even though decisions are no longer made 'in a sea of uncertainty' (Lave 1991), we know that new information will come over time, that may have significant bearing on the design and objectives of policies to shift development pathways and accelerate mitigation. New information may come from climate sciences (e.g., updated GWP values or available carbon budgets) (Quéré et al. 2018), impact sciences (e.g., re-evaluation of climate impacts associated with given emission pathways) (Ricke et al. 2018) or mitigation sciences (e.g., on availability of given technologies) (Lenzi et al. 2018; Giannousakis et al. 2020).

At the same time, economic and social systems are characterised by high degree of inertia, via long-lived capital stock or urban forms (Lecocq and Shalizi 2014), or more broadly mutually reinforcing physical, economic, and social constraints (Seto et al. 2016) that may lead to carbon lock-ins (Erickson et al. 2015). Risks associated with long-lasting fossil-fuel power plants have been the object of particular attention. For example, Pfeiffer et al. (2018) estimate that even if the current pipeline of power plants was cancelled, about 20% of the existing capacity might be stranded to remain compatible with 1.5°C or 2°C pathways – implying that additional capital accumulation would lead to higher sunk costs associated with stranded assets (Ansar et al. 2013; Johnson et al. 2015; Kriegler et al. 2018; Luderer et al. 2018b).

In the presence of uncertainty and inertia (or irreversibilities), hedging strategies may be considered, that include selection of risk-hedging strategies and processes to adjust decisions as new information becomes available. The notion of hedging against risks is also prominent in the adaptation literature, as exemplified by the terminology of 'climate resilient development' (Fankhauser and McDermott 2016) (AR6 WGII, Chapter18). There is also a growing literature on hedging strategies for individual actors (e.g., firms or investors) in the face of the uncertainties associated with mitigation (e.g., policy uncertainty or the associated carbon price uncertainty; e.g., Andersson et al. 2016 or Morris et al. 2018). On the other hand, there is often limited discussion of uncertainty and of its implication for hedging strategies in the accelerated mitigation pathway literature. Exceptions include (Capros et al. 2019), who elicit 'no-regret' and 'disruptive' mitigation options for the EU through a detailed sensitivity analysis, and (Watson et al. 2015) who discuss flexible strategies for the UK energy sector transition in the face of multiple uncertainties.

4.4.3.4   Black Swans (Such as the COVID-19 Crisis)

As the current COVID-19 crisis demonstrates, events happen that can derail the best-laid plans. Unexpected events beyond the range of human experience until then are called 'black swans', given the expectation that all swans are white. The only point to note here is that such events may also provide opportunities. In the COVID-19 case, for example, the experience of conducting many activities on-line, which reduces emissions from transport, may leave an imprint on how some of these activities are carried out in the post-COVID-19 world. Similarly, reduced air pollution seen during the pandemics may increase support for mitigation and strengthen the case for climate action. However, the emissions implications of recovery packages depend on choosing policies that support climate action while addressing the socio-economic implications of COVID-19 (Hepburn et al. 2020). Governments may be in a stronger position to do so due to their pivotal role in assuring the survival of many businesses during the pandemics. Given the magnitude of recovery packages and their implications (Pollitt et al. 2021), choosing the direction of recovery packages amounts to choosing a development pathway (Cross-Chapter Box 1 in Chapter 1).

4.4.3.5   Transformations Run Into Oppositions

As noted above, shifting development pathways and accelerating mitigation involve a broad range of stakeholders and decision-makers, at multiple geographical and temporal scales. They require a credible and trusted process for reconciling perspectives and balancing potential side-effects, managing winners and losers and implementing compensatory measures to ensure an inclusive just transition (Newell and Mulvaney 2013; Miller and Richter 2014; Gambhir et al. 2018; Diffenbaugh and Burke 2019). Such processes are designed to manage the risk of inequitable or non-representative power dynamics (Helsinki Design Lab 2011; Boulle et al. 2015; Kahane 2012). More generally, stakeholder processes can be subject to regulatory capture by special interests, or outright opposition from a variety of stakeholders. Information asymmetry between government and business may shape the results of consultative processes. Long experience of political management of change demonstrates that managing such risks is not easy, and requires sufficiently strong and competent institutions (Stiglitz 1998). The next section on Just Transition (Section 4.5) addresses this issue.

4.5   Equity, Including Just Transitions

Equity is an ethical and at times economic imperative, but it is also instrumentally an enabler of deeper ambition for accelerated mitigation (Hoegh-Guldberg et al. 2019). The literature supports a range of estimates of the net benefits – globally or nationally – of low-carbon transformation, and it identifies a number of difficulties in drawing definitive quantitative conclusions (e.g., comparisons of costs and benefits among different actors, the existence of non-economic impacts, comparison across time, uncertainty in magnitude) (Section 3.6). One of the most important of these dimensions is the distributional consequences of mitigation, as well as a range of equity considerations arising from the uncertainty in net benefits, as well as from the distribution of costs and benefits among winners and losers (Rendall 2019; Caney 2016; Lahn and Bradley 2016; Lenferna 2018a; Kartha et al. 2018b; Robiou Du Pont et al. 2017). Some equity approaches are even just seeking corrective justice including for historical emissions (Adler 2007). For an assessment of literature on fairness in NDCs, see Section 4.2.2.7.

Equity issues are often discussed in the literature via frameworks that are well-founded in the ethical literature and that have a strong bearing on effort-sharing, but have not yet been quantitatively modelled and expressed in the form of an emissions allocation quantified framework. These include, for example, ethical perspectives based in human rights (Johl and Duyck 2012), human capabilities (Klinsky et al. 2017b), environmental justice (Mohai et al. 2009; Schlosberg 2009), ecological debt (Srinivasana et al. 2008; Warlenius et al. 2015), transitional justice (Klinsky 2017; Klinsky and Brankovic 2018), and planetary boundaries (Häyhä et al. 2016).

While there is extensive literature on equity frameworks for national emissions allocations (CSO Equity Review 2015, 2017, 2018; Holz et al. 2018; Kemp-Benedict et al. 2018; Robiou du Pont and Meinshausen 2018; Fyson et al. 2020; Pozo et al. 2020; Pye et al. 2020), such studies have tended to focus on allocation of a global carbon budget among countries based on quantified equity frameworks. The implicit normative choices made in these analysis have limitations (Kartha et al. 2018a). Moreover, there are many ethical parameters that could be introduced to enrich the existing quantitative frameworks, such as progressivity (Holz et al. 2018), consumption-based accounting (Afionis et al. 2017), prioritarianism (Adler and Treich 2015), and a right to development (Moellendorf 2020). Introducing these ethical frames into conventional quantification approaches generally implies greater allocations for poorer and lower-emitting populations, suggesting that the approaches that are typically highlighted in emissions allocation analyses tends to favour wealthier and higher-emitting countries. Broader, more inclusive sharing of costs and burdens is seen as a way to enhance equity in procedures and outcomes.

Ultimately, equity consequences depend on how costs and benefits are initially incurred and how they are shared as per social contracts (Combet and Hourcade 2017), national policy, and international agreements. The literature suggests a relationship between the effectiveness of cooperative action and the perception of fairness of such arrangements. Winkler et al. (2018) demonstrate that countries have put forward a wide variety of indicators and approaches for explaining the fairness and ambition of their NDCs, reflecting the broader range of perspectives found in the moral philosophical literature cited above. Mbeva and Pauw (2016) further find that adaptation and financing issues take on greater salience in the national perspectives reflected in the NDCs.

Topics of equity and fairness have begun to receive a greater amount of attention within the energy and climate literature, namely through the approaches of gender and race (Pearson et al. 2017; Lennon 2017; Allen et al. 2019), climate justice (Roberts and Parks 2007; Routledge et al. 2018) (Roberts & Parks, 2006; Routledge et al. 2018), and energy justice (Sovacool and Dworkin 2014). While such approaches frequently envision justice and equity as an ethical imperative, justice also possesses the instrumental value of enabling deeper and more socially acceptable mitigation efforts (Klinsky and Winkler 2018).

A concrete focal point on these issues has been that of 'just transition'. Getting broad consensus for the transformational changes entailed in moving from a high- to a low-carbon economy means 'leaving no one behind', in other words, ensuring (sufficiently) equitable transition for the relevant affected individuals, workers, communities, sectors, regions and countries (Newell and Mulvaney, 2013; Jasanoff 2018). The concept of a 'just transition' owes its origin to the USA trade union movement of the 1980s. The earliest version of a just transition was called the 'Superfund for Workers' modelled on the 1980 Superfund program that designed federal funds for the clean-up of toxic substances from chemicals, mining and energy production (Stevis and Felli 2015). It was further taken up, for example in the collaboration of the International Trade Union Confederation (ITUC), the International Labour Organization (ILO) and the UN Environment Programme (UNEP) in promoting 'green jobs' as integral elements

of a just transition (ILO 2015; Rosemberg 2010). In recent years the concept of a 'just transition' has gained increased traction, for example incorporated in the outcome of the Rio+20 Earth Summit and more recently recognised in the preamble of the Paris Agreement, which states 'the imperative of a just transition of the workforce and the creation of decent work and quality jobs in accordance with nationally defined development priorities' (UNFCCC 2015a). Some heads of state and government signed a Solidarity and Just Transition Silesia Declaration first introduced at COP24 in Poland (HoSG 2018).

The literature identifies targeted and proactive measures from governments, agencies, and authorities to ensure that any negative social, environmental or economic impacts of economy-wide transitions are minimised, while benefits are maximised for those disproportionally affected (Healy and Barry 2017). While the precise definition varies by source, core elements tend to include: (i) investments in establishing low-emission and labour-intensive technologies and sectors (Mijn Cha et al. 2020); (ii) research and early assessment of the social and employment impacts of climate policies (Green and Gambhir 2020; Mogomotsi et al. 2018); (iii) social dialogue and democratic consultation of social partners and stakeholders (Swilling and Annecke 2012; Smith 2017); (iv) the creation of decent jobs; active labour markets policies; and rights at work (ILO 2015; UNFCCC 2016c); (v) fairness in energy access and use (Carley and Konisky 2020); (vi) economic diversification based on low-carbon investments; (vii) realistic training/retraining programs that lead to decent work; (viii) gender specific politics that promote equitable outcomes (Allwood 2020); (ix) the fostering of international cooperation and coordinated multilateral actions (Lenferna 2018b; Newell and Simms 2020); (x) redressing of past harms and perceived injustices (Setzer and Vanhala 2019; UNHRC 2020); and (xi) consideration of inter-generational justice concerns, such as the impacts of policy decisions on future generations (Newell and Mulvaney, 2013).

A just transition could therefore entail that the state intervenes more actively in the eradication of poverty, and creates jobs in lower-carbon sectors, in part to compensate for soon-to-be abandoned fossil-fuel-based sectors, and that governments, polluting industries, corporations and those more able to pay higher associated taxes pay for transition costs, provide a welfare safety net and adequate compensation for people, communities, places, and regions that have been impacted by pollution, marginalised or negatively impacted by a transition from a high- to low-carbon economy and society (Muttitt and Kartha 2020; Le Billon and Kristoffersen 2020; Kartha et al. 2018b). Reducing climate impacts is another important dimension of equity, in that the poor who are least responsible for climate change are most vulnerable to its impacts (AR6 WGII, Chapter 8). Focusing on financial losses alone however can obscure an important distinction between losses incurred by corporations and states and losses experienced by workers and communities. Processes established in the name of a just transition are also at risk of being co-opted by incumbent interests and powerful/wealthy agents (Green and Gambhir, 2020). Policy interventions associated with good governance, democratic oversight, and legal recourse can help overcome attempted co-optation of just transition, or use of COVID-19 recovery packages for continued carbon lock-in (Hepburn et al. 2020; SEI et al. 2020).

4

Box 4.6 | Selected Organisations and Movements Supporting a Just Transition

- 350.org (global)
- Asian Pacific Forum on Women, Law and Development (Asia Pacific)
- Blue Green Alliance (USA)
- Beyond Coal campaign (USA)
- Central Única dos Trabalhadores (Brazil)
- Climate Action Network (global)
- Climate Justice Alliance (USA)
- Cooperation Jackson (USA)
- Dejusticia (Colombia)
- Deutscher Gewerkschaftsbund (German Trade Union Confederation, Germany)
- DiEM25 (pan-European)
- European Union
- European Trade Union Confederation (EU)
- Grassroots Global Justice (USA)
- IndustriALL Global Union (global)
- Indigenous Environmental Network (USA)
- International Labor Organization (global)
- ITUC-affiliated Just Transition Centre (global)
- ITUC-affiliated Just Transition Centre (Americas)
- Just Transition Alliance (USA)
- Just Transition Centre (global)

- Just Transition Fund (USA)
- Kentuckians for the Commonwealth (USA)
- Labor Network for Sustainability (USA)
- Latrobe Valley Authority (Australia)
- Movement Generation (USA)
- NAACP (USA)
- National Union of Mineworkers of South Africa (South Africa)
- Pan African Climate Justice Alliance (Africa)
- Post Petroleum Transitions Roundtable (Mesa de Transición Post Petrolera) (Argentina)
- Powering Past Coal Alliance (global)
- Right to the city alliance (USA)
- Sierra Club (USA)
- Sunrise Movement (USA)
- The Leap Manifesto (Canada)
- The Trade Unions for Energy Democracy Initiative (global)
- Trade Union Confederation of the Americas (TUCA)
- Transition Towns Movement (UK)
- Women's Environment and Development Organization (global)

The just transition concept has thus become an international focal point tying together social movements, trade unions, and other key stakeholders to ensure equity is better accounted for in low-carbon transitions and to seek to protect workers and communities. It also forms a central pillar of the growing movement for a 'Green New Deal' – a roadmap for a broad spectrum of policies, programs, and legislation that aims to rapidly decarbonise the economy while significantly reducing economic inequality (Allam et al. 2021; Galvin and Healy 2020). The US Green New Deal Resolution (Ocasio-Cortez 2019) for example, positions structural inequality, poverty mitigation, and a just transition at its centre. The European Green Deal proposed in 2019 (European Commission 2019), including a €100 billion 'Just Transition Mechanism' to mitigate the social effects of transitioning away from jobs in fossil-based industries. National level green new deals with strong just transition components have been proposed in South Korea, Australia, Spain, UK, Puerto Rico, Canada, as well as regional proposals across Latin America and the Caribbean (Pollin 2020).

A just transition at national, regional and local scales can help to ensure that workers, communities, frontline communities and the energy-poor are not left behind in the transition. Moreover, a just transition necessitates that rapid decarbonisation does not perpetuate asymmetries between richer and poorer states and people (UNHRC 2020). Alliances around a just transition in countries across the world take many forms (Box 4.6).

As Figure 4.9 shows, no fewer than seven national commissions or task forces on a just transition existed as of 2020 as well as seven other sets of national policies and a multitude of other actors, networks, and movements. For instance, the German phase-out of coal subsidies involved a savings package for unemployed miners. Subsidy reform packages introduced by Iran, Namibia, the Philippines, Turkey, and United Kingdom provide similar compensating measures to affected groups (Sovacool 2017). Spain's just transition plan for coal miners includes early retirement, redundancy packages, silicosis compensation, retraining for green jobs, and priority job placement for former miners.

(a) Just Transition commissions, task forces and dialogues

Australia: La Trobe Valley Authority

Canada: Task Force on Just Transition for Canadian Coal Power Workers

China: Mine closure provisions in the 13th Five Year Plan for Coal Industry Development, 2016–2020

Costa Rica: National Decarbonisation Plan 2018–2050

Czech Republic: Czech Coal Commission

Finland: Working group to ensure a fair and just transition and acceptability of climate measures

France: 2018 Ecological Transition Contracts programme

Germany: German Commission on Growth, Structural Change and Employment (German Coal Commission)

Ghana: The National Dialogue on Decent Work and 'Just Transition' to a Sustainable Economy and Society

Greece: National Just Transition Fund for Lignite areas

Ireland: Just Transition Fund Ireland

Italy: Enel's Just Transition Framework and Futur-e project

New Zealand: 'Just Transitions Unit' within the ministry of Business, Innovation and Employment (MBIE)

Poland: The 1998 Mining Social Package and Special Privileges for the mining communes

Slovakia: Transformation Action Plan of coal region Upper Nitra

South Africa: National Planning Just Transition Dialogue + Presidential Climate Commission

Spain: Framework Agreement for a Just Transition on Coal Mining and Sustainable Development

UK: Scottish Just Transition Commission

United States: Partnership for Opportunity and Workforce and Economic Revitalisation Plan (POWER+)

(b) European Green Deal – Just Transitions Fund

(c) Platform for coal regions in transition

- Silesia, Lower Silesia, Greater Poland, Lesser Poland
- Moravia-Silesia, Usti, Karlovy Vary
- Western Macedonia
- Jiu Valley
- Midlands
- Brandenburg, Saxony, Saxony Anhalt, North Rhine-Westphalia
- Asturias, Aragón, Castilla-y-León
- Upper Nitra
- Zasavska, Savinjsko-Šaleška

Figure 4.9 | Just Transitions around the world, 2020. Panel (a) shows commissions, task forces, dialogues behind a just transition in many countries (Schweitzer and Tonn 2003; Thalmann 2004; Harrison 2013; Galgóczi 2014; Mendoza 2014; Adeoti et al. 2016; Ng et al. 2016; Gass and Echeverria 2017; Snell 2018; ILO 2018; Ministry of Employment and Labour Relations of Ghana 2018; Szpor, A. and Ziółkowska 2018; van Asselt and Moerenhout 2018; Bankwatch 2019; Commission on Growth Structural Change and Employment 2019; European Union 2019, 2020; Galgóczi 2019; Government of Canada 2019; Government of Costa Rica 2019; NPC (National Planning Commission) 2019; Ministry of Business Innovation & Employment New Zealand 2019; Piggot et al. 2019; Popp 2019; Strambo et al. 2019; Government of Spain 2019; Finnish Government 2020; Scottish Government 2020; White House 2016; Mijn Cha et al. 2020); **panel (b)** shows the funds related to the Just Transition within the European Union Green Deal, and **panel (c)** shows the European Union's Platform for Coal Regions in Transition.

4.6　　Knowledge Gaps

This section summarises knowledge gaps that require further research:

- Literature on mitigation pathways at the national level remains skewed towards large emitters. Many low-income countries have very few or no studies at all (Lepault and Lecocq 2021) (Section 4.2) (Annex III). Development of new studies and inclusion of associated scenarios in updated mitigation national mitigation pathway database would enhance understanding of mitigation at national level.

- Ex ante and ex post analysis of mitigation action and of mitigation plans by non-state actors, and their relationship with mitigation action and plans by governments is limited (Section 4.2.3).

- System analysis solutions are only beginning to be recognised in current literature on deep mitigation pathways, and rarely included in existing national policies or strategies (Section 4.2.5).

- While the technology elements of accelerated mitigation pathways at national level are generally well documented, studies of the economic and social implications of such pathways remain scarce (Section 4.2.6).

- Literature on the implication of development choices for emissions and for capacity to mitigate is limited (Section 4.3.2). In particular, more contributions from the research community working on development issues would be very useful here.

- Literature describing shifts in development pathways, and the conditions for such shifts (based on past experience or on models) remains scarce (Sections 4.3.1, 4.3.3 and 4.4.1). Studying shifts in development pathways requires new ways of thinking with interdisciplinary research and use of alternative frameworks and methods suited for understanding of change agents, determinants of change and adaptive management among other issues (Winkler 2018). Research is not only expected to produce knowledge and boost innovation, but also to help identify transformation pathways and to enlighten public debate and public decision-making on related political choices.

- Other research gaps concern the open ocean and blue carbon. There is limited knowledge about quantification of the blue carbon stocks. Research is required into what happens if the sequestration capacity of the ocean and marine ecosystems is damaged by climate change to the tipping point until the sink becomes an emitter, and on how to manage blue carbon (Section 4.4.2).

- Knowledge is limited on: (i) linking equity frameworks on mitigation with adaptation and most importantly with loss and damage, (ii) applying ethical parameters to enrich many of the existing quantitative frameworks, to assess fairness and ambition of NDCs; (iii) extending equity frameworks to quantify equitable international support, as the difference between equity-based national emissions scenarios and national domestic emissions scenarios (Sections 4.2.2.7 and 4.5).

4

Frequently Asked Questions (FAQs)

FAQ 4.1 | What is to be done over and above countries' existing pledges under the Paris Agreement to keep global warming well below 2°C?

Current pledges and efforts under the PA aimed at keeping global warming below 2°C are not enough, falling short by 14 to 23 GtCO$_2$.eq (Cross-Chapter Box 4 in this Chapter). There is a further shortfall of about 4 to 7 GtCO$_2$-eq in 2030 if the conditions are not fulfilled for those Parties that have made their pledges with conditions for support (Section 4.2.2.3). To cover up for these shortfalls will require taking actions across all sectors that can substantially reduce GHG emissions. Examples of such actions include shifting to low- or zero-emission power generation, such as renewables; changing food systems, such as diet changes away from land-intensive animal products; electrifying transport and developing 'green infrastructure', such as building green roofs, or improving energy efficiency by smart urban planning, which will change the layout of many cities. Because these different actions are connected, it means all relevant companies, industries and stakeholders would need to be involved to increase the support and chance of successful implementation (Section 4.2.5). The deployment of low-emission technology depends upon economic conditions (e.g., employment generation or capacity to mobilise investment), but also on social/cultural conditions (e.g., awareness and acceptability) and institutional conditions (e.g., political support and understanding), and the provision of relevant enabling conditions (Section 4.4.1). Encouraging stronger and more ambitious climate action by non-government and sub-national stakeholders, as well as international cooperative initiatives (ICIs) could make significant contributions to emissions reduction (Section 4.2.3).

FAQ 4.2 | What is to be done in the near term to accelerate mitigation and shift development pathways?

Increasing speed of implementation, breadth of action across all sectors of the economy, and depth of emission reduction faces important obstacles, that are rooted in the underlying structure of societies (Section 4.2.7). Addressing these obstacles amounts to shifting away from existing developmental trends (i.e., shifting development pathways, Cross-Chapter Box 5). This can be done by strengthening governance and institutional capacity, aligning technology and innovation systems with low-carbon development, facilitating behaviour change and providing adequate finance within the context of multi-objective policy packages and sequences (Section 4.4.1). Shifting development pathways towards sustainability broadens the scope for, and is thus a complement to, accelerated mitigation (Section 4.3).

FAQ 4.3 | Is it possible to accelerate mitigation in the near term while there are so many other development priorities? (Education, health, employment, etc.)

It is possible to accelerate mitigation while addressing other developmental priorities by implementing measures that simultaneously address both climate and development goals. Casting mitigation in the broader context of development pathways provides additional opportunities to articulate both (Section 4.3.1.4). Policies such as progressive taxation, investment in public transport, regulatory transparency, commitment to multilateral environmental governance, fiscal incentives for private investments, international technology development and transfer initiatives, and risk disclosure and efforts to improve underlying enabling conditions (improving governance and institutional capacity, fostering behavioural change and technological innovation, and provision of finance) address multiple objectives beyond mitigation, such as job creation, macroeconomic stability, economic growth, public health and welfare, providing energy access, providing formal housing, and providing mobility. How we manage our land and agriculture, growing cities, transport needs, our industries, and the way people are trained and employed all impact on GHG emissions and the options we have to reduce them. In turn, reducing GHG emissions can also contribute to reducing poverty, preventing hunger, improving health and wellbeing, and providing clean water and clean energy. Implementing right policies and investments can help to address the challenges of how to reduce emissions without constraining development. For example, in land use, widespread planting of a single tree species or crops for bioenergy (organic matter turned into renewable energy) could affect food and water supplies. Therefore, if bioenergy is to be relied upon to offset emissions, the right policies and investments are needed (see also Chapter 17).

References

Abadie, L.M., I. Galarraga, and D. Rübbelke, 2013: An analysis of the causes of the mitigation bias in international climate finance. *Mitig. Adapt. Strateg. Glob. Change*, **18(7)**, 943–955, doi:10.1007/s11027-012-9401-7.

Acar, S. and A.E. Yeldan, 2016: Environmental impacts of coal subsidies in Turkey: A general equilibrium analysis. *Energy Policy*, **90**, 1–15, doi:10.1016/j.enpol.2015.12.003.

Adler, M., 2007: Corrective Justice and Liability for Global Warming. *Univ. PA. Law Rev.*, **155(6)**, 1859–1867.

Adler, M.D. and N. Treich, 2015: Prioritarianism and Climate Change. *Environ. Resour. Econ.*, **62(2)**, 279–308, doi:10.1007/s10640-015-9960-7.

Adenle, A.A., H. Azadi, and J. Arbiol, 2015: Global assessment of technological innovation for climate change adaptation and mitigation in developing world. *J. Environ. Manage.*, **161**, 261–275, doi:10.1016/j.jenvman.2015.05.040.

Adenle, A.A., D.T. Manning, and J. Arbiol, 2017: Mitigating Climate Change in Africa: Barriers to Financing Low-Carbon Development. *World Dev.*, **100**, 123–132, doi.org/10.1016/j.worlddev.2017.07.033.

Adeoti, J., L. Chete, C. Beaton, and K. Clarke, 2016: *Compensation Mechanisms for Fuel Subsidy Removal in Nigeria*. The International Institute for Sustainable Development, Global Subsidies Initiative, Nigerian Institute of Social and Economic Research, Winnipeg, Canada, Geneva, Switzerland and Lagos, Nigeria, 68 pp.

Adler, M.D. and N. Treich, 2015: Prioritarianism and Climate Change. *Environ. Resour. Econ.*, **62(2)**, 279–308, doi:10.1007/s10640-015-9960-7.

Adshead, D., S. Thacker, L.I. Fuldauer, and J.W. Hall, 2019: Delivering on the Sustainable Development Goals through long-term infrastructure planning. *Glob. Environ. Change*, **59**, 101975, doi:10.1016/j.gloenvcha.2019.101975.

Afionis, S., M. Sakai, K. Scott, J. Barrett, and A. Gouldson, 2017: Consumption-based carbon accounting: Does it have a future? *Wiley Interdiscip. Rev. Clim. Change*, **8(1)**, e438, doi:10.1002/WCC.438.

Agénor, P.-R.R. and O. Canuto, 2015: Middle-income growth traps. *Res. Econ.*, **69(4)**, 641–660, 10.1016/j.rie.2015.04.003.

Aggarwal, P., 2017: 2°C target, India's climate action plan and urban transport sector. *Travel Behav. Soc.*, **6**, 110–116, doi:10.1016/j.tbs.2016.11.001.

Ai, Z., N. Hanasaki, V. Heck, T. Hasegawa, and S. Fujimori, 2021: Global bioenergy with carbon capture and storage potential is largely constrained by sustainable irrigation. *Nat. Sustain.*, **4(10)**, 884–891, doi:10.1038/s41893-021-00740-4.

Aldy, J.E., W.A. Pizer, and K. Akimoto, 2017: Comparing emissions mitigation efforts across countries. *Clim. Policy*, **17(4)**, 501–515, doi:10.1080/14693062.2015.1119098.

Allam, Z., A. Sharifi, D. Giurco, and S.A. Sharpe, 2021: On the Theoretical Conceptualisations, Knowledge Structures and Trends of Green New Deals. *Sustainability*, **13(22)**, 12529, doi:10.3390/su132212529.

Allen, E., H. Lyons, and J.C. Stephens, 2019: Women's leadership in renewable transformation, energy justice and energy democracy: Redistributing power. *Energy Res. Soc. Sci.*, **57**, 101233, doi:10.1016/j.erss.2019.101233.

Allwood, G., 2020: Mainstreaming Gender and Climate Change to Achieve a Just Transition to a Climate-Neutral Europe. *J. Common Mark. Stud.*, **58(S1)**, 173–186, doi:10.1111/jcms.13082.

Alongi, D.M., 2008: Mangrove forests: Resilience, protection from tsunamis, and responses to global climate change. *Estuar. Coast. Shelf Sci.*, **76(1)**, 1–13, doi:10.1016/j.ecss.2007.08.024.

Alongi, D.M., 2015: The Impact of Climate Change on Mangrove Forests. *Curr. Clim. Chang. Reports*, **1(1)**, 30–39, doi:10.1007/s40641-015-0002-x.

Altenburg, T. and D. Rodrik, 2017: Green Industrial Policy: Accelerating Structural Change Towards Wealthy Green Economies. In: *Green Industrial Policy. Concept, Policies, Country Experiences* [Altenburg, T. and C. Assmann, (eds.)], UN Environment; German Development Institute/Deutsches Institut für Entwicklungspolitik (DIE), Geneva, Switzerland, pp. 2–20.

Altieri, K. et al., 2015: *Pathways to deep decarbonisation in South Africa. Part of DDPP 2015 final report of the Deep Decarbonization Pathways Project*. Energy Research Centre, Sustainable Development Solutions Network, Institute for Sustainable Development and International Relations, Cape Town, New York, Paris, 52 pp.

Altieri, K.E. et al., 2016: Achieving development and mitigation objectives through a decarbonization development pathway in South Africa. *Clim. Policy*, **16(sup1)**, S78–S91, doi:10.1080/14693062.2016.1150250.

Alton, T. et al., 2014: Introducing carbon taxes in South Africa. *Appl. Energy*, **116**, 344–354, doi:10.1016/J.APENERGY.2013.11.034.

Álvarez-Espinosa, A.C. et al., 2018: Evaluación económica de los compromisos de Colombia en el marco de COP21. *Rev. Desarro. y Soc.*, (79), 15–54, doi:10.13043/dys.79.1.

Ameli, N., P. Drummond, A. Bisaro, M. Grubb, and H. Chenet, 2020: Climate finance and disclosure for institutional investors: Why transparency is not enough. *Clim. Change*, **160(4)**, 565–589, doi:10.1007/s10584-019-02542-2.

Amjath-Babu, T.S., P.K. Aggarwal, and S. Vermeulen, 2019: Climate action for food security in South Asia? Analyzing the role of agriculture in nationally determined contributions to the Paris agreement. *Clim. Policy*, **19(3)**, 283–298, doi:10.1080/14693062.2018.1501329.

Andersen, I. et al., 2021: Defining 'science-based targets'. *Natl. Sci. Rev.*, **8(7)**, doi:10.1093/nsr/nwaa186.

Andersson, M., P. Bolton, and F. Samama, 2016: Hedging Climate Risk. *Financ. Anal. J.*, **72(3)**, 13–32, doi:10.2469/faj.v72.n3.4.

Andrijevic, M., J. Crespo Cuaresma, T. Lissner, A. Thomas, and C.F. Schleussner, 2020: Overcoming gender inequality for climate resilient development. *Nat. Commun.*, **11(1)**, 1–8, doi:10.1038/s41467-020-19856-w.

Ansar, A., B. Caldecott, and J. Tilbury, 2013: *Stranded assets and the fossil fuel divestment campaign*. Smith School of Enterprise and the Environment, University of Oxford, Oxford, United Kingdom, 81 pp.

Antimiani, A., V. Costantini, O. Kuik, and E. Paglialunga, 2016: Mitigation of adverse effects on competitiveness and leakage of unilateral EU climate policy: An assessment of policy instruments. *Ecol. Econ.*, **128**, 246–259, doi:10.1016/j.ecolecon.2016.05.003.

Antwi-Agyei, P., A.J. Dougill, and L.C. Stringer, 2015: Impacts of land tenure arrangements on the adaptive capacity of marginalized groups: The case of Ghana's Ejura Sekyedumase and Bongo districts. *Land Use Policy*, **49**, 203–212, doi:10.1016/j.landusepol.2015.08.007.

Antwi-Agyei, P., A.J. Dougill, T.P. Agyekum, and L.C. Stringer, 2018: Alignment between nationally determined contributions and the sustainable development goals for West Africa. *Clim. Policy*, **18(10)**, 1296–1312, doi:10.1080/14693062.2018.1431199.

APERC, 2019: APEC Energy Demand and Supply. Outlook, vol. 1, 7th ed., Asia-Pacific Economic Cooperation Secretariat (APERC), Singapore, 198 pp.

Arango-Aramburo, S. et al., 2019: Climate impacts on hydropower in Colombia: A multi-model assessment of power sector adaptation pathways. *Energy Policy*, **128** (July 2018), 179–188, doi:10.1016/j.enpol.2018.12.057.

Arndt, C., R. Davies, K. Makrelov, and J. Thurlow, 2013: Measuring the Carbon Intensity of the South African Economy. *South African J. Econ.*, **81(3)**, 393–415, doi:10.1111/j.1813-6982.2012.01324.x.

Arneth, A. et al., 2021: Restoring Degraded Lands. *Annu. Rev. Environ. Resour.*, **46(1)**, doi:10.1146/annurev-environ-012320-054809.

Asakawa, K., K. Kimoto, S. Takeda, and T.H. Arimura, 2021: Double Dividend of the Carbon Tax in Japan: Can We Increase Public Support for Carbon Pricing? In: *Economics, Law, and Institutions in Asia Pacific*, Springer Japan, pp. 235–255.

Asensio, O.I., and M.A. Delmas, 2016: The dynamics of behavior change: Evidence from energy conservation. *J. Econ. Behav. Organ.*, **126**, 196–212, doi:10.1016/j.jebo.2016.03.012.

Asher, M.G. and A.S. Bali, 2017: Creating fiscal space to pay for pension expenditure in Asia. *Econ. Polit. Stud.*, **5(4)**, 501–514, doi:10.1080/2095 4816.2017.1384625.

Ashina, S., J. Fujino, T. Masui, T. Ehara, and G. Hibino, 2012: A roadmap towards a low-carbon society in Japan using backcasting methodology: Feasible pathways for achieving an 80% reduction in CO_2 emissions by 2050. *Energy Policy*, **41**, 584–598, doi:10.1016/j.enpol.2011.11.020.

Auffhammer, M. and C.D. Wolfram, 2014: Powering up China: Income distributions and residential electricity consumption. *Am. Econ. Rev.*, **104(5)**, 575–580, doi:10.1257/aer.104.5.575.

Ayers, J.M. and S. Huq, 2009: Supporting adaptation to climate change: What role for official development assistance? *Dev. Policy Rev.*, **27(6)**, 675–692, doi:10.1111/j.1467-7679.2009.00465.x.

Bachus, K., L. Van Ootegem, and E. Verhofstadt, 2019: 'No taxation without hypothecation': Towards an improved understanding of the acceptability of an environmental tax reform *J. Environ. Policy Plan.*, **21(4)**, 321–332, doi:10.1080/1523908X.2019.1623654.

Baek, J. and G. Gweisah, 2013: Does income inequality harm the environment? Empirical evidence from the United States. *Energy Policy*, **62**, 1434–1437, doi:10.1016/j.enpol.2013.07.097.

Bahn, O. and K. Vaillancourt, 2020: Implications of EMF 34 scenarios on renewable deployment and carbon abatement in Canada: Insights from a regionalized energy model. *Energy Policy*, **142** (April), doi:10.1016/j. enpol.2020.111518.

Bain, P.G., M.J. Hornsey, R. Bongiorno, and C. Jeffries, 2012: Promoting pro-environmental action in climate change deniers. *Nat. Clim. Change*, **2(8)**, 600–603, doi:10.1038/nclimate1532.

Bankwatch, 2019: *The transformation action plan for the Slovakia's Upper Nitra coal region. Bankwatch Network.* https://bankwatch.org/wp-content/uploads/2019/09/Transformation-Action-Plan-Upper-Nitra.pdf (Accessed June 15, 2020).

Banuri, T. and J.P. Weyant, 2001: Setting the Stage: Climate change and sustainable development. In: Climate Change 2001: Mitigation: Contribution of WGIII to the Third Assessment Report of the IPCC [Banuri, T. and J.P. Weyant, (eds.)]. Cambridge University Press, Cambridge, UK, pp. 74–114.

Bappenas, 2019: *Low Carbon Development Report: A paradigm shift towards a green economy in Indonesia. Minister (2001) of National Development Planning/ Head of National Development Planning Agency (Bappenas), Indonesia.* Jakarta, https://www.greengrowthknowledge.org/sites/default/files/downloads/policy-database//indonesia_lowcarbon_development_full%20report.pdf.

Bataille, C., H. Waisman, M. Colombier, L. Segafredo, and J. Williams, 2016a: The Deep Decarbonization Pathways Project (DDPP): Insights and emerging issues. *Clim. Policy*, **16(sup1)**, S1–S6, doi:10.1080/14693 062.2016.1179620.

Bataille, C. et al., 2016b: The need for national deep decarbonization pathways for effective climate policy. *Clim. Policy*, **16(sup1)**, S7–S26, doi:10.1080/14 693062.2016.1173005.

Bataille, C. et al., 2018: A review of technology and policy deep decarbonization pathway options for making energy-intensive industry production consistent with the Paris Agreement. *J. Clean. Prod.*, **187**, 960–973, doi. org/10.1016/j.jclepro.2018.03.107.

Bataille, C. et al., 2020: Net-zero deep decarbonization pathways in Latin America: Challenges and opportunities. *Energy Strateg. Rev.*, **30**, doi:10.1016/j.esr.2020.100510.

Bataille, C. G.F., 2020: Physical and policy pathways to net-zero emissions industry. *WIREs Clim. Change*, **11(2)**, doi:10.1002/wcc.633.

Baum, A., A. Hodge, and A. Mineshima, 2017: *Can They Do It All? Fiscal Space in Low-Income Countries.* International Monetary Fund, Washington, DC, USA, 41 pp.

Baumstark, L. et al., 2021: REMIND2.1: Transformation and innovation dynamics of the energy-economic system within climate and sustainability limits. *Geosci. Model Dev.*, **14(10)**, 6571–6603, doi:10.5194/gmd-14-6571-2021.

Beck, B., T. Surridge, and S. Hietkamp, 2013: The South African centre for carbon capture and storage delivering CCS in the developing world. *Energy Procedia*, **37**, 6502–6507, doi:10.1016/j.egypro.2013.06.580.

Beegle, K., A. Coudouel, and E. Monsalve, eds., 2018: *Realizing the Full Potential of Social Safety Nets in Africa.* The World Bank, San Francisco, USA 385 pp, https://openknowledge.worldbank.org/bitstream/handle/10986/29789/9781464811647.pdf?sequence=2&isAllowed=y (Accessed November 1, 2021).

Beiser-McGrath, L.F. and T. Bernauer, 2019: Could revenue recycling make effective carbon taxation politically feasible? *Sci. Adv.*, **5(9)**, doi:10.1126/sciadv.aax3323.

Benavides, C. et al., 2015: The impact of a carbon tax on the Chilean electricity generation sector. *Energies*, **8**, 2674–2700, doi:10.3390/en8042674.

Benner, C. and A. Karner, 2016: Low-wage jobs-housing fit: identifying locations of affordable housing shortages. *Urban Geogr.*, **37(6)**, 883–903, doi:10.1080/02723638.2015.1112565.

Bento, A.M., 2013: Equity Impacts of Environmental Policy. *Annu. Rev. Resour. Econ.*, **5(1)**, 181–196, doi:10.1146/annurev-resource-091912-151925.

Bento, A.M., M.L. Cropper, A.M. Mobarak, and K. Vinha, 2005: The effects of Urban spatial structure on travel demand in the United States. *Rev. Econ. Stat.*, **87(3)**, 466–478, doi:10.1162/0034653054638292.

Benveniste, H., O. Boucher, C. Guivarch, H. Le Treut, and P. Criqui, 2018: Impacts of nationally determined contributions on 2030 global greenhouse gas emissions: Uncertainty analysis and distribution of emissions. *Environ. Res. Lett.*, **13(1)**, doi:10.1088/1748-9326/aaa0b9.

Bergquist, P., M. Mildenberger, and L.C. Stokes, 2020: Combining climate, economic, and social policy builds public support for climate action in the US. *Environ. Res. Lett.*, **15(5)**, doi:10.1088/1748-9326/ab81c1.

Berry, A., 2019: The distributional effects of a carbon tax and its impact on fuel poverty: A microsimulation study in the French context. *Energy Policy*, **124**, 81–94, doi:10.1016/J.ENPOL.2018.09.021.

Berthe, A. and L. Elie, 2015: Mechanisms explaining the impact of economic inequality on environmental deterioration. *Ecol. Econ.*, **116**, 191–200, doi:10.1016/j.ecolecon.2015.04.026.

Bertram, C. et al., 2015: Carbon lock-in through capital stock inertia associated with weak near-term climate policies. *Technol. Forecast. Soc. Change*, **90(PA)**, 62–72, doi:10.1016/j.techfore.2013.10.001.

Bertram, C. et al., 2018: Targeted policies can compensate most of the increased sustainability risks in 1.5°C mitigation scenarios. *Environ. Res. Lett.*, **13(6)**, 064038, doi:10.1088/1748-9326/aac3ec.

Biagini, B., L. Kuhl, K.S. Gallagher, and C. Ortiz, 2014: Technology transfer for adaptation. *Nat. Clim. Change*, **4(9)**, 828–834, doi:10.1038/nclimate2305.

Biardeau, L.T., L.W. Davis, P. Gertler, and C. Wolfram, 2020: Heat exposure and global air conditioning. *Nat. Sustain.*, **3(1)**, 25–28, doi:10.1038/s41893-019-0441-9.

Bindoff, N.L., W.W.L. Cheung, J.G. Kairo, J. Arístegui, V.A. Guinder, R. Hallberg, N. Hilmi, N. Jiao, M.S. Karim, L. Levin, S. O'Donoghue, S.R. Purca Cuicapusa, B. Rinkevich, T. Suga, A. Tagliabue, and P. Williamson, 2019: Changing Ocean, Marine Ecosystems, and Dependent Communities. In: *IPCC Special Report on the Ocean and Cryosphere in a Changing Climate* [H.-O. Pörtner, D.C. Roberts, V. Masson-Delmotte, P. Zhai, M. Tignor, E. Poloczanska, K. Mintenbeck, A. Alegría, M. Nicolai, A. Okem, J. Petzold, B. Rama, N.M. Weyer (eds.)]. Cambridge University Press, Cambridge, UK, and New York, NY, USA, pp. 447–588.

Birmingham Energy Institute, 2018: *A Cool World Defining the Energy Conundrum of Cooling for All. University of Bringham.* https://www.birmingham.ac.uk/Documents/college-eps/energy/Publications/2018-clean-cold-report.pdf

Blazquez, J., L.C. Hunt, and B. Manzano, 2017: Oil subsidies and renewable energy in Saudi Arabia: A general equilibrium approach. *Energy J.*, **38(1)**, 29–45, doi:10.5547/01956574.38.SI1.jbla.

4

BloombergNEF, 2017: Global Storage Market to Double Six Times by 2030, Bloomberg New Energy Finance, London, UK, https://about.bnef.com/blog/global-storage-market-double-six-times-2030/ (Accessed November 1, 2021).

Bodnar, P. et al., 2018: Underwriting 1.5°C: competitive approaches to financing accelerated climate change mitigation. *Clim. Policy*, **18(3)**, 368–382, doi:10.1080/14693062.2017.1389687.

Böhringer, C., S. Peterson, T.F. Rutherford, J. Schneider, and M. Winkler, 2021: Climate policies after Paris: Pledge, Trade and Recycle: Insights from the 36th Energy Modeling Forum Study (EMF36). *Energy Econ.*, **103**, doi:10.1016/j.eneco.2021.105471.

Bolderdijk, J.W., L. Steg, E.S. Geller, P.K. Lehman, and T. Postmes, 2013: Comparing the effectiveness of monetary versus moral motives in environmental campaigning. *Nat. Clim. Change*, **3(4)**, 413–416, doi:10.1038/nclimate1767.

Boomsma, C. and L. Steg, 2014: The effect of information and values on acceptability of reduced street lighting. *J. Environ. Psychol.*, **39**, 22–31, doi:10.1016/j.jenvp.2013.11.004.

Borba, B.S.M.C. et al., 2012: Energy-related climate change mitigation in Brazil: Potential, abatement costs and associated policies. *Energy Policy*, **49**, 430–441, doi:10.1016/j.enpol.2012.06.040.

Borenstein, S. and L.W. Davis, 2016: The Distributional Effects of US Clean Energy Tax Credits. *Tax Policy Econ.*, **30(1)**, 191–234, doi:10.1086/685597.

Boulle, M. et al., 2015: *MAPS approach: learning and doing in the Global South. The MAPS Programme.* Mitigation Action Plans and Scenarios (MAPS), Cape Town, https://www.researchgate.net/publication/308899738_The_MAPS_approach_learning_and_doing_in_the_global_south.

Bowen, A., K. Kuralbayeva, and E.L. Tipoe, 2018: Characterising green employment: The impacts of 'greening' on workforce composition. *Energy Econ.*, **72**, 263–275, doi:10.1016/j.eneco.2018.03.015.

Boysen, L.R. et al., 2017: The limits to global-warming mitigation by terrestrial carbon removal. *Earth's Futur.*, **5(5)**, 463–474, doi:10.1002/2016EF000469.

Broekhoff, D., P. Erickson, and C.M. Lee, 2015: *What cities do best: Piecing together an efficient global climate governance.* Stockholm Environment Institute, Seattle, USA, https://www.sei.org/publications/what-cities-do-best-piecing-together-an-efficient-global-climate-governance/ (Accessed November 1, 2021).

Brown, T., D. Schlachtberger, A. Kies, S. Schramm, and M. Greiner, 2018: Synergies of sector coupling and transmission reinforcement in a cost-optimised, highly renewable European energy system. *Energy*, **160**, 720–739, doi:10.1016/J.ENERGY.2018.06.222.

Bruegge, C., T. Deryugina, and E. Myers, 2019: The Distributional Effects of Building Energy Codes. *J. Assoc. Environ. Resour. Econ.*, **6(S1)**, S95–S127, doi:10.1086/701189.

Brunner, S. and K. Enting, 2014: Climate finance: A transaction cost perspective on the structure of state-to-state transfers. *Glob. Environ. Change*, **27(1)**, 138–143, doi:10.1016/j.gloenvcha.2014.05.005.

Buchner, B. et al., 2019: Global Landscape of Climate Finance 2019 – CPI. https://climatepolicyinitiative.org/publication/global-landscape-of-climate-finance-2019/ (Accessed December 18, 2019).

Büchs, M. et al., 2020: *Wellbeing economies post-covid – Wellbeing Economy Alliance*, Wellbeing Economy Alliance, BARNSTAPLE, United Kingdom, 10 pp., https://wellbeingeconomy.org/ten-principles-for-building-back-better-to-create-wellbeing-economies-post-covid.

Bulavskaya, T. and F. Reynès, 2018: Job creation and economic impact of renewable energy in the Netherlands. *Renew. Energy*, **119**, 528–538, doi:10.1016/j.renene.2017.09.039.

Burch, S., A. Shaw, A. Dale, and J. Robinson, 2014: Triggering transformative change: A development path approach to climate response in communities. *Clim. Policy*, **14(4)**, 467–487.

Bureau, D., F. Henriet, and K. Schubert, 2019: Pour le climat: Une taxe juste, pas juste une taxe. *Notes du Cons. d'analyse économique*, **50(2)**, 1, doi:10.3917/ncae.050.0001.

Busch, T., H. Klee, and V.H. Hoffmann, 2008: Curbing greenhouse gas emissions on a sectoral basis: the Cement Sustainability Initiative. In: *Corporate Responses to Climate Change*, Routledge [Sullivan, R. (ed.)]. Routledge, Oxon, United Kingdom and New York, NY, USA, pp. 204–219.

Bustamante, M.M.C. et al., 2018: Engagement of scientific community and transparency in C accounting: The Brazilian case for anthropogenic greenhouse gas emissions from land use, land-use change and forestry. *Environ. Res. Lett.*, **13(5)**, 055005, doi:10.1088/1748-9326/aabb37.

Butnar, I. et al., 2020: A deep dive into the modelling assumptions for biomass with carbon capture and storage (BECCS): a transparency exercise. *Environ. Res. Lett.*, **15(8)**, 084008, doi:10.1088/1748-9326/ab5c3e.

Caetano, T., H. Winker, and J. Depledge, 2020: Towards zero carbon and zero poverty: Integrating national climate change mitigation and sustainable development goals. *Clim. Policy*, **20(7)**, 773–778, doi:10.1080/14693 062.2020.1791404.

Cain, M. et al., 2019: Improved calculation of warming-equivalent emissions for short-lived climate pollutants. *npj Clim. Atmos. Sci.*, **2(1)**, 29, doi:10.1038/s41612-019-0086-4.

Calfucoy, P., M. Torres Gunfaus, and H. Blanco, 2019: *Building capacities for long-term planning: The Mitigation Action Plans and Scenarios (MAPS) program*, Washington, DC, https://wriorg.s3.amazonaws.com/s3fs-public/building-capacities-long-term-planning-mitigation-action-plan-and-scenarios-maps-program-updated.pdf (Accessed November 1, 2021).

Calvin, K. et al., 2021: Bioenergy for climate change mitigation: Scale and sustainability. *GCB Bioenergy*, **13(9)**, 1346–1371, doi:10.1111/gcbb.12863.

Campagnolo, L. and M. Davide, 2019: Can the Paris deal boost SDGs achievement? An assessment of climate mitigation co-benefits or side-effects on poverty and inequality. *World Dev.*, **122**, 96–109, doi:10.1016/j.worlddev.2019.05.015.

Campbell, B.M., P. Thornton, R. Zougmoré, P. van Asten, and L. Lipper, 2014: ScienceDirect Sustainable intensification: What is its role in climate smart agriculture? *Curr. Opin. Environ. Sustain.*, **8**, 39–43, doi.org/10.1016/j.cosust.2014.07.002.

Caney, S., 2016: The Struggle for Climate Justice in a Non-Ideal World. *Midwest Stud. Philos.*, **40(1)**, 9–26, doi:10.1111/misp.12044.

Canzler, W. and D. Wittowsky, 2016: The impact of Germany's Energiewende on the transport sector – Unsolved problems and conflicts. *Util. Policy*, **41**, 246–251, doi:10.1016/j.jup.2016.02.011.

Cao, S. et al., 2010: Damage caused to the environment by reforestation policies in arid and semi-arid areas of China. *Ambio*, **39(4)**, 279–283, doi:10.1007/s13280-010-0038-z.

Capros, P. et al., 2019: Energy-system modelling of the EU strategy towards climate-neutrality. *Energy Policy*, **134**, doi:10.1016/J.ENPOL.2019.110960.

Carley, S. and D.M. Konisky, 2020: The justice and equity implications of the clean energy transition. *Nat. Energy*, **5**, 569–577, doi:10.1038/s41560-020-0641-6.

Carrara, S., 2020: Reactor ageing and phase-out policies: Global and regional prospects for nuclear power generation. *Energy Policy*, **147**, doi:10.1016/j.enpol.2020.111834.

Cartwright, A., 2015: *Better Growth, Better Cities: Rethinking and Redirecting Urbanisation in Africa.* Working Pa. New Climate Economy, Washington, DC, USA, 44 pp, https://newclimateeconomy.report/workingpapers/wp-content/uploads/sites/5/2016/04/NCE-APP-final.pdf (Accessed November 1, 2021).

CCFLA, 2017: *Localizing Climate Finance, Mapping Gaps and Opportunities, Designing Solutions*, New York, USA, https://ccacoalition.org/en/resources/localizing-climate-finance-mapping-gaps-and-opportunities-designing-solutions-0.

Central Compilation & Translation Press, 2016: The 13th Five-Year Plan for Economic and Social Development of the People's Republic of China. *Cent. Compil. Transl. Press*, 97–99.

Chadwick, A.E., 2017: Climate Change Communication. *Oxford Res. Encycl. Commun.*, doi:10.1093/acrefore/9780190228613.013.22.

Chai, Q.-M. and H.-Q. Xu, 2014: Modeling an emissions peak in China around 2030: Synergies or trade-offs between economy, energy and climate security. *Adv. Clim. Chang. Res.*, **5(4)**, 169–180, doi.org/10.1016/j.accre.2015.06.001.

Chan, S., R. Falkner, M. Goldberg, and H. van Asselt, 2018: Effective and geographically balanced? An output-based assessment of non-state climate actions. *Clim. Policy*, **18(1)**, 24–35, doi:10.1080/14693062.2016.1248343.

Charlier, D., B. Legendre, and A. Risch, 2019: Fuel poverty in residential housing: Providing financial support versus combatting substandard housing. *Appl. Econ.*, **51(49)**, 5369–5387, doi:10.1080/00036846.2019.1613501.

Chateau, J., R. Bibas, and E. Lanzi, 2018: *Impacts of Green Growth Policies on Labour Markets and Wage Income Distribution: A General Equilibrium Application to Climate and Energy Policies-Environment,* OECD Environment Working Papers, No. 137, OECD Publishing, Paris, France, doi: 10.1787/5jz2qck2b2vd-en.

Chen, J., P. Wang, L. Cui, S. Huang, and M. Song, 2018a: Decomposition and decoupling analysis of CO_2 emissions in OECD. *Appl. Energy*, **231**, 937–950, doi:10.1016/j.apenergy.2018.09.179.

Chen, J., X. Yin, and L. Mei, 2018b: Holistic Innovation: An Emerging Innovation Paradigm. *Int. J. Innov. Stud.*, **2(1)**, 1–13, doi:10.1016/J.IJIS.2018.02.001.

Chen, Y.-H.H., G.R. Timilsina, and F. Landis, 2013: Economic implications of reducing carbon emissions from energy use and industrial processes in Brazil. *J. Environ. Manage.*, **130**, 436–446, doi:10.1016/j.jenvman.2013.08.049.

Chen, Y., 2018: Comparing North-South technology transfer and South-South technology transfer: The technology transfer impact of Ethiopian Wind Farms. *Energy Policy*, **116**, 1–9, doi:10.1016/j.enpol.2017.12.051.

Chen, Y. and M.A.C. Hafstead, 2019: Using a Carbon Tax to Meet US International Climate Pledges. *Clim. Chang. Econ.*, **10(1)**, doi:10.1142/S2010007819500027.

Chenet, H., A. Hilke, and W. Duan, 2019: *Finance Sector Alignment with International Climate Goals Reviewing Options and Obstacles*.

Cheshmehzangi, A., 2016: China's New-type Urbanisation Plan (NUP) and the Foreseeing Challenges for Decarbonization of Cities: A Review. *Energy Procedia*, **104**, 146–152, doi:10.1016/j.egypro.2016.12.026.

Chester, M.V., 2019: Sustainability and infrastructure challenges. *Nat. Sustain.*, **2(4)**, 265–266, doi:10.1038/s41893-019-0272-8.

Child, M., C. Kemfert, D. Bogdanov, and C. Breyer, 2019: Flexible electricity generation, grid exchange and storage for the transition to a 100% renewable energy system in Europe. *Renew. Energy*, **139**, 80–101, doi:10.1016/j.renene.2019.02.077.

Chilvers, J. et al., 2017: Realising transition pathways for a more electric, low-carbon energy system in the United Kingdom: Challenges, insights and opportunities. *Proc. Inst. Mech. Eng. Part A J. Power Energy*, **231(6)**, 440–477, doi:10.1177/0957650917695448.

Chimhowu, A.O., D. Hulme, and L.T. Munro, 2019: The 'New' national development planning and global development goals: Processes and partnerships. *World Dev.*, **120**, 76–89, doi:10.1016/j.worlddev.2019.03.013.

China National Renewable Energy Centre, 2019: *China Renewable Energy Outlook 2019. Energy Research Institute of Academy of Macroeconomic Research/NDRC China National Renewable Energy Centre, Beijing, China*

Chiodi, A. et al., 2013: Modelling the impacts of challenging 2050 European climate mitigation targets on Ireland's energy system. *Energy Policy*, **53**, 169–189, doi:10.1016/j.enpol.2012.10.045.

Chunark, P. and B. Limmeechokchai, 2018: Thailand Energy System Transition to Keep Warming Below 1.5 Degrees. *Carbon Manag.*, **9(5)**, 515–531, doi: 10.1080/17583004.2018.1536169.

Chunark, P., B. Limmeechokchai, S. Fujimori, and T. Masui, 2017: Renewable energy achievements in CO_2 mitigation in Thailand's NDCs. *Renew. Energy*, **114**, 1294–1305, doi:10.1016/j.renene.2017.08.017.

Clack, C.T.M. et al., 2017: Evaluation of a proposal for reliable low-cost grid power with 100% wind, water, and solar. *Proc. Natl. Acad. Sci.*, **114(26)**, 6722–6727, doi:10.1073/PNAS.1610381114.

Clark, R., J. Reed, and T. Sunderland, 2018: Bridging funding gaps for climate and sustainable development: Pitfalls, progress and potential of private finance. *Land Use Policy*, **71**, 335–346, doi:10.1016/j.landusepol.2017.12.013.

Clarke, L. et al., 2016: Long-term abatement potential and current policy trajectories in Latin American countries. *Energy Econ.*, **56**, 513–525, doi:10.1016/j.eneco.2016.01.011.

Clarke L., K. Jiang, K. Akimoto, M. Babiker, G. Blanford, K. Fisher-Vanden, J.-C. Hourcade, V. Krey, E. Kriegler, A. Löschel, D. McCollum, S. Paltsev, S. Rose, P.R. Shukla, M. Tavoni, B. van der Zwaan, and D. P. van Vuuren, 2014: Assessing Transformation Pathways. In: *Climate Change 2014: Mitigation of Climate Change. Contribution of Working Group III to the Fifth Assessment Report of the Intergovernmental Panel on Climate Change* [Edenhofer, O., R. Pichs-Madruga, Y. Sokona, E. Farahani, S. Kadner, K. Seyboth, A. Adler, I. Baum, S. Brunner, P. Eickemeier, B. Kriemann, J. Savolainen, S. Schlömer, C. von Stechow, T. Zwickel and J.C. Minx (eds.)]. Cambridge University Press, Cambridge, United Kingdom and New York, NY, USA, pp. 413–510.

Clayton, S. et al., 2015: Psychological research and global climate change. *Nat. Clim. Change*, **5(7)**, 640–646, doi:10.1038/nclimate2622.

Climate Action Tracker, 2019: Climate Action Tracker: Country Assessments, NewClimate – Institute for Climate Policy and Global Sustainability gGmbH, Cologne, Germany and Climate Analytics gGmbH, Berlin, Germany, https://climateactiontracker.org/documents/698/CAT_2019-12-10_BriefingCOP25_WarmingProjectionsGlobalUpdate_Dec2019.pdf (updated November 2018 – June 2019).

Climate Action Tracker, 2020: *Pandemic recovery: Positive intentions vs policy*. Climate Action Tracker, Climate Analytics, NewClimate Institute, 25 pp., NewClimate – Institute for Climate Policy and Global Sustainability gGmbH, Cologne, Germany and Climate Analytics gGmbH, Berlin, Germany, https://climateactiontracker.org/documents/790/CAT_2020-09-23_Briefing_GlobalUpdate_Sept2020.pdf (Accessed November 1, 2021).

Climate Action Tracker, 2021: *Warming Projections Global Update*, NewClimate – Institute for Climate Policy and Global Sustainability gGmbH, Cologne, Germany and Climate Analytics gGmbH, Berlin, Germany, https://climateactiontracker.org/documents/853/CAT_2021-05-04_Briefing_Global-Update_Climate-Summit-Momentum.pdf (Accessed November 1, 2021).

Colander, D.C. and R. Kupers, (eds.), 2016: *Complexity and the art of public policy: Solving society's problems from the bottom up*. Princeton University Press, Princeton, NJ, USA, 320 pp.

Collier, P., 2007: *The Bottom Billion: Why the Poorest Countries are Failing and What Can Be Done About It*. Oxford University Press, Oxford, UK, 224 pp.

Combet, E. and J.C. Hourcade, 2014: Taxe carbone, retraites et déficits publics: Le coût caché du cloisonnement des expertises. *Rev. Econ. Polit.*, **124(3)**, 291, doi:10.3917/redp.243.0291.

Combet, E. and J.C. Hourcade, 2017: *Fiscalité carbone et finance climat, Un contrat social pour notre temps*. Les Petits Matins, Paris, France, 150 pp.

Commission on Growth Structural Change and Employment, 2019: *Commission on Growth, Structural Change and Employment – Final Report*. Berlin, Germany, 128 pp., https://www.bmwi.de/Redaktion/EN/Publikationen/commission-on-growth-structural-change-and-employment.pdf?__blob=publicationFile&v=3.

COMMIT, 2019: *Deliverable 2.2: Long-term, Low-emission Pathways in Australia, Brazil, Canada, China, EU, India, Indonesia, Japan, Republic of Korea, Russia, and United States*. The Hague, the Netherlands, https://www.researchgate.net/profile/Heleen-Van-Soest/publication/329521902_Long-term_Low-emission_Pathways_in_Australia_Brazil_Canada_China_EU_India_Indonesia_Japan_Republic_of_Korea_Russian_Federation_and_the_United_States/links/5c0d387e299bf139c74d4792/Long-term-Low-emission-Pathways-in-Australia-Brazil-Canada-China-EU-India-Indonesia-Japan-Republic-of-Korea-Russian-Federation-and-the-United-States.pdf?origin=publication_detail, 77 pp (Accessed November 1, 2021).

4

Committee on Climate Change, 2019: *Net Zero: The UK's contribution to stopping global warming*, Committee on Climate Change, London, United Kingdom, 275 pp., www.theccc.org.uk/publications (Accessed December 18, 2019).

Conley, T.G. and C.R. Udry, 2010: Learning about a new technology: Pineapple in Ghana. *Am. Econ. Rev.*, **100(1)**, 35–69, doi:10.1257/aer.100.1.35.

Cook, G. and J.P. Ponssard, 2011: A proposal for the renewal of sectoral approaches building on the cement sustainability initiative. *Clim. Policy*, **11(5)**, 1246–1256, doi:10.1080/14693062.2011.602552.

Cosbey, A., S. Droege, C. Fischer, and C. Munnings, 2019: Developing Guidance for Implementing Border Carbon Adjustments: Lessons, Cautions, and Research Needs from the Literature. *Rev. Environ. Econ. Policy*, **13(1)**, 3–22, doi.org/10.1093/reep/rey020.

CPC-CC, 2015: Opinions of the CPC Central Committee and the State Council on further promoting the development of Ecological Civilization, Communist Party of China Central Committee, Beijing, China.

CPLC, 2017: *Report of the High-Level Commission on Carbon Prices*, 2–3, Carbon Pricing Leadership Coalition, Washington D.C., USA 10 pp., https://www.connect4climate.org/sites/default/files/files/publications/CarbonPricingReortFinal.pdf (Accessed November 1, 2021).

Crippa, M. et al., 2021: *EDGAR v6.0 Greenhouse Gas Emissions*. European Commission, Joint Research Center (JRC), Brussels, Belgium, http://data.europa.eu/89h/97a67d67-c62e-4826-b873-9d972c4f670b (Accessed November 1, 2021).

Criqui, P., M. Jaccard, and T. Sterner, 2019: Carbon taxation: A tale of three countries. *Sustainability*, **11(22)**, 6280, doi:10.3390/su11226280.

Cronin, J.A., D. Fullerton, and S. Sexton, 2019: Vertical and Horizontal Redistributions from a Carbon Tax and Rebate. *J. Assoc. Environ. Resour. Econ.*, **6(S1)**, S169–S208, doi:10.1086/701191.

Crooks, S. et al., 2018: Coastal wetland management as a contribution to the US National Greenhouse Gas Inventory. *Nat. Clim. Change*, **8(12)**, 1109–1112, doi:10.1038/s41558-018-0345-0.

Cruz-Martinez, G., 2018: Revenue-Generating Potential of Taxation for Older-Age Social Pensions. *Ageing Int.*, **43(4)**, 415–437, doi:10.1007/s12126-017-9298-2.

CSO Equity Review, 2015: *Fair Shares: A Civil Society Equity Review of INDCs*. CSO Equity Review Coalition, Manila, London, Cape Town, Washington, et al., https://static1.squarespace.com/static/620ef5326bbf2d7627553dbf/t/622827f61f2e1746062ebec6/1646798856616/CSO.Equity.Review--2015--Fair.Shares.A.Civil.Society.Equity.Review.of.INDCs.pdf (Accessed November 1, 2021).

CSO Equity Review, 2017: *Equity and the Ambition Ratchet Towards a Meaningful 2018 Facilitative Dialogue Report*. CSO Equity Review Coalition, Manila, London, Cape Town, Washington, et al., https://static1.squarespace.com/static/620ef5326bbf2d7627553dbf/t/622827f61f2e1746062ebec6/1646798856616/CSO.Equity.Review--2015--Fair.Shares.A.Civil.Society.Equity.Review.of.INDCs.pdf (Accessed November 1, 2021).

CSO Equity Review, 2018: *After Paris: Inequality, Fair Shares, and the Climate Emergency*. CSO Equity Review Coalition, Manila, London, Cape Town, Washington, et al., https://static1.squarespace.com/static/620ef5326bbf2d7627553dbf/t/622827f61f2e1746062ebec6/1646798856616/CSO.Equity.Review--2015--Fair.Shares.A.Civil.Society.Equity.Review.of.INDCs.pdf (Accessed November 1, 2021).

Cui, L., R. Li, M. Song, and L. Zhu, 2019: Can China achieve its 2030 energy development targets by fulfilling carbon intensity reduction commitments? *Energy Econ.*, **83**, 61–73, doi:10.1016/J.ENECO.2019.06.016.

Cui, Z. et al., 2018: Pursuing sustainable productivity with millions of smallholder farmers. *Nature*, **555(7696)**, 363–366, doi:10.1038/nature25785.

Cunliffe, G.E., C. Holz, K.L. Mbeva, P. Pauw, and H. Winkler, 2019: *Comparative analysis of the NDCs of Canada, the European Union, Kenya and South Africa from an equity perspective*. Energy Research Centre, University of Cape Town, Cape Town, South Africa, 85 pp.

Da Silveira Bezerra, P.B. et al., 2017: The power of light: Socio-economic and environmental implications of a rural electrification program in Brazil. *Environ. Res. Lett.*, **12(9)**, doi:10.1088/1748-9326/aa7bdd.

Dafnomilis, I. et al., 2020: *Exploring the impact of COVID-19 pandemic on global emission projections: Assessment of green vs 'not green' recovery* PBL Netherlandz Environmental Assessment Agency, The Hague, Netherlands and NewClimate – Institute for Climate Policy and Global Sustainability gGmbH, Cologne, Germany, 44 pp., https://newclimate.org/wp-content/uploads/2020/09/COVID-19_Global_Emissions_Projections_Sept2020.pdf (Accessed November 1, 2021).

Dafnomilis, I. et al., 2021: Targeted green recovery measures in a post-COVID-19 world enable the energy transition, Working paper, 20 pp,. doi:10.21203/rs.3.rs-667715/v1.

Dagnet, Y. et al., 2017: *Designing the enhanced transparency framework part 2: Review under the Paris Agreement*. World Resources Institute, Washington, DC, USA., https://www.wri.org/research/designing-enhanced-transparency-framework-part-2-review-under-paris-agreement.

Dai, H.-C., H.-B. Zhang, and W.-T. Wang, 2017: The impacts of US withdrawal from the Paris Agreement on the carbon emission space and mitigation cost of China, EU, and Japan under the constraints of the global carbon emission space. *Adv. Clim. Chang. Res.*, **8(4)**, 226–234, doi:10.1016/j.accre.2017.09.003.

Dai, H., X. Xie, Y. Xie, J. Liu, and T. Masui, 2016: Green growth: The economic impacts of large-scale renewable energy development in China. *Appl. Energy*, **162**, 435–449, doi:10.1016/j.apenergy.2015.10.049.

Daioglou, V. et al., 2020: Implications of climate change mitigation strategies on international bioenergy trade. *Clim. Change*, **163(3)**, 1639–1658, doi:10.1007/s10584-020-02877-1.

Davis, L.W. and C.R. Knittel, 2019: Are Fuel Economy Standards Regressive? *J. Assoc. Environ. Resour. Econ.*, **6(S1)**, S37–S63, doi:10.1086/701187.

de Coninck, H., A. Revi, M. Babiker, P. Bertoldi, M. Buckeridge, A. Cartwright, W. Dong, J. Ford, S. Fuss, J.-C. Hourcade, D. Ley, R. Mechler, P. Newman, A. Revokatova, S. Schultz, L. Steg, and T. Sugiyama, 2018: Strengthening and Implementing the Global Response. In: *Global Warming of 1.5°C: An IPCC special report on the impacts of global warming of 1.5°C above pre-industrial levels and related global greenhouse gas emission pathways, in the context of strengthening the global response to the threat of climate change, sustainable development, and efforts to eradicate poverty.* [Masson-Delmotte, V., P. Zhai, H.-O. Pörtner, D. Roberts, J. Skea, P.R. Shukla, A. Pirani, W. Moufouma-Okia, C. Péan, R. Pidcock, S. Connors, J.B.R. Matthews, Y. Chen, X. Zhou, M.I. Gomis, E. Lonnoy, T. Maycock, M. Tignor, and T. Waterfield (eds.)]. Cambridge University Press, Cambridge, United Kingdom and New York, NY, USA, pp 313–443.

Deep Decarbonization Pathways Project, 2015: *Pathways to deep decarbonsiation: 2015 report. Published by the Sustainable Development Solutions Network (SDSN) and the Institute for Sustainable Development and International Relations (IDDRI).* Sustainable Development Solutions Network (SDSN) and Institute for Sustainable Development and International Relations (IDDRI), Paris and New York, 44 pp., https://www.iddri.org/sites/default/files/import/publications/ddpp_2015synthetisreport.pdf (Accessed November 1, 2021).

Deetman, S. et al., 2013: Deep greenhouse gas emission reductions in Europe: Exploring different options. *Energy Policy*, **55**, 152–164, doi:10.1016/j.enpol.2012.11.047.

Delgado, R., A.I. Cadena, M. Espinosa, C. Peña, and M. Salazar, 2014: A case study on Colombian mitigation actions. *Clim. Dev.*, **6(sup1)**, 12–24, doi:10.1080/17565529.2013.857587.

Delgado, R., T.B. Wild, R. Arguello, L. Clarke, and G. Romero, 2020: Options for Colombia's mid-century deep decarbonization strategy. *Energy Strateg. Rev.*, **32**, 100525, doi:10.1016/J.ESR.2020.100525.

den Elzen, M. et al., 2016: Contribution of the G20 economies to the global impact of the Paris agreement climate proposals. *Clim. Change*, **137(3–4)**, 655–665, doi:10.1007/s10584-016-1700-7.

den Elzen, M. et al., 2019: Are the G20 economies making enough progress to meet their NDC targets? *Energy Policy*, **126**, 238–250, doi:10.1016/j.enpol.2018.11.027.

den Elzen, M., I. Dafnomilis, and H. van Soest, 2021: PBL Climate Pledge NDC tool. *PBL Netherlands Environ. Assess. Agency*, https://themasites.pbl.nl/o/climate-ndc-policies-tool/ (Accessed October 7, 2021).

Deutscher Bundestag, 2002: *Enquete Commission on sustainable energy supply against the background of globalisation and liberalisation. Summary of final report*. Berlin, Germany, http://webarchiv.bundestag.de/archive/2007/0206/parlament/gremien/kommissionen/archiv14/ener/schlussbericht/engl.pdf (Accessed November 1, 2021).

Devarajan, S., D.S. Go, S. Robinson, and K. Thierfelder, 2011: Tax Policy to Reduce Carbon Emissions in a Distorted Economy: Illustrations from a South Africa CGE Model. *B.E.J. Econom. Anal. Policy*, **11(1)**, doi:10.2202/1935-1682.2376.

Dhar, S., M. Pathak, and P.R.R. Shukla, 2018: Transformation of India's transport sector under global warming of 2°C and 1.5°C scenario. *J. Clean. Prod.*, **172**, 417–427, doi:10.1016/j.jclepro.2017.10.076.

Di Gregorio, M. et al., 2016: *Integrating mitigation and adaptation in climate and land use policies in Brazil: a policy document analysis*. Centre for Climate Change Economics and Policy and Sustainability Research Institute, Leeds and London, United Kingdom, 54 pp., https://www.cccep.ac.uk/wp-content/uploads/2016/02/Working-Paper-257-Di-Gregorio-et-al-2016.pdf (Accessed November 1, 2021).

Diao, X., M. McMillan, and D. Rodrik, 2019: The Recent Growth Boom in Developing Economies: A Structural-Change Perspective. In: *The Palgrave Handbook of Development Economics* [Nissanke M. and J.A. Ocampo (eds.)]. Springer International Publishing, Cham, Switzerland, pp. 281–334.

Díaz, S., J. Settele, and E. Brondízio, 2019: *Global assessment report on biodiversity and ecosystem services. Summary for policymakers*. Intergovernmental Science-Policy Platform on Biodiversity and Ecosystem (IPBES), Bonn, Germany, 56 pp.

Diffenbaugh, N.S. and M. Burke, 2019: Global warming has increased global economic inequality. *Proc. Natl. Acad. Sci.* **116(20)**, 9808–9813, doi:10.1073/pnas.1816020116.

Dioha, M.O. and A. Kumar, 2020: Exploring sustainable energy transitions in sub-Saharan Africa residential sector: The case of Nigeria. *Renew. Sustain. Energy Rev.*, **117**, 109510, doi:10.1016/j.rser.2019.109510.

Dioha, M.O., N.V. Emodi, and E.C. Dioha, 2019: Pathways for low carbon Nigeria in 2050 by using NECAL2050. *Renew. Energy Focus*, **29** (June), 63–77, doi:10.1016/j.ref.2019.02.004.

Doelle, M., 2019: The heart of the Paris rulebook: Communicating ndcs and Accounting for Their Implementation. *Clim. Law*, **9(1–2)**, 3–20, doi:10.1163/18786561-00901002.

Dong, B., W. Wei, X. Ma, and P. Li, 2018: On the impacts of carbon tax and technological progress on China. *Appl. Econ.*, **50(4)**, 389–406, doi:10.1080/00036846.2017.1316826.

Dooley, K. and S. Kartha, 2018: Land-based negative emissions: Risks for climate mitigation and impacts on sustainable development. *Int. Environ. Agreements Polit. Law Econ.*, **18(1)**, 79–98, doi:10.1007/s10784-017-9382-9.

Dorband, I.I., M. Jakob, M. Kalkuhl, and J.C. Steckel, 2019: Poverty and distributional effects of carbon pricing in low- and middle-income countries – A global comparative analysis. *World Dev.*, **115**, 246–257, doi:10.1016/j.worlddev.2018.11.015.

Dorin, B., 2017: India and Africa in the global agricultural system (1961-2050): Towards a new socio-technical regime? *Econ. Polit. Wkly.*, **52(25–26)**, 5–13.

Douenne, T., 2020: The Vertical and Horizontal Distributive Effects of Energy Taxes: A Case Study of a French Policy. *Energy J.*, **41(3)**, doi:10.5547/01956574.41.3.tdou.

Douenne, T. and A. Fabre, 2020: French attitudes on climate change, carbon taxation and other climate policies. *Ecol. Econ.*, **169**, doi.org/10.1016/j.ecolecon.2019.106496.

Doumax-Tagliavini, V. and C. Sarasa, 2018: Looking towards policies supporting biofuels and technological change: Evidence from France. *Renew. Sustain. Energy Rev.*, **94**, 430–439, doi:10.1016/j.rser.2018.06.020.

Dreborg, K.H., 1996: Essence of backcasting. *Futures*, **28(9)**, 813–828, doi:10.1016/S0016-3287(96)00044-4.

Dreyfus, G., J. Borgford-Parnell, J. Fahey, B. Peters, and Xu, 2020: *Assessment of Climate and Development Benefits of Efficient and Climate-Friendly Cooling* [Molina, M. and Zaelke, D. (eds.)], https://www.ccacoalition.org/en/resources/assessment-climate-and-development-benefits-efficient-and-climate-friendly-cooling.

Druckman, A. and T. Jackson, 2015: Understanding households as drivers of carbon emissions. In: *Taking Stock of Industrial Ecology* [Clift, R. and A. Druckman (eds.)]. Springer International Publishing, Cham, Switzerland, pp. 181–203.

Duan, H., J. Mo, Y. Fan, and S. Wang, 2018: Achieving China's energy and climate policy targets in 2030 under multiple uncertainties. *Energy Econ.*, **70**, 45–60, doi:10.1016/J.ENECO.2017.12.022.

Dubash, N., R. Khosla, N.D.N. D. Rao, and A. Bhardwaj, 2018: India's energy and emissions future: An interpretive analysis of model scenarios. *Environ. Res. Lett.*, **13**(074018), doi:10.1088/1748-9326/aacc74.

Dubash, N.K., 2012: Toward Enabling and Inclusive Global Environmental Governance. *J. Environ. Dev.*, **21(1)**, 48–51, doi:10.1177/1070496511435550.

Dubash, N.K., 2021: Varieties of climate governance: The emergence and functioning of climate institutions. *Env. Polit.*, **30(sup1)**, 1–25, doi:10.1080/09644016.2021.1979775.

Dubois, G. et al., 2019: It starts at home? Climate policies targeting household consumption and behavioral decisions are key to low-carbon futures. *Energy Res. Soc. Sci.*, **52**, 144–158, doi:10.1016/j.erss.2019.02.001.

Dulal, H.B., 2017: Making cities resilient to climate change: Identifying 'win–win' interventions. *Local Environ.*, **22(1)**, 106–125, doi:10.1080/13549839.2016.1168790.

Duscha, V., J. Wachsmuth, J. Eckstein, and B. Pfluger, 2019: *GHG-neutral EU2050 – a scenario of an EU with net-zero greenhouse gas emissions and its implications*. Fraunhofer Institute for Systems and Innovation Research, Karlsruhe, Germany, 81 pp., https://www.umweltbundesamt.de/en/publikationen/ghg-neutral-eu2050 (Accessed November 1, 2021).

Ebi, K.L. et al., 2014: A new scenario framework for climate change research: Background, process, and future directions. *Clim. Change*, **122(3)**, doi:10.1007/s10584-013-0912-3.

Edwards, P.E.T., A.E. Sutton-Grier, and G.E. Coyle, 2013: Investing in nature: Restoring coastal habitat blue infrastructure and green job creation. *Mar. Policy*, **38**, 65–71, doi:10.1016/j.marpol.2012.05.020.

EFC, 2020: Synthesis Report 2020 on China's carbon neutrality: China's new growth pathway: from the 14th Five Year Plan to carbon neutrality, Energy Foundation China, Beijing, China, https://www.efchina.org/Reports-en/report-lceg-2020121 (Accessed November 1, 2021).

Ekholm, T., H. Ghoddusi, V. Krey, and K. Riahi, 2013: The effect of financial constraints on energy-climate scenarios. *Energy Policy*, **59**, 562–572, doi:10.1016/j.enpol.2013.04.001.

Elizondo, A., V. Pérez-Cirera, A. Strapasson, J.C. Fernández, and D. Cruz-Cano, 2017: Mexico's low-carbon futures: An integrated assessment for energy planning and climate change mitigation by 2050. *Futures*, **93**, 14–26, doi:10.1016/j.futures.2017.08.003.

Elliott, C., K. Levin, J. Thwaites, K. Mogelgaard, and Y. Dagnet, 2017: *Designing the enhanced transparency framework part 1: Reporting under the Paris Agreement*. World Resources Institute, Washington, DC, USA.

Energy Transitions Commission and Rocky Mountain Institute, 2019: *China 2050 : A Fully Developed Rich Zero-Carbon Economy*. https://www.energy-transitions.org/publications/china-2050-a-fully-developed-rich-zero-carbon-economy/#download-form.

4

Erb, K.H. et al., 2016: Exploring the biophysical option space for feeding the world without deforestation. *Nat. Commun.*, **7**, doi:10.1038/ncomms11382.

Erickson, P., S. Kartha, M. Lazarus, and K. Tempest, 2015: Assessing carbon lock-in. *Environ. Res. Lett.*, **10(8)**, 084023, doi:10.1088/1748-9326/10/8/084023.

Esquivel, V., 2016: Power and the Sustainable Development Goals: a feminist analysis. *Gend. Dev.*, **24(1)**, 9–23, doi:10.1080/13552074.2016.1147872.

Esteban, M. and J. Portugal-Pereira, 2014: Post-disaster resilience of a 100% renewable energy system in Japan. *Energy*, **68**, 756–764, doi:10.1016/j.energy.2014.02.045.

Esteban, M. et al., 2018: 100% renewable energy system in Japan: Smoothening and ancillary services. *Appl. Energy*, **224**, 698–707, doi:10.1016/j.apenergy.2018.04.067.

European Commission, 2013: *Summary report on the analysis of the responses received to the Consultative Communication on the future of Carbon Capture and Storage in Europe – Energía y Sociedad*. European Commission, Brussels, Belgium, https://energy.ec.europa.eu/system/files/2014-10/20130702_ccs_consultation_report_0.pdf (Accessed October 18, 2021).

European Commission, 2019: *The European Green Deal. COM(2019) 640 final*. European Commission (EC), Brussels, Belgium., https://eur-lex.europa.eu/legal-content/EN/TXT/?uri=COM%3A2019%3A640%3AFIN (Accessed November 1, 2021).

European Union, 2019: *Structural Support Action for Coal and Carbon Intensive Regions*. European Commission (EC), Brussels, Belgium, https://ec.europa.eu/energy/topics/oil-gas-and-coal/EU-coal-regions/coal-regions-transition_en (Accessed June 15, 2020).

European Union, 2020: *Financing the green transition: The European Green Deal Investment Plan and Just Transition Mechanism – Regional Policy – European Commission*. European Commission (EC), Brussels, Belgium, https://ec.europa.eu/regional_policy/en/newsroom/news/2020/01/14-01-2020-financing-the-green-transition-the-european-green-deal-investment-plan-and-just-transition-mechanism (Accessed December 15, 2020).

Fagerberg, J., S. Laestadius, and B.R. Martin, 2016: The Triple Challenge for Europe: The Economy, Climate Change, and Governance. *Challenge*, **59(3)**, 178–204, doi:10.1080/05775132.2016.1171668.

Fankhauser, S. and T.K.J. McDermott, 2016: Chapter 1: Climate-resilient development: an introduction. In: *The Economics of Climate-Resilient Development* [Fankhauser, S. and T.K.J. McDermott, (eds.)]. Edward Elgar Publishing, Cheltenham, UK, 1–14pp.

Fankhauser, S., A. Sahni, A. Savvas, and J. Ward, 2016: Where are the gaps in climate finance? *Clim. Dev.*, **8(3)**, 203–206, doi:10.1080/17565529.2015.1064811.

FAO, 2016: *The agricultural sectors in nationally determined contributions (NDCs): Priority areas for international support*. Food and Agriculture Organization of the United Nations, Rome, Italy. http://www.fao.org/3/a-i6400e.pdf, 23 pp (Accessed July 12, 2019).

Fargione, J.E. et al., 2018: Natural climate solutions for the United States. *Sci. Adv.*, **4(11)**, doi:10.1126/sciadv.aat1869.

Faria, P.C.S. and N. Labutong, 2019: A description of four science-based corporate GHG target-setting methods. *Sustain. Accounting, Manag. Policy J.*, **11(3)**, 591–612, doi:10.1108/SAMPJ-03-2017-0031.

Farrow, K., G. Grolleau, and L. Ibanez, 2017: Social Norms and Pro-environmental Behavior: A Review of the Evidence. *Ecol. Econ.*, **140**, 1–13, doi:10.1016/j.ecolecon.2017.04.017.

Fekete, H. et al., 2015: *How can the new climate agreement support robust national mitigation targets? Opportunities up to Paris and beyond*. Umweltbundesamt, Dessau-Roßlau, Germany, https://newclimate.org/wp-content/uploads/2015/12/climate_change_25_2015_how_can_the_climate_agreement_support_robust_national_mitigation_targets.pdf, 26 pp (Accessed July 12, 2019).

Fennessy, M.S. et al., 2019: Environmental controls on carbon sequestration, sediment accretion, and elevation change in the Ebro River Delta: Implications for wetland restoration. *Estuar. Coast. Shelf Sci.*, **222**, 32–42, doi:10.1016/J.ECSS.2019.03.023.

Ferleger, L., 2000: Arming American Agriculture for the Twentieth Century: How the USDA's Top Managers Promoted Agricultural Development. *Agricult. Hist.*, **74(2)**, 211–226.

Fernandez, M.A. and A.J. Daigneault, 2018: Money does grow on trees: Impacts of the Paris agreement on the New Zealand economy. *Clim. Chang. Econ.*, **9(3)**, 1850005, doi:10.1142/S2010007818500057.

Ferrante, L. and P.M. Fearnside, 2019: Brazil's new president and 'ruralists' threaten Amazonia's environment, traditional peoples and the global climate. *Environ. Conserv.*, **46(4)**, 261–263, doi:10.1017/S0376892919000213.

Figueres, C. et al., 2017: Three years to safeguard our climate. *Nature*, **546(7660)**, 593–595, doi:10.1038/546593a.

Finnish Government, 2020: *A fair transition towards a carbon neutral Finland – Roadmap for achieving the carbon neutrality target*. Government of Finland, Helsinki, Finland https://valtioneuvosto.fi/documents/10616/20764082/hiilineutraaliuden+tiekartta+03022020+en.pdf/e791931c-90e1-f74b-3be4-3dc0994f67f1/hiilineutraaliuden+tiekartta+03022020+en.pdf, 6 pp (Accessed November 1, 2021).

Fleischman, F. et al., 2020: Pitfalls of Tree Planting Show Why We Need People-Centered Natural Climate Solutions. *Bioscience*, **70(11)**, 947–950, doi:10.1093/biosci/biaa094.

Fleurbaey, M. and D. Blanchet, 2013: Beyond GDP: Measuring Welfare and Assessing Sustainability. *J. Reg. Sci.*, **54(1)**, 323, 10.1093/acprof:oso/9780199767199.001.0001.

Fleurbaey M., S. Kartha, S. Bolwig, Y.L. Chee, Y. Chen, E. Corbera, F. Lecocq, W. Lutz, M.S. Muylaert, R.B. Norgaard, C. Okereke, and A.D. Sagar, 2014: Sustainable Development and Equity. In: *Climate Change 2014: Mitigation of Climate Change. Contribution of Working Group III to the Fifth Assessment Report of the Intergovernmental Panel on Climate Change* [Edenhofer, O., R. Pichs-Madruga, Y. Sokona, E. Farahani, S. Kadner, K. Seyboth, A. Adler, I. Baum, S. Brunner, P. Eickemeier, B. Kriemann, J. Savolainen, S. Schlömer, C. von Stechow, T. Zwickel and J.C. Minx (eds.)]. Cambridge University Press, Cambridge, UK, and New York, NY, USA, pp. 283–350.

Fleurbaey, M. et al., 2018: *A Manifesto for Social Progress*. Cambridge University Press, Cambridge, United Kingdom and New York, NY, USA, 248 pp.

Forouli, A., A. Nikas, D.J. Van de Ven, J. Sampedro, and H. Doukas, 2020: A multiple-uncertainty analysis framework for integrated assessment modelling of several sustainable development goals. *Environ. Model. Softw.*, **131**, 104795, doi:10.1016/J.ENVSOFT.2020.104795.

Forster, P.M. et al., 2020: Current and future global climate impacts resulting from COVID-19. *Nat. Clim. Change*, **10(10)**, 913–919, doi:10.1038/s41558-020-0883-0.

Fouquet, R., 2010: The slow search for solutions: Lessons from historical energy transitions by sector and service. *Energy Policy*, **38(11)**, 6586–6596, doi:10.1016/j.enpol.2010.06.029.

Fouquet, R., 2016a: Path dependence in energy systems and economic development. *Nat. Energy*, **1(8)**, 16098, doi:10.1038/nenergy.2016.98.

Fouquet, R., 2016b: Historical energy transitions: Speed, prices and system transformation. *Energy Res. Soc. Sci.*, **22**, 7–12, doi:10.1016/j.erss.2016.08.014.

Fourqurean, J.W. et al., 2012: Seagrass ecosystems as a globally significant carbon stock. *Nat. Geosci.*, **5(7)**, 505–509, doi:10.1038/ngeo1477.

Fragkos, P., N. Tasios, L. Paroussos, P. Capros, and S. Tsani, 2017: Energy system impacts and policy implications of the European Intended Nationally Determined Contribution and low-carbon pathway to 2050. *Energy Policy*, **100**, 216–226, doi:10.1016/j.enpol.2016.10.023.

Fragkos, P. et al., 2021: Energy system transitions and low-carbon pathways in Australia, Brazil, Canada, China, EU-28, India, Indonesia, Japan, Republic of Korea, Russia and the United States. *Energy*, **216**, 119385, doi:10.1016/j.energy.2020.119385.

4

Frank, S. et al., 2017: Reducing greenhouse gas emissions in agriculture without compromising food security? *Environ. Res. Lett.*, **12(10)**, 105004, doi:10.1088/1748-9326/aa8c83.

Fridahl, M. and L. Johansson, 2017: An assessment of the potential for spurring transformational change through Nationally Appropriate Mitigation Actions (NAMAs). *Environ. Innov. Soc. Transitions*, **25**, 35–46, doi:10.1016/j.eist.2016.11.003.

Fuhrman, J. et al., 2020: Food–energy–water implications of negative emissions technologies in a +1.5°C future. *Nat. Clim. Change*, **10(10)**, 920–927, doi:10.1038/s41558-020-0876-z.

Fujimori, S., K. Oshiro, H. Shiraki, and T. Hasegawa, 2019: Energy transformation cost for the Japanese mid-century strategy. *Nat. Commun.*, **10(1)**, 4737, doi:10.1038/s41467-019-12730-4.

Fullerton, D. and E. Muehlegger, 2019: Who Bears the Economic Burdens of Environmental Regulations? *Rev. Environ. Econ. Policy*, **13(1)**, 62–82, doi:10.1093/reep/rey023.

Fuso Nerini, F. et al., 2019: Connecting climate action with other Sustainable Development Goals. *Nat. Sustain.*, **2(8)**, 674–680, doi:10.1038/s41893-019-0334-y.

Fyson, C.L. and M.L. Jeffery, 2019: Ambiguity in the Land Use Component of Mitigation Contributions Toward the Paris Agreement Goals. *Earth's Futur.*, **7(8)**, 873–891, doi:10.1029/2019EF001190.

Fyson, C.L., S. Baur, M. Gidden, and C.-F. Schleussner, 2020: Fair-share carbon dioxide removal increases major emitter responsibility. *Nat. Clim. Change*, **10(9)**, 836–841, doi:10.1038/s41558-020-0857-2.

Gable, S., H. Lofgren, and I.O. Rodarte, 2015: *Trajectories for Sustainable Development Goals: Framework and Country Applications*. World Bank, Washington, DC, USA, https://openknowledge.worldbank.org/handle/10986/23122 (Accessed November 1, 2021).

Galer, G., 2004: Preparing the ground? Scenarios and political change in South Africa. *Development*, **47(4)**, 26–34, doi:10.1057/palgrave.development.1100092.

Galgóczi, B., 2014: The long and winding road from black to green: Decades of structural change in the Ruhr region. *Int. J. Labour Res.*, **6(2)**, 217–268.

Galgóczi, B., 2019: *Phasing out Coal – A Just Transition Approach*. European Trade Union Institute , Brussels, Belgium, https://etui.org/sites/default/files/19%20WP%202019%2004%20Phasing%20out%20coal%20Galgoczi%20Web%20version.pdf, 45 pp (Accessed November 1, 2021).

Galvin, R. and N. Healy, 2020: The Green New Deal in the United States: What it is and how to pay for it. *Energy Res. Soc. Sci.*, **67**, doi:10.1016/j.erss.2020.101529.

Gambhir, A., F. Green, and P. Pearson, 2018: *Towards a just and equitable low-carbon energy transition*. Grantham Institute, Imperial College London, London, UK, 18 pp.

Garg, A. and S. S.Vishwanathan., 2021: Climate policies post Paris. In: *Climate ambition beyond emission numbers: Taking stock of progress by looking inside countries and sectors* [Waisman, H. et al., (eds.)]. Deep Decarbonization Pathways (DDP) Initiative-IDDRI. Paris, France, pp. 71–76.

Gass, P. and D. Echeverria, 2017: *Fossil Fuel Subsidy Reform and the Just Transition: Integrating approaches for complementary outcomes GSI REPORT*. https://www.iisd.org/system/files/publications/fossil-fuel-subsidy-reform-just-transition.pdf (Accessed December 15, 2020).

Gattuso, J.P. et al., 2018: Ocean solutions to address climate change and its effects on marine ecosystems. *Front. Mar. Sci.*, **5** (Oct), doi:10.3389/fmars.2018.00337.

Geels, F.W., B.K. Sovacool, T. Schwanen, and S. Sorrell, 2017: Socio-technical transitions for deep decarbonization. *Science*, **357(6357)**, 1242–1244, doi:10.1126/science.aao3760.

Geels, F.W., T. Schwanen, S. Sorrell, K. Jenkins, and B.K. Sovacool, 2018: Reducing energy demand through low-carbon innovation: A socio-technical transitions perspective and thirteen research debates. *Energy Res. Soc. Sci.*, **40** (June 2017), 23–35, doi:10.1016/j.erss.2017.11.003.

Giannousakis, A. et al., 2020: How uncertainty in technology costs and carbon dioxide removal availability affect climate mitigation pathways. *Energy*, **216**, 119253, doi:10.1016/j.energy.2020.119253.

Gilbert, A., B.K. Sovacool, P. Johnstone, and A. Stirling, 2017: Cost overruns and financial risk in the construction of nuclear power reactors: A critical appraisal. *Energy Policy*, **102**, 644–649, doi:10.1016/j.enpol.2016.04.001.

Gillingham, K.T., C.R. Knittel, J. Li, M. Ovaere, and M. Reguant, 2020: The Short-run and Long-run Effects of Covid-19 on Energy and the Environment. *Joule*, **4(7)**, 1337–1341, doi:10.1016/j.joule.2020.06.010.

GIZ, 2017: *Sectoral implementation of nationally determined contributions (NDCs)*. Deutsche Gesellschaft für Internationale Zusammenarbeit (GIZ) GmbH, Bonn and Eschborn, Germany, https://newclimate.org/2017/08/01/sectoral-implementation-of-nationally-determined-contributions-ndcs/, 12 pp. (Accessed July 12, 2019).

Glachant, M. and A. Dechezleprêtre, 2017: What role for climate negotiations on technology transfer? *Clim. Policy*, **17(8)**, 962–981, doi:10.1080/14693062.2016.1222257.

Global Cement and Concrete Association, 2020: *Climate Ambition: GCCA*. Global Cement and Concrete Association, London, United Kingdom, https://gccassociation.org/climate-ambition/ (Accessed October 18, 2021).

Glomsrød, S., T. Wei, B. Aamaas, M.T. Lund, and B.H. Samset, 2016: A warmer policy for a colder climate: Can China both reduce poverty and cap carbon emissions? *Sci. Total Environ.*, **568**, 236–244, doi:10.1016/j.scitotenv.2016.06.005.

Gomi, K., K. Shimada, and Y. Matsuoka, 2010: A low-carbon scenario creation method for a local-scale economy and its application in Kyoto city. *Energy Policy*, **38(9)**, 4783–4796, doi:10.1016/j.enpol.2009.07.026.

Gomi, K., Y. Ochi, and Y. Matsuoka, 2011: A systematic quantitative backcasting on low-carbon society policy in case of Kyoto city. *Technol. Forecast. Soc. Change*, **78(5)**, 852–871, doi:10.1016/j.techfore.2011.01.002.

Goulder, L.H., M.A.C. Hafstead, G. Kim, and X. Long, 2019: Impacts of a carbon tax across US household income groups: What are the equity-efficiency trade-offs? *J. Public Econ.*, **175**, 44–64, doi:10.1016/j.jpubeco.2019.04.002.

Government of Canada, 2019: Task Force: Just Transition for Canadian Coal Power Workers and Communities. Government of Canada, Ottawa, Canada, https://www.canada.ca/en/environment-climate-change/services/climate-change/task-force-just-transition.html (Accessed January 8, 2020).

Government of Costa Rica, 2019: *National Decarbonization Plan 2018-2050*. Government of Costa Rica, San José, Costa Rica, https://unfccc.int/sites/default/files/resource/NationalDecarbonizationPlan.pdf (Accessed 1 November 2021).

Government of India, 2015: *India's Intended Nationally Determined Contribution: Working Towards Climate Justice*. Ministry of Environment, Forest and Climate Change, Government of India, NewDelhi, India,. https://www4.unfccc.int/sites/ndcstaging/PublishedDocuments/India%20First/INDIA%20INDC%20TO%20UNFCCC.pdf, 38 pp (Accessed 1 November 2021).

Government of India, 2018: *Strategy for New India @ 75*. Government of India, New Delhi, India https://niti.gov.in/sites/default/files/2019-01/Strategy_for_New_India_0.pdf (Accessed November 1, 2021).

Government of Spain, 2019: *The just transition strategy within the strategic energy and climate framework*. Government of Spain, Madrid, Spain, 20 pp., https://www.miteco.gob.es/en/prensa/etj-english-interactive_tcm38-505653.pdf (Accessed November 1, 2021).

Grafakos, S., K. Trigg, M. Landauer, L. Chelleri, and S. Dhakal, 2019: Analytical framework to evaluate the level of integration of climate adaptation and mitigation in cities. *Clim. Change*, **154(1–2)**, 87–106, doi:10.1007/s10584-019-02394-w.

Grant, N., A. Hawkes, S. Mittal, and A. Gambhir, 2021: Confronting mitigation deterrence in low-carbon scenarios. *Environ. Res. Lett.*, **16(6)**, 064099, doi:10.1088/1748-9326/ac0749.

Grant, R., 2015: Sustainable African Urban Futures. *Am. Behav. Sci.*, **59(3)**, 294–310, doi:10.1177/0002764214550301.

4

Grassi, G. et al., 2017: The key role of forests in meeting climate targets requires science for credible mitigation. *Nat. Clim. Change*, **7(3)**, 220–226, doi:10.1038/nclimate3227.

Grassi, G. et al., 2018: Reconciling global-model estimates and country reporting of anthropogenic forest CO_2 sinks. *Nat. Clim. Change*, **8(10)**, 914–920, doi:10.1038/s41558-018-0283-x.

Grassi, G. et al., 2021: Critical adjustment of land mitigation pathways for assessing countries' climate progress. *Nat. Clim. Change*, **11(5)**, 425–434, doi:10.1038/s41558-021-01033-6.

Gray, L.K., T. Gylander, M.S. Mbogga, P.Y. Chen, and A. Hamann, 2011: Assisted migration to address climate change: Recommendations for aspen reforestation in western Canada. *Ecol. Appl.*, **21(5)**, 1591–1603, doi:10.1890/10-1054.1.

Green, F. and R. Denniss, 2018: Cutting with both arms of the scissors: The economic and political case for restrictive supply-side climate policies. *Clim. Change*, **150(1)**, 73–87, doi:10.1007/s10584-018-2162-x.

Green, F. and A. Gambhir, 2020: Transitional assistance policies for just, equitable and smooth low-carbon transitions: Who, what and how? *Clim. Policy*, **20(8)**, 902–921, doi:10.1080/14693062.2019.1657379.

Griliches, Z., 1957: Hybrid Corn: An Exploration in the Economics of Technological Change. *Econometrica*, **25(4)**, 501, doi:10.2307/1905380.

Grin, J., J. Rotmans, and J. Schot, 2010: *Transitions to sustainable development: New directions in the study of long term transformative change*. Routledge, New York, USA and Oxon, UK, 397 pp.

Griscom, B.W. et al., 2017: Natural climate solutions. *Proc. Natl. Acad. Sci.*, **114(44)**, 11645–11650, doi:10.1073/pnas.1710465114.

Grottera, C., A.O. Pereira, and E.L. La Rovere, 2017: Impacts of carbon pricing on income inequality in Brazil. *Clim. Dev.*, **9(1)**, 80–93, doi:10.1080/17565529.2015.1067183.

Grottera, C. et al., 2018: Linking electricity consumption of home appliances and standard of living: A comparison between Brazilian and French households. *Renew. Sustain. Energy Rev.*, **94** (July), 877–888, doi:10.1016/j.rser.2018.06.063.

Grubb, M., 2014: *Planetary Economics*. Routledge, Oxon, UK, and New York, NY, USA, 548 pp.

Grubb, M., J.C. Hourcade, and K. Neuhoff, 2015: The Three Domains structure of energy-climate transitions. *Technol. Forecast. Soc. Change*, **98**, 290–302, doi:10.1016/j.techfore.2015.05.009.

Grubb, M. et al., 2021: Induced innovation in energy technologies and systems a review of evidence and potential implications for CO_2 mitigation. *Environ. Res. Lett.*, **16(4)**, 043007, doi:10.1088/1748-9326/abde07.

Grubler, A., 2010: The costs of the French nuclear scale-up: A case of negative learning by doing. *Energy Policy*, **38(9)**, 5174–5188, doi:10.1016/j.enpol.2010.05.003.

Grubler, A. et al., 2018: A low energy demand scenario for meeting the 1.5°C target and sustainable development goals without negative emission technologies. *Nat. Energy*, **3(6)**, 515–527, doi:10.1038/s41560-018-0172-6.

Grunewald, N., S. Klasen, I. Martınez-Zarzoso, and C. Muris, 2017: The trade-off between income inequality and carbon dioxide emissions. *Ecol. Econ.*, **142**, 249–256, doi: 10.1016/j.ecolecon.2017.06.034.

Guan, D. et al., 2018: Structural decline in China's CO_2 emissions through transitions in industry and energy systems. *Nat. Geosci.*, **11(8)**, 551–555, doi:10.1038/s41561-018-0161-1.

Gupta, D., F. Ghersi, S.S. Vishwanathan, and A. Garg, 2019: Achieving sustainable development in India along low-carbon pathways: Macroeconomic assessment. *World Dev.*, **123**, 104623, doi:10.1016/J.WORLDDEV.2019.104623.

Haberl, H. et al., 2020: A systematic review of the evidence on decoupling of GDP, resource use and GHG emissions, part II: Synthesizing the insights. *Environ. Res. Lett.*, **15(6)**, 065003, doi:10.1088/1748-9326/AB842A.

Haines, A. et al., 2017: Short-lived climate pollutant mitigation and the Sustainable Development Goals. *Nat. Clim. Change*, **7(12)**, 863–869, doi:10.1038/s41558-017-0012-x.

Haites, E., 2018: Carbon taxes and greenhouse gas emissions trading systems: What have we learned? *Clim. Policy*, **18(8)**, 955–966, doi:10.1080/14693062.2018.1492897.

Halimanjaya, A. and E. Papyrakis, 2012: *Donor Characteristics and the Supply of Climate Change Aid*. DEV Working Paper 42. The School of International Development, University of East Anglia, Norwich, United Kingdom, 28 pp.

Hamilton, T.G.A. and S. Kelly, 2017: Low-carbon energy scenarios for sub-Saharan Africa: An input-output analysis on the effects of universal energy access and economic growth. *Energy Policy*, **105** (February), 303–319, doi:10.1016/j.enpol.2017.02.012.

Hammond, W., J. Axsen, and E. Kjeang, 2020: How to slash greenhouse gas emissions in the freight sector: Policy insights from a technology-adoption model of Canada. *Energy Policy*, **137** (November 2019), 111093, doi:10.1016/j.enpol.2019.111093.

Hanaoka, T. and T. Masui, 2018: Co-benefit Reductions of Short-Lived Climate Pollutants and Air Pollutants by 2050 while Achieving the 2 Degree Target in Asia. *J. Sustain. Dev. Energy, Water Environ. Syst.*, **6(3)**, 505–520, doi:10.13044/j.sdewes.d6.0218.

Hanger-Kopp, S., J. Lieu, and A. Nikas, 2019: *Narratives of Low-Carbon Transitions*. Routledge, Oxon, UK, and New York, NY, USA, 296 pp.

Hansen, K., B.V. Mathiesen, and I.R. Skov, 2019: Full energy system transition towards 100% renewable energy in Germany in 2050. *Renew. Sustain. Energy Rev.*, **102**, 1–13, doi:10.1016/j.rser.2018.11.038.

Hao, Y., H. Chen, and Q. Zhang, 2016: Will income inequality affect environmental quality? Analysis based on China's provincial panel data. *Ecol. Indic.*, **67**, 533–542, doi:10.1016/j.ecolind.2016.03.025.

Harper, A.B. et al., 2018: Land-use emissions play a critical role in land-based mitigation for Paris climate targets. *Nat. Commun.*, **9(1)**, doi:10.1038/s41467-018-05340-z.

Harrison, K., 2013: *The Political Economy of British Columbia's Carbon Tax*. OECD Environment Working Papers No.63, OECD, Paris, France, 22 pp, https://www.oecd-ilibrary.org/environment-and-sustainable-development/the-political-economy-of-british-columbia-s-carbon-tax_5k3z04gkkhkg-en.

Harvey, C.A. et al., 2014: Climate-Smart Landscapes: Opportunities and Challenges for Integrating Adaptation and Mitigation in Tropical Agriculture. *Conserv. Lett.*, **7(2)**, 77–90, doi:10.1111/conl.12066.

Hasegawa, T. et al., 2018: Risk of increased food insecurity under stringent global climate change mitigation policy. *Nat. Clim. Change*, **8(8)**, 699–703, doi:10.1038/s41558-018-0230-x.

Haut Conseil pour le Climat, 2019: Agir en cohérence avec les ambitions. Rapport annuel., Haut Conseil pour le Climat, Paris, France, 66 pp., https://www.hautconseilclimat.fr/wp-content/uploads/2019/09/hcc_rapport_annuel_2019_v2.pdf (Accessed November 1, 2021).

Häyhä, T., P.L. Lucas, D.P. van Vuuren, S.E. Cornell, and H. Hoff, 2016: From Planetary Boundaries to national fair shares of the global safe operating space – How can the scales be bridged? *Glob. Environ. Change*, **40**, 60-72, doi:10.1016/j.gloenvcha.2016.06.008.

He, J.-K., 2016: Global low-carbon transition and China's response strategies. *Adv. Clim. Chang. Res.*, **7(4)**, 204–212, doi.org/10.1016/j.accre.2016.06.007.

Healy, N. and J. Barry, 2017: Politicizing energy justice and energy system transitions: Fossil fuel divestment and a 'just transition.' *Energy Policy*, **108**, 451–459, doi:10.1016/j.enpol.2017.06.014.

Heck, V., D. Gerten, W. Lucht, and A. Popp, 2018: Biomass-based negative emissions difficult to reconcile with planetary boundaries. *Nat. Clim. Change*, **8(2)**, 151–155, doi:10.1038/s41558-017-0064-y.

Heidrich, O. et al., 2016: National climate policies across Europe and their impacts on cities strategies. *J. Environ. Manage.*, **168**, 36–45, doi:10.1016/j.jenvman.2015.11.043.

Hein, J., A. Guarin, E. Frommé, and P. Pauw, 2018: Deforestation and the Paris climate agreement: An assessment of REDD+ in the national climate action plans. *For. Policy Econ.*, **90**, 7–11, doi.org/10.1016/j.forpol.2018.01.005.

4

Helgenberger, S. et al., 2019: Future skills and job creation through renewable energy in South Africa: Assessing the co-benefits of decarbonising the power sector. IASS Studies, Council for Scientific and Industrial Research and Institute for Advanced Sustainability Studies, Pretoria and Postdam, doi: 10.2312/iass.2019.009.

Helsinki Design Lab, 2011: In Studio: Recipes for Systemic Change, SITRA, Helskinki, Finland, 335pp, http://www.helsinkidesignlab.org/peoplepods/themes/hdl/downloads/In_Studio-Recipes_for_Systemic_Change.pdf (Accessed November 1, 2021).

Hepburn, C., B. O'Callaghan, N. Stern, J. Stiglitz, and D. Zenghelis, 2020: Will COVID-19 fiscal recovery packages accelerate or retard progress on climate change? *Oxford Rev. Econ. Policy*, **36(sup1)**, S359–S381, doi:10.1093/oxrep/graa015.

Hering, J.G., D.A. Dzombak, S.A. Green, R.G. Luthy, and D. Swackhamer, 2014: Engagement at the science-policy interface. *Environ. Sci. Technol.*, **48(19)**, 11031–11033, doi:10.1021/es504225t.

Hermwille, L., A. Siemons, H. Förster, and L. Jeffery, 2019: Catalyzing mitigation ambition under the Paris Agreement: Elements for an effective Global Stocktake. *Clim. Policy*, **19(8)**, 988–1001, doi:10.1080/14693062.2019.1624494.

Herreras Martínez, S. et al., 2015: Possible energy futures for Brazil and Latin America in conservative and stringent mitigation pathways up to 2050. *Technol. Forecast. Soc. Change*, **98**, 186–210, doi:10.1016/j.techfore.2015.05.006.

Hess, D.J., 2018: Energy democracy and social movements: A multi-coalition perspective on the politics of sustainability transitions. *Energy Res. Soc. Sci.*, **40**, 177–189, doi:10.1016/j.erss.2018.01.003.

Hickel, J. et al., 2021: Urgent need for post-growth climate mitigation scenarios. *Nat. Energy*, **6(8)**, 766–768, doi:10.1038/s41560-021-00884-9.

Hochstenbach, C. and S. Musterd, 2018: Gentrification and the suburbanization of poverty: Changing urban geographies through boom and bust periods. *Urban Geogr.*, **39(1)**, doi:10.1080/02723638.2016.1276718.

Hodson, E.L. et al., 2018: US energy sector impacts of technology innovation, fuel price, and electric sector CO_2 policy: Results from the EMF 32 model intercomparison study. *Energy Econ.*, **73**, 352–370, doi:10.1016/j.eneco.2018.03.027.

Hoegh-Guldberg, O. et al., 2019: The human imperative of stabilizing global climate change at 1.5°C. *Science*, **365(6459)**, doi:10.1126/science.aaw6974.

Hoffman, S.G. and P. Durlak, 2018: The Shelf Life of a Disaster: Post-Fukushima Policy Change in The United States And Germany. *Sociol. Forum*, **33(2)**, 378–402, doi:10.1111/socf.12419.

Höhne, N., H. Fekete, M.G.J.J. den Elzen, A. F. Hof, and T. Kuramochi, 2018: Assessing the ambition of post-2020 climate targets: A comprehensive framework. *Clim. Policy*, **18(4)**, 425–441, doi:10.1080/14693062.2017.1294046.

Höhne, N. et al., 2019: Bridging the Gap: Enhancing Mitigation Ambition and Action at G20 Level and Globally. In UNEP Emissions Gap Report 2019. 28-38.

Höhne, N. et al., 2020: Emissions: World has four times the work or one-third of the time. *Nature*, **579(7797)**, 25–28, doi:10.1038/d41586-020-00571-x.

Holz, C., S. Kartha, and T. Athanasiou, 2018: Fairly Sharing 1.5: National Fair Shares of a 1.5°C – Compliant Global Mitigation Effort (D1500, Trans.). *Int. Environ. Agreements Polit. Law Econ.*, **18(1)**, 117–134, doi:10.1007/s10784-017-9371-z.

Hong, S. and B.W. Brook, 2018: A nuclear- to-gas transition in South Korea: Is it environmentally friendly or economically viable? *Energy Policy*, **112**, 67–73, doi:10.1016/J.ENPOL.2017.10.012.

Hong, S., C.J.A. Bradshaw, and B.W. Brook, 2014: South Korean energy scenarios show how nuclear power can reduce future energy and environmental costs. *Energy Policy*, **74(C)**, 569–578, doi:10.1016/J.ENPOL.2014.05.054.

Hoolohan, C. et al., 2019: Stepping-up innovations in the water–energy–food nexus: A case study of anaerobic digestion in the UK. *Geogr. J.*, **185(4)**, 391–405, doi:10.1111/geoj.12259.

Hornsey, M.J., E.A. Harris, P.G. Bain, and K.S. Fielding, 2016: Meta-analyses of the determinants and outcomes of belief in climate change. *Nat. Clim. Change*, **6(6)**, 622–626, doi:10.1038/nclimate2943.

HoSG, 2018: *Solidarity and just transition: Silesia Declaration. Supported by Heads of State and Government (HoSG) of several countries during UNFCCC COP 24*. Katowice.

Howard, J. et al., 2017: Clarifying the role of coastal and marine systems in climate mitigation. *Front. Ecol. Environ.*, **15(1)**, 42–50, doi:10.1002/fee.1451.

Hsu, A., A.J. Weinfurter, and K. Xu, 2017: Aligning subnational climate actions for the new post-Paris climate regime. *Clim. Change*, **142(3–4)**, 419–432, doi:10.1007/s10584-017-1957-5.

Hsu, A. et al., 2018: *Global climate action from cities, regions, and businesses*. New Climate Institute, Cologne and Berlin, Germany,106 pp., https://newclimate.org/2018/08/30/global-climate-action-from-cities-regions-and-businesses/ (Accessed December 4, 2019).

Hsu, A. et al., 2019: A research roadmap for quantifying non-state and subnational climate mitigation action. *Nat. Clim. Change*, **9(1)**, 11–17, doi:10.1038/s41558-018-0338-z.

Hsu, A., N. Höhne, T. Kuramochi, V. Vilariño, and B.K. Sovacool, 2020: Beyond states: Harnessing sub-national actors for the deep decarbonisation of cities, regions, and businesses. *Energy Res. Soc. Sci.*, **70**, 101738, doi:10.1016/j.erss.2020.101738.

Hu, W.-C., S.-M. Chung, J.-C. Lin, C.-T. Fan, and C.-A. Lien, 2017: An accelerating green growth for Taiwan's climate ambition. *Renew. Sustain. Energy Rev.*, **79**, 286–292, doi:10.1016/j.rser.2017.05.089.

Huang, H. et al., 2019: Emissions trading systems and social equity: A CGE assessment for China. *Appl. Energy*, **235**, 1254–1265, doi:10.1016/J.APENERGY.2018.11.056.

Huenteler, J., T.S. Schmidt, and N. Kanie, 2012: Japan's post-Fukushima challenge – implications from the German experience on renewable energy policy. *Energy Policy*, **45**, 6–11, doi:10.1016/j.enpol.2012.02.041.

Hummelbrunner, R. and H. Jones, 2013: *A guide for planning and strategy development in the face of complexity*. Overseas Development Institute, London, United Kingdom, 12 pp., https://cdn.odi.org/media/documents/8287.pdf (Accessed November 1, 2021).

Iacobuta, G., N.K. Dubash, P. Upadhyaya, M. Deribe, and N. Höhne, 2018: National climate change mitigation legislation, strategy and targets: A global update. *Clim. Policy*, **18(9)**, 1114–1132, doi:10.1080/14693062.2018.1489772.

IADB, 2012: *Room for Development: Housing Markets in Latin America and the Caribbean*. Inter-American Development Bank [Patricio Bouillon, C., (ed.)]. Inter-American Development Bank (IADB), Palgrave Macmillan, New York, USA, 456 pp.

IEA, 2015: *Technology Roadmap: Hydrogen and Fuel Cells*. International Energy Agency (IEA), Paris, France, 75pp., https://www.iea.org/reports/technology-roadmap-hydrogen-and-fuel-cells.

IEA, 2017: *Energy Technology Perspectives 2017*. International Energy Agency, Paris, France, 438 pp., https://iea.blob.core.windows.net/assets/a6587f9f-e56c-4b1d-96e4-5a4da78f12fa/Energy_Technology_Perspectives_2017-PDF.pdf (Accessed July 12, 2019).

IEA, 2020: *World Energy Outlook 2020*. International Energy Agency (IEA), Paris, France, 461 pp.

IEA and WBSCD, 2018: Technology roadmap low-carbon transition in the cement industry. International Energy Agency, Paris, France and World Business Council for Sustainable Development, Geneva, Switzerland, https://www.wbcsd.org/contentwbc/download/4586/61682/1.

Iftekhar, M.S., M. Polyakov, D. Ansell, F. Gibson, and G.M. Kay, 2017: How economics can further the success of ecological restoration. *Conserv. Biol.*, **31(2)**, 261–268, doi:10.1111/cobi.12778.

ILO, 2015: *Guidelines for a just transition towards environmentally sustainable economies and societies for all*. International Labour Organization (ILO), Geneva, Switzerland, 23 pp., http://www.ilo.org/wcmsp5/groups/public/---ed_emp/---emp_ent/documents/publication/wcms_432859.pdf.

ILO, 2018: *Just Transition Towards Environmentally Sustainable Economies and Societies for All*. International Labor Organization (ILO), Geneva, Switzerland, 22 pp., https://www.ilo.org/wcmsp5/groups/public/---ed_dialogue/---actrav/documents/publication/wcms_647648.pdf.

INPE, 2019a: INPE Database PRODES – Amazônia (Monitoramento do Desmatamento da Floresta Amazônica Brasileira por Satélite). Instituto Nacional de Pesquisas Espaciais, São José dos Campos/SP, Brazil http://www.obt.inpe.br/OBT/assuntos/programas/amazonia/prodes (Accessed December 19, 2019).

INPE, 2019b: INPE-EM database Deforestation-driven gross emissions. Instituto Nacional de Pesquisas Espaciais, São José dos Campos/SP, Brazil, http://inpe-em.ccst.inpe.br/en/deforestation-driven-gross-emissions-old-growth-forests-amz/ (Accessed December 19, 2019).

INPE, 2020: PRODES Amazônia. Amazon deforestation satellite monitoring (Monitoramento do Desmatamento da Floresta Amazônica Brasileira por Satélite). Brasilia. Instituto Nacional de Pesquisas. (Accessed November 1, 2021).

IPBES, 2019a: *Global assessment report on biodiversity and ecosystem services of the Intergovernmental Science-Policy Platform on Biodiversity and Ecosystem Services* [Díaz, S.et ak. (eds.)]. Intergovernmental Science-Policy Platform on Biodiversity and Ecosystem Services (IPBES), Bonn, Germany, 1148 pp.

IPBES, 2019b: *Summary for policymakers of the global assessment report on biodiversity and ecosystem services*. Intergovernmental Science-Policy Platform on Biodiversity and Ecosystem Services (IPBES), Bonn, Germany.

IPCC, 2014: *Climate Change 2014: Synthesis Report. Contribution of Working Groups I, II and III to the Fifth Assessment Report of the Intergovernmental Panel on Climate Change* [Core Writing Team, R.K. Pachauri and L.A. Meyer (eds.)]. IPCC, Geneva, Switzerland, 151 pp.

IPCC, 2018a: *Global Warming of 1.5°C: An IPCC special report on the impacts of global warming of 1.5°C above pre-industrial levels and related global greenhouse gas emission pathways, in the context of strengthening the global response to the threat of climate change, sustainable development, and efforts to eradicate poverty* [Masson-Delmotte, V., P. Zhai, H.-O. Pörtner, D. Roberts, J. Skea, P.R. Shukla, A. Pirani, W. Moufouma-Okia, C. Péan, R. Pidcock, S. Connors, J.B.R. Matthews, Y. Chen, X. Zhou, M.I. Gomis, E. Lonnoy, T. Maycock, M. Tignor, and T. Waterfield (eds.)]. Cambridge University Press, Cambridge, UK and New York, USA, 616 pp.

IPCC, 2018b: Summary for Policymakers. In: *Global Warming of 1.5°C: An IPCC special report on the impacts of global warming of 1.5°C above pre-industrial levels and related global greenhouse gas emission pathways, in the context of strengthening the global response to the threat of climate change, sustainable development, and efforts to eradicate poverty* [Masson-Delmotte, V., P. Zhai, H.-O. Pörtner, D. Roberts, J. Skea, P.R. Shukla, A. Pirani, W. Moufouma-Okia, C. Péan, R. Pidcock, S. Connors, J.B.R. Matthews, Y. Chen, X. Zhou, M.I. Gomis, E. Lonnoy, T. Maycock, M. Tignor, and T. Waterfield (eds.)]. UK and New York, NY, USA, pp. 32.

IPCC, 2019: *Climate Change and Land: An IPCC special report on climate change, desertification, land degradation, sustainable land management, food security, and greenhouse gas fluxes in terrestrial ecosystems* [P.R. Shukla, J. Skea, E. Calvo Buendia, V. Masson-Delmotte, H.-O. Pörtner, D. C. Roberts, P. Zhai, R. Slade, S. Connors, R. van Diemen, M. Ferrat, E. Haughey, S. Luz, S. Neogi, M. Pathak, J. Petzold, J. Portugal Pereira, P. Vyas, E. Huntley, K. Kissick, M. Belkacemi, J. Malley, (eds.)]. Cambridge University Press, Cambridge, UK and New York, NY, USA.

IPoSP, 2018: *Rethinking Society for the 21st Century*. International Panel on Social Progress, Volume 1: Socio-Economic Transformations. Cambridge University Press, Cambridge, United Kingdom, 366 pp.

Irfany, M.I. and S. Klasen, 2017: Affluence and emission trade-offs: Evidence from Indonesian households' carbon footprint. *Environ. Dev. Econ.*, **22(5)**, 546–570, doi:10.1017/S1355770X17000262.

Jacobson, M.Z., 2002: Control of fossil-fuel particulate black carbon and organic matter, possibly the most effective method of slowing global warming. *J. Geophys. Res. Atmos.*, **107(19)**, 16-1-16–22, doi:10.1029/2001JD001376.

Jacobson, M.Z., 2010: Short-term effects of controlling fossil-fuel soot, biofuel soot and gases, and methane on climate, Arctic ice, and air pollution health. *J. Geophys. Res. Atmos.*, **115(14)**, doi:10.1029/2009JD013795.

Jacobson, M.Z., 2019: The health and climate impacts of carbon capture and direct air capture. *Energy Environ. Sci.*, **12(12)**, 3567–3574, doi:10.1039/C9EE02709B.

Jacobson, M.Z. et al., 2017: 100% Clean and Renewable Wind, Water, and Sunlight All-Sector Energy Roadmaps for 139 Countries of the World. *Joule*, **1(1)**, 108–121, doi:10.1016/j.joule.2017.07.005.

Jacobson, M.Z. et al., 2019: Impacts of Green New Deal Energy Plans on Grid Stability, Costs, Jobs, Health, and Climate in 143 Countries. *One Earth*, **1(4)**, 449–463, doi:10.1016/j.oneear.2019.12.003.

Jakob, M., R. Soria, C. Trinidad, and O. Edenhofer, 2019: Green fiscal reform for a just energy transition in Latin America. *Econ. Open-Access, Open- Assess. E-Journal*, **13**, 1–11, 10.5018/economics-ejournal.ja.2019-17.

Jakob, M. et al., 2014: Feasible mitigation actions in developing countries. *Nat. Clim. Change*, **4(11)**, 961–968, doi:10.1038/nclimate2370.

Jakob, M. et al., 2016: Carbon Pricing Revenues Could Close Infrastructure Access Gaps. *World Dev.*, **84**, 254–265, doi:10.1016/J.WORLDDEV.2016.03.001.

Jasanoff, S., 2018: Just transitions: A humble approach to global energy futures. *Energy Res. Soc. Sci.*, **35**, 11–14, doi:10.1016/j.erss.2017.11.025.

Jayadev, G., B.D. Leibowicz, and E. Kutanoglu, 2020: US electricity infrastructure of the future: Generation and transmission pathways through 2050. *Appl. Energy*, **260** (November 2019), 114267, doi:10.1016/j.apenergy.2019.114267.

Jellinek, S. et al., 2019: Integrating diverse social and ecological motivations to achieve landscape restoration. *J. Appl. Ecol.*, **56(1)**, 246–252, doi:10.1111/1365-2664.13248.

Jia, G., E. Shevliakova, P. Artaxo, N. De Noblet-Ducoudré, R. Houghton, J. House, K. Kitajima, C. Lennard, A. Popp, A. Sirin, R. Sukumar, and L. Verchot, 2019: Land–Climate Interactions. In: *Climate Change and Land: An IPCC special report on climate change, desertification, land degradation, sustainable land management, food security, and greenhouse gas fluxes in terrestrial ecosystems* [P.R. Shukla, J. Skea, E. Calvo Buendia, V. Masson-Delmotte, H.-O. Pörtner, D.C. Roberts, P. Zhai, R. Slade, S. Connors, R. van Diemen, M. Ferrat, E. Haughey, S. Luz, S. Neogi, M. Pathak, J. Petzold, J. Portugal Pereira, P. Vyas, E. Huntley, K. Kissick, M, Belkacemi, J. Malley, (eds.)]. Cambridge University Press, Cambridge, United Kingdom and New York, NY, USA, 131–247 pp.

Jiang, K., X. Zhuang, R. Miao, and C. He, 2013: China's role in attaining the global 2°C target. *Clim. Policy*, **13(sup1)**, 55–69, doi:10.1080/14693062.2012.746070.

Jiang, K., K. Tamura, and T. Hanaoka, 2017: Can we go beyond INDCs: Analysis of a future mitigation possibility in China, Japan, EU and the US. *Adv. Clim. Chang. Res.*, **8(2)**, 117–122, doi:10.1016/j.accre.2017.05.005.

Jiang, K., C. He, H. Dai, J. Liu, and X. Xu, 2018: Emission scenario analysis for China under the global 1.5°C target. *Carbon Manag.*, **9(5)**, 481–491, doi:10.1080/17583004.2018.1477835.

Jiang, K.J. et al., 2016: China's low-carbon investment pathway under the 2°C scenario. *Adv. Clim. Chang. Res.*, **7(4)**, 229–234, doi:10.1016/j.accre.2016.12.004.

Johl, A. and S. Duyck, 2012: Promoting Human Rights in the Future Climate Regime. *Ethics, Policy Environ.*, **15(3)**, doi:10.1080/21550085.2012.730240.

Johnson, N. et al., 2015: Stranded on a low-carbon planet: Implications of climate policy for the phase-out of coal-based power plants.

Technol. Forecast. Soc. Change, **90(PA)**, 89–102, doi:10.1016/j. techfore.2014.02.028.

Jones, C. and D.M. Kammen, 2014: Spatial distribution of US household carbon footprints reveals suburbanization undermines greenhouse gas benefits of urban population density. *Environ. Sci. Technol.*, **48(2)**, 895–902, doi:10.1021/es4034364.

Jones, L. et al., 2013: *The political economy of local adaptation planning: Exploring barriers to Flexible and Forward-looking Decision Making in three districts in Ethiopia, Uganda and Mozambique*. Overseas Development Institute, London, United Kingdom, 29 pp., https://www.preventionweb.net/publication/political-economy-local-adaptation-planning-exploring-barriers-flexible-and-forward.

Jonsson, S., A. Ydstedt, and E. Asen, 2020: *Looking Back on 30 Years of Carbon Taxes in Sweden. Fiscal Fact No. 727*. Tax Foundation, Washington, DC, USA, 4 pp.

JRC, 2021: *Global Energy and Climate Outlook 2021: Advancing towards climate neutrality*. Joint Research Centre (European Commission), Brussels, Belgium, 130 pp.

Ju, Y. et al., 2021: Industrial decarbonization under Japan's national mitigation scenarios: A multi-model analysis. *Sustain. Sci.*, **16(2)**, 411–427, doi:10.1007/s11625-021-00905-2.

Kahane, A., 2012: Transformative scenario planning. In: *The Collaboratory*, Barrett-Koehler Publishers, Inc., San Francisco, USA, pp. 168.

Kairo, J.G., A.J. Hamza, and C. Wanjiru, 2018: Mikoko Pamoja. In: *A Blue Carbon Primer* [Windham-Myers, L., S. Crooks, and T.G. Troxler, (eds.)]. CRC Press, Boca Raton, FL, USA, pp. 341–350.

Kane, L. and M. Boulle, 2018: 'This was different': Transferring climate mitigation knowledge practices south to south with the MAPS programme. *Clim. Policy*, 8(9), 1177-1188, doi:10.1080/14693062.2017.1421520.

Karapin, R., 2016: *Political Opportunities for Climate Policy*. Cambridge University Press, Cambridge UK and New York, NY, USA, 344 pp.

Karlsson, M., E. Alfredsson, and N. Westling, 2020: Climate policy co-benefits: A review. *Clim. Policy*, **20(3)**, 292–316, doi:10.1080/14693062.2020.1724070.

Karner, A. and R.A. Marcantonio, 2018: Achieving Transportation Equity: Meaningful Public Involvement to Meet the Needs of Underserved Communities. *Public Work. Manag. Policy*, **23(2)**, 105–126, doi:10.1177/1087724X17738792.

Kartha, S. et al., 2018a: Cascading biases against poorer countries. *Nat. Clim. Change*, **8(5)**, 348–349, doi.org/10.1038/s41558-018-0152-7.

Kartha, S., S. Caney, N.K. Dubash, and G. Muttitt, 2018b: Whose carbon is burnable? Equity considerations in the allocation of a 'right to extract'. *Clim. Change*, **150**, 117–129, doi:10.1007/s10584-018-2209-z.

Kato, E. and A. Kurosawa, 2019: Evaluation of Japanese energy system toward 2050 with TIMES-Japan – Deep decarbonization pathways. *Energy Procedia*, **158**, 4141–4146, doi:10.1016/j.egypro.2019.01.818.

Kemp-Benedict, E., 2012: Telling better stories: Strengthening the story in story and simulation. *Environ. Res. Lett.*, **7(4)**, 41004, doi:10.1088/1748-9326/7/4/041004.

Kemp-Benedict, E., C. Holz, T. Athanasiou, S. Kartha, and P. Baer, 2018: *The Climate Equity Reference Calculator*. Climate Equity Reference Project (EcoEquity and Stockholm Environment Institute), Berkeley and Somerville, California, USA.

Keramidas, K. et al., 2021: *Global Energy and Climate Outlook 2020: A New Normal Beyond Covid-19*. European Commission, Joint Research Centre, Sevilla, Spain, 76 pp., https://publications.jrc.ec.europa.eu/repository/bitstream/JRC123203/kjna30558enn_geco2020.pdf.

Kettner, C., D. Kletzan-Slamanig, A. Köppl, B. Littig, and I. Zielinska, 2019: A Cross-Country Comparison of Sustainable Energy Development in Selected EU Members. *J. Sustain. Res.*, **1(2)**, doi:10.20900/jsr20190017.

Khanna, N. et al., 2019: Energy and CO_2 implications of decarbonization strategies for China beyond efficiency: Modeling 2050 maximum

renewable resources and accelerated electrification impacts. *Appl. Energy*, **242** (February 2019), 12–26, doi:10.1016/j.apenergy.2019.03.116.

Kharas, H. and J. McArthur, 2019: *Building the SDG economy: Needs, spending, and financing for universal achievement of the Sustainable Development Goals*. Global Economy & Development Working Paper 131, Brookings Institution, Washington, DC, USA , 38 pp., https://www.brookings.edu/research/building-the-sdg-economy-needs-spending-and-financing-for-universal-achievement-of-the-sustainable-development-goals/ (Accessed December 11, 2019).

Kharecha, P.A. and M. Sato, 2019: Implications of energy and CO_2 emission changes in Japan and Germany after the Fukushima accident. *Energy Policy*, **132**, 647–653, doi:10.1016/j.enpol.2019.05.057.

Khosla, R. and A. Bhardwaj, 2019: Urbanization in the time of climate change: Examining the response of Indian cities. *Wiley Interdiscip. Rev. Clim. Change*, **10(1)**, e560, doi:10.1002/wcc.560.

Kikstra, J.S. et al., 2021: Climate mitigation scenarios with persistent COVID-19-related energy demand changes. *Nat. Energy*, doi:10.1038/s41560-021-00904-8.

Kissinger, G., A. Gupta, I. Mulder, and N. Unterstell, 2019: Climate financing needs in the land sector under the Paris Agreement: An assessment of developing country perspectives. *Land Use Policy*, **83**, 256–269, doi:10.1016/j.landusepol.2019.02.007.

Kläy, A., A.B. Zimmermann, and F. Schneider, 2015: Rethinking science for sustainable development: Reflexive interaction for a paradigm transformation. *Futures*, **65**, 72–85, doi:10.1016/J.FUTURES.2014.10.012.

Klein, M., 2015: Public-private partnerships: Promise and hype. (June), Policy Research Working Paper number 7340, The World Bank, Washington, DC,18 pp., doi:10.1596/1813-9450-7340.

Klinsky, S., 2017: An initial scoping of transitional justice for global climate governance. *Clim. Policy*, **18(6)**, 1–14, doi:10.1080/14693062.2017.1377594.

Klinsky, S. and J. Brankovic, 2018: *The global climate regime and transitional justice*. Routledge, Oxon, UK and New York, USA, 196 pp.

Klinsky, S. and H. Winkler, 2018: Building equity in: strategies for integrating equity into modelling for a 1.5°C world. *Philos. Trans. R. Soc. A.*, **376(2119)**, 20160461, doi:10.1098/rsta.2016.0461.

Klinsky, S. et al., 2017a: Why equity is fundamental in climate change policy research. *Glob. Environ. Change*, **44**, 170–173, doi:10.1016/j.gloenvcha.2016.08.002.

Klinsky, S., D. Waskow, E. Northrop, and W. Bevins, 2017b: Operationalizing equity and supporting ambition: Identifying a more robust approach to 'respective capabilities'. *Clim. Dev.*, **9(4)**, 287–297, doi:http://dx.doi.org/10.1080/17565529.2016.1146121.

Köberle, A.C., P.R.R. Rochedo, A.F.P. Lucena, A. Szklo, and R. Schaeffer, 2020: Brazil's emission trajectories in a well-below 2°C world: The role of disruptive technologies versus land-based mitigation in an already low-emission energy system. *Clim. Change*, **162(4)**, 1823–1842, doi:10.1007/s10584-020-02856-6.

Kolsuz, G. and A.E. Yeldan, 2017: Economics of climate change and green employment: A general equilibrium investigation for Turkey. *Renew. Sustain. Energy Rev.*, **70**, 1240–1250, doi:10.1016/j.rser.2016.12.025.

Kongsager, R., B. Locatelli, and F. Chazarin, 2016: Addressing Climate Change Mitigation and Adaptation Together: A Global Assessment of Agriculture and Forestry Projects. *Environ. Manage.*, **57(2)**, 271–282, doi:10.1007/s00267-015-0605-y.

Kowarsch, M. et al., 2017: A road map for global environmental assessments. *Nat. Clim. Change*, **7**, 379, doi:10.1038/nclimate3307.

Krakowski, V., E. Assoumou, V. Mazauric, and N. Maïzi, 2016: Feasible path toward 40–100% renewable energy shares for power supply in France by 2050: A prospective analysis. *Appl. Energy*, **171**, 501–522, doi:10.1016/j.apenergy.2016.03.094.

Kriegler, E. et al., 2018: Short term policies to keep the door open for Paris climate goals. *Environ. Res. Lett.*, **13(7)**, 074022, doi:10.1088/1748-9326/aac4f1.

4

Kroeger, K.D., S. Crooks, S. Moseman-Valtierra, and J. Tang, 2017: Restoring tides to reduce methane emissions in impounded wetlands: A new and potent Blue Carbon climate change intervention. *Sci. Rep.*, **7(1)**, 1–12, doi:10.1038/s41598-017-12138-4.

Kuhlmann, S. and A. Rip, 2018: Next-Generation Innovation Policy and Grand Challenges. *Sci. Public Policy*, **45(4)**, 448–454, doi:10.1093/scipol/scy011.

Kuramochi, T., T. Wakiyama, and A. Kuriyama, 2017: Assessment of national greenhouse gas mitigation targets for 2030 through meta-analysis of bottom-up energy and emission scenarios: A case of Japan. *Renew. Sustain. Energy Rev.*, **77**, 924–944, doi:10.1016/j.rser.2016.12.093.

Kuramochi, T. et al., 2018: Ten key short-term sectoral benchmarks to limit warming to 1.5°C. *Clim. Policy*, **18(3)**, 287–305, doi:10.1080/14693 062.2017.1397495.

Kuramochi, T. et al., 2020: Beyond national climate action: The impact of region, city, and business commitments on global greenhouse gas emissions. *Clim. Policy*, **20(3)**, 275–291, doi:10.1080/14693062.2020.1740150.

Kuwae, T. and M. Hori, 2019: *Blue Carbon in Shallow Coastal Ecosystems: Carbon Dynamics, Policy, and Implementation*. Springer, Singapore.

Kwok, T.F., Y. Xu, X. Liu, and Y. Leung, 2018: The impacts of economic structure on China's carbon dioxide emissions: An analysis with reference to other East Asian economies. *Clim. Policy*, **18(10)**, 1235–1245, doi:10.1080/146 93062.2017.1418282.

La Rovere, E.L., 2017: Low-carbon development pathways in Brazil and 'Climate Clubs'. *Wiley Interdiscip. Rev. Clim. Change*, **8(1)**, e439, doi:10.1002/wcc.439.

La Rovere, E.L. et al., 2014a: *Economic and social implications: Brazilian GHG mitigation scenarios to 2030*. Brazilian Forum on Climate Change – FBMC. COPPE/UFRJ, Rio de Janeiro, https://www.mapsprogramme.org/wp-content/uploads/Summary_for_Decision_Makers_IES-Brasil.pdf.

La Rovere, E.L., A.O. Pereira, C.B.S. Dubeux, and W. Wills, 2014b: Climate change mitigation actions in Brazil. *Clim. Dev.*, **6(sup1)**, 25–33, doi:10.10 80/17565529.2013.812952.

La Rovere, E.L., W. Wills, C. Grottera, C.B.S.S. Dubeux, and C. Gesteira, 2018: Economic and social implications of low-emission development pathways in Brazil. *Carbon Manag.*, **9(5)**, 563–574, doi:10.1080/17583 004.2018.1507413.

Lachapelle, E. and M. Paterson, 2013: Drivers of national climate policy. *Clim. Policy*, **13(5)**, 547–571, doi:10.1080/14693062.2013.811333.

Lahn, B., 2018: In the light of equity and science: Scientific expertise and climate justice after Paris. *Int. Environ. Agreements Polit. Law Econ.*, **18(1)**, 29–43, doi:10.1007/s10784-017-9375-8.

Lahn, B. and G. Sundqvist, 2017: Science as a 'fixed point'? Quantification and boundary objects in international climate politics. *Environ. Sci. Policy*, **67(supC)**, 8–15, doi.org/10.1016/j.envsci.2016.11.001.

Lahn, G. and S. Bradley, 2016: Left Stranded? Extractives-Led Growth in a Carbon-Constrained World. *R. Inst. Int. Aff*. Royal Institute of International Affairs, London, United Kingdom, 38 pp., https://www.chathamhouse.org/sites/default/files/publications/research/2016-06-17-left-stranded-extractives-bradley-lahn-final.pdf (Accessed November 1, 2021).

Lampin, L.B.A.A., F. Nadaud, F. Grazi, and J.-C. C. Hourcade, 2013: Long-term fuel demand: Not only a matter of fuel price. *Energy Policy*, **62**, 780–787, doi:10.1016/j.enpol.2013.05.021.

Landa Rivera, G., F. Reynès, I. Islas Cortes, F.X. Bellocq, and F. Grazi, 2016: Towards a low-carbon growth in Mexico: Is a double dividend possible? A dynamic general equilibrium assessment. *Energy Policy*, **96**, 314–327, doi:10.1016/j.enpol.2016.06.012.

Lantz, V. and Q. Feng, 2006: Assessing income, population, and technology impacts on CO_2 emissions in Canada: Where's the EKC? *Ecol. Econ.*, **57(2)**, 229–238, doi:10.1016/j.ecolecon.2005.04.006.

Lap, T., R. Benders, F. van der Hilst, and A. Faaij, 2020: How does the interplay between resource availability, intersectoral competition and reliability affect a low-carbon power generation mix in Brazil for 2050? *Energy*, **195**, doi:10.1016/j.energy.2020.116948.

Lapola, D.M. et al., 2018: Limiting the high impacts of Amazon forest dieback with no-regrets science and policy action. *Proc. Natl. Acad. Sci.*, **115(46)**, 11671–11679, doi:10.1073/pnas.1721770115.

Lave, L.B., 1991: Formulating Greenhouse Policies in a Sea of Uncertainty. *Energy J.*, **12(1)**, doi:10.5547/issn0195-6574-ej-vol12-no1-2.

Le Billon, P. and B. Kristoffersen, 2020: Just cuts for fossil fuels? Supply-side carbon constraints and energy transition. *Environ. Plan. A*, **52(6)**, 1072–1092, doi:10.1177/0308518X18816702.

Le Quéré, C. et al., 2019: Drivers of declining CO_2 emissions in 18 developed economies. *Nat. Clim. Change*, **9**, 213–217, doi:10.1038/s41558-019-0419-7.

Le Quéré, C. et al., 2020: Temporary reduction in daily global CO_2 emissions during the COVID-19 forced confinement. *Nat. Clim. Change*, **10(7)**, 647–653, doi:10.1038/s41558-020-0797-x.

Leach, M. et al., 2018: Equity and sustainability in the anthropocene: A social-ecological systems perspective on their intertwined futures. *Glob. Sustain.*, **1(e13)**, 1–13, doi:10.1017/sus.2018.12.

Leal Filho, W. et al., 2018: Reinvigorating the sustainable development research agenda: The role of the sustainable development goals (SDG). *Int. J. Sustain. Dev. World Ecol.*, **25(2)**, 131–142, doi:10.1080/13504 509.2017.1342103.

Lecocq, F. and Z. Shalizi, 2014: The economics of targeted mitigation in infrastructure. *Clim. Policy*, **14(2)**, 187–208, doi:10.1080/1469 3062.2014.861657.

Lecocq, F., A. Nadaï, and C. Cassen, 2022: Getting models and modellers to inform long-term mitigation strategies. *Clim. Policy*, , doi:10.1080/14693 062.2021.2002250.

Lee, C.T. et al., 2018: Enabling low-carbon emissions for sustainable development in Asia and beyond. *J. Clean. Prod.*, **176**, 726–735, doi:10.1016/j.jclepro.2017.12.110.

Lefèvre, J., W. Wills, and J.-C. Hourcade, 2018: Combining low-carbon economic development and oil exploration in Brazil? An energy–economy assessment. *Clim. Policy*, **18(10)**, 1286–1295, doi:10.1080/14693 062.2018.1431198.

Lenferna, G.A., 2018a: If You're 'Still In' the Paris Climate Agreement, Then Show Us the Money. *Ethics, Policy Environ.*, **21(1)**, 52–55, doi:10.1080/21 550085.2018.1463626.

Lenferna, G.A., 2018b: Can we equitably manage the end of the fossil fuel era? *Energy Res. Soc. Sci.*, **35**, 217–223, doi:10.1016/j.erss.2017.11.007.

Lengefeld, E., G. Metternicht, and P. Nedungadi, 2020: Behavior change and sustainability of ecological restoration projects. *Restor. Ecol.*, **28(4)**, 724–729, doi:10.1111/rec.13159.

Lennon, M., 2017: Decolonizing energy: Black Lives Matter and technoscientific expertise amid solar transitions. *Energy Res. Soc. Sci.*, **30**, 18–27, doi:10.1016/j.erss.2017.06.002.

Lenzi, D., W.F. Lamb, J. Hilaire, M. Kowarsch, and J.C. Minx, 2018: Don't deploy negative emissions technologies without ethical analysis. *Nature*, **561(7723)**, 303–305, doi:10.1038/d41586-018-06695-5.

Lepault, C. and F. Lecocq, 2021: Mapping forward-looking mitigation studies at country level. *Environ. Res. Lett.*, **16(8)**, 083001, doi:10.1088/1748-9326/ac0ac8.

Levinson, A., 2019: Energy Efficiency Standards Are More Regressive Than Energy Taxes: Theory and Evidence. *J. Assoc. Environ. Resour. Econ.*, **6(S1)**, S7–S36, doi:10.1086/701186.

Li, J., M. Hamdi-Cherif, and C. Cassen, 2017: Aligning domestic policies with international coordination in a post-Paris global climate regime: A case for China. *Technol. Forecast. Soc. Change*, **125**, 258–274, doi:10.1016/J. TECHFORE.2017.06.027.

Lin, B. and H. Liu, 2015: CO_2 emissions of China's commercial and residential buildings: Evidence and reduction policy. *Build. Environ.*, **92**, 418–431, doi:10.1016/j.buildenv.2015.05.020.

Lipper, L. et al., 2014: Climate-smart agriculture for food security. *Nat. Clim. Change*, **4(12)**, 1068–1072, doi:10.1038/nclimate2437.

4

Liu, J. et al., 2018: Nexus approaches to global sustainable development. *Nat. Sustain.*, **1(9)**, 466–476, doi:10.1038/s41893-018-0135-8.

Locatelli, B., V. Evans, A. Wardell, A. Andrade, and R. Vignola, 2011: Forests and climate change in Latin America: Linking adaptation and mitigation. *Forests*, **2(1)**, 431–450, doi:10.3390/f2010431.

Locatelli, B., G. Fedele, V. Fayolle, and A. Baglee, 2016: Synergies between adaptation and mitigation in climate change finance. *Int. J. Clim. Chang. Strateg. Manag.*, **8(1)**, 112–128, doi:10.1108/IJCCSM-07-2014-0088.

Lofgren, H., M. Cicowiez, and C. Diaz-Bonilla, 2013: MAMS – A Computable General Equilibrium Model for Developing Country Strategy Analysis. *Handb. Comput. Gen. Equilib. Model.*, **1**, 159–276, doi:10.1016/B978-0-444-59568-3.00004-3.

Louis, J.N., S. Allard, F. Kotrotsou, and V. Debusschere, 2020: A multi-objective approach to the prospective development of the European power system by 2050. *Energy*, **191**, doi:10.1016/j.energy.2019.116539.

Lovejoy, T.E. and C. Nobre, 2018: Amazon Tipping Point. *Sci. Adv.*, **4(2)**, eaat2340, doi:10.1126/sciadv.aat2340.

Low-Carbon Asia Research Project, 2012: *Ten Actions toward Low Carbon Asia*. http://2050.nies.go.jp (Accessed December 18, 2019).

Lucena, A.F.P. et al., 2016: Climate policy scenarios in Brazil: A multi-model comparison for energy. *Energy Econ.*, **56**, 564–574, doi.org/10.1016/j.eneco.2015.02.005.

Luderer, G. et al., 2016: *Deep Decarbonization Towards 1.5°C–2°C Stabilization Policy findings from the ADVANCE project (first edition).* Postdam Institute for Climate Impact Research (PIK), Potsdam, Germany, 44 pp., http://www.fp7-advance.eu/sites/default/files/documents/WP7/ADVANCE-Synthesis-Report.pdf.

Luderer, G. et al., 2018a: Residual fossil CO_2 emissions in 1.5-2°C pathways. *Nat. Clim. Change*, **8(7)**, 626-633, doi:10.1038/s41558-018-0198-6.

Luderer, G. et al., 2018b: Residual fossil CO_2 emissions in 1.5–2 °C pathways. *Nat. Clim. Change*, **8(7)**, 626–633, doi:10.1038/s41558-018-0198-6.

Lui, S. et al., 2021: Correcting course: The emission reduction potential of international cooperative initiatives. *Clim. Policy*, **21(2)**, 232–250, doi:10.1080/14693062.2020.1806021.

Lund, H. and B.V. Mathiesen, 2009: Energy system analysis of 100% renewable energy systems – The case of Denmark in years 2030 and 2050. *Energy*, **34(5)**, 524–531, doi:10.1016/j.energy.2008.04.003.

Mace, M.J., C.L. Fyson, M. Schaeffer, and W.L. Hare, 2021: Large-Scale Carbon Dioxide Removal to Meet the 1.5°C Limit: Key Governance Gaps, Challenges and Priority Responses. *Glob. Policy*, **12(S1)**, 67–81, doi:10.1111/1758-5899.12921.

Maestre-Andrés, S., S. Drews, and J. van den Bergh, 2019: Perceived fairness and public acceptability of carbon pricing: A review of the literature. *Clim. Policy*, **19(9)**, 1186–1204, doi:10.1080/14693062.2019.1639490.

Malliet, P., F. Reynès, G. Landa, M. Hamdi-Cherif, and A. Saussay, 2020: Assessing Short-Term and Long-Term Economic and Environmental Effects of the COVID-19 Crisis in France. *Environ. Resour. Econ.*, **76(4)**, 867–883, doi:10.1007/s10640-020-00488-z.

Mandley, S.J., V. Daioglou, H.M. Junginger, D.P. van Vuuren, and B. Wicke, 2020: EU bioenergy development to 2050. *Renew. Sustain. Energy Rev.*, **127**, 109858, doi:10.1016/J.RSER.2020.109858.

Mansell, P., S.P. Philbin, T. Broyd, and I. Nicholson, 2019: Assessing the impact of infrastructure projects on global sustainable development goals. *Proc. Inst. Civ. Eng. Eng. Sustain.*, **173(4)**, 196–212, doi:10.1680/jensu.19.00044.

Markard, J., R. Raven, and B. Truffer, 2012: Sustainability transitions: An emerging field of research and its prospects. *Res. Policy*, **41(6)**, 955–967, doi:10.1016/j.respol.2012.02.013.

Maroun, C. and R. Schaeffer, 2012: Emulating new policy goals into past successes: Greenhouse gas emissions mitigation as a side effect of biofuels programmes in Brazil. *Clim. Dev.*, **4(3)**, 187–198, doi:10.1080/17565529.2012.668849.

Massetti, E., 2012: Short-term and long-term climate mitigation policy in Italy. *Wiley Interdiscip. Rev. Clim. Change*, **3(2)**, 171–183, doi:10.1002/wcc.159.

Mata, É. et al., 2020: A map of roadmaps for zero and low energy and carbon buildings worldwide. *Environ. Res. Lett.*, **15(11)**, 113003, doi:10.1088/1748-9326/abb69f.

Mathiesen, B.V., H. Lund, and K. Karlsson, 2011: 100% Renewable energy systems, climate mitigation and economic growth. *Appl. Energy*, **88(2)**, 488–501, doi:10.1016/j.apenergy.2010.03.001.

Mathur, R. and S. Shekhar, 2020: India's energy sector choices – options and implications of ambitious mitigation efforts. *Clim. Change*, **162(4)**, 1893–1911, doi:10.1007/s10584-020-02885-1.

Matsuoka, Y., M. Kainuma, J. Fujino, and T. Ehara, 2013: How to Approach Asian Low-Carbon Societies? *Glob. Environ. Res.*, **17**, 3–10.

Mattioli, G., C. Roberts, J.K. Steinberger, and A. Brown, 2020: The political economy of car dependence: A systems of provision approach. *Energy Res. Soc. Sci.*, **66**, 101486, doi:10.1016/j.erss.2020.101486.

Mawdsley, E., 2018: 'From billions to trillions': Financing the SDGs in a world 'beyond aid'. *Dialogues Hum. Geogr.*, **8(2)**, 191–195, doi:10.1177/2043820618780789.

Mazur, A. and E. Rosa, 1974: Energy and Life-Style: Massive energy consumption may not be necessary to maintain current living standards in America. *Science*, **186(4164)**, 607–610, doi:10.1126/science.186.4164.607.

Mazzucato, M. and G. Semieniuk, 2017: Public financing of innovation: New questions. *Oxford Rev. Econ. Policy*, **33(1)**, 24–48, doi:10.1093/oxrep/grw036.

Mbeva, K.L. and W.P. Pauw, 2016: *Self-Differentiation of Countries' Responsibilities Addressing Climate Change through Intended Nationally Determined Contributions*. Deutsches Institut für Entwicklungspolitik gGmbH, Bonn, Germany, 51 pp.

McCollum, D.L. et al., 2018: Energy investment needs for fulfilling the Paris Agreement and achieving the Sustainable Development Goals. *Nat. Energy*, **3(7)**, 589–599, doi:10.1038/s41560-018-0179-z.

McDowall, W. et al., 2017: Circular Economy Policies in China and Europe. *J. Ind. Ecol.*, **21(3)**, 651–661, doi:10.1111/jiec.12597.

McLeod, E. et al., 2011: A blueprint for blue carbon: Toward an improved understanding of the role of vegetated coastal habitats in sequestering CO_2. *Front. Ecol. Environ.*, **9(10)**, 552–560, doi:10.1890/110004.

McNeil, M.A. et al., 2016: Energy efficiency outlook in China's urban buildings sector through 2030. *Energy Policy*, **97**, 532–539, doi:10.1016/j.enpol.2016.07.033.

Meelen, T., B. Truffer, and T. Schwanen, 2019: Virtual user communities contributing to upscaling innovations in transitions: The case of electric vehicles. *Environ. Innov. Soc. Transitions*, **31**, 96–109, doi:10.1016/j.eist.2019.01.002.

Meheus, F. and D. McIntyre, 2017: Fiscal space for domestic funding of health and other social services. *Heal. Econ. Policy Law*, **12(2)**, 159–177, doi:10.1017/S1744133116000438.

Meinshausen, M., J. Guetschow, J. Lewis, and Z. Nicholls, 2021: NDC factsheets, doi:10.5281/zenodo.5710394.

Méjean, A., F. Lecocq, and Y. Mulugetta, 2015: Equity, burden sharing and development pathways: Reframing international climate negotiations. *Int. Environ. Agreements Polit. Law Econ.*, **15(4)**, 387–402, doi:10.1007/s10784-015-9302-9.

Mendoza, M.N., 2014: *Lessons Learned: Fossil Fuel Subsidies and Energy Sector Reform in the Philippines GSI REPORT*. International Institute for Sustainable Development, Winnipeg, Manitoba, Canada, www.iisd.org/gsi (Accessed December 15, 2020).

Messner, D., 2015: A social contract for low carbon and sustainable development: Reflections on non-linear dynamics of social realignments and technological innovations in transformation processes. *Technol. Forecast. Soc. Change*, **98**, 260–270, doi:10.1016/J.TECHFORE.2015.05.013.

Michaelowa, A., M. Allen, and F. Sha, 2018: Policy instruments for limiting global temperature rise to 1.5°C – can humanity rise to the challenge? *Clim. Policy*, **18(3)**, 275–286, doi:10.1080/14693062.2018.1426977.

4

Michaelowa, K. and A. Michaelowa, 2017: Transnational Climate Governance Initiatives: Designed for Effective Climate Change Mitigation? *Int. Interact.*, **43(1)**, 129–155, doi:10.1080/03050629.2017.1256110.

Mijn Cha, J., M. Wander, and M. Pastor, 2020: Environmental Justice, Just Transition, and a Low-Carbon Future for California. *Environ. Law Report.*, **50**, 10216.

Mikova, N., W. Eichhammer, and B. Pfluger, 2019: Low-carbon energy scenarios 2050 in north-west European countries: Towards a more harmonised approach to achieve the EU targets. *Energy Policy*, **130** (February), 448–460, doi:10.1016/j.enpol.2019.03.047.

Miller, C.A. and J. Richter, 2014: Social Planning for Energy Transitions. *Curr. Sustain. Energy Reports*, **1(3)**, 77–84, doi:10.1007/s40518-014-0010-9.

Millot, A., A. Krook-Riekkola, and N. Maïzi, 2020: Guiding the future energy transition to net-zero emissions: Lessons from exploring the differences between France and Sweden. *Energy Policy*, **139** (July 2019), 111358, doi:10.1016/j.enpol.2020.111358.

Millward-Hopkins, J., J.K. Steinberger, N.D. Rao, and Y. Oswald, 2020: Providing decent living with minimum energy: A global scenario. *Glob. Environ. Change*, **65**, 102168, doi:10.1016/j.gloenvcha.2020.102168.

Ministry of Business Innovation & Employment New Zealand, 2019: Just Transition. Government of New Zealand, Wellington, New Zealand, https://www.mbie.govt.nz/business-and-employment/economic-development/just-transition/ (Accessed January 8, 2020).

Ministry of Employment and Labour Relations of Ghana, 2018: Ghana National Dialogue on Decent Work. Accra, Ghana, https://www.un-page.org/ghana-holds-national-dialogue-decent-work-and-%E2%80%98just-transition%E2%80%99-green-economy (Accessed January 8, 2020).

Minx, J.C. et al., 2021: A comprehensive and synthetic dataset for global, regional, and national greenhouse gas emissions by sector 1970–2018 with an extension to 2019. *Earth Syst. Sci. Data*, **13**, 5213–5252, doi:10.5194/essd-13-5213-2021.

Mirzoev, Tokhir N., Ling Zhu, Yang Yang, Tian Zhang, Erik Roos, Andrea Pescatori, A.M., 2020: *Future of Oil and Fiscal Sustainability in the GCC Region*. International Monetary Fund, Washington, DC, USA, 45 pp., https://www.imf.org/-/media/Files/Publications/DP/2020/English/FOFSGCCEA.ashx (Accessed November 1, 2021).

Mittal, S., J.Y. Liu, S. Fujimori, and P.R. Shukla, 2018: An assessment of near-to-mid-term economic impacts and energy transitions under '2°C' and '1.5°C' scenarios for India. *Energies*, **11(9)**, doi:10.3390/en11092213.

MoEF, 2008: *India's National Action Plan on Climate Change (NAPCC)*. Prime Minister's Council On Climate Change, Ministry of Environment and Forests (MOEF), Government of India, New Delhi. 56 pp., https://moef.gov.in/wp-content/uploads/2018/04/Pg01-52_2.pdf (Accessed October 26, 2021).

MoEFCC, 2018: *Annual Report 2018-19*. Ministry of Environment, Forest and Climate Change (MOEFCC), Government of India. https://moef.gov.in/wp-content/uploads/2019/08/Annual-Report-2018-19-English.pdf (Accessed October 26, 2021).

MoEFCC, 2021: *Annual Report 2020-21*. Ministry of Environment, Forest and Climate Change, Government of India. https://moef.gov.in/wp-content/uploads/2017/06/Environment-AR-English-2020-21.pdf (Accessed October 26, 2021).

Moellendorf, D., 2020: Responsibility for Increasing Mitigation Ambition in Light of the Right to Sustainable Development. *Fudan J. Humanit. Soc. Sci.*, **13(2)**, 181–192, doi:10.1007/s40647-020-00277-4.

Mogomotsi, P.K., G.E.J. Mogomotsi, and W.L. Hambira, 2018: Paris agreement on climate change and Botswana's Vision 2036: An examination of linkages. *Chinese J. Popul. Resour. Environ.*, **16(1)**, 59–66, doi:10.1080/10042857.2018.1438000.

Mohai, P., D. Pellow, and J.T. Roberts, 2009: Environmental Justice. *Annu. Rev. Environ. Resour.*, **34(1)**, 405–430, doi:10.1146/annurev-environ-082508-094348.

Mohan, A., O. Geden, M. Fridahl, H.J. Buck, and G.P. Peters, 2021: UNFCCC must confront the political economy of net-negative emissions. *One Earth*, **4(10)**, 1348–1351, doi:10.1016/j.oneear.2021.10.001.

Moomaw, W.R., J.R. Moreira, K. Blok, D.L. Greene, K. Gregory, T. Jaszay, T. Kashiwagi, M. Levine, M. McFarland, N. Siva Prasad, L. Price, H.-H. Rogner, R. Sims, F. Zhou, P. Zhou, 2001: Technological and Economic Potential of Greenhouse Gas Emissions Reduction. In: *Contribution of Working Group III to the Third Assessment Report of the Intergovernmental Panel on Climate Change – Mitigation*. Cambridge University Press, Cambridge, UK and New York, NY, USA, pp. 167–300. https://www.ipcc.ch/site/assets/uploads/2018/03/3.pdf (Accessed July 12, 2019).

Morris, J., V. Srikrishnan, M. Webster, and J. Reilly, 2018: Hedging Strategies: Electricity Investment Decisions under Policy Uncertainty. *Energy J.*, **39(1)**, 101-122, doi:10.5547/01956574.39.1.jmor.

Mu, Y., S. Evans, C. Wang, and W. Cai, 2018a: How will sectoral coverage affect the efficiency of an emissions trading system? A CGE-based case study of China. *Appl. Energy*, **227**, 403–414, doi:10.1016/j.apenergy.2017.08.072.

Mu, Y., C. Wang, and W. Cai, 2018b: The economic impact of China's INDC: Distinguishing the roles of the renewable energy quota and the carbon market. *Renew. Sustain. Energy Rev.*, **81**, 2955–2966, doi:10.1016/j.rser.2017.06.105.

Munasinghe, M., 2001: Development, equity and sustainability (DES) in the context of climate change. In: *Cross-cutting issues guidance papers: IPCC supporting material for the Third Assessment Report* [Pachauri, R.K., T. Taniguchi, and K. Tanaka, (eds.)]. Intergovernmental Panel on Climate Change (IPCC), Geneva, Switzerland, 69–119 pp.

Munasinghe, M., 2007: *Making development more sustainable: Sustainomics framework and practical applications*. MIND Press, Colombo, Sri Lanka, 657 pp.

Mundaca, L., M. Mansoz, L. Neij, and G. Timilsina, 2013: Transaction costs analysis of low-carbon technologies. *Clim. Policy*, **13(4)**, 490–513, doi:10.1080/14693062.2013.781452.

Mundaca, L., J. Sonnenschein, L. Steg, N. Höhne, and D. Ürge-Vorsatz, 2019: The global expansion of climate mitigation policy interventions, the Talanoa Dialogue and the role of behavioural insights. *Environ. Res. Commun.*, **1(6)**, 061001, doi:10.1088/2515-7620/ab26d6.

Muttitt, G. and S. Kartha, 2020: Equity, climate justice and fossil fuel extraction: Principles for a managed phase out. *Clim. Policy*, **20(8)**, 1024–1042, doi:10.1080/14693062.2020.1763900.

Naidoo, C.P., 2020: Relating financial systems to sustainability transitions: Challenges, demands and design features. *Environ. Innov. Soc. Transitions*, **36**, 270–290, doi:10.1016/j.eist.2019.10.004.

Nair, S. and M. Howlett, 2017: Policy myopia as a source of policy failure: Adaptation and policy learning under deep uncertainty. *Policy Polit.*, **45(1)**, 103–118, doi:10.1332/030557316X14788776017743.

Nakicenovic, N. and R. Swart (Eds)2000: Special Report on Emissions Scenarios. Cambridge University Press, Cambridge, United Kingdom and New York, NY, USA, 599 pp., https://www.ipcc.ch/site/assets/uploads/2018/03/emissions_scenarios-1.pdf (Accessed July 12, 2019).

Nascimento, L. et al., 2021: *Greenhouse gas mitigation scenarios for major emitting countries – Analysis of current climate policies and mitigation commitments: 2021 update*. NewClimate Institute, PBL Netherlands Environmental Assessment Agency, and International Institute for Applied Systems Analysis, 132 pp., https://newclimate.org/wp-content/uploads/2021/10/NewClimate_EC-PBL_CurrentPolicies_Report_Oct21.pdf.

NDC Partnership, 2017: *PARTNERSHIP IN ACTION – ONE YEAR ON*. http://www4.unfccc.int/ndcregistry/Pages/Home.aspx (Accessed July 12, 2019).

Nemet, G.F., M. Jakob, J.C. Steckel, and O. Edenhofer, 2017: Addressing policy credibility problems for low-carbon investment. *Glob. Environ. Change*, **42**, 47–57, doi:10.1016/j.gloenvcha.2016.12.004.

Nepal, 2020: *The Fifteenth Plan (Fiscal Year 2019/20 2023/24)*. Government of Nepal, National Planning Commission, Kathmandu, Nepal, 731 pp., https://npc.gov.np/images/category/15th_plan_English_Version.pdf.

New, M., D. Reckien, D. Viner, C. Adler, S.-M. Cheong, C. Conde, A. Constable, E. Coughlan de Perez, A. Lammel, R. Mechler, B. Orlove, and W. Solecki, 2022: Decision Making Options for Managing Risk. In: *Climate Change 2022: Impacts, Adaptation, and Vulnerability. Contribution of Working Group II to the Sixth Assessment Report of the Intergovernmental Panel on Climate Change* [H.-O. Pörtner, D.C. Roberts, M. Tignor, E.S. Poloczanska, K. Mintenbeck, A. Alegría, M. Craig, S. Langsdorf, S. Löschke, V. Möller, A. Okem, B. Rama (eds.)]. Cambridge University Press. In Press.

NewClimate Institute, Data-Driven Lab, PBL, German Development Institute/ Deutsches Institut für Entwicklungspolitik (DIE), Blavatnik School of Government, University of Oxford, 2019: Global climate action from cities, regions and businesses: Impact of individual actors and cooperative initiatives on global and national emissions. [Kuramochi, T., et al. eds.)]. 2019 ed. NewClimate Institute and Data-Driven EnviroLab, Cologne, Germany, PBL, G.D. Institute, and Blavanik School of Government, University of Oxford, UK, 93pp.

Newell, P. and D. Mulvaney, 2013: The political economy of the 'just transition'. *Geogr. J.*, **179(2)**, 132–140, doi:10.1111/geoj.12008.

Newell, P. and A. Simms, 2020: Towards a fossil fuel non-proliferation treaty. *Clim. Policy*, **20(8)**, 1043–1054, doi:10.1080/14693062.2019.1636759.

Ng, S., N. Mabey, and J. Gaventa, 2016: *Pulling ahead on clean technology: China's 13th five year plan challenges Europe's low-carbon competitiveness*. E3G Briefing Paper, E3G, London, United Kingdom, 12 pp.

Nguyen, K.H., and M. Kakinaka, 2019: Renewable energy consumption, carbon emissions, and development stages: Some evidence from panel cointegration analysis. *Renew. Energy*, **132**, 1049–1057, doi:10.1016/j. renene.2018.08.069.

Nicholls, Z.R.J. et al., 2020: Reduced Complexity Model Intercomparison Project Phase 1: Introduction and evaluation of global-mean temperature response. *Geosci. Model Dev.*, **13(11)**, 5175–5190, doi:10.5194/ gmd-13-5175-2020.

Nieves, J.A., A.J. Aristizábal, I. Dyner, O. Báez, and D.H. Ospina, 2019: Energy demand and greenhouse gas emissions analysis in Colombia: A LEAP model application. *Energy*, **169**, 380–397, doi:10.1016/j.energy.2018.12.051.

Nilsson, L.J. et al., 2021: An industrial policy framework for transforming energy and emissions intensive industries towards zero emissions. *Clim. Policy*, **21(8)**, 1053–1065, doi:10.1080/14693062.2021.1957665.

Nilsson, M., D. Griggs, and M. Visbeck, 2016: Policy: Map the interactions between Sustainable Development Goals. *Nature*, **534(7607)**, 320–322, doi:10.1038/534320a.

Nisbet, E.G. et al., 2020: Methane Mitigation: Methods to Reduce Emissions, on the Path to the Paris Agreement. *Rev. Geophys.*, **58(1)**, doi:10.1029/2019RG000675.

Nobre, C.A., 2019: To save Brazil's rainforest, boost its science. *Nature*, **574(7779)**, 455–455, doi:10.1038/d41586-019-03169-0.

Nogueira de Oliveira, L.P. et al., 2016: Critical technologies for sustainable energy development in Brazil: Technological foresight based on scenario modelling. *J. Clean. Prod.*, **130**, 12–24, doi:10.1016/j.jclepro.2016.03.010.

Nong, D., 2018: General equilibrium economy-wide impacts of the increased energy taxes in Vietnam. *Energy Policy*, **123**, 471–481, doi:10.1016/J. ENPOL.2018.09.023.

Nong, D., S. Meng, and M. Siriwardana, 2017: An assessment of a proposed ETS in Australia by using the MONASH-Green model. *Energy Policy*, **108**, 281–291, doi:10.1016/J.ENPOL.2017.06.004.

NPC, 2011: *Our future - make it work: National development plan 2030*. National Planning Commission, The Presidency, Pretoria, South Africa, 484 pp., https://www.gov.za/sites/default/files/gcis_document/201409/ ndp-2030-our-future-make-it-workr.pdf (Accessed 23 August 2012).

NPC (National Planning Commission), 2019: *Draft Proposal - Version Two 2050 Vision and Pathways for a Just Transition to a low carbon, climate resilient economy and society*. Pretoria, South Africa, 35 pp.

Nunes, F.S.M., B.S. Soares-Filho, R. Rajão, and F. Merry, 2017: Enabling large-scale forest restoration in Minas Gerais state, Brazil. *Environ. Res. Lett.*, **12(4)**, 44022, doi:10.1088/1748-9326/aa6658.

NYDF Assessment Partners, 2020: *Balancing forests and development: Addressing infrastructure and extractive industries, promoting sustainable livelihoods*. Internationale Klimaschutzinitiative (IKI), Climate Focus, Amsterdam, The Netherlands, 109 pp., https://forestdeclaration.org/wp-content/uploads/2021/10/2020NYDFReport.pdf (Accessed October 18, 2021).

Nyong, A., F. Adesina, and B. Osman Elasha, 2007: The value of indigenous knowledge in climate change mitigation and adaptation strategies in the African Sahel. *Mitig. Adapt. Strateg. Glob. Change*, **12(5)**, 787–797, doi:10.1007/s11027-007-9099-0.

O'Neill, B., M. van Aalst, Z. Zaiton Ibrahim, L. Berrang Ford, S. Bhadwal, H. Buhaug, D. Diaz, K. Frieler, M. Garschagen, A. Magnan, G. Midgley, A. Mirzabaev, A. Thomas, and R. Warren, 2022: Key Risks Across Sectors and Regions Supplementary Material. In: *Climate Change 2022: Impacts, Adaptation, and Vulnerability. Contribution of Working Group II to the Sixth Assessment Report of the Intergovernmental Panel on Climate Change* [H.-O. Pörtner, D.C. Roberts, M. Tignor, E.S. Poloczanska, K. Mintenbeck, A. Alegría, M. Craig, S. Langsdorf, S. Löschke, V. Möller, A. Okem, B. Rama (eds.)]. Available from https://www.ipcc.ch/report/ar6/wg2/.

O'Neill, B.C. et al., 2014: A new scenario framework for climate change research: The concept of shared socio-economic pathways. *Clim. Change*, **122(3)**, 387–400, doi:10.1007/s10584-013-0905-2.

O'Neill, B.C. et al., 2017: The roads ahead: Narratives for shared socio-economic pathways describing world futures in the 21st century. *Glob. Environ. Change*, **42**, 169–180, doi:10.1016/j.gloenvcha.2015.01.004.

Obergassel, W., L. Hermwille, and S. Oberthür, 2021: Harnessing international climate governance to drive a sustainable recovery from the COVID-19 pandemic. *Clim. Policy*, 21(10), 1298-1306, doi:10.1080/14693 062.2020.1835603.

Ocasio-Cortez, A., 2019: *Resolution Recognizing the duty of the Federal Government to create a Green New Deal. H.Res.109*. House Resolution (H.Res.)109. 116th Congress, 1st Session, Washington, DC, https://www. congress.gov/bill/116th-congress/house-resolution/109/text (Accessed November 1, 2021).

OECD, 2017a: *Employment Implications of Green Growth: Linking jobs, growth, and green policies OECD REPORT FOR THE G7 ENVIRONMENT MINISTERS*. Organisation for Economic Co-operation and Development (OECD), Paris, France, 22 pp., www.oecd.org/greengrowth (Accessed December 11, 2019).

OECD, 2017b: *Investing in Climate, Investing in Growth*. Organisation for Economic Co-operation and Development (OECD), Paris, France, 309 pp., https://www.oecd.org/env/investing-in-climate-investing-in-growth-9789264273528-en.htm.

Oei, P.-Y., T. Burandt, K. Hainsch, K. Löffler, and C. Kemfert, 2020: Lessons from Modeling 100% Renewable Scenarios Using GENeSYS-MOD. *Econ. Energy Environ. Policy*, **9(1)**, 103–120, doi:10.5547/2160-5890.9.1.POEI.

Oshiro, K., M. Kainuma, and T. Masui, 2017a: Implications of Japan's 2030 target for long-term low emission pathways. *Energy Policy*, **110**, 581–587, doi:10.1016/j.enpol.2017.09.003.

Oshiro, K., T. Masui, and M. Kainuma, 2017b: Quantitative analysis of Japan's 2030 target based on AIM/CGE and AIM/enduse. In: *Post-2020 Climate Action: Global and Asian Perspectives* [Fujimori, S., M. Kainuma, T. Masui (eds.)]. Springer Singapore, Mizuho Information and Research Institute, Inc., Tokyo, Japan, pp. 143–156.

Oshiro, K., T. Masui, and M. Kainuma, 2018: Transformation of Japan's energy system to attain net-zero emission by 2050. *Carbon Manag.*, **9(5)**, 493–501, doi:10.1080/17583004.2017.1396842.

Ostrom, E., 2010: Beyond Markets and States: Polycentric Governance of Complex Economic Systems. *Am. Econ. Rev.*, **100(3)**, 641–672, doi:10.1257/AER.100.3.641.

4

Ouedraogo, N.S., 2017: Africa energy future: Alternative scenarios and their implications for sustainable development strategies. *Energy Policy*, **106**, 457–471, doi:10.1016/j.enpol.2017.03.021.

Ouyang, Z. et al., 2016: Improvements in ecosystem services from investments in natural capital. *Science*, **352(6292)**, 1455–1459, doi:10.1126/science.aaf2295.

Oyewo, A.S., A. Aghahosseini, M. Ram, A. Lohrmann, and C. Breyer, 2019: Pathway towards achieving 100% renewable electricity by 2050 for South Africa. *Sol. Energy*, **191** (June), 549–565, doi:10.1016/j.solener.2019.09.039.

Oyewo, A.S., A. Aghahosseini, M. Ram, and C. Breyer, 2020: Transition towards decarbonised power systems and its socio-economic impacts in West Africa. *Renew. Energy*, **154**, 1092–1112, doi:10.1016/j.renene.2020.03.085.

Paladugula, A.L. et al., 2018: A multi-model assessment of energy and emissions for India's transportation sector through 2050. *Energy Policy*, **116**, 10–18, doi:10.1016/j.enpol.2018.01.037.

Pan, X., M. den Elzen, N. Höhne, F. Teng, and L. Wang, 2017: Exploring fair and ambitious mitigation contributions under the Paris Agreement goals. *Environ. Sci. Policy*, **74**, 49–56, doi:10.1016/j.envsci.2017.04.020.

Pandza, K. and P. Ellwood, 2013: Strategic and ethical foundations for responsible innovation. *Res. Policy*, **42(5)**, 1112–1125, doi:10.1016/J.RESPOL.2013.02.007.

Parikh, K.S., J.K. Parikh, and P.P. Ghosh, 2018: Can India grow and live within a 1.5 degree CO_2 emissions budget? *Energy Policy*, **120**, 24–37, doi:10.1016/j.enpol.2018.05.014.

Patrizio, P. et al., 2018: Reducing US Coal Emissions Can Boost Employment. *Joule*, **2(12)**, 2633–2648, doi:10.1016/J.JOULE.2018.10.004.

Pauw, W.P. et al., 2018: Beyond headline mitigation numbers: We need more transparent and comparable NDCs to achieve the Paris Agreement on climate change. *Clim. Change*, **147(1–2)**, 23–29, doi:10.1007/s10584-017-2122-x.

Pauw, W.P., P. Castro, J. Pickering, and S. Bhasin, 2020: Conditional nationally determined contributions in the Paris Agreement: foothold for equity or Achilles heel? *Clim. Policy*, **20(4)**, 468–484, doi:10.1080/14693062.2019.1635874.

Pearson, A.R. et al., 2017: Race, Class, Gender and Climate Change Communication. In: *Oxford Research Encyclopedia of Climate Science*, Oxford University Press.

Pedde, S. et al., 2019: Archetyping shared socio-economic pathways across scales: An application to central Asia and European case studies. *Ecol. Soc.*, **24(4)**, doi:10.5751/ES-11241-240430.

Pelling, M.A and M. Garschagen, 2019: Put equity first in climate adaptation: Focusing on the bottom few percent, not averages, is the best way to tackle poverty. *Nature*, **569**, 327–329, doi: 10.1038/d41586-019-01497-9.

Pereira, A.M., R.M. Pereira, and P.G. Rodrigues, 2016: A new carbon tax in Portugal: A missed opportunity to achieve the triple dividend? *Energy Policy*, **93**, 110–118, doi:10.1016/j.enpol.2016.03.002.

Perrier, Q. and P. Quirion, 2018: How shifting investment towards low-carbon sectors impacts employment: Three determinants under scrutiny. *Energy Econ.*, **75**, 464–483, doi:10.1016/J.ENECO.2018.08.023.

Peters, G.P. and O. Geden, 2017: Catalysing a political shift from low to negative carbon. *Nat. Clim. Change*, **7(9)**, 619–621, doi:10.1038/nclimate3369.

Peters, G.P., R.M. Andrew, S. Solomon, and P. Friedlingstein, 2015: Measuring a fair and ambitious climate agreement using cumulative emissions. *Environ. Res. Lett.*, **10(10)**, 105004, doi:10.1088/1748-9326/10/10/105004.

Peters, G.P. et al., 2017: Key indicators to track current progress and future ambition of the Paris Agreement. *Nat. Clim. Change*, **7**, 118–122, doi:10.1038/NCLIMATE3202.

Pettifor, A., 2020: *The Case for the Green New Deal*. Verso, London, UK, New York, NY, USA, 208 pp.

Pezzoni, M., R. Veugelers, and F. Visentin, 2019: *How fast is this novel technology going to be a hit?* C.E.P.R. Discussion Papers, Centre for Economic Policy Research, London, United Kingdom, https://ideas.repec.org/p/cpr/ceprdp/13447.html (Accessed December 22, 2020).

Pfeiffer, A., C. Hepburn, A. Vogt-Schilb, and B. Caldecott, 2018: Committed emissions from existing and planned power plants and asset stranding required to meet the Paris Agreement. *Environ. Res. Lett.*, **13(5)**, 054019, doi:10.1088/1748-9326/aabc5f.

Piggot, G., M. Boyland, A. Down, and A.R. Torre, 2019: *Realizing a just and equitable transition away from fossil fuels*. Stockholm Environment Institute (SEI), Seattle, USA, 12 pp., https://www.sei.org/publications/just-and-equitable-transition-fossil-fuels/ (Accessed January 8, 2020).

Piggot, G., C. Verkuijl, H. van Asselt, and M. Lazarus, 2020: Curbing fossil fuel supply to achieve climate goals. *Clim. Policy*, **20(8)**, doi:10.1080/14693062.2020.1804315.

Pizer, W.A. and S. Sexton, 2019: The Distributional Impacts of Energy Taxes. *Rev. Environ. Econ. Policy*, **13(1)**, 104–123, doi:10.1093/reep/rey021.

Poffenbarger, H.J., B.A. Needelman, and J.P. Megonigal, 2011: Salinity influence on methane emissions from tidal marshes. *Wetlands*, **31(5)**, 831–842, doi:10.1007/s13157-011-0197-0.

Pollin, R., 2020: An Industrial Policy Framework to Advance a Global Green New Deal. In: *The Oxford Handbook of Industrial Policy*, [Oqubay, A., C. Cramer, H.-J. Chang, and R. KozulWright, (eds.)]. Oxford University Press, Oxford, UK, doi: 10.1093/oxfordhb/9780198862420.013.16.

Pollin, R. and B. Callaci, 2019: The Economics of Just Transition: A Framework for Supporting Fossil Fuel–Dependent Workers and Communities in the United States. *Labor Stud. J.*, **44(2)**, 93–138, doi:10.1177/0160449X18787051.

Pollitt, H., E. Alexandri, U. Chewpreecha, and G. Klaassen, 2015: Macroeconomic analysis of the employment impacts of future EU climate policies. *Clim. Policy*, **15(5)**, 604–625, doi:10.1080/14693062.2014.953907.

Pollitt, H., R. Lewney, B. Kiss-Dobronyi, and X. Lin, 2021: Modelling the economic effects of COVID-19 and possible green recovery plans: a post-Keynesian approach. *Clim. Policy*, 21(10), 1257–1271, doi:10.1080/14693062.2021.1965525.

Polonara, F., L.J.M. Kuijpers, and R.A. Peixoto, 2017: Potential impacts of the montreal protocol kigali amendment to the choice of refrigerant alternatives. *Int. J. Heat Technol.*, **35** (Special Issue 1), S1–S8, doi:10.18280/ijht.35Sp0101.

Popp, R., 2019: *A Just Transition of European Coal Regions. Assessing stakeholder positions towards the transition away from coal*. E3G, London, UK, 20 pp., https://www.euki.de/wp-content/uploads/2019/02/E3G_2019_Stakeholder_Mappings_European_Coal_Regions_Final-1.pdf (Accessed November 1, 2021).

Portugal-Pereira, J. et al., 2016: Overlooked impacts of electricity expansion optimisation modelling: The life cycle side of the story. *Energy*, **115**, 1424–1435, doi:10.1016/j.energy.2016.03.062.

Portugal-Pereira, J. et al., 2018: Better late than never, but never late is better: Risk assessment of nuclear power construction projects. *Energy Policy*, **120**, 158–166, doi:10.1016/j.enpol.2018.05.041.

Powlson, D.S., C.M. Stirling, C. Thierfelder, R.P. White, and M.L. Jat, 2016: Does conservation agriculture deliver climate change mitigation through soil carbon sequestration in tropical agro-ecosystems? *Agric. Ecosyst. Environ.*, **220**, 164–174, doi:10.1016/j.agee.2016.01.005.

Pozo, C., Á. Galán-Martín, D.M. Reiner, N. Mac Dowell, and G. Guillén-Gosálbez, 2020: Equity in allocating carbon dioxide removal quotas. *Nat. Clim. Change*, **10(7)**, 640–646, doi:10.1038/s41558-020-0802-4.

PPMC and SLoCaT, 2016: *Transport and climate change synthesis of analytical products by the paris process on mobility and climate (PPMC)*. Paris Process on Mobility and Climate (PPMC) and Partnership on Sustainable, Low Carbon Transport (SLoCaT). http://www.ppmc-transport.org/wp-content/uploads/2016/11/E2_Synthesis-Report.pdf (Accessed July 12, 2019).

Pradhan, A., C. Chan, P.K. Roul, J. Halbrendt, and B. Sipes, 2018a: Potential of conservation agriculture (CA) for climate change adaptation and food security under rainfed uplands of India: A transdisciplinary approach. *Agric. Syst.*, **163**, 27–35, doi:10.1016/j.agsy.2017.01.002.

4

Pradhan, B.B., R.M. Shrestha, A. Pandey, and B. Limmeechokchai, 2018b: Strategies to Achieve Net Zero Emissions in Nepal. *Carbon Manag.*, **9(5)**, 533–548, doi:10.1080/17583004.2018.1536168.

Pradhan, P., L. Costa, D. Rybski, W. Lucht, and J.P. Kropp, 2017: A Systematic Study of Sustainable Development Goal (SDG) Interactions. *Earth's Futur.*, **5(11)**, 1169–1179, doi:10.1002/2017EF000632.

Pretty, J.N. et al., 2006: Resource-conserving agriculture increases yields in developing countries. *Environ. Sci. Technol.*, **40(4)**, 1114–1119, doi:10.1021/es051670d.

Prognos, Öko-Institut, Wuppertal-Institut, 2020: *Towards a Climate-Neutral Germany. Executive Summary conducted for Agora Energiewende, Agora Verkehrswende and Stiftung Klimaneutralität*. Stiftung Denkfabrik Klimaneutralität, Berlin, Germany, 175 pp., https://www.stiftung-klima. de/app/uploads/2020/11/2020_KNDE_Langfassung_WEB.pdf (Accessed October 18, 2021).

Pye, S. et al., 2016: Exploring national decarbonization pathways and global energy trade flows: A multi-scale analysis. *Clim. Policy*, **16(sup1)**, S92–S109, doi:10.1080/14693062.2016.1179619.

Pye, S. et al., 2020: An equitable redistribution of unburnable carbon. *Nat. Commun.*, **11**, 3968, doi:10.1038/s41467-020-17679-3.

Quéré, C. et al., 2018: Global Carbon Budget 2018. *Earth Syst. Sci. Data*, **10(4)**, 2141–2194, doi:10.5194/essd-10-2141-2018.

Quinet, A. et al., 2019: *The Value for Climate Action: A Shadow Price of Carbon for Evaluation of Investments and Public Policies*, Paris, France, 187 pp., https://www.strategie.gouv.fr/sites/strategie.gouv.fr/files/atoms/files/ fs-the-value-for-climate-action-final-web.pdf (Accessed November 1, 2021).

Rajamani, L., 2017: Guiding principles and general obligation (Article 2.2 and Article 3). In: *The Paris Agreement on climate change: Analysis and commentary. ISBN: 9780198803768* [Klein, D., P. Carazo, J. Bulmer, M. Doelle, and A. Higham, (eds.)]. Oxford University Press, Oxford, UK.

Rajamani, L. and J. Brunnée, 2017: The legality of downgrading nationally determined contributions under the Paris agreement: Lessons from the US disengagement. *J. Environ. Law*, **29(3)**, 537–551, doi:10.1093/jel/eqx024.

Rajamani, L. et al., 2021: National 'fair shares' in reducing greenhouse gas emissions within the principled framework of international environmental law. *Clim. Policy*, 21(8), 983–1004, doi:10.1080/14693062.2021.1970504.

Ramalingam, B., 2013: *Aid on the edge of chaos: Rethinking international cooperation in a complex world*. Oxford University Press, Oxford, UK, 480 pp.

Ramanathan, V. and Y. Xu, 2010: The Copenhagen accord for limiting global warming: Criteria, constraints, and available avenues. *Proc. Natl. Acad. Sci.*, **107(18)**, 8055–8062, doi:10.1073/pnas.1002293107.

Randelli, F. and B. Rocchi, 2017: Analysing the role of consumers within technological innovation systems: The case of alternative food networks. *Environ. Innov. Soc. Transitions*, **25**, 94–106, doi:10.1016/j. eist.2017.01.001.

Rao, N.D. and J. Min, 2018: Less global inequality can improve climate outcomes. *Wiley Interdiscip. Rev. Clim. Change*, **9(2)**, doi:10.1002/wcc.513.

Rao, N.D., P. Sauer, M. Gidden, and K. Riahi, 2019: Income inequality projections for the Shared Socio-economic Pathways (SSPs). *Futures*, **105**, 27–39, doi: 10.1016/j.futures.2018.07.001.

Raskin, P. and R. Swart, 2020: Excluded futures: The continuity bias in scenario assessments. *Sustain. Earth*, **3(1)**, 8, doi:10.1186/s42055-020-00030-5.

Raskin, P. et al., 2002: *Great transition: The promise and lure of the times ahead*. Stockholm Environment Institute, Boston, USA, https://greattransition.org/ documents/Great_Transition.pdf (Accessed November 1, 2021).

Rasul, G., 2016: Managing the food, water, and energy nexus for achieving the Sustainable Development Goals in South Asia. *Environ. Dev.*, **18**, 14–25, doi:10.1016/j.envdev.2015.12.001.

Raubenheimer, S. et al., 2015: *Stories from the South: Exploring low-carbon development pathways*. MAPS team (Mitigation Action Plans and Scenarios), Edited by Stefan Raubenheimer. Cape Town, South Africa, 328 pp.

Rauter, R., D. Globocnik, E. Perl-Vorbach, and R.J. Baumgartner, 2019: Open innovation and its effects on economic and sustainability innovation performance. *J. Innov. Knowl.*, **4(4)**, 226–233, doi:10.1016/J. JIK.2018.03.004.

Rendall, M., 2019: Discounting, climate change, and the ecological fallacy. *Ethics*, **129(3)**, 441–463, doi:10.1086/701481.

Renner, S., J. Lay, and M. Schleicher, 2019: The effects of energy price changes: Heterogeneous welfare impacts and energy poverty in Indonesia. *Environ. Dev. Econ.*, **24(2)**, 180–200, doi:10.1017/S1355770X18000402.

Rentschler, J. and M. Bazilian, 2017: Policy Monitor – Principles for Designing Effective Fossil Fuel Subsidy Reforms. *Rev. Environ. Econ. Policy*, **11(1)**, 138–155, doi:10.1093/reep/rew016.

Revi, A., 2017: Re-imagining the United Nations' Response to a Twenty-first-century Urban World: doi.org/10.1177/2455747117740438, **2(2)**, ix–xv, doi:10.1177/2455747117740438.

Riahi, K. et al., 2015: Locked into Copenhagen pledges – Implications of short-term emission targets for the cost and feasibility of long-term climate goals. *Technol. Forecast. Soc. Change*, **90**, 8–23, doi:10.1016/j. techfore.2013.09.016.

Riahi, K. et al., 2017: The Shared Socio-economic Pathways and their energy, land use, and greenhouse gas emissions implications: An overview. *Glob. Environ. Change*, **42**, 153–168, doi:10.1016/j.gloenvcha.2016.05.009.

Riahi, K. et al., 2021: Implications of avoiding temperature overshoot for the attainability and costs of stringent mitigation targets. *Nat. Clim. Change*, Accepted.

Richter, P.M., R. Mendelevitch, and F. Jotzo, 2018: Coal taxes as supply-side climate policy: A rationale for major exporters? *Clim. Change*, **150(1–2)**, 43–56, doi:10.1007/s10584-018-2163-9.

Ricke, K., L. Drouet, K. Caldeira, and M. Tavoni, 2018: Country-level social cost of carbon. *Nat. Clim. Change*, **8(10)**, 895–900, doi:10.1038/ s41558-018-0282-y.

Ringel, M., 2017: Energy efficiency policy governance in a multi-level administration structure – evidence from Germany. *Energy Effic.*, **10(3)**, 753–776, doi:10.1007/s12053-016-9484-1.

Roberts, C. et al., 2018a: The politics of accelerating low-carbon transitions: Towards a new research agenda. *Energy Res. Soc. Sci.*, **44**, 304–311, doi:10.1016/j.erss.2018.06.001.

Roberts, D., 2016: The New Climate Calculus: 1.5°C = Paris Agreement, Cities, Local Government, Science and Champions (PLSC 2). *Urbanisation*, **1(2)**, 71–78, doi:10.1177/2455747116672474.

Roberts, J.T. and B.C. Parks, 2007: *A climate of injustice: Global inequality, North-South politics, and climate policy*. MIT Press, Cambridge, MA, USA, 404 pp.

Roberts, S.H., B.D. Foran, C.J. Axon, B.S. Warr, and N.H. Goddard, 2018b: Consequences of selecting technology pathways on cumulative carbon dioxide emissions for the United Kingdom. *Appl. Energy*, **228**, 409–425, doi:10.1016/j.apenergy.2018.06.078.

Robertson, S., 2021: Transparency, trust, and integrated assessment models: An ethical consideration for the Intergovernmental Panel on Climate Change. *WIREs Clim. Change*, **12(1)**, doi:10.1002/wcc.679.

Robiou du Pont, Y. and M. Meinshausen, 2018: Warming assessment of the bottom-up Paris Agreement emissions pledges. *Nat. Commun.*, **9(1)**, 4810, doi:10.1038/s41467-018-07223-9.

Robiou Du Pont, Y. et al., 2017: Equitable mitigation to achieve the Paris Agreement goals. *Nat. Clim. Change*, **7(1)**, 38, doi:10.1038/nclimate3186.

Rochedo, P.R.R. et al., 2018: The threat of political bargaining to climate mitigation in Brazil. *Nat. Clim. Change*, **8(8)**, 695–698, doi:10.1038/ s41558-018-0213-y.

Rockström, J. et al., 2017: A roadmap for rapid decarbonization. *Science*, **355(6331)**, 1269–1271, doi:10.1126/science.aah3443.

Rodrik, D., 2016: Premature deindustrialization. *J. Econ. Growth*, **21(1)**, 1–33, doi:10.1007/s10887-015-9122-3.

4

Roelfsema, M. et al., 2018: The Global Stocktake. Keeping track of implementing the Paris Agreement. *PBL Netherlands Environ. Assess. Agency*, PBL Netherlands Environmental Assedssment Agency, The Hague, The Netherlands, https://themasites.pbl.nl/global-stocktake-indicators/ (Accessed July 12, 2019).

Roelfsema, M. et al., 2020: Taking stock of national climate policies to evaluate implementation of the Paris Agreement. *Nat. Commun.*, **11(1)**, 2096, doi:10.1038/s41467-020-15414-6.

Rogelj, J. and C.-F. Schleussner, 2019: Unintentional unfairness when applying new greenhouse gas emissions metrics at country level. *Environ. Res. Lett.*, **14**(11), 114039, doi:10.1088/1748-9326/ab4928.

Rogelj, J. et al., 2016: Paris Agreement climate proposals need a boost to keep warming well below 2°C. *Nature*, **534(7609)**, 631–639, doi:10.1038/nature18307.

Rogelj, J. et al., 2017: Understanding the origin of Paris Agreement emission uncertainties. *Nat. Commun.*, **8**, 15748, doi:10.1038/ncomms15748.

Rogelj, J., D. Shindell, K. Jiang, S. Fifita, P. Forster, V. Ginzburg, C. Handa, H. Kheshgi, S. Kobayashi, E. Kriegler, L. Mundaca, R. Séférian, and M.V. Vilariño, 2018a: Mitigation Pathways Compatible with 1.5°C in the Context of Sustainable Development. In: *Global Warming of 1.5°C: An IPCC special report on the impacts of global warming of 1.5°C above pre-industrial levels and related global greenhouse gas emission pathways, in the context of strengthening the global response to the threat of climate change* [Masson-Delmotte, V., P. Zhai, H.-O. Pörtner, D. Roberts, J. Skea, P.R. Shukla, A. Pirani, W. Moufouma-Okia, C. Péan, R. Pidcock, S. Connors, J.B.R. Matthews, Y. Chen, X. Zhou, M.I. Gomis, E. Lonnoy, T. Maycock, M. Tignor, and T. Waterfield (eds.)]. Cambridge University Press, Cambridge, UK, and New York, NY, USA, pp. 93–174.

Rogelj, J. et al., 2018b: Scenarios towards limiting global mean temperature increase below 1.5°C. *Nat. Clim. Change*, **8(4)**, 325–332, doi:10.1038/s41558-018-0091-3.

Rogelj, J., O. Geden, A. Cowie, and A. Reisinger, 2021: Net-zero emissions targets are vague: three ways to fix. *Nat.*, **591**, 365–368, doi: 10.1038/d41586-021-00662-3

Rogge, K.S. and K. Reichardt, 2016: Policy mixes for sustainability transitions: An extended concept and framework for analysis. *Res. Policy*, **45(8)**, 1620–1635, doi:10.1016/J.RESPOL.2016.04.004.

Rogge, K.S. et al., 2015: *Green change: Renewable energies, policy mix and innovation*. Fraunhofer ISI, Karlsruhe, Germany, 43 pp., http://sro.sussex.ac.uk/id/eprint/66004/ (Accessed December 19, 2019).

Romañach, S.S. et al., 2018: Conservation and restoration of mangroves: Global status, perspectives, and prognosis. *Ocean Coast. Manag.*, **154**, 72–82, doi:10.1016/J.OCECOAMAN.2018.01.009.

Rose, S.K., R. Richels, G. Blanford, and T. Rutherford, 2017: The Paris Agreement and next steps in limiting global warming. *Clim. Change*, **142(1–2)**, 255–270, doi:10.1007/s10584-017-1935-y.

Rosemberg, A., 2010: Building a Just Transition: The linkages between climate change and employment. In: *Climate Change and Labour: The Need for a "Just Transition". International Journal of Labour Research*, **2(2)**, 125–161.

Rosenbloom, D., 2017: Pathways: An emerging concept for the theory and governance of low-carbon transitions. *Glob. Environ. Change*, **43**, 37–50, doi:10.1016/j.gloenvcha.2016.12.011.

Rosenbloom, D., J. Meadowcroft, S. Sheppard, S. Burch, and S. Williams, 2018: Transition experiments: Opening up low-carbon transition pathways for Canada through innovation and learning. *Can. Public Policy*, **44(4)**, 368–383, doi:10.3138/cpp.2018-020.

Rosentreter, J.A., D.T. Maher, D.V. Erler, R.H. Murray, and B.D. Eyre, 2018: Methane emissions partially offset 'blue carbon' burial in mangroves. *Sci. Adv.*, **4(6)**, doi:10.1126/sciadv.aao4985.

Routledge, P., A. Cumbers, and K.D. Derickson, 2018: States of just transition: Realising climate justice through and against the state. *Geoforum*, **88**, 78–86, doi:10.1016/j.geoforum.2017.11.015.

Roy, J., P. Tschakert, H. Waisman, S. Abdul Halim, P. Antwi-Agyei, P. Dasgupta, B. Hayward, M. Kanninen, D. Liverman, C. Okereke, P.F. Pinho, K. Riahi, and A.G. Suarez Rodriguez, 2018: Sustainable Development, Poverty Eradication and Reducing Inequalities. In: *Global Warming of 1.5°C: An IPCC special report on the impacts of global warming of 1.5°C above pre-industrial levels and related global greenhouse gas emission pathways, in the context of strengthening the global response to the threat of climate change* [Masson-Delmotte, V., P. Zhai, H.-O. Pörtner, D. Roberts, J. Skea, P.R. Shukla, A. Pirani, W. Moufouma-Okia, C. Péan, R. Pidcock, S. Connors, J.B.R. Matthews, Y. Chen, X. Zhou, M.I. Gomis, E. Lonnoy, T. Maycock, M. Tignor, and T. Waterfield (eds.)]. Cambridge University Press, Cambridge, UK and New York, USA, pp. 445–540.

Rozenberg, J. and M. Fay, 2019: *Beyond the Gap: How Countries Can Afford the Infrastructure They Need while Protecting the Planet*. [Rozenberg, J. and M. Fay, (eds.)]. World Bank, Washington, DC, 175 pp.

RSA, 2011: National Climate Change Response White Paper. Government Gazette No. 34695, Notice 757 of 2011. Government of South Africa, Pretoria, South Africa, 49 pp.

Runge, C.F., 1984: Institutions and the Free Rider: The Assurance Problem in Collective Action. *J. Polit.*, **46(1)**, 154–181, doi:10.2307/2130438.

Sachs, J.D. et al., 2019: Six Transformations to achieve the Sustainable Development Goals. *Nat. Sustain.*, **2**(9), 805–814, doi:10.1038/s41893-019-0352-9.

Safarzyńska, K., 2018: Integrating behavioural economics into climate-economy models: Some policy lessons. *Clim. Policy*, **18(4)**, 485–498, doi:10.1080/14693062.2017.1313718.

Sager, L., 2019: Income inequality and carbon consumption: Evidence from Environmental Engel curves. *Energy Econ.*, **84**, 104507, doi:10.1016/j.eneco.2019.104507.

Samadi, S., J. Terrapon-Pfaff, S. Lechtenböhmer, and K. Knoop, 2018: Long-term low greenhouse gas emission development strategies for achieving the 1.5°C target – insights from a comparison of German bottom-up energy scenarios. *Carbon Manag.*, **9(5)**, 549–562, doi:10.1080/17583004.2018.1475174.

Sanjuán, M.A., C. Argiz, P. Mora, and A. Zaragoza, 2020: Carbon dioxide uptake in the roadmap 2050 of the spanish cement industry. *Energies*, **13(13)**, 3452, doi:10.3390/en13133452.

Sathaye, J., A. Najam, C. Cocklin, T. Heller, F. Lecocq, J. Llanes-Regueiro, J. Pan, G. Petschel-Held , S. Rayner, J. Robinson, R. Schaeffer, Y. Sokona, R. Swart, H. Winkler, 2007: Sustainable Development and Mitigation. In: Climate Change 2007: Mitigation. *Contribution of Working Group III to the Fourth Assessment Report of the Intergovernmental Panel on Climate Change* [Metz, B., O.D. Davidson, P. Bosch, R. Dave, and L.M. Meyer (eds.)]. Cambridge University Press, Cambridge, UK and New York, NY, USA.

Sathaye, J. et al., 2009: Opportunities to change development pathways toward lower greenhouse gas emissions through energy efficiency. *Energy Effic.*, **2(4)**, doi:10.1007/s12053-009-9044-z.

Saveyn, B., L. Paroussos, and J.C. Ciscar, 2012: Economic analysis of a low-carbon path to 2050: A case for China, India and Japan. *Energy Econ.*, **34(sup3)**, doi:10.1016/j.eneco.2012.04.010.

SB Chairs, 2021: *Preparing for the first global stock-take. Revised non-paper by the Chairs of the SBSTA and SBI (15 September 2021)*. United Nations Framework Convention on Climate Change (UNFCCC), Bonn, 10 pp., https://unfccc.int/sites/default/files/resource/REV_Non-paper_on_Preparing_for_GST1_forSBs_15Sept.pdf (Accessed November 1, 2021).

Scenario Building Team, 2007: *Long Term Mitigation Scenarios: Strategic Options for South Africa*. Department of Environment Affairs and Tourism South Africa, Pretoria, South Africa, https://open.uct.ac.za/bitstream/handle/11427/16804/Scenario_Building_Team_Long_Term_Mitigation_2007.pdf?sequence%20=%201 (Accessed November 1, 2021).

Schelly, C., 2014: Residential solar electricity adoption: What motivates, and what matters? A case study of early adopters. *Energy Res. Soc. Sci.*, **2**, 183–191, doi:10.1016/j.erss.2014.01.001.

4

Schiffer, H.-W., 2015: Europe's Road to a Sustainable Energy-Supply System. *Energy Environ.*, **26(1–2)**, 111–126, doi:10.1260/0958-305x.26.1-2.111.

Schlosberg, D., 2009: *Defining environmental justice: Theories, movements, and nature*. Oxford University Press, Oxford, UK, 238 pp.

Schmid, E. and B. Knopf, 2012: Ambitious mitigation scenarios for Germany: A participatory approach. *Energy Policy*, **51**, 662–672, doi:10.1016/j.enpol.2012.09.007.

Schot, J. and W.E. Steinmueller, 2018: Three frames for innovation policy: R&D, systems of innovation and transformative change. *Res. Policy*, **47(9)**, 1554–1567, doi:10.1016/J.RESPOL.2018.08.011.

Schot, J., L. Kanger, and G. Verbong, 2016: The roles of users in shaping transitions to new energy systems. *Nat. Energy*, **1**, 16054, doi:10.1038/nenergy.2016.54.

Schramski, S., C. McCarty, and G. Barnes, 2018: Household adaptive capacity: A social networks approach in rural South Africa. *Clim. Dev.*, **10(3)**, 230–242, doi:10.1080/17565529.2017.1301861.

Schrobback, P., D. Adamson, and J. Quiggin, 2011: Turning Water into Carbon: Carbon Sequestration and Water Flow in the Murray–Darling Basin. *Environ. Resour. Econ.*, **49(1)**, 23–45, doi:10.1007/s10640-010-9422-1.

Schweitzer, M. and Tonn, B., 2003: Non-energy benefits of the US Weatherization Assistance Program: A summary of their scope and magnitude. *Appl. Energy*, **76(4)**, 321–335, doi: 10.1016/S0306-2619(03)00003-5.

Schweizer, V.J. and E. Kriegler, 2012: Improving environmental change research with systematic techniques for qualitative scenarios. *Environ. Res. Lett.*, **7(4)**, 044011, doi:10.1088/1748-9326/7/4/044011.

Scott, A., 2017: *Making governance work for water – energy – food nexus approaches*. Climate and Development Knowledge Network, London, United Kingdom, 15 pp., https://cdkn.org/resource/working-paper-making-governance-work-water-energy-food-nexus-approaches/?loclang=en_gb (Accessed November 1, 2021).

Scott, A., L. Worrall, and S. Patel, 2018: *Aligning energy development and climate objectives in Nationally Determined Contributions*. Climate and Development Knowledge Network (CDKN), London, UK, 28 pp., https://media.africaportal.org/documents/CDKN_Aligning-Energy-Working-Paper_final-web.pdf (Accessed November 1, 2021).

Scottish Government, 2020a: *Just Transition Commission*. https://www.gov.scot/groups/just-transition-commission, Scottish Government, Edinburgh, United Kingdom (Accessed November 1, 2021).

Scottish Government, 2020b: Securing a green recovery on a path to net zero: Climate change plan 2018–2032 – update. Scottish Government, Edinburgh, United Kingdom, https://www.gov.scot/publications/securing-green-recovery-path-net-zero-update-climate-change-plan-20182032/, 253 pp. (Accessed January 6, 2021).

Scottish Government, 2021: Energy statistics for Scotland. Q4 2020 figures. https://www.gov.scot/binaries/content/documents/govscot/publications/statistics/2018/10/quarterly-energy-statistics-bulletins/documents/energy-statistics-summary---march-2021/energy-statistics-summary---march-2021/govscot%3Adocument/Scotland%2BEnergy%2BSt (Accessed November 1, 2021).

SEI et al., 2019: *The Production Gap: The discrepancy between countries' panned fossil fuel production and global production levels consistent with limiting warming to 1.5°C or 2°C*. Stockholm Environment Institute (SEI), Seattle, USA, 70 pp., https://productiongap.org/2019report/.

SEI, IISD, ODI, E3G, and UNEP, 2020: *The Production Gap Report: 2020 Special Report*. Stockholm Environment Institute (SEI), Seattle, USA, International Institute for Sustainable Development, Winnipeg, Manitoba, Canada, Overseas Development Institute, London, United Kingdom, E3G, London, United Kingdom, United Nations Environmental Program, New York, USA, 66 pp., http://productiongap.org/2020report.

Sekera, J. and A. Lichtenberger, 2020: Assessing Carbon Capture: Public Policy, Science, and Societal Need. *Biophys. Econ. Sustain.*, **5(3)**, 1–28, doi:10.1007/s41247-020-00080-5.

Sen Roy, S. and S. Sen Roy, 2018: *Linking Gender to Climate Change Impacts in the Global South*. Springer International Publishing, Cham, Switzerland, 1–25 pp.

Service, O. et al., 2014: *EAST Four simple ways to apply behavioural insights*. Behavioural Insights Ltd., London, United Kingdom, 53 pp., http://behaviouralinsights.co.uk/publications/east-four-simple-ways-apply-behavioural-insights.

Seto, K.C. et al., 2016: Carbon Lock-In: Types, Causes, and Policy Implications. *Annu. Rev. Environ. Resour.*, **41(1)**, 425–452, doi:10.1146/annurev-environ-110615-085934.

Setzer, J. and L.C. Vanhala, 2019: Climate change litigation: A review of research on courts and litigants in climate governance. *Wiley Interdiscip. Rev. Clim. Change*, **10(3)**, doi:10.1002/wcc.580.

Seyfang, G. and A. Smith, 2007: Grassroots innovations for sustainable development: Towards a new research and policy agenda. *Env. Polit.*, **16(4)**, 584–603, doi:10.1080/09644010701419121.

Seyfang, G., S. Hielscher, T. Hargreaves, M. Martiskainen, and A. Smith, 2014: A grassroots sustainable energy niche? Reflections on community energy in the UK. *Environ. Innov. Soc. Transitions*, **13**, 21–44, doi:10.1016/j.eist.2014.04.004.

Shah, Z. et al., 2019: If you care, I care: Perceived social support and public engagement via SNSs during crises. *Technol. Soc.*, **59**, 101195, doi:10.1016/j.techsoc.2019.101195.

Shahiduzzaman, M. and A. Layton, 2017: Decomposition analysis for assessing the United States 2025 emissions target: How big is the challenge? *Renew. Sustain. Energy Rev.*, **67**, 372–383, doi:10.1016/j.rser.2016.08.042.

Sharma, S.S., 2011: Determinants of carbon dioxide emissions: Empirical evidence from 69 countries. *Appl. Energy*, **88(1)**, 376–382, doi:10.1016/j.apenergy.2010.07.022.

Sharmina, M. et al., 2016: A nexus perspective on competing land demands: Wider lessons from a UK policy case study. *Environ. Sci. Policy*, **59**, 74–84, doi:10.1016/j.envsci.2016.02.008.

Shawoo, Z. and C.L. McDermott, 2020: Justice through polycentricity? A critical examination of climate justice framings in Pakistani climate policymaking. *Clim. Policy*, **20(2)**, 199–216, doi:10.1080/14693062.2019.1707640.

Shell Global, 2014: New Lenses on Future Cities. Shell International BV, The Hague, The Netherlands, 55 pp., https://www.shell.com/energy-and-innovation/the-energy-future/scenarios/new-lenses-on-future-cities.html (Accessed November 22, 2019).

Shiller, R.J., 2019: *Narrative economics: How stories go viral and drive major economic events*. Princeton University Press, Princeton, USA, 377 pp.

Shindell, D. et al., 2012: Simultaneously mitigating near-term climate change and improving human health and food security. *Science*, **335(6065)**, 183–189, doi:10.1126/science.1210026.

Shindell, D. et al., 2017: A climate policy pathway for near- and long-term benefits. *Science*, **356(6337)**, 493–494, doi:10.1126/science.aak9521.

Shiraki, H. et al., 2021: The role of renewables in the Japanese power sector: Implications from the EMF35 JMIP. *Sustain. Sci.*, **16(2)**, 375–392, doi:10.1007/s11625-021-00917-y.

Shirizadeh, B., Q. Perrier, and P. Quirion, 2020: How Sensitive are Optimal Fully Renewable Power Systems to Technology Cost Uncertainty? *Energy J.*, **43(1)**, doi:10.5547/01956574.43.1.BSHI.

Shukla, P.R., S. Dhar, and D. Mahapatra, 2008: Low-carbon society scenarios for India. *Clim. Policy*, **8**, S156–S176, doi:10.3763/cpol.2007.0498.

Siagian, U.W.R., B.B. Yuwono, S. Fujimori, and T. Masui, 2017: Low-carbon energy development in Indonesia in alignment with Intended Nationally Determined Contribution (INDC) by 2030. *Energies*, **10(1)**, doi:10.3390/en10010052.

Siikamäki, J., J.N. Sanchirico, and S.L. Jardine, 2012: Global economic potential for reducing carbon dioxide emissions from mangrove loss. *Proc. Natl. Acad. Sci.*, **109(36)**, 14369–14374, doi:10.1073/pnas.1200519109.

Silva Herran, D. and S. Fujimori, 2021: Beyond Japanese NDC: Energy and macroeconomic transitions towards 2050 in emission pathways with multiple ambition levels. *Sustain. Sci.*, **16(2)**, 489–501, doi:10.1007/s11625-021-00930-1.

Simonet, G., J. Subervie, D. Ezzine-de-Blas, M. Cromberg, and A.E. Duchelle, 2019: Effectiveness of a REDD+ Project in Reducing Deforestation in the Brazilian Amazon. *Am. J. Agric. Econ.*, **101(1)**, 211–229, doi:10.1093/ajae/aay028.

Singh, C., 2018: Is participatory watershed development building local adaptive capacity? Findings from a case study in Rajasthan, India. *Environ. Dev.*, **25**, 43–58, doi:10.1016/j.envdev.2017.11.004.

SIPRI, 2020: *How does world military expenditure compare with government expenditure on health and education, or with overseas aid to developing countries?* Stockholm International Peace Research Institute (SIPRI), Stockholm, Sweden, https://sipri.org/databases/milex/frequently-asked-questions#9-how-does-world (Accessed November 1, 2021).

Smil, V., 2016: *Energy transitions: Global and national perspectives – 2nd ed.* Praeger, Santa Barbara, CA, USA , 297 pp.

Smith, A., T. Hargreaves, S. Hielscher, M. Martiskainen, and G. Seyfang, 2016: Making the most of community energies: Three perspectives on grassroots innovation. *Environ. Plan. A Econ. Sp.*, **48(2)**, 407–432, doi:10.1177/0308518X15597908.

Smith, H.J., E. Kruger, J. Knot, and J.N. Blignaut, 2017: Conservation agriculture in South Africa: lessons from case studies. In: *Conservation agriculture for Africa: building resilient farming systems in a changing climate* [Kassam, A. H., Mkomwa, S., Friedrich, T. (eds.)]. Plant Production and Protection Division, Food and Agriculture Organization of the United Nations Rome, Italy, pp. 214–245.

Smith, J.B. et al., 2011: Development and climate change adaptation funding: Coordination and integration. *Clim. Policy*, **11(3)**, 987–1000, doi:10.1080/14693062.2011.582385.

Smith, S., 2017: *Just Transition: A Report for the OECD*. International Trade Union Confederation (ITUC), Brussels, Belgium, 23 pp., https://www.oecd.org/environment/cc/g20-climate/collapsecontents/Just-Transition-Centre-report-just-transition.pdf (Accessed November 1, 2021).

Snell, D., 2018: 'Just transition'? Conceptual challenges meet stark reality in a 'transitioning' coal region in Australia. *Globalizations*, **15(4)**, 550–564, doi:10.1080/14747731.2018.1454679.

Solano Rodriguez, B., P. Drummond, and P. Ekins, 2017: Decarbonizing the EU energy system by 2050: An important role for BECCS. *Clim. Policy*, **17**, S93–S110, doi:10.1080/14693062.2016.1242058.

Soterroni, A.C. et al., 2018: Future environmental and agricultural impacts of Brazil's Forest Code. *Environ. Res. Lett.*, **13(7)**, 074021, doi:10.1088/1748-9326/aaccbb.

Soterroni, A.C. et al., 2019: Expanding the Soy Moratorium to Brazil's Cerrado. *Sci. Adv.*, **5(7)**, eaav7336, doi:10.1126/sciadv.aav7336.

Soussana, J.-F. et al., 2019: Matching policy and science: Rationale for the '4 per 1000 - soils for food security and climate' initiative. *Soil Tillage Res.*, **188**, 3–15, doi.org/10.1016/j.still.2017.12.002.

Sovacool, B.K., 2013: Expanding renewable energy access with pro-poor public private partnerships in the developing world. *Energy Strateg. Rev.*, **1(3)**, 181–192, doi:10.1016/j.esr.2012.11.003.

Sovacool, B.K., 2016: How long will it take? Conceptualizing the temporal dynamics of energy transitions. *Energy Res. Soc. Sci.*, **13**, 202–215, doi:10.1016/j.erss.2015.12.020.

Sovacool, B.K., 2017: Reviewing, Reforming, and Rethinking Global Energy Subsidies: Towards a Political Economy Research Agenda. *Ecol. Econ.*, **135**, 150–163, doi:10.1016/j.ecolecon.2016.12.009.

Sovacool, B.K. and M.H. Dworkin, 2014: *Global energy justice: Problems, principles, and practices*. Cambridge University Press, Cambridge, United Kingdom and New York, NY, USA, 1–391 pp.

Sovacool, B.K., P. Schmid, A. Stirling, G. Walter, and G. MacKerron, 2020: Differences in carbon emissions reduction between countries pursuing renewable electricity versus nuclear power. *Nat. Energy*, **5(11)**, 928–935, doi:10.1038/s41560-020-00696-3.

Spencer, T. et al., 2015: *Beyond the Numbers: Understanding the Transformation Induced by INDCs*. Institut du developpement durable et des relations internationales (IDDRI), Paris, France, 80 pp., https://inis.iaea.org/search/search.aspx?orig_q=RN:48078532 (Accessed November 1, 2021).

Srinivasana, U.T. et al., 2008: The debt of nations and the distribution of ecological impacts from human activities. *Proc. Natl. Acad. Sci.*, **105(5)**, 1768–1773, doi:10.1073/PNAS.0709562104.

State of California, 2018: Executive Order B-55-18 to Achieve Carbon Neutrality. https://www.ca.gov/archive/gov39/wp-content/uploads/2018/09/9.10.18-Executive-Order.pdf (Accessed January 6, 2021).

Statistics Sweden, 2020: *Downloaded data on Carbon tax revenues and GDP*. www.scb.se.

Staub-Kaminski, I., A. Zimmer, M. Jakob, and R. Marschinski, 2014: Climate policy in practice: A typology of obstacles and implications for integrated assessment modeling. *Clim. Chang. Econ.*, **5(1)**, doi:10.1142/S2010007814400041.

Steckel, J.C. et al., 2017: From climate finance toward sustainable development finance. *Wiley Interdiscip. Rev. Clim. Change*, **8(1)**, e437, doi:10.1002/wcc.437.

Steffen, W. and M. Stafford Smith, 2013: Planetary boundaries, equity and global sustainability: Why wealthy countries could benefit from more equity. *Curr. Opin. Environ. Sustain.*, **5(3–4)**, 403–408, doi:10.1016/j.cosust.2013.04.007.

Steffen, W. et al., 2015: Planetary boundaries: Guiding human development on a changing planet. *Science*, **347(6223)**, doi:10.1126/science.1259855.

Stenzel, F. et al., 2021: Irrigation of biomass plantations may globally increase water stress more than climate change. *Nat. Commun.*, **12(1)**, 1512, doi:10.1038/s41467-021-21640-3.

Stephan, B., S. Schurig, and A. Leidreiter, 2016: *What Place for Renewables in the INDCs?* World Future Council, Hamburg, Germany, 12 pp., https://www.worldfuturecouncil.org/wp-content/uploads/2016/03/WFC_2016_What_Place_for_Renewables_in_the_INDCs.pdf (Accessed July 12, 2019).

Stern, N.,2010: Imperfections in the Economics of Public Policy, Imperfections in Markets, and Climate Change. *Journal of the European Economic Association*, **8(2–3)**, 253–288, 10.1111/j.1542-4774.2010.tb00504.x,

Sterner, T., 2007: Environmental tax reform: The Swedish experience. *Eur. Environ.*, **4(6)**, 20–25, doi:10.1002/eet.3320040606.

Stevis, D. and R. Felli, 2015: Global labour unions and just transition to a green economy. *Int. Environ. Agreements Polit. Law Econ.*, **15(1)**, 29–43, doi:10.1007/s10784-014-9266-1.

Stiglitz, J., 1998: Distinguished Lecture on Economics in Government: The Private Uses of Public Interests: Incentives and Institutions. *J. Econ. Perspect.*, **12(2)**, 3–22, doi:10.1257/jep.12.2.3.

Stiglitz, J. et al., 2017: *Report of the high-level commission on carbon prices. Supported by the World Bank Group; Agence de l'Environnement et de la Maitrise de l'Energie; Ministere de la transition ecologique et solidaire, Republique Francaise*. Carbon Pricing Leadership Coalition, Washington, DC, USA, 61 pp., https://www.carbonpricingleadership.org/report-of-the-highlevel-commission-on-carbon-prices (Accessed November 1, 2021).

Strambo, C., J. Burton, and A. Atteridge, 2019: *The end of coal? Planning a 'just transition' in South Africa*. Stockholm Environment Institute (SEI), Seattle, USA, 15 pp., https://www.sei.org/wp-content/uploads/2019/02/planning-a-just-transition-in-south-africa.pdf (Accessed November 1, 2021).

Sugiyama, M. et al., 2019: Japan's long-term climate mitigation policy: Multi-model assessment and sectoral challenges. *Energy*, **167**, 1120–1131, doi:10.1016/j.energy.2018.10.091.

Sugiyama, M. et al., 2021: EMF 35 JMIP study for Japan's long-term climate and energy policy: Scenario designs and key findings. *Sustain. Sci.*, **16(2)**, 355–374, doi:10.1007/S11625-021-00913-2.

Sumabat, A.K. et al., 2016: Decomposition analysis of Philippine CO_2 emissions from fuel combustion and electricity generation. *Appl. Energy*, **164**, 795–804, doi:10.1016/j.apenergy.2015.12.023.

4

Sunderlin, W.D. et al., 2014: How are REDD+ Proponents Addressing Tenure Problems? Evidence from Brazil, Cameroon, Tanzania, Indonesia, and Vietnam. *World Dev.*, **55**, 37–52, doi:10.1016/j.worlddev.2013.01.013.

Sutton-Grier, A.E. and A. Moore, 2016: Leveraging Carbon Services of Coastal Ecosystems for Habitat Protection and Restoration. *Coast. Manag.*, **44(3)**, 259–277, doi:10.1080/08920753.2016.1160206.

Sutton-Grier, A.E., K. Wowk, and H. Bamford, 2015: Future of our coasts: The potential for natural and hybrid infrastructure to enhance the resilience of our coastal communities, economies and ecosystems. *Environ. Sci. Policy*, **51**, 137–148, doi:10.1016/j.envsci.2015.04.006.

Swilling, M. and E. Annecke, 2012: *Just transitions: Explorations of sustainability in an unfair world*. UCT Press, Cape Town, South Africa, 360 pp.

Szpor, A. and Ziółkowska, K., 2018: *The transformation of the Polish coal sector*. International Institute for Sustainable Development, Winipeg, Manitoba, Canada, 21 pp., https://www.iisd.org/sites/default/files/publications/transformation-polish-coal-sector.pdf (Accessed November 1, 2021).

Taillardat, P., D.A. Friess, and M. Lupascu, 2018: Mangrove blue carbon strategies for climate change mitigation are most effective at the national scale. *Biol. Lett.*, **14(10)**, 20180251, doi:10.1098/rsbl.2018.0251.

Tait, L., 2017: Towards a multidimensional framework for measuring household energy access: Application to South Africa. *Energy Sustain. Dev.*, **38**, 1–9, doi:10.1016/j.esd.2017.01.007.

Tait, L. and M. Euston-Brown, 2017: What role can African cities play in low-carbon development? A multilevel governance perspective of Ghana, Uganda and South Africa. *J. Energy South. Africa*, **28(3)**, 43, doi:10.17159/2413-3051/2017/v28i3a1959.

Tallis, H.M. et al., 2018: An attainable global vision for conservation and human well-being. *Front. Ecol. Environ.*, **114**, 6722–6728, doi:10.1002/fee.1965.

Task Force on Climate-Related Financial Disclosures, 2019: *Task Force on Climate-Related Financial Disclosures: Status Report*. Financial Stability Board, Bank for International Settlements, Basel, Switzerland, 135 pp., https://assets.bbhub.io/company/sites/60/2020/10/2019-TCFD-Status-Report-FINAL-0531191.pdf.

Tegmark, M., 2017: *Life 3.0: Being human in the age of artificial intelligence*. Penguin Random House, London, United Kingdom, 364 pp.

Telaye, A., P. Benitez, S. Tamru, H.A. Medhin, and M.A. Toman, 2019: *Exploring Carbon Pricing in Developing Countries: A Macroeconomic Analysis in Ethiopia*. The World Bank, Washington, DC, Policy Research Working Paper 8860, 29 pp.

Thacker, S. et al., 2019: Infrastructure for sustainable development. *Nat. Sustain.*, **2(4)**, 324–331, doi:10.1038/s41893-019-0256-8.

Thalmann, P., 2004: The public acceptance of green taxes: 2 Million voters express their opinion. *Public Choice*, **119**(1–2), 179–217, doi:10.1023/b:puch.0000024165.18082.db.

The Energy and Climate Intelligence Unit, 2019: *Countdown to zero: Plotting progress towards delivering net zero emissions by 2050*. Energy and Climate Intelligence Unit, London, United Kingdom, 16 pp., https://ca1-eci.edcdn.com/reports/ECIU_Countdown_to_Net_Zero.pdf?v=1561459809.

Thepkhun, P., B. Limmeechokchai, S. Fujimori, T. Masui, and R.M. Shrestha, 2013: Thailand's Low-Carbon Scenario 2050: The AIM/CGE analyses of CO_2 mitigation measures. *Energy Policy*, **62**, 561–572, doi:10.1016/j.enpol.2013.07.037.

Thomas Klaus, Carla Vollmer, Harry Lehmann, and Klaus Müschen, 2010: *Energy target 2050: 100 % renewable electricity supply*. Federal Environment Agency Germany, Dessau-Roßlau, Germany, 44 pp., https://www.researchgate.net/publication/279526291_2050_Energy_Target_100_renewable_electricity_supply (Accessed October 18, 2021).

Thomas, N. et al., 2017: Distribution and drivers of global mangrove forest change, 1996–2010. *PLoS One*, **12(6)**, 1–14, doi:10.1371/journal.pone.0179302.

Thornton, P.K. and M. Herrero, 2015: Adapting to climate change in the mixed crop and livestock farming systems in sub-Saharan Africa. *Nat. Clim. Change*, **5**, 830–836, doi:10.1038/nclimate2754.

Thornton, P.K. et al., 2018: A Qualitative Evaluation of CSA Options in Mixed Crop-Livestock Systems in Developing Countries. In: *Climate Smart Agriculture* [Lipper, L., N. McCarthy, D. Zilberman, S. Asfaw, and G. Branca, (eds.)]. Food and Agriculture Organization of the United Nations, Rome, Italy, pp. 385–423.

Tokoro, T. et al., 2014: Net uptake of atmospheric CO_2 by coastal submerged aquatic vegetation. *Glob. Chang. Biol.*, **20(6)**, 1873–1884, doi:10.1111/gcb.12543.

Tume, S.J.P., J.N. Kimengsi, and Z.N. Fogwe, 2019: Indigenous Knowledge and Farmer Perceptions of Climate and Ecological Changes in the Bamenda Highlands of Cameroon: Insights from the Bui Plateau. *Climate*, **7(12)**, doi:10.3390/cli7120138.

TWI2050 – The World in 2050, 2018: *Transformations to Achieve the Sustainable Development Goals – Report prepared by The World in 2050 initiative*. International Institute for Applied Systems Analysis (IIASA), Laxenburg, Austria, 157 pp., https://pure.iiasa.ac.at/id/eprint/15347/ (Accessed November 1, 2021).

UN, 2017: Work of the Statistical Commission pertaining to the 2030 Agenda for Sustainable Development. UN Documents A/RES/71/313, https://undocs.org/Home/Mobile?FinalSymbol=A%2FRES%2F71%2F313&Language=E&DeviceType=Desktop&LangRequested=False (Last Accessed May 30, 2022), 25 pp.

UN, 2018: Report of the Inter-Agency and Expert Group on Sustainable Development Goal Indicators. UN Document E/CN.3/2018/2, https://undocs.org/Home/Mobile?FinalSymbol=E%2FCN.3%2F2018%2F2&Language=E&DeviceType=Desktop&LangRequested=False (last accessed May 30, 2022), 13 pp.

UN, 2019: *Report of the Inter-Agency and Expert Group on Sustainable Development Goal Indicators – Note by the Secretary-General*. UN Document E/CN.3/2019/2, https://documents-dds-ny.un.org/doc/UNDOC/GEN/N18/451/31/PDF/N1845131.pdf?OpenElement (Last Accessed May 31, 2022), 15 pp.

UN, 2020a: 'Enhance solidarity' to fight COVID-19, Chinese President urges, also pledges carbon neutrality by 2060. UN News, United Nations, New York, USA, https://news.un.org/en/story/2020/09/1073052 (Accessed December 8, 2020).

UN, 2020b: UN chief hails Republic of Korea's vow to achieve carbon neutrality. UN News, United Nations, New York, USA, https://news.un.org/en/story/2020/10/1076342 (Accessed December 8, 2020).

UN, 2020c: Climate action: UN chief encouraged by Japan's 2050 net zero pledge. UN News, United Nations, New York, USA, https://news.un.org/en/story/2020/10/1076132 (Accessed December 8, 2020).

Ünal, A.B., L. Steg, and M. Gorsira, 2018: Values Versus Environmental Knowledge as Triggers of a Process of Activation of Personal Norms for Eco-Driving. *Environ. Behav.*, **50(10)**, 1092–1118, doi:10.1177/0013916517728991.

UNEP, 2015: *Aligning the Financial System with Sustainable Development: Pathways to Scale*. Inquiry: Design of a Sustainable Financial System and United Nations Environment Programme (UNEP), Geneva, Switzerland, 25 pp., https://www.unenvironment.org/ru/node/10493 (Accessed November 20, 2019).

UNEP, 2016: *The Adaptation Finance Gap Report 2016*. United Nations Environment Programme (UNEP), Nairobi, Kenya, 50 pp., https://climateanalytics.org/media/agr2016.pdf (Accessed November 1, 2021).

UNEP, 2017a: *The Emissions Gap Report 2017*. United Nations Environment Programme (UNEP), Nairobi, Kenya, 89 pp., https://wedocs.unep.org/bitstream/handle/20.500.11822/22070/EGR_2017.pdf?sequence=1&isAllowed=y (Accessed November 1, 2021).

UNEP, 2017b: *Consuming Differently, Consuming Sustainably: Behavioural Insights for Policymaking*. United Nations Environment Programme (UNEP), Nairobi, Kenya, 55 p., https://sustainabledevelopment.un.org/content/documents/2404Behavioral%20Insights.pdf (Accessed November 1, 2021).

4

UNEP, 2018a: *The Adaptation Gap Report 2018*. United Nations Environment Programme (UNEP), Nairobi, Kenya, 84 pp., https://wedocs.unep.org/bitstream/handle/20.500.11822/27114/AGR_2018.pdf?sequence=3 (Accessed November 1, 2021).

UNEP, 2018b: Emissions gap report 2018. United Nations Environment Programme (UNEP), Nairobi, Kenya, 85 pp., https://wedocs.unep.org/bitstream/handle/20.500.11822/26895/EGR2018_FullReport_EN.pdf?isAllowed=y&sequence=1 (Accessed November 1, 2021).

UNEP, 2020a: *Emissions gap report 2020*. United Nations Environment Programme (UNEP), Nairobi, Kenya. 101 pp., https://wedocs.unep.org/xmlui/bitstream/handle/20.500.11822/34426/EGR20.pdf?sequence=3 (Accessed November 1, 2021)

UNEP, 2020b: *Oil and Gas Methane Partnership (OGMP) 2.0 Framework | Climate & Clean Air Coalition*. United Nations Environment Programme (UNEP), Nairobi, Kenya, 18 pp., https://www.ccacoalition.org/en/resources/oil-and-gas-methane-partnership-ogmp-20-framework (Accessed October 18, 2021).

UNEP, 2021: *The emissions gap report 2021*. United Nations Environment Programme (UNEP), Nairobi, Kenya, 79 pp., , https://www.unep.org/resources/emissions-gap-report-2021 (Accessed November 1, 2021).

UNEP - Finance Initiative, 2020: Task Force on Climate-related financial disclosures. *UNEP - Financ. Initiat.*

UNEP and IEA, 2020: *UNEP and IEA report: Cooling Emissions and Policy Synthesis (GEN - 1142.00) Eurovent.*

United Nations Environment Program (UNEP), Nairobi, Kenya and International Energy Agency (IEA), Paris, France, 49 pp., https://wedocs.unep.org/bitstream/handle/20.500.11822/33094/CoolRep.pdf?sequence=1&isAllowed=y (Accessed December 8, 2020).

UNEP and WMO, 2011: *Integrated Assessment of Black Carbon and Tropospheric Ozone*. World Meteorological Organization (WMO), Geneva, Switzerland, 283 pp., https://library.wmo.int/doc_num.php?explnum_id=7737 (Accessed November 1, 2021).

UNEP Inquiry, 2016: The Financial System We Need – From Momentum to Transformation. *Financ. Syst. We Need*. United Nations Environment Program (UNEP), Nairobi, Kenya, https://wedocs.unep.org/bitstream/handle/20.500.11822/20716/The_Financial_System_We_Need_From_Momentum_to_Transformation.pdf?sequence=1&isAllowed=y (Accessed November 1, 2021).

UNFCCC, 2014: Decision 1/CP.20: *Lima Call for Action*. FCCC/CP/2014/10/Add.1, United Nations Framework Convention on Climate Change (UNFCCC), 43 pp., https://undocs.org/Home/Mobile?FinalSymbol=FCCC%2FCP%2F2014%2F10%2FAdd.1&Language=E&DeviceType=Desktop&LangRequested=False* (Accessed November 1, 2021).

UNFCCC, 2015a: *Synthesis report on the aggregate effect of the intended nationally determined contributions*. Note by the Secretariat, FCCC/CP/2015/7, United Nations Framework Convention on Climate Change (UNFCCC), 66 pp., https://undocs.org/Home/Mobile?FinalSymbol=FCCC%2FCP%2F2015%2F7&Language=E&DeviceType=Desktop&LangRequested=False (Accessed November 1, 2021).

UNFCCC, 2015b: *Paris Agreement*. Annex to decision 1/CP.21. FCCC/CP/2015/10/Add.1, United Nations Framework Convention on Climate Change (UNFCCC), 36 pp., https://undocs.org/Home/Mobile?FinalSymbol=FCCC%2FCP%2F2015%2F10%2FAdd.1&Language=E&DeviceType=Desktop&LangRequested=False (Accessed November 1, 2021).

UNFCCC, 2016a: Aggregate effect of the intended nationally determined contributions: an update - Synthesis report by the secretariat. FCCC/CP/2016/2, United Nations Framework Convention on Climate Change (UNFCCC), 75 pp., https://unfccc.int/resource/docs/2016/cop22/eng/02.pdf (Accessed November 1, 2021).

UNFCCC, 2016b: *Aggregate effect of the intended nationally determined contributions: An update*. FCCC/CP/2016/2, United Nations Framework Convention on Climate Change (UNFCCC), 78 pp., https://unfccc.int/resource/docs/2016/cop22/eng/02.pdf (Accessed November 1, 2021).

UNFCCC, 2016c: *Just transition of the workforce, and the creation of decent work and quality jobs. Technical Paper*. FCCC/TP/2016/7, United Nations Framework Convention on Climate Change (UNFCCC), 59 pp., https://documents-dds-ny.un.org/doc/UNDOC/GEN/G16/240/43/PDF/G1624043.pdf?OpenElement (Accessed November 1, 2021).

UNFCCC, 2018a: Decision 19/CM1, FCCC/PA/CMA/2018/3/Add.2: *Matters Relating to Article 14 of the Paris Agreement and Paragraphs 99–101 of Decision 1/CP.21*. United Nations Framework Convention on Climate Change (UNFCCC), 53–58 pp., https://unfccc.int/sites/default/files/resource/cma2018_3_add2_new_advance.pdf (Accessed November 1, 2021).

UNFCCC, 2018b: Decision 18/CM1, FCCC/PA/CMA/2018/3/Add.2: Modalities, procedures and guidelines for the transparency framework for action and support referred to in Article 13 of the Paris Agreement. United Nations Framework Convention on Climate Change (UNFCCC), 18–52 pp., https://unfccc.int/sites/default/files/resource/cma2018_3_add2_new_advance.pdf (Accessed November 1, 2021).

UNFCCC, 2018c: Decision 4/CMA.1: *Further guidance in relation to the mitigation section of decision 1/CP.21. Decision x/CMA.1*. FCCC/PA/CMA/2018/3/Add.1, United Nations Framework Convention on Climate Change (UNFCCC), 37 pp., https://unfccc.int/documents/193407 (Accessed November 1, 2021).

UNFCCC, 2021: *Nationally determined contributions under the Paris Agreement. Synthesis report by the secretariat. FCCC/PA/CMA/2021/8*, United Nations Framework Convention on Climate Change (UNFCCC), 42 pp., https://unfccc.int/sites/default/files/resource/cma2021_08_adv_1.pdf (Accessed November 1, 2021).

UNHRC, 2020: *International solidarity and climate change: Report of the Independent Expert on human rights and international solidarity*. UN Doc. A/HRC/44/44, 20 pp., https://undocs.org/Home/Mobile?FinalSymbol=A%2FHRC%2F44%2F44&Language=E&DeviceType=Desktop&LangRequested=False (Accessed November 1, 2021).

Urban, F., 2018: China's rise: Challenging the North-South technology transfer paradigm for climate change mitigation and low-carbon energy. *Energy Policy*, **113** (August 2017), 320–330, doi:10.1016/j.enpol.2017.11.007.

Vaillancourt, K., O. Bahn, E. Frenette, and O. Sigvaldason, 2017: Exploring deep decarbonization pathways to 2050 for Canada using an optimization energy model framework. *Appl. Energy*, **195**, 774–785, doi:10.1016/j.apenergy.2017.03.104.

Valadkhani, A., I. Roshdi, and R. Smyth, 2016: A multiplicative environmental DEA approach to measure efficiency changes in the world's major polluters. *Energy Econ.*, **54**, 363–375, doi:10.1016/j.eneco.2015.12.018.

van Asselt, H. and T.S.H. Moerenhout, 2018: Reforming Egypt's Fossil Fuel Subsidies in the Context of a Changing Social Contract. In: *The Politics of Fossil Fuel Subsidies and their Reform*. [J. Skovgaard, and H. van Asselt (eds.)], Cambridge University Press, Cambridge, United Kingdom and New York, NY, USA, pp. 265–282.

van den Berg, N.J. et al., 2019: Implications of various effort-sharing approaches for national carbon budgets and emission pathways. *Clim. Change*, **162(4)**, 1805–1822, doi:10.1007/s10584-019-02368-y.

van den Broek, K., J.W. Bolderdijk, and L. Steg, 2017: Individual differences in values determine the relative persuasiveness of biospheric, economic and combined appeals. *J. Environ. Psychol.*, **53**, 145–156, doi:10.1016/j.jenvp.2017.07.009.

van der Linden, S., E. Maibach, and A. Leiserowitz, 2015: Improving Public Engagement With Climate Change: Five 'Best Practice' Insights From Psychological Science. *Perspect. Psychol. Sci.*, **10(6)**, 758–763, doi:10.1177/1745691615598516.

van der Voorn, T., Å. Svenfelt, K.E. Björnberg, E. Fauré, and R. Milestad, 2020: Envisioning carbon-free land use futures for Sweden: A scenario study on conflicts and synergies between environmental policy goals. *Reg. Environ. Change*, **20(2)**, 1–10, doi:10.1007/s10113-020-01618-5.

4

van der Zwaan, B. et al., 2016: Energy technology roll-out for climate change mitigation: A multi-model study for Latin America. *Energy Econ.*, **56**, 526–542, doi:10.1016/j.eneco.2015.11.019.

van Heerden, J. et al., 2016: The economic and environmental effects of a carbon tax in South Africa: A dynamic CGE modelling approach. *South African J. Econ. Manag. Sci.*, **19(5)**, 714–732, doi:10.17159/2222-3436/2016/v19n5a3.

van Meijl, H. et al., 2018: On the macroeconomic impact of bioenergy and biochemicals – Introducing advanced bioeconomy sectors into an economic modelling framework with a case study for the Netherlands. *Biomass and Bioenergy*, **108**, 381–397, doi:10.1016/J.BIOMBIOE.2017.10.040.

Vandyck, T., K. Keramidas, B. Saveyn, A. Kitous, and Z. Vrontisi, 2016: A global stocktake of the Paris pledges: Implications for energy systems and economy. *Glob. Environ. Change*, **41**, 46–63, doi:10.1016/j.gloenvcha.2016.08.006.

Vaughan, N.E. and C. Gough, 2016: Expert assessment concludes negative emissions scenarios may not deliver. *Environ. Res. Lett.*, **11(9)**, 1–7, doi:10.1088/1748-9326/11/9/095003.

Ven, D.-J. Van de et al., 2019: Integrated policy assessment and optimisation over multiple sustainable development goals in Eastern Africa. *Environ. Res. Lett.*, **14(9)**, 094001, doi:10.1088/1748-9326/AB375D.

Vergara, W. et al., 2016: *The Economic Case for Landscape Restoration in Latin America*. World Resources Insite, Washington DC, USA, 62 pp.

Veysey, J. et al., 2014: Pathways to Mexico's climate change mitigation targets: A multi-model analysis. *Energy Econ.*, **56**, 587–599, doi:10.1016/j.eneco.2015.04.011.

Victor, N., C. Nichols, and C. Zelek, 2018: The US power sector decarbonization: Investigating technology options with MARKAL nine-region model. *Energy Econ.*, **73** (November), 410–425, doi:10.1016/j.eneco.2018.03.021.

Viebahn, P., D. Vallentin, and S. Höller, 2014: Prospects of carbon capture and storage (CCS) in India's power sector – An integrated assessment. *Appl. Energy*, **117**, 62–75, doi:10.1016/J.APENERGY.2013.11.054.

Vishwanathan, S.S. and A. Garg, 2020: Energy system transformation to meet NDC, 2°C, and well below 2°C targets for India. *Clim. Change*, **162(4)**, 1877–1891, doi:10.1007/s10584-019-02616-1.

Vishwanathan, S.S., A. Garg, and V. Tiwari, 2018a: *Coal transitions in India: Assessing India's energy transition options*. Institut du Développement Durable et des Relations Internationales, Paris, France and Climate Strategies, London, United Kingdom, 52 pp., https://www.iddri.org/sites/default/files/PDF/Publications/Catalogue%20Iddri/Rapport/20180609_ReportCOAL_India.pdf.

Vishwanathan, S.S., A. Garg, V. Tiwari, and P.R. Shukla, 2018b: India in 2°C and well below 2°C worlds: Opportunities and challenges. *Carbon Manag.*, **9(5)**, 459–479, doi:10.1080/17583004.2018.1476588.

Vogt-Schilb, A. and S. Hallegatte, 2017: Climate policies and nationally determined contributions: Reconciling the needed ambition with the political economy. *Wiley Interdiscip. Rev. Energy Environ.*, **6(6)**, e256, doi:10.1002/wene.256.

Vogt-Schilb, A. et al., 2019: Cash transfers for pro-poor carbon taxes in Latin America and the Caribbean. *Nat. Sustain.*, **2(10)**, 941–948, doi:10.1038/s41893-019-0385-0.

Voigt, C. and F. Ferreira, 2016: Differentiation in the Paris Agreement. *Clim. Law*, **6**, 58–74, doi:doi 10.1163/18786561-00601004.

Von Stechow, C. et al., 2016: 2°C and SDGs: United they stand, divided they fall? *Environ. Res. Lett.*, **11(3)**, doi:10.1088/1748-9326/11/3/034022.

Voß, J.-P., J. Newig, B. Kastens, J. Monstadt, and B. Nölting, 2007: Steering for Sustainable Development: A Typology of Problems and Strategies with respect to Ambivalence, Uncertainty and Distributed Power. *J. Environ. Policy Plan.*, **9(3–4)**, 193–212, doi:10.1080/15239080701622881.

Waage, J. et al., 2015: Governing the UN Sustainable Development Goals: interactions, infrastructures, and institutions. *Lancet Glob. Heal.*, **3(5)**, e251–e252, doi:10.1016/S2214-109X(15)70112-9.

Waisman, H. et al., 2019: A pathway design framework for national low greenhouse gas emission development strategies. *Nat. Clim. Change*, **9(4)**, 261–268, doi:10.1038/s41558-019-0442-8.

Wakiyama, T. and T. Kuramochi, 2017: Scenario analysis of energy saving and CO_2 emissions reduction potentials to ratchet up Japanese mitigation target in 2030 in the residential sector. *Energy Policy*, **103**, 1–15, doi:10.1016/j.enpol.2016.12.059.

Wall Street Journal, 2019: *Economists' Statement on Carbon Dividends Organized by the Climate Leadership Council*. https://www.wsj.com/articles/economists-statement-on-carbon-dividends-11547682910 (Accessed December 11, 2019).

Wang, K., Y. Mao, J. Chen, and S. Yu, 2018: The optimal research and development portfolio of low-carbon energy technologies: A study of China. *J. Clean. Prod.*, **176**, 1065–1077, doi:10.1016/J.JCLEPRO.2017.11.230.

Wang, M. and C. Feng, 2017: Decomposition of energy-related CO_2 emissions in China: An empirical analysis based on provincial panel data of three sectors. *Appl. Energy*, **190**, 772–787, doi:10.1016/j.apenergy.2017.01.007.

Wang, Q., M. Lu, Z. Bai, and K. Wang, 2020: Coronavirus pandemic reduced China's CO_2 emissions in short-term, while stimulus packages may lead to emissions growth in medium- and long-term. *Appl. Energy*, **278**, 115735, doi:10.1016/j.apenergy.2020.115735.

Warlenius, R., G. Pierce, and V. Ramasar, 2015: Reversing the arrow of arrears: The concept of 'ecological debt' and its value for environmental justice. *Glob. Environ. Change*, **30**, 21–30, doi:10.1016/J.GLOENVCHA.2014.10.014.

Watson, J., R. Gross, I. Ketsopoulou, and M. Winskel, 2015: The impact of uncertainties on the UK's medium-term climate change targets. *Energy Policy*, **87**, 685–695, doi:10.1016/J.ENPOL.2015.02.030.

Watts, N. et al., 2019: The 2019 report of The Lancet Countdown on health and climate change: nsuring that the health of a child born today is not defined by a changing climate. *Lancet*, **304**(10211), 1836–1878, doi:/10.1016/S0140-6736(19)32596-6.

WBGU, 2011: *World in transition: A social contract for sustainability*. German Advisory Council on Global Change, Berlin, 396 pp, https://www.wbgu.de/fileadmin/user_upload/wbgu/publikationen/hauptgutachten/hg2011/pdf/wbgu_jg2011_en.pdf.

Wei, W., Y. Zhao, J. Wang, and M. Song, 2019: The environmental benefits and economic impacts of Fit-in-Tariff in China. *Renew. Energy*, **133**, 401–410, doi:10.1016/J.RENENE.2018.10.064.

Weitz, N., H. Carlsen, M. Nilsson, and K. Skånberg, 2018: Towards systemic and contextual priority setting for implementing the 2030 agenda. *Sustain. Sci.*, **13(2)**, 531–548, doi:10.1007/s11625-017-0470-0.

White House, 2016: Investing in Coal Communities, Workers, and Technology: The POWER+ Plan. https://obamawhitehouse.archives.gov/sites/default/files/omb/budget/fy2016/assets/fact_sheets/investing-in-coal-communities-workers-and-technology-the-power-plan.pdf (Accessed January 8, 2020).

Wiedenhofer, D. et al., 2017: Unequal household carbon footprints in China. *Nat. Clim. Change*, **7(1)**, 75–80, doi:10.1038/nclimate3165.

Wiedmann, T., M. Lenzen, L.T. Keyßer, and J.K. Steinberger, 2020: Scientists' warning on affluence. *Nat. Commun.*, **11(1)**, 1–10, doi:10.1038/s41467-020-16941-y.

Willenbockel, D., H. Hoka Osiolo, and S. Bawakyillenuo, 2017: Exploring the Macroeconomic Impacts of Low-Carbon Energy Transitions: A Simulation Analysis for Kenya and Ghana. *IDS Bull.*, **48(5–6)**, doi:10.19088/1968-2017.163.

Windham-Myers, L., S. Crooks, and T.G. Troxler, 2018: *A Blue Carbon Primer: The State of Coastal Wetland Carbon Science, Practice and Policy*. 1st Edition. [Windham-Myers, L., S. Crooks, and T.G. Troxler, (eds.)]. CRC Press, Boca Raton, USA, 532 pp.

Winkler, H., 2017a: Mitigation (Article 4). In: *The Paris Agreement on climate change: Analysis and commentary*. [Klein, D., P. Carazo, J. Bulmer, M. Doelle, and A. Higham, (eds.)], Oxford University Press, Oxford, UK, pp. 135–159.

4

Winkler, H., 2017b: Reducing energy poverty through carbon tax revenues in South Africa. *J. Energy South. Africa*, **28(3)**, 12–26, doi:10.17159/2413-3051/2017/v28i3a2332.

Winkler, H., 2018: *Reducing inequality and carbon emissions: Innovation of developmental pathways*. Academy of Science of South Africa, Pretoria, South Africa.

Winkler, H., and A. Marquard, 2009: Changing development paths: From an energy-intensive to low-carbon economy in South Africa. *Clim. Dev.*, **1(1)**, 47–65, doi:10.3763/cdev.2009.0003.

Winkler, H., K. Baumert, O. Blanchard, S. Burch, and J. Robinson, 2007: What factors influence mitigative capacity? *Energy Policy*, **35(1)**, 692–703, doi:10.1016/j.enpol.2006.01.009.

Winkler, H., A. Boyd, M. Torres Gunfaus, and S. Raubenheimer, 2015: Reconsidering development by reflecting on climate change. *Int. Environ. Agreements Polit. Law Econ.*, **15(4)**, 369–385, doi:10.1007/s10784-015-9304-7.

Winkler, H. et al., 2017: Information for a developmental approach to mitigation: Linking sectoral and economy-wide models for Brazil, Chile, Colombia, Peru and South Africa. *Clim. Dev.*, **9(6)**, 559–570, doi:10.1080/17565529.2016.1174660.

Winkler, H. et al., 2018: Countries start to explain how their climate contributions are fair: More rigour needed. *Int. Environ. Agreements Polit. Law Econ.*, **18**, 99–115, doi:10.1007/s10784-017-9381-x.

Withana S., 2016: Overcoming Obstacles to Green Fiscal Reform. *Int. J. Green Growth Dev.*, **2(2)**, 161–188.

Wollenberg, E. et al., 2016: Reducing emissions from agriculture to meet the 2°C target. *Glob. Chang. Biol.*, **22(12)**, 3859–3864, doi:10.1111/gcb.13340.

World Bank, 2007: *Results-based National Development Strategies: Assessment and Challenges Ahead. The World bank*. The World Bank, Washington, DC, USA, 96 pp.

World Bank, 2009: *: World Development Report 2009: Reshaping Economic Geography*. The World Bank, Washington, DC, USA, 383 pp.

World Bank, 2020: *World Development Indicators*. The World Bank, Washington, DC, USA, https://databank.worldbank.org.

World Economic Forum, 2018: Eight Futures of Work: Scenarios and their Implications. The World Economic Forum (WEF), Geneva, Switzerland, 18 pp., https://www.weforum.org/whitepapers/eight-futures-of-work-scenarios-and-their-implications (Accessed November 22, 2019).

World Meteorological Organization, 2018: *Scientific Assessment of Ozone Depletion: 2018 - Executive Summary*. Global Ozo. World Meteorological Organization (WMO), Geneva, Switzerland, 67 pp.

Wright, J.G., T. Bischof-Niemz, J.R. Calitz, C. Mushwana, and R. van Heerden, 2019: Long-term electricity sector expansion planning: A unique opportunity for a least cost energy transition in South Africa. *Renew. Energy Focus*, **30** (September), 21–45, doi:10.1016/j.ref.2019.02.005.

Wu, R., H. Dai, Y. Geng, Y. Xie, and X. Tian, 2019: Impacts of export restructuring on national economy and CO_2 emissions: A general equilibrium analysis for China. *Appl. Energy*, **248**, 64–78, doi:10.1016/j.apenergy.2019.04.024.

Prognos, Öko-Institut, Wuppertal-Institut., 2021: *Klimaneutrales Deutschland 2045. Wie Deutschland seine Klimaziele schon vor 2050 erreichen kann Zusammenfassung im Auftrag von Stiftung Klimaneutralität, Agora Energiewende und Agora Verkehrswende* Prognos AG, Berlin, Germany, Öko-Institut e. V., Berlin, Germany, and Wuppertal Institut für Klima, Umwelt, 31 pp., https://static.agora-energiewende.de/fileadmin/Projekte/2021/2021_04_KNDE45/A-EW_209_KNDE2045_Zusammenfassung_DE_WEB.pdf (Accessed October 18, 2021).

Wylie, L., A.E. Sutton-Grier, and A. Moore, 2016: Keys to successful blue carbon projects: Lessons learned from global case studies. *Mar. Policy*, **65**, 76–84, doi:10.1016/j.marpol.2015.12.020.

Xiao, L. and R. Zhao, 2017: China's new era of ecological civilization. *Science*, **358(6366)**, 1008–1009, doi:10.1126/science.aar3760.

Xu, Y. and V. Ramanathan, 2017: Well below 2°C: Mitigation strategies for avoiding dangerous to catastrophic climate changes. *Proc. Natl. Acad. Sci.*, **114(39)**, 10315–10323, doi:10.1073/pnas.1618481114.

Xunzhang, P., C. Wenying, L.E. Clarke, W. Lining, and L. Guannan, 2017: China's energy system transformation towards the 2°C goal: Implications of different effort-sharing principles. *Energy Policy*, **103**, 116–126, doi:10.1016/j.enpol.2017.01.020.

Yang, X., J. Pang, F. Teng, R. Gong, and C. Springer, 2021: The environmental co-benefit and economic impact of China's low-carbon pathways: Evidence from linking bottom-up and top-down models. *Renew. Sustain. Energy Rev.*, **136**, 110438, doi:10.1016/J.RSER.2020.110438.

Yeo, S., 2019: Where climate cash is flowing and why it's not enough. *Nature*, **573(7774)**, 328–331, doi:10.1038/d41586-019-02712-3.

Young, J. and M. Brans, 2017: Analysis of factors affecting a shift in a local energy system towards a 100% renewable energy community. *J. Clean. Prod.*, **169**, 117–124, doi:10.1016/j.jclepro.2017.08.023.

Zadek, S. and N. Robins, 2016: *Financing sustainable development: Moving from momentum to transformation in a time of turmoil*, : United Nations Environmental Program, New York, USA https://www.un.org/pga/71/wp-content/uploads/sites/40/2017/02/Financing-Sustainable-Development-in-a-time-of-turmoil.pdf (Accessed November 1, 2021).

Zappa, W., M. Junginger, and M. van den Broek, 2019: Is a 100% renewable European power system feasible by 2050? *Appl. Energy*, **233–234** (August 2018), 1027–1050, doi:10.1016/j.apenergy.2018.08.109.

Zauberman, G., B.K. Kim, S.A. Malkoc, and J.R. Bettman, 2009: Discounting time and time discounting: Subjective time perception and intertemporal preferences. *J. Mark. Res.*, **46(4)**, 543–556, doi:10.1509/jmkr.46.4.543.

Zevallos, P., T.P. Takahashi, M.P. Cigaran, and K. Coetzee, 2014: Mitigation Action in Peru: A case study for energy efficiency. *Clim. Dev.*, **6(sup1)**, 43–48, doi: 10.1080/17565529.2013.867251.

Zhang, H.-B., H.-C. Dai, H.-X. Lai, and W.-T. Wang, 2017: US withdrawal from the Paris Agreement: Reasons, impacts, and China's response. *Adv. Clim. Chang. Res.*, **8(4)**, 220–225, doi:10.1016/j.accre.2017.09.002.

Zhao, Y. et al., 2018: Scenario analysis of the carbon pricing policy in China's power sector through 2050: Based on an improved CGE model. *Ecol. Indic.*, **85**, 352–366, doi:10.1016/J.ECOLIND.2017.10.028.

Zhou, N. et al., 2019: A roadmap for China to peak carbon dioxide emissions and achieve a 20% share of non-fossil fuels in primary energy by 2030. *Appl. Energy*, **239** (December 2018), 793–819, doi:10.1016/j.apenergy.2019.01.154.

Zou, J. et al., 2016: *Pursuing an innovative development pathway: Understanding China's NDC*. National Center for Climate Change Strategy and International Cooperation (NCSC) and Partnership for Market Readiness (PMR), Beijing and Washington, DC, http://documents.worldbank.org/curated/en/312771480392483509/pdf/110555-WP-FINAL-PMR-China-Country-Paper-Digital-v1-PUBLIC-ABSTRACT-SENT.pdf.

4

5

Demand, Services and Social Aspects of Mitigation

Coordinating Lead Authors:
Felix Creutzig (Germany), Joyashree Roy (India/Thailand)

Lead Authors:
Patrick Devine-Wright (United Kingdom/Ireland), Julio Díaz-José (Mexico), Frank W. Geels (United Kingdom/the Netherlands), Arnulf Grubler (Austria), Nadia Maïzi (France/Algeria), Eric Masanet (the United States of America), Yacob Mulugetta (Ethiopia/United Kingdom), Chioma Daisy Onyige (Nigeria), Patricia E. Perkins (Canada), Alessandro Sanches-Pereira (Brazil), Elke Ursula Weber (the United States of America)

Contributing Authors:
Jordana Composto (the United States of America), Anteneh Getnet Dagnachew (the Netherlands/Ethiopia), Nandini Das (India), Robert Frank (the United States of America), Bipashyee Ghosh (India/United Kingdom), Niko Heeren (Switzerland/Norway), Linus Mattauch (Germany/United Kingdom), Josephine Mylan (United Kingdom), Gregory F. Nemet (the United States of America/Canada), Mani Nepal (Nepal), Leila Niamir (Iran/Germany), Nick Pidgeon (United Kingdom), Narasimha D. Rao (the United States of America), Lucia A. Reisch (United Kingdom), Julia Steinberger (Switzerland/United Kingdom), Linda Steg (the Netherlands), Cass R. Sunstein (the United States of America), Charlie Wilson (United Kingdom), Caroline Zimm (Austria)

Review Editors:
Nicholas Eyre (United Kingdom), Can Wang (China)

Chapter Scientists:
Nandini Das (India), Leila Niamir (Iran/Germany)

This chapter should be cited as:
Creutzig, F., J. Roy, P. Devine-Wright, J. Díaz-José, F.W. Geels, A. Grubler, N. Maïzi, E. Masanet, Y. Mulugetta, C.D. Onyige, P.E. Perkins, A. Sanches-Pereira, E.U. Weber, 2022: Demand, services and social aspects of mitigation. In IPCC, 2022: *Climate Change 2022: Mitigation of Climate Change. Contribution of Working Group III to the Sixth Assessment Report of the Intergovernmental Panel on Climate Change* [P.R. Shukla, J. Skea, R. Slade, A. Al Khourdajie, R. van Diemen, D. McCollum, M. Pathak, S. Some, P. Vyas, R. Fradera, M. Belkacemi, A. Hasija, G. Lisboa, S. Luz, J. Malley, (eds.)]. Cambridge University Press, Cambridge, UK and New York, NY, USA. doi: 10.1017/9781009157926.007.

Table of Contents

5

Executive Summary

Assessment of the social science literature and regional case studies reveals how social norms, culture, and individual choices interact with infrastructure and other structural changes over time. This provides new insight into climate change mitigation strategies, and how economic and social activity might be organised across sectors to support emission reductions. To enhance well-being, people demand services and not primary energy and physical resources *per se*. Focusing on demand for services and the different social and political roles people play broadens the participation in climate action.

Potential of Demand-side Actions and Service Provisioning Systems

Demand-side mitigation and new ways of providing services can help *avoid*, *shift*, and *improve* final service demand. Rapid and deep changes in demand make it easier for every sector to reduce greenhouse gas (GHG) emissions in the short and medium term (*high confidence*). {5.2, 5.3}

The indicative potential of demand-side strategies to reduce emissions of direct and indirect CO_2 and non-CO_2 GHG emissions in three end-use sectors (buildings, land transport, and food) is 40–70% globally by 2050 (*high confidence*). Technical mitigation potentials compared to the 2050 emissions projection of two scenarios consistent with policies announced by national governments until 2020 amount to 6.8 $GtCO_2$ for building use and construction, 4.6 $GtCO_2$ for land transport and 8.0 $GtCO_2$-eq for food demand, and amount to 4.4 $GtCO_2$ for industry. Mitigation strategies can be classified as Avoid-Shift-Improve (ASI) options, that reflect opportunities for socio-cultural, infrastructural, and technological change. The greatest 'Avoid' potential comes from reducing long-haul aviation and providing short-distance low-carbon urban infrastructures. The greatest 'Shift' potential would come from switching to plant-based diets. The greatest 'Improve' potential comes from within the building sector, and in particular increased use of energy-efficient end-use technologies and passive housing. {5.3.1, 5.3.2, Figure 5.7, Figure 5.8, Table 5.1, Chapter 5 Supplementary Material II, Table 5.SM.2}

Socio-cultural and lifestyle changes can accelerate climate change mitigation (*medium confidence*). Among 60 identified actions that could change individual consumption, individual mobility choices have the largest potential to reduce carbon footprints. Prioritising car-free mobility by walking and cycling and adoption of electric mobility could save 2 tCO_2-eq cap^{-1} yr^{-1}. Other options with high mitigation potential include reducing air travel, heating and cooling set-point adjustments, reduced appliance use, shifts to public transit, and shifting consumption towards plant-based diets. {5.3.1, 5.3.1.2, Figure 5.8}

Leveraging improvements in end-use service delivery through behavioural and technological innovations, and innovations in market organisation, leads to large reductions in upstream resource use (*high confidence*). Analysis of indicative potentials range from a factor 10- to 20-fold improvement in the case of available energy (exergy) analysis, with the highest improvement potentials at the end-user and service-provisioning levels. Realisable service-level efficiency improvements could reduce upstream energy demand by 45% in 2050. {5.3.2, Figure 5.10}

Alternative service provision systems, for example those enabled through digitalisation, sharing economy initiatives and circular economy initiatives, have to date made a limited contribution to climate change mitigation (*medium confidence*). While digitalisation through specific new products and applications holds potential for improvement in service-level efficiencies, without public policies and regulations, it also has the potential to increase consumption and energy use. Reducing the energy use of data centres, networks, and connected devices is possible in managing low-carbon digitalisation. Claims on the benefits of the circular economy for sustainability and climate change mitigation have limited evidence. {5.3.4, 5.3.4.1, 5.3.4.2, Figure 5.12, Figure 5.13}

Social Aspects of Demand-side Mitigation Actions

***Decent living standards and well-being* for all are achievable through the implementation of high-efficiency low demand mitigation pathways (*medium confidence*).** Decent living standards (DLS) – a benchmark of minimum material conditions for human well-being – overlaps with many Sustainable Development Goals (SDGs). Minimum requirements of energy use consistent with enabling well-being for all is between 20 and 50 GJ per person per year (cap^{-1} yr^{-1}) depending on the context. {5.2.2.1, 5.2.2.2, Box 5.3}

Providing better services with less energy and resource input has high technical potential and is consistent with providing well-being for all (*medium confidence*). Assessment of 19 demand-side mitigation options and 18 different constituents of well-being show that positive impacts on well-being outweigh negative ones by a factor of 11. {5.2, 5.2.3, Figure 5.6}

Demand-side mitigation options bring multiple interacting benefits (*high confidence*). Energy services to meet human needs for nutrition, shelter, health, and so on are met in many different ways, with different emissions implications that depend on local contexts, cultures, geography, available technologies, and social preferences. In the near term, many less-developed countries and poor people everywhere require better access to safe and low-emissions energy sources to ensure decent living standards and increase energy savings from service improvements by about 20–25%. {5.2, 5.4.5, Figure 5.3, Figure 5.4, Figure 5.5, Figure 5.6, Box 5.2, Box 5.3}

Granular technologies and decentralised energy end use, characterised by modularity, small unit sizes and small unit costs, diffuse faster into markets and are associated with faster technological learning benefits, greater efficiency, more opportunities to escape technological lock-in, and greater employment (*high confidence*). Examples include solar photovoltaic systems, batteries, and thermal heat pumps. {5.3, 5.5, 5.5.3}

Wealthy individuals contribute disproportionately to higher emissions and have a high potential for emissions reductions

while maintaining decent living standards and well-being (*high confidence*). Individuals with high socio-economic status are capable of reducing their GHG emissions by becoming role models of low-carbon lifestyles, investing in low-carbon businesses, and advocating for stringent climate policies. {5.4.1, 5.4.3, 5.4.4, Figure 5.14}

Demand-side solutions require both motivation and capacity for change (*high confidence*). Motivation by individuals or households worldwide to change energy consumption behaviour is generally low. Individual behavioural change is insufficient for climate change mitigation unless embedded in structural and cultural change. Different factors influence individual motivation and capacity for change in different demographics and geographies. These factors go beyond traditional socio-demographic and economic predictors and include psychological variables such as awareness, perceived risk, subjective and social norms, values, and perceived behavioural control. Behavioural nudges promote easy behaviour change, for example 'Improve' actions such as making investments in energy efficiency, but fail to motivate harder lifestyle changes (*high confidence*). {5.4}

Meta-analyses demonstrate that behavioural interventions, including the way choices are presented to consumers,[1] work synergistically with price signals, making the combination more effective (*medium confidence*). Behavioural interventions through nudges, and alternative ways of redesigning and motivating decisions, alone provide small to medium contributions to reduce energy consumption and GHG emissions. Green defaults, such as automatic enrolment in 'green energy' provision, are highly effective. Judicious labelling, framing, and communication of social norms can also increase the effect of mandates, subsidies, or taxes. {5.4, 5.4.1, Table 5.3a, Table 5.3b}

Coordinated change in several domains leads to the emergence of new low-carbon configurations with cascading mitigation effects (*high confidence*). Demand-side transitions involve interacting and sometimes antagonistic processes on the behavioural, socio-cultural, institutional, business, and technological dimensions. Individual- or sectoral-level change may be stymied by reinforcing social, infrastructural, and cultural lock-ins. Coordinating the way choices are presented to end users and planners, physical infrastructures, new technologies and related business models can rapidly realise system-level change. {5.4.2, 5.4.3, 5.4.4, 5.4.5, 5.5}

Cultural change, in combination with new or adapted infrastructure, is necessary to enable and realise many 'Avoid' and 'Shift' options (*medium confidence*). By drawing support from diverse actors, narratives of change can enable coalitions to form, providing the basis for social movements to campaign in favour of (or against) societal transformations. People act and contribute to climate change mitigation in their diverse capacities as consumers, citizens, professionals, role models, investors, and policymakers. {5.4, 5.5, 5.6}

Collective action as part of social or lifestyle movements underpins system change (*high confidence*). Collective action and social organising are crucial to shift the possibility space of public policy on climate change mitigation. For example, climate strikes have given voice to youth in more than 180 countries. In other instances, mitigation policies allow the active participation of all stakeholders, resulting in building social trust, new coalitions, legitimising change, and thus initiate a positive cycle in climate governance capacity and policies. {5.4.2, Figure 5.14}

Transition pathways and changes in social norms often start with pilot experiments led by dedicated individuals and niche groups (*high confidence*). Collectively, such initiatives can find entry points to prompt policy, infrastructure, and policy reconfigurations, supporting the further uptake of technological and lifestyle innovations. Individuals' agency is central as social change agents and narrators of meaning. These bottom-up socio-cultural forces catalyse a supportive policy environment, which enables changes. {5.5.2}

The current effects of climate change, as well as some mitigation strategies, are threatening the viability of existing business practices, while some corporate efforts also delay mitigation action (*medium confidence*). Policy packages that include job creation programmes help to preserve social trust, livelihoods, respect, and dignity of all workers and employees involved. Business models that protect rent-extracting behaviour may sometimes delay political action. Corporate advertisement and marketing strategies may also attempt to deflect corporate responsibility to individuals or aim to appropriate climate care sentiments in their own brand building. {5.4.3, 5.6.4}

Middle actors – professionals, experts, and regulators – play a crucial, albeit underestimated and underutilised, role in establishing low-carbon standards and practices (*medium confidence*). Building managers, landlords, energy efficiency advisers, technology installers, and car dealers influence patterns of mobility and energy consumption by acting as middle actors or intermediaries in the provision of building or mobility services and need greater capacity and motivation to play this role. {5.4.3}

Social influencers and thought leaders can increase the adoption of low-carbon technologies, behaviours, and lifestyles (*high confidence*). Preferences are malleable and can align with a cultural shift. The modelling of such shifts by salient and respected community members can help bring about changes in different service provisioning systems. Between 10% and 30% of committed individuals are required to set new social norms. {5.2.1, 5.4}

Preconditions and Instruments to Enable Demand-side Transformation

Social equity reinforces capacity and motivation for mitigating climate change (*medium confidence*). Impartial governance

---

[1] The way choices are presented to consumers is known as 'choice architecture' in the field of behavioural economics.

such as fair treatment by law and order institutions, fair treatment by gender, and income equity, increases social trust, thus enabling demand-side climate policies. High status (often high carbon) item consumption may be reduced by taxing absolute wealth without compromising well-being. {5.2, 5.4.2, 5.6}

Policies that increase the political access and participation of women, racialised, and marginalised groups increase the democratic impetus for climate action (*high confidence*). Including more differently situated knowledge and diverse perspectives makes climate mitigation policies more effective. {5.2, 5.6}

Carbon pricing is most effective if revenues are redistributed or used impartially (*high confidence*). A carbon levy earmarked for green infrastructures or saliently returned to taxpayers corresponding to widely accepted notions of fairness increases the political acceptability of carbon pricing. {5.6, Box 5.11}

Greater contextualisation and granularity in policy approaches better addresses the challenges of rapid transitions towards zero-carbon systems (*high confidence*). Larger systems take more time to evolve, grow, and change compared to smaller ones. Creating and scaling up entirely new systems takes longer than replacing existing technologies and practices. Late adopters tend to adopt faster than early pioneers. Obstacles and feasibility barriers are high in the early transition phases. Barriers decrease as a result of technical and social learning processes, network building, scale economies, cultural debates, and institutional adjustments. {5.5, 5.6}

The lockdowns implemented in many countries in response to the COVID-19 pandemic demonstrated that behavioural change at a massive scale and in a short time is possible (*high confidence*). COVID-19 accelerated some specific trends, such as increased uptake of urban cycling. However, the acceptability of collective social change over a longer term towards less resource-intensive lifestyles depends on social mandate building through public participation, discussion and debate over information provided by experts, to produce recommendations that inform policymaking. {Box 5.2}

Mitigation policies that integrate and communicate with the values people hold are more successful (*high confidence*). Values differ between cultures. Measures that support autonomy, energy security and safety, equity and environmental protection, and fairness resonate well in many communities and social groups. Changing from a commercialised, individualised, entrepreneurial training model to an education cognisant of planetary health and human well-being can accelerate climate change awareness and action. {5.4.1, 5.4.2}

Changes in consumption choices that are supported by structural changes and political action enable the uptake of low-carbon choices (*high confidence*). Policy instruments applied in coordination can help to accelerate change in a consistent desired direction. Targeted technological change, regulation, and public policy can help in steering digitalisation, the sharing economy, and circular economy towards climate change mitigation. {5.3, 5.6}

Complementarity in policies helps in the design of an optimal demand-side policy mix (*medium confidence*). In the case of energy efficiency, for example, this may involve CO_2 pricing, standards and norms, and information feedback. {5.3, 5.4, 5.6}

5.1   Introduction

The *Sixth Assessment Report* of the IPCC (AR6), for the first time, features a chapter on demand, services, and social aspects of mitigation. It builds on the AR4 and AR5, which linked behaviour and lifestyle change to mitigating climate change (IPCC 2007; Roy and Pal 2009; IPCC 2014a), the Global Energy Assessment (Roy et al. 2012), and the AR5, which identified sectoral demand-side mitigation options across chapters (IPCC 2014a; IPCC 2014b; Creutzig et al. 2016b). The literature on the nature, scale, implementation and implications of demand-side solutions, and associated changes in lifestyles, social norms, and well-being, has been growing rapidly (Creutzig et al. 2021a) (Box 5.2). Demand-side solutions support near-term climate change mitigation (Méjean et al. 2019; Wachsmuth and Duscha 2019) and include consumers' technology choices, behaviours, lifestyle changes, coupled with production-consumption infrastructures and systems, service provision strategies, and associated socio-technical transitions. This chapter's assessment of the social sciences (also see Chapter 5 Supplementary Material I) reveals that social dynamics at different levels offer diverse entry points for acting on and mitigating climate change (Jorgenson et al. 2018).

Three entry points are relevant for this chapter. First, well-designed demand for services scenarios are consistent with adequate levels of well-being for everyone (Rao and Baer 2012; Grubler et al. 2018; Mastrucci et al. 2020; Millward-Hopkins et al. 2020), with high and/or improved quality of life (Max-Neef 1995), improved levels of happiness (Easterlin et al. 2010) and sustainable human development (Arrow et al. 2013; Dasgupta and Dasgupta 2017).

Second, demand-side solutions support staying within planetary boundaries (Haberl et al. 2014; Matson et al. 2016; Hillebrand et al. 2018; Andersen and Quinn 2020; UNDESA 2020; Hickel et al. 2021; Keyßer and Lenzen 2021). Demand side solutions entail fewer environmental risks than many supply-side technologies (Von Stechow et al. 2016). Additionally they make carbon dioxide removal technologies, such as bioenergy with carbon capture and storage (BECCS) less relevant (Van Vuuren et al. 2018) but modelling studies (Grubler et al. 2018; Hickel et al. 2021; Keyßer and Lenzen 2021) still require ecosystem-based carbon dioxide removal. In the IPCC's Special Report on Global Warming of 1.5°C (SR1.5) (IPCC 2018), four stylised scenarios have explored possible pathways towards stabilising global warming at 1.5°C (IPCC 2014a, Figure SPM.3a) (Figure 5.1) One of these scenarios, LED-19, investigates the scope of demand-side solutions (Figure 5.1). The comparison of scenarios reveals that such low energy demand pathways eliminate the need for technologies with high uncertainty, such as BECCS. Third, interrogating demand for services from the well-being perspective also opens new avenues for assessing mitigation potentials (Brand-Correa and Steinberger 2017; Mastrucci and Rao 2017; Rao and Min 2018a; Mastrucci and Rao 2019; Baltruszewicz et al. 2021). Arguably, demand-side interventions often operate institutionally or in terms of restoring natural functioning and have so far been politically sidelined but COVID-19 revealed interesting perspectives (Box 5.2). Such demand-side solutions also support near-term goals towards climate change mitigation and reduce the need for politically challenging high global carbon prices (Méjean et al. 2019) (Box 5.11). The well-being focus

emphasises equity and universal need satisfaction, compatible with progress towards meeting the Sustainable Development Goals (SDGs) (Lamb and Steinberger 2017).

The requisites for well-being include collective and social interactions as well as consumption-based material inputs. Moreover, rather than material inputs *per se*, people need and demand services for dignified survival, sustenance, mobility, communication, comfort and material well-being (Nakićenović et al. 1996b; Johansson et al. 2012; Creutzig et al. 2018). These services may be provided in many different context-specific ways using physical resources (biomass, energy, materials, etc.) and available technologies (e.g., cooking tools, appliances). Here we understand demand as demand for services (often requiring material input), with particular focus on services that are required for well-being (such as lighting, accessibility, shelter, etc.), and that are shaped by culturally and geographically differentiated social aspects, choice architectures and the built environment (infrastructures).

Focusing on demand for services broadens the climate solution space beyond technological switches confined to the supply side, to include solutions that maintain or improve well-being related to nutrition, shelter and mobility while (sometimes radically) reducing energy and material input levels (Creutzig et al. 2018; Cervantes Barron 2020; Baltruszewicz et al. 2021; Kikstra et al. 2021b). This also recognises that mitigation policies are politically, economically and socially more feasible, as well as more effective, when there is a two-way alignment between climate action and well-being (OECD 2019a). There is *medium evidence* and *high agreement* that well-designed demand for services scenarios are consistent with adequate levels of well-being for everyone (Rao and Baer 2012; Grubler et al. 2018; Rao et al. 2019b; Millward-Hopkins et al. 2020; Kikstra et al. 2021b), with high and/or improved quality of life (Max-Neef 1995; Vogel et al. 2021) and improved levels of happiness (Easterlin et al. 2010) and sustainable human development (Gadrey and Jany-Catrice 2006; Arrow et al. 2013; Dasgupta and Dasgupta 2017). While demand for services is high as development levels increase, and related emissions are growing in many countries (Yumashev et al. 2020; Bamisile et al. 2021), there is also evidence that provisioning systems delink services provided from emissions (Conte Grand 2016; Patra et al. 2017; Kavitha et al. 2020). Various mitigation strategies, often classified into Avoid-Shift-Improve (ASI) options, effectively reduce primary energy demand and/or material input (Haas et al. 2015; Haberl et al. 2017; Samadi et al. 2017; Hausknost et al. 2018; Haberl et al. 2019; Van den Berg et al. 2019; Ivanova et al. 2020). Users' participation in decisions about how services are provided, not just their technological feasibility, is an important determinant of their effectiveness and sustainability (Whittle et al. 2019; Vanegas Cantarero 2020).

Sector-specific mitigation approaches (Chapters 6–11) emphasise the potential of mitigation via improvements in energy- and materials-efficient manufacturing (Gutowski et al. 2013; Gramkow and Anger-Kraavi 2019; Olatunji et al. 2019; Wang et al. 2019), new product design (Fischedick et al. 2014), energy-efficient buildings (Lucon et al. 2014), shifts in diet (Bajželj et al. 2014; Smith et al. 2014), transport infrastructure design (Sims et al. 2014), and compact urban forms (Seto et al. 2014). In this chapter, service-related mitigation strategies are categorised as 'Avoid', 'Shift', or 'Improve' options to

5

show how mitigation potentials, and social groups who can deliver them, are much broader than usually considered in traditional sector-specific presentations. ASI originally arose from the need to assess the staging and combinations of inter-related mitigation options in the provision of transportation services (Hidalgo and Huizenga 2013). In the context of transportation services, ASI seeks to mitigate emissions through *avoiding* as much transport service demand as possible (e.g., through telework to eliminate commutes, mixed-use urban zoning to shorten commute distances), *shifting* remaining demand to more efficient modes (e.g., bus rapid transit replacing passenger vehicles), and *improving* the carbon intensity of modes utilised (e.g., electric buses powered by renewables) (Creutzig et al. 2016a). This chapter summarises ASI options and potentials across sectors and generalises the definitions. 'Avoid' refers to all mitigation options that reduce unnecessary (in the sense of being not required to deliver the desired service output) energy consumption by redesigning service provisioning systems; 'Shift' refers to the switch to already existing competitive efficient technologies and service provisioning systems; and 'Improve' refers to improvements in efficiency in existing technologies. The Avoid-Shift-Improve framing operates in three domains: Socio-cultural, where social norms, culture, and individual choices play an important role – a category especially, but not only, relevant for 'Avoid' options; Infrastructure, which provides the cost and benefit landscape for realising options and is particularly relevant for 'Shift' options; and Technologies, especially important for the 'Improve' options.

'Avoid', 'Shift', and 'Improve' choices will be made by individuals and households, instigated by salient and respected role models and novel social norms, but will require support by adequate infrastructures designed by urban planners and building and transport professionals, corresponding investments, and a political culture supportive of mitigation action. This is particularly true for many 'Avoid' and 'Shift' decisions that are difficult because they encounter psychological barriers of breaking routines, habits and imagining new lifestyles and the social costs of not conforming to society (Kaiser 2006). Simpler 'Improve' decisions like energy efficiency investments, on the other hand, can be triggered and sustained by traditional policy instruments, complemented by behavioural nudges.

A key concern about climate change mitigation policies is that they may reduce quality of life. Based on growing literature, in this chapter we adopt the concept of decent living standards (DLS, explained further in relation to other individual and collective well-being measures and concepts in the Social Science Primer, Chapter 5 Supplementary Material I) as a universal set of service requirements essential for achieving basic human well-being. DLS includes the dimensions of nutrition, shelter, living condition, clothing, health care, education, and mobility (Frye et al. 2018; Rao and Min 2018b). DLS provides a fair, direct way to understand the basic low-carbon energy needs of society and specifies the underlying minimum material and energy requirements. This chapter also comprehensively assesses related well-being metrics that result from demand-side action, observing overall positive effects (Section 5.3). Similarly, ambitious low-emissions demand-side scenarios suggest that well-being could be maintained or improved while reducing global final energy demand, and some current literature estimates that it is possible to meet decent living standards for all within the 2°C warming window (Grubler et al. 2018; Burke 2020; Keyßer and Lenzen 2021) (Section 5.4). A key concern here is how to blend new technologies

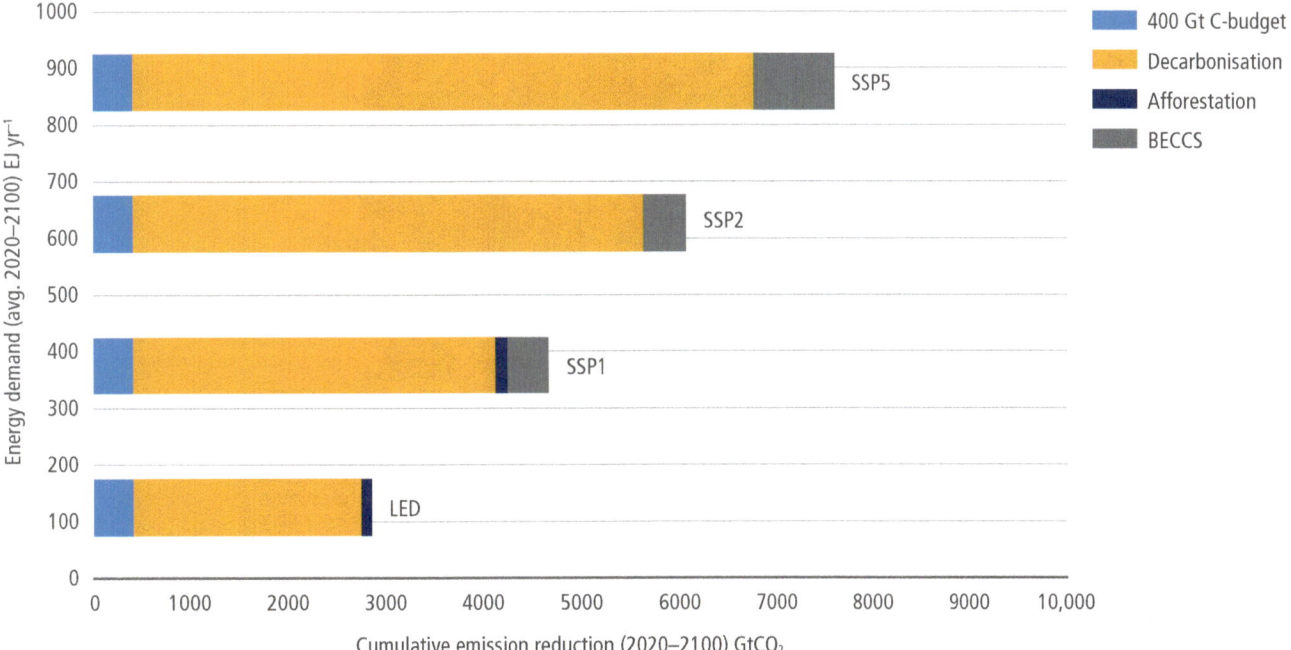

Figure 5.1 | Low Energy Demand Scenario needs no BECCS and needs less decarbonisation effort. Dependence of the size of the mitigation effort to reach a 1.5°C climate target (cumulative GtCO$_2$ emission reduction 2020–2100 by option) as a function of the level of energy demand (average global final energy demand 2020–2100 in EJ yr^{-1}) in baseline and corresponding 1.5°C scenarios (1.9 W m^{-2} radiative forcing change) based on the IPCC Special Report on Global Warming of 1.5°C (data obtained from the Scenario Explorer database, LED baseline emission data obtained from authors). In this figure an example of remaining carbon budget of 400 Gt has been taken from Rogelj et al. (2019) for illustrative purposes. 400 Gt is also the number given in Table SPM.2 (IPCC 2021, p. 29) for a probability of 67% to limit global warming to 1.5°C.

with social change to integrate Improving ways of living, Shifting modalities and Avoiding certain kinds of emissions altogether (Section 5.6).

Social practice theory emphasises that material stocks and social relations are key in forming and maintaining habits (Reckwitz 2002; Haberl et al. 2021). This chapter reflects these insights by assessing the role of infrastructures and social norms in GHG emission-intensive or low-carbon lifestyles (Section 5.4).

A core operational principle for sustainable development is equitable access to services to provide well-being for all, while minimising resource inputs and environmental and social externalities/trade-offs, underpinning the Sustainable Development Goals (Princen 2003; Lamb and Steinberger 2017; Dasgupta and Dasgupta 2017). Sustainable development is not possible without changes in

consumption patterns within the widely recognised constraints of planetary boundaries, resource availability, and the need to provide decent living standards for all (Langhelle 2000; Toth and Szigeti 2016; O'Neill et al. 2018). Inversely, reduced poverty and higher social equity offer opportunities for delinking demand for services from emissions, for example via more long-term decision-making after having escaped poverty traps and by reduced demand for non-well-being-enhancing status consumption (Nabi et al. 2020; Ortega-Ruiz et al. 2020; Parker and Bhatti 2020; Teame and Habte 2020) (Section 5.3).

Throughout this chapter we discuss how people can realise various opportunities to reduce GHG emission-intensive consumption (Sections 5.2 and 5.3), and act in various roles (Section 5.4), within an enabling environment created by policy instruments and infrastructure that build on social dynamics (Section 5.6).

Box 5.1 | Bibliometric Foundation of Demand-side Climate Change Mitigation

A bibliometric overview of the literature found 99,065 academic peer-reviewed papers identified with 34 distinct search queries addressing relevant content of this chapter (Creutzig et al. 2021a). The literature is growing rapidly (15% yr^{-1}) and the literature body assessed in the AR6 period (2014–2020) is twice as large as all literature published before.

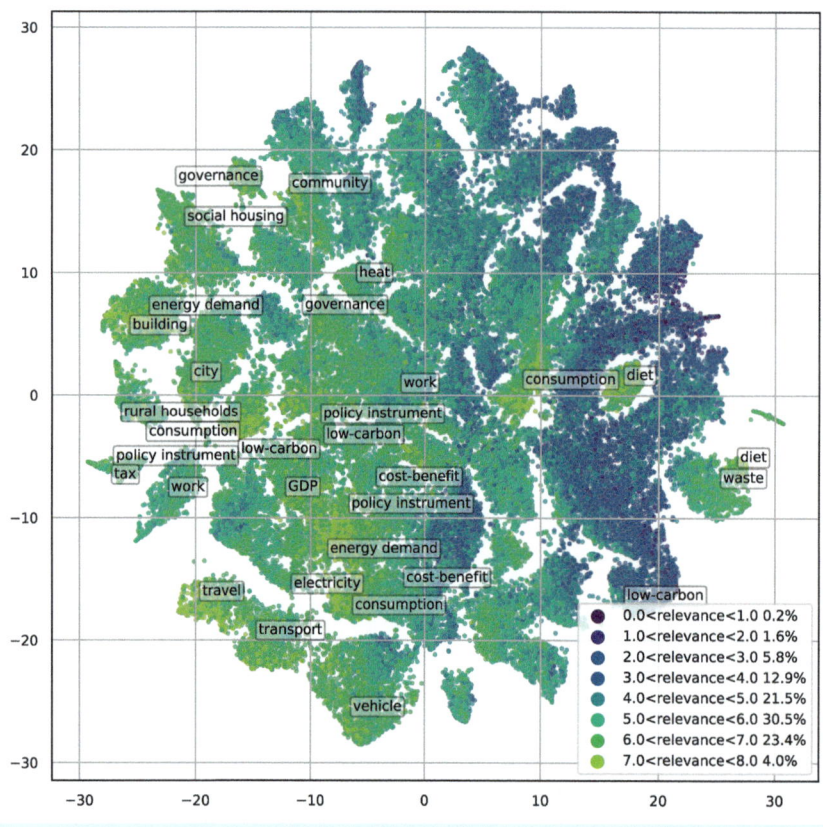

Box 5.1, Figure 1 | Map of the literature on demand, services and social aspects of climate change mitigation. Dots show document positions obtained by reducing the 60-dimensional topic scores to two dimensions aiming to preserve similarity in overall topic score. The two axes therefore have no direct interpretation but represent a reduced version of similarities between documents across 60 topics. Documents are coloured by query category. Topic labels of the 24 most relevant topics are placed in the centre of each of the large clusters of documents associated with each topic. % value in caption indicates the proportion of studies in each 'relevance' bracket. Source: reused with permission from Creutzig et al. (2021a).

Box 5.1 (continued)

A large part of the literature is highly repetitive and/or includes no concepts or little quantitative or qualitative data of relevance to this chapter. For example, a systematic review on economic growth and decoupling identified more than 11,500 papers treating this topic, but only 834 of those, that is, 7%, included relevant data (Wiedenhofer et al. 2020). In another systematic review, assessing quantitative estimates of consumption-based solutions (Ivanova et al. 2020), only 0.8% of papers were considered after consistency criteria were enforced. Altogether, we relied on systematic reviews wherever possible. Other important papers were not captured by systematic reviews but are included in this chapter through expert judgement. Based on topical modelling and relevance coding of resulting topics, the full literature body can be mapped into two dimensions, where spatial relationships indicate topical distance (Box 5.1, Figure 1). The interpretation of topics demonstrates that the literature organises in four clusters of high relevance for demand-side solutions (housing, mobility, food, and policy), whereas other clusters (nature, energy supply) are relatively less relevant.

Section 5.2 provides evidence on the links among mitigation and well-being, services, equity, trust, and governance. Section 5.3 quantifies the demand-side opportunity space for mitigation, relying on the Avoid-Shift-Improve framework. Section 5.4 assesses the relevant contribution of different parts of society to climate change mitigation. Section 5.5 evaluates the overall dynamics of social transition processes while Section 5.6 summarises insights on governance and policy packages for demand-side mitigation and well-being. A Social Science Primer (Chapter 5 Supplementary Material I) defines and discusses key terms and social science concepts used in the context of climate change mitigation.

Box 5.2 | COVID-19, Service Provisioning and Climate Change Mitigation

There is now *high evidence* and *high agreement* that the COVID-19 pandemic has increased the political feasibility of large-scale government actions to support the services for provision of public goods, including climate change policies. Many behavioural changes due to COVID-19 reinforce sufficiency and emphasis on solidarity, economies built around care, livelihood protection, collective action, and basic service provision, linked to reduced emissions.

COVID-19 led to direct and indirect health, economic, and confinement-induced hardships and suffering, mostly for the poor, and reset habits and everyday behaviours of the well-off too, enabling a reflection on the basic needs for a good life. Although COVID-19 and climate change pose different kinds of threats and therefore elicit different policies, there are several lessons from COVID-19 for advancing climate change mitigation (Klenert et al. 2020; Manzanedo and Manning 2020; Stark 2020). Both crises are global in scale, requiring holistic societal response; governments can act rapidly, and delay in action is costly (Bouman et al. 2020a; Klenert et al. 2020). The pandemic highlighted the role of individuals in collective action and many people felt morally compelled and responsible to act for others (Budd and Ison, 2020). COVID-19 also taught the effectiveness of rapid collective action (physical distancing, wearing masks, etc.) as contributions to the public good. The messaging about social distancing, wearing masks and handwashing during the pandemic called attention to the importance of effective public information (e.g., also about reducing personal carbon footprints), recognising that rapid pro-social responses are driven by personal and socio-cultural norms (Bouman et al. 2020a; Sovacool et al. 2020a). In contrast, low trust in public authorities impairs the effectiveness of policies and polarises society (Bavel et al. 2020; Hornsey 2020).

During the shutdown, emissions declined relatively most in aviation, and absolutely most in car transport (Le Quéré et al. 2020, Sarkis et al. 2020), and there were disproportionally strong reductions in GHG emissions from coal (Bertram et al. 2021) (Chapter 2). At their peak, CO_2 emissions in individual countries decreased by 17% on average (Le Quéré et al. 2020). Global energy demand was projected to drop by 5% in 2020, energy-related CO_2 emissions by 7%, and energy investment by 18% (IEA 2020a). COVID-19 shock and recovery scenarios project final energy demand reductions of 1–36 EJyr^{-1} by 2025 and cumulative CO_2 emission reductions of 14–45 GtCO_2 by 2030 (Kikstra et al. 2021a). Plastics use and waste generation increased during the pandemic (Klemeš et al. 2020; Prata et al. 2020). Responses to COVID-19 had important connections with energy demand and GHG emissions due to quarantine and travel restrictions (Sovacool et al. 2020a). Reductions in mobility and economic activity reduced energy use in sectors such as industry and transport, but increased energy use in the residential sector (Diffenbaugh et al. 2020). COVID-19 induced behavioural changes that may translate into new habits, some beneficial and some harmful for climate change mitigation. New digitally-enabled service accessibility patterns (videoconferencing, telecommuting) played an important role in sustaining various service needs while avoiding demand for individual mobility. However, public transit lost customers to cars, personalised two wheelers, walking and cycling, while suburban and rural living gained popularity, possibly with long-term consequences. Reduced air travel, pressures for more localised

Box 5.2 (continued)

food and manufacturing supply chains (Hobbs 2020; Nandi et al. 2020; Quayson et al. 2020), and governments' revealed willingness to make large-scale interventions in the economy also reflect sudden shifts in service provisions and GHG emissions, some likely to be lasting (Aldaco et al. 2020; Bilal et al. 2020; Boyer 2020; Hepburn et al. 2020; Norouzi et al. 2020; Prideaux et al. 2020; Sovacool et al. 2020a). If changes in some preference behaviours, for example for larger homes and work environments to enable home working and online education, lead to sprawling suburbs or gentrification with linked environmental consequences, this could translate into long-term implications for climate change (Beaunoyer et al. 2020; Diffenbaugh et al. 2020). Recovering from the pandemic by adopting low energy demand practices – embedded in new travel, work, consumption and production behaviour and patterns – could reduce carbon prices for a 1.5°C consistent pathway by 19%, reduce energy supply investments until 2030 by USD1.8 trillion, and lessen pressure on the upscaling of low-carbon energy technologies (Kikstra et al. 2021a).

COVID-19 drove hundreds of millions of people below poverty thresholds, reversing decades of poverty reduction accomplishments (Krieger 2020; Mahler et al. 2020; Patel et al. 2020; Sumner et al. 2020) and raising the spectre of intersecting health and climate crises that are devastating for the most vulnerable (Flyvbjerg 2020; Phillips et al. 2020). Like those of climate change, pandemic impacts fall heavily on disadvantaged groups, exacerbate the uneven distribution of future benefits, amplify existing inequities, and introduce new ones (Beaunoyer et al. 2020; Devine-Wright et al. 2020). Addressing such inequities is a positive step towards the social trust that leads to improved climate policies as well as individual actions. Increased support for care workers and social infrastructures within a solidarity economy is consistent with lower-emission economic transformation (Shelley 2017; Di Chiro 2019; Pichler et al. 2019; Smetschka et al. 2019).

Fiscally, the pandemic may have slowed the transition to a sustainable energy world: governments redistributed public funding to combat the disease, adopted austerity and reduced capacity. Of nearly 300 policies implemented to counteract the pandemic, the vast majority are related to rescue, including worker and business compensation, and only 4% of these focus on green policies with potential to reduce GHG emissions in the long term; some rescue policies also assist emissions-intensive business (Hepburn et al. 2020; Leach et al. 2021). However, climate investments can double as the basis of the COVID-19 recovery (Stark 2020), with policies focused on both economic multipliers and climate impacts, such as clean physical infrastructure, natural capital investment, clean research and development (R&D) and education and training (Hepburn et al. 2020). This requires attention to investment priorities, including often-underprioritised social investment, given how inequality intersects with, and is a recognised core driver of, environmental damage and climate change (Millward-Hopkins et al. 2020).

5.2 Services, Well-being and Equity in Demand-side Mitigation

As outlined in section 5.1, mitigation, equity and well-being go hand in hand to motivate actions. Global, regional, and national actions and policies that advance inclusive well-being and build social trust strengthen governance. There is *high evidence* and *high agreement* that demand-side measures cut across all sectors, and can bring multiple benefits (Mundaca et al. 2019; Wachsmuth and Duscha 2019; Geels 2020; Niamir et al. 2020b; Garvey et al. 2021; Roy et al. 2021). Since effective demand requires affordability, one of the necessary conditions for acceleration of mitigation through demand-side measures is wide and equitable participation from all sectors of society. Low-cost low-emissions technologies, supported by institutions and government policies, can help meet service demand and advance both climate and well-being goals (Steffen et al. 2018a; Khosla et al. 2019). This section introduces metrics of well-being and their relationship to GHG emissions, and clarifies the concept of service provisioning.

5.2.1 Metrics of Well-being and their Relationship to Greenhouse Gas Emissions

There is *high evidence* and *high agreement* in the literature that human well-being and related metrics provide a societal perspective which is inclusive, compatible with sustainable development, and generates multiple ways to mitigate emissions. Development targeted to basic needs and well-being for all entails less carbon intensity than GDP-focused growth (Rao et al. 2014; Lamb and Rao 2015).

Current socioeconomic systems are based on high-carbon economic growth and resource use (Steffen et al. 2018b). Several systematic reviews confirm that economic growth is tightly coupled with increasing CO_2 emissions (Ayres and Warr 2005; Tiba and Omri 2017; Mardani et al. 2019; Wiedenhofer et al. 2020) although the level of emissions depends on inequality (Baležentis et al. 2020; Liu et al. 2020b), and on geographic and infrastructural constraints that force consumers to use fossil fuels (Pottier et al. 2021). Different patterns emerge in the causality of the energy–growth nexus: (i) energy consumption causes economic growth; (ii) growth causes energy consumption; (iii) bidirectional causality; and (iv) no significant causality (Ozturk 2010). In a systematic review, Mardani et al. (2019) found that in most cases, energy use and economic growth have a bidirectional causal effect, indicating that as economic growth increases, further CO_2 emissions are stimulated at higher levels; in turn, measures designed to lower GHG emissions may reduce economic growth. However, energy substitution and efficiency gains may offer opportunities to break the bidirectional dependency (Komiyama 2014; Brockway et al. 2017; Shuai et al. 2019). Worldwide trends reveal that at best only relative decoupling (resource use grows at a slower pace than GDP) was the norm during the twentieth century (Jackson 2009; Krausmann et al. 2009; Ward et al. 2016; Jackson 2016), while absolute decoupling (when material use declines as GDP grows) is rare, observed only during recessions or periods of low or no economic growth (Heun and Brockway 2019; Hickel and Kallis 2019; Vadén et al. 2020; Wiedenhofer et al. 2020). Recent trends in OECD countries demonstrate the potential for absolute decoupling of economic growth not only from territorial but also from consumption-based emissions (Le Quéré et al. 2019), albeit at scales insufficient for mitigation pathways (Vadén et al. 2020) (Chapter 2).

Energy demand and demand for GHG-intensive products increased from 2010 until 2020 across all sectors and categories. 2019 witnessed a reduction in energy demand growth rate to below 1% and 2020 an overall decline in energy demand, with repercussions for energy supply disproportionally affecting coal via merit order effects (Bertram et al. 2021) (Cross-Chapter Box 1 in Chapter 1). There was a slight but significant shift from high-carbon beef consumption to medium-carbon intensive poultry consumption. Final energy use in buildings grew from 118 EJ in 2010 to around 128 EJ in 2019 (increased about 8%). The highest increase was observed in non-residential buildings, with a 13% increase against 8% in residential energy demand (IEA 2019a). While electricity accounted for one-third of building energy use in 2019, fossil fuel use also increased at a marginal annual average growth rate of 0.7% since 2010 (IEA 2020a). Energy-related CO_2 emissions from buildings have risen in recent years after flattening between 2013 and 2016. Direct and indirect emissions from electricity and commercial heat used in buildings rose to 10 $GtCO_2$ in 2019, the highest level ever recorded. Several factors have contributed to this rise, including growing energy demand for heating and cooling with rising air conditioner ownership and extreme weather events. A critical issue remains how comfortable people feel with temperatures they will be exposed to in the future and this depends on physical, psychological and behavioural factors (Singh et al. 2018; Jacobs et al. 2019). Literature now shows *high evidence* and *high agreement* around the observation that policies and infrastructure interventions that lead to change in human preferences are more valuable for climate change mitigation. In economics, welfare evaluations are predominantly based on the preference approach. Preferences are typically assumed to be fixed, so that only changes in relative prices will reduce emissions. However, as decarbonisation is a societal transition, individuals' preferences do shift and this can contribute to climate change mitigation (Gough 2015). Even if preferences are assumed to change in response to policy, it is nevertheless possible to evaluate policy, and demand-side solutions, by approaches to well-being and welfare that are based on deeper concepts of preferences across disciplines (Roy and Pal 2009; Fleurbaey and Tadenuma 2014; Komiyama 2014; Dietrich and List 2016; Mattauch and Hepburn 2016). In cases of past societal transitions, such as smoking reduction, there is evidence that societies guided the processes of shifting preferences, and values changed along with changing relative prices (Nyborg and Rege 2003; Stuber et al. 2008; Brownell and Warner 2009). Further evidence on changing preferences in consumption choices pertinent to decarbonisation includes Grinblatt et al. (2008) and Weinberger and Goetzke (2010) for mobility; Erb et al. (2016), Muller et al. (2017), and Costa and Johnson (2019) for diets; and Baranzini et al. (2017) for solar panel uptake. If individuals' preferences

and values change during a transition to the low-carbon economy, then this overturns conclusions on what count as adequate or even optimal policy responses to climate change mitigation in economics (Jacobsen et al. 2012; Schumacher 2015; Dasgupta et al. 2016; Daube and Ulph 2016; Ulph and Ulph 2021). In particular, if policy instruments, such as awareness campaigns, infrastructure development or education, can change people's preferences, then policies or infrastructure provision – socially constrained by deliberative decision making – which change both relative prices and preferences, are more valuable for mitigation than previously thought (Creutzig et al. 2016b; Mattauch et al. 2016; Mattauch et al. 2018). The provisioning context of human needs is participatory, so transformative mitigation potential arises from social as well as technological change (Lamb and Steinberger 2017). Many dimensions of well-being and 'basic needs' are social, not individual, in character (Schneider 2016), so extending well-being and DLS analysis to emissions also involves understanding individual situations in social contexts. This includes building supports for collective strategies to reduce emissions (Chan et al. 2019), going beyond individual consumer choice. Climate policies that affect collective behaviour fairly are the most acceptable policies across political ideologies (Clayton 2018); thus collective preferences for mitigation are synergistic with evolving policies and norms in governance contexts that reduce risk, ensure social justice and build trust (Atkinson et al. 2017; Cramton et al. 2017; Milkoreit 2017; Tvinnereim et al. 2017; Smith and Reid 2018; Carattini et al. 2019).

Because of data limitations, which can make cross-country comparisons difficult, health-based indicators and in particular life expectancy (Lamb et al. 2014) have sometimes been proposed as quick and practical ways to compare local or national situations, climate impacts, and policy effects (Decancq et al. 2009; Sager 2017; Burstein et al. 2019). A number of different well-being metrics are valuable in emphasising the constituents of what is needed for a decent life in different dimensions (Lamb and Steinberger 2017; Porter et al. 2017; Smith and Reid 2018). The SDGs overlap in many ways with such indicators, and the data needed to assess progress in meeting the SDGs is also useful for quantifying well-being (Gough 2017). For the purposes of this chapter, indicators directly relating GHG emissions to well-being for all are particularly relevant.

Well-being can be categorised either as 'hedonic' or 'eudaimonic'. Hedonic well-being is related to a subjective state of human motivation, balancing pleasure over pain, and has gained influence in psychology assessing 'subjective well-being', assuming that the individual is motivated to enhance personal freedom, self-preservation and enhancement (Sirgy 2012; Brand-Correa and Steinberger 2017; Lamb and Steinberger 2017; Ganglmair-Wooliscroft and Wooliscroft 2019). Eudaimonic well-being focuses on the individual in the broader context, associating happiness with virtue (Sirgy 2012), allowing for the creation of social institutions and political systems and considering their ability to enable individuals to flourish. Eudaimonic analysis supports numerous development approaches (Fanning and O'Neill 2019) such as the capabilities (Sen 1985), human needs (Doyal and Gough 1991; Max-Neef et al. 1991) and models of psychosocial well-being (Ryan and Deci 2001). Measures of well-being differ somewhat in developed and developing countries (Sulemana et al. 2016; Ng and Diener 2019); for example, food insecurity, associated everywhere with lower subjective well-being, is more strongly associated with poor subjective well-being in more-developed countries (Frongillo et al. 2019); in wealthier countries, the relationship between living in rural areas is less strongly associated with negative well-being than in less-developed countries (Requena 2016); and income inequality is negatively associated with subjective well-being in developed countries, but positively so in less-developed countries (Ngamaba et al. 2018). This chapter connects demand-side climate mitigation options to multiple dimensions of well-being, going beyond the single dimensional metric of GDP which is at the core of IAMs. Many demand side-mitigation solutions generate positive and negative impacts on wider dimensions of human well-being which are not always quantifiable (*medium evidence, medium agreement*).

5.2.1.1   Services for Well-being

Well-being needs are met through services. Provision of services associated with low energy demand is a key component of current and future efforts to reduce carbon emissions. Services can be provided in various culturally-appropriate ways, with diverse climate implications. There is *high evidence* and *high agreement* in the literature that many granular service provision systems can make 'demand' more flexible, provide new options for mitigation, support access to basic needs, and enhance human well-being. Energy services offer an important lens to analyse the relationship between energy systems and human well-being (Jackson and Papathanasopoulou 2008; Druckman and Jackson 2010; Mattioli 2016; Walker et al. 2016; Fell 2017; Brand-Correa et al. 2018; King et al. 2019; Pagliano and Erba 2019; Whiting et al. 2020). Direct and indirect services provided by energy, rather than energy itself, deliver well-being benefits (Kalt et al. 2019). For example, illumination and transport are intermediary services in relation to education, health care, meal preparation, sanitation, and so on, which are basic human needs. Sustainable consumption and production revolve around 'doing more and better with the same' and thereby increasing well-being from economic activities 'by reducing resource use, degradation and pollution along the whole lifecycle, while increasing quality of life' (UNEP 2010). Although energy is required for delivering human development by supporting access to basic needs (Lamb and Rao 2015; Lamb and Steinberger 2017), a reduction in primary energy use and/or shift to low-carbon energy, if associated with the maintenance or improvement of services, can not only ensure better environmental quality but also directly enhance well-being (Roy et al. 2012). The correlation between human development and emissions is not necessarily coupled in the long term, which implies there is a need to prioritise human well-being and the environment over economic growth (Steinberger et al. 2020). At the interpersonal and community levels, cultural specificities, infrastructure, norms, and relational behaviours differ (Box 5.3). For example, demand for space heating and cooling depends on building materials and designs, urban planning, vegetation, clothing and social norms as well as geography, incomes, and outside temperatures (Brand-Correa et al. 2018; Campbell et al. 2018; Ivanova et al. 2018; IEA 2019b; Dreyfus et al. 2020). In personal mobility, different variable needs satisfiers (e.g., street space allocated to cars, buses or bicycles) can help satisfy human needs, such as accessibility to jobs, health care, and education. Social interactions and normative values play a crucial

role in determining energy demand. Hence, demand-side and service-oriented mitigation strategies are most effective if geographically and culturally differentiated (Niamir et al. 2020a).

Decent living standards (DLS) serves as a socio-economic benchmark as it views human welfare not in relation to consumption but rather in terms of services which together help meet human needs (e.g., nutrition, shelter, health, etc.), recognising that these service needs may be met in many different ways (with different emissions implications) depending on local contexts, cultures, geography, available technologies, social preferences, and other factors. Therefore, one key way of thinking about providing well-being for all with low carbon emissions centres around prioritising ways of providing services for DLS in a low-carbon way (including choices of needs satisfiers, and how these are provided or made accessible). They may be supplied to individuals or groups or communities, both through formal markets and/or informally, for example by collaborative work, in coordinated ways that are locally appropriate, designed and implemented in accordance with overlapping local needs.

The most pressing DLS service shortfalls, as shown in Figure 5.2, lie in the areas of nutrition, mobility, and communication. Gaps in regions such as Africa and the Middle East are accompanied by current levels of service provision in the highly industrialised countries at much higher than DLS levels for the same three service categories. The lowest population quartile by income worldwide faces glaring shortfalls in housing, mobility, and nutrition. Meeting these service needs using low-emissions energy sources is a top priority. Reducing GHG emissions associated with high levels of consumption and material throughput by those far above DLS levels has potential to address both emissions and inequality in energy and emission footprints (Otto et al. 2019). This, in turn, has further potential benefits; under the conditions of 'fair' income reallocation to public services, this can reduce national carbon footprint by up to 30% while allowing the consumption of those at the bottom to increase (Millward-Hopkins and Oswald 2021). The challenge then is to address the upper limits of consumption. When consumption only just supports the satisfaction of basic needs, any decrease causes deficiencies in human-need satisfaction. This is quite unlike the case of consumption that exceeds the limits of basic needs, in which deprivation causes a subjective discomfort (Brand-Correa et al. 2020). Therefore, to collectively remain within environmental limits, the establishment of minimum and maximum standards of consumption, or sustainable consumption corridors, (Wiedmann et al. 2020) has been suggested, depending on the context. In some countries, carbon-intensive ways of satisfying human needs have been locked-in, for example via car-dependent infrastructures (Jackson and Papathanasopoulou 2008; Druckman and Jackson 2010; Mattioli 2016; King et al. 2019), and both infrastructure reconfiguration and adaptation are required to organise need satisfaction in low-carbon ways (see also Section 10.2).

There is *high evidence* and *high agreement* in the literature that vital dimensions of human well-being correlate with consumption, but only up to a threshold. High potential for mitigation lies in using low-carbon energy for new basic needs satisfaction while cutting emissions of those whose basic needs are already met (Grubler et al. 2018; Rao and Min 2018b; Rao et al. 2019b; Millward-Hopkins et al. 2020;

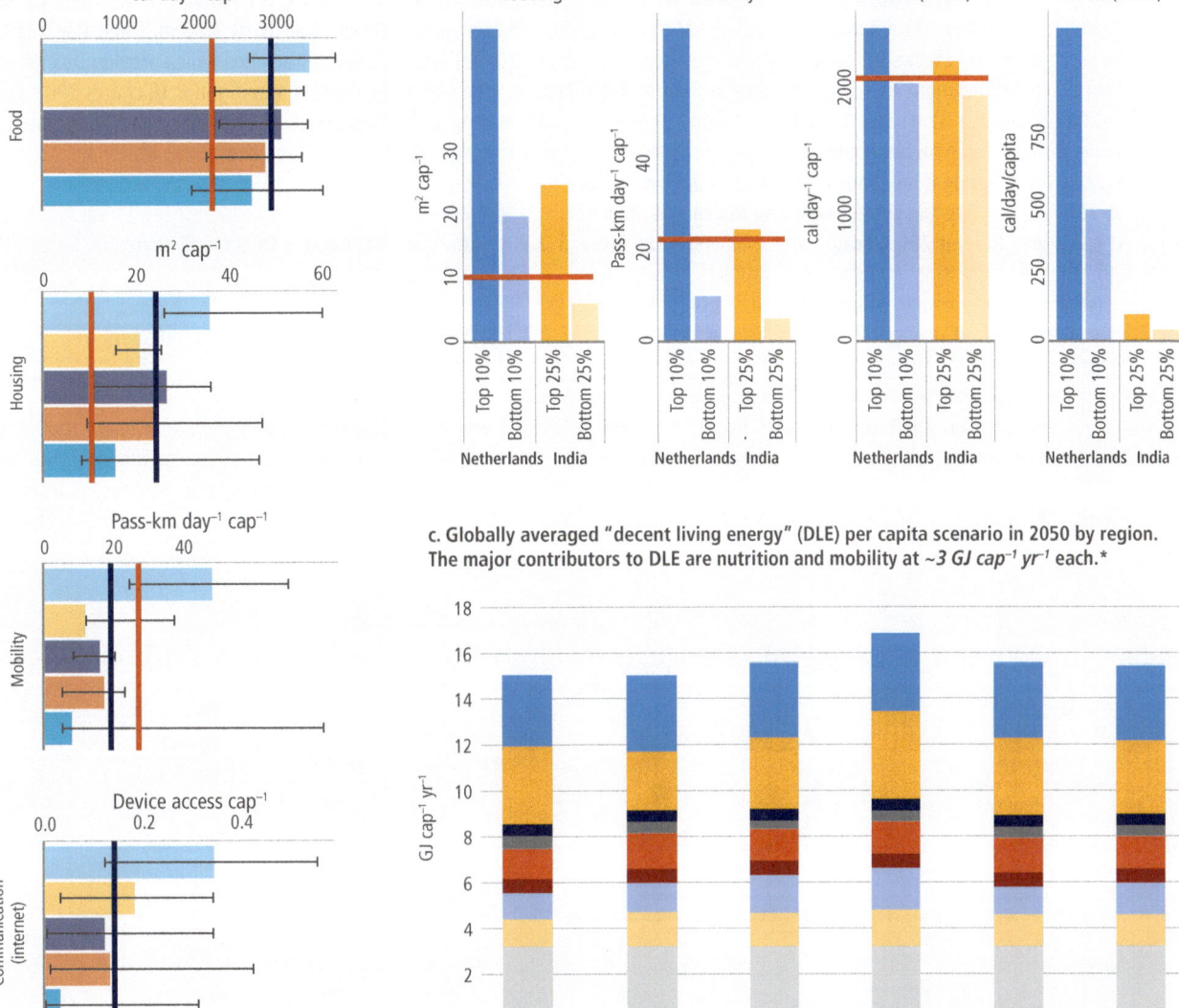

a. Across country heterogeneity (annual average per capita energy consumption).

b. Within country heterogeneity in service levels as a function of income differences for the Netherlands (bottom and 10% of incomes) and India (bottom and top 25% of incomes).

c. Globally averaged "decent living energy" (DLE) per capita scenario in 2050 by region. The major contributors to DLE are nutrition and mobility at ~3 GJ cap⁻¹ yr⁻¹ each.*

Developed Countries
Eastern Europe and West-Central Asia
Latin America and Caribbean
Asia and Developing Pacific
Africa and Middle East
Global average
Decent Living Standards (DLS) threshold (Rao et al. 2019)

Other (power supply and retail and freight activities)
Mobility
Communication and information
Education
Healthcare
Clothing
Hygiene
Shelter and living conditions
Nutrition

*Calculation is based on Millward-Hopkins et al. (2020)

Figure 5.2² | Heterogeneity in access to and availability of services for human well-being within and across countries. Panel **(a)** Across-country differences in panel (a) food (meat and other), (b) housing, (c) mobility, (d) communication (mobile phones and high-speed internet access). Variation in service levels across countries within a region is shown as error bars (black). Values proposed as decent standards of living threshold (Rao et al. 2019b) are shown as red dashed lines. Global average values are shown as blue dashed lines. Panel **(b)** Within-country differences in service levels as a function of income differences for the Netherlands (bottom and top 10% of incomes) and India (bottom and top 25% of incomes) (Grubler et al. 2012b) (data update 2016). Panel **(c)** Decent living energy (DLE) scenario using global, regional and DLS dimensions for final energy consumption at 149 EJ (15.3 GJ cap⁻¹ yr⁻¹) in 2050 (Millward-Hopkins et al. 2020), requiring advanced technologies in all sectors and radical demand-side changes. Values are shown for five world regions based on the AR6 WGIII Regional breakdown. We use passenger kilometres per day per capita (km day⁻¹ cap⁻¹) as a metric for mobility only as a reference, however, transport and social inclusion research suggest the aim is to maximise accessibility and not travel levels or travelled distance.

---

² The countries and areas classification in this figure deviate from the standard classification scheme adopted by WGIII as set out in Annex II, section 1.

Keyßer and Lenzen 2021). Decent living standards indicators serve as tools to clarify this socio-economic benchmark and identify well-being for all compatible mitigation potential. Energy services provisioning opens up avenues of efficiency and possibilities for decoupling energy services demand from primary energy supply, while needs satisfaction leads to the analysis of the factors influencing the energy demand associated with the achievement of well-being (Brand-Correa and Steinberger 2017; Tanikawa et al. 2021). Vital dimensions of well-being correlate with consumption, but only up to a threshold: decent living energy thresholds range from about 13 to 18.4 GJ cap^{-1} yr^{-1} of final energy consumption but the current consumption ranges from under 5 GJ cap^{-1} yr^{-1} to over 200 GJ cap^{-1} yr^{-1} (Millward-Hopkins et al. 2020), thus a mitigation strategy that protects minimum levels of essential-goods service delivery for DLS, but critically views consumption beyond the point of diminishing returns of needs satisfaction, is able to sustain well-being while generating emissions reductions (Goldemberg et al. 1988; Jackson and Marks 1999; Druckman and Jackson 2010; Girod and De Haan 2010; Vita et al. 2019a; Baltruszewicz et al. 2021). Such relational dynamics are relevant both within and between countries, due to variances in income levels, lifestyle choice (see also Section 5.4.4), geography,

resource assets and local contexts. Provisioning for human needs is recognised as participatory and inter-relational; transformative mitigation potential can be found in social as well as technological change (Mazur and Rosa 1974; Goldemberg et al. 1985; Lamb and Steinberger 2017; O'Neill et al. 2018; Hayward and Roy 2019; Vita et al. 2019a). More equitable societies which provide DLS for all can devote attention and resources to mitigation (Richards 2003; Dubash 2013; Rafaty 2018; Oswald et al. 2021). For further exploration of these concepts, see Chapter 5 Supplementary Material I.

5.2.2 Inequity in Access to Basic Energy Use and Services

5.2.2.1 Variations in Access to Needs-satisfiers for Decent Living Standards

There is very *high evidence* and *very high agreement* that globally, there are differences in the amount of energy that societies require to provide the basic needs for everyone. At present nearly one-third of the world's population are 'energy poor', facing challenges

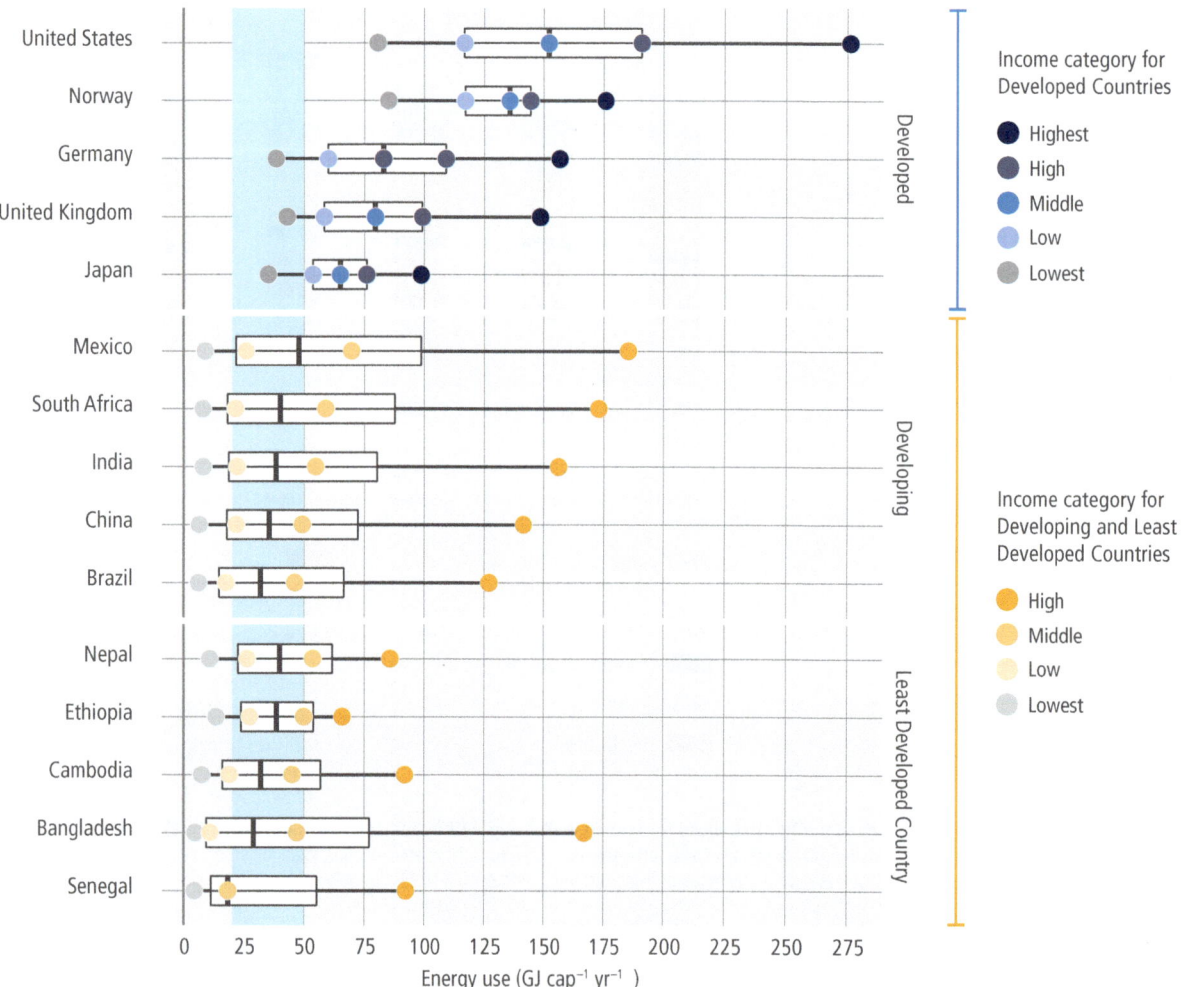

Figure 5.3 | Energy use per capita per year of three groups of countries ranked by socio-economic development and displayed for each country based on four or five different income groups (according to data availability) as well as geographical representation. The final energy use for decent living standards (20–50 GJ cap^{-1} yr^{-1}) (Rao et al. 2019b) is indicated in the blue column as a reference for global range, rather than dependent on each country. Source: data based on Oswald et al. (2020).

in both access and affordability, that is, more than 2.6 billion people have little or no access to energy for clean cooking. About 1.2 billion lack energy for cleaning, sanitation and water supply, lighting, and basic livelihood tasks (Sovacool and Drupady 2016; Rao and Pachauri 2017).The current per capita energy requirement to provide a decent standard of living range from around 5 to 200 GJ cap^{-1} yr^{-1} (Steckel et al. 2013; Lamb and Steinberger 2017; Rao et al. 2019b; Millward-Hopkins et al. 2020), which shows the level of inequality that exists; this depends on the context, such as geography, culture, infrastructure or how services are provided (Brand-Correa et al. 2018) (Box 5.3). However, through efficient technologies and radical demand-side transformations, the final energy requirements for providing DLS by 2050 is estimated at 15.3 GJ cap^{-1} yr^{-1} (Millward-Hopkins et al. 2020). Recent DLS estimates for Brazil, South Africa, and India are in the range between 15 and 25 GJ cap^{-1} yr^{-1} (Rao et al. 2019b).The most gravely energy poor are often those living in informal settlements, particularly women, in sub-Saharan Africa and developing Asia, whose socially-determined responsibilities for food, water, and care are highly labour-intensive and made more intense by climate change (Guruswamy 2016; Wester et al. 2019). In Brazil, India and South Africa, where inequality is extreme (Alvaredo et al. 2018) mobility (51–60%), food production and preparation (21–27%) and housing (5–12%) dominate total energy needs (Rao et al. 2019b). Minimum requirements of energy use consistent with enabling well-being for all is between 20 and 50 GJ cap^{-1} yr^{-1} depending on context (Rao et al. 2019b). Inequality in access to and availability of services for human well-being varies in extreme degree across countries and income groups. In developing countries, the bottom 50% receive about 10% of the energy used in land transport and less than 5% in air transport, while the top 10% use about 45% of the energy for land transport and around 75% for air transport (Oswald et al. 2020). Within-country analysis shows that particular groups in China – women born in the rural West with disadvantaged family backgrounds – face unequal opportunities for energy consumption (Shi 2019). Figure 5.3 shows the wide variation across world regions in people's access to some of the basic material prerequisites for meeting DLS, and variations in energy consumption, providing a starting point for comparative global analysis.

Box 5.3 | Inequities in Access to and Levels of End-use Technologies and Infrastructure Services

Acceleration in mitigation action needs to be understood from a societal perspective. Technologies, access and service equity factors sometimes change rapidly. Access to technologies, infrastructures and products, and the services they provide, are essential for raising global living standards and improving human well-being (Alkire and Santos 2014; Rao and Min 2018b). Yet access to and levels of service delivery are distributed extremely inequitably as of now. How fast such inequities can be reduced by granular end-use technologies is illustrated by the cellphone (households with mobiles), comparing the situation between 2000 and 2018. In this eighteen-year period, cellphones changed from a very inequitably-distributed technology to one with almost universal access, bringing accessibility benefits especially to populations with very low disposable income and to those whose physical mobility is limited (Porter 2016). Every human has the right to a dignified decent life, to live in good health and to participate in society. This is a daunting challenge, requiring that in the next decade governments build out infrastructure to provide billions of people with access to a number of services and basic amenities in comfortable homes, nutritious food, and transit options (Rao and Min 2018b). For a long time, this challenge was thought to also be an impediment to developing countries' participation in global climate mitigation efforts. However, recent research shows that this need not be the case (Millward-Hopkins et al. 2020; Rao et al. 2019b).

Several of the Sustainable Development Goals (SDGs) (UN 2015) deal with providing access to technologies and service infrastructures to the share of population so far excluded, showing that the UN 2030 Agenda has adopted a multidimensional perspective on poverty. Multidimensional poverty indices, such as the Social Progress Indicator and the Individual Deprivation Measure, go beyond income and focus on tracking the delivery of access to basic services by the poorest population groups, both in developing countries (Fulton et al. 2009; Alkire and Santos 2014; Alkire and Robles 2017; Rao and Min 2018b), and in developed countries (Townsend 1979; Aaberge and Brandolini 2015; Eurostat 2018). At the same time, the SDGs, primarily SDG 10 on reducing inequalities within and among countries, promote a more equitable world, both in terms of inter- as well as intra-national equality.

Access to various end-use technologies and infrastructure services features directly in the SDG targets and among the indicators used to track their progress (UN 2015; UNESC 2017): Basic services in households (SDG 1.4.1), Improved water sources (SDG 6.1.1); Improved sanitation (SDG 6.1.2); Electricity (SDG 7.1.1); Internet – fixed broadband subscriptions (SDG 17.6.2); Internet – proportion of population using (SDG 17.8.1). Transport (public transit, cars, mopeds or bicycles) and media technologies (mobile phones, TVs, radios, PCs, Internet) can be seen as proxies for access to mobility and communication, crucial for participation in society and the economy (Smith et al. 2015). In addition, SDG 10 is a more conventional income-based inequality goal, referring to income inequality (SDG 10.1), social, economic and political inclusion of all (SDG 10.2.), and equal opportunities and reduced inequalities of outcome (SDG 10.3).

5

Box 5.3 (continued)

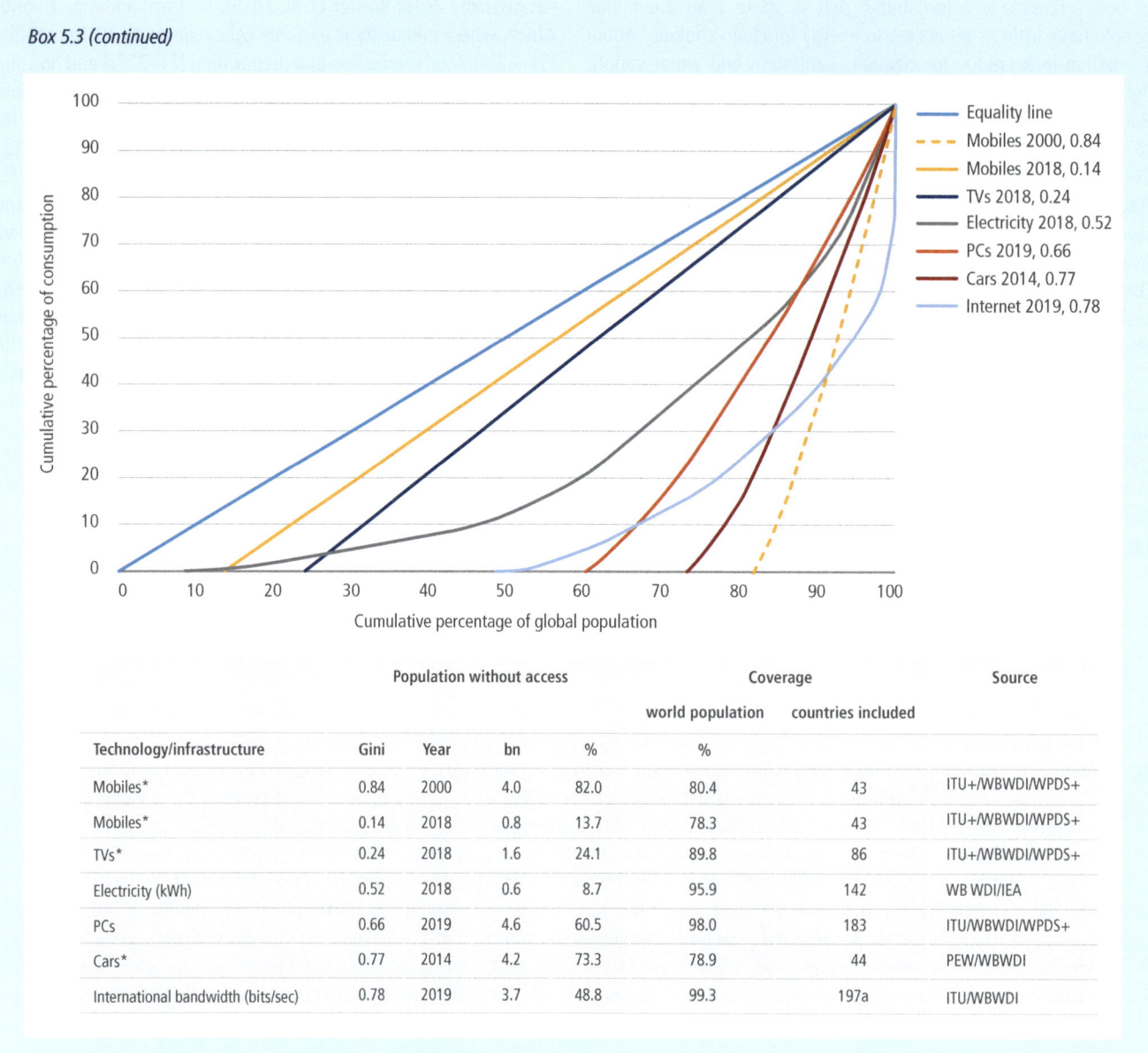

| Technology/infrastructure | Population without access | | | | Coverage | | Source |
	Gini	Year	bn	%	world population %	countries included	
Mobiles*	0.84	2000	4.0	82.0	80.4	43	ITU+/WBWDI/WPDS+
Mobiles*	0.14	2018	0.8	13.7	78.3	43	ITU+/WBWDI/WPDS+
TVs*	0.24	2018	1.6	24.1	89.8	86	ITU+/WBWDI/WPDS+
Electricity (kWh)	0.52	2018	0.6	8.7	95.9	142	WB WDI/IEA
PCs	0.66	2019	4.6	60.5	98.0	183	ITU/WBWDI/WPDS+
Cars*	0.77	2014	4.2	73.3	78.9	44	PEW/WBWDI
International bandwidth (bits/sec)	0.78	2019	3.7	48.8	99.3	197a	ITU/WBWDI

Box 5.3, Figure 1 | International inequality in access and use of goods and services. Upper panel: International Lorenz curves and Gini coefficients accounting for the share of population living in households without access (origin of the curves on the y-axis), multiple ownership not considered. **Lower panel:** Gini, number of people without access, access rates and coverage in terms of share of global population and number of countries included. *Reduced samples lead to underestimation of inequality. A sample, for example, of around 80% of world population (taking the same 43 countries as for mobiles and cars) led to a lower Gini of around 0.48 (−0.04) for electricity. The reduced sample was kept for mobiles in 2018 to allow for comparability with 2000. Source: Zimm (2019).

5.2.2.2   Variations in Energy Use

There is *high evidence* and *high agreement* in the literature that through equitable distribution, well-being for all can be assured at the lowest-possible energy consumption levels (Steinberger and Roberts 2010; Oswald et al. 2020) by reducing emissions related to consumption as much as possible, while assuring DLS for everyone (Annecke 2002; de Zoysa 2011; Ehrlich and Ehrlich 2013; Spangenberg 2014; Toroitich and Kerber 2014; Kenner 2015; Toth and Szigeti 2016; Smil 2017; Otto et al. 2019; Baltruszewicz et al. 2021). For example, at similar levels of human development, per capita energy demand

in the US was 63% higher than in Germany (Arto et al. 2016); those patterns are explained by context in terms of various climate, cultural and historical factors influencing consumption. Context matters even in within-country analysis, for example, electricity consumption in the US shows that efficiency innovations do exert positive influence on savings of residential energy consumption, but the relationship is mixed; on the contrary, affluence (household income and home size) and context (geographical location) drive resource utilisation significantly (Adua and Clark 2019); affluence is central to any future prospect in terms of environmental conditions (Wiedmann et al. 2020). In China, inequality of energy consumption and expenditure

5

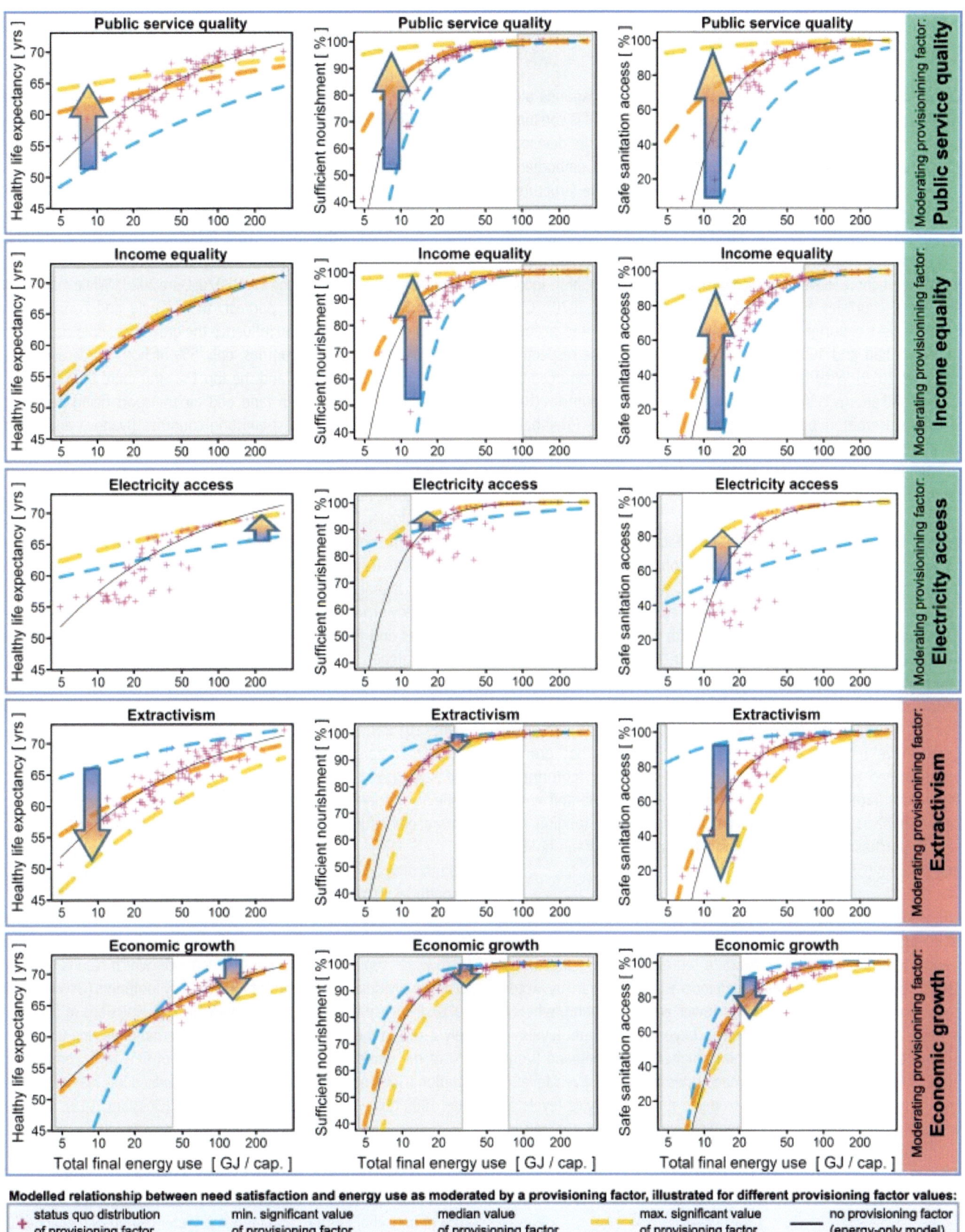

Figure 5.4 | Improving services for well-being is possible, often at huge margin, at a given (relatively low) level of energy use. Source: reused with permission from Vogel et al. (2021).

varies highly depending on the energy type, end-use demand and climatic region (Wu et al. 2017).

Consumption is energy- and materials-intensive and expands along with income. About half of the energy used in the world is consumed by the richest 10% of people, most of whom live in developed countries, especially when one includes the energy embodied in the goods they purchase from other countries and the structure of consumption as a function of income level (Arto et al. 2016; Wolfram et al. 2016; Santillán Vera et al. 2021). International trade plays a central role, being responsible for shifting burdens in most cases from low-income developing countries producers to high-income developed countries as consumers (Wiedmann et al. 2020). China is the largest exporter to the EU and United States, and accounts for nearly half and 40% of their imports in energy use respectively (Wu et al. 2019). Wealthy countries have exported or outsourced their climate and energy crisis to low- and middle-income countries (Baker 2018), exacerbated by intensive international trade (Steinberger et al. 2012; Scherer et al. 2018). Therefore, issues of total energy consumption are inseparably related to the energy inequity among the countries and regions of the world.

Within the energy use induced by global consumer products, household consumption is the biggest contributor, contributing to around three-quarters of the global total (Wu et al. 2019). A more granular analysis of household energy consumption reveals that the lowest two quintiles in countries with average annual income below USD15,000 cap^{-1} yr^{-1} consume less energy than the international energy requirements for DLS (20–50 GJ cap^{-1}); 77% of people consume less than 30 GJ cap^{-1} yr^{-1} and 38% consume less than 10 GJ cap^{-1} yr^{-1} (Oswald et al. 2020). Many energy-intensive goods have high price elasticity (>1.0), implying that growing incomes lead to over-proportional growth of energy footprints in these consumption categories. Highly unequally distributed energy consumption is concentrated in the transport sector, ranging from vehicle purchase to fuels, and most unequally in package holidays and aviation (Gössling 2019; Oswald et al. 2020).

Socio-economic dynamics and outcomes affect whether provisioning of goods and services is achieved at low energy demand levels (Figure 5.4). Specifically, multivariate regression shows that public service quality, income equality, democracy, and electricity access enable higher need satisfaction at lower energy demand, whereas extractivism and economic growth beyond moderate levels of affluence reduce need satisfaction at higher energy demand (Vogel et al. 2021). Altogether, this demonstrates that at a given level of energy provided, there is large scope to improve service levels for well-being by modifying socio-economic context without increasing energy supply (Figure 5.4).

5.2.2.3   Variations in Consumption-based Emissions

The carbon footprint of a nation is equal to the direct emissions occurring due to households' transport, heating and cooking, as well as the impact embodied in the production of all consumed goods and services (Wiedmann and Minx 2008; Davis and Caldeira 2010; Hübler 2017; Vita et al. 2019a). There are large differences in carbon footprints between the poor and the rich. As a result of energy use inequality, the lowest global emitters (the poorest 10% in developing countries) in 2013 emitted about 0.1 tCO_2 cap^{-1} yr^{-1}, whereas the highest global emitters (the top 1% in the richest countries) emitted about 200–300 tCO_2 cap^{-1} yr^{-1} (World Bank 2019). The poorest 50% of the world's population are responsible for only about 10% of total lifetime consumption emissions, in contrast about 50% of the world's GHG emissions can be attributed to consumption by the world's richest 10%, with the average carbon footprint of the richest being 175 times higher than that of the poorest 10% (Chancel and Piketty 2015). This richest 10% consumed the global carbon budget by nearly 30% during the period 1990–2015 (Kartha et al. 2020; Gore 2020). While mitigation efforts often focus on the poorest, the lifestyle and consumption patterns of the affluent often influence the growing middle class (Otto et al. 2019). Across EU countries, only 5% of households are living within 1.5°C climate limits and the top 1% emit more than 22 times the target on average, with land and air transport being particular characteristics of the highest-emitting countries (Ivanova and Wood 2020).

In low-income nations – which can exhibit per-capita carbon footprints 30 times lower than wealthy nations (Hertwich and Peters 2009) – emissions are predominantly domestic and driven by provision of essential services (shelter, low-meat diets, clothing). Per capita carbon footprints average 1.6 tonnes per year for the lowest income category, then quickly increase to 4.9 and 9.8 tonnes for the two middle-income categories and finally to an average of 17.9 tonnes for the highest income category. Global CO_2 emissions remain concentrated: the top 10% of emitters contribute about 35–45% of the total, while the bottom 50% contribute just 13–15% of global emissions (Chancel and Piketty 2015; Hubacek et al. 2017). In wealthy nations, services such as private road transport, frequent air travel, private jet ownership, meat-intensive diets, entertainment and leisure add significant emissions, while a considerable fraction of the carbon footprint is imported from abroad, embedded in goods and services (Hubacek et al. 2017).

High-income households consume and demand energy at an order of magnitude greater than what is necessary for DLS (Oswald et al. 2020). Energy-intensive goods, such as package holidays, have a higher income elasticity of demand than less energy-intensive goods like food, water supply and housing maintenance, which results in high-income individuals having much higher energy footprints (Oswald et al. 2020). Evidence highlights highly unequal GHG emissions in aviation: only 2–4% of the global population flew internationally in 2018, with 1% of the world population emitting 50% of CO_2 from commercial aviation (Gössling and Humpe 2020). Some individuals may add more than 1600 tCO_2 yr^{-1} individually by air travel (Gössling 2019).

The food sector dominates in all income groups, comprising 28% of households' carbon footprint, with cattle and rice the major contributors (Scherer et al. 2018); food also accounts for 48% and 70% of household impacts on land and water resources respectively, and consumption of meat, dairy, and processed food rise fast as incomes increase (Ivanova et al. 2016). Roughly 20–40% of food produced worldwide is lost to waste before it reaches the market, or is wasted by households, the energy embodied in wasted food was estimated at around 36 EJ yr^{-1}, and during the period 2010–2016 global food loss and waste equalled 8–10% of total GHG emissions (Godfray and Garnett 2014; Springmann et al. 2018; Mbow et al. 2019). Global agri-food supply chains are crucial in the variation of per capita food consumption-related-GHG footprints, mainly in the case of red meat and dairy (Kim et al. 2020) since the highest per capita food-consumption-related GHG emissions do not correlate perfectly with the income status of countries. Thus, it is also crucial to focus on high-emitting individuals and groups within countries, rather than only those who live in high-emitting countries, since the top 10% of emitters live on all continents and one-third of them are from the developing world (Chakravarty et al. 2009; Pan et al. 2019).

The environmental impact of increasing equity across income groups can be either positive or negative (Hubacek et al. 2017; Rao and Min 2018a; Scherer et al. 2018; Millward-Hopkins et al. 2020). Projections for achieving equitable levels of service provision globally predict large increases in global GHG emissions and demand for key resources (Blomsma and Brennan 2017), especially in passenger transport, which is predicted to increase nearly three-fold between 2015 and 2050, from 44 trillion to 122 trillion passenger-kilometres (OECD 2019a), and associated infrastructure needs, increasing freight (Murray et al. 2017), increasing demand for cooling (IEA 2018), and shifts to carbon-intensive high-meat diets (OECD/FAO 2018).

Increasing incomes for all to attain DLS raises emissions and energy footprints, but only slightly (Chakravarty et al. 2009; Jorgenson et al. 2016; Scherer et al. 2018; Millward-Hopkins et al. 2020; Oswald et al. 2020; Oswald et al. 2021). The amount of energy needed for a high global level of human development is dropping (Steinberger and Roberts 2010) and could by 2050 be reduced to 1950 levels (Millward-Hopkins et al. 2020) requiring a massive deployment of technologies across the different sectors as well as demand-side reduction consumption. The consumption share of the bottom half of the world's population represents less than 20% of all energy footprints, which is less than what the top 5% of people consume (Oswald et al. 2020).

Income inequality itself also raises carbon emissions (Hao et al. 2016; Sinha 2016; Uzar and Eyuboglu 2019; Baloch et al. 2020; Oswald et al. 2020; Wiedmann et al. 2020; Vogel et al. 2021). Wide inequality can increase status-based consumption patterns, where individuals spend more to emulate the standards of the high-income group (the Veblen effect); inequality also diminishes environmental efforts by reducing social cohesion and cooperation (Jorgenson et al. 2017) and finally, inequality also operates by inducing an increase in working hours that leads to higher economic growth and, consequently, higher emissions and ecological footprint, so working time reduction is key for policy to both reduce emissions and protect employment (Fitzgerald et al. 2015; Fitzgerald et al. 2018).

5.2.3   Equity, Trust, and Participation in Demand-side Mitigation

There is *high evidence* and *high agreement* in literature that socio-economic equity builds not only well-being for all, but also trust and effective participatory governance, which in turn strengthen demand-side climate mitigation. Equity, participation, social trust, well-being,

governance and mitigation are parts of a continuous interactive and self-reinforcing process (Figure 5.5). Chapter 5 Supplementary Material I (Section 5.SM.1) contains more detail on these links, drawing from social science literature.

Economic growth in equitable societies is associated with lower emissions than in inequitable societies (McGee and Greiner 2018), and income inequality is associated with higher global emissions (Ravallion et al. 1997; McGee and Greiner 2018; Rao and Min 2018c; Diffenbaugh and Burke 2019; Fremstad and Paul 2019; Liu and Hao 2020). Relatively slight increases in energy consumption and carbon emissions produce great increases in human development and well-being in less-developed countries, and the amount of energy needed for a high global level of human development is dropping (Steinberger and Roberts 2010). Equitable and democratic societies which provide high quality public services to their population have high well-being outcomes at lower energy use than those which do not, whereas those which prioritise economic growth beyond moderate incomes and extractive sectors display a reversed effect (Vogel et al. 2021).

Well-designed climate mitigation policies ameliorate constituents of well-being (Creutzig et al. 2021b). The study shows that of all demand-side option effects on well-being, 79% are positive, 18% are neutral (or not relevant or specified), and only 3% are negative (*high confidence*) (Creutzig et al. 2021b) (Figure 5.6). Figure 5.6 illustrates that active mobility (cycling and walking), efficient buildings and prosumer choices of renewable technologies have the most encompassing beneficial effects on well-being, with no negative outcomes detected. Urban and industry strategies are highly positive overall for well-being, but they will also reshape supply-side businesses with transient intermediate negative effects. Shared mobility, like all the others, has overall highly beneficial effects on well-being, but also displays a few negative consequences, depending on implementation, such as a minor decrease in personal security for patrons of ride-sourcing.

Well-being improvements are most notable in health, air, and energy (*high confidence*). These categories are also most substantiated in the literature, often under the framing of co-benefits. In many cases, co-benefits outweigh the mitigation benefits of specific GHG emission reduction strategies. Food (*medium confidence*), mobility (*high confidence*), and water (*medium confidence*) are further categories where well-being is improved. Mobility has entries with highest well-being rankings for teleworking, compact cities, and urban system approaches. Effects on well-being in water and sanitation mostly come from buildings and urban solutions. Social dimensions, such as personal security, social cohesion, and especially political stability, are less predominantly represented. An exception is economic stability, suggesting that demand-side options generate stable opportunities to participate in economic activities (*high confidence*). Although the relation between demand-side mitigation strategies and the social aspects of human well-being is important, this has been less reflected in the literature so far, and hence the assessment finds more neutral/unknown interactions (Figure 5.6).

Policies designed to foster higher well-being for all via climate mitigation include reducing emissions through wider participation in climate action, building more effective governance for improved mitigation,

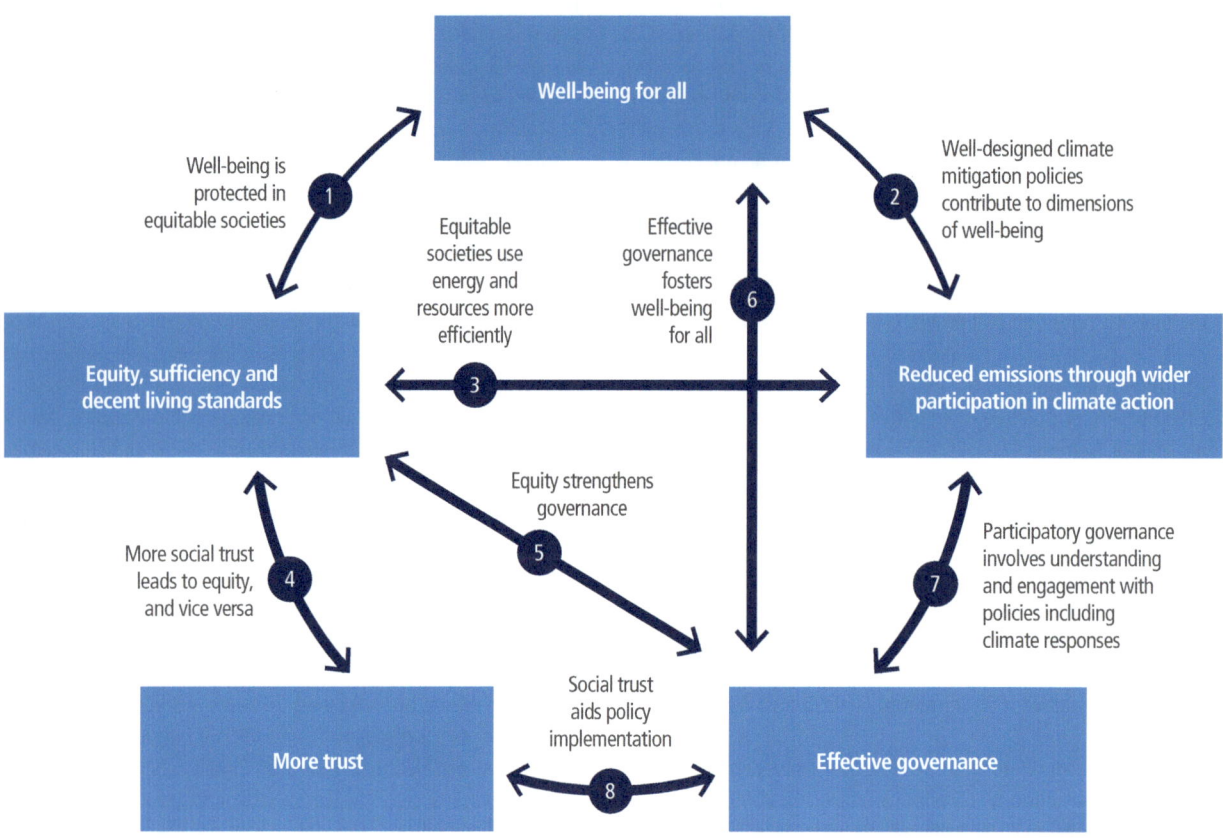

Figure 5.5 | Well-being, equity, trust, governance and climate mitigation: positive feedbacks. Well-being for all, increasingly seen as the main goal of sustainable economies, reinforces emissions reductions through a network of positive feedbacks linking effective governance, social trust, equity, participation and sufficiency. This diagram depicts relationships noted in this chapter text and explained further in the Social Science Primer (Chapter 5 Supplementary Material I). The width of the arrows corresponds to the level of confidence and degree of evidence from recent social sciences literature.

and including social trust, greater equity, and informal-sector support as integral parts of climate policies. Public participation facilitates social learning and people's support of and engagement with climate change priorities; improved governance is closely tied to effective climate policies (Phuong et al. 2017). Better education, health care, valuing of social diversity, and reduced poverty – characteristics of more equal societies – all lead to resilience, innovation, and readiness to adopt progressive and locally-appropriate mitigation policies, whether high-tech or low-tech, centralised or decentralised (Tanner et al. 2009; Lorenz 2013; Chu 2015; Cloutier et al. 2015; Mitchell 2015; Martin and Shaheen 2016; Vandeweerdt et al. 2016; Turnheim et al. 2018). Moreover, these factors are the ones identified as enablers of high need satisfaction at lower energy use (Vogel et al. 2021).

There is less policy lock-in in more equitable societies (Seto et al. 2016). International communication, networking, and global connections among citizens are more prevalent in more equitable societies, and these help spread promising mitigation approaches (Scheffran et al. 2012). Climate-related injustices are addressed where equity is prioritised (Klinsky and Winkler 2014). Thus, there is high confidence in the literature that addressing inequities in income, wealth, and DLS not only raises overall well-being and furthers the SDGs but also improves the effectiveness of climate change mitigation policies. For example, job creation, retraining for new jobs, local production of

livelihood necessities, social provisioning, and other positive steps toward climate mitigation and adaptation are all associated with more equitable and resilient societies (Okvat and Zautra 2011; Bentley 2014; Klinsky et al. 2016; Roy et al. 2018a). At all scales of governance, the popularity and sustainability of climate policies requires attention to the fairness of their health and economic implications for all, and participatory engagement across social groups – a responsible development framing (Cazorla and Toman 2001; Dulal et al. 2009; Chuku 2010; Shonkoff et al. 2011; Navroz 2019; Hofstad and Vedeld 2020; Muttitt and Kartha 2020; Roy and Schaffartzik 2020; Temper et al. 2020; Waller et al. 2020). Far from being secondary or even a distraction from climate mitigation priorities, an equity focus is intertwined with mitigation goals (Klinsky et al. 2016). Demand-side climate mitigation options have pervasive ancillary, equity-enhancing benefits, for example for health, local livelihoods, and community forest resources (Chhatre and Agrawal 2009; Garg 2011; Shaw et al. 2014; Serrao-Neumann et al. 2015; Klausbruckner et al. 2016; Salas and Jha 2019) (Figure 5.6). Limiting climate change risks is fundamental to collective well-being (Max-Neef et al. 1989; Yamin et al. 2005; Nelson et al. 2013; Gough 2015; Gough 2017; Pecl et al. 2017; Tschakert et al. 2017). Section 5.6 discusses well-designed climate policies more fully, with examples. Rapid changes in social norms which are underway and which underlie socially-acceptable climate policy initiatives are discussed in section 5.4.

Figure 5.6 | Two-way link between demand-side climate mitigation strategies and multiple dimensions of human well-being and SDGs. All demand-side mitigation strategies improve well-being in sum, though not necessarily in each individual dimension. Incumbent business (in contrast to overall economic performance) may be challenged. Source: Creutzig et al. (2021b).

Mitigation strategies / Well-being dimensions	Food (2)	Water (6)	Air (7,11)	Health (3)	Sanitation (6)	Energy (7)	Shelter (11)	Mobility (11)	Education (4)	Communication	Social protection (1,2,8,10)	Participation (5,10,16)	Personal Security (5,16)	Social cohesion (10,16)	Political stability (11,16)	Economic stability (8)	Material provision (9,12)
Sufficiency (adequate floor space, etc.)	[+1]	[+2]	[+2]	[+3]	[+1]	[+3]	[+1]	[+1]	[+1]	[+2]	[+1]	[+1]		[+2]		[+2]	[+2]
Efficiency	[+2]	[+2]	[+3/-1]	[+3/-1]	[+1]	[+3]	[+2]		[+1]	[+1]		[+1]	[+1]	[+2/-1]		[+2]	[+2/-1]
Lower carbon and renewable energy	[+2/-1]	[+2/-1]	[+3]	[+3]		[+3]	[+1]	[+1]	[+1]	[+2]		[+1]	[+1]	[+2/-1]		[+2/-1]	[+2]
Food waste	[+1]	[+2]	[+2]	[+2]	[+1]	[+1]				[+1]	[-1/+1]	[+1]			[+1]	[+1]	
Over-consumption	[+1]	[+1/-1]	[+1/-1]	[+3]		[+1/-1]						[+2]			[+1]		
Plant based diets	[+2]	[+2]	[+3]	[+3]		[+2]	[+1]		[-1]	[-1]	[+3]	[+1]	[+1/-1]	[-1]	[+2]	[+2]	[+2]
Teleworking and online education system	[+1]	[+1]	[+3]	[+2]		[+2]	[+1]	[+2]	[+1]	[+2]	[+1]	[+2]	[+2]	[+2]	[+2]	[+1]	[+2]
Non-motorised transport	[+2]	[+1]	[+1]	[+3]		[+2]		[+3]	[+1]	[+3]	[+1]	[+1]	[+2]	[+2]	[+2]	[+1]	
Shared mobility	[+1]	[+2]	[+3]	[+2]		[+1]		[+2]		[+1]	[+2]	[+1]	[+1/-1]	[+1/-1]	[-1]	[+2]	[+2]
Electric vehicles (EVs)	[+1]	[+1/-1]	[+2]	[+1]	[+1]	[+3]		[+2]			[+3]	[+2]	[+1]	[+1/-1]	[-1]	[+2]	[-1]
Compact city	[+2/-1]	[+1]	[+2/-1]	[+3/-1]	[+1]	[+3/-1]	[-1]	[+3]	[+1]	[+1/-1]	[+2]	[+1]	[+1]	[+1/-1]		[+1]	[+1]
Circular and shared economy	[+2]	[+1]	[+2]	[+2]	[+2]	[+3]	[+2/-1]	[+3]	[+1]	[+1]	[+1]	[+1]	[+2]	[+1]	[+1]	[+2]	[+3]
Systems approach in urban policy and practice	[+1]	[+2]	[+3]	[+3]	[+2]	[+3]	[+2]	[+3]		[+1]	[-1]	[-1]	[+2]	[+1]	[+1]	[+1]	[+3]
Nature-Based Solutions	[+2]	[+1/-1]	[+3/-1]	[+3]	[+1]	[+3]	[+1/-1]	[+1]	[+2]	[+2]	[+2]	[+3]	[+1]	[+2/-2]	[+1]	[+3]	[+1]
Using less material by design	[+2]	[+2]	[+3]	[+2]	[+2]	[+3]	[+2]	[+2]	[+1]	[+2]	[+1]	[+1]	[+2]	[+1]	[+1]	[+2]	[+3]
Product life extension	[+2]	[+2]	[+3]	[+1]	[+2]	[+3]	[+2]	[+2]	[+1]	[+2]	[+1]	[+1]	[+2]	[+1]	[+1]	[+2]	[+3]
Energy efficiency	[+2]	[+2]	[+3]	[+1]	[+2]	[+3]	[+2]	[+2]	[+1]	[+2]	[+1]	[+2]	[+1]		[+1]	[+2]	[+2]
Circular economy	[+2]	[+2]	[+3]	[+1]	[+2]	[+3]	[+2]	[+2]	[+1]	[+2]	[+1]	[+1]	[+2]	[+1]	[+1]	[+2]	[+3]

Legend:
- High positive impact [+3]
- Medium positive impact [+2]
- Low positive impact [+1]
- Overall neutral
- No impact
- Low negative impact [-1]
- Medium negative impact [-2]
- • Confidence level

The distinction between necessities and luxuries helps to frame a growing stream of social sciences literature with climate policy relevance (Arrow et al. 2004; Ramakrishnan and Creutzig 2021). Given growing public support worldwide for strong sustainability, sufficiency, and sustainable consumption, changing demand patterns and reduced demand are accompanying environmental and social benefits (Jackson 2008; Fedrigo et al. 2010; Schroeder 2013; Figge et al. 2014; Spangenberg and Germany 2016; Spengler 2016; Burke 2020; Mont et al. 2020). Beyond a threshold, increased material consumption is not closely correlated with improvements in human progress (Frank 1999; Kahneman and Deaton 2010; Steinberger and Roberts 2010; Roy et al. 2012; Oishi et al. 2018; Xie et al. 2018; Vita et al. 2019b; Wang et al. 2019; Vita et al. 2020). Policies focusing on the 'super-rich', also called the 'polluter elite', are gaining attention for moral or norms-based as well as emissions-control reasons (Kenner 2019; Otto et al. 2019; Pascale et al. 2020; Stratford 2020) (Section 5.2.2.3). Conspicuous consumption by the wealthy is the cause of a large proportion of emissions in all countries, related to expenditures on such things as air travel, tourism, large private vehicles and large homes (Brand and Boardman 2008; Roy and Pal 2009; Roy et al. 2012; Brand and Preston 2010; Gore 2015; Hubacek et al. 2017; Jorgenson et al. 2017; Sahakian 2018; Gössling 2019; Kenner 2019; Lynch et al. 2019; Osuoka and Haruna 2019).

Since no country now meets its citizens' basic needs at a level of resource use that is globally sustainable, while high levels of life satisfaction for those just escaping extreme poverty require even more resources, the need for transformative shifts in governance and policies is large (O'Neill et al. 2018; Vogel et al. 2021).

Inequitable societies use energy and resources less efficiently.
Higher income inequality is associated with higher carbon emissions, at least in developed countries (Grunewald et al. 2011; Golley and Meng 2012; Chancel et al. 2015; Grunewald et al. 2017; Jorgenson et al. 2017; Sager 2017; Klasen 2018; Liu et al. 2019); reducing inequality in high-income countries helps to reduce emissions (Klasen 2018). There is high agreement in the literature that alienation or distrust weakens collective governance and fragments political approaches towards climate action (Smit and Pilifosova 2001; Adger et al. 2003; Hammar and Jagers 2007; Van Vossole 2012; Bulkeley and Newell 2015; Smith and Howe 2015; ISSC et al. 2016; Alvaredo et al. 2018; Smith and Mayer 2018; Fairbrother et al. 2019; Hayward and Roy 2019; Kulin and Johansson Sevä 2019; Liao et al. 2019).

Populism and politics of fear are less prevalent under conditions of more income equality (Chevigny 2003; Bryson and Rauwolf 2016; O'Connor 2017; Fraune and Knodt 2018; Myrick and Evans Comfort 2019). Ideology and other social factors also play a role in populist climate scepticism, but many of these also relate to resentment of elites and desire for engagement (Swyngedouw 2011; Lockwood 2018; Huber et al. 2020). 'Climate populism' movements are driven by an impetus for justice (Beeson 2019; Hilson 2019). When people feel powerless and/or that climate change is too big a problem to solve because others are not acting, they may take less action themselves (Williams and Jaftha 2020). However, systems for benefit-sharing can build trust and address large-scale 'commons dilemmas', in the context of strong civil society (Barnett 2003; Mearns and Norton 2009; Inderberg et al. 2015; Sovacool et al. 2015; Hunsberger et al. 2017;

Soliev and Theesfeld 2020). Leadership is also important in fostering environmentally-responsible group behaviours (Liu and Hao 2020).

In some less-developed countries, higher income inequality may in fact be associated with lower per capita emissions, but this is because people who are excluded by poverty from access to fossil fuels must rely on biomass (Klasen 2018). Such energy poverty – the fact that millions of people do not have access to energy sources to help meet human needs – implies the opposite of development (Guruswamy 2010; Guruswamy 2020). In developing countries, livelihood improvements do not necessarily cause increases in emissions (Peters et al. 2012; Reusser et al. 2013; Creutzig et al. 2015a; Chhatre and Agrawal 2009; Baltruszewicz et al. 2021) and poverty alleviation causes negligible emissions (Chakravarty et al. 2009). Greater equity is an important step towards sustainable service provisioning (Godfray et al. 2018; Dorling 2019; Timko 2019).

As discussed in Section 5.6, policies to assist the low-carbon energy transition can be designed to include additional benefits for income equality, besides contributing to greater energy access for the poor (Burke and Stephens 2017; Frank 2017; Healy and Barry 2017; Sen 2017; Chapman et al. 2018; La Viña et al. 2018; Chapman and Fraser 2019; Piggot et al. 2019; Sunderland et al. 2020). Global and intergenerational climate inequities impact people's well-being, which affects their consumption patterns and political actions (Albrecht et al. 2007; Fritze et al. 2008; Gori-Maia 2013; Clayton et al. 2015; Pizzigati 2018) (Box 5.4).

Consumption reductions, both voluntary and policy-induced, can have positive and double-dividend effects on efficiency as well as reductions in energy and materials use (Mulder et al. 2006; Harriss and Shui 2010; Figge et al. 2014; Grinde et al. 2018; Spangenberg and Lorek 2019; Vita et al. 2020). Less waste, better emissions control and more effective carbon policies lead to better governance and stronger democracies. Systems-dynamics models linking strong emissions-reducing policies and strong social equity policies show that a low-carbon transition in conjunction with social sustainability is possible, even without economic growth (Kallis et al. 2012; Jackson and Victor 2016; Stuart et al. 2017; Chapman and Fraser 2019; D'Alessandro et al. 2019; Gabriel and Bond 2019; Huang et al. 2019; Victor 2019). Such degrowth pathways may be crucial in combining technical feasibility of mitigation with social development goals (Hickel et al. 2021; Keyßer and Lenzen 2021).

Multi-level or polycentric governance can enhance well-being and improve climate governance and social resilience, due to varying adaptive, flexible policy interventions at different times and scales (Kern and Bulkeley 2009; Lidskog and Elander 2009; Amundsen et al. 2010; Keskitalo 2010; Lee and Koski 2015; Jokinen et al. 2016; Lepeley 2017; Marquardt 2017; Di Gregorio et al. 2019). Institutional transformation may also result from socio-ecological stresses that accompany climate change, leading to more effective governance structures (David Tàbara et al. 2018; Patterson and Huitema 2019; Barnes et al. 2020). An appropriate, context-specific mix of options facilitated by policies can deliver both higher well-being and reduced disparity in access to basic needs for services concurrently with climate mitigation (Thomas and Twyman 2005; Mearns and Norton 2009;

Klinsky and Winkler 2014; Lamb et al. 2014; Lamb and Steinberger 2017). Hence, nurturing equitable human well-being through provision of decent living standards for all goes hand in hand with climate change mitigation (ISSC et al. 2016; OECD 2019a). There is *high confidence* in the literature that addressing inequities in income, wealth, and DLS not only raises overall well-being and furthers the SDGs but also improves the effectiveness of climate change mitigation policies.

Participatory governance involves understanding and engagement with policies, including climate policies. Greater public participation in climate policy processes and governance, by increasing the diversity of ideas and stakeholders, builds resilience and allows broader societal transformation towards systemic change, even in complex, dynamic and contested contexts (Dombrowski 2010; Wise et al. 2014; Haque et al. 2015; Jodoin et al. 2015; Mitchell 2015; Kaiser 2020; Alegria 2021). This sometimes involves complex policy discussions that can lead to governance innovations, also influencing social norms (Martinez 2020). A specific example are citizen assemblies, deliberating public policy challenges, such as climate change (Devaney et al. 2020). Activist climate movements are changing policies as well as normative values (Section 5.4 and the Social Science Primer, Chapter 5 Supplementary Material I). Environmental justice and climate justice activists worldwide have called attention to the links between economic and environmental inequities, collected and publicised data about them, and demanded stronger mitigation (Goodman 2009; Schlosberg and Collins 2014; Jafry 2019; Cheon 2020). Youth climate activists, and Indigenous leaders, are also exerting growing political influence towards mitigation (Helferty and Clarke 2009; White 2011; Powless 2012; Petheram et al. 2015; UN 2015; Curnow and Gross 2016; Grady-Benson and Sarathy 2016; Claeys and Delgado Pugley 2017; O'Brien et al. 2018; Rowlands and Gomez Peña 2019; Bergmann and Ossewaarde 2020; Han and Ahn 2020; Nkrumah 2021). Indigenous resurgence (activism fuelled by ongoing colonial social and environmental injustices, land claims, and deep spiritual and cultural commitment to environmental

protection) not only strengthens climate leadership in many countries, but also changes broad social norms by raising knowledge of Indigenous governance systems which supported sustainable lifeways over thousands of years (Wildcat 2014; Chanza and De Wit 2016; Whyte 2017; Whyte 2018, Temper et al. 2020). Related trends include recognition of the value of traditional ecological knowledge, Indigenous governance principles, decentralisation, and appropriate technologies (Lange et al. 2007; Goldthau 2014; Whyte 2017).

Social trust aids policy implementation. More equal societies display higher trust, which is a key requirement for successful implementation of climate policies (Rothstein and Teorell 2008; Carattini et al. 2015; Klenert et al. 2018; Patterson et al. 2018). Inter-personal trust among citizens often promotes pro-environment behaviour by influencing perceptions (Harring and Jagers 2013), enhancing cooperation, and reducing free-riding and opportunistic behaviour (Gür 2020). Individual support for carbon taxes and energy innovations falls when collective community support is lacking (Bolsen et al. 2014; Smith and Mayer 2018; Simon 2020). Social trust has a positive influence on civic engagement among local communities, NGOs, and self-help groups for local clean cooking fuel installation (Nayak et al. 2015).

Section 5.6 includes examples of climate mitigation policies and policy packages which address the interrelationships shown in Figure 5.5. Improving well-being for all through climate mitigation includes emissions-reduction goals in policy packages that ensure equitable outcomes, prioritise social trust-building, support wide public participation in climate action including within the informal sector, and facilitate institutional change for effective multi-level governance, as integral components of climate strategies. This strategic approach, and its feasibility of success, rely on complex contextual factors that may differ widely, especially between the Global North and Global South (Atteridge et al. 2012; Patterson et al. 2018; Jewell and Cherp 2020; Singh et al. 2020; Singh et al. 2021).

Box 5.4 | Gender, Race, Intersectionality and Climate Mitigation

There is *high evidence* and *high agreement* that empowering women benefits both mitigation and adaptation, because women prioritise climate change in their voting, purchasing, community leadership, and work, both professionally and at home (*high evidence, high agreement*). Increasing voice and agency for those marginalised in intersectional ways by indigeneity, race, ethnicity, dis/ability, and other factors has positive effects for climate policy (*high evidence, high agreement*).

Climate change affects people differently along all measures of difference and identity, which have intersectional impacts linked to economic vulnerability and marginalisation (Morello Frosch et al. 2009; Dankelman 2010; Habtezion 2013; Godfrey and Torres 2016; Walsh 2016; Flatø et al. 2017; Goodrich et al. 2019; Perkins 2019; Gür 2020). Worldwide, racialised and Indigenous people bear the brunt of environmental and climate injustices through geographic location in extraction and energy 'sacrifice zones', areas most impacted by extreme weather events, and/or through inequitable energy access (Aubrey 2019; Jafry 2019; Gonzalez 2020; Lacey-Barnacle et al. 2020; Porter et al. 2020; Temper et al. 2020) Disparities in climate change vulnerability not only reflect pre-existing inequalities, they also reinforce them. For example, inequities in income and in the ownership and control of household assets, familial responsibilities due to male out-migration, declining food and water access, and increased disaster exposure can undermine women's ability to achieve economic independence, enhance human capital, and maintain physical and mental health and well-being (Chandra et al. 2017; Eastin 2018; Das et al. 2019). Studies during the COVID-19 crisis have found that, in general, women's economic and productive lives have been affected disproportionately to men's (Alon et al. 2020; ILO 2020). Women have less access to social protections and their capacity to absorb economic shocks is very low, so they face a 'triple burden' during crises – including those

5

Box 5.4 (continued)

resulting from climate change – and this is heightened for women in the less-developed countries and for those who are intersectionally vulnerable (Coates et al. 2020; McLaren et al. 2020; Wenham et al. 2020; Azong and Kelso 2021; Erwin et al. 2021; Maobe and Atela 2021; Nicoson 2021; Sultana 2021; Versey 2021). Because men currently hold the majority of energy-sector jobs, energy transition will impact them economically and psychologically; benefits, burdens and opportunities on both the demand and supply sides of the mitigation transition have a range of equity implications (Pearl-Martinez and Stephens 2017; Standal et al. 2020; Mang-Benza 2021). Mitigating gendered climate impacts requires addressing inequitable power relations throughout society (Wester and Lama 2019).

Women's well-being and gender-responsive climate policy have been emphasised in international agreements including the Paris Agreement (UNFCCC 2015), Convention on the Elimination of all Forms of Discrimination Against Women General Recommendation 37 (Vijeyarasa 2021), and the 2016 Decision 21/CP.22 on Gender and Climate Change (UNFCCC 2016; Larson et al. 2018). Increasing the participation of women and marginalised social groups, and addressing their special needs, helps to meet a range of SDGs, improve disaster and crisis response, increase social trust, and improve climate mitigation policy development and implementation (Alber 2009; Whyte 2014; Elnakat and Gomez 2015; Salehi et al. 2015; Buckingham and Kulcur 2017; Cohen 2017; Kronsell 2017; Lee and Zusman 2019).

Women have a key role in the changing energy economy due to their demand for and end use of energy resources in socially-gendered productive roles in food production and processing, health, care, education, clothing purchases and maintenance, commerce, and other work, both within and beyond the home (Räty and Carlsson-Kanyama 2009; Oparaocha and Dutta 2011; Bob and Babugura 2014; Macgregor 2014; Perez et al. 2015; Bradshaw 2018; Clancy and Feenstra 2019; Clancy et al. 2019; Fortnam et al. 2019; Rao et al. 2019a; Quandt 2019; Horen Greenford et al. 2020; Johnson 2020). Women's work and decision-making are central in the food chain and agricultural output in most developing countries, and in household management everywhere. Emissions from cooking fuels can cause serious health damage, and unsustainable extraction of biofuels can also hurt mitigation (Bailis et al. 2015), so considering health, biodiversity and climate tradeoffs and co-benefits is important (Rosenthal et al. 2018; Aberilla et al. 2020; Mazorra et al. 2020). Policies on energy use and consumption are often focused on technical issues related to energy supply, thereby overlooking demand-side factors such as household decision-making, unpaid work, livelihoods and care (Himmelweit 2002; Perch 2011; Fumo 2014; Hans et al. 2019; Huyer and Partey 2020). Such gender-blindness represents the manifestation of wider issues related to political ideology, culture and tradition (Carr and Thompson 2014; Thoyre 2020; Perez et al. 2015; Fortnam et al. 2019).

Women, and all those who are economically and/or politically marginalised, often have less access to energy and use less, not just because they may be poorer but case studies show because their consumption choices are more ecologically inclined and their energy use is more efficient (Lee et al. 2013; Permana et al. 2015; Li et al. 2019). Women's carbon footprints are about 6–28% lower than men's (with high variation across countries), mostly based on their lower meat consumption and lower vehicle use (Isenhour and Ardenfors 2009; Räty and Carlsson-Kanyama 2009; Räty and Carlsson-Kanyama 2010; Barnett et al. 2012; Medina and Toledo-Bruno 2016; Ahmad et al. 2017; Fernström Nåtby and Rönnerfalk 2018; Li et al. 2019). Gender-based income redistribution in the form of pay equity for women could reduce emissions if the redistribution is revenue neutral (Terry 2009; Dengler and Strunk 2018). Also, advances in female education and reproductive health, especially voluntary family planning, can contribute greatly to reducing world population growth (Abel et al. 2016; Dodson et al. 2020).

Carbon emissions are lower per capita in countries where women have more political 'voice', controlling for GDP per capita and a range of other factors (Ergas and York 2012). While most people recognise that climate change is happening (Lewis et al. 2018; Ballew et al. 2019), climate denialism is more prevalent among men (McCright and Dunlap 2011; Anshelm and Hultman 2014; Nagel 2015; Jylhä et al. 2016), while women are more likely to be environmental activists, and to support stronger environmental and climate policies (Stein 2004; McCright and Xiao 2014, Whyte 2014). Racialised groups are more likely to be concerned about climate change and to take political action to support climate mitigation policies (Leiserowitz and Akerlof 2010; Godfrey and Torres 2016; Schuldt and Pearson 2016; Pearson et al. 2017; Ballew et al. 2020; Johnson 2020). This underscores the important synergies between equity and mitigation. The contributions of women, racialised people, and indigenous people, who are socially positioned as those first and most affected by climate change – and therefore experts on appropriate climate responses – are substantial (Dankelman and Jansen 2010; Wickramasinghe 2015; Black 2016; Vinyeta et al. 2016; Pearse 2017). Equitable power, participation, and agency in climate policymaking is hence an effective contribution for improving governance and decision-making on climate change mitigation (Reckien et al. 2017; Collins 2019). Indigenous knowledge is an important source of guidance for biodiversity conservation, impact assessment, governance, disaster preparedness and resilience (Salick and Ross 2009; Green and Raygorodetsky 2010; Speranza et al. 2010; Mekuriaw Bizuneh 2013; Mekuriaw 2017), and women are often the local educators, passing on and utilising traditional and indigenous knowledge (Ketlhoilwe 2013; Onyige 2017; Azong et al. 2018).

Higher female political participation, controlled for other factors, leads to higher stringency in climate policies, and results in lower GHG emissions (Cook et al. 2019). Gender equity is also correlated with lower per capita CO_2-eq emissions (Ergas and York 2012).

In societies where women have more economic equity, their votes push political decision-making in the direction of environmental and sustainable development policies, less high-emission militarisation, and more emphasis on equity and social policies such as via wealth and capital gains taxes (Ergas and York 2012; Resurrección 2013; UNEP 2013; Glemarec et al. 2016; Bryan et al. 2018; Crawford 2019). Changing social norms on race and climate are linked and policy-relevant (Benegal 2018; Elias et al. 2018; Slocum 2018; Gach 2019; Wallace-Wells 2019; Temple 2020; Drolet 2021). For all these reasons, climate policies are strengthened by including more differently-situated knowledge and diverse perspectives, such as feminist expertise in the study of power (Bell et al. 2020; Lieu et al. 2020); clarifying equity goals (e.g., distinguishing among 'reach, 'benefit', and 'empowerment'; obtaining disaggregated data and using clear empirical equity measures; and confronting deeply-ingrained inequities in society (Lau et al. 2021). Inclusivity in climate governance spans mitigation–adaptation, supply–demand and formal–informal sector boundaries in its positive effects (Morello Frosch et al. 2009; Dankelman 2010; Bryan and Behrman 2013; Habtezion 2013; Godfrey and Torres 2016; Walsh 2016; Flatø et al. 2017; Wilson et al. 2018; Goodrich et al. 2019; Perkins 2019; Bell et al. 2020; Gür 2020).

5.3 Mapping the Opportunity Space

Reducing global energy demand and resource inputs while improving well-being for all requires an identification of options, services and pathways that do not compromise essentials of a decent living. To identify such a solution space, this section summarises socio-cultural, technological and infrastructural interventions through the Avoid-Shift-Improve concept. ASI (Section 5.1) provides a categorisation of options aimed at continuously eliminating waste in the current systems of service provision (Section 5.3.1.1). It also concisely presents demand-side options to reduce GHG emissions by individual choices which can be leveraged by supporting policies, technologies and infrastructure. Two key concepts for evaluating the efficiency of service provision systems are: resource cascades and exergy. These concepts provide powerful analytical lenses through which to identify and substantially reduce energy and resource waste in service provision systems, both for decent living standards (Section 5.3.2) and higher well-being levels. They typically focus on end-use conversion and service delivery improvements as the most influential opportunities for system-wide waste reductions. Review of the state of modelling low energy and resource demand pathways in long-term climate mitigation scenarios (recognising the importance of such scenarios for illuminating technology and policy pathways for more efficient service provision) and summary of the mitigation potentials estimated from relevant scenarios to date are in Section 5.3.3. Finally, it reviews the role of three megatrends that are transforming delivery of services in innovative ways – digitalisation, the sharing economy, and the circular economy (Section 5.3.4). The review of megatrends makes an assessment highlighting the potential risks of rebound effects, and even accelerated consumption; it also scopes for proactive and vigilant policies to harness their potential for future energy and resource demand reductions, and, conversely, avoiding undesirable outcomes.

5.3.1 Efficient Service Provision

This section organises demand reductions under the ASI framework. It presents service-oriented demand-side solutions consistent with decent living standards (Creutzig et al. 2018) (Table 5.1). The sharing economy, digitalisation, and the circular economy can all contribute to ASI strategies, with the circular economy tentatively more on the supply side, and the sharing economy and digitalisation tentatively more on the demand side (Section 5.3.4). These new service delivery models go beyond sectoral boundaries (IPCC sector chapter boundaries are explained in Chapter 12) and take advantage of technological innovations, design concepts, and innovative forms of cooperation, cutting across sectors to contribute to systemic changes worldwide. Some of these changes can be realised in the short term, such as energy access, while others may take a longer period, such as radical and systemic eco-innovations like shared electric autonomous vehicles. It is important to understand benefits and distributional impacts of these systemic changes.

5.3.1.1 Integration of Service Provision Solutions with Avoid-Shift-Improve Framework

Assessment of service-related mitigation options within the ASI framework is aided by decomposition of emissions intensities into explanatory contributing factors, which depend on the type of service delivered. Table 5.1 shows ASI options in selected sectors and services. It summarises resource, energy, and emissions intensities commonly used by type of service (Cuenot et al. 2010; Lucon et al. 2014; Fischedick et al. 2014). Also relevant are the concepts of service provision adequacy (Arrow et al. 2004; Samadi et al. 2017), establishing the extents to which consumption levels exceed (e.g., high-calorie diets contributing to health issues (Roy et al. 2012); excessive food waste) or fall short (e.g., malnourishment) of service level sufficiency (e.g., recommended calories) (Millward-Hopkins et al. 2020); and service level efficiency (e.g., effect of occupancy on the energy intensity of public transit passenger-km travelled (Schäfer and Yeh 2020). Service-oriented solutions are discussed in Table 5.1. Implementation of these solutions requires combinations of institutional, infrastructural, behavioural, socio-cultural, and business changes which are mentioned in Section 5.2 and discussed in Section 5.4.

Opportunities for avoiding waste associated with the provision of services, or avoiding overprovision of or excess demand for services, exist across multiple service categories. 'Avoid' options are relevant in all end-use sectors, namely, teleworking and avoiding long-haul flights, adjusting dwelling size to household size, and avoiding short-

Table 5.1 | Avoid-Shift-Improve options in selected sectors and services. Many options, such as urban form and infrastructures, are systemic, and influence several sectors simultaneously. Linkages to concepts presented in sectoral chapters are indicated in parentheses in the first column. Source: adapted from Creutzig at al. (2018).

Service	Emission decomposition factors	Avoid	Shift	Improve
Mobility [passenger-km] *(Chapters 8, 10, 11, 16)*	$kgCO_2 = $ (passenger km)* $(MJ\ pkm^{-1})*(kgCO_2\ MJ^{-1})$	**Innovative mobility to reduce passenger-km:** Integrate transport and land-use planning Smart logistics Teleworking Compact cities Fewer long-haul flights Local holidays	**Increased options for mobility MJ pkm^{-1}:** Modal shifts, from car to cycling, walking, or public transit Modal shift from air travel to high-speed rail	**Innovation in equipment design MJ pkm^{-1} and CO$_2$-eq MJ^{-1}:** Lightweight vehicles Hydrogen vehicles Electric vehicles Eco-driving
Shelter [square metres] *(Chapters 8, 9, 11)*	$kgCO_2 = $ (square metres)* (tonnes material m^{-2})* (kg CO$_2$ tonne material^{-1})	**Innovative dwellings to reduce square metres:** Smaller decent dwellings Shared common spaces Multigenerational housing	**Materials-efficient housing tonnes material m^{-2}:** Less material-intensive dwelling designs Shift from single-family to multi-family dwellings	**Low emission dwelling design kgCO$_2$ tonne^{-1} material:** Use wood as material Use low-carbon production processes for building materials (e.g., cement and steel)
Thermal comfort [indoor temperature] *(Chapters 9, 16)*	$kgCO_2 = (\Delta°C\ m^3$ to warm or cool) (MJ m^{-3})* (kgCO$_2$ MJ^{-1})	**Choice of healthy indoor temperature $\Delta°C\ m^3$:** Reduce m^2 as above Change temperature set-points Change dress code Change working times	**Design options to reduce MJ $\Delta°C^{-1}$ m^{-3}:** Architectural design (shading, natural ventilation, etc.)	**New technologies to reduce MJ $\Delta°C^{-1}$ m^{-3} and kgCO$_2$ MJ^{-1}:** Solar thermal devices Improved insulation Heat pumps District heating
Goods [units] *(Chapters 11, 12)*	$kgCO_2 = $ (product units)* (kg material product^{-1})* (kgCO$_2$ kg material^{-1})	**More service per product:** Reduce consumption quantities Long lasting fabric, appliances Sharing economy	**Innovative product design kg material product^{-1}:** Materials-efficient product designs	**Choice of new materials kgCO$_2$ kg material^{-1}:** Use of low-carbon materials New manufacturing processes and equipment use
Nutrition [calories consumed] *(Chapters 6, 12)*	$kgCO_2$-eq = (calories consumed)* (calories produced calories consumed^{-1})* (kgCO$_2$-eq calorie produced^{-1})	**Reduce calories produced/calories consumed and optimise calories consumed:** Keep calories in line with daily needs and health guidelines Reduce waste in supply chain and after purchase	**Add more variety in food plate to reduce kgCO$_2$-eq cal^{-1} produced:** Dietary shifts from ruminant meat and dairy to other protein sources while maintaining nutritional quality	**Reduce kgCO$_2$-eq cal^{-1} produced:** Improved agricultural practices Energy efficient food processing
Lighting [lumens] *(Chapters 9, 16)*	$kgCO_2 = $ lumens* (kWh lumen^{-1})* (kgCO$_2$ kWh^{-1})	**Minimise artificial lumen demand:** Occupancy sensors Lighting controls	**Design options to increase natural lumen supply:** Architectural designs with maximal daylighting	**Demand innovation lighting technologies kWh lumens^{-1} and power supply kgCO$_2$ kWh^{-1}:** LED lamps

lifespan products and food waste. Cities and built environments can play an additional role. For example, more compact designs and higher accessibility reduce travel demand and translate into lower average floor space and corresponding heating/cooling and lighting demand, and thus reductions of between 5% to 20% of GHG emissions of end-use sectors (Creutzig et al. 2021b). Avoidance of food loss and wastage – which equalled 8–10% of total anthropogenic GHG emissions from 2010–2016 (Mbow et al. 2019), while millions suffer from hunger and malnutrition – is a prime example (Chapter 12). A key challenge in meeting global nutrition services is therefore to avoid food loss and waste while simultaneously raising nutrition levels to equitable standards globally. Literature results indicate that in developed economies, consumers are the largest source of food waste, and that behavioural changes such as meal planning, use of leftovers, and avoidance of over-preparation can be important service-oriented solutions (Gunders et al. 2017; Schanes et al. 2018), while improvements to expiration labels by regulators would reduce unnecessary disposal of unexpired items (Wilson et al. 2017) and improved preservation in supply chains would reduce spoilage (Duncan and Gulbahar 2019). Around 931 million tonnes of food waste was generated in 2019 globally, 61% of which came from households, 26% from food service and 13% from retail.

Demand-side mitigations are achieved through changing *Socio-cultural factors*, *Infrastructure use* and *Technology adoption* by various social actors in urban and other settlements, food choice and waste management (*high confidence*) (Figure 5.7). In all sectors, end-use strategies can help reduce the majority of emissions, ranging from 28.7% (4.4 GtCO$_2$) emission reductions in the industry sector, to 44.2% (8.0 GtCO$_2$-eq) in the food sector, to 66.75% (4.6 GtCO$_2$) emission reductions in the land transport sector, and 66% (6.8 GtCO$_2$) in the buildings sector. These numbers are median estimates and represent benchmark accounting. Estimates are approximations, as they are simple products of individual assessments for each of the three options listed above. If interactions were taken into account, the full mitigation potentials may be higher or lower, independent of relevant barriers to realising the median potential estimates. See more in Chapter 5 Supplementary Material II, Table 5.SM.2.

The technical mitigation potential of food loss and waste reductions globally has been estimated at 0.1–5.8 GtCO$_2$-eq (*high confidence*) (Poore and Nemecek 2018; Smith, et al. 2019) (Section 7.4.5, Figure 5.7 and Table 12.3). Coupling food waste reductions with dietary shifts can further reduce energy, land, and resource demand in upstream food provision systems, leading to substantial GHG emissions benefits. The estimated technical potential for GHG emissions reductions associated with shifts to sustainable healthy diets is 0.5–8 $GtCO_2$-eq (*high confidence*) (Smith et al. 2013; Jarmul et al. 2020; Creutzig et al. 2021b) (Figure 5.7, Table 12.2). Current literature on health, diets, and emissions indicates that sustainable food systems providing healthy diets for all are within reach but require significant cross-sectoral action, including improved agricultural practices, dietary shifts among consumers, and food waste reductions in production, distribution, retail, and consumption (Erb et al. 2016; Muller et al. 2017; Graça et al. 2019; Willett and al. 2019) (Table 12.9).

Reduced food waste and dietary shifts have highly relevant repercussions in the land-use sector that underpin the high GHG emission reduction potential. Demand-side measures lead to changes in consumption of land-based resources and can save GHG emissions by reducing or improving management of residues or making land areas available for other uses such as afforestation or bioenergy production (Smith et al. 2013; Hoegh-Guldberg et al. 2019). Deforestation is the second-largest source of anthropogenic greenhouse gas emissions, caused mainly by expanding forestry and agriculture, and in many cases this agricultural expansion is driven by trade demand for food. For example, across the tropics, cattle and oilseed products account for half the deforestation carbon emissions, embodied in international trade to China and Europe (Creutzig et al. 2019a; Pendrill et al. 2019). Benefits from shifts in diets and resulting lowered land pressure are also reflected in reductions of land degradation and emissions.

Increased demand for biomass can increase the pressure on forest and conservation areas (Cowie et al. 2013) and poses a heightened risk for biodiversity, livelihoods, and intertemporal carbon balances (Lamb et al. 2016; Creutzig et al. 2021c), requiring policy and regulations to ensure sustainable forest management, which depends on forest type, region, climate, and ownership. This suggests that demand-side actions hold sustainability advantages over the intensive use of bioenergy and BECCS, but also enable land use for bioenergy by saving agricultural land for food.

In the transport sector, ASI opportunities exist at multiple levels, comprehensively summarised in Bongardt et al. (2013), Sims et al. (2014), and Roy et al. (2021) (Chapter 10). Modelling based on a plethora of bottom-up insights and options reveals that a balanced portfolio of ASI policies brings global transport sector emissions in line with global warming of not more than 1.5°C (Gota et al. 2019). For example, telework may be a significant lever for avoiding road transport associated with daily commutes, achievable through digitalisation, but its savings depend heavily on the modes, distances, and types of office use avoided (Hook et al. 2020) and whether additional travel is induced due to greater available time (Mokhtarian 2002) or vehicle use by other household members (Kim et al. 2015; de Abreu e Silva and Melo 2018). More robustly, avoiding kilometres travelled through improved urban planning and smart logistical systems can lead to fuel, and, hence, emissions savings (Creutzig et al. 2015a; IEA 2016; IEA 2017a; Wiedenhofer et al. 2018), or through avoiding long-haul flights (IEA 2021). For example, reallocating road and parking space to exclusive public transit lanes,

protected bike lanes and pedestrian priority streets can reduce vehicle kilometres travelled in urban areas (ITF 2021). At the vehicle level, lightweighting strategies (Fischedick et al. 2014) and avoiding inputs of carbon-intensive materials into vehicle manufacturing can also lead to significant emissions savings through improved fuel economy (Das et al. 2016; Hertwich et al. 2019; IEA 2019b).

Figure 5.7 shows socio-cultural factors can contribute up to 15% to land transport GHG emissions reduction by 2050, with 5% as our central estimate. Active mobility, such as walking and cycling, has 2–10% potential in GHG emissions reduction. Well designed teleworking policies can reduce transport-related GHG emissions by at least 1%. A systematic review demonstrates that 26 of 39 studies identified suggest that teleworking reduces energy use, induced mainly by distance travelled, and only eight studies suggest that teleworking increases or has a neutral impact on energy use (Hook et al. 2020). Infrastructure use (specifically urban planning and shared pooled mobility) has about 20–50% (on average) potential in land transport GHG emissions reduction, especially via redirecting the ongoing design of existing infrastructures in developing countries, and with 30% as our central estimate (Section 5.3.4.2). Technology adoption, particularly banning combustion and diesel engines and 100% EV targets (and other zero-carbon fuels, especially in freight) and efficient lightweight cars, can contribute to between 30% and 70% of GHG emissions reduction from land transport in 2050, with 50% as our central estimate (see Chapter 5 Supplementary Material II, Table 5.SM.2 and Chapter 10, Sections 10.4 and 10.7), consistent with scenario modelling (Figure 10.27) and based on rapid reduction in the GHG emission footprint of vehicle production. These numbers are consistent with the end of fossil fuel-based new cars in 2035 in major economies and of 100% of vehicles being zero-emission vehicles in 2050. Other economies that display vehicles obtained on second hand markets may phase out fossil fuel cars only after 2050, hence limiting the overall mitigation potential of electric vehicles to well below 100% in 2050. Higher energy use and CO_2-footprint in BEV production compared to ICE production are to be met with more rapid decarbonisation of the industry sector and by the reduced need for overall vehicle stock, due to socio-cultural and infrastructure measures. Ehrenberger et al. (2021) shows that the development of technologies, fleets, and their use are decisive factors in reducing the use of fossil energies, resulting in 26–65% CO_2 emissions reduction potential until 2040 for the case of Germany. Electric vehicles can be used to provide new shared services. In this case, reductions of CO_2 emissions of close to 20% can be obtained in a scenario where 20% of car trips and all bus feeder trips are replaced, but considerably higher reductions are possible when shared pooled mobility replaces private vehicle trips in urban areas (ITF 2017b, ITF 2017d). A study shows that ICE vehicles reduce CO_2 emissions to 60% or 80% of current emissions levels by 2050 (Hill et al. 2019). Similarly, the power grid decarbonisation is assumed to improve to either 50% or 80% over current rates, with 80% being the expected decarbonisation and 50% a more conservative estimate. Each possibility for EV adoption rate, ICE efficiency improvement, and power decarbonisation is combined (Hill et al. 2019). Beyond consuming less energy, EVs enable greater use of low-carbon and renewable energy sources than is possible for conventional petroleum-based fuels. These technical advantages lead to the potential for greatly reducing petroleum use, air pollution and carbon emissions. International collaboration could better leverage

5

Demand-side mitigation can be achieved through changes in socio-cultural factors, infrastructure design and use, and end-use technology adoption by 2050.

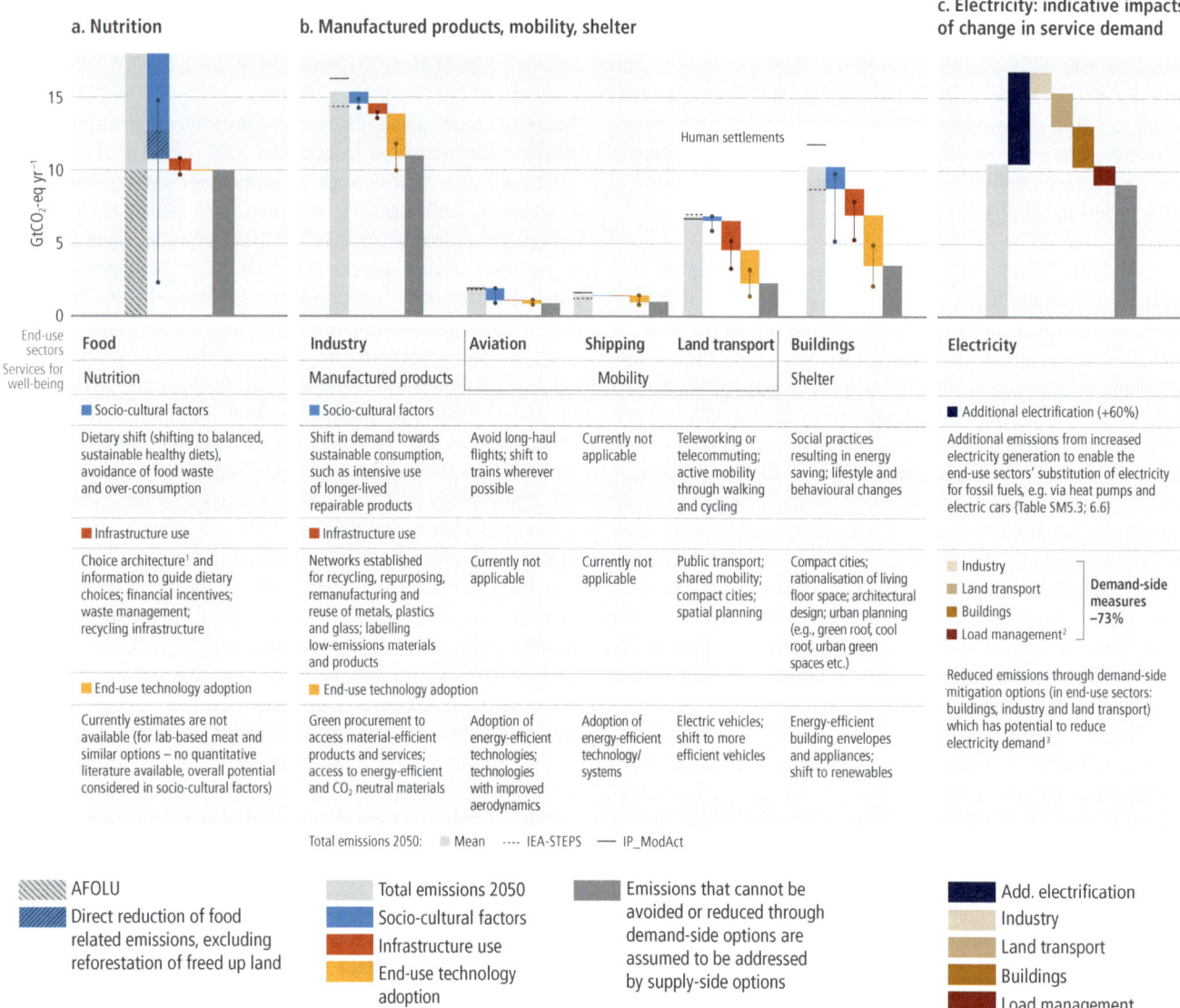

a. Nutrition

b. Manufactured products, mobility, shelter

c. Electricity: indicative impacts of change in service demand

	Food	Industry	Aviation	Shipping	Land transport	Buildings	Electricity
End-use sectors							
Services for well-being	Nutrition	Manufactured products		Mobility		Shelter	

■ Socio-cultural factors (Food / Industry)

Food	Industry	Aviation	Shipping	Land transport	Buildings	Electricity
Dietary shift (shifting to balanced, sustainable healthy diets), avoidance of food waste and over-consumption	Shift in demand towards sustainable consumption, such as intensive use of longer-lived repairable products	Avoid long-haul flights; shift to trains wherever possible	Currently not applicable	Teleworking or telecommuting; active mobility through walking and cycling	Social practices resulting in energy saving; lifestyle and behavioural changes	**■ Additional electrification (+60%)** Additional emissions from increased electricity generation to enable the end-use sectors' substitution of electricity for fossil fuels, e.g. via heat pumps and electric cars {Table SM5.3; 6.6}

■ Infrastructure use (Food / Industry)

Food	Industry	Aviation	Shipping	Land transport	Buildings
Choice architecture[1] and information to guide dietary choices; financial incentives; waste management; recycling infrastructure	Networks established for recycling, repurposing, remanufacturing and reuse of metals, plastics and glass; labelling low-emissions materials and products	Currently not applicable	Currently not applicable	Public transport; shared mobility; compact cities; spatial planning	Compact cities; rationalisation of living floor space; architectural design; urban planning (e.g., green roof, cool roof, urban green spaces etc.)

■ Industry
■ Land transport   **Demand-side measures –73%**
■ Buildings
■ Load management[2]

■ End-use technology adoption (Food / Industry)

Food	Industry	Aviation	Shipping	Land transport	Buildings
Currently estimates are not available (for lab-based meat and similar options – no quantitative literature available, overall potential considered in socio-cultural factors)	Green procurement to access material-efficient products and services; access to energy-efficient and CO$_2$ neutral materials	Adoption of energy-efficient technologies; technologies with improved aerodynamics	Adoption of energy-efficient technology/ systems	Electric vehicles; shift to more efficient vehicles	Energy-efficient building envelopes and appliances; shift to renewables

Reduced emissions through demand-side mitigation options (in end-use sectors: buildings, industry and land transport) which has potential to reduce electricity demand[3]

Total emissions 2050: ▨ Mean ···· IEA-STEPS —— IP_ModAct

Legend:
- ▨ AFOLU
- ▨ Direct reduction of food related emissions, excluding reforestation of freed up land
- ▨ Total emissions 2050
- ▨ Socio-cultural factors
- ▨ Infrastructure use
- ▨ End-use technology adoption
- ▨ Emissions that cannot be avoided or reduced through demand-side options are assumed to be addressed by supply-side options
- ■ Add. electrification
- ■ Industry
- ■ Land transport
- ■ Buildings
- ■ Load management

[1] The presentation of choices to consumers, and the impact of that presentation on consumer decision-making.

[2] Load management refers to demand-side flexibility that cuts across all sectors and can be achieved through incentive design like time of use pricing/monitoring by artificial intelligence, diversification of storage facilities, etc.

[3] The impact of demand-side mitigation on electricity sector emissions depends on the baseline carbon intensity of electricity supply, which is scenario dependent.

Figure 5.7 | Demand-side mitigation options and indicative potentials. Demand-side mitigation response options related to demand for services have been categorised into three broad domains: 'socio-cultural factors', associated with individual choices, behaviour and lifestyle change, social norms and culture; 'infrastructure use', related to the design and use of supporting hard and soft infrastructure that enables changes in individual choices and behaviour; and 'end-use technology adoption', which refers to the uptake of technologies by end users. Demand-side mitigation is a central element of the IMP-LD and IMP-SP scenarios (Section 3.3). Food (nutrition) demand-side potentials in 2050 assessment is based on bottom-up studies and estimated following the 2050 baseline for the food sector presented in peer-reviewed literature (more information in Chapter 5 Supplementary Material II and Chapter 7, Section 7.4.5). Industry (manufactured products), land transport, aviation and shipping (mobility), and buildings (shelter) assessment of potentials for total emissions in 2050 are estimated based on approximately 500 bottom-up studies representing all global regions (detailed list is in Table 5. SM.2). Baseline is provided by the sectoral mean GHG emissions in 2050 of the two scenarios consistent with policies announced by national governments until 2020. The heights of the coloured columns represent the potentials represented by the median value. These are based on a range of values available in the case studies from literature shown in Chapter 5 Supplementary Material II. The range is shown by the dots connected by dotted lines representing the highest and the lowest potentials reported in the literature. The demand-side potential of socio-cultural factors in food has two parts. The median value of direct emissions (mostly non-CO$_2$) reduction through socio-cultural factors is 1.9 GtCO$_2$-eq without considering land-use change through reforestation of freed up land. If changes in land-use patterns enabled by this change in food demand are considered, the indicative potential could reach 7 GtCO$_2$-eq. The 'electricity' panel presents how sectoral demand-side mitigation options (industry, transport and buildings) can change demand on the electricity distribution system. Electricity accounts for an increasing proportion of final energy demand in 2050 ('additional electrification' bar) in line with multiple bottom-up studies (detailed list is in Table 5.SM.3) and Chapter 6 (Section 6.6). These studies are used to compute the impact of end-use electrification which increases overall electricity demand. Some of the projected increase in electricity demand can be avoided through demand-side mitigation options in the domains of socio-cultural factors and infrastructure use strategies in end-use electricity use in buildings, industry and land transport found in literature based on bottom-up assessments (Section 5.3 and Chapter 5 Supplementary Material II).

5

existing efforts to promote zero-emission vehicles. The establishment of a zero-emission vehicle deployment target and an electric mobility target for 2035 would help in establishing a common long-term global electric-drive vision (Lutsey 2015).

Socio-cultural factors such as avoiding long-haul flights and shifting to train wherever possible can contribute between 10% and 40% to aviation GHG emissions reduction by 2050 (Figure 5.7). Maritime transport (shipping) emits around 940 $MtCO_2$ annually and is responsible for about 2.5% of global GHG emissions (IMO 2020). Technology measures and management measures, such as slow steaming, weather routing, contra-rotating propellers, and propulsion efficiency devices can deliver more fuel savings between 1% and 40% than the investment required (Bouman et al. 2017) (Chapter 5, Supplementary Material II, Table 5.SM.2).

In the buildings sector, avoidance strategies can occur at the end use or individual building operation level. End-use technologies and strategies such as the use of daylighting (Bodart and De Herde 2002) and lighting sensors can avoid demand for lumens from artificial light, while passive houses, thermal mass, and smart controllers can avoid demand for space conditioning services. Eliminating standby power losses can avoid energy wasted for no useful service in many appliances and devices, which may reduce household electricity use by up to 10% (Roy et al. 2012). At the building level, smaller dwellings can reduce overall demand for lighting and space conditioning services, while smaller dwellings, shared housing, and building lifespan extension can all reduce the overall demand for carbon-intensive building materials such as concrete and steel (Material Economics 2018; Hertwich et al. 2019; IEA 2019b; Pauliuk et al. 2021). Emerging strategies for materials efficiency, such as 3D printing to optimise the geometries and minimise the materials content of structural elements, may also play a key role if thermal performance and circularity can be improved (Mahadevan et al. 2020; Adaloudis and Bonnin Roca 2021). Several scenarios estimate an 'Avoid' potential in the building sector, which includes reducing waste in superfluous floor space, heating and IT equipment, and energy use, of between 10% and 30%, in one case even by 50% (Nadel and Ungar 2019) (Chapter 9).

Socio-cultural factors and behavioural and social practices in energy saving, like adaptive heating and cooling by changing temperature, can contribute about 15% to GHG emissions reduction in the buildings sector by 2050 (Figure 5.7). Infrastructure use such as compact city and urban planning interventions, living floor space rationalisation, and access to low-carbon architectural design has about 20% potential in building sector GHG emissions reduction. Technology adoption, particularly access to energy efficient technologies, and installation of renewable energy technologies can contribute between 30% and 70% to GHG emissions reduction in the buildings sector (Chapters 8 and 9 and Chapter 5 Supplementary Material II, Table 5.SM.2).

Service efficiency strategies are emerging to avoid materials demand at the product level, including dematerialisation strategies for various forms of packaging (Worrell and Van Sluisveld 2013) and the concept of 'products as services', in which product systems are designed and maintained for long lifespans to provide a marketable service (Oliva and Kallenberg 2003), thereby reducing the number of products

sold and tonnes of materials needed to provide the same service to consumers, consistent with circular economy and materials efficiency principles (Chapter 11). Successful examples of this approach have been documented for carpets (Stubbs and Cocklin 2008), copiers (Roy 2000), kitchens (Liedtke et al. 1998), vehicles (Williams 2006; Ceschin and Vezzoli 2010) and more (Roy 2000).

'Shift' strategies unique to the service-oriented perspective generally involve meeting service demands at much lower lifecycle energy, emissions, and resource intensities (Roy and Pal 2009), through such strategies as shifting from single-family to multi-family dwellings (reducing the materials intensity per unit floor area (Ochsendorf et al. 2011)), shifting from passenger cars to rail or bus (reducing fuel, vehicle manufacturing, and infrastructure requirements (Chester and Horvath 2009)), shifting materials to reduce resource and emissions intensities (e.g., low-carbon concrete blends (Scrivener and Gartner 2018)) and shifting from conventional to additive manufacturing processes to reduce materials requirements and improve end-use product performance (Huang et al. 2016, 2017).

An important consideration in all ASI strategies is the potential for unintended rebound effects (Sorrell et al. 2009; Brockway et al. 2021) as indicated in Figures 5.8, 5.12, and 5.13a, which must be carefully avoided through various regulatory and behavioural measures (Santarius et al. 2016). In many developing country contexts, rebound effects can help in accelerated provision of affordable access to modern energy and a minimum level of per capita energy consumption (Saunders et al. 2021; Chakravarty and Roy 2021). Extending the lifespan of energy inefficient products may lead to net increases in emissions (Gutowski et al. 2011), whereas automated car sharing may reduce the number of cars manufactured at the expense of increased demand for passenger kilometres due to lower travel opportunity cost (Wadud et al. 2016) (Section 5.3.2).

Avoiding short lifespan products in favour of products with longer lifespan as a socio-cultural factor; and infrastructure use measures such as increasing the re-usability and recyclability of products' components and materials, and adopting materials-efficient services and CO_2-neutral materials, have about 29% indicative potential by 2050. (Chapter 11 and Chapter 5 Supplementary Material II, Table 5.SM.2).

In summary, sector-specific demand-side mitigation options reflect the important role of socio-cultural, technological and infrastructural factors and the interdependence among them (Figure 5.7). The assessment in Figure 5.7 shows that by 2050 high emission reduction potential can be realised with demand-side actions alone, which can be complementary to supply-side interventions, with considerable impact by reducing the need for capacity addition on the electricity supply system. Integrated cross-sectoral actions shown through sector coupling is also important for investment decision-making and policy framing going beyond sector boundaries (*high evidence* and *high agreement*).

5.3.1.2   Household Consumption Options to Reduce GHG Emissions

A systematic review of options to reduce the GHG emissions associated with household consumption activities identified

5

6,990 peer-reviewed journal papers, with 771 options that were aggregated into 61 consumption option categories (Ivanova et al. 2020) (Figure 5.8). Consistently with previous research (Herendeen and Tanaka 1976; Pachauri and Spreng 2002; Pachauri 2007; Ivanova et al. 2016), a hierarchical list of mitigation options emerges. Choosing low-carbon options, such as car-free living, plant-based diets with no or very little animal products, low-carbon sources of electricity and heating at home, as well as local holiday plans, can reduce an individual's carbon footprint by up to 9 tCO$_2$-eq. Realising these options requires substantial policy support to overcome infrastructural, institutional and socio-cultural lock-in (Sections 5.4 and 5.6).

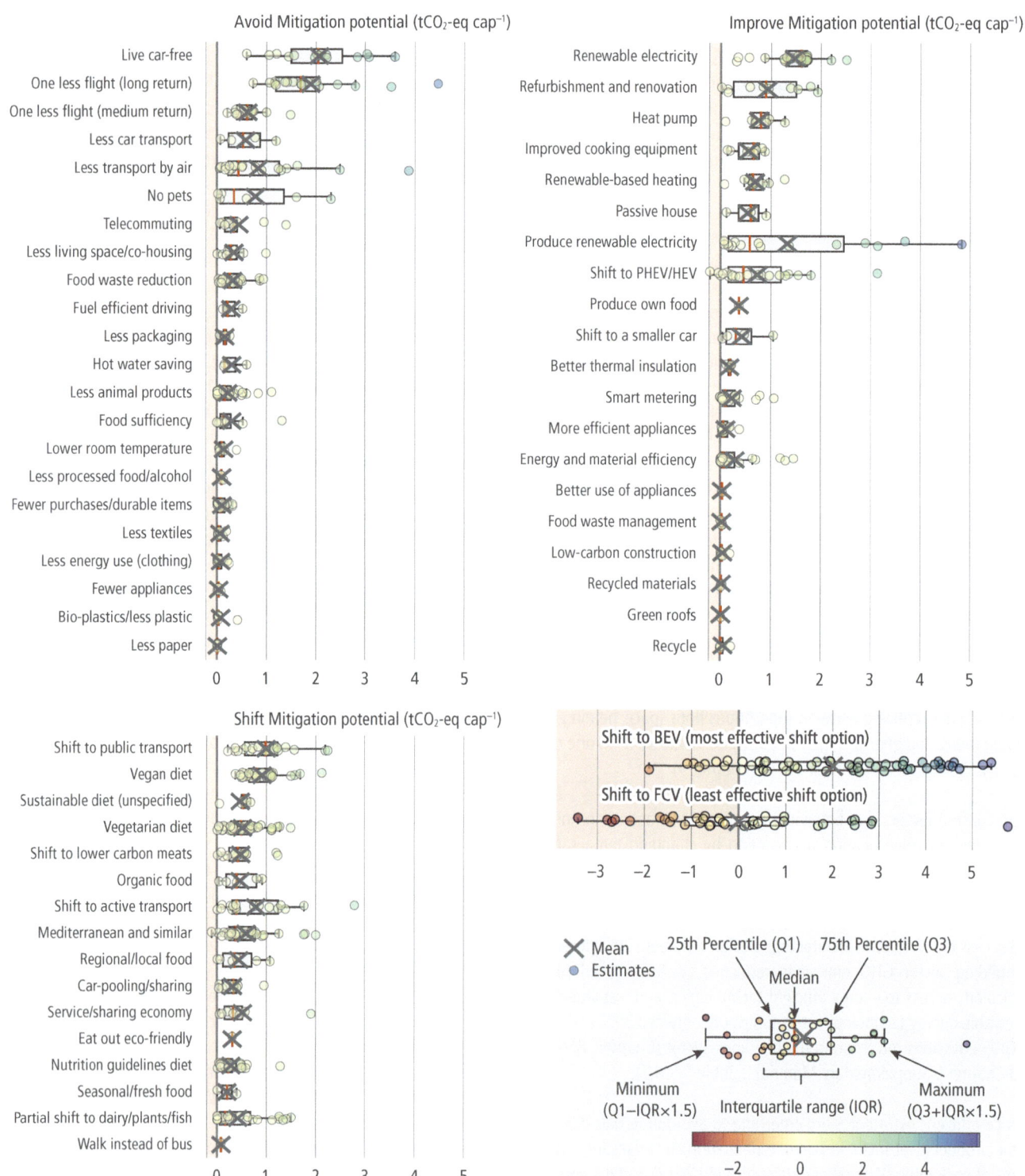

Figure 5.8 | Synthesis of 60 demand-side options ordered by the median GHG mitigation potential found across all estimates from the literature. The grey crosses are averages. The boxes represent the 25th percentile, median and 75th percentiles of study results. The whiskers or dots show the minimum and maximum mitigation potentials of each option. Negative values (in the red area) represent the potentials for backfire due to rebound, i.e., a net increase of GHG emissions due to adopting the option. Source: with permission from Ivanova et al. (2020).

5.3.2 Technical Tools to Identify Avoid-Shift-Improve Options

Service delivery systems to satisfy a variety of service needs (e.g., mobility, nutrition, thermal comfort, etc.) comprise a series of interlinked processes to convert primary resources (e.g., coal, minerals) into useable products (e.g., electricity, copper wires, lamps, light bulbs). It is useful to differentiate between conversion and processing steps 'upstream' of end users (mines, power plants, manufacturing facilities) and 'downstream', that is, those associated with end-users, including service levels, and direct well-being benefits for people (Kalt et al. 2019). Illustrative examples of such resource processing systems

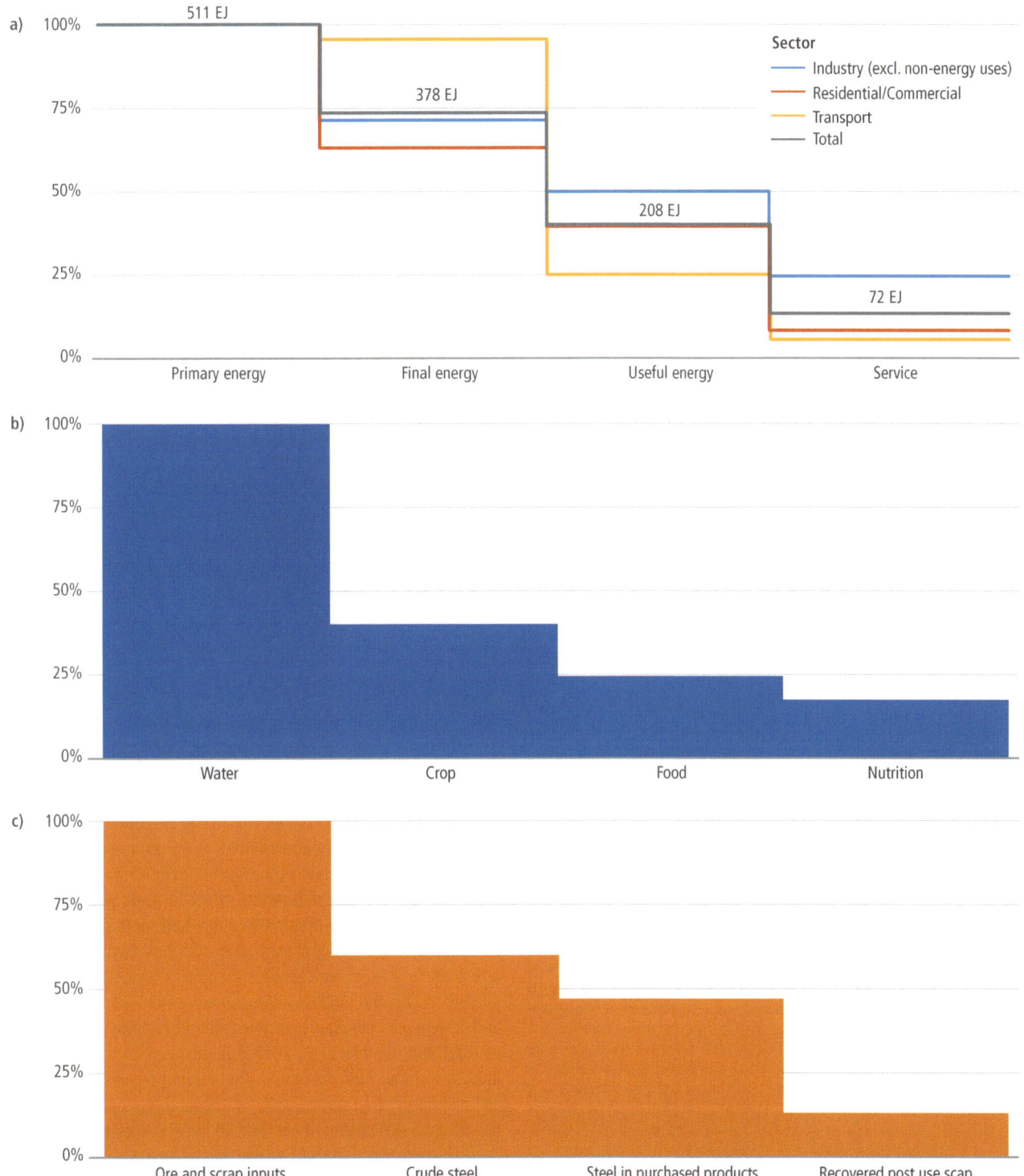

Figure 5.9 | Resource processing steps and efficiency cascades (in percentage of primary resource inputs [vertical axis] remaining at respective steps until ultimate service delivery) for illustrative global service delivery systems for energy (panel (a), disaggregated into three sectoral service types and the aggregate total), food (panel (b), water use in agriculture and food processing, delivery and use), and materials (panel (c), example steel). The aggregate efficiencies of service delivery chains is with 13–17% low. Source: TWI2050 (2018).

and associated conversion losses drawn from the literature are shown in Figure 5.9, in the form of resource processing cascades for energy (direct energy conversion efficiencies (Nakićenović et al. 1993; De Stercke 2014)), water use in food production systems (water use efficiency and embodied water losses in food delivery and consumption (Lundqvist et al. 2008; Sadras et al. 2011)), and materials (Ayres and Simonis 1994; Fischer-Kowalski et al. 2011), using the example of steel manufacturing, use and recycling at the global level (Allwood and Cullen 2012). Invariably, conversion losses along the entire service delivery systems are substantial, ranging from 83% (water) to 86% (energy) and 87% (steel) of primary resource inputs (TWI2050 2018). In other words, only between 14 to 17% of the harnessed primary resources remain at the level of ultimate service delivery.

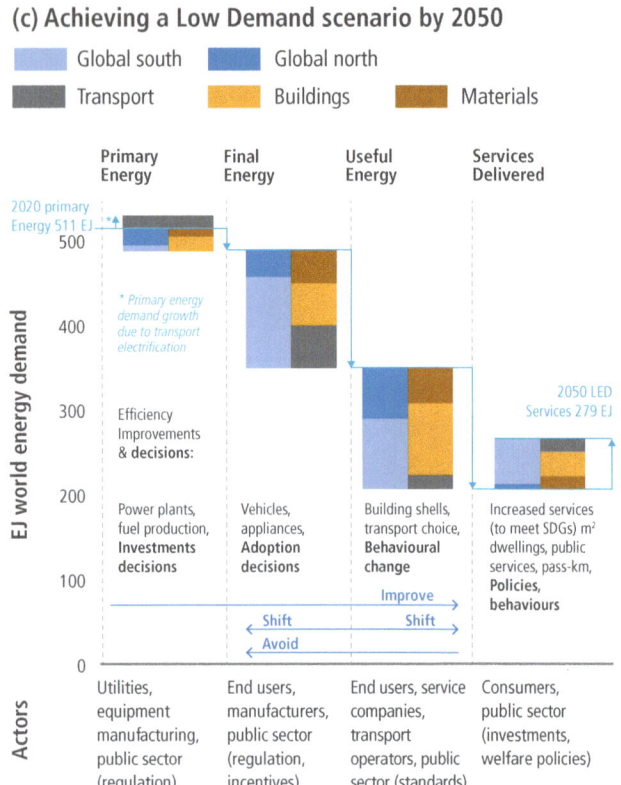

(c) Achieving a Low Demand scenario by 2050

Improved service provisioning systems enable increases in service levels and at the same time a reduction in upstream energy demand by 45%.

Figure 5.10 | Realisable energy efficiency improvements by region and by end-use type between 2020 and 2050 in an illustrative Low Energy Demand scenario (in EJ). Efficiency improvements are decomposed by respective steps in the conversion chain from primary energy to final, and useful, energy, and to service delivery, and disaggregated by region (developed and developing countries) and end-use type (buildings, transport, materials). Improvements are dominated by improved efficiency in service delivery (153 EJ) and by more efficient end-use energy conversion (134 EJ). Improvements in service efficiency in transport shown here are conservative in this scenario but could be substantially higher with the full adoption of integrated urban shared mobility schemes. Increases in energy use due to increases in service levels and system effects of transport electrification (grey bars on top of first pair in the bar charts) that counterbalance some of the efficiency improvements are also shown. Examples of options for efficiency improvements and decision involved (grey text in the chart), the relative weight of generic demand-side strategies (Avoid-Shift-Improve blue arrows), as well as prototype actors involved, are also illustrated. Data source: Figure 5.9 and Grubler et al. (2018).

Examples of conversion losses on the supply side of resource processing systems include, for instance: for energy, electricity generation (global output/input conversion efficiency of electric plants of 45% as shown in energy balance statistics (IEA 2020b)); for water embodied in food, irrigation water use efficiency (some 40% (Sadras et al. 2011)) and calorific conversion efficiency (food calories in to food calories out) in meat production of 60% (Lundqvist et al. 2008), or for materials, globally only 47% of primary iron ore extracted and recovered steel scrap end up as steel in purchased products, (i.e., a loss of 57%) (Allwood and Cullen 2012).

A substantial part of losses happens at the end-use point and in final service delivery (where losses account for 47% to 60% of aggregate systems losses for steel and energy respectively, and 23% in the case of water embodied in food). The efficiency of service delivery (Brand-Correa and Steinberger 2017) has usually both a technological component (efficiency of end-use devices such as cars, light bulbs) and a behavioural component (i.e., how efficiently end-use devices are used, e.g., load factors) (Dietz et al. 2009; Laitner et al. 2009; Norton 2012; Kane and Srinivas 2014; Ehrhardt-Martinez 2015; Thaler 2015; Lopes et al. 2017). Using the example of mobility, where service levels are usually expressed by passenger-km, service delivery efficiency is thus a function of the fuel efficiency of the vehicle and its drivetrain (typically only about 20%–25% for internal combustion engines, but close to 100% for electric motors) plus how many passengers the vehicle actually transports (load factor, typically as low as 20–25%, i.e. one passenger per vehicle that could seat four to five), that is, an aggregate end-use efficiency of between 4–6% only. Aggregated energy end-use efficiencies at the global level are estimated as low as 20% (De Stercke 2014), 13% for steel (recovered post-use scrap) (Allwood and Cullen 2012), and some 70% for food (including distribution losses and food waste of some 30%) (Lundqvist et al. 2008).

To harness additional gains in efficiency by shifting the focus in service delivery systems to the end user can translate into large upstream resource reductions. For each unit of improvement at the end-use point of the service delivery system (examples shown in Figure 5.9), primary resource inputs are reduced between a factor of 6 to 7 units (water, steel, energy) (TWI2050 2018). For example, reducing energy needs for final service delivery equivalent to 1 EJ, reduces primary energy needs by some 7 EJ. There is thus *high evidence* and *high agreement* in the literature that the leverage effect for improvements in end-use service delivery efficiency through behavioural, technological, and market organisational innovations is very large, ranging from a factor 6 to 7 (resource cascades) to up to a factor 10 to 20 (exergy analysis), with the highest improvement potentials at the end-user and service provisioning levels (for systemic reviews see Nakićenović et al. (1996a), Grubler et al. (2012b), and Sousa et al. (2017)). Also, the literature shows *high agreement* that current conversion efficiencies are invariably low, particularly for those components at the end-use and service-delivery back end of service provisioning systems. It also suggests that efficiencies might actually be even lower than those revealed by direct input-output resource accounting, as discussed above (Figure 5.9). Illustrative exergy efficiencies of entire national or global service delivery systems range from 2.5% (USA (Ayres 1989)) to 5% (OECD average (Grubler et al. 2012b)) and 10% (global (Nakićenović et al., 1996)). Studies that adopt more restricted systems boundaries, either leaving out upstream resource processing/conversion or conversely end-use and service provision, show typical exergetic efficiencies between 15% (city of Geneva (Grubler et al. 2012a)) to below 25% (Japan, Italy, and Brazil, albeit with incomplete systems coverage that miss important conversion losses (Nakićenović et al. 1996b)). These findings are confirmed by more recent exergy efficiency studies that also include longitudinal time trend analysis (Cullen and Allwood 2010; Brockway et al. 2014; Serrenho et al. 2014; Brockway et al. 2015; Guevara et al. 2016). Figure 5.10 illustrates how energy demand reductions can be realised by improving the resource efficiency cascades shown in Figure 5.9.

5.3.3   Low Demand Scenarios

Long-term mitigation scenarios play a crucial role in climate policy design in the near term, by illuminating transition pathways, interactions between supply-side and demand-side interventions, their timing, and the scales of required investments needed to achieve mitigation goals (Chapter 3). Historically, most long-term mitigation scenarios have taken technology-centric approaches with heavy reliance on supply-side solutions and the use of carbon dioxide removal, particularly in 1.5°C scenarios (Rogelj et al. 2018). Comparatively less attention has been paid to deep demand-side reductions incorporating socio-cultural change and the cascade effects (Section 5.3.2) associated with ASI strategies, primarily due to limited past representation of such service-oriented interventions in long-term integrated assessment models (IAMs) and energy systems models (ESMs) (Grubler et al. 2018; van de Ven et al. 2018; Napp et al. 2019). There is ample evidence of savings from sector- or issue-specific bottom-up studies (Section 5.3.1.2). However, these savings typically get lost in the dominant narrative provided by IAMs and ESMs and in their aggregate-level evaluations of combinations of ASI and efficiency strategies. As a result, their interaction effects do not typically get equal focus alongside supply-side and carbon dioxide removal options (Samadi et al. 2017; Van Vuuren et al. 2018; Van den Berg et al. 2019).

In response to 1.5°C ambitions, and a growing desire to identify participatory pathways with less reliance on carbon dioxide removal which has high uncertainty, some recent IAM and ESM mitigation scenarios have explored the role of deep demand-side energy and resource use reduction potentials at global and regional levels. Table 5.2 summarises long-term scenarios that aimed to: minimise service-level energy and resource demand as a central mitigation tenet; specifically evaluate the role of behavioural change and ASI strategies; and/or achieve a carbon budget with limited or no carbon dioxide removal. From assessment of this emerging body of literature, several general observations arise and are presented below.

First, socio-cultural changes within transition pathways can offer gigatonne-scale CO_2 savings potential at the global level, and therefore represent a substantial overlooked strategy in traditional mitigation scenarios. Two lifestyle change scenarios conducted with the IMAGE IAM suggested that behaviour and cultural changes such as heating and cooling set-point adjustments, shorter showers, reduced appliance use, shifts to public transit, less meat-intensive diets, and improved recycling can deliver an additional 1.7 Gt and 3 $GtCO_2$ savings in 2050, beyond the savings achieved in traditional technology-centric mitigation scenarios for the 2°C and 1.5°C ambitions, respectively (van Sluisveld et al. 2016; Van Vuuren et al. 2018). In its Sustainable Development Scenario, the IEA's behavioural change and resource efficiency wedges deliver around 3 $GtCO_2$-eq reduction in 2050, combined savings, roughly equivalent to those of solar PV that same year (IEA 2019a). In Europe, a Global Change Assessment Model (GCAM) scenario evaluating combined lifestyle changes such as teleworking, travel avoidance, dietary shifts, food waste reductions, and recycling reduced cumulative EU 27 CO_2 emissions 2011–2050 by up to 16% compared to an SSP2 baseline (van de Ven et al. 2018). Also in Europe, a multi-regional input-output analysis suggested that adoption of low-carbon consumption practices could reduce carbon footprints by 25%, or 1.4 Gt (Moran et al. 2020). A global transport scenario suggests that transport sector emissions can decline from business-as-usual 18 $GtCO_2$-eq to 2 $GtCO_2$-eq if ASI strategies are deployed (Gota et al. 2019), a value considerably below the estimates provided in IAM scenarios that have limited or no resolution in ASI strategies (Chapter 10).

The IEA's Net-Zero Emissions by 2050 (NZE) scenario, in which behavioural changes lead to 1.7 $GtCO_2$ savings in 2030, expresses the substantial mitigation opportunity in terms of low-carbon technology equivalencies: to achieve the same emissions reductions, the global share of EVs in the NZE would have to increase from 20% to 45% by 2030 or the number of installed heat pumps in homes would have to increase from 440 to 660 million by 2030 (IEA 2021).

In light of the limited number of mitigation scenarios that represent socio-behavioural changes explicitly, there is *medium evidence* in the literature that such changes can reduce emissions at regional and global levels, but *high agreement* within that literature that such changes hold up to gigatonne-scale CO_2 emissions reduction potentials.

Second, pursuant to the ASI principle, deep demand reductions require parallel pursuit of behavioural change and advanced energy-efficient technology deployment; neither is sufficient on its own. The LED scenario (Figure 5.10) combines behavioural and technological change consistent with numerous ASI strategies that leverage digitalisation, sharing, and circular economy megatrends to deliver decent living standards while reducing global final energy demand in 2050 to 245 EJ (Grubler et al. 2018). This value is 40% lower than final energy demand in 2018 (IEA 2019a), and a lower 2050 outcome than other IAM/ESM scenarios with primarily technology-centric mitigation approaches (Teske et al. 2015; IEA 2017b). In the IEA's B2DS scenario, Avoid/Shift in the transport sector accounts for around 2 $GtCO_2$-eq yr^{-1} in 2060, whereas parallel vehicle efficiency improvements increase the overall mitigation wedge to 5.5 $GtCO_2$-eq yr^{-1} in 2060 (IEA 2017b). Through a combination of behavioural change and energy-efficient technology adoption, the IEA's NZE requires only 340 EJ of global final energy demand with universal energy access in 2050, which is among the lowest of IPCC net zero SR1.5 scenarios (IEA 2021).

Table 5.2 | Summary of long-term scenarios with elements that aimed to minimise service-level energy and resource demand.

#	Scenario [Temp]	IAM/ESM	Final energy	Global scenarios – Scope	Focused demand reduction element(s) – Sectors^a	Key demand reduction measures considered (A, S, I)^b	Baseline scenario	Mitigation potential^c – CO2 (Gt)	Mitigation potential^c – Final energy	Mitigation potential^c – Primary energy
1	Lifestyle change scenario [2°C]	IMAGE	–	Whole scenario	R, T, I	A: set-points, smaller houses, reduced shower times, wash temperatures, standby loss, reduced car travel, reduced plastics; S: from cars to bikes, rail; I: improved plastic recycling	2°C technology-centric scenario in 2050	1.9	–	–
2	Sustainable Development scenario [1.8°C]	World Energy Model (WEM)	398 EJ in 2040	Behavioural change wedge and resource efficiency wedge	T, I	S: shifts from cars to mass transit, building lifespan extension, materials-efficient construction, product reuse; I: improved recycling	Stated policies in 2050	3	–	–
3	Beyond 2 Degrees scenario [1.75°C]	ETP-TIMES	377 EJ in 2050	Transport Avoid/Shift wedge and material efficiency wedge	T, I	A: shorter car trips, optimised truck routing and utilisation; S: shifts from cars to mass transit; I: plastics and metal recycling, production yield improvements	Stated policies in 2060	2.8	–	–
4	Lifestyle change scenario [1.5°C]	IMAGE	322 EJ in 2050	Whole scenario	R, C, T, I	A: set-points, reduced appliance use; S: from cars to mass transit, less meat-intensive diets, cultured meat; I: best available technologies across sectors	1.5°C technology-centric scenario in 2050	3.1	–	–
5	Low Energy Demand scenario [1.5°C]	MESSAGE	245 EJ in 2050	Whole scenario	R, C, T, I, F	A: device integration, telework, shared mobility, material efficiency, dematerialisation, reduced paper; S: multi-purpose dwellings, healthier diets; I: best available technologies across sectors	Final energy in 2020	–	179 EJ	–
6	Advanced Energy [R]evolution	–	279 EJ in 2050	Whole scenario	R, C, T, I	S: shifts from cars to mass transit; I: best available technologies across sectors	Continuation of current trends and policies in 2050	–	260 EJ	–
7	Limited BECCS – lifestyle change [1.5°C]	IMAGE	–	Whole scenario	R, C, T, F	A: set-points, reduced appliance use; S: from cars to mass transit, less meat-intensive diets, cultured meat; I: best available technologies across sectors	1.5°C technology-centric scenario in 2050	2.2 Gt	–	82 EJ
8	Lifestyle scenario [1.5°C]	AIM	374 EJ in 2050	Whole scenario	T, I, F	A: reduced transport services demand, reduced demand for industrial goods; S: less meat-intensive diets	1.5°C supply technology-centric scenario in 2050	–	42 EJ	–
9	Transport scenario [1.5°C]	Bottom-up construction	–	Whole scenario	T	A: multiple options; S: multiple options; I: multiple options		89% vs BAU: 16GtCO2	–	–
10	Net Zero Emissions 2050 scenario	World Energy Model (WEM)	–	Behaviour change wedge	R, T	A: set-points, line drying, reduced wash temperatures, telework, reduced air travel; S: shifts to walking, cycling; I: eco-driving	Stated policies in 2030	2	–	–
11	Decent living with minimum energy	Bottom-up construction	149 EJ in 2050	Whole scenario	R, T, I, F	A: activity levels for mobility, shelter, nutrition, etc., consistent with decent living standards; S: shifts away from animal-based foods, shifts to public transit, etc.; I: energy efficiency consistent with best available technologies	IEA Stated Policies Scenario in 2050	–	75%	–
12	Net-Zero Emissions by 2050 Scenario (NZE)	Hybrid model based on WEM and ETP-TIMES	340 EJ in 2050	Behavioural change reductions	R, C, T, I	A: heating, air conditioning, and hot water set-points, reduce international flights, line drying, vehicle light-weighting, materials-efficient construction, building lifespan extension; S: shifts from regional flights to high-speed rail, cars to walking, cycling or public transport; I: eco-driving, plastics recycling	Stated policies in 2050	2.6	37 EJ	–

5

| # | Scenario [Temp] | IAM/ESM | Final energy | Global scenarios | | Focused demand reduction element(s) | | Baseline scenario | Mitigation potential[c] | | |
				Scope	Sectors[a]	Key demand reduction measures considered (A, S, I)[b]			CO$_2$ (Gt)	Final energy	Primary energy
Regional scenarios											
13	Urban mitigation wedge	–	540 EJ in global cities in 2050	Whole scenario	R, C, T	A: reduced transport demand S: mixed-use developments I: vehicle efficiency, building codes and retrofits		Current trends to 2050	–	180 EJ	–
14	France 2072 collective society	TIMES-Fr	4.2 EJ in France in 2072	Whole scenario	R, T	A: less travel by car and plane, longer building and device lifespans, less spending S: shared housing, shifts from cars to walking, biking, mass transit		Final energy in 2014	–	1.7 EJ	–
15	EU 27 lifestyle change – enthusiastic profile	GCAM	–	Whole scenario	R, T, F	A: telework, avoid short flights, closer holidays, food waste reduction, car sharing, set-points S: vegan diet, shifts to cycling and public transit I: eco-driving, composting, paper, metal, plastic, and glass recycling		SSP2, cumulative emissions 2011–2050	16%	–	–
16	Europe broader regime change scenario	IMAGE	35 EJ in EU in 2050	Whole scenario	R, T	A: reduced passenger and air travel, smaller dwellings, fewer appliances, reduced shower times, set points, avoid standby losses S: car sharing, shifts to public transit I: best available technologies		SSP2 in 2050	–	10 EJ	–
17	EU Carbon-CAP	EXIOBASE 3 MRIO	–	Whole scenario	R, T, F	90 demand-side behaviour change opportunities spanning A-S-I including changes to consumption patterns, reducing consumption, and switching to using goods with lower-carbon production and low-carbon use phases.		Present day consumption footprint	1.4	–	–
18	France 'négawatt' scenario	Bottom-up construction		Sufficiency wedge	R, C, T, I, F	A: increase building capacity utilisation, reduced appliance use, car sharing, telework, reduced goods consumption, less packaging S: shifts to attached buildings; shifts from cars and air to public transit and active mobility, car sharing, freight shifts to rail and water, shifts away from animal proteins I: reduced speed limits, vehicle efficiency, increased recycling		Business as usual in 2050 (~2,300 TWh primary energy)	–	–	~500 TWh
19	The Netherlands household energy behavioural changes	BENCH-NLD agent-based model	–	Individual energy behavioural changes and social dynamics; considering carbon pricing	R	A: reduce energy consumption through changing lifestyle, habits and consumption patterns S: to green energy provider; investment in solar PVs (prosumers) I: investment in insulation and energy-efficient appliances		SSP2 in 2030	50%	–	–
20	The Netherlands household energy behavioural changes	BENCH-NLD agent-based model	–	Individual energy behavioural changes and social dynamics	R	A: reduce energy consumption S: investment in solar PVs (prosumers) I: investment in insulation and energy-efficient appliances		SSP2 in 2050	56%	51–71%	–
21	Spain household energy behavioural changes	BENCH-ESP agent-based model	–	Individual energy behavioural changes and social dynamics	R	A: reduce energy consumption S: investment in solar PVs (prosumers) I: investment in insulation and energy-efficient appliances		SSP2 in 2050	44%	16–64%	–
22	A Societal Transformation Scenario for Staying Below 1.5°C	Global calculator	187 EJ in 2050	Whole scenario	R, C, I, F	A: reduce energy, material and land use consumption		n/a	Down to 9.1 GtCO$_2$ in 2050		

Sources: a van Sluisveld et al. (2016); b IEA (2019a); c IEA (2017b); d Van Vuuren et al. (2018); e Grubler et al. (2018); f Teske et al. (2015); g Esmeijer et al. (2018); h Liu et al. (2018); i Gota et al. (2019); j IEA (2020a); k Millward-Hopkins et al. (2020); l IEA (2021); m Creutzig et al. (2015b); n Millot et al. (2018); o van de Ven et al. (2018); p van Sluisveld et al. (2018); q Moran et al. (2020); r négawatt Association (2018); s Niamir et al. (2020c); t, u Niamir et al. (2020a); v Kuhnhenn et al. (2020).

[a] R = residential (Chapters 8, 9); C = commercial (Chapters 8, 9); T = transport (Chapters 8, 10); I = industry (Chapter 11), F = food (Chapters 6, 12).

[b] A= Avoid; S = Shift; I = Improve, BAU = business as usual.

[c] Relative to indicated baseline scenario value in stated year.

Third, low demand scenarios can reduce both supply-side capacity additions and the need for carbon capture and removal technologies to reach emissions targets. Of the scenarios listed in Table 5.2, one (LED-MESSAGE) reaches 2050 emissions targets with no carbon capture or removal technologies (Grubler et al. 2018), whereas others report significant reductions in reliance on bioenergy with carbon capture and storage (BECCS) compared to traditional technology-centric mitigation pathways (Liu et al. 2018; Van Vuuren et al. 2018; Napp et al. 2019), with the IEA's NZE notably requiring the least carbon dioxide removal (1.8 Gt in 2050) and primary bioenergy (100 EJ in 2050) compared to IPCC net zero SR1.5 scenarios (IEA 2021).

Fourth, the costs of reaching mitigation targets may be lower when incorporating ASI strategies for deep energy and resource demand reductions. The TIAM-Grantham low demand scenarios displayed reduction in mitigation costs (0.87–2.4% of GDP), while achieving even lower cumulative emissions to 2100 (228 to ~475 GtCO$_2$) than its central demand scenario (741 to 1066 GtCO$_2$), which had a cost range of (2.4–4.1% of GDP) (Napp et al. 2019). The GCAM behavioural change scenario concluded that domestic emission savings would contribute to reducing the costs of achieving the internationally agreed climate goal of the EU by 13.5% to 30% (van de Ven et al. 2018). The AIMS lifestyle case indicated that mitigation costs, expressed as global GDP loss, would be 14% lower than the SSP2 reference scenario in 2100, for both 2°C and 1.5°C mitigation targets (Liu et al. 2018). These findings mirror earlier AIM results, which indicated lower overall mitigation costs for scenarios focused on energy service demand reductions (Fujimori et al. 2014). In the IEA's NZE, behavioural changes that avoid energy and resource demand save USD4 trillion (cumulatively 2021–2050) compared to if those emissions reductions were achieved through low-carbon electricity and hydrogen deployment (IEA 2021).

Based on the limited number of long-term mitigation scenarios that explicitly represent demand reductions enabled by ASI strategies, there is *medium evidence* but with *high agreement* within the literature that such scenarios can reduce dependence on supply-side capacity additions and carbon capture and removal technologies, with opportunites for lower overall mitigation costs.

If the limitations within most IAMs and ESMs regarding non-inclusion of granular ASI strategy analysis can be addressed, it will expand and improve long-term mitigation scenarios (Van den Berg et al. 2019). These include broader inclusion of mitigation costs for behavioural interventions (van Sluisveld et al. 2016), much greater incorporation of rebound effects (Krey et al. 2019), including from improved efficiencies (Brockway et al. 2021) and avoided spending (van de Ven et al. 2018), improved representation of materials cycles to assess resource cascades (Pauliuk et al. 2017), broader coverage of behavioural change (Samadi et al. 2017; Saujot et al. 2020), improved consideration of how economic development affects service demand (Semieniuk et al. 2021), explicit representation of intersectoral linkages related to digitalisation, sharing economy, and circular economy strategies (Section 5.3.4), and institutional, political, social, entrepreneurial, and cultural factors (van Sluisveld et al. 2018). Addressing the current significant modelling limitations will require increased investments in data generation and collection, model development, and inter-model comparisons, with a particular focus on socio-behavioural research, which has been underrepresented in mitigation research funding to date (Overland and Sovacool 2020).

COVID-19 interacts with demand-side scenarios (Box 5.2). Energy demand will mostly likely be reduced between 2020 and 2030 compared to the default pathway, and if recovery is steered towards low energy demand, carbon prices for a 1.5°C-consistent pathway will be reduced by 19%, energy supply investments until 2030 will be reduced by USD1.8 trillion, and the pressure to rapidly upscale renewable energy technologies will be softened (Kikstra et al. 2021a).

5.3.4   Transformative Megatrends

The sharing economy, the circular economy, and digitalisation have all received much attention from the research, advocacy, business models and policy communities as potentially transformative trends for climate change mitigation (IEA 2017a; Material Economics 2018; TWI2050 2019). All are essentially emerging and contested concepts (Gallie 1955) that have the common goal of increasing convenience for users and rendering economic systems more resource efficient, but which exhibit variability in the literature on their definitions and system boundaries. Historically, both sharing and circular economies have been commonplace in developing countries, where reuse, repair, and waste scavenging and recycling comprise the core of informal economies facilitated by human interventions (Wilson et al. 2006; Asim et al. 2012; Pacheco et al. 2012). Digitalisation is now propelling sharing and circular economy concepts in developed and developing countries alike (Roy et al. 2021), and the three megatrends are highly interrelated, as seen in Figure 5.11. For example, many sharing economy concepts rely on corporate or, to lesser degree, non-profit digital platforms that enable efficient information and opportunity sharing, thus making it part of the digitalisation trend. Parts of the sharing economy are also included in some circular economy approaches, as shared resource use renders utilisation of material more efficient. Digital approaches to material management also support the circular economy, such as through waste exchanges and industrial symbiosis. Digitalisation aims more broadly to deliver services in more efficient, timely, intelligent, and less resource-intensive ways (i.e., by moving bits and not atoms), through the use of increasingly interconnected physical and digital systems in many facets of economies. With rising digitalisation also comes the risk of increased electricity use to power billions of devices and the internet infrastructure that connects them, as well as growing quantities of e-waste, presenting an important policy agenda for monitoring and balancing the carbon and resource costs and benefits of digitalisation (Malmodin and Lundén 2018; TWI2050 2019). Rebound effects and instigated consumption of digitalisation are risking to lead to a net increase in GHG emissions (Belkhir and Elmeligi 2018). The determinants and possible scales of mitigation potentials associated with each megatrend are discussed below.

5

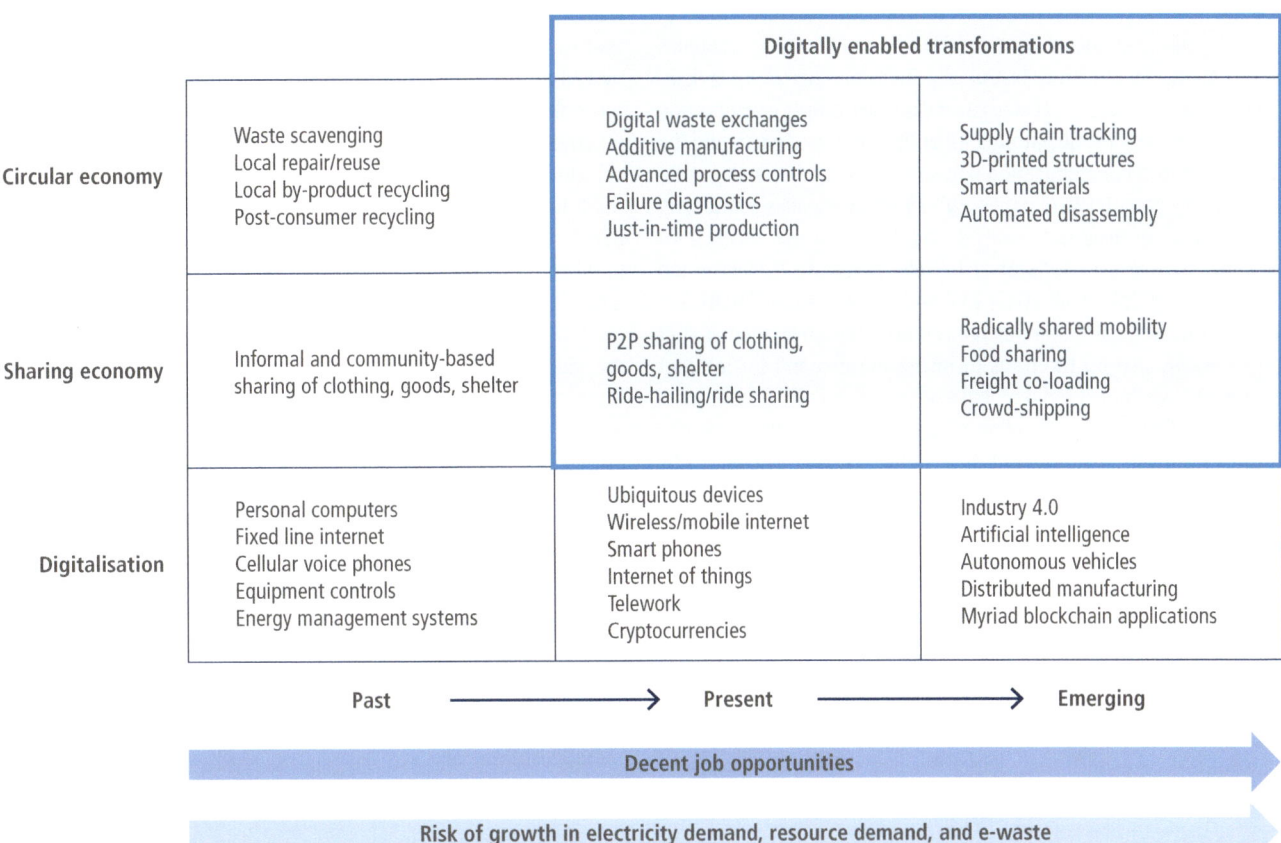

Figure 5.11 | The growing nexus between digitalisation, the sharing economy, and the circular economy in service delivery systems. While these trends started mostly independently, rapid digitalisation is creating new synergistic opportunities with systemic potential to improve the quality of jobs, particularly in developing economies. Widespread digitalisation may lead to net increases in electricity use, demand for electronics manufacturing resources, and e-waste, all of which must be monitored and managed via targeted policies.

5.3.4.1 Digitalisation

In the context of service provision, there are numerous opportunities for consumers to buy, subscribe to, adopt, access, install or use digital goods and services (Wilson et al. 2020b). Digitalisation has opened up new possibilities across all domains of consumer activity, from travel and retail to domestic living and energy use. Digital platforms allow surplus resources to be identified, offered, shared, transacted and exchanged (Frenken 2017). Real-time information flows on consumers' preferences and needs mean service provision can be personalised, differentiated, automated, and optimised (TWI2050 2019). Rapid innovation cycles and software upgrades drive continual improvements in performance and responsiveness to consumer behaviour. These characteristics of digitalisation enable new business models and services that affect both service demand, from shared ride-hailing (ITF 2017a) to smart heating (IEA 2017a), and how services are provisioned, from online farmers' markets (Richards and Hamilton 2018) to peer-to-peer electricity trading to enable distributed power systems (Morstyn et al. 2018).

In many cases, digitalisation provides a 'radical functionality' that enables users to do or accomplish something that they could not do before (Nagy et al. 2016). Indeed the consumer appeal of digital innovations varies widely, from choice, convenience, flexibility and control to relational and social benefits (Pettifor and Wilson 2020).

Reviewing over 30 digital goods and services for mobility, food buying and domestic living, Wilson et al. (2020b) also found shared elements of appeal across multiple innovations including (i) making use of surplus, (ii) using not owning, (iii) being part of wider networks, and (iv) exerting greater control over service provisioning systems. Digitalisation thus creates a strong value proposition for certain consumer niches. Concurrent diffusion of many digital innovations amplifies their disruptive potential (Schuelke-Leech 2018; Wilson et al. 2019b). Besides basic mobile telephone service for communication, digital innovations have been primarily geared to population groups with high purchasing power, and too little to the needs of poor and vulnerable people.

The long-term sustainability implications of digitalised services hinge on four factors: (i) the direct energy demands of connected devices and the digital infrastructures (i.e., data centres and communication networks) that provide necessary computing, storage, and communication services (Section 9.4.6); (ii) the systems-level energy and resource efficiencies that may be gained through the provision of digital services (Wilson et al. 2020b); (iii) the resource, material, and waste management requirements of the billions of ICT devices that comprise the world's digital systems (Belkhir and Elmeligi 2018; Malmodin and Lundén 2018) and (iv) the magnitude of potential rebound effects or induced energy demands that might unleash unintended and unsustainable demand growth, such as autonomous

5

vehicles inducing more frequent and longer journeys due to reduced travel costs (Wadud et al. 2016). Estimating digitalisation's direct energy demand has historically been hampered by lack of consistent global data on IT device stocks, their power consumption characteristics, and usage patterns, for both consumer devices and the data centres and communication networks behind them. As a result, quantitative estimates vary widely, with literature values suggesting that consumer devices, data centres, and data networks account for anywhere from 6% to 12% of global electricity use (Gelenbe and Caseau 2015; Cook et al. 2017; Malmodin and Lundén 2018). For example, within the literature on data centres, top-down models that project energy use on the basis of increasing demand for internet services tend to predict rapid global energy use growth, (Andrae and Edler 2015; Belkhir and Elmeligi 2018; Liu et al. 2020a), whereas bottom-up models that consider data centre technology stocks and their energy efficiency trends tend to predict slower but still positive growth (Shehabi et al. 2018; Hintemann and Hinterholzer 2019;

Malmodin 2020; Masanet et al. 2020). Yet there is growing concern that remaining energy efficiency improvements might be outpaced by rising demand for digital services, particularly as data-intensive technologies such as artificial intelligence, smart and connected energy systems, distributed manufacturing systems, and autonomous vehicles promise to increase demand for data services even further in the future (TWI2050 2019; Masanet et al. 2020; Strubell et al. 2020). Rapid digitalisation is also contributing to an expanding e-waste problem, estimated to be the fastest growing domestic waste stream globally (Forti et al. 2020).

As digitalisation proliferates, an important policy objective is therefore to invest in data collection and monitoring systems and energy demand models of digitalised systems to guide technology and policy investment decisions for addressing potential direct energy demand growth (IEA 2017a) and potentially concomitant growth in e-waste.

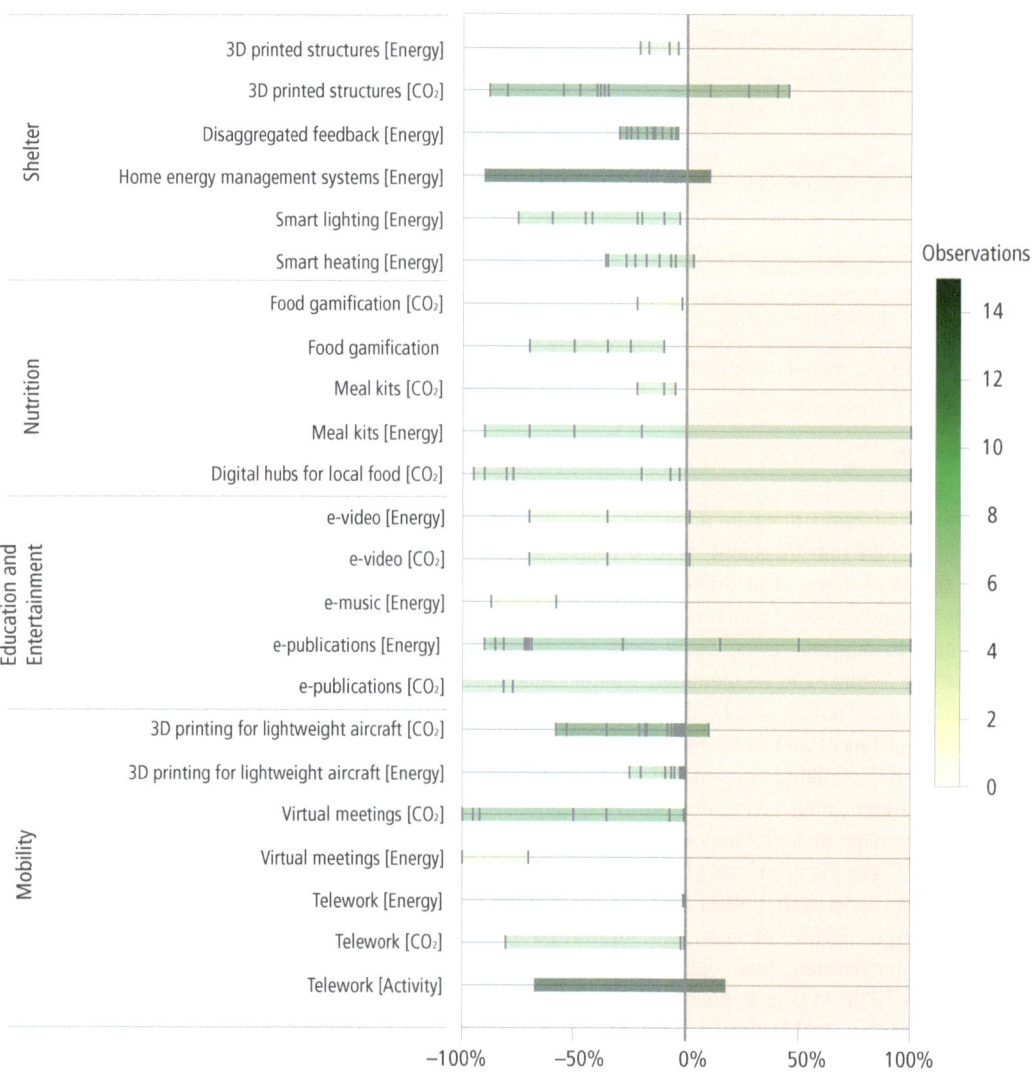

Figure 5.12 | Studies assessing net changes in CO$_2$ emissions, energy use, and activity levels indicate mitigation potentials for numerous end-user-oriented digitalisation solutions, but also risk of increased emissions due to inefficient substitutions, induced demand, and rebound effects. 90 studies were assessed with 207 observations (indicated by vertical bars) including those based on empirical research, attributional and consequential lifecycle assessments, and techno-economic analyses and scenarios at different scales, which are not directly comparable but are useful for indicating the directionality and determinants of net emissions, energy, and activity effects. Sources: Erdmann and Hilty (2010); Gebler et al. (2014); Huang et al. (2016); Verhoef et al. (2018); Alhumayani et al. (2020); Court and Sorrell (2020); Hook et al. (2020); IEA (2020a); Saade et al. (2020); Torres-Carrillo et al. (2020); Wilson et al. (2020c); Yao et al. (2020); Muñoz et al. (2021).

However, the net systems-level energy and resource efficiencies gained through the provision of digital services could play an important role in dealing with climate change and other environmental challenges (Masanet and Matthews 2010; Melville 2010; Elliot 2011; Watson et al. 2012; Gholami et al. 2013; Añón Higón et al. 2017). As shown in Figure 5.12, assessments of numerous digital service opportunities for mobility, nutrition, shelter, and education and entertainment suggest that net emissions benefits can be delivered at the systems level, although these effects are highly context dependent. Importantly, evidence of potential negative outcomes due to rebound effects, induced demand, or life-cycle trade-offs can also be observed. For example, telework has been shown to reduce emissions where long and/or energy-intensive commutes are avoided, but can lead to net emissions increases in cases where greater non-work vehicle use occurs or only short, low-emissions commutes (e.g., via public transit) are avoided (Hook et al. 2020; IEA 2020a; Viana Cerqueira et al. 2020). Similarly, substitution of physical media by digital alternatives may lead to emissions increases where greater consumption is fuelled, whereas a shift to 3D printed structures may require more emissions-intensive concrete formulations or result in reduced thermal energy efficiency, leading to life-cycle emissions increases (Mahadevan et al. 2020; Yao et al. 2020).

Furthermore, digitalisation, automation and artificial intelligence, as general-purpose technologies, may lead to a plethora of new products and applications that are likely to be efficient on their own but that may also lead to undesirable changes or absolute increases in demand for products (Figure 5.12). For example, last-mile delivery in logistics is both expensive and cumbersome. Battery-powered drones enable a delivery of goods at similar lifecycle emissions to delivery vans (Stolaroff et al. 2018). At the same time, drone delivery is cheaper in terms of time (immediate delivery) and monetary costs (automation saves the highest-cost component: personnel) (Sudbury and Hutchinson 2016). As a result, demand for package delivery may increase rapidly. Similarly, automated vehicles reduce the costs of time, parking, and personnel, and therefore may dramatically increase vehicle mileage (Wadud et al. 2016; Cohen and Cavoli 2019). On-demand electric scooters offer mobility access preferable to passenger cars, but can replace trips otherwise taken on public transit (de Bortoli and Christoforou 2020) and can come with significant additional energy requirements for night-time system rebalancing (Hollingsworth et al. 2019; ITF 2020). The energy requirements of cryptocurrencies is also a growing concern, although considerable uncertainty exists surrounding the energy use of their underlying blockchain infrastructure (Vranken 2017; de Vries 2018; Stoll et al. 2019). For example, while it is clear that the energy requirements of global Bitcoin mining have grown significantly since 2017, recent literature indicates a wide range of estimates for 2020 (47 TWh to 125 TWh) due to data gaps and differences in modelling approaches (Lei et al. 2021). Initial estimates of the computational intensity of artificial intelligence algorithms suggest that energy requirements may be enormous without concerted effort to improve efficiencies, especially on the computational side (Strubell et al. 2020). Efficiency gains enabled by digitalisation, in terms of reduced GHG emissions or energy use per service unit, may be overcompensated by activity/scale effects.

Maximising the mitigation potential of digitalisation trends involves diligent monitoring and proactive management of both direct and indirect demand effects, to ensure that a proper balance is maintained. Direct energy demand can be managed through continued investments in, and incentives for, energy-efficient data centres, networks, and end-use devices (Masanet et al. 2011; Avgerinou et al. 2017; IEA 2017a; Koronen et al. 2020). Shifts to low-carbon power are a particularly important strategy being undertaken by data centre and network operators (Cook et al. 2014; Huang et al. 2020), which might be adopted across the digital device spectrum as a proactive mitigation strategy where data demands outpace hardware efficiency gains, which may be approaching limits in the near future (Koomey et al. 2011). Most recently, data centres are being investigated as a potential resource for demand response and load balancing in renewable power grids (Koronen et al. 2020; Zheng et al. 2020), while a large bandwidth for improving software efficiency has been suggested for overcoming slowing hardware efficiency gains (Leiserson et al. 2020). Ensuring efficiency benefits of digital services while avoiding potential rebound effects and demand surges will require early and proactive public policies to avoid excess energy use (TWI2050 2019; WBGU 2019), which will also necessitate investments in data collection and monitoring systems to ensure that net mitigation benefits are realised and that unintended consequences can be identified early and properly managed (IEA 2017a).

Within a small but growing body of literature on the net effects of digitalisation, there is *medium evidence* that digitalised consumer services can reduce overall emissions, energy use, and activity levels, with *medium agreement* on the scale of potential savings, with the important caveat that induced demand and rebound effects must be managed carefully to avoid negative outcomes.

5.3.4.2   The Sharing Economy

Opportunities to increase service per product include peer-to-peer based sharing of goods and services such as housing, mobility, and tools. Hence, consumable products become durable goods delivering a 'product service', which potentially could provide the same level of service with fewer products (Fischedick et al. 2014).The sharing economy is an old practice of sharing assets between many without transferring ownership, which has been made new through focuses on sharing underutilised products and assets in ways that promote flexibility and convenience, often in a highly developed context via gig economy or online platforms. However, the sharing economy offers the potential to shift from 'asset-heavy' ownership to 'asset-light' access, especially in developing countries (Retamal 2019). General conclusions on the sharing economy as a framework for climate change mitigation are challenging and are better broken down to specific subsystems (Mi and Coffman 2019) (Chapter 5 Supplementary Material I, 5.SM.4.3).

Shared mobility

Shared mobility is characterised by the sharing of an asset (e.g., a bicycle, e-scooter, vehicle), and the use of technology (i.e., apps and the Internet) to connect users and providers. It succeeded by identifying market inefficiencies and transferring control over transactions to consumers. Even though most shared mobility providers operate privately, their services can be considered as part of a public transport system in so far as it is accessible to most transport users and does not require private asset ownership. Shared mobility reduces GHG emissions if it substitutes for more GHG-intensive travel (usually private car travel) (Martin and Shaheen 2011; Shaheen and Chan 2016; Santos 2018; Axsen and Sovacool 2019; Shaheen and Cohen 2019), and especially if it changes consumer behaviour in the long run 'by shifting personal transportation choices from ownership to demand-fulfilment' (Mi and Coffman 2019).

Demand is an important driver for energy use and emissions because decreased cost of travel time by sharing an asset (e.g., a vehicle) could lead to an increase in emissions, but a high level of vehicle sharing could reduce negative impacts associated with this (Brown and Dodder 2019). One example is the megacity Kolkata, India, which has as many as twelve different modes of public transportation that co-exist and offer means of mobility to its 14 million citizens (Box 5.8). Most public transport modes are shared mobility options ranging from sharing between two people in a rickshaw or between a few hundred in metro or suburban trains. Sharing also happens informally as daily commuters avail shared taxis and neighbours borrow each other's car or bicycle for urgent or day trips.

Shared mobility using private vehicle assets is categorised into four models (Santos 2018): peer-to-peer platforms where individuals can rent the vehicle when not in use (Ballús-Armet et al. 2014); short-term rental managed and owned by a provider (Enoch and Taylor 2006; Schaefers et al. 2016; Bardhi and Eckhardt 2012); Uber-like ridehailing services (Wallsten 2015; Angrist et al. 2017); and ride pooling using private vehicles shared by passengers to a common destination (Liyanage et al. 2019; Shaheen and Cohen 2019). The latest model – ride pooling – is promising in terms of congestion and per capita CO_2 emissions reductions and is a common practice in developing countries, however it is challenging in terms of waiting and travel time, comfort, and convenience, relative to private cars (Santos 2018; Shaheen and Cohen 2019). The other three models often yield profits to private parties, but remain mostly unrelated to reduction in CO_2 emissions (Santos 2018). Shared travel models, especially Uber-like models, are criticised because of the flexibilisation of labour, especially in developing countries, in which unemployment rates and unregulated labour markets lay a foundation of precarity that lead many workers to seek out wide-ranging means towards patching together a living (Ettlinger 2017; Wells et al. 2020). Despite the advantages of shared mobility, such as convenience and affordability, consumers may also perceive risk formed by possible physical injury from strangers or unexpected poor service quality (Hong et al. 2019).

From a mitigation perspective, the current state of shared mobility looks at best questionable (Fishman et al. 2014; Ricci 2015; Martin 2016; Zhang and Mi 2018; Creutzig et al. 2019b; Mi and Coffman 2019; Zhang et al. 2019). Transport entrepreneurs and government officials often conflate 'smart' and 'shared' vehicles with 'sustainable' mobility, a conflation not withstanding scrutiny (Noy and Givoni 2018). Surveys demonstrate that many users take free-floating car sharing instead of public transit, rather than to replace their private car (Herrmann et al. 2014); while in the United States, ride-hailing and sharing data indicate that these services have increased road congestion and lowered transit ridership, with an insignificant change in vehicle ownership, and may further lead to net increases in energy use and CO_2 emissions due to deadheading (Diao et al. 2021; Ward et al. 2021). If substitution effects and deadheading, which is the practice of allowing employees of a common carrier to use a vehicle as a non-revenue passenger, are accounted for, flexible motor-cycle sharing in Djakarta, Indonesia, is at best neutral to overall GHG emissions (Suatmadi et al. 2019). Passenger surveys conducted in Denver, Colorado, US, indicated that around 22% of all trips travelled with Uber and Lyft would have been travelled by transit, 12% would have walked or biked, and another 12% of passengers would not have travelled at all (Henao and Marshall 2019).

Positive effects can be realised directly in bike sharing due to its very low marginal transport emissions. For example, in 2016, bike sharing in Shanghai, China, reduced CO_2 emissions by 25 $ktCO_2$, with additional benefits to air quality (Zhang and Mi 2018). However, bike-sharing can also increase emissions from motor vehicle usage when inventory management is not optimised during maintenance, collection, and redistribution of dock-less bikes (Fishman et al. 2014; Zhang et al. 2019; Mi and Coffman 2019).

Shared mobility scenarios demonstrate that GHG emission reduction can be substantial when mobility systems and digitalisation are regulated. One study modelled that ride pooling with electric cars (6 to 16 seats), which shifts the service to a more efficient transport mode, improves its carbon intensity by cutting GHG emissions by one-third (International Transport Forum 2016). Another study found that shared autonomous taxis had the potential to reduce per-mile GHG emissions to 63–82% below those of projected hybrid vehicles in 2030, 87% to 94% lower than a privately owned, gasoline-powered vehicle in 2014 (Greenblatt and Saxena 2015). This also realises 95% reduction in space required for public parking; and total vehicle kilometres travelled would be 37% lower than the present day, although each vehicle would travel ten times the total distance of current vehicles (International Transport Forum 2016). Studies of Berlin, Germany, and Lisbon, Portugal, demonstrate that sharing strategies could reduce the number of cars by more than 90%, also saving valuable street space for human-scale activity (Bischoff and Maciejewski 2016; Martinez and Viegas 2017; Creutzig et al. 2019b). The impacts will depend on sharing levels – concurrent or sequential – and the future modal split among public transit, automated electric vehicles fleets, and shared or pooled rides. Evidence from attributional lifecycle assessments (LCAs) of ride-hailing, whether Uber-like or by taxi, suggests that the key determinants of net emissions effects are average vehicle occupancy and vehicle powertrain, with high-occupancy and electric drivetrain cars delivering the greatest emissions benefits, even rivalling traditional metro/urban rail and bus options (Figure 5.13b). It is possible that shared automated electric vehicle fleets could become widely used without many shared rides, and single- or even zero-occupant vehicles will continue to be the majority of vehicle trips. It is also feasible that shared rides could become more common, if automation makes route deviation more efficient, more cost effective, and more convenient, increasing total travel substantially (Wadud et al. 2016). Car sharing with automated vehicles could even worsen congestion and emissions by generating additional travel demand (Rubin et al. 2016). Travel time in autonomous vehicles can be used for other activities but driving and travel costs are expected to decrease, which most likely will induce additional demand for auto travel (Moeckel and Lewis 2017) and could even create incentives for further urban sprawl. More generally, increased efficiency generated by big data and smart algorithms may generate rebound effects in demand and potentially compromise the public benefits of their efficiency promise (Gossart 2015).

In many countries, shared mobility and ride pooling are often the norm. Here the challenge is to improve service quality to keep users in shared mobility and public transport (Box 5.8). A key barrier in cities like Nairobi, Kenya, is the lack of public involvement of users and sustainability experts in designing transport systems, leaving planning to transport engineers, and thus preventing inclusive shared mobility system design (Klopp 2012).

Altogether, travel behaviour, business models, and especially public policy will be key components in determining how impacts of pooling and shared automated electric vehicles unfold (Shaheen and Cohen 2019). Urban-scale governance of smart mobility holds potential for prioritising public transit and the use of public spaces for human activities, managing the data as a digital sustainable commons (e.g., via the installation of a Central Information Officer, as in Tel Aviv, Israel), and managing the social and environmental risks of smart mobility to realise its benefits (Creutzig et al. 2019b). Pricing of energy use and GHG emissions will be helpful to achieve these goals. The governance of shared mobility is complicated, as it involves many actors, and is key to realising wider benefits of shared mobility (Akyelken et al. 2018). New actors, networks and technologies enabling shared mobility are already fundamentally challenging how transport is governed worldwide. This is not a debate about state versus non-state actors but instead about the role the state takes within these new networks to steer, facilitate, and also reject different elements of the mobility system (Docherty et al. 2018).

Shared accommodation

In developing countries and in many student accommodations globally, shared accommodation allows affordable housing for a large part of the population. For example, living arrangements are built expressly around the practice of sharing toilets, bathrooms and kitchens. While the sharing of such facilities does connote a lower level of service provision and quality of life, it provides access for a consumer base with very low and unreliable incomes. Thus, sharing key facilities can help guarantee the provision of affordable housing (Gulyani et al. 2018). In developed countries, large-scale developments are targeting students and 'young professionals' by offering shared accommodation and services. Historically shared accommodation has been part of the student life due to its flexible and affordable characteristics. However, the expansion of housing supply through densification can use shared facilities as

an instrument to 'commercialize small housing production, while housing affordability and accessibility are threatened' (Uyttebrouck et al. 2020).

With respect to travel accommodation, several models are emerging in which accommodation is offered to, or shared with, travellers by private individuals organised by business-driven or non-profit online platforms. Accommodation sharing includes peer-to-peer, ICT-enabled, short-term renting, swapping, borrowing or lending of existing privately-owned lodging facilities (Möhlmann 2015; Voytenko Palgan et al. 2017).

With shared accommodation services via the platform economy, there may be risks of negative sustainability effects, such as rebound effects caused by increased travel frequency (Tussyadiah and Pesonen 2016). This is particularly a problem if apartments are removed from long-term rental markets, thus indirectly inducing construction activities, with substantial GHG emissions of their own. However, if a host shares their accommodation with a guest, the use of some resources, such as heating and lighting, is shared, thereby leading to more efficient resource use per capita (Chenoweth 2009; Voytenko Palgan et al. 2017). Given the nascence of shared accommodation via the platform economy, quantifications of its systems-level energy and emissions impacts are lacking in the literature, representing an important area for future study.

Mitigation potentials of sharing economy strategies

Sharing economy initiatives play a central role in enabling individuals to share underutilised products. While the literature on the net effects of sharing economy strategies is still limited, available studies have presented different mitigation potentials to date, as shown in Figure 5.13. For many sharing economy strategies, there is a risk of negative rebound and induced demand effects, which may occur by changing consuming patterns, for example if savings from sharing housing are used to finance air travel. Thus, the mitigation potentials of sharing economy strategies will depend on stringent public policy and consumer awareness that reins in runaway consumption effects. Shared economy solutions generally relate to the 'Avoid' and 'Shift' strategies (Sections 5.1 and 5.3.2). On the one hand, they hold potential for providing similar or improved services for well-being (mobility, shelter) at reduced energy and resource input, with the proper policy signals and consumer responses. On the other hand, shared economy strategies may increase emissions, for example shared mobility may shift activity away from public transit and lead to lower vehicle occupancy, deadheading, and use of inefficient shared vehicles (Jones and Leibowicz 2019; Merlin 2019; Bonilla-Alicea et al. 2020; Ward et al. 2021). Similarly to digitalisation, there is *medium evidence* that the sharing economy can reduce overall emissions, energy use, and activity levels, with *medium agreement* on the scale of potential savings if induced demand and rebound effects can be carefully managed to avoid negative outcomes.

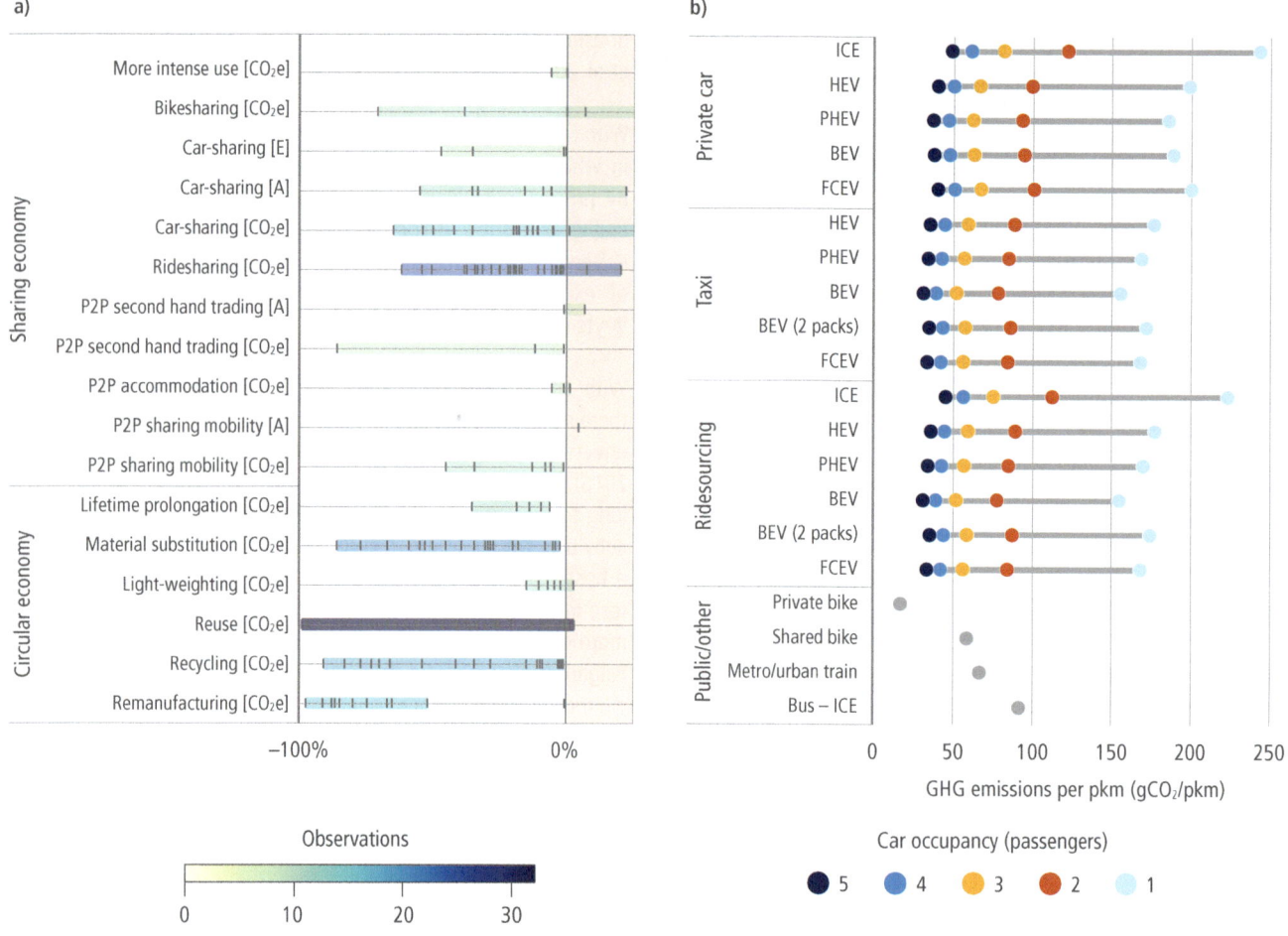

Figure 5.13 | (a) Published estimates from 72 studies with 185 observations (indicated by vertical bars) of the relative mitigation potential of different shared and circular economy strategies, demonstrating limited observations for many emerging strategies, a wide variance in estimated benefits for most strategies, and within the sharing economy, risk of increased emissions due to inefficient substitutions, induced demand, and rebound effects. Mitigation potentials are conditional on corresponding public policy and/or regulation. **(b)** Attributional LCA comparisons of ridesharing mobility options, which highlight the large effects of vehicle occupancy and vehicle technology on total CO_2 emissions per passenger-km and the preferability of high-occupancy and non-ICE configurations for emissions reductions compared to private cars. Also indicated are possible emissions increases associated with shared car mobility when it substitutes for non-motorised and public transit options. BEV = battery electric vehicle; FCEV = fuel cell electric vehicle; HEV = hybrid electric vehicle; ICE = internal combustion engine; PHEV = plug-in hybrid electric vehicle. Sources: data from Jacobson and King (2009); Firnkorn and Müller (2011); Baptista et al. (2014); Liu et al. (2014); Namazu and Dowlatabadi (2015); Nijland et al. (2015); IEA (2016); Koh (2016); Martin and Shaheen (2016); Rabbitt and Ghosh (2016); Bruck et al. (2017); Bullock et al. (2017); Clewlow and Mishra (2017); Fremstad (2017); ITF (2017a,b,c); Nasir et al. (2017); Nijland and van Meerkerk (2017); Rademaekers et al. (2017); Skjelvik et al. (2017); Yin et al. (2017); Campbell (2018); Favier et al. (2018); Ghisellini et al. (2018); Hopkinson et al. (2018); IEA (2018); ITF (2018); Lokhandwala and Cai (2018); Makov and Font Vivanco (2018); Malmqvist et al. (2018); Material Economics (2018); Nasr et al. (2018); Yu et al. (2018); Zhang and Mi (2018); Brambilla et al. (2019); Brütting et al. (2019); Buyle et al. (2019); Castro and Pasanen (2019); Coulombel et al. (2019); Eberhardt et al. (2019); IEA (2019b); ITF (2019); Jones and Leibowicz (2019); Ludmann (2019); Merlin (2019); Nußholz et al. (2019); Bonilla-Alicea et al. (2020); Cantzler et al. (2020); Churkina et al. (2020); Gallego-Schmid et al. (2020); Hertwich et al. (2020); ITF (2020a,b); Liang et al. (2020); Miller (2020); Wilson et al. (2020c); Yan et al. (2020); Cordella et al. (2021); Diao et al. (2021); Pauliuk et al. (2021); Ward et al. (2021); Wolfram et al. (2021).

The circular economy

While the demand for energy and materials will increase until 2060 following the traditional linear model of production and consumption, resulting in serious environmental consequences (OECD 2019b), the circular economy (CE) provides strategies for reducing societal needs for energy and primary materials to deliver the same level of service with lower environmental impacts. The CE framework embodies multiple schools of thought with roots in a number of related concepts (Blomsma and Brennan 2017; Murray et al. 2017), including cradle to cradle (McDonough and Braungart 2002), performance economy (Stahel 2016), biomimicry (Benyus 1997), green economy (Loiseau et al. 2016) and industrial ecology (Saavedra et al. 2018). As a result,

there are also many definitions of CE: a systematic literature review identified 114 different definitions (Kirchherr et al. 2017). One of the most comprehensive models is suggested by the Netherlands Environmental Assessment Agency (Potting et al. 2018), which defines ten strategies for circularity: Refuse (R0), Rethink (R1), Reduce (R2), Reuse (R3), Repair (R4), Refurbish (R5), Remanufacture (R6), Repurpose (R7), Recycle (R8), and Recover energy (R9). Overall, the definition of CE is contested, with varying boundary conditions chosen. As illustrated in Figure 5.11, the CE overlaps with both the sharing economy and digitalisation megatrends.

In line with the principles of SDG 12 (responsible consumption and production), the essence of building a CE is to retain as much value as possible from products and components when they reach the end of their useful life in a given application (Lewandowski 2016; Lieder and Rashid 2016; Stahel 2016; Linder and Williander 2017). This requires an integrated approach during the design phase that, for example, extends product usage and ensures recyclability after use (de Coninck et al. 2018). While traditional 'Improve' strategies tend to focus on direct energy and carbon efficiency, service-oriented strategies focus on reducing lifecycle emissions through harnessing the leverage effect (Creutzig et al. 2018). The development of closed-loop models in service-oriented businesses can increase resource and energy efficiency, reducing emissions and contributing to climate change mitigation goals at national, regional, and global levels (Johannsdottir 2014; Korhonen et al. 2018). Key examples include remanufacturing of consumer products to extend lifespans while maintaining adequate service levels (Klausner et al. 1998), reuse of building components to reduce demand for primary materials and construction processes (Shanks et al. 2019), and improved recycling to reduce upstream resource pressures (IEA 2019b; IEA 2017b).

Among the many schools of thought on the CE and climate change mitigation, two different trends can be distinguished from the literature to date. First, there are publications, many of them not peer-reviewed, that eulogise the perceived benefits of the CE, but in many cases stop short of providing a quantitative assessment. Promotion of CE from this perspective has been criticised as a greenwashing attempt by industry to avoid serious regulation (Isenhour 2019). Second, there are more methodologically rigorous publications, mostly originating in the industrial ecology field, but sometimes investigating only limited aspects of the CE (Bocken et al. 2017; Cullen 2017; Goldberg 2017). Conclusions on CE's mitigation potential also differ, with diverging definitions of the CE. A systematic review identified 3,244 peer-reviewed articles addressing CE and climate change, but only 10% of those provide insights on how the CE can support mitigation, and most of them found only small potentials to reduce GHG emissions (Cantzler et al. 2020). Recycling is the CE category most investigated, while reuse and reduce strategies have seen comparatively less attention (Cantzler et al. 2020). However, mitigation potentials were also context- and material-specific, as illustrated by the ranges shown in Figure 5.13a.

There are three key concerns relating to the effectiveness of the CE concept. First, many proposals on the CE insufficiently reflect on thermodynamic constraints that limit the potential of recycling from both mass conservation and material quality perspectives or ignore the considerable amount of energy needed to reuse materials (Cullen 2017). Second, demand for materials and resources will likely outpace efficiency gains in supply chains, becoming a key driver of GHG emissions and other environmental problems, rendering the CE alone an insufficient strategy to reduce emissions (Bengtsson et al. 2018). In fact, the empirical literature points out that only 6.5% of all processed materials (4 Gt yr^{-1}) globally originate from recycled sources (Haas et al. 2015). The low degree of circularity is explained by the high proportion of processed materials (44%) used to provide energy, thus not available for recycling; and the high rate of net additions to stocks of 17 Gt yr^{-1}. As long as long-lived material stocks (e.g., in buildings and infrastructure) continue

to grow, strategies targeting end-of-pipe materials cannot keep pace with primary materials demand (Krausmann et al. 2017; Haas et al. 2020). Instead, a significant reduction of societal stock growth, and decisive eco-design, are suggested to advance the CE (Haas et al. 2015). Third, cost-effectiveness underlying CE activities may concurrently also increase energy intensity and reduce labour intensity, causing systematically undesirable effects. To a large extent, the distribution of costs and benefits of material and energy use depend on institutions in order to include demand-side solutions. Thus, institutional conditions have an essential role to play in setting rules differentiating profitable from nonprofitable activities in CE (Moreau et al. 2017). Moreover, the prevalence of CE practices such as reuse, refurbishment, and recycling can differ substantially between developed and developing economies, leading to highly context-specific mitigation potentials and policy approaches (McDowall et al. 2017).

One report estimates that the CE can contribute to more than 6 GtCO$_2$ emission reductions in 2030, including strategies such as material substitution in buildings (Blok et al. 2016). Reform of the tax system towards GHG emissions and the extraction of raw materials substituting taxes on labour is a key precondition to achieve such a potential. Otherwise, rebound effects tend to take back a high share of marginal CE efforts. A 50% reduction of GHG emissions in industrial processes, including the production of goods in steel, cement, plastic, paper, and aluminium, from 2010 until 2050, is impossible to attain only with reuse and radical product innovation strategies, but will need to also rely on the reduction of primary input (Allwood et al. 2010).

CE strategies generally correspond to the 'Avoid' strategy for primary materials (Sections 5.1 and 5.3.2). CE strategies in industrial settings improve well-being mostly indirectly, via the reduction of environmental harm and climate impact. They can also save monetary resources of consumers by reducing the need for consumption. It may seem counterintuitive, but reducing consumers' need to consume a particular product or service (e.g., reducing energy consumption) may increase consumption of another product or service (e.g., travel) associated with some type of energy use, or lead to greater consumption if additional secondary markets are created. Hence, carbon emissions could rise if the rebound effect is not considered (Chitnis et al. 2013; Zink and Geyer 2017).

Looking at 'Shift' strategies (Sections 5.1 and 5.3.2), the role of individuals as consumers and users has received less attention than other aspects of the CE (e.g., technological interventions as 'Improve' strategies and waste minimisation as 'Avoid' strategies) within mainstream debates to date. One explanation is that CE has roots in the field of industrial ecology, which has historically emphasised materials systems more than the end user. By shifting this perspective from the supply side to the demand side in the CE, users are, for the most part, discussed as social entities that now must form new relations with businesses to meet their needs. That is, the demand-side approach largely replaces the concept of a consumer with that of a user, who must either accept or reject new business models for service provision, stimulated by the pushes and pulls of prices and performance (Hobson 2019).

Relevant contributions to climate change mitigation at gigatonne scale by the CE will remain out of scope if decision-makers and industry fail to reduce primary inputs (*high confidence*). Systemic (consequential) analysis is required to avoid the risk that scaling effects negate efficiency gains; such analysis is however rarely applied to date. For example, material substitution or refurbishment of buildings brings risk of increasing emissions despite improving or avoiding current materials (Castro and Pasanen 2019; Eberhardt et al. 2019). Besides, CE concepts that extend the lifetime of products and increase the fraction of recycling are useful but are both thermodynamically limited and will remain relatively small in scale as long as demand for primary materials continues to grow, and scale effects dominate. In spite of presenting a large body of literature on CE in general, only a small but growing body of literature exists on the net effects of its strategies from a quantitative perspective, with key knowledge gaps remaining on specific CE strategies. There is *medium evidence* that the CE can reduce overall emissions, energy use, and activity levels, with *medium evidence* that the sharing economy can reduce overall emissions, energy use, and activity levels, with *medium agreement* on the scale of potential savings.

5.4 Transition Toward High Well-being and Low-carbon-demand Societies

Demand-side mitigation involves individuals (e.g., consumption choices), culture (e.g., social norms, values), corporate (e.g., investments), institutions (e.g., political agency), and infrastructure change (*high evidence, high agreement*). These five drivers of human behaviour either contribute to the status quo of a global high-carbon, consumption- and GDP growth-oriented economy or help generate the desired change to a low-carbon energy-services, well-being, and equity-oriented economy (Jackson 2016; Cassiers et al. 2018; Yuana et al. 2020; Nielsen et al. 2021) (Figure 5.14). Each driver has novel implications for the design and implementation of demand-side mitigation policies. They show important synergies, making energy demand mitigation a dynamic problem where the packaging and/or sequencing of different policies play a role in their effectiveness, demonstrated in Sections 5.5 and 5.6. The Social Science Primer (Chapter 5 Supplementary Material I) describes theory and empirical insights about the interplay between individual agency, the social and physical context of demand-side decisions in the form of social roles and norms, infrastructure and technological constraints and affordances, and other formal and informal institutions. Incremental interventions on all five fronts change social practices, affecting simultaneously energy and well-being (Schot and Kanger 2018). Transformative change will require coordinated use of all five drivers, as described in Figure 5.14 and, using novel insights about behaviour change for policy design and implementation (*high evidence, high agreement*). In particular, socio-economic factors, such as equity, public service quality, electricity access and democracy are found to be highly significant in enabling need satisfaction at low energy use, whereas economic growth beyond moderate incomes and extractive economic activities are observed to be prohibiting factors (Vogel et al. 2021).

5.4.1 Behavioural Drivers

Behaviour change by individuals and households requires both *motivation* to change and *capacity* for change (option availability/knowledge; material/cognitive resources to initiate and maintain change) (Moser and Ekstrom 2010; Michie et al. 2011) and is best seen as part of more encompassing collective action. Motivation for

Demand side mitigation is about more than behavioural change. Reconfiguring the way services are provided while simultaneously changing social norms and preferences will help reduce emissions and access. Transformation happens through societal, technological and institutional changes.

Tilting the balance towards less resource intensive service provisioning

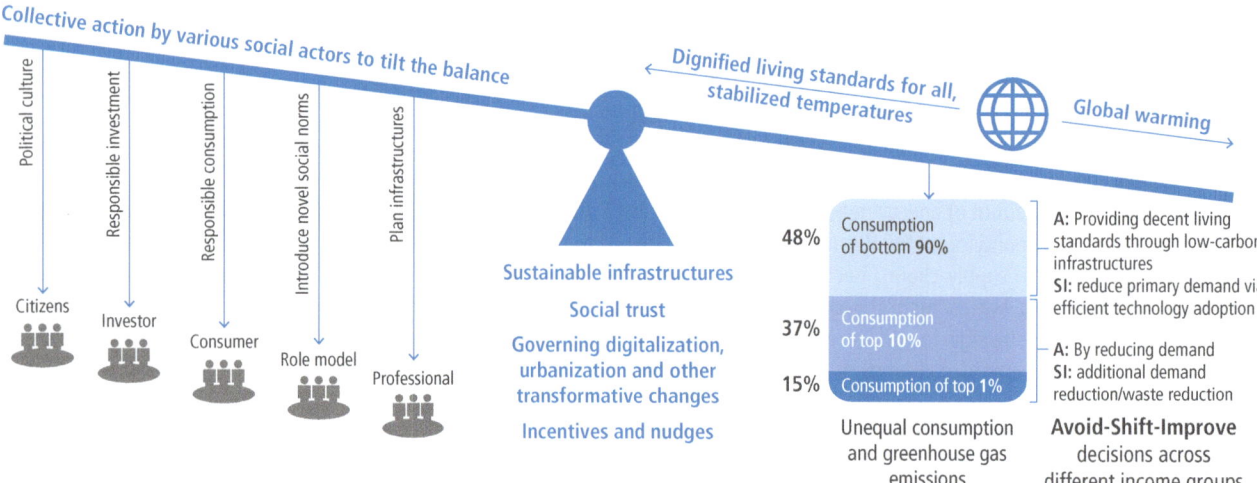

Figure 5.14 | Role of people, demand-side action and consumption in reversing a planetary trajectory to a warming Earth towards effective climate change mitigation and dignified living standards for all.

change for collective good comes from economic, legal, and social incentives, and regard for deeper intrinsic value of concern for others over extrinsic values. Capacity for change varies; people in informal settlements or rural areas are incapacitated by socio-political realities and have limited access to new energy-service options.

Motivation and effort required for behaviour change increase from 'Improve' to 'Shift' to 'Avoid' decisions. 'Improve' requires changes in personal purchase decisions, 'Shift' involves changes in behavioural routines, 'Avoid' also involves changes in deeper values or mindsets. People set easy goals for themselves and more difficult ones for others (Attari et al. 2016) and underestimate the energy savings of behaviour changes that make a large difference (Attari et al. 2010). Most personal actions taken so far have small mitigation potential (recycling, ecodriving), and people refrain from options advocated more recently with high impact (less flying, living car free) (Dubois et al. 2019).

As individuals pursue a broad set of goals and use calculation-, emotion-, and rule-based processes when they make energy decisions, demand-side policies can use a broad range of behavioural tools that complement subsidies, taxes, and regulations (Chakravarty and Roy 2016; Mattauch et al. 2016; Niamir 2019) (*high evidence, high agreement*). The provision of targeted information, social advertisements, and influence of trusted in-group members and/role models or admired role models like celebrities can be used to create better climate change knowledge and awareness (Niamir 2019; Niamir et al. 2020b; Niamir et al. 2020c). Behavioural interventions like communicating changes in social norms can accelerate behaviour change by creating tipping points (Nyborg et al. 2016). When changes in energy-demand decisions (such as switching to a plant-based diet, (Box 5.5)) are motivated by the creation and activation of a social identity consistent with this and other behaviours, positive spillover can accelerate behaviour change (Truelove et al. 2014), both within a domain or across settings, for example from work to home (Maki and Rothman 2017).

Box 5.5 | Dietary Shifts in UK Society Towards Lower-emission Foods

Meat eating is declining in the UK, alongside a shift from carbon-intensive red meat towards poultry. This is due to the interaction of behavioural, socio-cultural and organisational drivers (Vinnari and Vinnari 2014). Reduced meat consumption is primarily driven by issues of personal health and animal welfare, instead of climate or environment concerns (Latvala et al. 2012; Dibb and Fitzpatrick 2014; Hartmann and Siegrist 2017; Graça et al. 2019). Social movements have promoted shifts to a vegan diet (Morris et al. 2014; Laestadius et al. 2016) yet their impact on actual behaviour is the subject of debate (Taufik et al. 2019; Harguess et al. 2020; Sahakian et al. 2020). Companies have expanded new markets in non-meat products (MINTEL 2019). Both corporate food actors and new entrants offering more innovative 'meat alternatives' view consumer preferences as an economic opportunity, and are responding by increasing the availability of meat replacement products. No significant policy change has taken place in the UK to enable dietary shift (Wellesley and Froggatt 2015); however the Climate Change Committee has recommended dietary shift in the Sixth Carbon Budget (Climate Change Committee 2020), involving reduced consumption of high-carbon meat and dairy products by 20% by 2030, with further reductions in later years in order to reach net zero GHG emissions by 2050. Agricultural policies serve to support meat production with large subsidies that lower production cost and effectively increase the meat intensity of diets at a population level (Simon 2003; Godfray et al. 2018). Deeper, population-wide reductions in meat consumption are hampered by these lock-in mechanisms which continue to stabilise the existing meat production-consumption system. The extent to which policymakers are willing to actively stimulate reduced meat consumption thus remains an open question (Godfray et al. 2018). See more in Chapter 5 Supplementary Material I, Section 5.SM.6.4.

People's general perceptions of climate risks, first covered in AR5, motivate behaviour change; more proximate and personal feelings of being at risk triggered by extreme weather and climate-linked natural disasters will increase concern and willingness to act (Bergquist et al. 2019), though the window of increased support is short (Sisco et al. 2017). 67% of individuals in 26 countries see climate change as a major threat to their country, an increase from 53% in 2013, though 29% also consider it a minor or no threat (Fagan and Huang 2019). Concern that the COVID-19 crisis may derail this momentum due to a finite pool of worry (Weber 2006) appears to be unwarranted: Americans' positions on climate change in 2020 matched high levels of concern measured in 2019 (Leiserowitz et al. 2020). Younger, female, and more educated individuals perceive climate risks to be larger (Weber 2016; Fagan and Huang 2019). Moral values and political ideology influence climate risk perception and beliefs about the outcomes and effectiveness of climate action (Maibach et al. 2011).

Motivation for demand-side solutions can be increased by focusing on personal health or financial risks and benefits that clearly matter to people (Petrovic et al. 2014). Consistent with climate change as a normally distant, non-threatening, statistical issue (Gifford 2011; Fox-Glassman and Weber 2016), personal experience with climate-linked flooding or other extreme weather events increases perceptions of risk and willingness to act (Weber 2013; Atreya and Ferreira 2015; Sisco et al. 2017) when plausible mediators and moderators are considered Brügger et al. (2021), confirmed in all 24 countries studied by Broomell et al. (2015). Discounting the future matters (Hershfield et al. 2014): across multiple countries, individuals more focused on future outcomes are more likely to engage in environmental actions (Milfont et al. 2012).

There is *medium evidence* and *high agreement* that demographics, values, goals, personal and social norms differentially determine

ASI behaviours, in the Netherlands and Spain (Abrahamse and Steg 2009; Niamir 2019; Niamir et al. 2020b), the OECD (Ameli and Brandt 2015), and 11 European countries (Mills and Schleich 2012; Roy et al. 2012). Education and income increase 'Shift' and 'Improve' behaviour, whereas personal norms help to increase the more difficult 'Avoid' behaviours (Mills and Schleich 2012). Socio-demographic variables (household size and income) predict energy use, but psychological variables (perceived behavioural control, perceived responsibility) predict *changes* in energy use; younger households are more likely to adopt 'Improve' decisions, whereas education increases 'Avoid'

decisions (Ahmad et al. 2015). In India and developing countries, 'Avoid' decisions are made by individuals championing a cause, while 'Improve' and 'Shift' behaviour are increased by awareness programmes and promotional materials highlighting environmental and financial benefits (Chakravarty and Roy 2016; Roy et al. 2018a). Cleaner cookstove adoption Box 5.6), a widely studied 'Improve' solution in developing countries (Nepal et al. 2010; Pant et al. 2014), goes up with income, education, and urban location. Female education and investments in reproductive health are evident measures to reduce world population growth (Abel et al. 2016).

Box 5.6 | Socio-behavioural Aspects of Deploying Cookstoves

Universal access to clean and modern cooking energy could cut premature deaths from household air pollution by two-thirds, while reducing forest degradation and deforestation and contributinh to the reduction of up to 50% of CO_2 emissions from cooking (relative to baseline by 2030) (IEA 2017c; Dagnachew et al. 2019). However, in the absence of policy reform and substantial energy investments, 2.3 billion people will have no access to clean cooking fuels such as biogas, LPG, natural gas or electricity in 2030 (IEA 2017c). Studies reveal that a combination of drivers influence adoption of new cookstove appliances, including affordability, behavioural and cultural aspects (lifestyles, social norms around cooking and dietary practices), information provision, availability, aesthetic qualities of the technology, perceived health benefits, and infrastructure (spatial design of households and cooking areas). The increasing efficiency improvements in electric cooking technologies could enable households to shift to electrical cooking at mass scale. The use of pressure cookers and rice cookers is now widespread in South Asia and beginning to penetrate the African market as consumer attitudes are changing towards household appliances with higher energy efficiencies (Batchelor et al. 2019). There are shifts towards electric and LPG stoves in Bhutan (Dendup and Arimura 2019), India (Pattanayak et al. 2019), Ecuador (Martínez et al. 2017; Gould et al. 2018) and Ethiopia (Tesfamichael et al. 2021); and improved biomass stoves in China (Smith et al. 1993). Significant subsidy, information (Dendup and Arimura 2019), social marketing and availability of technology in the local markets are some of the key policy instruments helping to adopt improved cookstoves (Pattanayak et al. 2019). There is no one-size-fits-all solution to household air pollution – different levels of shift and improvement occur in different cultural contexts, indicating the importance of socio-cultural and behavioural aspects in shifts in cooking practices. See more in Chapter 5 Supplementary Material I, Section 5.SM.6.2.

There is *high agreement* in the literature that the updating of educational systems from a commercialised, individualised, entrepreneurial training model to an education cognisant of planetary health and human well-being can accelerate climate change awareness and action (Mendoza and Roa 2014; Dombrowski et al. 2016) (Supplementary Material I Chapter 5).

There is *high evidence* and *high agreement* that people's core values affect climate-related decisions and climate policy support by shaping beliefs and identities (Dietz 2014; Steg 2016; Hayward and Roy 2019). People with altruistic and biospheric values are more likely to act on climate change and support climate policies than those with hedonic or egoistic values (Taylor et al. 2014), because these values are associated with higher awareness and concern about climate change, stronger belief that personal actions can help mitigate climate change, and stronger feelings of responsibility for taking climate action (Dietz 2014; Steg 2016). Research also suggest that egalitarian, individualistic, and hierarchical worldviews (Wildavsky and Dake 1990) have their role, and that successful solutions require policy-makers of all three worldviews to come together and communicate with each other (Chuang et al. 2020).

Core values also influence which costs and benefits are considered (Hahnel et al. 2015; Gölz and Hahnel 2016; Steg 2016). Information provision and appeals are thus more effective when tailored to those values (Bolderdijk et al. 2013; Boomsma and Steg 2014), as implemented by the energy cultures framework (Stephenson et al. 2015; Klaniecki et al. 2020). Awareness, personal norms, and perceived behavioural control predict willingness to change energy-related behaviour above and beyond traditional socio-demographic and economic predictors (Schwartz 1977; Ajzen 1985; Stern 2000), as do perceptions of self-efficacy (Bostrom et al. 2019). However, such motivation for change is often not enough, as actors also need capacity for change and help to overcome individual, institutional and market barriers (Young et al. 2010; Bray et al. 2011; Carrington et al. 2014).

Table 5.4 describes common obstacles to demand-side energy behaviour change, from loss aversion to present bias (for more detail see Chapter 5 Supplementary Material I). Choice architecture refers to interventions ('nudges') that shape the choice context and how choices are presented, with seemingly-irrelevant details (e.g., option order or labels) often more important than option price (Thaler and Sunstein 2009). There is *high evidence* and *high agreement* that choice architecture nudges shape energy decisions by capturing deciders' attention; engaging their desire to contribute to the social good; facilitating accurate assessment of risks, costs, and benefits; and making complex information more accessible (Yoeli et al. 2017; Zangheri et al. 2019). Climate-friendly choice architecture includes the setting of proper defaults, the salient positioning of green options (in stores and online), forms of framing, and communication of social norms (Johnson et al. 2012). Simplifying access to greener options (and hence lowering effort) can promote ASI changes (Mani et al. 2013). Setting effective 'green' defaults may be the most effective policy to mainstream low-carbon energy choices (Sunstein and Reisch 2014), adopted in many contexts (Jachimowicz et al. 2019) and deemed acceptable in many countries (Sunstein et al. 2019). Table 5.3a lists how often different choice-architecture tools were used in many countries over the past 10 years to change ASI behaviours, and how often each tool was used to enhance an economic incentive. These tools have been tested mostly in developed countries. Reduction in energy use (typically electricity consumption) is the most widely studied behaviour (because metering is easily observable). All but one tool was applied to increase this 'Avoid' behaviour, with demand-side reductions from 0% to up to 20%, with most values below 3% (see also meta-analyses by Hummel and Maedche (2019); Nisa et al. (2019); van der Linden and Goldberg (2020); Stankuniene et al. (2020); and Khanna et al. (2021). Behavioural, economic, and legal instruments are most effective when applied as an internally consistent ensemble where they can reinforce each other, a concept referred to as 'policy packaging' in transport policy research (Givoni 2014). A meta-analysis, combining evidence of psychological and economic studies, demonstrates that feedback, monetary incentives and social comparison operate synergistically and are together more effective than the sum of individual interventions (Khanna et al. 2021). The same meta-analysis also shows that combined with monetary incentives, nudges and choice architecture can reduce global GHG emissions from household energy use by 5–6% (Khanna et al. 2021).

Choice architecture has been depicted as an anti-democratic attempt at manipulating the behaviour of actors without their awareness or approval (Gumbert 2019). Such critiques ignore the fact that there is no neutral way to present energy-use-related decisions, as every presentation format and choice environment influences choice, whether intentionally or not. Educating households and policy makers about the effectiveness of choice architecture and adding these behavioural tools to existing market- and regulation-based tools in a transparent and consultative way can provide desired outcomes with increased effectiveness, while avoiding charges of manipulation or deception. People consent to choice-architecture tools if their use is welfare-enhancing, policymakers are transparent about their goals and processes, public deliberation and participation are encouraged, and the choice architect is trusted (Sunstein et al. 2019).

Table 5.3a | Inventory of behavioural interventions experimentally tested to change energy behaviours.

Behavioural tool	# of papers	# in developed countries	# in other countries	Energy demand behaviour	Avoid	Shift	Improve	Economic incentive
Set the proper defaults	27	26	1	**Carbon Offset Programme (3)** Löfgren et al. (2012); Araña and León (2013) **Energy Source (4)** Kaiser et al. (2020); Wolske et al. (2020)* **Energy Use (16)** Jachimowicz et al. (2019); Nisa et al. (2019); Grilli and Curtis (2021)* **Investment in Energy Efficiency (7)** Theotokis and Manganari (2015); Ohler et al. (2020) **Mode of Transportation (1)** Goodman et al. (2013)	11	12	9	6
Reach out during transitions	10	9	1	**Energy Use (4)** Verplanken (2006); Jack and Smith (2016); Iweka et al. (2019)* **Investment in Energy Efficiency (4)** Gimpel et al. (2020) **Mode of Transportation (2)** Verplanken et al. (2008)	1	3	7	1
Provide timely feedback and reminders	256	246	10	**Energy Use (252)** Darby (2006); Buckley (2019)* Abrahamse et al. (2005); Fischer (2008); Steg (2008); Faruqui et al. (2010); Delmas et al. (2013); McKerracher and Torriti (2013); Karlin et al. (2015); Andor and Fels (2018); Bergquist et al. (2019); Iweka et al. (2019); Nisa et al. (2019); Zangheri et al. (2019); Ahir and Chakraborty (2021); Grilli and Curtis (2021); Khanna et al. (2021)* **Mode of Transportation (3)** Steg (2008); Sanguinetti et al. (2020)*	244	6	7	33

Behavioural tool	# of papers	# in developed countries	# in other countries	Energy demand behaviour	Avoid	Shift	Improve	Economic incentive
Make information intuitive and easy to access	247	235	12	**Energy Source (3)** Havas et al. (2015); Jagger et al. (2019) **Energy Use (202)** Henryson et al. (2000); Darby (2006); Carlsson-Kanyama and Lindén (2007); Chen et al. (2017); Iwafune et al. (2017); Burkhardt et al. (2019); Henry et al. (2019); Wong-Parodi et al. (2019); Mi et al. (2020); Stojanovski et al. (2020) [Abrahamse et al. (2005); Ehrhardt-Martinez and Donnelly (2010); Delmas et al. (2013); Andor and Fels (2018); Bergquist et al. (2019); Buckley (2019); Iweka et al. (2019); Nisa et al. (2019); Zangheri et al. (2019); Wolske et al. (2020); Ahir and Chakraborty (2021); Grilli and Curtis (2021); Khanna et al. (2021)]* **Investment in Energy Efficiency (30)** Larrick and Soll (2008); Steg (2008); Andor and Fels (2018)* **Mode of Transportation (19)** Steg (2008); Pettifor et al. (2017)*	197	38	24	33
Make behaviour observable and provide recognition	58	53	5	**Energy Use (24)** Abrahamse et al. (2005); Delmas et al. (2013); Bergquist et al. (2019); Iweka et al. (2019); Nisa et al. (2019); Grilli and Curtis (2021)* **Investment in Energy Efficiency (30)** Pettifor et al. (2017)* **Mode of Transportation (4)** Pettifor et al. (2017)*	27	28	5	6
Communicate a norm	138	131	7	**Energy Source (1)** Hafner et al. (2019) **Energy Use (116)** Nolan et al. (2008); Ayers and Forsyth (2009); Allcott (2011); Costa and Kahn (2013); Allcott and Rogers (2014) Abrahamse et al. (2005); Abrahamse and Steg (2013); Delmas et al. (2013); Andor and Fels (2018); Bergquist et al. (2019); Buckley (2019); Iweka et al. (2019); Nisa et al. (2019); Ahir and Chakraborty (2021); Khanna et al. (2021)* **Investment in Energy Efficiency (15)** Pettifor et al. (2017); Niamir et al. (2020b); Grilli and Curtis (2021)* **Mode of Transportation (7)** Bamberg et al. (2007); Bergquist et al. (2019)*	106	21	16	15
Reframe consequences in terms people care about	74	68	6	**Energy Source (5)** Wolske et al. (2018); Hafner et al. (2019); Grilli and Curtis (2021)* **Energy Use (47)** Abrahamse et al. (2005); Darby (2006); Delmas et al. (2013); Chen et al. (2017); Eguiguren-Cosmelli (2018); Bergquist et al. (2019); Ghesla et al. (2020); Mi et al. (2020); Khanna et al. (2021)* **Investment in Energy Efficiency (22)** Andor and Fels (2018);* Forster et al. (2021) **Mode of Transportation (2)** Nepal et al. (2010); Mattauch et al. (2016)	41	18	19	18
Obtain a commitment	52	47	5	**Energy Source (1)** Jagger et al. (2019) **Energy Use (47)** Ghesla et al. (2020); Abrahamse et al. (2005); Steg (2008); Delmas et al. (2013); Andor and Fels (2018); Iweka et al. (2019); Nisa et al. (2019); Grilli and Curtis (2021); Khanna et al. (2021)* **Investment in Energy Efficiency (1)** Steg (2008)* **Mode of Transportation (5)** Matthies et al. (2006); Steg (2008)*	45	4	4	10

Note: Papers in this review of behavioural interventions to reduce household energy demand were collected through a systemic literature search up to August 2021. Studies are included in the reported counts if they are (i) experimental, (ii) peer-reviewed or highly cited reports, (iii) the intervention is behavioural, and (iv) the targeted behaviour is household energy demand. 559 papers are included in the review. Each paper was coded for: type of behavioural intervention, country of study, energy demand behaviour targeted, whether the target is an 'Avoid', 'Shift', or 'Improve' behaviour, and whether the intervention includes an economic incentive. Some papers do not report all elements. The energy demand behaviour column provides the count of papers that focus on each behaviour type (in parentheses after the behaviour). The citations that follow are not exhaustive but exemplify papers in the category, selected for impact, range, and recency. The asterisk (*) indicates references that are meta-analyses or systematic reviews. Papers within meta-analyses and systematic reviews that meet the inclusion criteria are counted individually in the total counts. The full reference list is available at https://osf. io/9463u/.

Table 5.3b | Summary of effects of behavioural interventions in Table 5.3a.

Behavioural tool	Results (expressed in household energy savings, unless otherwise stated)	Results summary
Set proper default	Meta-analyses find a medium to strong effect of defaults on environmental behaviour. Jachimowicz et al. (2019) report a strong average effect of defaults on environmental behaviour (Cohen's d = 0.75, confidence interval 0.39–1.12), though not as high as for consumer decisions. They find that defaults, across domains, are more effective when they reflect an endorsement (recommendation by a trusted source) or endowment (reflecting the status quo). Nisa et al. (2019)* report a medium average effect size (Cohen's d =0.35; range 0.04–0.55).	
Reach out during transitions	The few interventions that focus on transitions and measure behaviour change (rather than energy savings) report mixed, moderate effect sizes. People were unwilling to change their behaviour if they were satisfied with current options (Mahapatra and Gustavsson 2008). Iweka et al. (2019) find that effective messages can prompt habit disruption.	
Timely feedback and reminders	The average effects of meta-analyses of feedback interventions on household energy use reductions range from 1.8% to 7.7%, with large variations (Delmas et al. 2013; Buckley 2019; Nisa et al. 2019; Buckley 2020; Ahir and Chakraborty 2021; Khanna et al. 2021). The same is true for two literature reviews (Abrahamse et al. 2005; Bergquist et al. 2019). Most studies find a 4–10% average reduction during the intervention; some studies find a non-significant result (Dünnhoff and Duscha 2008) or a negative reduction (Winett et al. 1978). Real-time feedback is most effective, followed by personalised feedback (Buckley 2019; Buckley 2020). A review by Darby et al. (2006) finds direct feedback (from the meter or display monitor) is more effective than indirect feedback (via billing) (5–15% savings vs 0–10% savings). Feedback effects (Cohen's d = 0.241) are increased when combined with a monetary incentive (Cohen's d = 0.96) and with a social comparison and a monetary incentive (Cohen's d = 0.714) (Khanna et al. 2021). Sanguinetti et al. (2020) find that onboard feedback results in a 6.6% improvement in the fuel economy of cars (Cohen's d: 0.07, [range 0.05–0.08]).	

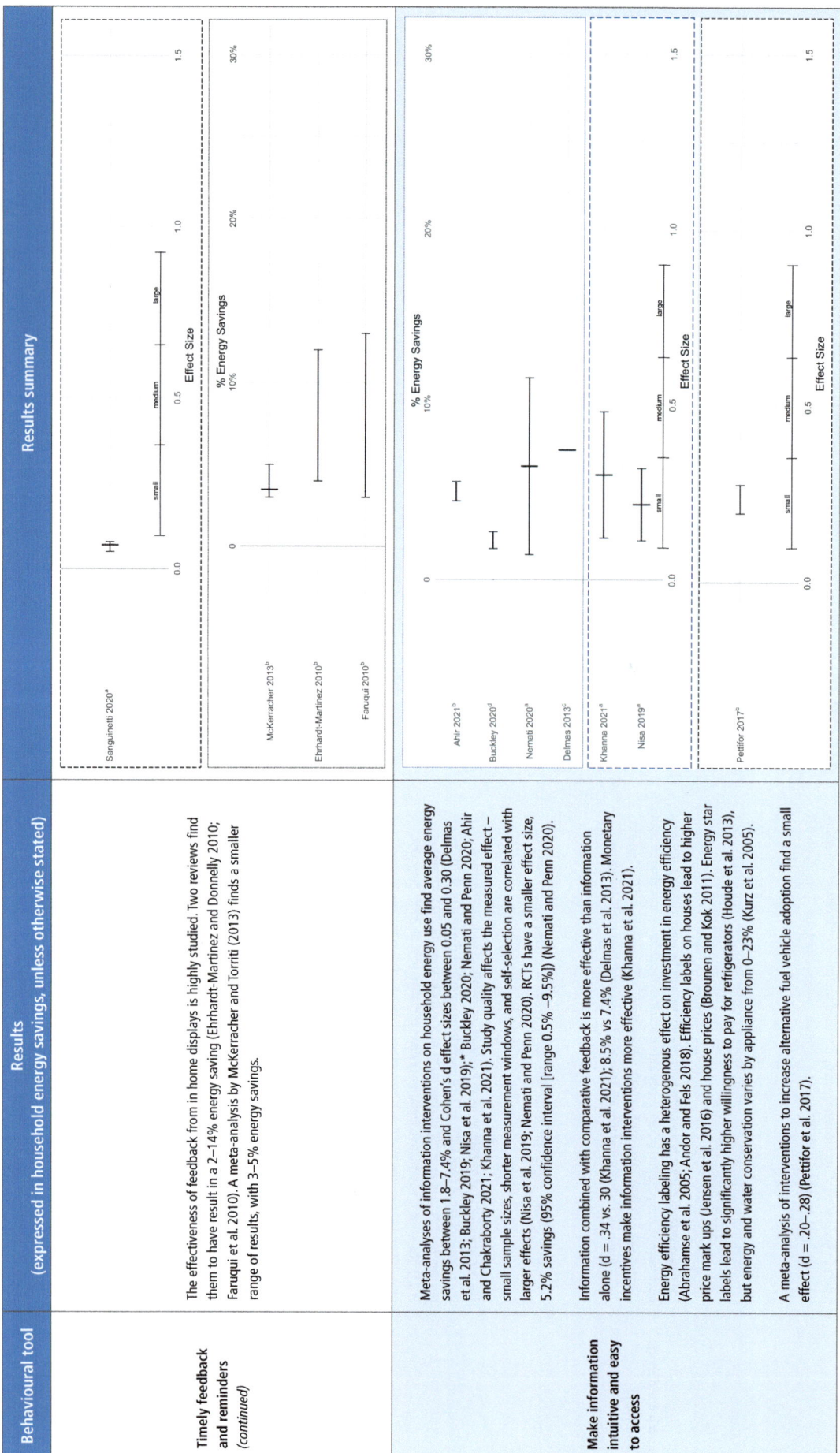

Behavioural tool	Results (expressed in household energy savings, unless otherwise stated)	Results summary
Timely feedback and reminders (*continued*)	The effectiveness of feedback from in home displays is highly studied. Two reviews find them to have result in a 2–14% energy saving (Ehrhardt-Martinez and Donnelly 2010; Faruqui et al. 2010). A meta-analysis by McKerracher and Torriti (2013) finds a smaller range of results, with 3–5% energy savings.	
Make information intuitive and easy to access	Meta-analyses of information interventions on household energy use find average energy savings between 1.8–7.4% and Cohen's d effect sizes between 0.05 and 0.30 (Delmas et al. 2013; Buckley 2019; Nisa et al. 2019);* Buckley 2020; Nemati and Penn 2020; Ahir and Chakraborty 2021; Khanna et al. 2021). Study quality affects the measured effect – small sample sizes, shorter measurement windows, and self-selection are correlated with larger effects (Nisa et al. 2019; Nemati and Penn 2020). RCTs have a smaller effect size, 5.2% savings (95% confidence interval [range 0.5% –9.5%]) (Nemati and Penn 2020). Information combined with comparative feedback is more effective than information alone (d = .34 vs. 30 (Khanna et al. 2021); 8.5% vs 7.4% (Delmas et al. 2013). Monetary incentives make information interventions more effective (Khanna et al. 2021). Energy efficiency labeling has a heterogenous effect on investment in energy efficiency (Abrahamse et al. 2005; Andor and Fels 2018). Efficiency labels on houses lead to higher price mark ups (Jensen et al. 2016) and house prices (Brounen and Kok 2011). Energy star labels lead to significantly higher willingness to pay for refrigerators (Houde et al. 2013), but energy and water conservation varies by appliance from 0–23% (Kurz et al. 2005). A meta-analysis of interventions to increase alternative fuel vehicle adoption find a small effect (d = .20–.28) (Pettifor et al. 2017).	

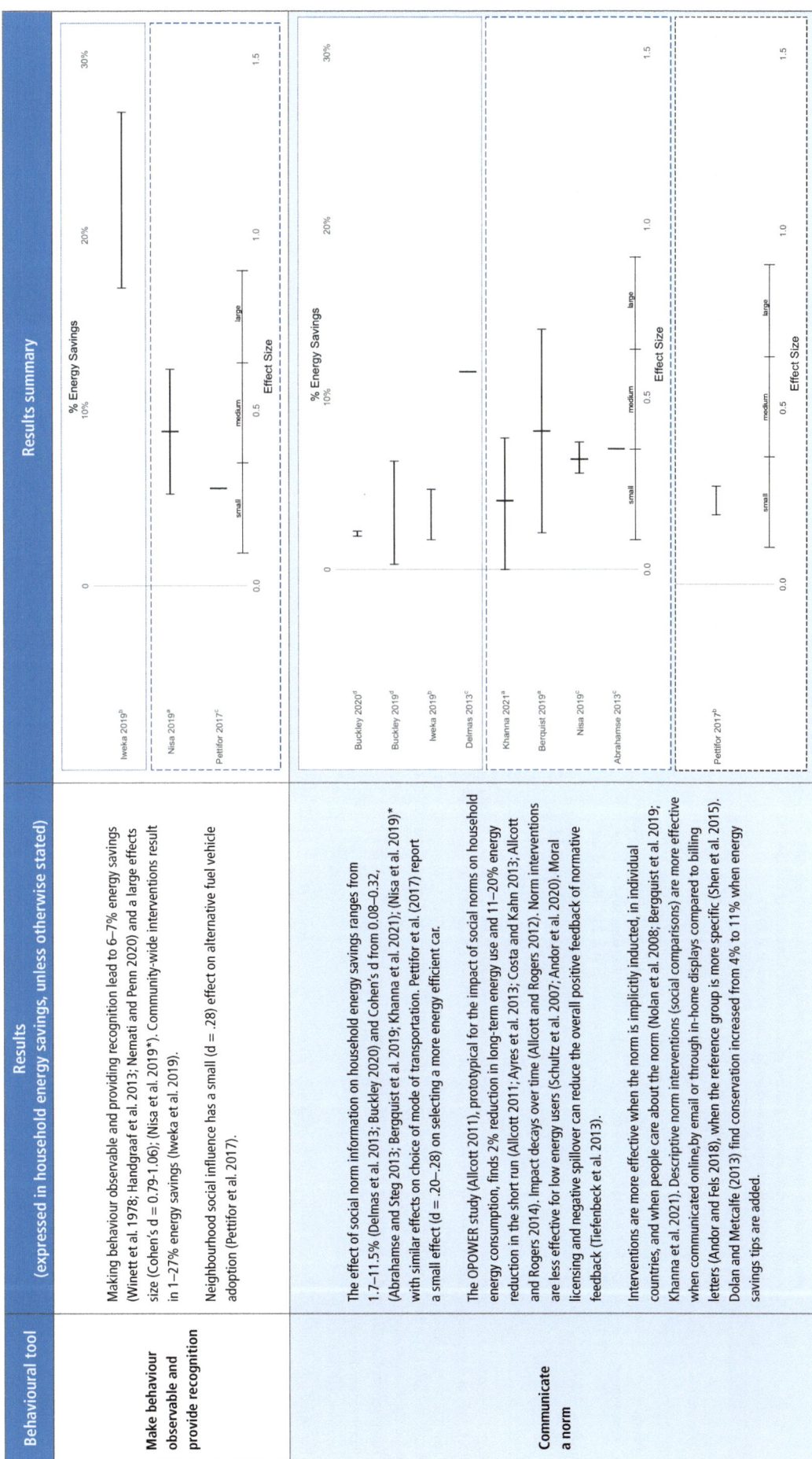

Behavioural tool	Results (expressed in household energy savings, unless otherwise stated)
Make behaviour observable and provide recognition	Making behaviour observable and providing recognition lead to 6–7% energy savings (Winett et al. 1978; Handgraaf et al. 2013; Nemati and Penn 2020) and a large effects size (Cohen's d = 0.79-1.06); (Nisa et al. 2019*). Community-wide interventions result in 1–27% energy savings (Iweka et al. 2019). Neighbourhood social influence has a small (d = .28) effect on alternative fuel vehicle adoption (Pettifor et al. 2017).
Communicate a norm	The effect of social norm information on household energy savings ranges from 1.7–11.5% (Delmas et al. 2013; Buckley 2020) and Cohen's d from 0.08–0.32, (Abrahamse and Steg 2013; Bergquist et al. 2019; Khanna et al. 2021); (Nisa et al. 2019)* with similar effects on choice of mode of transportation. Pettifor et al. (2017) report a small effect (d = .20–.28) on selecting a more energy efficient car. The OPOWER study (Allcott 2011), prototypical for the impact of social norms on household energy consumption, finds 2% reduction in long-term energy use and 11–20% energy reduction in the short run (Allcott 2011; Ayres et al. 2013; Costa and Kahn 2013; Allcott and Rogers 2014). Impact decays over time (Allcott and Rogers 2012). Norm interventions are less effective for low energy users (Schultz et al. 2007; Andor et al. 2020). Moral licensing and negative spillover can reduce the overall positive feedback of normative feedback (Tiefenbeck et al. 2013). Interventions are more effective when the norm is implicitly inducted, in individual countries, and when people care about the norm (Nolan et al. 2008; Bergquist et al. 2019; Khanna et al. 2021). Descriptive norm interventions (social comparisons) are more effective when communicated online,by email or through in-home displays compared to billing letters (Andor and Fels 2018), when the reference group is more specific (Shen et al. 2015). Dolan and Metcalfe (2013) find conservation increased from 4% to 11% when energy savings tips are added.

5

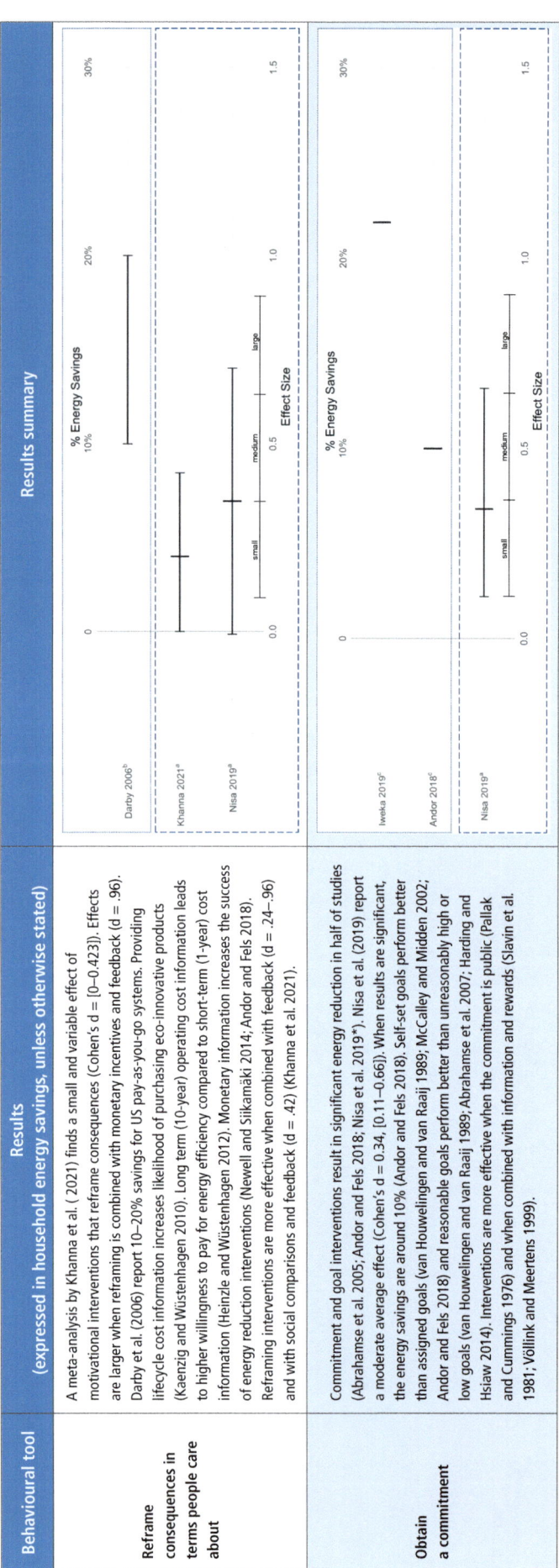

Behavioural tool	Results (expressed in household energy savings, unless otherwise stated)	Results summary
Reframe consequences in terms people care about	A meta-analysis by Khanna et al. (2021) finds a small and variable effect of motivational interventions that reframe consequences (Cohen's d = [0–0.423]). Effects are larger when reframing is combined with monetary incentives and feedback (d = .96). Darby et al. (2006) report 10–20% savings for US pay-as-you-go systems. Providing lifecycle cost information increases likelihood of purchasing eco-innovative products (Kaenzig and Wüstenhagen 2010). Long term (10-year) operating cost information leads to higher willingness to pay for energy efficiency compared to short-term (1-year) cost information (Heinzle and Wüstenhagen 2012). Monetary information increases the success of energy reduction interventions (Newell and Siikamäki 2014; Andor and Fels 2018). Reframing interventions are more effective when combined with feedback (d = .24–.96) and with social comparisons and feedback (d = .42) (Khanna et al. 2021).	
Obtain a commitment	Commitment and goal interventions result in significant energy reduction in half of studies (Abrahamse et al. 2005; Andor and Fels 2018; Nisa et al. 2019*). Nisa et al. (2019) report a moderate average effect (Cohen's d = 0.34, [0.11–0.66)). When results are significant, the energy savings are around 10% (Andor and Fels 2018). Self-set goals perform better than assigned goals (van Houwelingen and van Raaij 1989; McCalley and Midden 2002; Andor and Fels 2018) and reasonable goals perform better than unreasonably high or low goals (van Houwelingen and van Raaij 1989; Abrahamse et al. 2007; Harding and Hsiaw 2014). Interventions are more effective when the commitment is public (Pallak and Cummings 1976) and when combined with information and rewards (Slavin et al. 1981; Völlink and Meertens 1999).	

Note: The second column describes the effects of each of the eight behavioural tools. The third column plots the results of meta-analyses and reviews that focus on each tool. Effects are reported as described in the referenced paper, either as percentage of energy saved (dotted box) or by the effect size, measured as Cohen's d (dashed box).

*Two responses to Nisa et al. (2019) challenge their conclusion that behavioural interventions have a small impact on household energy use (Stern 2020; van der Linden and Goldberg, 2020). We report the raw data collected and used in Nisa et al. (2019). Our data summary supports the arguments by Stern (2020) and van der Linden and Goldberg (2020) that interventions should be evaluated in combination, as well as individually, and that the results are highly sensitive to the chosen estimator.

[a] Range reported as 95% confidence interval of results used in the meta-analysis or review.

[b] Range reported as all results included in the meta-analysis or review.

[c] No range reported.

[d] Range indicates the reported results within a meta-analysis; this applies when multiple intervention types in a meta-analysis are classified as a single behavioural tool.

5.4.2   Socio-cultural Drivers of Climate Mitigation

Collective behaviours and social organisation are part of everyday life, and feeling part of active collective action renders mitigation measures efficient and pervasive (Climact 2018). Social and cultural processes play an important role in shaping what actions people take on climate mitigation, interacting with individual, structural, institutional and economic drivers (Barr and Prillwitz 2014). Just like infrastructure, social and cultural processes can 'lock in' societies to carbon-intensive patterns of service delivery. They also offer potential levers to change normative ideas and social practices in order to achieve extensive emissions cuts (*high confidence*) (Table 5.4).

In terms of cultural processes, we can distinguish two levels of analysis: specific meanings associated with particular technologies or practices, and general narratives about climate change mitigation. Specific **meanings** (e.g., comfort, status, identity and agency) are associated with many technologies and everyday social practices that deliver energy services, from driving a car to using a cookstove (*high evidence, high agreement*) (Section 5.5). Meanings are symbolic and influence the willingness of individuals to use existing technologies or shift to new ones (Wilhite and Ling 1995; Wilhite 2009; Sorrell 2015). Symbolic motives are more important predictors of technology adoption than instrumental motives (Steg 2005; Noppers et al. 2014; Noppers et al. 2015; Noppers et al. 2016) (see case study on app cabs in Kolkata, India (Box 5.8)). If an individual's pro-environmental behaviour is associated with personal meaning than it also increases subjective well-being (Zawadzki et al. 2020). Status consciousness is highly relevant in GHG emission-intensive consumption choices (cars, houses). However, inversely framing energy-saving behaviour as high status is a promising strategy for emission reduction (Ramakrishnan and Creutzig 2021).

At a broader level, **narratives** about climate mitigation circulate within and across societies, as recognised in SR1.5, and are broader than the meanings associated with specific technologies (*high evidence, high agreement*). Narratives enable people to imagine and make sense of the future through processes of interpretation, understanding, communication and social interaction (Smith et al. 2017). Stories about climate change are relevant for mitigation in numerous ways. They can be utopian or dystopian (e.g., *The great derangement* by Amitav Ghosh) (Ghosh 2016), for example presenting apocalyptic stories and imagery to capture people's attention and evoke emotional and behavioural response (O'Neill and Smith 2014). Reading climate stories has been shown to cause short-term influences on attitudes towards climate change, increasing the belief that climate change is human caused and increasing its issue priority (Schneider-Mayerson et al. 2020). Climate narratives can also be used to justify scepticism of science, drawing together coalitions of diverse actors into social movements that aim to prevent climate action (Lejano and Nero 2020). Narratives are also used in integrated assessment and energy system models that construct climate stabilisation scenarios, for example in the choice of parameters, their interpretation and model structure (Ellenbeck and Lilliestam 2019). One important narrative choice of many models involves framing climate change as market failure (which leads to the result that carbon pricing is required).

While such a choice can be justified, other model framings can be equally justified (Ellenbeck and Lilliestam 2019).

Power and agency shape which climate narratives are told and how prevalent they are (O'Neill and Smith 2014; Schneider-Mayerson et al. 2020). For example, narratives have been used by indigenous communities to imagine climate futures divergent from top-down, government-led narratives (Streeby 2018). The uptake of new climate narratives is influenced by political beliefs and trust. Policymakers can enable emissions reduction by employing narratives that have broad societal appeal, encourage behavioural change and complement regulatory and fiscal measures (Terzi 2020). Justice narratives may not have universal appeal: in a UK study, justice narratives polarised individuals along ideological lines, with lower support amongst individuals with right-wing beliefs; by contrast, narratives centred on saving energy, avoiding waste and patriotic values were more widely supported across society (Whitmarsh and Corner 2017). More research is needed to assess if these findings are prevalent in diverse socio-cultural contexts, as well as the role played by social media platforms to influence emerging narratives of climate change (Pearce et al. 2019).

Trust in organisations is a key predictor of the take-up of novel energy services (Lutzenhiser 1993), particularly when financial incentives are high (Stern et al. 1985; Joskow 1995). Research has shown that if there is low public trust in utility companies, service delivery by community-based non-profit organisations in the US (Stern et al. 1985) or public/private partnerships in Mexico (Friedmann and Sheinbaum 1998), offer more effective solutions, yet only if public trust is higher in these types of organisations. UK research shows that acceptance of shifts to less resource-intensive service provision (e.g., more resource-efficient products, extending product lifetimes, community schemes for sharing products) varies depending on factors including trust in suppliers and manufacturers, affordability, quality and hygiene of shared products, and fair allocation of responsibilities (Cherry et al. 2018). Trust in other people plays an important role in the sharing economy (Li and Wang 2020), for example predicting shifts in transport mode, specifically car sharing involving rides with strangers (Acheampong and Siiba 2019) (Section 5.3.4.2).

Action on climate mitigation is influenced by our perception of what other people commonly do, think or expect, known as social norms (*high evidence, high agreement*) (Cialdini 2006) (Table 5.3), even though people often do not acknowledge this (Nolan et al. 2008; Noppers et al. 2014). Changing social norms can encourage societal transformation and social tipping points to address climate mitigation (Nyborg et al. 2016; Otto et al. 2020). Providing feedback to people about how their own actions compare to others' can encourage mitigation (Delmas et al. 2013), although the overall effect size is not strong (Abrahamse and Steg 2013). Trending norms are behaviours that are becoming more popular, even if currently practised by a minority. Communicating messages that the number of people engaging in a mitigation behaviour (e.g., giving a financial donation to an environmental conservation organisation) is increasing – a simple low-cost policy intervention – can encourage shifts to the targeted behaviour, even if the effect size is relatively small (Mortensen et al. 2019).

Socially comparative feedback seems to be more effective when people strongly identify with the reference group (De Dominicis et al. 2019). Descriptive norms (perceptions of behaviours common in others) are more strongly related to mitigation actions when injunctive norms (perceptions of whether certain behaviours are commonly approved or disapproved) are also strong, when people are not strongly personally involved with mitigation topics (Göckeritz et al. 2010), when people are currently acting inconsistently with their preferences, when norm-based interventions are supported by other interventions and when the context supports norm-congruent actions (Miller and Prentice 2016). A descriptive norm prime ('most other people try to reduce energy consumption') together with injunctive norm feedback ('you are very good at saving energy') is a very effective combination to motivate further energy savings (Bonan et al. 2020). Second-order beliefs (perceptions of what others in the community believe) are particularly important for leveraging descriptive norms (Jachimowicz et al. 2018).

Behavioural contagion, which describes how ideas and behaviours often spread like infectious diseases, is a major contributor to the climate crisis (Sunstein 2019). But harnessing contagion can also mitigate warming. Carbon-heavy consumption patterns have become the norm only in part because we're not charged for environmental damage we cause (Pigou 1920). The deeper source of these patterns has been peer influence (Frank 1999), because what we do influences others. A rooftop solar installation early in the adoption cycle, for example, spawns a copycat installation in the same neighbourhood within four months, on average. With such installations thus doubling every four months, a single new order results in 32 additional installations in just two years. And contagion doesn't stop there, since each family also influences friends and relatives in distant locations.

Harnessing contagion can also underwrite the investment necessary for climate stability. If taxed more heavily, top earners would spend less, shifting the frames of reference that shape spending of those just below, and so on – each step simultaneously reducing emissions and liberating resources for additional green investment (Frank 2020). Many resist, believing that higher taxes would make it harder to buy life's special extras. But that belief is a cognitive illusion (Frank 2020). Acquiring special things, which are inherently in short supply, requires outbidding others who also want them. When top tax rates rise in tandem, relative bidding power is completely unchanged, so the same penthouse apartments would end up in the same hands as before. More generally, behavioural contagion is important to leverage all relevant social tipping points for stabilising Earth's climate (Otto et al. 2020).

For new climate policies and mitigation technologies to be rapidly and extensively implemented, they must be socially acceptable to those who are directly impacted by those policies and technologies (medium evidence, high agreement). Policies that run counter to social norms or cultural meanings are less likely to be effective in reducing emissions (Demski et al. 2015; Perlaviciute et al. 2018; Roy et al. 2018b). More just and acceptable implementation of renewable energy technologies requires taking account of the cultural meanings, emotional attachments and identities linked to particular landscapes and places where those technologies

are proposed (Devine-Wright 2009) and enabling fairness in how decisions are taken and costs and benefits distributed (Wolsink 2007). This is important for achieving the goal of SDG 7 (increased use of renewable energy resources) in developing countries while achieving energy justice (Calzadilla and Mauger 2017). 'Top-down' imposition of climate policies by governments can translate into local opposition when perceived to be unjust and lacking transparency (high evidence, high agreement). Policymakers can build trust and increase the legitimacy of new policies by implementing early and extensive public and stakeholder participation, avoiding 'Nimby' (Not In My Back Yard) assumptions about objectors and adopting 'Just Transition' principles (Owens 2000; Wolsink 2007; Wüstenhagen et al. 2007; Dietz and Stern 2008; Devine-Wright 2011; Heffron and McCauley 2018). Participatory mechanisms that enable deliberation by a representative sample of the public (Climate Assembly UK 2020) can inform policymaking and increase the legitimacy of new and difficult policy actions (Dryzek et al. 2019).

Collective action by civil society groups and social movements can work to enable or constrain climate mitigation. Civil society groups can advocate policy change, provide policy research and open up opportunities for new political reforms (high evidence, high agreement) as recognised in previous IPCC reports (IPCC 2007). Grassroots environmental initiatives, including community energy groups, are collective responses to, and critiques of, normative ways that everyday material needs (e.g., food, energy, making) are produced, supplied and circulated (Schlosberg and Coles 2016). Such initiatives can reconcile lower carbon footprints with higher life satisfaction and higher incomes (Vita et al. 2020). Local initiatives such as Transition Towns and community energy projects can lead to improvements in energy efficiency, ensure a decent standard of living and increase renewable energy uptake, while building on existing social trust, and, in turn, building social trust and initiating engagement, capacity building, and social capital formation (Hicks and Ison 2018). Another example are grassroot initiatives that aim to reduce food loss and waste, even as overall evidence on their effectiveness remains limited (Mariam et al. 2020). However, community energy initiatives are not always inclusive and require policy support for widespread implementation across all socio-economic groups (Aiken et al. 2017). In addition, more evidence is required of the impacts of community energy initiatives (Creamer et al. 2018; Bardsley et al. 2019).

Civil society social movements are a primary driver of social and institutional change (high evidence, high agreement) and can be differently positioned as, on the one hand, 'insider' social movements (e.g., World Wildlife Fund) that seek to influence existing state institutions through lobbying, advice and research and, on the other hand, 'outsider' social movements (e.g., Rising Tide, Extinction Rebellion) that advocate radical reform through protests and demonstrations (Newell 2005; Caniglia et al. 2015). Civil society social movements frame grievances that resonate with society, mobilise resources to coordinate and sustain mass collective action, and operate within – and seek to influence – external conditions that enable or constrain political change (Caniglia et al. 2015). When successful, social movements open up windows of opportunity (so called 'Overton Windows') to unlock structural change (high evidence, high agreement) (Szałek 2013; Piggot 2018).

5

Climate social movements advocate new narratives or framings for climate mitigation (e.g., 'climate emergency') (della Porta and Parks 2014); criticise positive meanings associated with high emission technologies or practices (see case studies on diet and solar PV, (Boxes 5.5 and 5.7)); show disapproval for high-emission behaviours (e.g., through 'flight shaming'); model behaviour change (e.g., shifting to veganism or public transport – see case study on mobility in Kolkata, India (Box 5.8)); demonstrate against extraction and use of fossil fuels (Cheon and Urpelainen 2018); and aim to increase a sense of agency amongst certain social groups (e.g., young people or indigenous communities) that structural change is possible. Climate strikes have become internationally prevalent, for example the September 2019 strikes involved participants in more than 180 countries (Rosane 2019; Fisher and Nasrin 2020; Martiskainen et al. 2020). Enabled by digitalisation, these have given voice to youth on climate (Lee et al. 2020) and created a new cohort of active citizens engaged in climate demonstrations (Fisher 2019). Research on bystanders shows that marches increase positive beliefs about marchers and collective efficacy (Swim et al. 2019).

Countermovement coalitions work to oppose climate mitigation (*high confidence*). Examples include efforts in the US to oppose mandatory limits on carbon emissions supported by organisations from the coal and electrical utility sectors (Brulle 2019). There is evidence that US opposition to climate action by carbon-connected industries is broad-based, highly organised, and matched with extensive lobbying (Cory et al., 2021). Social movements can also work to prevent policy changes, for example in France the Gilet Jaunes objected to increases in fuel costs on the grounds that they unfairly distributed the costs and benefits of price rises across social groups, for example between urban, peri-urban and rural areas (Copland 2019).

Religion could play an important role in enabling collective action on climate mitigation by providing cultural interpretations of change and institutional responses that provide resources and infrastructure to sustain collective actions (Roy et al. 2012; Haluza-DeLay 2014; Caniglia et al. 2015; Hulme 2015). Religion can be an important cultural resource towards sustainability at individual, community and institutional levels (Ives and Kidwell 2019), providing leverage points for inner transformation towards sustainability (Woiwode et al. 2021). Normative interpretations of climate change for and from religious communities are found in nearly every geography, and often observe popular movements for climate action drawing on religious symbols or metaphors (Jenkins et al. 2018). This suggests the value for policymakers of involving religious constituencies as significant civil society organisations in devising and delivering climate responses.

Box 5.7 | Solar PV and the Agency of Consumers

As an innovative technology, solar PV was strongly taken up by consumers (Nemet 2019). Several key factors explain its success. First, modular design made it applicable to different scales of deployment in different geographical contexts (e.g., large-scale grid-connected projects and smaller-scale off-grid projects) and allowed its application by companies taking advantage of emerging markets (Shum and Watanabe 2009). Second, culturally, solar PV symbolised an environmentally progressive technology that was valued by users (Morris and Jungjohann 2016). Large-scale adoption led to policy change (i.e., the introduction of feed-in tariffs that guaranteed a financial return) that in turn enabled improvements to the technology by companies. Over time, this has driven large-scale reductions in cost and increase in deployment worldwide. The relative importance of drivers varied across contexts. In Japan, state subsidies were lower yet did not hinder take-up because consumer behaviour was motivated by non-cost symbolic aspects. In Germany, policy change arose from social movements that campaigned for environmental conservation and opposed nuclear power, making solar PV policies politically acceptable. In summary, the seven-decade evolution of solar PV shows an evolution in which the agency of consumers has consistently played a key role in multiple countries, such that deriving 30–50% of global electricity supply from solar is now a realistic possibility (Creutzig et al. 2017). See more in Chapter 5 Supplementary Material I, 5.SM.6.1.

5.4.3   Business and Corporate Drivers

Businesses and corporate organisations play a key role in the mitigation of global warming, through their own commitments to zero-carbon footprints (Mendiluce 2021), decisions to invest in researching and implementing new energy technologies and energy-efficient measures, and the supply-side interaction with changing consumer preferences and behaviours, such as via marketing. Business models and strategies work both as a barrier to and an accelerator of decarbonisation. Still existing locked-in infrastructures and business models advantages fossil fuel industry over renewable and energy efficient end use industry (Klitkou et al. 2015). The fossil fuel energy generation and delivery system therefore epitomises a barrier to the acceptance and implementation of new and cleaner renewable energy technologies (Kariuki 2018). A good number of corporate agents have attempted to derail climate change mitigation by targeted lobbying and doubt-inducing media strategies (Oreskes and Conway 2011). A number of corporations that are involved in both upstream and downstream supply chains of fossil fuel companies make up the majority of organisations opposed to climate action (Dunlap and McCright 2015; Brulle 2019; Cory et al. 2021). Corporate advertisement and brand-building strategies also attempt to deflect corporate responsibility to individuals, and/or to appropriate climate care sentiments in their own brand building; climate change mitigation is uniquely framed through choice of products and consumption, avoiding the notion of the political collective action sphere (Doyle 2011; Doyle et al. 2019).

Business and corporations are also agents of change towards decarbonisation, as demonstrated in the case of PV and battery electric cars (Teece 2018). Beyond new low-carbon technologies, strong sustainability business models are characterised by identifying nature as the primary stakeholder, strong local anchorage, the creation of diversified income sources, and deliberate limitations on economic growth (Brozovic 2019). However, such business models are difficult to maintain if generally traditional business models, which require short-term accounting, prevail.

Liability of fossil fuel business models and insurance against climate damages are key concerns of corporations and business. Limitations and regulation on GHG emissions will compel reductions in demand for fossil fuel companies' products (Porter and Kramer 2006). According to a report by the Advisory Scientific Committee of the European Systemic Risk Board, insurance industries are very likely to incur losses due to liability risks (ESRB 2016). The divestment movement adds additional pressure on fossil fuel related investments (Braungardt et al. 2019), even though fossil fuel financing remains resilient (Curran 2020). Companies, businesses and organisations, especially those in the carbon-intensive energy sector, might face liability claims for their contribution to climate change. A late transition to a low-carbon economy would exacerbate the physical costs of climate change on governments, businesses and corporations (ESRB 2016).

Despite the seemingly positive roles that businesses and corporate organisations tend to play towards sustainable transitions, there is a need to highlight the dynamic relationship between sustainable and unsustainable trends (Antal et al. 2020), or example, the production of sport utility vehicles (SUVs) in the automobile market at the same time that car manufacturers are producing electric vehicles. An analysis of the role of consumers as drivers of unsustainability for businesses and corporate organisations is very important here as this trend will offset the sustainability progress being made by these businesses and organisations (Antal et al. 2020).

Professional actors, such as building managers, landlords, energy efficiency advisers, technology installers and car dealers, influence patterns of mobility and energy consumption (Shove 2003) by acting as 'middle actors' (Janda and Parag 2013; Parag and Janda 2014) or intermediaries in the provision of building or mobility services (Grandclément et al. 2015; De Rubens et al. 2018). Middle actors can bring about change in several different directions, be it, upstream, downstream or sideways. They can redefine professional ethics around sustainability issues, and, as influencers on the process of diffusion of innovations (Rogers 2003), professionals can enable or obstruct improvements in efficient service provision or shifts towards low-carbon technologies (e.g., air and ground source heat pumps, solar hot water, underfloor heating, programmable thermostats, and mechanical ventilation with heat recovery) and mobility technologies (e.g., electric vehicles).

5.4.4   Institutional Drivers

The allocation of political power to incumbent actors and coalitions has contributed to lock-in of particular institutions, stabilising the interests of incumbents through networks that include policymakers, bureaucracies, advocacy groups and knowledge institutions (*high agreement, high evidence*). There is *high evidence* and *high agreement* that institutions are central in addressing climate change mitigation. Indeed, social provisioning contexts, including equity, democracy, public services and high quality infrastructure, are found to facilitate high levels of need satisfaction at lower energy use, whereas economic growth beyond moderate incomes and dependence on extractive industries inhibit it (Vogel et al. 2021). They shape and interact with technological systems (Unruh 2000; Foxon et al. 2004; Seto et al. 2014) and represent rules, norms and conventions that organise and structure actions (Vatn 2015) and help create new path dependency or strengthen existing path dependency (Mattioli et al. 2020) (see case studies in Boxes 5.5 to 5.8 and Chapter 5 Supplementary Material I). These drive behaviour of actors through formal (e.g., laws, regulations, and standards) or informal (e.g., norms, habits, and customs) processes, and can create constraints on policy options (Breukers and Wolsink 2007). For example, the car-dependent transport system is maintained by interlocking elements and institutions, consisting of (i) the automotive industry; (ii) the provision of car infrastructure; (iii) the political economy of urban sprawl; (iv) the provision of public transport; (v) cultures of car consumption (Mattioli et al. 2020). The behaviour of actors, their processes and implications on policy options and decisions are discussed further in Section 5.6.

Box 5.8 | Shifts from Private to Public Transport in an Indian Megacity

In densely populated, fast-growing megacities, policymakers face the difficult challenge of preventing widespread adoption of petrol or diesel fuelled private cars as a mode of transport. The megacity of Kolkata in India provides a useful case study. As many as twelve different modes of public transportation, each with its own system structure, actors and meanings, co-exist and offer means of mobility to its 14 million citizens. Most of the public transport modes are shared mobility options, ranging from sharing between two people in a rickshaw or a few hundred in metro or sub-urban trains. Sharing also happens informally as daily commuters avail shared taxis and neighbours borrow each other's car or bicycle for urgent or day trips.

Box 5.8 (continued)

A key role is played by the state government, in collaboration with other stakeholders, to improve the system as whole and formalise certain semi-formal modes of transport. An important policy consideration has been to make Kolkata's mobility system more efficient (in terms of speed, reliability and avoidance of congestion) and sustainable through strengthening coordination between different mode-based regimes (Ghosh 2019) and more comfortable with air conditioned space in a hot and humid climate (Roy et al. 2018b). Policymakers have introduced multiple technological, behavioural and socio-cultural measures to tackle this challenge. New buses have been purchased by public authorities (Ghosh and Schot 2019). These have been promoted to middle class workers in terms of modernity, efficiency and comfort, and implemented using premium fares. Digitalisation and the sharing economy have encouraged take-up of shared taxi rides ('app cabs'), being low cost and fast, but also influenced by levels of social trust involved in rides with strangers (Acheampong and Siiba 2019; Ghosh and Schot 2019). Rickshaws have been improved through use of LNG and cycling has been banned from busy roads. These measures contributed positively to halving greenhouse gas emissions per unit of GDP tin one decade within the Kolkata metropolitan area, with potential for further reduction (Colenbrander et al. 2016). However, social movements have opposed some changes due to concerns about social equity, since many of the new policies cater to middle class aspirations and preferences, at the cost of low-income and less privileged communities.

To conclude, urban mobility transitions in Kolkata show interconnected policy, institutional and socio-cultural drivers for socio-technical change. Change has unfolded in complex interactions between multiple actors, sustainability values and megatrends, where direct causalities are hard to identify. However, the prominence of policy actors as change agents is clear as they are changing multiple regimes from within. The state government initiated infrastructural change in public bus systems, coordinated with private and non-governmental actors such as auto-rickshaw operators and app cab owners, who hold crucial agency in offering public transport services in the city. The latter can directly be attributed to the global momentum of mobility-as-a-service platforms, at the intersection of digitalisation and sharing economy trends. More thoughtful action at a policy level is required to sustain and coordinate the diversity of public transport modes through infrastructure design and reflect on the overall direction of change (Roy et al. 2018b; Schot and Steinmueller 2018). See more in Chapter 5 Supplementary Material I, Section 5.SM.6.3.

5.4.5   Technological and Infrastructural Drivers

Technologies and infrastructures shape social practices and their design matters for effective mitigation measures (*high evidence, high agreement*). There are systemic interconnections between infrastructures and practices (Cass et al. 2018; Haberl et al. 2021), and their intersection explains their relevance (Thacker et al. 2019). The design of a new electricity system to meet new emerging demand based on intermittent renewable sources can lead to a change in consumption habits and the adaption of lifestyles compliant with more power supply interruption (Maïzi et al. 2017; Maïzi and Mazauric 2019). The quality of the service delivery impacts directly the potential user uptake of low-carbon technologies among rural households. In the state of Himachal Pradesh in India, a shift from LPG to electricity among rural households, with induction stoves, has been successful due to the availability of stable and continuous electricity, which has been difficult to achieve in any other Indian state (Banerjee et al. 2016). In contrast, in South Africa, people who were using electricity earlier are now adopting LPG to diversify the energy source for cooking due to high electricity tariffs and frequent blackouts (Kimemia and Annegarn 2016) (Box 5.5 and Chapter 5 Supplementary Material I).

From a welfare point of view, infrastructure investments are not constrained by revealed or stated preferences (*high evidence, high agreement*). Preferences change with social and physical environment, and infrastructure interventions can be justified by objective measures, such as public health and climate change mitigation, not only given preferences (*high agreement, high evidence*). Specifically, there is a case for more investment in low-carbon transport infrastructure than assumed in environmental economics as it induces low-carbon preferences (Creutzig et al. 2016a; Mattauch et al. 2016; Mattauch et al. 2018). Changes in infrastructure provision for active travel may contribute to uptake of more walking and cycling (Frank et al. 2019). These effects contribute to higher uptake of low-carbon travel options, albeit the magnitude of effects depends on design choices and context (Goodman et al. 2013; Goodman et al. 2014; Song et al. 2017; Javaid et al. 2020; Abraham et al. 2021). Infrastructure is thus not only required to make low-carbon travel possible but can also be a pre-condition for the formation of low-carbon mobility preferences (see case study in Box 5.8).

The dynamic interaction of habits and infrastructures also predict CO_2-intensive choices. When people move from a city with good public transport to a car-dependent city, they are more likely to own fewer vehicles due to learned preferences for lower levels of car ownership (Weinberger and Goetzke 2010). When individuals moving to a new city with extensive public transport were given targeted material about public transport options, the modal share of public transport increased significantly (Bamberg et al. 2003). Similarly, an exogenous change to route choice in public transport makes commuters change their habitual routes (Larcom et al. 2017).

5

Table 5.4 | Main features, insights, and policy implications of five drivers of decision and action. Entries in each column are independent lists, not intended to line up with each other.

Driver	How does driver contribute to status quo bias?	What needs to change?	Driver's policy implications	Examples
Behavioural	– Habits and routines formed under different circumstances do not get updated – Present bias penalises upfront costs and discourages energy efficiency investments – Loss aversion magnifies the costs of change – When climate change is seen as distant, it is not feared – Nuclear power and accident potential score high on psychological dread	– New goals (sustainable lifestyle) – New capabilities (online real-time communication) – New resources (increased education) – Use of full range of incentives and mechanisms to change demand-side behaviour	– Policies need to be context specific and coordinate economic, legal, social, and infrastructural tools and nudges – Relate climate action to salient local risks and issues	– India's new LPG scale up policy uses insights about multiple behavioural drivers of adoption and use – Rooftop solar adoption expanded in Germany, when feed-in tariffs removed risk from upfront-cost recovery – Nuclear power policies in Germany post Fukushima affected by emotional factors
Socio-cultural	– Cultural norms (e.g., status, comfort, convenience) support existing behaviour – Lack of social trust reduces willingness to shift behaviour (e.g., adopt car sharing) – Fear of social disapproval decreases willingness to adopt new behaviours – Lack of opportunities to participate in policy create reactance against 'top-down' imposition – Unclear or dystopian narratives of climate response reduce willingness to change and to accept new policies and technologies	– Create positive meanings and norms around low-emission service delivery (e.g., mass transit) – Community initiatives to build social trust and engagement, capacity building, and social capital formation – Climate movements that call out the insufficient, highly problematic state of delayed climate action – Public participation in policymaking and technology implementation that increases trust, builds capacity and increases social acceptance – Positive narratives about possible futures that avoid emissions (e.g., emphasis upon health and slow/active travel)	– Embed policies in supportive social norms – Support collective action on climate mitigation to create social trust and inclusion – Involve arts and humanities to create narratives for policy process	– Communicate descriptive norms to electricity end users – Community energy initiative – REScoop – Fridays For Future
Business and corporate	– Lock-in mechanisms that make incumbent firms reluctant to change: core capabilities, sunk investments in staff and factories, stranded assets	– New companies (like car-sharing companies, renewable energy start-ups) that pioneer new business models or energy service provisions	– Influence consumer behaviour via product innovation – Provide capital for clean energy innovation	– Electrification of transport opens up new markets for more than a hundred million new vehicles
Institutional	– Lock-in mechanisms related to power struggles, lobbying, political economy	– New policy instruments, policy discussions, policy platforms, implementation agencies, including capacity	– Feed-in tariffs and other regulations that turn energy consumers into prosumers	– Mobility case study, India's LPG policy sequence
Infrastructural	– Various lock-in mechanisms such as sunk investments, capabilities, embedding in routines/lifestyles	– Many emerging technologies, which are initially often more expensive, but may benefit from learning curves and scale economies that drive costs down	– Systemic governance to avoid rebound effects	– Urban walking and bike paths – Stable and continuous electricity supply fostering induction stoves

5.5　An Integrative View on Transitioning

5.5.1　Demand-side Transitions as Multi-dimensional Processes

Several integrative frameworks including social practice theory (Røpke 2009; Shove and Walker 2014), the energy cultures framework (Stephenson et al. 2015; Jürisoo et al. 2019) and socio-technical transitions theory (McMeekin and Southerton 2012; Geels et al. 2017) conceptualise demand-side transitions as multi-dimensional and interacting processes (*high evidence, high agreement*). Social practice theory emphasises interactions between artefacts, competences, and cultural meanings (Røpke 2009; Shove and Walker 2014). The energy cultures framework highlights feedbacks between materials, norms, and behavioural practices (Stephenson et al. 2015; Jürisoo et al. 2019). Socio-technical transitions theory addresses interactions

between technologies, user practices, cultural meanings, business, infrastructures, and public policies (McMeekin and Southerton 2012; Geels et al. 2017) and can thus accommodate the five drivers of change and stability discussed in Section 5.4.

Section 5.4 shows with *high evidence* and *high agreement* that the relative influence of different drivers varies between demand-side solutions. The deployment of 'Improve' options like LEDs and clean cookstoves mostly involves technological change, adoption by consumers who integrate new technologies in their daily life practices (Smith et al. 1993; Sanderson and Simons 2014; Franceschini and Alkemade 2016), and some policy change. Changes in meanings are less pertinent for those 'Improve' options that are primarily about technological substitution. Other 'Improve' options, like clean cookstoves, involve both technological substitution and changes in cultural meanings and traditions.

Deployment of 'Shift' options like enhanced public transport involves substantial behavioural change and transitions to new or expanded provisioning systems, which may include new technologies (buses, trams), infrastructures (light rail, dedicated bus lanes), institutions (operational licences, performance contracts), financial arrangements, and new organisations (with particular responsibilities and oversight) (*high evidence, high agreement*) (Deng and Nelson 2011; Turnheim and Geels 2019). Changes in cultural meanings can facilitate 'Shift' options. Shifts towards low-meat diets, for instance, are motivated by costs and by beliefs about the undesirability of meat that relate more to issues like health, nutrition and animal welfare than climate change (De Boer et al. 2014; Mylan 2018).

'Avoid' options that reduce service levels (e.g., sufficiency or downshifting) imply very substantial behavioural and cultural changes that may not resonate with mainstream consumers (Dubois et al. 2019). Other 'Avoid' options like teleworking also require changes in cultural meanings and beliefs (about the importance of supervision, coaching, social contacts, or office politics), as well as changes in behaviour, institutions, business, and technology (including good internet connections and office space at home). Because these interconnected changes were not widespread, teleworking remained stuck in small niches and did not diffuse widely before the COVID-19 crisis (Hynes 2014; Hynes 2016; Belzunegui-Eraso and Erro-Garcés 2020; Stiles 2020). As preferences change, new infrastructures and social settings can also elicit new desires associated with emerging low-energy demand service provisioning systems (Section 5.4.5).

Demand-side transitions involve interactions between radical social or technical innovations (such as the Avoid-Shift-Improve options discussed in Section 5.3) and existing socio-technical systems, energy cultures, and social practices (*high evidence, high agreement*) (Stephenson et al. 2015; Geels et al. 2017). Radical innovations such as teleworking, plant-based burgers, car sharing, vegetarianism, or electric vehicles initially emerge in small, peripheral niches (Kemp et al. 1998; Schot and Geels 2008), constituted by R&D projects, technological demonstration projects (Borghei and Magnusson 2016; Rosenbloom et al. 2018b), local community initiatives or grassroots projects by environmental activists (Hargreaves et al. 2013a; Hossain 2016). Such niches offer protection from mainstream selection pressures and nurture the development of radical innovations (Smith and Raven 2012). Many low-carbon niche innovations, such as those described in Section 5.3, face uphill struggles against existing socio-technical systems, energy cultures, and social practices that are stabilised by multiple lock-in mechanisms (*high evidence, high agreement*) (Klitkou et al. 2015; Seto et al. 2016; Clausen et al. 2017; Ivanova et al. 2018). Demand-side transitions therefore do not happen easily and involve interacting processes and struggles on the behavioural, socio-cultural, institutional, business and technological dimensions (Nikas et al. 2020) (Section 5.4).

5.5.2 Phases in Transitions

Transitions often take several decades, unfolding through several phases. Although there is variability across innovations, sectors, and countries, the transitions literature distinguishes four phases, characterised by generic core processes and challenges: (i) emergence, (ii) early adaptation, (i) diffusion, (iv) stabilisation (*high confidence*) (Rotmans et al. 2001; Markard et al. 2012; Geels et al. 2017) (Cross-Chapter Box 12 in Chapter 16). These four phases do not imply that transitions are linear, teleological processes, because set-backs or reversals may occur as a result of learning processes, conflicts, or changing coalitions (*very high confidence*) (Geels and Raven 2006; Messner 2015; Davidescu et al. 2018). There is also no guarantee that technological, social, or business model innovations progress beyond the first phase.

In the first phase, radical innovations emerge in peripheral niches, where researchers, inventors, social movement organisations or community activists dedicate time and effort to their development (*high confidence*) (Kemp et al. 1998; Schot and Geels 2008). Radical social, technical and business model innovations are initially characterised by many uncertainties about technical performance, consumer interest, institutions and cultural meanings. Learning processes are therefore essential and can be stimulated through R&D, demonstration projects, local community initiatives or grassroots projects (Borghei and Magnusson 2016; Hossain 2016; Rosenbloom et al. 2018b; van Mierlo and Beers 2020). Typical challenges are fragmentation and high rates of project failure (den Hartog et al. 2018; Dana et al. 2021), limited funding (Auerswald and Branscomb 2003), limited consumer interest, and socio-cultural acceptance problems due to being perceived as strange or unfamiliar (Lounsbury and Glynn 2001).

In the second phase, social or technical innovations are appropriated or purchased by early adopters, which increases visibility and may provide a small but steady flow of financial resources (*high evidence, high agreement*) (Zimmerman and Zeitz 2002; Dewald and Truffer 2011). Learning processes, knowledge sharing and codification activities help stabilise the innovation, leading to best practice guidelines, standards, and formalised knowledge (*high evidence, high agreement*) (Raven et al. 2008; Borghei and Magnusson 2018). User innovation may lead to the articulation of new routines and social practices, often in tandem with the integration of new technologies into people's daily lives (Nielsen et al. 2016; Schot et al. 2016). Radical innovations remain confined to niches in the second phase because adoption is limited to small, dedicated groups (Schot et al. 2016), innovations are expensive or do not appeal to wider groups, or because complementary infrastructure are missing (Markard and Hoffmann 2016).

In the third phase, radical innovations diffuse into wider communities and mainstream markets. Typical drivers are performance improvements, cost reductions, widespread consumer interest, investments in infrastructure and complementary technologies, institutional support and strong cultural appeal (*high evidence, high agreement*) (Wilson 2012; Markard and Hoffmann 2016; Malone et al. 2017; Raven et al. 2017; Kanger et al. 2019). The latter may be related to wider cultural shifts such as increased public attention to climate change and new framings like 'climate emergency' which gained traction before the Covid-19 pandemic (Bouman et al. 2020b). These concerns may not last, however, since public attention typically follows cycles (Downs 1972; Djerf-Pierre 2012).

This phase often involves multiple struggles: economic competition between low-carbon innovations and existing technologies and practices, business struggles between incumbents and new entrants (Hockerts and Wüstenhagen 2010), cultural and framing struggles in public opinion arenas (Kammermann and Dermont 2018; Rosenbloom 2018; Hess 2019a), and political struggles over adjustments in policies and institutions, which shape markets and innovations (Meadowcroft 2011; Roberts and Geels 2019). The lock-in mechanisms of existing practices and systems tend to weaken in the third phase, either because competing innovations erode their economic viability, cultural legitimacy or institutional support (Turnheim and Geels 2012; Roberts 2017; Kuokkanen et al. 2018; Leipprand and Flachsland 2018) or because exogenous shocks and pressures disrupt the status quo (Kungl and Geels 2018; Simpson 2019).

In the fourth phase, the diffusing innovations replace or substantially reconfigure existing practices and systems, which may lead to the downfall or reorientation of incumbent firms (Bergek et al. 2013; McMeekin et al. 2019). The new system becomes institutionalised and anchored in professional standards, technical capabilities, infrastructures, educational programmes, regulations and institutional logics, user habits, and views of normality, which create new lock-ins (Galaskiewicz 1985; Shove and Southerton 2000; Barnes et al. 2018).

'Avoid', 'Shift' and 'Improve' options vary with regard to the four transition phases. Incremental 'Improve' options, such as energy-efficient appliances or stand-alone insulation measures, are not transitions but upgrades of existing technologies. They have progressed furthest since they build on existing knowledge and do not require wider changes (Geels et al. 2018). Some radical 'Improve' options, which have a different technological knowledge base, are beginning to diffuse, moving from phase two to three in multiple countries. Examples are electric vehicles, light-emitting diodes (LED), or passive house designs (Franceschini and Alkemade 2016; Berkeley et al. 2017). Many 'Shift' and 'Avoid/Reduce' options like heat pumps, district heating, passive house designs, compact cities, less meat initiatives, flight and car use reduction have low momentum in most countries, and are mostly in the first phase of isolated initiatives and projects (Bergman 2013; Morris et al. 2014; Bows-Larkin 2015; Bush et al. 2016; Kivimaa and Martiskainen 2018; Hoolohan et al. 2018). Structural transitions in Dutch cities, Copenhagen, and more recently Paris, however, demonstrate that transitions towards low-carbon lifestyles, developed around cycling, are possible (Colville-Andersen 2018). Low-carbon demand-side transitions are often still in early phases (*high evidence, high agreement*).

5.5.3   Feasible Rate of Change

Transitional change is usually slow in the first and second transition phases, because experimentation, social and technological learning, and stabilisation processes take a long time, often decades, and remain restricted to small niches (*high confidence*) (Wilson 2012; Bento 2013; Bento et al. 2018b). Transitional change accelerates in the third phase, as radical innovations diffuse from initial niches into mainstream markets, propelled by the self-reinforcing mechanisms discussed above. The rate of adoption (diffusion) of new practices,

processes, artefacts, and behaviours is determined by a wide range of factors at the macro- and micro-scales, which have been identified by several decades of diffusion research in multiple disciplines (Mansfield 1968; Martino et al. 1978; Davis 1979; Mahajan et al. 1990; Ausubel 1991; Grubler 1991; Feder and Umali 1993; Bayus 1994; Comin and Hobijn 2003; Rogers 2003; Van den Bulte and Stremersch 2004; Meade and Islam 2006; Peres et al. 2010).

Diffusion rates are determined by two broad categories of variables: those intrinsic to the technology, product or practice under consideration (typically performance, costs, benefits), and those intrinsic to the adoption environment (e.g., socio-economic and market characteristics).

Despite differences, the literature offers three robust conclusions on acceleration (*high evidence, high agreement*): First, size matters. Acceleration of transitions is more difficult for social, economic, or technological systems of larger size (in terms of number of users, financial investments, infrastructure, powerful industries) (Wilson 2009; Wilson 2012). Size also matters at the level of the systems component involved in a transition. Components with smaller unit-scale ('granular' and thus relatively cheap), such as light bulbs or household appliances, turn over much faster (often within a decade) than large-scale, capital-intensive lumpy technologies and infrastructures (such as transport systems) where rates of change typically involve several decades, even up to a century (Grubler 1991; Leibowicz 2018). Also, the creation of entirely new systems (diffusion) takes longer time than replacements of existing technologies or practices (substitution) (Grübler et al. 1999); and late adopters tend to adopt faster than early pioneers (Wilson 2012; Grubler 1996).

Arguments about scale in the energy system date back at least to the 1970s when Schumacher, Lovins and others argued the case for smaller-scale, distributed technologies (Schumacher 1974; Lovins 1976; Lovins 1979). In *Small is Profitable* Lovins and colleagues evidenced over 200 reasons why decentralised energy resources, from distributed generation to end-use efficiency, made good business sense in addition to their social, human-centred benefits (Lovins et al. 2003). More recent advances in digital, solar and energy storage technologies have renewed technical and economic arguments in favour of adopting decentralised approaches to decarbonisation (Cook et al. 2016; Jain et al. 2017; Lovins et al. 2018). Smaller-scale technologies from microprocessors to solar panels show dramatically faster cost and performance improvement trajectories than large-scale energy supply facilities (Trancik 2014; Sweerts et al. 2020, Creutzig et al. 2021) (Figure 5.15). Analysing the performance of over 80 energy technologies historically, Wilson et al. (2020a) found that smaller scale, more 'granular' technologies are empirically associated with faster diffusion, lower investment risk, faster learning, more opportunities to escape lock-in, more equitable access, more job creation, and higher social returns on innovation investment. These advantages of more granular technologies are consistent with accelerated low-carbon transformation (Wilson et al. 2020a).

Second, complexity matters, which is often related to unit scale (Ma et al. 2008). Acceleration is more difficult for options with higher degrees of complexity (e.g., carbon capture, transport and storage, or a hydrogen economy) representing higher technological and investment risks that

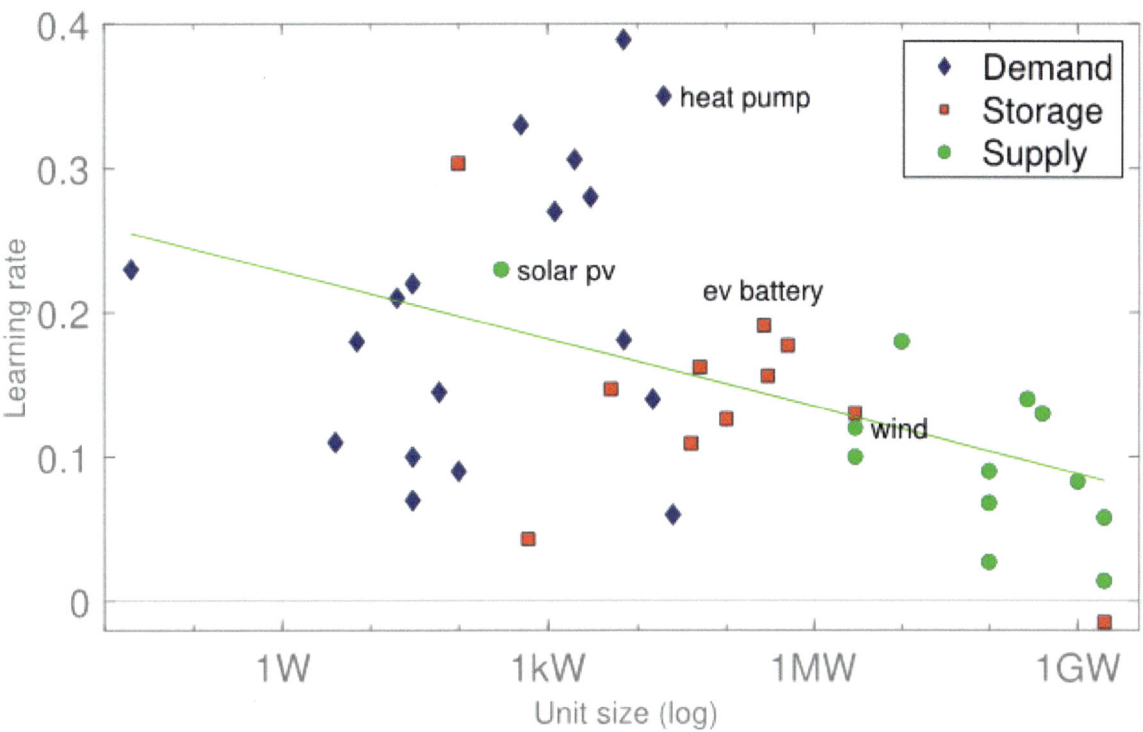

Figure 5.15 | Demand technologies show high learning rates. Learning from small-scale granular technologies outperforms learning from larger supply-side technologies. Line is linear fit of log unit size to learning rate for all 41 technologies plotted. Source: Creutzig et al. (2021); based on Sweerts et al. (2020).

can slow down change. Options with lower complexity are easier to accelerate because they involve less experimentation and debugging and require less adoption efforts and risk.

Third, agency, structure and meaning can accelerate transitions. The creation and mobilisation of actor coalitions is widely seen as important for acceleration, especially if these involve actors with technical skills, financial resources and political capital (Kern and Rogge 2016; Hess 2019b; Roberts and Geels 2019). Changes in

policies and institutions can also accelerate transitions, especially if these create stable and attractive financial incentives or introduce technology-forcing standards or regulations (Brand et al. 2013; Kester et al. 2018; Roberts et al. 2018). Changes in meanings and cultural norms can also accelerate transitions, especially when they affect consumer practices, enhance social acceptance, and create legitimacy for stronger policy support (Lounsbury and Glynn 2001; Rogers 2003; Buschmann and Oels 2019). Adoption of most advanced practices can support leapfrogging of polluting technologies (Box 5.9).

Box 5.9 | Is Leapfrogging Possible?

The concept of leapfrogging emerged in development economics (Soete 1985), energy policy (Goldemberg 1991) and environmental regulation (Perkins 2003, which provides a first critical review of the concept), and refers to a development strategy that skips traditional and polluting development in favour of the most advanced concepts. For instance, in rural areas without telephone landlines or electricity access (cables), a direct shift to mobile telephony or distributed, locally-sourced energy systems is promoted, or economic development policies for pre-industrial economies forego the traditional initial emphasis on heavy industry industrialisation, instead focusing on services like finance or tourism. Often leapfrogging is enabled by learning and innovation externalities where improved knowledge and technologies become available for late adopters at low costs. The literature highlights many cases of successful leapfrogging but also highlights limitations (Watson and Sauter 2011); with example case studies for China (Gallagher 2006; Chen and Li-Hua 2011); Mexico (Gallagher and Zarsky 2007); and Japan and Korea (Cho et al. 1998). Increasingly the concept is being integrated into the literature of low-carbon development, including innovation and technology transfer policies (Pigato et al. 2020), highlighting in particular the importance of contextual factors of successful technology transfer and leapfrogging including: domestic absorptive capacity and technological capabilities (Cirera and Maloney 2017); human capital, skills, and relevant technical know-how (Nelson and Phelps 1966); the size of the market (Keller 2004); greater openness to trade (Sachs and Warner 1995; Keller 2004); geographical proximity to investors and financing (Comin et al. 2012); environmental regulatory proximity (Dechezleprêtre et al. 2015); and stronger protection of intellectual property rights (Dechezleprêtre et al. 2013; Dussaux et al. 2017). The existence of a technological potential for leapfrogging therefore needs to be considered within a wider context of social, institutional, and economic factors that influence whether leapfrogging potentials can be realised (*high evidence, high agreement*).

There are also some contentious topics in the debate on accelerated low-carbon transitions. First, while acceleration is desirable to mitigate climate change, there is a risk that accelerating change too much may short-cut crucial experimentation and social and technological learning in 'formative phases' (Bento 2013; Bento et al. 2018b) and potentially lead to a pre-mature lock-in of solutions that later turn out to have negative impacts (Cowan 1990; Cowan 1991) (*high evidence, medium agreement*).

Second, there is an ongoing debate about the most powerful leverage points and policies for speeding up change in social and technological systems. Farmer et al. (2019) suggested 'sensitive intervention points' for low-carbon transitions, but do not quantify the impacts on transformations. Grubler et al. (2018) proposed an end-user and efficiency-focused strategy to achieve rapid emission reductions and quantified their scenario with a leading IAM. However, discussion of the policy implications of such a strategy have only just started (Wilson et al. 2019a), suggesting an important area for future research.

The last contentious issue is if policies can or should substitute for lack of economic or social appeal of change or for technological risks. Many large-scale supply-side climate mitigation options, such as CCS or nuclear power, involve high technological risks, critically depend on a stable carbon price, and are controversial in terms of social and environmental impacts (Sovacool et al. 2014; Smith et al. 2016; Wilson et al. 2020a) (*high evidence, medium agreement*). There is continuing debate if and how policies could counterbalance these impacts in order to accelerate transitions (Nordhaus 2019; Lovins 2015). Some demand-side options like large-scale public transport infrastructures such as 'Hyperloop' (Decker et al. 2017) or concepts such as the Asian Super Grid (maglev fast train coupled with superconducting electricity transmission networks) (AIGC 2017) may face similar challenges, which adds weight and robustness to those demand-side options that are more decentralised, granular in scale, and provide potential tangible consumer benefits besides being low-carbon (like more efficient buildings and appliances, 'soft' urban mobility options (walking and cycling), digitalisation, among others (Grubler et al. 2018)).

A robust conclusion from this review is that there are no generic acceleration policies that are independent from the nature of what changes, by whom and how. Greater contextualisation and granularity in policy approaches is therefore important to address the challenges of rapid transitions towards zero-carbon systems (*high evidence, high agreement*).

5.6   Governance and Policy

5.6.1   Governing Mitigation: Participation and Social Trust

In demand-side mitigation, governance is key to drive the multidimensional changes needed to meet service needs within a society that provide people with a decent living while increasingly reducing resource and energy input levels (Rojas-Rueda et al. 2012; Batchelor et al. 2018; OECD 2019a). Impartial governance, understood as equal treatment of everyone by the rule of law, creates social trust and is thus a key enabler of inclusive and participatory demand-side climate policies (Rothstein 2011). Inclusive and broad-based participation itself also leads to greater social trust and thus is also a key enabler of demand-side climate mitigation (Section 5.2). Higher social trust and inclusive participatory processes also reduce inequality, restrain opportunistic behaviour and enhance cooperation (Drews and van den Bergh 2016; Gür 2020) (Section 5.2). Altogether, broad-based participatory processes are central to the successful implementation of climate policies (Rothstein and Teorell 2008; Klenert et al. 2018) (*high evidence, medium agreement*). A culture of cooperation feeds back to increase social trust and enables action that reduce GHG emissions (Carattini et al. 2015; Jo and Carattini 2021), and requires including explicit consideration of the informal sector (Box 5.10). More equitable societies also have the institutional flexibility to allow for mitigation to advance faster, given their readiness to adopt locally-appropriate mitigation policies; they also suffer less from policy lock-in (Tanner et al. 2009; Lorenz 2013; Chu 2015; Cloutier et al. 2015; Martin 2016; Seto et al. 2016; Vandeweerdt et al. 2016; Turnheim et al. 2018).

Box 5.10 | The Informal Sector and Climate Mitigation

The informal economy represents a large and growing portion of socio-economic activities (Charmes 2016; Muchie et al. 2016; Mbaye and Gueye 2018), including much of the work done by women worldwide. It accounts for an estimated 61% of global employment in the world; 90% in developing countries, 67% in emerging countries, and 18% in developed countries (Berik 2018), representing roughly 30% of GDP across a range of countries (Durán Heras 2012; Narayan 2017). Due to its importance, policies which support informal-sector climate mitigation activities may be extremely efficient (Garland 2015). For example, environmental and energy taxes may have negative gross costs when the informal sector dominates economic activity since these taxes indirectly tax the informal sector; informal production may substitute for energy-intensive goods, with strong welfare-enhancing effects (Bento et al. 2018a). The informal sector can assemble social and financial capital, create jobs, and build low-carbon local economies (Ruzek 2015). Constraints on small and informal-sector firms' ability to build climate resilience include financial and data barriers, limited access to information technology, and policy exclusion (Kraemer-Mbula and Wunsch-Vincent 2016; Crick et al. 2018a; Crick et al. 2018b).

Informal-sector innovation is often underrated. It gives marginalised people access to welfare-enhancing innovations, building on alternative knowledge and socially-embedded reciprocal exchange (Jaffe and Koster 2019; Sheikh 2019; Sheikh and Bhaduri 2020). Large improvements in low-emission, locally-appropriate service provision are possible by facilitating informal-sector service providers'

Box 5.10 (continued)

access to low-energy technologies (while taking care not to additionally burden the unpaid and marginalised), through such means as education, participatory governance, government policies to assist the informal sector, social services, health care, credit provision, and removing harmful policies and regulatory silos. The importance of the informal economy, especially in low-income countries, opens many possibilities for new approaches to decent living standards service provision along with climate resilience (Rynikiewicz and Chetaille 2006; Backstränd et al. 2010; Porio 2011; Kriegler et al. 2014; Taylor and Peter 2014; Brown and McGranahan 2016; Chu 2016; Satterthwaite et al. 2018; Boran 2019; Hugo and du Plessis 2019; Schröder et al. 2019; Javaid et al. 2020).

Public information and understanding of the CO_2-eq emissions implied by consumption patterns can unleash great creativity for meeting service needs fairly and with lower emissions (Darier and Schüle 1999; Sterman and Sweeney 2002; Lorenzoni et al. 2007; Billett 2010; Marres 2011; Zapico Lamela et al. 2011; Polonsky et al. 2012; Williams et al. 2019). Community-based mapping, social learning, green infrastructure development, and participatory governance facilitate such information-sharing (Tauhid and Zawani 2018; Mazeka et al. 2019; Sharifi 2020), strengthening mitigation policies (Loiter and Norberg-Bohm 1999; Stokes and Warshaw 2017; Zhou et al. 2019).

Since informal settlements are usually dense, upgrading them supports low-carbon development pathways which leapfrog less-efficient housing, transport and other service provision, using locally-appropriate innovations (Satterthwaite et al. 2018). Examples of informal-sector mitigation include digital banking in Africa; mobility in India using collective transport; food production, meal provision, and reduction of food waste in Latin America (e.g., soup kitchens in Brazil, community kitchens in Lima, Peru); informal materials recycling, space heating and cooling, and illumination (Hordijk 2000; Baldez 2003; Maumbe 2006; Gutberlet 2008; Chaturvedi and Gidwani 2011; Nandy et al. 2015; Rouse and Verhoef 2016; Ackah 2017).

5.6.2 Policies to Strengthen Avoid-Shift-Improve

There is high untapped potential of demand-side mitigation options if considered holistically within the domains of Avoid-Shift-Improve (Sections 5.3 and 5.4, Tables 5.1, 5.2, and 5.3a,b). Within the demand-side mitigation options opportunity space, policies currently focus more on efficiency and 'Improve' options and relatively less on 'Shift' and 'Avoid' options (Dubois et al. 2019; Moberg et al. 2019). Current demand-side policies are fragmented, piecemeal and too weak to drive demand-side transitions commensurate with 1.5°C or 2°C climate goals (Wilson et al. 2012; Fawcett et al. 2019; Mundaca et al. 2019; Moberg et al. 2019) (*high evidence, high agreement*). However, increasingly policy mix in a number of countries has seen a rise in prohibitions on fossil fuel use as a way to weaken lock-ins, for example, on fossil fuel heating in favour of low-carbon alternatives (Rosenbloom et al. 2020). Policies that are aimed at behaviour and lifestyle changes carry a perception of political risks for policymakers, which may explain why policy instruments focus more on information provision and adoption of incentives than on regulation and investment (Rosenow et al. 2017; Moberg et al. 2019). Acceleration of demand-side transitions would thus require both a broadening of demand-side options and the creation of comprehensive and targeted policy mixes (Kern et al. 2017; Rosenow et al. 2017; IPCC 2018) that strengthen the five drivers of decision and action identified in Section 5.4, Table 5.4 and in Tables 5.5–5.7 (*high evidence, high agreement*). Demand-side transitions in developing and emerging economies would also require stronger administrative capacity as well as technical and financial support (UN-Habitat 2013; Creutzig et al. 2016b).

Systematic categorisation of demand-side policy options in different sectors and services through the Avoid-Shift-Improve framework enables identification of major entry points and possible associated social struggles to overcome for the policy instruments/interventions as discussed below.

5.6.2.1 'Avoid' Policies

There is *high evidence* and *high agreement* that 'Avoid' policies that affect lifestyle changes offer opportunities for cost-effective reductions in energy use and emissions, but would need to overcome political sensitivities around government efforts to shape and modify individual-level behaviour (Rosenow et al. 2017; Grubb et al. 2020) (Table 5.5). These policies include ways to help avoid travel growth through integrated city planning or building retrofits to help avoid demand for transport, heating or cooling (Bakker et al. 2014; Lucon et al. 2014; de Feijter et al. 2019), which interact with existing infrastructure. Dense pedestrianised cities and towns and medium-density transit corridors are better placed to implement policies for car reductions than 'sprawled' cities characterised by low-density, auto-dependent and separated land uses (Seto et al. 2014; Newman and Kenworthy 2015; Newman et al. 2017; Bakker et al. 2014).

Cities face pressing priorities like poverty reduction, meeting basic services and building human and institutional capacity. These are met with highly accessible walkable and cyclable cities, connected with public transit corridors, enabling equal accessibility for all citizens, and enabling a high level of service provisioning (UN-Habitat 2013; Creutzig et al. 2016b). Infrastructure development costs less than for car dependent cities. However, it requires a mindset shift for urban and transport planners (*medium evidence, high agreement*).

Policies that support the avoidance of higher-emission lifestyles and improve well-being are facilitated by the introduction of smart technologies, infrastructures and practices (Amini et al. 2019). They

5

include regulations and measures for investment in high-quality ICT infrastructure and regulations to restrict number plates, as well as company policy around flexible working conditions (Lachapelle et al. 2018; Shabanpour et al. 2018). Working-from-home arrangements may advantage certain segments of society such as male, older, higher-educated and highly-paid employees, potentially exacerbating existing inequalities in the labour market (Lambert et al. 2020;

Bonacini et al. 2021). In the absence of distributive or other equity-based measures, the potential gains in terms of emissions reduction may therefore be counteracted by the cost of increasing inequality. This potential growth in inequality is likely to be more severe in poorer countries that will additionally suffer from a lack of international funding for achieving the SDGs (*high evidence, medium agreement*) (Barbier and Burgess 2020; UN 2020).

Table 5.5 | Examples of policies to enable 'Avoid' options.

Mitigation option	Perceived struggles to overcome	Policy to overcome struggles (Incentives)
Reduce passenger km	– Existing paradigms and planning practices and car dependency (Rosenow et al. 2017; Grubb et al. 2020) – Financial and capacity barrier in many developing countries – Status dimension of private cars	– Integrated city planning to avoid travel growth, car reduction, building retrofits to avoid heating or cooling demand (Bakker et al. 2014; Lucon et al. 2014; de Feijter et al. 2019) – Public-private partnership to overcome financial barrier (Roy et al. 2018b) (Box 5.8) – Taxation of status consumption; reframing of low-carbon transport as high status (Hoor 2020; Ramakrishnan and Creutzig 2021)
Reduce/Avoid food waste	Little visible political and social momentum to prevent food waste in the Global North	Strengthen national nutrition guidelines for health safety; improve education/awareness on food waste; policies to eliminate ambiguous food labelling include well-defined and clear date labelling systems for food (Wilson et al. 2017); policies to support R&D to improve packaging to extend shelf life (Thyberg and Tonjes 2016); charging according to how much food households throw away
Reduce size of dwellings	Size of dwellings getting larger in many countries	Compact city design, taxing residential properties with high per capita area, progressive taxation of high status consumption (Ramakrishnan and Creutzig 2021)
Reduce/Avoid heating, cooling and lighting in dwellings	Change in individual behaviour in dress codes and working times	Temperature set point as norm; building energy codes that set building standards; bioclimatic and/or zero emissions buildings; cities and buildings that incorporate features like daylighting and increased building depth, height, and compactness (Steemers 2003; Creutzig et al. 2016a)
Sharing economy for more service per product	Lack of inclusivity and involvement of users in design. Digital divide, unequal access and unequal digital literacy (Pouri and Hilty 2018). Political or power relations among actors involved in the sharing economy (Curtis and Lehner 2019)	Lower prices for public parking, and subsidies towards the purchase of electric vehicles for providers of electric vehicle sharing services (Jung and Koo 2018)

5.6.2.2　'Shift' Policies

As indicated in Table 5.6, 'Shift' policies have various forms such as the demand for low-carbon materials for buildings and infrastructure in manufacturing and services and shift from meat-based protein, mainly beef, to plant-based diets of other protein sources (*high evidence, high agreement*) (Springmann et al. 2016a;

Ritchie et al. 2018; Willett et al. 2019). Governments also play a direct role beyond nudging citizens with information about health and well-being. While the effectiveness of these policies on behaviour change overall may be limited (Pearson-Stuttard et al. 2017; Shangguan et al. 2019), there is some room for policy to influence actors upstream, such as industry and supermarkets, which may give rise to longer-term, structural change.

Table 5.6 | Examples of policies to enable 'Shift' options.

Mitigation option	Perceived struggles to overcome	Policy to overcome struggles (Incentives)
More walking, less car use, train rather air travel	Adequate infrastructure may be absent, speed a part of modern life	– Congestion charges (Pearson-Stuttard et al. 2017; Shangguan et al. 2019); deliberate urban design including cycling lanes, shared micromobility, and extensive cycling infrastructure; synchronised/integrated transport system and timetable – Fair street space allocation (Creutzig et al. 2020)
Multifamily housing	Zonings that favour single family homes have been dominant in planning (Hagen 2016)	Taxation, relaxation of single-family zoning policies and land use regulation (Geffner 2017)
Shifting from meat to other protein	Minimal meat required for protein intake, especially in developing countries for population suffering from malnutrition and when plant-based protein is lacking (Garnett 2011; Sunguya et al. 2014; Behrens et al. 2017; Godfray et al. 2018); dominance of market-based instruments limits governments' role to nudging citizens with information about health and well-being, and point-of-purchase labelling (Pearson-Stuttard et al. 2017; Shangguan et al. 2019)	– Tax on meat/beef in wealthier countries and/or households (Edjabou and Smed 2013; Säll and Gren 2015) – Nationally recommended diets (Garnett 2011; Sunguya et al. 2014; Behrens et al. 2017; Godfray et al. 2018)
Material-efficient product design, packaging	Resistance by architects and builders who might perceive risks with lean designs. Cultural and social norms. Policy measures not keeping up with changes on the ground such as increased consumption of packaging	Embodied carbon standards for buildings (IEA 2019c)
Architectural design with shading and ventilation	Lack of education, awareness and capacity for new thinking, local air pollution	Incentives for increased urban density and incentives to encourage architectural forms with lower surface-to-volume ratios and increased shading support (Creutzig et al. 2016a)

Mobility services is one of the key areas where a combination of market-based and command-and-control measures have been implemented to persuade large numbers of people to get out of their automobiles and take up public transport and cycling alternatives (Gehl et al. 2011). Congestion charges are often complemented by other measures, such as company subsidies for bicycles, to incentivise the shift to public mobility services. Attracting people to public transport requires sufficient spatial coverage of transport with adequate level of provision, and good quality service at affordable fares (Sims et al. 2014; Moberg et al. 2019) (*high evidence, high agreement*). Cities such as Bogota, Colombia, Buenos Aires, Argentina, and Santiago, Chile, have seen rapid growth of cycling, resulting in a six-fold increase in cyclists (Pucher and Buehler 2017). Broadly, the history and type of city determines how quickly the transition to public modes of transport can be achieved. For example, cities in developed countries enjoy an advantage in that there is a network of high-quality public transport predating the advent of automobiles, whereas cities in less developed countries are latecomers to large-scale network infrastructure (UN-Habitat 2013; Gota et al. 2019).

5.6.2.3 'Improve' Policies

'Improve' policies focus on the efficiency and enhancement of technological performance of services (Table 5.7). In mobility services,

'Improve' policies aim at improving vehicles, comfort, fuels, transport operations and management technologies; and in buildings, they include policies for improving efficiency of heating systems and retrofitting existing buildings. Efficiency improvements in electric cooking appliances, together with the ongoing decrease in prices of renewable energy technologies, are opening policy opportunities to support households to adopt electrical cooking at mass scale (*medium evidence, medium agreement*) (IEA 2017c; Puzzolo et al. 2019). These actions towards cleaner energy for cooking often come with cooking-related reduction of GHG emissions, even though the extent of the reductions is highly dependent on context and technology and fuel pathways (*high evidence, high agreement*) (Martínez et al. 2017; Mondal et al. 2018; Rosenthal et al. 2018; Serrano-Medrano et al. 2018; Dagnachew et al. 2019) (Box 5.6).

Table 5.7 highlights the significant progress made in the uptake of the electrical vehicle (EV) in Europe, driven by a suite of incentives and policies. Increased activity in widening electric vehicle use is also occurring in developing countries. The Indian Government's proposal to reach the target of a 100% electric vehicle fleet by 2030 has stimulated investment in charging infrastructure that can facilitate diffusion of larger EVs (Dhar et al. 2017). Although the proposal was not converted into a policy, India's large and growing two-wheeler market has benefitted from the policy attention on EVs, showing a significant potential for increasing the share of electric two- and three-wheelers

Table 5.7 | Examples of policies to enable 'Improve' options

Mitigation option	Perceived struggles to overcome	Policy to overcome struggles (Incentives)
Lightweight vehicles, hydrogen cars, electric vehicles, ecodriving	Adequate infrastructure may be absent, speed a part of modern life	Monetary incentives and traffic regulations favouring electric vehicles; investment in public charging infrastructure; car purchase tax calculated by a combination of weight, CO_2 and NO_x emissions (Haugneland and Kvisle 2015; Globisch et al. 2018; Gnann et al. 2018; Lieven and Rietmann 2018; Rietmann and Lieven 2019)
Use low-carbon materials in dwelling design	Manufacturing and R&D costs, recycling processes and aesthetic performance (Orsini and Marrone 2019). Access to secondary materials in the building sector (Nußholz et al. 2019)	Increasing recycling of construction and demolition waste; incentives must be available to companies in the waste collection and recovery markets to offer recovered material at higher value (Nußholz et al. 2019)
Better insulation and retrofitting	– Policies to advance retrofitting and GHG emission reductions in buildings are laden with high expectations since they are core components of politically ambitious city climate targets (Haug et al. 2010) – Building owners' to implement measures identified in auditing results – Lack of incentive for building owners to invest in higher efficiency than required norms (Trencher et al. 2016)	Grants and loans through development banks, building and heating system labels, and technical renovation requirements to continuously raise standards (Ortiz et al. 2019; Sebi et al. 2019); disclosure of energy use, financing and technical assistance (Sebi et al. 2019)
Widen low-carbon energy access	Access to finance, capacity, robust policies, affordability for poor households for off-grid solutions until recently (Rolffs et al. 2015; Fuso Nerini et al. 2018; Mulugetta et al. 2019)	Feed-in tariffs and auctions to stimulate investment. Pay-as-you-go end-user financing scheme where customers pay a small up-front fee for the equipment, followed by monthly payments, using mobile payment system (Rolffs et al. 2015; Yadav et al. 2019)
Improve illumination-related emission	Lack of supply-side solutions for low-carbon electricity provision	Building energy codes that set building standards; grants and other incentives for R&D
Improve efficiency of cooking appliances	Reliability of power in many countries is not guaranteed; electricity tariff is high in many countries; cooking appliances are mostly imported using scarce foreign currency	Driven by a combination of government support for appliance purchases, shifting subsidies from kerosene or LPG to electricity; community-level consultation and awareness campaigns about the hazards associated with indoor air pollution from the use of fuelwood, coal and kerosene, as well as education on the multiple benefits of electric cooking (Martínez-Gómez et al. 2016; Yangka and Diesendorf 2016; Martínez et al. 2017; Gould and Urpelainen 2018; Dendup and Arimura 2019; Pattanayak et al. 2019)
Shift to LED lamps	People spend increasing amounts of time indoors, with heavy dependence on and demand for artificial lighting (Ding et al. 2020)	Government incentives, utility incentive (Bertoldi et al. 2021). EU bans on directional and non-directional halogen bulbs (Franceschini et al. 2018)
Solar water heating	Dominance of incumbent energy source i.e., electricity; cheap conventional energy; high initial investment costs and long payback (Joubert et al. 2016)	Subsidy for solar heaters (Li et al. 2013; Bessa and Prado 2015; Sgouridis et al. 2016)

5

in the short term (Ahmad and Creutzig 2019). Similar opportunities exist for China, where e-bikes have replaced car trips and are reported to act as intermediate links in multimodal mobility (Cherry et al. 2016).

In recent years, policy interest has arisen to address the energy access challenge in Africa using low-carbon energy technologies to meet energy for poverty reduction and climate action simultaneously (Rolffs et al. 2015; Fuso Nerini et al. 2018; Mulugetta et al. 2019). This aspiration has been bolstered on the technical front by significant advances in appliance efficiency such as light-emitting diode (LED) technology, complemented by the sharp reduction in the cost of renewable energy technologies, and largely driven by market-stimulating policies and public R&D to mitigate risks (*high evidence, high agreement*) (Alstone et al. 2015; Zubi et al. 2019).

5.6.3 Policies in Transition Phases

Demand-side policies tend to vary for different transition phases (*high evidence, high agreement*) (Roberts and Geels 2019; Sandin

et al. 2019). In the first phase, which is characterised by the emergence or introduction of radical innovations in small niches, policies focus on: (i) supporting R&D and demonstration projects to enable learning and capability developments, (ii) nurturing the building of networks and multi-stakeholder interactions, and (iii) providing future orientation through visions or targets (Brown et al. 2003; López-García et al. 2019; Roesler and Hassler 2019). In the second phase, the policy emphasis shifts towards upscaling of experiments, standardisation, cost reduction, and the creation of early market niches (Borghei and Magnusson 2018; Ruggiero et al. 2018). In the third and later phases, comprehensive policy mixes are used to stimulate mass adoption, infrastructure creation, social acceptance and business investment (Fichter and Clausen 2016; Geels et al. 2018; Strauch 2020). In the fourth phase, transitions can also be stimulated through policies that weaken or phase out existing regimes, such as removing inefficient subsidies (for cheap petrol or fuel oil) that encourage wasteful consumption, increasing taxes on carbon-intensive products and practices (Box 5.11), or substantially tightening regulations and standards (Kivimaa and Kern 2016; David 2017; Rogge and Johnstone 2017).

Box 5.11 | Carbon Pricing and Fairness

Whether the public supports specific policy instruments for reducing greenhouse gas emissions is determined by cultural and political world views (Cherry et al. 2017; Kotchen et al. 2017; Alberini et al. 2018) and national positions in international climate negotiations, with major implications for policy design. For example, policy proposals need to circumvent 'solution aversion': that is, individuals are more doubtful about the urgency of climate change mitigation if the proposed policy contradicts their political worldviews (Campbell and Kay 2014). While there are reasons to believe that carbon pricing is the most efficient way to reduce emissions, a recent literature – focusing on populations in Western Europe and North America and carbon taxes – documents that efficiency features alone is not what makes citizens like or dislike carbon pricing schemes (Kallbekken et al. 2011; Carattini et al. 2017; Klenert et al. 2018).

Citizens tend to ignore or doubt the idea that pricing carbon emissions reduces GHG emissions (Kallbekken et al. 2011; Douenne and Fabre 2019; Maestre-Andrés et al. 2019). Further, citizens have fairness concerns about carbon pricing (Büchs and Schnepf 2013; Douenne and Fabre 2019; Maestre-Andrés et al. 2019), even if higher carbon prices can be made progressive by suitable use of revenues (Rausch et al. 2011; Williams et al. 2015; Klenert and Mattauch 2016). There are also non-economic properties of policy instruments that matter for public support: Calling a carbon price a 'CO$_2$ levy' alleviates solution aversion (Kallbekken et al. 2011; Carattini et al. 2017). It may be that the word 'tax' evokes a feeling of distrust in government and fears of high costs, low benefits and distributional effects (Strand 2020). Trust in politicians is negatively correlated with higher carbon prices (Hammar and Jagers 2006; Rafaty 2018) and political campaigns for a carbon tax can lower public support for them (Anderson et al. 2019). Few developing countries have adopted carbon taxes, probably due to high costs, relatively low benefits, and distributional effects (Strand 2020).

To address these realities regarding support for carbon pricing, some studies have examined whether specific uses of the revenue can increase public support for higher carbon prices (Carattini et al. 2017; Beiser-McGrath and Bernauer 2019). Doubt about the environmental effectiveness of carbon pricing may be alleviated if revenue from carbon pricing is earmarked for specific uses (Kallbekken et al. 2011; Carattini et al. 2017) and higher carbon prices may then be supported (Beiser-McGrath and Bernauer 2019). This is especially the case for using the proceeds on 'green investment' in infrastructure or energy efficiency programmes (Kotchen et al. 2017). Further, returning the revenues to individuals in a salient manner may increase public support and alleviate fairness proposals, given sufficient information (Carattini et al. 2017; Klenert et al. 2018). Perceived fairness is one of the strongest predictors of policy support (Jagers et al. 2010; Whittle et al. 2019).

5.6.4 Policy Sequencing and Packaging to Strengthen Enabling Conditions

Policy coordination is critical to manage infrastructure interdependence across sectors, and to avoid trade-off effects (Raven and Verbong 2007; Hiteva and Watson 2019), specifically requiring the consideration of interactions among supply-side and demand-side measures (*high evidence, high agreement*) (Kivimaa and Virkamäki 2014; Rogge and Reichardt 2016; de Coninck et al. 2018; Edmondson et al. 2019). For example, the amount of electricity required for cooking can overwhelm the grid which can lead to failure, causing end-users to shift back to traditional biomass or fossil fuels (Ateba et al. 2018; Israel-Akinbo et al. 2018); thus grid stability policies need to be undertaken in conjunction.

Policymakers operate in a politically dynamic national and international environment, and their policies often reflect their contextual situations and constraints with regards to climate-related reforms (Levin et al. 2012; Copland 2019), including differentiation between developed and developing countries (*high evidence, high agreement*) (Beer and Beer 2014; Roy et al. 2018c). Variables such as internal political stability, equity, informality (Box 5.10), macro-economic conditions, public debt, governance of policies, global oil prices, quality of public services, and the maturity of green technologies play important roles in determining policy directions.

Sequencing policies appropriately is a success factor for climate policy regimes (*high evidence, high agreement*). In most situations policy measures require a preparatory phase that prepares the ground by lowering the costs of policies, communicating the costs and benefits to citizens, and building coalitions for policies, thus reducing political resistance (Meckling et al. 2017). This policy sequencing aims to incrementally relax or remove barriers over time to enable significant cumulative increases in policy stringency and create coalitions that support future policy development (Pahle et al. 2018). German policies on renewables began with funding for research, design and development (RD&D), then subsidies for demonstration projects during the 1970s and 1980s, and continued to larger-scale projects such as 'Solar Roofs' programmes in the 1990s, including scaled-up feed-in tariffs for solar power (Jacobsson and Lauber 2006). These policies led to industrial expansion in wind and solar energy systems, giving rise to powerful renewables interest coalitions that defend existing measures and lend political support for further action. Policy sequencing has also been deployed to introduce technology bans and strict performance standards with a view to eliminating emissions as the end goal, and may involve simultaneous support for low-carbon options while deliberately phasing out established technological regimes (Rogge and Johnstone 2017).

As a key contending policy instrument, carbon pricing also requires embedding into policy packages (*high evidence, medium agreement*). Pricing may be regressive and perceived as additional costs by households and industry, making investments in green infrastructure politically unfeasible, as examples from France and Australia show (Copland 2019; Douenne and Fabre 2020). Reforms that would push up household energy expenses are often left aside for fear of how citizens, especially the poor, would react or cope with higher bills (*high evidence, medium agreement*) (Martinez and Viegas 2017; Tesfamichael et al. 2021). This makes it important to precede carbon pricing with investments in renewable energy and low-carbon transport modes (Biber et al. 2017; Tvinnereim and Mehling 2018), and especially support for developing countries by building up low-carbon energy and mobility infrastructures and technologies, thus reducing resistance to carbon pricing (Creutzig 2019). Additionally, carbon pricing receives higher acceptance if fairness and distributive considerations are made explicit in revenue distribution (Box 5.11).

The effectiveness of a policy package is determined by design decisions as well as the wider governance context that include the political environment, institutions for coordination across scales, bureaucratic traditions, and judicial functioning (*high evidence, high agreement*) (Howlett and Rayner 2013; Rogge and Reichardt 2013; Rosenow et al. 2016). Policy packages often emerge through interactions between different policy instruments as they operate in either complementary or contradictory ways, resulting from conflicting policy goals (Cunningham et al. 2013; Givoni et al. 2013). An example includes the acceleration in shift from traditional biomass to the adoption of modern cooking fuel for 80 million households in rural India over a very short period of four years (2016–2020), which employed a comprehensive policy package including financial incentives, infrastructural support and strengthening of the supply chain to induce households to shift towards a clean cooking fuel from the use of biomass (Kumar 2019). This was operationalised by creating a LPG supply chain by linking oil and gas companies with distributors to assure availability, and create infrastructure for local storage along with an improvement of the rural road network, especially in the rural context (Sankhyayan and Dasgupta 2019). State governments initiated separate policies to increase the distributorship of LPG in their states (Kumar et al. 2016). Similarly, policy actions for scaling up electric vehicles need to be well designed and coordinated where EV policy, transport policy and climate policy are used together, working on different decision points and different aspects of human behaviour (Barton and Schütte 2017). The coordination of the multiple policy actions enables co-evolution of multiple outcomes that involve shifting towards renewable energy production, improving access to charging infrastructure, carbon pricing and other GHG measures (Wolbertus et al. 2018).

Design of policy packages should consider not only policies that support low-carbon transitions but also those that challenge existing carbon-intensive regimes, generating not just policy 'winners' but also 'losers' (*high evidence, high agreement*) (Carley and Konisky 2020). The winners include low-carbon innovators and entrepreneurs, while the potential losers include incumbents with vested interests in sustaining the status quo (Mundaca et al. 2018; Monasterolo and Raberto 2019). Low-carbon policy packages would benefit from looking beyond climate benefits to include non-climate benefits such as health benefits, fuel poverty reductions and environmental co-benefits (Ürge-Vorsatz et al. 2014; Sovacool et al. 2020b). The uptake of decentralised energy services using solar PV in rural areas in developing countries is one such example where successful initiatives are linked to the convergence of multiple policies that include import tariffs, research incentives for R&D, job creation programmes, policies to widen health and education services, and strategies for increased safety for women and children (Kattumuri and Kruse 2019; Gebreslassie 2020).

5

The energy-efficient lighting transition in Europe represents a good case of the formation of policy coalitions that led to the development of policy packages. As attention to energy efficiency in Europe increased in the 1990s, policymakers attempted to stimulate energy-saving lamp diffusion through voluntary measures. But policies stimulated only limited adoption. Consumers perceived compact fluorescent lamps (CFLs) as giving 'cold' light, being unattractively shaped, taking too long to achieve full brightness, unsuitable for many fixtures, and unreliable (Wall and Crosbie 2009). Still, innovations by major CFL and LED multinationals continued. Increasing political attention to climate change and criticisms from environmental NGOs (e.g. WWF, Greenpeace) strengthened awareness about the inefficiency of incandescent light bulbs (ILBs), which led to negative socio-cultural framings that associated ILBs with energy waste (Franceschini and Alkemade 2016). The combined pressures from the lighting industry, NGOs and member states led the European Commission to introduce the 2009 ban of ILBs of more than 80W, progressing to lower-wattage bans in successive years. While the ILB ban initially mainly boosted CFL diffusion, it also stimulated LED uptake. LED prices decreased quickly by more than 85% between 2008 and 2012 (Sanderson and Simons 2014), because of scale economies, standardisation and commoditisation of LED chip technology, and improved manufacturing techniques. Because of further rapid developments to meet consumer tastes, LEDs came to be seen as the future of domestic lighting (Franceschini et al. 2018). Acknowledging these changing views, the 2016 and 2018 European bans on directional and non-directional halogen bulbs explicitly intended to further accelerate the LED transition and reduce energy consumption for residential lighting.

In summary, more equitable societies are associated with high levels of social trust and enable actions that reduce GHG emissions. To this end, people play an important role in the delivery of demand-side mitigation options within which efficiency and 'Improve' options dominate. Policies that are aimed at behaviour and lifestyle changes come with political risks for policymakers. However, the potential exists for broadening demand-side interventions to include 'Avoid' and 'Shift' policies. Longer term thinking and implementation that involves careful sequencing of policies as well as designing policy packages that address multiple co-benefits would be critical to manage interactions among supply-side and demand-side options to accelerate mitigation.

5.7   Knowledge Gaps

Knowledge gap 1: Better metric to measure actual human well-being

Knowledge on climate action that starts with the social practices and how people live in various environments, cultures, contexts and attempts to improve their well-being, is still in its infancy. In models, climate solutions remain supply-side oriented, and evaluated against GDP, without acknowledging the reduction in well-being due to climate impacts. GDP is a poor metric of human well-being, and climate policy evaluation requires better grounding in relation to decent living standards and/or similar benchmarks. Actual solutions will invariably include demand, service provisioning and

end use. Literature on how gender, informal economies mostly in developing countries, and solidarity and care frameworks translate into climate action, but also how climate action can improve the life of marginalised groups, remains scarce. The working of economic systems under a well-being-driven rather than GDP-driven paradigm requires better understanding.

Knowledge gap 2: Evaluation of climate implications of the digital economy

The digital economy, as well as shared and circular economy, is emerging as a template for great narratives, hopes and fears. Yet, there are few systematic evaluations of what is already happening and what can govern it towards a better narrative. Research needs to better gauge energy trends for rapidly evolving systems like data centres, increased use of social media and influence of consumption and choices, AI, blockchain; and implications of digital divides among social groups and countries on well-being. Governance decisions on AI, indirectly fostering either climate harming or climate mitigating activities remain unexplored. Better integration of mitigation models and consequential lifecycle analysis is needed for assessing how digitalisation, shared economy and circular economy change material and energy demand.

Knowledge gap 3: Scenario modelling of services

Scenarios start within parameter-rich models carrying more than a decade-long legacy of supply-side technologies that are not always gauged in recent technological developments. Service provisioning systems are not explicitly modelled, and diversity in concepts and patterns of lifestyles rarely considered. A new class of flexible and modular models with focus on services and activities, based on a variety of data sources including big data collected and compiled, is needed. There is scope for more sensitivity analysis on two aspects to better guide further detailed studies on societal response to policy. These aspects need to explore which socio-behavioural aspects and/or organisation changes has the biggest impact on energy/emissions reductions, and on the scale for take-back effects, due to interdependence on inclusion or exclusion of groups of people. Models mostly consider behavioural change free, and don't account for how savings due to 'Avoid' measures may be re-spent. Most quantitatively measurable service indicators, for example passenger-kilometres travelled or tonne-kilometres of freight transport are also inadequate to measure services in the sense of well-being contributions. More research is needed on how to measure, for example, accessibility, social inclusion etc. Otherwise, services will also be poorly represented in scenarios.

Knowledge gap 4: Dynamic interaction between individual, social, and structural drivers of change

Better understanding is required on: (i) more detailed causal mechanisms in the mutual interactions between individual, social, and structural drivers of change and how these vary over time, that

5

is, what is their relative importance in different transition phases; (ii) how narratives associated with specific technologies, group identities, and climate change influence each other and interact over time to enable and constrain mitigation outcomes; (iii) how social media influences the development and impacts of narratives about low-carbon transitions; (iv) the effects of social movements (for climate justice, youth climate activism, fossil fuel divestment, and climate action more generally) on social norms and political change, especially in less developed countries; (v) how existing provisioning systems and social practices destabilise through the weakening of various lock-in mechanisms, and resulting deliberate strategies for accelerating demand-side transitions; (vi) a dynamic understanding of feasibility, which addresses the dynamic mechanisms that lower barriers or drive mitigation options over the barriers; (vii) how shocks like prolonged pandemic impact willingness and capacity to change and their permanency for various social actors and country contexts. The debate on the most powerful leverage points and policies for speeding up change in social and technological systems need to be resolved with more evidence. Discussion on the policy interdependence and implications of end-user and efficiency focused strategies have only just started suggesting an important area for future research.

Frequently Asked Questions (FAQs)

FAQ 5.1 | What can every person do to limit warming to 1.5°C?

People can be educated through knowledge transfer so they can act in different roles, and in each role everyone can contribute to limit global warming to 1.5°C. Citizens with enough knowledge can organise and put political pressure on the system. Role models can set examples to others. Professionals (e.g., engineers, urban planners, teachers, researchers) can change professional standards in consistency with decarbonisation; for example urban planners and architects can design physical infrastructures to facilitate low-carbon mobility and energy use by making walking and cycling safe for children. Rich investors can make strategic plans to divest from fossils and invest in carbon-neutral technologies. Consumers, especially those in the top 10% of the world population in terms of income, can limit consumption, especially in mobility, and explore the good life consistent with sustainable consumption.

Policymakers support individual actions in certain contexts, not only by economic incentives, such as carbon pricing, but also by interventions that understand complex decision-making processes, habits, and routines. Examples of such interventions include, but are not limited to, choice architectures and nudges that set green options as default, shift away from cheap petrol or gasoline, increasing taxes on carbon-intensive products, or substantially tightening regulations and standards to support shifts in social norms, and thus can be effective beyond the direct economic incentive.

FAQ 5.2 | How does society perceive transformative change?

Humaninduced global warming, together with other global trends and events, such as digitalisation and automation, and the COVID-19 pandemic, induce changes in labour markets, and bring large uncertainty and ambiguity. History and psychology reveal that societies can thrive in these circumstances if they openly embrace uncertainty on the future and try out ways to improve life. Tolerating ambiguity can be learned, for example by interacting with history, poetry and the arts. Sometimes religion and philosophy also help.

As a key enabler, novel narratives created in a variety of ways, such as by advertising, images and the entertainment industry, help to break away from the established meanings, values and discourses and the status quo. For example, discourses that frame comfortable public transport services to avoid stress from driving cars on busy, congested roads help avoid car driving as a status symbol and create a new social norm to shift to public transport. Discourses that portray plant-based protein as healthy and natural promote and stabilise particular diets. Novel narratives and inclusive processes help strategies to overcome multiple barriers. Case studies demonstrate that citizens support transformative changes if participatory processes enable a design that meets local interests and culture. Promising narratives specify that even as speed and capabilities differ, humanity embarks on a joint journey towards well-being for all and a healthy planet.

FAQ 5.3 | Is demand reduction compatible with growth of human well-being?

There is a growing realisation that mere monetary value of income growth is insufficient to measure national welfare and individual well-being. Hence, any action towards climate change mitigation is best evaluated against a set of indicators that represent a broader variety of needs to define individual well-being, macroeconomic stability, and planetary health. Many solutions that reduce primary material and fossil energy demand, and thus reduce GHG emissions, provide better services to help achieve well-being for all.

Economic growth measured by total or individual income growth is a main driver of GHG emissions. Only a few countries with low economic growth rates have reduced both territorial and consumption-based GHG emissions, typically by switching from fossil fuels to renewable energy and by reduction in energy use and switching to low/zero carbon fuels, but until now at insufficient rates and levels for stabilising global warming at 1.5°C. High deployment of low/zero carbon fuels and associated rapid reduction in demand for and use of coal, gas, and oil can further reduce the interdependence between economic growth and GHG emissions.

References

Aaberge, R. and A. Brandolini, 2015: Multidimensional Poverty and Inequality. In: *Handbook of Income Distribution* [Atkinson, A. and F. Bourguignon, (eds.)], Vol. 2, Elsevier, Amsterdam, the Netherlands, pp. 141–216.

Abel, G.J., B. Barakat, S. KC, and W. Lutz, 2016: Meeting the Sustainable Development Goals leads to lower world population growth. *Proc. Natl. Acad. Sci.*, **113(50)**, 14294–14299, doi:10.1073/PNAS.1611386113.

Aberilla, J.M., A. Gallego-Schmid, L. Stamford, and A. Azapagic, 2020: Environmental sustainability of cooking fuels in remote communities: Life cycle and local impacts. *Sci. Total Environ.*, **713**, 136445, doi:10.1016/J.SCITOTENV.2019.136445.

Abraham, C.J., A.J. Rix, I. Ndibatya, and M.J. Booysen, 2021: Ray of hope for sub-Saharan Africa's paratransit: Solar charging of urban electric minibus taxis in South Africa. *Energy Sustain. Dev.*, **64**, 118–127, doi:10.1016/J.ESD.2021.08.003.

Abrahamse, W. and L. Steg, 2009: How do socio-demographic and psychological factors relate to households' direct and indirect energy use and savings? *J. Econ. Psychol.*, **30(5)**, 711–720, doi:10.1016/j.joep.2009.05.006.

Abrahamse, W. and L. Steg, 2013: Social influence approaches to encourage resource conservation: A meta-analysis. *Glob. Environ. Change*, **23(6)**, 1773–1785, doi:10.1016/j.gloenvcha.2013.07.029.

Abrahamse, W., L. Steg, C. Vlek, and T. Rothengatter, 2005: A review of intervention studies aimed at household energy conservation. *J. Environ. Psychol.*, **25(3)**, 273–291, doi:10.1016/j.jenvp.2005.08.002.

Abrahamse, W., L. Steg, C. Vlek, and T. Rothengatter, 2007: The effect of tailored information, goal setting, and tailored feedback on household energy use, energy-related behaviors, and behavioral antecedents. *J. Environ. Psychol.*, **27(4)**, 265–276, doi:10.1016/j.jenvp.2007.08.002.

Acheampong, R.A. and A. Siiba, 2019: Modelling the determinants of car-sharing adoption intentions among young adults: the role of attitude, perceived benefits, travel expectations and socio-demographic factors. *Transportation (Amst).*, **47**, 2557–2580, doi:10.1007/s11116-019-10029-3.

Ackah, M., 2017: Informal E-waste recycling in developing countries: review of metal(loid)s pollution, environmental impacts and transport pathways. *Environ. Sci. Pollut. Res.*, **24(31)**, 24092–24101, doi:10.1007/s11356-017-0273-y.

Adaloudis, M. and J. Bonnin Roca, 2021: Sustainability tradeoffs in the adoption of 3D Concrete Printing in the construction industry. *J. Clean. Prod.*, **307**, 127201, doi.org/10.1016/j.jclepro.2021.127201.

Adger, W.N. et al., 2003: Governance for Sustainability: Towards a 'Thick' Analysis of Environmental Decisionmaking. *Environ. Plan. A Econ. Sp.*, **35(6)**, 1095–1110, doi:10.1068/a35289.

Adua, L. and B. Clark, 2019: Even for the environment, context matters! States, households, and residential energy consumption. *Environ. Res. Lett.*, **14(6)**, 064008, doi:10.1088/1748-9326/AB1ABF.

Ahir, R.K. and B. Chakraborty, 2021: A meta-analytic approach for determining the success factors for energy conservation. *Energy*, **230** (September 1, 2021), 120821, doi:10.1016/j.energy.2021.120821.

Ahmad, S. and F. Creutzig, 2019: Spatially contextualized analysis of energy use for commuting in India. *Environ. Res. Lett.*, **14(4)**, 045007, doi:10.1088/1748-9326/ab011f.

Ahmad, S., G. Baiocchi, and F. Creutzig, 2015: CO_2 Emissions from Direct Energy Use of Urban Households in India. *Environ. Sci. Technol.*, **49(19)**, 11312–11320, doi:10.1021/es505814g.

Ahmad, S., S. Pachauri, and F. Creutzig, 2017: Synergies and trade-offs between energy-efficient urbanization and health. *Environ. Res. Lett.*, **12(11)**, doi:10.1088/1748-9326/aa9281.

AIGC, 2017: *Asia International Grid Connection Study Group Interim Report*. Renewable Energy Institute, Tokyo, Japan, 60 pp. https://www.renewable-ei.org/en/activities/reports/img/20170419/ASGInterimReport_170419_Web_en.pdf (Accessed December 16, 2019).

Aiken, G.T., L. Middlemiss, S. Sallu, and R. Hauxwell-Baldwin, 2017: Researching climate change and community in neoliberal contexts: an emerging critical approach. *Wiley Interdiscip. Rev. Clim. Change*, **8(4)**, e463, doi:10.1002/WCC.463.

Ajzen, I., 1985: From Intentions to Actions: A Theory of Planned Behavior. In: *Action Control*, [Kuhl, J. and Beckmann, J. (eds.)]. Springer Berlin, Heidelberg, Germany, pp. 11–39.

Akyelken, N., D. Banister, and M. Givoni, 2018: The Sustainability of Shared Mobility in London: The Dilemma for Governance. *Sustainability*, **10(2)**, 420, doi:10.3390/su10020420.

Alber, G., 2009: Gender and Climate Change Policy. In: *Population Dynamics and Climate Change* [Guzmán, J.M., G. Martinez, G. McGranahan, D. Schensul, and C. Tacoli, (eds.)], United Nations Population Fund/International Institute for Environment and Development, New York, NY, USA and London, UK, pp. 149–163.

Alberini, A., A. Bigano, M. Ščasný, and I. Zvěřinová, 2018: Preferences for Energy Efficiency vs. Renewables: What Is the Willingness to Pay to Reduce CO_2 Emissions? *Ecol. Econ.*, **144**, 171–185, doi:10.1016/j.ecolecon.2017.08.009.

Albrecht, G. et al., 2007: Solastalgia: The Distress Caused by Environmental Change. *Australas. Psychiatry*, **15**, S95–S98, doi:10.1080/10398560701701288.

Aldaco, R. et al., 2020: Food waste management during the COVID-19 outbreak: a holistic climate, economic and nutritional approach. *Sci. Total Environ.*, **742**, 140524, doi:10.1016/j.scitotenv.2020.140524.

Alegria, M.E.O., 2021: *Optimization of Agro-Socio-Hydrological Networks under Water Scarcity Conditions*. TU Dresden, Germany, 182 pp.

Alhumayani, H., M. Gomaa, V. Soebarto, and W. Jabi, 2020: Environmental assessment of large-scale 3D printing in construction: A comparative study between cob and concrete. *J. Clean. Prod.*, **270**, 122463, doi:10.1016/J.JCLEPRO.2020.122463.

Alkire, S. and M.E. Santos, 2014: Measuring Acute Poverty in the Developing World: Robustness and Scope of the Multidimensional Poverty Index. *World Dev.*, **59**, 251–274, doi:10.1016/j.worlddev.2014.01.026.

Alkire, S. and G. Robles, 2017: *Multidimensional Poverty Index – Summer 2017: brief methodological note and results*. Oxford Poverty and Human Development Initiative, Oxford, UK, 20 pp. https://ophi.org.uk/multidimensional-poverty-index-summer-2017-brief-methodological-note-and-results/.

Allcott, H., 2011: Social norms and energy conservation. *J. Public Econ.*, **95(9)**, 1082–1095, doi:10.1016/j.jpubeco.2011.03.003.

Allcott, H. and T.T. Rogers, 2012: *How long do treatment effects last? Persistence and durability of a descriptive norms intervention's effect on energy conservation*. https://dash.harvard.edu/bitstream/handle/1/9804492/RWP12-045_Rogers.pdf.

Allcott, H. and T. Rogers, 2014: The short-run and long-run effects of behavioral interventions: Experimental evidence from energy conservation. *Am. Econ. Rev.*, **104(10)**, 3003–3037, doi:10.1257/aer.104.10.3003.

Allwood, J.M. and J.M. Cullen, 2012: *Sustainable Materials with Both Eyes Open. Future Buildings, Vehicles, Products and Equipment – Made Efficiently and Made with Less New Material*. UIT Cambridge Ltd., Cambridge, UK, 356 pp.

Allwood, J.M., J.M. Cullen, and R.L. Milford, 2010: Options for Achieving a 50% Cut in Industrial Carbon Emissions by 2050. *Environ. Sci. Technol.*, **44(6)**, 1888–1894, doi:10.1021/es902909k.

5

Alon, T., M. Doepke, J. Olmstead-Rumsey, and M. Tertilt, 2020: *The Impact of COVID-19 on Gender Equality*. National Bureau of Economic Research, Cambridge, MA, USA.

Alstone, P., D. Gershenson, and D.M. Kammen, 2015: Decentralized energy systems for clean electricity access. *Nat. Clim. Change*, **5(4)**, 305–314, doi:10.1038/nclimate2512.

Alvaredo, F., L. Chancel, T. Piketty, E. Saez, and G. Zucman, 2018: *World Inequality Report 2018*. 344 pp. www.wid.world/team (Accessed November 20, 2019).

Ameli, N. and N. Brandt, 2015: Determinants of households' investment in energy efficiency and renewables: evidence from the OECD survey on household environmental behaviour and attitudes. *Environ. Res. Lett.*, **10(4)**, doi:10.1088/1748-9326/10/4/044015.

Amini, M.H., H. Arasteh, and P. Siano, 2019: Sustainable smart cities through the lens of complex interdependent infrastructures: Panorama and state-of-the-art. In: *Studies in Systems, Decision and Control*, [M. Hadi Amini, Kianoosh G. Boroojeni, S. S. Iyengar, Panos M. Pardalos, Frede Blaabjerg, Asad M. Madni (eds.)], Vol. 186, Springer International Publishing, Zurich, Switzerland, pp. 45–68.

Amis, J.M., and B.D. Janz, 2020: Leading Change in Response to COVID-19. *J. Appl. Behav. Sci.*, **56(3)**, 272–278, doi:10.1177/0021886320936703.

Amundsen, H., F. Berglund, and H. Westskogh, 2010: Overcoming barriers to climate change adaptation-a question of multilevel governance? *Environ. Plan. C Gov. Policy*, **28(2)**, 276–289, doi:10.1068/c0941.

Andersen, C.B., and J. Quinn, 2020: Human Appropriation of Net Primary Production. *Encycl. World's Biomes*,, 22–28, doi:10.1016/B978-0-12-409548-9.12434-0.

Anderson, S., I.E. Marinescu, and B. Shor, 2019: Can Pigou at the Polls Stop US Melting the Poles? *SSRN Electron. J.*, doi:10.2139/ssrn.3400772.

Andor, M., A. Gerster, J. Peters and C. Schmidt, 2020: *Social Norms and Energy Conservation Beyond the US*. RWI, Essen, Germany, 25 pp. https://www.sciencedirect.com/science/article/abs/pii/S0095069620300747.

Andor, M.A. and K.M. Fels, 2018: Behavioral Economics and Energy Conservation – A Systematic Review of Non-price Interventions and Their Causal Effects. *Ecol. Econ.*, **148**, 178–210, doi:10.1016/j.ecolecon.2018.01.018.

Andrae, A. and T. Edler, 2015: On Global Electricity Usage of Communication Technology: Trends to 2030. *Challenges*, **6(1)**, 117–157, doi:10.3390/challe6010117.

Angrist, J.D., S. Caldwell, and J. V Hall, 2017: *Uber vs. Taxi: A Driver's Eye View*. 75 pp.

Annecke, W., 2002: The rich get richer and the poor get renewables: the WSSD, energy and women, a malevolent perspective. *Agenda*, **17(52)**, 8–16.

Añón Higón, D., R. Gholami, and F. Shirazi, 2017: ICT and environmental sustainability: A global perspective. *Telemat. Informatics*, **34(4)**, 85–95, doi:10.1016/J.TELE.2017.01.001.

Anshelm, J. and M. Hultman, 2014: A green fatwā? Climate change as a threat to the masculinity of industrial modernity. *NORMA*, **9(2)**, 84–96, doi:10.1080/18902138.2014.908627.

Antal, M., G. Mattioli, and I. Rattle, 2020: Let's focus more on negative trends: A comment on the transitions research agenda. *Environ. Innov. Soc. Transitions*, **34**, 359–362, doi:10.1016/J.EIST.2020.02.001.

Araña, J. and C. León, 2013: Can Defaults Save the Climate? Evidence from a Field Experiment on Carbon Offsetting Programs. *Environ. Resour. Econ.*, **54(4)**, 613–626.

Arrow, K. et al., 2004: Are We Consuming Too Much? *J. Econ. Perspect.*, **18(3)**, 147–172, doi:10.1257/0895330042162377.

Arrow, K.J., P. Dasgupta, L.H. Goulder, K.J. Mumford, and K. Oleson, 2013: Sustainability and the measurement of wealth: further reflections. *Environ. Dev. Econ.*, **18(4)**, 504–516, doi:10.1017/s1355770x13000193.

Arto, I., I. Capellán-Pérez, R. Lago, G. Bueno, and R. Bermejo, 2016: The energy requirements of a developed world. *Energy Sustain. Dev.*, **33**, 1–13, doi:0.1016/j.esd.2016.04.001.

Asim, M., S.A. Batool, and M.N. Chaudhry, 2012: Scavengers and their role in the recycling of waste in Southwestern Lahore. *Resour. Conserv. Recycl.*, **58**, 152–162, doi.org/10.1016/j.resconrec.2011.10.013.

Ateba, B.B., J.J. Prinsloo, and E. Fourie, 2018: The impact of energy fuel choice determinants on sustainable energy consumption of selected South African households. *J. Energy South. Africa*, **29(3)**, 51–65, doi:10.17159/2413-3051/2018/v29i3a4714.

Atkinson, R., T. Dörfler, M. Hasanov, E. Rothfuß, and I. Smith, 2017: Making the case for self-organisation: Understanding how communities make sense of sustainability and climate change through collective action. *Int. J. Sustain. Soc.*, **9(3)**, 193–209, doi:10.1504/IJSSOC.2017.088300.

Atreya, A. and S. Ferreira, 2015: Seeing is Believing? Evidence from Property Prices in Inundated Areas. *Risk Anal.*, **35(5)**, 828–848, doi:10.1111/risa.12307.

Attari, S.Z. et al., 2010: Public perceptions of energy consumption and savings. *Proc. Natl. Acad. Sci.*, **107(37)**, 16054–16059, doi:10.1073/pnas.1001509107.

Attari, S.Z., D.H. Krantz, and E.U. Weber, 2016: Energy conservation goals: What people adopt, what they recommend, and why. *Judgm. Decis. Mak.*, **11(4)**, 342–351.

Atteridge, A., M.K. Shrivastava, N. Pahuja, and H. Upadhyay, 2012: Climate Policy in India: What Shapes International, National and State Policy? *Ambio*, **41(1)**, 68–77, doi:10.1007/S13280-011-0242-5.

Aubrey, S.B., 2019: Violence against the earth begets violence against women. *Arizona J. Environ. Law Policy*, **10(Fall 2019)**, 34–67.

Auerswald, P.E. and L.M. Branscomb, 2003: Valleys of Death and Darwinian Seas : Financing the Invention to Innovation Transition in the United States. *Technology*, **28(3–4)**, 227–239, doi:10.1023/A:1024980525678.

Ausubel, J.H., 1991: Rat-race dynamics and crazy companies. The diffusion of technologies and social behavior. *Technol. Forecast. Soc. Change*, **39(1–2)**, 11–22, doi:10.1016/0040-1625(91)90025-B.

Avgerinou, M., P. Bertoldi, and L. Castellazzi, 2017: Trends in Data Centre Energy Consumption under the European Code of Conduct for Data Centre Energy Efficiency. *Energies*, **10(10)**, 1–18, doi:10.3390/en10101470.

Axsen, J. and B.K. Sovacool, 2019: The roles of users in electric, shared and automated mobility transitions. *Transp. Res. Part D Transp. Environ.*, **71**, 1–21, doi:10.1016/J.TRD.2019.02.012.

Ayers, J. and T. Forsyth, 2009: Community-Based Adaptation to Climate Change. *Environ. Sci. Policy Sustain. Dev.*, **51(4)**, 22–31, doi:10.3200/ENV.51.4.22-31.

Ayres, I., S. Raseman, and A. Shih, 2013: Evidence from Two Large Field Experiments that Peer Comparison Feedback Can Reduce Residential Energy Usage. *J. Law, Econ. Organ.*, **29(5)**, 992–1022.

Ayres, R.U., 1989: *Energy Inefficiency in the US Economy: A New Case for Conservation*. International Institute for Applied Systems Analysis, Laxenburg, Austria, 28 pp. http://pure.iiasa.ac.at/id/eprint/3220/ (Accessed September 12, 2019).

Ayres, R.U., and U.E. Simonis, 1994: *Industrial Metabolism: Restructuring for Sustainable Development*. United Nations University Press, Tokyo, Japan, 376 pp.

Ayres, R.U. and B. Warr, 2005: Accounting for growth: The role of physical work. *Struct. Change Econ. Dyn.*, **16(2)**, 181–209, doi:10.1016/j.strueco.2003.10.003.

Azong, M., C.J. Kelso, and K. Naidoo, 2018: Vulnerability and resilience of female farmers in Oku, Cameroon, to Climate Change. *African Sociol. Rev.*, **22(1)**.

Azong, M.N. and C.J. Kelso, 2021: Gender, ethnicity and vulnerability to climate change: The case of matrilineal and patrilineal societies in Bamenda Highlands Region, Cameroon. *Glob. Environ. Change*, **67**, 102241, doi:10.1016/J.GLOENVCHA.2021.102241.

Backstränd, K., J. Khan, A. Kronsell, and E. Lövbrand, eds., 2010: *Environmental Politics and Deliberative Democracy: Examining the Promise of New Modes of Governance*. Edward Elgar Publishing Limited, Cheltenham, UK, 256 pp.

5

Bailis, R., R. Drigo, A. Ghilardi, and O. Masera, 2015: The carbon footprint of traditional woodfuels. *Nat. Clim. Change*, **5(3)**, 266–272, doi:10.1038/nclimate2491.

Bajželj, B. et al., 2014: Importance of food-demand management for climate mitigation. *Nat. Clim. Change*, **4(10)**, 924–929, doi:10.1038/nclimate2353.

Baker, L., 2018: Of embodied emissions and inequality: Rethinking energy consumption. *Energy Res. Soc. Sci.*, **36**(December 2017), 52–60, doi:10.1016/j.erss.2017.09.027.

Bakker, S., M. Zuidgeest, H. de Coninck, and C. Huizenga, 2014: Transport, Development and Climate Change Mitigation: Towards an Integrated Approach. *Transp. Rev.*, **34(3)**, 335–355, doi:10.1080/01441647.2014.903531.

Baldez, L., 2003: Women's Movements and Democratic Transition in Chile, Brazil, East Germany, and Poland. *Comp. Polit.*, **35(3)**, 253, doi:10.2307/4150176.

Baležentis, T., G. Liobikienė, D. Štreimikienė, and K. Sun, 2020: The impact of income inequality on consumption-based greenhouse gas emissions at the global level: A partially linear approach. *J. Environ. Manage.*, **267**, 110635, doi:10.1016/J.JENVMAN.2020.110635.

Ballew, M. et al., 2020: Which racial/ethnic groups care most about climate change? Yale Program on Climate Change Communication. Yale University and George Mason University, New Haven, CT, USA, https://climatecommunication.yale.edu/publications/race-and-climate-change/ (Accessed June 5, 2020).

Ballew, M.T. et al., 2019: Climate Change in the American Mind: Data, Tools, and Trends. *Environ. Sci. Policy Sustain. Dev.*, **61(3)**, 4–18, doi:10.1080/00139157.2019.1589300.

Ballús-Armet, I., S.A. Shaheen, K. Clonts, and D. Weinzimmer, 2014: Peer-to-Peer Carsharing. *Transp. Res. Rec. J. Transp. Res. Board*, **2416(1)**, 27–36, doi:10.3141/2416-04.

Baloch, M.A., Danish, S.U. Khan, and Z.Ş. Ulucak, 2020: Analyzing the relationship between poverty, income inequality, and CO₂ emission in Sub-Saharan African countries. *Sci. Total Environ.*,, 139867, **740** doi:10.1016/j.scitotenv.2020.139867.

Baltruszewicz, M. et al., 2021: Household final energy footprints in Nepal, Vietnam and Zambia: composition, inequality and links to well-being. *Environ. Res. Lett.*, **16(2)**, 025011, doi:10.1088/1748-9326/ABD588.

Bamberg, S., D. Rölle, and C. Weber, 2003: Does habitual car use not lead to more resistance to change of travel mode? *Transportation (Amst).*, **30(1)**, 97–108, doi:10.1023/A:1021282523910.

Bamberg, S., M. Hunecke, and A. Blöbaum, 2007: Social context, personal norms and the use of public transportation: Two field studies. *J. Environ. Psychol.*, **27(3)**, 190–203, doi:10.1016/J.JENVP.2007.04.001.

Bamisile, O. et al., 2021: Impact of economic development on CO₂ emission in Africa; the role of BEVs and hydrogen production in renewable energy integration. *Int. J. Hydrogen Energy*, **46(2)**, 2755–2773, doi:10.1016/J.IJHYDENE.2020.10.134.

Banerjee, M., R. Prasad, I.H. Rehman, and B. Gill, 2016: Induction stoves as an option for clean cooking in rural India. *Energy Policy*, **88**, 159–167, doi:10.1016/j.enpol.2015.10.021.

Baptista, P., S. Melo, and C. Rolim, 2014: Energy, Environmental and Mobility Impacts of Car-sharing Systems. Empirical Results from Lisbon, Portugal. *Procedia – Soc. Behav. Sci.*, **111**, 28–37, doi:10.1016/j.sbspro.2014.01.035.

Baranzini, A., S. Carattini, and M. Péclat, 2017: *What drives social contagion in the adoption of solar photovoltaic technology?* Centre for Climate Change Economics and Policy and Grantham Research Institute on Climate Change and the Environment, London, UK, 38 pp. http://www.lse.ac.uk/GranthamInstitute/publication/what-drives-social-contagion-in-the-adoption-of-solar-photovoltaic-technology/ (Accessed June 23, 2021).

Barbier, E.B. and J.C. Burgess, 2020: Sustainability and development after COVID-19. *World Dev.*, **135**, 105082, doi:10.1016/j.worlddev.2020.105082.

Bardhi, F. and G.M. Eckhardt, 2012: Access-Based Consumption: The Case of Car Sharing. *J. Consum. Res.*, **39(4)**, 881–898, doi:10.1086/666376.

Bardsley, N. et al., 2019: Domestic thermal upgrades, community action and energy saving: A three-year experimental study of prosperous households. *Energy Policy*, **127**, 475–485, doi:10.1016/j.enpol.2018.11.036.

Barnes, J., R. Durrant, F. Kern, and G. MacKerron, 2018: The institutionalisation of sustainable practices in cities: how initiatives shape local selection environments. *Environ. Innov. Soc. Transitions*, **29**, 68–80, doi:10.1016/j.eist.2018.04.003.

Barnes, M.L. et al., 2020: Social determinants of adaptive and transformative responses to climate change. *Nat. Clim. Change*, **10**, doi:10.1038/s41558-020-0871-4.

Barnett, J., 2003: Security and climate change. *Glob. Environ. Change*, **13(1)**, 7–17, doi:10.1016/S0959-3780(02)00080-8.

Barnett, J., K. Burningham, G. Walker, and N. Cass, 2012: Imagined publics and engagement around renewable energy technologies in the UK. *Public Underst. Sci.*, **21**(1), 36–50, doi:10.1177/0963662510365663.

Barr, S. and J. Prillwitz, 2014: A smarter choice? Exploring the behaviour change agenda for environmentally sustainable mobility. *Environ. Plan. C Gov. Policy*, **32(1)**, 1–19, doi:10.1068/c1201.

Barton, B. and P. Schütte, 2017: Electric vehicle law and policy: A comparative analysis. *J. Energy Nat. Resour. Law*, **35(2)**, 147–170, doi:10.1080/02646811.2017.1262087.

Batchelor, S. et al., 2018: Solar electric cooking in Africa: Where will the transition happen first? *Energy Res. Soc. Sci.*, **40**, 257–272, doi:10.1016/j.erss.2018.01.019.

Batchelor, S., E. Brown, N. Scott, and J. Leary, 2019: Two birds, one stone – reframing cooking energy policies in Africa and Asia. *Energies*, **12(9)**, 1591, doi:10.3390/en12091591.

Bavel, J.J. Van et al., 2020: Using social and behavioural science to support COVID-19 pandemic response. *Nat. Hum. Behav.*, **4(5)**, 460–471, doi:10.1038/s41562-020-0884-z.

Bayus, B.L., 1994: Are product life cycles really getting shorter? *J. Prod. Innov. Manag.*, **11(4)**, 300–308, doi:10.1016/0737-6782(94)90085-X.

Beaunoyer, E., S. Dupéré, and M.J. Guitton, 2020: COVID-19 and digital inequalities: Reciprocal impacts and mitigation strategies. *Comput. Human Behav.*, **111**, 106424, doi:10.1016/j.chb.2020.106424.

Beer, C.T., 2014: Climate Justice, the Global South, and Policy Preferences of Kenyan Environmental NGOs. *Glob. South*, **8(2)**, 84–100, doi:10.2979/globalsouth.8.2.84.

Beeson, M., 2019: *Environmental Populism: The Politics of Survival in the Anthropocene*. Palgrave Macmillan, Singapore, 131 pp.

Behrens, P. et al., 2017: Evaluating the environmental impacts of dietary recommendations. *Proc. Natl. Acad. Sci.*, **114(51)**, 13412–13417, doi:10.1073/pnas.1711889114.

Beiser-McGrath, L.F. and T. Bernauer, 2019: Could revenue recycling make effective carbon taxation politically feasible? *Sci. Adv.*, **5(9)**, doi:10.1126/sciadv.aax3323.

Belkhir, L. and A. Elmeligi, 2018: Assessing ICT global emissions footprint: Trends to 2040 & recommendations. *J. Clean. Prod.*, **177**, 448–463, doi:10.1016/J.JCLEPRO.2017.12.239.

Bell, S.E., C. Daggett, and C. Labuski, 2020: Toward feminist energy systems: Why adding women and solar panels is not enough☆. *Energy Res. Soc. Sci.*, **68**, 101557, doi:10.1016/J.ERSS.2020.101557.

Belzunegui-Eraso, A. and A. Erro-Garcés, 2020: Teleworking in the Context of the Covid-19 Crisis. *Sustainability*, **12(9)**, 3662, doi:10.3390/SU12093662.

Benegal, S.D., 2018: The spillover of race and racial attitudes into public opinion about climate change. *Env. Polit.*, **27(4)**, 733–756, doi:10.1080/09644016.2018.1457287.

Bengtsson, M., E. Alfredsson, M. Cohen, S. Lorek, and P. Schroeder, 2018: Transforming systems of consumption and production for achieving the sustainable development goals: moving beyond efficiency. *Sustain. Sci.*, **13(6)**, 1533–1547, doi:10.1007/s11625-018-0582-1.

5

Bentley, M., 2014: An ecological public health approach to understanding the relationships between sustainable urban environments, public health and social equity. *Health Promot. Int.*, **29(3)**, 528–537, doi:10.1093/heapro/dat028.

Bento, A.M., M.R. Jacobsen, and A.A. Liu, 2018a: Environmental policy in the presence of an informal sector. *J. Environ. Econ. Manage.*, **90**, 61–77, doi:10.1016/j.jeem.2018.03.011.

Bento, N., 2013: *New Evidence in Technology Scaling Dynamics and the Role of the Formative Phase*. International Institute for Applied Systems Analysis, Laxenburg, Austria, 45 pp. http://pure.iiasa.ac.at/id/eprint/10752/ (Accessed July 12, 2021).

Bento, N., C. Wilson, and L.D. Anadon, 2018b: Time to get ready: Conceptualizing the temporal and spatial dynamics of formative phases for energy technologies. *Energy Policy*, **119**(May), 282–293, doi:10.1016/j.enpol.2018.04.015.

Benyus, J., 1997: *Biomimicry: Innovation inspired by nature*. 320 pp. William Morrow Paperbacks, New York, USA.

Bergek, A., C. Berggren, T. Magnusson, and M. Hobday, 2013: Technological discontinuities and the challenge for incumbent firms: Destruction, disruption or creative accumulation? *Res. Policy*, **42**, 1210–1224, doi:10.1016/j.respol.2013.02.009.

Bergman, N., 2013: Why is renewable heat in the UK underperforming? A socio-technical perspective. *Proc. Inst. Mech. Eng. Part A J. Power Energy*, **227(1)**, 124–131, doi:10.1177/0957650912471291.

Bergmann, Z. and R. Ossewaarde, 2020: Youth climate activists meet environmental governance: ageist depictions of the FFF movement and Greta Thunberg in German newspaper coverage. *J. Multicult. Discourses*, **15(3)**, 267–290, doi:10.1080/17447143.2020.1745211.

Bergquist, M., A. Nilsson, and P. Wesley Schultz, 2019: Experiencing a severe weather event increases concern about climate change. *Front. Psychol.*, **10**(FEB), 220, doi:10.3389/fpsyg.2019.00220.

Berik, G., 2018: *Toward more inclusive measures of economic well-being: Debates and practices*. International Labour Organization, Geneva, Switzerland, 32 pp. https://www.ilo.org/global/topics/future-of-work/publications/research-papers/WCMS_649127/lang--en/index.htm (Accessed March 3, 2020).

Berkeley, N., D. Bailey, A. Jones, and D. Jarvis, 2017: Assessing the transition towards Battery Electric Vehicles: A Multi-Level Perspective on drivers of, and barriers to, take up. *Transp. Res. Part A Policy Pract.*, **106**(October), 320–332, doi:10.1016/j.tra.2017.10.004.

Bertoldi, P., P. Economidou, V. Palermo, B. Boza-Kiss, and V. Todeschi, 2021: How to finance energy renovation of residential buildings: Review of current and emerging financing instruments in the EU. *Wiley Interdiscip. Rev. Energy Environ.*, **10(1)**, e384, doi:10.1002/wene.384.

Bertram, C. et al., 2021: COVID-induced low power demand and market forces starkly reduce CO_2 emissions. *Nat. Clim. Change*, **11**, 193–196, doi:10.1038/s41558-021-00987-x.

Bessa, V.M.T., and R.T.A. Prado, 2015: Reduction of carbon dioxide emissions by solar water heating systems and passive technologies in social housing. *Energy Policy*, **83**, 138–150, doi:10.1016/j.enpol.2015.04.010.

Biber, E., N. Kelsey, and J. Meckling, 2017: The Political Economy of Decarbonization: A Research Agenda. *Brooklyn Law Rev.*, **82(2)**. https://brooklynworks.brooklaw.edu/blr/vol82/iss2/8.

Bilal et al., 2020: Environmental pollution and COVID-19 outbreak: insights from Germany. *Air Qual. Atmos. Heal.*, **13**, 1385–1394, doi:10.1007/s11869-020-00893-9.

Billett, S., 2010: Dividing climate change: global warming in the Indian mass media. *Clim. Change*, **99(1–2)**, 1–16, doi:10.1007/s10584-009-9605-3.

Bischoff, J. and M. Maciejewski, 2016: Autonomous Taxicabs in Berlin – A Spatiotemporal Analysis of Service Performance. *Transp. Res. Procedia*, **19**, 176–186, doi:10.1016/J.TRPRO.2016.12.078.

Black, T., 2016: Race, gender, and climate justice: Dimensions of social and environmental inequality. In: *Systemic crises of global climate change: intersections of race, class and gender* [Godfrey, P. and D. Torres, (eds.)], Routledge, Abingdon, UK and New York, NY, USA, pp. 172–184.

Blok, K. et al., 2016: *Implementing Circular Economy Globally Makes Paris Targets Achievable*. Ecofys and Circle Economy, Utrecht, the Netherlands, 18 pp. https://assets.website-files.com/5d26d80e8836af2d12ed1269/5dea481576d89489dff8782e_ircle-economy-ecofys-2016-implementing-circular-economy-globally-makes-paris-targets-achievable.pdf (Accessed October 11, 2021).

Blomsma, F., and G. Brennan, 2017: The Emergence of Circular Economy: A New Framing Around Prolonging Resource Productivity. *J. Ind. Ecol.*, **21(3)**, 603–614, doi:10.1111/jiec.12603.

Bob, U. and A. Babugura, 2014: Contextualising and conceptualising gender and climate change in Africa. *Agenda*, **28(3)**, 3–15, doi:10.1080/10130950.2014.958907.

Bocken, N.M.P., E.A. Olivetti, J.M. Cullen, J. Potting, and R. Lifset, 2017: Taking the Circularity to the Next Level: A Special Issue on the Circular Economy. *J. Ind. Ecol.*, **21(3)**, 476–482, doi:10.1111/jiec.12606.

Bodart, M. and A. De Herde, 2002: Global energy savings in offices buildings by the use of daylighting. *Energy Build.*, **34(5)**, 421–429, doi:10.1016/S0378-7788(01)00117-7.

Bolderdijk, J.W., M. Gorsira, K. Keizer, and L. Steg, 2013: Values Determine the (In)Effectiveness of Informational Interventions in Promoting Pro-Environmental Behavior. *PLoS One*, **8(12)**, e83911, doi:10.1371/journal.pone.0083911.

Bolsen, T., T.J. Leeper, and M.A. Shapiro, 2014: Doing What Others Do: Norms, Science, and Collective Action on Global Warming. *Am. Polit. Res.*, **42(1)**, 65–89, doi:10.1177/1532673X13484173.

Bonacini, L., G. Gallo, and S. Scicchitano, 2021: Working from home and income inequality: risks of a 'new normal' with COVID-19. *J. Popul. Econ.*, **34(1)**, 303–360, doi:10.1007/s00148-020-00800-7.

Bonan, J., C. Cattaneo, G. D'Adda, and M. Tavoni, 2020: The interaction of descriptive and injunctive social norms in promoting energy conservation. *Nat. Energy*, **5(11)**, 900–909, doi:10.1038/s41560-020-00719-z.

Bongardt, D. et al., 2013: *Low-carbon Land Transport: Policy Handbook*. Routledge, New York, NY, USA.

Bonilla-Alicea, R.J., B.C. Watson, Z. Shen, L. Tamayo, and C. Telenko, 2020: Life cycle assessment to quantify the impact of technology improvements in bike-sharing systems. *J. Ind. Ecol.*, **24(1)**, 138–148, doi:10.1111/jiec.12860.

Boomsma, C. and L. Steg, 2014: The effect of information and values on acceptability of reduced street lighting. *J. Environ. Psychol.*, **39**, 22–31, doi:10.1016/j.jenvp.2013.11.004.

Boran, I., 2019: *Political theory and global climate action: recasting the public sphere*. 1st ed. Routledge, New York, NY, USA, 108 pp.

Borghei, B. and T. Magnusson, 2016: Niche experiments with alternative powertrain technologies: the case of electric city-buses in Europe. *Int. J. Automot. Technol. Manag.*, **16(3)**, 274, doi:10.1504/ijatm.2016.080787.

Borghei, B.B. and T. Magnusson, 2018: Niche aggregation through cumulative learning: A study of multiple electric bus projects. *Environ. Innov. Soc. Transitions*, **28**(C), 108–121, doi:10.1016/j.eist.2018.01.004.

Bostrom, A., A.L. Hayes, and K.M. Crosman, 2019: Efficacy, Action, and Support for Reducing Climate Change Risks. *Risk Anal.*, **39(4)**, 805–828, doi:10.1111/RISA.13210.

Bouman, E.A., E. Lindstad, A.I. Rialland, and A.H. Strømman, 2017: State-of-the-art technologies, measures, and potential for reducing GHG emissions from shipping – A review. *Transp. Res. Part D Transp. Environ.*, **52**, 408–421, doi:10.1016/j.trd.2017.03.022.

Bouman, T., L. Steg, and T. Dietz, 2020a: Insights from early COVID-19 responses about promoting sustainable action. *Nat. Sustain.*, **4**, 194–200, doi:10.1038/s41893-020-00626-x.

Bouman, T. et al., 2020b: When worry about climate change leads to climate action: How values, worry and personal responsibility relate to various climate actions. *Glob. Environ. Change*, **62**, 102061, doi:10.1016/j.gloenvcha.2020.102061.

Bows-Larkin, A., 2015: All adrift: aviation, shipping, and climate change policy. *Clim. Policy*, **15(6)**, 681–702, doi:10.1080/14693062.2014.965125.

Boyer, R., 2020: *Les capitalismes à l'épreuve de la pandémie*. La Découverte, Paris, France, 200 pp.

Bradshaw, S., 2018: Sex disaggregation alone will not energize equality. *Nat. Energy*, **3(10)**, 813–815, doi:10.1038/s41560-018-0247-4.

Brambilla, G., M. Lavagna, G. Vasdravellis, and C.A. Castiglioni, 2019: Environmental benefits arising from demountable steel-concrete composite floor systems in buildings. *Resour. Conserv. Recycl.*, **141**(October 2018), 133–142, doi:10.1016/j.resconrec.2018.10.014.

Brand-Correa, L.I. and J.K. Steinberger, 2017: A Framework for Decoupling Human Need Satisfaction From Energy Use. *Ecol. Econ.*, **141**, 43–52, doi:10.1016/j.ecolecon.2017.05.019.

Brand-Correa, L.I., J. Martin-Ortega, and J.K. Steinberger, 2018: Human Scale Energy Services: Untangling a 'golden thread'. *Energy Res. Soc. Sci.*, **38**(August 2017), 178–187, doi:10.1016/j.erss.2018.01.008.

Brand-Correa, L.I., G. Mattioli, W.F. Lamb, and J.K. Steinberger, 2020: Understanding (and tackling) need satisfier escalation. *Sustain. Sci. Pract. Policy*, **16(1)**, 309–325, doi:10.1080/15487733.2020.1816026.

Brand, C. and B. Boardman, 2008: Taming of the few – The unequal distribution of greenhouse gas emissions from personal travel in the UK. *Energy Policy*, **36(1)**, 224–238, doi:10.1016/j.enpol.2007.08.016.

Brand, C. and J.M. Preston, 2010: '60-20 emission' – The unequal distribution of greenhouse gas emissions from personal, non-business travel in the UK. *Transp. Policy*, **17(1)**, 9–19, doi:10.1016/j.tranpol.2009.09.001.

Brand, C., J. Anable, and M. Tran, 2013: Accelerating the transformation to a low carbon passenger transport system: The role of car purchase taxes, feebates, road taxes and scrappage incentives in the UK. *Transp. Res. Part A Policy Pract.*, **49**, 132–148, doi:10.1016/j.tra.2013.01.010.

Braungardt, S., J. van den Bergh, and T. Dunlop, 2019: Fossil fuel divestment and climate change: Reviewing contested arguments. *Energy Res. Soc. Sci.*, **50**, 191–200, doi:10.1016/j.erss.2018.12.004.

Bray, J., N. Johns, and D. Kilburn, 2011: An Exploratory Study into the Factors Impeding Ethical Consumption. *J. Bus. Ethics*, **98(4)**, 597–608, doi:10.1007/s10551-010-0640-9.

Breukers, S. and M. Wolsink, 2007: Wind energy policies in the Netherlands: Institutional capacity-building for ecological modernisation. *Env. Polit.*, **16(1)**, 92–112, doi:10.1080/09644010601073838.

Brockway, P. et al., 2017: Energy Rebound as a Potential Threat to a Low-Carbon Future: Findings from a New Exergy-Based National-Level Rebound Approach. *Energies*, **10(1)**, 51, doi:10.3390/en10010051.

Brockway, P.E., J.R. Barrett, T.J. Foxon, and J.K. Steinberger, 2014: Divergence of Trends in US and UK Aggregate Exergy Efficiencies 1960–2010. *Environ. Sci. Technol.*, **48(16)**, 9874–9881, doi:10.1021/ES501217T.

Brockway, P.E., J.K. Steinberger, J.R. Barrett, and T.J. Foxon, 2015: Understanding China's past and future energy demand: An exergy efficiency and decomposition analysis. *Appl. Energy*, **155**, 892–903, doi:10.1016/J.APENERGY.2015.05.082.

Brockway, P.E., S. Sorrell, G. Semieniuk, M.K. Heun, and V. Court, 2021: Energy efficiency and economy-wide rebound effects: A review of the evidence and its implications. *Renew. Sustain. Energy Rev.*, **141**, 110781, doi:10.1016/J.RSER.2021.110781.

Broomell, S.B., D.V. Budescu, and H.H. Por, 2015: Personal experience with climate change predicts intentions to act. *Glob. Environ. Change*, **32**, 67–73, doi:10.1016/J.GLOENVCHA.2015.03.001.

Brounen, D. and N. Kok, 2011: On the economics of energy labels in the housing market. *J. Environ. Econ. Manage.*, **62(2)**, 166–179, doi:10.1016/j.jeem.2010.11.006.

Brown, D. and G. McGranahan, 2016: The urban informal economy, local inclusion and achieving a global green transformation. *Habitat Int.*, **53**, 97–105, doi:10.1016/j.habitatint.2015.11.002.

Brown, H.S., P. Vergragt, K. Green, and L. Berchicci, 2003: Learning for sustainability transition through bounded socio-technical experiments in personal mobility. *Technol. Anal. Strateg. Manag.*, **15(3)**, 291–316, doi:10.1080/09537320310001601496.

Brown, K.E. and R. Dodder, 2019: Energy and emissions implications of automated vehicles in the U.S. energy system. *Transp. Res. Part D Transp. Environ.*, **77**(November), 132–147, doi:10.1016/j.trd.2019.09.003.

Brownell, K.D. and K.E. Warner, 2009: The perils of ignoring history: Big tobacco played dirty and millions died. How similar is big food? *Milbank Q.*, **87(1)**, 259–294, doi:10.1111/j.1468-0009.2009.00555.x.

Brozovic, D., 2019: Business model based on strong sustainability: Insights from an empirical study. *Bus. Strateg. Environ.*, **29(2)**, 763–778, doi:10.1002/bse.2440.

Bruck, B.P., V. Incerti, M. Iori, and M. Vignoli, 2017: Minimizing CO_2 emissions in a practical daily carpooling problem. *Comput. Oper. Res.*, **81**, 40–50, doi:10.1016/j.cor.2016.12.003.

Brügger, A., C. Demski, and S. Capstick, 2021: How Personal Experience Affects Perception of and Decisions Related to Climate Change: A Psychological View. *Weather. Clim. Soc.*, **13(3)**, 397–408, doi:10.1175/WCAS-D-20-0100.1.

Brulle, R.J., 2019: Networks of Opposition: A Structural Analysis of U.S. Climate Change Countermovement Coalitions 1989–2015. *Sociol. Inq.*, **91(3)**, 603–624, doi:10.1111/SOIN.12333.

Brütting, J., C. De Wolf, and C. Fivet, 2019: The reuse of load-bearing components. *IOP Conf. Ser. Earth Environ. Sci.*, **225(1)**, doi:10.1088/1755-1315/225/1/012025.

Bryan, E., and J.A. Behrman, 2013: *Community based adaptation to climate change: A theoretical framework, overview of key issues and discussion of gender differentiated priorities and participation*. International Food Policy Research Institute (IFPRI), Washington, DC, USA.

Bryan, E., Q. Bernier, M. Espinal, and C. Ringler, 2018: Making climate change adaptation programmes in sub-Saharan Africa more gender responsive: insights from implementing organizations on the barriers and opportunities. *Clim. Dev.*, **10(5)**, 417–431, doi:10.1080/17565529.2017.1301870.

Bryson, J., and P. Rauwolf, 2016: *Trust, Communication, and Inequality*. 7 pp. University of Bath, UK.

Büchs, M. and S.V. Schnepf, 2013: Who emits most? Associations between socio-economic factors and UK households' home energy, transport, indirect and total CO_2 emissions. *Ecol. Econ.*, **90**, 114–123, doi:10.1016/j.ecolecon.2013.03.007.

Buckingham, S. and R. Kulcur, 2017: It's not just the numbers: Challenging Masculinist Working Practices in Climate Change Decision-Making in UK Government and Environmental Non-Governmental Organizations. In: *Climate Change and Gender in Rich Countries: Work, Public Policy and Action* [Cohen, M.G. (ed.)], Routledge, Abingdon, UK, pp. 35–51.

Buckley, P., 2019: *Incentivising households to reduce electricity consumption: A meta-analysis of the experimental evidence*. HAL, Paris, France, 51 pp. https://econpapers.repec.org/paper/haljournl/hal-02485494.htm (Accessed August 9, 2020).

Buckley, P., 2020: Prices, information and nudges for residential electricity conservation: A meta-analysis. *Ecol. Econ.*, **172**, 106635, doi:10.1016/j.ecolecon.2020.106635.

Budd, L. and S. Ison, 2020: Responsible Transport: A post-COVID agenda for transport policy and practice. *Transp. Res. Interdiscip. Perspect.*, **6**, 100151, doi:10.1016/j.trip.2020.100151.

Bulkeley, H. and P. Newell, 2015: *Governing Climate Change*. [Weiss, T.G. (ed.)]. Routledge, Abingdon, UK.

Bullock, C., F. Brereton, and S. Bailey, 2017: The economic contribution of public bike-share to the sustainability and efficient functioning of cities. *Sustain. Cities Soc.*, **28**, 76–87, doi:10.1016/j.scs.2016.08.024.

Burke, M.J., 2020: Energy-Sufficiency for a Just Transition: A Systematic Review. *Energies*, **13(10)**, 2444, doi:10.3390/en13102444.

Burke, M.J. and J.C. Stephens, 2017: Energy democracy: Goals and policy instruments for sociotechnical transitions. *Energy Res. Soc. Sci.*, **33**, 35–48, doi:10.1016/j.erss.2017.09.024.

5

Burkhardt, J., K. Gillingham, and P. Kopalle, 2019: *Experimental Evidence on the Effect of Information and Pricing on Residential Electricity Consumption*. Working Paper 25576, National Bureau of Economic Research, Cambridge, MA, USA, 71 pp. http://www.nber.org/papers/w25576.pdf (Accessed September 8, 2020).

Burstein, R. et al., 2019: Mapping 123 million neonatal, infant and child deaths between 2000 and 2017. *Nature*, **574(7778)**, 353–358, doi:10.1038/s41586-019-1545-0.

Buschmann, P. and A. Oels, 2019: The overlooked role of discourse in breaking carbon lock-in: The case of the German energy transition. *Wiley Interdiscip. Rev. Clim. Change*, **10**(e574), 1–14, doi:10.1002/wcc.574.

Bush, R.E., C.S.E. Bale, and P.G. Taylor, 2016: Realising local government visions for developing district heating: Experiences from a learning country. *Energy Policy*, **98**, 84–96, doi:10.1016/j.enpol.2016.08.013.

Buyle, M., W. Galle, W. Debacker, and A. Audenaert, 2019: Sustainability assessment of circular building alternatives: Consequential LCA and LCC for internal wall assemblies as a case study in a Belgian context. *J. Clean. Prod.*, **218(2019)**, 141–156, doi:10.1016/j.jclepro.2019.01.306.

Calzadilla, P.V. and R. Mauger, 2017: The UN's new sustainable development agenda and renewable energy: the challenge to reach SDG7 while achieving energy justice. J. Energy Nat. Resour. Law, **36(2)**, 233–254, doi:10.1080/02646811.2017.1377951.

Campbell, A., 2018: Mass timber in the circular economy: Paradigm in practice? *Proc. Inst. Civ. Eng. Eng. Sustain.*, **172(3)**, 141–152, doi:10.1680/jensu.17.00069.

Campbell, I., A. Kalanki, and S. Sachar, 2018: *Solving the Global Cooling Challenge How to Counter the Climate Threat from Room Air Conditioners*. Rocky Mountain Institute, New York, USA, https://rmi.org/wp-content/uploads/2018/11/Global_Cooling_Challenge_Report_2018.pdf (Accessed December 9, 2020).

Campbell, T.H. and A.C. Kay, 2014: Solution aversion: On the relation between ideology and motivated disbelief. *J. Pers. Soc. Psychol.*, **107(5)**, 809–824, doi:10.1037/a0037963.

Caniglia, B.S., R.J. Brulle, and A. Szasz, 2015: Civil Society, Social Movements and Climate Change. In: *Climate Change and Society: Sociological Perspective* [Dunlap, R.E. and R.J. Brulle, (eds.)], Oxford University Press, Oxford, UK, pp. 235–268.

Cantzler, J. et al., 2020: Saving resources and the climate? A systematic review of the circular economy and its mitigation potential. *Environ. Res. Lett.*, **15(12)**, 123001, doi:10.1088/1748-9326/abbeb7.

Carattini, S., A. Baranzini, and J. Roca, 2015: Unconventional Determinants of Greenhouse Gas Emissions: The role of trust. *Environ. Policy Gov.*, **25(4)**, 243–257, doi:10.1002/eet.1685.

Carattini, S., A. Baranzini, P. Thalmann, F. Varone, and F. Vöhringer, 2017: Green Taxes in a Post-Paris World: Are Millions of Nays Inevitable? *Environ. Resour. Econ.*, **68(1)**, 97–128, doi:10.1007/s10640-017-0133-8.

Carattini, S., S. Levin, and A. Tavoni, 2019: Cooperation in the Climate Commons. *Rev. Environ. Econ. Policy*, **13(2)**, 227–247, doi:10.1093/reep/rez009.

Carley, S. and D.M. Konisky, 2020: The justice and equity implications of the clean energy transition. *Nat. Energy*, **5(8)**, 569–577, doi:10.1038/s41560-020-0641-6.

Carlsson-Kanyama, A., and A.-L. Lindén, 2007: Energy efficiency in residences – Challenges for women and men in the North. *Energy Policy*, **35(4)**, 2163–2172, doi:10.1016/j.enpol.2006.06.018.

Carr, E.R. and M.C. Thompson, 2014: Gender and Climate Change Adaptation in Agrarian Settings: Current Thinking, New Directions, and Research Frontiers. *Geogr. Compass*, **8(3)**, 182–197, doi:10.1111/gec3.12121.

Carrington, M.J., B.A. Neville, and G.J. Whitwell, 2014: Lost in translation: Exploring the ethical consumer intention-behavior gap. *J. Bus. Res.*, **67(1)**, 2759–2767, doi:10.1016/j.jbusres.2012.09.022.

Cass, N., T. Schwanen, and E. Shove, 2018: Infrastructures, intersections and societal transformations. *Technol. Forecast. Soc. Change*, **137**, 160–167, doi:10.1016/J.TECHFORE.2018.07.039.

Cassiers, I., K. Maréchal, and D. Méda, 2018: *Post-growth economics and society: exploring the paths of a social and ecological transition*. [Cassiers, I., K. Maréchal, and D. Méda, (eds.)]. Routledge, Abingdon, UK.

Castro, R. and P. Pasanen, 2019: How to design buildings with Life Cycle Assessment by accounting for the material flows in refurbishment. *IOP Conf. Ser. Earth Environ. Sci.*, **225(1)**, doi:10.1088/1755-1315/225/1/012019.

Cazorla, M. and M. Toman, 2001: International Equity and Climate Change Policy. In: *Climate Change Economics and Policy: An RFF Anthology* [Toman, M., (ed.)], Routledge, Abingdon, UK, pp. 235–245.

Cervantes Barron, K., 2020: Adequate service provision as the guide for energy transitions and international development. University of Cambridge, Cambridge, UK, 212 pp. https://www.repository.cam.ac.uk/bitstream/handle/1810/323462/KCB_Thesis.pdf?sequence=1&isAllowed=y (Accessed September 26, 2021).

Ceschin, F. and C. Vezzoli, 2010: The role of public policy in stimulating radical environmental impact reduction in the automotive sector: The need to focus on product-service system innovation. *Int. J. Automot. Technol. Manag.*, **10(2–3)**, doi:10.1504/IJATM.2010.032631.

Chakravarty, D. and J. Roy, 2016: The global south: New estimates and insights from urban India. In: *Rethinking Climate and Energy Policies: New Perspectives on the Rebound Phenomenon* [Santarius, T., H.J. Walnum, and C. Aall, (eds.)], Springer International Publishing, Cham, Switzerland, pp. 55–72.

Chakravarty, D. and J. Roy, 2021: Solar Microgrids in Rural India: A Case Study of Household Benefits. *Ecol. Econ. Soc. INSEE J.*, **4(2)**, 65–93, doi:10.37773/EES.V4I2.140.

Chakravarty, S. et al., 2009: Sharing global CO_2 emission reductions among one billion high emitters. *Proc. Natl. Acad. Sci.*, **106(29)**, 11884–11888, doi:10.1073/pnas.0905232106.

Chan, S. et al., 2019: Promises and risks of nonstate action in climate and sustainability governance. *Wiley Interdiscip. Rev. Clim. Change*, **10(3)**, 1–8, doi:10.1002/wcc.572.

Chancel, L., and T. Piketty, 2015: *Carbon and inequality: from Kyoto to Paris Trends in the global inequality of carbon emissions (1998-2013) & prospects for an equitable adaptation fund*. Paris School of Economics, Paris, France, 50 pp, http://piketty.pse.ens.fr/files/ChancelPiketty2015.pdf (Accessed July 4, 2019).

Chandra, A., K.E. McNamara, P. Dargusch, A.M. Caspe, and D. Dalabajan, 2017: Gendered vulnerabilities of smallholder farmers to climate change in conflict-prone areas: A case study from Mindanao, Philippines. *J. Rural Stud.*, **50**, 45–59, doi:10.1016/j.jrurstud.2016.12.011.

Chanza, N. and A. De Wit, 2016: Enhancing climate governance through indigenous knowledge: Case in sustainability science. *S. Afr. J. Sci.*, **112(3–4)**, doi:10.17159/sajs.2016/20140286.

Chapman, A. and T. Fraser, 2019: Japan's mega solar boom: quantifying social equity expectations and realities at the local scale. *Sustain. Sci.*, **14(2)**, 355–374, doi:10.1007/s11625-018-0613-y.

Chapman, A.J., B.C. Mclellan, and T. Tezuka, 2018: Prioritizing mitigation efforts considering co-benefits, equity and energy justice: Fossil fuel to renewable energy transition pathways. *Appl. Energy*, **219(2018)**, 187–198, doi:10.1016/j.apenergy.2018.03.054.

Charmes, J., 2016: The Informal Economy: Definitions, Size, Contribution and Main Characteristics. In: *The Informal Economy in Developing Nations: Hidden Engine of Innovation?* [Kraemer-Mbula, E. and S. Wunsch-Vincent, (eds.)], *Intellectual Property, Innovation and Economic Development*, Cambridge University Press, Cambridge, UK, pp. 13–52.

Chaturvedi, B. and V. Gidwani, 2011: The Right to Waste: Informal Sector Recyclers and Struggles for Social Justice in Post-Reform Urban India. In: *India's New Economic Policy A Critical Analysis* [Ahmed, W., A. Kundu, and R. Peet, (eds.)], Routledge, New York, NY, USA, pp. 125–153.

Chen, D. and R. Li-Hua, 2011: Modes of technological leapfrogging: Five case studies from China. *J. Eng. Technol. Manag.*, **28(1–2)**, 93–108, doi:10.1016/j.jengtecman.2010.12.006.

5

Chen, V.L., M.A. Delmas, S.L. Locke, and A. Singh, 2017: Information strategies for energy conservation: A field experiment in India. *Energy Econ.*, **68(2017)**, 215–227, doi:10.1016/j.dib.2017.11.084.

Chenoweth, J., 2009: Is tourism with a low impact on climate possible? *Worldw. Hosp. Tour. Themes*, **1(3)**, 274–287, doi:10.1108/17554210910980611.

Cheon, A., 2020: Advocacy, social movements, and climate change. In: *Handbook of U.S. Environmental Policy* [Konisky, D.M. (ed.)], Edward Elgar Publishing, pp. 315–327.

Cheon, A. and J. Urpelainen, 2018: *Activism and the fossil fuel industry*. Routledge, Abingdon, UK, 242 pp.

Cherry, C., K. Scott, J. Barrett, and N. Pidgeon, 2018: Public acceptance of resource-efficiency strategies to mitigate climate change. *Nat. Clim. Change*, **8(11)**, 1007–1012, doi:10.1038/s41558-018-0298-3.

Cherry, C.R., H. Yang, L.R. Jones, and M. He, 2016: Dynamics of electric bike ownership and use in Kunming, China. *Transp. Policy*, **45(1)**, 127–135, doi:10.1016/j.tranpol.2015.09.007.

Cherry, T.L., S. Kallbekken, and S. Kroll, 2017: Accepting market failure: Cultural worldviews and the opposition to corrective environmental policies. *J. Environ. Econ. Manage.*, **85(9)**, 193–204, doi:10.1016/j.jeem.2017.05.004.

Chester, M.V. and A. Horvath, 2009: Environmental assessment of passenger transportation should include infrastructure and supply chains. *Environ. Res. Lett.*, **4(2)**, doi:10.1088/1748-9326/4/2/024008.

Chevigny, P., 2003: The populism of fear: Politics of crime in the Americas. *Punishm. Soc.*, **5(1)**, 77–96, doi:10.1177/1462474503005001293.

Chhatre, A. and A. Agrawal, 2009: Trade-offs and synergies between carbon storage and livelihood benefits from forest commons. *Proc. Natl. Acad. Sci.*, **106(42)**, 17667–17670, doi:10.1073/pnas.0905308106.

Chitnis, M., S. Sorrell, A. Druckman, S.K. Firth, and T. Jackson, 2013: Turning lights into flights: Estimating direct and indirect rebound effects for UK households. *Energy Policy*, **55**, 234–250, doi:10.1016/j.enpol.2012.12.008.

Cho, D.-S., D.-J. Kim, and D.K. Rhee, 1998: Latecomer Strategies: Evidence from the Semiconductor Industry in Japan and Korea. *Organ. Sci.*, **9(4)**, 489–505, doi.org/10.1287/orsc.9.4.489.

Chu, E., 2016: The political economy of urban climate adaptation and development planning in Surat, India. *Environ. Plan. C Gov. Policy*, **34(2)**, 281–298, doi:10.1177/0263774X15614174.

Chu, S., 2015: Car restraint policies and mileage in Singapore. *Transp. Res. Part A Policy Pract.*, **77**, 404–412, doi:10.1016/j.tra.2015.04.028.

Chuang, F., E. Manley, and A. Petersen, 2020: The role of worldviews in the governance of sustainable mobility. *Proc. Natl. Acad. Sci.*, **117(8)**, 4034–4042, doi:10.1073/pnas.1916936117.

Chuku, C.A., 2010: Pursuing an integrated development and climate policy framework in Africa: Options for mainstreaming. *Mitig. Adapt. Strateg. Glob. Change*, **15(1)**, 41–52, doi:10.1007/s11027-009-9203-8.

Churkina, G. et al., 2020: Buildings as a global carbon sink. *Nat. Sustain.*, **3(4)**, 269–276, doi:10.1038/s41893-019-0462-4.

Cialdini, R.B., 2006: *Influence: The psychology of persuasion*. Harper Collins, New York, NY, USA.

Cirera, X. and W.F. Maloney, 2017: *The Innovation Paradox: Developing-Country Capabilities and the Unrealized Promise of Technological Catch-Up*. World Bank, Washington, DC, USA, 186 pp.

Claeys, P. and D. Delgado Pugley, 2017: Peasant and indigenous transnational social movements engaging with climate justice. *Can. J. Dev. Stud. / Rev. Can. D'études du développement*, **38(3)**, 325–340, doi:10.1080/02255189.2016.1235018.

Clancy, J. and M. Feenstra, 2019: *Women, Gender Equality and the Energy Transition in the EU*. European Parliament's Policy Department for Citizens' Rights and Constitutional Affairs, Brussels, Belgium, https://www.europarl.europa.eu/RegData/etudes/STUD/2019/608867/IPOL_STU(2019)608867_EN.pdf.

Clancy, J. et al., 2019: Gender in the transition to sustainable energy for all: From evidence to inclusive policies. *Energ. Int. Netw. Gend. Sustain. Energy*, 1–105. https://energia.org/assets/2019/04/Gender-in-the-transition-to-sustainable-energy-for-all_-From-evidence-to-inclusive-policies_FINAL.pdf.

Clausen, J., E. Göll, and V. Tappeser, 2017: Sticky Transformation – How path dependencies in socio-technical regimes are impeding the transformation to a Green Economy. *J. Innov. Manag.*, **5(2)**, 111–138, doi:10.1007/BF00727536.

Clayton, S., 2018: The Role of Perceived Justice, Political Ideology, and Individual or Collective Framing in Support for Environmental Policies. *Soc. Justice Res.*, **31(3)**, 219–237, doi:10.1007/s11211-018-0303-z.

Clayton, S. et al., 2015: Psychological research and global climate change. *Nat. Clim. Change*, **5(7)**, 640–646, doi:10.1038/nclimate2622.

Clewlow, R.R. and G.S. Mishra, 2017: *Disruptive Transportation: The Adoption, Utilization, and Impacts of Ride-Hailing in the United States*. UC Davis Institute of Transportation Studies, Davis, California.

Climact, 2018: *Net Zero by 2050: from whether to how*. Climact, Louvain-la-Neuve, Belgium, 35 pp. https://europeanclimate.org/wp-content/uploads/2019/11/09-18-net-zero-by-2050-from-whether-to-how.pdf (Accessed November 4, 2020).

Climate Assembly UK, 2020: *The path to net zero*. Climate Assembly UK, https://www.climateassembly.uk/report/read/final-report-exec-summary.pdf (Accessed December 10, 2020).

Climate Change Committee, 2020: *Sixth Carbon Budget: The UK's path to Net Zero*. Climate Change Committee, London, UK. https://www.theccc.org.uk/publication/sixth-carbon-budget/ (Accessed September 7, 2021).

Cloutier, G. et al., 2015: Planning adaptation based on local actors' knowledge and participation: a climate governance experiment. *Clim. Policy*, **15(4)**, 458–474, doi:10.1080/14693062.2014.937388.

Coates, S.J., L.K. Andersen, and M.D. Boos, 2020: Balancing public health and private wealth: lessons on climate inaction from the COVID-19 pandemic. *Int. J. Dermatol.*, doi:10.1111/ijd.14917.

Cohen, M., 2017: Gendered Emissions: Counting Greenhouse Gas Emissions by Gender and Why it Matters. In: *Climate Change and its Discontents* [Fanelli, C. and B. Evans, (eds.)]. Alternate Routes Critical Social Research.

Cohen, T. and C. Cavoli, 2019: Automated vehicles: exploring possible consequences of government (non)intervention for congestion and accessibility. *Transp. Rev.*, **39(1)**, 129–151, doi:10.1080/01441647.2018.1524401.

Colenbrander, S. et al., 2016: Can low-carbon urban development be pro-poor? The case of Kolkata, India. *Environ. Urban.*, **29(1)**, 139–158, doi:10.1177/0956247816677775.

Collins, C., 2019: *Can Improving Women's Representation in Environmental Governance Reduce Greenhouse Gas Emissions?* Climate Institute, New York, NY, USA, 7 pp. http://climate.org/can-improving-womens-representation-in-environmental-governance-reduce-greenhouse-gas-emissions/ (Accessed July 4, 2019).

Colville-Andersen, M., 2018: *Copenhagenize: the definitive guide to global bicycle urbanism*. Island Press, Washington, DC, USA, 275 pp.

Comin, D. and B. Hobijn, 2003: *Cross-country technology adoption: Making the theories face the facts*. Federal Reserve Bank of New York, New York, NY, USA, 49 pp. http://hdl.handle.net/10419/60558 (Accessed May 23, 2021).

Comin, D., M. Dmitriev, and E. Rossi-Hansberg, 2012: Heavy technology: The process of technological diffusion over time and space. *VoxEU CEPR*. https://voxeu.org/article/heavy-technology-process-technological-diffusion-over-time-and-space (Accessed August 4, 2020).

Conte Grand, M., 2016: Carbon emission targets and decoupling indicators. *Ecol. Indic.*, **67**, 649–656, doi:10.1016/J.ECOLIND.2016.03.042.

Cook, G., T. Dowdall, D. Pomerantz, and Y. Wang, 2014: *Clicking Clean: How Companies are Creating the Green Internet*. Greenpeace Inc, Washington, DC, USA, https://www.greenpeace.org/usa/wp-content/uploads/legacy/Global/usa/planet3/PDFs/clickingclean.pdf (Accessed May 23, 2021).

5

Cook, G. et al., 2017: *Clicking Clean: Who is Winning the Race to Build A Green Internet?* Greenpeace Inc, Washington, DC, USA, 102 pp. http://www.clickclean.org/downloads/ClickClean2016%20HiRes.pdf. (Accessed May 23, 2021).

Cook, N.J., T. Grillos, and K.P. Andersson, 2019: Gender quotas increase the equality and effectiveness of climate policy interventions. *Nat. Clim. Change*, **9(4)**, 330–334, doi:10.1038/s41558-019-0438-4.

Cook, S., M. Brucoli, and M. Stevns, 2016: *Distributed Energy Systems: Flexible and Efficient Power for the New Energy Era.* 64 pp. Arup & Siemens. https://www.arup.com/perspectives/publications/research/section/distributed-energy-systems-flexible-and-efficient-power-for-the-new-energy-era.

Copland, S., 2019: Anti-politics and Global Climate Inaction: The Case of the Australian Carbon Tax. *Crit. Sociol.*, **46(4–5)**, 623–641, doi:10.1177/0896920519870230.

Cordella, M., F. Alfieri, and J. Sanfelix, 2021: Reducing the carbon footprint of ICT products through material efficiency strategies: A life cycle analysis of smartphones. *J. Ind. Ecol.*, **25(2)**, 448–464, doi:10.1111/JIEC.13119.

Cory, J., M. Lerner, and I. Osgood, 2021: Supply Chain Linkages and the Extended Carbon Coalition. *Am. J. Pol. Sci.*, **65(1)**, 69–87, doi:10.1111/AJPS.12525.

Costa, D.L., and M.E. Kahn, 2013: Energy conservation "nudges" and environmentalist ideology: Evidence from a randomized residential electricity field experiment. *J. Eur. Econ. Assoc.*, **11(3)**, 680–702, doi:10.1111/jeea.12011.

Costa, V. and A. Johnson, 2019: Global Food and Nutrition Trends: Driving Positive Momentum for Grains. *Cereal Foods World*, **64(3)**, doi:10.1094/CFW-64-3-0032.

Coulombel, N., V. Boutueil, L. Liu, V. Viguié, and B. Yin, 2019: Substantial rebound effects in urban ridesharing: Simulating travel decisions in Paris, France. *Transp. Res. Part D Transp. Environ.*, **71**(December 2018), 110–126, doi:10.1016/j.trd.2018.12.006.

Court, V. and S. Sorrell, 2020: Digitalisation of goods: A systematic review of the determinants and magnitude of the impacts on energy consumption. *Environ. Res. Lett.*, **15(4)**, doi:10.1088/1748-9326/ab6788.

Cowan, R., 1990: Nuclear Power Reactors: A Study in Technological Lock-in. *J. Econ. Hist.*, **50(3)**, 541–567, doi:10.1017/S0022050700037153.

Cowan, R., 1991: Tortoises and hares: Choice among technologies of unknown merit. *Econ. J.*, **101**, 801–814, doi:10.1016/s0262-4079(11)61100-7.

Cowie, A., G. Berndes, and T. Smith, 2013: *On the Timing of Greenhouse Gas Mitigation Benefits of Forest-Based Bioenergy.* IEA Bioenergy. https://www.ieabioenergy.com/wp-content/uploads/2013/10/On-the-Timing-of-Greenhouse-Gas-Mitigation-Benefits-of-Forest-Based-Bioenergy.pdf.

Cramton, P., A. Ockenfels, and J. Tirole, 2017: Translating the Collective Climate Goal Into a Common Climate Commitment. *Rev. Environ. Econ. Policy*, **11(1)**, 165–171, doi:10.1093/reep/rew015.

Crawford, N.C., 2019: *Pentagon Fuel Use, Climate Change, and the Costs of War.* 46 pp. Watson Institute of Public Affairs and Law, Brown University. https://watson.brown.edu/costsofwar/files/cow/imce/papers/Pentagon%20Fuel%20Use%2C%20Climate%20Change%20and%20the%20Costs%20of%20War%20Revised%20November%202019%20Crawford.pdf (Accessed October 31, 2019).

Creamer, E. et al., 2018: Community energy: Entanglements of community, state, and private sector. *Geogr. Compass*, **12(7)**, doi:10.1111/gec3.12378.

Creutzig, F., 2019: The Mitigation Trinity: Coordinating Policies to Escalate Climate Mitigation. *One Earth*, **1(1)**, 76–85, doi:10.1016/j.oneear.2019.08.007.

Creutzig, F. et al., 2015a: Transport: A roadblock to climate change mitigation? *Science*, **350(6263)**, 911–912, doi:10.1126/science.aac8033.

Creutzig, F., G. Baiocchi, R. Bierkandt, P.-P.P. Pichler, and K.C. Seto, 2015b: Global typology of urban energy use and potentials for an urbanization mitigation wedge. *Proc. Natl. Acad. Sci.*, **112(20)**, 6283–6288, doi:10.1073/pnas.1315545112.

Creutzig, F. et al., 2016a: Urban infrastructure choices structure climate solutions. *Nat. Clim. Change*, **6(12)**, 1054, doi:10.1038/nclimate3169.

Creutzig, F. et al., 2016b: Beyond technology: demand-side solutions for climate change mitigation. *Annu. Rev. Environ. Resour.*, **41(1)**, 173–198, doi:10.1146/annurev-environ-110615-085428.

Creutzig, F. et al., 2018: Towards demand-side solutions for mitigating climate change. *Nat. Clim. Change*, **8(4)**, 260–263, doi:10.1038/s41558-018-0121-1.

Creutzig, F. et al., 2019a: Assessing human and environmental pressures of global land-use change 2000–2010. *Glob. Sustain.*, **2**, doi:10.1017/SUS.2018.15.

Creutzig, F. et al., 2019b: Leveraging Digitalization for Sustainability in Urban Transport. *Glob. Sustain.*, **2**(e14), 1–6, doi:10.1017/sus.2019.11.

Creutzig, F. et al., 2020: Fair street space allocation: ethical principles and empirical insights. *Transp. Rev.*, **40(6)**, 711–733, doi:10.1080/01441647.2020.1762795.

Creutzig, F. et al., 2021a: A typology of 100,000 publications on demand, services and social aspects of climate change mitigation. *Environ. Res. Lett.*, **16(3)**, 033001, doi:10.1088/1748-9326/abd78b.

Creutzig, F. et al., 2021b: Demand-side solutions to climate change mitigation consistent with high levels of wellbeing. *Nat. Clim. Change*, **12**, 36–46.

Creutzig, F. et al., 2021c: Considering sustainability thresholds for BECCS in IPCC and biodiversity assessments. *GCB Bioenergy*, **13(4)**, 510–515, doi:10.1111/gcbb.12798.

Crick, F., S.M.S.U. Eskander, S. Fankhauser, and M. Diop, 2018a: How do African SMEs respond to climate risks? Evidence from Kenya and Senegal. *World Dev.*, **108**, 157–168, doi:10.1016/j.worlddev.2018.03.015.

Crick, F., K.E. Gannon, M. Diop, and M. Sow, 2018b: Enabling private sector adaptation to climate change in sub-Saharan Africa. *Wiley Interdiscip. Rev. Clim. Change*, **9(2)**, e505, doi:10.1002/wcc.505.

Cuenot, F., L. Fulton, and J. Staub, 2010: The prospect for modal shifts in passenger transport worldwide and impacts on energy use and CO_2. *Energy Policy*, **41**, 98–106, doi:10.1016/j.enpol.2010.07.017.

Cullen, J., 2017: Circular economy: theoretical benchmark or perpetual motion machine? *Circ. Econ.*, **21**, 483–486, doi:10.1111/jiec.12599.

Cullen, J.M. and J.M. Allwood, 2010: Theoretical efficiency limits for energy conversion devices. *Energy*, **35(5)**, 2059–2069, doi:10.1016/j.energy.2010.01.024.

Cunningham, P., J. Edler, K. Flanagan, and P. Laredo, 2013: *Innovation policy mix and instrument interaction: a review.* 47 pp. https://media.nesta.org.uk/documents/innovation_policy_mix_and_instrument_interaction.pdf.

Curnow, J. and A. Gross, 2016: Injustice is not an investment: student activism, climate justice, and the fossil fuel divestment campaign. In: *Contemporary Youth Activism: Advancing Social Justice in the United States* [Connor, J. and Rosen, S. (ed.)], ABC-CLIO, Santa Barbara, CA, USA, 433 pp.

Curran, G., 2020: Divestment, energy incumbency and the global political economy of energy transition: the case of Adani's Carmichael mine in Australia. *Clim. Policy*, **20(8)**, 949–962, doi:10.1080/14693062.2020.1756731.

Curtis, S.K. and M. Lehner, 2019: Defining the sharing economy for sustainability. *Sustainability*, **11(3)**, doi:10.3390/su11030567.

D'Alessandro, S., A Cieplinski, T. Distefano, and P. Guarnieri, 2019: Societal transition for a sustainable economy. *Agrochimica*, Special Issue December 2019, pp. 293–336.

Dagnachew, A.G., P.L. Lucas, and D.P. van Vuuren, and A.F. Hof, 2019: *Towards Universal Access to Clean Cooking Solutions in Sub-Saharan Africa: An integrated assessment of the cost, health and environmental implications of policies and targets.* PBL Netherlands Environmental Assessment Agency, The Hague, the Netherlands, 60 pp. https://www.pbl.nl/sites/default/files/downloads/pbl-2019-clean-cooking-solutions-sub-saharan-africa_3421_0.pdf (Accessed July 22, 2020).

Dana, L.-P., C. Gurău, F. Hoy, V. Ramadani, and T. Alexander, 2021: Success factors and challenges of grassroots innovations: Learning from failure. *Technol. Forecast. Soc. Change*, **164(119600)**, doi:10.1016/j.techfore.2019.03.009.

Dankelman, I., 2010: *Gender and climate change: an introduction.* [Dankelman, I., (ed.)]. Routledge/Earthscan, London, UK, 284 pp.

5

Dankelman, I. and W.H.M. Jansen, 2010: Gender, Environment and Climate Change: understanding the linkages. doi:10.4324/9781849775274.

Darby, S., 2006: *The effectiveness of feedback on energy consumption: a review for DEFRA of the literature on metering, billing and direct displays*. Environmental Change Institute, Oxford University, Oxford, UK, 24 pp. https://www.eci.ox.ac.uk/research/energy/downloads/smart-metering-report.pdf (Accessed November 28, 2020).

Darier, É. and R. Schüle, 1999: Think globally, act locally'? Climate change and public participation in Manchester and Frankfurt. *Local Environ.*, **4(3)**, 317–329, doi:10.1080/13549839908725602.

Das, K., G. Pradhan, and S. Nonhebel, 2019: Human energy and time spent by women using cooking energy systems: A case study of Nepal. *Energy*, **182**, 493–501, doi:10.1016/j.energy.2019.06.074.

Das, S. et al., 2016: Vehicle lightweighting energy use impacts in U.S. light-duty vehicle fleet. *Sustain. Mater. Technol.*, **8**, 5–13, doi:10.1016/j.susmat.2016.04.001.

Dasgupta, A. and P. Dasgupta, 2017: Socially Embedded Preferences, Environmental Externalities, and Reproductive Rights. *Popul. Dev. Rev.*, **43(3)**, 405–441, doi:10.1111/padr.12090.

Dasgupta, P., D. Southerton, A. Ulph, and D. Ulph, 2016: Consumer Behaviour with Environmental and Social Externalities: Implications for Analysis and Policy. *Environ. Resour. Econ.*, **65(1)**, 191–226, doi:10.1007/s10640-015-9911-3.

Daube, M. and D. Ulph, 2016: Moral Behaviour, Altruism and Environmental Policy. *Environ. Resour. Econ.*, **63(2)**, 505–522, doi:10.1007/s10640-014-9836-2.

David, M., 2017: Moving beyond the heuristic of creative destruction: Targeting exnovation with policy mixes for energy transitions. *Energy Res. Soc. Sci.*, **33**, 138–146, doi:10.1016/j.erss.2017.09.023.

David Tàbara, J. et al., 2018: Positive tipping points in a rapidly warming world. *Curr. Opin. Environ. Sustain.*, **31**, 120–129, doi:10.1016/j.cosust.2018.01.012.

Davidescu, S., R. Hiteva, and T. Maltby, 2018: Two steps forward, one step back: Renewable energy transitions in Bulgaria and Romania. *Public Adm.*, **96(3)**, 611–625, doi:10.1111/padm.12522.

Davis, S., 1979: *The Diffusion of Process Innovations*. Cambridge University Press, Cambridge, UK, 193 pp.

Davis, S.J. and K. Caldeira, 2010: Consumption-based accounting of CO$_2$ emissions. *Proc. Natl. Acad. Sci.*, **107(12)**, 5687–5692, doi:10.1073/pnas.0906974107.

de Abreu e Silva, J., and P.C. Melo, 2018: Does home-based telework reduce household total travel? A path analysis using single and two worker British households. *J. Transp. Geogr.*, **73**, 148–162, doi:10.1016/j.jtrangeo.2018.10.009.

De Boer, J., H. Schösler, and H. Aiking, 2014: "Meatless days" or "less but better"? Exploring strategies to adapt Western meat consumption to health and sustainability challenges. *Appetite*, **76**, 120–128, doi:10.1016/j.appet.2014.02.002.

de Bortoli, A. and Z. Christoforou, 2020: Consequential LCA for territorial and multimodal transportation policies: method and application to the free-floating e-scooter disruption in Paris. *J. Clean. Prod.*, **273**, 122898, doi:10.1016/J.JCLEPRO.2020.122898.

de Coninck, H., A. Revi, M. Babiker, P. Bertoldi, M. Buckeridge, A. Cartwright, W. Dong, J. Ford, S. Fuss, J.-C. Hourcade, D. Ley, R. Mechler, P. Newman, A. Revokatova, S. Schultz, L. Steg, and T. Sugiyama, 2018: Strengthening and implementing the global response. In: *Global Warming of 1.5°C: an IPCC special report on the impacts of global warming of 1.5°C above pre-industrial levels and related global greenhouse gas emission pathways, in the context of strengthening the global response to the threat of climate change, sustainable development, and efforts to eradicate poverty*. [Masson-Delmotte, V., P. Zhai, H.-O. Pörtner, D. Roberts, J. Skea, P.R. Shukla, A. Pirani, W. Moufouma-Okia, C. Péan, R. Pidcock, S. Connors, J.B.R. Matthews, Y. Chen, X. Zhou, M.I. Gomis, E. Lonnoy, T. Maycock, M. Tignor, and T. Waterfield (eds.)]. Cambridge University Press, Cambridge, UK, and New York, NY, USA, pp. 313–443.

De Dominicis, S., R. Sokoloski, C.M. Jaeger, and P.W. Schultz, 2019: Making the smart meter social promotes long-term energy conservation. *Palgrave Commun.*, **5(1)**, 1–8, doi:10.1057/s41599-019-0254-5.

de Feijter, F.J., B.J.M. van Vliet, and Y. Chen, 2019: Household inclusion in the governance of housing retrofitting: Analysing Chinese and Dutch systems of energy retrofit provision. *Energy Res. Soc. Sci.*, **53**, 10–22, doi:10.1016/j.erss.2019.02.006.

De Rubens, Z.G., L. Noel, and B.K. Sovacool, 2018: Dismissive and deceptive car dealerships create barriers to electric vehicle adoption at the point of sale. *Nat. Energy*, **3**, 501–507, doi:10.1038/s41560-018-0152-x.

De Stercke, S., 2014: *Dynamics of Energy Systems: a Useful Perspective*. International Institute for Applied Systems Analysis, Laxenburg, Austria, 68 pp. http://pure.iiasa.ac.at/id/eprint/11254/1/IR-14-013.pdf (Accessed July 22, 2020).

de Vries, A., 2018: Bitcoin's Growing Energy Problem. *Joule*, **2(5)**, 801–805, doi:10.1016/j.joule.2018.04.016.

de Zoysa, U., 2011: Millennium consumption goals: A fair proposal from the poor to the rich. *Sustain. Sci. Pract. Policy*, **7(1)**, 1–5, doi:10.1080/15487733.2011.11908060.

Decancq, K., A. Decoster, and E. Schokkaert, 2009: The Evolution of World Inequality in Well-being. *World Dev.*, **37(1)**, 11–25, doi:10.1016/j.worlddev.2007.12.006.

Dechezleprêtre, A., M. Glachant, and Y. Ménière, 2013: What Drives the International Transfer of Climate Change Mitigation Technologies? Empirical Evidence from Patent Data. *Environ. Resour. Econ.*, **54(2)**, 161–178, doi:10.1007/s10640-012-9592-0.

Dechezleprêtre, A., E. Neumayer, and R. Perkins, 2015: Environmental regulation and the cross-border diffusion of new technology: Evidence from automobile patents. *Res. Policy*, **44(1)**, 244–257, doi:10.1016/j.respol.2014.07.017.

Decker, K. et al., 2017: *Conceptual Feasibility Study of the Hyperloop Vehicle for Next-Generation Transport*. NASA, Cleveland, OH, USA, 22 pp. https://ntrs.nasa.gov/search.jsp?R=20170001624 (Accessed December 16, 2019).

della Porta, D. and L. Parks, 2014: Framing Processes in the Climate Movement: from climate change to climate justice. In: *Handbook of the climate change movement* [Dietz, M. and H. Garrelts, (eds.)], Routledge, New York, NY, USA, pp. 19–30.

Delmas, M.A., M. Fischlein, and O.I. Asensio, 2013: Information strategies and energy conservation behavior: A meta-analysis of experimental studies from 1975 to 2012. *Energy Policy*, **61**, 729–739, doi:10.1016/j.enpol.2013.05.109.

Demski, C., C. Butler, K.A. Parkhill, A. Spence, and N.F. Pidgeon, 2015: Public values for energy system change. *Glob. Environ. Change*, **34**, 59–69, doi:10.1016/j.gloenvcha.2015.06.014.

den Hartog, H. et al., 2018: Low-carbon promises and realities: Lessons from three socio-technical experiments in Shanghai. *J. Clean. Prod.*, **181**, 692–702, doi:10.1016/j.jclepro.2018.02.003.

Dendup, N., and T.H. Arimura, 2019: Information leverage: The adoption of clean cooking fuel in Bhutan. *Energy Policy*, **125**, 181–195, doi:10.1016/j.enpol.2018.10.054.

Deng, T. and J.D. Nelson, 2011: Recent developments in bus rapid transit: A review of the literature. *Transp. Rev.*, **31(1)**, 69–96, doi:10.1080/01441647.2010.492455.

Dengler, C. and B. Strunk, 2018: The Monetized Economy Versus Care and the Environment: Degrowth Perspectives On Reconciling an Antagonism. *Fem. Econ.*, **24(3)**, 160–183, doi:10.1080/13545701.2017.1383620.

Devaney, L., D. Torney, P. Brereton, and M. Coleman, 2020: Ireland's Citizens' Assembly on Climate Change: Lessons for Deliberative Public Engagement and Communication. *Environ. Commun.*, **14(2)**, 141–146, doi:10.1080/17524032.2019.1708429.

Devine-Wright, P., 2009: Rethinking NIMBYism: The role of place attachment and place identity in explaining place-protective action. *J. Community Appl. Soc. Psychol.*, **19(6)**, 426–441, doi:10.1002/casp.1004.

Devine-Wright, P., 2011: Public engagement with large-scale renewable energy technologies: Breaking the cycle of NIMBYism. *Wiley Interdiscip. Rev. Clim. Change*, **2(1)**, 19–26, doi:10.1002/wcc.89.

Devine-Wright, P. et al., 2020: "Re-placed" – Reconsidering relationships with place and lessons from a pandemic. *J. Environ. Psychol.*, **72**, 101514, doi:10.1016/j.jenvp.2020.101514.

Dewald, U. and B. Truffer, 2011: Market formation in technological innovation systems-diffusion of photovoltaic applications in Germany. *Ind. Innov.*, **18(3)**, 285–300, doi:10.1080/13662716.2011.561028.

Dhar, S., M. Pathak, and P.R. Shukla, 2017: Electric vehicles and India's low carbon passenger transport: a long-term co-benefits assessment. *J. Clean. Prod.*, **146**, 139–148, doi:10.1016/j.jclepro.2016.05.111.

Di Chiro, G., 2019: Care not growth: Imagining a subsistence economy for all. *Br. J. Polit. Int. Relations*, **21(2)**, 303–311, doi:10.1177/1369148119836349.

Di Gregorio, M. et al., 2019: Multi-level governance and power in climate change policy networks. *Glob. Environ. Change*, **54**, 64–77, doi:10.1016/j.gloenvcha.2018.10.003.

Diao, M., H. Kong, and J. Zhao, 2021: Impacts of transportation network companies on urban mobility. *Nat. Sustain.*, **4(6)**, 494–500, doi:10.1038/s41893-020-00678-z.

Dibb, S. and I. Fitzpatrick, 2014: *Let's talk about meat: changing dietary behaviour for the 21st century*. Eating Better, 32 pp. https://www.eating-better.org/uploads/Documents/LetsTalkAboutMeat.pdf (Accessed December 10, 2019).

Dietrich, F. and C. List, 2016: Reason-based choice and context-dependence: an explanatory framework. *Econ. Philos.*, **32(2)**, 175–229, doi:10.1017/S0266267115000474.

Dietz, T., 2014: Understanding environmentally significant consumption. *Proc. Natl. Acad. Sci.*, **111(14)**, 5067–5068, doi:10.1073/pnas.1403169111.

Dietz, T. and P.C. Stern, 2008: *Public participation in environmental assessment and decision making*. National Academies Press, Washington, DC, USA, 305 pp.

Dietz, T., G.T. Gardner, J. Gilligan, P.C. Stern, and M.P. Vandenbergh, 2009: Household actions can provide a behavioral wedge to rapidly reduce US carbon emissions. *Proc. Natl. Acad. Sci.*, **106(44)**, 18452–18456, doi:10.1073/pnas.0908738106.

Diffenbaugh, N.S. and M. Burke, 2019: Global warming has increased global economic inequality. *Proc. Natl. Acad. Sci.*, **116(20)**, 9808–9813, doi:10.1073/pnas.1816020116.

Diffenbaugh, N.S. et al., 2020: The COVID-19 lockdowns: a window into the Earth System. *Nat. Rev. Earth Environ.*, **1(9)**, 470–481, doi:10.1038/s43017-020-0079-1.

Ding, Q., X. Liang, H. Chen, M. Liu, and J. Yang, 2020: Study on Policy and Standard System of LED Lighting Industry in EU. *E3S Web Conf.*, **194**, 2016, doi:10.1051/e3sconf/202019402016.

Djerf-Pierre, M., 2012: Green metacycles of attention: Reassessing the attention cycles of environmental news reporting 1961–2010. *Public Underst. Sci.*, **22(4)**, 495–512, doi:10.1177/0963662511426819.

Docherty, I., G. Marsden, and J. Anable, 2018: The governance of smart mobility. *Transp. Res. Part A Policy Pract.*, **115**(October 2017), 114–125, doi:10.1016/j.tra.2017.09.012.

Dodson, J.C., P. Dérer, P. Cafaro, and F. Götmark, 2020: Population growth and climate change: Addressing the overlooked threat multiplier. *Sci. Total Environ.*, **748**, 141346, doi:10.1016/J.SCITOTENV.2020.141346.

Dolan, P. and R. Metcalfe, 2013: *Neighbors, Knowledge, and Nuggets: Two Natural Field Experiments on the Role of Incentives on Energy Conservation*. CEP Discussion Papers dp1222, Centre for Economic Performance, London School of Economics and Political Science, London, UK, https://ideas.repec.org/p/cep/cepdps/dp1222.html.

Dombrowski, K., 2010: Filling the gap? An analysis of non-governmental organizations responses to participation and representation deficits in global climate governance. *Int. Environ. Agreements Polit. Law Econ.*, **10(4)**, 397–416, doi:10.1007/s10784-010-9140-8.

Dombrowski, U., S. Ernst, and A. Reimer, 2016: A New Training for Factory Planning Engineers to Create Awareness of Climate Change. *Procedia CIRP*, **48**, 443–448, doi:10.1016/j.procir.2016.04.083.

Dorling, D., 2019: *Inequality and the 1%*. 3rd ed. Verso, London, UK, 272 pp.

Douenne, T. and A. Fabre, 2019: *Can We Reconcile French People with the Carbon Tax? Disentangling Beliefs from Preferences*. FAERE, French Association of Environmental and Resource Economists.

Douenne, T. and A. Fabre, 2020: French attitudes on climate change, carbon taxation and other climate policies. *Ecol. Econ.*, **169**, doi:10.1016/j.ecolecon.2019.106496.

Downs, A., 1972: Up and Down with Ecology: The Issue Attention Cycle. *Public Interest*, **28**, pp. 38–50.

Doyal, L. and I. Gough, 1991: Introduction. In: *A Theory of Human Need*, Palgrave, London, UK, pp. 1–2.

Doyle, J., 2011: Where has all the oil gone? BP branding and the discursive elimination of climate change risk. In: *Culture, environment and eco-politics* [Heffernan, N. and D. Wragg, (eds.)], Cambridge Scholars Publishing, Newcastle, UK, pp. 200–225.

Doyle, J., N. Farrell, and M.K. Goodman, 2019: The cultural politics of climate branding: Project Sunlight, the biopolitics of climate care and the socialisation of the everyday sustainable consumption practices of citizens-consumers. *Clim. Change*, **163(1)**, 117–133, doi:10.1007/s10584-019-02487-6.

Drews, S. and J.C.J.M. van den Bergh, 2016: What explains public support for climate policies? A review of empirical and experimental studies. *Clim. Policy*, **16(7)**, 855–876, doi:10.1080/14693062.2015.1058240.

Dreyfus, G. et al., 2020: *Assessment of climate and development benefits of efficient and climate-friendly cooling*. Institute for Governance & Sustainable Development and Centro Mario Molina, La Jolla, CA, USA, https://ccacoalition.org/en/resources/assessment-climate-and-development-benefits-efficient-and-climate-friendly-cooling (Accessed December 9, 2020).

Drolet, J.L., 2021: Societal adaptation to climate change. In: *The Impacts of Climate Change* [Letcher, T.M., (ed.)], Elsevier, Amsterdam, the Netherlands, pp. 365–377.

Druckman, A. and T. Jackson, 2010: The bare necessities: How much household carbon do we really need? *Ecol. Econ.*, **69(9)**, 1794–1804, doi:10.1016/j.ecolecon.2010.04.018.

Dryzek, J.S. et al., 2019: The crisis of democracy and the science of deliberation. *Science*, **363(6432)**, 1144–1146, doi:10.1126/scienceaaw2694.

Dubash, N.K., 2013: The politics of climate change in India: Narratives of equity and cobenefits. *Wiley Interdiscip. Rev. Clim. Change*, **4(3)**, 191–201, doi:10.1002/wcc.210.

Dubois, G. et al., 2019: It starts at home? Climate policies targeting household consumption and behavioral decisions are key to low-carbon futures. *Energy Res. Soc. Sci.*, **52**, 144–158, doi:10.1016/j.erss.2019.02.001.

Dulal, H., K. Shah, and N. Ahmad, 2009: Social Equity Considerations in the Implementation of Caribbean Climate Change Adaptation Policies. *Sustainability*, **1(3)**, 363–383, doi:10.3390/su1030363.

Duncan, G. and A. Gulbahar, 2019: *Climate change mitigation and food loss and waste reduction: Exploring the business case*. CCAFS Report No. 18. CGIAR Research Program on Climate Change, Wageningen, the Netherlands, https://ccafs.cgiar.org/resources/publications/climate-change-mitigation-and-food-loss-and-waste-reduction-exploring (Accessed August 25, 2021).

Dunlap, R.E., and A.M. McCright, 2015: Challenging climate change: The denial countermovement. In: *Climate Change and Society: Sociological Perspective* [Dunlap, R.E. and R.J. Brulle, (eds.)], Oxford University Press, Oxford, UK, pp. 300–332.

Dünnhoff, E. and M. Duscha, 2008: Effiziente Beratungsbausteine zur Minderung des Stromverbrauchs in privaten Haushalten. Endbericht [Efficient building blocks for energy counseling aimed at reducing electricity consumption in private households]. *Inst. für Energie-und Umweltforsch*.

Durán Heras, M.A. (ed.), 2012: *Unpaid Work in the Global Economy*. Fundación BBVA, Spain, 511 pp.

5

Dussaux, D., A. Dechezleprêtre, and M. Glachant, 2017: *Intellectual property rights protection and the international transfer of low-carbon technologies*. Centre for Climate Change Economics and Policy Working Paper No. 323, Grantham Research Institute on Climate Change and the Environment Working Paper No. 288, London, UK, 48 pp. https://www.lse.ac.uk/granthaminstitute/publication/intellectual-property-rights-protection-international-transfer-low-carbon-technologies/ (Accessed April 12, 2021).

Easterlin, R.A., L.A. McVey, M. Switek, O. Sawangfa, and J.S. Zweig, 2010: The happiness-income paradox revisited. *Proc. Natl. Acad. Sci.*, **107(52)**, doi:10.1073/pnas.1015962107.

Eastin, J., 2018: Climate change and gender equality in developing states. *World Dev.*, **107**, 289–305, doi:10.1016/j.worlddev.2018.02.021.

Eberhardt, L.C.M., H. Birgisdottir, and M. Birkved, 2019: Potential of Circular Economy in Sustainable Buildings. *IOP Conf. Ser. Mater. Sci. Eng.*, **471(9)**, doi:10.1088/1757-899X/471/9/092051.

Edjabou, L.D. and S. Smed, 2013: The effect of using consumption taxes on foods to promote climate friendly diets – The case of Denmark. *Food Policy*, **39**, 84–96, doi:10.1016/j.foodpol.2012.12.004.

Edmondson, D.L., F. Kern, and K.S. Rogge, 2019: The co-evolution of policy mixes and socio-technical systems: Towards a conceptual framework of policy mix feedback in sustainability transitions. *Res. Policy*, **48(10)**, Article 103555, doi:10.1016/j.respol.2018.03.010.

Eguiguren-Cosmelli, J.M., 2018: Responsiveness of low-income households to hybrid price/non-price policies in the presence of energy shortages: evidence from Colombia. *Energy Effic.*, **11(3)**, 641–661, doi:10.1007/S12053-017-9595-3.

Ehrhardt-Martinez, K., 2015: Behaviour wedge profiles for cities. *eceee 2015 Summer Study energy Effic. First fuel now*, **Panel: 3.**, 691–702.

Ehrhardt-Martinez, K., K.A. Donnelly, and J.A. Laitner, 2010: *Advanced Metering Initiatives and Residential Feedback Programs: A Meta-Review for Household Electricity-Saving Opportunities*. American Council for an Energy-Efficient Economy, Washington, DC, USA, 140 pp. https://www.aceee.org/sites/default/files/publications/researchreports/e105.pdf (Accessed February 13, 2020).

Ehrlich, P.R., and A.H. Ehrlich, 2013: Can a collapse of global civilization be avoided? *Proc. R. Soc. B Biol. Sci.*, **280(1754)**, 1–9, doi:10.1098/rspb.2012.2845.

Elias, T., N.S. Dahmen, D.D. Morrison, D. Morrison, and D.L. Morris, 2018: Understanding Climate Change Perceptions and Attitudes Across Racial/Ethnic Groups. *Howard J. Commun.*, **30(1)**, 38–56, doi:10.1080/10646175.2018.1439420.

Ellenbeck, S. and J. Lilliestam, 2019: How modelers construct energy costs: Discursive elements in Energy System and Integrated Assessment Models. *Energy Res. Soc. Sci.*, **47**, 69–77, doi:10.1016/j.erss.2018.08.021.

Elliot, S., 2011: Transdisciplinary Perspectives on Environmental Sustainability: A Resource Base and Framework for IT-Enabled Business Transformation. *MIS Q.*, **35(1)**, 197, doi:10.2307/23043495.

Elnakat, A. and J.D. Gomez, 2015: Energy engenderment: An industrialized perspective assessing the importance of engaging women in residential energy consumption management. *Energy Policy*, **82(1)**, 166–177, doi:10.1016/j.enpol.2015.03.014.

Enoch, M.P. and J. Taylor, 2006: A worldwide review of support mechanisms for car clubs. *Transp. Policy*, **13(5)**, 434–443, doi:10.1016/J.TRANPOL.2006.04.001.

Erb, K.-H. et al., 2016: Exploring the biophysical option space for feeding the world without deforestation. *Nat. Clim. Change*, **48(7)**, 829–834, doi.org/10.1038/ncomms11382.

Erdmann, L. and L.M. Hilty, 2010: Scenario Analysis. *J. Ind. Ecol.*, **14(5)**, 826–843, doi:10.1111/J.1530-9290.2010.00277.X.

Ergas, C. and R. York, 2012: Women's status and carbon dioxide emissions: A quantitative cross-national analysis. *Soc. Sci. Res.*, **41(4)**, 965–976, doi:10.1016/j.ssresearch.2012.03.008.

Erwin, A. et al., 2021: Intersectionality shapes adaptation to social-ecological change. *World Dev.*, **138**, 105282, doi:10.1016/J.WORLDDEV.2020.105282.

ESRB, 2016: *Too late, too sudden: Transition to a low-carbon economy and systemic risk*. European Systemic Risk Board, Frankfurt am Main, Germany.

Ettlinger, N., 2017: Open innovation and its discontents. *Geoforum*, **80**, 61–71, doi:10.1016/j.geoforum.2017.01.011.

Eurostat, 2018: Glossary: Material deprivation. *Eurostat Stat. Explain.*, https://ec.europa.eu/eurostat/statistics-explained/index.php?title=Glossary:Material_deprivation_rate (Accessed February 21, 2019).

Fagan, M. and C. Huang, 2019: How people worldwide view climate change. Pew Research Center. https://www.pewresearch.org/fact-tank/2019/04/18/a-look-at-how-people-around-the-world-view-climate-change/ (Accessed November 30, 2019).

Fairbrother, M., I. Johansson Sevä, and J. Kulin, 2019: Political trust and the relationship between climate change beliefs and support for fossil fuel taxes: Evidence from a survey of 23 European countries. *Glob. Environ. Change*, **59**, doi:10.1016/j.gloenvcha.2019.102003.

Fanning, A.L. and D.W. O'Neill, 2019: The Wellbeing–Consumption paradox: Happiness, health, income, and carbon emissions in growing versus non-growing economies. *J. Clean. Prod.*, **212**, 810–821, doi:10.1016/j.jclepro.2018.11.223.

Farmer, J.D. et al., 2019: Sensitive intervention points in the post-carbon transition. *Science*, **364(6436)**, 132–134, doi:10.1126/science.aaw7287.

Faruqui, A., S. Sergici, and A. Sharif, 2010: The impact of informational feedback on energy consumption – A survey of the experimental evidence. *Energy*, **35(4)**, 1598–1608, doi:10.1016/j.energy.2009.07.042.

Favier, A., C. De Wolf, K. Scrivener, and G. Habert, 2018: *A sustainable future for the European Cement and Concrete Industry*. ETH Zurich, Zürich, Switzerland.

Fawcett, T., J. Rosenow, and P. Bertoldi, 2019: Energy efficiency obligation schemes: their future in the EU. *Energy Effic.*, **12(1)**, 57–71, doi:10.1007/s12053-018-9657-1.

Feder, G. and D.L. Umali, 1993: The adoption of agricultural innovations: A review. *Technol. Forecast. Soc. Change*, **43(3)**, 215–239, doi.org/10.1016/0040-1625(93)90053-A.

Fedrigo, D. et al., 2010: Sustainable Consumption and Production. *J. Ind. Ecol.*, **14(1)**, 10–12, doi.org/10.1111/j.1530-9290.2009.00214.x.

Fell, M.J., 2017: Energy services : A conceptual review. *Energy Res. Soc. Sci.*, **27(2017)**, 129–140, doi:10.1016/j.erss.2017.02.010.

Fernström Nåtby, K. and H. Rönnerfalk, 2018: Gender Equality and CO_2-Emissions: A Panel Data Study. Lund University, Department of Economics, Sweden, 40 pp. https://lup.lub.lu.se/student-papers/search/publication/8934039 (Accessed July 4, 2019).

Fichter, K. and J. Clausen, 2016: Diffusion Dynamics of Sustainable Innovation – Insights on Diffusion Patterns Based on the Analysis of 100 Sustainable Product and Service Innovations. *J. Innov. Manag.*, **4(2)**, 30–67, doi:10.24840/2183-0606_004.002_0004.

Figge, F., W. Young, and R. Barkemeyer, 2014: Sufficiency or efficiency to achieve lower resource consumption and emissions? I role of the rebound effect. *J. Clean. Prod.*, **69**, 216–224, doi:10.1016/j.jclepro.2014.01.031.

Firnkorn, J. and M. Müller, 2011: What will be the environmental effects of new free-floating car-sharing systems? The case of car2go in Ulm. *Ecol. Econ.*, **70(8)**, 1519–1528, doi:10.1016/j.ecolecon.2011.03.014.

Fischedick, M., J. Roy, A. Abdel-Aziz, A. Acquaye, J. Allwood, J.P. Ceron, Y. Geng, H. Kheshgi, A. Lanza, D. Perczyk, L. Price, E. Santalla, C. Sheinbaum, and K. Tanaka, Kanako, 2014: Industry. In: *Climate Change 2014: Mitigation of Climate Change. Contri-bution of Working Group III to the Fifth Assessment Report of the Intergovernmental Panel on Climate Change* [Edenhofer, O., R. Pichs-Madruga, Y. Sokona, E. Farahani, S. Kadner, K. Seyboth, A. Adler, I. Baum, S. Brunner, P. Eickemeier, B. Kriemann, J. Savolainen, S. Schlömer, C. von Stechow, T. Zwickel and J.C. Minx, (eds.)], Cambridge University Press, Cambridge, UK and New York, NY, USA, pp. 739–810.

5

Fischer-Kowalski, M. et al., 2011: Methodology and indicators of economy-wide material flow accounting: State of the art and reliability across sources. *J. Ind. Ecol.*, **15(6)**, 855–876, doi:10.1111/j.1530-9290.2011.00366.x.

Fischer, C., 2008: Feedback on household electricity consumption: A tool for saving energy? *Energy Effic.*, **1(1)**, 79–104, doi:10.1007/s12053-008-9009-7.

Fisher, D.R., 2019: The broader importance of #FridaysForFuture. *Nat. Clim. Change*, **9(6)**, 430–431, doi:10.1038/s41558-019-0484-y.

Fisher, D.R. and S. Nasrin, 2020: Climate activism and its effects. *Wiley Interdiscip. Rev. Clim. Change*, **12(1)**, doi:10.1002/wcc.683.

Fishman, E., S. Washington, and N. Haworth, 2014: Bike share's impact on car use: Evidence from the United States, Great Britain, and Australia. *Transp. Res. Part D Transp. Environ.*, **31**, 13–20, doi:10.1016/j.trd.2014.05.013.

Fitzgerald, J.B., A.K. Jorgenson, and B. Clark, 2015: Energy consumption and working hours: a longitudinal study of developed and developing nations, 1990–2008. *Environ. Sociol.*, **1(3)**, 213–223, doi:10.1080/23251042.2015.1046584.

Fitzgerald, J.B., J.B. Schor, and A.K. Jorgenson, 2018: Working Hours and Carbon Dioxide Emissions in the United States, 2007–2013. *Soc. Forces*, **96(4)**, 1851–1874, doi:10.1093/SF/SOY014.

Flatø, M., R. Muttarak, and A. Pelser, 2017: Women, Weather, and Woes: The Triangular Dynamics of Female-Headed Households, Economic Vulnerability, and Climate Variability in South Africa. *World Dev.*, **90**, 41–62, doi:10.1016/j.worlddev.2016.08.015.

Fleurbaey, M. and K. Tadenuma, 2014: Universal Social Orderings: An Integrated Theory of Policy Evaluation, Inter-Society Comparisons, and Interpersonal Comparisons. *Rev. Econ. Stud.*, **81(3)**, 1071–1101, doi:10.1093/restud/rdu006.

Flyvbjerg, B., 2020: The law of regression to the tail: How to survive Covid-19, the climate crisis, and other disasters. *Environ. Sci. Policy*, **114(2020)**, 614–618, doi:10.1016/j.envsci.2020.08.013.

Forster, H.A., H. Kunreuther, and E.U. Weber, 2021: Planet or pocketbook? Environmental motives complement financial motives for energy efficiency across the political spectrum in the United States. *Energy Res. Soc. Sci.*, **74**, 101938, doi:10.1016/j.erss.2021.101938.

Forti V., Baldé C.P., Kuehr R., B.G., 2020: *The Global E-waste Monitor 2020: Quantities, flows and the circular economy potential*. United Nations University (UNU)/United Nations Institute for Training and Research (UNITAR) – co-hosted SCYCLE Programme, International Telecommunication Union (ITU) & International Solid Waste Association (ISWA), Bonn/Geneva/Rotterdam, 120 pp. https://www.itu.int/en/ITU-D/Environment/Documents/Toolbox/GEM_2020_def.pdf.

Fortnam, M. et al., 2019: The Gendered Nature of Ecosystem Services. *Ecol. Econ.*, **159**, 312–325, doi:10.1016/j.ecolecon.2018.12.018.

Fox-Glassman, K.T. and E.U. Weber, 2016: What makes risk acceptable? Revisiting the 1978 psychological dimensions of perceptions of technological risks. *J. Math. Psychol.*, **75**, 157–169, doi:10.1016/j.jmp.2016.05.003.

Foxon, T., Z. Makuch, M. Mata, and P. Pearson, 2004: *Governance for Industrial Transformation*. 96–112 pp.

Franceschini, S. and F. Alkemade, 2016: Non-disruptive regime changes – The case of competing energy efficient lighting trajectories. *Environ. Innov. Soc. Transitions*, **21**, 56–68, doi:10.1016/j.eist.2016.04.003.

Franceschini, S., M. Borup, and J. Rosales-Carreón, 2018: Future indoor light and associated energy consumption based on professionals' visions: A practice- and network-oriented analysis. *Technol. Forecast. Soc. Change*, **129**, 1–11, doi:10.1016/j.techfore.2018.01.013.

Frank, L.D., A. Hong, and V.D. Ngo, 2019: Causal evaluation of urban greenway retrofit: A longitudinal study on physical activity and sedentary behavior. *Prev. Med. (Baltim).*, **123**, 109–116, doi:10.1016/j.ypmed.2019.01.011.

Frank, R.H., 1999: *Luxury Fever: Weighing the Cost of Excess*. Princeton University Press, Princeton, NJ, USA.

Frank, R.H., 2020: *Under the Influence: Putting Peer Pressure to Work*. Princeton University Press, Princeton, NJ, USA.

Frank, S., 2017: Reducing greenhouse gas emissions in agriculture without compromising food security? *Environ. Res. Lett.*, **12**, doi:10.1088/1748-9326/aa8c83.

Fraune, C. and M. Knodt, 2018: Sustainable energy transformations in an age of populism, post-truth politics, and local resistance. *Energy Res. Soc. Sci.*, **43**, 1–7, doi:10.1016/j.erss.2018.05.029.

Fremstad, A., 2017: Does Craigslist Reduce Waste? Evidence from California and Florida. *Ecol. Econ.*, **132**, 135–143, doi:10.1016/J.ECOLECON.2016.10.018.

Fremstad, A. and M. Paul, 2019: The Impact of a Carbon Tax on Inequality. *Ecol. Econ.*, **163**, 88–97, doi:10.1016/j.ecolecon.2019.04.016.

Frenken, K., 2017: Political economies and environmental futures for the sharing economy. *Philos. Trans. R. Soc. A Math. Phys. Eng. Sci.*, **375(2095)**, doi:10.1098/rsta.2016.0367.

Friedmann, R. and C. Sheinbaum, 1998: Mexican electric end-use efficiency: Experiences to date. *Annu. Rev. Energy Environ.*, **23(1)**, 225–252, doi:10.1146/annurev.energy.23.1.225.

Fritze, J.C.G., G.A. Blashki, S. Burke, and J. Wiseman, 2008: Hope, despair and transformation: Climate change and the promotion of mental health and wellbeing. *Int. J. Ment. Health Syst.*, **2(1)**, 13, doi:10.1186/1752-4458-2-13.

Frongillo, E.A., H.T. Nguyen, M.D. Smith, and A. Coleman-Jensen, 2019: Food Insecurity Is More Strongly Associated with Poor Subjective Well-Being in More-Developed Countries than in Less-Developed Countries. *J. Nutr.*, **149(2)**, 330–335, doi:10.1093/jn/nxy261.

Frye, I. et al., 2018: *Decent Standard of Living Index: Final Report*. 1–69 pp. http://spii.org.za/wp-content/uploads/2018/11/DSL-Report-SD-v3.doc.pdf (Accessed November 30, 2019).

Fujimori, S., M. Kainuma, T. Masui, T. Hasegawa, and H. Dai, 2014: The effectiveness of energy service demand reduction: A scenario analysis of global climate change mitigation. *Energy Policy*, **75**, doi:10.1016/j.enpol.2014.09.015.

Fulton, L., P. Cazzola, and F. Cuenot, 2009: IEA Mobility Model (MoMo) and its use in the ETP 2008. *Energy Policy*, **37(10)**, 3758–3768, doi:10.1016/j.enpol.2009.07.065.

Fumo, N., 2014: A review on the basics of building energy estimation. *Renew. Sustain. Energy Rev.*, **31**, 53–60, doi:10.1016/j.rser.2013.11.040.

Fuso Nerini, F. et al., 2018: Mapping synergies and trade-offs between energy and the Sustainable Development Goals. *Nat. Energy*, **3(1)**, 10–15, doi:10.1038/s41560-017-0036-5.

Gabriel, C.A. and C. Bond, 2019: Need, Entitlement and Desert: A Distributive Justice Framework for Consumption Degrowth. *Ecol. Econ.*, **156**, 327–336, doi:10.1016/j.ecolecon.2018.10.006.

Gach, E., 2019: Normative Shifts in the Global Conception of Climate Change: The Growth of Climate Justice. *Soc. Sci.*, **8(1)**, 24, doi:10.3390/socsci8010024.

Gadrey, J. and F. Jany-Catrice, 2006: *The new indicators of well-being and development*. Palgrave Macmillan, London, UK, 135 pp.

Galaskiewicz, J., 1985: Professional Networks and the Institutionalization of a Single Mind Set. *Am. Sociol. Rev.*, **50(5)**, 639–658, doi:10.2307/2095379.

Gallagher, K.P. and L. Zarsky, 2007: *The enclave economy: foreign investment and sustainable development in Mexico's Silicon Valley*. [Gottlieb, R. and H.R. Luce, (eds.)]. Massachusetts Institute of Technology, Cambridge, MA, USA, and London, UK, 214 pp.

Gallagher, K.S., 2006: Limits to leapfrogging in energy technologies? Evidence from the Chinese automobile industry. *Energy Policy*, **34(4)**, 383–394, doi:10.1016/j.enpol.2004.06.005.

Gallego-Schmid, A., H.M. Chen, M. Sharmina, and J.M.F. Mendoza, 2020: Links between circular economy and climate change mitigation in the built environment. *J. Clean. Prod.*, **260**, 121115, doi:10.1016/j.jclepro.2020.121115.

Gallie, W.B., 1955: Essentially Contested Concepts. *Proc. Aristot. Soc.*, **56**, 167–198, doi:10.2307/4544562.

5

Ganglmair-Wooliscroft, A. and B. Wooliscroft, 2019: Well-Being and Everyday Ethical Consumption. *J. Happiness Stud.*, **20(1)**, 141–163, doi:10.1007/s10902-017-9944-0.

Garg, A., 2011: Pro-equity Effects of Ancillary Benefits of Climate Change Policies: A Case Study of Human Health Impacts of Outdoor Air Pollution in New Delhi. *World Dev.*, **39(6)**, 1002–1025, doi:10.1016/j.worlddev.2010.01.003.

Garland, A.M. (ed) 2015: *Urban Opportunities: Perspectives on Climate Change, Resilience, Inclusion, and the Informal Economy*. Wilson Center, Washington, DC, USA, 181 pp.

Garnett, T., 2011: Where are the best opportunities for reducing greenhouse gas emissions in the food system (including the food chain)? *Food Policy*, **36**(SUPPL. 1), doi:10.1016/j.foodpol.2010.10.010.

Garvey, A., J.B. Norman, A. Owen, and J. Barrett, 2021: Towards net zero nutrition: The contribution of demand-side change to mitigating UK food emissions. *J. Clean. Prod.*, **290**, 125672, doi:10.1016/J.JCLEPRO.2020.125672.

Gebler, M., A.J.M. Schoot Uiterkamp, and C. Visser, 2014: A global sustainability perspective on 3D printing technologies. *Energy Policy*, **74**(C), doi:10.1016/j.enpol.2014.08.033.

Gebreslassie, M.G., 2020: Solar home systems in Ethiopia: Sustainability challenges and policy directions. *Sustain. Energy Technol. Assessments*, **42**, doi:10.1016/j.seta.2020.100880.

Geels, F. and R. Raven, 2006: Non-linearity and expectations in niche-development trajectories: Ups and downs in Dutch biogas development (1973–2003). *Technol. Anal. Strateg. Manag.*, **18(3–4)**, 375–392, doi:10.1080/09537320600777143.

Geels, F.W., 2020: Changing the Climate Change Discourse. *Joule*, **4(1)**, 18–20, doi:10.1016/J.JOULE.2019.12.011.

Geels, F.W., B.K. Sovacool, T. Schwanen, and S. Sorrell, 2017: Sociotechnical transitions for deep decarbonization. *Science*, **357(6357)**, 1242–1244, doi:10.1126/science.aao3760.

Geels, F.W., T. Schwanen, S. Sorrell, K. Jenkins, and B.K. Sovacool, 2018: Reducing energy demand through low carbon innovation: A sociotechnical transitions perspective and thirteen research debates. *Energy Res. Soc. Sci.*, **40**, 23–35, doi:10.1016/j.erss.2017.11.003.

Geffner, T., 2017: Land Use Zoning in America: The Case for Inclusionary Policy. *Anthós*, **8(1)**, doi:10.15760/anthos.2017.49.

Gehl, J., B.B. Svarre, and J. Risom, 2011: Cities for People. *Plan. News*, **37(4)**, 6–8.

Gelenbe, E. and Y. Caseau, 2015: The impact of information technology on energy consumption and carbon emissions. *Ubiquity*, **1530–2180**(June), 1–15, doi:10.1145/2755977.

Ghesla, C., M. Grieder, and R. Schubert, 2020: Nudging the poor and the rich – A field study on the distributional effects of green electricity defaults. *Energy Econ.*, **86**, doi:10.1016/j.eneco.2019.104616.

Ghisellini, P., M. Ripa, and S. Ulgiati, 2018: Exploring environmental and economic costs and benefits of a circular economy approach to the construction and demolition sector. A literature review. *J. Clean. Prod.*, **178**, 618–643, doi:10.1016/j.jclepro.2017.11.207.

Gholami, R., A.B. Sulaiman, T. Ramayah, and A. Molla, 2013: Senior managers' perception on green information systems (IS) adoption and environmental performance: Results from a field survey. *Inf. Manag.*, **50(7)**, 431–438, doi:10.1016/J.IM.2013.01.004.

Ghosh, A., 2016: *The great derangement*. University of Chicago Press, Chicago, IL, USA, 182 pp.

Ghosh, B., 2019: Transformation beyond experimentation: Sustainability transitions in megacities. University of Sussex, Brighton, UK, 246 pp. http://sro.sussex.ac.uk/id/eprint/82511/ (Accessed December 10, 2019).

Ghosh, B. and J. Schot, 2019: Towards a novel regime change framework: Studying mobility transitions in public transport regimes in an Indian megacity. *Energy Res. Soc. Sci.*, **51**, 82–95, doi:10.1016/J.ERSS.2018.12.001.

Gifford, R., 2011: The Dragons of Inaction: Psychological Barriers That Limit Climate Change Mitigation and Adaptation. *Am. Psychol.*, **66(4)**, 290–302, doi:10.1037/a0023566.

Gimpel, H., V. Graf, and V. Graf-Drasch, 2020: A comprehensive model for individuals' acceptance of smart energy technology – A meta-analysis. *Energy Policy*, **138**(March 2020), 111196, doi:10.1016/j.enpol.2019.111196.

Girod, B. and P. De Haan, 2010: More or Better? A Model for Changes in Household Greenhouse Gas Emissions due to Higher Income. *J. Ind. Ecol.*, **14(1)**, 31–49, doi:10.1111/j.1530-9290.2009.00202.x.

Givoni, M., 2014: Addressing transport policy challenges through policy-packaging. *Transp. Res. Part A Policy Pract.*, **60**, 1–8, doi:10.1016/j.tra.2013.10.012.

Givoni, M., J. Macmillen, D. Banister, and E. Feitelson, 2013: From Policy Measures to Policy Packages. *Transp. Rev.*, **33(1)**, 1–20, doi:10.1080/01441647.2012.744779.

Glemarec, Y., F. Bayat-Renoux, and O. Waissbein, 2016: Removing barriers to women entrepreneurs' engagement in decentralized sustainable energy solutions for the poor. *AIMS Energy*, **4(1)**, 136–172, doi:10.3934/energy.2016.1.136.

Globisch, J., P. Plötz, E. Dütschke, and M. Wietschel, 2018: *Consumer evaluation of public charging infrastructure for electric vehicles*. Fraunhofer-Institut für System- und Innovationsforschung ISI, Karlsruhe, http://nbn-resolving.de/urn:nbn:de:0011-n-497713-14.

Gnann, T. et al., 2018: Fast charging infrastructure for electric vehicles: Today's situation and future needs. *Transp. Res. Part D Transp. Environ.*, **62**, 314–329, doi:10.1016/j.trd.2018.03.004.

Göckeritz, S. et al., 2010: Descriptive mormative belief and conservative behaviour: The moderating roles of personal involvement and injunctive normative belief. *Eur. J. Soc. Psychol.*, **40**, 514–523, doi:10.1002/ejsp.643.

Godfray, H. et al., 2018: Meat consumption, health, and the environment. *Science*, **361(6399)**, doi:10.1126/science.aam5324.

Godfray, H.C.J. and T. Garnett, 2014: Food security and sustainable intensification. *Philos. Trans. R. Soc. London B Biol. Sci.*, **369(1639)**, 20120273, doi:10.1098/rstb.2012.0273.

Godfrey, P. and D. Torres (eds.), 2016: *Systemic Crises of Global Climate Change: Intersection of race, class and gender*. Routledge, Abingdon, UK and New York, NY, USA.

Goldberg, T., 2017: What about the Circularity of Hazardous Materials? *J. Ind. Ecol.*, **21(3)**, 491–493, doi:10.1111/jiec.12585.

Goldemberg, J., 1991: Leapfrogging: A New Energy Policy for Developing Countries. *World Energy Counc.*, 27–30.

Goldemberg, J., T.B. Johansson, A.K.N. Reddy, and R.H. Williams, 1985: Basic needs and much more with one kilowatt per capita (energy). *Ambio*, **14(4–5)**, 190–200, doi:10.2307/4313148.

Goldemberg, J., T.B. Johansson, A.K.N. Reddy, and R.H. Williams, 1988: *Energy for a sustainable world*. Wiley-Eastern, New Delhi, India.

Goldthau, A., 2014: Rethinking the governance of energy infrastructure: Scale, decentralization and polycentrism. *Energy Res. Soc. Sci.*, **1**, 134–140, doi:10.1016/j.erss.2014.02.009.

Golley, J. and X. Meng, 2012: Income inequality and carbon dioxide emissions: The case of Chinese urban households. *Energy Econ.*, **34(6)**, 1864–1872, doi:10.1016/J.ENECO.2012.07.025.

Gölz, S. and U.J.J. Hahnel, 2016: What motivates people to use energy feedback systems? A multiple goal approach to predict long-term usage behaviour in daily life. *Energy Res. Soc. Sci.*, **21**, 155–166, doi:10.1016/j.erss.2016.07.006.

Gonzalez, C.G., 2020: Climate Change, Race, and Migration. *J. Law Polit. Econ.*, **1(1)**, 109–146, doi:10.4337/JHRE.2016.01.02.

Goodman, A., S. Sahlqvist, and D. Ogilvie, 2013: Who uses new walking and cycling infrastructure and how? Longitudinal results from the UK iConnect study. *Prev. Med. (Baltim).*, **57(5)**, 518–524, doi:10.1016/j.ypmed.2013.07.007.

Goodman, A., S. Sahlqvist, and D. Ogilvie, 2014: New walking and cycling routes and increased physical activity: One- and 2-year findings from the UK iConnect study. *Am. J. Public Health*, **104(9)**, 38–46, doi:10.2105/AJPH.2014.302059.

Goodman, J., 2009: From global justice to climate justice? Justice ecologism in an era of global warming. *New Polit. Sci.*, **31(4)**, 499–514, doi:10.1080/07393140903322570.

Goodrich, C.G., P.B. Udas, and H. Larrington-Spencer, 2019: Conceptualizing gendered vulnerability to climate change in the Hindu Kush Himalaya: Contextual conditions and drivers of change. *Environ. Dev.*, **31**, 9–18, doi:10.1016/j.envdev.2018.11.003.

Gore, T., 2015: *Extreme Carbon Inequality: Why the Paris climate deal must put the poorest, lowest emitting and most vulnerable people first*. Oxfam International, London, UK, 14 pp. https://oxfamilibrary.openrepository.com/handle/10546/582545 (Accessed September 12, 2019).

Gore, T., 2020: *Confronting carbon inequality*. Oxfam, https://www.oxfam.org/en/research/confronting-carbon-inequality (Accessed October 2, 2021).

Gori-Maia, A., 2013: Relative Income, Inequality and Subjective Wellbeing: Evidence for Brazil. *Soc. Indic. Res.*, **113(3)**, 1193–1204, doi:10.1007/s11205-012-0135-4.

Gossart, C., 2015: Rebound Effects and ICT: A Review of the Literature. In: *ICT Innovations for Sustainability* [Hilty, L.M. and B. Aebischer, (eds.)], Springer, ETH Zurich, Switzerland, pp. 435–448.

Gössling, S., 2019: Celebrities, air travel, and social norms. *Ann. Tour. Res.*, **79**, 102775, doi:10.1016/j.annals.2019.102775.

Gössling, S. and A. Humpe, 2020: The global scale, distribution and growth of aviation: Implications for climate change. *Glob. Environ. Change*, **65**, 102194, doi:10.1016/j.gloenvcha.2020.102194.

Gota, S., C. Huizenga, K. Peet, N. Medimorec, and S. Bakker, 2019: Decarbonising transport to achieve Paris Agreement targets. *Energy Effic.*, **12(2)**, 363–386, doi:10.1007/s12053-018-9671-3.

Gough, I., 2015: Climate change and sustainable welfare: the centrality of human needs. *Cambridge J. Econ.*, **39**, 1191–1214, doi:10.1093/cje/bev039.

Gough, I., 2017: *Heat, Greed and Human Need: Climate Change, Capitalism and Sustainable Wellbeing*. Elgar, London, UK, 283 pp.

Gould, C.F. and J. Urpelainen, 2018: LPG as a clean cooking fuel: Adoption, use, and impact in rural India. *Energy Policy*, **122**, 395–408, doi:10.1016/j.enpol.2018.07.042.

Gould, C.F. et al., 2018: Government policy, clean fuel access, and persistent fuel stacking in Ecuador. *Energy Sustain. Dev.*, **46**, 111–122, doi:10.1016/j.esd.2018.05.009.

Graça, J., C.A. Godinho, and M. Truninger, 2019: Reducing meat consumption and following plant-based diets: Current evidence and future directions to inform integrated transitions. *Trends Food Sci. Technol.*, **91**, 380–390, doi:10.1016/j.tifs.2019.07.046.

Grady-Benson, J. and B. Sarathy, 2016: Fossil fuel divestment in US higher education: student-led organising for climate justice. *Local Environ.*, **21(6)**, 661–681, doi:10.1080/13549839.2015.1009825.

Gramkow, C. and A. Anger-Kraavi, 2019: Developing Green: A Case for the Brazilian Manufacturing Industry. *Sustainability*, **11(23)**, 6783, doi:10.3390/su11236783.

Grandclément, C., A. Karvonen, and S. Guy, 2015: Negotiating comfort in low energy housing: The politics of intermediation. *Energy Policy*, **84**, 213–222, doi:10.1016/j.enpol.2014.11.034.

Green, D. and G. Raygorodetsky, 2010: Indigenous knowledge of a changing climate. *Clim. Change*, **100(2)**, 239–242, doi:10.1007/s10584-010-9804-y.

Greenblatt, J.B. and S. Saxena, 2015: Autonomous taxis could greatly reduce greenhouse-gas emissions of US light-duty vehicles. *Nat. Clim. Change*, **5(9)**, 860–863, doi:10.1038/nclimate2685.

Grilli, G. and J. Curtis, 2021: Encouraging pro-environmental behaviours: A review of methods and approaches. *Renew. Sustain. Energy Rev.*, **135**, 110039, doi:10.1016/j.rser.2020.110039.

Grinblatt, M., M. Keloharju, and S. Ikaheimo, 2008: Social Influence and Consumption: Evidence from the Automobile Purchases of Neighbors. *Rev. Econ. Stat.*, **90(4)**, 735–753, doi:10.2139/ssrn.995855.

Grinde, B., R.B. Nes, I.F. MacDonald, and D.S. Wilson, 2018: Quality of Life in Intentional Communities. *Soc. Indic. Res.*, **137(2)**, 625–640, doi:10.1007/s11205-017-1615-3.

Grubb, M. et al., 2020: Consumption-oriented policy instruments for fostering greenhouse gas mitigation. *Clim. Policy*, **20(sup1)**, S58–S73, doi:10.1080/14693062.2020.1730151.

Grubler, A., 1991: Energy in the 21st century: From resource to environmental and lifestyle constraints. *Entropie Rev. Sci. Tech. Thermodyn.*, **164**, 29–33.

Grubler, A., 1996: Time for a change: on the patterns of diffusion of innovation. *Daedalus*, **125(3)**, 19–42.

Grubler, A. et al., 2012a: Policies for the Energy Technology Innovation System (ETIS). In: *Global Energy Assessment – Toward a Sustainable Future*, Cambridge University Press, Cambridge, UK and New York, NY, USA and the International Institute for Applied Systems Analysis, Laxenburg, Austria, pp. 1665–1744.

Grubler, A. et al., 2012b: Energy Primer. In: *Global Energy Assessment – Toward a Sustainable Future*, Cambridge University Press, Cambridge, UK and New York, NY, USA and the International Institute for Applied Systems Analysis, Laxenburg, Austria, pp. 99–150.

Grubler, A. et al., 2018: A low energy demand scenario for meeting the 1.5°C target and sustainable development goals without negative emission technologies. *Nat. Energy*, **3(6)**, 515–527, doi:10.1038/s41560-018-0172-6.

Grubler, A., N. Nakićenović, and D.G. Victor, 1999: Dynamics of energy technologies and global change. *Energy Policy*, **27(5)**, 247–280, doi:10.1016/S0301-4215(98)00067-6.

Grunewald, N., S. Klasen, I. Martinez-Zarzoso, and C. Muris, 2011: *Income Inequality and Carbon Emissions*.

Grunewald, N. et al., 2017: The Trade-off Between Income Inequality and Carbon Dioxide Emissions. *Ecol. Econ.*, **142**, 249–256, doi:10.1016/j.ecolecon.2017.06.034.

Guevara, Z., T. Sousa, and T. Domingos, 2016: Insights on Energy Transitions in Mexico from the Analysis of Useful Exergy 1971–2009. *Energies 2016, Vol. 9, Page 488*, **9(7)**, 488, doi:10.3390/EN9070488.

Gulyani, S., D. Talukdar, and E.M. Bassett, 2018: A sharing economy? Unpacking demand and living conditions in the urban housing market in Kenya. *World Dev.*, **109**, 57–72, doi:10.1016/j.worlddev.2018.04.007.

Gumbert, T., 2019: Anti-Democratic Tenets? Behavioural-Economic Imaginaries of a Future Food System. *Polit. Gov.*, **7(4)**, doi:10.17645/pag.v7i4.2216.

Gunders, D. et al., 2017: *Wasted: How America is Losing up to 40% of its Food from Farm to Fork to Landfill*. Natural Resources Defense Council, New York, NY, USA.

Gür, N., 2020: Does social trust promote behaviour aimed at mitigating climate change? *Econ. Aff.*, **40(1)**, 36–49, doi:10.1111/ecaf.12384.

Guruswamy, L., 2010: Energy Justice and Sustainable Development. *Colo. J. Int. Environ. Law Policy*, **231**.

Guruswamy, L. (ed.), 2016: *International energy and poverty: The emerging contours*. Routledge, Abingdon, UK, 329 pp.

Guruswamy, L., 2020: Global Energy Poverty: the Relevance of Faith and Reason. *Belmont Law Rev.*, **7(2)**, 199–244.

Gutberlet, J., 2008: Organized and informal recycling: social movements contributing to sustainability. In: *Waste Management and the Environment IV* [Zamorano, M., C.A. Brebbia, A.G. Kungolos, and V. Popov, (eds.)], WIT Press, Southampton, UK, pp. 223–232.

Gutowski, T.G., S. Sahni, A. Boustani, and S.C. Graves, 2011: Remanufacturing and Energy Savings. *Environ. Sci. Technol.*, **45(10)**, 4540–4547, doi:10.1021/es102598b.

Gutowski, T.G., J.M. Allwood, C. Herrmann, and S. Sahni, 2013: A Global Assessment of Manufacturing: Economic Development, Energy Use, Carbon Emissions, and the Potential for Energy Efficiency and Materials Recycling. *Annu. Rev. Environ. Resour.*, **38(1)**, 81–106, doi:10.1146/annurev-environ-041112-110510.

5

Haas, W., F. Krausmann, D. Wiedenhofer, and M. Heinz, 2015: How Circular is the Global Economy?: An Assessment of Material Flows, Waste Production, and Recycling in the European Union and the World in 2005. *J. Ind. Ecol.*, **19(5)**, 765–777, doi:10.1111/jiec.12244.

Haas, W., F. Krausmann, D. Wiedenhofer, C. Lauk, and A. Mayer, 2020: Spaceship earth's odyssey to a circular economy – a century long perspective. *Resour. Conserv. Recycl.*, **163**, 105076, doi.org/10.1016/j.resconrec.2020.105076.

Haberl, H., K.-H. Erb, and F. Krausmann, 2014: Human Appropriation of Net Primary Production: Patterns, Trends, and Planetary Boundaries. *Annu. Rev. Environ. Resour.*, **39**(October 2014), 363–391, doi:10.1146/ANNUREV-ENVIRON-121912-094620.

Haberl, H., D. Wiedenhofer, K.H. Erb, C. Görg, and F. Krausmann, 2017: The Material Stock–Flow–Service Nexus: A New Approach for Tackling the Decoupling Conundrum. *Sustainability*, **9(7)**, 1049, doi:10.3390/su9071049.

Haberl, H. et al., 2019: Contributions of sociometabolic research to sustainability science. *Nat. Sustain.*, **2(3)**, 173–184, doi:10.1038/s41893-019-0225-2.

Haberl, H. et al., 2021: Stocks, flows, services and practices: Nexus approaches to sustainable social metabolism. *Ecol. Econ.*, **182**(April 2021), 106949, doi:10.1016/J.ECOLECON.2021.106949.

Habtezion, S., 2013: *Gender and Climate Change Asia and the Pacific*. United Nations Development Programme, New York, NY, USA, 6 pp. https://www.undp.org/publications/gender-and-climate-change-asia-and-pacific (Accessed November 26, 2021).

Hafner, R., D. Elmes, D. Read, and M.P. White, 2019: Exploring the role of normative, financial and environmental information in promoting uptake of energy efficient technologies. *J. Environ. Psychol.*, **63**, 26–35, doi:10.1016/j.jenvp.2019.03.004.

Hagen, B., 2016: The role of planning in minimizing the negative impacts of global climate change. *Urban Plan.*, **1(3)**, 13–24, doi:10.17645/up.v1i3.671.

Hahnel, U.J.J. et al., 2015: The power of putting a label on it: green labels weigh heavier than contradicting product information for consumers' purchase decisions and post-purchase behavior. *Front. Psychol.*, **6**, 1392, doi:10.3389/fpsyg.2015.01392.

Haluza-DeLay, R., 2014: Religion and climate change: varieties in viewpoints and practices. *Wiley Interdiscip. Rev. Clim. Change*, **5(2)**, 261–279, doi:10.1002/wcc.268.

Hammar, H. and S.C. Jagers, 2006: Can trust in politicians explain individuals' support for climate policy? The case of CO_2 tax. *Clim. Policy*, **5(6)**, 613–625, doi:10.1080/14693062.2006.9685582.

Hammar, H. and S.C. Jagers, 2007: What is a fair CO_2 tax increase? On fair emission reductions in the transport sector. *Ecol. Econ.*, **61(2–3)**, 377–387, doi:10.1016/j.ecolecon.2006.03.004.

Han, H. and S.W. Ahn, 2020: Youth Mobilization to Stop Global Climate Change: Narratives and Impact. *Sustainability.* **12(10)**, 4127, doi:10.3390/SU12104127.

Handgraaf, M.J.J., M.A. Van Lidth de Jeude, and K.C. Appelt, 2013: Public praise vs. private pay: Effects of rewards on energy conservation in the workplace. *Ecol. Econ.*, **86**, 86–92, doi:10.1016/j.ecolecon.2012.11.008.

Hans, A., S. Hazra, S. Das, and A. Patel, 2019: Encountering Gendered Spaces in Climate Change Policy in India: Migration and Adaptation. *J. Migr. Aff.*, **II(1)**, 1–24, doi:10.36931/jma.2019.2.1.1-24.

Hao, Y., H. Chen, and Q. Zhang, 2016: Will income inequality affect environmental quality? Analysis based on China's provincial panel data. *Ecol. Indic.*, **67**, 533–542, doi:10.1016/j.ecolind.2016.03.025.

Haque, K.N.H., F.A. Chowdhury, and K.R. Khatun, 2015: Participatory environmental governance and climate change adaptation: Mainstreaming of tidal river management in South-West Bangladesh. In: *Land and Disaster Management Strategies in Asia* [Ha, H. (ed.)], Springer, India, pp. 189–208.

Harding, M. and A. Hsiaw, 2014: Goal setting and energy conservation. *J. Econ. Behav. Organ.*, **107**, 209–227, doi:10.1016/j.jebo.2014.04.012.

Harguess, J.M., N.C. Crespo, and M.Y. Hong, 2020: Strategies to reduce meat consumption: A systematic literature review of experimental studies. *Appetite*, **144**, 104478, doi:10.1016/j.appet.2019.104478.

Harring, N. and S.C. Jagers, 2013: Should We Trust in Values? Explaining Public Support for Pro-Environmental Taxes. *Sustainability*, **5(2013)**, 210–227, doi:10.3390/su5010210.

Harriss, R. and B. Shui, 2010: Consumption, not CO_2 emissions: Reframing perspectives on climate change and sustainability. *Environment*, **52(6)**, 8–15, doi:10.1080/00139157.2010.522461.

Hartmann, C. and M. Siegrist, 2017: Consumer perception and behaviour regarding sustainable protein consumption: A systematic review. *Trends Food Sci. Technol.*, **61**, 11–25, doi:10.1016/j.tifs.2016.12.006.

Haug, C. et al., 2010: Navigating the dilemmas of climate policy in Europe: Evidence from policy evaluation studies. *Clim. Change*, **101(3)**, 427–445, doi:10.1007/s10584-009-9682-3.

Haugneland, P. and H.H. Kvisle, 2015: Norwegian electric car user experience. *Int. J. Automot. Technol. Manag.*, **15(2)**, 194–221, doi:10.1504/IJATM.2015.068548.

Hausknost, D. et al., 2018: Investigating patterns of local climate governance: How low-carbon municipalities and intentional communities intervene in social practices. *Environ. Policy Gov.*, **28(6)**, 371–382, doi:10.1002/eet.1804.

Havas, L., J. Ballweg, C. Penna, and D. Race, 2015: Power to change: Analysis of household participation in a renewable energy and energy efficiency programme in Central Australia. *Energy Policy*, **87**(December 2015), 325–333, doi:10.1016/j.enpol.2015.09.017.

Hayward, B. and J. Roy, 2019: Sustainable Living: Bridging the North-South Divide in Lifestyles and Consumption Debates. *Annu. Rev. Environ. Resour.*, **44(6)**, 1–9, doi:10.1146/annurev-environ-101718-033119.

Healy, N. and J. Barry, 2017: Politicizing energy justice and energy system transitions: Fossil fuel divestment and a "just transition". *Energy Policy*, **108**, 451–459, doi:10.1016/j.enpol.2017.06.014.

Heffron, R.J. and D. McCauley, 2018: What is the 'Just Transition'? *Geoforum*, **88**, 74–77, doi:10.1016/j.geoforum.2017.11.016.

Heinzle, S.L. and R. Wüstenhagen, 2012: Dynamic Adjustment of Eco-labeling Schemes and Consumer Choice – the Revision of the EU Energy Label as a Missed Opportunity? *Bus. Strateg. Environ.*, **21(1)**, 60–70, doi:10.1002/bse.722.

Helferty, A. and A. Clarke, 2009: Student-led campus climate change initiatives in Canada. *Int. J. Sustain. High. Educ.*, **10(3)**, 287–300, doi:10.1108/14676370910972594.

Henao, A. and W.E. Marshall, 2019: The impact of ride hailing on parking (and vice versa). *J. Transp. Land Use*, **12(1)**, doi:10.5198/jtlu.2019.1392.

Henry, M.L., P.J. Ferraro, and A. Kontoleon, 2019: The behavioural effect of electronic home energy reports: Evidence from a randomised field trial in the United States. *Energy Policy*, **132**, 1256–1261, doi:10.1016/j.enpol.2019.06.039.

Henryson, J., T. Håkansson, and J. Pyrko, 2000: Energy efficiency in buildings through information – Swedish perspective. *Energy Policy*, **28(3)**, 169–180, doi:10.1016/S0301-4215(00)00004-5.

Hepburn, C. et al., 2020: Will COVID-19 fiscal recovery packages accelerate or retard progress on climate change? *Oxford Rev. Econ. Policy*, **36(Supplement_1)**, S359–S381, doi:10.1093/oxrep/graa015.

Herendeen, R. and J. Tanaka, 1976: Energy cost of living. *Energy*, **1(2)**, 165–178, doi:10.1016/0360-5442(76)90015-3.

Herrmann, S., F. Schulte, and S. Voß, 2014: Increasing acceptance of free-floating car sharing systems using smart relocation strategies: A survey based study of car2go hamburg. *Lecture Notes in Computer Science*, Vol. 8760, 151–162.

Hershfield, H.E., H.M. Bang, and E.U. Weber, 2014: National Differences in Environmental Concern and Performance Are Predicted by Country Age. *Psychol. Sci.*, **25(1)**, 152–160, doi:10.1177/0956797613501522.

Hertwich, E.G. and G.P. Peters, 2009: Carbon footprint of nations: A global, trade-linked analysis. *Environ. Sci. Technol.*, **43(16)**, 6414–6420, doi:10.1021/es803496a.

Hertwich, E.G. et al., 2019: Material efficiency strategies to reducing greenhouse gas emissions associated with buildings, vehicles, and electronics – a review. *Environ. Res. Lett.*, **14(4)**, 043004, doi:10.1088/1748-9326/ab0fe3.

Hertwich, E.G. et al., 2020: *Resource Efficiency and Climate Change: Material Efficiency Strategies for a Low-Carbon Future*. United Nations Environment Programme, Nairobi, Kenya.

Hess, D.J., 2019a: Coalitions, framing, and the politics of energy transitions: Local democracy and community choice in California. *Energy Res. Soc. Sci.*, **50**, 38–50, doi:10.1016/j.erss.2018.11.013.

Hess, D.J., 2019b: Cooler coalitions for a warmer planet: A review of political strategies for accelerating energy transitions. *Energy Res. Soc. Sci.*, **57**, 101246, doi:10.1016/j.erss.2019.101246.

Heun, M.K. and P.E. Brockway, 2019: Meeting 2030 primary energy and economic growth goals: Mission impossible? *Appl. Energy*, **251**, 112697, doi:10.1016/j.apenergy.2019.01.255.

Hickel, J. and G. Kallis, 2019: Is Green Growth Possible? *New Polit. Econ.*, **25(4)**, 469–486, doi:10.1080/13563467.2019.1598964.

Hickel, J. et al., 2021: Urgent need for post-growth climate mitigation scenarios. *Nat. Energy*, **6(8)**, 766–768, doi:10.1038/s41560-021-00884-9.

Hicks, J. and N. Ison, 2018: An exploration of the boundaries of 'community' in community renewable energy projects: Navigating between motivations and context.' *Energy Policy*, **113**, 523–534, doi:10.1016/j.enpol.2017.10.031.

Hidalgo, D. and C. Huizenga, 2013: Implementation of sustainable urban transport in Latin America. *Res. Transp. Econ.*, **40(1)**, 66–77, doi:10.1016/j.retrec.2012.06.034.

Hillebrand, H. et al., 2018: Biodiversity change is uncoupled from species richness trends: Consequences for conservation and monitoring. *J. Appl. Ecol.*, **55(1)**, 169–184, doi:10.1111/1365-2664.12959.

Hilson, C., 2019: Climate Populism, Courts, and Science. *J. Environ. Law*, **31(3)**, 395–398, doi:10.1093/jel/eqz021.

Himmelweit, S., 2002: Making visible the hidden economy: The case for gender-impact analysis of economic policy. *Fem. Econ.*, **8(1)**, 49–70, doi:10.1080/13545700110104864.

Hintemann, R. and S. Hinterholzer, 2019: Energy consumption of data centers worldwide: How will the Internet become green? In: *Proceedings of the 6th International Conference on ICT for Sustainability*, Lappeenranta, Finland, 8 pp. http://ceur-ws.org/Vol-2382/ICT4S2019_paper_16.pdf (Accessed December 4, 2021).

Hiteva, R. and J. Watson, 2019: Governance of interactions between infrastructure sectors: The making of smart grids in the UK. *Environ. Innov. Soc. Transitions*, **32**, 140–152, doi:10.1016/j.eist.2019.02.006.

Hobbs, J.E., 2020: Food supply chains during the COVID-19 pandemic. *Can. J. Agric. Econ. Can. d'agroeconomie*, **68(2)**, 171–176, doi:10.1111/cjag.12237.

Hobson, K., 2019: 'Small stories of closing loops': social circularity and the everyday circular economy. *Clim. Change*, doi:10.1007/s10584-019-02480-z.

Hockerts, K. and R. Wüstenhagen, 2010: Greening Goliaths versus emerging Davids: Theorizing about the role of incumbents and new entrants in sustainable entrepreneurship. *J. Bus. Ventur.*, **25(5)**, 481–492, doi:10.1016/j.jbusvent.2009.07.005.

Hoegh-Guldberg, O. et al., 2019: *The Ocean as a Solution to Climate Change: Five Opportunities for Action*. World Resources Institute., Washington, DC, USA, https://oceanpanel.org/sites/default/files/2019-10/HLP_Report_Ocean_Solution_Climate_Change_final.pdf (Accessed October 29, 2021).

Hofstad, H. and T. Vedeld, 2020: *Urban climate governance and co-creation – In Cape Town, Copenhagen, Gothenburg and Oslo*. Norwegian Institute for Urban and Regional Research, Oslo. Norway, 115 pp. https://oda.oslomet.no/oda-xmlui/handle/20.500.12199/3126 (Accessed June 12, 2020).

Hollingsworth, J., B. Copeland, and J.X. Johnson, 2019: Are e-scooters polluters? The environmental impacts of shared dockless electric scooters. *Environ. Res. Lett.*, **14(8)**, doi:10.1088/1748-9326/ab2da8.

Hong, J.H., B.C. Kim, and K.S. Park, 2019: Optimal risk management for the sharing economy with stranger danger and service quality. *Eur. J. Oper. Res.*, **279(3)**, 1024–1035, doi:10.1016/j.ejor.2019.06.020.

Hook, A., V. Court, B.K. Sovacool, and S. Sorrell, 2020: A systematic review of the energy and climate impacts of teleworking. *Environ. Res. Lett.*, **15(9)**, doi:10.1088/1748-9326/ab8a84.

Hoolohan, C., C. McLachlan, and S. Mander, 2018: Food related routines and energy policy: A focus group study examining potential for change in the United Kingdom. *Energy Res. Soc. Sci.*, **39**, 93–102, doi:10.1016/j.erss.2017.10.050.

Hoor, M., 2020: The bicycle as a symbol of lifestyle, status and distinction. A cultural studies analysis of urban cycling (sub)cultures in Berlin. *Appl. Mobilities*, 1–18, doi:10.1080/23800127.2020.1847396.

Hopkinson, P., H.M. Chen, K. Zhou, Y. Wang, and D. Lam, 2018: Recovery and reuse of structural products from end-of-life buildings. *Proc. Inst. Civ. Eng. Eng. Sustain.*, **172(3)**, 119–128, doi:10.1680/jensu.18.00007.

Hordijk, M.A., 2000: Of Dreams and Deeds: the role of local initiatives for community-based environmental management in Lima, Peru. https://dare.uva.nl/search?identifier=6f7a4580-e9b6-454d-9d7e-c8225ee89234 (Accessed December 9, 2019).

Horen Greenford, D., T. Crownshaw, C. Lesk, K. Stadler, and H.D. Matthews, 2020: Shifting economic activity to services has limited potential to reduce global environmental impacts due to the household consumption of labour. *Environ. Res. Lett.*, **15(6)**.

Hornsey, M.J., 2020: Why Facts Are Not Enough: Understanding and Managing the Motivated Rejection of Science. *Curr. Dir. Psychol. Sci.*, **29(6)**, 583–591, doi:10.1177/0963721420969364.

Hossain, M., 2016: Grassroots innovation: A systematic review of two decades of research. *J. Clean. Prod.*, **137**, 973–981, doi:10.1016/j.jclepro.2016.07.140.

Houde, S., A. Todd, A. Sudarshan, J.A. Flora, and K.C. Armel, 2013: Real-time Feedback and Electricity Consumption: A Field Experiment Assessing the Potential for Savings and Persistence. *Energy J.*, **34(1)**, 87–102, doi:10.5547/01956574.34.1.4.

Howlett, M. and J. Rayner, 2013: Patching vs packaging in policy formulation: Assessing policy portfolio design. *Polit. Gov.*, **1(2)**, 170–182, doi:10.12924/pag2013.01020170.

Huang, H. et al., 2019: Emissions trading systems and social equity: A CGE assessment for China. *Appl. Energy*, **235**, 1254–1265, doi:10.1016/j.apenergy.2018.11.056.

Huang, P. et al., 2020: A review of data centers as prosumers in district energy systems: Renewable energy integration and waste heat reuse for district heating. *Appl. Energy*, **258**, 114109, doi:10.1016/J.APENERGY.2019.114109.

Huang, R. et al., 2016: Energy and emissions saving potential of additive manufacturing: the case of lightweight aircraft components. *J. Clean. Prod.*, **135**, 1559–1570, doi:10.1016/j.jclepro.2015.04.109.

Huang, R. et al., 2017: Environmental and Economic Implications of Distributed Additive Manufacturing: The Case of Injection Mold Tooling. *J. Ind. Ecol.*, **21(S1)**, S130–S143, doi:10.1111/jiec.12641.

Hubacek, K., G. Baiocchi, K. Feng, L. Sun, and J. Xue, 2017: Global carbon inequality. *Energy, Ecol. Environ.*, **2(6)**, 361–369, doi:10.1007/s40974-017-0072-9.

Huber, J., W.K. Viscusi, and J. Bell, 2020: Dynamic relationships between social norms and pro-environmental behavior: evidence from household recycling. *Behav. Public Policy*, **4(1)**, 1–25, doi:10.1017/bpp.2017.13.

Hübler, M., 2017: The inequality-emissions nexus in the context of trade and development: A quantile regression approach. *Ecol. Econ.*, **134**, 174–185, doi:10.1016/j.ecolecon.2016.12.015.

Hugo, J. and C. du Plessis, 2019: A quantitative analysis of interstitial spaces to improve climate change resilience in Southern African cities. *Clim. Dev.*, **12(7)**, 1–9, doi:10.1080/17565529.2019.1664379.

Hulme, M., 2015: Varieties of religious engagement with climate change. In: *Routledge Handbook of Religion and Ecology* [Jenkins, W., M.E. Tucker, and J. Grim, (eds.)], Routledge, Abingdon, UK, pp. 239.

Hummel, D. and A. Maedche, 2019: How effective is nudging? A quantitative review on the effect sizes and limits of empirical nudging studies. *J. Behav. Exp. Econ.* **80**, 47–58, doi:10.1016/j.socec.2019.03.005.

Hunsberger, C. et al., 2017: Climate change mitigation, land grabbing and conflict: towards a landscape-based and collaborative action research agenda. *Can. J. Dev. Stud.*, **38(3)**, 305–324, doi:10.1080/02255189.2016.1250617.

Huyer, S. and S. Partey, 2020: Weathering the storm or storming the norms? Moving gender equality forward in climate-resilient agriculture: Introduction to the Special Issue on Gender Equality in Climate-Smart Agriculture: Approaches and Opportunities. *Clim. Change*, **158(1)**, 1–12, doi:10.1007/s10584-019-02612-5.

Hynes, M., 2014: Telework Isn't Working: A Policy Review. *Econ. Soc. Rev. (Irel.)*, **45(4)**, 579–602.

Hynes, M., 2016: Developing (tele)work? A multi-level sociotechnical perspective of telework in Ireland. *Res. Transp. Econ.*, **57**, 21–31, doi:10.1016/j.retrec.2016.06.008.

IEA, 2016: *Energy Technology Perspectives 2016*. OECD, Paris, France, 418 pp.

IEA, 2017a: *Digitalization & Energy*. OECD, Paris, France, 185 pp.

IEA, 2017b: *Energy Technology Perspectives 2017: Catalysing Energy Technology Transformations*. OECD, Paris, France, 443 pp.

IEA, 2017c: *Energy Access Outlook 2017: From Poverty to Prosperity*. OECD, Paris, France.

IEA, 2018: *The Future of Cooling: Opportunities for energy-efficient air conditioning*. OECD, Paris, France, 92 pp.

IEA, 2019a: *World Energy Outlook 2019*. OECD, Paris, France.

IEA, 2019b: *Material efficiency in clean energy transitions*. OECD, Paris, France, 162 pp.

IEA, 2019c: *SDG7: Data and Projections – Access to affordable, reliable, sustainable and modern energy for all*. OECD, Paris, France, https://www.iea.org/reports/sdg7-data-and-projections (Accessed December 6, 2019).

IEA, 2020a: *World Energy Outlook 2020*. OECD, Paris, France.

IEA, 2020b: *World Energy Balances: Overview*. OECD, Paris, France, https://www.iea.org/reports/world-energy-balances-overview (Accessed July 12, 2021).

IEA, 2021: *Net Zero by 2050: A Roadmap for the Global Energy Sector*. OECD, Paris, France, 224 pp.

ILO, 2020: *Policy Brief The COVID-19 response: Getting gender equality right for a better future for women at work*. International Labour Organization, Geneva, Switzerland.

IMO, 2020: *Fourth IMO GHG Study 2020*. International Maritime Organization, London, UK, 524 pp. https://www.imo.org/en/OurWork/Environment/Pages/Fourth-IMO-Greenhouse-Gas-Study-2020.aspx (Accessed June 21, 2021).

Inderberg, T.H., S.H. Eriksen, K.L. O'Brien, and L. Sygna (eds.) 2015: *Climate change adaptation and development: transforming paradigms and practices*. Routledge, Abingdon, UK and New York, NY, USA, 296 pp.

International Transport Forum, 2016: *Shared mobility: innovation for liveable cities*. International Transport Forum, Paris, France, 56 pp.

IPCC, 2007: *Climate Change 2007: Mitigation. Contribution of Working Group III to the Fourth Assessment Report of the Intergovernmental Panel on Climate Change*. [Metz, B., O.R. Davidson, P.R. Bosch, R. Dave, and L.A. Meyer, (eds.)]. Cambridge University Press, Cambridge, UK and New York, NY, USA, 861 pp.

IPCC, 2014a: Summary for Policymakers. In: *Climate Change 2014: Mitigation of Climate Change. Contribution of Working Group III to the Fifth Assessment Report of the Intergovernmental Panel on Climate Change* [Edenhofer, O., R. Pichs-Madruga, Y. Sokona, E. Farahani, S. Kadner, K. Seyboth, A. Adler, I. Baum, S. Brunner, P. Eickemeier, B. Kriemann, J. Savolainen, S. Schlömer, C. von Stechow, T. Zwickel and J.C. Minx (eds.)], Cambridge University Press, Cambridge, UK and New York, NY, USA, pp. 1–30.

IPCC, 2014b: *Climate Change 2014: Mitigation of Climate Change: Working Group III contribution to the Fifth Assessment Report of the Intergovernmental Panel on Climate Change*. [Edenhofer, O., R. Pichs-Madruga, Y. Sokona, E. Farahani, S. Kadner, K. Seyboth, A. Adler, I. Baum, S. Brunner, P. Eickemeier, B. Kriemann, J. Savolainen, S. Schlömer, C. von Stechow, T. Zwickel and J.C. Minx (eds.)]. Cambridge University Press, Cambridge, UK and New York, NY, USA.

IPCC, 2018: *Global Warming of 1.5°C. An IPCC Special Report on the impacts of global warming of 1.5°C above pre-industrial levels and related global greenhouse gas emission pathways, in the context of strengthening the global response to the threat of climate change, sustainable development, and efforts to eradicate poverty*. [Masson-Delmotte, V., P. Zhai, H.-O. Pörtner, D. Roberts, J. Skea, P.R. Shukla, A. Pirani, W. Moufouma-Okia, C. Péan, R. Pidcock, S. Connors, J.B.R. Matthews, Y. Chen, X. Zhou, M.I. Gomis, E. Lonnoy, T. Maycock, M. Tignor, and T. Waterfield (eds.)]. Cambridge University Press, Cambridge, UK and New York, NY, USA pp.

IPCC, 2021: Summary for Policymakers. In: *Climate Change 2021: The Physical Science Basis. Contribution of Working Group I to the Sixth Assessment Report of the Intergovernmental Panel on Climate Change* [Masson-Delmotte, V., P. Zhai, A. Pirani, S.L. Connors, C. Péan, S. Berger, N. Caud, Y. Chen, L. Goldfarb, M.I. Gomis, M. Huang, K. Leitzell, E. Lonnoy, J.B.R. Matthews, T.K. Maycock, T. Waterfield, O. Yelekçi, R. Yu, and B. Zhou (eds.)]. In press.

Isenhour, C., 2019: A consuming globalism: On power and the post-Paris Agreement politics of climate and consumption. In: *Power and Politics in Sustainable Consumption Research and Practice* [Isenhour, C., M Martiskainen, and L Middlemiss (eds.)], Routledge, Abingdon, UK, pp. 21–44.

Isenhour, C. and M. Ardenfors, 2009: Gender and sustainable consumption: Policy implications. *Int. J. Innov. Sustain. Dev.*, **4(2–3)**, 135–149, doi:10.1504/IJISD.2009.028068.

Israel-Akinbo, S., J. Snowball, and G. Fraser, 2018: The energy transition patterns of low-income households in South Africa: An evaluation of energy programme and policy. *J. Energy South. Africa*, **29(3)**, 75–85, doi:10.17159/2413-3051/2017/v29i3a3310.

ISSC, IDS, and UNESCO, 2016: *World Social Science Report 2016, Challenging Inequalities; Pathways to a Just World*. UNESCO Publishing, Paris, France, 359 pp.

ITF, 2017a: *Transition to Shared Mobility: How large cities can deliver inclusive transport services*. International Transport Forum, Paris, France.

ITF, 2017b: *Shared Mobility Simulations for Helsinki*. International Transport Forum, Paris, France, 95 pp.

ITF, 2017c: *Shared Mobility Simulations for Auckland*. International Transport Forum, Paris, France, 91 pp.

ITF, 2018: *Shared Mobility Simulations for Dublin. Case-specific policy analysis*. International Transport Forum, Paris, France, 97 pp.

ITF, 2019: *ITF Transport Outlook 2019*. OECD Publishing, Paris, France, 200 pp.

ITF, 2020a: *Good to Go? Assessing the Environmental Performance of New Mobility*. International Transport Forum, Paris, France, https://www.itf-oecd.org/good-go-assessing-environmental-performance-new-mobility (Accessed June 21, 2021).

ITF, 2020b: *Shared Mobility Simulations for Lyon*. International Transport Forum, Paris, France, 91 pp.

ITF, 2021: *Reversing Car Dependency: Summary and Conclusions*. International Transport Forum, Paris, France, 43 pp. www.itf-oecd.org/avoiding-car-dependency (Accessed August 25, 2021).

Ivanova, D. and R. Wood, 2020: The unequal distribution of household carbon footprints in Europe and its link to sustainability. *Glob. Sustain.*, **3**, doi:10.1017/SUS.2020.12.

Ivanova, D. et al., 2016: Environmental Impact Assessment of Household Consumption. *J. Ind. Ecol.*, **20(3)**, 526–536, doi:10.1111/jiec.12371.

Ivanova, D. et al., 2018: Carbon mitigation in domains of high consumer lock-in. *Glob. Environ. Change*, **52**, 117–130, doi:10.1016/j.gloenvcha.2018.06.006.

Ivanova, D. et al., 2020: Quantifying the potential for climate change mitigation of consumption options. *Environ. Res. Lett.*, **15(9)**, 093001, doi:10.1088/1748-9326/ab8589.

Ives, C.D. and J. Kidwell, 2019: Religion and social values for sustainability. *Sustain. Sci.*, **14(5)**, 1355–1362, doi:10.1007/S11625-019-00657-0.

Iwafune, Y., Y. Mori, T. Kawai, and Y. Yagita, 2017: Energy-saving effect of automatic home energy report utilizing home energy management system data in Japan. *Energy*, **125** (15 April 2017), 382–392, doi:10.1016/j.energy.2017.02.136.

Iweka, O., S. Liu, A. Shukla, and D. Yan, 2019: Energy and behaviour at home: A review of intervention methods and practices. *Energy Res. Soc. Sci.*, **57**(November 2019), 101238, doi:10.1016/j.erss.2019.101238.

Jachimowicz, J.M., O.P. Hauser, J.D. O'Brien, E. Sherman, and A.D. Galinsky, 2018: The critical role of second-order normative beliefs in predicting energy conservation. *Nat. Hum. Behav.*, **2(10)**, 757–764, doi:10.1038/s41562-018-0434-0.

Jachimowicz, J.M., S. Duncan, E.U. Weber, and E.J. Johnson, 2019: When and why defaults influence decisions: a meta-analysis of default effects. *Behav. Public Policy*, **3(02)**, 159–186, doi:10.1017/bpp.2018.43.

Jack, B.K. and G. Smith, 2016: *Charging Ahead: Prepaid Electricity Metering in South Africa*. Working Paper 22895, National Bureau of Economic Research, Cambridge, MA, USA, 41 pp. http://www.nber.org/papers/w22895.pdf (Accessed June 21, 2021).

Jackson, T., 2008: Live Better by Consuming Less?: Is There a "Double Dividend" in Sustainable Consumption? *J. Ind. Ecol.*, **9(1–2)**, 19–36, doi:10.1162/1088198054084734.

Jackson, T., 2009: *Prosperity without growth? The transition to a sustainable economy*. Sustainable Development Commission, 133 pp.

Jackson, T., 2016: *Prosperity without growth: foundations for the economy of tomorrow*. 2nd ed. Routledge, Abingdon, UK, 310 pp.

Jackson, T. and N. Marks, 1999: Consumption, sustainable welfare and human needs – With reference to UK expenditure patterns between 1954 and 1994. *Ecol. Econ.*, **28(3)**, 421–441, doi:10.1016/S0921-8009(98)00108-6.

Jackson, T. and E. Papathanasopoulou, 2008: Luxury or "lock-in"? An exploration of unsustainable consumption in the UK: 1968 to 2000. *Ecol. Econ.*, **68(1–2)**, 80–95, doi:10.1016/j.ecolecon.2008.01.026.

Jackson, T. and P.A. Victor, 2016: Does slow growth lead to rising inequality? Some theoretical reflections and numerical simulations. *Ecol. Econ.*, **121**, 206–219, doi:10.1016/j.ecolecon.2015.03.019.

Jacobs, C. et al., 2019: Patterns of outdoor exposure to heat in three South Asian cities. *Sci. Total Environ.*, **674**, 264–278, doi:10.1016/J.SCITOTENV.2019.04.087.

Jacobsen, G.D., M.J. Kotchen, and M.P. Vandenbergh, 2012: The behavioral response to voluntary provision of an environmental public good: Evidence from residential electricity demand. *Eur. Econ. Rev.*, **56**, 946–960, doi:10.1016/j.euroecorev.2012.02.008.

Jacobson, S.H. and D.M. King, 2009: Fuel saving and ridesharing in the US: Motivations, limitations, and opportunities. *Transp. Res. Part D Transp. Environ.*, **14(1)**, 14–21, doi:10.1016/j.trd.2008.10.001.

Jacobsson, S. and V. Lauber, 2006: The politics and policy of energy system transformation—explaining the German diffusion of renewable energy technology. *Energy Policy*, **34(3)**, 256–276.

Jaffe, R. and M. Koster, 2019: The Myth of Formality in the Global North: Informality-as-Innovation in Dutch Governance. *Int. J. Urban Reg. Res.*, **43(3)**, 563–568, doi:10.1111/1468-2427.12706.

Jafry, T., (ed.) 2019: *Handbook of climate justice*. Routledge, Abingdon, UK and New York, NY, USA, 542 pp.

Jagers, S.C., Å. Löfgren, and J. Stripple, 2010: Attitudes to personal carbon allowances: Political trust, fairness and ideology. *Clim. Policy*, **10(4)**, 410–431, doi:10.3763/cpol.2009.0673.

Jagger, P., I. Das, S. Handa, L.A. Nylander-French, and K.B. Yeatts, 2019: Early Adoption of an Improved Household Energy System in Urban Rwanda. *Ecohealth*, **16(1)**, 7–20, doi:10.1007/s10393-018-1391-9.

Jain, R.K., J. Qin, and R. Rajagopal, 2017: Data-driven planning of distributed energy resources amidst socio-technical complexities. *Nat. Energy*, **2(8)**, 17112, doi:10.1038/nenergy.2017.112.

Janda, K.B. and Y. Parag, 2013: A middle-out approach for improving energy performance in buildings. *Build. Res. Inf.*, **41(1)**, 39–50, doi:10.1080/09613218.2013.743396.

Jarmul, S. et al., 2020: Climate change mitigation through dietary change: a systematic review of empirical and modelling studies on the environmental footprints and health effects of 'sustainable diets.' *Environ. Res. Lett.*, **15(12)**, 123014, doi:10.1088/1748-9326/abc2f7.

Javaid, A., S. Bamberg, and F. Creutzig, 2020: Determinants of low-carbon transport mode adoption: Systematic review of reviews. *Environ. Res. Lett*, **15(10)**, 103002, doi:10.1088/1748-9326/aba032.

Jenkins, W., E. Berry, and L.B. Kreider, 2018: Religion and Climate Change. *Annu. Rev. Environ. Resour.*, **43**, 85–108, doi:10.1146/annurev-environ-102017-025855.

Jewell, J. and A. Cherp, 2020: On the political feasibility of climate change mitigation pathways: Is it too late to keep warming below 1.5°C? *Clim. Change*, **11(1)**, e621, doi:10.1002/WCC.621.

Jo, A. and S. Carattini, 2021: Trust and CO$_2$ Emissions: Cooperation on a Global Scale. *J. Econ. Behav. Organ.*, **190(10)**, 992–937, doi:10.1016/j.jebo.2021.08.010.

Jodoin, S., S. Duyck, and K. Lofts, 2015: Public Participation and Climate Governance: An Introduction. *Rev. Eur. Comp. Int. Environ. Law*, **24(2)**, 117–122, doi:10.1111/reel.12126.

Johannsdottir, L., 2014: Transforming the linear insurance business model to a closed-loop insurance model: A case study of Nordic non-life insurers. *J. Clean. Prod.*, **83**, 341–355, doi:10.1016/j.jclepro.2014.07.010.

Johansson, T., A. Patwardhan, N. Nakićenović, and L. Gomez-Echeverri, 2012: *Global Energy Assessment – Toward a Sustainable Future*., Cambridge University Press, Cambridge, UK and New York, NY, USA, and the International Institute for Applied Systems Analysis, Laxenburg, Austria.

Johnson, C., 2020: Is demand side response a woman's work? Domestic labour and electricity shifting in low income homes in the United Kingdom. *Energy Res. Soc. Sci.*, **68**, doi:10.1016/j.erss.2020.101558.

Johnson, E.J. et al., 2012: Beyond nudges: Tools of a choice architecture. *Mark. Lett.*, **23(2)**, 487–504, doi:10.1007/s11002-012-9186-1.

Jokinen, M., S. Sarkki, and H.I. Heikkinen, 2016: The Well-being effects of localized multi-level environmental governance: Case of Kilpisjärvi. *Nord. Geogr. Publ.*, **45(2)**, 19–36.

Jones, E.C. and B.D. Leibowicz, 2019: Contributions of shared autonomous vehicles to climate change mitigation. *Transp. Res. Part D Transp. Environ.*, **72**, 279–298, doi:10.1016/j.trd.2019.05.005.

Jorgenson, A., J. Schor, and X. Huang, 2017: Income Inequality and Carbon Emissions in the United States: A State-level Analysis, 1997–2012. *Ecol. Econ.*, **134**, 40–48, doi:10.1016/j.ecolecon.2016.12.016.

Jorgenson, A.K., J.B. Schor, K.W. Knight, and X. Huang, 2016: Domestic Inequality and Carbon Emissions in Comparative Perspective. *Sociol. Forum*, **31**(September), 770–786, doi:10.1111/socf.12272.

Jorgenson, A.K. et al., 2018: Social science perspectives on drivers of and responses to global climate change. *WIREs Clim. Change*, **10**(February 2018), 1–17, doi:10.1002/wcc.554.

Joskow, P.L., 1995: Utility-Subsidized Energy-Efficiency Programs. *Annu. Rev. Energy Environ.*, **20(1)**, 526–534, doi:10.1146/annurev.eg.20.110195.002522.

Joubert, E.C., S. Hess, and J.L. Van Niekerk, 2016: Large-scale solar water heating in South Africa: Status, barriers and recommendations. *Renew. Energy*, **97**, 809–822, doi:10.1016/j.renene.2016.06.029.

Jung, J. and Y. Koo, 2018: Analyzing the effects of car sharing services on the reduction of greenhouse gas (GHG) emissions. *Sustainability*, **10(2)**, doi:10.3390/su10020539.

Jürisoo, M., N. Serenje, F. Mwila, F. Lambe, and M. Osborne, 2019: Old habits die hard: Using the energy cultures framework to understand drivers of household-level energy transitions in urban Zambia. *Energy Res. Soc. Sci.*, **53**, 59–67, doi:10.1016/j.erss.2019.03.001.

Jylhä, K.M., C. Cantal, N. Akrami, and T.L. Milfont, 2016: Denial of anthropogenic climate change: Social dominance orientation helps explain the conservative male effect in Brazil and Sweden. *Pers. Individ. Dif.*, **98**, 184–187, doi:10.1016/j.paid.2016.04.020.

Kaenzig, J. and R. Wüstenhagen, 2010: The Effect of Life Cycle Cost Information on Consumer Investment Decisions Regarding Eco-Innovation. *J. Ind. Ecol.*, **14(1)**, 121–136, doi:10.1111/j.1530-9290.2009.00195.x.

Kahneman, D. and A. Deaton, 2010: High income improves evaluation of life but not emotional well-being. *Proc. Natl. Acad. Sci.*, **107(38)**, 16489–16493, doi:10.1073/pnas.1011492107.

Kaiser, C.M., 2020: State Steering in Polycentric Governance Systems: Climate Policy Integration in Ontario and California's Transportation Sectors. York University, Toronto, Canada, https://yorkspace.library.yorku.ca/xmlui/handle/10315/37701 (Accessed October 2, 2021).

Kaiser, F.G., 2006: A general measure of ecological behavior. *J. Appl. Soc. Psychol.*, **28(5)**, 395–422, doi:10.1111/j.1559-1816.1998.tb01712.x.

Kaiser, M., M. Bernauer, C.R. Sunstein, and L.A. Reisch, 2020: The power of green defaults: the impact of regional variation of opt-out tariffs on green energy demand in Germany. *Ecol. Econ.*, **174**, 106685, doi:10.1016/j.ecolecon.2020.106685.

Kallbekken, S., S. Kroll, and T.L. Cherry, 2011: Do you not like Pigou, or do you not understand him? Tax aversion and revenue recycling in the lab. *J. Environ. Econ. Manage.*, **62(1)**, 53–64, doi:10.1016/j.jeem.2010.10.006.

Kallis, G., C. Kerschner, and J. Martinez-Alier, 2012: The economics of degrowth. *Ecol. Econ.*, **84**, 172–180, doi:10.1016/j.ecolecon.2012.08.017.

Kalt, G., D. Wiedenhofer, C. Görg, and H. Haberl, 2019: Conceptualizing energy services: A review of energy and well-being along the Energy Service Cascade. *Energy Res. Soc. Sci.*, **53**(November 2018), 47–58, doi:10.1016/j.erss.2019.02.026.

Kammermann, L. and C. Dermont, 2018: How beliefs of the political elite and citizens on climate change influence support for Swiss energy transition policy. *Energy Res. Soc. Sci.*, **43**, 48–60, doi:10.1016/j.erss.2018.05.010.

Kane, R. and N. Srinivas, 2014: Unlocking the Potential of Behavioral Energy Efficiency: Methodology for Calculating Technical, Economic, and Achievable Savings Potential. In: *Proceedings of the 2014 ACEEE 2014: The Next Generation: Reaching for High Energy Savings*, pp. 198–209.

Kanger, L., F.W. Geels, B. Sovacool, and J. Schot, 2019: Technological diffusion as a process of societal embedding: Lessons from historical automobile transitions for future electric mobility. *Transp. Res. Part D Transp. Environ.*, **71**, 47–66, doi:10.1016/j.trd.2018.11.012.

Kariuki, D., 2018: Barriers to Renewable Energy Technologies Development. *Energy Today*, https://www.researchgate.net/publication/348936339_Barriers_to_Renewable_Energy_Technologies_Development (Accessed December 2, 2020).

Karlin, B., J.F. Zinger, and R. Ford, 2015: The effects of feedback on energy conservation: A meta-analysis. *Psychol. Bull.*, **141(6)**, 1205–1227, doi:10.1037/a0039650.

Kartha, S., E. Kemp-Benedict, E. Ghosh, A. Nazareth, and T. Gore, 2020: *The carbon inequality era*. Stockholm Environment Institute and Oxfam International, Oxford, UK, 51 pp.

Kattumuri, R. and T. Kruse, 2019: Renewable technologies in Karnataka, India: jobs potential and co-benefits. *Clim. Dev.*, **11(2)**, 124–137, doi:10.1080/17565529.2017.1410085.

Kavitha, N.V., N. Gandhimathi, and S. Gandhimathi, 2020: Do carbon emissions and economic growth decouple in India? An empirical analysis based on Tapio decoupling model. *Stud. Indian Place Names*, **40(25)**, 146–152.

Keller, W., 2004: International Technology Diffusion. *J. Econ. Lit.*, **42(3)**, 752–782, doi:10.1257/0022051042177685.

Kemp, R., J. Schot, and R. Hoogma, 1998: Regime shifts to sustainability through processes of niche formation: The approach of strategic niche management. *Technol. Anal. Strateg. Manag.*, **10(2)**, 175–195, doi:10.1080/09537329808524310.

Kenner, D. 2015: *Inequality of overconsumption: The ecological footprint of the richest*. GSI Working Paper 2015/2. Global Sustainability Institute, Anglia Ruskin University, Cambridge, UK.

Kenner, D., 2019: *Carbon Inequality: The Role of the Richest in Climate Change – 1st Edition*. Routledge, Abingdon, UK, 146 pp.

Kern, F., and K.S. Rogge, 2016: The pace of governed energy transitions: Agency, international dynamics and the global Paris agreement accelerating decarbonisation processes? *Energy Res. Soc. Sci.*, **22**, 13–17, doi:10.1016/j.erss.2016.08.016.

Kern, F., P. Kivimaa, and M. Martiskainen, 2017: Policy packaging or policy patching? The development of complex energy efficiency policy mixes. *Energy Res. Soc. Sci.*, **23**, 11–25, doi:10.1016/j.erss.2016.11.002.

Kern, K. and H. Bulkeley, 2009: Cities, Europeanization and Multi-level Governance: Governing Climate Change through Transnational Municipal Networks. *JCMS*, **47(2)**, 309–332.

Keskitalo, E.C.H. (ed.) 2010: *Developing Adaptation Policy and Practice in Europe: Multi-level Governance of Climate Change*. Springer Nature, Dordecht, The Netherlands.

Kester, J., L. Noel, G. Zarazua de Rubens, and B.K. Sovacool, 2018: Policy mechanisms to accelerate electric vehicle adoption: A qualitative review from the Nordic region. *Renew. Sustain. Energy Rev.*, **94**(September 2017), 719–731, doi:10.1016/j.rser.2018.05.067.

Ketlhoilwe, M.J., 2013: Improving resilience to protect women against adverse effects of climate change. *Clim. Dev.*, **5(2)**, 153–159, doi:10.1080/17565529.2013.789788.

Keyßer, L.T. and M. Lenzen, 2021: 1.5°C degrowth scenarios suggest the need for new mitigation pathways. *Nat. Commun. 2021 121*, **12(1)**, 1–16, doi:10.1038/s41467-021-22884-9.

Khanna, T.M. et al., 2021: A multi-country meta-analysis on the role of behavioural change in reducing energy consumption and CO_2 emissions in residential buildings. *Nat. Energy*, **6**(September 2021), 925–932, doi:10.1038/s41560-021-00866-x.

Khosla, R., N. Sircar, and A. Bhardwaj, 2019: Energy demand transitions and climate mitigation in low-income urban households in India. *Environ. Res. Lett.*, **14(9)**, 095008, doi:10.1088/1748-9326/AB3760.

Kikstra, J.S. et al., 2021a: Climate mitigation scenarios with persistent COVID-19-related energy demand changes. *Nat. Energy*, pp. 1114–1123, doi:10.1038/s41560-021-00904-8.

Kikstra, J.S., A. Mastrucci, J. Min, K. Riahi, and N.D. Rao, 2021b: Decent living gaps and energy needs around the world. *Environ. Res. Lett.*, **16(9)**, 095006, doi:10.1088/1748-9326/AC1C27.

Kim, B.F. et al., 2020: Country-specific dietary shifts to mitigate climate and water crises. *Glob. Environ. Change*, **62**, 101926, doi:10.1016/j.gloenvcha.2019.05.010.

Kim, S.-N., S. Choo, and P.L. Mokhtarian, 2015: Home-based telecommuting and intra-household interactions in work and non-work travel: A seemingly unrelated censored regression approach. *Transp. Res. Part A Policy Pract.*, **80**, 197–214, doi:10.1016/j.tra.2015.07.018.

Kimemia, D. and H. Annegarn, 2016: Domestic LPG interventions in South Africa: Challenges and lessons. *Energy Policy*, **93**, 150–156, doi:10.1016/j.enpol.2016.03.005.

King, D.A., M.J. Smart, and M. Manville, 2019: The Poverty of the Carless: Toward Universal Auto Access. *J. Plan. Educ. Res.*, doi:10.1177/0739456X18823252.

Kirchherr, J., D. Reike, and M. Hekkert, 2017: Conceptualizing the circular economy: An analysis of 114 definitions. *Resour. Conserv. Recycl.*, **127**, 221–232.

Kivimaa, P. and V. Virkamäki, 2014: Policy mixes, policy interplay and low carbon transitions: The case of passenger transport in Finland. *Environ. Policy Gov.*, **24(1)**, 28–41, doi:10.1002/eet.1629.

5

Kivimaa, P. and F. Kern, 2016: Creative destruction or mere niche support? Innovation policy mixes for sustainability transitions. *Res. Policy*, **45(1)**, 205–217, doi:10.1016/j.respol.2015.09.008.

Kivimaa, P. and M. Martiskainen, 2018: Energy Research & Social Science Dynamics of policy change and intermediation : The arduous transition towards low-energy homes in the United Kingdom. *Energy Res. Soc. Sci.*, **44**(October 2017), 83–99, doi:10.1016/j.erss.2018.04.032.

Klaniecki, K., I.A. Duse, L.M. Lutz, J. Leventon, and D.J. Abson, 2020: Applying the energy cultures framework to understand energy systems in the context of rural sustainability transformation. *Energy Policy*, **137**, 111092, doi:10.1016/J.ENPOL.2019.111092.

Klasen, S., 2018: Inequality and Greenhouse Gas Emissions. *J. Income Distrib.*, **26(3)**, 1–14.

Klausbruckner, C., H. Annegarn, L.R.F. Henneman, and P. Rafaj, 2016: A policy review of synergies and trade-offs in South African climate change mitigation and air pollution control strategies. *Environ. Sci. Policy*, **57**, 70–78, doi:10.1016/j.envsci.2015.12.001.

Klausner, M., W.M. Grimm, and C. Hendrickson, 1998: Reuse of Electric Motors in Consumer Products. *J. Ind. Ecol.*, **2(2)**, 89–102, doi:10.1162/jiec.1998.2.2.89.

Klemeš, J.J., Y. Van Fan, R.R. Tan, and P. Jiang, 2020: Minimising the present and future plastic waste, energy and environmental footprints related to COVID-19. *Renew. Sustain. Energy Rev.*, **127**, 109883, doi:10.1016/j.rser.2020.109883.

Klenert, D. and L. Mattauch, 2016: How to make a carbon tax reform progressive: The role of subsistence consumption. *Econ. Lett.*, **138**, 100–103, doi:10.1016/j.econlet.2015.11.019.

Klenert, D. et al., 2018: Making carbon pricing work for citizens. *Nat. Clim. Change*, **8(8)**, 669–677, doi:10.1038/s41558-018-0201-2.

Klenert, D., F. Funke, L. Mattauch, and B. O'Callaghan, 2020: Five Lessons from COVID-19 for Advancing Climate Change Mitigation. *Environmental and Resource Economics.*, **76(4)**, 751–778, doi:10.2139/ssrn.3622201.

Klinsky, S. and H. Winkler, 2014: Equity, sustainable development and climate policy. *Clim. Policy*, **14(1)**, 1–7, doi:10.1080/14693062.2014.859352.

Klinsky, S. et al., 2016: Why equity is fundamental in climate change policy research. *Glob. Environ. Change*, doi:10.1016/j.gloenvcha.2016.08.002.

Klitkou, A., S. Bolwig, T. Hansen, and N. Wessberg, 2015: The role of lock-in mechanisms in transition processes: The case of energy for road transport. *Environ. Innov. Soc. Transitions*, **16**, 22–37, doi:10.1016/j.eist.2015.07.005.

Klopp, J.M., 2012: Towards a Political Economy of Transportation Policy and Practice in Nairobi. *Urban Forum*, **23(1)**, 1–21, doi:10.1007/s12132-011-9116-y.

Koh, H., 2016: A new app to save food at the 11th Hour. *Eco-Business*, November 15.

Komiyama, H., 2014: *Beyond the limits to growth: New ideas for sustainability from Japan*. Springer Japan, Tokyo, Japan, 103 pp.

Konrad, K., 2016: Expectation dynamics: Ups and downs of alternative fuels. *Nat. Energy*, **1(16022)**, doi:10.1038/nenergy.2016.22.

Koomey, J.G., S. Berard, M. Sanchez, and H. Wong, 2011: Implications of historical trends in the electrical efficiency of computing. *IEEE Ann. Hist. Comput.*, **33(3)**, doi:10.1109/MAHC.2010.28.

Korhonen, J., A. Honkasalo, and J. Seppälä, 2018: Circular Economy: The Concept and its Limitations. *Ecol. Econ.*, **143**, 37–46, doi:10.1016/j.ecolecon.2017.06.041.

Koronen, C., M. Åhman, and L.J. Nilsson, 2020: Data centres in future European energy systems – energy efficiency, integration and policy. *Energy Effic.*, **13(1)**, doi:10.1007/s12053-019-09833-8.

Kotchen, M.J., Z.M. Turk, and A.A. Leiserowitz, 2017: Public willingness to pay for a US carbon tax and preferences for spending the revenue. *Environ. Res. Lett*, **12**, 94012, doi:10.1088/1748-9326/aa822a.

Kraemer-Mbula, E. and S. Wunsch-Vincent, (eds.), 2016: Chapter 7: Innovation policy and the informal economy: Towards a new policy framework, Comment 7.1. In: *The Informal Economy in Developing Nations: Hidden Engine of Innovation?, Intellectual Property, Innovation and Economic Development*, Cambridge University Press, Cambridge, UK, pp. 327–331.

Krausmann, F. et al., 2009: Growth in global materials use, GDP and population during the 20th century. *Ecol. Econ.*, **68(10)**, 2696–2705, doi:10.1016/j.ecolecon.2009.05.007.

Krausmann, F. et al., 2017: Global socioeconomic material stocks rise 23-fold over the 20th century and require half of annual resource use. *Proc. Natl. Acad. Sci.*, **114(8)**, 1880–1885, doi:10.1073/PNAS.1613773114.

Krey, V. et al., 2019: Looking under the hood: A comparison of techno-economic assumptions across national and global integrated assessment models. *Energy*, **172**, 1254–1267, doi:10.1016/J.ENERGY.2018.12.131.

Krieger, N., 2020: ENOUGH: COVID-19, Structural Racism, Police Brutality, Plutocracy, Climate Change – and Time for Health Justice, Democratic Governance, and an Equitable, Sustainable Future. *Am. J. Public Health*, **110(11)**, 1620–1623, doi:10.2105/ajph.2020.305886.

Kriegler, E. et al., 2014: A new scenario framework for climate change research: The concept of shared climate policy assumptions. *Clim. Change*, **122(3)**, 401–414, doi:10.1007/s10584-013-0971-5.

Kronsell, A., 2017: The contribution of feminist perspectives to climate governance. In: *Understanding Climate Change through Gender Relations* [Buckingham, S. and V. Le Masson, (eds.)], Routledge, Abingdon, UK, pp. 104–120.

Kuhnhenn, K., L. Costa, E. Mahnke, L. Schneider, and S. Lange, 2020: *A Societal Transformation Scenario for Staying Below 1.5°C*. Heinrich Böll Foundation, Berlin, Germany, https://www.boell.de/sites/default/files/2020-12/A Societal Transformation Scenario for Staying Below 1.5C.pdf?dimension1=division_iup (Accessed October 29, 2021).

Kulin, J. and I. Johansson Sevä, 2019: The Role of Government in Protecting the Environment: Quality of Government and the Translation of Normative Views about Government Responsibility into Spending Preferences. *Int. J. Sociol.*, **49(2)**, 110–129, doi:10.1080/00207659.2019.1582964.

Kumar, P., R.K. Rao, and N.H. Reddy, 2016: Sustained uptake of LPG as cleaner cooking fuel in rural India: Role of affordability, accessibility, and awareness. *World Dev. Perspect.*, **4**, 33–37, doi:10.1016/j.wdp.2016.12.001.

Kumar, S.V., 2019: *Rural roads and the SDGs*. The Energy and Resources Institute, New Delhi, India, https://www.teriin.org/sites/default/files/2019-05/rural-roads-sdgs.pdf.

Kungl, G. and F.W. Geels, 2018: Sequence and alignment of external pressures in industry destabilisation: Understanding the downfall of incumbent utilities in the German energy transition (1998–2015). *Environ. Innov. Soc. Transitions*, **26**, 78–100, doi.org/10.1016/j.eist.2017.05.003.

Kuokkanen, A. et al., 2018: Agency in regime destabilization through the selection environment: The Finnish food system's sustainability transition. *Res. Policy*, **47(8)**, 1513–1522, doi:10.1016/j.respol.2018.05.006.

Kurz, T., N. Donaghue, and I. Walker, 2005: Utilizing a social-ecological framework to promote water and energy conservation: A field experiment. *J. Appl. Soc. Psychol.*, **35(6)**, 1281–1300, doi:10.1111/j.1559-1816.2005.tb02171.x.

La Viña, A.G., J.M. Tan, T.I.M. Guanzon, M.J. Caleda, and L. Ang, 2018: Navigating a trilemma: Energy security, equity, and sustainability in the Philippines' low-carbon transition. *Energy Res. Soc. Sci.*, **35**, 37–47, doi:10.1016/j.erss.2017.10.039.

Lacey-Barnacle, M., R. Robison, and C. Foulds, 2020: Energy justice in the developing world: a review of theoretical frameworks, key research themes and policy implications. *Energy Sustain. Dev.*, **55**, 122–138, doi:10.1016/J.ESD.2020.01.010.

Lachapelle, U., G.A. Tanguay, and L. Neumark-Gaudet, 2018: Telecommuting and sustainable travel: Reduction of overall travel time, increases in non-motorised travel and congestion relief? *Urban Stud.*, **55(10)**, 2226–2244, doi:10.1177/0042098017708985.

Laestadius, L.I., R.A. Neff, C.L. Barry, and S. Frattaroli, 2016: No Meat, Less Meat, or Better Meat: Understanding NGO Messaging Choices Intended to

5

Alter Meat Consumption in Light of Climate Change. *Environ. Commun.*, **10(1)**, 84–103, doi:10.1080/17524032.2014.981561.

Laitner, J.A. "Skip," K. Ehrhardt-Martinez, and V. McKinney, 2009: Examining the scale of the Behaviour Energy Efficiency Continuum. In: *Proceedings of the 2009 eceee Summer Study*, Panel 1. T, European Council for an Energy Efficient Economy, Stockholm, Sweden, pp. 217–223.

Lamb, A. et al., 2016: The potential for land sparing to offset greenhouse gas emissions from agriculture. *Nat. Clim. Change*, **6**(5), 488–492, doi:10.1038/nclimate2910.

Lamb, W.F. and N.D. Rao, 2015: Human development in a climate-constrained world: What the past says about the future. *Glob. Environ. Change*, **33**, 14–22, doi:10.1016/j.gloenvcha.2015.03.010.

Lamb, W.F. and J.K. Steinberger, 2017: Human well-being and climate change mitigation. *Wiley Interdiscip. Rev. Clim. Change*, **8(6)**, doi:10.1002/wcc.485.

Lamb, W.F. et al., 2014: Transitions in pathways of human development and carbon emissions. *Environ. Res. Lett.*, **9(1)**, doi:10.1088/1748-9326/9/1/014011.

Lambert, H. et al., 2020: COVID-19 as a global challenge: towards an inclusive and sustainable future. *Lancet Planet. Heal.*, **4(8)**, e312–e314, doi:10.1016/S2542-5196(20)30168-6.

Lange, A., C. Vogt, and A. Ziegler, 2007: On the importance of equity in international climate policy: An empirical analysis. *Energy Econ.*, **29(3)**, 545–562, doi:10.1016/j.eneco.2006.09.002.

Langhelle, O., 2000: Sustainable Development and Social Justice: Expanding the Rawlsian Framework of Global Justice. *Environ. Values,* **9(3)**, 295–323.

Larcom, S., F. Rauch, and T. Willems, 2017: The Benefits of Forced Experimentation: Striking Evidence from the London Underground Network. *Q. J. Econ.*, **132(4)**, 2019–2055, doi:10.1093/qje/qjx020.

Larrick, R.P. and J.B. Soll, 2008: The MPG illusion. *Science*, **320(5883)**, 1593–1594, doi:10.1126/science.1154983.

Larson, A.M. et al., 2018: Gender lessons for climate initiatives: A comparative study of REDD+ impacts on subjective wellbeing. *World Dev.*, **108**, 86–102, doi:10.1016/j.worlddev.2018.02.027.

Latvala, T. et al., 2012: Diversifying meat consumption patterns: Consumers' self-reported past behaviour and intentions for change. *Meat Sci.*, **92(1)**, 71–77, doi:10.1016/j.meatsci.2012.04.014.

Lau, J.D., D. Kleiber, S. Lawless, and P.J. Cohen, 2021: Gender equality in climate policy and practice hindered by assumptions. *Nat. Clim. Change,* **11(3)**, 186–192, doi:10.1038/s41558-021-00999-7.

Le Quéré, C. et al., 2019: Drivers of declining CO2 emissions in 18 developed economies. *Nat. Clim. Change*, **9(3)**, 213–217, doi:10.1038/s41558-019-0419-7.

Le Quéré, C. et al., 2020: Temporary reduction in daily global CO2 emissions during the COVID-19 forced confinement. *Nat. Clim. Change*, **10(7)**, 647–653, doi:10.1038/s41558-020-0797-x.

Leach, M., H. MacGregor, I. Scoones, and A. Wilkinson, 2021: Post-pandemic transformations: How and why COVID-19 requires us to rethink development. *World Dev.*, **138**, 105233, doi:10.1016/j.worlddev.2020.105233.

Lee, E., N.-K. Park, and J.H. Han, 2013: Gender Difference in Environmental Attitude and Behaviors in Adoption of Energy-Efficient Lighting at Home. *J. Sustain. Dev.*, **6(9)**, doi:10.5539/jsd.v6n9p36.

Lee, K., N. Gjersoe, S. O'Neill, and J. Barnett, 2020: Youth perceptions of climate change: A narrative synthesis. *Wiley Interdiscip. Rev. Clim. Change*, **11(3)**, 1–24, doi:10.1002/wcc.641.

Lee, S. and E. Zusman, 2019: Participatory climate governance in Southeast Asia: Lessons learned from gender-responsive climate mitigation. In: *Routledge Handbook of Climate Justice* [Jafry, T., (ed.)], Routledge, New York, USA, pp. 393–404.

Lee, T. and C. Koski, 2015: Multilevel governance and urban climate change mitigation. *Environ. Plan. C Gov. Policy*, **33(6)**, 1501–1517, doi:10.1177/0263774X15614700.

Lei, N., E. Masanet, and J. Koomey, 2021: Best practices for analyzing the direct energy use of blockchain technology systems: Review and policy recommendations. *Energy Policy*, **156**, 112422, doi:10.1016/J.ENPOL.2021.112422.

Leibowicz, B.D., 2018: Policy recommendations for a transition to sustainable mobility based on historical diffusion dynamics of transport systems. *Energy Policy*, **119**, 357–366, doi:10.1016/j.enpol.2018.04.066.

Leipprand, A. and C. Flachsland, 2018: Energy Research & Social Science Regime destabilization in energy transitions : The German debate on the future of coal. *Energy Res. Soc. Sci.*, **40**, 190–204, doi:10.1016/j.erss.2018.02.004.

Leiserowitz, A. and K. Akerlof, 2010: *Race, ethnicity and public responses to climate change*. Yale University and George Mason University, New Haven, CT, USA, https://climatecommunication.yale.edu/wp-content/uploads/2016/02/2010_04_Race-Ethnicity-and-Public-Responses-to-Climate-Change.pdf (Accessed June 5, 2020).

Leiserowitz, A. et al., 2020: *Climate change in the American mind*. Yale University and George Mason University. New Haven, CT, USA,, doi:10.31234/osf.io/z3wtx.

Leiserson, C.E. et al., 2020: There's plenty of room at the Top: What will drive computer performance after Moore's law? *Science,* **368(6495)**, doi:10.1126/SCIENCE.AAM9744.

Lejano, R.P. and S.J. Nero, 2020: *The Power of Narrative: Climate Skepticism and the Deconstruction of Science*. Oxford University Press, Oxford, UK.

Lepeley, M.-T., 2017: Bhutan's Gross National Happiness: An Approach to Human Centred Sustainable Development. *South Asian J. Hum. Resour. Manag.*, **4(2)**, 174–184, doi:10.1177/2322093717731634.

Levin, K., B. Cashore, S. Bernstein, and G. Auld, 2012: Overcoming the tragedy of super wicked problems: Constraining our future selves to ameliorate global climate change. *Policy Sci.*, **45(2)**, 123–152, doi:10.1007/s11077-012-9151-0.

Lewandowski, M., 2016: Designing the business models for circular economy – Towards the conceptual framework. *Sustainability*, **8(1)**, 1–28, doi:10.3390/su8010043.

Lewis, G.B., R. Palm, and B. Feng, 2018: Cross-national variation in determinants of climate change concern. *Env. Polit.*, **28(5)**, 793–821, doi:10.1080/09644016.2018.1512261.

Li, J., J. Zhang, D. Zhang, and Q. Ji, 2019: Does gender inequality affect household green consumption behaviour in China? *Energy Policy*, **135**, 111071, doi:10.1016/j.enpol.2019.111071.

Li, L. and W. Wang, 2020: The effects of online trust-building mechanisms on trust in the sharing economy: The perspective of providers. *Sustainability*, **12(5)**, doi:10.3390/su12051717.

Li, W., T.H. Rubin, and P.A. Onyina, 2013: Comparing solar water heater popularization policies in China, Israel and Australia: The roles of governments in adopting green innovations. *Sustain. Dev.*, **21(3)**, 160–170, doi:10.1002/sd.1547.

Liang, S., H. Gu, R. Bergman, and S.S. Kelley, 2020: Comparative life-cycle assessment of a mass timber building and concrete alternative. *Wood Fiber Sci.*, **52(2)**, 217–229, doi:10.22382/wfs-2020-019.

Liao, L., M.E. Warner, and G.C. Homsy, 2019: Sustainability's forgotten third E: what influences local government actions on social equity? *Local Environ.*, **24(12)**, 1197–1208, doi:10.1080/13549839.2019.1683725.

Lidskog, R. and I. Elander, 2009: Addressing climate change democratically. Multi-level governance, transnational networks and governmental structures. *Sustain. Dev.*, **18(1)**, doi:10.1002/sd.395.

Lieder, M. and A. Rashid, 2016: Towards circular economy implementation: a comprehensive review in context of manufacturing industry. *J. Clean. Prod.*, **115**, 36–51, doi.org/10.1016/j.jclepro.2015.12.042.

Liedtke, C., H. Rohn, M. Kuhndt, and R. Nickel, 1998: Applying Material Flow Accounting: Ecoauditing and Resource Management at the Kambium Furniture Workshop. *J. Ind. Ecol.*, **2(3)**, 131–147, doi:10.1162/jiec.1998.2.3.131.

5

Lieu, J., A.H. Sorman, O.W. Johnson, L.D. Virla, and B.P. Resurrección, 2020: Three sides to every story: Gender perspectives in energy transition pathways in Canada, Kenya and Spain. *Energy Res. Soc. Sci.*, **68**, 101550, doi:10.1016/J.ERSS.2020.101550.

Lieven, T. and N. Rietmann, 2018: Do policy measures in fact promote electric mobility? A study across 20 countries. In: *Transport and the City* [Ricci, S. and C.A. Brebbia, (eds.)], Edward Elgar Publications, London, UK, pp. 41–50.

Linder, M. and M. Williander, 2017: Circular Business Model Innovation: Inherent Uncertainties. *Bus. Strateg. Environ.*, **26(2)**, 182–196, doi:10.1002/bse.1906.

Liu, C.J. and F. Hao, 2020: The impact of social and ecological factors on environmentally responsible behavior. *J. Clean. Prod.*, **254**, 120173, doi:10.1016/j.jclepro.2020.120173.

Liu, J.Y. et al., 2018: Socioeconomic factors and future challenges of the goal of limiting the increase in global average temperature to 1.5°C. *Carbon Manag.*, **9(5)**, 447–457, doi:10.1080/17583004.2018.1477374.

Liu, Q., S. Wang, W. Zhang, J. Li, and Y. Kong, 2019: Examining the effects of income inequality on CO_2 emissions: Evidence from non-spatial and spatial perspectives. *Appl. Energy*, **236**, 163–171, doi:10.1016/J.APENERGY.2018.11.082.

Liu, Y. et al., 2020a: Energy consumption and emission mitigation prediction based on data center traffic and PUE for global data centers. *Glob. Energy Interconnect.*, **3(3)**, 272–282, doi.org/10.1016/j.gloei.2020.07.008.

Liu, Y., M. Zhang, and R. Liu, 2020b: The impact of income inequality on Carbon emissions in China; A Household-level analysis. *Sustainability*, **12(7)**, 2715.

Liu, Z., T. Li, Q. Jiang, and H. Zhang, 2014: Life Cycle Assessment–based Comparative Evaluation of Originally Manufactured and Remanufactured Diesel Engines. *J. Ind. Ecol.*, **18(4)**, 567–576, doi:10.1111/JIEC.12137.

Liyanage, S. et al., 2019: Flexible Mobility On-Demand: An Environmental Scan. *Sustainability*, **11(5)**, 1262, doi:10.3390/su11051262.

Lockwood, M., 2018: Right-wing populism and the climate change agenda: exploring the linkages. *Env. Polit.*, 27(4), 712–732, doi:10.1080/09644016.2018.1458411.

Löfgren, Å., P. Martinsson, M. Hennlock, and T. Sterner, 2012: Are experienced people affected by a pre-set default option – Results from a field experiment. *J. Environ. Econ. Manage.*, **63(1)**, 66–72.

Loiseau, E. et al., 2016: Green economy and related concepts: An overview. *J. Clean. Prod.*, **139**, 361–371, doi.org/10.1016/j.jclepro.2016.08.024.

Loiter, J.M., and V. Norberg-Bohm, 1999: Technology policy and renewable energy: public roles in the development of new energy technologies. Energy Policy, 27(2), 85–97.

Lokhandwala, M. and H. Cai, 2018: Dynamic ride sharing using traditional taxis and shared autonomous taxis: A case study of NYC. *Transp. Res. Part C Emerg. Technol.*, **97**(November 2017), 45–60, doi:10.1016/j.trc.2018.10.007.

Lopes, M.A.R., C.H. Antunes, A. Reis, and N. Martins, 2017: Estimating energy savings from behaviours using building performance simulations. *Build. Res. Inf.*, **45(3)**, 303–319, doi:10.1080/09613218.2016.1140000.

López-García, D., L. Calvet-Mir, M. Di Masso, and J. Espluga, 2019: Multi-actor networks and innovation niches: university training for local Agroecological Dynamization. *Agric. Human Values*, **36(3)**, 567–579, doi:10.1007/s10460-018-9863-7.

Lorenz, D.F., 2013: The diversity of resilience: contributions from a social science perspective. *Nat. Hazards*, **67(1)**, 7–24, doi:10.1007/s11069-010-9654-y.

Lorenzoni, I., S. Nicholson-Cole, and L. Whitmarsh, 2007: Barriers perceived to engaging with climate change among the UK public and their policy implications. *Glob. Environ. Change*, **17(3–4)**, 445–459, doi:10.1016/J.GLOENVCHA.2007.01.004.

Lounsbury, M. and M.A. Glynn, 2001: Cultural entrepreneurship: Stories, legitimacy, and the acquisition of resources. *Strateg. Manag. J.*, **22(6–7)**, 545–564, doi:10.1002/smj.188.

Lovins, A.B., 1976: Energy Strategy: The Road Not Taken? *Economics*, **55**, 65, doi:10.2307/20039628.

Lovins, A., 1979: *Soft Energy Paths: Toward a Durable Peace*. Harper & Row, New York, NY, USA.

Lovins, A., 2015: The nuclear distraction. *Bulletin of the Atomic Scientists*, https://thebulletin.org/commentary/the-nuclear-distraction/ (Accessed December 16, 2019).

Lovins, A. et al., 2003: *Small is Profitable: The Hidden Economic Benefits of Making Electrical Resources the Right Size*. Rocky Mountain Institute, New York, NY, USA, 398 pp.

Lovins, A.B., T. Palazzi, R. Laemel, and E. Goldfield, 2018: Relative deployment rates of renewable and nuclear power: A cautionary tale of two metrics. *Energy Res. Soc. Sci.*, **38**, 188–192, doi.org/10.1016/j.erss.2018.01.005.

Lucon, O. et al., 2014: Buildings. In: *Climate Change 2014: Mitigation of Climate Change. Contribution of Working Group III to the Fifth Assessment Report of the Intergovernmental Panel on Climate Change* [Edenhofer, O., R. Pichs-Madruga, Y. Sokona, E. Farahani, S. Kadner, K. Seyboth, A. Adler, I. Baum, S. Brunner, P. Eickemeier, B. Kriemann, J. Savolainen, S. Schlömer, C. von Stechow, T. Zwickel and J.C. Minx (eds.)], Cambridge University Press, Cambridge, UK and New York, NY, USA, pp. 671–738.

Ludmann, S., 2019: Ökologische Betrachtung des Peer-to-Peer Sharing. In: *Digitale Kultur des Teilens* [Behrendt, S., C, Henseling, and G. Scholl (eds.)] Springer Fachmedien Wiesbaden, Wiesbaden, Germany, pp. 71–93.

Lundqvist, J., C. de Fraiture, and D. Molden, 2008: *Saving Water: From Field to Fork – Curbing Losses and Wastage in the Food Chain*. Stockholm International Water Institute, Stockholm, Sweden, 36 pp. http://www.siwi.org/publications/ (Accessed May 23, 2021).

Lutzenhiser, L., 1993: Social and behavioral aspects of energy use contents introduction. *Annu. Rev. Energy Env.*, **18**, 247–289, doi:10.1146/annurev.eg.18.110193.001335.

Lynch, M.J., M.A. Long, P.B. Stretesky, and K.L. Barrett, 2019: Measuring the Ecological Impact of the Wealthy: Excessive Consumption, Ecological Disorganization, Green Crime, and Justice. *Soc. Curr.*, **6(4)**, 377–395, doi:10.1177/2329496519847491.

Ma, T., A. Grubler, N. Nakicenovic, and W.B. Arthur, 2008: *Technologies as agents of change: A simulation model of the evolving complexity of the global energy system*. International Institute for Applied Systems Analysis, Laxenburg, Austria, http://pure.iiasa.ac.at/id/eprint/8762/ (Accessed May 23, 2021).

Macgregor, S., 2014: Only Resist: Feminist Ecological Citizenship and the Post-politics of Climate Change. *Hypatia*, **29(3)**, 617–633, doi:10.1111/hypa.12065.

Maestre-Andrés, S., S. Drews, and J. van den Bergh, 2019: Perceived fairness and public acceptability of carbon pricing: a review of the literature. *Clim. Policy*, **19(9)**, 1186–1204, doi:10.1080/14693062.2019.1639490.

Mahadevan, M., A. Francis, and A. Thomas, 2020: A simulation-based investigation of sustainability aspects of 3D printed structures. *J. Build. Eng.*, **32**, 101735, doi.org/10.1016/j.jobe.2020.101735.

Mahajan, V., E. Muller, and F.M. Bass, 1990: New product diffusion models in marketing: A review and directions for research. *J. Mark.*, **54(1)**, 1–26, doi:10.2307/1252170.

Mahapatra, K. and L. Gustavsson, 2008: An adopter-centric approach to analyze the diffusion patterns of innovative residential heating systems in Sweden. *Energy Policy*, **36(2)**, 577–590, doi:10.1016/J.ENPOL.2007.10.006.

Mahler, D.G., C. Lakner, R.A.C. Aguilar, and H. Wu, 2020: Updated estimates of the impact of COVID-19 on global poverty. *World Bank Blog*, https://blogs.worldbank.org/opendata/updated-estimates-impact-covid-19-global-poverty-turning-corner-pandemic-2021 (Accessed November 26, 2020).

Maibach, E.W., A. Leiserowitz, C. Roser-Renouf, and C.K. Mertz, 2011: Identifying Like-Minded Audiences for Global Warming Public Engagement Campaigns: An Audience Segmentation Analysis and Tool Development. *PLoS One*, **6(3)**, e17571, doi:10.1371/journal.pone.0017571.

Maïzi, N. and V. Mazauric, 2019: From centralized to decentralized power systems: The shift on finitude constraints. *Energy Procedia*, **158(2019)**, 4262–4267, doi:10.1016/j.egypro.2019.01.800.

Maïzi, N. et al., 2017: Maximizing intermittency in 100% renewable and reliable power systems: A holistic approach applied to Reunion Island in 2030. *Appl. Energy*, **227**, 332–341, doi:10.1016/j.apenergy.2017.08.058.

Maki, A. and A.J. Rothman, 2017: Understanding proenvironmental intentions and behaviors: The importance of considering both the behavior setting and the type of behavior. *J. Soc. Psychol.*, **157(5)**, 517–531, doi:10.1080/00224545.2016.1215968.

Makov, T. and D. Font Vivanco, 2018: Does the Circular Economy Grow the Pie? The Case of Rebound Effects From Smartphone Reuse. *Front. Energy Res.*, **6**, 39, doi:10.3389/fenrg.2018.00039.

Malmodin, J., 2020: The power consumption of mobile and fixed network data services – The case of streaming video and downloading large files. In: *Proceedings of the Electronics Goes Green 2020+ Conference, Berlin, Germany, September 1*, 87–96.

Malmodin, J. and D. Lundén, 2018: The energy and carbon footprint of the global ICT and E&M sectors 2010–2015. *Sustainability*, **10(9)**, 3027, doi:10.3390/su10093027.

Malmqvist, T. et al., 2018: Design and construction strategies for reducing embodied impacts from buildings – Case study analysis. *Energy Build.*, **166**, 35–47, doi:10.1016/J.ENBUILD.2018.01.033.

Malone, E., N.E. Hultman, K.L. Anderson, and V. Romeiro, 2017: Energy Research & Social Science Stories about ourselves : How national narratives influence the diff usion of large-scale energy technologies. **31**(July), 70–76, doi:10.1016/j.erss.2017.05.035.

Mang-Benza, C., 2021: Many shades of pink in the energy transition: Seeing women in energy extraction, production, distribution, and consumption. *Energy Res. Soc. Sci.*, **73**, 101901, doi:10.1016/J.ERSS.2020.101901.

Mani, A., S. Mullainathan, E. Shafir, and J. Zhao, 2013: Poverty impedes cognitive function. *Science*, **341(6149)**, 976–980, doi:10.1126/science.1238041.

Mansfield, E., 1968: *The Economics of Technological Change*. W.W. Norton & Co., New York, NY, USA, 150 pp.

Manzanedo, R.D. and P. Manning, 2020: COVID-19: Lessons for the climate change emergency. *Sci. Total Environ.*, **742**, 140563, doi:10.1016/j.scitotenv.2020.140563.

Maobe, A. and J. Atela, 2021: *Gender Intersectionality and Disaster Risk Reduction-Context Analysis*. UK Research and Innovation (UKRI) Global Challenges Research Fund (GCRF) Urban Disaster Risk Hub, Edinburgh, UK, https://tomorrowscities.org/sites/default/files/resources/2021-03/Gender Intersectionality and Disaster Risk Reduction.pdf (Accessed October 2, 2021).

Mardani, A., D. Streimikiene, F. Cavallaro, N. Loganathan, and M. Khoshnoudi, 2019: Carbon dioxide (CO_2) emissions and economic growth: A systematic review of two decades of research from 1995 to 2017. *Sci. Total Environ.*, **649**, 31–49, doi:10.1016/j.scitotenv.2018.08.229.

Mariam, N., K. Valerie, D. Karin, W.-R. Angelika, and L. Nina, 2020: Limiting food waste via grassroots initiatives as a potential for climate change mitigation: a systematic review. *Environ. Res. Lett.*, **15(12)**, 123008, doi:10.1088/1748-9326/ABA2FE.

Markard, J. and V.H. Hoffmann, 2016: Analysis of complementarities: Framework and examples from the energy transition. *Technol. Forecast. Soc. Change*, **111**, 63–75, doi:10.1016/j.techfore.2016.06.008.

Markard, J., R. Raven, and B. Truffer, 2012: Sustainability transitions : An emerging field of research and its prospects. *Res. Policy*, **41(6)**, 955–967, doi:10.1016/j.respol.2012.02.013.

Marquardt, J., 2017: Conceptualizing power in multi-level climate governance. *J. Clean. Prod.*, **154**, 167–175, doi:10.1016/j.jclepro.2017.03.176.

Marres, N., 2011: The costs of public involvement: everyday devices of carbon accounting and the materialization of participation. *Econ. Soc.*, **40(4)**, 510–533, doi:10.1080/03085147.2011.602294.

Martin, C.J., 2016: The sharing economy: A pathway to sustainability or a nightmarish form of neoliberal capitalism? *Ecol. Econ.*, **121**, 149–159, doi.org/10.1016/j.ecolecon.2015.11.027.

Martin, E. and S. Shaheen, 2016: *Impacts of car2go on Vehicle Ownership, Modal Shift, Vehicle Miles Traveled, and Greenhouse Gas Emissions: An Analysis of Five North American Cities*. Transportation Sustainability Research Center, Berkeley, CA, USA, 25 pp. http://innovativemobility.org/wp-content/uploads/2016/07/Impactsofcar2go_FiveCities_2016.pdf (Accessed July 23, 2021).

Martin, E.W. and S.A. Shaheen, 2011: Greenhouse gas emission impacts of carsharing in North America. *IEEE Trans. Intell. Transp. Syst.*, **12(4)**, 1074–1086, doi:10.1109/TITS.2011.2158539.

Martínez-Gómez, J., D. Ibarra, S. Villacis, P. Cuji, and P.R. Cruz, 2016: Analysis of LPG, electric and induction cookers during cooking typical Ecuadorian dishes into the national efficient cooking program. *Food Policy*, **59**, 88–102, doi:10.1016/j.foodpol.2015.12.010.

Martínez, J., J. Martí-Herrero, S. Villacís, A.J.J. Riofrio, and D. Vaca, 2017: Analysis of energy, CO_2 emissions and economy of the technological migration for clean cooking in Ecuador. *Energy Policy*, **107**, 182–187, doi:10.1016/j.enpol.2017.04.033.

Martinez, L.M. and J.M. Viegas, 2017: Assessing the impacts of deploying a shared self-driving urban mobility system: An agent-based model applied to the city of Lisbon, Portugal. *Int. J. Transp. Sci. Technol.*, **6(1)**, 13–27, doi:10.1016/J.IJTST.2017.05.005.

Martinez, N.B., 2020: The Politics of Sociocultural Impacts in Mexico's Ongoing Energy Transition. UC Berkeley, CA, USA, https://escholarship.org/uc/item/7pm2p7g7 (Accessed October 2, 2021).

Martino, J.P., K.-L. Chen, and R.C. Lenz, 1978: *Predicting the Diffusion Rate of Industrial Innovations*. University of Dayton Research Institute Technical Report UDRI-TR-78-42, Springfield, VA, USA.

Martiskainen, M. et al., 2020: Contextualizing climate justice activism: Knowledge, emotions, motivations, and actions among climate strikers in six cities. *Glob. Environ. Change*, **65**, 102180, doi:10.1016/j.gloenvcha.2020.102180.

Masanet, E. and H.S. Matthews, 2010: Exploring Environmental Applications and Benefits of Information and Communication Technology. *J. Ind. Ecol.*, **14(5)**, 687–691, doi:10.1111/J.1530-9290.2010.00285.X.

Masanet, E., A. Shehabi, N. Lei, S. Smith, and J. Koomey, 2020: Recalibrating global data center energy-use estimates: Growth in energy use has slowed owing to efficiency gains that smart policies can help maintain in the near term. *Science*, **367(6481)**, doi:10.1126/science.aba3758.

Masanet, E.R., R.E. Brown, A. Shehabi, J.G. Koomey, and B. Nordman, 2011: Estimating the energy use and efficiency potential of U.S. data centers. *Proc. IEEE*, **99(8)**, 1440–1453, doi:10.1109/JPROC.2011.2155610.

Mastrucci, A. and N.D. Rao, 2017: Decent housing in the developing world: Reducing life-cycle energy requirements. *Energy Build.*, **152**, 629–642, doi:10.1016/j.enbuild.2017.07.072.

Mastrucci, A. and N.D. Rao, 2019: Bridging India's housing gap: lowering costs and CO_2 emissions. *Build. Res. Inf.*, **47(1)**, 8–23, doi:10.1080/09613218.2018.1483634.

Mastrucci, A., J. Min, A. Usubiaga-Liaño, and N.D. Rao, 2020: A Framework for Modelling Consumption-Based Energy Demand and Emission Pathways. *Environ. Sci. Technol.*, **54(3)**, 1799–1807, doi:10.1021/ACS.EST.9B05968.

Material Economics, 2018: *The Circular Economy: a Powerful Force for Climate Mitigation*. Material Economics, Stockholm, Sweden, 176 pp. https://materialeconomics.com/publications/the-circular-economy-a-powerful-force-for-climate-mitigation-1.

Matson, P., W.C. Clark, and K. Andersson, 2016: *Pursuing Sustainability*. Princeton University Press, Princeton, NJ, USA.

Mattauch, L. and C. Hepburn, 2016: Climate Policy When Preferences Are Endogenous – and Sometimes They Are. *Midwest Stud. Philos.*, **40(1)**, 76–95, doi:10.1111/misp.12048.

Mattauch, L., M. Ridgway, and F. Creutzig, 2016: Happy or liberal? Making sense of behavior in transport policy design. *Transp. Res. Part D Transp. Environ.*, **45**(June 2016), 64–83, doi:10.1016/j.trd.2015.08.006.

5

Mattauch, L., C. Hepburn, and N. Stern, 2018: *Pigou Pushes Preferences: Decarbonisation and Endogenous Values*. Climate Change Economics and Policy Working Paper 346/Grantham Research Institute on Climate Change and the Environment Working Paper 314. London School of Economics and Political Science, London, UK, 37 pp. http://www.lse.ac.uk/GranthamInstitute/wp-content/uploads/2018/12/working-paper-314-Mattauch-et-al.pdf (Accessed July 4, 2019).

Matthies, E., C.A. Klockner, and C.L. Preissner, 2006: Applying a Modified Moral Decision Making Model to Change Habitual Car Use: How Can Commitment be Effective? *Appl. Psychol.*, **55(1)**, 91–106, doi:10.1111/j.1464-0597.2006.00237.x.

Mattioli, G., 2016: Transport needs in a climate-constrained world. A novel framework to reconcile social and environmental sustainability in transport. *Energy Res. Soc. Sci.*, **18**, 118–128, doi:10.1016/j.erss.2016.03.025.

Mattioli, G., C. Roberts, J.K. Steinberger, and A. Brown, 2020: The political economy of car dependence: A systems of provision approach. *Energy Res. Soc. Sci.*, **66**, doi:10.1016/j.erss.2020.101486.

Maumbe, B.M., 2006: Digital Financial Service Delivery to Poor Communities in South Africa: A Preliminary Assessment. *Int. Rev. Bus. Res. Pap.*, **2(2)**, 72–79.

Max-Neef, M., 1995: Economic growth and quality of life: a threshold hypothesis. *Ecol. Econ.*, **15(2)**, 115–118, doi.org/10.1016/0921-8009(95)00064-X.

Max-Neef, M., A. Elizalde, and Martín Hopenhayn, 1989: *Human scale development: An option for the future*. Development Dialogue **1(1)**, pp. 7–80.

Max-Neef, M.A., M. Hopenhayn, and A. Elizalde, 1991: *Human scale development: conception, application and further reflections*. 2nd ed. The Apex Press, New York, NY, USA.

Mazeka, B., C. Sutherland, S. Buthelezi, and D. Khumalo, 2019: Community-Based Mapping Methodology for Climate Change Adaptation: A Case Study of Quarry Road West Informal Settlement, Durban, South Africa. In: *The Geography of Climate Change Adaptation in Urban Africa* [Cobbinah, P.B. and Addaney, M. (eds.)] Springer International Publishing, Cham, Switzerland, pp. 57–88.

Mazorra, J., E. Sánchez-Jacob, C. de la Sota, L. Fernández, and J. Lumbreras, 2020: A comprehensive analysis of cooking solutions co-benefits at household level: Healthy lives and well-being, gender and climate change. *Sci. Total Environ.*, **707**, 135968, doi:10.1016/J.SCITOTENV.2019.135968.

Mazur, A., and E. Rosa, 1974: Energy and life-style. *Science*, **186(4164)**, 607–610, doi:10.1126/science.186.4164.607.

Mbaye, A.A. and F. Gueye, 2018: The Competitiveness Challenge of the Formal Sector in Francophone Africa: Understanding the Role of the Informal Sector and the Business Environment. In: *Africa's Competitiveness in the Global Economy* [Adeleye, I. and M. Esposito (eds.)], Springer International Publishing, Cham, Switzerland, pp. 25–51.

Mbow, C. C. Rosenzweig, L.G. Barioni, T.G. Benton, M. Herrero, M. Krishnapillai, E. Liwenga, P. Pradhan, M.G. Rivera-Ferre, T. Sapkota, F.N. Tubiello, Y. Xu, 2019: Food security. In: *Climate Change and Land: an IPCC special report on climate change, desertification, land degradation, sustainable land management, food security, and greenhouse gas fluxes in terrestrial ecosystems* [P.R. Shukla, J. Skea, E. Calvo Buendia, V. Masson-Delmotte, H.-O. Pörtner, D.C. Roberts, P. Zhai, R. Slade, S. Connors, R. van Diemen, M. Ferrat, E. Haughey, S. Luz, S. Neogi, M. Pathak, J. Petzold, J. Portugal Pereira, P. Vyas, E. Huntley, K. Kissick, M. Belkacemi, J. Malley, (eds.)]. Cambridge University Press, Cambridge, UK and New York, NY, USA, pp. 437–550.

McCalley, L.T. and C.J.H. Midden, 2002: Energy conservation through product-integrated feedback: The roles of goal-setting and social orientation. *J. Econ. Psychol.*, **23(5)**, 589–603, doi:10.1016/S0167-4870(02)00119-8.

McCright, A.M. and R.E. Dunlap, 2011: Cool dudes: The denial of climate change among conservative white males in the United States. *Glob. Environ. Change*, **21(4)**, 1163–1172, doi:10.1016/j.gloenvcha.2011.06.003.

McCright, A.M. and C. Xiao, 2014: Gender and Environmental Concern: Insights from Recent Work and for Future Research. *Soc. Nat. Resour.*, **27(10)**, 1109–1113, doi:10.1080/08941920.2014.918235.

McDonough, W., and M. Braungart, 2002: *Cradle to cradle: remaking the way we make things*. North Point Press, 193 pp.

McDowall, W. et al., 2017: Circular Economy Policies in China and Europe. *J. Ind. Ecol.*, **21(3)**, 651–661, doi.org/10.1111/jiec.12597.

McGee, J.A., and P.T. Greiner, 2018: Can Reducing Income Inequality Decouple Economic Growth from CO_2 Emissions? *Socius Sociol. Res. A Dyn. World*, **4**, 1–11, doi:10.1177/2378023118772716.

McKerracher, C. and J. Torriti, 2013: Energy consumption feedback in perspective: integrating Australian data to meta-analyses on in-home displays. *Energy Effic.*, **6(2)**, 387–405, doi:10.1007/s12053-012-9169-3.

McLaren, H.J., K.R. Wong, K.N. Nguyen, and K.N.D. Mahamadachchi, 2020: Covid-19 and women's triple burden: Vignettes from Sri Lanka, Malaysia, Vietnam and Australia. *Soc. Sci.*, **9(5)**, 87, doi:10.3390/SOCSCI9050087.

McMeekin, A. and D. Southerton, 2012: Sustainability transitions and final consumption: Practices and socio-technical systems. *Technol. Anal. Strateg. Manag.*, **24(4)**, 345–361, doi:10.1080/09537325.2012.663960.

McMeekin, A., F.W. Geels, and M. Hodson, 2019: Mapping the winds of whole system reconfiguration: Analysing low-carbon transformations across production, distribution and consumption in the UK electricity system **(1990–2016)**. *Res. Policy*, **48(5)**, 1216–1231, doi:10.1016/j.respol.2018.12.007.

Meade, N. and T. Islam, 2006: Modelling and forecasting the diffusion of innovation – A 25-year review. *Int. J. Forecast.*, **22(3)**, 519–545, doi:10.1016/j.ijforecast.2006.01.005.

Meadowcroft, J., 2011: Environmental Innovation and Societal Transitions Engaging with the politics of sustainability transitions. *Environ. Innov. Soc. Transitions*, **1(1)**, 70–75, doi:10.1016/j.eist.2011.02.003.

Mearns, R. and A. Norton, 2009: *Social dimensions of climate change : equity and vulnerability in a warming world*. World Bank, Washington, DC, USA, 319 pp.

Meckling, J., T. Sterner, and G. Wagner, 2017: Policy sequencing toward decarbonization. *Nat. Energy*, **2(12)**, 918–922, doi:10.1038/s41560-017-0025-8.

Medina, M.A.P. and A.G. Toledo-Bruno, 2016: Ecological footprint of university students: Does gender matter? *Autumn 2016 Glob. J. Environ. Sci. Manag.*, **2(4)**, 339–344, doi:10.22034/gjesm.2016.02.04.003.

Méjean, A., C. Guivarch, J. Lefèvre, and M. Hamdi-Cherif, 2019: The transition in energy demand sectors to limit global warming to 1.5°C. *Energy Effic.*, **12(2)**, 441–462, doi:10.1007/s12053-018-9682-0.

Mekuriaw, A., 2017: Towards a methodological approach to document and analyze local knowledge of climate change: with evidence from Rift Balley and Blue Nile Basins, Ethiopia. In: *Climate Change Adaptation in Africa: Fostering Resilience and Capacity to Adapt* [Leal Filho, W. et al. (eds.)], Springer, Cham, Switzerland, pp. 689–710.

Mekuriaw Bizuneh, A., 2013: *Climate Variability and Change in the Rift Valley and Blue Nile Basin*. Logos Verlag, Berlin, Germany.

Melville, N.P., 2010: Information Systems Innovation for Environmental Sustainability. *MIS Q.*, **34(1)**, 1–21, doi:10.2307/20721412.

Mendiluce, M., 2021: Your Company Pledged to Reduce Its Carbon Footprint. Now What? *Harvard Business Review*.

Mendoza, M.E.B., and O.G.M. Roa, 2014: Educomunicación y medio ambiente: en la búsqueda y construcción de fisuras. *Rev. Investig. Agrar. y Ambient.*, **5(1)**, doi:10.22490/21456453.960.

Merlin, L.A., 2019: Transportation Sustainability Follows From More People in Fewer Vehicles, Not Necessarily Automation. *J. Am. Plan. Assoc.*, **85(4)**, 501–510, doi:10.1080/01944363.2019.1637770.

Messner, D., 2015: A social contract for low carbon and sustainable development: Reflections on non-linear dynamics of social realignments and technological innovations in transformation processes. *Technol. Forecast. Soc. Change*, **98**, 260–270, doi:10.1016/j.techfore.2015.05.013.

Mi, L. et al., 2020: Evaluating the effect of eight customized information strategies on urban households' electricity saving: A field experiment in China. *Sustain. Cities Soc.*, **62**(November 2020), 102344, doi:10.1016/j.scs.2020.102344.

Mi, Z. and D.M. Coffman, 2019: The sharing economy promotes sustainable societies. *Nat. Commun.*, **10(1)**, 5–7, doi:10.1038/s41467-019-09260-4.

Michie, S., M.M. van Stralen, and R. West, 2011: The behaviour change wheel: A new method for characterising and designing behaviour change interventions. *Implement. Sci.*, **6(1)**, 42, doi:10.1186/1748-5908-6-42.

Milfont, T.L., J. Wilson, and P. Diniz, 2012: Time perspective and environmental engagement: A meta-analysis. *Int. J. Psychol.*, **47(5)**, 325–334, doi:10.1080/00207594.2011.647029.

Milkoreit, M., 2017: Imaginary politics: Climate change and making the future. *Elementa*, **5(62)**, doi:10.1525/elementa.249.

Miller, D.T. and D.A. Prentice, 2016: Changing Norms to Change Behavior. *Annu. Rev. Psychol.*, **67(1)**, 339–361, doi:10.1146/annurev-psych-010814-015013.

Miller, S.A., 2020: The role of cement service-life on the efficient use of resources. *Environ. Res. Lett.*, **15(2)**, 024004, doi:10.1088/1748-9326/AB639D.

Millot, A. et al., 2018: France 2072: Lifestyles at the core of carbon neutrality challenges. In: *Limiting Global Warming to Well Below 2°C: Energy System Modelling and Policy Development. Lecture Notes in Energy 54* [Giannakidis, G., K.B. Karlsson, M. Labriet, and B. Gallachóir, (eds.)], Vol. 64, Springer Verlag, Berlin, Germany, pp. 173–190.

Mills, B. and J. Schleich, 2012: Residential energy-efficient technology adoption, energy conservation, knowledge, and attitudes: An analysis of European countries. *Energy Policy*, **49**, 616–628, doi:10.1016/J.ENPOL.2012.07.008.

Millward-Hopkins, J. and Y. Oswald, 2021: 'Fair' inequality, consumption and climate mitigation. *Environ. Res. Lett.*, **16(3)**, 034007, doi:10.1088/1748-9326/ABE14F.

Millward-Hopkins, J., J.K. Steinberger, N.D. Rao, and Y. Oswald, 2020: Providing decent living with minimum energy: A global scenario. *Glob. Environ. Change*, **65**, 102168, doi:10.1016/j.gloenvcha.2020.102168.

MINTEL, 2019: MINTEL Global New Products Database. https://www.mintel.com/global-new-products-database/features (Accessed November 27, 2020).

Mitchell, J.K., 2015: Governance of megacity disaster risks: Confronting the contradictions. In: *Risk Governance: The Articulation of Hazard, Politics and Ecology* [Fra Paleo, U., (ed.)], Springer, Dordrecht, the Netherlands, pp. 413–439.

Moberg, K.R. et al., 2019: Mobility, food and housing: responsibility, individual consumption and demand-side policies in European deep decarbonisation pathways. *Energy Effic.*, **12(2)**, 497–519, doi:10.1007/s12053-018-9708-7.

Moeckel, R. and R. Lewis, 2017: Two decades of smart growth in Maryland (U.S.A): impact assessment and future directions of a national leader. *Urban, Plan. Transp. Res.*, **5(1)**, 22–37, doi:10.1080/21650020.2017.1304240.

Möhlmann, M., 2015: Collaborative consumption: determinants of satisfaction and the likelihood of using a sharing economy option again. *J. Consum. Behav.*, **14(3)**, 193–207, doi:10.1002/cb.1512.

Mokhtarian, P.L., 2002: Telecommunications and travel: The case for complementarity *J. Ind. Ecol.*, **6(2)**, 43–57, doi:10.1162/108819802763471771.

Monasterolo, I. and M. Raberto, 2019: The impact of phasing out fossil fuel subsidies on the low-carbon transition. *Energy Policy*, **124**, 355–370, doi:10.1016/j.enpol.2018.08.051.

Mondal, M.A.H., E. Bryan, C. Ringler, D. Mekonnen, and M. Rosegrant, 2018: Ethiopian energy status and demand scenarios: Prospects to improve energy efficiency and mitigate GHG emissions. *Energy*, **149**, 161–172, doi:10.1016/j.energy.2018.02.067.

Mont, O., Y.V. Palgan, K. Bradley, and L. Zvolska, 2020: A decade of the sharing economy: Concepts, users, business and governance perspectives. *J. Clean. Prod.*, **269**, 122215, doi:10.1016/j.jclepro.2020.122215.

Moran, D. et al., 2020: Quantifying the potential for consumer-oriented policy to reduce European and foreign carbon emissions. *Clim. Policy*, **20**(sup1), doi:10.1080/14693062.2018.1551186.

Moreau, V., M. Sahakian, P. van Griethuysen, and F. Vuille, 2017: Coming Full Circle: Why Social and Institutional Dimensions Matter for the Circular Economy. *J. Ind. Ecol.*, **21(3)**, 497–506, doi:10.1111/jiec.12598.

Morello Frosch, R., M. Pastor, J. Sadd, and S. Shonkoff, 2009: *The Climate Gap: Inequalities in How Climate Change Hurts Americans & How to Close the Gap*. Equity Research Institute, https://dornsife.usc.edu/pere/climategap/ (Accessed December 3, 2020).

Morris, C., J. Kirwan, and R. Lally, 2014: Less Meat Initiatives: An Initial Exploration of a Diet-focused Social Innovation in Transitions to a More Sustainable Regime of Meat Provisioning. *Int. J. Sociol. Agric. Food*, **21(2)**, 189–208.

Morstyn, T., N. Farrell, S.J. Darby, and M.D. McCulloch, 2018: Using peer-to-peer energy-trading platforms to incentivize prosumers to form federated power plants. *Nat. Energy*, **3(2)**, doi:10.1038/s41560-017-0075-y.

Mortensen, C.R. et al., 2019: Trending Norms: A Lever for Encouraging Behaviors Performed by the Minority. *Soc. Psychol. Personal. Sci.*, **10(2)**, 201–210, doi:10.1177/1948550617734615.

Moser, S.C. and J.A. Ekstrom, 2010: A framework to diagnose barriers to climate change adaptation. *Proc. Natl. Acad. Sci.*, **107(51)**, 22026, doi:10.1073/PNAS.1007887107.

Muchie, M., S. Bhaduri, A. Baskaran, and F.A. Sheikh (eds.), 2016: *Informal Sector Innovations: Insights from the Global South*. Routledge, Abingdon, UK, 178 pp.

Mulder, L.B., E. Van Dijk, D. De Cremer, and H.A.M. Wilke, 2006: Undermining trust and cooperation: The paradox of sanctioning systems in social dilemmas. *J. Exp. Soc. Psychol.*, **42**, 147–162, doi:10.1016/j.jesp.2005.03.002.

Muller, A. et al., 2017: Strategies for feeding the world more sustainably with organic agriculture. *Nat. Commun.*, **8(1)**, doi:10.1038/s41467-017-01410-w.

Mulugetta, Y., E. Ben Hagan, and D. Kammen, 2019: *Energy access for sustainable development*. Institute of Physics Publishing, Bristol, UK.

Mundaca, L., H. Busch, and S. Schwer, 2018: 'Successful' low-carbon energy transitions at the community level? An energy justice perspective.' *Appl. Energy*, **218**, 292–303, doi:10.1016/j.apenergy.2018.02.146.

Mundaca, L., D. Ürge-Vorsatz, and C. Wilson, 2019: Demand-side approaches for limiting global warming to 1.5°C. *Energy Effic.*, **12(2)**, 343–362, doi:10.1007/s12053-018-9722-9.

Muñoz, I. et al., 2021: Life cycle assessment of integrated additive–subtractive concrete 3D printing. *Int. J. Adv. Manuf. Technol.*, **112(7)**, 2149–2159, doi:10.1007/S00170-020-06487-0.

Murray, A., K. Skene, and K. Haynes, 2017: The Circular Economy: An Interdisciplinary Exploration of the Concept and Application in a Global Context. *J. Bus. Ethics*, **140(3)**, 369–380, doi:10.1007/s10551-015-2693-2.

Muttitt, G. and S. Kartha, 2020: Equity, climate justice and fossil fuel extraction: principles for a managed phase out. *Clim. Policy*, 1–19, doi:10.1080/14693062.2020.1763900.

Mylan, J., 2018: Sustainable consumption in everyday life: A qualitative study of UK consumer experiences of meat reduction. *Sustainability*, **10(7)**, 2307, doi:10.3390/su10072307.

Myrick, J.G. and S. Evans Comfort, 2019: The Pope May Not Be Enough: How Emotions, Populist Beliefs, and Perceptions of an Elite Messenger Interact to Influence Responses to Climate Change Messaging. *Mass Commun. Soc.*, **23(1)**, 1–21, doi:10.1080/15205436.2019.1639758.

Nabi, A.A. et al., 2020: Relationship between population growth, price level, poverty incidence, and carbon emissions in a panel of 98 countries. *Environ. Sci. Pollut. Res.*, **27(2020)**, 31778–31792, doi:10.1007/s11356-020-08465-1.

Nadel, S. and L. Ungar, 2019: *Halfway there: Energy efficiency can cut energy use and greenhouse gas emissions in half by 2050*. American Council for an Energy-Efficient Economy, Washington, DC, USA, 70 pp. https://www.aceee.org/sites/default/files/publications/researchreports/u1907.pdf.

Nagel, J., 2015: *Gender and climate change: Impacts, science, policy*. Routledge, Abingdon, UK, 249 pp.

Nagy, D., J. Schuessler, and A. Dubinsky, 2016: Defining and identifying disruptive innovations. *Ind. Mark. Manag.*, **57**, doi:10.1016/j.indmarman.2015.11.017.

Nakićenović, N. et al., 1993: Long term strategies for mitigating global warming. *Energy*, **18(5)**, 401–609, doi:10.1016/0360-5442(93)90019-A.

Nakićenović, N., P.V. Gilli, and R. Kurz, 1996a: Regional and global exergy and energy efficiencies. *Energy*, **21(3)**, 223–237, doi:10.1016/0360-5442(96)00001-1.

Nakićenović, N., A. Grübler, H. Ishitani, T. Johansson, G. Marland, J.R. Moreira, H-H. Rogner, 1996b: Energy Primer. In: *Climate Change 1995: Impacts, Adaptations and Mitigation of Climate Change: Scientific-Technical Analyses. Contribution of Working Group II to the Second Assessment Report of the Intergovernmental Panel on Climate Change* [Watson, R.T., M.C. Zinyowera, and R.H. Moss, (eds.)], Cambridge University Press, Cambridge, UK, and New York, NY, USA, pp. 77–94.

Namazu, M. and H. Dowlatabadi, 2015: Characterizing the GHG emission impacts of carsharing: A case of Vancouver. *Environ. Res. Lett.*, **10(12)**, doi:10.1088/1748-9326/10/12/124017.

Nandi, S., J. Sarkis, A.A. Hervani, and M.M. Helms, 2020: Redesigning Supply Chains using Blockchain-Enabled Circular Economy and COVID-19 Experiences. *Sustain. Prod. Consum.*, **27**, 10–22, doi:10.1016/j.spc.2020.10.019.

Nandy, B. et al., 2015: Recovery of consumer waste in India – A mass flow analysis for paper, plastic and glass and the contribution of households and the informal sector. *Resour. Conserv. Recycl.*, **101**, 167–181, doi:10.1016/j.resconrec.2015.05.012.

Napp, T.A. et al., 2019: The role of advanced demand-sector technologies and energy demand reduction in achieving ambitious carbon budgets. *Appl. Energy*, **238**, pp. 351–367, doi:10.1016/j.apenergy.2019.01.033.

Narayan, L., 2017: Contextualizing unpaid care work and women empowerment. *Int. J. Appl. Res.*, **3(7)**, 654–659.

Nasir, M.H.A., A. Genovese, A.A. Acquaye, S.C.L. Koh, and F. Yamoah, 2017: Comparing linear and circular supply chains: A case study from the construction industry. *Int. J. Prod. Econ.*, **183**, 443–457, doi:10.1016/j.ijpe.2016.06.008.

Nasr, N. et al., 2018: *Redefining value: manufacturing revolution-remanufacturing, refurbishment, repair and direct reuse in the circular economy*. United Nations Environment Programme, Nairobi, Kenya, 267 pp.

Navroz, D., 2019: *India in a Warming World: Integrating Climate Change and Development – Google Books*. [Dubash, N., (ed.)]. Oxford University Press, Oxford, UK.

Nayak, B.P., C. Werthmann, and V. Aggarwal, 2015: Trust and cooperation among urban poor for transition to cleaner and modern cooking fuel. *Environ. Innov. Soc. Transitions*, **14**, 116–127, doi:10.1016/j.eist.2014.09.002.

négaWatt Association, 2018: *négaWatt scenario 2017–2050: A blueprint for a succesful energy transition in France*. négaWatt Association, Valence, France, https://negawatt.org/IMG/pdf/181128_negawatt-scenario_eng_12p.pdf (Accessed December 5, 2021).

Nelson, E.J. et al., 2013: Climate change's impact on key ecosystem services and the human well-being they support in the US. *Front. Ecol. Environ.*, **11(9)**, 483–893, doi:10.1890/120312.

Nelson, R. and E.S. Phelps, 1966: Investment in Humans, Technological Diffusion, and Economic Growth. *Am. Econ. Rev.*, **56(1)**, 69–75, doi:10.1016/b978-0-12-554002-5.50015-7.

Nemati, M. and J. Penn, 2020: The impact of information-based interventions on conservation behavior: A meta-analysis. *Resour. Energy Econ.*, **62**, 101201, doi:10.1016/j.reseneeco.2020.101201.

Nepal, M., A. Nepal, and K. Grimsrud, 2010: Unbelievable but improved cookstoves are not helpful in reducing firewood demand in Nepal. *Environ. Dev. Econ.*, **16(1)**, 1–23, doi:10.1017/S1355770X10000409.

Newell, P., 2005: Climate for Change? Civil Society and the Politics of Global Warming. In: *Global Civil Society 2005/6* [Glasius, M., M. Kaldor, and H. Anheier, (eds.)], SAGE Publications Inc., pp. 120–149.

Newell, R.G. and J. Siikamäki, 2014: Nudging Energy Efficiency Behavior: The Role of Information Labels. *J. Assoc. Environ. Resour. Econ.*, **1(4)**, 555–598, doi:10.1086/679281.

Newman, P. and J.R. Kenworthy, 2015: *The End of Automobile Dependence: How Cities are Moving Beyond Car-based Planning*. Island Press, Washington, DC, USA, 320 pp.

Newman, P., T. Beatley, and H. Boyer, 2017: *Resilient Cities: Overcoming Fossil Fuel Dependence*. 2nd ed. Island Press, Washington, DC, USA, 264 pp.

Ng, W. and E. Diener, 2019: Affluence and Subjective Well-Being: Does Income Inequality Moderate their Associations? *Appl. Res. Qual. Life*, **14(1)**, 155–170, doi:10.1007/s11482-017-9585-9.

Ngamaba, K.H., M. Panagioti, and C.J. Armitage, 2018: Income inequality and subjective well-being: a systematic review and meta-analysis. *Qual. Life Res.*, **27(3)**, 577–596, doi:10.1007/s11136-017-1719-x.

Niamir, L., 2019: Behavioural Climate Change Mitigation: from individual energy choices to demand-side potential. University of Twente, Enschede, the Netherlands, 267 pp.

Niamir, L., T. Filatova, A. Voinov, and H. Bressers, 2018: Transition to low-carbon economy: Assessing cumulative impacts of individual behavioral changes. *Energy Policy*, **118**, 325–345, doi:10.1016/j.enpol.2018.03.045.

Niamir, L., O. Ivanova, and T. Filatova, 2020a: Economy-wide impacts of behavioral climate change mitigation: Linking agent-based and computable general equilibrium models. *Environ. Model. Softw.*, **134**, 104839, doi:10.1016/j.envsoft.2020.104839.

Niamir, L., O. Ivanova, T. Filatova, A. Voinov, and H. Bressers, 2020b: Demand-side solutions for climate mitigation: Bottom-up drivers of household energy behavior change in the Netherlands and Spain. *Energy Res. Soc. Sci.*, **62(101356)**, 101356, doi:10.1016/j.erss.2019.101356.

Niamir, L. et al., 2020c: Assessing the macroeconomic impacts of individual behavioral changes on carbon emissions. *Clim. Change*, **158**, 141–160, doi:10.1007/s10584-019-02566-8.

Nicoson, C., 2021: Towards climate resilient peace: an intersectional and degrowth approach. *Sustain. Sci.*, **16(4)**, 1147–1158, doi:10.1007/S11625-021-00906-1.

Nielsen, K.R., L.A. Reisch, and J. Thøgersen, 2016: Sustainable user innovation from a policy perspective: a systematic literature review. *J. Clean. Prod.*, **133**, 65–77, doi:10.1016/j.jclepro.2016.05.092.

Nielsen, K.S., K.A. Nicholas, F. Creutzig, T. Dietz, and P.C. Stern, 2021. The role of high-socioeconomic-status people in locking in or rapidly reducing energy-driven greenhouse gas emissions. *Nature Energy* **6(11)**, 1011–1016, doi:10.1038/s41560-021-00900-y.

Nijland, H. and J. van Meerkerk, 2017: Mobility and environmental impacts of car sharing in the Netherlands. *Environ. Innov. Soc. Transitions*, **23**, 84–91, doi:10.1016/j.eist.2017.02.001.

Nijland, H., J. Van Meerkerk, and A. Hoen, 2015: *Impact of car sharing on mobility and CO₂ emissions*. PBL Netherlands Environmental Assessment Agency, The Hague, the Netherlands, 12 pp. https://www.pbl.nl/sites/default/files/downloads/PBL_2015_Note_Impact_of_car_sharing_1842.pdf (Accessed December 9, 2020).

Nikas, A. et al., 2020: The desirability of transitions in demand: Incorporating behavioural and societal transformations into energy modelling. *Energy Res. Soc. Sci.*, **70**, 101780, doi:10.1016/J.ERSS.2020.101780.

Nisa, C.F., J.J. Bélanger, B.M. Schumpe, and D.G. Faller, 2019: Meta-analysis of randomised controlled trials testing behavioural interventions to promote household action on climate change. *Nat. Commun.*, **10(1)**, 4545, doi:10.1038/s41467-019-12457-2.

Nkrumah, B., 2021: Beyond Tokenism: The "Born Frees" and Climate Change in South Africa. *Int. J. Ecol.*, **2021**, doi:10.1155/2021/8831677.

Nolan, J.M., P.W. Schultz, R.B. Cialdini, N.J. Goldstein, and V. Griskevicius, 2008: Normative social influence is underdetected. *Personal. Soc. Psychol. Bull.*, **34(7)**, 913–923, doi:10.1177/0146167208316691.

5

Noppers, E.H., K. Keizer, J.W. Bolderdijk, and L. Steg, 2014: The adoption of sustainable innovations: Driven by symbolic and environmental motives. *Glob. Environ. Change*, **25(1)**, 52–62, doi:10.1016/j.gloenvcha.2014.01.012.

Noppers, E.H., K. Keizer, M. Bockarjova, and L. Steg, 2015: The adoption of sustainable innovations: The role of instrumental, environmental, and symbolic attributes for earlier and later adopters. *J. Environ. Psychol.*, **44**, 74–84, doi:10.1016/j.jenvp.2015.09.002.

Noppers, E.H., K. Keizer, M. Milovanovic, and L. Steg, 2016: The importance of instrumental, symbolic, and environmental attributes for the adoption of smart energy systems. *Energy Policy*, **98**, 12–18, doi:10.1016/j.enpol.2016.08.007.

Nordhaus, T., 2019: The Empty Radicalism of the Climate Apocalypse. *Issues Sci. Technol.*, **35(4)**, 69–78.

Norouzi, N., G. Zarazua de Rubens, S. Choubanpishehzafar, and P. Enevoldsen, 2020: When pandemics impact economies and climate change: Exploring the impacts of COVID-19 on oil and electricity demand in China. *Energy Res. Soc. Sci.*, **68**, 101654, doi:10.1016/j.erss.2020.101654.

Norton, B., 2012: No Title. *Saving waste: Energy use and waste analysis by end-use*. Presentation. November 13.

Noy, K, and M. Givoni, 2018: Is 'Smart Mobility' Sustainable? Examining the Views and Beliefs of Transport's Technological Entrepreneurs. *Sustainability*, **10(2)**, 422, doi:10.3390/su10020422.

Nußholz, J.L.K., F. Nygaard Rasmussen, and L. Milios, 2019: Circular building materials: Carbon saving potential and the role of business model innovation and public policy. *Resour. Conserv. Recycl.*, **141**(November 2018), 308–316, doi:10.1016/j.resconrec.2018.10.036.

Nyborg, K. and M. Rege, 2003: On social norms: the evolution of considerate smoking behavior. *J. Econ. Behav. Organ.*, **52(3)**, 323–340, doi:10.1016/S0167-2681(03)00031-3.

Nyborg, K. et al., 2016: Social norms as solutions. *Science*, **354(6308)**, 42–43, doi:10.1126/science.aaf8317.

O'Brien, K., E. Selboe, and B. Hayward, 2018: Exploring youth activism on climate change: dutiful, disruptive, and dangerous dissent. *Ecol. Soc.*, **23(3)**, doi:10.5751/ES-10287-230342.

O'Connor, N., 2017: Three connections between rising economic inequality and the rise of populism. *Irish Stud. Int. Aff.*, **28**, 29–43, doi:10.3318/isia.2017.28.5.

O'Neill, D.W. et al., 2018: A good life for all within planetary boundaries. *Nat. Sustain.*, **1(2)**, 88–95, doi:10.1038/s41893-018-0021-4.

O'Neill, S.J. and N. Smith, 2014: Climate change and visual imagery. *Wiley Interdiscip. Rev. Clim. Change*, **5(1)**, 73–87, doi:10.1002/wcc.249.

Ochsendorf, J. et al., 2011: *Methods, impacts, and opportunities in the concrete building life cycle*. Concrete Sustainability Hub, Massachusetts Institute of Technology, Cambridge, MA, USA, 119 pp. http://cshub.mit.edu/sites/default/files/documents/MIT Buildings LCA Report.pdf.

OECD, 2019a: *Accelerating Climate Action: Refocusing Policies through a Well-being Lens*. Organisation for Economic Co-operation and Development, Paris, France, 193 pp.

OECD, 2019b: *Global Material Resources Outlook to 2060*. Organisation for Economic Co-operation and Development, Paris, France, 212 pp.

OECD/FAO, 2018: *OECD-FAO Agricultural Outlook 2018–2027*. OECD Publishing, Paris, France and FAO, Rome, Italy, 108 pp.

Ohler, A.M., D.G. Loomis, and K. Ilves, 2020: A study of electricity savings from energy star appliances using household survey data. *Energy Policy*, **144**(September 2020), 111607, doi:10.1016/j.enpol.2020.111607.

Oishi, S., K. Kushlev, and U. Schimmack, 2018: Progressive taxation, income inequality, and happiness. *Am. Psychol.*, **73(2)**, 157–168, doi:10.1037/amp0000166.

Okvat, H.A. and A.J. Zautra, 2011: Community Gardening: A Parsimonious Path to Individual, Community, and Environmental Resilience. *Am. J. Community Psychol.*, **47(3–4)**, 374–387, doi:10.1007/s10464-010-9404-z.

Olatunji, O.O. et al., 2019: Competitive advantage of carbon efficient supply chain in manufacturing industry. *J. Clean. Prod.*, **238**, 117937, doi:10.1016/j.jclepro.2019.117937.

Oliva, R. and R. Kallenberg, 2003: Managing the transition from products to services. *Int. J. Serv. Ind. Manag.*, **14(2)**, 160–172, doi:10.1108/09564230310474138.

Onyige, C.D., 2017: Women, indigenous knowledge and climate change in Nigeria. *Osun Sociol. Rev.*, **4(1 & 2)**.

Oparaocha, S. and S. Dutta, 2011: Gender and energy for sustainable development. *Curr. Opin. Environ. Sustain.*, **3(4)**, 265–271, doi:10.1016/j.cosust.2011.07.003.

Oreskes, N. and E.M. Conway, 2011: *Merchants of Doubt: How a Handful of Scientists Obscured the Truth on Issues from Tobacco Smoke to Global Warming*. 1st ed. Bloomsbury Press, New York, USA, London, UK, New Delhi, India and Sydney, Australia.

Orsini, F. and P. Marrone, 2019: Approaches for a low-carbon production of building materials: A review. *J. Clean. Prod.*, **241**, doi:10.1016/j.jclepro.2019.118380.

Ortega-Ruiz, G., A. Mena-Nieto, and J.E. García-Ramos, 2020: Is India on the right pathway to reduce CO_2 emissions? Decomposing an enlarged Kaya identity using the LMDI method for the period 1990–2016. *Sci. Total Environ.*, **737**, 139638, doi:10.1016/j.scitotenv.2020.139638.

Ortiz, J., N. Casquero-Modrego, and J. Salom, 2019: Health and related economic effects of residential energy retrofitting in Spain. *Energy Policy*, **130**, 375–388, doi:10.1016/j.enpol.2019.04.013.

Osuoka, A. and A. Haruna, 2019: *Boiling Over: Global Warming, Hunger and Violence in the Lake Chad Basin*. http://saction.org/books/boiling_over.pdf.

Oswald, Y., A. Owen, and J.K. Steinberger, 2020: Large inequality in international and intranational energy footprints between income groups and across consumption categories. *Nat. Energy*, **5(2020)**, 231–239, doi:10.1038/s41560-020-0579-8.

Oswald, Y., J.K. Steinberger, D. Ivanova, and J. Millward-Hopkins, 2021: Global redistribution of income and household energy footprints: a computational thought experiment. *Glob. Sustain.*, **4**, doi:10.1017/SUS.2021.1.

Otto, I.M., K.M. Kim, N. Dubrovsky, and W. Lucht, 2019: Shift the focus from the super-poor to the super-rich. *Nat. Clim. Change*, **9(2)**, 82–84, doi:10.1038/s41558-019-0402-3.

Otto, I.M. et al., 2020: Social tipping dynamics for stabilizing Earth's climate by 2050. *Proc. Natl. Acad. Sci.*, **117(5)**, 2354–2365, doi:10.1073/pnas.1900577117.

Overland, I. and B.K. Sovacool, 2020: The misallocation of climate research funding. *Energy Res. Soc. Sci.*, **62**, 101349, doi:10.1016/j.erss.2019.101349.

Owens, S., 2000: 'Engaging the Public': Information and Deliberation in Environmental Policy. *Environ. Plan. A Econ. Sp.*, **32(7)**, 1141–1148, doi:10.1068/a3330.

Ozturk, I., 2010: A literature survey on energy-growth nexus. *Energy Policy*, **38(1)**, 340–349, doi:10.1016/j.enpol.2009.09.024.

Pachauri, S., 2007: *An energy analysis of household consumption: Changing patterns of direct and indirect use in India*. 1st ed. Springer-Verlag Berlin.

Pachauri, S. and D. Spreng, 2002: Direct and indirect energy requirements of households in India. *Energy Policy*, **30(6)**, 511–523, doi:10.1016/S0301-4215(01)00119-7.

Pacheco, E.B.A.V., L.M. Ronchetti, and E. Masanet, 2012: An overview of plastic recycling in Rio de Janeiro. *Resour. Conserv. Recycl.*, **60** (March) pp. 140–146, doi:10.1016/j.resconrec.2011.12.010.

Pagliano, L. and S. Erba, 2019: Energy sufficiency in (strongly intertwined) building and city design – Examples for temperate and Mediterranean climates. *Proceedings of the 2019 eceee Summer Study*, European Council for an Energy Efficient Economy, Stockholm, Sweden, pp. 1505–1514.

Pahle, M. et al., 2018: Sequencing to ratchet up climate policy stringency. *Nat. Clim. Change*, **8(10)**, 861–867, doi:10.1038/s41558-018-0287-6.

5

Pallak, M.S. and W. Cummings, 1976: Commitment and Voluntary Energy Conservation. *Personal. Soc. Psychol. Bull.*, **2(1)**, 27–30, doi:10.1177/0146 16727600200105.

Pan, X. et al., 2019: Carbon Palma Ratio: A new indicator for measuring the distribution inequality of carbon emissions among individuals. *J. Clean. Prod.*, **241**, 118418, doi:10.1016/j.jclepro.2019.118418.

Pant, K.P., S.K. Pattanayak, and M.B.M. Thakuri, 2014: Climate change, cookstoves and coughs and colds: Thinking global acting locally in rural Nepal. In: *Environment and Development Economics: Essays in Honour of Sir Partha Dasgupta* [Barrett, S., K.-G. Mäler, and E.S. Maskin, (eds.)], Oxford University Press, Oxford, pp. 145–168.

Parag, Y. and K.B. Janda, 2014: More than filler: Middle actors and socio-technical change in the energy system from the "middle-out." *Energy Res. Soc. Sci.*, **3**(C), 102–112, doi:10.1016/j.erss.2014.07.011.

Parker, S. and M.I. Bhatti, 2020: Dynamics and drivers of per capita CO_2 emissions in Asia. *Energy Econ.*, **89(2020)**, 104798, doi:10.1016/j.eneco. 2020.104798.

Pascale, A., S. Chakravarty, P. Lant, S. Smart, and C. Greig, 2020: The rise of (sub)nations? Sub-national human development, climate targets, and carbon dioxide emissions in 163 countries. *Energy Res. Soc. Sci.*, **68**, 101546, doi:10.1016/j.erss.2020.101546.

Patel, J.A. et al., 2020: Poverty, inequality and COVID-19: the forgotten vulnerable. *Public Health*, **183**, 110–111, doi:10.1016/j.puhe.2020.05.006.

Patra, S.K. and M. Muchie, 2017: Science, technology and innovation in BRICS countries: Introduction to the special issue. *African J. Sci. Technol. Innov. Dev.*, **9(5)**, 499–501, doi:10.1080/20421338.2017.1380586.

Pattanayak, S.K. et al., 2019: Experimental evidence on promotion of electric and improved biomass cookstoves. *Proc. Natl. Acad. Sci.*, **116(27)**, 13282–13287, doi:10.1073/pnas.1808827116.

Patterson, J.J. and D. Huitema, 2019: Institutional innovation in urban governance: The case of climate change adaptation. *J. Environ. Plan. Manag.*, **62(3)**, 374–398, doi:10.1080/09640568.2018.1510767.

Patterson, J.J. et al., 2018: Political feasibility of 1.5°C societal transformations: the role of social justice. *Curr. Opin. Environ. Sustain.*, **31**, 1–9, doi:10.1016/ J.COSUST.2017.11.002.

Pauliuk, S., A. Arvesen, K. Stadler, and E.G. Hertwich, 2017: Industrial ecology in integrated assessment models. *Nat. Clim. Change*, **7**, pp. 13–20, doi:10.1038/ nclimate3148.

Pauliuk, S. et al., 2021: Global Scenarios of Resource and Emissions Savings from Systemic Material Efficiency in Buildings and Cars. *Nat. Commun.*, **12**, doi:10.1038/s41467-021-25300-4.

Pearce, W., S. Niederer, S.M. Özkula, and N. Sánchez Querubín, 2019: The social media life of climate change: Platforms, publics, and future imaginaries. *Wiley Interdiscip. Rev. Clim. Change*, **10(2)**, doi:10.1002/wcc.569.

Pearl-Martinez, R. and J.C. Stephens, 2017: Toward a gender diverse workforce in the renewable energy transition. *Sustain. Sci. Pract. Policy*, **12(1)**, doi:10. 1080/15487733.2016.11908149.

Pearse, R., 2017: Gender and climate change. *Wiley Interdiscip. Rev. Clim. Change*, **8(2)**, e451, doi:10.1002/wcc.451.

Pearson-Stuttard, J. et al., 2017: Comparing effectiveness of mass media campaigns with price reductions targeting fruit and vegetable intake on US cardiovascular disease mortality and race disparities. *Am. J. Clin. Nutr.*, **106(1)**, 199–206, doi:10.3945/ajcn.

Pearson, A.R. et al., 2017: Race, Class, Gender and Climate Change Communication. In: *Oxford Research Encyclopedia of Climate Science*, Oxford University Press, Oxford, UK.

Pecl, G.T. et al., 2017: Biodiversity redistribution under climate change: Impacts on ecosystems and human well-being. *Science*, **355(6332)**, doi:10.1126/ science.aai9214.

Pendrill, F. et al., 2019: Agricultural and forestry trade drives large share of tropical deforestation emissions. *Glob. Environ. Change*, **56**(March), 1–10, doi:10.1016/j.gloenvcha.2019.03.002.

Perch, L., 2011: *Mitigation of what and by what? Adaptation by whom and for whom? Dilemmas in delivering for the poor and the vulnerable in international climate policy.*, IPC-IG, Brasilia Brazil, https://www.ipc-undp. org/pub/IPCWorkingPaper79.pdf.

Peres, R., E. Muller, and V. Mahajan, 2010: Innovation diffusion and new product growth models: A critical review and research directions. *Int. J. Res. Mark.*, **27(2)**, 91–106, doi:10.1016/j.ijresmar.2009.12.012.

Perez, C. et al., 2015: How resilient are farming households and communities to a changing climate in Africa? A gender-based perspective. *Glob. Environ. Change*, **34**, 95–107, doi:10.1016/j.gloenvcha.2015.06.003.

Perkins, P.E., 2019: Climate justice, commons, and degrowth. *Ecol. Econ.*, **160**, 183–190, doi:10.1016/j.ecolecon.2019.02.005.

Perkins, R., 2003: Environmental leapfrogging in developing countries: A critical assessment and reconstruction. *Nat. Resour. Forum*, **27(3)**, 177–188, doi:10.1111/1477-8947.00053.

Perlaviciute, G., G. Schuitema, P. Devine-Wright, and B. Ram, 2018: At the heart of a sustainable energy transition: The public acceptability of energy projects. *IEEE Power Energy Mag.*, **16(1)**, 49–55, doi:10.1109/MPE.2017.2759918.

Permana, A.S., N.A. Aziz, and H.C. Siong, 2015: Is mom energy efficient? A study of gender, household energy consumption and family decision making in Indonesia. *Energy Res. Soc. Sci.*, **6**, 78–86, doi:10.1016/j.erss.2014.12.007.

Peters, M. et al., 2012: Tropical Forage-based Systems to Mitigate Greenhouse Gas Emissions. In: *Eco-Efficiency: From Vision to Reality* [Hershey, C.H., (ed.)], International Center for Tropical Agriculture (CIAT), Cali, Colombia.

Petheram, L., N. Stacey, and A. Fleming, 2015: Future sea changes: Indigenous women's preferences for adaptation to climate change on South Goulburn Island, Northern Territory (Australia). *Clim. Dev.*, **7(4)**, 339–352, doi:10.1080/ 17565529.2014.951019.

Petrovic, N., J. Madrigano, and L. Zaval, 2014: Motivating mitigation: when health matters more than climate change. *Clim. Change*, **126**, 245–254, doi:10.1007/s10584-014-1192-2.

Pettifor, H. and C. Wilson, 2020: Low carbon innovations for mobility, food, homes and energy: A synthesis of consumer attributes. *Renew. Sustain. Energy Rev.*, **130**, doi:10.1016/j.rser.2020.109954.

Pettifor, H., C. Wilson, J. Axsen, W. Abrahamse, and J. Anable, 2017: Social influence in the global diffusion of alternative fuel vehicles – A meta-analysis. *J. Transp. Geogr.*, **62**(June), 247–261, doi:10.1016/j.jtrangeo.2017.06.009.

Phillips, C.A. et al., 2020: Compound climate risks in the COVID-19 pandemic. *Nat. Clim. Change*, **10(7)**, 586–588, doi:10.1038/s41558-020-0804-2.

Phuong, L.T.H., G.R. Biesbroek, and A.E.J. Wals, 2017: The interplay between social learning and adaptive capacity in climate change adaptation: A systematic review. *NJAS – Wageningen J. Life Sci.*, **82**, 1–9, doi:10.1016/ j.njas.2017.05.001.

Pichler, P.P., I.S. Jaccard, U. Weisz, and H. Weisz, 2019: International comparison of health care carbon footprints. *Environ. Res. Lett.*, **14(6)**, 064004, doi:10.1088/1748-9326/ab19e1.

Pigato, M.A. et al., 2020: *Technology Transfer and Innovation for Low-Carbon Development*. World Bank, Washington, DC, USA, 192 pp.

Piggot, G., 2018: The influence of social movements on policies that constrain fossil fuel supply. *Clim. Policy*, **18(7)**, 942–954, doi:10.1080/14693062.20 17.1394255.

Piggot, G., M. Boyland, A. Down, and A.R. Torre, 2019: *Realizing a just and equitable transition away from fossil fuels*. Stockholm Environment Institute, Stockholm, Sweden.

Pigou, A., 1920: *The Economics of Welfare*. Macmillan, London, UK.

Pizzigati, S., 2018: Can an Unequal Earth Beat Climate Change? Inequality. org, https://inequality.org/great-divide/can-an-unequal-earth-beat-climate-change/ (Accessed July 4, 2019).

Polonsky, M.J., A. Vocino, S.L. Grau, R. Garma, and A.S. Ferdous, 2012: The impact of general and carbon-related environmental knowledge on attitudes and behaviour of US consumers. *J. Mark. Manag.*, **28(3–4)**, 238–263, doi:10.1080/0267257X.2012.659279.

5

Poore, J. and T. Nemecek, 2018: Reducing food's environmental impacts through producers and consumers. *Science*, **360(6392)**, 987–992, doi:10.1126/science.aaq0216.

Porio, E., 2011: Vulnerability, adaptation, and resilience to floods and climate change-related risks among marginal, riverine communities in Metro Manila. *Asian J. Soc. Sci.*, **39(4)**, 425–445, doi:10.1163/156853111X597260.

Porter, G., 2016: Mobilities in rural Africa: New connections, new challenges. *Ann. Am. Assoc. Geogr.*, **106(2)**, 434–441, doi:10.1080/00045608.2015.1100056.

Porter, L. et al., 2020: Climate Justice in a Climate Changed World. *Plan. Theory*, **21(2)**, 293–321, doi:10.1080/14649357.2020.1748959.

Porter, M.E. and M.R. Kramer, 2006: Strategy & Society: The link between competitive advantage and corporate social responsibility. *Harv. Bus. Rev.*, **84(12)**, 78–92.

Porter, M.E., S. Stern, and M. Green, 2017: *Social Progress Index 2017*. Social Progress Imperative, Washington, DC, USA, 95 pp.

Pottier, A., E. Combet, J. Cayla, S. De Lauretis, and F. Nadaud, 2021: *Who emits CO₂? Landscape of ecological inequalities in France from a critical perspective*. FEEM Working Paper No. 14.2021, Fondazione Eni Enrico Mattei (FEEM), Milan, Italy.

Potting, J. et al., 2018: *Circular Economy: What We Want To Know and Can Measure*. PBL Netherlands Environmental Assessment Agency, The Hague, the Netherlands, 20 pp.

Pouri, M.J. and L.M. Hilty, 2018: Conceptualizing the Digital Sharing Economy in the Context of Sustainability. *Sustainability*, **10(12)**, 4453, doi:10.3390/su10124453.

Powless, B., 2012: An Indigenous Movement to Confront Climate Change. *Globalizations*, **9(3)**, 411–424, doi:10.1080/14747731.2012.680736.

Prata, J.C., A.L.P. Silva, T.R. Walker, A.C. Duarte, and T. Rocha-Santos, 2020: COVID-19 Pandemic Repercussions on the Use and Management of Plastics. *Environ. Sci. Technol.*, **54(13)**, 7760–7765, doi:10.1021/acs.est.0c02178.

Prideaux, B., M. Thompson, and A. Pabel, 2020: Lessons from COVID-19 can prepare global tourism for the economic transformation needed to combat climate change. *Tour. Geogr.*, **22(3)**, 667–678, doi:10.1080/14616688.2020.1762117.

Princen, T., 2003: Principles for Sustainability: From Cooperation and Efficiency to Sufficiency. *Glob. Environ. Polit.*, **3(1)**, 33–50, doi:10.1162/152638003763336374.

Pucher, J. and R. Buehler, 2017: Cycling towards a more sustainable transport future. *Transp. Rev.*, **37(6)**, 689–694, doi:10.1080/01441647.2017.1340234.

Puzzolo, E. et al., 2019: Supply Considerations for Scaling Up Clean Cooking Fuels for Household Energy in Low- and Middle-Income Countries. *GeoHealth*, **3(12)**, pp. 370–390, doi:10.1029/2019GH000208.

Quandt, A., 2019: Variability in perceptions of household livelihood resilience and drought at the intersection of gender and ethnicity. *Clim. Change*, **152**, 1–15, doi:10.1007/s10584-018-2343-7.

Quayson, M., C. Bai, and V. Osei, 2020: Digital Inclusion for Resilient Post-COVID-19 Supply Chains: Smallholder Farmer Perspectives. *IEEE Eng. Manag. Rev.*, **48(3)**, 104–110, doi:10.1109/EMR.2020.3006259.

Rabbitt, N. and B. Ghosh, 2016: Economic and environmental impacts of organised Car Sharing Services: A case study of Ireland. *Res. Transp. Econ.*, **57**, 3–12, doi:10.1016/j.retrec.2016.10.001.

Rademaekers, K., K. Svatikova, J. Vermeulen, T. Smit, and L. Baroni, 2017: *Environmental potential of the collaborative economy*. European Commission, Directorate-General for Environment.

Rafaty, R., 2018: Perceptions of corruption, political distrust, and the weakening of climate policy. *Glob. Environ. Polit.*, **18(3)**, 106–129, doi:10.1162/glep_a_00471.

Ramakrishnan, A. and F. Creutzig, 2021: Status consciousness in energy consumption: a systematic review. *Environ. Res. Lett.*, **16(5)**, 053010, doi:10.1088/1748-9326/ABF003.

Rao, N.D. and P. Baer, 2012: "Decent Living" Emissions: A Conceptual Framework. *Sustainability*, **4(4)**, 656–681, doi:10.3390/su4040656.

Rao, N.D. and S. Pachauri, 2017: Energy access and living standards: some observations on recent trends. *Environ. Res. Lett.*, **12(2)**, 025011, doi:10.1088/1748-9326/aa5b0d.

Rao, N.D. and J. Min, 2018a: Less global inequality can improve climate outcomes. *Wiley Interdisip. Rev. Clim. Change*, **9(2)**, doi:10.1002/wcc.513.

Rao, N.D. and J. Min, 2018b: Decent Living Standards: Material Prerequisites for Human Wellbeing. *Soc. Indic. Res.*, **138(1)**, 225–244, doi:10.1007/s11205-017-1650-0.

Rao, N.D. and J. Min, 2018c: *Is less global inequality good for climate change?* IIASA. https://pure.iiasa.ac.at/id/eprint/15078/1/RaoMin-GlobalInequalityandEmissionsWIRES2018-postacceptance.pdf.

Rao, N.D., K. Riahi, and A. Grubler, 2014: Climate impacts of poverty eradication. *Nat. Clim. Change*, **4(9)**, 749–751, doi:10.1038/nclimate2340.

Rao, N., E. T. Lawson, W. N. Raditloaneng, D. Solomon, and M. N. Angula, 2019a: Gendered vulnerabilities to climate change: insights from the semi-arid regions of Africa and Asia. *Clim. Dev.*, **11(1)**, 14–26, doi:10.1080/17565529.2017.1372266.

Rao, N.D., J. Min, and A. Mastrucci, 2019b: Energy requirements for decent living in India, Brazil and South Africa. *Nat. Energy*, **4(12)**, 1025–1032, doi:10.1038/s41560-019-0497-9.

Räty, R. and A. Carlsson-Kanyama, 2009: *Comparing energy use by gender, age and income in some European countries*. FOI, Swedish Defence Research Agency, Stockholm, Sweden, 40 pp. pp. https://www.compromisorse.com/upload/estudios/000/101/foir2800.pdf (Accessed September 12, 2019).

Räty, R. and A. Carlsson-Kanyama, 2010: Energy consumption by gender in some European countries. *Energy Policy*, **38(1)**, 646–649, doi.org/10.1016/j.enpol.2009.08.010.

Rausch, S., G.E. Metcalf, and J.M. Reilly, 2011: Distributional impacts of carbon pricing: A general equilibrium approach with micro-data for households. *Energy Econ.*, **33**(SUPPL. 1), doi:10.1016/j.eneco.2011.07.023.

Ravallion, M., M. Heil, and J. Jalan, 1997: *A less poor world, but a hotter one? Carbon emissions, economic growth and income inequality*. World Bank, Washington, DC, USA.

Raven, R. and G. Verbong, 2007: Multi-regime interactions in the Dutch energy sector: The case of combined heat and power technologies in the Netherlands 1970–2000. *Technol. Anal. Strateg. Manag.*, **19(4)**, 491–507, doi:10.1080/09537320701403441.

Raven, R. et al., 2017: Unpacking sustainabilities in diverse transition contexts: solar photovoltaic and urban mobility experiments in India and Thailand. *Sustain. Sci.*, **12(4)**, 579–596, doi:10.1007/s11625-017-0438-0.

Raven, R.P.J.M., E. Heiskanen, M. Hodson, and B. Brohmann, 2008: The Contribution of Local Experiments and Negotiation Processes to Field-Level Learning in Emerging (Niche) Technologies: Meta-Analysis of 27 New Energy Projects in Europe. *Bull. Sci. Technol. Soc.*, **28(6)**, 464–477, doi:10.1177/0270467608317523.

Reckien, D. et al., 2017: Climate change, equity and the Sustainable Development Goals: an urban perspective. *Environ. Urban.*, **29(1)**, 159–182, doi:10.1177/0956247816677778.

Reckwitz, A., 2002: Toward a Theory of Social Practices: A Development in Culturalist Theorizing. *Eur. J. Soc. Theory*, **5(2)**, 243–263, doi:10.1177/13684310222225432.

Requena, F., 2016: Rural–Urban Living and Level of Economic Development as Factors in Subjective Well-Being. *Soc. Indic. Res.*, **128(2)**, 693–708, doi:10.1007/s11205-015-1051-1.

Resurrección, B.P., 2013: Persistent women and environment linkages in climate change and sustainable development agendas. *Womens. Stud. Int. Forum*, **40**, 33–43, doi:10.1016/j.wsif.2013.03.011.

Retamal, M., 2019: Collaborative consumption practices in Southeast Asian cities: Prospects for growth and sustainability. *J. Clean. Prod.*, **222**, 143–152, doi.org/10.1016/j.jclepro.2019.02.267.

Reusser, D. et al., 2013: Relating climate compatible development and human livelihood. *Energy Procedia*, **40**, 192–201.

Ricci, M., 2015: Bike sharing: A review of evidence on impacts and processes of implementation and operation. *Res. Transp. Bus. Manag.*, **15**, 28–38, doi:10.1016/j.rtbm.2015.03.003.

Richards, M., 2003: *Poverty reduction, equity and climate change: challenges for global governance*. Overseas Development Institute, London, UK, https://cdn.odi.org/media/documents/2792.pdf (Accessed December 17, 2019).

Richards, T.J. and S.F. Hamilton, 2018: Food waste in the sharing economy. *Food Policy*, **75**, 109–123, doi.org/10.1016/j.foodpol.2018.01.008.

Rietmann, N. and T. Lieven, 2019: How policy measures succeeded to promote electric mobility – Worldwide review and outlook. *J. Clean. Prod.*, **206**, 66–75, doi:10.1016/j.jclepro.2018.09.121.

Ritchie, H., D.S. Reay, and P. Higgins, 2018: Potential of Meat Substitutes for Climate Change Mitigation and Improved Human Health in High-Income Markets. *Front. Sustain. Food Syst.*, **2**, 16, doi:10.3389/fsufs.2018.00016.

Roberts, C. and F.W. Geels, 2019: Conditions for politically accelerated transitions: Historical institutionalism, the multi-level perspective, and two historical case studies in transport and agriculture. *Technol. Forecast. Soc. Change*, **140**(December 2018), 221–240, doi:10.1016/j.techfore.2018.11.019.

Roberts, C. et al., 2018: The politics of accelerating low-carbon transitions: Towards a new research agenda. *Energy Res. Soc. Sci.*, **44**(February), 304–311, doi:10.1016/j.erss.2018.06.001.

Roberts, J.C.D., 2017: Discursive destabilisation of socio-technical regimes: Negative storylines and the discursive vulnerability of historical American railroads. *Energy Res. Soc. Sci.*, **31**(May), 86–99, doi:10.1016/j.erss.2017.05.031.

Roesler, T. and M. Hassler, 2019: Creating niches – The role of policy for the implementation of bioenergy village cooperatives in Germany. *Energy Policy*, **124**, 95–101, doi:10.1016/j.enpol.2018.07.012.

Rogelj, J., D. Shindell, K. Jiang, S. Fifita, P. Forster, V. Ginzburg, C. Handa, H. Kheshgi, S. Kobayashi, E. Kriegler, L. Mundaca, R. Séférian, and M.V. Vilariño, 2018: Mitigation pathways compatible with 1.5°C in the context of sustainable development. In: *Global Warming of 1.5°C an IPCC special report on the impacts of global warming of 1.5°C above pre-industrial levels and related global greenhouse gas emission pathways, in the context of strengthening the global response to the threat of climate change, sustainable development, and efforts to eradicate poverty* [Masson-Delmotte, V., P. Zhai, H.-O. Pörtner, D. Roberts, J. Skea, P.R. Shukla, A. Pirani, W. Moufouma-Okia, C. Péan, R. Pidcock, S. Connors, J.B.R. Matthews, Y. Chen, X. Zhou, M.I. Gomis, E. Lonnoy, T. Maycock, M. Tignor, and T. Waterfield (eds.)], Cambridge University Press, Cambridge, UK and New York, NY, USA, pp. 93–174.

Rogelj, J., P.M. Forster, E. Kriegler, C.J. Smith, and R. Séférian, 2019: Estimating and tracking the remaining carbon budget for stringent climate targets. *Nature*, **571**(7765), 335–342, doi:10.1038/s41586-019-1368-z.

Rogers, E.M., 2003: *Diffusion of Innovations*. Fifth edit. Free Press of Glencoe and Macmillan, New York, USA and London, UK, 576 pp.

Rogge, K.S. and K. Reichardt, 2013: *Towards a more comprehensive policy mix conceptualization for environmental technological change: A literature synthesis*. Working Papers "Sustainability and Innovation" S3/2013, Fraunhofer Institute for Systems and Innovation Research (ISI), Karlsruhe, Germany, 67 pp. https://www.econstor.eu/bitstream/10419/77924/1/749915005.pdf (Accessed December 17, 2019).

Rogge, K.S. and K. Reichardt, 2016: Policy mixes for sustainability transitions: An extended concept and framework for analysis. *Res. Policy*, **45**(8), 1620–1635, doi:10.1016/j.respol.2016.04.004.

Rogge, K.S. and P. Johnstone, 2017: Exploring the role of phase-out policies for low-carbon energy transitions: The case of the German Energiewende. *Energy Res. Soc. Sci.*, **33**, 128–137, doi:10.1016/j.erss.2017.10.004.

Rojas-Rueda, D., A. de Nazelle, O. Teixidó, and M.J. Nieuwenhuijsen, 2012: Replacing car trips by increasing bike and public transport in the greater Barcelona metropolitan area: A health impact assessment study. *Environ. Int.*, **49**, 100–109, doi:10.1016/j.envint.2012.08.009.

Rolffs, P., D. Ockwell, and R. Byrne, 2015: Beyond technology and finance: pay-as-you-go sustainable energy access and theories of social change. *Environ. Plan. A*, **47**(12), 2609–2627, doi:10.1177/0308518X15615368.

Røpke, I., 2009: Theories of practice – New inspiration for ecological economic studies on consumption. *Ecol. Econ.*, **68**(10), 2490–2497, doi:10.1016/j.ecolecon.2009.05.015.

Rosane, O., 2019: 7.6 Million Join Week of Global Climate Strikes. *EcoWatch*, https://www.ecowatch.com/global-climate-strikes-week-2640790405.html (Accessed December 1, 2020).

Rosenbloom, D., 2018: Framing low-carbon pathways: A discursive analysis of contending storylines surrounding the phase-out of coal-fired power in Ontario. *Environ. Innov. Soc. Transitions*, **27**, 129–145, doi:10.1016/j.eist.2017.11.003.

Rosenbloom, D., B. Haley, and J. Meadowcroft, 2018a: Critical choices and the politics of decarbonization pathways: Exploring branching points surrounding low-carbon transitions in Canadian electricity systems. *Energy Res. Soc. Sci.*, **37**, 22–36, doi:10.1016/j.erss.2017.09.022.

Rosenbloom, D., J. Meadowcroft, S. Sheppard, S. Burch, and S. Williams, 2018b: Transition Experiments: Opening Up Low-Carbon Transition Pathways for Canada through Innovation and Learning. *Can. Public Policy*, **44**(4), 1–6, doi:10.3138/cpp.2018-020.

Rosenbloom, D., J. Markard, F.W. Geels, and L. Fuenfschilling, 2020: Opinion: Why carbon pricing is not sufficient to mitigate climate change – and how "sustainability transition policy" can help. *Proc. Natl. Acad. Sci.*, **117**(16), 8664–8668, doi:10.1073/PNAS.2004093117.

Rosenow, J., T. Fawcett, N. Eyre, and V. Oikonomou, 2016: Energy efficiency and the policy mix. *Build. Res. Inf.*, **44**(5–6), 562–574, doi:10.1080/09613218.2016.1138803.

Rosenow, J., F. Kern, and K. Rogge, 2017: The need for comprehensive and well targeted instrument mixes to stimulate energy transitions: The case of energy efficiency policy. *Energy Res. Soc. Sci.*, **33**, 95–104, doi:10.1016/j.erss.2017.09.013.

Rosenthal, J., A. Quinn, A.P. Grieshop, A. Pillarisetti, and R.I. Glass, 2018: Clean cooking and the SDGs: Integrated analytical approaches to guide energy interventions for health and environment goals. *Energy Sustain. Dev.*, **42**, 152–159, doi:10.1016/j.esd.2017.11.003.

Rothstein, B., 2011: *The Quality of Government: Corruption, Social Trust, and Inequality in International Perspective*. University of Chicago Press, Chicago, IL, USA.

Rothstein, B. and J. Teorell, 2008: What Is Quality of Government? A Theory of Impartial Government Institutions. *Governance*, **21**(2), 165–190, doi:10.1111/j.1468-0491.2008.00391.x.

Rotmans, J., R. Kemp, and M. Van Asselt, 2001: More evolution than revolution: Transition management in public policy. *Foresight*, **3**(1), 15–31, doi:10.1108/14636680110803003.

Rouse, M. and G. Verhoef, 2016: Mobile banking in Africa: The current state of play. In: *The Book of Payments: Historical and Contemporary Views on the Cashless Society* [Batiz-Lazo, B. and L. Efthymiou, (eds.)], Palgrave Macmillan, London, UK, pp. 233–257.

Rowlands, L. and N. Gomez Peña, 2019: *We will not be silenced: Climate activism from the frontlines to the UN*. Civicus, https://www.civicus.org/documents/WeWillNotBeSilenced_eng_Nov19.pdf (Accessed October 2, 2021).

Roy, B. and A. Schaffartzik, 2020: Talk renewables, walk coal: The paradox of India's energy transition. *Ecol. Econ.*, **180**, 106871, doi:10.1016/j.ecolecon.2020.106871.

Roy, J. and S. Pal, 2009: Lifestyles and climate change: link awaiting activation. *Curr. Opin. Environ. Sustain.*, **1**(2), 192–200, doi:10.1016/j.cosust.2009.10.009.

Roy, J. et al., 2012: Lifestyles, Well-Being and Energy. In: *Global Energy Assessment – Toward a Sustainable Future*, Cambridge University Press, Cambridge, UK, New York, NY, USA and Laxenburg, Austria, pp. 1527–1548.

Roy, J., P. Tschakert, H. Waisman, S. Abdul Halim, P. Antwi-Agyei, P. Dasgupta, B. Hayward, M. Kanninen, D. Liverman, C. Okereke, P.F. Pinho, K. Riahi, and A.G. Suarez Rodriguez, 2018a: Sustainable Development, Poverty Eradication and Reducing Inequalities. In: *Global Warming of 1.5°C. An IPCC Special Report on the impacts of global warming of 1.5°C above pre-industrial levels and related global greenhouse gas emission pathways, in the context of strengthening the global response to the threat of climate change, sustainable development, and efforts to eradicate poverty* [Masson-Delmotte, V., P. Zhai, H.-O. Pörtner, D. Roberts, J. Skea, P.R. Shukla, A. Pirani, W. Moufouma-Okia, C. Péan, R. Pidcock, S. Connors, J.B.R. Matthews, Y. Chen, X. Zhou, M.I. Gomis, E. Lonnoy, T. Maycock, M. Tignor, and T. Waterfield (eds.)]. Cambridge University Press, Cambridge, UK and New York, NY, USA, pp. 445–538.

Roy, J. et al., 2018b: Where is the hope? Blending modern urban lifestyle with cultural practices in India. *Curr. Opin. Environ. Sustain.*, **31**, 96–103, doi:10.1016/j.cosust.2018.01.010.

Roy, J. et al., 2018c: Governing National Actions for Global Climate Change Stabilization: Examples from India. In: *Climate Change Governance and Adaptation* [Barua, A., V. Narain, and S. Vij, (eds.)], CRC Press, pp. 137–159.

Roy, J., S. Some, N. Das, and M. Pathak, 2021: Demand side climate change mitigation actions and SDGs: literature review with systematic evidence search. *Environ. Res. Lett.*, **16(4)**, 043003, doi:10.1088/1748-9326/ABD81A.

Roy, R., 2000: Sustainable product-service systems. *Futures*, **32(3–4)**, 289–299, doi:10.1016/S0016-3287(99)00098-1.

Rubin, E.S., M.L. Azevedo, P. Jaramillo, and S. Yeh, 2016: A review of learning rates for electricity supply technologies. *Energy Policy*, **86**, 198–218, doi:10.1016/j.enpol.2015.06.011.

Ruggiero, S., M. Martiskainen, and T. Onkila, 2018: Understanding the scaling-up of community energy niches through strategic niche management theory: Insights from Finland. *J. Clean. Prod.*, **170**, 581–590, doi:10.1016/j.jclepro.2017.09.144.

Ruzek, W., 2015: The Informal Economy as a Catalyst for Sustainability. *Sustainability*, **7(1)**, doi:10.3390/su7010023.

Ryan, R.M. and E.L. Deci, 2001: On happiness and human potentials: a review of research on hedonic and eudaimonic well-being. *Annu. Rev. Psychol.*, **52**, 141–166, doi:10.1146/annurev.psych.52.1.141.

Rynikiewicz, C. and A. Chetaille, 2006: *Poverty reduction, climate change mitigation and adaptation: The need for intermediate public policies harnessing technology appropriation*. The future of science, technology and innovation : 40th anniversary conference, Science Policy Research Unit, Falmer, UK, https://pdfs.semanticscholar.org/c59f/90000428a5c81e12daf3b9a7a96983996813.pdf?_ga=2.171553252.57338894.1575697081-1617201598.1561360840 (Accessed November 30, 2019).

Saade, M.R.M., A. Yahia, and B. Amor, 2020: How has LCA been applied to 3D printing? A systematic literature review and recommendations for future studies. *J. Clean. Prod.*, **244**, 118803, doi:10.1016/J.JCLEPRO.2019.118803.

Saavedra, Y.Y.M.B. et al., 2018: Theoretical contribution of industrial ecology to circular economy. *J. Clean. Prod.*, **170**, 1514–1522, doi:10.1016/J.JCLEPRO.2017.09.260.

Sachs, J.D. and A.M. Warner, 1995: *Natural Resource Abundance and Economic Growth*. Working Paper 5398, National Bureau of Economic Research, Cambridge, MA, USA, 47 pp. https://www.nber.org/papers/w5398 (Accessed December 17, 2019).

Sadras, V.O., P. Grassini, and P. Steduto, 2011: *Status of water use efficiency of main crops: SOLAW Background Thematic Report-TR07*. UN Food and Agriculture Organization, Rome, Italy, 41 pp. http://www.fao.org/fileadmin/templates/solaw/files/thematic_reports/TR_07_web.pdf (Accessed December 20, 2019).

Sager, L., 2017: *Income inequality and carbon consumption: evidence from environmental Engel curves*, Centre for Climate Change Economics and Policy and Grantham Research Institute on Climate Change and the Environment, London, UK, 55 pp. http://www.lse.ac.uk/GranthamInstitute/publication/income-inequality-and-carbon-consumption-evidence-from-environmental-engel-curves/ (Accessed July 4, 2019).

Sahakian, M., 2018: Toward a more solidaristic sharing economy. In: *Social Change and the Coming of Post-Consumer Society* [Cohen, M.J., H.S. Brown, and P.J. Vergragt, (eds.)], Routledge, Abingdon, UK, pp. 43–60.

Sahakian, M., L. Godin, and I. Courtin, 2020: Promoting 'pro', 'low', and 'no' meat consumption in Switzerland: The role of emotions in practices. *Appetite*, **150**, 104637, doi:10.1016/j.appet.2020.104637.

Salas, R.N. and A.K. Jha, 2019: Climate change threatens the achievement of effective universal healthcare. *BMJ*, **366**, doi:10.1136/bmj.l5302.

Salehi, S., Z. Pazuki Nejad, H. Mahmoudi, and A. Knierim, 2015: Gender, responsible citizenship and global climate change. *Womens. Stud. Int. Forum*, **50**, 30–36, doi:10.1016/j.wsif.2015.02.015.

Salick, J. and N. Ross, 2009: Traditional peoples and climate change. *Glob. Environ. Change*, **19(2)**, 137–139, doi:10.1016/j.gloenvcha.2009.01.004.

Säll, S. and I.M. Gren, 2015: Effects of an environmental tax on meat and dairy consumption in Sweden. *Food Policy*, **55**, 41–53, doi:10.1016/j.foodpol.2015.05.008.

Samadi, S. et al., 2017: Sufficiency in energy scenario studies: Taking the potential benefits of lifestyle changes into account. *Technol. Forecast. Soc. Change*, **124**, 126–134, doi:10.1016/j.techfore.2016.09.013.

Sanderson, S.W. and K.L. Simons, 2014: Light emitting diodes and the lighting revolution: The Emergence of a solid-state lighting industry. *Res. Policy*, **43(10)**, 1730–1746, doi:10.1016/j.respol.2014.07.011.

Sandin, S., L. Neij, and P. Mickwitz, 2019: Transition governance for energy efficiency –insights from a systematic review of Swedish policy evaluation practices. *Energy. Sustain. Soc.*, **9(1)**, 17, doi:10.1186/s13705-019-0203-6.

Sanguinetti, A., E. Queen, C. Yee, and K. Akanesuvan, 2020: Average impact and important features of onboard eco-driving feedback: A meta-analysis. *Transp. Res. Part F-Traffic Psychol. Behav.*, **70**, 1–14, doi:10.1016/j.trf.2020.02.010.

Sankhyayan, P. and S. Dasgupta, 2019: 'Availability' and/or 'Affordability': What matters in household energy access in India? *Energy Policy*, **131**(April), 131–143, doi:10.1016/j.enpol.2019.04.019.

Santarius, T., H.J. Walnum, and C. Aall, 2016: *Rethinking climate and energy policies: New perspectives on the rebound phenomenon*. Springer Cham.

Santillán Vera, M., A. de la Vega Navarro, and J. Islas Samperio, 2021: Climate change and income inequality: An I-O analysis of the structure and intensity of the GHG emissions in Mexican households. *Energy Sustain. Dev.*, **60**, 15–25, doi:10.1016/J.ESD.2020.11.002.

Santos, G., 2018: Sustainability and Shared Mobility Models. Sustainability, 10(9), 3194, doi:10.3390/su10093194Satterthwaite, D. et al., 2018: *Responding to climate change in cities and in their informal settlements and economies*. 61 pp. IIED and IIED-América Latina, https://pubs.iied.org/sites/default/files/pdfs/migrate/G04328.pdf (Accessed November 30, 2019).

Saujot, M., T. Le Gallic, and H. Waisman, 2020: Lifestyle changes in mitigation pathways: policy and scientific insights. *Environ. Res. Lett.*, **16(1)**, 015005, doi:10.1088/1748-9326/ABD0A9.

Saunders, H.D. et al., 2021: Energy Efficiency: What has it Delivered in the Last 40 years? *Annu. Rev. Energy Environ.*, **46,** 135–165, doi:10.1146/ANNUREV-ENVIRON-012320-084937.

Schaefers, T., S.J. Lawson, and M. Kukar-Kinney, 2016: How the burdens of ownership promote consumer usage of access-based services. *Mark. Lett.*, **27(3)**, 569–577, doi:10.1007/s11002-015-9366-x.

Schäfer, A.W. and S. Yeh, 2020: A holistic analysis of passenger travel energy and greenhouse gas intensities. *Nat. Sustain.*, **3(6)**, doi:10.1038/s41893-020-0514-9.

Schanes, K., K. Dobernig, and B. Gözet, 2018: Food waste matters – A systematic review of household food waste practices and their policy implications. *J. Clean. Prod.*, **182**, 978–991.

Scheffran, J., E. Marmer, and P. Sow, 2012: Migration as a contribution to resilience and innovation in climate adaptation: Social networks and co-development in Northwest Africa. *Appl. Geogr.*, **33(1)**, 119–127, doi:10.1016/j.apgeog.2011.10.002.

Scherer, L. et al., 2018: Trade-offs between social and environmental Sustainable Development Goals. *Environ. Sci. Policy*, **90**(September), 65–72, doi:10.1016/j.envsci.2018.10.002.

Schlosberg, D. and L.B. Collins, 2014: From environmental to climate justice: climate change and the discourse of environmental justice. *Wiley Interdisc. Rev. Clim. Change*, **5**(3), 359–374, doi:10.1002/wcc.275.

Schlosberg, D. and R. Coles, 2016: The new environmentalism of everyday life: Sustainability, material flows and movements. *Contemp. Polit. Theory*, **15**(2), 160–181, doi:10.1057/CPT.2015.34.

Schneider-Mayerson, M. et al., 2020: Environmental Literature as Persuasion: An Experimental Test of the Effects of Reading Climate Fiction. *Environ. Commun.*, doi:10.1080/17524032.2020.1814377.

Schneider, S.M., 2016: Income Inequality and Subjective Wellbeing: Trends, Challenges, and Research Directions. *J. Happiness Stud.*, **17**(4), 1719–1739, doi:10.1007/s10902-015-9655-3.

Schot, J. and F.W. Geels, 2008: Strategic niche management and sustainable innovation journeys: Theory, findings, research agenda, and policy. *Technol. Anal. Strateg. Manag.*, **20**(5), 537–554, doi:10.1080/09537320802292651.

Schot, J. and L. Kanger, 2018: Deep transitions: Emergence, acceleration, stabilization and directionality. *Res. Policy*, **47**(6), 1045–1059, doi:10.1016/j.respol.2018.03.009.

Schot, J. and W.E. Steinmueller, 2018: Three frames for innovation policy: R&D, systems of innovation and transformative change. *Res. Policy*, **47**(9), 1554–1567, doi:10.1016/j.respol.2018.08.011.

Schot, J., L. Kanger, and G. Verbong, 2016: The roles of users in shaping transitions to new energy systems. *Nat. Energy*, **1**(5), 1–7, doi:10.1038/NENERGY.2016.54.

Schröder, P. et al., 2019: Advancing sustainable consumption and production in cities – A transdisciplinary research and stakeholder engagement framework to address consumption-based emissions and impacts. *J. Clean. Prod.*, **213**, 114–125, doi.org/10.1016/j.jclepro.2018.12.050.

Schroeder, P., 2013: Assessing effectiveness of governance approaches for sustainable consumption and production in China. *J. Clean. Prod.*, **63**, 64–73, doi:10.1016/j.jclepro.2013.05.039.

Schuelke-Leech, B.A., 2018: A model for understanding the orders of magnitude of disruptive technologies. *Technol. Forecast. Soc. Change*, **129**, doi:10.1016/j.techfore.2017.09.033.

Schuldt, J.P. and A.R. Pearson, 2016: The role of race and ethnicity in climate change polarization: evidence from a U.S. national survey experiment. *Clim. Change*, **136**(3–4), 495–505, doi:10.1007/s10584-016-1631-3.

Schultz, P.W., J.M. Nolan, R.B. Cialdini, N.J. Goldstein, and V. Griskevicius, 2007: The Constructive, Destructive, and Reconstructive Power of Social Norms. *Psychol. Sci.*, **18**(5), 429–434, doi:10.1111/j.1467-9280.2007.01917.x.

Schumacher, E.F., 1974: *Small is Beautiful: A Study of Economics as if People Mattered*. Abacus, London, UK, 255 pp.

Schumacher, I., 2015: The endogenous formation of an environmental culture. *Eur. Econ. Rev.*, **76**, 200–221, doi:10.1016/j.euroecorev.2015.03.002.

Schwartz, S.H., 1977: Normative influences on altruism. *Adv. Exp. Soc. Psychol.*, **10**(C), 221–279, doi:10.1016/S0065-2601(08)60358-5.

Scrivener, K.L. and E.M. Gartner, 2018: Eco-efficient cements: Potential economically viable solutions for a low-CO$_2$ cement-based materials industry. *Cem. Concr. Res.*, **114**, 2–26, doi:10.1016/J.CEMCONRES.2018.03.015.

Sebi, C., S. Nadel, B. Schlomann, and J. Steinbach, 2019: Policy strategies for achieving large long-term savings from retrofitting existing buildings. *Energy Effic.*, **12**(1), 89–105, doi:10.1007/s12053-018-9661-5.

Semieniuk, G., L. Taylor, A. Rezai, and D.K. Foley, 2021: Plausible energy demand patterns in a growing global economy with climate policy. *Nat. Clim. Change 2021 114*, **11**(4), 313–318, doi:10.1038/s41558-020-00975-7.

Sen, A., 1985: Well-being, agency and freedom: The Dewey Lectures 1984. *J. Philos.*, **82**(April), 169–221, doi:10.2307/2026184.

Sen, B., 2017: *How States can boost renewables, with benefits for all*. Institute for Policy Studies, Washington, DC, USA, https://ips-dc.org/report-how-states-can-boost-renewables-with-benefits-for-all/.

Serrano-Medrano, M. et al., 2018: Promoting LPG, clean woodburning cookstoves or both? Climate change mitigation implications of integrated household energy transition scenarios in rural Mexico. *Environ. Res. Lett.*, **13**(11), doi:10.1088/1748-9326/aad5b8.

Serrao-Neumann, S., F. Crick, B. Harman, G. Schuch, and D.L. Choy, 2015: Maximising synergies between disaster risk reduction and climate change adaptation: Potential enablers for improved planning outcomes. *Environ. Sci. Policy*, **50**, 46–61, doi:10.1016/j.envsci.2015.01.017.

Serrenho, A.C., T. Sousa, B. Warr, R.U. Ayres, and T. Domingos, 2014: Decomposition of useful work intensity: The EU (European Union)-15 countries from 1960 to 2009. *Energy*, **76**, 704–715, doi:10.1016/J.ENERGY.2014.08.068.

Seto, K.C., S. Dhakal, A. Bigio, H. Blanco, G.C. Delgado, D. Dewar, L. Huang, A. Inaba, A. Kansal, S. Lwasa, J.E. McMahon, D.B. Müller, J. Murakami, H. Nagendra, and A. Ramaswami, 2014: Human Settlements, Infrastructure, and Spatial Planning. In: *Climate Change 2014: Mitigation of Climate Change. Contribution of Working Group III to the Fifth Assessment Report of the Intergovernmental Panel on Climate Change* [Edenhofer, O., R. Pichs-Madruga, Y. Sokona, E. Farahani, S. Kadner, K. Seyboth, A. Adler, I. Baum, S. Brunner, P. Eickemeier, B. Kriemann, J. Savolainen, S. Schlömer, C. von Stechow, T. Zwickel and J.C. Minx, (eds.)], Cambridge University Press Cambridge, UK, and New York, NY, USA, pp. 67–76.

Seto, K.C. et al., 2016: Carbon Lock-In: Types, Causes, and Policy Implications. *Annu. Rev. Environ. Resour.*, **41**(1), 425–452, doi:10.1146/annurev-environ-110615-085934.

Sgouridis, S. et al., 2016: RE-mapping the UAE's energy transition: An economy-wide assessment of renewable energy options and their policy implications. *Renew. Sustain. Energy Rev.*, **55**, 1166–1180, doi:10.1016/j.rser.2015.05.039.

Shabanpour, R., N. Golshani, M. Tayarani, J. Auld, and A. (Kouros) Mohammadian, 2018: Analysis of telecommuting behavior and impacts on travel demand and the environment. *Transp. Res. Part D Transp. Environ.*, **62**, 563–576, doi:10.1016/j.trd.2018.04.003.

Shaheen, S. and N. Chan, 2016: Mobility and the Sharing Economy: Potential to Facilitate the First- and Last-Mile Public Transit Connections. *Built Environ.*, **42**(4), 573–588, doi:10.2148/benv.42.4.573.

Shaheen, S. and A. Cohen, 2019: Shared ride services in North America: definitions, impacts, and the future of pooling. *Transp. Rev.*, **39**(4), 427–442, doi:10.1080/01441647.2018.1497728.

Shangguan, S. et al., 2019: A Meta-Analysis of Food Labeling Effects on Consumer Diet Behaviors and Industry Practices. *Am. J. Prev. Med.*, **56**(2), 300–314, doi:10.1016/j.amepre.2018.09.024.

Shanks, W. et al., 2019: How much cement can we do without? Lessons from cement material flows in the UK. *Resour. Conserv. Recycl.*, **141**, 441–454, doi:10.1016/J.RESCONREC.2018.11.002.

Sharifi, A., 2020: Trade-offs and conflicts between urban climate change mitigation and adaptation measures: A literature review. *J. Clean. Prod.*, **276**, 122813, doi:10.1016/j.jclepro.2020.122813.

Shaw, C., S. Hales, P. Howden-Chapman, and R. Edwards, 2014: Health co-benefits of climate change mitigation policies in the transport sector. *Nat. Clim. Change*, **4**(6), 427–433, doi:10.1038/nclimate2247.

Shehabi, A., S.J. Smith, E. Masanet, and J. Koomey, 2018: Data center growth in the United States: decoupling the demand for services from electricity use. *Environ. Res. Lett.*, **13**(12), 124030, doi:10.1088/1748-9326/aaec9c.

Sheikh, F.A., 2019: Undervaluation of informal sector innovations: Making a case for revisiting methodology. *African J. Sci. Technol. Innov. Dev.*, **11**(4), 505–512, doi:10.1080/20421338.2018.1532630.

Sheikh, F.A. and S. Bhaduri, 2020: Grassroots innovations in the informal economy: insights from value theory. *Oxford Dev. Stud.*, **48**(1), 85–99, doi:10.1080/13600818.2020.1717453.

5

Shelley, S., 2017: More and better jobs in a low carbon future: provocations and possibilities. 35th International Labour Process Conference, *'Reconnecting work and political economy'*, Sheffield, UK, 22 pp, https://uhra.herts.ac.uk/bitstream/handle/2299/19605/Accepted_Manuscript.pdf?sequence=2 (Accessed November 12, 2019).

Shi, X., 2019: Inequality of opportunity in energy consumption in China. *Energy Policy*, **124**(May 2018), 371–382, doi:10.1016/j.enpol.2018.09.029.

Shonkoff, S.B., R. Morello-Frosch, M. Pastor, and J. Sadd, 2011: The climate gap: Environmental health and equity implications of climate change and mitigation policies in California – a review of the literature. *Clim. Change*, **109**(sup1), 485–503, doi:10.1007/s10584-011-0310-7.

Shove, E., 2003: *Comfort, Cleanliness and Convenience: The Social Organization of Normality*. 1st ed. Berg Publishers/Bloomsbury, Oxford, UK, 240 pp.

Shove, E. and D. Southerton, 2000: Defrosting the freezer: From Novelty to convenience. A Narrative of Normalization. *J. Mater. Cult.*, **5**(3), 301–319, doi:10.1177/135918350000500303.

Shove, E. and G. Walker, 2014: What Is Energy For? Social Practice and Energy Demand. *Theory, Cult. Soc.*, **31**(5), 41–58, doi:10.1177/0263276414536746.

Shuai, C., X. Chen, Y. Wu, Y. Zhang, and Y. Tan, 2019: A three-step strategy for decoupling economic growth from carbon emission: Empirical evidences from 133 countries. *Sci. Total Environ.*, **646**, 524–543, doi:10.1016/j.scitotenv.2018.07.045.

Simon, D.R., 2003: *Meatonomics: how the rigged economics of meat and dairy make you consume too much – and how to eat better, live longer, and spend smarter*. Conari Press, Newburyport, MA, USA, 289 pp.

Simon, F., 2020: Expert: 'Lack of trust' hampers energy efficiency services industry. *Euractiv*, June 16.

Simpson, N.P., 2019: Accommodating landscape-scale shocks: Lessons on transition from Cape Town and Puerto Rico. *Geoforum*, **102**, 226–229, doi.org/10.1016/j.geoforum.2018.12.005.

Sims, R., R. Schaeffer, F. Creutzig, X. Cruz-Núñez, M. D'Agosto, D. Dimitriu, M. J. Figueroa Meza, L. Fulton, S. Kobayashi, O. Lah, A. McKinnon, P. Newman, M. Ouyang, J. J. Schauer, D. Sperling, and G. Tiwari, 2014: Transport. In: *Climate Change 2014: Mitigation of Climate Change. Contribution of Working Group III to the Fifth Assessment Report of the Intergovernmental Panel on Climate Change* [Edenhofer, O., R. Pichs-Madruga, Y. Sokona, E. Farahani, S. Kadner, K. Seyboth, A. Adler, I. Baum, S. Brunner, P. Eickemeier, B. Kriemann, J. Savolainen, S. Schlömer, C. von Stechow, T. Zwickel and J.C. Minx, (eds.)], Cambridge University Press, Cambridge, United Kingdom and New York, NY, USA, pp. 559–670.

Singh, C., J. Ford, D. Ley, A. Bazaz, and A. Revi, 2020: Assessing the feasibility of adaptation options: methodological advancements and directions for climate adaptation research and practice. *Clim. Change 2020*, **162**(2), 255–277, doi:10.1007/S10584-020-02762-X.

Singh, C., M. Madhavan, J. Arvind, and A. Bazaz, 2021: Climate change adaptation in Indian cities: A review of existing actions and spaces for triple wins. *Urban Clim.*, **36**, 100783, doi:10.1016/J.UCLIM.2021.100783.

Singh, T., C. Siderius, and Y. Van der Velde, 2018: When do Indians feel hot? Internet searches indicate seasonality suppresses adaptation to heat. *Environ. Res. Lett.*, **13**(5), 054009, doi:10.1088/1748-9326/AABA82.

Sinha, A., 2016: Trilateral association between SO_2/NO_2 emission, inequality in energy intensity, and economic growth: A case of Indian cities. *Atmos. Pollut. Res.*, **7**(4), 647–658, doi:10.1016/j.apr.2016.02.010.

Sirgy, M.J., 2012: *The psychology of quality of life: Hedonic well-being, life satisfaction, and eudaimonia*. 2nd ed. Springer Netherlands, Dordrecht, the Netherlands, 622 pp.

Sisco, M.R., V. Bosetti, and E.U. Weber, 2017: When do extreme weather events generate attention to climate change? *Clim. Change*, **143**(1–2), 227–241, doi:10.1007/s10584-017-1984-2.

Skjelvik, J.M., A.M. Erlandsen, and O. Haavardsholm, 2017: *Environmental impacts and potential of the sharing economy*. Nordic Council of Ministers, Copenhagen, Denmark, 554 pp.

Slavin, R.E., J.S. Wodarski, and B.L. Blackburn, 1981: A group contingency for electricity conservation in master-metered apartments. *J. Appl. Behav. Anal.*, **14**(3), 357–363, doi:10.1901/jaba.1981.14–357.

Slocum, R., 2018: Climate Politics and Race in the Pacific Northwest. *Soc. Sci.*, **7**(10), 192, doi:10.3390/socsci7100192.

Smetschka, B. et al., 2019: Time Matters: The Carbon Footprint of Everyday Activities in Austria. *Ecol. Econ.*, **164**, 106357, doi:10.1016/j.ecolecon.2019.106357.

Smil, V., 2017: *Energy and civilization: a history*. MIT Press, Cambridge, MA, USA, 552 pp.

Smit, B., O. Pilifosova, I. Burton, B. Challenger, S. Huq, R.J.T. Klein, and G. Yohe, 2001: Adaptation to Climate Change in the Context of Sustainable Development and Equity. In: *Climate Change 2001: Impacts, Adaptation and Vulnerability. Contribution of Working Group II to the Third Assessment Report of the Intergovernmental Panel on Climate Change* [McCarthy, J., Canziani, O., Leary, N., Dokken, D., and White, K. (eds.)]. Cambridge University Press, Cambridge, UK, pp. 879–912.

Smith, A. and R. Raven, 2012: What is protective space? Reconsidering niches in transitions to sustainability. *Res. Policy*, **41**(6), 1025–1036, doi:10.1016/j.respol.2011.12.012.

Smith, E.K. and A. Mayer, 2018: A social trap for the climate? Collective action, trust and climate change risk perception in 35 countries. *Glob. Environ. Change*, **49**, 140–153, doi:10.1016/j.gloenvcha.2018.02.014.

Smith, J. et al., 2017: Gathering around stories: Interdisciplinary experiments in support of energy system transitions. *Energy Res. Soc. Sci.*, **31**, 284–294, doi:10.1016/j.erss.2017.06.026.

Smith, K.R., G.U. Shuhua, H. Kun, and Q. Daxiong, 1993: One hundred million improved cookstoves in China: How was it done? *World Dev.*, **21**(6), 941–961, doi:10.1016/0305-750X(93)90053-C.

Smith, P. et al., 2013: How much land-based greenhouse gas mitigation can be achieved without compromising food security and environmental goals? *Glob. Change Biol.*, **19**(8), 2285–2302, doi:10.1111/gcb.12160.

Smith, P., M. Bustamante, H. Ahammad, H. Clark, H. Dong, E.A. Elsiddig, H. Haberl, R. Harper, J. House, M. Jafari, O. Masera, C. Mbow, N.H. Ravindranath, C.W. Rice, C. Robledo Abad, A. Romanovskaya, F. Sperling, and F. Tubiello, 2014: Agriculture, Forestry and Other Land Use (AFOLU). In: *Climate Change 2014: Mitigation of Climate Change. Contribution of Working Group III to the Fifth Assessment Report of the Intergovernmental Panel on Climate Change* [Edenhofer, O., R. Pichs-Madruga, Y. Sokona, E. Farahani, S. Kadner, K. Seyboth, A. Adler, I. Baum, S. Brunner, P. Eickemeier, B. Kriemann, J. Savolainen, S. Schlömer, C. von Stechow, T. Zwickel and J.C. Minx (eds.)], Cambridge University Press, Cambridge, UK and New York, NY, USA, pp. 881–922.

Smith, P. and N.C. Howe, 2015: *Climate change as social drama: global warming in the public sphere*. Cambridge University Press, Cambridge, UK, 242 pp.

Smith, P. et al., 2016: Biophysical and economic limits to negative CO_2 emissions. *Nat. Clim. Change*, **6**(1), 42–50, doi:10.1038/nclimate2870.

Smith, P., J. Nkem, K. Calvin, D. Campbell, F. Cherubini, G. Grassi, V. Korotkov, A.L. Hoang, S. Lwasa, P. McElwee, E. Nkonya, N. Saigusa, J.-F. Soussana, and M.A. Taboada, 2019: Interlinkages between desertification, land degradation, food security and greenhouse gas fluxes: Synergies, trade-offs and integrated response options. In: *Climate Change and Land: an IPCC special report on climate change, desertification, land degradation, sustainable land management, food security, and greenhouse gas fluxes in terrestrial ecosystems* [Shukla, P.R., J. Skea, E. Calvo Buendia, V. Masson-Delmotte, H.-O. Portner, D.C. Roberts, P. Zhai, R. Slade, S. Connors, R. van Diemen, M. Ferrat, E. Haughey, S. Luz, S. Neogi, M. Pathak, J. Petzold, J. Portugal Pereira, P. Vyas, E. Huntley, K. Kissick, M. Belkacemi, and J. Malley, (eds.)], Cambridge University Press, Cambridge, UK and New York, NY, USA, pp. 551–672.

Smith, T. et al., 2015: *The English Indices of Deprivation 2015*. Department for Communities and Local Government, London, UK, 126 pp.

5

Smith, T.S.J., and L. Reid, 2018: Which 'being' in wellbeing? Ontology, wellness and the geographies of happiness. *Prog. Hum. Geogr.*, **42(6)**, 807–829, doi:10.1177/0309132517717100.

Soete, L., 1985: International diffusion of technology, industrial development and technological leapfrogging. *World Dev.*, **13(3)**, 409–422, doi.org/10.1016/0305-750X(85)90138-X.

Soliev, I. and I. Theesfeld, 2020: Benefit sharing for solving transboundary commons dilemma in central Asia. *Int. J. Commons*, **14(1)**, 61–77, doi:10.5334/ijc.955.

Song, Y., J. Preston, and D. Ogilvie, 2017: New walking and cycling infrastructure and modal shift in the UK: A quasi-experimental panel study. *Transp. Res. Part A Policy Pract.*, **95**(January 2017), 320–333, doi.org/10.1016/j.tra.2016.11.017.

Sorrell, S., 2015: Reducing energy demand: A review of issues, challenges and approaches. *Renew. Sustain. Energy Rev.*, **47**, 74–82, doi:10.1016/J.RSER.2015.03.002.

Sorrell, S., J. Dimitropoulos, and M. Sommerville, 2009: Empirical estimates of the direct rebound effect: A review. *Energy Policy*, **37(4)**, 1356–1371, doi:10.1016/J.ENPOL.2008.11.026.

Sousa, T. et al., 2017: The Need for Robust, Consistent Methods in Societal Exergy Accounting. *Ecol. Econ.*, **141**, 11–21, doi:10.1016/j.ecolecon.2017.05.020.

Sovacool, B.K. and I.M. Drupady, 2016: *Energy access, poverty, and development: the governance of small-scale renewable energy in developing Asia*. Routledge, Abingdon, UK, 328 pp.

Sovacool, B.K., A. Gilbert, and D. Nugent, 2014: An international comparative assessment of construction cost overruns for electricity infrastructure. *Energy Res. Soc. Sci.*, **3**(C), 152–160, doi:10.1016/j.erss.2014.07.016.

Sovacool, B.K. et al., 2015: Integrating social science in energy research. *Energy Res. Soc. Sci.*, **6**, 95–99, doi:10.1016/j.erss.2014.12.005.

Sovacool, B.K., D. Furszyfer Del Rio, and S. Griffiths, 2020a: Contextualizing the Covid-19 pandemic for a carbon-constrained world: Insights for sustainability transitions, energy justice, and research methodology. *Energy Res. Soc. Sci.*, **68**, 101701, doi:10.1016/j.erss.2020.101701.

Sovacool, B.K., M. Martiskainen, A. Hook, and L. Baker, 2020b: Beyond cost and carbon: The multidimensional co-benefits of low carbon transitions in Europe. *Ecol. Econ.*, **169**, doi:10.1016/j.ecolecon.2019.106529.

Spangenberg, J., 2014: Institutional change for strong sustainable consumption: Sustainable consumption and the degrowth economy. *Sustain. Sci. Pract. Policy*, **10(1)**, 62–77, doi:10.1080/15487733.2014.11908125.

Spangenberg, J.H. and S. Germany, 2016: Sufficiency, Degrowth and Sustainable Consumption. *Sustainable Consumption and Social Justice in a Constrained World SCORAI Europe Workshop Proceedings*, Budapest, Hungary, Sustainable Consumption Transitions Series, Issue 6, 25–33.

Spangenberg, J.H. and S. Lorek, 2019: Sufficiency and consumer behaviour: From theory to policy. *Energy Policy*, **129**, 1070–1079, doi:10.1016/j.enpol.2019.03.013.

Spengler, L., 2016: Two types of 'enough': sufficiency as minimum and maximum. *Env. Polit.*, **25(5)**, 921–940, doi:10.1080/09644016.2016.1164355.

Speranza, C.I., B. Kiteme, P. Ambenje, U. Wiesmann, and S. Makali, 2010: Indigenous knowledge related to climate variability and change: Insights from droughts in semi-arid areas of former Makueni District, Kenya. *Clim. Change*, **100(2)**, 295–315, doi:10.1007/s10584-009-9713-0.

Springmann, M. et al., 2016: Global and regional health effects of future food production under climate change: A modelling study. *Lancet*, **387(10031)**, 1937–1946, doi:10.1016/S0140-6736(15)01156-3.

Springmann, M. et al., 2018: Options for keeping the food system within environmental limits. *Nature*, **562(7728)**, 519–525, doi:10.1038/s41586-018-0594-0.

Stahel, W., 2016: The circular economy. *Nature*, **531(7595)**, 435–438, doi:10.1038/531435a.

Standal, K., M. Talevi, and H. Westskog, 2020: Engaging men and women in energy production in Norway and the United Kingdom: The significance of social practices and gender relations. *Energy Res. Soc. Sci.*, **60**, 101338, doi:10.1016/J.ERSS.2019.101338.

Stankuniene, G., D. Streimikiene, and G.L. Kyriakopoulos, 2020: Systematic Literature Review on Behavioral Barriers of Climate Change Mitigation in Households. *Sustainability*, **12(18)**, 7369, doi:10.3390/SU12187369.

Stark, C., 2020: Covid-19 recovery and climate change. *IPPR Progress. Rev.*, **27(2)**, 132–139, doi:10.1111/newe.12207.

Steckel, J.C., R.J. Brecha, M. Jakob, J. Stre, and G. Luderer, 2013: Development without energy? Assessing future scenarios of energy consumption in developing countries. *Ecol. Econ.*, **90**, 53–67, doi:10.1016/j.ecolecon.2013.02.006.

Steemers, K., 2003: Energy and the city: density, buildings and transport. *Energy Build.*, **35(1)**, 3–14, doi.org/10.1016/S0378-7788(02)00075-0.

Steffen, B., D. Hischier, and T.S. Schmidt, 2018a: Historical and projected improvements in net energy performance of power generation technologies. *Energy Environ. Sci.*, **11(12)**, 3524–3530, doi:10.1039/C8EE01231H.

Steffen, W. et al., 2018b: Trajectories of the Earth System in the Anthropocene. *Proc. Natl. Acad. Sci.*, **115(33)**, 8252–8259, doi:10.1073/pnas.1810141115.

Steg, L., 2005: Car use: Lust and must. Instrumental, symbolic and affective motives for car use. *Transp. Res. Part A Policy Pract.*, **39(2–3 special issue)**, 147–162, doi:10.1016/j.tra.2004.07.001.

Steg, L., 2008: Promoting household energy conservation. *Energy Policy*, **36(12)**, 4449–4453, doi:10.1016/j.enpol.2008.09.027.

Steg, L., 2016: Values, Norms, and Intrinsic Motivation to Act Proenvironmentally. *Annu. Rev. Environ. Resour.*, **41(1)**, 277–292, doi:10.1146/annurev-environ-110615-085947.

Stein, R. (ed.), 2004: *New Perspectives on Environmental Justice: Gender, Sexuality, and Activism*. Rutgers University Press, New Brunswick, NJ, USA.

Steinberger, J.K. et al., 2012: Pathways of human development and carbon emissions embodied in trade. *Nat. Clim. Change*, **2(2)**, 81–85, doi:10.1038/nclimate1371.

Steinberger, J.K., W.F. Lamb, and M. Sakai, 2020: Your money or your life? The carbon-development paradox. *Environ. Res. Lett.*, **15(4)**, 044016, doi:10.1088/1748-9326/AB7461.

Steinberger, J.K., and J.T. Roberts, 2010: From constraint to sufficiency: The decoupling of energy and carbon from human needs, 1975–2005. *Ecol. Econ.*, **70(2)**, 425–433, doi:10.1016/j.ecolecon.2010.09.014.

Stephenson, J. et al., 2015: The energy cultures framework: Exploring the role of norms, practices and material culture in shaping energy behaviour in New Zealand. *Energy Res. Soc. Sci.*, **7**, 117–123, doi:10.1016/j.erss.2015.03.005.

Sterman, J.D. and L.B. Sweeney, 2002: Cloudy skies: assessing public understanding of global warming. *Syst. Dyn. Rev.*, **18(2)**, 207–240, doi:10.1002/sdr.242.

Stern, P.C., 2000: New Environmental Theories: Toward a Coherent Theory of Environmentally Significant Behavior. *J. Soc. Issues*, **56(3)**, 407–424, doi:10.1111/0022-4537.00175.

Stern, P.C. et al., 1985: The effectiveness of incentives for residential energy conservation. *Evol. Rev.*, **10(2)**, 147–176.

Stiles, J., 2020: Strategic niche management in transition pathways: Telework advocacy as groundwork for an incremental transformation. *Environ. Innov. Soc. Transitions*, **34**, 139–150, doi:10.1016/J.EIST.2019.12.001.

Stojanovski, O., G.W. Leslie, F.A. Wolak, J.E.H. Wong, and M.C. Thurber, 2020: Increasing the energy cognizance of electricity consumers in Mexico: Results from a field experiment. *J. Environ. Econ. Manage.*, **102**(July 2020), 102323, doi:10.1016/j.jeem.2020.102323.

Stokes, L.C., and C. Warshaw, 2017: Renewable energy policy design and framing influence public support in the United States. *Nat. Energy*, **2(8)**, 17107, doi:10.1038/nenergy.2017.107.

Stolaroff, J.K. et al., 2018: Energy use and life cycle greenhouse gas emissions of drones for commercial package delivery. *Nat. Commun.*, **9(1)**, 409, doi:10.1038/s41467-017-02411-5.

Stoll, C., L. Klaaßen, and U. Gallersdörfer, 2019: The Carbon Footprint of Bitcoin. *Joule*, **3(7)**, doi:10.1016/j.joule.2019.05.012.

5

Strand, J., 2020: *Supporting Carbon Tax Implementation in Developing Countries through Results-Based Payments for Emissions Reductions*. Policy Research Working Paper No. 9443. World Bank, Washington, DC, USA.

Stratford, B., 2020: The Threat of Rent Extraction in a Resource-constrained Future. *Ecol. Econ.*, **169**, 106524, doi:10.1016/j.ecolecon.2019.106524.

Strauch, Y., 2020: Beyond the low-carbon niche: Global tipping points in the rise of wind, solar, and electric vehicles to regime scale systems. *Energy Res. Soc. Sci.*, **62**, doi:10.1016/j.erss.2019.101364.

Streeby, S., 2018: *Imagining the Future of Climate Change World-Making through Science Fiction and Activism*. University of California Press, Berkeley, CA, USA.

Strubell, E., A. Ganesh, and A. McCallum, 2020: Energy and policy considerations for deep learning in NLP. In: *Proceedings of the 57th Annual Meeting of the Association for Computational Linguistics,* Florence, Italy, 3645–3650.

Stuart, D., R. Gunderson, and B. Petersen, 2017: Climate Change and the Polanyian Counter-movement: Carbon Markets or Degrowth? *New Polit. Econ.*, **24(1)**, 89–102, doi:10.1080/13563467.2017.1417364.

Stubbs, W. and C. Cocklin, 2008: An ecological modernist interpretation of sustainability: The Case of Interface Inc. *Bus. Strateg. Environ.*, **17(8)**, 512–523, doi:10.1002/bse.544.

Stuber, J., S. Galea, and B.G. Link, 2008: Smoking and the emergence of a stigmatized social status. *Soc. Sci. Med.*, **67(3)**, 420–430, doi:10.1016/j.socscimed.2008.03.010.

Suatmadi, A.Y., F. Creutzig, and I.M. Otto, 2019: On-demand motorcycle taxis improve mobility, not sustainability. *Case Stud. Transp. Policy*, **7(2)**, 218–229, doi:10.1016/J.CSTP.2019.04.005.

Sudbury, A.W. and E.B. Hutchinson, 2016: A Cost Analysis Of Amazon Prime Air (Drone Delivery). *J. Econ. Educ.*, **16(1)**, 1–12.

Sulemana, I., L. McCann, and H.S. James, 2016: Perceived environmental quality and subjective well-being: are African countries different from developed countries? *Int. J. Happiness Dev.*, **3(1)**, 64, doi:10.1504/ijhd.2016.076209.

Sultana, F., 2021: Climate change, COVID-19, and the co-production of injustices: a feminist reading of overlapping crises. *Soc. Cult. Geogr.*, **22(4)**, 447–460, doi:10.1080/14649365.2021.1910994.

Sumner, A., C. Hoy, and E. Ortiz-Juarez, 2020: *Estimates of the impact of COVID-19 on global poverty*. WIDER Working Paper 2020/43. United Nations University World Institute for Development Economics Research (UNU-WIDER), Helsinki, Finland.

Sunderland, L. A. Jahn, M. Hogan, J. Rosenow, and R. Cowart, 2020: *Equity in the energy transition Who pays and who benefits?* Regulatory Assistance Project, Brussels, Belgium.

Sunguya, B.F. et al., 2014: Strong nutrition governance is a key to addressing nutrition transition in low and middle-income countries: Review of countries' nutrition policies. *Nutr. J.*, **13(1)**, doi:10.1186/1475-2891-13-65.

Sunstein, C.R., 2019: *Conformity: The Power of Social Influences*. New York University Press, New York, NY, USA, 192 pp.

Sunstein, C.R. and L.A. Reisch, 2014: Automatically Green: Behavioral Economics and Environmental Protection. *Harvard Environ. Law Rev.*, **38(1)**, 127–158, doi:10.2139/ssrn.2245657.

Sunstein, C.R., L.A. Reisch, and M. Kaiser, 2019: Trusting nudges? Lessons from an international survey. *J. Eur. Public Policy*, **26(10)**, 1417–1443, doi:10.1080/13501763.2018.1531912.

Sweerts, B., R.J. Detz, and B. van der Zwaan, 2020: Evaluating the Role of Unit Size in Learning-by-Doing of Energy Technologies. *Joule*, **4(5)**, 967–970, doi.org/10.1016/j.joule.2020.03.010.

Swim, J.K., N. Geiger, and M.L. Lengieza, 2019: Climate Change Marches as Motivators for Bystander Collective Action. *Front. Commun.*, **4**, 4, doi:10.3389/FCOMM.2019.00004.

Swyngedouw, E., 2011: Climate Change as Post-Political and Post-Democratic Populism. In: *Politik im Klimawandel*, Nomos, Baden-Baden, Germany, pp. 65–81.

Szałek, B.Z., 2013: Some Praxiological Reflections on the So-called 'Overton Window of Political Possibilities', 'Framing' and Related Problems. *Real. Polit. Estim. – Comments – Forecast.*, **(04)**, 237–257.

Tanikawa, H. et al., 2021: A framework of indicators for associating material stocks and flows to service provisioning: Application for Japan 1990–2015. *J. Clean. Prod.*, **285**, 125450, doi:10.1016/J.JCLEPRO.2020.125450.

Tanner, T., T. Mitchell, E. Polack, and B. Guenther, 2009: Urban Governance for Adaptation: Assessing Climate Change Resilience in Ten Asian Cities. *IDS Work. Pap.*, **2009(315)**, 1–47, doi:10.1111/j.2040-0209.2009.00315_1.x.

Taufik, D., M.C.D. Verain, E.P. Bouwman, and M.J. Reinders, 2019: Determinants of real-life behavioural interventions to stimulate more plant-based and less animal-based diets: A systematic review. *Trends Food Sci. Technol.*, **93**, 281–303, doi:10.1016/j.tifs.2019.09.019.

Tauhid, F.A. and H. Zawani, 2018: Mitigating climate change related floods in urban poor areas: Green infrastructure approach. *J. Reg. City Plan.*, **29(2)**, 98–112, doi:10.5614/jrcp.2018.29.2.2.

Taylor, A. and C. Peter, 2014: *Strengthening Climate Resilience in African Cities A Framework for Working with Informality*. Climate and Development Knowledge Network (CDKN), 20 pp. https://cdkn.org/wp-content/uploads/2014/05/CDKN_ACC_WP_final_web-res.pdf (Accessed October 11, 2021).

Taylor, A.L., S. Dessai, and W. Bruine de Bruin, 2014: Public perception of climate risk and adaptation in the UK: A review of the literature. *Clim. Risk Manag.*, **4**, 1–16, doi:10.1016/j.crm.2014.09.001.

Teame, G.T. and A.T. Habte, 2020: Economic Growth and Carbon Dioxide Emissions in East African Countries: A Pooled Mean Group Approach. *Int. J. Bus. Econ. Res.*, **9(4)**, 160–169, doi:10.11648/j.ijber.20200904.11.

Teece, D.J., 2018: Tesla and the Reshaping of the Auto Industry. *Manag. Organ. Rev.*, **14(3)**, 501–512, doi:10.1017/mor.2018.33.

Temper, L. et al., 2020: Movements shaping climate futures: A systematic mapping of protests against fossil fuel and low-carbon energy projects. *Environ. Res. Lett*, **15**, 123004.

Temple, J., 2020: Why we need broader coalitions to combat environmental racism and climate change *MIT Technol. Rev.* https://www.technologyreview.com/2020/06/11/1003162/a-green-new-deal-architect-explains-how-the-protests-and-climate-crisis-are-connected/ (Accessed June 19, 2020).

Terry, G., 2009: No climate justice without gender justice: an overview of the issues. *Gend. Dev.*, **17(1)**, 5–18, doi:10.1080/13552070802696839.

Terzi, A., 2020: Crafting an effective narrative on the green transition. *Energy Policy*, **147**, doi:10.1016/j.enpol.2020.111883.

Tesfamichael, M., Y. Mulugetta, A.D. Beyene, and S. Sebsibie, 2021: Counting the cost: Coping with tariff increases amidst power supply shortfalls in urban households in Ethiopia. *Energy Res. Soc. Sci.*, **71**, 101860, doi:10.1016/j.erss.2020.101860.

Teske, S. et al., 2015: *Energy [R]evolution: A sustainable world energy outlook 2015*. Greenpeace International, Hamburg, Germany, https://elib.dlr.de/98314/.

Thacker, S. et al., 2019: Infrastructure for sustainable development. *Nat. Sustain.*, **2(4)**, 324–331, doi:10.1038/s41893-019-0256-8.

Thaler, R. and C. Sunstein, 2009: *Nudge: Improving decisions about health, wealth, and happiness*. Penguin Books Ltd, New York, NY, USA.

Thaler, R.H., 2015: *Misbehaving: the making of behavioral economics*. W.W. Norton & Co., New York, NY, USA, 415 pp.

Theotokis, A. and E. Manganari, 2015: The Impact of Choice Architecture on Sustainable Consumer Behavior: The Role of Guilt. *J. Bus. Ethics*, **131(2)**, 423–437, doi:10.1007/s10551-014-2287-4.

Thomas, D.S.G. and C. Twyman, 2005: Equity and justice in climate change adaptation amongst natural-resource-dependent societies. *Glob. Environ. Change*, **15(2)**, 115–124, doi:10.1016/j.gloenvcha.2004.10.001.

Thoyre, A., 2020: Home climate change mitigation practices as gendered labor. *Womens. Stud. Int. Forum*, **78**, 102314, doi:10.1016/j.wsif.2019.102314.

Thyberg, K.L. and D.J. Tonjes, 2016: Drivers of food waste and their implications for sustainable policy development. *Resour. Conserv. Recycl.*, **106**, 110–123, doi:10.1016/j.resconrec.2015.11.016.

Tiba, S. and A. Omri, 2017: Literature survey on the relationships between energy, environment and economic growth. *Renew. Sustain. Energy Rev.*, **69**(August 2015), 1129–1146, doi:10.1016/j.rser.2016.09.113.

Tiefenbeck, V., T. Staake, K. Roth, and O. Sachs, 2013: For better or for worse? Empirical evidence of moral licensing in a behavioral energy conservation campaign. *Energy Policy*, **57**, 160–171, doi:10.1016/j.enpol.2013.01.021.

Timko, M.T., 2019: A World Without Waste. *IEEE Eng. Manag. Rev.*, **47**(1), 106–109, doi:10.1109/EMR.2019.2900636.

Toroitich, I.K. and G. Kerber, 2014: Diakonia, Sustainability, and Climate Change. *Ecum. Rev.*, **66**(3), 288–301, doi:10.1111/erev.12106.

Torres-Carrillo, S., H.R. Siller, C. Vila, C. López, and C.A. Rodríguez, 2020: Environmental analysis of selective laser melting in the manufacturing of aeronautical turbine blades. *J. Clean. Prod.*, **246**, 119068, doi:10.1016/J.JCLEPRO.2019.119068.

Toth, G. and C. Szigeti, 2016: The historical ecological footprint: From over-population to over-consumption. *Ecol. Indic.*, **60**, 283–291, doi:10.1016/j.ecolind.2015.06.040.

Townsend, P., 1979: *Poverty in the United Kingdom: A Survey of Household Resources and Standards of Living.* Penguin Books Ltd, Middlesex, England; New York, New York; Ringwood, Victoria, Australia; Markham, Ontario, Canada; Auckland, New Zealand, 1216 pp.

Trancik, J.E., 2014: Renewable energy: Back the renewables boom. *Nature*, **507**(7492), 300–302, doi:10.1038/507300a.

Trencher, G. et al., 2016: Innovative policy practices to advance building energy efficiency and retrofitting: Approaches, impacts and challenges in ten C40 cities. *Environ. Sci. Policy*, **66**, 353–365, doi:10.1016/j.envsci.2016.06.021.

Truelove, H.B., A.R. Carrico, E.U. Weber, K.T. Raimi, and M.P. Vandenbergh, 2014: Positive and negative spillover of pro-environmental behavior: An integrative review and theoretical framework. *Glob. Environ. Change*, **29**, 127–138, doi:10.1016/j.gloenvcha.2014.09.004.

Tschakert, P. et al., 2017: Climate change and loss, as if people mattered: values, places, and experiences. *Wiley Interdiscip. Rev. Clim. Change*, **8**(5), e476, doi:10.1002/wcc.476.

Turnheim, B. and F.W. Geels, 2012: Regime destabilisation as the flipside of energy transitions: Lessons from the history of the British coal industry (1913–1997). *Energy Policy*, **50**, 35–49, doi:10.1016/j.enpol.2012.04.060.

Turnheim, B. and F.W. Geels, 2019: Incumbent actors, guided search paths, and landmark projects in infra-system transitions: Re-thinking Strategic Niche Management with a case study of French tramway diffusion (1971–2016). *Res. Policy*, **48**(6), 1412–1428, doi:10.1016/j.respol.2019.02.002.

Turnheim, B., P. Kivimaa, and F. Berkhout, eds., 2018: *Innovating Climate Governance: Moving Beyond Experiments*. Cambridge University Press, Cambridge, UK, 250 pp.

Tussyadiah, I.P. and J. Pesonen, 2016: Impacts of Peer-to-Peer Accommodation Use on Travel Patterns. *J. Travel Res.*, **55**(8), 1022–1040, doi:10.1177/0047287515608505.

Tvinnereim, E. and M. Mehling, 2018: Carbon pricing and deep decarbonisation. *Energy Policy*, **121**, 185–189, doi:10.1016/j.enpol.2018.06.020.

Tvinnereim, E., K. Fløttum, Ø. Gjerstad, M.P. Johannesson, and Å.D. Nordø, 2017: Citizens' preferences for tackling climate change. Quantitative and qualitative analyses of their freely formulated solutions. *Glob. Environ. Change*, **46**, 34–41, doi:10.1016/j.gloenvcha.2017.06.005.

TWI2050, 2018: *Transformations to Achieve the Sustainable Development Goals – Report prepared by The World in 2050 Initiative*. International Institute for Applied Systems Analysis (IIASA), Laxenburg, Austria, 154 pp.

TWI2050, 2019: *The Digital Revolution and Sustainable Development: Opportunities and Challenges*. International Institute for Applied Systems Analysis (IIASA), Laxenburg, Austria, 100 pp.

Ulph, A., and D. Ulph, 2021: Environmental policy when consumers value conformity. *J. Environ. Econ. Manage.*, **109**(September 2021), 102172, doi:10.1016/j.jeem.2018.09.001.

UN-Habitat, 2013: *Planning and design for sustainable urban mobility: Global report on human settlements 2013*. United Nations Human Settlements Programme, Nairobi, Kenya, 348 pp.

UN, 2015: *Transforming Our World: The 2030 Agenda for Sustainable Development*. 41 pp. https://sustainabledevelopment.un.org/post2015/transformingourworld (Accessed October 11, 2021).

UN, 2020: *Shared Responsibility, Global Solidarity: Responding to the socio-economic impacts of COVID-19.*, New York, https://www.imf.org/en/News/Articles/2020/03/27/sp032720-opening-remarks-at-press-briefing-following-imfc-conference-call (Accessed December 7, 2020).

UNDESA, 2020: *World Social Report 2020*. Department of Economic and Social Affairs, 216 pp.

UNEP, 2010: *ABC of SCP: Clarifying Concepts on Sustainable Consumption and Production*. United Nations Environment Programme, Nairobi, Kenya.

UNEP, 2013: *Women and natural resources: unlocking the peacebuilding potential*. United Nations Environment Programme, Nairobi, Kenya. 1–70 pp.

UNESC, 2017: *Report of the UN Inter-agency and Expert Group on Sustainable Development Goal Indicators*. 49 pp. https://digitallibrary.un.org/record/821651?ln=en.

UNFCCC, 2016: Decision 1/CP.21: Adoption of the Paris Agreement. In: Report of the Conference of the Parties on its twenty-first session, held in Paris from 30 November to 13 December 2015. Addendum: Part two: Action taken by the Conference of the Parties at its twenty-first session. FCCC/CP/2015/10/ Add.1, United Nations Framework Convention on Climate Change (UNFCCC), pp. 1–36.

UNFCCC, 2016: Decision 21/CP.22: Gender and climate change. In: *Report of the Conference of the Parties on its twenty-second session, held in Marrakech from 7 to 18 November 2016*. FCCC/CP/2016/10/Add.2, United Nations Framework Convention on Climate Change, Marrakech, pp. 17–20, https://unfccc.int/resource/docs/2016/cop22/eng/10a02.pdf (Accessed December 4, 2020).

Unruh, G.C., 2000: Understanding carbon lock-in. *Energy Policy*, **28**(12), 817–830, doi:10.1016/S0301-4215(00)00070-7.

Ürge-Vorsatz, D., S.T. Herrero, N.K. Dubash, and F. Lecocq, 2014: Measuring the co-benefits of climate change mitigation. *Annu. Rev. Environ. Resour.*, **39**, 549–582, doi:10.1146/annurev-environ-031312-125456.

Uyttebrouck, C., E. van Bueren, and J. Teller, 2020: Shared housing for students and young professionals: evolution of a market in need of regulation. *J. Hous. Built Environ.*, (0123456789), doi:10.1007/s10901-020-09778-w.

Uzar, U. and K. Eyuboglu, 2019: The nexus between income inequality and CO_2 emissions in Turkey. *J. Clean. Prod.*, **227**, 149–157, doi:10.1016/j.jclepro.2019.04.169.

Vadén, T. et al., 2020: Decoupling for ecological sustainability: A categorisation and review of research literature. *Environ. Sci. Policy*, **112**(July 2), 236, doi:10.1016/J.ENVSCI.2020.06.016.

van de Ven, D.J., M. González-Eguino, and I. Arto, 2018: The potential of behavioural change for climate change mitigation: a case study for the European Union. *Mitig. Adapt. Strateg. Glob. Change*, **23**(6), 835–886, doi:10.1007/s11027-017-9763-y.

Van den Berg, N.J. et al., 2019: Improved modelling of lifestyle changes in Integrated Assessment Models: Cross-disciplinary insights from methodologies and theories. *Energy Strateg. Rev.*, **26**, 100420, doi:10.1016/j.esr.2019.100420.

Van den Bulte, C., and S. Stremersch, 2004: Social Contagion and Income Heterogeneity in New Product Diffusion: A Meta-Analytic Test. *Mark. Sci.*, **23**(4), 530–544, doi:10.1287/mksc.1040.0054.

van der Linden, S. and M.H. Goldberg, 2020: Alternative meta-analysis of behavioral interventions to promote action on climate change yields different conclusions. *Nat. Commun.*, **11**(1), 3915, doi:10.1038/s41467-020-17613-7.

van Houwelingen, J.H. and W.F. van Raaij, 1989: The Effect of Goal-Setting and Daily Electronic Feedback on In-Home Energy Use. *J. Consum. Res.*, **16**(1), 98, doi:10.1086/209197.

van Mierlo, B. and P.J. Beers, 2020: Understanding and governing learning in sustainability transitions: A review. *Environ. Innov. Soc. Transitions*, **34**(September 2017), 255–269, doi.org/10.1016/j.eist.2018.08.002.

van Sluisveld, M.A.E., S.H. Martínez, V. Daioglou, and D.P. van Vuuren, 2016: Exploring the implications of lifestyle change in 2°C mitigation scenarios using the IMAGE integrated assessment model. *Technol. Forecast. Soc. Change*, **102**, 309–319, doi:10.1016/j.techfore.2015.08.013.

van Sluisveld, M.A.E. et al., 2018: Aligning integrated assessment modelling with socio-technical transition insights: An application to low-carbon energy scenario analysis in Europe. *Technol. Forecast. Soc. Change*, 151(Feb), 119177, doi:10.1016/j.techfore.2017.10.024.

Van Vossole, J., 2012: Global Climate Governance: A Legitimation Crisis: Capitalism, Power, and Alienation from Marxist and Polanyian Perspectives. *Rev. (Fernand Braudel Center)*, **35**(1), 1–27.

Van Vuuren, D.P. et al., 2018: Alternative pathways to the 1.5°C target reduce the need for negative emission technologies. *Nat. Clim. Change*, **8**(5), 391–397, doi:10.1038/s41558-018-0119-8.

Vandeweerdt, C., B. Kerremans, and A. Cohn, 2016: Climate voting in the US Congress: the power of public concern. *Env. Polit.*, **25**(2), 268–288, doi:10.1080/09644016.2016.1116651.

Vanegas Cantarero, M.M., 2020: Of renewable energy, energy democracy, and sustainable development: A roadmap to accelerate the energy transition in developing countries. *Energy Res. Soc. Sci.*, **70**, 101716, doi:10.1016/J.ERSS.2020.101716.

Vatn, A., 2015: *Environmental governance: institutions, policies and actions.* Edward Elgar Publications, Cheltenham, UK.

Verhoef, L.A., B.W. Budde, C. Chockalingam, B. García Nodar, and A.J.M. van Wijk, 2018: The effect of additive manufacturing on global energy demand: An assessment using a bottom-up approach. *Energy Policy*, **112**, doi:10.1016/j.enpol.2017.10.034.

Verplanken, B., 2006: Beyond frequency: Habit as mental construct. *Br. J. Soc. Psychol.*, **45**(3), 639–656, doi:10.1348/014466605X49122.

Verplanken, B., I. Walker, A. Davis, and M. Jurasek, 2008: Context change and travel mode choice: Combining the habit discontinuity and self-activation hypotheses. *J. Environ. Psychol.*, **28**(2), 121–127, doi:10.1016/j.jenvp.2007.10.005.

Versey, H.S., 2021: Missing Pieces in the Discussion on Climate Change and Risk: Intersectionality and Compounded Vulnerability: *Policy Insights from Behav. Brain Sci.*, **8**(1), 67–75, doi:10.1177/2372732220982628.

Viana Cerqueira, E.D., B. Motte-Baumvol, L.B. Chevallier, and O. Bonin, 2020: Does working from home reduce CO_2 emissions? An analysis of travel patterns as dictated by workplaces. *Transp. Res. Part D Transp. Environ.*, **83**(June), 2020, doi:10.1016/j.trd.2020.102338.

Victor, P., 2019: *Managing Without Growth – Slower by Design, Not Disaster.* 2nd ed. Centre for the Understanding of Sustainable Prosperity (CUSP), 413 pp.

Vijeyarasa, R., 2021: Quantifying CEDAW: Concrete Tools for Enhancing Accountability for Women's Rights. *Harv. Hum. Rights J.*, **34**(2021).

Vinnari, M. and E. Vinnari, 2014: A Framework for Sustainability Transition: The Case of Plant-Based Diets. *J. Agric. Environ. Ethics*, **27**(3), 369–396, doi:10.1007/s10806-013-9468-5.

Vinyeta, K., K. Whyte, and K. Lynn, 2016: *Climate Change Through an Intersectional Lens: Gendered Vulnerability and Resilience in Indigenous Communities in the United States.* US Department of Agriculture, Forest Service, Pacific Northwest Research Station, https://www.researchgate.net/publication/291523872_Climate_change_through_an_intersectional_lens_Gendered_vulnerability_and_resilience_in_indigenous_communities_in_the_United_States (Accessed July 4, 2019).

Vita, G., E.G. Hertwich, K. Stadler, and R. Wood, 2019a: Connecting global emissions to fundamental human needs and their satisfaction. *Environ. Res. Lett.*, **14**(1), 014002, doi:10.1088/1748-9326/aae6e0.

Vita, G. et al., 2019b: The Environmental Impact of Green Consumption and Sufficiency Lifestyles Scenarios in Europe: Connecting Local Sustainability Visions to Global Consequences. *Ecol. Econ.*, **164**(March), 106322, doi:10.1016/j.ecolecon.2019.05.002.

Vita, G. et al., 2020: Happier with less? Members of European environmental grassroots initiatives reconcile lower carbon footprints with higher life satisfaction and income increases. *Energy Res. Soc. Sci.*, **60**, doi:10.1016/j.erss.2019.101329.

Vogel, J., J.K. Steinberger, D.W. O'Neill, W.F. Lamb, and J. Krishnakumar, 2021: Socio-economic conditions for satisfying human needs at low energy use: An international analysis of social provisioning. *Glob. Environ. Change*, **69**(July 2021), 102287, doi:10.1016/J.GLOENVCHA.2021.102287.

Völlink, T. and R.M. Meertens, 1999: De effectiviteit van elektronische feedback over het energie-en waterverbruik door middel van teletekst bij huishoudens. (The effectiveness of electronic feedback on household energy use and water use by means of text TV). In: *Sociale psychologie en haar toepassingen* (*Social psychology and its applications*) [Meertens, R.M., R. Vermunt, J.B.F. De Wit, and J.F. Ybema (eds.)]. Eburon, Delft, the Netherlands, pp. 79–91.

Von Stechow, C. et al., 2016: 2°C and SDGs: united they stand, divided they fall? *Environ. Res. Lett.*, **11**(3), 034022, doi:10.1088/1748-9326/11/3/034022.

Voytenko Palgan, Y., L. Zvolska, and O. Mont, 2017: Sustainability framings of accommodation sharing. *Environ. Innov. Soc. Transitions*, **23**, 70–83, doi:10.1016/J.EIST.2016.12.002.

Vranken, H., 2017: Sustainability of bitcoin and blockchains. *Curr. Opin. Environ. Sustain.*, **28**, 1–9, doi:10.1016/j.cosust.2017.04.011.

Wachsmuth, J. and V. Duscha, 2019: Achievability of the Paris targets in the EU – the role of demand-side-driven mitigation in different types of scenarios. *Energy Effic.*, **12**(2), 403–421, doi:10.1007/s12053-018-9670-4.

Wadud, Z., D. MacKenzie, and P. Leiby, 2016: Help or hindrance? The travel, energy and carbon impacts of highly automated vehicles. *Transp. Res. Part A Policy Pract.*, **86**, 1–18, doi.org/10.1016/j.tra.2015.12.001.

Walker, G., N. Simcock, and R. Day, 2016: Necessary energy uses and a minimum standard of living in the United Kingdom: Energy justice or escalating expectations? *Energy Res. Soc. Sci.*, **18**, 129–138, doi:10.1016/j.erss.2016.02.007.

Wall, R. and T. Crosbie, 2009: Potential for reducing electricity demand for lighting in households: An exploratory socio-technical study. *Energy Policy*, **37**(3), 1021–1031, doi:10.1016/j.enpol.2008.10.045.

Wallace-Wells, D., 2019: Rhiana Gunn-Wright on the Rapid Evolution of Climate Policy. *Intelligencer*, September 20.

Waller, L. et al., 2020: Contested framings of greenhouse gas removal and its feasibility: Social and political dimensions. *WIREs Clim. Change*, **11**(4), doi:10.1002/wcc.649.

Wallsten, S., 2015: *The Competitive Effects of the Sharing Economy: How is Uber Changing Taxis?* Technology Policy Institute, Washington, DC, USA, 22 pp. https://techpolicyinstitute.org/wp-content/uploads/2015/06/the-competitive-effects-of-the-2007713.pdf (Accessed July 14, 2019).

Walsh, E., 2016: Why We Need Intersectionality to Understand Climate Change. *intercontinentalcry.org*, https://intercontinentalcry.org/need-intersectionality-understand-climate-change/ (Accessed December 3, 2020).

Wang, D., T. Schwanen, and Z. Mao, 2019: Does exposure to richer and poorer neighborhoods influence wellbeing? *Cities*, **95**, doi:10.1016/j.cities.2019.102408.

Ward, J.D. et al., 2016: Is Decoupling GDP Growth from Environmental Impact Possible? *PLoS One*, **11**(10), e0164733, doi:10.1371/journal.pone.0164733.

Ward, J.W., J.J. Michalek, and C. Samaras, 2021: Air Pollution, Greenhouse Gas, and Traffic Externality Benefits and Costs of Shifting Private Vehicle Travel to Ridesourcing Services. *Environ. Sci. Technol.*, **55**(19), 13174–13185, doi:10.1021/acs.est.1c01641.

Watson, J. and R. Sauter, 2011: Sustainable innovation through leapfrogging: A review of the evidence. *Int. J. Technol. Glob.*, **5(3–4)**, 170–189, doi.org/10.1504/IJTG.2011.039763.

Watson, R.T., J. Corbett, M.C. Boudreau, and J. Webster, 2012: An information strategy for environmental sustainability. *Commun. ACM*, **55(7)**, 28, doi:10.1145/2209249.2209261.

WBGU, 2019: *Digital Momentum for the UN Sustainability Agenda in the 21st Century*. WBGU (German Advisory Council on Global Change), Berlin, Germany, 28 pp. https://www.wbgu.de/fileadmin/user_upload/wbgu/publikationen/politikpapiere/pp10_2019/pdf/WBGU_PP10_EN.pdf (Accessed July 14, 2019).

Weber, E.U., 2006: Experience-based and description-based perceptions of long-term risk: Why global warming does not scare us (yet). *Clim. Change*, **77(1–2)**, 103–120, doi:10.1007/s10584-006-9060-3.

Weber, E.U., 2013: Psychology: Seeing is believing. *Nat. Clim. Change*, **3**(April 2013), doi:10.1038/nclimate1845.

Weber, E.U., 2016: What shapes perceptions of climate change? New research since 2010. *Wiley Interdiscip. Rev. Clim. Change*, **7(1)**, 125–134, doi:10.1002/wcc.377.

Weinberger, R. and F. Goetzke, 2010: Unpacking Preference: How Previous Experience Affects Auto Ownership in the United States. *Urban Stud.*, **47(10)**, 2111–2128, doi:10.1177/0042098009357354.

Wellesley, L. and A. Froggatt, 2015: Changing Climate, Changing Diets: Pathways to Lower Meat Consumption. Chatham House, London, UK, https://www.chathamhouse.org/2015/11/changing-climate-changing-diets-pathways-lower-meat-consumption.

Wells, P., X. Wang, L. Wang, H. Liu, and R. Orsato, 2020: More friends than foes? The impact of automobility-as-a-service on the incumbent automotive industry. *Technol. Forecast. Soc. Change*, **154**(November 2018), 119975, doi:10.1016/j.techfore.2020.119975.

Wenham, C., J. Smith, and R. Morgan, 2020: COVID-19: the gendered impacts of the outbreak. *Lancet*, **395(10227)**, 846–848, doi:10.1016/S0140-6736(20)30526-2.

Wester, M. and P.D. Lama, 2019: Women as agents of change? Reflections on women in climate adaptation and mitigation in the Global North and the Global South. In: *Climate Hazards, Disasters, and Gender Ramifications* [Kinnvall, C. and H. Rydstrom, (eds.)], Routledge, Abingdon, UK, pp. 67–85.

Wester, P., A. Mishra, A. Mukherji, and A.B. Shrestha, 2019: *The Hindu Kush Himalaya Assessment: Mountains, Climate Change, Sustainability and People*. Springer, Cham, Switzerland, 627 pp.

White, R., 2011: Climate change, uncertain futures and the sociology of youth. *Youth Stud. Aust.*, **30(3)**, 13–19.

Whiting, K., L.G. Carmona, L. Brand-Correa, and E. Simpson, 2020: Illumination as a material service: A comparison between Ancient Rome and early 19th century London. *Ecol. Econ.*, **169**, 106502, doi:10.1016/j.ecolecon.2019.106502.

Whitmarsh, L. and A. Corner, 2017: Tools for a new climate conversation: A mixed-methods study of language for public engagement across the political spectrum. *Glob. Environ. Change*, **42**, 122–135, doi:10.1016/j.gloenvcha.2016.12.008.

Whittle, C., L. Whitmarsh, P. Hagger, P. Morgan, and G. Parkhurst, 2019: User decision-making in transitions to electrified, autonomous, shared or reduced mobility. *Transp. Res. Part D Transp. Environ.*, **71**(January), 302–319, doi:10.1016/j.trd.2018.12.014.

Whyte, K., 2017: Indigenous climate change studies: Indigenizing futures, decolonizing the anthropocene. *Engl. Lang. Notes*, **55(1–2)**, 153–162, doi:10.1215/00138282-55.1-2.153.

Whyte, K.P., 2014: A concern about shifting interactions between indigenous and non-indigenous parties in US climate adaptation contexts. *Interdiscip. Environ. Rev.*, **15(2/3)**, 114, doi:10.1504/IER.2014.063658.

Whyte, K.P., 2018: Indigenous science (fiction) for the Anthropocene: Ancestral dystopias and fantasies of climate change crises. *Environ. Plan. E Nat. Sp.*, **1(1–2)**, 224–242, doi:10.1177/2514848618777621.

Wickramasinghe, A., 2015: Energy for rural women: beyond energy access. In: *International Energy and Poverty: The emerging contours* [Guruswamy, L., (ed.)], Routledge, Abingdon, UK and New York, NY, USA, pp. 231–244.

Wiedenhofer, D., B. Smetschka, L. Akenji, M. Jalas, and H. Haberl, 2018: Household time use, carbon footprints, and urban form: a review of the potential contributions of everyday living to the 1.5°C climate target. *Curr. Opin. Environ. Sustain.*, **30**(February 2018), 7–17, doi:10.1016/j.cosust.2018.02.007.

Wiedenhofer, D. et al., 2020: A systematic review of the evidence on decoupling of GDP, resource use and GHG emissions, part I: Bibliometric and conceptual mapping. *Environ. Res. Lett.*, **15(6)**, 063002, doi:10.1088/1748-9326/ab842a.

Wiedmann, T. and J. Minx, 2008: A Definition of "Carbon Footprint." In: *Ecological Economics Research Trends* [Pertsova, C.C., (ed.)], Nova Science Publishers, New York, NY, USA.

Wiedmann, T., M. Lenzen, L.T. Keyßer, and J.K. Steinberger, 2020: Scientists' warning on affluence. *Nat. Commun.*, **11(1)**, 1–10, doi:10.1038/s41467-020-16941-y.

Wildavsky, A. and K. Dake, 1990: Theories of Risk Perception: Who Fears What and Why? *Daedalus*, **119(4)**, 41–60.

Wildcat, D.R., 2014: Introduction: Climate change and indigenous peoples of the USA. In: *Climate Change and Indigenous Peoples in the United States: Impacts, Experiences and Actions* [Maldonado, J.K., B. Colombi, and R. Pandya (eds.)] Springer International Publishing, pp. 1–7.

Wilhite, H., 2009: The conditioning of comfort. *Build. Res. Inf.*, **37(1)**, 84–88, doi:10.1080/09613210802559943.

Wilhite, H. and R. Ling, 1995: Measured energy savings from a more informative energy bill. *Energy Build.*, **22(2)**, 145–155, doi:10.1016/0378-7788(94)00912-4.

Willett, W. et al., 2019: Food in the Anthropocene: the EAT–Lancet Commission on healthy diets from sustainable food systems. *Lancet*, **393(10170)**, 447–492, doi:10.1016/S0140-6736(18)31788-4.

Williams, A., 2006: Product-service systems in the automotive industry: The case of micro-factory retailing. *J. Clean. Prod.*, **14(2)**, doi:10.1016/j.jclepro.2004.09.003.

Williams, D.S., M. Máñez Costa, C. Sutherland, L. Celliers, and J. Scheffran, 2019: Vulnerability of informal settlements in the context of rapid urbanization and climate change. *Environ. Urban.*, **31(1)**, 157–176, doi:10.1177/0956247818819694.

Williams, M. and B. Jaftha, 2020: Attitudes, beliefs and readiness to act on climate change: A preregistered replication. *Ecopsychology*.

Williams, R.C. et al., 2015: The Initial Incidence of a Carbon Tax Across Income Groups. *Natl. Tax J.*, **68(1)**, 195–214.

Wilson, C., 2009: *Meta-analysis of unit and industry level scaling dynamics in energy technologies and climate change mitigation scenarios*. International Institute for Applied Systems Analysis (IIASA), Laxenburg, Austria, 119 pp.

Wilson, C., 2012: Up-scaling, formative phases, and learning in the historical diffusion of energy technologies. *Energy Policy*, **50**, 81–94, doi:10.1016/j.enpol.2012.04.077.

Wilson, C., A. Grubler, K.S. Gallagher, and G.F. Nemet, 2012: Marginalization of end-use technologies in energy innovation for climate protection. *Nat. Clim. Change*, **2(11)**, 780–788, doi:10.1038/nclimate1576.

Wilson, C., N. Bento, B. Boza-Kiss, and A. Grubler, 2019a: Near-term actions for transforming energy-service efficiency to limit global warming to 1.5°C. In: Proceedings of the *eceee 2019 Summer Study on energy efficiency: Is efficient sufficient?*, Belambra, Presqu'île de Giens, France.

Wilson, C., H. Pettifor, E. Cassar, L. Kerr, and M. Wilson, 2019b: The potential contribution of disruptive low-carbon innovations to 1.5°C climate mitigation. *Energy Effic.*, **12(2)**, doi:10.1007/s12053-018-9679-8.

Wilson, C. et al., 2020a: Granular technologies to accelerate decarbonization. *Science*, **368(6486)**, 36–39, doi:10.1126/science.aaz8060.

Wilson, C., L. Kerr, F. Sprei, E. Vrain, and M. Wilson, 2020b: Potential Climate Benefits of Digital Consumer Innovations. *Annu. Rev. Environ. Resour.*, **45(1)**, doi:10.1146/annurev-environ-012320-082424.

Wilson, C., L. Kerr, F. Sprei, E. Vrain, and M. Wilson, 2020c: Potential Climate Benefits of Digital Consumer Innovations. *Annu. Rev. Environ. Resour.*, **45**, 113–144, doi:10.1146/ANNUREV-ENVIRON-012320-082424.

Wilson, D.C., C. Velis, and C. Cheeseman, 2006: Role of informal sector recycling in waste management in developing countries. *Habitat Int.*, **30(4)**, 797–808, doi.org/10.1016/j.habitatint.2005.09.005.

Wilson, J.R. et al., 2018: Adaptive comanagement to achieve climate-ready fisheries. *Conserv. Lett.*, **11(6)**, e12452, doi:10.1111/conl.12452.

Wilson, N.L.W., B.J. Rickard, R. Saputo, and S.-T. Ho, 2017: Food waste: The role of date labels, package size, and product category. *Food Qual. Prefer.*, **55**, 35–44, doi:10.1016/J.FOODQUAL.2016.08.004.

Winett, R.A., J.H. Kagel, R.C. Battalio, and R.C. Winkler, 1978: Effects of monetary rebates, feedback, and information on residential electricity conservation. *J. Appl. Psychol.*, **63(1)**, 73–80, doi:10.1037/0021-9010.63.1.73.

Wise, R.M. et al., 2014: Reconceptualising adaptation to climate change as part of pathways of change and response. *Glob. Environ. Change*, **28**, 325–336, doi:10.1016/j.gloenvcha.2013.12.002.

Woiwode, C. et al., 2021: Inner transformation to sustainability as a deep leverage point: fostering new avenues for change through dialogue and reflection. *Sustain. Sci.*, **16(3)**, 841–858, doi:10.1007/S11625-020-00882-Y.

Wolbertus, R., M. Kroesen, R. van den Hoed, and C.G. Chorus, 2018: Policy effects on charging behaviour of electric vehicle owners and on purchase intentions of prospective owners: Natural and stated choice experiments. *Transp. Res. Part D Transp. Environ.*, **62**, 283–297, doi:10.1016/j.trd.2018.03.012.

Wolfram, P., T. Wiedmann, and M. Diesendorf, 2016: Carbon footprint scenarios for renewable electricity in Australia. *J. Clean. Prod.*, **124**, 236–245, doi:10.1016/j.jclepro.2016.02.080.

Wolfram, P., Q. Tu, N. Heeren, S. Pauliuk, and E.G. Hertwich, 2021: Material efficiency and climate change mitigation of passenger vehicles. *J. Ind. Ecol.*, **25(2)**, 494–510, doi:10.1111/JIEC.13067.

Wolsink, M., 2007: Wind power implementation: The nature of public attitudes: Equity and fairness instead of "backyard motives." *Renew. Sustain. Energy Rev.*, **11(6)**, 1188–1207, doi:10.1016/j.rser.2005.10.005.

Wolske, K.S., A. Todd, M. Rossol, J. McCall, and B. Sigrin, 2018: Accelerating demand for residential solar photovoltaics: Can simple framing strategies increase consumer interest? *Glob. Environ. Change*, **53**(November), 68–77, doi:10.1016/j.gloenvcha.2018.08.005.

Wolske, K.S., K.T. Gillingham, and P.W. Schultz, 2020: Peer influence on household energy behaviours. *Nat. Energy*, **5(3)**, 202–212, doi:10.1038/s41560-019-0541-9.

Wong-Parodi, G., T. Krishnamurti, J. Gluck, and Y. Agarwal, 2019: Encouraging energy conservation at work: A field study testing social norm feedback and awareness of monitoring. *Energy Policy*, **130**(July 2019), 197–205, doi:10.1016/j.enpol.2019.03.028.

World Bank, 2019: CO$_2$ emissions (metric tons per capita). *World Bank Data*. Washington, DC, USA, https://data.worldbank.org/indicator/EN.ATM.CO2E.PC (Accessed December 11, 2019).

Worrell, E. and M.A.E. Van Sluisveld, 2013: Material efficiency in Dutch packaging policy. *Philos. Trans. R. Soc. A Math. Phys. Eng. Sci.*, **371(1986)**, doi:10.1098/rsta.2011.0570.

Wu, S., X. Zheng, and C. Wei, 2017: Measurement of inequality using household energy consumption data in rural China. *Nat. Energy*, **2(10)**, 795–803, doi:10.1038/s41560-017-0003-1.

Wu, X.D., J.L. Guo, J. Meng, and G.Q. Chen, 2019: Energy use by globalized economy: Total-consumption-based perspective via multi-region input-output accounting. *Sci. Total Environ.*, **662**, 65–76, doi:10.1016/j.scitotenv.2019.01.108.

Wüstenhagen, R., M. Wolsink, and M.J. Bürer, 2007: Social acceptance of renewable energy innovation: An introduction to the concept. *Energy Policy*, **35(5)**, 2683–2691, doi:10.1016/j.enpol.2006.12.001.

Xie, B., M.J. Hurlstone, and I. Walker, 2018: Correct me if I'm wrong: groups outperform individuals in the climate stabilization task. *Front. Psychol.*, **9**, 17–28, doi:10.3389/fpsyg.2018.02274.

Yadav, P., A.P. Heynen, and D. Palit, 2019: Pay-As-You-Go financing: A model for viable and widespread deployment of solar home systems in rural India. *Energy Sustain. Dev.*, **48**, 139–153, doi:10.1016/j.esd.2018.12.005.

Yamin, F., A. Rahman, and S. Huq, 2005: Vulnerability, Adaptation and Climate Disasters: A Conceptual Overview. *IDS Bull.*, **36(4)**, 1–14, doi:10.1111/j.1759-5436.2005.tb00231.x.

Yan, L. et al., 2020: Quantifying and analyzing traffic emission reductions from ridesharing: A case study of Shanghai. *Transp. Res. Part D Transp. Environ.*, **89**(November), 102629, doi:10.1016/j.trd.2020.102629.

Yangka, D. and M. Diesendorf, 2016: Modeling the benefits of electric cooking in Bhutan: A long term perspective. *Renew. Sustain. Energy Rev.*, **59**, 494–503, doi:10.1016/j.rser.2015.12.265.

Yao, Y., M. Hu, F. Di Maio, and S. Cucurachi, 2020: Life cycle assessment of 3D printing geo-polymer concrete: An ex-ante study. *J. Ind. Ecol.*, **24(1)**, doi:10.1111/jiec.12930.

Yin, B., L. Liu, N. Coulombel, and V. Viguié, 2017: Evaluation of ridesharing impacts using an integrated transport land-use model: A case study for the Paris region. *Transp. Res. Procedia*, **27**, 824–831, doi:10.1016/j.trpro.2017.12.083.

Yoeli, E. et al., 2017: Behavioral science tools to strengthen energy & environmental policy. *Behav. Sci. Policy*, **3(1)**, 68–79, doi:10.1353/bsp.2017.0006.

Young, W., K. Hwang, S. McDonald, and C.J. Oates, 2010: Sustainable consumption: green consumer behaviour when purchasing products. *Sustain. Dev.*, **18(1)**, 20–31, doi:10.1002/sd.394.

Yu, A., Y. Wei, W. Chen, N. Peng, and L. Peng, 2018: Life cycle environmental impacts and carbon emissions: A case study of electric and gasoline vehicles in China. *Transp. Res. Part D Transp. Environ.*, **65**(September), 409–420, doi:10.1016/j.trd.2018.09.009.

Yuana, S.L., F. Sengers, W. Boon, M.A. Hajer, and R. Raven, 2020: A dramaturgy of critical moments in transition: Understanding the dynamics of conflict in socio-political change. *Environ. Innov. Soc. Transitions*, **37**, 156–170, doi:10.1016/j.eist.2020.08.009.

Yumashev, A., B. Ślusarczyk, S. Kondrashev, and A. Mikhaylov, 2020: Global Indicators of Sustainable Development: Evaluation of the Influence of the Human Development Index on Consumption and Quality of Energy. *Energies*, **13(11)**, 2768, doi:10.3390/en13112768.

Zangheri, Serrenho, and Bertoldi, 2019: Energy Savings from Feedback Systems: A Meta-Studies' Review. *Energies*, **12(19)**, 3788, doi:10.3390/en12193788.

Zapico Lamela, J.L., M. Turpeinen, and M. Guath, 2011: Kilograms or cups of tea: comparing footprints for better CO$_2$ understanding. *PsychNology*, **9(1)**, 43–54.

Zawadzki, S.J., L. Steg, and T. Bouman, 2020: Meta-analytic evidence for a robust and positive association between individuals' pro-environmental behaviors and their subjective wellbeing. *Environ. Res. Lett.*, **15(12)**, 123007, doi:10.1088/1748-9326/ABC4AE.

Zhang, Y. and Z. Mi, 2018: Environmental benefits of bike sharing: A big data-based analysis. *Appl. Energy*, **220**(December 2017), 296–301, doi:10.1016/j.apenergy.2018.03.101.

Zhang, Y., D. Lin, and Z. Mi, 2019: Electric fence planning for dockless bike-sharing services. *J. Clean. Prod.*, **206**, 383–393, doi:10.1016/j.jclepro.2018.09.215.

Zheng, J., A.A. Chien, and S. Suh, 2020: Mitigating Curtailment and Carbon Emissions through Load Migration between Data Centers. *Joule*, **4(10)**, doi:10.1016/j.joule.2020.08.001.

Zhou, S. and D. Noonan, 2019: Justice Implications of Clean Energy Policies and Programs in the United States: A Theoretical and Empirical Exploration. *Sustainability*, **11(3)**, 807, doi:10.3390/su11030807.

5

Zimm, C., 2019: Methodological issues in measuring international inequality in technology ownership and infrastructure service use. *Dev. Stud. Res.*, **6(1)**, 92–105, doi:10.1080/21665095.2019.1605533.

Zimmerman, M.A., and G.J. Zeitz, 2002: Beyond Survival: Achieving New Venture Growth by Building Legitimacy. *Acad. Manag.*, **27(3)**, 414–431, doi:10.5465/amr.2002.7389921.

Zink, T. and R. Geyer, 2017: Circular Economy Rebound. *J. Ind. Ecol.*, **21(3)**, 593–602, doi:10.1111/jiec.12545.

Zubi, G., G.V. Fracastoro, J.M. Lujano-Rojas, K. El Bakari, and D. Andrews, 2019: The unlocked potential of solar home systems; an effective way to overcome domestic energy poverty in developing regions. *Renew. Energy*, **132**, 1425–1435, doi:10.1016/j.renene.2018.08.093.

5

6

Energy Systems

Coordinating Lead Authors:

Leon Clarke (the United States of America), Yi-Ming Wei (China)

Lead Authors:

Angel De La Vega Navarro (Mexico), Amit Garg (India), Andrea N. Hahmann (Chile/Denmark), Smail Khennas (Algeria), Inês Margarida Lima de Azevedo (the United States of America/ Portugal), Andreas Löschel (Germany), Ajay Kumar Singh (India), Linda Steg (the Netherlands), Goran Strbac (Serbia/United Kingdom), Kenichi Wada (Japan)

Contributing Authors:

Hossein Ameli (Germany), Nils Angliviel de La Beaumelle (France/the United States of America), John Bistline (the United States of America), Edward Byers (Austria/Ireland), Katherine Calvin (the United States of America), Kiran Chawla (India), Yiyun Ryna Cui (China), Steven J. Davis (the United States of America), Julianne DeAngelo (the United States of America), Subash Dhar (India/Denmark), Jacqueline Sophie Edge (South Africa/United Kingdom), Robert Germeshausen (Germany), Mohamad Hejazi (Syria/United States of America), Gokul Iyer (India), Louise Jeffery (United Kingdom), Matti Juhani Koivisto (Finland/Denmark), Gunnar Luderer (Germany), David McCollum (the United States of America), Matteo Muratori (Italy), Gregory F. Nemet (the United States of America/Canada), Omkar Patange (India), Mónica Santillán Vera (Mexico), Udayan Singh (India), Benjamin Kenneth Sovacool (Denmark/United Kingdom), Loreta Stankeviciute (Lithuania), Falko Ueckerdt (Germany), Cintia B. Uvo (Brazil/Sweden/Italy), Heleen van Soest (the Netherlands), Janet Veldstra (the Netherlands)

Review Editors:

Joseph Kow Essandoh-Yeddu (Ghana), Arthur Lee (the United States of America)

Chapter Scientists:

Rong Han (China), Daniel Alejandro Pacheco-Rojas (Mexico), Biying Yu (China)

This chapter should be cited as:

Clarke, L., Y.-M. Wei, A. De La Vega Navarro, A. Garg, A.N. Hahmann, S. Khennas, I.M.L. Azevedo, A. Löschel, A.K. Singh, L. Steg, G. Strbac, K. Wada, 2022: Energy Systems. In IPCC, 2022: *Climate Change 2022: Mitigation of Climate Change. Contribution of Working Group III to the Sixth Assessment Report of the Intergovernmental Panel on Climate Change* [P.R. Shukla, J. Skea, R. Slade, A. Al Khourdajie, R. van Diemen, D. McCollum, M. Pathak, S. Some, P. Vyas, R. Fradera, M. Belkacemi, A. Hasija, G. Lisboa, S. Luz, J. Malley, (eds.)]. Cambridge University Press, Cambridge, UK and New York, NY, USA. doi: 10.1017/9781009157926.008.

Table of Contents

Executive Summary

Warming cannot be limited to well below 2°C without rapid and deep reductions in energy system carbon dioxide (CO_2) and greenhouse gas (GHG) emissions. In scenarios limiting warming to 1.5°C (>50%) with no or limited overshoot (2°C (>67%) with action starting in 2020), net energy system CO_2 emissions (interquartile range) fall by 87–97% (60–79%) in 2050. In 2030, in scenarios limiting warming to 1.5°C (>50%) with no or limited overshoot, net CO_2 and GHG emissions fall by 35–51% and 38–52% respectively. In scenarios limiting warming to 1.5°C (>50%) with no or limited overshoot (2°C (>67%)), net electricity sector CO_2 emissions reach zero globally between 2045 and 2055 (2050 and 2080). (*high confidence*) {6.7}

Limiting warming to well below 2°C will require substantial energy system changes over the next 30 years. This includes reduced fossil fuel consumption, increased production from low- and zero-carbon energy sources, and increased use of electricity and alternative energy carriers. Coal consumption without carbon capture and storage (CCS) falls by 67–82% (interquartile range) in 2030 in scenarios limiting warming to 1.5°C (>50%) with no or limited overshoot. Oil and gas consumption fall more slowly. Low-carbon sources produce 93–97% of global electricity by 2050 in scenarios that limit warming to 2°C (>67%) with action starting in 2020. In scenarios limiting warming to 1.5°C (>50%) with no or limited overshoot (2°C (>67%) with action starting in 2020), electricity supplies 48–58% (36–47%) of final energy in 2050, up from 20% in 2019. (*high confidence*) {6.7}

Net-zero energy systems will share common characteristics, but the approach in every country will depend on national circumstances. Common characteristics of net-zero energy systems will include: (i) electricity systems that produce no net CO_2 or remove CO_2 from the atmosphere; (ii) widespread electrification of end uses, including light-duty transport, space heating, and cooking; (iii) substantially lower use of fossil fuels than today; (iv) use of alternative energy carriers such as hydrogen, bioenergy, and ammonia to substitute for fossil fuels in sectors less amenable to electrification; (v) more efficient use of energy than today; (vi) greater energy system integration across regions and across components of the energy system; and (vii) use of CO_2 removal (e.g., direct air carbon capture and storage (DACCS) and bioenergy with carbon capture and storage (DACCS, BECCS)) to offset any residual emissions. (*high confidence*) {6.6}

Energy demands and energy sector emissions have continued to rise. From 2015 to 2019, global final energy consumption grew by 6.6%, CO_2 emissions from the global energy system grew by 4.6%, and total GHG emissions from energy supply rose by 2.7%. Methane emissions, mainly fugitive emissions from oil, gas, and coal, accounted for 18% of GHG emissions in 2019. Coal electricity capacity grew by 7.6% between 2015 and 2019, as new builds in some countries offset declines in others. Total consumption of oil and oil products increased by 5%, and natural gas consumption grew by 15%. Declining energy intensity in almost all regions has been balanced by increased energy consumption. (*high confidence*) {6.3}

Prices have dropped rapidly over the last five years for several key energy system mitigation options, notably solar photovoltaics (PV), wind power, and batteries. From 2015 to 2020, the prices of electricity from PV and wind dropped 56% and 45%, respectively, and battery prices dropped by 64%. Electricity from PV and wind is now cheaper than electricity from fossil sources in many regions, electric vehicles are increasingly competitive with internal combustion engines, and large-scale battery storage on electricity grids is increasingly viable. (*high confidence*) {6.3, 6.4}

Global wind and solar PV capacity and generation have increased rapidly. Solar PV grew by 170% (to 680 TWh); wind grew by 70% (to 1420 TWh) from 2015 to 2019. Policy, societal pressure to limit fossil generation, low interest rates, and cost reductions have all driven wind and solar PV deployment. Solar PV and wind together accounted for 21% of total low-carbon electricity generation and 8% of total electricity generation in 2019. Nuclear generation grew 9% between 2015 and 2019 and accounted for 10% of total generation in 2019 (2790 TWh); hydroelectric power grew by 10% and accounted for 16% (4290 TWh) of total generation. In total, low- and zero-carbon electricity generation technologies produced 37% of global electricity in 2019. (*high confidence*) {6.3, 6.4}

If investments in coal and other fossil infrastructure continue, energy systems will be locked in to higher emissions, making it harder to limit warming to well below 2°C. Many aspects of the energy system – physical infrastructure; institutions, laws, and regulations; and behaviour – are resistant to change or take many years to change. New investments in coal-fired electricity without CCS are inconsistent with limiting warming to well below 2°C. (*high confidence*) {6.3, 6.7}

Limiting warming to well below 2°C will strand fossil-related assets, including fossil infrastructure and unburned fossil fuel resources. The economic impact of stranded assets could amount to trillions of dollars. Coal assets are most vulnerable over the coming decade; oil and gas assets are more vulnerable toward mid-century. CCS can allow fossil fuels to be used longer, reducing potential stranded assets. (*high confidence*) {6.7}

A low-carbon energy transition will shift investment patterns and create new economic opportunities. Total energy investment needs will rise, relative to today, over the next decades, if warming is limited to 2°C (>67%) or lower. These increases will be far less pronounced, however, than the reallocations of investment flows that are likely to be seen across sub-sectors, namely from fossil fuels (extraction, conversion, and electricity generation) without CCS and toward renewables, nuclear power, CCS, electricity networks and storage, and end-use energy efficiency. A significant and growing share of investments between now and 2050 will be made in emerging economies, particularly in Asia. (*high confidence*) {6.7}

6

Climate change will affect many future local and national low-carbon energy systems. The impacts, however, are uncertain, particularly at the regional scale. Climate change will alter hydropower production, bioenergy and agricultural yields, thermal power plant efficiencies, and demands for heating and cooling, and it will directly impact power system infrastructure. Climate change will not affect wind and solar resources to the extent that it would compromise their ability to reduce emissions. (*high confidence*) {6.5}

Electricity systems powered predominantly by renewables will be increasingly viable over the coming decades, but it will be challenging to supply the entire energy system with renewable energy. Large shares of variable solar PV and wind power can be incorporated in electricity grids through batteries, hydrogen, and other forms of storage; transmission; flexible non-renewable generation; advanced controls; and greater demand-side responses. Because some applications (e.g., air travel) are not currently amenable to electrification, 100% renewable energy systems would likely need to include alternative fuels such as hydrogen or biofuels. Economic, regulatory, social, and operational challenges increase with higher shares of renewable electricity and energy. The ability to overcome these challenges in practice is not fully understood. (*high confidence*) {6.6}

Multiple energy supply options are available to reduce emissions over the next decade. Nuclear power and hydropower are already established technologies. Solar PV and wind are now cheaper than fossil-generated electricity in many locations. Bioenergy accounts for about a tenth of global primary energy. Carbon capture is widely used in the oil and gas industry, with early applications in electricity production and biofuels. It will not be possible to widely deploy all of these and other options without efforts to address the geophysical, environmental-ecological, economic, technological, socio-cultural, and institutional factors that can facilitate or hinder their implementation. (*high confidence*) {6.4}

Some mitigation options can provide more immediate and cost-effective emissions reductions than others, but a comprehensive approach will be required over the next 10 years to limit warming to well below 2°C. There are substantial, cost-effective opportunities to reduce emissions rapidly in several sectors, including electricity generation and light-duty transportation. But near-term reductions in these sectors will not be sufficient to limit warming to well below 2°C. A broad-based approach across the energy sector will be necessary to reduce emissions over the next 10 years and to set the stage for still deeper reductions beyond 2030. (*high confidence*) {6.4, 6.6, 6.7}

Enhanced integration across energy system sectors and across scales will lower costs and facilitate low-carbon energy system transitions. Greater integration between the electricity sector and end use sectors can facilitate integration of variable renewable energy (VRE) options. Energy systems can be integrated across district, regional, national, and international scales. (*high confidence*) {6.4, 6.6}

The viable speed and scope of a low-carbon energy system transition will depend on how well it can support sustainable development goals (SDGs) and other societal objectives. Energy systems are linked to a range of societal objectives, including energy access, air and water pollution, health, energy security, water security, food security, economic prosperity, international competitiveness, employment. These linkages and their importance vary among regions. Energy sector mitigation and efforts to achieve SDGs generally support one another, though there are important region-specific exceptions. (*high confidence*) {6.1, 6.7}

The economic outcomes of low-carbon transitions in some sectors and regions may be on a par with, or superior to those of an emissions-intensive future. Cost reductions in key technologies, particularly in electricity and light-duty transport, have increased the economic attractiveness of near-term low-carbon transitions. Long-term mitigation costs are not well understood and depend on policy design and implementation, and the future costs and availability of technologies. Advances in low-carbon energy resources and carriers such as next-generation biofuels, hydrogen produced from electrolysis, synthetic fuels, and carbon-neutral ammonia would substantially improve the economics of net-zero energy systems. (*medium confidence*) {6.4, 6.7}

6

6.1   Introduction

The global energy system is the largest source of CO_2 emissions (Chapter 2). Reducing energy sector emissions is therefore essential to limit warming. The energy systems of the future will be very different from those of today if the world successfully limits warming to well below 2°C. Energy will be provided, converted, and used in different ways than it is today (Figure 6.1). Achieving and responding to these changes presents an impressive range of challenges and opportunities.

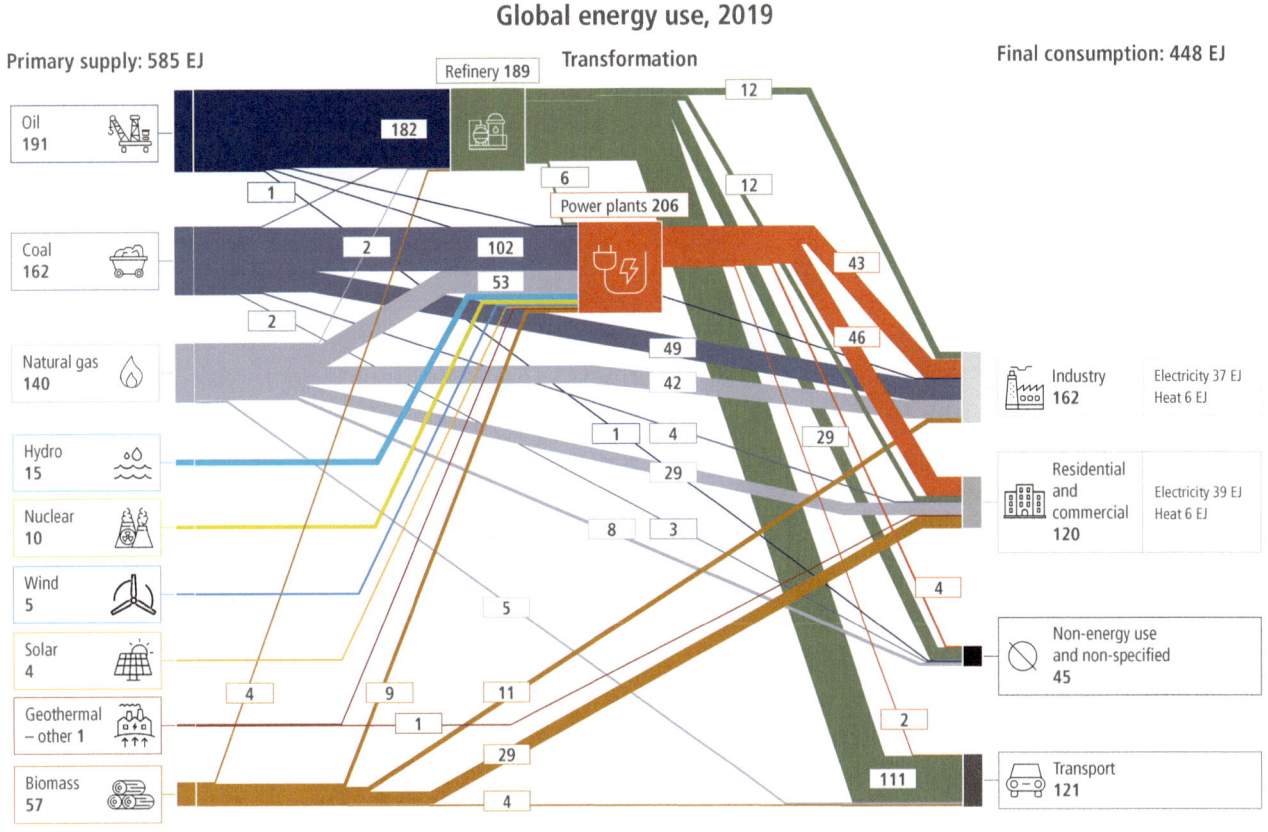

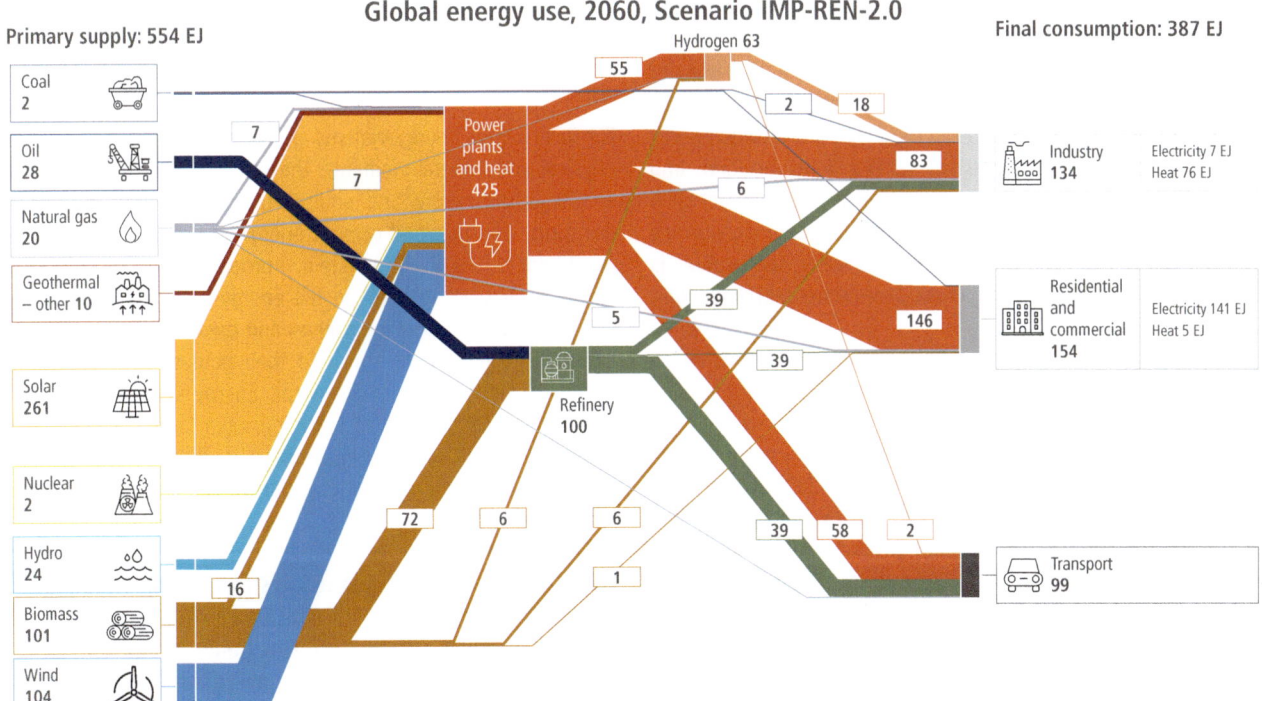

Figure 6.1 | Global energy flows within the 2019 global energy system (top panel) and within two illustrative future, net-zero CO_2 emissions global energy systems (bottom panels).

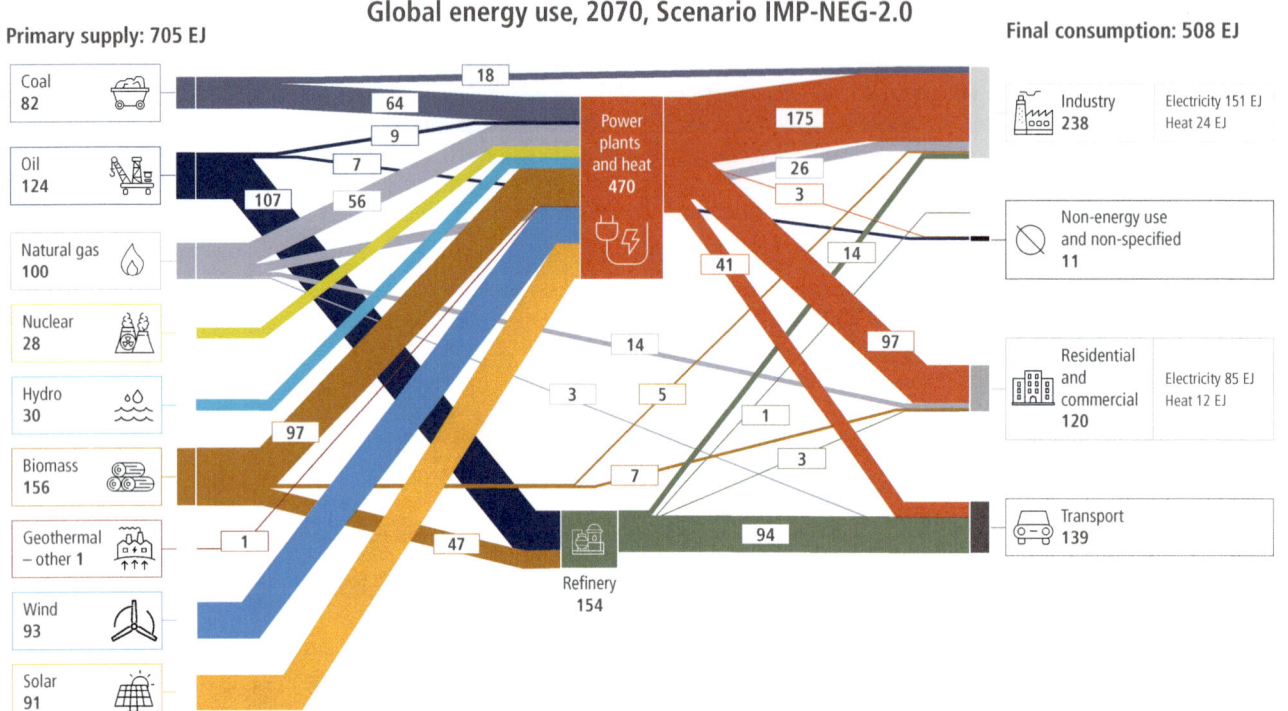

Figure 6.1 (continued): Global energy flows within the 2019 global energy system (top panel) and within two illustrative future, net-zero CO₂ emissions global energy systems (bottom panels). Source: IEA, AR6 Scenarios Database. Flows below 1 EJ are not represented. Agricultural energy and energy own use are included in industry. Captured methane is included in natural gas supply where appropriate. The illustrative net-zero scenarios correspond to the years in which net energy system CO_2 emissions reach zero – 2060 in IMP-Ren and 2070 in IMP-Neg-2.0. Source: data from IMP-Ren: Luderer et al. (2022); IMP-Neg-2.0: Riahi, K. et al. (2021).

Within this context, this chapter has two main objectives. First, it aims to assess specific, individual mitigation options in energy supply, energy transformation, and energy transportation and transmission. This assessment is complementary to a set of chapters that explore mitigation options in agriculture, forestry, and other land uses (Chapter 7), urban systems and other settlements (Chapter 8), buildings (Chapter 9), transport (Chapter 10), industry (Chapter 11), and cross-sectoral perspectives (Chapter 12). Second, this chapter aims to assess system-level mitigation opportunities and challenges across the entirety of energy systems. These systems include energy supply, transformation, transmission, storage, transportation, and end uses. They also include the societal systems that interact with the physical energy system. As energy systems become increasingly integrated and interconnected, a system-wide perspective is necessary for understanding mitigation opportunities and challenges.

Within this context, this chapter addresses six topics, each of which is addressed in a separate section. First, Section 6.2 defines the scope of the energy system. Section 6.3 then discusses the recent trends in energy systems that might exert the most significant influence on energy system evolution and options for reducing emissions. Section 6.4 assesses the status and potential of individual energy supply, transformation, storage, transportation and transmission, and integration mitigation options in the energy sector. Section 6.5 explores how climate change might affect energy systems and alter potential energy system mitigation options and strategies. Section 6.6 identifies key characteristics of net-zero energy systems – those that emit very little or no CO₂. Section 6.7 explores transition pathways toward and through net-zero energy systems.

Across all of these sections, the chapter aims to explore the ways that energy sector mitigation options and strategies interact with Sustainable Development Goals (SDGs) and other societal and environmental goals.

6.2   The Scope of the Energy System and its Possible Evolution

For this chapter, energy systems are defined broadly to include both physical and societal elements. The physical infrastructure includes all the infrastructure and equipment used to extract, transform, transport, transmit, and convert energy to provide energy services. In addition to the physical system, a broad range of societal systems and dynamics are relevant to the energy system. Human societies use energy to transport themselves and the goods that they use and consume, to heat, cool, and light their homes, to cook their food, and to produce goods and services. Energy systems are therefore tied to the systems involved in the provision of these various goods and services. All energy users engage in the operation of energy systems by demanding energy at particular times and in particular forms. They can adjust their behaviour and demands, for example, by using less energy or by changing when they use energy. Consumers can invest in equipment that reduces their energy needs, and they can invest in technologies that transform energy (e.g., rooftop solar) or store energy (e.g., batteries). Firms and governments invest in equipment to produce, transform, and transport energy such as power plants, refineries, electric transmission lines, and oil tankers. All aspects of energy systems are governed by laws, regulations, and actual institutions that reside within businesses and governments at all levels. This includes, for example, rules for trading emissions permits, deciding when particular electricity generation technologies might come online, water management and related environmental rules that define the availability of hydropower or influence water availability for cooling power plants, regulations for injecting CO_2 into underground reservoirs or disposing of nuclear waste, and even company policies regarding work hours or teleworking, which can have important implications for energy demand profiles. Many people are employed in the energy sector, and energy system mitigation will eliminate some jobs while creating others.

This broader view of energy systems is essential for understanding energy system mitigation, as these broader societal and institutional factors can have an important influence on energy system transformations and the potential to rapidly reduce energy CO_2 emissions. Energy system mitigation is as much about the challenges of societal change as it is about the challenges of changes in physical infrastructure, technologies, and operations. While this chapter does not attempt to draw a specific boundary around all the different systems that interact with the energy system, it frequently explores these broader system interactions when assessing different mitigation options and strategies.

There is no single spatial scale at which energy systems might be defined and assessed. They can be assessed at the scales of homes, cities, states or provinces, countries, regions, or the entire world. These different scales are frequently both distinct with their own internal dynamics yet al.o connected to one another. This chapter most frequently assesses energy systems from the country and global perspective.

Because the energy system is so complex, it can be hard to define particular parts of it precisely, and there may be competing definitions

in the literature. For the purposes of this chapter, 'energy supply' encompasses all primary energy, conversion, and transmission processes with the exception of those that use final energy to provide energy services in the end-use sectors (transport, buildings, industry and agriculture). The 'energy system' includes energy end uses sectors along with energy supply. 'Low-emissions' is used for energy technologies that produce little CO_2 or no CO_2 or that remove CO_2 from the atmosphere. Similarly, 'low-carbon' transitions is used to describe transitions that limit likely to 2°C (>67%) or below. 'Net-zero' energy systems refer to those that produce very little or no CO_2 or may even sequester CO_2 from the atmosphere.

6.3   Recent Energy System Trends and Developments

Global energy sector emissions continue to grow but at a decreasing rate

Current energy sector emissions trends, if continued, will not limit global temperature change to well below 2°C (*high confidence*). Global energy system fossil fuel CO_2 emissions grew by 4.6% between 2015 and 2019 (1.1% yr^{-1}), reaching 38 $GtCO_2$ yr^{-1} and accounting for approximately two-thirds of annual global anthropogenic GHG emissions. In 2020, with the worldwide COVID-19 pandemic, energy sector CO_2 emissions dropped by roughly 2 $GtCO_2$ yr^{-1} (Figure 6.2). However global energy-related CO_2 emissions are projected to rebound by nearly 5% in 2021, approaching the 2018–19 peak (IEA 2021d).

Coal was the single largest contributor to energy sector CO_2 emissions between 2015 and 2019, accounting for about 44% of energy sector CO_2 emissions in 2019. Oil accounted for about 34% and natural gas accounted for about 22% of energy sector CO_2 emissions. Coal, oil and natural gas CO_2 emissions grew respectively by 1.2%, 2% and

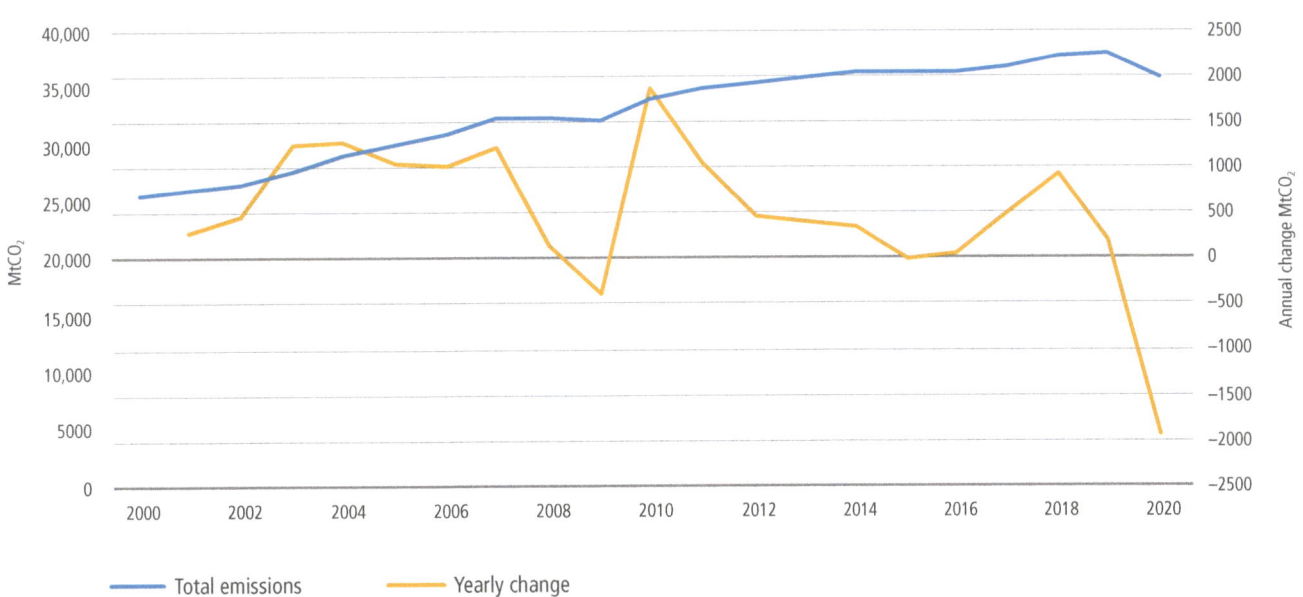

Figure 6.2 | Global energy sector fossil fuel CO_2 emissions and annual change 2000–2019 (MtCO$_2$ yr^{-1}). Source: adapted from Minx et al. (2021a); Crippa et al. (2021).

12.7% (annual rates of 0.31%, 0.5% and 3%) (Figure 6.3). The electricity sector remains the single largest source of energy sector CO_2 emissions, accounting for about 36% in 2019, followed by industry at 22% and transport (excluding international shipping and aviation transport) at about 18% (Figure 6.3). Shipping and aviation accounted for a little over 3%. These proportions have remained relatively unchanged over the last decade. Recent trends reinforce the near-term challenges facing energy sector mitigation – electricity sector emissions continue to rise despite rapid deployment of wind and solar power (see below); transportation emissions continue to rise, and petroleum remains the dominant fuel, despite advances in batteries and electric cars (see below). Some specific sectors, such as shipping and aviation, may present longer-term challenges.

Energy supply GHG emissions, including CO_2 and non-CO_2 greenhouse gases, reached 20 $GtCO_2$-eq yr^{-1} in 2019, rising by 2.7% between 2015 and 2019 (0.66% yr^{-1}). Approximately 18%

of energy supply emissions were non-CO_2 emissions. Electricity and heat contributed approximately 69% of total energy supply GHG emissions in 2019 (Figure 6.3). This growth has occurred despite the high penetration of solar PV and wind power, particularly in Asia and developed countries.

Fugitive emissions from fossil fuel production, primarily methane, accounted for about 18% of sector supply emissions in 2019, with 2.6 Gt CO_2-eq yr^{-1} linked to oil and gas production and 1.3 $GtCO_2$-eq yr^{-1} to coal mining (Crippa et al. 2021). Oil and gas operations produced 2.9 $GtCO_2$.eq yr^{-1} in 2019 (82 Mt yr^{-1} as methane), split roughly equally between the two (IEA 2020a). There remains a high degree of uncertainty in methane emissions estimates from oil and gas operations despite the emergence of new data from satellites and other measurement campaigns. According to a recent study (Hmiel et al. 2020), methane emissions are underestimated by about 25 to 40%.

(a) Global energy sector CO₂ emissions by fuel

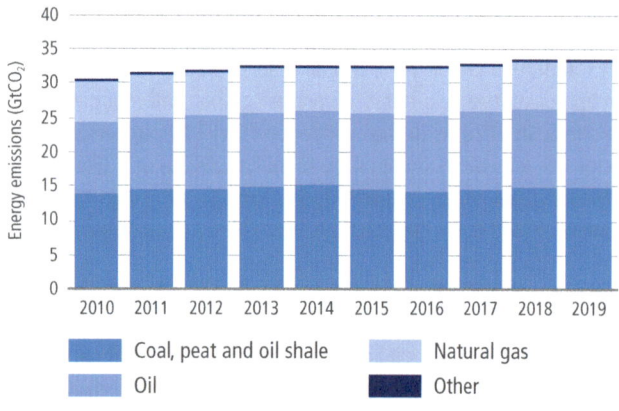

(b) Global energy sector CO₂ emissions by sector

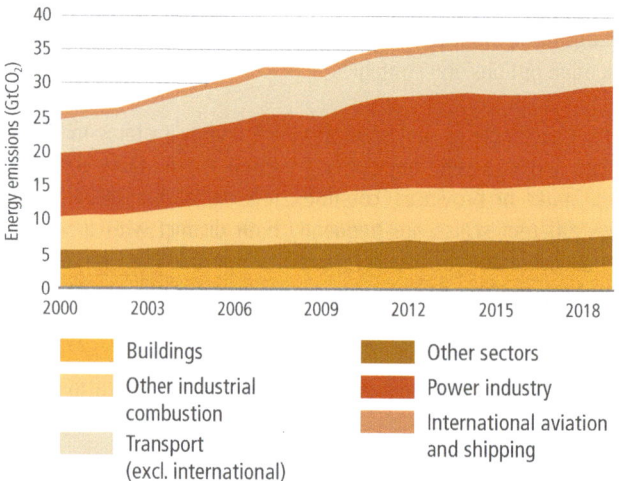

(c) Global energy supply GHG emissions by sector

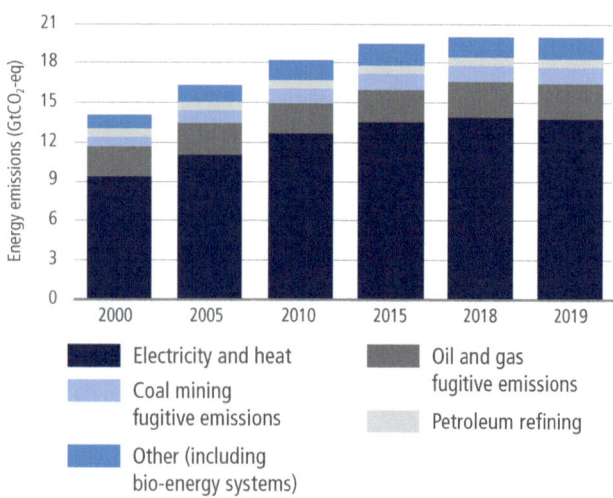

(d) Global energy supply GHG emissions by region

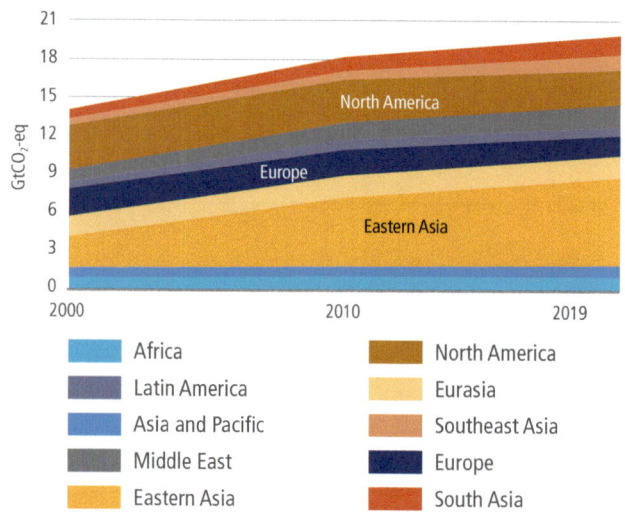

Figure 6.3 | Global energy sector CO₂ emissions and global energy supply GHG emission. Source: Panel (a): data from IEA (2020a); other panels: data from Crippa et al. (2021).

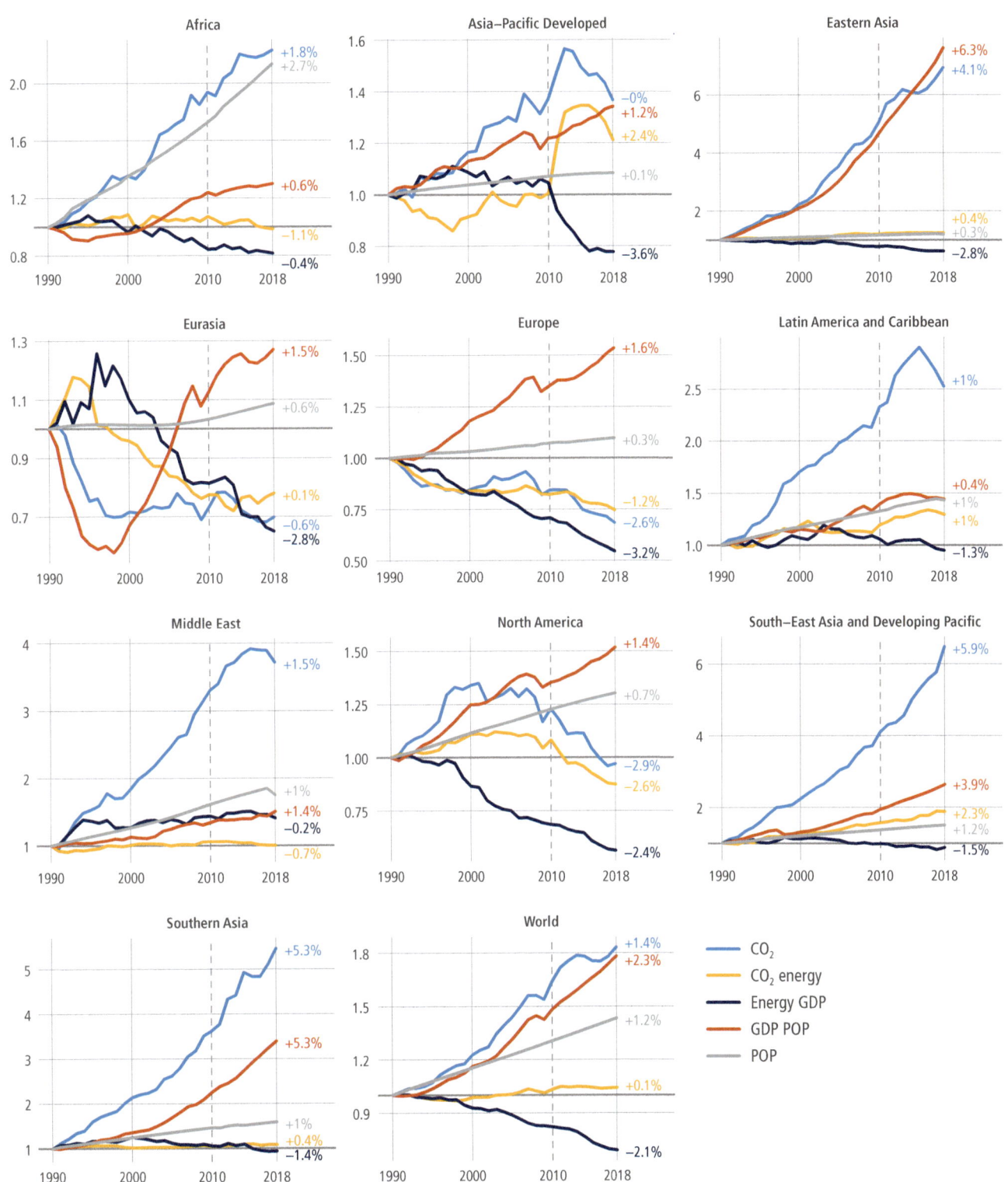

Figure 6.4 | Drivers of greenhouse gas emissions across selected regions. Source: Lamb et al. 2021.

Increasing global energy sector GHG emissions have been driven by rising emissions in some large developing and emerging countries; however, per capita emissions in these countries remain well below those in developed countries (Yu et al. 2019). From 2015 to 2019, Eastern Asia, Southern Asia, and South-East Asia energy sector CO_2 emissions grew by 2.4% yr^{-1}, 2.6% yr^{-1}, and 5.1% yr^{-1}, respectively. The relative and absolute shares of Europe and North America have continued to decline, partly due to the growth in other countries (Figure 6.3).

Despite the declining energy intensity, global energy system CO_2 emissions have closely tracked GDP per capita (Figure 6.4). This is especially true in the Asian economies, which have experienced rapid GDP per capita growth in the past decades and a massive rise in energy demand. Similarly, emissions have declined in times of economic downturns – for example, in Eurasia in the 1990s and globally in 2009 and 2020. Population growth has also contributed to emissions growth globally and in most regions, particularly Africa, but the effect of population growth has been less than that of economic growth. Since 2015, energy intensity has been declining (IEA 2020b), limiting the impact of economic and population growth. However, there is no region where this factor alone would have been sufficient to decrease CO_2 emissions from the energy system. In Europe and North America, the only two regions where emissions decreased meaningfully since 2010, a steady decrease in the carbon intensity of energy was a significant downward driver. The reduction in carbon intensity in the EU is due primarily to the increase of renewable electricity production coupled with the low levels of fossil fuel-based production in the energy mix (Dyrstad et al. 2019).

Global energy production and demand continue to grow, but at a declining rate

Recent changes in the energy system can be viewed within the context of longer-term trends in energy supply and use. Over the last decade, there has been a significant increase in the total primary energy supply (TPES) and major changes in energy sources. From 2015 to 2019, TPES grew by 6.6% (1.6% yr^{-1}) from 569 EJ yr^{-1} to 606 EJ yr^{-1}. Natural gas consumption grew most quickly during this period, at 3.5% yr^{-1}. Coal, oil and oil products grew at annual rates of 0.23% yr^{-1} and 0.83% yr^{-1}, respectively. In 2019, the shares of coal, oil, and natural gas in global TPES were 27%, 31% and 23%, representing only a modest shift from 2015, when the shares were 28%, 32% and 22%, respectively. Renewables, excluding hydropower, grew at an annual rate of 12% yr^{-1} during this period; however, their share remains marginal in 2019, with just 2.2% of the TPES compared to 1.5% in 2015 (Figure 6.5). Bioenergy (including traditional bioenergy) accounted for 9.4% of the TPES, a similar share compared with 2015.

The total final energy consumption (TFC) grew by 6.6% (1.6% yr^{-1}) from 2015 to 2019, rising from 392 EJ yr^{-1} to 418 EJ yr^{-1}. This is a slower growth rate than the previous decade (2.8% yr^{-1}) (Figure 6.5). In 2019, oil products used for transportation accounted for 41% of TFC. The penetration of non-fossil fuels is still marginal despite the significant growth of electric vehicles in recent years. Coal still accounted for 9.5% of TFC in 2019, dropping from 11.7% in 2015. Coal is mainly used as a primary energy source in industry and, to a lesser extent, in the residential sector. The share of electricity increased modestly, from 18.6% in 2015 to 20.2% in 2019, reflecting increasing access in developing countries and increasing use of electricity for a wide variety of end uses in the residential sector (Box 6.1). Heat accounts for approximately 3% of TFC, used mainly in industry and the residential sector. Biofuels and waste accounted for 10.4% of TFC in 2019, only modestly changed compared with 2015.

There are important differences in fuel use across countries. While developed countries almost exclusively use modern fuels, many countries still obtain a significant fraction of their energy from traditional bioenergy (fuelwood and charcoal). Traditional bioenergy

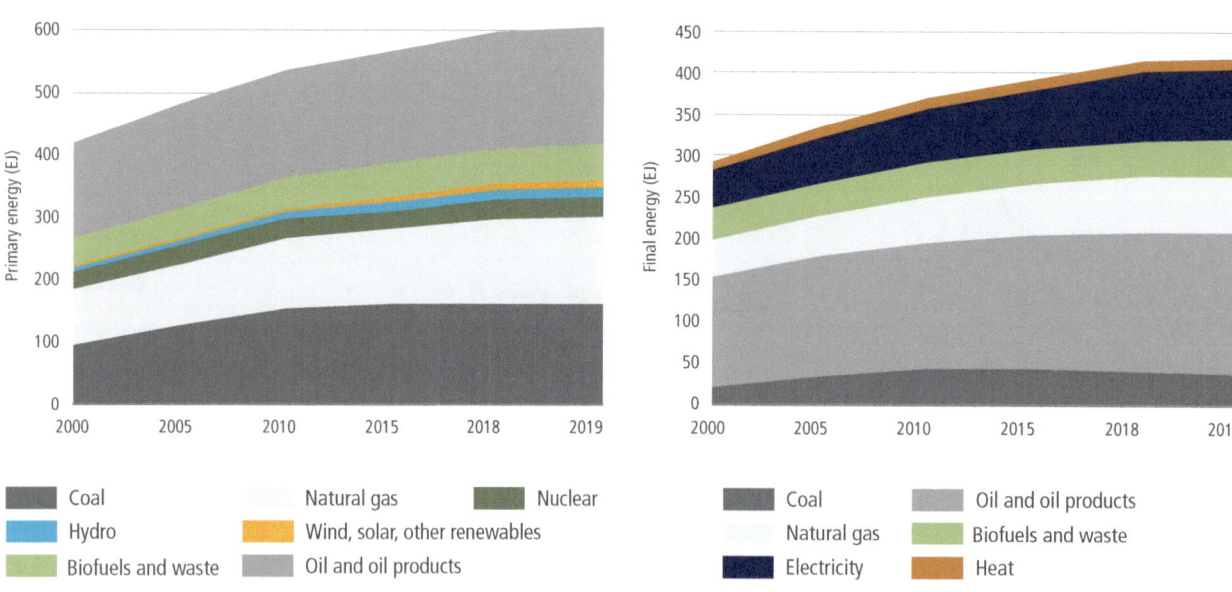

Figure 6.5 | World total primary energy supply (TPES) (EJ) and total final energy consumption (TFC) 2000–2019. Primary energy in this figure is based on IEA accounting methods and not direct equivalents for several energy sources. Final energy does not include industry own use and losses. Source: adapted from IEA world energy balances, Minx et al. (2021b) database for IPCC.

(fuelwood and charcoal) is particularly important in sub-Saharan countries and some Asian countries such as India, particularly in the residential sector for cooking. Africa is still characterised by a high share of traditional bioenergy in TPES and TFC. In 2019, biomass and waste in Africa accounted for 44% of the TPES. The global average was 9.4%.

Asia has been particularly important in TFC growth since 2015. In 2019, Eastern Asia accounted for more 24% of TFC (1.52% annual growth from 2015). In contrast, TFC has increased by only 0.58% in Europe and 1.24% in North America. Despite an increase of 2.05% over the same period, Africa's TFC remains relatively low (6.1% of global TFC), particularly in sub-Saharan countries. Approximately 860 million people, mostly in sub-Saharan Africa and some Asian countries, lacked access to electricity and about 2.65 billion to clean-cooking facilities in 2018 (IEA 2019a). Achieving universal energy access (SDG 7) will require energy transitions in the domestic sector, including new developments in off-grid energy technologies, emphasis on rationalising energy subsidies, and increasing efforts to address health concerns related to the use of traditional fuels (Box 6.1).

Non-climate factors continue to drive energy systems changes

While energy system changes are vital to climate mitigation, recent energy system changes have arisen in response to a much broader set of factors. Important factors include economic growth, energy access, energy justice, energy security, air pollution, technological progress in low-emissions technologies, local job creation. Several of these are discussed here.

Energy access. Between 2000 and 2019, the proportion of the population with access to electricity increased from 73% to 90% (IEA 2020c). Although most of those people gaining access to energy have gained access to fossil fuel-based electricity, an increasing number are gaining access to electricity from renewable sources. Low-emissions, decentralised systems are proving a cost-effective way to provide electricity in rural areas (Scott et al. 2016; Muchunku et al. 2018; IEA 2019b), although the use of diesel generators continues in some remote areas. Between 2000 and 2019 the proportion of the population with access to clean cooking (modern fuels and/or improved biomass cookstoves) rose from 52% to 66%.

Energy security. The ability of countries to maintain access to reliable and affordable energy resources continues to shape energy policy. Energy security is perceived as a national security issue and often prioritised over climate concerns (Nyman 2018). The linkage between climate and energy security is now widely recognised (Blarke and Lund 2007; Toke and Vezirgiannidou 2013; La Viña et al. 2018; World Energy Council 2020; Fu et al. 2021; United Nations 2021). Approaches to energy security are frequently driven by the scope of domestic energy resources. For example, energy security concerns have led to continued reliance on domestic coal production and consumption (Jakob et al. 2020) and increased investment in domestic renewable generation (Konstantinos and Ioannidis 2017). Liquefied natural gas (LNG) Importers have diversified their sources as reliance on LNG has increased (Vivoda 2019).

Air pollution. The energy system is an important source of air pollution, including both indoor and outdoor air pollution. Efforts to address air pollution in several countries and regions (the USA, Mexico, China, India, European Union, Africa, Southeast Asia, among others) have had an importance influence on energy system changes (Bollen and Brink 2014; Fang et al. 2019). Policies aimed at controlling nitrogen oxides (NO_x) and sulphur dioxide (SO_2) emissions have driven emissions abatement efforts and coal fleet retirements (Singh and Rao 2015; Drake and York, 2021). In some places, the prospect of reducing local air pollution remains more salient to policymakers and the public than climate mitigation when deciding to tighten regulations on coal use (Brauers and Oei 2020).

Technology and costs. Costs for renewable technologies have fallen significantly in recent years, driving significant changes in electricity production and transportation (see below). These advances are not divorced from climate and other environmental concerns (Kuik, Branger and Quirion 2019; Timilsina and Shah 2020). Recent advances in PV cells, for example, can be traced in part to aggressive deployment policies spurred by energy security, climate, and other environmental concerns (Kreuz and Müsgens 2017) (Sections 6.3.5 and 6.4.2). The falling costs of batteries, manly Li-ion batteries, has boosted the competitiveness of electric vehicles (Nykvist et al. 2015) (Section 6.3.7).

Box 6.1 | Energy Access, Energy Systems, and Sustainability

Successful mitigation must work in tandem with fundamental development goals such as access to modern forms of energy. In many developing countries, access to electricity, clean cooking fuels, and modern and efficient energy remain an essential societal priority. This is particularly true in sub-Saharan Africa and several Asian countries. SDG 7 on universal access to modern energy includes targets on modern energy services, renewable energy, and energy efficiency, which implies a profound transformation of the current energy systems. Although there are different definitions of energy access, the ultimate goal is universal access to clean and modern fuels.

Despite progress in some countries such as India, Bangladesh and Kenya, 860 million people were without access to electricity in 2018, compared with 1.2 billion in 2010. About 2.65 billion households were cooking with solid fuels, distributed across Asia and Africa (IEA et al. 2020). Around 850 million people in sub-Saharan Africa relied on traditional biomass (firewood and charcoal) for cooking, and 60 million relied on kerosene and coal to meet their energy needs (IEA 2018a). Air pollution was likely responsible for 1.1 million deaths across Africa in 2019 (Fisher et al. 2021). It has been estimated that 2.2 billion people will still be dependent on inefficient and polluting energy sources for cooking by 2030, mainly in Asia and Sub-Saharan Africa, and 650 million people are likely to remain without access to electricity in 2030, 90% of whom will reside in Sub-Saharan Africa (IEA et al. 2020).

6

Box 6.1 (continued)

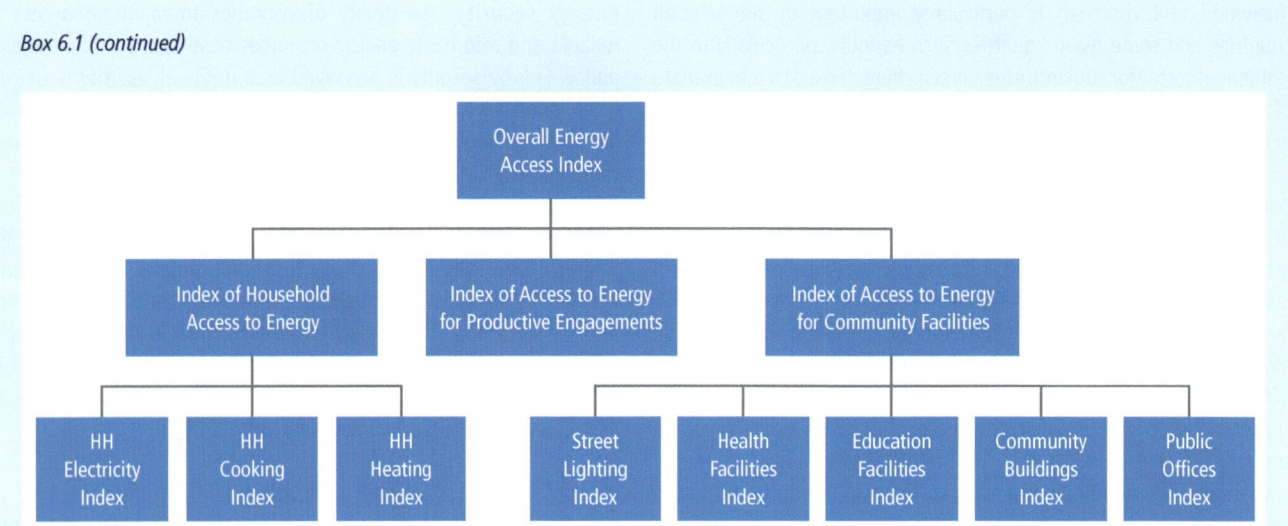

Box 6.1, Figure 1 | Measuring access to energy. Source: with permission from ESMAP-World Bank 2015.

Research indicates that decentralised and on-grid renewables are likely the least cost options to provide universal access to electricity by 2030 (Section 6.4.2). Natural gas, LPG, and improved biomass cookstoves are the most important options for cooking. Universal access to electricity and clean cooking requires a rapid shift from traditional biomass to cleaner fuels and/or clean cooking technologies (IEA et al. 2020). It has been estimated that the provision of electricity and clean cooking for all would require USD786 billion in cumulative investment to 2030, equal to 3.4% of total energy sector investment over the period (IEA 2017).

Even without universal access to modern energy, increased access will substantially affect energy systems, particularly electricity systems through the deployment of renewable energy, LPG, and biomass supply chains. Universal access for households, however, will have a minimal impact on global energy demand; it has been estimated that universal access for household will increase energy demand by 0.2% in 2030 (37 Mtoe yr^{-1}) relative to a future without any change in access to modern energy (IEA 2017).

There have been initial efforts to phase out coal but only modest declines in use

Global coal consumption has been declining, with small fluctuations, since it peaked in 2013 (IEA 2020d). Coal is faring differently across regions. Coal use has been decreasing in the OECD regions, particularly in the USA and the European Union (EU), while remaining mostly flat in China after a period of growth, and it is continuing to increase in other major developing Asian economies (IEA 2020d). Trends in the electricity sector, where most coal is being consumed, are similar. Growth in coal-fired electricity generation capacity in the Asia Pacific region has offset retirements in North America and Europe (Jakob et al. 2020; Global Energy Monitor et al., 2021).

Reductions in coal consumption have been driven in large part by non-climate factors, most notably environmental regulations to address air pollution, rapidly declining costs of renewables, and lower natural gas prices, especially inexpensive unconventional gas in the USA. (Culver and Hong 2016; Diluiso et al.2021; Vinichenko et al. 2021). Older coal-fired power plants that cannot meet new environmental regulations, or have become unprofitable or uncompetitive, have been closed in many regions. Moreover, coal power expansion has slowed down in Asia, as countries have suspended and cancelled new

projects for reasons such as overcapacity, environmental constraints, and the development of renewables (Box 6.2).

Different regions have replaced retired coal with different energy sources. Old coal fleets have been replaced approximately half by gas and half by renewables in the USA, mainly by renewables in the EU, and by advanced coal plants and renewables in Asia (EMBER 2020). Replacing old coal with new coal facilities is inconsistent with limiting warming to 2°C or below (*high confidence*) (Pfeiffer et al. 2016, 2018; Smith et al. 2019; Tong et al. 2019) (Section 6.7.4).

Major coal-consuming countries with abundant coal reserves remain far from phasing out coal (Edenhofer et al. 2018; Spencer et al. 2018). In most developing countries with large coal reserves, coal use has been increasing to support energy security and because it is perceived to have lower costs than alternatives (Steckel et al. 2015; Kalkuhl et al.2019). However, coal faces increasing business risks from the decreasing costs of alternative, low-emissions energy sources and increasing focus on air pollution and other environmental impacts from coal mining and use (Garg et al. 2017; Sovacool et al. 2021). Continued coal builds, mostly in developing countries, will increase the risks of stranded assets (Farfan Orozco 2017; Cui et al. 2019; Saygin et al. 2019) (Box 6.13).

Economic, social, and employment impacts of accelerated coal phase-outs tend to be significant in coal-dependent regions. Tailored reemployment has been used to support coal transitions in some regions. Although some estimates show higher employment opportunities from low-carbon energy (Garrett-Peltier 2017), results vary across regions. Moreover, even with a net increase in total employment, in the long run, renewable jobs are often located outside of coal regions and require different skill sets from the coal industry (Spencer et al. 2018). In a broader sense, achieving a 'just transition' also requires managing the impacts on regional economic development for coal-dependent communities and the effects of higher energy prices for consumers and energy-intensive industries through a comprehensive policy package (Green and Gambhir 2020; Jakob et al. 2020) (Box 6.2).

Box 6.2 | Status and Challenges of a Coal Phase-out

Limiting global warming to 2°C or below requires a rapid shift away from unabated coal consumption – coal without CCS – in the energy system by 2050 (IPCC 2018a; Section 6.7; Chapter 3). This will require cancellation of new coal power projects and accelerated retirement of existing coal plants (Edenhofer et al. 2018; Kriegler et al. 2018; Pfeiffer et al. 2018; Smith et al. 2019; Tong et al. 2019). To limit warming to 2°C or lower, and without new builds, existing coal plants will need to retire 10 to 25 years earlier than the historical average operating lifetime. Completing all planned projects will further reduce the viable lifetime of all plants by 5 to 10 years if warming is to be limited to 2°C or lower (Cui et al. 2019). Phasing-out coal in the next few decades will present economic, social, and security challenges. These will vary across regions based on the characteristics of existing coal infrastructure, the availability of alternatives, economic development, and technological and institutional lock-in (Jakob et al. 2020).

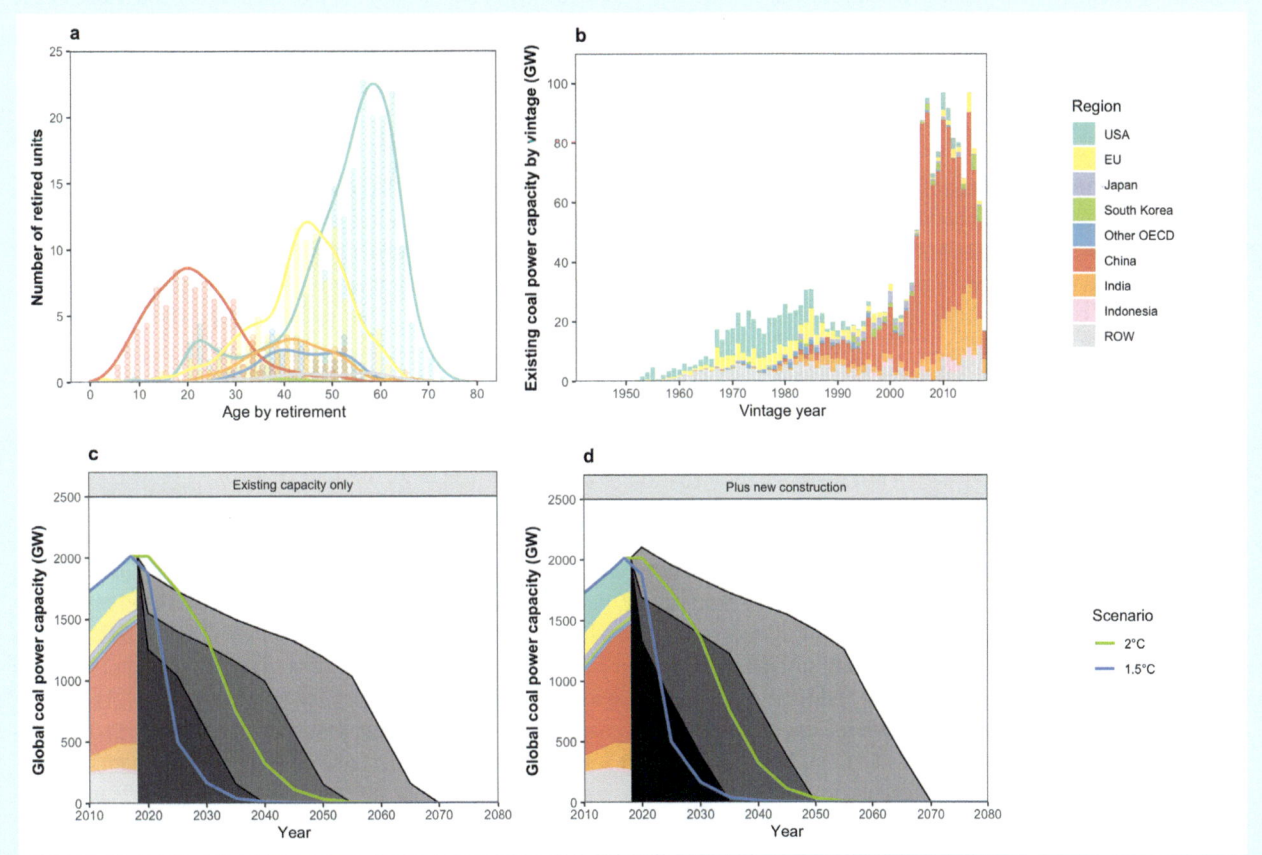

Box 6.2, Figure 1 | Retirement of coal-fired power plants to limit warming to 1.5°C and 2°C or lower. (a) Historical facility age at retirement, **(b)** the vintage year of existing units, **(c)** global coal capacity under different plant lifetimes, compared to capacity levels consistent with a well-below 2°C (green) and 1.5°C (blue) pathway assuming no new coal plants, and **(d)** and assuming plants currently under construction come online as scheduled, but those in planning or permitting stages are not built. Source: with permission from Cui et al. (2019).

6

Box 6.2 (continued)

Between 2015 and 2019, global coal power capacity grew by 146 GW, or 7.6%, as new builds offset retirements in some countries (Global Energy Monitor et al. 2021). Meanwhile, an increasing number of countries and regions have committed to or operationalised coal phase-outs (Jewell et al. 2019; Watts et al. 2019; Littlecott et al. 2021). Actions are being taken by various international and sub-national actors, including national and sub-national governments, public and private power companies, and financial institutions and pension funds that have committed not to fund new coal or coal-based infrastructure (yan Nie et al. 2016; Buckley 2019; Auger et al. 2021). Although these initial efforts are not yet sufficient in limiting warming to 1.5°C, and most have occurred in regions with older coal fleets, these examples provide insight into possible coal phase-out strategies (Spencer et al. 2018) and help identify the mechanisms driving the move away from coal, such as market, technology, policy, or other societal objectives. They also enable better understanding of the possible character of oil and gas phase-downs that would ultimately be needed to limit warming two well below 2°C (Section 6.7.4) (Raimi et al. 2019).

Europe. Several European countries are part of the Powering Past Coal Alliance (PPCA) and have committed to phase out unabated coal on or before 2030 (Jewell et al. 2019). Because these countries represent a small share of global coal generation capacity and have mostly ageing coal plants, they tend to face fewer changes in phasing out coal. The effectiveness of PPCA in countries with younger coal fleets has thus been questioned (Jewell et al. 2019; Blondeel et al. 2020). Germany recently joined the PPCA and has committed to phase out unabated coal by 2038. As part of its commitment to phase out coal, Germany is implementing a set of measures that include compensation for power plant closures, labour market measures for coal workers, and substantial support of structural change in coal-mining regions. Poland, another coal-heavy country in Europe, has not indicated a coal phase-out target and faces substantial challenges (Whitley et al. 2017; Antosiewicz et al. 2020). European efforts to phase out coal indicate that appropriate financial instruments are needed (Rentier et al. 2019), and a just transition for workers are important to gain broad public support and help those most affected by the phase-out (Johnstone and Hielscher 2017; Osička et al. 2020).

North America. Coal use has been declining in North America. In the USA, the primary driver has been the availability of cheap shale gas and ageing coal fleets. Coal use in the USA has dropped by over 50% since 2008 (EIA 2019). The recently announced Nationally Determined Contribution (NDC) by the Biden Administration sets a 100% carbon-free electricity goal by 2035 (The White House 2021), indicating a phase-out not only of unabated coal electricity generation, but also of natural gas generation. As one of the two founding countries of the PPCA, Canada has committed to phasing out unabated coal power by 2030 (Government of Canada 2018). Declining coal use in both the USA and Canada has decreased GHG emissions, local air pollutants, and cooling water use (Harris et al. 2015; Kondash et al. 2019). However, there have been concerns about social and economic consequences, particularly at the local level. For instance, the USA has lost about 50,000 coal mining jobs between 2011 and 2021 (US Bureau of Labor Statistics, 2021), with significant regional and economic inequities (Bodenhamer 2016; Abraham 2017; Greenberg 2018). Comprehensive social programmes, such as retirement compensation, training for reemployment, and business support for economic diversification, have been suggested as means to support a just transition (Homagain et al. 2015; Patrizio et al. 2018; Grubert 2020).

Asia. After a period of rapid growth, coal expansion has slowed in Asia, but it still the primary driver of the global increase in coal demand (IEA 2020e). China's coal consumption reached a plateau under policy efforts during the 13th Five-Year Plan (2016–2020), and new coal plants are being built at a slower rate than previously. Both China and India have suspended and cancelled many new coal power projects and retired a small set of old, dirty, inefficient coal plants (CEA 2019; Global Energy Monitor et al. 2021). These efforts are largely due to non-climate reasons, such air pollution and health (Singh and Rao 2015; Gass et al. 2016; Peng et al. 2018; Malik et al. 2020), overcapacity (Blondeel and Van de Graaf 2018), and rural electrification and renewable investments (Aklin et al. 2017; Thapar et al. 2018). However, as new builds offset retirements, coal generation capacity has continued to grow in both countries since 2015 (Global Energy Monitor et al. 2021). Other fast-growing Southeast Asian countries, such as Indonesia, Vietnam, and the Philippines have experienced strong growth in coal use (IEA 2020b), but an increasing number of new coal power projects are being cancelled (Littlecott et al. 2021). Coal projects in these countries are decreasingly likely to proceed because they rely on international financing, and China, Japan, USA, and other G7 countries have pledged to end overseas coal financing (Schiermeier 2021).

Africa. New coal power projects in Africa have been declining since 2016, with only South Africa and Zimbabwe currently building new coal plants and several others with planned projects (Littlecott et al. 2021). However, these projects also largely depend on international financing and are thus less likely to be implemented (see above). In South Africa, employment in the coal mining sector has dropped by almost half since the 1980s and has been estimated to fall from 77,000 today to 22,000 to 42,000 by 2050 (Cock 2019; Strambo et al. 2019). Policy and financial support are essential to ensure a sustainable transition for these workers (Swilling et al. 2016).

Solar and wind energy have grown dramatically, but global shares remain low relative to other sources

Global PV and wind electric capacities grew 170% and 70%, respectively, between 2015 and 2019. Total solar and wind capacities in 2019 were 609 GW and 623 GW (Figure 6.6) and generation was 680 TWh yr^{-1} and 1420 TWh yr^{-1}. The combined share of solar and wind in the total global electricity generation in 2019 was around 8% (5.5% wind, 2.5% solar), up from around 5% in 2015 (IEA 2021a). Since 2015, the cost of solar PVs has declined by over 60%. Offshore wind costs have fallen by 32%, and onshore wind costs have fallen by 23% (Section 6.4). PV was around 99% of total solar capacity in 2019; onshore wind was about 95% of total wind capacity. Concentrating solar power (CSP) deployment has also continued to grow, but it remains far below PV. Prior to 2010, 50% of all wind capacity was in Europe, but since then, capacity growth in Asia (led by China), has surpassed the growth in Europe. As a consequence, Europe's share in global solar capacity has declined from 74% in 2010 to 24% in 2019. Asia's share in wind and solar capacity in 2019 was 41% and 56%, followed by Europe (31% and 24%) and North America (20% and 12%) (IRENA 2020a, 2021a).

Although the shares of wind and solar remain low in the global total electricity generation, recent growth rates signal the potential for these technologies to support substantial mitigation. The prospects for a continuation of recent growth rates will depend on meeting key challenges such as rapidly integrating wind and solar into electricity grids (Section 6.6.2, Box 6.8) and retiring fossil power plants (see above).

Low-carbon energy sources beyond wind and solar have continued to grow

Low-carbon energy sources such as nuclear, hydropower, bioenergy, geothermal, marine, and fossil or bioenergy with carbon capture, use and storage (CCUS) have continued to grow since 2015 (IEA 2017, 2021a). Hydroelectric power grew from 3890 TWh yr^{-1} (14.0 EJ yr^{-1}) in 2015 to 4290 TWh yr^{-1} (15.5 EJ yr^{-1}) in 2019, or 10.3%; nuclear power grew from 2570 TWh yr^{-1} (9.3 EJ yr^{-1}) to 2790 TWh yr^{-1} (10.1 EJ yr^{-1}), or 8.6%. Hydroelectric and nuclear shares in global total electricity generation remained around 16% and 10%, respectively (IEA 2017, 2021a). Global biofuels production grew from 3.2 EJ yr^{-1} to 4.0 EJ yr^{-1} from 2015 to 2019 (IEA 2017, 2021a). Bioenergy accounted for 2.4% of electricity generation in 2019. Geothermal energy sources produced 92 TWh yr^{-1} (0.33 EJ yr^{-1}) of electricity in 2019, up from 80 TWh yr^{-1} (0.28 EJ yr^{-1}) in 2015 (IEA 2017, 2021a). At present, there are 28 commercially operating CCUS facilities with a CO_2 removal capacity of around 40 million tonnes yr^{-1} (Mtpa). Only two of these are associated with electricity production: the majority are in industrial applications – 37 commercial projects, accounting for about 75 Mtpa, are in various stages of development and construction (Global CCS Institute 2020). The share of marine energy in global electricity generation has remained at approximately 1 TWh yr^{-1} since 2015. In total, low- and zero-carbon electricity generation technologies produced 37% of global electricity in 2019.

Battery prices have dropped substantially, spurring deployment in electricity and transportation

Recent years have seen a rapid decline in the cost of energy storage, particularly batteries (Section 6.4.4). The price of lithium-ion batteries (LIBs) has declined by 97% in the past three decades, and by 90% in the past decade alone (IEA 2021a; Ziegler and Trancik 2021). These declines have important implications for the energy systems, most notably in supporting increased deployment of variable renewable energy (VRE) generation and electrification of the vehicle fleet.

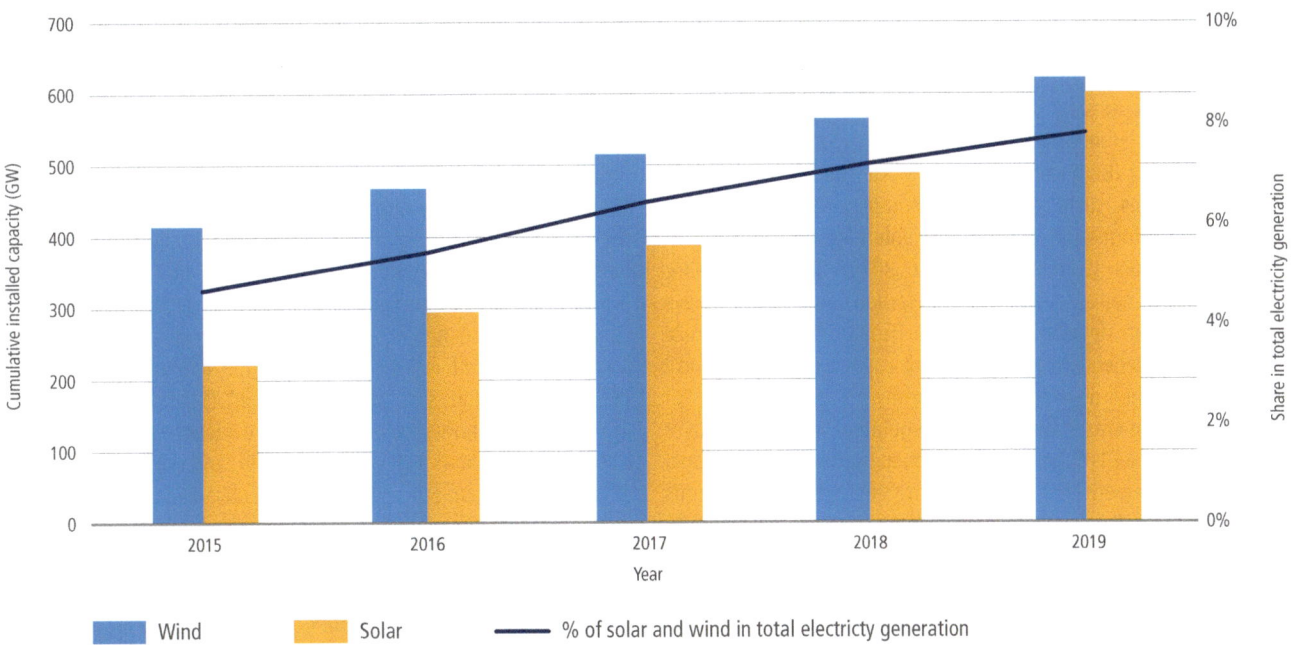

Figure 6.6 | Global solar and wind electricity installed capacities (GW) from 2015–2019 and their combined share in total electricity generation.
Source: data from IEA (2021a) and IRENA (2021).

Battery electricity storage has emerged as important for supporting the flexibility of electricity systems as they accommodate rising shares of VRE. Although pumped-storage hydropower systems accounted for 160 GW, or over 90%, of total energy storage capacity in 2019 (IEA 2020c), battery energy storage systems, led by LIB technology, have accounted for over 90% of new capacity addition since 2015 (IRENA 2019a). In 2019, 10 GW of batteries were connected at the grid and consumer level, rising from 0.6 GW in 2015 (IEA WEO 2019; IEA 2020c).

In California in the USA, legislation was passed to procure around 1.3 GW energy storage (excluding pumped storage) by 2020. One of the largest utility-scale battery storage facilities (300 MW) recently went online in California (Vistra Corp. 2021). Other major projects are in Florida in the USA (409 MW), London in the UK (320 MW), Lithuania (200 MW), Australia (150 MW), Chile (112 MW) and Germany (90 MW), (IRENA 2019a; ARENA 2020; Katz 2020).

The drop in battery prices has also had important implications in the transportation sector. Automotive LIB production rose from around 40 GWh in 2015 to 160 GWh in 2020 (32%). The stock of battery electric vehicles (BEVs) grew from around 0.7 million in 2015 to 4.8 million in 2019 (IEA 2020d). The number of publicly accessible vehicle chargers reached 1.3 million in 2020, 30% of which were fast chargers. The average battery size of BEVs reached 67 kWh in 2019 due to consumer preferences and government incentives for long-range vehicles (Agency 2020; IEA 2021b).

The energy policy landscape continues to evolve

The current energy sector policy landscape consists of policy mixes or policy packages, including regulatory, market-based and other approaches. These mixes have evolved over time and include many sectoral but also some economy-wide policy instruments, such as carbon pricing subsidies.

Governments have chosen a mix of policies and institutional mechanisms that consists of regulatory instruments, like efficiency and technology standards, economic instruments (e.g., carbon pricing, subsidies) (Bertram et al. 2015; Martin and Saikawa 2017) and other policies, such as government interventions to provide infrastructure, information policies, and voluntary actions by non-government actors (Somanathan et al. 2014). In recent years, regulatory instruments to promote low-carbon infrastructure have gained traction in developing countries (Finon 2019). The choice of policies has depended on institutional capacities, technological maturity and other developmental priorities of governments. For example, governments have favoured regulatory instruments over economic instruments when there has been sufficient institutional capacity to implement and monitor the regulations and standards (Hughes and Urpelainen 2015). Furthermore, institutional capacity has also determined the extent of implemented measures (Adenle et al. 2017). Market conditions and technological maturity are other important determinants of policy mixes being deployed in the energy sector. For example, subsidies for mitigation like feed-in-tariffs have worked best when the technologies are in nascent stages of development (Gupta et al. 2019a).

On the other hand, market-based instruments like emissions rading schemes (ETS) and auctions coupled with a regulatory framework have been a favourable strategy for more mature technologies (Polzin et al. 2015; Kitzing et al. 2018). FIT, tax incentives, and renewable portfolio standards – despite potentially substantial programme costs (Andor and Voss 2016; Abrell et al. 2019) – have played a significant role in attracting foreign direct investments in the renewable sector (Wall et al. 2019). Subsidies and carbon pricing have also played an important role in mainstreaming these renewable energy sources (Best and Burke 2018). Recently, subsidy-free investments in renewables, such as wind offshore (Jansen et al. 2020), backed by power purchase agreements, have gained momentum (Frankfurt School-UNEP Centre and BNEF 2020). Similar considerations apply for policy mixes targeted to other sectors – for example, transport and buildings.

The role of carbon pricing is still limited though increasing. Different measures have been suggested to improve the performance of the ETS, such as 'price floors and caps' and other carbon pricing schemes (Campiglio 2016; Bataille et al. 2018; Goulder and Morgenstern 2018). In 2020, 61 regional, national and sub-national carbon pricing instruments, representing 22% of the global GHG emissions, were in action or scheduled for implementation (World Bank 2019). Over 51% of emissions covered are priced at less than USD10 per tCO_2-eq. At present, however, only 5% of the global emissions covered under carbon pricing initiatives are consistent with the range of carbon prices that have been suggested as needed to limit warming to well below 2°C (Stiglitz and Stern 2017). Most of the carbon pricing schemes have taken place in the OECD countries. The limited application of carbon pricing instruments in developing, and emerging economies may be due to political economy constraints (Campiglio 2016; Finon 2019). Carbon pricing had a sizeable impact on emissions – for example, the EU ETS impacts emissions from electricity in Germany (Schäfer 2019) and manufacturing in France (Colmer et al. 2020), respectively. Emissions reductions could be increased with higher carbon prices and without free allocation of allowances.

In the absence of a global comprehensive carbon price, regional regulatory policies for fossil fuels supply and key demand sectors like transport, industry and buildings (Chapters 9–11), coupled with regional carbon pricing instruments, were implemented to help initiate the climate actions consistent with the Paris Agreement (Kriegler et al. 2018). However, differences in the stringency of climate regulation have triggered fear that regulation reduces the competitiveness of industries in regulated countries and leads to industry relocation and 'carbon leakage' (Schenker et al. 2018). In recent years, however, there is little evidence of carbon leakage (Naegele and Zaklan 2019; Schäfer 2019), and even positive effects of carbon pricing on efficiency have been observed (e.g., Löschel et al. 2019, for German manufacturing firms, and Germeshausen 2020 for German power plants). However, with asymmetric rising carbon prices, discussions about specific policy mechanisms to address carbon leakage like carbon border adjustments (Cosbey et al. 2019) were amplified. Furthermore, multiple policies – often implemented by different governmental levels (national vs sub-national) – interacted with each other and thereby affected their environmental and economic effectiveness. Recent examples include interactions of ETS with renewable support policies (e.g. Boehringer and Behrens 2015; Del Rio 2017), energy efficiency policies (e.g. Wiese et al. 2018) or electricity market reform (e.g. Teng et al. 2017), respectively.

Apart from explicit carbon pricing, various implicit carbon pricing mechanisms, such as fossil fuel taxes and removal of fossil fuel subsidies (Box 6.3) and regulatory instruments, are used by many countries as part of their climate policies. In addition, public provision and procurement of low-carbon infrastructure and technologies such as energy-efficient devices, renewable energy, and upgrades in electricity grids through state-sponsored institutions and public-private partnerships have played an important role in low-carbon development (e.g., Baron 2016).

Box 6.3 | Energy Subsidies

Energy subsidies continue to be widely applied. Global fossil fuel subsidies represent more than half of total energy subsidies with predominantly adverse environmental, economic, and social effects (*high confidence*).

Energy subsidies can be defined as policy measures in the energy sector to lower the prices for consumers, raise the prices for producers, or reduce energy production costs (IEA 1999). There are subsidies for fossil fuels, renewables, and energy efficiency measures. The majority of the renewable subsidies are generation-based incentives for solar, wind or biomass in the form of feed-in-tariffs (Chapter 13), with total annual renewable subsidy estimates of about USD150 billion yr^{-1} globally (IEA 2018b). Estimates of fossil fuel subsidies can vary by an order of magnitude. For the year 2017, the IEA estimated fossil fuel subsidies of USD300 billion using IEA's pre-tax, price-gap method (IEA 2018b), while the International Monetary Fund (IMF) included unpriced externalities in calculating subsidies of USD5.2 trillion or 6.5% of global GDP (Coady et al. 2017, 2019; World Bank 2019). It has been estimated that the amount spent on fossil fuel subsidies was around double the amount of subsidies spent on renewables (IEA 2018b). There are adverse environmental, economic and social consequences of fossil fuel subsidies (Rentschler and Bazilian 2017). More than 75% of the distortions created by fossil fuel subsidies are domestic, and studies indicate that reforming them can have substantial in-country benefits (Coady et al. 2017, 2019). Some of the G20 countries have implemented subsidy reforms based on low oil prices (Jewell et al. 2018).

Fossil fuel subsidies most commonly pursue non-climate objectives, for example, enhanced access to energy sources (*high confidence*). In some cases, these energy access subsidies have helped extend modern energy sources to the poor (Kimemia and Annegarn 2016) and thereby contribute to SDG 7. However, the subsidies have proven to be regressive in most cases, with little benefit reaching the poor (Lockwood 2015). For example, Indonesia has introduced LPG subsidies for cooking. The kerosene-to-LPG conversion programme ('Zero Kero') was launched in 2007 and provided mainly households with free initial LPG equipment and LPG at a low subsidised price (Imelda et al. 2018b; Thoday et al. 2018). Besides the national government, provincial governments and industry played a crucial role in implementation. Overall, the LPG conversion programme in Indonesia reduced cooking kerosene use (Andadari et al. 2014; Imelda et al. 2018b) and GHG emissions (Permadi et al. 2017) with positive health effects (Imelda et al. 2018b; Thoday et al. 2018). However, the programme is generally viewed as regressive and has failed to reduce traditional solid fuel use (Andadari et al. 2014; Toft 2016; Thoday et al. 2018). Furthermore, even if the programme decreased GHG emissions relative to continued kerosene use, these subsidies are still targeted at fossil fuels and contribute to GHG emissions.

India started a large LPG programme in 2015 that provided a capital cost subsidy to poor households (e.g., Gould 2018; Jose et al. 2018; Kar et al. 2019). While the programme has increased adoption of LPG in India (e.g., Sharma et al. 2019), it has not yet achieved a sustained use of LPG and replacement of solid fuels for cooking, amplifying the need for complementary policy measures (Gould 2018; Kar et al. 2019; Mani et al. 2020). The climate impacts of switching from biomass to LPG depend on the degree of biomass combustion in stoves and the extent to which biomass originates from non-renewable sources (Singh and Rao 2015; Jose et al. 2018). Barriers to increasing LPG use for cooking further included abundance of solid fuels at zero (monetary) costs (Mani et al. 2020) as well as benefits of solid fuels, such as maintaining the traditional taste of food and space heating in colder seasons (Gould 2018; Sharma et al. 2020).

6.4   Mitigation Options

6.4.1   Elements of Characterisation

This section characterises energy system mitigation options and discusses which factors enable and inhibit their implementation.

We touch on a broad range of factors that may enable and inhibit the implementation of mitigation options by considering six dimensions that affect their feasibility (Table 6.1 and Annex II.11). The assessment aims to identify which mitigation options can be readily implemented and which face barriers that would need to be overcome before they can be deployed at scale.

Table 6.1 | Dimensions and indicators to assess the barriers and enablers of implementing mitigation options in low-carbon energy systems.

Metric	Indicators
Geophysical: Are the required resources available?	– Physical potential: physical constraints to implementation – Geophysical resources (including geological storage capacity): availability of resources needed for implementation – Land use: claims on land where an option would be implemented
Environmental-ecological: What are the wider environmental and ecological impacts of the option?	– Air pollution: increase or decrease in air pollutants, such as NH_4, CH_4 and fine dust – Toxic waste, ecotoxicity and eutrophication – Water quantity and quality: changes in the amount of water available for other uses – Biodiversity: changes in conserved primary forest or grassland that affect biodiversity, and management to conserve and maintain land carbon stocks
Technological: Can the required technology be upscaled soon?	– Simplicity: is the option technically simple to operate, maintain and integrate? – Technology scalability: can the option be scaled up technically? – Maturity and technology readiness: research and development (R&D) and time needed to implement the option
Economic: What economic conditions can support or inhibit the implementation of the option?	– Costs in 2030 and in the long term: investment costs, costs in USD tCO_2-eq^{-1} – Employment effects and economic growth: decrease or increase in jobs and economic welfare
Socio-cultural: What social conditions could support or inhibit acceptance, adoption, and use of the option before 2030?	– Public acceptance: the extent to which the public supports the option and will change their behaviour accordingly – Effects on health and well-being – Distributional effects: equity and justice across groups, regions, and generations, including energy, water, and food security and poverty
Institutional: What institutional conditions could support or inhibit the implementation of the option?	– Political acceptance: the extent to which politicians support the option – Institutional capacity and governance, cross-sectoral coordination: capability of institutions to implement and handle the option – Legal and administrative capacity

6.4.2 Energy Sources and Energy Conversion

6.4.2.1 Solar Energy

Solar photovoltaic (PV) is increasingly competitive with other forms of electricity generation, and is the low-cost option in many applications (*high confidence*). Costs have declined by 62% since 2015 (*high confidence*) and are anticipated to decline by an additional 16% by 2030 if current trends continue (*low confidence, medium evidence*). Key areas for continued improvement are grid integration and non-module costs for rooftop systems (*high confidence*). Most deployment is now utility-scale (*high confidence*). Global future potential is not limited by solar irradiation, but by grid integration needed to address its variability, as well as access to finance, particularly in developing countries (*high confidence*).

The global technical potential of direct solar energy far exceeds that of any other renewable energy resource and is well beyond the total amount of energy needed to support ambitious mitigation over the current century (*high confidence*). Estimates of global solar resources have not changed since the IPCC's Fifth Assessment Report (AR5) (Lewis 2007; Besharat et al. 2013) even as precision and near-term forecasting have improved (Diagne et al. 2013; Abreu et al. 2018). Approximately 120,000 TW of sunlight reaches the Earth's surface continuously, almost 10,000 times average world energy consumption; factoring in competition for land use leaves a technical potential of about 300 PWh yr^{-1} (1080 EJ yr^{-1}) for solar PV, roughly double current consumption (Dupont et al. 2020). The technical potential for concentrating solar power (CSP) is estimated to be 45–82 PWh yr^{-1} (162–295 EJ yr^{-1}) (Dupont et al. 2020). Areas with the highest solar irradiation are: western South America; northern, eastern and southwestern Africa; and the Middle East and Australia (Figure 6.7) (Prǎvǎlie et al. 2019).

In many parts of the world, the cost of electricity from PV is below the cost of electricity generated from fossil fuels; in some, it is

below the operating costs of electricity generated from fossil fuels (*high confidence*). The weighted average cost of PV in 2019 was USD68 MWh^{-1}, near the bottom of the range of fossil fuel prices (IRENA 2019b). The cost of electricity from PV has fallen by 89% since 2000 and 69% since AR5, at a rate of –16% per year. The 5:95 percentile range for PV in 2019 was USD52–190 MWh^{-1} (IRENA 2021b). Differences in solar insolation, financing costs, equipment acquisition, installation labour, and other sources of price dispersion explain this range (Nemet et al. 2016; Vartiainen et al. 2020) and scale. For example, in India, rooftop installations cost 41% more than utility-scale installations, and commercial-scale costs are 39% higher than utility-scale. Significant differences in regional cost persist (Kazhamiaka et al. 2017; Vartiainen et al. 2020), with particularly low prices in China, India, and parts of Europe. Globally, the range of global PV costs is quite similar to the range of coal and natural gas prices.

PV costs (Figure 6.8) have fallen for various reasons: lower silicon costs, automation, lower margins, automation, higher efficiency, and a variety of incremental improvements (Fu et al. 2018; Green 2019) (Chapter 16). Increasingly, the costs of PV electricity are concentrated in the installation and related 'soft costs' (marketing, permitting) associated with the technology rather than in the modules themselves, which now account for only 30% of installed costs of rooftop systems (O'Shaughnessy et al. 2019; IRENA 2021b). Financing costs are a significant barrier in developing countries (Ondraczek et al. 2015) and growth there depends on access to low-cost finance (Creutzig et al. 2017).

CSP costs have also fallen, albeit at about half the rate of PV: –9% yr^{-1} since AR5. The lowest prices for CSP are now competitive with more expensive fossil fuels, although the average CSP cost is above the range for fossil-based power generation. Other data sources put recent CSP costs at USD120 MWh^{-1}, in the middle of the fossil range (Lilliestam et al. 2020). Continuing the pace of change since AR5 will make CSP competitive with fossil fuels in sunny locations, although

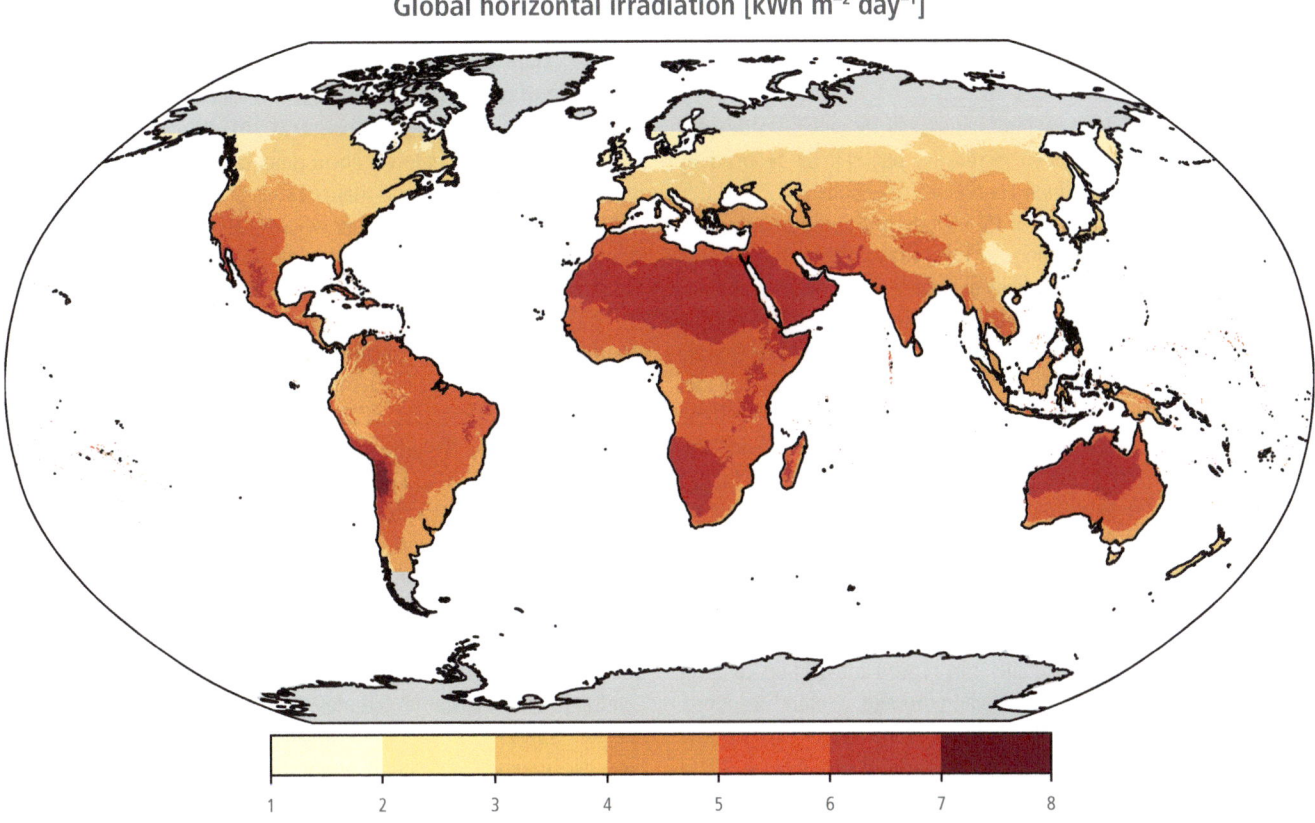

Figure 6.7 | Distribution of the daily mean global horizontal irradiation (GHI, kWh m⁻² day⁻¹). Source: Global Solar Atlas (ESMAP 2019).

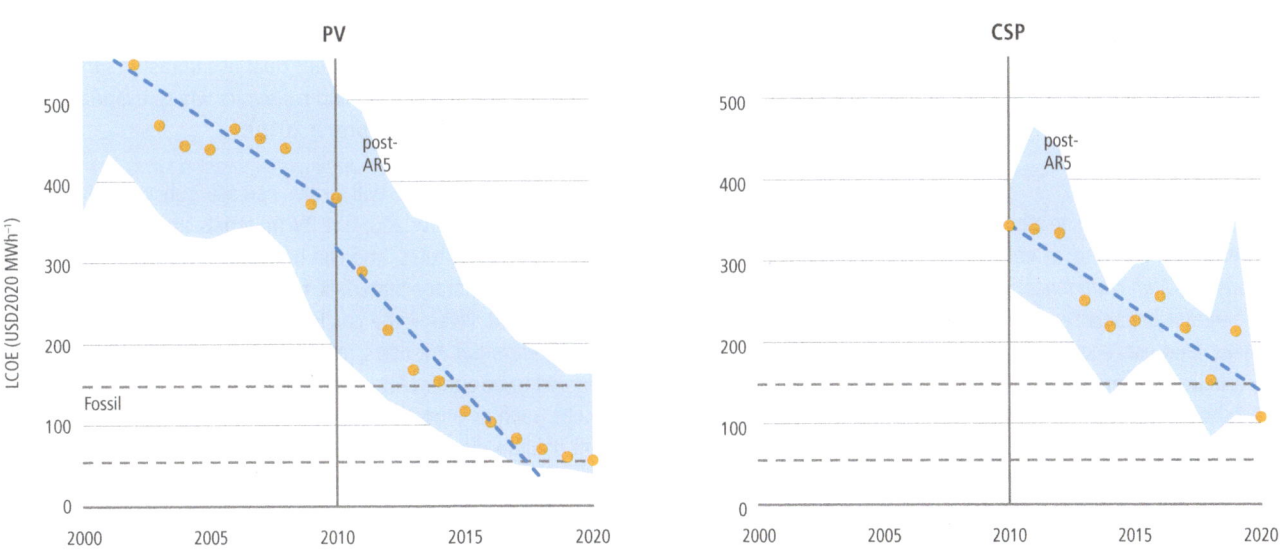

Figure 6.8 | Levelised costs of electricity (LCOE) of solar energy technologies 2000–2020. Range of fossil fuel LCOE indicated as dashed lines USD50–177 MWh⁻¹. Linear fit lines were applied to data for AR4–AR5 and post-AR5 (2012). Yellow dots are capacity-weighted global averages for utility-scale installations. The blue area shows the range between the 5th and 95th percentile in each year. Data: IRENA (2021b).

it will be difficult for CSP to compete with PV and even hybrid PV-battery systems. CSP electricity can be more valuable, however, because CSP systems can store heat longer than PV battery systems.

The share of total costs of PV-intensive electricity systems attributed to integration costs has been increasing but can be reduced by enhancing grid flexibility (*high confidence*) (Sections 6.4.3 and 6.6, and Box 6.8). The total costs of PV include grid integration, which varies tremendously depending on PV's share of electricity, other supply sources like wind, availability of storage, transmission capacity, and demand flexibility (Heptonstall and Gross 2020). Transmission costs can add USD1–10 MWh^{-1} or 3–33% to the cost of utility-scale PV (Gorman et al. 2019). Distributed (rooftop) PV involves a broader set of grid integration costs – including grid reinforcement, voltage balancing and control, and impacts on other generations – and has a larger range of integration costs from USD2–25 MWh^{-1}, which is –3% to +37% (Hirth et al. 2015; Wu et al. 2015; Gorman et al. 2019). Other meta-analyses put the range at USD1–7 MWh^{-1} in the USA (Luckow et al. 2015.; Wiser et al. 2017), while a comprehensive study put the range at USD12–18 MWh^{-1} for up to 35% renewables and USD25–46 MWh^{-1} above 35% renewables (Heptonstall and Gross 2020). Increased system flexibility can reduce integration costs of solar energy (Wu et al. 2015) including storage, demand response, sector-coupling (Brown et al. 2018; Bogdanov et al. 2019), and increase complementarity between wind and solar (Heide et al. 2010) (Sections 6.4.3 and 6.4.4).

Since solar PV panels have very low operating costs, they can, at high penetrations and in the absence of adequate incentives to shift demand, depress prices in wholesale electricity markets, making it difficult to recoup investment, and potentially reducing incentives for new installations (Hirth 2013; Millstein et al. 2021). Continued cost reductions help address this issue of value deflation, but only partially. Comprehensive solutions depend on adding transmission and storage (Das et al. 2020) and, more fundamentally, adjustments to electricity market design (Roques and Finon 2017; Bistline and Young 2019).

The most important ways to minimise PV's impact on the environment lie in recycling materials at end of life and making smart land-use decisions (*medium confidence*). A comprehensive assessment of PV's environmental impacts requires lifecycle analysis (LCA) of resource depletion, land-use, ecotoxicity, eutrophication, acidification, ozone, and particulates, among other things (Mahmud et al. 2018). LCA studies show that solar PVs produce far less CO_2 per unit of electricity than fossil generation, but PV CO_2 emissions vary due to the carbon intensity of manufacturing energy and offset electricity (Grant and Hicks 2020). Concerns about systemic impacts, such as reducing the Earth's albedo by covering surfaces with dark panels, have shown to be trivial compared to the mitigation benefits (Nemet 2009) (Box 6.7). Even though GHG LCA estimates span a considerable range of 9–250 gCO_2 kWh^{-1} (de Wild-Scholten 2013; Kommalapati et al. 2017), recent studies that reflect higher efficiencies and manufacturing improvements find lower lifecycle emissions, including a range of 18–60 gCO_2 kWh^{-1} (Wetzel and Borchers 2015) and central estimates of 80 gCO_2 kWh^{-1} (Hou et al. 2016), 50 gCO_2 kWh^{-1} (Nugent and Sovacool 2014), and 20 gCO_2 kWh^{-1} (Louwen et al. 2016). These recent values are an order of magnitude lower than coal, and natural gas and further decarbonisation of the energy system will make them lower still. Thin films and organics produce half the lifecycle emissions of silicon wafer PV, mainly because they use less material (Lizin et al. 2013; Hou et al. 2016). Novel materials promise even lower environmental impacts, especially with improvements to their performance ratios and reliability (Gong et al. 2015; Muteri et al. 2020). Higher efficiencies, longer lifetimes, sunny locations, less carbon-intensive manufacturing inputs, and shifting to thin films could reduce future lifecycle impacts.

Another environmental concern with large PV power plants is the conversion of land to collect solar energy (Hernandez et al. 2015). Approximately 2 hectares of land are needed for 1 MW of solar electricity capacity (Perpiña Castillo et al. 2016; Kabir et al. 2018); at 20% efficiency, a square of PV panels of 550 km by 550 km, comprising 0.2% of Earth's land area, could meet global energy demand. Land conversion can have local impacts, especially near cities and where land used for solar competes with alternative uses, such as agriculture. Large installations can also adversely impact biodiversity (Hernandez et al. 2014), especially where the above-ground vegetation is cleared and soils are typically graded. Landscape fragmentation creates barriers to the movement of species. However, a variety of means have emerged to mitigate land use issues. Substitution among renewables can reduce land conversion (Tröndle 2020). Solar can be integrated with other uses through 'agrivoltaics' (the use of land for both agriculture and solar production) (Dupraz et al. 2011) by, for example, using shade-tolerant crops (Dinesh and Pearce 2016). Combining solar and agriculture can also create income diversification, reduced drought stress, higher solar output due to radiative cooling, and other benefits (Elamri et al. 2018; Hassanpour Adeh et al. 2018; Barron-Gafford et al. 2019). PV installations floating on water also avoid land-use conflicts (Sahu et al. 2016; Lee et al. 2020), as does dual-use infrastructure, such as landfills (Jäger-Waldau 2020) and reservoirs where evaporation can also be reduced (Farfan and Breyer 2018).

Material demand for PV will likely increase substantially to limit warming to well below 2°C, but PV materials are widely available, have possible substitutes, and can be recycled (*medium confidence*) (Box 6.4). The primary materials for PV are silicon, copper, glass, aluminium, and silver – the costliest being silicon, and glass being the most essential by mass, at 70%. None of these materials is considered to be either critical or potentially scarce (IEA 2020e). Thin-film cells, such as amorphous silicon, cadmium telluride and copper indium gallium diselenide (CIGS), use far less material (though they use more glass), but account for less than 10% of the global solar market. Other thin-films, such as those based on perovskites, organic solar cells, or earth-abundant, non-toxic materials such as kesterites, either on their own, or layered on silicon, could further reduce material use per energy produced (Box 6.4).

After a typical lifetime of 30 years of use, PV modules can be recycled to prevent environmental contamination from the toxic materials within them, reusing valuable materials and avoiding waste accumulation. Recycling allows the reuse of nearly all – 83% in one study – of the components of PV modules, other than plastics (Ardente et al. 2019) and would add less than 1% to lifecycle GHG emissions (Latunussa et al. 2016). Glass accounts for 70% of the mass of a solar cell and is relatively easy to recycle. Recycling technology is advancing, but the scale and share of recycling is still small (Li et al. 2020d). By 2050, however, end-of-life PV could total 80 MT and comprise 10% of global electronic waste (Stolz and Frischknecht 2017), although most of it is glass. IEA runs a programme to enable PV recycling by sharing best practices to minimise recycling lifecycle impacts. Ensuring that a substantial amount of panels are recycled at end of life will likely require policy incentives, as the market value of the recovered materials, aside from aluminium and copper, is likely to be too low to justify recycling on its own (Deng et al. 2019). A near-term priority is maximising the recovery of silver, silicon, and aluminium, the most valuable PV material components (Heath et al. 2020).

Many alternative PV materials are improving in efficiency and stability, providing longer-term pathways for continued PV costs reductions and better performance (*high confidence*). While solar PV based on semi-conductors constructed from wafers of silicon still captures 90% of the market, new designs and materials have the potential to reduce costs further, increase efficiency, reduce resource use, and open new applications. The most significant technological advance within silicon PV in the past 10 years has been the widespread adoption of the passivated emitter and rear cell (PERC) design (Green 2015), which now accounts for the majority of production. This advance boosts efficiency over traditional aluminium backing by increasing reflectivity within the cell and reducing electron-hole recombination (Blakers 2019). Bifacial modules increase efficiency by using reflected light from the ground or roof on the backside of modules (Guerrero-Lemus et al. 2016). Integrating PV into buildings can reduce overall costs and improve building energy performance (Shukla et al. 2016). Concentrating PV uses lenses or mirrors that collect and concentrate light onto high efficiency PV cells (Li et al. 2020a). Beyond crystalline silicon, thin films of amorphous silicon, cadmium telluride, and copper indium gallium selenide (among others) have the potential for much lower costs while their efficiencies have increased (Green et al. 2019). Perovskites, inexpensive and easy to produce crystalline structures, have increased in efficiency by a factor of six in the past decade; the biggest challenge is light-induced degradation as well as finding lead-free efficient compounds, or establishing lead recycling at the end of the lifecycle of the device (Petrus et al. 2017; Chang et al. 2018; Wang et al. 2019b; Zhu et al. 2020). Organic solar cells are made of carbon-based semiconductors like the ones found in the displays made from organic light emitting diodes (OLEDs) and can be processed in thin films on large areas with scalable and fast coating processes on plastic substrates. The main challenges are raising the efficiency and improving their lifetime (Ma et al. 2020; Riede et al. 2021). Quantum dots, spherical semi-conductor nanocrystals, can be tuned to absorb specific wavelengths of sunlight, giving them the potential for high efficiency with very little material use (Kramer et al. 2015). A common challenge for all emerging solar cell technologies is developing the corresponding production equipment. Hybrids of silicon with layers of quantum dots and perovskites have the potential to take advantage of the benefits of all three, although those designs require that these new technologies have stability and scale that match those of silicon (Chang et al. 2017; Palmstrom et al. 2019). This broad array of alternatives to making PV from crystalline

silicon offer realistic potential for lower costs, reduced material use, and higher efficiencies in future years (Victoria et al. 2021).

Besides PV, alternative solar technologies exist, including CSP, which can provide special services in high-temperature heat and diurnal storage, even if it is more costly than PV and its potential for deployment is limited. CSP uses reflective surfaces, such as parabolic mirrors, to focus sunlight on a receiver to heat a working fluid, which is subsequently transformed into electricity (Islam et al. 2018). Solar heating and cooling are also well established technologies, and solar energy can be utilised directly for domestic or commercial applications such as drying, heating, cooling, and cooking (Ge et al. 2018). Solar chimneys, (still purely conceptual), heat air using large transparent greenhouse-like structures and channel the warm air to turbines in tall chimneys (Kasaeian et al. 2017). Solar energy can also be used to produce solar fuels, for example, hydrogen or synthetic gas (syngas) (Montoya et al. 2016; Nocera 2017; Detz et al. 2018). In addition, research proceeds on space-based solar PV, which takes advantage of high insolation and a continuous solar resource (Kelzenberg et al. 2018), but faces the formidable obstacle of developing safe, efficient, and inexpensive microwave or laser transmission to the Earth's surface (Yang et al. 2016). CSP is the most widely adopted of these alternative solar technologies.

Like PV, CSP facilities can deliver large amounts of power (up to 200 MW per unit) and maintain substantial thermal storage, which is valuable for load balancing over the diurnal cycle (McPherson et al. 2020). However, unlike PV, CSP can only use direct sunlight, constraining its cost-effectiveness to North Africa, the Middle East, Southern Africa, Australia, the Western USA, parts of South America (Peru, Chile), and the Western part of China (Deng et al. 2015; Dupont et al. 2020). Parabolic troughs, central towers and parabolic dishes are the three leading solar thermal technologies (Wang et al. 2017d). Parabolic troughs represented approximately 70% of new capacity in 2018 with the balance made up by central tower plants (Islam et al. 2018). Especially promising research directions are on tower-based designs that can achieve high temperatures, useful for industrial heat and energy storage (Mehos et al. 2017), and direct steam generation designs (Islam et al. 2018). Costs of CSP have fallen by nearly half since AR5 (Figure 6.8) albeit at a slower rate than PV. Since AR5, almost all new CSP plants have storage (Figure 6.9) (Thonig 2020).

Solar energy elicits favourable public responses in most countries (*high confidence*) (Mcgowan and Sauter 2005; Ma et al. 2015; Hanger et al. 2016; Bessette and Arvai 2018; Jobin and Siegrist 2018; Roddis et al. 2019; Hazboun and Boudet 2020). Solar energy is perceived as clean and environmentally friendly with few downsides (Faiers and Neame 2006; Whitmarsh et al. 2011b). Key motivations for homeowners to adopt PV systems are expected financial gains, environmental benefits, the desire to become more self-sufficient, and peer expectations (Korcaj et al. 2015; Vasseur and Kemp 2015; Palm 2017). Hence, the observability of PV systems can facilitate adoption (Boudet 2019). The main barriers to the adoption of solar PV by households are its high upfront costs, aesthetics, landlord-tenant incentives, and concerns about performance and reliability (Faiers and Neame 2006; Whitmarsh et al. 2011b; Vasseur and Kemp 2015).

6

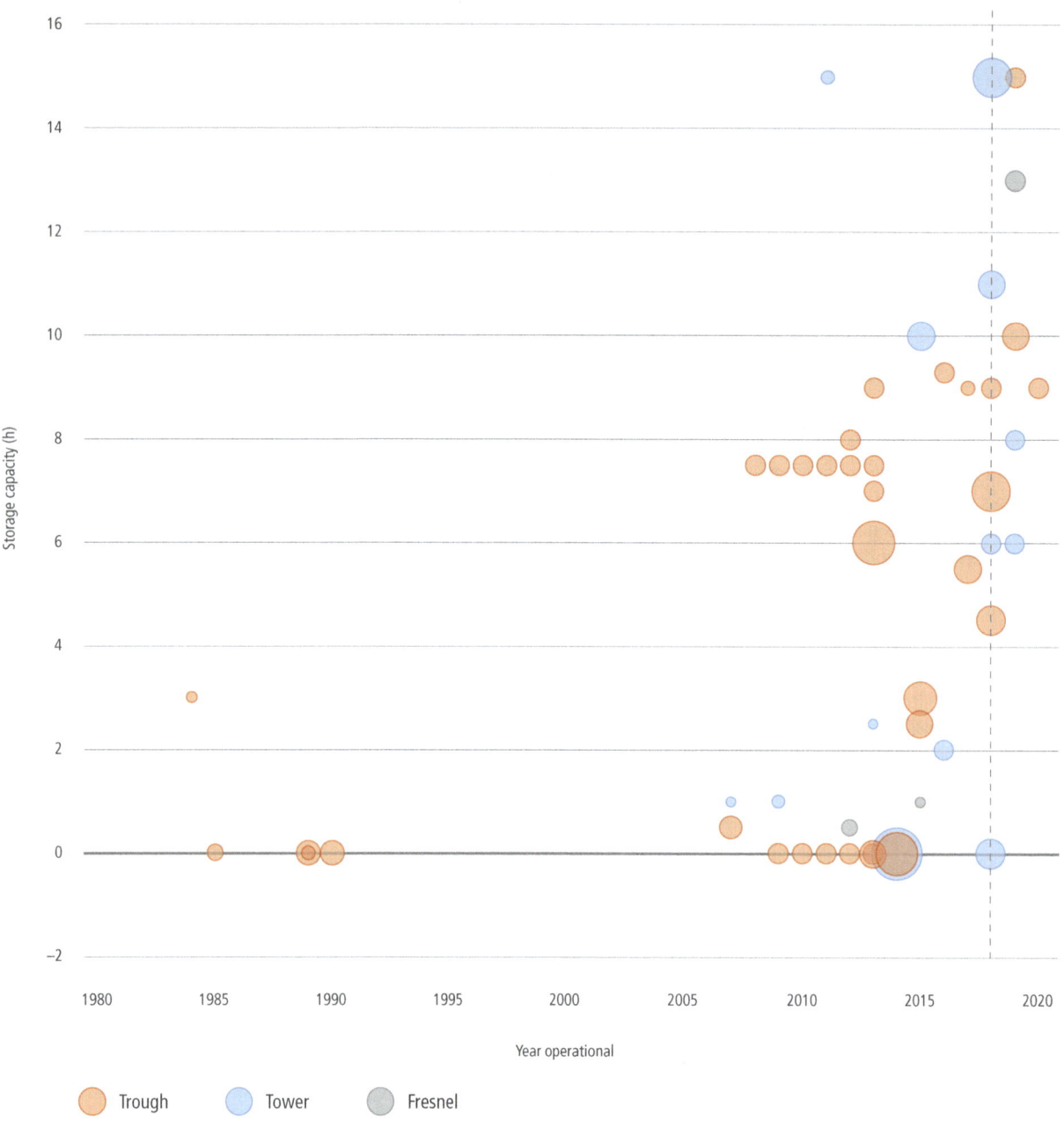

Figure 6.9 | CSP plants by storage capacity in hours (vertical), year of installation (horizontal), and size of plant in MW (circle size). Since AR5, almost all new CSP plants have storage (Thonig 2020). Source: with permission from https://csp.guru/metadata.html.

6.4.2.2   Wind Energy

Wind power is increasingly competitive with other forms of electricity generation and is the low-cost option in many applications (*high confidence*). Costs have declined by 18% and 40% on land and offshore since 2015 (*high confidence*), and further reductions can be expected by 2030 (*medium confidence*). Critical areas for continued improvement are technology advancements and economies of scale (*high confidence*). Global future potential is primarily limited by onshore land availability in wind power-rich areas, lack of supporting infrastructure, grid integration, and access to finance (especially in developing countries) (*high confidence*).

Energy from wind is abundant, and the estimated technical potentials surpass the total amount of energy needed to limit warming to well below 2°C (*high confidence*). Recent global estimates of potentially exploitable wind energy resource are in the range of 557–717 PWh yr^{-1} (2005–2580 EJ yr^{-1}) (Eurek et al. 2017; Bosch et al. 2017, 2018; McKenna et al. 2022), or 20–30 times the 2017 global electricity demand. Studies have suggested that 'bottom-up' approaches may overestimate technical potentials (Miller et al. 2015; Kleidon and Miller 2020). But even in the most conservative 'top-down' approaches, the technical wind potential surpasses the amount needed to limit warming to well below 2°C (Bosch et al. 2017; Eurek et al. 2017; Volker et al. 2017). The projected climate change

Wind power density (100 m) [Wm⁻²]

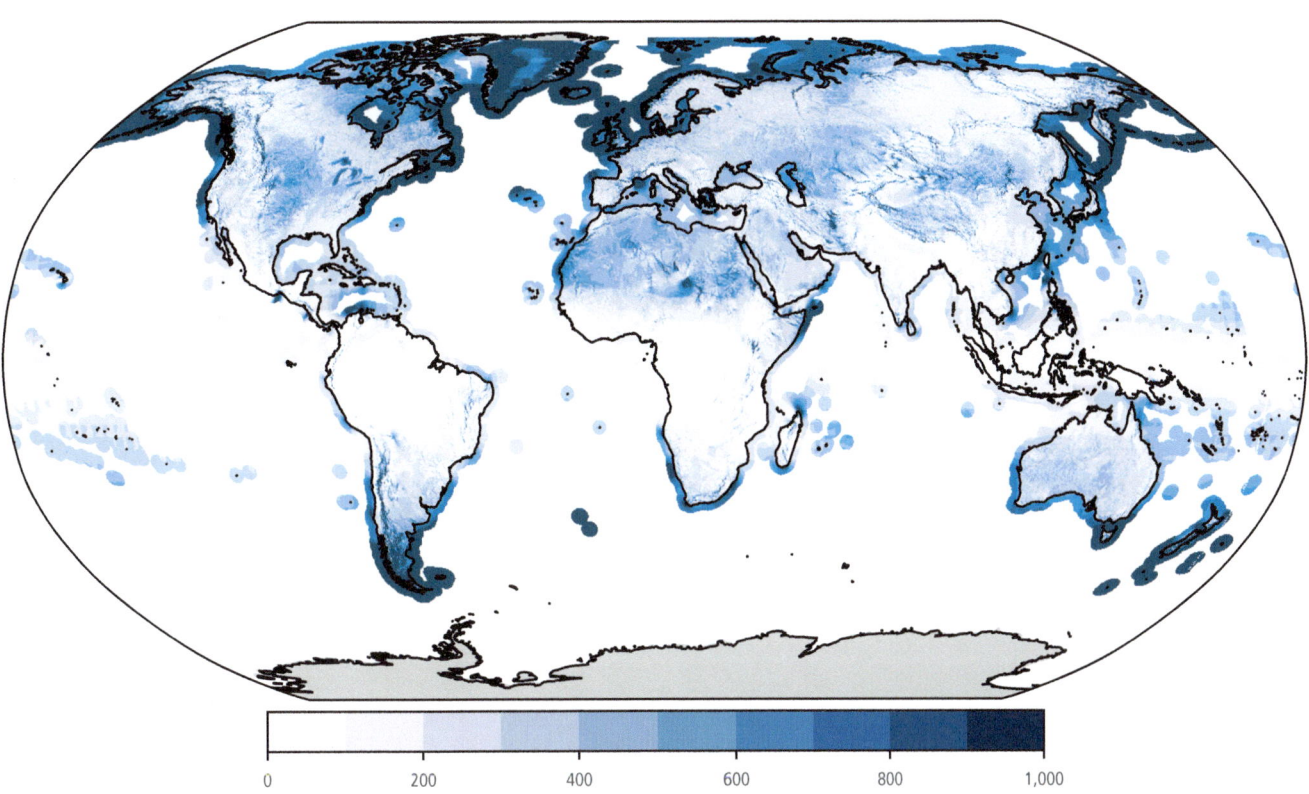

Figure 6.10 | Mean wind power density [W m⁻²] at 100 m above ground level over land and within 100 km of the coastline. Source: Global Wind Atlas, available at: https://globalwindatlas.info/.

mitigation from wind energy by 2100 ranges from 0.3°C–0.8°C depending on the precise socio-economic pathway and wind energy expansion scenario followed (Barthelmie and Pryor 2021). Wind resources are unevenly distributed over the globe and by time of the year (Petersen and Troen 2012), but potential hotspots exist on every continent (Figure 6.10) as expressed by the wind power density (a quantitative measure of wind energy available at any location). Technical potentials for onshore wind power vary considerably, often because of inconsistent assessments of suitability factors (McKenna et al. 2020). The potential for offshore wind power is larger than for onshore because offshore wind is stronger and less variable (Bosch et al. 2018). Offshore wind is more expensive, however, because of higher costs for construction, maintenance, and transmission. Wind power varies at a range of time scales, from annual to sub-seconds; the effects of local short-term variability can be offset by power plant control, flexible grid integration, and storage (Barra et al. 2021) (Section 6.4.3). In some regions, interannual variations in wind energy resources could be important for optimal power system design (Wohland et al. 2019a; Coker et al. 2020).

Wind power cost reductions (Figure 6.11) are driven mainly by larger capacity turbines, larger rotor diameters and taller hub heights – larger swept areas increase the energy captured and the capacity factors for a given wind speed; taller towers provide access to higher wind speeds (Beiter et al. 2021). All major onshore wind markets have experienced rapid growth in both rotor diameter (from 81.2 m

in 2010 to 120 m in 2020) (IRENA 2021b), and average power ratings (from 1.9 MW in 2010 to 3 MW in 2020). The generation capacity of offshore wind turbines grew by a factor of 3.7 in less than two decades, from 1.6 MW in 2000 to 6 MW in 2020 (Wiser et al. 2021). Floating foundations could revolutionise offshore wind power by tapping into the abundant wind potential in deeper waters. This technology is particularly important for regions where coastal waters are too deep for fixed-bottom wind turbines. Floating wind farms potentially offer economic and environmental benefits compared with fixed-bottom designs due to less-invasive activity on the seabed during installation, but the long-term ecological effects are unknown and meteorological conditions further offshore and in deeper waters are harsher on wind turbine components (IRENA 2019c). A radical new class of wind energy converters has also been conceived under the name of airborne wind energy systems that can harvest strong, high-altitude winds (typically between 200–800m), which are inaccessible by traditional wind turbines (Cherubini et al. 2015). This technology has seen development and testing of small devices (Watson et al. 2019).

Wind capacity factors have increased over the last decade (Figure 6.11). The capacity factor for onshore wind farms increased from 27% in 2010 to 36% in 2020 (IRENA 2021a). The global average offshore capacity factor has decreased from a peak of 45% in 2017. This has been driven by the increased share of offshore development in China, where projects are often near-shore and use smaller wind turbines than in Europe

6

Onshore wind energy, 2010–2020

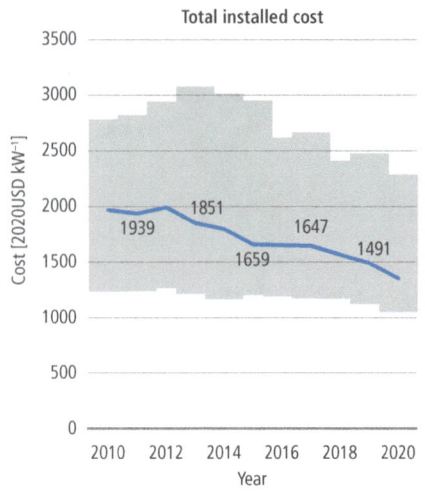
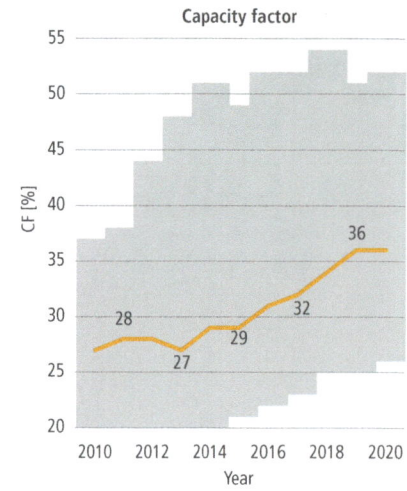
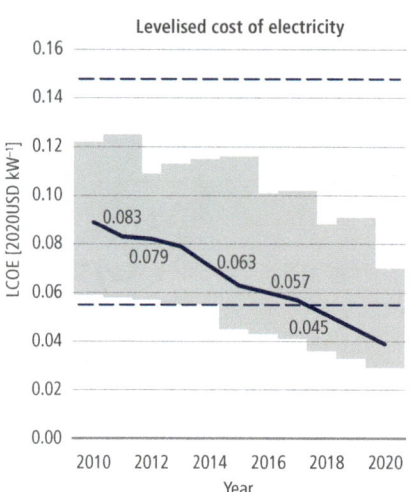

Offshore wind energy, 2010–2020

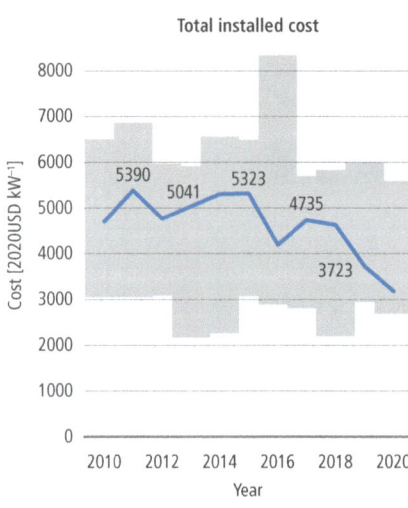
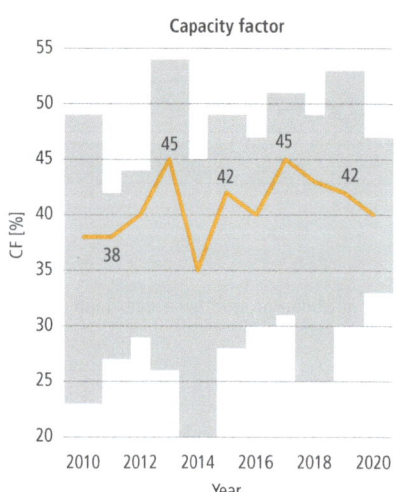
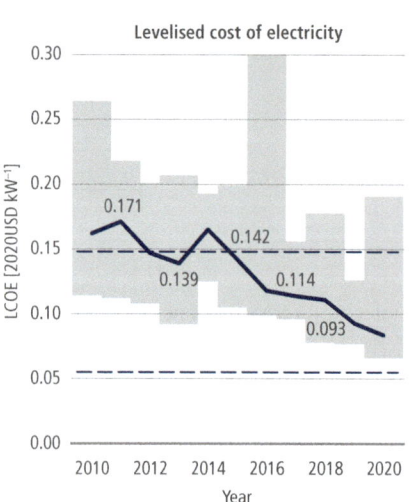

Figure 6.11 | Global weighted average total installed costs, capacity factors, and LCOE for onshore (top) and offshore (bottom) wind power of existing power plants per year (2010–2020). The shaded area represents the 5th and 95th percentiles, and the red dashed line represents the fossil fuel cost range. Source: with permission from IRENA (2021a).

(IRENA 2021b). Improvements in capacity factors also come from increased functionality of wind turbines and wind farms. Manufactures can adapt the wind turbine generator to the wind conditions. Turbines for windy sites have smaller generators and smaller specific capacity per rotor area, and therefore operate more efficiently and reach full capacity for a longer time period (Rohrig et al. 2019).

Electricity from onshore wind is less expensive than electricity generated from fossil fuels in a growing number of markets (*high confidence*). The global average LCOE onshore declined by 38% from 2010 to 2020 (Figure 6.11), reaching USD0.039 kWh^{-1}. However, the decrease in cost varies substantially by region. Since 2014, wind costs have declined more rapidly than the majority of experts predicted (Wiser et al. 2021). New modelling projects onshore wind LCOE of USD.037 kWh^{-1} by 2030 (Junginger et al. 2020a), and additional reductions of 37–39% have been predicted by 2050 (Wiser et al. 2021). The future cost of offshore wind is more uncertain because

other aspects besides increases in capacity factors influence the cost (Junginger et al. 2020b).

The cost of the turbine (including the towers) makes up the largest component of wind LCOE. Total installed costs for both onshore and offshore wind farms have decreased since 2015 (Figure 6.11), but the total installed costs for onshore wind projects are very site- and market-specific, as reflected in the range of LCOEs. China, India, and the USA have experienced the largest declines in total installed costs. In 2020, typical country-average total installed costs were around USD1150 kW^{-1} in China and India, and between USD1403–2472 kW^{-1} elsewhere (IRENA 2021b). Total installed costs of offshore wind farms declined by 12% between 2010 and 2020. But, because some of the new offshore wind projects have moved to deeper waters and further offshore, there are considerable year-to-year variations in their price (IRENA 2021b). Projects outside China in recent years have typically been built in deeper waters

(10–55 m) and up to 120 km offshore, compared to around 10 m in 2001–2006, when distances rarely exceeded 20 km. With the shift to deeper waters and sites further from ports, the total installed costs of offshore wind farms rose, from an average of around USD2500 kW^{-1} in 2000 to around USD5127 kW^{-1} by 2011–2014, before falling to around USD3185 kW^{-1} in 2020 (IRENA 2020a). The full cost of wind power includes the transmission and system integration costs (Sections 6.4.3 and 6.4.6). A new technology in development is the co-location of wind and solar PV power farms, also known as hybrid power plants. Co-locating wind, solar PV, and batteries can lead to synergies in electricity generation, infrastructure, and land usage, which may lower the overall plant cost compared to single technology systems (Lindberg et al. 2021).

Wind power plants pose relatively low environmental impact, but sometimes locally significant ecological effects (*high confidence*). The environmental impact of wind technologies, including CO_2 emissions, is concentrated in the manufacturing, transport, and building stage and in disposal as the end-of-life of wind turbines is reached (Liu and Barlow 2017; Mishnaevsky 2021). The operation of wind turbines produces no waste or pollutants. The LCA for wind turbines is strongly influenced by the operating lifetime, quality of wind resources, conversion efficiency, and size of the wind turbines (Kaldellis and Apostolou 2017; Laurent et al. 2018). All wind power technologies repay their carbon footprint in less than a year (Bonou et al. 2016).

Wind farms can cause local ecological impacts, including on animal habitat and movements, biological concerns, bird and bat fatalities from collisions with rotating blades, and health concerns (Morrison and Sinclair 2004). The impacts on animal habitats and collisions can be resolved or reduced by selectively stopping some wind turbines in high-risk locations, often without affecting the productivity of the wind farm (de Lucas et al. 2012). Many countries now require environmental studies of impacts of wind turbines on wildlife prior to project development, and, in some regions, shutdowns are required during active bird migration (de Lucas et al. 2012). Offshore wind farms can also impact migratory birds and other sea species (Hooper et al. 2017). Floating foundations pose lower environmental impacts at build stage (IRENA 2019c), but their cumulative long-term impacts are unclear (Goodale and Milman 2016). Recent studies find weak associations between wind farm noise and measures of long-term human health (Poulsen et al. 2018a, b, 2019a, b).

Public support for onshore and particularly offshore wind energy is generally high, although people may oppose specific wind farm projects (*high confidence*) (e.g., Bell et al. 2005; Batel and Devine-Wright 2015; Rand and Hoen 2017; Steg 2018). People generally believe that wind energy is associated with environmental benefits and that it is relatively cheap. Yet, some people believe wind turbines can cause noise and visual aesthetic pollution, threaten places of symbolic value (Devine-Wright and Wiersma 2020; Russell et al. 2020), and have adverse effects on wildlife (Bates and Firestone 2015), which challenges public acceptability (Rand and Hoen 2017). Support for local wind projects is higher when people believe fair decision-making procedures have been implemented (Dietz and Stern 2008; Aitken 2010a). Evidence is mixed whether distance from wind turbines or financial compensation increases public acceptability of wind turbines (Cass et al. 2010; Rand and Hoen 2017; Rudolph et al. 2018; Hoen et al. 2019). Offshore wind farms projects have higher public support, but can also face resistance (Bidwell 2017; Rudolph et al. 2018).

Common economic barriers to wind development are high initial cost of capital, long payback periods, and inadequate access to capital. Optimal wind energy expansion is most likely to occur in the presence of a political commitment to establish, maintain, and improve financial support instruments, technological efforts to support a local supply chains, and grid investments integrate VRE electricity (Diógenes et al. 2020).

Box 6.4 | Critical Strategic Minerals and a Low-carbon Energy System Transition

The secure supply of many metals and minerals (e.g., cobalt, copper, lithium, and rare earth elements (REEs)) is critical to supporting a low-emissions energy system transition (Sovacool et al. 2020). A low-carbon energy system transition will increase the demand for these minerals to be used in technologies like wind turbines, PV cells, and batteries (World Bank 2020). Reliance on these minerals has raised questions about possible constraints to a low-carbon energy system transition, including supply chain disruptions (Chapter 10.6). Concerns have also been raised about mining for these materials, which frequently results in severe environmental impacts (Sonter et al. 2020), and metal production itself is energy-intensive and difficult to decarbonise (Sovacool et al. 2020).

Wind energy depends on two critical REEs – neodymium and dysprosium – used in magnets in high-performance generators (Pavel et al. 2017; Li et al. 2020b). Silicon-wafer-based solar PV, which accounted for 95% of PV production in 2020, does not use REEs but utilises aluminium, copper, and silver (IEA 2021a). Lithium, nickel, cobalt, and phosphorous are used in batteries. Many critical minerals are used in EVs, including aluminium and copper in manufacturing the necessary EV charging infrastructure, and neodymium in permanent magnet motors.

These strategic minerals are found in a limited number of countries, and concerns have been raised that geopolitical factors could disrupt the supply chain necessary for a low-carbon energy system transition. However, excluding cobalt and lithium, no single country holds more than a third of the world reserves. The known supply of some strategic minerals is still close to 600 years at current levels of demand (BP 2020), but increased demand would cut more quickly into supplies.

6

There are alternatives to the strategic minerals currently used to support a low-carbon transition. Wind turbines can be manufactured without permanent magnets to reduce the need for strategic minerals, but the production costs are higher, and their efficiency is reduced (Månberger and Stenqvist 2018). Alternatives to silicon, such as thin films, could be used to produce PVs. Thin-films use much less material than silicon-based PV, but they contain other potentially critical metals like tellurium, cadmium, and gallium. Alternatives to lithium-ion batteries, such as sodium-ion batteries, are becoming more practical and feasible (Sovacool et al. 2020).

6.4.2.3 Hydroelectric Power

Hydropower is technically mature, proved worldwide as a primary source of renewable electricity, and may be used to balance electricity supply by providing flexibility and storage. The LCOE of hydropower is lower than the cheapest new fossil fuel-fired option. However, the future mitigation potential of hydropower depends on minimising environmental and social impacts during the planning stages, reducing the risks of dam failures, and modernising the ageing hydropower fleet to increase generation capacity and flexibility (*high confidence*).

Estimates of global gross theoretical available hydropower potential varies from 31–128 PWh yr^{-1} (112–460 EJ yr^{-1}), exceeding total electricity production in 2018 (Banerjee et al. 2017; BP 2020;

IEA 2021d). This potential is distributed over 11.8 million locations (Figure 6.12), but many of the locations cannot be developed for (current) technical, economic, or political reasons. The estimated technical potential of hydropower is 8–30 PWh yr^{-1} (29–108 EJ yr^{-1}), and its estimated economic potential is 8–15 PWh yr^{-1} (29–54 EJ yr^{-1}) (Zhou et al. 2015; van Vliet et al. 2016c). Actual hydropower generation in 2019 was 4.2 PWh (15.3 EJ), providing about 16% of global electricity and 43% of global electricity from renewables (BP 2020; IEA 2020f; Killingtveit 2020). Asia holds the largest hydropower potential (48%), followed by South America (19%) (Hoes et al. 2017).

Hydropower is a mature technology with locally adapted solutions (*high confidence*) (Zhou et al. 2015; Killingtveit 2020). The peak efficiency of hydroelectric plants is greater than 85%. Hydropower plants without storage or with small storage typically produce

Gross hydropower potential [GWh yr^{-1}]

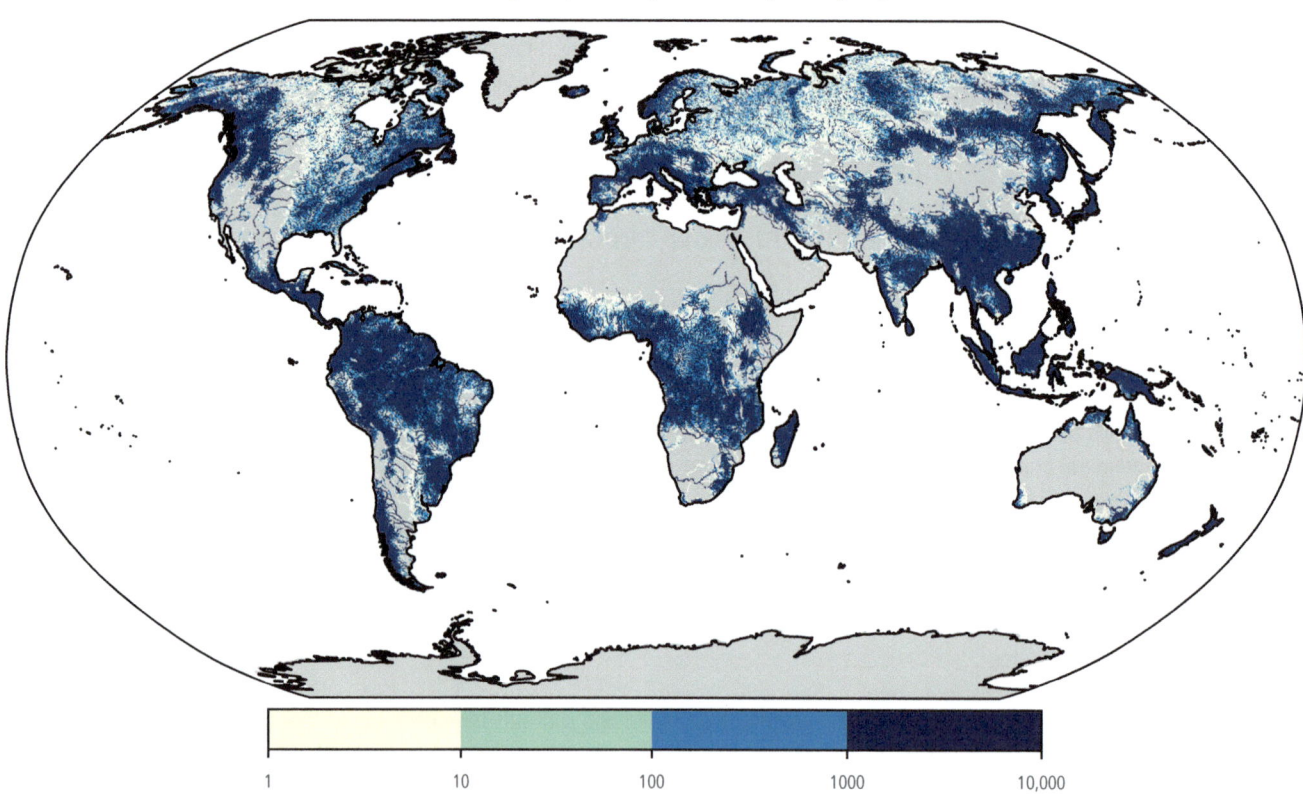

Figure 6.12 | Global map of gross hydropower potential distribution [GWh yr^{-1}]. Source: data from Hoes et al. (2017).

a few kWs to 10 MWs (examples of plants producing higher amounts do exist), and are useful for providing electricity at a scale from households to small communities (El Bassam et al. 2013; Towler 2014). However, hydropower plants without or with small storage may be susceptible to climate variability, especially droughts, when the amount of water may not be sufficient to generate electricity (Premalatha et al. 2014) (Section 6.5).

Hydropower plants with storage may produce 10 GW, reaching over 100 TWh yr^{-1} (0.36 EJ yr^{-1}), but generally require large areas. Pumped storage hydropower stores energy by pumping water to higher reservoirs during low-demand periods (Killingtveit 2020). The storage in hydropower systems provides flexibility to compensate for rapid variations in electricity loads and supplies. The regulating characteristics of the storage play an important role in assuring continuity of energy supply from renewable sources (Yang et al. 2018b).

Hydropower is one of the lowest-cost electricity technologies (Mukheibir 2013; IRENA 2021b). Its operation and maintenance costs are typically 2–2.5% of the investment costs per kW yr^{-1} for a lifetime of 40–80 years (Killingtveit 2020). Construction costs are site-specific. The total cost for an installed large hydropower project varies from USD10,600–804,500 kW^{-1} if the site is located far away from transmission lines, roads, and infrastructure. Investment costs increase for small hydropower plants and may be as high as USD100,000 kW^{-1} or more for the installation of plants of less than 1 MW – 20% to 80% more than for large hydropower plants (IRENA 2015). During the past 100 years, total installed costs and LCOE have risen by a few percent, but the LCOE of hydropower remains lower than the cheapest new fossil fuel-fired option (IRENA 2019b, 2021).

Hydroelectric power plants may pose serious environmental and societal impacts (*high confidence*) (McCartney 2009). Dams may lead to fragmentation of ecological habitats because they act as barriers for migration of fish and other land and water-borne fauna, sediments, and water flow. These barriers can be mitigated by sediment passes and fish migration aids, and with provision of environmental flows. Below dams, there can be considerable alterations to vegetation, natural river flows, retention of sediments and nutrients, and water quality and temperature. Construction of large reservoirs leads to loss of land, which may result in social and environmental consequences. Minimising societal and environmental impacts requires taking into account local physical, environmental, climatological, social, economic, and political aspects during the planning stage (Killingtveit 2020). Moreover, when large areas of land are flooded by dam construction, they generate GHGs (Prairie et al. 2018; Phyoe and Wang 2019; Maavara et al. 2020). On the other hand, hydropower provides flexible, competitive low-emission electricity, local economic benefits (e.g., by increasing irrigation and electricity production in developing countries), and ancillary services such as municipal water supply, irrigation and drought management, navigation and recreation, and flood control (IRENA 2021b). However, the long-term economic benefits to communities affected by reservoirs are a subject of debate (de Faria et al. 2017; Catolico et al. 2021).

Public support for hydroelectric energy is generally high (Steg 2018), and higher than support for coal, gas, and nuclear. Yet, public support for hydro seems to differ for existing and new projects (*high confidence*). Public support is generally high for small- and medium-scale hydropower in regions where hydropower was historically used (Gormally et al. 2014). Additionally, there is high support for existing large hydropower projects in Switzerland (Rudolf et al. 2014; Plum et al. 2019), Canada (Boyd et al. 2019), and Norway (Karlstrøm and Ryghaug 2014), where it is a trusted and common energy source. Public support seems lower for new hydropower projects (Hazboun and Boudet 2020), and the construction of new large hydropower plants has been met with strong resistance in some areas (Vince 2010; Bronfman et al. 2015). People generally perceive hydroelectric energy as clean and a non-contributor to climate change and environmental pollution (Kaldellis et al. 2013). For example, in Sweden, people believed that existing hydropower projects have as few negative environmental impacts as solar, and even less than wind (Ek 2005). However, in areas where the construction of new large-scale hydroelectric energy is met with resistance, people believe that electricity generation from hydro can cause environmental, social, and personal risks (Bronfman et al. 2012; Kaldellis et al. 2013).

The construction time of hydroelectric power plants is longer than many other renewable technologies, and that construction time may be extended by the additional time it takes to fill the reservoir. This extended timeline can create uncertainty in the completion of the project. The uncertainty is due to insecurity in year-to-year variations in precipitation and the water inflows required to fill reservoirs. This is especially critical in the case of trans-boundary hydroelectric power plants, where filling up the reservoirs can have large implications on downstream users in other nations. As a result of social and environmental constraints, only a small fraction of potential economic hydropower projects can be developed, especially in developed countries. Many developing countries have major undeveloped hydropower potential, and there are opportunities to develop hydropower combined with other economic activities such as irrigation (Lacombe et al. 2014). Competition for hydropower across country borders can lead to conflict, which could be exacerbated if climate alters rainfall and streamflow (Ito et al. 2016).

6.4.2.4 Nuclear Energy

Nuclear power can deliver low-carbon energy at scale (*high confidence*). Doing so will require improvements in managing construction of reactor designs that hold the promise of lower costs and broader use (*medium confidence*). At the same time, nuclear power continues to be affected by cost overruns, high upfront investment needs, challenges with final disposal of radioactive waste, and varying public acceptance and political support levels (*high confidence*).

There are sufficient resources for substantially increasing nuclear deployment (*medium confidence*). Estimates for identified uranium resources have been increasing steadily over the years. Conventional uranium resources have been estimated to be sufficient for over 130 years of supply at current levels of use; 100 years were estimated in 2009 (Hahn 1983; NEA/IAEA 2021). In the case of future uranium resource scarcity, thorium or recycling of spent fuel might be used as alternatives. Interest in these alternatives has waned with better understanding of uranium deposits, their availability, and low prices (IAEA 2005; OECD NEA 2015).

There are several possible nuclear technology options for the period from 2030 to 2050 (*medium confidence*). In addition to electricity, nuclear can also be used to produce low-carbon hydrogen and freshwater (Kavvadias and Khamis 2014; Kayfeci et al. 2019).

- **Large reactors.** The nuclear industry has entered a new phase of reactor construction, based on evolutionary designs. These reactors achieve improvements over previous designs through small to moderate modifications, including improved redundancy, increased application of passive safety features, and significant improvements to containment design to reduce the risk of a major accident (MIT 2018). Examples include European – EPR, Korean – APR1400, USA – AP1000, Chinese – HPR1000 or Russian – VVER-1200.
- **Long-term operation (LTO) of the current fleet.** Continued production from nuclear power will depend in part on life extensions of the existing fleet. By the end of 2020, two-thirds of nuclear power reactors will have been operational for over 30 years. The design lifetime of most of existing reactors is 30–40 years. Engineering assessments have established that reactors can operate safely for longer if key replaceable components (e.g., steam generator, mechanical and electrical equipment, instrumentation and control parts) are changed or refurbished (IAEA 2018). The first lifetime extension considered in most of the countries typically is 10–20 years (IEA 2020j).
- **Small modular reactors (SMR).** There are more than 70 SMR designs at different stages of consideration and development, from the conceptual phase to licensing and construction of first-of-a-kind facilities (IAEA 2020). Due to smaller unit sizes, the SMRs are expected to have lower total investment costs, although the cost per unit of generation might be higher than conventional large reactors (Mignacca and Locatelli 2020). Modularity and off-site pre-production may allow greater efficiency in construction, shorter delivery times, and overall cost optimisation (IEA 2019c). SMR designs aim to offer an increased load-following capability that makes them suitable to operate in smaller systems and in systems with increasing shares of VRE sources. Their market development by the early 2030s will strongly depend on the successful deployment of prototypes during the 2020s.

Nuclear power costs vary substantially across countries (*high confidence*). First-of-a-kind projects under construction in Northern America and Europe have been marked by delays and costs overruns (Berthelemy and Rangel 2015). Construction times have exceeded 13–15 years and cost has surpassed three to four times initial budget estimates (IEA 2020j). In contrast, most of the recent projects in Eastern Asia (with construction starts from 2012) were implemented within five to six years (IAEA 2021). In addition to region-specific factors, future nuclear costs will depend on the ability to benefit from the accumulated experience in controlling the main drivers of cost. These cost drivers fall into four categories: design maturity; project management; regulatory stability and predictability; and multi-unit and series effects (NEA 2020). With lessons learned from first-of-a-kind projects, the cost of electricity for new builds are expected to be in the range of USD42–102 MWh^{-1} depending on the region (IEA 2020j).

Lifetime extensions are significantly cheaper than new builds and cost competitive with other low-carbon technologies. The overnight cost of lifetime extensions is estimated in the range of USD390–630 kWe^{-1} for Europe and North America, and the LCOE in the range of USD30–36 MWh^{-1} for extensions of 10–20 years (IEA 2020j).

Cost-cutting opportunities, such as design standardisation and innovations in construction approaches, are expected to make SMRs competitive against large reactors by 2040 (Rubio and Tricot 2016) (*medium confidence*). As SMRs are under development, there is substantial uncertainty regarding the construction costs. Vendors have estimated first-of-a-kind LCOEs at USD131–190 MWh^{-1}. Effects of learning for nth-of-a-kind SMR are anticipated to reduce the first-of-a-kind LCOE by 19–32%.

Despite low probabilities, the potential for major nuclear accidents exists, and the radiation exposure impacts could be large and long-lasting (Steinhauser et al. 2014). However, new reactor designs with passive and enhanced safety systems reduce the risk of such accidents significantly (*high confidence*). The (normal) activity of a nuclear reactor results in low volumes of radioactive waste, which requires strictly controlled and regulated disposal. On a global scale, roughly 421 kt of spent nuclear fuel have been produced since 1971 (IEA 2014). Out of this volume, 2–3% is high-level radioactive waste, which presents challenges in terms of radiotoxicity and decay longevity, and ultimately entails permanent disposal.

Nuclear energy is found to be favourable regarding land occupation (Cheng and Hammond 2017; Luderer et al. 2019) and ecological impacts (Brook and Bradshaw 2015; Gibon et al. 2017). Similarly, bulk material requirements per unit of energy produced are low (e.g., aluminum, copper, iron, rare earth metals) (Vidal et al. 2013; Luderer et al. 2019). Water-intensive inland nuclear power plants may contribute to localised water stress and competition for water uses. The choice of cooling systems (closed-loop instead of once-through) can significantly moderate withdrawal rates of freshwater (Meldrum et al. 2013; Fricko et al. 2016; Mouratiadou et al. 2016; Jin et al. 2019). Reactors situated on the seashore are not affected by water scarcity issues (Abousahl et al. 2021). Lifecycle analysis (LCA) studies suggest that the overall impacts on human health (in terms of disability adjusted life years (DALYs)) from the normal operation of nuclear power plants are substantially lower than those caused by fossil fuel technologies and are comparable to renewable energy sources (Treyer et al. 2014; Gibon et al. 2017).

Nuclear power continues to suffer from limited public and political support in some countries (*high confidence*). Public support for nuclear energy is consistently lower than for renewable energy and natural gas, and in many countries as low as support for energy from coal and oil (Corner et al. 2011; Pampel 2011; Hobman and Ashworth 2013). The major nuclear accidents (i.e., Three Mile Island, Chernobyl, and Fukushima) decreased public support (Poortinga et al. 2013; Bird et al. 2014). The public remains concerned about the safety risks of nuclear power plants and radioactive materials (Pampel 2011; Bird et al. 2014; Tsujikawa et al. 2016). At the same time, some groups see nuclear energy as a reliable energy source, beneficial for the economy and helpful in climate change mitigation. Public support for nuclear energy is higher when people are concerned about energy security, including concerns about the availability of energy and high energy prices (Groot et al. 2013; Gupta et al. 2019b), and when they expect local benefit (Wang et al. 2020c). Public support also increases when trust in managing bodies is higher (de Groot and Steg 2011). Similarly, transparent and participative decision-making processes enhance perceived procedural fairness and public support (Sjoberg 2004).

Because of the sheer scale of the investment required (individual projects can exceed USD10 billion in value), nearly 90% of nuclear power plants under construction are run by state-owned or controlled companies, with governments assuming significant part of the risks and costs. For countries that choose nuclear power in their energy portfolio, stable political conditions and support, clear regulatory regimes, and adequate financial framework are crucial for successful and efficient implementation.

Many countries have adopted technology-specific policies for low-carbon energy courses, and these policies influence the competitiveness of nuclear power. For example, feed-in-tariffs and feed-in premiums for renewables widely applied in the EU (Kitzing et al. 2012) or renewable portfolio standards in the USA (Barbose et al. 2016) impact wholesale electricity price (leading occasionally to low or even negative prices), which affects the revenues of existing nuclear and other plants (Bruninx et al. 2013; Newbery et al. 2018; Lesser 2019).

Nuclear power's long-term viability may hinge on demonstrating to the public and investors that there is a long-term solution to spent nuclear fuel. Evidence from countries steadily progressing towards first final disposals – Finland, Sweden and France – suggests that broad political support, coherent nuclear waste policies, and a well-managed, consensus-based decision-making process are critical for accelerating this process (Metlay 2016). Proliferation concerns surrounding nuclear power are related to fuel cycle (i.e., uranium enrichment and spent fuel processing). These processes are implemented in a very limited number of countries following strict national and internationals norms and rules, such as the International Atomic Energy Agency (IAEA) guidelines, treaties and conventions. Most of the countries that might introduce nuclear power in the future for their climate change mitigation benefits do not envision developing their own full fuel cycle, significantly reducing any risks that might be linked to proliferation (IAEA 2014, 2019).

6.4.2.5   Carbon Dioxide Capture, Utilisation and Storage

Since AR5, there have been increased efforts to develop novel platforms that reduce the energy penalty associated with CO_2 capture, develop CO_2 utilisation pathways as a substitute to geologic storage, and establish global policies to support CCS (*high confidence*). CCS can be used within electricity and other sectors. While it increases the cost of electricity, CCS has the potential to contribute significantly to low-carbon energy system transitions (IPCC 2018).

The theoretical global geologic storage potential is about 10,000 $GtCO_2$, with more than 80% of this capacity existing in saline aquifers (*medium confidence*). Not all the storage capacity is usable because geologic and engineering factors limit the actual storage capacity to an order of magnitude below the theoretical potential, which is still more than the CO_2 storage requirement through 2100 to limit temperature change to 1.5°C (Martin-Roberts et al. 2021) (*high confidence*). One of the key limiting factors associated with geologic CO_2 storage is the global distribution of storage capacity (Table 6.2). Most of the available storage capacity exists in saline aquifers. Capacity in oil and gas reservoirs and coalbed methane fields is limited. Storage potential in the USA alone is >1000 $GtCO_2$, which is more than 10% of the world total (NETL 2015). The Middle East has more than 50% of global enhanced oil recovery potential (Selosse and Ricci 2017). It is likely that oil and gas reservoirs will be developed as geologic sinks before saline aquifers because of existing infrastructure and extensive subsurface data (Alcalde et al. 2019; Hastings and Smith 2020). Notably, not all geologic storage is utilisable. In places with limited geologic storage, international CCS chains are being considered, where sources and sinks of CO_2 are located in two or more countries (Sharma and Xu 2021). For economic long-term storage, the desirable conditions are a depth of 800–3000 m, thickness of greater than 50 m and permeability greater than 500 mD (Chadwick et al. 2008; Singh et al. 2021). Even in reservoirs with large storage potential, the rate of injection might be limited by the subsurface pressure of the reservoir (Baik et al. 2018). It is estimated that geologic sequestration is reliable with overall leakage rates at <0.001% yr^{-1} (Alcalde et al. 2018). In many cases, geological storage resources are not located close to CO_2 sources, increasing costs and reducing viability (Garg et al. 2017a).

CO_2 utilisation (CCU) – instead of geologic storage – could present an alternative method of decarbonisation (*high confidence*). The global CO_2 utilisation potential, however, is currently limited to 1–2 $GtCO_2$ yr^{-1} for use of CO_2 as a feedstock (Hepburn et al. 2019;

Table 6.2 | Geologic storage potential across underground formations globally. These represent order-of-magnitude estimates. Data: Selosse and Ricci (2017).

Reservoir type	Africa	Australia	Canada	China	CSA	EEU	FSU	India	MEA	Mexico	ODA	USA	WEU
Enhanced oil recovery	3	0	3	1	8	2	15	0	38	0	1	8	0
Depleted oil and gas fields	20	8	19	1	33	2	191	0	252	22	47	32	37
Enhanced coalbed methane recovery	8	30	16	16	0	2	26	8	0	0	24	90	12
Deep saline aquifers	1000	500	667	500	1000	250	1000	500	500	250	1015	1000	250

CSA: Central and South America, EEU: Eastern Europe, FSU: Former Soviet Union, MEA: Middle East, ODA: Other Asia (except China and India), WEU: Western Europe.

Kätelhön et al. 2019) but could increase to 20 $GtCO_2$ by the mid-century (*medium confidence*). CCU involves using CO_2 as a feedstock to synthesise products of economic value and as substitute to fossil feedstock. However, several CO_2 utilisation avenues might be limited by energy availability. Depending on the utilisation pathway, the CO_2 may be considered sequestered for centuries (e.g., cement curing, aggregates), decades (plastics), or only a few days or months (e.g., fuels) (Hepburn et al. 2019). Moreover, when carbon-rich fuel end-products are combusted, CO_2 is emitted back into the atmosphere. Because of the presence of several industrial clusters (regions with high density of industrial infrastructure) globally, a number of regions demonstrate locations where CO_2 utilisation potential could be matched with large point sources of CO_2 (Wei et al. 2020).

The technological development for several CO_2 utilisation pathways is still in the laboratory, prototype, and pilot phases, while others have been fully commercialised (such as urea manufacturing). Technology development in some end uses is limited by purity requirements for CO_2 as a feedstock. The efficacy of CCU processes depends on additional technological constraints such as CO_2 purity and pressure requirements. For instance, urea production requires CO_2 pressurised to 122 bar and purified to 99.9%. While most utilisation pathways require purity levels of 95–99%, algae production may be carried out with atmospheric CO_2 (Voldsund et al. 2016; Ho et al. 2019).

Existing post-combustion approaches relying on absorption are technologically ready for full-scale deployment (*high confidence*). More novel approaches using membranes and chemical looping that might reduce the energy penalty associated with absorption are in different stages of development – ranging from laboratory phase to prototype phase (Abanades et al. 2015) (*high confidence*). There has been significant progress in post-combustion capture technologies that used absorption in solvents such as monoethanolamine (MEA). There are commercial-scale application of solvent-based absorption at two electricity generating facilities – Boundary Dam since 2015 and Petra Nova (temporarily suspended) since 2017, with capacities of 1 and 1.6 $MtCO_2$ yr^{-1} respectively (Mantripragada et al. 2019; Giannaris et al. 2020a). Several second- and third-generation capture technologies are being developed with the aim of not just lowering costs but also enhancing other performance characteristics such as improved ramp-up and lower water consumption. These include processes such as chemical looping, which also has the advantage of being capable of co-firing with biomass with a better efficiency (Bhave et al. 2017; Yang et al. 2019). Another important technological development is the Allam cycle, which utilises CO_2 as a working fluid

and operates based on oxy-combustion capture. Applications using the Allam Cycle can deliver net energy efficiency greater than 50% and nearly 100% CO_2 capture, but they are quite sensitive to oxygen and CO_2 purity needs (Scaccabarozzi et al. 2016; Ferrari et al. 2017).

CO_2 capture costs present a key challenge, remaining higher than USD50 tCO_2^{-1} for most technologies and regions; novel technologies could help reduce some costs (*high confidence*). The capital cost of a coal or gas electricity generation facility with CCS is almost double that of one without CCS (Rubin et al. 2015; Zhai and Rubin 2016; Bui et al. 2018). Additionally, the energy penalty increases the fuel requirement for electricity generation by 13–44%, leading to further cost increases (Table 6.3).

In addition to reductions in capture costs, other approaches to reduce CCS costs rely on utilising the revenues from co-products such as oil, gas, or methanol, and on clustering of large-point sources to reduce infrastructure costs. The potential for such reductions is limited in several regions due to low sink availability, but it could jump-start initial investments (*medium confidence*). Injecting CO_2 into hydrocarbon formations for enhanced oil or gas recovery can produce revenues and lower costs (Edwards and Celia 2018). While enhanced oil recovery potential is <5% of the actual CCS needs, they can enable early pilot and demonstration projects (Núñez-López and Moskal 2019; Núñez-López et al. 2019). Substantial portions of CO_2 are effectively stored during enhanced oil recovery (Menefee and Ellis 2020; Sminchak et al. 2020). By clustering together of several CO_2 sources, overall costs may be reduced by USD10 tCO_2^{-1} (Abotalib et al. 2016; Garg et al. 2017a), but geographical circumstances determine the prospects of these cost reductions via economies of scale. The major pathways for CO_2 utilisation via methanol, methane, liquid fuel production, and cement curing have costs greater than USD500 tCO_2^{-1} (Hepburn et al. 2019). The success of these pathways therefore depends on the value of such fuels and on the values of other alternatives.

The public is largely unfamiliar with carbon capture, use and storage technologies (L'Orange Seigo et al. 2014; Tcvetkov et al. 2019) (*high confidence*), and many people may not have formed stable attitudes and risk perceptions regarding these technologies (Daamen et al. 2006; Jones et al. 2015; Van Heek et al. 2017) (*medium confidence*). In general, low support has been reported for CCS technologies (Allen and Chatterton 2013; Demski et al. 2017). When presented with neutral information on CCS, people favour other mitigation options such as renewable energy and energy efficiency (de Best-Waldhober et al. 2009; Scheer et al. 2013; Karlstrøm and Ryghaug 2014). Although few totally reject CCS, specific CCS projects have faced strong local

Table 6.3 | Costs and efficiency parameters of CCS in electric power plants. Data: Muratori et al. (2017a).

	Capital cost [USD kW^{-1}]	Efficiency [%]	CO_2 capture cost [USD tCO_2^{-1}]	CO_2 avoided cost [USD tCO_2^{-1}]
Coal (steam plant) + CCS	5800	28%	63	88
Coal (IGCC) + CCS	6600	32%	61	106
Natural gas (CC) + CCS	2100	42%	91	33
Oil (CC) + CCS	2600	39%	105	95
Biomass (steam plant) + CCS	7700	18%	72	244
Biomass (IGCC) + CCS	8850	25%	66	242

resistance, which has contributed to the cancellation of CCS projects (Terwel et al. 2012; L'Orange Seigo et al. 2014). Communities may also consider CCU to be lower-risk and view it more favourably than CCS (Arning et al. 2019).

CCS requires considerable increases in some resources and chemicals, most notably water. Power plants with CCS could shut down periodically due to water scarcity. In several cases, water withdrawals for CCS are 25–200% higher than plants without CCS (Rosa et al. 2020b; Yang et al. 2020) due to energy penalty and cooling duty. The increase is slightly lower for non-absorption technologies. In regions prone to water scarcity such as the Southwestern USA or Southeast Asia, this may limit deployment and result in power plant shutdowns during the summer months (Liu et al. 2019b; Wang et al. 2019c). The water use could be managed by changing heat integration strategies and implementing reuse of wastewater (Magneschi et al. 2017; Giannaris et al. 2020b).

Because CCS always adds cost, policy instruments are required for it to be widely deployed (*high confidence*). Relevant policy instruments include financial instruments such as emission certification and trading, legally enforced emission restraints, and carbon pricing (Haszeldine 2016; Kang et al. 2020). There are some recent examples of policy instruments specifically focused on promoting CCS. The recent 45Q tax credits in the USA offer nationwide tax credits for

CO_2 capture projects above USD35–50 tCO_2^{-1} which offset CO_2 capture costs at some efficient plants (Esposito et al. 2019). Similarly, California's low-carbon fuel standard offers benefits for CO_2 capture at some industrial facilities such as biorefineries and refineries (Von Wald et al. 2020).

6.4.2.6   Bioenergy

Bioenergy has the potential to be a high-value and large-scale mitigation option to support many different parts of the energy system. Bioenergy could be particularly valuable for sectors with limited alternatives to fossil fuels (e.g., aviation, heavy industry), production of chemicals and products, and, potentially, in carbon dioxide removal (CDR) via BECCS or biochar. While traditional biomass and first-generation biofuels are widely used today, the technology for large-scale production from advanced processes is not competitive, and growing dedicated bioenergy crops raises a broad set of sustainability concerns. Its long-term role in low-carbon energy systems is therefore uncertain (*high confidence*). (Note that this section focuses on the key technological developments for deployment of commercial bioenergy.)

Bioenergy is versatile: technology pathways exist to produce multiple energy carriers from biomass – electricity, liquid fuels, gaseous fuels, hydrogen, and solid fuels – as well as other value-added products

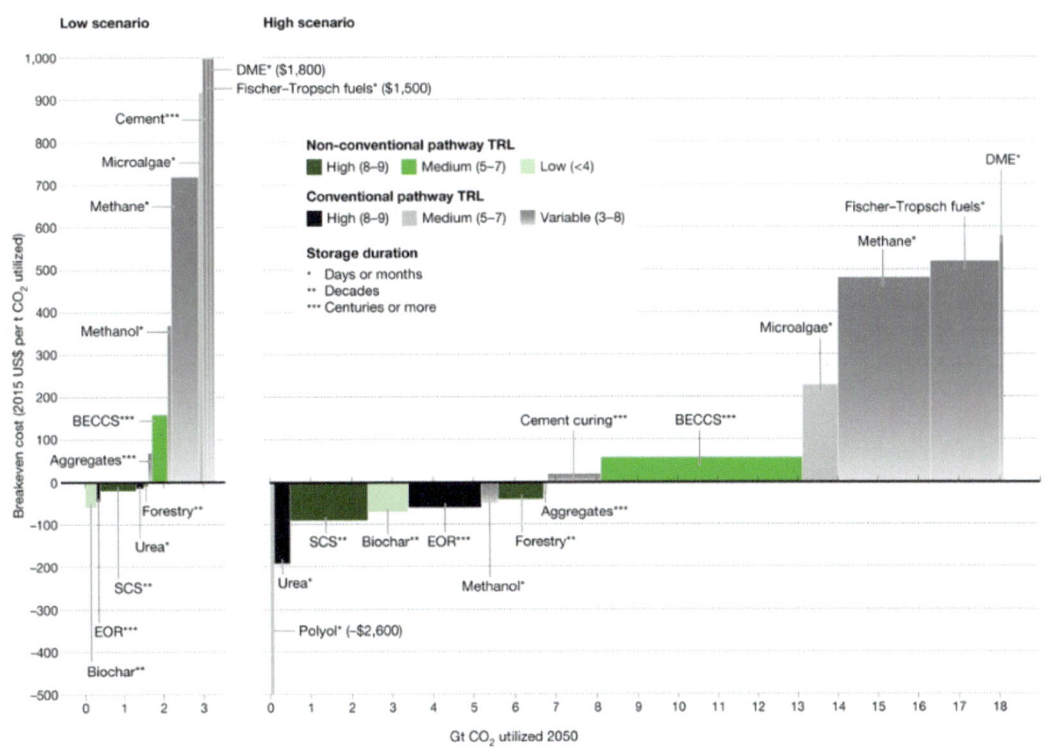

Figure 6.13 | Costs and potential for different CO_2 utilisation pathways. Source: with permission from Hepburn et al. (2019).

(*high confidence*). Different chemical and biological conversion pathways exist to convert diverse biomass feedstocks into multiple final energy carriers (Figure 6.14). Currently, biomass is mostly used to produce heat, or for cooking purposes (traditional biomass), electricity, or first-generation sugar-based biofuels (e.g., ethanol produced via fermentation), as well as biodiesel produced from vegetable oils and animal fats. Electricity generated from biomass contributes about 3% of global generation. Tens of billions of gallons of first-generation biofuels are produced per year. The processing requirements (drying, dewatering, pelletising) of different feedstocks for producing electricity from biomass are energy-intensive, and when utilising current power plants, the efficiency is around 22%, with an increase up to 28% with advanced technologies (Zhang et al. 2020).

Scaling up bioenergy use will require advanced technologies such as gasification, Fischer-Tropsch processing, hydrothermal liquefaction (HTL), and pyrolysis. These pathways could deliver several final energy carriers starting from multiple feedstocks, including forest biomass, dedicated cellulosic feedstocks, crop residues, and wastes (Figure 6.14). While potentially cost-competitive in the future, pyrolysis, Fischer-Tropsch, and HTL are not currently cost-competitive (IEA 2018c; Molino et al. 2018; Prussi et al. 2019), and scaling-up these processes will require robust business strategies and optimised use of co-products (Lee and Lavoie 2013). Advanced biofuels production processes are at the pilot or demonstration stage and

will require substantial breakthroughs or market changes to become competitive. Moreover, fuels produced from these processes require upgrading to reach 'drop-in' conditions – that is, conditions in which they may be used directly consistent with current standards in existing technologies (van Dyk et al. 2019). Additional opportunities exist to co-optimise second-generation biofuels and engines (Ostadi et al. 2019; Salman et al. 2020). In addition, gaseous wastes, or high-moisture biomass, such as dairy manure, wastewater sludge and organic municipal solid waste (MSW) could be utilised to produce renewable natural gas. Technologies for producing biogas (e.g., digestion) tend to be less efficient than thermochemical approaches and often produce large amounts of CO_2, requiring the produced fuels to undergo significant upgrading (Melara et al. 2020).

A major scale-up of bioenergy production will require dedicated production of advanced biofuels. First-generation biofuels produced directly from food crops or animal fats have limited potential and lower yield per land area than advanced biofuels. Wastes and residues (e.g., from agricultural, forestry, animal manure processing) or biomass grown on degraded, surplus, and marginal land can provide opportunities for cost-effective and sustainable bioenergy at significant but limited scale (Morris et al. 2013; Saha and Eckelman 2018; Fajardy and Mac Dowell 2020; Spagnolo et al. 2020). Assessing the potential for a major scale-up of purpose-grown bioenergy is challenging due to its far-reaching linkages to issues

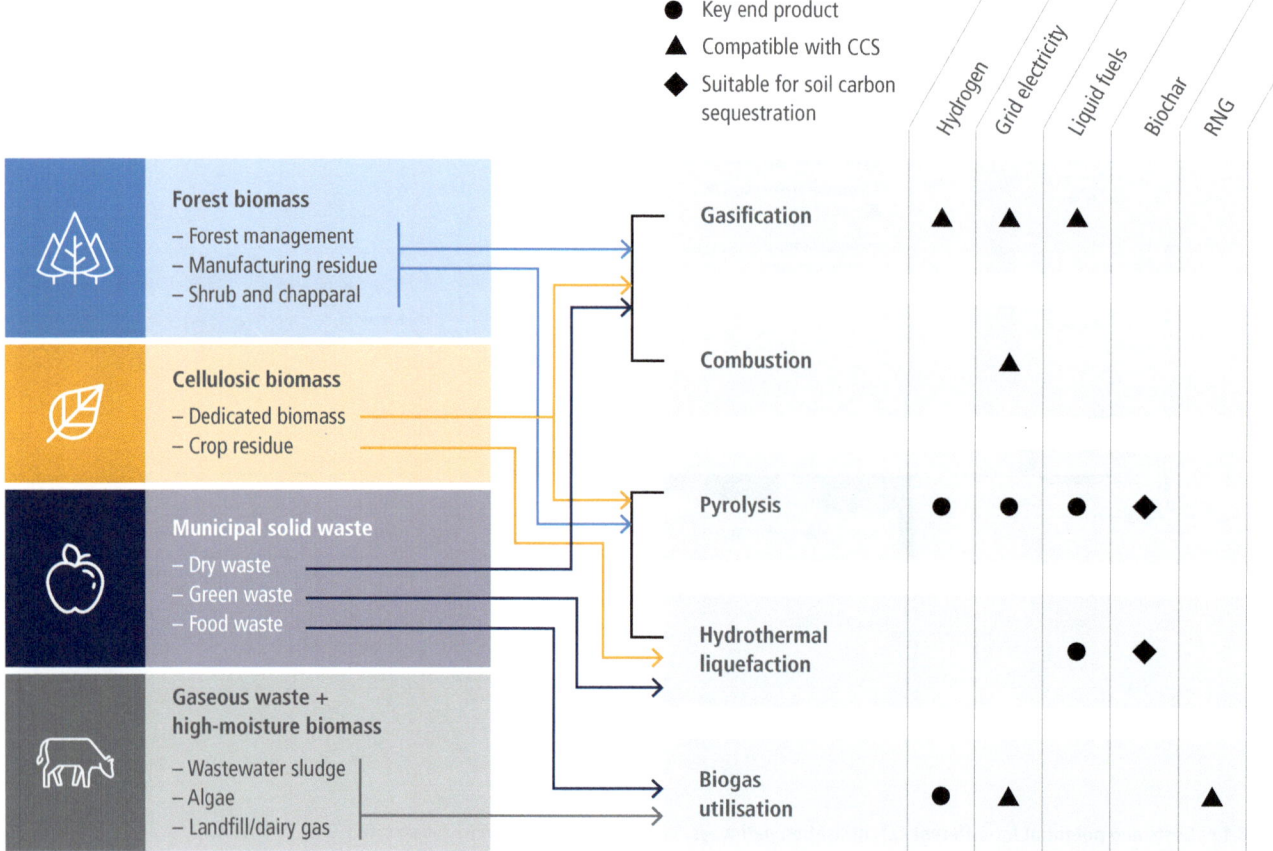

Figure 6.14 | Range of advanced bioenergy conversion pathways (excluding traditional biomass, direct heat generation, first-generation biofuels, and non-energy products) based on feedstock, targeted end product, and compatibility with carbon dioxide removal (CDR) via carbon capture and storage (CCS) and soil carbon sequestration. Source: modified with permission from Baker et al. (2020).

beyond the energy sector, including competition with land for food production and forestry, water use, impacts on ecosystems, and land-use change (IPCC 2020; Roe et al. 2021) (Chapter 12). These factors, rather than geophysical characteristics, largely define the potential for bioenergy and explain the difference in estimates of potential in the literature. Biomass resources are not always in close proximity to energy demand, necessitating additional infrastructure or means to transport biomass or final bioenergy over larger distances and incur additional energy use (Baik et al. 2018; Singh et al. 2021).

An important feature of bioenergy is that it can be used to remove carbon from the atmosphere by capturing CO_2 in different parts of the conversion process and then permanently storing the CO_2 (BECCS or biochar) (Smith et al. 2016; Fuss et al. 2018) (Chapters 3 and 7, and Section 12.5). Some early opportunities for low-cost BECCS are being utilised in the ethanol sector but these are applicable only in the near-term at the scale of ≤ 100 MtCO$_2$ yr^{-1} (Sanchez et al. 2018). Several technological and institutional barriers exist for large-scale BECCS implementation, including large energy requirements for CCS, limit and cost of biomass supply and geologic sinks for CO_2 in several regions, and cost of CO_2 capture technologies (*high confidence*). Besides BECCS, biofuels production through pyrolysis and hydrothermal liquefaction creates biochar, which could also be used to store carbon as 80% of the carbon sequestered in biochar will remain in the biochar permanently (Chapter 7). In addition to its ability to sequester carbon, biochar can be used as a soil amendment (Wang et al. 2014b).

First-generation bioenergy is currently competitive in some markets though, on average, its costs are higher than other forms of final energy. Bioenergy from waste and residues from forestry and agriculture is also currently competitive, but the supply is limited (Aguilar et al. 2020). These costs are context-dependent, and regions having large waste resources are already producing low-cost bioenergy (Jin and Sutherland 2018). In the future, technology costs are anticipated to decrease, but bioenergy produced through cellulosic feedstocks may remain more expensive than fossil alternatives. Large-scale deployment of early opportunities, especially in the liquid fuel sector, may reduce the technological costs associated with biomass conversion (IEA 2020g). At the same time, the cost of feedstocks may rise as bioenergy requirements increase, especially in scenarios with large bioenergy deployment (Muratori et al. 2020). The costs of bioenergy production pathways are highly uncertain (Table 6.4).

- **Electricity.** The costs of baseload electricity production with biomass are higher than corresponding fossil electricity production with and without CCS, and are likely to remain as such without carbon pricing (Bhave et al. 2017). The additional cost associated with CO_2 capture are high for conventional solvent-based technologies. However, upcoming technologies such as chemical looping are well-suited to biomass and could reduce CCS costs.
- **Hydrogen.** The costs of hydrogen production from biomass are somewhat higher than, but comparable, to that produced by natural gas reforming with CCS. Further, the incremental costs for incorporating CCS in this process are less than 5% of the levelised costs in some cases, since the gasification route creates a high-purity stream of CO_2 (Muratori et al. 2017a; Sunny et al. 2020). While these processes have fewer ongoing prototypes/demonstrations, the costs of biomass-based hydrogen (with or without CCS) are substantially cheaper than that produced from electrolysis utilising solar/wind resources (Kayfeci et al. 2019; Newborough and Cooley 2020), even though electrolysis costs are dropping.
- **Liquid biofuels.** First-generation sugar-based biofuels (e.g., ethanol produced via fermentation) or biodiesel produced from vegetable oils and animal fats, are produced in several countries at large scale and costs competitive with fossil fuels. However, supply is limited. The costs for second-generation processes (Fischer-Tropsch and cellulosic ethanol) are higher in most regions (Li et al. 2019). Technological learning is projected to reduce these costs by half (IEA 2020g).

Large-scale bioenergy production will require more than wastes/residues and cultivation on marginal lands, which may raise conflicts with SDGs relevant to environmental and societal priorities (Heck et al. 2018; Gerten et al. 2020) (Chapter 12). These include competition with food crops, implications for biodiversity, potential deforestation to support bioenergy crop production, energy security implications from bioenergy trade, point-of-use emissions and associated effects on air quality, and water use and fertiliser use (Fajardy and Mac Dowell 2018; Fuss et al. 2018; Tanzer and Ramírez 2019; Brack and King 2020). Overall, the environmental impact of bioenergy production at scale remains uncertain and varies by region and application.

Alleviating these issues would require some combination of increasing crop yields, improving conversion efficiencies, and developing advanced biotechnologies for increasing the fuel yield per tonne of feedstock (Henry et al. 2018). Policy structures would be necessary to

Table 6.4 | The costs of electricity generation, hydrogen production, and second-generation liquid fuels production from biomass in 2020. These costs are adapted from Bhave et al. (2017), Daioglou et al. (2020), NREL (2020a, 2020b), Witcover and Williams (2020), and Lepage et al. (2021).

	Unit	Low	Median	High
Bioelectricity with CCS	USD MWh^{-1}	74	86	160
Bioelectricity without CCS	USD MWh^{-1}	66	84	112
Biohydrogen with CCS[a]	USD kg^{-1}	1.63	2.37	2.41
Biohydrogen without CCS[a]	USD kg^{-1}	1.59	1.79	2.37
Liquid biofuels with CCS	USD gge^{-1}	1.34	4.20	7.85
Liquid biofuels without CCS	USD gge^{-1}	1.15	4.00	7.60

[a] Using cellulosic feedstocks.

6

retain biodiversity, manage water use, limit deforestation and land-use change emissions, and ultimately optimally integrate bioenergy with transforming ecosystems. Large-scale international trade of biomass might be required to support a global bioeconomy, raising questions about infrastructure, logistics, financing options, and global standards for bioenergy production and trade (Box 6.10). Additional institutional and economic barriers are associated with accounting of carbon dioxide removal, including BECCS (Fuss et al. 2014; Muratori et al. 2016; Fridahl and Lehtveer 2018).

Lifecycle emissions impacts from bioenergy are subject to large uncertainties and could be incompatible with net-zero emissions in some contexts. Due to the potentially large energy conversion requirements and associated GHG emissions (Chapters 7 and 12), bioenergy systems may fail to deliver near-zero emissions depending on operating conditions and regional contexts (Elshout et al. 2015; Daioglou et al. 2017; Staples et al. 2017; Hanssen et al. 2020; Lade et al. 2020). As a result, bioenergy carbon neutrality is debated and depends on factors such as the source of biomass, conversion pathways and energy used for production and transport of biomass, and land-use changes, as well as assumed analysis boundary and considered time

scale (Zanchi et al. 2012; Wiloso et al. 2016; Booth 2018; Fan et al. 2021). Similarly, the lifecycle emissions of BECCS remain uncertain and will depend on how effectively bioenergy conversion processes are optimised (Fajardy and Mac Dowell 2017; Tanzer and Ramírez 2019).

Acceptability of bioenergy is relatively low compared to other renewable energy sources like solar and wind (Poortinga et al. 2013; Ma et al. 2015; Peterson et al. 2015; EPCC 2017) and comparable to natural gas (Scheer et al. 2013). People also know relatively little about bioenergy compared to other energy sources (Whitmarsh et al. 2011a; EPCC 2017) and tend be be more ambivalent towards bioenergy compared to other mitigation options (Allen and Chatterton 2013). People evaluate biomass from waste products (e.g., food waste) more favourably than grown-for-purpose energy crops, which are more controversial (Plate et al. 2010; Demski et al. 2015). The most pressing concerns for use of woody biomass are air pollution and loss of local forests (Plate et al. 2010). Various types of bioenergy additionally raise concerns about landscape impacts (Whitmarsh et al. 2011a) and biodiversity (Immerzeel et al. 2014). Moreover, many people do not see biomass as a renewable energy source, possibly because it involves burning of material.

Box 6.5 | Methane Mitigation Options for Coal, Oil, and Gas

Methane emissions mainly from coal, oil, and gas currently represent in 2019 about 18% of energy supply sector greenhouse gas (GHG) emissions and 90% of global energy supply non-CO_2 emissions in 2019 (Minx et al. 2021b). While approximately 80% of the lifecycle methane emissions in the coal sector occur during underground mining, oil and gas emissions are spread throughout upstream, midstream, and downstream stages (Alvarez et al. 2018; IPCC 2019). For this reason, methane reductions from coal mining can be accomplished through coal mine methane recovery (where methane and coal are recovered simultaneously) and from the ventilation air, which can cumulatively reduce methane emissions by 50–75% (Zhou et al. 2016; Singh and Hajra 2018). Governments incentivise such operations through a number of emissions trading and offset programmes (Haya et al. 2020). Methane emissions in the oil and gas sector can be reduced by leak detection and repair, relevant across varying time scales (hours to decades) and regional scopes (component/facility level to continental) (Fox et al. 2019). Around 50% of the methane emitted from oil and gas infrastructure can be mitigated at net-negative costs; that is, the market price of the recovered methane is higher than the mitigation costs (IEA 2021e). As CO_2 emissions are reduced and fossil fuel consumption decreases, methane emissions associated with these supply chains are anticipated to decline (Section 6.7). That said, substantial 'legacy' methane emissions – methane leaks after abandonment – will remain, even if a complete fossil fuel phase-out takes place. These legacy emissions are estimated to be less than 1–4% of overall methane emissions across all fossil fuel sources (Kholod et al. 2020; Williams et al. 2021b). Even without a complete phase-out, 50–80% of methane emissions from coal, oil and gas could be avoided with currently available technologies at less than USD50 tCO_2-eq^{-1} (Harmsen et al. 2019; Höglund-Isaksson et al. 2020). Methane recovery from abandoned coal mines could offset most project costs (Singh and Sahu 2018). For abandoned oil and gas wells, low plugging costs could be offset through methane recovery, while high plugging costs would likely require some market or policy support (Kang et al. 2019).

6.4.2.7   Fossil Energy

Fossil fuels could play a role in climate change mitigation if strategically deployed with CCS (*high confidence*). On the one hand, the primary mechanism for reducing emissions is to eliminate the unabated fossil fuel use. On the other hand, fossil energy combined with CCS provides a means of producing low-carbon energy while still utilising the available base of fossil energy worldwide and limiting stranded assets. While Section 6.4.2.5 discusses the important aspects of CCS

with fossil fuels, this section aims to elucidate the feasibility criteria around these fuels itself.

Fossil fuel reserves have continued to rise because of advanced exploration and utilisation techniques (*high confidence*). A fraction of these available reserves can be used consistent with mitigation goals when paired with CCS opportunities in close geographical proximity (*high confidence*). Based on continued exploration, the fossil fuel resource base has increased significantly; for example, a 9% increase in gas reserves and 12% in oil reserves was observed in the USA between 2017 and 2018. This increase is a result of advanced exploration techniques, which are often subsidised (Lazarus and van Asselt 2018; MA et al. 2018). Fossil reserves are distributed unevenly throughout the globe. Coal represents the largest remaining resource (close to 500 ZJ). Conventional oil and gas resources are an order of magnitude smaller (15–20 ZJ each). Technological advances have increased the reserves of unconventional fossil in the last decade. Discovered ultimate recoverable resources of unconventional oil and gas are comparable to conventional oil and gas (Fizaine et al. 2017).

It is unlikely that resource constraints will lead to a phase-out of fossil fuels, and instead, such a phase-out would require policy action. Around 80% of coal, 50% of gas, and 20% of oil reserves are likely to remain unextractable under 2°C constraints (McGlade and Ekins 2015; Pellegrini et al. 2020). Reserves are more likely to be utilised in a low-carbon transition if they can be paired with CCS. Availability of CCS technology not only allows continued use of fossil fuels as a capital resource for countries but also paves the way for CDR through BECCS (Haszeldine 2016; Pye et al. 2020). While the theoretical geologic CO_2 sequestration potential is vast, there are limits on how much resource base could be utilised based on geologic, engineering, and source-sink mapping criteria (Budinis et al. 2017).

Technological changes have continued to drive down fossil fuel extraction costs. Significant decarbonisation potential also exists via diversification of the fossil fuel uses beyond combustion (high evidence). The costs of extracting oil and gas globally have gone down by utilising hydraulic fracturing and directional drilling for resources in unconventional reservoirs (Wachtmeister and Höök 2020). Although the extraction of these resources is still more expensive than those derived from conventional reservoirs, the large availability of unconventional resources has significantly reduced global prices. The emergence of liquefied natural gas (LNG) markets has also provided opportunities to export natural gas significant distances from the place of production (Avraam et al. 2020). The increase in availability of natural gas has been accompanied by an increase in the production of natural gas liquids as a co-product to oil and gas. Over the period from 2014 to 2019, exports of natural gas liquids increased by 160%. Natural gas liquids could potentially be a lower-carbon alternative to liquid fuels and hydrocarbons. On the demand side, natural gas can be used to produce hydrogen using steam methane reforming, which is a technologically mature process (Sections 6.4.4 and 6.4.5). When combined with 90% CO_2 capture, the costs of producing hydrogen are around USD1.5–2 $kg(H_2)^{-1}$ (Collodi et al. 2017; Newborough and Cooley 2020), considerably less than hydrogen produced via electrolysis.

Significant potential exists for gasifying deep-seated coal deposits *in situ* to produce hydrogen. Doing so reduces fugitive methane emissions from underground coal mining. The integration costs of this process with CCS are less than with natural gas reforming. The extent to which coal gasification could be compatible with low-carbon energy would depend on the rate of CO_2 capture and the ultimate use of the gas (Verma and Kumar 2015). Similarly, for ongoing underground mining projects, coal mine methane recovery can be economic for major coal producers such as China and India.

Coal mine methane and ventilation air methane recovery can reduce the fugitive methane emissions by 50–75% (Zhou et al. 2016; Singh and Sahu 2018).

The cost of producing electricity from fossil sources has remained roughly the same with some regional exceptions while the costs of producing transport fuels has gone down significantly (*high confidence*). The cost of producing electricity from fossil fuels has remained largely static, with the exception of some regional changes, for example, a 40% cost reduction in the USA for natural gas (Rai et al. 2019), where the gas wellhead price has declined by almost two-thirds due to large reserves. Similarly, the global price of crude oil has declined from almost USD100 bbl^{-1} to USD55 bbl^{-1} in the last five years.

The energy return of investment (EROI) is a useful indicator of full fossil lifecycle costs. Fossil fuels create significantly more energy per unit energy invested – or in other words have much larger EROI – than most cleaner fuels such as biomass or electrolysis-derived hydrogen, where intensive processing reduces EROI (Hall et al. 2014). That said, recent years have seen a decrease in fossil EROI, especially as underground coal mining still represents a substantial portion of global production. Exploitation of unconventional gas reservoirs is also energy intensive and has led to a reduction in EROI. The primary energy EROI of fossil fuels has converged at about 30, which represents a 20-point decrease from the 1995 value for coal (Brockway et al. 2019). When processing and refining stages are considered, these EROI values further decrease.

Several countries have large reserves of fossil fuels. Owing to climate constraints, these may become stranded, causing considerable economic impacts (*high confidence*) (Sections 6.7.3 and 6.7.4, and Box 6.13). While global fossil energy resources are greater than 600 ZJ, more than half of these resources would likely be unburnable, even in the presence of CCS (McGlade and Ekins 2015; Pye et al. 2020). This would entail a significant capital loss for the countries with large reserves. The total amount of stranded assets in such a case would amount to USD1–4 trillion at present value (Box 6.13).

Apart from CO_2 emissions and air pollutants from fossil fuel combustion, other environmental impacts include fugitive methane leakages and implications to water systems. While the rate of methane leakage from unconventional gas systems is uncertain, their overall GHG impact is less than coal (Tanaka et al. 2019; Deetjen and Azevedo 2020). The stated rate of leakage in such systems ranges from 1–8%, and reconciling different estimates requires a combination of top-down and bottom-up approaches (Zavala-Araiza et al. 2015; Grubert and Brandt 2019). Similarly, for coal mining, fugitive methane emissions have grown, despite some regulations on the degree to which emission controls must be deployed. Recent IPCC inventory guidance also notes considerable CO_2 emissions resulting from spontaneous combustion of the coal surface, and accounting for these emissions will likely increase the overall lifecycle emissions by 1–5% (IPCC 2019; Singh 2019; Fiehn et al. 2020).

Another key issue consistently noted with unconventional wells (both oil and gas, and coalbed methane) is the large water requirements (Qin et al. 2018). The overall water footprint of unconventional

6

reservoirs is higher than conventional reservoirs because of higher lateral length and fracturing requirements (Scanlon et al. 2017; Kondash et al. 2018). Moreover, produced water from such formations is moderately to highly brackish, and treating such waters has large energy consumption (Bartholomew and Mauter 2016; Singh and Colosi 2019).

Oil and coal consistently rank among the least preferred energy sources in many countries (*high confidence*). The main perceived advantage of fossil energy is the relatively low costs, and emphasising these costs might increase acceptability somewhat (Pohjolainen et al. 2018; Boyd et al. 2019; Hazboun and Boudet 2020). Acceptability of fossil fuels is, on average, similar to acceptability of nuclear energy, although evaluations are less polarised. People evaluate natural gas as somewhat more acceptable than other fossil fuels, although they generally oppose hydraulic fracturing (Clarke et al. 2016). Yet, natural gas is evaluated as less acceptable than renewable energy sources, although evaluations of natural gas and biogas are similar (Liebe and Dobers 2019; Plum et al. 2019). Acceptability of fossil energy tends to be higher in countries and regions that strongly rely on them for their energy production (Pohjolainen et al. 2018; Boyd et al. 2019). Combining fossil fuels with CCS can increase their acceptability (Van Rijnsoever et al. 2015; Bessette and Arvai 2018). Some people seem ambivalent about natural gas, as they perceive both benefits (e.g., affordability, less carbon emissions than coal) and disadvantages (e.g., finite resource, contributing to climate change) (Blumer et al. 2018).

Fossil fuel subsidies have been valued in the order of USD0.5–5 trillion annually by various estimates which have the tendency to introduce economic inefficiency within systems (Jakob et al. 2015; Merrill et al. 2015) (*high confidence*). Subsequent reforms have been suggested by different researchers who have estimated reductions in CO_2 emissions may take place if these subsidies are removed (Mundaca 2017). Such reforms could create the necessary framework for

enhanced investments in social welfare – through sanitation, water, clean energy – with differentiating impacts (Edenhofer 2015).

6.4.2.8   Geothermal Energy

Geothermal energy is heat stored in the Earth's subsurface and is a renewable resource that can be sustainably exploited. The geophysical potential of geothermal resources is 1.3 to 13 times the global electricity demand in 2019 (*medium confidence*). Geothermal energy can be used directly for various thermal applications, including space heating and industrial heat input, or converted to electricity depending on the source temperature (Limberger et al. 2018; Moya et al. 2018; REN21 2019).

Suitable aquifers underlay 16% of the Earth's land surface and store an estimated 110,000–1,400,000 PWh (400,000–1,450,000 EJ) that could theoretically be used for direct heat applications. For electricity generation, the technical potential of geothermal energy is estimated to be between 30 PWh yr^{-1} (108 EJ yr^{-1}) (to 3 km depth) and 300 PWh yr^{-1} (1080 EJ yr^{-1}) (to 10 km depth). For direct thermal uses, the technical potential is estimated to range from 2.7–86 PWh yr^{-1} (9.7–310 EJ yr^{-1}) (IPCC 2011). Despite the potential, geothermal direct heat supplies only 0.15% of the annual global final energy consumption. The technical potential for electricity generation, depending on the depth, can meet one third to almost three times the global final consumption – based on International Energy Agency (IEA) database for IPCC. The mismatch between potential and developed geothermal resources is caused by high upfront costs, decentralised geothermal heat production, lack of uniformity among geothermal projects, geological uncertainties, and geotechnical risks (IRENA 2017a; Limberger et al. 2018). A limited number of countries have a long history in geothermal. At least in two countries (Iceland and New Zealand), geothermal accounts for 20–25% of electricity generation (Pan et al. 2019; Spittler et al. 2020). Furthermore, in Iceland approximately 90% of the households are heated with

Geothermal energy, 2010–2020

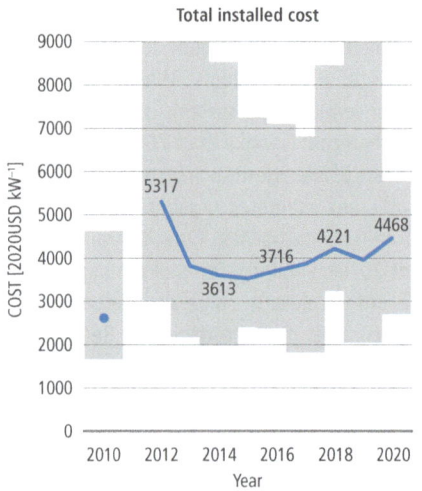

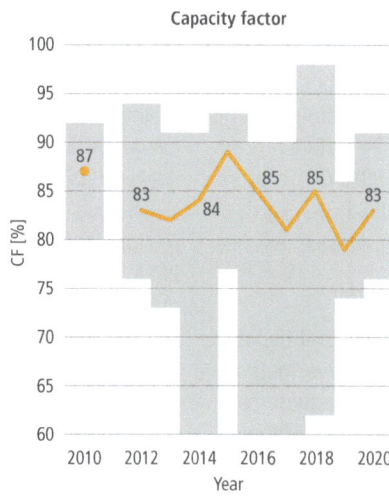

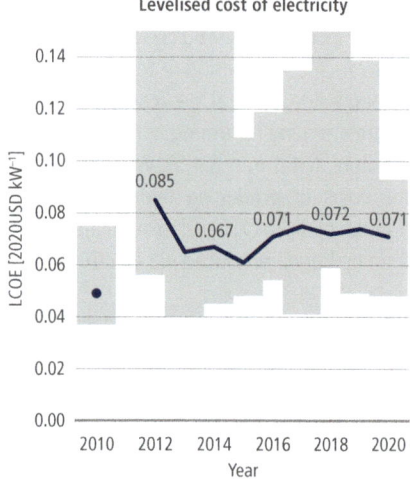

Figure 6.15 | Global weighted average total installed costs, capacity factors and levelised costs of electricity (LCOE) for geothermal power per year (2010–2020). The shaded area represents the 5% and 95% percentiles. Source: with permission from IRENA (2021a).

geothermal energy. In Kenya, as of July 2019, geothermal accounted for 734 MW effective capacity spread over 10 power plants and approximately one third of the total installed capacity (Kahlen 2019).

There are two main types of geothermal resources: convective hydrothermal resources, in which the Earth's heat is carried by natural hot water or steam to the surface; and hot, dry rock resources, in which heat cannot be extracted using water or steam, and other methods must be developed. There are three basic types of geothermal power plants: (i) dry steam plants use steam directly from a geothermal reservoir to turn generator turbines; (ii) flash steam plants take high-pressure hot water from deep inside the Earth and convert it to steam to drive generator turbines; and (iii) binary cycle power plants transfer the heat from geothermal hot water to another liquid. Many of the power plants in operation today are dry steam plants or flash plants (single, double and triple) harnessing temperatures of more than 180°C.

However, medium temperature fields are increasingly used for electricity generation or combined heat and power. The use of medium temperature fields has been enabled through the development of binary cycle technology, in which a geothermal fluid is used via heat exchangers. Increasing binary generation technologies are now being utilised instead of flash steam power plants. This will result in almost 100% injection and essentially zero GHG emissions, although GHG emissions from geothermal power production are generally small compared to traditional baseload thermal energy power generation facilities (Fridriksson et al. 2016).

Additionally, new technologies are being developed like Enhanced Geothermal Systems (EGS), which is in the demonstration stage (IRENA 2018), deep geothermal technology, which may increase the prospects for harnessing the geothermal potential in a large number of countries, or shallow-geothermal energy, which represents a promising supply source for heating and cooling buildings (Narsilio and Aye 2018). Successful large-scale deployment of shallow geothermal energy will depend not only on site-specific economic performance but also on developing suitable governance frameworks (Bloemendal et al. 2018; García-Gil et al. 2020). Technologies for direct uses like district heating, geothermal heat pumps, greenhouses, and other applications, are widely used and considered mature. Given the limited number of plants commissioned, economic indicators (Figure 6.15) vary considerably depending on site characteristics.

Public awareness and knowledge of geothermal energy is relatively low (*high confidence*). Geothermal energy is evaluated as less acceptable than other renewable energy sources such as solar and wind, but is preferred over fossil and nuclear energy, and in some studies, over hydroelectric energy (*high confidence*) (Pellizzone et al. 2015; Steel et al. 2015; Karytsas et al. 2019; Hazboun and Boudet 2020). Some people are concerned about the installation of geothermal facilities close to their homes, similar to solar and wind projects (Pellizzone et al. 2015). The main concerns about geothermal energy, particularly for large-scale, high-temperature geothermal power generation plants, involve water usage, water scarcity, and seismic risks of drilling (Dowd et al. 2011). Moreover, noise, smell and damages to the landscape have been reasons for protests against specific projects (Walker 1995).

However, with the implementation of modern technologies, geothermal presents fewer adverse environmental impacts. At the same time, people perceive geothermal energy as relatively environmentally friendly (Tampakis et al. 2013).

6.4.2.9 Marine Energy

The ocean is a vast source of energy (Hoegh-Guldberg et al. 2019). Ocean energy can be extracted from tides, waves, ocean thermal energy conversion (OTEC), currents, and salinity gradients (Bindoff et al. 2019). Their technical potentials, without considering possible exclusion zones, are explored below. Tidal energy, which uses elevation differences between high and low tides, appears in two forms: potential energy (rise and fall of the tide); and current energy (from tidal currents). The global technically harvestable tidal power from areas close to the coast is estimated as about 1.2 PWh yr^{-1} (4.3 EJ yr^{-1}) (IRENA 2020b). The potential for tidal current energy is estimated to be larger than that for tidal range or barrage (Melikoglu 2018). Ocean wave energy is abundant and predictable and can be extracted directly from surface waves or pressure fluctuations below the surface (Melikoglu 2018). Its global theoretical potential is 29.5 PWh yr^{-1} (106 EJ yr^{-1}), which means that wave energy alone could meet all global energy demand (Mørk et al. 2010; IRENA 2020b). The temperature gradients in the ocean can be exploited to produce energy, and its total estimated available resource could be up to 44.0 PWh yr^{-1} (158 EJ yr^{-1}) (Rajagopalan and Nihous 2013). Salinity gradient energy, also known as osmotic power, has a global theoretical potential of over 1.6 PWh yr^{-1} (6.0 EJ yr^{-1}) (IRENA 2020b). The greatest advantage of most marine energy, excluding wave energy, is that their sources are highly regular and predictable, and energy can be furthermore generated both day and night. An additional use of sea water is to develop lower-cost district cooling systems near the sea (Hunt et al. 2019). The greatest barrier to most marine technology advances is the relatively high upfront costs, uncertainty on environmental regulation and impact, need for investments and insufficient infrastructure (Kempener and Neumann 2014a, b). There are also concerns about technology maturity and performance; thus, not all have the potential to become economically viable (IRENA 2020b).

6.4.2.10 Waste-to-Energy

Waste-to-energy (WTE) is a strategy to recover energy from waste in a form of consumable heat, electricity, or fuel (Zhao et al. 2016). Thermal (incineration, gasification, and pyrolysis) and biological (anaerobic digestion and landfill gas to energy) technologies are commonly used (Ahmad et al. 2020). When WTE technologies are equipped with proper air pollution reduction facilities they can contribute to clean electricity production and reduction of GHG emissions. However, if not properly operated, they can exacerbate air quality issues.

In 2019, there were more than 1,200 WTE incineration facilities worldwide, with estimated capacity of 310 million tonnes per year (UNECE 2020). It is estimated that treatment of a minimum of 261 million tonnes/year of waste could produce 283 TWh (1 EJ) of power and heat by 2022 (Awasthi et al. 2019). Incineration plants can reduce the mass of waste by 70–80% and the volume of waste by 80–90% (Haraguchi et al. 2019). Incineration technology can reduce water and soil pollution (Gu et al. 2019). However, if not properly handled, dust, and gases such as SO_2, HCL, HF, NO_2, and dioxins in the flue gases can harm the environment (Mutz et al. 2017). Anaerobic digestion technology has a positive environmental impact and the ability to reduce GHG emissions (Ayodele et al. 2018; Cudjoe et al. 2020). The by-product of the anaerobic digestion process could be used as a nutrient-rich fertiliser for enhancing soil richness for agricultural purposes (Wainaina et al. 2020). Due to the potential negative impacts on domestic environment and residents' health, WTE projects such as incineration encounter substantial opposition from the local communities in which they are located (Baxter et al. 2016; Ren et al. 2016). Therefore, for WTE to be deployed more widely, policies would need to be tailored with specific guidelines focused on mitigating emissions, which may have an adverse effect on the environment.

Depending on the origin of the waste used, the integration of WTE and carbon capture and storage (CCS) could enable waste to be a net-zero or even net negative emissions energy source (Kearns 2019; Wienchol et al. 2020). For example, in Europe only, the integration of CCS with WTE facilities has the potential to capture about 60 to 70 million tonnes of carbon dioxide annually (Tota et al. 2021).

Waste-to-energy is an expensive process compared to other energy sources such as fossil fuels and natural gas (Mohammadi and Harjunkoski 2020). However, the environmental and economic benefits make its high financial costs justifiable. In 2019, the global WTE market size was valued at USD31 billion, and it is predicted to experience 7.4% annual growth until 2027 (UNECE 2020).

6.4.3   Energy System Integration

Greenhouse gases are emitted across all economic activities. Therefore, cost-effective decarbonisation requires a 'system of systems' approach that considers the interaction between different energy sectors and systems. Flexibility technologies and advanced control of integrated energy systems (e.g., considering the interaction between electricity, heating/cooling, gas/hydrogen, transport sectors) could reduce energy infrastructure investments substantially in future low-carbon energy systems (Strbac et al. 2015b; Jacobson et al. 2019).

The electricity grid will serve as a backbone of future low-carbon energy systems. Integration of large amounts of VRE generation (Hansen et al. 2019), particularly wind and solar generation (Bistline and Young 2019; Perez et al. 2019), presents economic and technical challenges to electricity system management across different time scales from sub-seconds, hours, days, seasons, to multiple years. Furthermore, electrification of segments of the transport and heat sectors could disproportionately increase peak demand relative to supply (Bistline et al. 2021). Increases in peak demand may require reinforcing network infrastructures and generation in the historical passive system operation paradigm (Strbac et al. 2020).

These challenges to electricity system management can be addressed through system integration and a digitalised control paradigm

involving advanced information and communication technologies. Real-time maintenance of supply-demand balance and sufficient flexibility technologies such as electricity storage, flexible demand, and grid forming converters (Strbac et al. 2015a; López Prol and Schill 2021) would be increasingly valuable for incorporating larger amounts of VRE generation. This flexibility will be particularly important to deal with sudden losses of supply, for example, due to a failure of a large generator or interconnector or a rapid increase in demand (Teng et al. 2017; Chamorro et al. 2020).

The transition to a digitalised-based electricity system control paradigm would facilitate radical changes in the security of supply, moving from the traditional approach of redundancy in assets to a smart control paradigm. Advanced control and communication systems can significantly reduce the electricity system investment and operation costs (Harper et al. 2018; Münster et al. 2020).

6.4.3.1   Importance of Cross-sector Coupling for Cost-effective Energy System Decarbonisation

Integrated whole-system approaches can reduce the costs of low-carbon energy system transitions (*high confidence*). A lack of flexibility in the electricity system may limit the cost-effective integration of technologies as part of broader net-zero energy systems. At the same time, the enormous latent flexibility hidden in heating and cooling, hydrogen, transport, gas systems, and other energy systems provides opportunities to take advantage of synergies and to coordinate operations across systems (Martin et al. 2017; Zhang et al. 2018; Martinez Cesena and Mancarella 2019; Pavičević et al. 2020; Bogdanov et al. 2021) (Figure 6.16).

Sector coupling can significantly increase system flexibility, driven by the application of advanced technologies (Clegg and Mancarella 2016; Heinen et al. 2016; Bogdanov et al. 2019; Solomon et al. 2019; Zhang et al. 2019b; Zhang and Fujimori 2020; Zhao et al. 2021). For example, district heating infrastructure can generate both heat and power. Cooling systems and electrified heating systems in buildings can provide flexibility through preheating and precooling via thermal energy storage (Z. Li et al. 2016; G. Li et al. 2017). System balancing services can be provided by electric vehicles (EVs) based on vehicle-to-grid concepts and deferred charging through smart control of EV batteries without compromising customers' requirements for transport (Aunedi and Strbac 2020).

Hydrogen production processes (power-to-gas and vice versa) and hydrogen storage can support short-term and long-term balancing in the energy systems and enhance resilience (Stephen and Pierluigi 2016; Strbac et al. 2020). However, the economic benefits of flexible power-to-gas plants, energy storage, and other flexibility technological and options will depend on the locations of VRE sources, storage sites, gas, hydrogen, and electricity networks (Jentsch et al. 2014; Heymann and Bessa 2015; Ameli et al. 2020). Coordinated operation of gas and electricity systems can bring significant benefits in supplying heat demands. For example, hybrid heating can eliminate investment in electricity infrastructure reinforcement by switching to heat pumps in off-peak hours and gas boilers in peak hours (Fischer et al. 2017; Dengiz et al. 2019;

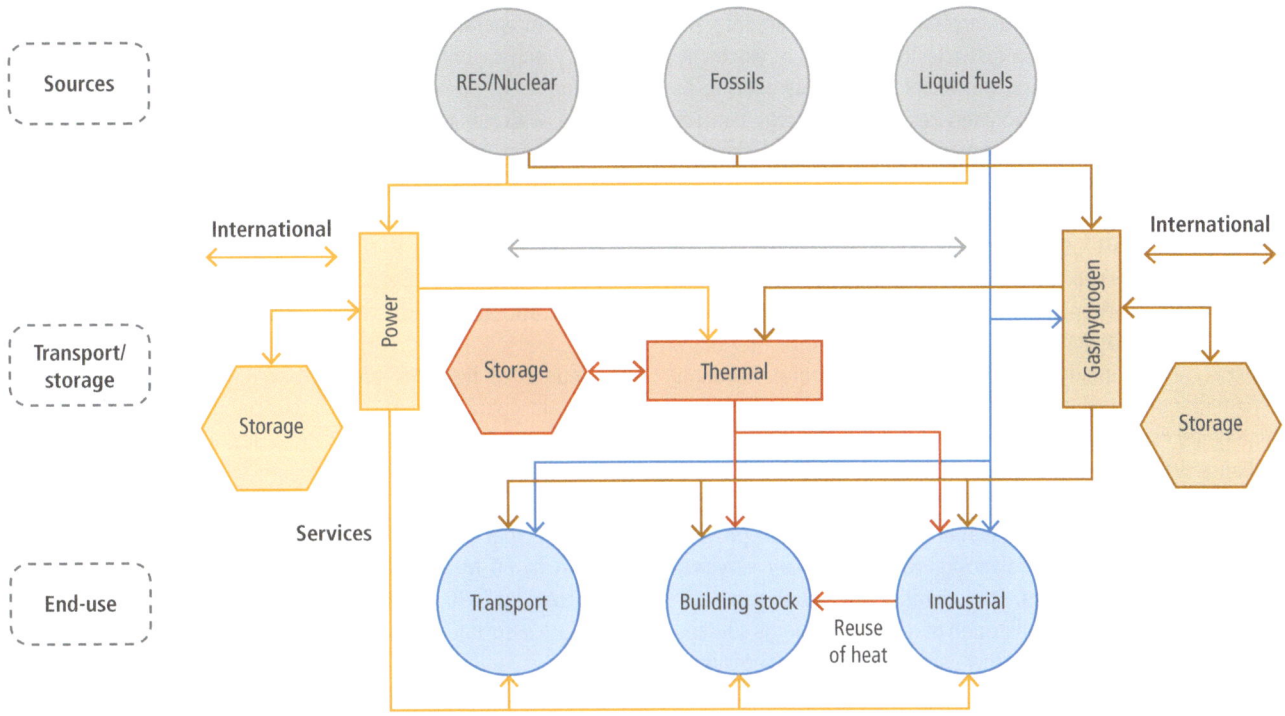

Figure 6.16 | Interaction between different energy sectors. Source: extracted with permission from Münster et al. (2020).

Bistline et al. 2021). The heat required by direct air carbon capture and storage (DACCS) could be effectively supplied by inherent heat energy in nuclear plants, enhancing overall system efficiency (Realmonte et al. 2019).

Rather than incremental planning, strategic energy system planning can help minimise long-term mitigation costs (*high confidence*). With a whole-system perspective, integrated planning can consider both short-term operation and long-term investment decisions, covering infrastructure from local to national and international, while meeting security of supply requirements and incorporating the flexibility provided by different technologies and advanced control strategies (Zhang et al. 2018; O'Malley et al. 2020; Strbac et al. 2020). Management of conflicts and synergies between local district and national level energy system objectives, including strategic investment in local hydrogen and heat infrastructure, can drive significant whole-system cost savings (Zhang et al. 2019b; Fu et al. 2020). For example, long-term planning of the offshore grid infrastructure to support offshore wind development, including interconnection between different countries and regions, can provide significant savings compared to a short-term incremental approach in which every offshore wind farm is individually connected to the onshore grid (E3G 2021).

6.4.3.2   Role of Flexibility Technologies

Flexibility technologies – including energy storage, demand-side response, flexible/dispatchable generation, grid-forming converters, and transmission interconnection – as well as advanced control systems – can facilitate cost-effective and secure low-carbon energy systems (*high confidence*). Flexibility technologies have already

been implemented, but they can be enhanced and deployed more widely. Due to their interdependencies and similarities, there can be both synergies and conflicts for utilising these flexibility options (Bistline et al. 2021). It will therefore be important to coordinate the deployment of the potential flexibility technologies and smart control strategies. Important electricity system flexibility options include the following:

- **Flexible/dispatchable generation.** Advances in generation technologies, for example, gas/hydrogen plants and nuclear plants, can enable them to provide flexibility services. These technologies would start more quickly, operate at lower power output, and make faster output changes, enabling more secure and cost-effective integration of VRE generation and end-use electrification. There are already important developments in increasing nuclear plants flexibility (e.g., in France (Office of Nuclear Energy 2021)) and the development of small modular reactors, which could support system balancing (FTI Consulting 2018).

- **Grid-forming converters (inverters).** The transition from conventional electricity generation, applying mainly synchronous machines to inverter-dominated renewable generation, creates significant operating challenges. These challenges are mainly associated with reduced synchronous inertia, system stability, and 'black start' capability. Grid-forming converters will be a cornerstone for the control of future electricity systems dominated by VRE generation. These converters will address critical stability challenges, including the lack of system inertia, frequency and voltage regulation, and black start services while reducing or eliminating the need to operate conventional generation (Tayyebi et al. 2019).

6

- **Interconnection.** Electricity interconnections between different regions can facilitate more cost-effective renewable electricity deployment. Interconnection can enable large-scale sharing of energy and provide balancing services. Backup energy carriers beyond electricity, such as ammonia, can be shared through gas/ammonia/hydrogen-based interconnections, strengthening temporal coupling of multiple sectors in different regions (Bhagwat et al. 2017; Brown et al. 2018) (Section 6.4.5).
- **Demand-side response.** Demand-side schemes – including, for example, smart appliances, EVs, and building-based thermal energy storage (Heleno et al. 2014) – can provide flexibility services across multiple time frames and systems. Through differentiation between essential and non-essential needs during emergency conditions, smart control of demands can significantly enhance system resilience (Chaffey 2016).
- **Energy storage.** Energy storage technologies (Section 6.4.4) can act as both demand and generation sources. They can provide services such as system balancing, various ancillary services, and network management. Long-duration energy storage can significantly enhance the utilisation of renewable energy sources and reduce the need for firm low-carbon generation (Sepulveda et al. 2021).

6.4.3.3 Role of Digitalisation and Advanced Control Systems

A digitalised energy system can significantly reduce energy infrastructure investments while enhancing supply security and resilience (*high confidence*) (Andoni et al. 2019; Strbac et al. 2020). Significant progress has been made in the development of technologies essential for the transition to a digitalised energy control paradigm, although the full implementation is still under development. Electrification and the increased integration of the electricity system with other systems will fundamentally transform the operational and planning paradigm of future energy infrastructure. A fully intelligent and sophisticated coordination of the multiple systems through smart control will support this paradigm shift. This shift will provide significant savings through better utilisation of existing infrastructure locally, regionally, nationally, and internationally. Supply system reliability will be enhanced through advanced control of local infrastructure (Strbac et al. 2015a). Furthermore, this paradigm shift offers the potential to increase energy efficiency through a combination of technologies that gather and analyse data and consequently optimise energy use in real-time.

The transition to advanced data-driven control of energy system operations (Cremer et al. 2019; Sun et al. 2019a) will require advanced information and communication technologies and infrastructure, including the internet, wireless networks, computers, software, middleware, smart sensors, internet of things components, and dedicated technological developments (Hossein Motlagh et al. 2020). The transition will raise standardisation and cyber-security issues, given that digitalisation can become a single point of failure for the complete system (Ustun and Hussain 2019; Unsal et al. 2021). Implementing peer-to-peer energy trading based on blockchain is expected to be one of the key elements of next-generation electricity systems (Qiu et al. 2021). This trading will enable consumers to drive system operation and future design, increasing overall system efficiency and security of supply while reducing emissions without sacrificing users' privacy (Andoni et al. 2019; Ahl et al. 2020). When deployed with smart contracts, this concept will be suitable for energy systems involving many participants, where a prerequisite is digitalisation (e.g., smart meters, end-use demand control systems) (Juhar and Khaled 2018; Teufel et al. 2019).

6.4.3.4 System Benefits of Flexibility Technologies and Advanced Control Systems

New sources of flexibility and advanced control systems provide a significant opportunity to reduce low-carbon energy system costs by enhancing operating efficiency and reducing energy infrastructure and low-carbon generation investments, while continuing to meet security requirements (*high confidence*). In the USA, for example, one study found that flexibility in buildings alone could reduce US CO_2 emissions by 80 Mt yr^{-1} and save USD18 billion yr^{-1} in electricity system costs by 2030 (Satchwell et al. 2021). Key means for creating savings are associated with the following:

- **Efficient energy system operation.** Flexibility technologies such as storage, demand-side response, interconnection, and cross-system control will enable more efficient, real-time demand and supply balancing. This balancing has historically been provided by conventional fossil-fuel generation (Nuytten et al. 2013).
- **Savings in investment in low-carbon/renewable generation capacity.** System flexibility sources can absorb or export surplus electricity, thus reducing or avoiding energy curtailment and reducing the need for firm low-carbon capacity such as nuclear and fossil-fuel plants with CCS (Newbery et al. 2013; Solomon et al. 2019). For example, one study found that flexibility technologies and advanced control systems could reduce the need for nuclear power by 14 GW and offshore wind by 20 GW in the UK's low-carbon transition (Strbac et al. 2015b).
- **Reduced need for backup capacity.** System flexibility can reduce energy demand peaks, reducing the required generation capacity to maintain the security of supply, producing significant savings in generation investments (Strbac et al. 2020).
- **Deferral or avoidance of electricity network reinforcement/ addition.** Flexibility technologies supported by advanced control systems can provide significant savings in investment in electricity network reinforcement that might emerge from increased demand, for example, driven by electrification of transport and heat sectors. Historical network planning and operation standards are being revised considering alternative flexibility technologies, which would further support cost-effective integration of decarbonised transport and heat sectors (Strbac et al. 2020).

6.4.4 Energy Storage for Low-carbon Grids

Energy storage technologies make low-carbon electricity systems more cost-effective, allowing VRE technologies to replace more expensive firm low-carbon generation technologies (Carbon Trust 2016) and

Table 6.5 | Suitability of low-carbon energy storage technologies, in terms of the grid services they can provide, and overall features such as technology maturity: where Low represents an emerging technology; Med represents a maturing technology; and High a fully mature technology. The opportunity for the cost of a technology to reduce over the next decade is represented by Low, Med and High and the lifetime of installations by: Long, for projects lasting more than 25 years; Med for those lasting 15–25 years; Short, for those lasting less than 15 years.

Suitability factor	PHS	CAES	LAES	TES	FES	LiB	Scap	RFB	PtX	RHFC
Upgrade deferral	•	•	•	•	•	•	•	•	•	•
Energy arbitrage	•	•	•	•		•		•	•	•
Capacity firming	•	•	•	•		•		•	•	•
Seasonal storage				•					•	•
Stability	•				•	•	•		•	
Frequency regulation	•	•	•		•	•	•	•	•	•
Voltage support	•	•	•		•	•	•	•	•	•
Black start	•	•	•			•				
Short-term reserve	•	•	•			•		•	•	•
Fast reserve	•	•	•		•	•		•	•	•
Islanding		•	•	•		•				
Uninterruptible power supply					•	•	•	•		•
Maturity	High	High	Med	Low	High	Med	Low	Low	Low	Low
Opportunity to reduce costs	Low	Low	Low	Med	Med	High	High	High	Med	High
Lifetime	Long	Long	Long	Long	Med	Short	Med	Med	Med	Short
Roundtrip efficiency	60–80%	30–60%	55–90%	70–80%	90%	>95%	>95%	80–90%	35–60%	<30%

Note: PHS – Pumped Hydroelectric Storage; CAES – Compressed Air Energy Storage; LAES – Liquid Air Energy Storage; TES – Thermal Energy Storage; FES – Flywheel Energy Storage; LIB – Li-ion Batteries; Scap – Supercapacitors; RFB – Redox Flow Batteries; RHFC – Reversible Hydrogen Fuel Cells; PtX – Power to fuels. Source: PHS – Barbour et al. 2016, Yang 2016, IRENA 2017b; CAES – Luo et al. 2014, Brandon et al. 2015, IRENA 2017b; LAES – Luo et al. 2014, Highview 2019; TES – Brandon et al. 2015, Gallo et al. 2016, Smallbone et al. 2017; FES – IRENA 2017b, Yulong et al. 2017; LIB – IRENA 2015b, Hammond and Hazeldine 2015, Nykvist and Nilsson 2015, Staffell, I. and Rustomji, M. et al. 2016, IRENA 2017b, Schmidt et al. 2017c, May et al. 2018; Scap – Brandon et al. 2015, Gur 2018; RFB – IRENA 2017b; RHFC – IEA 2015, Gur 2018.

reducing investment costs in backup generation, interconnection, transmission, and distribution network upgrades (*high confidence*). Energy system decarbonisation relies on increased electrification (Section 6.6.2.3). Meeting increasing demands with variable renewable sources presents challenges and could lead to costly infrastructure reinforcements. Energy storage enables electricity from variable renewables to be matched against evolving demands across both time and space, using short-, medium- and long-term storage of excess energy for delivery later or at a different location. In 2017, an estimated 4.67 TWh (0.017 EJ) of electricity storage was in operation globally (IRENA 2017b). If the integration of renewables is doubled from 2014 levels by 2030, the total capacity of global electricity storage could triple, reaching 11.89–15.27 TWh (0.043–0.055 EJ) (IRENA 2017b).

Energy storage technologies can provide a range of different grid services (Table 6.5). Energy storage enhances security of supply by providing real-time system regulation services (voltage support, frequency regulation, fast reserve, and short-term reserve). A greater proportion of variable renewable sources reduces system inertia, requiring more urgent responses to changes in system frequency, which rapid response storage technologies can provide (stability requires responses within sub-second time scale for provision of frequency and voltage control services). Energy storage also provides intermittent renewable sources with flexibility, allowing them to contribute a greater proportion of electrical energy and avoiding curtailment (capacity firming). Investment costs in backup generation, interconnection, transmission, and distribution network

upgrades can thus be reduced (upgrade deferral), meaning that less low-carbon generation will need to be built while still reducing emissions. In the event of an outage, energy storage reserves can keep critical services running (islanding) and restart the grid (black start). The ability to store and release energy as required provides a range of market opportunities for buying and selling of energy (arbitrage).

No single, sufficiently mature energy storage technology can provide all the required grid services – a portfolio of complementary technologies working together can provide the optimum solution (*high confidence*). Different energy storage technologies can provide these services and support cost-effective energy system decarbonisation (Carbon Trust 2016). To achieve very low-carbon systems, significant volumes of storage will be required (Strbac et al. 2015a; Section 6.4.3.2). There are few mature global supply chains for many of the less-developed energy storage technologies. This means that, although costs today may be relatively high, there are significant opportunities for future cost reductions, both through technology innovation and through manufacturing scale. Adding significant amounts of storage will reduce the price variation and, therefore, the profitability of additional and existing storage, increasing investment risk.

Energy storage extends beyond electricity storage and includes technologies that can store energy as heat, cold, and both liquid and gaseous fuels. Energy storage is a conversion technology, enabling energy to be converted from one form to another. This diversification improves the overall resilience of energy systems, with each system

6

being able to cover supply shortfalls in the others. For example, storage can support the electrification of heating or cooling, as well as transport through electric vehicles, powered by batteries or by fuel cells. Storage significantly reduces the need for costly reinforcement of local distribution networks through smart charging schemes and the ability to flow electricity back to the grid (e.g., through vehicle-to-grid). By capturing otherwise wasted energy streams, such as heat or cold, energy storage improves the efficiency of many systems, such as buildings, data centres and industrial processes.

6.4.4.1 Energy Storage Technologies

Pumped hydroelectric storage (PHS). PHS makes use of gravitational potential energy, using water as the medium. Water is pumped into an elevated reservoir using off-peak electricity and stored for later release when electricity is needed. These closed-loop hydropower plants have been in use for decades and account for 97% of worldwide electricity storage capacity (IRENA 2017b; IEA 2018b). PHS is best suited to balancing daily energy needs at a large scale, and advances in the technology now allow rapid response and power regulation in both generating and pumping mode (Valavi and Nysveen 2018; Dong et al. 2019; Kougias et al. 2019). The construction itself can cause disruption to the local community and environment (Hayes et al. 2019), the initial investment is costly, and extended construction periods delay return on investment (Section 6.4.2.3). In addition, locations for large-scale PHS plants are limited.

Advanced pump-turbines are being developed, allowing both reversible and variable-speed operation, supporting frequency control and grid stability with improved round-trip efficiencies (Ardizzon et al. 2014). New possibilities are being explored for small-scale PHS installations and expanding the potential for siting (Kougias et al. 2019). For example, in underwater PHS, the upper reservoir is the sea, and the lower is a hollow deposit at the seabed. Seawater is pumped out of the deposit to store off-peak energy and re-enters

through turbines to recharge it (Kougias et al. 2019). Using a similar concept, underground siting in abandoned mines and caverns could be developed reasonably quickly (IEA 2020h). Storage of energy as gravitational potential can also be implemented using materials other than water, such as rocks and sand. Pumped technology is a mature technology (Rehman et al. 2015; Barbour et al. 2016) and can be important in supporting the transition to future low-carbon electricity grids (IHA 2021).

Batteries. There are many types of batteries, all having unique features and suitability, but their key feature is their rapid response time. A rechargeable battery cell is charged by using electricity to drive ions from one electrode to another, with the reverse occurring on discharge, producing a usable electric current (Crabtree et al. 2015). While lead-acid batteries (LABs) have been widely used for automotive and grid applications for decades (May et al. 2018), LIBs are increasingly being used in grid-scale projects (Crabtree et al. 2015), displacing LABs. The rapid response time of batteries makes them suitable for enhanced frequency regulation and voltage support, enabling the integration of variable renewables into electricity grids (Strbac and Aunedi 2016). Batteries can provide almost all electricity services, except for seasonal storage. LIBs, in particular, can store energy and power in small volumes and with low weight, making them the default choice for EVs (Placke et al. 2017). EV batteries are expected to form a distributed storage resource as this market grows, both impacting and supporting the grid (Staffell and Rustomji 2016).

Drawbacks of batteries include relatively short lifespans and the use of hazardous or costly materials in some variants. While LIB costs are decreasing (Schmidt et al. 2017; Vartiainen et al. 2020), the risk of thermal runaway, which could ignite a fire (Gur 2018; Wang et al. 2019a), concerns about long-term resource availability (Olivetti et al. 2017; Sun et al. 2017), and concerns about global cradle-to-grave impacts (Peters et al. 2017; Kallitsis et al. 2020) need to be addressed.

Table 6.6 | Technical characteristics of a selected range of battery chemistries, categorised as those which precede LIBs (white background), LIBs (yellow background) and post LIBs (blue background).

Battery type	Technology maturity	Lifespan (cycles)	Energy density (Wh L⁻¹)	Specific energy (Wh kg⁻¹)	Price (USD kWh⁻¹) in 2017
Lead acid	High	300–800 [e]	102–106 [e]	38–60 [e]	70–160 [e]
Ni MH	High	600–1200 [e]	220–250 [e]	42–110 [e]	210–365 [e]
Ni Cd	High	1350 [b]	100 [b]	60 [b]	700
High-temperature Na batteries	High	1000 [e]	150–280 [h]	80–120 [a]	315–490 [h]
LIB state of the art	High	1000–6000 [e]	200–680 [c]	110–250 [c]	176 [f]
LIB energy-optimised	Under development		600–850 [c]	300–440 [c]	
Classic Li Metal (CLIM)	Under development		800–1050 [c]	420–530 [c]	
Metal Sulphur (Li S)	Near commercialisation	100–500 [e]	350–680 [c, h]	360–560 [c, h]	36–130 [e]
Metal Sulphur (Na S)	Under development	5000–10,000 [h]			
Metal Air (Li/air)	Under development	20–100 [e]		470–900 [d]	70–200 [e]
Metal Air (Zn/air)	Under development	150–450 [e]		200–410 [d]	70–160 [e]
Na ion	Under development	500 [g]		600 [g]	
All-solid-state	Under development			278–479 [c]	
Redox	Under development	>12,000–14,000 [i]	15–25 [i]	10–20 [i]	66 [i]

Note: With the exception of the All-solid-state batteries, all use liquid electrolytes. Source: [a] Mahmoudzadeh et al. 2017; [b] Manzetti and Mariasiu 2015; [c] Placke et al. 2017; [d] Nykvist and Nilsson 2015; [e] Cano et al. 2018; [f] Bloomberg Energy Finance, 2019; [g] You and Manthiram 2017; [h] Fotouhi et al. 2017; [i] IRENA 2017b; [j] Yang et al. 2020.

The superior characteristics of LIBs will keep them the dominant choice for EV and grid applications in the medium term (*high confidence*). There are, however, several next-generation battery chemistries (Placke et al. 2017), which show promise (*high confidence*). Cost reductions through economies of scale are a key area for development. Extending the life of the battery can bring down overall costs and mitigate the environmental impacts (Peters et al. 2017). Understanding and controlling battery degradation is therefore important. The liquid, air-reactive electrolytes of conventional LIBs are the main source of their safety issues (Janek and Zeier 2016; Gur 2018), so all-solid-state batteries, in which the electrolyte is a solid, stable material, are being developed. They are expected to be safe, be durable, and have higher energy densities (Janek and Zeier 2016). New chemistries and concepts are being explored, such as lithium-sulphur batteries to achieve even higher energy densities (Van Noorden 2014; Blomgren 2017) and sodium chemistries because sodium is more abundant than lithium (Hwang et al. 2017). Cost-effective recycling of batteries will address many sustainability issues and prevent hazardous and wasteful disposal of used batteries (Harper et al. 2019). Post-LIB chemistries include metal sulphur, metal-air, metal ion (besides lithium) and all-solid-state batteries.

Compressed air energy storage (CAES). With CAES, off-peak electricity is used to compress air in a reservoir – either in salt caverns for large-scale or in high-pressure tanks for smaller-scale installations. The air is later released to generate electricity. While conventional CAES has used natural gas to power compression, new low-carbon CAES technologies, such as isothermal or adiabatic CAES, control thermal losses during compression and expansion (Wang et al. 2017c). Fast responses and higher efficiencies occur in small-scale CAES installations, scalable to suit the application as a distributed energy store, offering a flexible, low-maintenance alternative (Luo et al. 2014; Venkataramani et al. 2016).

CAES is a mature technology in use since the 1970s. Although CAES technologies have been developed, there are not many installations at present (Wang et al. 2017b; Blanc et al. 2020). While the opportunities for CAES are significant, with a global geological storage potential of about 6.5 PW (Aghahosseini and Breyer 2018), a significant amount of initial investment is required. Higher efficiencies and energy densities can be achieved by exploiting the hydrostatic pressure of deep water to compress air within submersible reservoirs (Pimm et al. 2014). CAES is best suited to bulk diurnal electricity storage for buffering VRE sources and services, which do not need a very rapid response. In contrast to PHS, CAES has far more siting options and poses few environmental impacts.

Liquid air energy storage (LAES). LAES uses electricity to liquefy air by cooling it to −196°C and storing it in this condensed form (largely liquid nitrogen) in large, insulated tanks. To release electricity, the 'liquid air' is evaporated through heating, expanding to drive gas turbines. Low-grade waste heat can be utilised, providing opportunities for integrating with industrial processes to increase system efficiency. There are clear, exploitable synergies with the existing liquid gas infrastructure (Peters and Sievert 2016).

LAES provides bulk daily storage of electricity, with the additional advantage of being able to capture waste heat from industrial processes. This technology is in the early commercial stage (Brandon et al. 2015; Regen 2017). Advances in whole systems integration can be developed to integrate LAES with industrial processes, making use of their waste heat streams. LAES uniquely removes contaminants in the air and could potentially incorporate CO_2 capture (Taylor et al. 2012).

Thermal energy storage (TES). TES refers to a range of technologies exploiting the ability of materials to absorb and store heat or cold, either within the same phase (sensible TES), through phase changes (latent TES), or through reversible chemical reactions (thermochemical TES). Pumped Thermal Energy Storage (PTES), a hybrid form of TES, is an air-driven electricity storage technology storing both heat and cold in gravel beds, using a reversible heat-pump system to maintain the temperature difference between the two beds and gas compression to generate and transfer heat (Regen 2017). TES technologies can store both heat and cold energy for long periods, for example, in underground water reservoirs for balancing between seasons (Dahash et al. 2019; Tian et al. 2019), storing heat and cold to balance daily and seasonal temperatures in buildings and reducing heat build-up in applications generating excessive waste heat, such as data centres and underground operations.

TES can be much cheaper than batteries and has the unique ability to capture and reuse waste heat and cold, enabling the efficiency of many industrial, buildings, and domestic processes to be greatly improved (*high confidence*). Integration of TES into energy systems is particularly important, as the global demand for cooling is expected to grow (Elzinga et al. 2014; Peters and Sievert 2016). Sensible TES is well developed and widely used; latent TES is less developed with few applications. Thermochemical TES is the least developed, with no application yet (Prieto et al. 2016; Clark et al. 2020). The potential for high-density storage of industrial heat for long periods in thermochemical TES (Brandon et al. 2015) is high, with energy densities comparable to that of batteries (Taylor et al. 2012), but material costs are currently prohibitive, ranging from hundreds to thousands of dollars per tonne.

Flywheel energy storage (FES). Flywheels are charged by accelerating a rotor/flywheel. Energy is stored in the spinning rotor's inertia which is only decelerated by friction (minimised by magnetic bearings in a vacuum), or by contact with a mechanical, electric motor. They can reach full charge very rapidly, their state of charge can be easily determined (Amiryar and Pullen 2017), and they operate over a wide range of temperatures. While they are more expensive to install than batteries and supercapacitors, they last a long time and are best suited to stationary grid storage, providing high power for short periods (minutes). Flywheels can be used in vehicles, but not as the primary energy source.

Flywheels are a relatively mature storage technology but not widely used, despite their many advantages over electrochemical storage (Dragoni 2017). Conventional flywheels require costly, high tensile strength materials, but high-energy flywheels, using lightweight rotor materials, are being developed (Hedlund et al. 2015; Amiryar and Pullen 2017).

6

Supercapacitors – also known as ultracapacitors or double layer capacitors (Scap). Supercapacitors consist of a porous separator sandwiched between two electrodes, immersed in a liquid electrolyte (Gur 2018). When a voltage is applied across the electrodes, ions in the electrolyte form electric double layers at the electrode surfaces, held by electrostatic forces. This structure forms a capacitor, storing electrical charge (Brandon et al. 2015; Lin et al. 2017) and can operate from –40°C to 65°C.

Supercapacitors can supply high peaks of power very rapidly for short periods (seconds up to minutes) and are able to fulfil the grid requirements for frequency regulation, but they would need to be hybridised with batteries for automotive applications. Their commercial status is limited by costly materials and additional power electronics required to stabilise their output (Brandon et al. 2015). Progress in this area includes the development of high-energy supercapacitors, LIB-supercapacitor devices (Gonzalez et al. 2016), and cheaper materials (Wang et al. 2017a), all providing the potential to improve the economic case for supercapacitors, either by reducing manufacturing costs or extending their service portfolio.

Redox flow batteries (RFB). Redox flow batteries use two separate electrolyte solutions, usually liquids, but solid or gaseous forms may also be involved, stored in separate tanks, and pumped over or through electrode stacks during charge and discharge, with an ion-conducting membrane separating the liquids. The larger the tank, the greater the energy storage capacity, whereas more and larger cells in the stack increase the power of the flow battery. This decoupling of energy from power enables RFB installations to be uniquely tailored to suit the requirements of any given application. There are two commercially available types today: vanadium and zinc bromide, and both operate at near ambient temperatures, incurring minimal operational costs.

RFBs respond rapidly and can perform all the same services as LIBs, except for onboard electricity for EVs. Lower cost chemistries are emerging, to enable cost-effective bulk energy storage (Brandon et al. 2015). A new membrane-free design eliminates the need for a separator and also halves the system requirements, as the chemical reactions can coexist in a single electrolyte solution (Navalpotro et al. 2017; Arenas et al. 2018).

Power to fuels (PtX) (see also Section 6.4.3.1). The process of using electricity to generate a gaseous fuel, such as hydrogen or ammonia, is termed power-to-gas (PtG/P2G) (IEA 2020h). When injected into the existing gas infrastructure (Section 6.4.5), it has the added benefit of decarbonising gas (Brandon et al. 2015). Electricity can be used to generate hydrogen, which is then converted back into electricity using combined-cycle gas turbines that have been converted to run on hydrogen. For greater compatibility with existing gas systems and appliances, the hydrogen can be combined with captured carbon dioxide to form methane and other synthetic fuels (Thema et al. 2019), however, methane has high global warming potential and its supply chain emissions have been found to be significant (Balcombe et al. 2013).

PtX can provide all required grid services, depending on how it is integrated. However, a significant amount of PtX is required for storage to produce electricity again (Bogdanov et al. 2019) due to the low roundtrip efficiency of converting electricity to fuel and back again. However, portable fuels (hydrogen, methane, ammonia, synthetic hydrocarbons) are useful in certain applications, for example, in energy systems lacking the potential for renewables. The high energy density of chemical storage is essential for more demanding applications, such as transporting heavy goods and heating or cooling buildings (IEA 2020h). Research is needed into more efficient and flexible electrolysers which last longer and cost less (Brandon et al. 2015).

Hydrogen and reversible hydrogen fuel cells (H/RHFC). Hydrogen is a flexible fuel with diverse uses, capable of providing electricity, heat, and long-term energy storage for grids, industry, and transport, and has been widely used industrially for decades (Section 6.4.5.1). Hydrogen can be produced in various ways and stored in significant quantities in geological formations at moderate pressures, often for long periods, providing seasonal storage (Gabrielli et al. 2020). A core and emerging implementation of PtX is hydrogen production through electrolysers. Hydrogen is a carbon-free fuel holding three times the energy of an equivalent mass of gasoline but occupying a larger volume. An electrolyser uses excess electricity to split water into hydrogen and oxygen through the process of electrolysis. A fuel cell performs the reverse process of recombining hydrogen and oxygen back into water, converting chemical energy into electricity (Elzinga et al. 2014). Reversible hydrogen fuel cells (RHFCs) can perform both functions in a single device, however, they are still in the pre-commercial stage, due to prohibitive production costs.

Hydrogen can play an important role in reducing emissions and has been shown to be the most cost-effective option in some cases, as it builds on existing systems (Staffell et al. 2018). Fuel cell costs need to be reduced and the harmonies between hydrogen and complementary technologies, such as batteries, for specific applications need to be explored further. Hydrogen can provide long-duration storage to deal with prolonged extreme events, such as very low output of wind generation, to support resilience of future low-carbon energy systems. Research in this technology focuses on improving roundtrip efficiencies, which can be as high as 80% with recycled waste heat and in high-pressure electrolysers, incorporating more efficient compression (Matos et al. 2019). Photo-electrolysis uses solar energy to directly generate hydrogen from water (Amirante et al. 2017).

6.4.4.2 Societal Dimensions of Energy Storage

Public awareness and knowledge about electricity storage technologies, their current state, and their potential role in future energy systems is limited (Jones et al. 2018). For instance, people do not perceive energy system flexibility and storage as a significant issue, or assume storage is already taking place. Public perceptions differ across storage technologies. Hydrogen is considered a modern and clean technology, but people also have safety concerns. Moreover, the public is uncertain about hydrogen storage size and the possibility of storing hydrogen in or near residential areas (Eitan and Fischhendler 2021). Battery storage both on the household and community level was perceived as slightly positive in one study in the UK (Ambrosio-Albala et al. 2020). However, financial costs are seen as a main barrier. The potential of EV batteries to function as flexible storage is limited by the current numbers of EV owners and concerns that one's car battery might not be fully loaded when needed.

6.4.5   Energy Transport and Transmission

The linkage between energy supply and distribution, on the one hand, and energy use on the other is facilitated by various mechanisms for transporting energy. As the energy system evolves, the way that energy is transported will also evolve.

6.4.5.1   Hydrogen: Low-carbon Energy Fuel

Hydrogen is a promising energy carrier for a decarbonised world (Box 6.9). It can be utilised for electricity, heat, transport, industrial demand, and energy storage (Abdin et al. 2020). In low-carbon energy systems, hydrogen is expected to be utilised in applications that are not as amenable to electrification, such as a fuel for heavy-duty road transport and shipping, or as a chemical feedstock (Schemme et al. 2017; Griffiths et al. 2021). Hydrogen could also provide low-carbon heat for industrial processes or be utilised for direct reduction of iron ore (Vogl et al. 2018). Hydrogen could replace natural gas-based electricity generation (do Sacramento et al. 2013) in certain regions and support the integration of variable renewables into electricity systems by providing a means of long-term electricity storage. Hydrogen-based carriers, such as ammonia and synthetic hydrocarbons, can likewise be used in energy-intensive industries and the transport sector (Schemme et al. 2017; IRENA 2019b) (e.g., synthetic fuels for aviation). These hydrogen-based energy carriers are easier to store than hydrogen. At present hydrogen has limited applications – mainly being produced onsite for the creation of methanol and ammonia (IEA 2019c), as well as in refineries.

Low- or zero-carbon produced hydrogen is not currently competitive for large-scale applications, but it is likely to have a significant role in future energy systems, due to its wide-range of applications (*high confidence*). Key challenges for hydrogen are: (i) cost-effective low/zero carbon production; (ii) delivery infrastructure cost; (iii) land area (i.e., 'footprint') requirements of hydrogen pipelines, compressor stations, and other infrastructure; (iv) challenges in using existing pipeline infrastructure; (v) maintaining hydrogen purity; (vi) minimising hydrogen leakage; and (vii) the cost and performance of end uses. Furthermore, it is necessary to consider the public perception and social acceptance of hydrogen technologies and their related infrastructure requirements (Iribarren et al. 2016; Scott and Powells 2020).

Hydrogen production. Low- or zero-carbon hydrogen can be produced from multiple sources. While there is no consensus on the hydrogen production spectrum, 'blue' hydrogen (Goldmann and Dinkelacker 2018) generally refers to hydrogen produced from natural gas combined with CCS through processes such as steam methane reforming (SMR) (Sanusi and Mokheimer 2019) and advanced gas reforming (Zhou et al. 2020). Low-carbon hydrogen could also be produced from coal coupled with CCS (Hu et al. 2020) (Table 6.7). Current estimates are that adding CCS to produce hydrogen from SMR will add on average 50% on the capital cost, 10% to fuel, and 100% to operating costs. For coal gasification, CCS will add 5% to the capital and fuel costs and 130% to operating costs (Staffell et al. 2018; IEA 2019d). Further, biomass gasification could produce renewable hydrogen, and when joined with CCS could provide negative carbon emissions. 'Green' hydrogen (Jaszczur et al. 2016) is most often referred to as hydrogen produced from zero-carbon electricity sources such as solar power and wind power (Schmidt et al. 2017) (Table 6.8). Nuclear power could also provide clean hydrogen, via electrolysis or thermochemical water splitting (EERE 2020).

Table 6.7 | Key performance and cost characteristics of different non-electric hydrogen production technologies, including carbon capture and storage (CCS).

Technology	LHV efficiency (%)		Carbon intensity (kgCO$_2$ (kgH$_2$)$^{-1}$)	Cost estimates* (USD (kgH$_2$)$^{-1}$)	
	Current	Long-term		Current	Long-term
Steam methane reforming (SMR)	65 [e]	74 [e,f]	1.0–3.6 [e,i]	1.0–2.7 [a,b,c,d,e]	1.5–2.6 [e]
Advanced gas reforming	–	81–84 [e,f]	0.9–2.9 [e]	1.3–2.1 [e]	1.2–3.4 [e,f]
Hydrogen from coal gasification	54 [e]	54 [(5)]	2.1–5.5 [e,i]	1.8–3.1 [a,b,c,d,e]	2.4–3.3 [e]
Hydrogen from biomass gasification	53.6 [g]	40–60 [e]	Potential to achieve negative emission [e,h]	4.9 [e]	2.9–5.9 [e,f]

Source: [a] CSIRO 2021; [b] IEA 2020; [c] IRENA 2019; [d] Hydrogen Council 2020; [e] CCC 2018; [f] BEIS 2021; [g] Ishaq et al. 2021; [h] Al-Mahtani et al. 2021; [i] IEA 2019.

* USD per GBP exchange rate: 0.72 (August 2021); LHV: Lower Heating Values; Long-term refers to 2040 and 2050 according to different references.

Table 6.8 | Efficiency and cost characteristics of electrolysis technologies for hydrogen production.

Technology	LHV efficiency (%)		CAPEX (USD kW$_e$$^{-1}$)		Cost estimates*,† (USD (kgH$_2$)$^{-1}$)	
	Current	Long-term [b,e,f,h]	Current [g]	Long-term [g]	Current	Long-term
Alkaline Electrolysers	58–77 [a,b,e,f,h]	70–82	500–1400	200–700	2.3–6.9 [a,b,c,e]	0.9–3.9 [c,e]
Polymer electrolyte membrane (PEM)	54–72 [a,b,e,f,h]	67–82	1100–1800	200–900	3.5–9.3 [a,d,e,f]	2.2–7.2 [e,f]
Solid oxide electrolyser cell (SOEC)	74–81 [b,t,h]	77–92	2800–5600	500–1000	4.2 [e]	2.6–3.6 [e]

Source: [a] CSIRO 2021; [b] IEA 2020; [c] IRENA 2019; [d] Hydrogen Council 2020; [e] CCC 2018; [f] BEIS 2021; [g] IEA 2019; [h] Christensen 2020.

* USD per GBP exchange rate: 0.72 (August 2021); † The cost of hydrogen production from electrolysers is highly dependent on the technology, source of electricity, and operating hours, and some values provided are based on the assumptions made in the references.

Hydrogen can even be produced by pyrolysis of methane (Sánchez-Bastardo et al. 2020) – sometimes called 'turquoise' hydrogen, solar thermochemical water splitting, biological hydrogen production (cyanobacteria) (Velazquez Abad and Dodds 2017) – and microbes that use light to make hydrogen (under research) (EIA 2020).

Hydrogen energy carriers. Hydrogen can be both an energy carrier itself, be converted further into other energy carriers (such as synthetic fuels) and be a means of transporting other sources of energy. For example, hydrogen could be transported in its native gaseous form or liquefied. Hydrogen can also be combined with carbon and transported as a synthetic hydrocarbons (Gumber and Gurumoorthy 2018) (IRENA 2019d) as well as be transported via liquid organic hydrogen carriers (LOHCs) or ammonia (IRENA 2019d). For synthetic hydrocarbons such as methane or methanol to be considered zero carbon, the CO_2 used to produce them would need to come from the atmosphere either directly through DACCS or indirectly through BECCS (IRENA 2019b). LOHCs are organic substances in liquid or semi-solid states, which store hydrogen based on reversible catalytic hydrogenation and de-hydrogenation of carbon double bounds (Niermann et al. 2019; Rao and Yoon 2020). Hydrogen produced from electrolysis could also be seen as an electricity energy carrier. This is an example of the PtX processes (Section 6.4.4), entailing the conversion of electricity to other energy carriers for subsequent use.

Ammonia is a promising cost-effective hydrogen carrier (Creutzig et al. 2019). Onsite generation of hydrogen for the production of ammonia already occurs today, and the ammonia (NH_3) could be subsequently 'cracked' (with a 15–25% energy loss) to reproduce hydrogen (Hansgen et al. 2010; Montoya et al. 2015; Bell and Torrente-Murciano 2016). Because the energy density of ammonia is 38% higher than liquid hydrogen (Osman and Sgouridis 2018), it is potentially a suitable energy carrier for long-distance transport and storage (Salmon et al. 2021). Moreover, ammonia is more easily condensable (liquefied at 0.8 MPa, 20°C), which provides economically viable hydrogen storage and supply systems. Ammonia production and transport are also established industrial processes (about 180 MMT yr^{-1}) (Valera-Medina et al. 2017), and hence ammonia is considered to be a scalable and cost-effective hydrogen-based energy carrier. At present, most ammonia is used in fertilisers (about 80%), followed by many industrial processes, such as the manufacturing of mining explosives and petrochemicals (Jiao and Xu 2018). In contrast to hydrogen, ammonia can be used directly as a fuel without any phase change for internal combustion engines, gas turbines, and industrial furnaces (Kobayashi et al. 2019). Ammonia can also be used in low- and high-temperature fuel cells (Lan and Tao 2014), whereby both electricity and hydrogen can be produced without any nitrogen oxide (NO_x) emissions. Furthermore, ammonia provides the flexibility to be dehydrogenated for hydrogen-use purposes. Ammonia is considered a carbon-free sustainable fuel for electricity generation, since in a complete combustion, only water and nitrogen are produced (Valera-Medina et al. 2017). Like hydrogen, ammonia could facilitate management of VRE, due to its cost-effective grid-scale energy storage capabilities. In this regard, production of ammonia via hydrogen from low- or zero-carbon generation technologies along with ammonia energy recovery

technologies (Afif et al. 2016) could play a major role in forming a hydrogen and/or ammonia economy to support decarbonisation. However, there are serious concerns regarding the ability to safely use ammonia for all these purposes, given its toxicity – whereas hydrogen is not considered toxic.

In general, challenges around hydrogen-based energy carriers – including safety issues around flammability, toxicity, storage, and consumption – require new devices and techniques to facilitate their large-scale use. Relatively high capital costs and large electricity requirements are also challenges for technologies that produce hydrogen energy carriers. Yet, these energy carriers could become economically viable through the availability of low-cost electricity generation and excess of renewable energy production (Daiyan et al. 2020). A key challenge in use of ammonia is related to the significant amount of NO_x emissions, which is released from nitrogen and oxygen combustion, and unburned ammonia. Both have substantial air pollution risks, which can result in lung and other injuries, and can reduce visibility (EPA 2001). Due to the low flammability of hydrogen energy carriers such as liquefied hydrogen (Nilsson et al. 2016) and ammonia (Li et al. 2018), a stable combustion (Lamas and Rodriguez 2019; Zengel et al. 2020) in the existing gas turbines is not currently feasible. In recent developments, however, the proportion of hydrogen in gas turbines has been successfully increased, and further development of gas turbines may enable them to operate on 100% hydrogen by 2030 (Pflug et al. 2019).

Long-distance hydrogen transport. Hydrogen can allow regional integration and better utilisation of low- or zero-carbon energy sources (Boxes 6.9 and 6.10). Hydrogen produced from renewables or other low-carbon sources in one location could be transported for use elsewhere (Philibert 2017; Ameli et al. 2020). Depending on the distance to the user and specific energy carrier utilised (e.g., gaseous hydrogen or LOHC), various hydrogen transport infrastructures, distribution systems, and storage facilities would be required (Hansen 2020; Schönauer and Glanz 2021) (Figure 6.17).

Hydrogen can be liquefied and transported at volume over the ocean without pressurisation. This requires a temperature of −253°C and is therefore energy-intensive and costly (Niermann et al. 2021). Once it reaches its destination, the hydrogen needs to be re-gasified, adding further cost. A demonstration project is under development exporting liquid hydrogen from Australia to Japan (Yamashita et al. 2019). Hydrogen could also be transported as ammonia by ocean in liquid form. Ammonia is advantageous because it is easier to store than hydrogen (Zamfirescu and Dincer 2008; Soloveichik 2016; Nam et al. 2018). Liquid ammonia requires temperatures below −33°C and is therefore more straightforward and less costly to transport than liquefied hydrogen and even liquefied natural gas (Singh and Sahu 2018). A project exporting ammonia from Saudi Arabia to Japan is under consideration (Nagashima 2018). LOHCs could also be used to transport hydrogen at ambient temperature and pressure. This advantageous property of LOHCs makes them similar to oil products, meaning they can be transported in existing oil infrastructure including oil tankers and tanks (IEA 2019; Niermann et al. 2019). A project is under development to export hydrogen from Brunei to Japan using LOHCs (Kurosaki 2018).

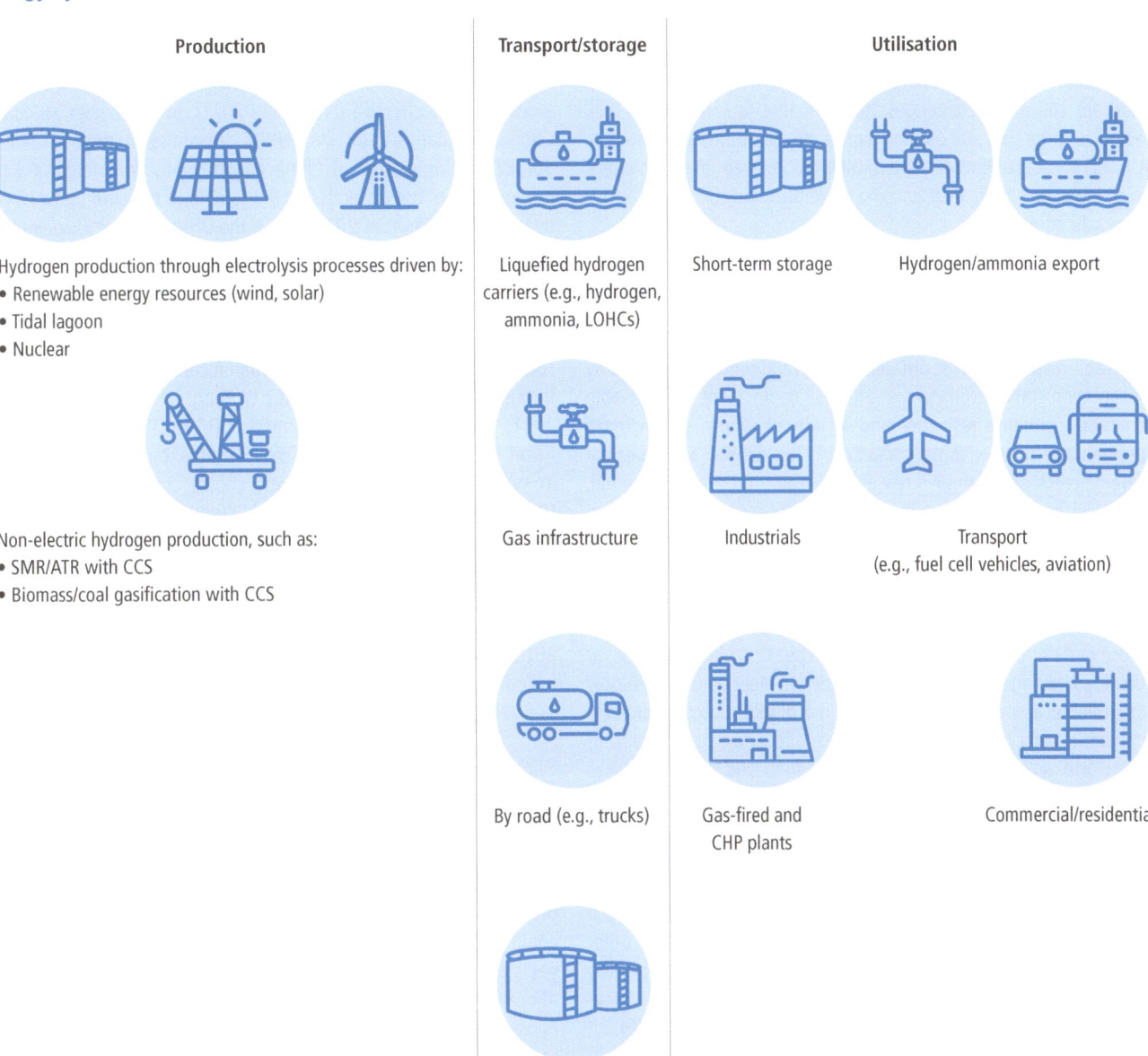

Figure 6.17 | Hydrogen value chain. Hydrogen can be produced by various means and input and fuel sources. These processes have different emissions implications. Hydrogen can be transported by various means and in various forms, and it can be stored in bulk for longer-term use. It also has multiple potential end uses. CHP: Combined heat and power.

Intra-regional hydrogen transportation. Within a country or region, hydrogen would likely be pressurised and delivered as compressed gas. About three times as much compressed hydrogen by volume is required to supply the same amount of energy as natural gas. Security of supply is therefore more challenging in hydrogen networks than in natural gas networks. Storing hydrogen in pipelines (linepack) would be important to maintaining security of supply (Ameli et al. 2017, 2019). Due to the physics of hydrogen, in most cases exiting gas infrastructure would need to be upgraded to transport hydrogen. Transporting hydrogen in medium- or high-pressure networks most often would require reinforcements in compressor stations and pipeline construction routes (Dohi et al. 2016). There are several recent examples of efforts to transport hydrogen by pipeline. For example, in the Iron Mains Replacement Programme in the UK, the existing low-pressure gas distribution pipes are being converted from iron to plastic (Committee on Climate Change 2018). In the Netherlands, an existing low-pressure 12 km natural gas pipeline has been used for transporting hydrogen (Dohi et al. 2016).

To bypass gas infrastructure in transporting hydrogen, methane can be transported using the existing gas infrastructure, while hydrogen can be produced close to the demand centres. This approach will only make sense if the methane is produced in a manner that captures carbon from the atmosphere and/or if CCS is used when the methane is used to produce hydrogen.

Bulk hydrogen storage. Currently, hydrogen is stored in bulk in chemical processes such as metal and chemical hydrides as well as in geologic caverns (Andersson and Grönkvist 2019; Caglayan et al. 2019) (e.g., salt caverns operate in Sweden) (Elberry et al. 2021). There are still many challenges, however, due to salt or hard rock geologies, large size, and minimum pressure requirements of the sites (IEA 2019c). Consequently, alternative carbon-free energy carriers, which store hydrogen, may become more attractive (Lan et al. 2012; Kobayashi et al. 2019).

6.4.5.2   Electricity Transmission

Given the significant geographical variations in the efficiency of renewable resources across different regions and continents, electricity transmission could facilitate cost-effective deployment of renewable generation, enhance resilience and security of supply, and increase operational efficiency (*high confidence*). The diurnal and seasonal characteristics of different renewable energy sources such as wind, solar, and hydropower can vary significantly by location. Through enhanced electricity transmission infrastructure, more wind turbines can be deployed in areas with high wind potential and more solar panels in areas with larger solar irradiation. Increases in electricity transmission and trade can also enhance operational efficiency and reduce or defer the need for investment in peaking plants, storage, or other load management techniques needed to meet security of supply requirements associated with localised use of VRE sources. Increased interconnectivity of large-scale grids also allows the aggregation of 'smart grid' solutions such as flexible heating and cooling devices for flexible demand in industrial, commercial, and domestic sectors (Hakimi et al. 2020) and EVs (Muratori and Mai 2020; Li et al. 2021). In general, interconnection is more cost-optimal for countries that are geographically close to each other and can benefit from the diversity of their energy mixes and usage (Schlachtberger et al. 2017). Such developments are not without price, however, and among other concerns, raise issues surrounding land use, public acceptance, and resource acquisition for materials necessary for renewable developments (Capellán-Pérez et al. 2017; Vakulchuk et al. 2020).

A number of studies have demonstrated the cost benefits of interconnected grids in a range of geographical settings, including across the USA (Bloom et al. 2020), Europe (Newbery et al. 2013; Cluet et al. 2020), between Australia and parts of Asia (Halawa et al. 2018), and broader global regions, for example between the Middle East and Europe or North Africa and Europe (Tsoutsos et al. 2015). While there is growing interest in interconnection among different regions or continents, a broad range of geopolitical and socio-techno-economic challenges would need to be overcome to support this level of international cooperation and large-scale network expansion (Bertsch et al. 2017; Palle 2021).

Status of electricity transmission technology. Long-distance electricity transmission technologies are already available. High voltage alternating current (HVAC), high-voltage direct current (HVDC), and ultra HVDC (UHVDC) technologies are well-established and widely used for bulk electricity transmission (Alassi et al. 2019). HVDC is used with underground cables or long-distance overhead lines (typically voltages between 100–800 kV) (Alassi et al. 2019) where HVAC is infeasible or not economic. A project development agreement, worth approximately USD17 billion, was signed in January

2021 that would connect 10 GW of PVs in the north of Australia via a 4500 km 3 GW HVDC cable to Singapore, suggesting that this would be cost effective (Sun Cable 2021). In September 2019, the Changji-Guquan ±1,100 kV UHVDC transmission project built by State Grid Corporation of China was officially completed and put into operation. The transmission line is able to transmit up to 12 GW over 3341 km (Pei et al. 2020). This is the UHVDC transmission project with the highest voltage level, the largest transmission capacity, and the longest transmission distance in the world (Liu 2015).

Other technologies that could expand the size of transmission corridors and/or improve the operational characteristics include low-frequency AC transmission (LFAC) (Y. Tang et al. 2021; Xiang et al. 2021) and half-wave AC transmission (HWACT) (Song et al. 2018; Xu et al. 2019). LFAC is technically feasible, but the circumstances in which it is the best economic choice compared to HVDC or HVAC still needs to be established (Xiang et al. 2016). HWACT is restricted to very long distances, and it has not been demonstrated in practice, so its feasibility is unproven. There are still a number of technological challenges for long-distance transmission networks such as protection systems for DC or hybrid AC-DC networks (Chaffey 2016; Franck C. et al. 2017), improvement in cabling technology, and including the use of superconductors and nanocomposites (Ballarino et al. 2016; Doukas 2019), which require advanced solutions.

Challenges, barriers, and recommendations. The main challenge to inter-regional transmission is the absence of appropriate market designs and regulatory and policy frameworks. In addition, there are commercial barriers for further enhancement of cross-border transmission. The differing impacts of cross-border interconnections on costs and revenues for generation companies in different regions could delay the development of these interconnectors. It is not yet clear how the investment cost of interconnections should be allocated and recovered, although there is growing support for allocating costs in accordance with the benefits delivered to the market participants. Increased cross-border interconnection may also require new business models which provide incentives for investment and efficient operation, manage risks and uncertainties, and facilitate coordinated planning and governance (Poudineh and Rubino 2017).

Optimising the design and operation of the interconnected transmission system, both onshore and offshore grids, also requires more integrated economic and reliability approaches (Moreno et al. 2012) to ensure the optimal balance between the economics and the provision of system security while maximising the benefits of smart network technologies.

A wide range of factors, including generation profiles, demand profiles circuit losses, reliability characteristics, and maintenance, as well as the uncertainties around them will need to be considered in designing and operating long-distance transmission systems if they are to be widely deployed (Djapic et al. 2008; Du 2009; De Sa and Al Zubaidy 2011; E3G 2021). Public support for extending transmission systems will also be crucial, and studies indicate that such support is frequently low (Vince 2010; Perlaviciute et al. 2018).

6.4.6 Demand-side Mitigation Options from an Energy Systems Perspective

Demand-side measures are fundamental to an integrated approach to low-carbon energy systems (*high confidence*). Mitigation options, such as wind parks, CCS, and nuclear power plants, may not be implemented when actors oppose these options. Further, end users, including consumers, governments, businesses and industry, would need to adopt the relevant options, and then use these as intended; user adoption can be a key driver to scale up markets for low-carbon technologies. This section discusses which factors shape the likelihood that end users engage in relevant mitigation actions, focusing on consumers; strategies to promote mitigation actions are discussed in Section 6.7.6.1.

A wide range of actions of end users would reduce carbon emissions in energy systems (Abrahamse et al. 2007; Dietz 2013; Hackmann et al. 2014; Creutzig et al. 2018; Grubler et al. 2018), including:

- use of low-carbon energy sources and carriers. Actors can produce and use their own renewable energy (e.g., install solar PV, solar water heaters, heat pumps), buy shares in a renewable energy project (e.g., wind shares), or select a renewable energy provider.
- adoption of technologies that support flexibility in energy use and sector coupling, thereby providing flexibility services by balancing demand and renewable energy supply. This would reduce the need to use fossil fuels to meet demand when renewable energy production is low and put less pressure on deployment of low-emission energy supply systems. Examples are technologies to store energy (e.g., batteries and EVs) or that automatically shift appliances on or off (e.g., fridges, washing machines).
- adoption of energy-efficient appliances and systems and increase of resource efficiency of end uses so that less energy is required to provide the same service. Examples are insulating buildings, and passive or energy-positive buildings.
- change behaviour to reduce overall energy demand or to match energy demand to available energy supplies. Examples include adjusting indoor temperature settings, reducing showering time, reducing car use or flying, and operating appliances when renewable energy production is high.
- purchase and use products and services that are associated with low GHG emissions during their production (e.g., reduce dairy and meat consumption) or for transporting products (e.g., local products). Also, end users can engage in behaviour supporting a circular economy, by reducing waste (e.g., of food), sharing products (e.g., cars, equipment), and refurbishing products (e.g., repair rather than buying new products) so that fewer new products are used.

Various factors shape whether such mitigation actions are feasible and considered by end users, including contextual factors, individual abilities, and motivational factors. Mitigation actions can be facilitated and encouraged by targeting relevant barriers and enablers (Section 6.7.6.1).

Contextual factors, such as physical and climate conditions, infrastructure, available technology, regulations, institutions, culture, and financial conditions define the costs and benefits of mitigation options that enable or inhibit their adoption (*high confidence*). Geographic location and climate factors may make some technologies, such as solar PV or solar water heaters, impractical (Chang et al. 2009). Culture can inhibit efficient use of home heating or PV (Sovacool and Griffiths 2020), low-carbon diets (Dubois et al. 2019), and advanced fuel choices (Van Der Kroon et al. 2013). Also, favourable financial conditions promote the uptake of PV (Wolske and Stern 2018), good facilities increase recycling (Geiger et al. 2019), and vegetarian meal sales increase when more vegetarian options are offered.

Mitigation actions are more likely when individuals feel capable to adopt them (Pisano and Lubell 2017; Geiger et al. 2019), which may depend on income and knowledge. Low-income groups may lack resources to invest in refurbishments and energy-efficient technology with high upfront costs (Chang et al. 2009; Andrews-Speed and Ma 2016; Wolske and Stern 2018). Yet, higher-income groups can afford more carbon-intensive lifestyles (Golley and Meng 2012; Frederiks et al. 2015; Wiedenhofer et al. 2017; Namazkhan et al. 2019; Santillán Vera and de la Vega Navarro 2019; Mi et al. 2020). Knowledge of the causes and consequences of climate change and of ways to reduce GHG emissions is not always accurate, but lack of knowledge is not a main barrier to mitigation actions (Boudet 2019).

Motivation to engage in mitigation action, reflecting individuals' reasons for actions, depends on general goals that people strive for in their life (i.e., values). People who strongly value protecting the environment and other people are more likely to consider climate impacts and to engage in a wide range of mitigation actions than those who strongly value individual consequences of actions, such as pleasure and money (Taylor et al. 2014; Steg 2016). Values affect which types of costs and benefits people consider and prioritise when making choices, including individual, affective, social, and environmental costs and benefits (Gowdy 2008; Steg 2016).

First, people are more likely to engage in mitigation behaviour (i.e., energy savings, energy efficiency, resource efficiency in buildings, low-carbon energy generation) when they believe such behaviour has more individual benefits than costs (Harland et al. 1999; Steg and Vlek 2009; Kastner and Stern 2015; Korcaj et al. 2015; Kardooni et al. 2016; Kastner and Matthies 2016; Wolske et al. 2017), including financial benefits, convenience, comfort, autonomy, and independence in energy supply (Wolske and Stern 2018). Yet, financial consequences seem less important for decisions to invest in energy-efficiency and renewable energy production than people indicate (Zhao et al. 2012).

Second, people are less likely to engage in mitigation behaviours that are unpleasurable or inconvenient (Steg 2016), and more likely to do so when they expect to derive positive feelings from such actions (Smith et al. 1994; Pelletier et al. 1998; Steg 2005; Carrus et al. 2008; Brosch et al. 2014; Taufik et al. 2016). Positive feelings may be elicited when behaviour is pleasurable, but also when it is perceived as meaningful (Bolderdijk et al. 2013; Taufik et al. 2015).

Third, social costs and benefits can affect climate action (Farrow et al. 2017), although people do not always recognise this (Nolan et al. 2008; Noppers et al. 2014). People engage more in mitigation actions when they think others expect them to do so and when others act as well

(Harland et al. 1999; Nolan et al. 2008; Rai et al. 2016). Being part of a group that advocates mitigation encourages such actions (Biddau et al. 2016; Fielding and Hornsey 2016; Jans et al. 2018). Talking with peers can reduce uncertainties and confirm benefits about adoption of renewable energy technology (Palm 2017), and peers can provide social support (Wolske et al. 2017). People may engage in mitigation actions when they think this would signal something positive about them (Milinski et al. 2006; Griskevicius et al. 2010; Noppers et al. 2014; Kastner and Stern 2015). Social influence can also originate from political and business leaders (Bouman and Steg 2019); GHG emissions are lower when legislators have strong environmental records (Jensen and Spoon 2011; Dietz et al. 2015).

Fourth, mitigation actions, including saving energy and hot water, limiting meat consumption, and investing in energy efficiency, resource efficiency in buildings, and renewable energy generation are more likely when people care more strongly about others and the environment (Steg et al. 2015; Van Der Werff and Steg 2015; Wolske et al. 2017). People across the world generally strongly value the environment (Steg 2016; Bouman and Steg 2019), suggesting that they are motivated to mitigate climate change. The more individuals are aware of the climate impact of their behaviour, the more they think their actions can help reduce such impacts, which strengthens

their moral norms to act accordingly, and promotes mitigation actions (Steg and de Groot 2010; Jakovcevic and Steg 2013; Chen 2015; Wolske et al. 2017).

Initial mitigation actions can encourage engagement in other mitigation actions when people experience that such actions are easy and effective (Lauren et al. 2016), and when initial actions make them realise they are a pro-environmental person, motivating them to engage in more mitigation actions so as to be consistent (van der Werff et al. 2014; Lacasse 2015, 2016; Peters et al. 2018). This implies it would be important to create conditions that make it likely that initial mitigation actions motivate further actions.

6.4.7 Summary of Mitigation Options

Designing feasible, desirable, and cost-effective energy sector mitigation strategies requires comparison between the different mitigation options. One such metric is the cost of delivering one unit of energy, for example, the levelised cost, or USD MWh^{-1}, of electricity produced from different sources. Levelised costs of electricity (LCOE) are useful because they normalise the costs per unit of service provided. While useful in characterising options in broad strokes,

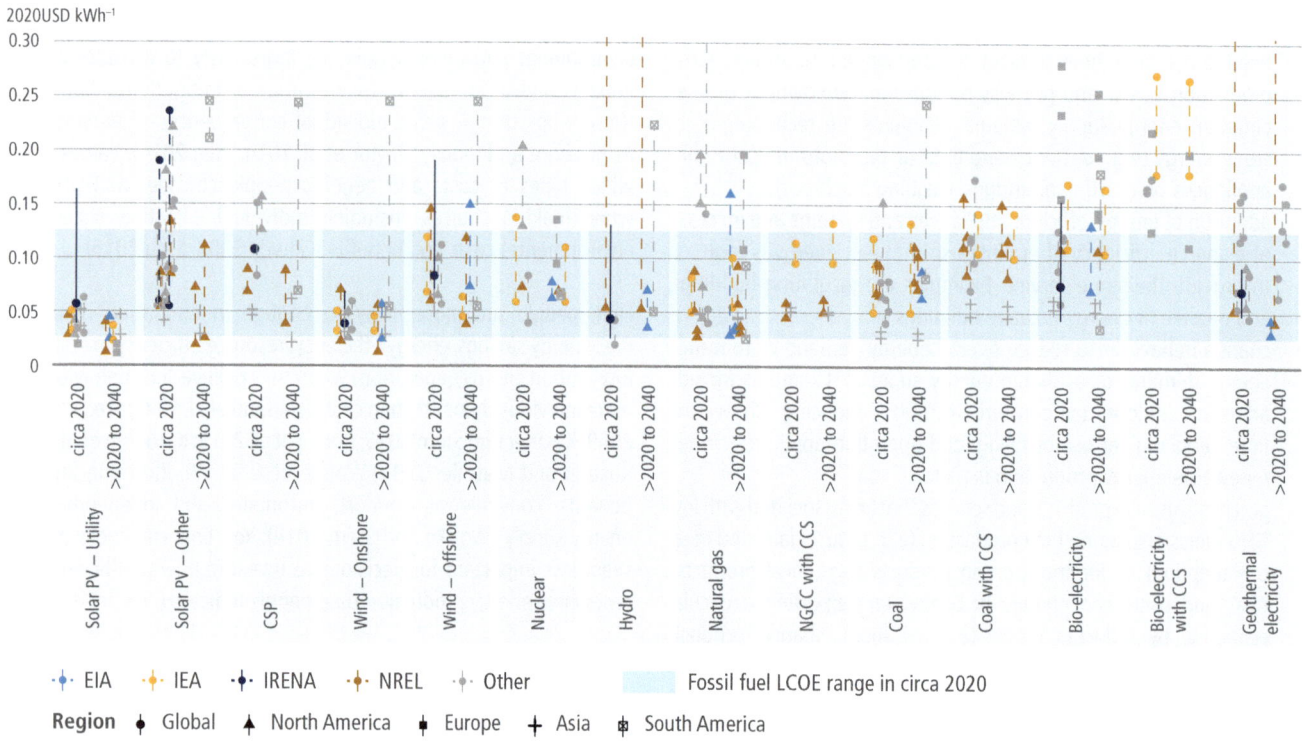

Figure 6.18 | Range of LCOE (in USD kWh^{-1}) from recent studies for different electricity-generating technologies circa 2020 and in the future between 2020–2040. LCOEs are primarily taken from recent studies, because the costs of some technologies are changing rapidly. To make the figure more tractable across the studies, we highlight the data from IEA WEO 2020 STEPS scenario in yellow (IEA 2020), the EIA AEO 2021 in light blue (EIA 2021), NREL ATB 2021 in brown, (NREL 2021), and IRENA's 2020 Renewable Power Generation Costs in dark blue (IRENA 2021). All other studies are shown in light grey markers. Marker shapes identify the regions included in the studies. Studies that included several regions are labelled as global. Only sources that provided LCOEs are included. Ranges for studies frequently reflect variations among regional estimates. Studies that are shown as a mid-point and a solid line represent studies that reported either a median or an average, and that had either a confidence interval or a minimum and a maximum reported. Dashed lines with markers at the end represent the range of values reported in studies that had several point estimates for either different regions or used different assumptions. All estimates were converted to USD2020. The publication year was used if no USD year was provided. Some studies included transmissions costs, and some of the CCS studies included storage and sequestration costs, while others did not. Vertical axis is capped at USD2020 0.30 kWh^{-1}, but some estimates for hydro, geothermal, natural gas and bioelectricity were higher than 0.30. The grey horizontal band denotes the range of fossil fuel electricity LCOEs circa 2020.

Table 6.9 | Examples of cost of mitigation for selected electricity options. Results represent variations in mitigation options and displaced fossil generation. LCOEs are illustrative, but consistent with recent estimates. Negative values mean that the mitigation option is cheaper than the displaced option, irrespective of emissions benefits. NGCC: natural gas combined cycle.

		Baseline			
		New coal	Existing coal	New NGCC	Existing NGCC
	Baseline emissions rate (tCO$_2$ MWh^{-1})	0.8	0.9	0.34	0.42
	LCOEs (USD2020 kWh^{-1})	0.065	0.041	0.044	0.028
Utility scale solar PV (poor resource site)	0.100	USD44 tCO$_2$-eq^{-1}	USD66 tCO$_2$-eq^{-1}	USD165 tCO$_2$-eq^{-1}	USD171 tCO$_2$-eq^{-1}
Utility scale solar PV (good resource site)	0.035	−38 USD tCO$_2$-eq^{-1}	−7 USD tCO$_2$-eq^{-1}	−26 USD tCO$_2$-eq^{-1}	USD17 tCO$_2$-eq^{-1}

it is important to acknowledge and understand several caveats associated with these metrics, particularly when applied globally. They may be constructed with different discount rates; they require information on energy input costs for options that require energy inputs (e.g., fossil electricity generation, biofuels); they depend on local resource availability, for example, solar insolation for solar power, wind classes for wind power, and rainfall and streamflow for hydropower; and actual implementation costs may include additional elements, for example, the costs of managing electricity grids heavily dependent on VRE electricity sources. These complicating factors vary across regions, some depend strongly on the policy environment in which mitigation options are deployed, and some depend on how technologies are constructed and operated.

The literature provides multiple LCOE estimates for mitigation options today and in the future (see Table 6.9 for electricity generation options). LCOE ranges for low- and zero-carbon electricity technologies overlap with LCOE's of fossil generation without CCS. For example, LCOEs for utility solar and wind today and in the future overlap with those of new coal and gas without CCS (IEA WEO 2020; Lazard, 2020; NREL 2021) (Figure 6.18). Some of the overlap stems from differences in assumptions or regional conditions that apply to all technologies (e.g., variations in assumed discount rates), but the overlap also reflects the fact that low- and zero-carbon electricity generation options are, and will be, less expensive than emitting options in many regions. Future cost projections also illustrate that several technologies are anticipated to experience further cost declines over the coming decades, reinforcing the increasingly competitiveness of low- and zero-carbon electricity. For example, IEA's LCOEs estimates for offshore wind halve between 2020 and 2040 in several regions (IEA WEO 2020).

A more direct metric of mitigation options is the cost to reduce one tonne of CO$_2$ or equivalent GHGs, or USD tCO$_2$-eq^{-1} avoided. In addition to the comparison challenges noted above, this metric must account for the costs and emissions of the emitting options that are being displaced by the low-carbon option. Assumptions about the displaced option can lead to very different mitigation cost estimates (Table 6.9). Despite these challenges, these metrics are useful for identifying broad trends and making broad comparisons, even from the global perspective in this assessment. But local information will always be critical to determine which options are most cost-effective in any specific applications.

The feasibility and desirability of mitigation options extends well beyond the market economic costs of installation and operation (Section 6.4.1). Figure 6.19 summarises the barriers and enablers for implementing different mitigation options in energy systems. The feasibility of different options can be enhanced by removing barriers and/or strengthening enablers of the implementation of the options. The feasibility of options may differ across context (e.g., region), time (e.g., 2030 versus 2050), scale (e.g., small versus large) and the long-term warming goal (e.g., 1.5°C versus 2°C).

6.5   Climate Change Impacts on the Energy System

6.5.1   Climate Impacts on the Energy System

Many components of the energy system are affected by individual weather events and climate conditions (Table 6.10). In addition, a range of compounding effects can be anticipated, as the complex, interconnected climate and energy systems are influenced by multiple weather and climate conditions. This raises the question of whether the energy system transformation needed to limit warming will be impacted by climate change.

The impacts of *climate change* on the energy system can be divided into three areas: impacts on the energy supply; impacts on energy consumption; and impacts on energy infrastructure. The rest of this section focuses on how the *future changes* in climate drivers might affect the ability of the energy system transformation needed to mitigate climate change. The discussion of energy infrastructure in this section is limited to electricity system vulnerability.

6

Figure 6.19 | Summary of the extent to which different factors would enable or inhibit the deployment of mitigation options in energy systems. Blue bars indicate the extent to which the indicator enables the implementation of the option (E) and orange bars indicate the extent to which an indicator is a barrier (B) to the deployment of the option, relative to the maximum possible barriers and enablers assessed. An X signifies that the indicator is not applicable or does not affect the feasibility of the option, while a forward slash indicates that there is no or limited evidence whether the indicator affects the feasibility of the option. The shading indicates the level of confidence, with darker shading signifying higher levels of confidence. Appendix II provides an overview of the factors affecting the feasibility of options and how they differ across context (e.g., region), time (e.g., 2030 versus 2050), and scale (e.g., small versus large), and includes a line of sight on which the assessment is based. The assessment method is explained in Annex II.11.

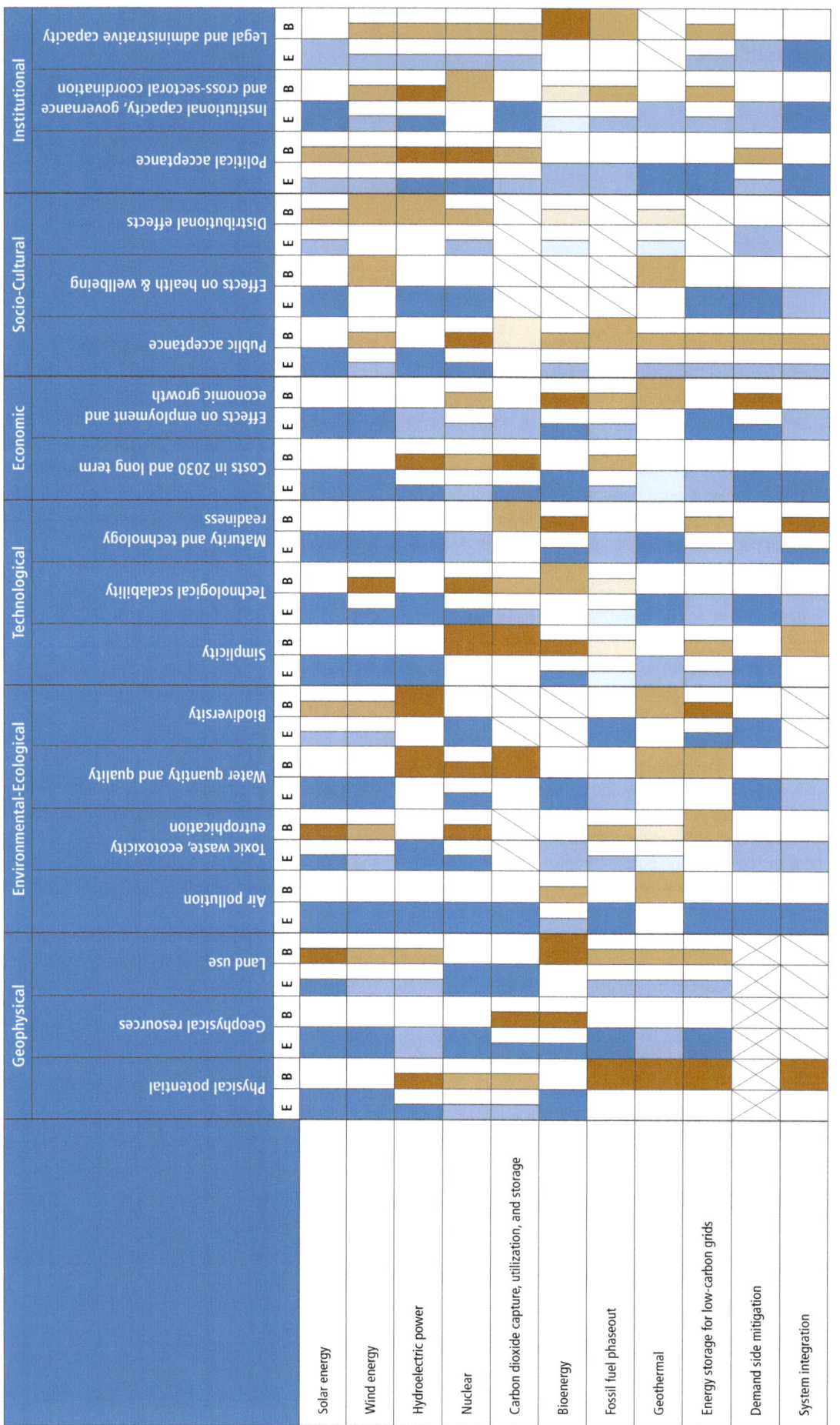

Table 6.10 | Relevance of the key climatic impact drivers (and their respective changes in intensity, frequency, duration, timing, and spatial extent) for major categories of activities in the energy sector. The climate impact drivers (CIDs) are identified in Table 12.1 in Chapter 12 of WGI AR6 report. The relevance is assessed as: positive/negative (+ or −), or both (±). D&O: Design and Operation; CF: Capacity Factor.

Relevance of the climate impact driver: Positive | Positive or negative | Negative

6.5.2   Impacts on Energy Supply

The increased weather dependency of future low-carbon electricity systems amplifies the possible impacts of climate change (Staffell and Pfenninger 2018). However, *globally* climate change impacts on electricity generation – including hydro, wind and solar power potentials – should not compromise climate mitigation strategies (*high confidence*). Many of the changes in the climate system will be geographically complex at the regional and local levels. Thus, *regionally* climate change impacts on electricity generation could be significant. Climate change impacts on bioenergy potentials are more uncertain because of uncertainties associated with the crop response to climate change, future water availability and crop deployment. Climate change can reduce the efficiency of thermal power generation and increase the risk of power plant shutdowns during droughts. The potential additional cooling water needs of CCS can increase these risks.

6.5.2.1   Hydropower

The impacts of climate change on hydropower will vary by region. High latitudes in the northern hemisphere are anticipated to experience increased runoff and hydropower potential. For other regions, studies find both increasing and decreasing runoff and hydropower potential. Areas with decreased runoff are anticipated to experience reduced hydropower production and increased water conflict among different economic activities (*high confidence*).

Hydropower production is directly related to the availability of water. Changes in runoff and its seasonality and changes in temperature and precipitation intensity will influence hydroelectricity production

(IHA 2019). In general, increased precipitation will increase water availability and hydropower production. Increased precipitation intensity, however, may impact on the integrity of dam structures and affect power production by increasing debris accumulation and vegetation growth. Additionally, increased precipitation intensity results in the silting of the reservoirs or increases the amount of water spilt, resulting in erosion (Schaeffer et al. 2012; IHA 2019). Climate change will likely lead to higher air temperatures, resulting in more surface evaporation, less water storage, and loss of equipment efficiency (Ebinger and Vergara 2011; Mukheibir 2013; Fluixá-Sanmartín et al. 2018; Hock et al. 2019). Climate change may alter the demands for water use by other sectors that often rely on stored water in multi-purpose reservoirs, and may therefore generate conflicts over water use. The increased need for water for irrigation and/or industry can affect the availability of water for hydropower generation (Spalding-Fecher et al. 2016; Solaun and Cerdá 2017). Higher temperatures increase glacier melt, increasing water availability for hydropower while the glaciers exist. Changes in the timing of snow and ice melt may require upgrading in storage capacity and adaptation of the hydropower plant management for fully exploiting the increase in water availability.

The conclusions regarding climate change impacts on hydropower vary due to differences in modelling assumptions and methodology, such as choice of the climate and hydrological models, choice of metrics (e.g., projected production vs hydropower potential), level of modelling details between local and global studies, reservoir operation assumptions. Also important is how hydropower production matches up with other reservoir purposes, accounting for other water and energy users, and how the competing uses are impacted by climate change (van Vliet et al. 2016b; Turner et al. 2017). Nonetheless,

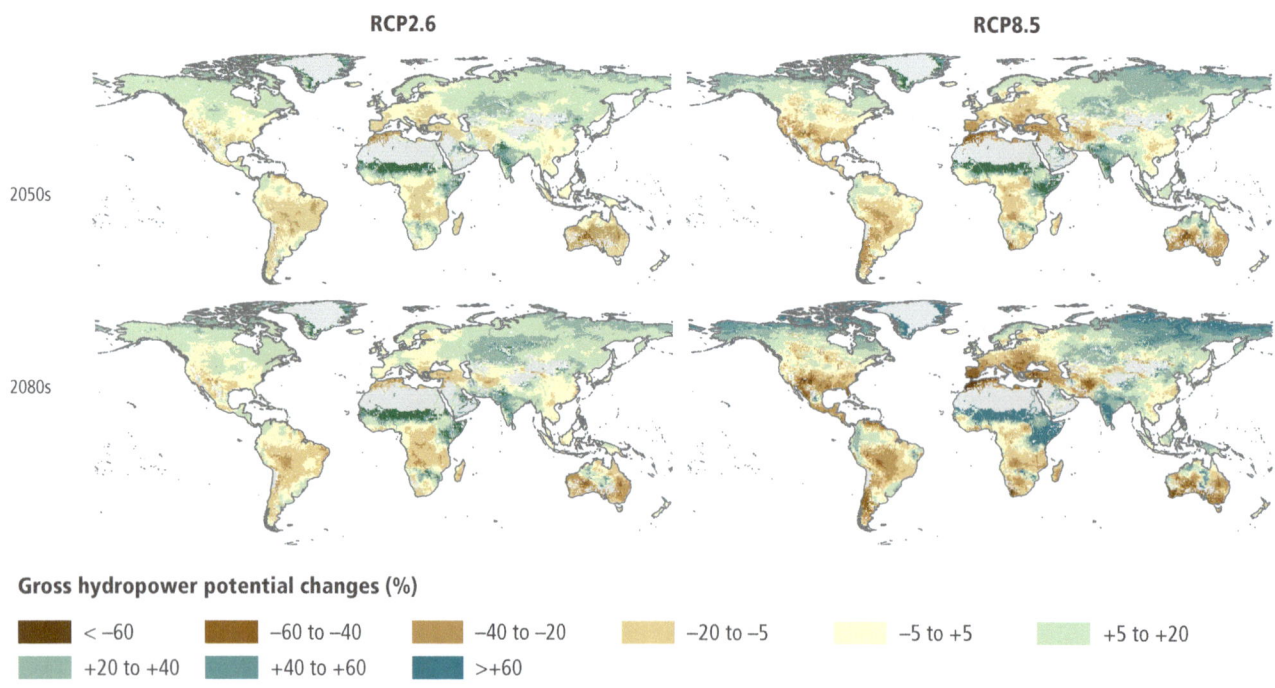

Gross hydropower potential changes (%)

■ < –60	■ –60 to –40	■ –40 to –20	■ –20 to –5	■ –5 to +5	■ +5 to +20
■ +20 to +40	■ +40 to +60	■ >+60			

Figure 6.20 | Global spatial patterns of changes in gross hydropower potential based on climate forcing from five climate models. Changes are shown for the 2050s (upper) and the 2080s (lower) for the low-emission scenario (RCP2.6; left) and highest emission scenario (RCP8.5; right) scenarios relative to the control period (1971–2000). Source: data from van Vliet et al. (2016b).

analyses consistently demonstrate that the global impact of climate change on hydropower will be small, but the regional impacts will be larger, and will be both positive and negative (Figure 6.20). Gross global hydropower potential in the 2050s has been estimated to slightly decrease (Hamududu and Killingtveit 2012) between 0.4% (for the low-emission scenario) and 6.1% (for the highest-emission scenario) for the 2080s compared to 1971–2000 (van Vliet et al. 2016a).

Regional changes in hydropower are estimated from 5–20% increases for most areas in high latitudes (van Vliet et al. 2016b; Turner et al. 2017) to decreases of 5–20% in areas with increased drought conditions (Cronin et al. 2018). Models show a consistent increase in streamflow and hydropower production by 2080 in high latitudes of the northern hemisphere and parts of the tropics (Figure 6.20) (e.g., central Africa and southern Asia) while decreasing in the USA, southern and central Europe, Southeast Asia and southern South America, Africa and Australia (van Vliet et al. 2016c,a). Decreases in hydropower production are indicated for parts of North America, central and southern Europe, the Middle East, central Asia and Southern South America. Studies disagree on the changes in hydropower production in China, central South America, and partially in southern Africa (Hamududu and Killingtveit 2012; van Vliet et al. 2016b; Solaun and Cerdá 2019; Fan et al. 2020).

6.5.2.2   Wind Energy

Climate change will not substantially impact future wind resources and will not compromise the ability of wind energy to support low-carbon transitions (*high confidence*). Changing wind variability may have a small-to-modest impact on backup energy and storage needs (*low confidence*); however, current evidence is largely from studies focused on Europe.

Long-term global wind energy resources are not expected to substantially change in future climate scenarios (Karnauskas et al. 2018; Pryor et al. 2020; Yalew et al. 2020). However, recent research has indicated consistent shifts in the geographic position of atmospheric jets in the high-emission scenarios (Harvey et al. 2014), which would decrease wind power potentials across the Northern Hemisphere mid-latitudes and increase wind potentials across the tropics and the Southern Hemisphere. However, the climate models used to make these assessments differ in how well they can reproduce the historical wind resources and wind extremes, which raises questions about the robustness of their predictions of future wind resources (Pryor et al. 2020).

There are many regional studies on changes in wind resources from climate change. For Europe, there is medium evidence and moderate agreement that wind resources are already increasing and will continue to increase in Northern Europe and decrease in Southern Europe (Carvalho et al. 2017; Devis et al. 2018; Moemken et al. 2018). For North America, the various studies have low agreement for the changes in future wind resources in part because the year-to-year variations in wind resources are often larger than the future change due to climate change (Johnson and Erhardt 2016; Chen 2020; Costoya et al. 2020; Wang et al. 2020b). Studies show increases in future wind resources in windy areas in South America (Ruffato-

Ferreira et al. 2017; de Jong et al. 2019). No robust future changes in wind resources have been identified in China (Xiong et al. 2019). However, none of the global or regional studies of the effects of climate change on wind resources considers the fine-scale dependence of wind resources on the topography and wind direction (Sanz Rodrigo et al. 2016; Dörenkämper et al. 2020) or the effect of expanding wind energy exploitation (Volker et al. 2017; Lundquist et al. 2019). There is limited evidence that extreme wind speeds, which can damage wind turbines, will increase due to climate change (Pes et al. 2017; Pryor et al. 2020). Nevertheless, projected changes in Europe and North America – regions where the most extensive analysis has been undertaken – are expected to be within the estimates embedded in the design standards of wind turbines (Pryor and Barthelmie 2013).

Future wind generation in Europe could decrease in summer and autumn, increasing in winter in northern-central Europe but decreasing in southernmost Europe (Carvalho et al. 2017). Towards 2100, intra-annual variations increase in most of Europe, except around the Mediterranean area (Reyers et al. 2016), but this may reflect natural multi-decadal variability (Wohland et al. 2019b). Wind speeds may become more homogeneous over large geographical regions in Europe due to climate change, increasing the likelihood of large areas experiencing high or low wind speeds simultaneously (Wohland et al. 2017). These changes could result in fewer benefits in the transmission of wind generation between countries and increased system integration costs. Europe could require a modest increase (up to 7%) in backup energy towards the end of the 21st century due to more homogeneous wind conditions over Europe (Wohland et al. 2017; Weber et al. 2018). However, other studies report that the impact of climate change is substantially smaller than interannual variability, with no significant impact on the occurrence of extreme low wind production events in Europe (Van Der Wiel et al. 2019). If European electricity systems are designed to manage the effects of existing weather variability on wind power, they can likely also cope with climate change impacts on wind power (Ravestein et al. 2018). Changes in wind-generation variability caused by climate change are also reported for North America (Haupt et al. 2016; Losada Carreño et al. 2018), with modest impacts on electricity system operation (Craig et al. 2019).

6.5.2.3   Solar Energy

Climate change is not expected to substantially impact global solar insolation and will not compromise the ability of solar energy to support low-carbon transitions (*high confidence*). Models show dimming and brightening in certain regions, driven by cloud, aerosol and water vapour trends (Chapter 12 of IPCC AR6 WGI). The increase in surface temperature, which affects all regions, decreases solar power output by reducing the PV panel efficiency. In some models and climate scenarios, the increases in solar insolation are counterbalanced by reducing efficiency due to rising surface air temperatures, which increase significantly in all models and scenarios (Jerez et al. 2015; Bartók et al. 2017; Emodi et al. 2019). Increases in aerosols would reduce the solar resource available and add to maintenance costs (Chapter 12 of IPCC AR6 WGI).

In many emission scenarios, the effect on solar PV from temperature-induced efficiency losses is smaller than the effect expected from changes on solar insolation due to variations in water vapour and clouds in most regions. Also, future PV technologies will likely have higher efficiency, which would offset temperature-related declines (Müller et al. 2019). Cloud cover is projected to decrease in the subtropics (around −0.05% per year), including parts of North America, vast parts of Europe and China, South America, South Africa and Australia (*medium agreement, medium evidence*). Thus, models project modest (<3%) increases in solar PV by the end of the century for southern Europe, northern and southern Africa, Central America, and the Caribbean (Emodi et al. 2019). There are several studies projecting decreasing solar production, but these are generally influenced by other factors, for example, increasing air pollution (Ruosteenoja et al. 2019). The multi-model means for solar insolation in regional models decrease 0.60 W m^{-2} per decade from 2006 to 2100 over most of Europe (Bartók et al. 2017), with the most significant decreases in the Northern countries (Jerez et al. 2015).

6.5.2.4   Bioenergy

Climate change can affect biomass resource potential directly, via changes in the suitable range (i.e., the area where bioenergy crops can grow) and/or changes in yield, and indirectly, through changes in land availability. Increases in CO_2 concentration increase biomass yield; climate changes (e.g., temperature, precipitation, and so on) can either increase or decrease the yield and suitable range.

Climate change will shift the suitable range for bioenergy towards higher latitudes, but the net change in the total suitable area is uncertain (*high confidence*). Several studies show northward shifts in the suitable range for bioenergy in the northern hemisphere (Tuck et al. 2006; Barney and DiTomaso 2010; Bellarby et al. 2010; Hager et al. 2014; Wang et al. 2014a; Preston et al. 2016; Conant et al. 2018; Cronin et al. 2018), but the net effect of climate change on total suitable area varies by region, species, and climate model (Barney and DiTomaso 2010; Hager et al. 2014; Wang et al. 2014a).

The effect of climate change on bioenergy crop yields will vary across region and feedstock (*high confidence*); however, in general, yields will decline in low latitudes (*medium confidence*) and increase in high latitudes (*low confidence*) (Haberl et al. 2010; Cosentino et al. 2012; Preston et al. 2016; Cronin et al. 2018; Mbow et al. 2019). However, the average change in yield varies significantly across studies, depending on the feedstock, region, and other factors (Beringer et al. 2011; Kyle et al. 2014; Mbow et al. 2019; Dolan et al. 2020). Only a few studies extend the modelling of climate change impacts on bioenergy to quantify the effect on bioenergy deployment or its implications on the energy system (Calvin et al. 2013, 2019; Kyle et al. 2014; Thornton et al. 2017). These studies find that changes in deployment are of the same sign as changes in yield; that is, if yields increase, then deployment increases.

Some of the uncertainty in the sign and magnitude of the impacts of climate change on bioenergy potential is due to uncertainties in CO_2 fertilisation (the increase in photosynthesis due to increases in atmospheric CO_2 concentration) (Haberl et al. 2011; Bonjean Stanton et al. 2016; Cronin et al. 2018; Solaun and Cerdá 2019; Yalew et al. 2020). For example, earlier studies found that, without CO_2 fertilisation,

climate change will reduce global bioenergy potential by about 16%; with CO_2 fertilisation, however, climate change increases this potential by 45% (Haberl et al. 2011). However, newer studies in the USA find little effect of CO_2 fertilisation on switchgrass yield (Dolan et al. 2020). There is also a considerable uncertainty across climate and crop models in estimating bioenergy potential (Hager et al. 2014).

6.5.2.5   Thermal Power Plants

The operation of thermal power plants will be affected by climate change, deriving from changes in the ambient conditions like temperature, humidity and water availability (Schaeffer et al. 2012) (*high confidence*). Changes in ambient temperature have relatively small impacts on coal-fired and nuclear power plants (Rankine cycle); however, gas-fired power plants (Brayton or combined-cycle) may have their thermal efficiency and power output significantly decreased (De Sa and Al Zubaidy 2011; Schaeffer et al. 2012). Droughts decrease potential cooling water for thermal power plants and increase the probability of water outlet temperatures exceeding regulatory limits, leading to lower production or shutdowns. Thermal power utilisation has been reported to be, on average, 3.8% lower during drought years globally (van Vliet et al. 2016c), and further significant decreases in available thermal power plant capacity due to climate change are projected (Koch et al. 2014; van Vliet et al. 2016b; Yalew et al. 2020). An increase in climate-related nuclear power disruptions has been reported in the past decades globally (Ahmad 2021).

Carbon capture may increase cooling water usage significantly, especially in retrofits, with up to 50% increase in water usage for coal-fired power plants globally, depending on the CCS technology (Rosa et al. 2020) (Section 6.4). In Asia, planned coal capacity is expected to be vulnerable to droughts, sea level rise, and rising air temperatures, and this may be exacerbated by incorporating carbon capture (Wang et al. 2019c). Recently, however, studies have proposed designs of CCS with a minimal increase in water requirements (Magneschi et al. 2017; Mikunda et al. 2021).

Older thermal power plants can be retrofitted to mitigate climate impacts by altering and redesigning the cooling systems (Westlén 2018), although the costs for these solutions may be high. For example, dry cooling may be used instead of once-through cooling; however, it lowers thermal efficiency and would leave plants vulnerable to ambient temperature increase (Ahmad 2021). Closed-circuit cooling is much less sensitive to water temperature than once-through cooling (Bonjean Stanton et al. 2016). Modifying policies and regulation of water and heat emissions from power plants may also be used to mitigate plant reliability problems induced by climate change (Eisenack 2016; Mu et al. 2020), albeit with potential impacts for other water users and ecology. Improvements in water use and thermal efficiencies and the use of transmission capabilities over large geographical regions to mitigate risks on individual plants are also possible mitigation options (Miara et al. 2017).

6.5.3   Impacts on Energy Consumption

Heating demand will decrease, and cooling demand will increase in response to climate change. Peak load may increase more than energy consumption, and the changing spatial and temporal load patterns can impact transmission and needs for storage, demands-side management, and peak-generating capacity (*high confidence*).

Climate change will decrease heating demands, especially in cold regions, and it will increase cooling demands, especially in warm regions (Yalew et al. 2020). Recent studies report significant net impacts, with the commercial and industrial sectors and substantial air condition penetration driving an increase in energy demand (Davis and Gertler 2015; Levesque et al. 2018; De Cian and Sue Wing 2019; van Ruijven et al. 2019; Yalew et al. 2020). For example, globally, De Cian and Sue Wing (2019) found a 7–17% increase in energy consumption due to climate change in 2050, with the range depending on the climate change scenario. The overall effects of climate change on building energy consumption are regionally dependent. For example, Zhang et al. (2019) find that reduced heating will outweigh increased cooling in the residential buildings in Europe, but the reverse will be true in China.

While many studies have focused on energy consumption, climate extremes are expected to alter peak energy demands, with the potential for blackouts, brownouts, and other short-term energy system impacts (Yalew et al. 2020). For example, peak energy demand during heatwaves can coincide with reduced transmission and distribution capacity at higher temperatures. In large cities, extreme heat events increase cooling degree days significantly, with the urban heat island effect compounding the impact (Morakinyo et al. 2019). One study found that total electricity consumption at the end of the century in the USA could increase on average by 20% during summer months and decrease on average by 6% in the winter (Ralston Fonseca et al. 2019). While the average increase in consumption is modest, climate change is projected to have severe impacts on the frequency and intensity of peak electricity loads (Auffhammer et al. 2017). Bartos et al. (2016) find that peak per-capita summertime load in the USA may rise by 4.2–15% by mid-century. Efficient cooling technologies and other demand-side measures can limit cooling energy loads during periods of particularly high demand (IEA 2018; Dreyfus et al. 2020).

Box 6.6 | Energy Resilience

In February 2021, the state of Texas was hit by three major storms and suffered significant scale power outages. More than 4.5 million homes and businesses on the Texas electric grid were left without electricity for days, limiting the ability to heat homes during dangerously low temperatures and leading to food and clean water shortages (Busby et al. 2021). The Texas and other events – for example, Typhoon Haiyan in Southeast Asia in 2013; the Australian bush fires in 2019–2020; forest fires in 2018 in California; water shortages in Cape Town, South Africa in 2018 and the western USA during 2021 – raise the question of whether future low-carbon energy systems will be more or less resilient than those of today.

Some characteristics of low-carbon energy systems will make them less resilient. Droughts reduce hydroelectric electricity generation (Gleick 2016; van Vliet et al. 2016c); wind farms do not produce electricity in calm conditions or shut down in very strong winds (Petersen and Troen 2012); solar PV generation is reduced by clouds and is less efficient under extreme heat, dust storms, and wildfires (Perry and Troccoli 2015; Jackson and Gunda 2021). In addition, the electrification of heating will increase the weather dependence of electricity consumption (Staffell and Pfenninger 2018; Gea-Bermúdez et al. 2021). Non-renewable generation, for example, from nuclear and fossil power plants, are also vulnerable to high temperatures and droughts as they depend on water for cooling (Cronin et al. 2018; Ahmad 2021).

But some aspects of low-carbon energy systems will make them more resilient. Wind and solar farms are often spread geographically, which reduces the chances of being affected by the same extreme weather event (Perera et al. 2020). The diversification of energy sources, in which each component has different vulnerabilities, increases resilience. Less reliance on thermal electricity generation technologies will reduce the risks of curtailment or efficiency losses from droughts and heat waves (Lohrmann et al. 2019). More generally, increased electricity system integration and flexibility (Section 6.4.3) and weatherisation of generators increases electricity system resilience (Busby et al. 2021; Heffron et al. 2021). Likewise, local district micro-grids with appropriate enabling technologies (e.g., distributed generation, energy storage, greater demand-side participation, electric vehicles) may ensure access to electricity during major long-duration power outage events and radically enhance the resilience of supply of essential demand (Stout et al. 2019).

6

6.5.4   Impacts on Electricity System Vulnerability

While long-term trends are important for electricity system planning, short-term effects associated with loss of power can be disruptive and lead to significant economic losses along with cascading impacts on health and safety. Extreme weather and storms threaten the electricity system in different ways, affecting system resilience, reliability, and adequacy (Moreno-Mateos et al. 2020). The implications of climate change for electricity system vulnerability will depend on the degree to which climate change alters the frequency and intensity of extreme weather events. The complex compounding effects of simultaneous events (e.g., high winds and lightning occurring at the same time) are not well understood.

High wind speeds can shear lines through mechanical failure or cause lines to collide, causing transient events (Panteli and Mancarella 2015; Yalew et al. 2020). Hurricane conditions can damage electricity system infrastructures, including utility-scale wind and solar PV plants. Electricity systems may experience high demand when lines are particularly at risk from mechanical failure from wind and storm-related effects. However, except for medium evidence of increases in heavy precipitation associated with tropical cyclones, there is limited evidence that extreme wind events will increase in frequency or intensity in the future (Kumar et al. 2015; Pryor et al. 2020).

Wildfires pose a significant threat to electricity systems in dry conditions and arid regions (Dian et al. 2019). With climate change, wildfires will probably become more frequent (Flannigan et al. 2013) and more difficult to address, given that they frequently coincide with dry air and can be exacerbated by high winds (Mitchell 2013).

Lightning can cause wildfires or common-mode faults on electricity systems associated with vegetation falling on power substations or overhead lines but is more generally associated with flashovers and overloads (Balijepalli et al. 2005). Climate change may change the probability of lightning-related events (Romps et al. 2014).

Snow and icing can impact overhead power lines by weighing them down beyond their mechanical limits, leading to collapse and cascading outages (Feng et al. 2015). Snow can also lead to flashovers on lines due to wet snow accumulation on insulators (Yaji et al. 2014; Croce et al. 2018) and snow and ice can impact wind turbines (Davis et al. 2016). Climate change will lower the risk of snow and ice conditions (McColl et al. 2012), but there is still an underlying risk of sporadic acute cold conditions such as those associated with the winter storms in Texas in 2021 (Box 6.6).

Flooding poses a threat to the transmission and distribution systems by inundating low-lying substations and underground cables. Coastal flooding also poses a threat to electricity system infrastructure. Rising sea levels from climate change and associated storm surge may also pose a significant risk for coastal electricity systems (Entriken and Lordan 2012).

Temperature increases influence electricity load profiles and electricity generation, as well as potentially impact supporting information and communication infrastructure. Heat can pose direct impacts to electricity system equipment such as transformers. Referred to as 'solar heat faults', they occur under high temperatures and low wind speeds and can be exacerbated by the urban heat island effect (McColl et al. 2012). Increasing temperatures affect system adequacy by reducing electric transmission capacity, simultaneously increasing peak load due to increased air conditioning needs (Bartos et al. 2016).

Box 6.7 | Impacts of Renewable Energy Production on Climate

While climate change will affect energy systems (Section 6.5), the reverse is potentially also true: increasing the use of renewable energy sources could affect local climate. Large solar PV arrays and hydroelectric dams darken the land surface, and wind turbines extract the wind's kinetic energy near the Earth's surface. Their environmental impacts of renewable energy production are mostly confined to areas close to the production sources and have been shown to be trivial compared to the mitigation benefits of renewable energy (*high confidence*).

Solar energy. Observations and model simulations have addressed whether large-scale solar PV power plants can alter the local and regional climate. In rural areas at the local scale, large-scale solar PV farms change the surface characteristics and affect air temperatures (Taha 2013). Measurements in rural Arizona, USA show local night-time temperatures 3°C–4°C warmer at the PV farm than surroundings (Barron-Gafford et al. 2016). In contrast, measurements in urban settings show that solar PV panels on roofs provide a cooling effect (Taha 2013; Ma et al. 2017). On the regional scale, modelling studies suggest cooling in urban areas (0.11–0.53°C) and warming in rural areas (up to 0.27°C) (Millstein and Menon 2011). Global climate model simulations show that solar panels induce regional cooling by converting part of the incoming solar energy to electricity (Hu et al. 2016). However, converting the generated electricity to heat in urban areas increases regional and local temperatures, compensating for the cooling effect.

Wind energy. Surface temperature changes in the vicinity of wind farms have been detected (Smith et al. 2013; Lee and Lundquist 2017; Takle et al. 2019; Xia et al. 2019) in the form of night-time warming. Data from field campaigns suggest that a 'suppression of cooling' can explain the observed warming (Takle et al. 2019). Regional and climate models have been used to describe the interactions between turbines and the atmosphere and find minor impacts (Vautard et al. 2014). More sophisticated models confirm the local warming effect of wind farms but report that the impact on the regional area is slight and occasional (Wang et al. 2019d). Wind turbines alter the transport and dissipation of momentum near the surface but do not directly impact the Earth's energy balance

Box 6.7 (continued)

(Fischereit et al. 2021). However, the secondary modifications to the energy and water exchanges have added implications for the climate system (Jacobson and Archer 2012).

Hydropower. The potential climate impacts of hydropower concentrate on the GHG emissions from organic matter decomposition when the carbon cycle is altered by the flooding of the hydroelectric power plant reservoir (Ocko and Hamburg 2019), but emissions from organic matter decomposition decrease over time. The darker surface of the reservoir, compared to the lighter surrounding land may counterbalance part of the reduced GHG emissions by hydropower production (Wohlfahrt et al. 2021). However, these impacts vary significantly among facilities due to the surrounding land properties and the area inundated by the reservoir.

6.6   Key Characteristics of Net-zero Energy Systems

6.6.1   What is a Net-zero Energy System?

Limiting warming to well below 2°C requires that CO_2 emissions from the energy sector be reduced to near zero or even below zero (Section 6.7; Chapter 3). Policies, technologies, behaviours, investments, and other factors will determine the speed at which countries transition to net-zero energy systems – those that emit very little or no emissions. An understanding of these future energy systems can help to chart a course toward them over the coming decades.

This section synthesises current understanding of net-zero energy systems. Discussions surrounding efforts to limit warming are frequently communicated in terms of the point in time at which net anthropogenic CO_2 emissions reach zero, accompanied by substantial reductions in non-CO_2 emissions (IPCC 2018, Chapter 3). Net-zero GHG goals are also common, and they require net-negative CO_2 emissions to compensate for residual non-CO_2 emissions. Economy-wide CO_2 and GHG goals appear in many government and corporate decarbonisation strategies, and they are used in a variety of ways. Most existing carbon-neutrality commitments from countries and sub-national jurisdictions aim for economies with very low emissions rather than zero emissions. Offsets, carbon dioxide removal (CDR) methods, and/or land sink assumptions are used to achieve net-zero goals (Kelly Levin et al. 2020).

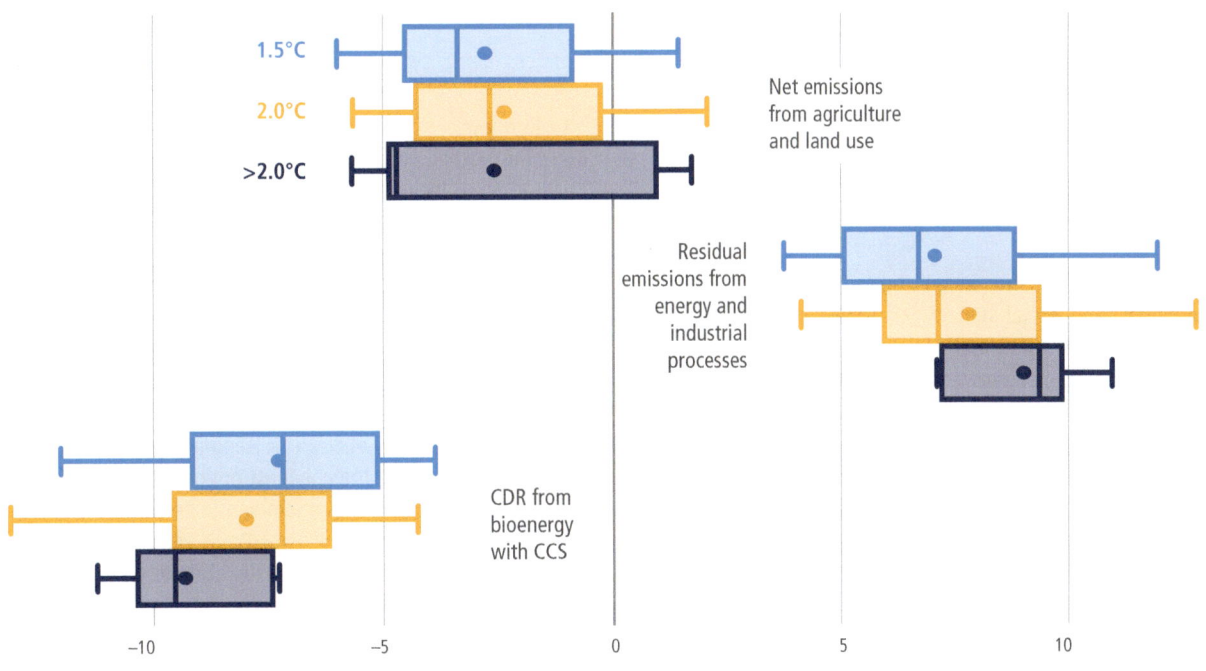

Figure 6.21 | Residual emissions and carbon dioxide removal (CDR) when global energy and industrial CO_2 emissions reach net-zero. Residual emissions and CDR in net-zero scenarios from the AR6 Scenarios Database show global differences across warming levels (light blue = scenarios that limit warming to 1.5°C (>50%) with no or limited overshoot and scenarios that return warming to 1.5°C (>50%) after a high overshoot; yellow = scenarios that limit warming to 2°C (>67%) and scenarios that limit warming to 2°C (>50%); dark blue = scenarios that limit warming to 2.5°C (>50%), scenarios that limit warming to 3°C (>50%), scenarios that limit warming to 4°C (>50%), and scenarios that exceed warming of 4°C (≥50%)). In each case, the boxes show the 25th to 75th percentile ranges, and whiskers show the 5th and 95th percentiles. Lines and circles within the boxes denote the median and mean values, respectively.

Precisely describing a net-zero energy system is complicated by the fact that different scenarios attribute different future CO_2 emissions to the energy system, even under scenarios where economy-wide CO_2 emissions reach net zero. It is also complicated by the dependence of energy system configurations on unknown future conditions such as population and economic growth, and technological change. The energy system is not the only source or sink of CO_2 emissions. Terrestrial systems may store or emit carbon, and CDR options like BECCS or DACCS can be used to store CO_2, relieving pressure on the energy system (Chapter 3). The location of such CDR options is ambiguous, as it might be deployed within or outside of the energy sector (Figure 6.21), and many CDR options, such as DACCS, would be important energy consumers (Bistline and Blanford 2021a) (Section 6.6.2). If CDR methods are deployed outside of the energy system (e.g., net negative agriculture, forestry, and land-use CO_2 emissions), it is possible for the energy system to still emit CO_2 but have economy-wide emissions of zero or below. When global energy and industrial CO_2 emissions reach net zero, the space remaining for fossil energy emissions is determined by deployment of CDR options (Figure 6.21).

This section focuses on energy systems that produce very little or no CO_2 emissions, referred to in this chapter as 'net-zero energy systems'. While energy systems may not reach net zero concurrently with economy-wide CO_2 or GHG emissions, they are a useful benchmark for planning a path to net zero. Note that the focus here is on energy systems with net-zero CO_2 emissions from fossil fuel combustion and industrial processes, but the lessons will be broadly applicable to net-zero GHG energy systems as well. Net-zero GHG energy systems would incorporate the major efforts made to reduce non-CO_2 emissions (e.g., CH_4 from oil, gas and coal as discussed in Section 6.4) and would also need to incorporate more CDR to compensate for remaining non-CO_2 GHG emissions. Energy sector emissions in many countries may not reach net zero at the same time as global energy system emissions (Figure 6.25 and Cross-Chapter Box 3 in Chapter 3).

6.6.2 Configurations of Net-zero Energy Systems

Net-zero energy systems entail trade-offs across economic, environmental, and social dimensions (Davis et al. 2018). Many socio-economic, policy, and market uncertainties will also influence the configuration of net-zero energy systems (Smith et al. 2015; van Vuuren et al. 2018; Bistline et al. 2019; Krey et al. 2019; Azevedo et al. 2021, Pye et al. 2021). There are reasons that countries might focus on one system configuration versus another, including cost, resource endowments, related industrial bases, existing infrastructure, geography, governance, public acceptance, and other policy priorities (Section 6.6.4 and Chapter 18 of WGII).

Explorations of net-zero energy systems have been emerging in the detailed systems modelling literature (Azevedo et al. 2021; Bistline 2021b). Reports associated with net-zero economy-wide targets for countries and sub-national entities typically do not provide detailed roadmaps or modelling but discuss high-level guiding principles, though more detailed studies are emerging at national levels (Capros et al. 2019; Wei et al. 2020; Duan et al. 2021; Williams et al. 2021a). Most analysis has focused on identifying potential decarbonisation technologies and

pathways for different sectors, enumerating opportunities and barriers for each, their costs, highlighting robust insights, and characterising key uncertainties (Davis et al. 2018; Hepburn et al. 2019).

The literature on the configuration of net-zero energy systems is limited in a few respects. On the one hand, there is a robust integrated assessment literature that provides characterisations of these systems in broad strokes (the AR6 database), offering internally consistent global scenarios to link global warming targets to regional/national goals. All integrated assessment scenarios that discuss net-zero energy system CO_2 emissions provide high-level characterisations of net-zero systems. Because these characterisations have less temporal, spatial, technological, regulatory, and societal detail, however, they may not consider the complexities that could ultimately influence regional, national, or local pathways. High-fidelity models and analyses are needed to assess the economic and environmental characteristics and the feasibility of many aspects of net-zero or net-negative emissions energy systems (*high confidence*) (Blanford et al. 2018; Bistline and Blanford 2020). For example, evaluating the competitiveness of electricity sector technologies requires temporal, spatial, and technological detail to accurately represent system investments and operations (Collins et al. 2017; Santen et al. 2017; Helistoe et al. 2019; Bistline 2021c; Victoria et al. 2021).

Configurations of net-zero energy systems will vary by region but are likely to share several common characteristics (*high confidence*) (Figure 6.22). We focus on seven of those common characteristics in the remainder of this subsection.

6.6.2.1 Limited and/or Targeted Use of Fossil Fuels

Net-zero energy systems will use far less fossil fuel than today (*high confidence*). The precise quantity of fossil fuels will largely depend on the relative costs of such fuels, electrification, alternative fuels, and CDR (Section 6.6.2.4) in the energy system (*high confidence*). All of these are affected by regional differences in resources (McGlade and Ekins 2015), existing energy infrastructure (Tong et al. 2019), demand for energy services, and climate and energy policies. Fossil fuel use may persist, for example, if and where the costs of such fuels and the compensating carbon management (e.g., CDR, CCS) are less than non-fossil energy. For most applications, however, it is likely that electrification (McCollum et al. 2014; Madeddu et al. 2020; Zhang and Fujimori 2020) or use of non-fossil alternative fuels (Zeman and Keith 2008; Graves et al. 2011; Hänggi et al. 2019; Ueckerdt et al. 2021) will prove to be the cheapest options. Most residual demand for fossil fuels is likely to predominantly be petroleum and natural gas given their high energy density (Davis et al. 2018), while demand for coal in net-zero energy systems is likely to be very low (Luderer et al. 2018; Jakob et al. 2020, Section 6.7.4) (*high confidence*).

There is considerable flexibility regarding the overall quantity of liquid and gaseous fuels that will be required in net-zero energy systems (*high confidence*) (Figure 6.22 and Section 6.7.4). This will be determined by the relative value of such fuels as compared to systems which rely more or less heavily on zero-emissions electricity. In turn, the share of any fuels that are fossil or fossil-derived is uncertain and will depend on the feasibility of CCS and CDR technologies and

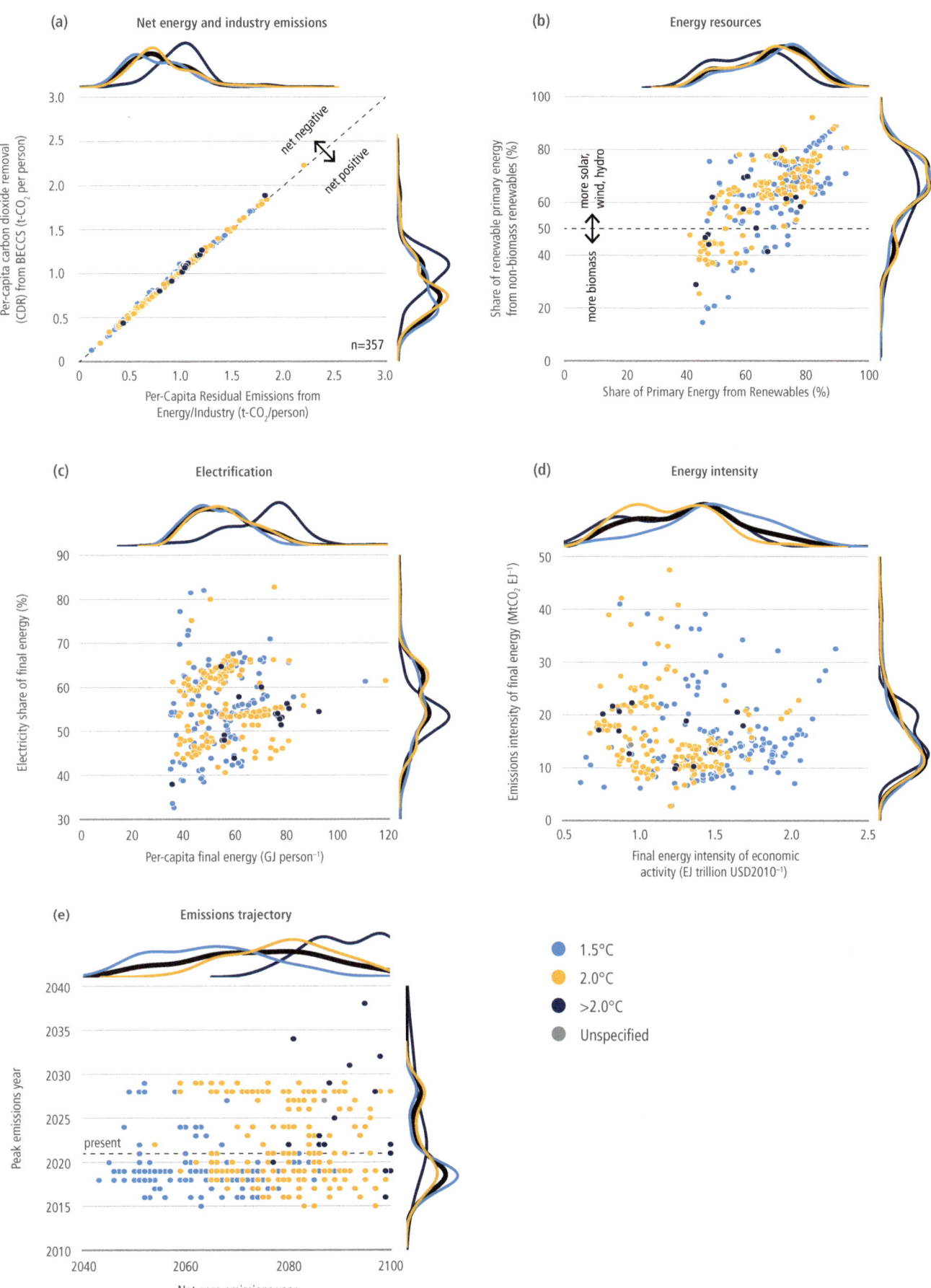

Figure 6.22 | Characteristics of global net-zero energy systems when global energy and industrial CO₂ emissions reach net-zero.

Figure 6.22 (continued): Characteristics of global net-zero energy systems when global energy and industrial CO₂ emissions reach net-zero. Scenarios reaching net-zero emissions show differences in residual emissions and carbon removal **(a)**, energy resources **(b)**, electrification **(c)**, energy intensity (as measured here by energy GDP^{-1}) **(d)**, and emissions trajectory **(e)**, particularly with respect to warming levels (light blue = scenarios that limit warming to 1.5°C (>50%) with no or limited overshoot and scenarios that return warming to 1.5°C (>50%) after a high overshoot; yellow = scenarios that limit warming to 2°C (>67%) and scenarios that limit warming to 2°C (>50%); dark blue = scenarios that limit warming to 2.5°C (>50%), scenarios that limit warming to 3°C (>50%), scenarios that limit warming to 4°C (>50%), and scenarios that exceed warming of 4°C (≥50%); grey = unspecified warming). Points represent individual scenarios from the AR6 Scenarios Database, with probability density distributions shown along each axis for each warming level (colours corresponding to warming levels) and for all scenarios (black).

long-term sequestration as compared to alternative, carbon-neutral fuels. Moreover, to the extent that physical, biological, and/or socio-political factors limit the availability of CDR (Smith et al. 2015; Field and Mach 2017), carbon management efforts may prioritise residual emissions related to land use and other non-energy sources.

6.6.2.2   Zero or Negative CO₂ Emissions from Electricity

Net-zero energy systems will rely on decarbonised or net-negative CO₂ emissions electricity systems, due to the many lower-cost options for producing zero-carbon electricity and the important role of end-use electrification in decarbonising other sectors (*high confidence*).

There are many possible configurations and technologies for zero- or net-negative-emissions electricity systems (*high confidence*). These systems could entail a mix of variable renewables, dispatchable renewables (e.g., biomass, hydropower), other firm, dispatchable ('on-demand') low-carbon generation (e.g., nuclear, CCS-equipped capacity), energy storage, transmission, carbon removal options (e.g., BECCS, DACCS), and demand management (Luderer et al. 2017; Bistline et al. 2018; Jenkins et al. 2018b; Bistline and Blanford 2021b). The marginal cost of deploying electricity sector mitigation options increases as electricity emissions approach zero; in addition, the most cost-effective mix of system resources changes as emissions approach zero and, therefore, so do the implications of electricity sector mitigation for sustainability and other societal goals (Mileva et al. 2016; Bistline et al. 2018; Sepulveda et al. 2018; Jayadev et al. 2020; Cole et al. 2021). Key factors influencing the electricity mix include relative costs and system benefits, local resource bases, infrastructure availability, regional integration and trade, co-benefits, societal preferences and other policy priorities, all of which vary by country and region (Section 6.6.4). Many of these factors depend on when the net-zero point is reached (Figure 6.22).

Based on their increasing economic competitiveness, VRE technologies, especially wind and solar power, will likely comprise large shares of many regional generation mixes (*high confidence*) (Figure 6.22). While wind and solar will likely be prominent electricity resources, this does not imply that 100% renewable energy systems will be pursued under all circumstances, since economic and operational challenges increase nonlinearly as shares approach 100% (Box 6.8) (Frew et al. 2016; Imelda et al. 2018b; Shaner et al. 2018; Bistline and Blanford 2021a; Cole et al. 2021). Real-world experience planning and operating regional electricity systems with high instantaneous and annual shares of renewable generation is accumulating, but debates continue about how much wind and solar should be included in different systems, and the cost-effectiveness of mechanisms for managing variability (Box 6.8). Either firm, dispatchable generation (including nuclear, CCS-equipped capacity, dispatchable renewables such as geothermal, and fossil units run with low capacity factors and CDR to balance emissions) or seasonal energy storage (alongside

other balancing resources discussed in Box 6.8) will be needed to ensure reliability and resource adequacy with high percentages of wind and solar (Jenkins et al. 2018b; Dowling et al. 2020; Denholm et al. 2021) though each option involves uncertainty about costs, timing, and public acceptance (Albertus et al. 2020).

Electricity systems require a range of different functional roles – for example, providing energy, capacity, or ancillary services. As a result, a range of different types of generation, energy storage, and transmission resources may be deployed in these systems (Baik et al. 2021). There are many options for each of these roles, each with their strengths and weaknesses (Sections 6.4.3 and 6.4.4), and deployment of these options will be influenced by the evolution of technological costs, system benefits, and local resources (Fell and Linn 2013; Hirth 2015; Bistline et al. 2018; Mai et al. 2018; Veers et al. 2019).

System management is critical for zero- or negative-emissions electricity systems. Maintaining reliability will increasingly entail system planning and operations that account for characteristics of supply- and demand-side resources (Hu et al. 2018). Coordinated planning and operations will likely become more prevalent across portions of the electricity system (e.g., integrated generation, transmission, and distribution planning), across sectors, and across geographies (EPRI 2017; Konstantelos et al. 2017; Chan et al. 2018; Bistline and Young 2019) (Section 6.4.3).

Energy storage will be increasingly important in net-zero energy systems, especially in systems with shares of VRE (*high confidence*). Deployment of energy storage will vary based on the system benefits and values of different options (Arbabzadeh et al. 2019; Denholm and Mai 2019). Diurnal storage options like lithium-ion batteries have different value than storing and discharging electricity over longer periods through long-duration energy storage with less frequent cycling, which require different technologies, supporting policies, and business models (Gallo et al. 2016; Blanco and Faaij 2017; Albertus et al. 2020; Dowling et al. 2020; Sepulveda et al. 2021) (Section 6.4.4). The value of energy storage varies with the level of deployment and on the competitiveness of economic complements such as VRE options (Mileva et al. 2016; Bistline and Young 2020) and substitutes such as flexible demand (Brown et al. 2018; Merrick et al. 2018), transmission (Schlachtberger et al. 2017; Brown et al. 2018; Merrick et al. 2018; Bistline and Young 2019), trade (Bistline et al. 2020b), dispatchable generators (Hittinger and Lueken 2015; Gils et al. 2017; Arbabzadeh et al. 2019), direct air capture (DAC) (Daggash et al. 2019), and efficiencies in system operations (Tuohy et al. 2015).

The approach to other sectors could impact on electricity sector planning, and the role of some technologies (e.g., hydrogen, batteries, CCS) could depend on deployment in other sectors. CCS offers opportunities for CO₂ removal when fuelled with syngas or biomass containing carbon captured from the atmosphere (Hepburn et al. 2019); however, concerns about lifecycle environmental impacts, uncertain costs, and public acceptance are potential barriers to widespread deployment (Section 6.4.2). It is unclear whether CDR options like BECCS will be included in the electricity mix to offset continued emissions in other parts of the energy system or beyond (MacDowell et al. 2017; Bauer et al. 2018a; Luderer et al. 2018). Some applications may also rely on power to fuels (PtX) electricity conversion to create low-emissions synthetic fuels (Sections 6.6.2.6, 6.4.4, and 6.4.5), which could impact on electricity system planning and operations. Additionally, if DAC technologies are used, electricity and heat requirements to operate DAC could impact electricity system investments and operations (Realmonte et al. 2019; Bistline and Blanford 2021a).

Box 6.8 | 100% Renewables in Net-zero Energy Systems

The decreasing cost and increasing performance of renewable energy has generated interest in the feasibility of providing nearly all energy services with renewables. Renewable energy includes wind power, solar power, hydroelectric power, bioenergy, geothermal energy, tidal power, and ocean power. There are two primary frames around which 100% renewable energy systems are discussed: 100% renewable electricity systems and 100% renewable energy systems, considering not only electricity but all aspects of the energy system.

It is technically feasible to use very high renewable shares (e.g., above 75% of annual regional generation) to meet hourly electricity demand under a range of conditions, especially when VRE options, notably wind and solar, are complemented by other resources (*high confidence*). There are currently many grids with high renewable shares and large anticipated roles for VRE sources, in particular wind and solar (Section 6.4), in future low-carbon electricity systems. An increasingly large set of studies examines the feasibility of high renewable penetration and economic drivers under different policy, technology, and market scenarios (Cochran et al. 2014; Deason 2018; Jenkins et al. 2018b; Bistline et al. 2019; Hansen et al. 2019; Dowling et al. 2020; Blanford et al. 2021; Denholm et al. 2021). High wind and solar penetration involves technical and economic challenges due to their unique characteristics such as spatial and temporal variability, short- and long-term uncertainty, and non-synchronous generation (Cole et al. 2017). These challenges become increasingly important as renewable shares approach 100% (Sections 6.6.2.2 and 6.4.3).

There are many balancing options in systems with very high renewables (Milligan et al. 2015; Jenkins et al. 2018b; Mai et al. 2018; Bistline 2021a; Denholm et al. 2021).

- **Energy storage.** Energy storage technologies like batteries, pumped hydro, and hydrogen can provide a range of system services (Balducci et al. 2018; Bistline et al. 2020a) (Section 6.4.4). Lithium-ion batteries have received attention as costs fall and installations increase, but very high renewable shares typically entail either dispatchable generation or long-duration storage in addition to short-duration options (Jenkins et al. 2018b; Arbabzadeh et al. 2019; Schill 2020). Energy storage technologies are part of a broad set of options (including synchronous condensers, demand-side measures, and even inverter-based technologies themselves) for providing grid services (Castillo and Gayme 2014; EPRI 2019a).
- **Transmission and trade.** To balance differences in resource availability, high renewable systems will very likely entail investments in transmission capacity (Mai et al. 2014; Macdonald et al. 2016; Pleßmann and Blechinger 2017; Zappa et al. 2019) (Section 6.4.5) and changes in trade (Abrell and Rausch 2016; Bistline et al. 2019). These increases will likely be accompanied by expanded balancing regions to take advantage of geographical smoothing.
- **Dispatchable ('on-demand') generation.** Dispatchable generation could include flexible fossil units or low-carbon fuels such as hydrogen with lower minimum load levels (Denholm et al. 2018; Bistline 2019), renewables like hydropower, geothermal, or biomass (Hirth 2016; Hansen et al. 2019), or flexible nuclear (Jenkins et al. 2018a). The composition depends on costs and other policy goals, though in all cases, capacity factors are low for these resources (Mills et al. 2020).
- **Demand management:** Many low-emitting and high-renewables systems also utilise increased load flexibility in the forms of energy efficiency, demand response, and demand flexibility, utilising newly electrified end uses such as electric vehicles to shape demand profiles to better match supply (Ameli et al. 2017; Hale 2017; Brown et al. 2018; Imelda et al. 2018a; Bistline 2021a).
- **Sector coupling:** Sector coupling includes increased end-use electrification and PtX electricity conversion pathways, which may entail using electricity to create synthetic fuels such as hydrogen (Davis et al. 2018; Ueckerdt et al. 2021) (Sections 6.4.3, 6.4., 6.4.5, 6.6.4.3, and 6.6.4.6).

Deployment of integration options depends on their relative costs and value, regulations, and electricity market design. There is considerable uncertainty about future technology costs, performance, availability, scalability, and public acceptance (Kondziella and Bruckner 2016; Bistline et al. 2019). Deploying balanced resources likely requires operational, market design, and other institutional changes, as well as technological changes in some cases (Denholm et al. 2021; Cochran et al. 2014). Mixes will differ based on resources, system size, flexibility, and whether grids are isolated or interconnected.

6

Box 6.8 (continued)

Although there are no technical upper bounds on renewable electricity penetration, the economic value of additional wind and solar capacity typically decreases as their penetration rises, creating economic challenges at higher deployment levels (Hirth 2013; Gowrisankaran et al. 2016; Cole et al. 2021; Denholm et al. 2021; Millstein et al. 2021). The integration options above, as well as changes to market design, can mitigate these challenges but likely will not solve them, especially since these options can exhibit declining value themselves (De Sisternes et al. 2016; Bistline 2017; Denholm and Mai 2019) and may be complements or substitutes to each other.

Energy systems that are 100% renewable (including all parts of the energy sector, and not only electricity generation) raise a range of technological, regulatory, market, and operational challenges that make their competitiveness uncertain (*high confidence*). These systems require decarbonising all electricity, using this zero-carbon electricity broadly, and then utilising zero-carbon energy carriers for all end uses not served by electricity, for example, air travel, long-distance transport, and high-temperature process heat. Broader questions emerge regarding the attractiveness of supplying all energy, and not just electricity, with renewables (Figure 6.22). Integrated assessment and energy systems research suggest large roles for renewables, but energy and electricity shares are far from 100%, even with stringent emissions reductions targets and optimistic assumptions about future cost reductions (Bauer et al. 2018; Bistline et al. 2018; Jenkins et al. 2018b; Huntington et al. 2020) (Section 6.7.1). Scenarios with 100% renewable energy systems are an emerging subset in the decarbonisation literature, especially at regional levels (Hansen et al. 2019; Denholm et al. 2021). Many 100% renewables studies focus more heavily on electrification for decarbonising end uses, and include less biofuels and hydrogen than the broader literature on deep decarbonisation (Bauer et al. 2018a). These studies typically assume a constrained set of available technologies to demonstrate the technical feasibility of very high renewable systems and do not optimise to find least-cost, technology-neutral decarbonisation pathways, and many 100% renewables studies focus on the electricity sector or a limited number of sectors (Jenkins et al. 2018a; Hansen et al. 2019). In addition to renewables, studies broadly agree that including additional low-carbon options – including not only low-carbon electricity but also targeted use of fossil fuels with and without CCS (Section 6.6.2.1) and alternative fuels for sectors that are difficult to electrify (Section 6.6.2.4) – can lower the cost of decarbonisation, even with very high shares of renewables (Figure 6.22). However, there is disagreement about the magnitude of cost savings from larger portfolios, which depend on context- and scenario-specific assumptions about technologies, markets, and policies.

6.6.2.3   Widespread Electrification of End Uses

Net-zero energy systems will rely more heavily on increased use of electricity (electrification) in end uses (*high confidence*). The literature on net-zero energy systems almost universally calls for increased electrification (Sugiyama 2012; Williams et al. 2012; Kriegler et al. 2014a; Williams et al. 2014; Rogelj et al. 2015a; Sachs et al. 2016; Luderer et al. 2018; Sven et al. 2018; Schreyer et al. 2020). At least 30% of the global final energy needs are expected to be served by electricity, with some estimates suggesting upwards of 80% of total energy use being electrified (Figure 6.22, panel c). Increased electrification is especially valuable in net-zero energy systems in tandem with decarbonised electricity generation or net-negative emissions electricity generation (Section 6.5.4.2). Flexible electric loads (electric vehicles, smart appliances) can in turn facilitate incorporation of VRE electricity options, increase system flexibility, and reduce needs for grid storage (Section 6.4.3) (Mathiesen et al. 2015; Lund et al. 2018).

Several end uses, such as passenger transportation (light-duty electric vehicles, two and three wheelers, buses, rail) as well as building energy uses (lighting, cooling) are likely to be electrified in net-zero energy systems (*high confidence*). Variations in projections of electrification largely result from differences in expectations about the ability and cost-competitiveness of electricity to serve other end uses such as non-rail freight transport, aviation, and heavy industry (McCollum et al. 2014; Bataille et al. 2016; EPRI 2018; Breyer et al. 2019)

(Section 6.5.4.4), especially relative to biofuels and hydrogen ('low-carbon fuels') (McCollum et al. 2014; Sachs et al. 2016; Rockström et al. 2017), the prospects for which are still quite uncertain (Section 6.4). The emergence of CDR technologies and the extent to which they allow for residual emissions as an alternative to electrification will also affect the overall share of energy served by electricity (Section 6.6.2.7).

Regions endowed with cheap and plentiful low-carbon electricity resources (wind, solar, hydropower) are likely to emphasise electrification, while those with substantial bioenergy resources or availability of other liquid fuels might put less emphasis on electrification, particularly in hard-to-electrify end uses (*medium confidence*). For example, among a group of Latin American countries, relative assumptions about liquid fuels and electricity result in an electrification range of 28–82% for achieving a net-zero energy system (Bataille et al. 2020). Similarly, the level of penetration of biofuels that can substitute for electrification will depend on regional circumstances such as land-use constraints, competition with food, and sustainability of biomass production (Section 6.6.2.4).

Electrification of most buildings services, with the possible exception of space heating in extreme climates, is expected in net-zero energy systems (*high confidence*) (Chapter 9). Space cooling and water heating are expected to be largely electrified. Building electrification is expected to rely substantially on heat pumps, which will help lower emissions both through reduced thermal requirements and higher efficiencies

(Mathiesen et al. 2015; Sven et al. 2018; Rissman et al. 2020). The level of electrification for heating will depend on the trade-offs between building or household level heat pumps versus more centralised district heating network options (Mathiesen et al. 2015; Brown et al. 2018), as well as the cost and performance of heat pumps in more extreme climates and regional grid infrastructure (EPRI 2018; Waite and Modi 2020).

A significant share of transportation, especially road transportation, is expected to be electrified in net-zero energy systems (*high confidence*). In road transportation, two- and three-wheelers, light-duty vehicles (LDVs), and buses, are especially amenable to electrification, with more than half of passenger LDVs expected to be electrified globally in net-zero energy systems (*medium confidence*) (Fulton et al. 2015; Sven et al. 2018; Khalili et al. 2019; Bataille et al. 2020). Long-haul trucks, large ships, and aircraft are expected to be harder to electrify without technological breakthroughs (Fulton et al. 2015; Mathiesen et al. 2015), although continued improvements in battery technology may enable electrification of long-haul trucks (Nykvist and Olsson 2021) (Chapter 10). Due to the relative ease of rail electrification, near complete electrification of rail and a shift of air and truck freight to rail is expected in net-zero energy systems (Fulton et al. 2015; Rockström et al. 2017; Sven et al. 2018; Khalili et al. 2019). The degree of modal shifts and electrification will depend on local factors such as infrastructure availability and location accessibility. Due to the challenges associated with electrification of some transport modes, net-zero energy systems may include some residual emissions associated with the freight sector that are offset through CDR technologies (Muratori et al. 2017b), or reliance on low and zero-carbon fuels instead of electrification.

A non-trivial number of industry applications could be electrified as a part of a net-zero energy system, but direct electrification of heavy industry applications such as cement, primary steel manufacturing, and chemical feedstocks is expected to be challenging (*medium confidence*) (Davis et al. 2018; Philibert 2019; Madeddu et al. 2020; van Sluisveld et al. 2021). Process and boiler heating in industrial facilities are anticipated to be electrified in net-zero energy systems. Emissions intensity reductions for cement and concrete production can be achieved through the use of electrified cement kilns, while emissions associated with steel production can be reduced through the use of an electric arc furnace (EAF) powered by decarbonised electricity (Rissman et al. 2020). Electricity can also be used to replace thermal heat such as resistive heating, EAFs, and laser sintering (Madeddu et al. 2020; Rissman et al. 2020). One study found that as much as 60% of the energy end-use in European industry could be met with direct electrification using existing and emerging technologies (Madeddu et al. 2020). Industry electrification for different regions will depend on the economics and availability of alternative emissions mitigation strategies such as carbon neutral fuels and CCS (Davis et al. 2018; Madeddu et al. 2020).

6.6.2.4 Alternative Fuels in Sectors not Amenable to Electrification

Net-zero energy systems will need to rely on alternative fuels – notably hydrogen or biofuels – in several sectors that are not amenable to electricity and otherwise hard to decarbonise (*medium confidence*).

Useful carbon-based fuels (e.g., methane, petroleum, methanol), hydrogen, ammonia, or alcohols can be produced with net-zero CO_2 emissions and without fossil fuel inputs (Sections 6.4.4 and 6.4.5). For example, liquid hydrocarbons can be synthesised via hydrogenation of non-fossil carbon by processes such as Fischer-Tropsch (MacDowell et al. 2017) or by conversion of biomass (Tilman et al. 2009). The resulting energy-dense fuels can serve applications that are difficult to electrify, but it is not clear if and when the combined costs of obtaining necessary feedstocks and producing these fuels without fossil inputs will be less than continuing to use fossil fuels and managing the related carbon through, for example, CCS or CDR (Ueckerdt et al. 2021).

CO_2 emissions from some energy services are expected to be particularly difficult to cost-effectively avoid, among them: aviation; long-distance freight by ships; process emissions from cement and steel production; high-temperature heat (e.g., >1000°C); and electricity reliability in systems with high penetration of variable renewable energy sources (NAS) (Davis et al. 2018; Luderer et al. 2018; Sepulveda et al. 2018; Chiaramonti 2019; Bataille 2020; Madeddu et al. 2020; Rissman et al. 2020; Thiel and Stark 2021). The literature focused on these services and sectors is growing, but remains limited, and provides minimal guidance on the most promising or attractive technological options and systems for avoiding these sectors' emissions. Technological solutions do exist, but those mentioned in the literature are prohibitively expensive, exist only at an early stage, and/or are subject to much broader concerns about sustainability (e.g., biofuels) (Davis et al. 2018).

Liquid biofuels today supply about 4% of transportation energy worldwide, mostly as ethanol from grain and sugar cane and biodiesel from oil seeds and waste oils (Davis et al. 2018). These biofuels could conceivably be targeted to difficult-to-electrify sectors, but face substantial challenges related to their lifecycle carbon emissions, cost, and further scalability (Tilman et al. 2009; Staples et al. 2018), (Section 6.4.2). The extent to which biomass will supply liquid fuels or high temperature heat for industry in a future net-zero energy system will thus depend on advances in conversion technology that enable use of feedstocks such as woody crops, agricultural residues, algae, and wastes, as well as competing demands for bioenergy and land, the feasibility of other sources of carbon-neutral fuels, and integration of bioenergy production with other objectives, including CDR, economic development, food security, ecological conservation, and air quality (Fargione 2010; Williams and Laurens 2010; Creutzig et al. 2015; Chatziaras et al. 2016; Laurens 2017; Lynd 2017; Bauer et al. 2018a, b; Strefler et al. 2018; Muratori et al. 2020b; Fennell et al. 2021) (Section 6.4.2.6).

Costs are the main barrier to synthesis of net-zero emissions fuels (*high confidence*), particularly costs of hydrogen (a constituent of hydrocarbons, ammonia, and alcohols) (Section 6.4.5). Today, most hydrogen is supplied by steam reformation of fossil methane (CH_4 into CO_2 and H_2) at a cost of 1.30– USD1.50 kg^{-1} (Sherwin 2021). Non-fossil hydrogen can be obtained by electrolysis of water, at current costs of USD5–7 kgH_2^{-1} (assuming relatively low electricity costs and high utilisation rates) (Graves et al. 2011; DOE 2020a; Newborough and Cooley 2020; Peterson et al. 2020). At these costs for electrolytic hydrogen, synthesised net-zero emissions fuels would cost at least USD1.6 per litre of diesel equivalent (or USD6 $gallon^{-1}$ and USD46 GJ^{-1}, assuming non-fossil carbon feedstock costs

6

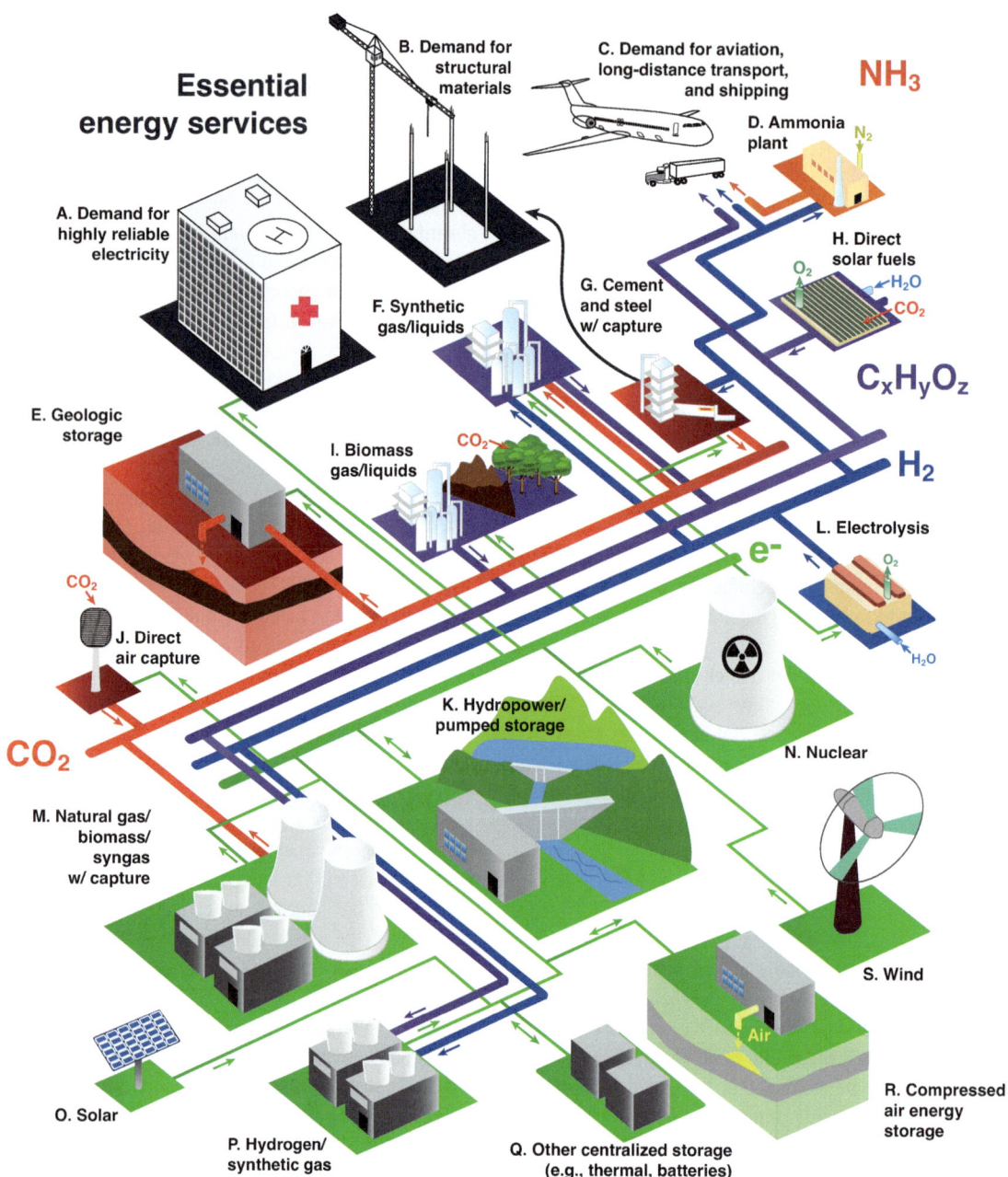

Figure 6.23 | Schematic of net-zero emissions energy system, including methods to address difficult-to-electrify sectors. Source: with permission from Davis et al. (2018).

of USD100 per tonne of CO_2 and low process costs of USD0.05 litre^{-1} or USD1.5 GJ^{-1}). Similar calculations suggest that synthetic hydrocarbon fuels could currently avoid CO_2 emissions at a cost of USD936–1404 tonne^{-1} (Ueckerdt et al. 2021). However, economies of scale are expected to bring these costs down substantially in the future (IRENA 2020c; Ueckerdt et al. 2021), and R&D efforts are targeting 60–80% reductions in costs (to less than USD2 kg^{-1} (H_2)$^{-1}$) possibly by use of less mature but promising technologies such as high-temperature electrolysis and thermochemical water splitting (Kuckshinrichs et al. 2017; Pes et al. 2017; Schmidt et al. 2017; Saba et al. 2018; DOE, 2018, 2020b). Technologies capable of producing hydrogen directly from water and sunlight (photoelectrochemical cells or photocatalysts) are also under development, but are at

an early stage (Nielander et al. 2015; DOE 2020a). High hydrogen production efficiencies have been demonstrated, but costs, capacity factors, and lifetimes need to be improved in order to make such technologies feasible for net-zero emissions fuel production at scale (McKone et al. 2014; DOE 2020a; Newborough and Cooley 2020).

The carbon contained in net-zero emissions hydrocarbons must have been removed from the atmosphere either through DAC, or, in the case of biofuels, by photosynthesis (which could include CO_2 captured from the exhaust of biomass or biogas combustion) (Zeman and Keith 2008; Graves et al. 2011). A number of different groups are now developing DAC technologies, targeting costs of USD100 per tonne of CO_2 or less (Darton and Yang 2018; Keith et al. 2018; Fasihi et al. 2019).

Box 6.9 | The Hydrogen Economy

The phrase 'hydrogen economy' is often used to describe future energy systems in which hydrogen plays a prominent role. These future energy systems would not use hydrogen for all end uses; they would use hydrogen to complement other energy carriers, mainly electricity, where hydrogen might have advantages. Hydrogen could provide long-term electricity storage to support high-penetration of intermittent renewables and could enable trading and storage of electricity between different regions to overcome seasonal or production capability differences (Dowling et al. 2020; Sepulveda et al. 2021). It could also be used in lieu of natural gas for peaking generation, provide process heat for industrial needs, or be used in the metal sector via direct reduction of iron ore (Chapter 11). Clean hydrogen could be used as a feedstock in the production of various chemicals and synthetic hydrocarbons. Finally, hydrogen-based fuel cells could power vehicles. Recent advances in battery storage make electric vehicles the most attractive alternative for light-duty transport. However, fuel cell technology could complement electric vehicles in supporting the decarbonisation of heavy-duty transport segments (e.g., trucks, buses, ships, and trains) (Chapter 10).

Hydrogen production costs have historically been prohibitive, but recent technological developments are bringing costs down. These developments include improvements in hydrogen production technologies in terms of efficiency and capital costs (e.g., steam methane reforming) (Alrashed and Zahid 2021; Boretti and Banik 2021) and the emergence of alternative production technologies such as electrolysers (Dawood et al. 2020). These technological changes, along with decreasing costs of renewable power, are increasing the viability of hydrogen. Other improvements in hydrogen-based technologies are also emerging quickly. Gas turbines now run on blended fuels containing 5–95% hydrogen by volume (GE 2020) and could operate entirely on hydrogen by 2030 (Pflug et al. 2019). Fuel cell costs have decreased by 80–95% since the early 2000s, while power density and durability have improved (Jouin et al. 2016; IEA 2019e; Kurtz et al. 2019).

For hydrogen to support decarbonisation, it will need to be produced from zero-carbon or extremely low-carbon energy sources. One such production category is 'green hydrogen'. While there is no unified definition for green hydrogen, it can be produced by the electrolysis of water using electricity generated without carbon emissions (such as renewables). Hydrogen can also be produced through biomass gasification with carbon capture and storage (BECCS), leading to negative carbon emissions (Arnaiz del Pozo et al. 2021). Additionally, 'blue hydrogen' can be produced from natural gas through the process of auto-thermal reforming (ATR) or steam methane reforming, combined with CCS technology that would absorb most of the resulting CO_2 (80–90%).

However, the potential role of hydrogen in future energy systems depends on more than just production methods and costs. For some applications, the competitiveness of hydrogen also depends on the availability of the infrastructure needed to transport and deliver it at relevant scales (Lee et al. 2021). Transporting hydrogen through existing gas pipelines is generally not feasible without changes to the infrastructure itself (Gumber and Gurumoorthy 2018; Muratori et al. 2018). Existing physical barriers, such as steel embrittlement and degradation of seals, reinforcements in compressor stations, and valves, require retrofitting during the conversion to H_2 distribution or new dedicated pipelines to be constructed (Dohi et al. 2016). The capacity to leverage and convert existing gas infrastructure to transport hydrogen will vary regionally, but in many cases could be the most economically viable pathway (Cerniauskas et al. 2020; Brändle et al. 2021; Brooks 2021; Wettengel 2021). Hydrogen could also be transported as liquid gas or as liquid organic hydrogen carriers such as ammonia, for which industry knowledge exists (Demir et al. 2018; Wulf et al. 2018; Hong et al. 2021). Additionally, improvements in fuel cell technologies are needed to make hydrogen-based transport economically viable. There are also safety concerns associated with the flammability (Nilsson et al. 2017) and storage (Andersson and Grönkvist 2019; Caglayan et al. 2019) of hydrogen which will need to be considered.

6.6.2.5 Using Less Energy and Using It More Efficiently

Demand-side or demand reduction strategies include technology efficiency improvements, strategies that reduce energy consumption or demand for energy services (such as reducing the use of personal transportation, often called 'conservation') (Creutzig et al. 2018), and strategies such as load curtailment.

Net-zero energy systems will use energy more efficiently than those of today (*high confidence*). Energy efficiency and energy use reduction strategies are generally identified as being flexible and cost-effective, with the potential for large-scale deployment (Chapters 5, 9, 10, and 11). For this reason, existing studies find that energy efficiency and demand reduction strategies will be important contributors to net-zero energy systems (Creutzig et al. 2018; Davis et al. 2018; DeAngelo et al. 2021). Lower demand reduces the need for low-carbon energy or alternative fuel sources.

Characterising efficiency of net-zero energy systems is problematic due to measurement challenges (*high confidence*). Efficiency itself is difficult to define and measure across full economies (Saunders et al. 2021). There is no single definition of energy efficiency and the definition understandably depends on the context used (Patterson 1996), which ranges from device-level efficiency all the way to the efficient use of energy throughout an economy. Broadly, energy-efficient strategies allow for the same level of services or output while using less energy. At the level of the entire economy, measures such as primary or final energy per capita or per GDP are often used as a proxy for energy efficiency; these measures reflect not only efficiency, but also many other factors such as industrial structure, endowed natural resources, consumer preferences, policies, and regulations. Energy efficiency and other demand-side strategies represent such a large set of technologies, strategies, policies, market and consumers' responses and policies that aggregate measures can be difficult to define (Saunders et al. 2021).

Measurement issues notwithstanding, virtually all studies that address net-zero energy systems assume improved energy intensity in the future (*high confidence*). The overall efficiency outcomes and the access to such improvements across different nations, however, are not clear. Energy consumption will increase over time – despite energy efficiency improvements – due to population growth and development (DeAngelo et al. 2021).

A study (DeAngelo et al. 2021) reviewed 153 integrated asset management scenarios that attain net-zero energy sector CO_2 emissions and found that, under a scenario with net-zero emissions: global final energy per capita lies between 21–109 GJ per person (median: 57), in comparison to 2018 global final energy use of 55 GJ per person; many countries use far more energy per capita than today as their incomes increase; global final energy use per unit of economic output ranges from 0.7–2.2 EJ per trillion USD (median: 1.5), in comparison to 5 EJ per trillion USD in 2018; and the median final energy consumption is 529 EJ. By comparison, final energy consumption would be 550 EJ if current energy consumption per capita continued under a future population of 10 billion people. Across all scenarios, total final energy consumption is higher today than in the year in which net-zero emissions are attained, and regionally, only the OECD+EU and Eurasia have lower median total final energy than in 2010.

Net-zero energy systems will be characterised by greater efficiency and more efficient use of energy across all sectors (*high confidence*). Road transportation efficiency improvements will require a shift from liquid fuels (Chapters 5 and 10). Emissions reductions will come from a transition to electricity, hydrogen, or synthetic fuels produced with low-carbon energy sources or processes. Vehicle automation, ride-hailing services, online shopping with door delivery services, and new solutions like last mile delivery with drones may result in increased service share. Lighter vehicles, a shift to public transit, and incorporation of two- and three-wheelers will be features of a net-zero energy system (Chapter 10). Teleworking and automation of work may provide reductions in driving needs. Other sectors, such as air travel and marine transportation may rely on alternative fuels such as biofuels, synthetic fuels, ammonia, produced with zero carbon energy source (Section 6.6.2.4).

Under net-zero energy systems, buildings would by characterised by improved construction materials, an increase in multi-family

dwellings, early retirement of inefficient buildings, smaller floor areas, and smart controls to optimise energy use in the building, namely for heating, cooling, LED lighting, and water heating (Chapter 9). End uses would utilise electricity, or potentially hydrogen, produced from zero-carbon sources. The use of electricity for heating and cooking may often be a less efficient process at converting primary energy to energy services than using natural gas, but using natural gas would require CDR in order to be considered net-zero emissions. Changes in behaviour may modestly lower demand. Most economies would have buildings with more efficient technologies powered by zero-carbon electricity, and developing economics would shift from biomass to electricity, raising their energy consumption as population and wealth increase under net-zero energy systems.

Industry has seen major efficiency improvements in the past, but many processes are now close to their thermodynamic limits. Electrification and breakthrough processes (such as producing steel with electricity and hydrogen), using recycled materials, using heat more efficiently by improving thermal insulation, and using waste heat for heat pumps, as well using advanced sensors, monitoring, and visualisation and communication technologies may provide further efficiency improvements (Chapter 11).

6.6.2.6   Greater Reliance on Integrated Energy System Approaches

Energy systems integration refers to connected planning and operations across energy carriers, including electricity, fuels, and thermal resources. Coordinated planning could be important in lowering system costs, increasing reliability, minimising environmental impacts, and ensuring that costs of R&D and infrastructure account for not just current needs but also for those of future energy systems (Section 6.4.3). Integration includes not only the physical energy systems themselves but also simultaneous societal objectives (e.g., sustainable development goals), innovation processes (e.g., coordinating R&D to increase the likelihood of beneficial technological spillovers), and other institutional and infrastructural transformations (Sachs et al. 2019). Given system variability and differences in regional resources, there are economic and technical advantages to greater coordination of investments and policies across jurisdictions, sectors, and levels of government (Schmalensee and Stavins 2017). Coordinated planning and operations can improve system economics by sharing resources, increasing the utilisation of capital-intensive assets, enhancing the geographical diversity of resource bases, and smoothing demand. But integration could require regulatory and market frameworks to facilitate and appropriate price signals to align incentives and to coordinate investments and operations.

Carbon-neutral energy systems are likely to be more interconnected than those of today (*high confidence*). The many possible feedstocks, energy carriers, and interconversion processes imply a greater need for the integration of production, transport, storage, and consumption of different fuels (Davis et al. 2018). For instance, electrification is expected to play an important role in decarbonising light-duty vehicles (Chapter 10, Section 6.4.3), yet the electricity and transport sectors have few direct interactions today. Systems integration and sectoral coupling are increasingly relevant to ensure that net-zero energy systems are reliable, resilient, and affordable (EPRI 2017; Martin et al. 2017; Buttler and Spliethoff 2018; O'Malley et al. 2020). Deep decarbonisation offers new opportunities and challenges for integrating different sectors as well as supply- and demand-side options. For instance, increasing electrification will change daily and seasonal load shapes, and end-use flexibilities and constraints could impact the desirability of different supply-side technologies (Brown et al. 2018; EPRI 2019b). The feasibility of net-zero energy system configurations could depend on demonstrating cross-sector benefits like balancing VRE sources in the electricity sector, and on offering the flexibility to produce multiple products. For instance, low-emissions synthetic fuels could help to bridge stationary and mobile applications, since fuel markets have more flexibility than instantaneously balanced electricity markets due to the comparative ease and cost of large-scale, long-term storage of chemical fuels (Davis et al. 2018).

There are few detailed archetypes of integrated energy systems that provide services with zero- or net-negative CO_2 emissions (such as Jacobson et al. 2019), so there is considerable uncertainty about integration and interactions across parts of the system. Although alternate configurations, trade-offs, and pathways are still being identified, common elements include fuels and processes like zero- or negative-CO_2 electricity generation and transmission, hydrogen production and transport, synthetic hydrocarbon production and transport, ammonia production and transport, and carbon management, where linkages across pathways could include the use of electricity to produce hydrogen via electrolysis (Smith et al. 2016; Moore 2017; Davis et al. 2018; Jenkins et al. 2018b; Shih et al. 2018; van Vuuren et al. 2018). Linked analytical frameworks are increasing being used to understand the potential role for system coupling with greater temporal resolution, spatial resolution, and heterogeneity of consumer and firm decisions (Bohringer and Rutherford 2008; Bistline and de la Chesnaye 2017; Collins et al. 2017; Gerboni et al. 2017; Santen et al. 2017; Pye et al. 2021).

Challenges associated with integrating net-zero energy systems include rapid technological change, the importance of behavioural dimensions in domains with limited experience and data, policy changes and interactions, and path dependence. Technological cost and public acceptance will influence the degree of integration. Sectoral pathways will likely be adaptive and adjust based on the resolution of uncertainties over time, and the relative competitiveness will evolve as the technological frontier evolves, which is a complex and path-dependent function of deployment, R&D, and inter-industry spillovers. Supply-side options interact with demand-side measures in increasingly integrated energy systems (Sorrell 2015; van Vuuren et al. 2018).

6.6.2.7 Carbon Dioxide Removal

While CDR is likely necessary for net-zero energy systems, the scale and mix of strategies is unclear –nonetheless some combination of BECCS and DACCS are likely to be part of net-zero energy systems (*high confidence*). Studies indicate that energy-sector CDR may potentially remove 5–12 $GtCO_2$ annually globally in net-zero energy systems (Fuss et al. 2018) (Figure 6.22; Section 6.7; Chapter 12). CDR

is not intended as a replacement for emissions reduction, but rather as a complementary effort to offset residual emissions from sectors that are not decarbonised and from other low-carbon technologies such as fossil CCS (McLaren et al. 2019; Gaffney et al. 2020; Iyer et al. 2021).

CDR covers a broad set of methods and implementation options (Chapters 7 and 12). The two CDR methods most relevant to the energy sector are BECCS, which is used to produce energy carriers, and DACCS which is an energy user (Smith et al. 2016; Singh and Colosi 2021). BECCS has value as an electricity generation technology, providing firm, dispatchable power to support electricity grids with large amounts of VRE sources, and reducing the reliance on other means to manage these grids, including electricity storage (Mac Dowell et al. 2017; Bistline and Blanford 2021a). BECCS may also be used to produce liquid fuels or gaseous fuels, including hydrogen (Section 6.4.2.6) (Muratori et al. 2020b). For instance, CO_2 from bio-refineries could be captured at <USD45 tCO_2^{-1} (Sanchez et al. 2018). Similarly, while CO_2 capture is expensive in the electricity sector, its integration with hydrogen via biomass gasification can be achieved at an incremental capital cost of 3–35% (Muratori et al. 2020b) (Section 6.4). As with all uses of bioenergy, linkages to broad sustainability concerns may limit the viable development, as will the presence of high-quality geologic sinks in close proximity (Melara et al. 2020).

DACCS offers a modular approach to CDR (Creutzig et al. 2019), but it could be a significant consumer of energy. DAC could also interact with other elements of the energy systems as the captured CO_2 could be reused to produce low-carbon methanol and other fuels (Hoppe et al. 2018; Realmonte et al. 2019; Zhang and Fujimori 2020). DACCS might also offer an alternative for use of excess electricity produced by variable renewables (Wohland et al. 2018), though there are uncertainties about the economic performance of this integrated approach.

6.6.3 The Institutional and Societal Characteristics of Net-zero Energy Systems

The transition to net-zero energy systems is not just technological; it requires shifts in institutions, organisations, and society more generally. As such, it involves institutional changes alongside changes in supply, technology, or markets (Andrews-Speed 2016, Pai et al. 2021). Institutional relationships between governments and energy sector actors (e.g., consumers, electricity companies) affect the nature of net-zero systems, as these entities may collaborate on or dispute net-zero goals and measures to achieve them. For example, following the Fukushima disaster, Japan placed emphasis on government-utility-public cooperation on use of nuclear power as a means of reducing carbon emissions (Sklarew 2018). Institutions are instrumental in shaping net-zero energy systems in multiple ways, complemented by and interacting with the behaviours of actors and policy regimes in these systems (Figure 6.24).

One level of institutional interactions reflects embedded institutions, norms, beliefs, and ideas that would need to change to support net-zero energy systems. This applies, for example, to the objectives of modern economies and the potentially contradictory dynamics embedded in

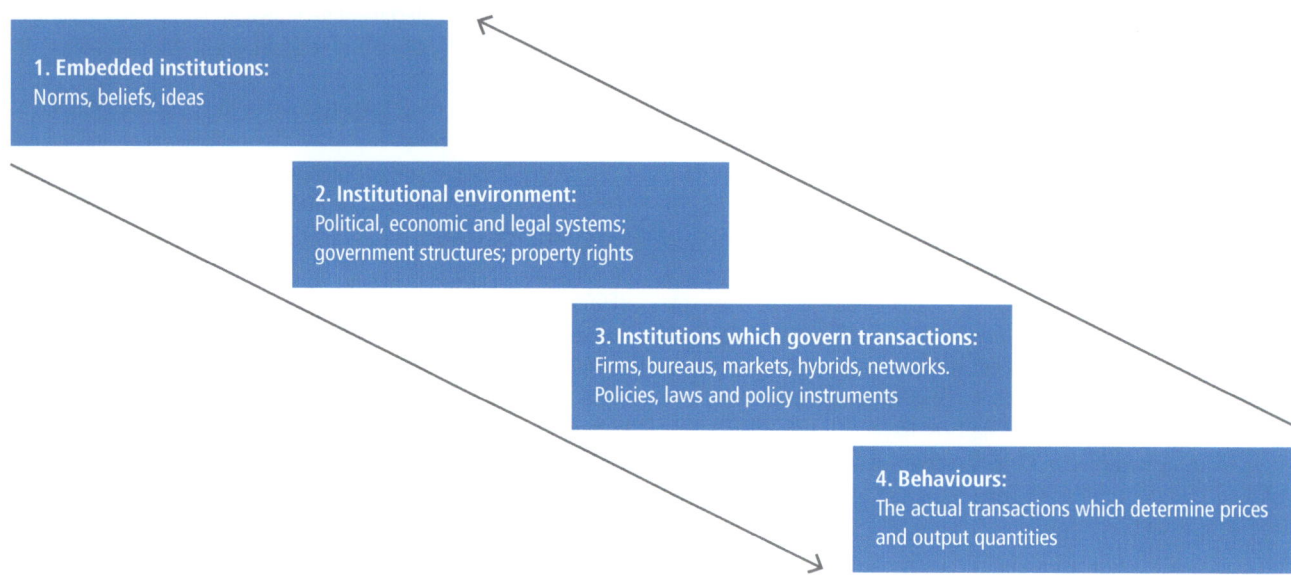

Figure 6.24 | A four-level framework for institutional change. The diagram depicts three levels of institutions (1–3) which collectively govern actor behaviours (4). Source: with permission from Andrews-Speed (2016).

the concept of 'green growth' (Stegemann and Ossewaarde 2018; Stoknes and Rockström 2018). The institutional environment – the political and legal systems that govern exchanges and protect property rights – would also need to be different in net-zero energy systems. In this setting, changing regulations or subsidies that continue to favour carbon-intensive systems over the technologies of a net-zero energy system might prove difficult (Sovacool 2017). More generally, net-zero energy systems will need new regulatory frameworks to undertake new challenges, from managing a more interconnected grid to adequately governing underground storage of CO_2. Institutions may also govern specific transactions, such as firms or networks that supply energy fuels or services. Current actors are typically resistant to disruptions, even if such disruptions may broadly benefit society (Kungl 2015; Schmid et al. 2017; Mori 2018).

For example, one energy system characterised by differentiated institutional interactions is the USA, where delivery of liquid fuels is lightly regulated, while electricity delivery is closely regulated (Dworkin et al. 2013). Reforming this two-pronged system for decarbonisation would require four types of institutional change: (i) changes to the control systems that coordinate generation and transmission through a pyramidal architecture for the operational control, dispatch, and delivery of electricity with a primary emphasis on reliability; (ii) changes to the financing of central-station power plants through long-term bonds, as valued by Wall Street ratings analysts; (iii) changes to the structure of investor-owned utilities that attract private investors who expected decades of technological stability to yield long-term, low-risk revenues; and (iv) changes to regulations to restructure and limit excessive returns and easy entry of new retail competitors, all recognising local and national concerns through state and federal regulatory agencies. The example shows how decision-making and the infrastructures involved are layered, and can create 'nested hierarchies' where institutions fulfil multiple roles for energy governance or regulation simultaneously

(Stern et al. 2016b). Internationally and across different parts of the energy system, institutional challenges such as these could become even more stark and complex (Van de Graaf 2013).

6.6.4 Regional Circumstances and Net-zero Energy Systems

Countries have flexibility to pursue options that make the most sense for their national circumstances (Figure 6.25). They may emphasise supply transformation over demand reduction; deploy different resources; engage at different levels in international energy trade; support different energy industries; focus on different energy carriers (e.g., electricity, hydrogen); or focus more on distributed or integrated systems, among others. Many factors may influence the long-term net-zero energy systems that are appropriate for any country's national circumstances, including the following.

Future technology. Technological transitions have often been driven by the relative merits of different technology options. Recent trends in the use of PV cells, wind power, and in batteries, for example, have been spurred by their increasing economic competitiveness (Section 6.3). Yet future technology cannot be fully predicted, so it provides only a partial guide today for charting a path toward future systems.

Indigenous energy resources. Countries may emphasise approaches that take advantage of indigenous energy resources such as solar power, wind, hydroelectric resources, land for bioenergy crops, CO_2 storage capability, or fossil resources to be used with CCS. Countries with less abundant resources may put greater emphasis on demand reductions and regional integration. Countries with resource bases that are easily tradeable, like low-carbon electricity or bioenergy, may choose to trade those resources rather than use them domestically (Box 6.10, Section 6.4.3, 6.4.5).

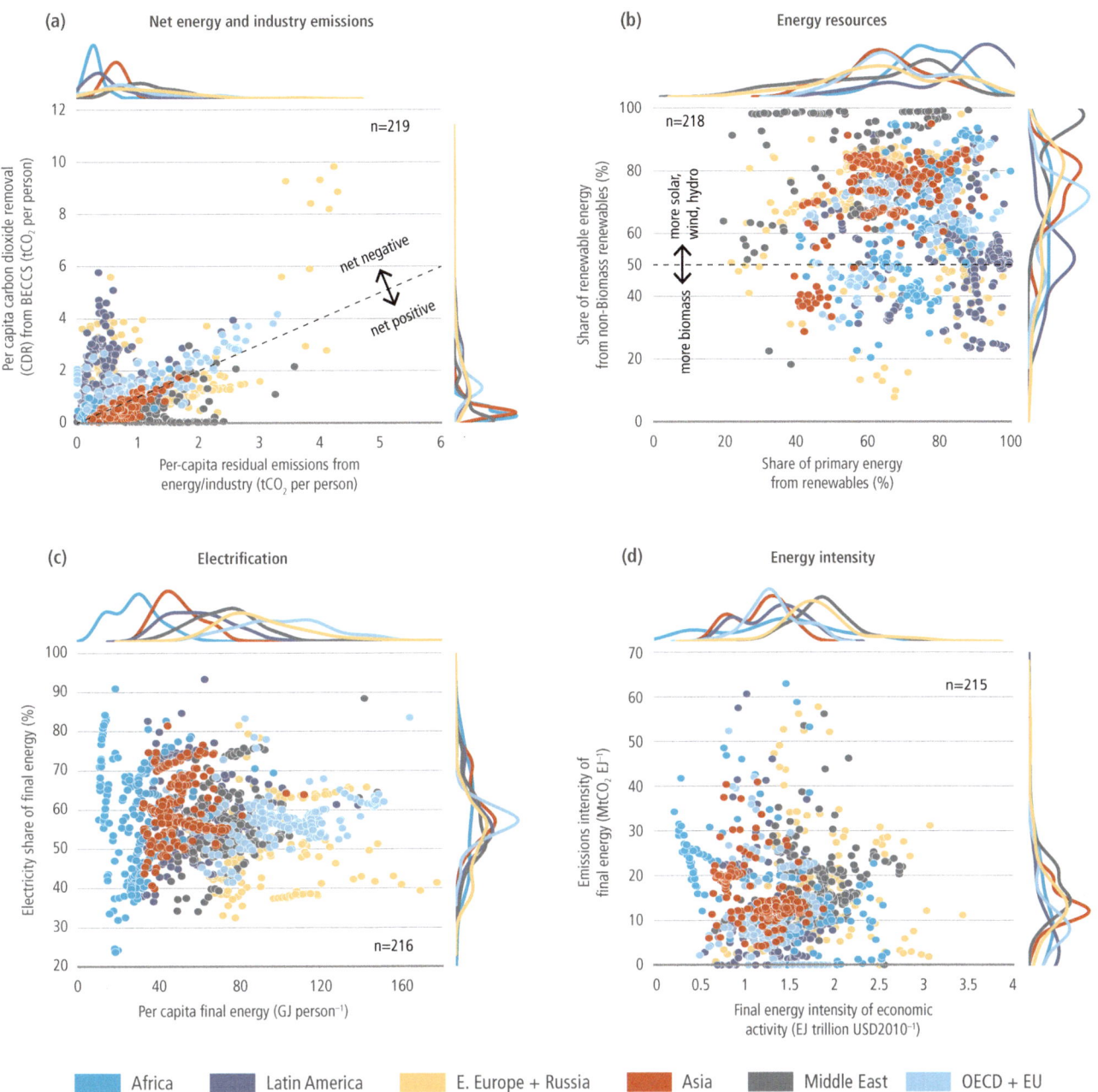

Figure 6.25 | Characteristics of regional energy systems and emissions when global energy and industrial CO₂ emissions reach net-zero. Regional differences are shown for: **(a)** residual emissions and carbon removal; **(b)** energy resources; **(c)** electrification; and **(d)** energy intensity. Distributions of scenarios are shown along each axis for each region. Colour scheme is shown in (a). Points represent individual scenarios from the AR6 Scenarios Database (R6 regions dataset).

Regional climate. Climate influences heating and cooling demand, both of which influence countries' energy demands and energy infrastructure to meet those demands (Section 6.5). In addition to daily demand profiles, heating and cooling are seasonal, influencing which energy sources may serve these loads and the seasonal storage they require. Cooling is almost entirely served by electricity today, and heating has commonly been served by non-electric fuels. In low-carbon energy systems, heating may be increasingly served by electricity (Section 6.6.4), meaning that the influence of regional climate may be strongest on countries' electricity systems.

Current energy system configuration. Future sectoral energy demands and the potential for demand-side transformation are partially determined by existing infrastructure (e.g., building stocks, transport infrastructure). Countries with less developed or growing energy systems will have more flexibility to create the systems that best match their long-term goals, but there may be substantial challenges in transitioning directly to the most advanced low-carbon technology options, and countries may have different capacities to absorb technology from other countries.

6

Regional integration. Regional integration will allow countries to bridge energy gaps using external linkages, including regional electricity integration and trade in hydrogen, biomass, and other fuels. Countries with greater integration can rely more heavily on imports and may therefore rely less on indigenous resources (Box 6.10).

Societal preferences. Citizens in every country have preferences for certain technological options or mitigation approaches over others that will influence energy system choices. The public generally prefers a future energy system based largely on renewables. Preferences for non-renewable energy differ across regions and groups. For example, studies have found that people in the UK, Germany, the Netherlands, and Switzerland prefer renewable energy and personal energy efficiency and savings to nuclear, fossil fuels and CCS (Jones et al. 2012; Scheer et al. 2013; Demski et al. 2017; Bessette and Arvai 2018; Steg 2018; Volken et al. 2018). Studies have found that people with higher education levels, higher incomes, females, and liberals prefer renewables to fossil fuels and nuclear (Van Rijnsoever et al. 2015; Bertsch et al. 2016; Blumer et al. 2018; Jobin et al. 2019). The willingness to pay for renewable electricity differs by source (Ma et al. 2015; Sundt and Rehdanz 2015).

Technological leadership, economic opportunities, and growth. Countries may emphasise technologies in which they intend to have technological leadership and a competitive advantage. These could emerge over time or be based on current areas of opportunity or leadership. Industrial policy will influence future energy system as technological choices can benefit or hamper incumbents or new market actors.

Energy security. Countries emphasising import security will tend to rely more heavily on indigenous resources (Section 6.3). Some indigenous resources may raise security of supply issues that will influence energy system configurations. Bioenergy and hydropower, for example, can be subject to import climate risks (Section 6.5), and significant integration of VRE technologies will influence electricity system infrastructure and management (Section 6.6.2, Box 6.8).

Other factors. Countries will consider a wide range of other factors in building toward low-carbon energy systems. Population density, for example, will influence building and transportation energy demands; economic transitions will influence industrial energy demands. Societal priorities beyond climate, notably SDGs may influence technology choices and types of energy systems (Sections 6.3 and 6.7.7).

Box 6.10 | Regional Integration of Energy Systems

Energy systems are linked across countries in many ways: countries transport crude oil across the ocean in supertankers, pipelines carry oil and natural gas across country boundaries, electric power lines cross country boundaries, and countries trade industrial commodities that carry embodied energy or that are essential inputs to mitigation technologies. Future systems will generate electricity using different mixes of technologies, produce and transport different carriers (e.g., hydrogen or biofuels), and use far less fossil fuel, among other major changes. Important examples include electricity, hydrogen, and biomass.

Electricity system integration. Net-zero energy systems will rely more heavily on electricity generated from low-emissions technologies. Given the significant variations in the location of low-carbon electricity resources and the temporal variability of some renewable electricity sources, notably solar and wind power, regional electricity grids could reduce overall costs of net-zero energy systems (Section 6.4.5). Furthermore, electricity transmission interconnections could significantly reduce local energy balancing costs and investment in peaking plants needed to meet security of supply requirements, and it could increase system resilience, especially in the case of extreme events such as heat waves or cold spells (Fasihi and Bogdanov 2016). Important challenges to regional electricity integration include geopolitical concerns from cross-border trade and societal and technological challenges associated with building new transmission lines.

Hydrogen trade. Hydrogen may play an important role in future net-zero energy systems, particularly in applications where electricity is not economically advantageous (Box 6.9). Hydrogen can be used to decarbonise regions in which it is produced, and it can also be transported long distances to facilitate decarbonisation of sectors distant from sources of low-cost supply. Methods of long-distance, high-volume hydrogen transport could include liquid storage, chemical carriers, and gaseous delivery via pipelines (Section 6.4.5). In net-zero systems with substantial wind and solar power generation, hydrogen can be generated through electrolysis and then shipped to other locations. Important challenges to hydrogen trade include cost-effective low-carbon production, cost of delivery infrastructure, storage, and end-use technology costs and safety.

Trade in biomass. Biomass may also play an important role in net-zero energy systems (Section 6.6.4, Chapter 3). Large-scale bioenergy production and consumption is likely to trigger global biomass trade. Global bioenergy trade volumes presently exceed 1 EJ yr^{-1}, of which 60% is directly traded for energy purposes (Proskurina et al. 2019a). Established trade mechanisms include wood pellet transport, ethanol, and biodiesel (Proskurina et al. 2019b). In a net-zero global energy system, bioenergy trade could be greater than current trade of coal or natural gas, but less than that of petroleum (Sharmina et al. 2017; Mandley et al. 2020). Some studies indicate that Latin America and Africa could become key exporting regions, with the EU, the USA, and East Asia emerging as key importers (Alsaleh and Abdul-Rahim 2018; Rentizelas et al. 2019). Studies have found that net bioenergy exports could be as high as 10% of GDP for some Latin American countries, while other regions like the EU may be faced with burgeoning import reliance (Daioglou et al. 2020b; Mahlknecht et al. 2020). In addition to challenges associated with bioenergy production (Section 6.4 and Chapter 7), important challenges to biomass trade include differences in sustainability criteria and land/biomass definitions in different jurisdictions, and difficulties in establishing consistent monitoring and auditing systems (Lamers et al. 2016).

6.7   Low-carbon Energy System Transitions in the Near and MediumTerm

6.7.1   Low-carbon Energy System Transition Pathways

6.7.1.1   Energy System Emissions

Without additional efforts to reduce emissions, it is very unlikely that energy system CO_2 emissions will decrease sufficiently to limit warming to well below 2°C (*high confidence*). Scenarios assuming improvements in technology but no additional climate policies beyond those in place today provide a benchmark for comparison against energy-related CO_2 emissions in mitigation scenarios (Figure 6.26). Emissions in these reference scenarios increase through 2050 but span a broad range (Riahi et al. 2017; Wei et al. 2018) (Chapter 3, Figure 3.16). The highest emission levels are about four times current emissions; the lowest are modestly below today's emissions. Emissions in these scenarios increase in most regions, but they diverge significantly across regions (Bauer et al. 2017). Asia and the Middle East and Africa account for the majority of increased emissions across these scenarios (Figure 6.27). While it is unlikely that there will be no new climate policies in the future, these scenarios

nonetheless support the conclusion that the energy sector will not be decarbonised without explicit policy actions to reduce emissions.

Warming cannot be limited to well below 2°C without rapid and deep reductions in energy system GHG emissions (*high confidence*). Energy sector CO_2 emissions fall by 87–97% (interquartile range) by 2050 in scenarios limiting warming to 1.5°C (>50%) with no or limited overshoot and 60–79% in scenarios limiting warming to 2°C (>67%) with action starting in 2020 (Figure 6.26). Energy sector GHG emissions fall by 85–95% (interquartile range) in scenarios limiting warming to 1.5°C (>50%) with no or limited overshoot, and 62–78% in scenarios limiting warming to 2°C (>67%) with action starting in 2020 (Figure 6.26). In 2030, in scenarios limiting warming to 1.5°C (>50%) with no or limited overshoot, net CO_2 and GHG emissions fall by 35–51% and 38–52% respectively. Key characteristics of emissions pathways – the year of peak emissions, the year when net emissions reach zero, and the pace of emissions reductions – vary widely across countries and regions. These differences arise from differences in economic development, demographics, resource endowments, land use, and potential carbon sinks (Schaeffer, et al. 2020; Schreyer, et al. 2020; van Soest, Heleen et al. 2021) (Figure 6.27, Figure 6.28, Box 6.11). If countries do not move quickly

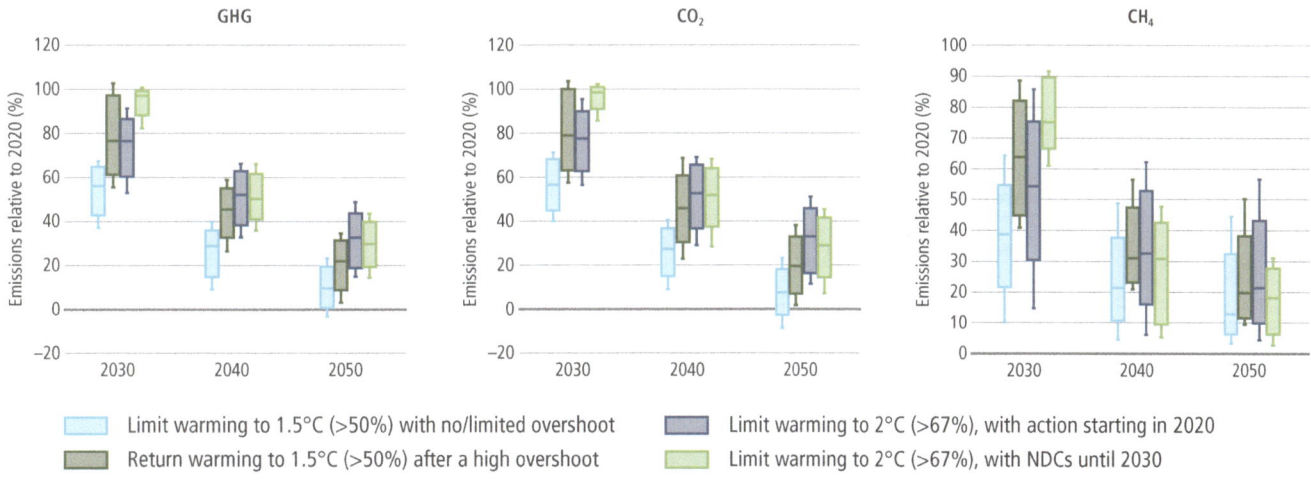

Figure 6.26 | Projected energy sector GHG emissions for the 1.5°C scenarios (without and with overshoot), and likely below 2°C scenarios (without and with delayed policy action) during 2020–2050 (Source: AR6 Scenarios Database). Boxes indicate 25th and 75th percentiles, while whiskers indicate 5th and 95th percentiles. GHG emissions are inclusive of energy sector CO_2, CH_4, N_2O emissions and 80% of global HFC emissions. Number of model-scenario combinations in AR6 Scenarios Database: limit warming to 1.5°C (>50%) with no or limited overshoot: 77; return warming to 1.5°C (>50%) after a high overshoot: 110; limit warming to 2(C (>67%) with action starting in 2020: 164; limit warming to 2°C (>67%) with NDCs until 2030: 97.

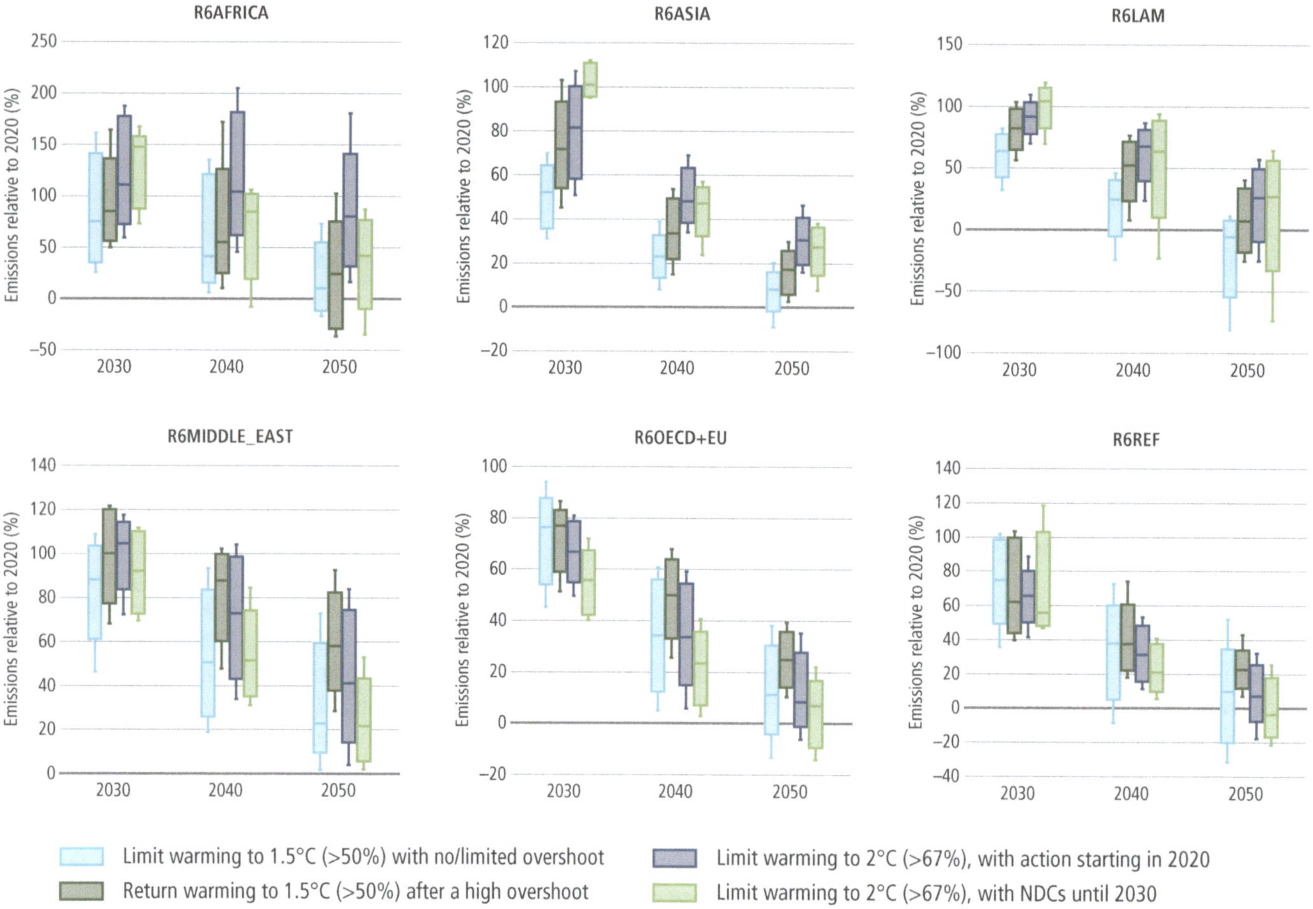

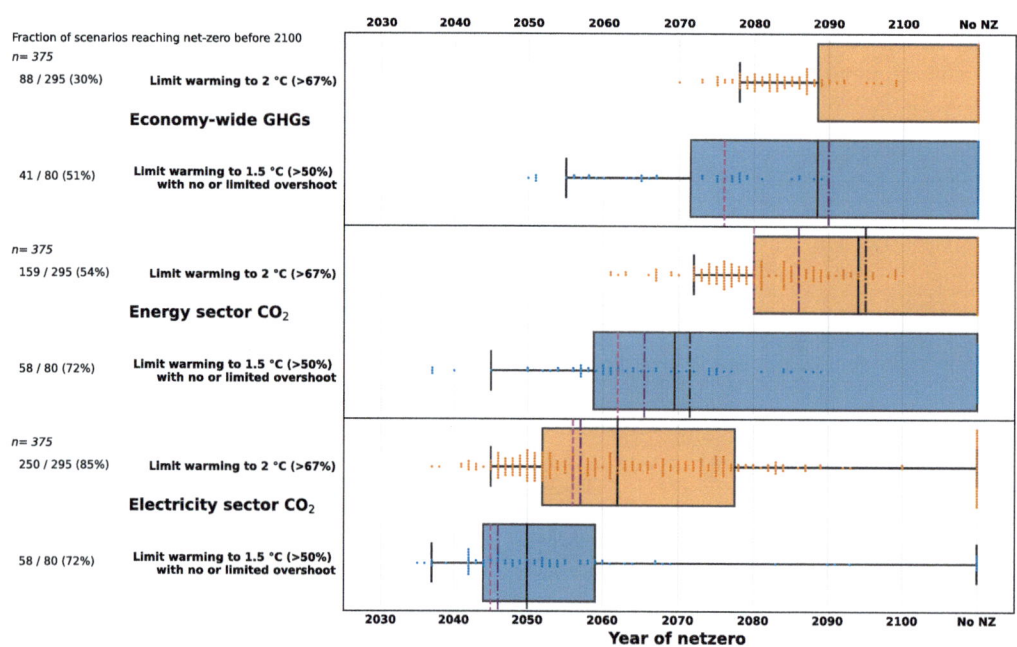

Figure 6.27 | Net regional (R6) CO$_2$ emissions from energy across scenarios that limit/return warming to 1.5°C (>50%) with no or limited/after a high overshoot, and scenarios that limit warming to 2°C (>67%) with action starting in 2020 or with NDCs until 2030, during 2020–2050 (Source: AR6 Scenarios Database). Boxes indicate 25th and 75th percentiles, while whiskers indicate 5th and 95th percentiles. Most mitigation scenarios are based on a cost-minimising framework that does not consider historical responsibility or other equity approaches.

Figure 6.28 | The timing of net-zero emissions for full economy greenhouse gases (GHGs), energy sector CO$_2$, and electricity sector CO$_2$. Boxes indicate 25th and 75th percentiles, centre black line is the median, while whiskers indicate 1.5x the inter-quartile range. The vertical dashed lines represent the median point at which emissions in the scenarios have dropped by 95% (pink) and 97.5% (purple), respectively. Dots represent individual scenarios. The fraction indicates the number of scenarios reaching net-zero by 2100 out of the total sample. Source: AR6 Scenario Database.

to reduce emissions – if reductions are delayed – a more rapid energy transition will subsequently be required to limit warming to 2°C or lower (Rogelj et al. 2015a, 2018a; IPCC 2018).

The timing of net-zero energy system emissions varies substantially across scenarios. In scenarios limiting warming to 1.5°C (>50%) with no or limited overshoot (2°C (>67%)), the energy system reaches net-zero CO_2 emissions (interquartile range) from 2060 onwards (2080–). (Figure 6.28). However, net emissions reach near-zero more quickly. For example, in scenarios limiting warming to 1.5°C (>50%) with no or limited overshoot (2°C (>67%)) net energy system CO_2 emissions drop by 95% between 2056 and 2075 (2073 and 2093). Net full economy GHG emissions reach zero more slowly than net CO_2 emissions. In some scenarios, net energy system CO_2 and total GHG emissions do not reach zero this century, offset by CDR in other sectors.

The timing of emissions reductions will vary across the different parts of the energy sector (Figure 6.28). To decarbonise most cost-effectively, global net CO_2 emissions from electricity generation will likely reach zero before the rest of the energy sector (*medium confidence*). In scenarios limiting warming to 1.5°C (>50%) with no or limited overshoot (2°C (>67%)), net electricity sector CO_2 emissions

(interquartile range) reach zero globally between 2044 and 2055 (2052 and 2078) (Figure 6.28). It is likely to be less costly to reduce net CO_2 emissions close to or below zero in the electricity sector than in other sectors, because there are relatively more low-emissions options in electricity. Sectors such as long-distance transport, air transport, and process heat are anticipated to face greater challenges to decarbonisation than the electricity sector (Clark and Herzog 2014; Rogelj et al. 2015b, 2018b; IPCC 2018; Luderer et al. 2018).

In addition, there are potential options to remove CO_2 from the atmosphere in the electricity sector, notably BECCS, which would allow electricity sector emissions to drop below zero. Without CDR options, electricity sector emissions may not fall all the way to zero. If CDR is accomplished in other sectors and not in electricity, some fossil fuel plants may still lead to positive net electricity sector CO_2 emissions, even in net-zero economies (Bistline and Blanford 2021b; Williams et al. 2021a).

We lack sufficient understanding to pin down precise dates at which energy system CO_2 emissions in individual countries, regions, or sectors will reach net zero. Net-zero timing is based on many factors that are not known today or are bound up in development of key technologies, such as energy storage, bioenergy, or hydrogen. Some

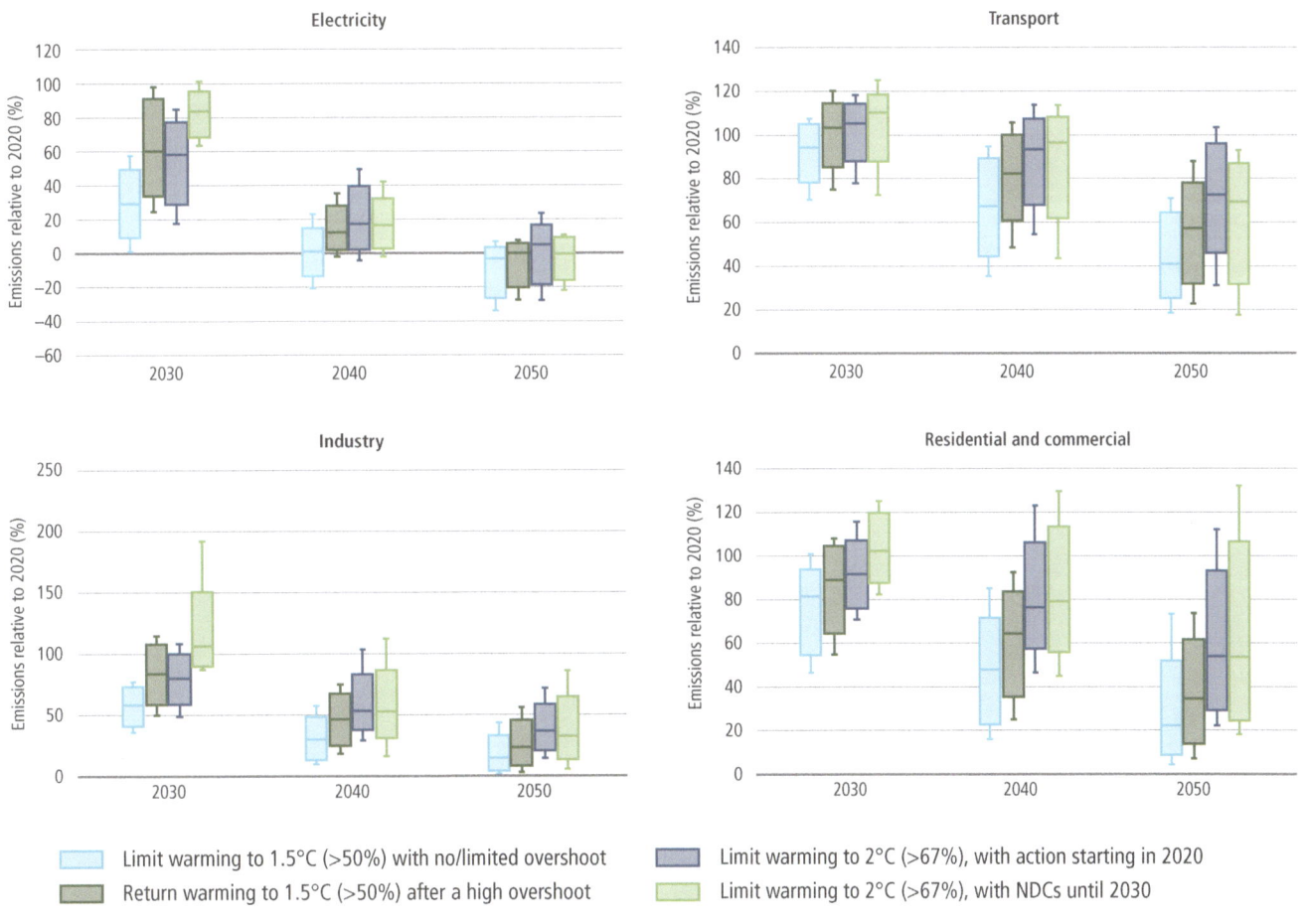

Figure 6.29 | Reductions in CO_2 emissions relative to 2020 levels for scenarios that limit/return warming to 1.5°C (>50%) with no or limited/after a high, overshoot, and scenarios that limit warming to 2°C (>67%), with action starting in 2020 or NDCs until 2030, during 2030–2050. Boxes indicate 25th and 75th percentiles while whiskers indicate 5th and 95th percentiles. Source: AR6 Scenarios Database.

countries have low-carbon resource bases that could support deep emissions reductions, while others do not. Timing is also affected by the availability of CDR options, whether these options are in the energy sector or elsewhere, and the discount rate used to assess strategies (Bednar et al. 2019; Emmerling et al. 2019). Moreover, while many scenarios are designed to minimise global mitigation costs, many other frameworks exist for allocating mitigation effort across countries (van den Berg et al. 2019) (Chapter 4).

6.7.1.2   Low-carbon Energy Transition Strategies

There are multiple technological routes to reduce energy system emissions (Section 6.6). Here we discuss three of these: (i) decarbonising primary energy and electricity generation; (ii) switching to electricity, bioenergy, hydrogen, and other fuels produced from low-carbon sources; and (iii) limiting energy use through improvement of efficiency and conservation. CDR is discussed in Section 6.7.1.3 Fossil fuel transitions are discussed in Section 6.7.4.

Decarbonising primary energy and electricity generation. Limiting warming to well below 2°C requires a rapid and dramatic increase in energy produced from low- or zero-carbon sources (*high*

confidence). Low- and zero-carbon technologies produce 74–82% (interquartile range) of primary energy in 2050 in scenarios limiting warming to 1.5°C (>50%) with no or limited overshoot and 55–68% in scenarios limiting warming to 2°C (>67%) (Figure 6.29). The share of low-carbon technologies in global primary energy supply today is below 20% (Chapter 3, Section 6.3, and Figure 6.29). The percentage of low- and zero-carbon energy will depend in part on the evolution of energy demand – the more that energy demand grows, the more energy from low- and zero-carbon sources will be needed, and the higher the percentage of total primary energy these sources will represent.

Low- and zero-carbon sources produce 97–99% of global electricity in 2050 in scenarios limiting warming to 1.5°C (>50%) with no or limited overshoot and 93–97% in scenarios limiting warming to 2°C (>67%) (Figure 6.29) (*medium confidence*). Decarbonising electricity generation, in tandem with increasing use of electricity (see below), is an essential near-term strategy for limiting warming. The increase in low- and zero-carbon electricity will occur while electricity demand grows substantially. Studies have projected that global electricity demand will roughly double by 2050 and quadruple to quintuple by 2100 irrespective of efforts to reduce emissions (Bauer et al. 2017; Luderer et al. 2017; IEA 2019a).

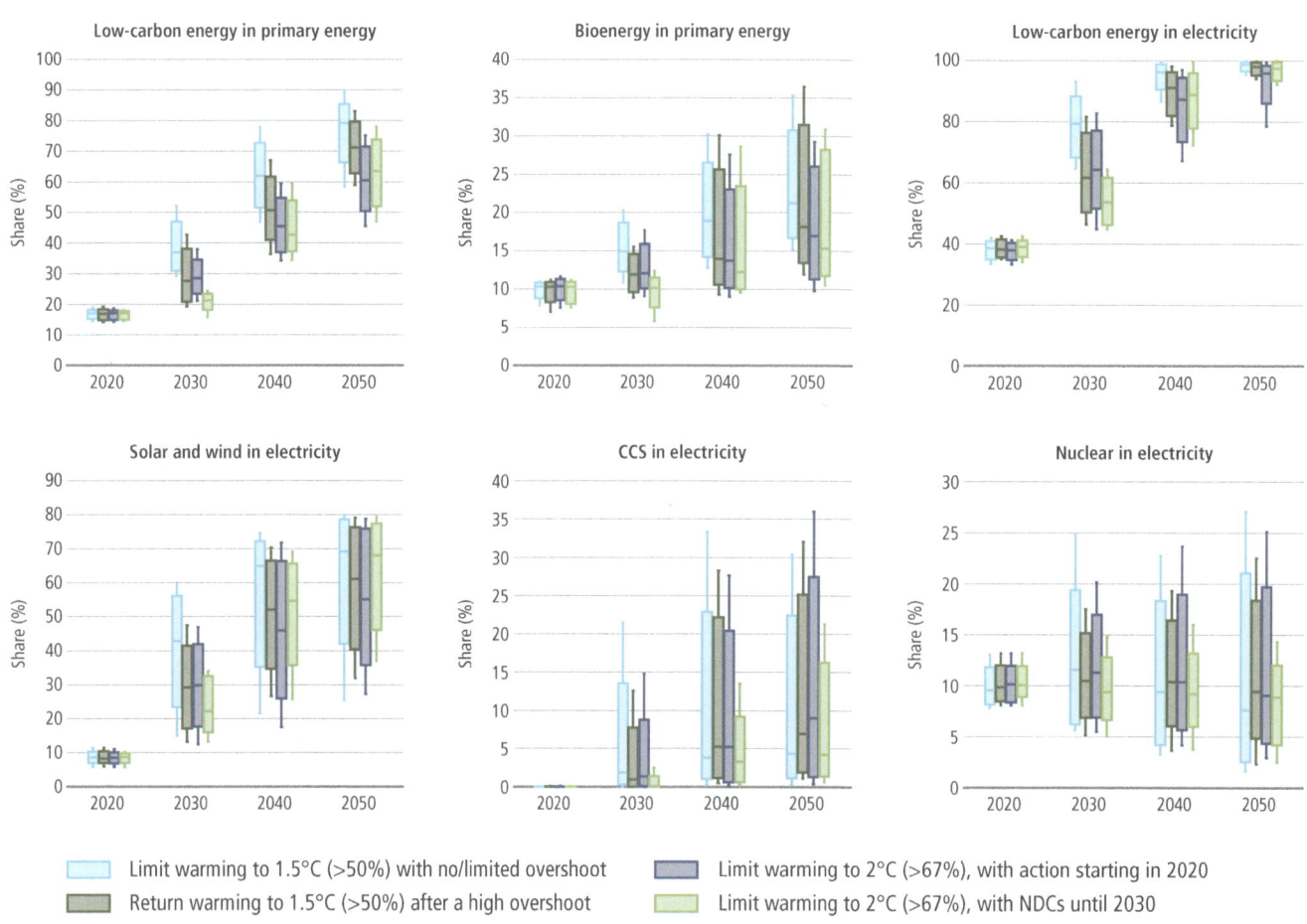

Figure 6.30 | Shares of low-carbon energy (all sources except unabated fossil fuels) and bioenergy (including both traditional and commercial biomass) in total primary energy, and solar+wind, CCS and nuclear in electricity for scenarios that limit/return warming to 1.5°C (>50%) with no or limited/after a high, overshoot, and scenarios that limit warming to 2°C (>67%), with action starting in 2020 or NDCs until 2030, during 2030–2050 (Source: AR6 Scenarios Database). Boxes indicate 25th and 75th percentiles while whiskers indicate 5th and 95th percentiles.

Renewable energy, especially generation from solar and wind, is likely to have an important role in many low-carbon electricity systems. The contributions of wind and solar electricity will depend on their levelised costs relative to other options, integration costs, system value, and the ability to integrate variable resources into the grid (Section 6.6). Electric sector technology mixes will vary by region but will typically include additional resources such as hydropower, nuclear power, fossil generation with CCS, energy storage resources, and geothermal energy, among others. Contributions of different options vary widely across scenarios based on different assumptions about these factors (Figure 6.30).

Nonetheless, it is likely that wind and solar will dominate low-carbon generation and capacity growth over the next couple of decades due to supporting policies in many countries, and due to their significant roles in early electric sector decarbonisation, alongside reductions in coal generation (Bistline and Blanford 2021b; Pan et al. 2021). Clean firm technologies play important roles in providing flexibility and on-demand generation for longer durations, though deployment of these technologies is typically associated with deeper decarbonisation levels (e.g., beyond 70–80% reductions), which are likely to be more important after 2030 in many regions, and with more limited CDR deployment (Baik et al. 2021; Bistline and Blanford 2021a; Williams et al. 2021a).

Box 6.11 | Illustrative Low-carbon Energy System Transitions

There are multiple possible strategies to transform the energy system to reach net-zero CO_2 emissions and to limit warming to 2°C (>67%) or lower. All pathways rely on the strategies for net-zero CO_2 energy systems highlighted in Section 6.6.2, but they vary in the emphasis that they put on different aspects of these strategies and the pace at which they approach net-zero emissions. The pathway that any country or region might follow will depend on a wide variety of factors (Section 6.6.4), including, for example, resource endowments, trade and integration with other countries and regions, carbon sequestration potential, public acceptability of various technologies, climate, the nature of domestic industries, the degree of urbanisation, and the relationship with other societal priorities such as energy access, energy security, air pollution, and economic competitiveness. The Illustrative Mitigation Pathways presented in this box demonstrate four distinct strategies for energy system transformations and how each plays out for a different region, aligned with global strategies that would limit warming to 2.0°C (>67%) or to 1.5°C (>50%). Each pathway represents a very different vision of a net-zero energy system. Yet, all these pathways share the common characteristic of a dramatic system-wide transformation over the coming decades.

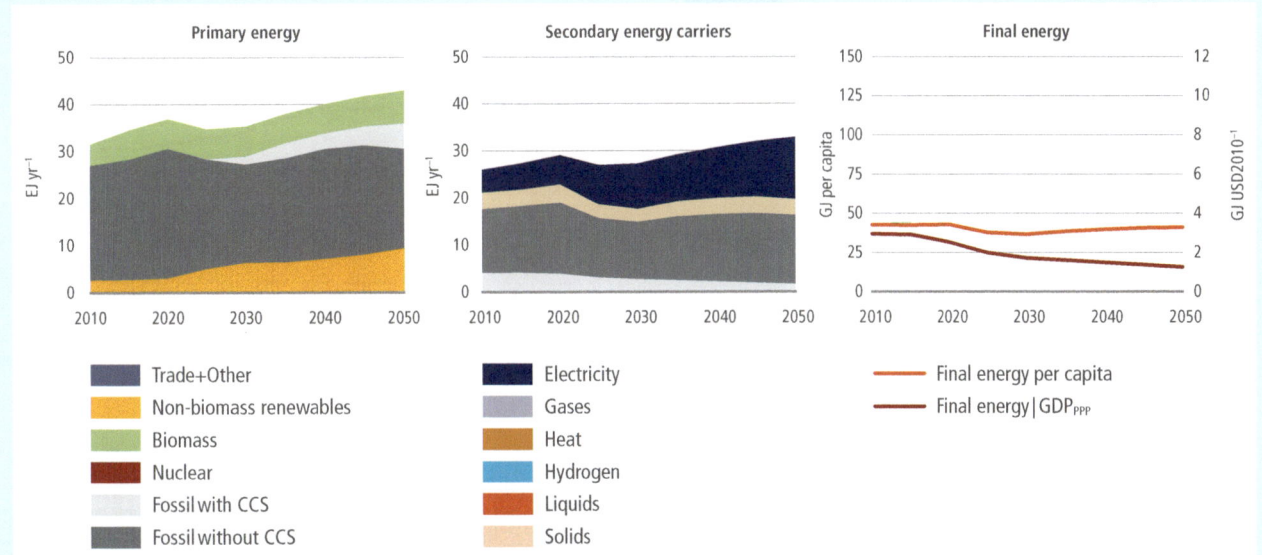

Box 6.11, Figure 1 | Illustrative Mitigation Pathway 2.0-Neg: Latin America & Caribbean (LAM) in a scenario that limits warming to 2°C (>67%) (LAM net-zero economy 2040–2045, net-zero energy system 2045–2050). Supply-side focus with growing dependency on carbon dioxide removal and agriculture, forestry and other land-use (AFOLU), thus achieves net-zero CO_2 relatively early.

Box 6.11 (continued)

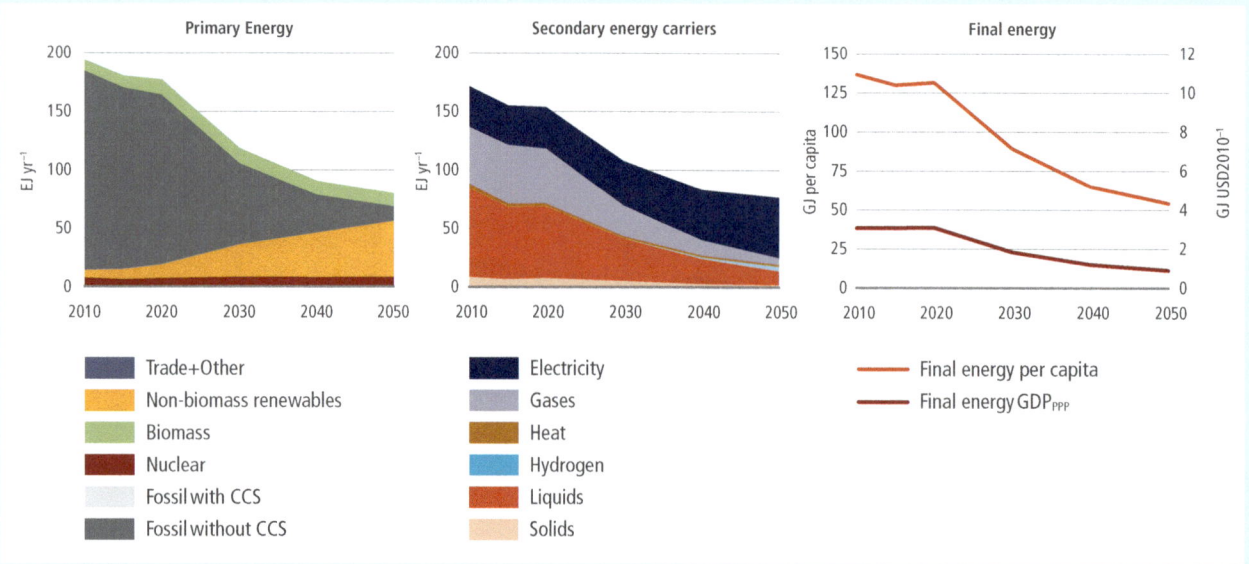

Box 6.11, Figure 2 | Illustrative Mitigation Pathway 1.5-Renewables: Africa (AF) in a scenario that limts warming to 1.5°C (>50%) (AF net-zero economy, 2055–2060, AF net-zero energy system 2055–2060). Rapid expansion of non-biomass renewables, high electrification, and a fossil fuel phase-out.

Box 6.11, Figure 3 | Illustrative Mitigation Pathway 1.5-Low Demand: Developed Countries (DEV) in a scenario that limits warming to 1.5°C (>50%) (DEV net-zero economy, 2055–2060, net-zero energy system 2075–2080). Major reduction of energy demand, high electrification, and gradual fossil fuel phase-out.

Box 6.11 (continued)

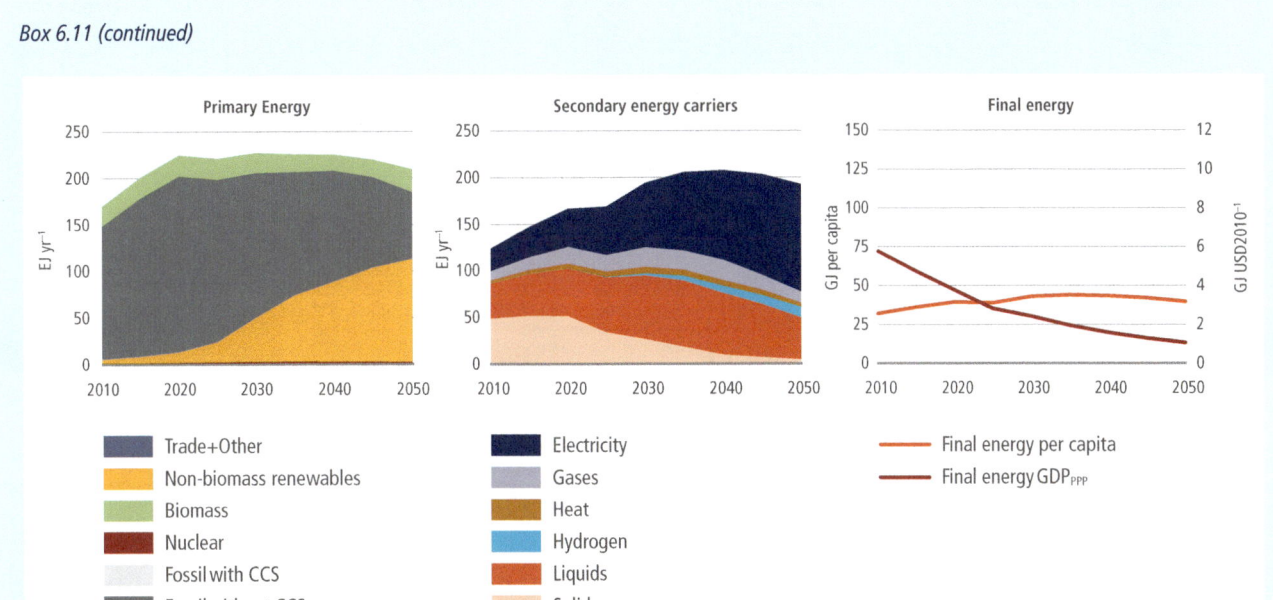

Box 6.11, Figure 4 | Illustrative Mitigation Pathway 1.5-Shifting Pathways: Asia and Pacific (APC) in a scenario that limits warming to 1.5°C (>50%) (APC net-zero economy, 2075–2080, net-zero energy system 2090–2095). Renewables, high electrification, fossil fuel phase-out and low agriculture, forestry and other land-use (AFOLU) emissions. Reaches net-zero CO$_2$ relatively late.

Box 6.11, Table 1 | Summary of selected Illustrative Mitigation Pathways energy system characteristics in 2050 for the chosen regions.

		Energy sector CO$_2$ Reduction 2020–2050	Energy intensity		Variable renewable electricity generation		Low-carbon electricity capacity additions		CO$_2$ removal BECCS, AFOLU, Total	GDP per capita		Year net-zero CO$_2$ emissions		
		%	MJ/PPP USD2010		EJ yr^{-1} (%)		GW yr^{-1}		GtCO$_2$ yr^{-1}	PPP USD2010 per person		Full economy	Energy sector	Electricity
	Region	2050	2020	2050	2020	2050	2020	2050	2050	2020	2050			
IMP-Neg	LAM	124	3	2.1	0.5 (9)	7.7 (53)	15.4	21.5	1.1, 0.2, 1.9	12,952	24,860	2040–2045	2045–2050	2025–2030
IMP-Ren	AF	85	7.6	1.9	0.1 (5)	18 (84)	5	217	0.1, 0, 0.1	2965	8521	2055–2060	2055–2060	2025–2030
IMP-LD	DEV	92	3.1	0.9	4.6 (13)	37 (72)	52	188	0, 0.6, 0.6	42,945	61,291	2055–2060	2075–2080	2045–2050
IMP-SP	APC	76	3.8	1.1	3 (7)	91 (79)	123	603	0.1, 0.4, 0.4	10,514	37,180	2075–2080	2085–2090	2085–2090

Switching to low-carbon energy carriers. Switching to energy carriers produced from low-carbon sources will be an important strategy for energy sector decarbonisation. Accelerated electrification of end uses such as light duty transport, space heating, and cooking is a critical near-term mitigation strategy (Sugiyama 2012; Zou et al. 2015; Rockström et al. 2017; IEA 2019f; Waisman et al. 2019; B. Tang et al. 2021). Electricity supplies 48–58% (interquartile range) of the global final energy demand by 2050 in scenarios limiting warming to 1.5°C (>50%) with no or limited overshoot and 36–47% in scenarios limiting warming to 2°C (>67%) (Figure 6.29). Globally, the current level of electrification is about 20%.

Indirect electrification encompasses the use of electricity to produce hydrogen and synthetic fuels (efuels or power fuels). The extent of indirect electrification of final energy will depend on resource endowments and other regionally specific circumstances. Although indirect electrification is less efficient compared to direct electrification, it allows low-carbon fuels to be imported from regions with abundant low-carbon electricity generation resources (Fasihi and Bogdanov 2016; Lehtveer et al. 2019; Fasihi and Breyer 2020) (Box 6.10 on regional integration).

6

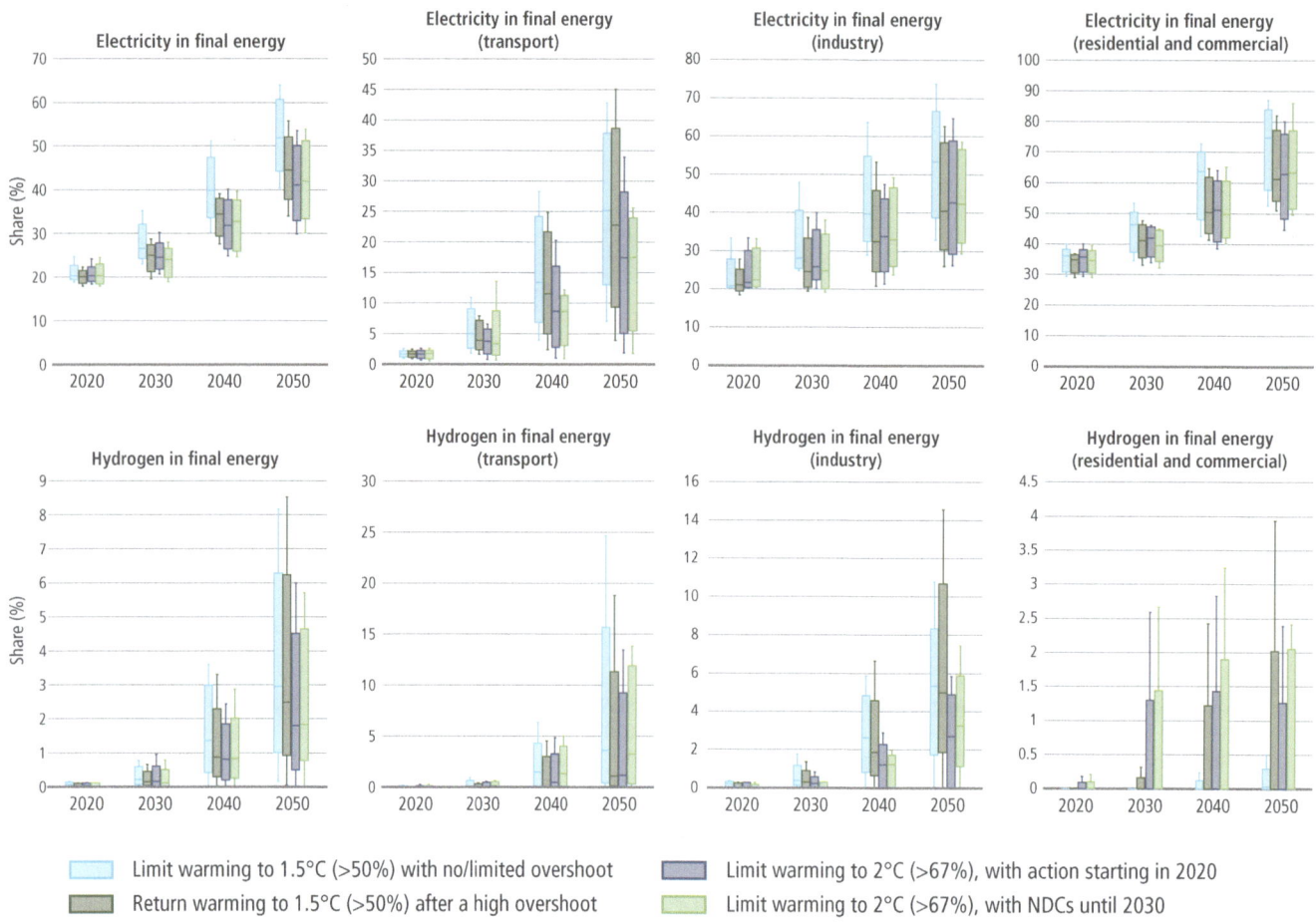

Figure 6.31 | Shares of electricity and hydrogen in final energy in scenarios that limit/return warming to 1.5°C (>50%) with no or limited/after a high, overshoot, and scenarios that limit warming to 2°C (>67%), with action starting in 2020 or NDCs until 2030, during 2030–2050 (Source: AR6 Scenarios Database). Boxes indicate 25th and 75th percentiles while whiskers indicate 5th and 95th percentiles.

While electrifying end uses is a key decarbonisation strategy, some end uses such as long-distance transport (freight, aviation, and shipping) and energy-intensive industries will be harder to electrify. For these sectors, alternative fuels or energy carriers such as biofuels, hydrogen, ammonia or synthetic methane, may be needed (Section 6.6 and Box 6.9). Most scenarios find that hydrogen consumption will grow gradually, becoming more valuable when the energy system has become predominantly low-carbon (Figure 6.31).

Reducing energy demand. Energy service demand is expected to continue to increase with growth of the economy, but there is great uncertainty about how much it will increase (Bauer et al. 2017; Riahi et al. 2017; Yu et al. 2018). Given the need to produce low-carbon energy, the scale of energy demand is a critical determinant of the mitigation challenge (Riahi et al. 2012). Higher energy demand calls for more low-carbon energy and increases the challenge; lower energy demand reduces the need for low-carbon sources and therefore can ease a low-carbon transition. Recent studies have shown that tempering the growth of energy demand, while ensuring services and needs are still satisfied, can materially affect the need for technological CDR (Section 6.7.1.3) (Grubler et al. 2018; van Vuuren et al. 2018). Two of the Illustrative Mitigation Pathways (IMP-SP, IMP-LD) feature substantially lower final energy demand

across buildings, transport, and industry than most other pathways in the literature. In some cases, energy demand levels are lower in 2050 (and later) than in 2019. These lower demands result in less reliance on bioenergy and a more limited role for CDR (Figure 3.18).

6.7.1.3   Technology Options to Offset Residual Emissions

CDR technologies can offset emissions from sectors that are difficult to decarbonise (Section 6.6), altering the timeline and character of energy sector transitions. A number of studies suggest that CDR is no longer a choice, but rather a necessity to limit warming to 1.5°C (Rogelj et al. 2015a; Detz et al. 2018; Luderer et al. 2018; Strefler et al. 2018; van Vuuren et al. 2018). The reliance on CDR varies across scenarios and is tightly linked to future energy demand and the rate of emission reductions in the next two decades: deeper near-term emissions reductions will reduce the need to rely on CDR to constrain cumulative CO_2 emissions. Some studies have argued that only with a transition to lower energy demands will it be possible to largely eliminate the need for engineered CDR options (Grubler et al. 2018; van Vuuren et al. 2018). Overall, the amount of CDR will depend on CO_2 capture costs, lifestyle changes, reduction in non-CO_2 GHGs, and utilisation of zero-emission end-use fuels (Muratori et al. 2017; van Vuuren et al. 2018).

There is substantial uncertainty about the amount of CDR that might ultimately be deployed. In most scenarios that limit warming to 1.5°C, CDR deployment is fairly limited through 2030 at less than 1 $GtCO_2$ yr^{-1}. The key projected increase in CDR deployment (BECCS and DAC only) occurs between 2030 and 2050, with annual CDR in 2050 projected at 2.5–7.5 $GtCO_2$ yr^{-1} in 2050 (interquartile range) in scenarios limiting warming to 1.5°C (>50%) with limited or no overshoot, and 0.7–1.4 $GtCO_2$ yr^{-1} in 2050 in scenarios limiting warming to 2°C (>67%) with action starting in 2020. This characteristic of scenarios largely reflects substantial capacity addition of BECCS power plants. BECCS is also deployed in multiple ways across sectors. For instance, the contribution (interquartile range) of BECCS to electricity is 1–5% in 2050 in scenarios limiting warming to 1.5°C (>50%) with no or limited overshoot, and 0–5% in scenarios that limit warming to 2°C (>67%) with action starting in 2020. The contribution (interquartile range) of BECCS to liquid fuels is 9–21% in 2050 in scenarios limiting

warming to 1.5°C (>50%) with no or limited overshoot and 2–11% in scenarios that limit warming to 2°C (>67%) with action starting in 2020. Large-scale deployment of CDR allows flexibility in timing of emissions reduction in hard-to-decarbonise sectors.

CDR will influence the potential fossil-related stranded assets (Box 6.13). Availability of low-cost CDR can help reduce premature retirement for some fossil fuel infrastructure. CDR can allow countries to reach net-zero emissions without phasing out all fossil fuels. Specific infrastructure could also be extended if it is used to burn biomass or other non-emitting sources. For example, existing coal-fired power plants, particularly those with CCS, could be co-fired with biomass (Woolf et al. 2016; Lu et al. 2019; Pradhan et al. 2021). In many scenarios, energy sector CDR is deployed to such an extent that energy sector CO_2 emissions become negative in the second half of the century (Chapter 3).

Box 6.12 | Taking Stock of the Energy System Transition

The Global Stocktake is a regularly occurring process under the UN Framework Convention on Climate Change (UNFCCC) in which efforts will be made to understand progress on, among other things, global mitigation. Collective progress of countries towards the Paris Agreement goal will be assessed and its outcome will inform Parties in updating and enhancing their Nationally Determined Contributions (NDCs). This box explores potential indicators to understand energy system mitigation progress.

CO_2 emissions from fuel combustion are the bottom line on energy system progress. Beyond CO_2 emissions, primary energy demand by energy sources, final energy consumption by sectors, and total electricity demand provide a first order assessment of energy system transitions. The year at which CO_2 emissions peak is also important. The Kaya Identity can be used to decompose energy system CO_2 emissions into carbon intensity of the energy system (CO_2 emissions from fossil-fuel combustion and industry divided by energy use), energy intensity (energy use divided by economic output), and economic output. The impacts of energy and climate policy are reflected in the changes of carbon intensity and energy intensity. Carbon intensity captures decarbonisation of energy supply systems, for example, through fuel switching from fossil fuels to non-fossil fuels, upscaling of low-carbon energy sources, and deploying carbon dioxide removal technologies. The carbon intensity of electricity is specifically important, given the role of the electricity sector in near-term mitigation. Economy-wide energy intensity represents efforts of demand-side energy, such as energy conservation, increase of energy performance of technologies, structural change of economy, and development of efficient urban infrastructure.

Beyond these aggregate indicators, a second order assessment would capture more details, such as the electrification rate, share of renewables, nuclear, CCS or other low-carbon technologies in electricity generation, land area used for energy production, and the number of EVs or PHEVs. Consumption of coal, oil and gas captures the underlying factors of CO_2 emissions. The emphasis of these indicators could differ across countries in the context of national specific circumstances. Technology- or project-based statistics are also useful to check the progress of the low-carbon transition, for example, the number of CCS facilities.

A critical challenge in the assessment of energy sector progress is how to measure societal, institutional, and political progress. These factors are difficult to quantify, yet they are fundamental determinants of the ability to reduce emissions. Public opinion, special interest politics, implications of mitigation for employment, energy subsidies, and energy policies are all critical indicators of progress. In addition, while much of the literature focuses on national-level action, mitigation is increasingly being led by cities, states, provinces, businesses, and other sub-national or non-national actors. Understanding the progress of these actors will be critical to assess energy system mitigation progress. New research is needed to better assess these 'societal' indicators and the role of non-national actors.

6.7.2   Investments in Technology and Infrastructure

Total global energy investment was roughly USD1940 billion yr^{-1} in 2019 (IEA 2021f). This total can be broken down into the following main categories: fossil-related energy supply, including

oil, gas, and coal extraction and fossil electricity generation (USD990 billion yr^{-1}); renewable electricity, primarily solar and wind (USD340 billion yr^{-1}); nuclear energy (USD40 billion yr^{-1}); electricity networks (USD270 billion yr^{-1}); and end-use energy efficiency (USD270 billion yr^{-1}).

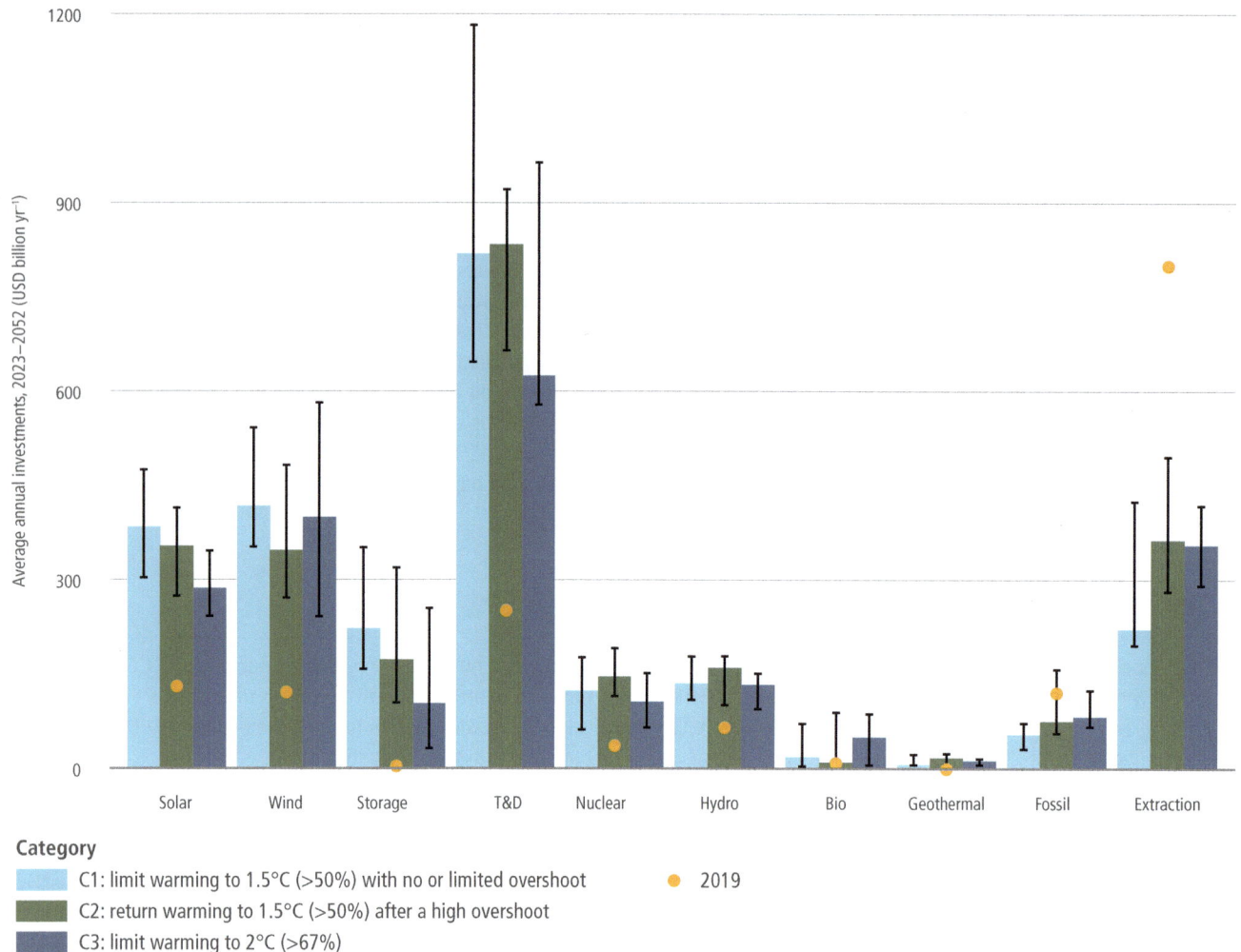

Figure 6.32 | Global average annual investments from 2023 to 2052 (undiscounted, in USD billion yr⁻¹) for electricity supply sub-sectors and for extraction of fossil fuels in scenarios that limit warming to 2°C (>67%) or lower (C1-C3) (Source: AR6 Scenarios Database and Chapter 3). Historical investments are also shown for comparison (Source: IEA 2021; approximations are made for hydro and geothermal based on available data; solar and wind values are for 2020). T&D: transmission and distribution of electricity. Bars show median values across models-scenarios, and whiskers the interquartile ranges. See Chapters 3 and 15 for additional information on investments and finance.

Energy investment needs are projected to rise, according to investment-focused scenario studies found in the literature (McCollum et al. 2018a; Zhou et al. 2019; Bertram et al. 2021). While these increases are projected to occur in emissions-intensive pathways as well as low-carbon pathways, they are projected to be largest in low-carbon pathways. Average annual global energy investments over the 2016–2050 period range (across six models) from USD2100 to 4100 billion yr⁻¹ in pathways limiting warming to 2°C (>67%) and from USD2400 to 4700 billion yr⁻¹ in pathways limiting warming to 1.5°C (>50%) with no or limited overshoot (McCollum et al. 2018). Whatever the scenario, a significant and growing share of investments between now and 2050 will be channelled toward infrastructure build-out in emerging economies, particularly in Asia (Zhou et al. 2019).

More widespread electrification of buildings, transport, and industry means particularly substantial investment in the electricity system. According to C1–C3 pathways in the IPCC's *Sixth Assessment Report* (AR6 Scenarios Database), such investments could be at the following average annual levels (inter-quartile range, USD2015)

over the 2023–2052 timeframe: USD1670 to 3070 billion yr⁻¹ (C1), USD1600 to 2780 billion yr⁻¹ (C2), and USD1330 to 2680 billion yr⁻¹ (C3) (see also Section 3.6.1.3).

Beyond these sector-wide numbers, a key feature of stringent mitigation pathways is a pronounced reallocation of investment flows across sub-sectors, namely from unabated fossil fuels (extraction, conversion, and electricity generation) and toward renewables, nuclear power, CCS, electricity networks and storage, and end-use energy efficiency (McCollum et al. 2018a; Bertram et al. 2021; IEA 2021f) (Figure 6.32). Investments in solar, wind, and electricity transmission, distribution, and storage increase the most in mitigation scenarios. Up to 2050, the bulk of these investments are made in OECD and Asian countries (Figure 6.33). While fossil fuel extraction investments exhibit a marked downscaling across all regions, compared to reference scenarios, the declines are especially strong in the Middle East, Reforming Economies of Eastern Europe and the Former Soviet Union (REF), and OECD.

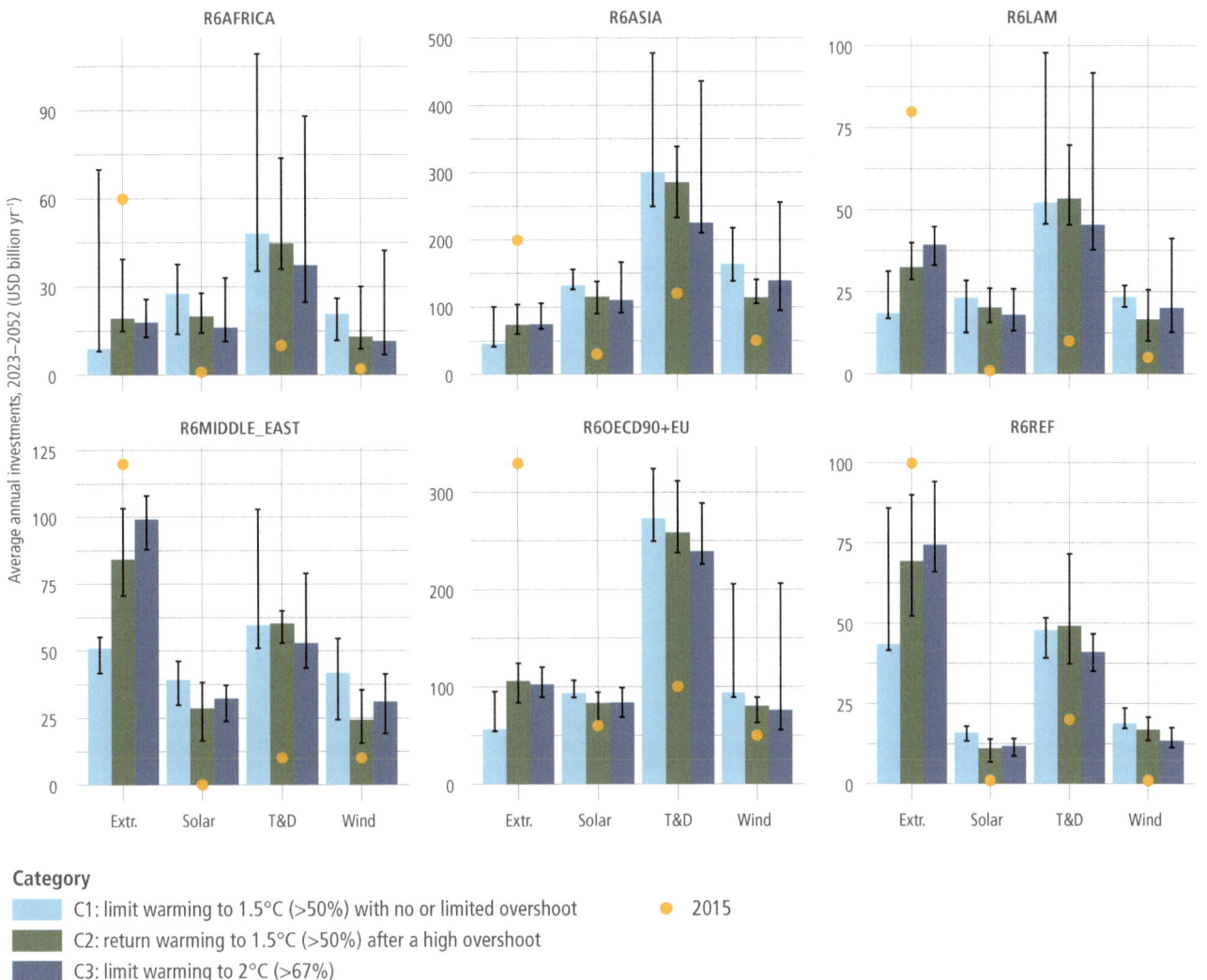

Category

- C1: limit warming to 1.5°C (>50%) with no or limited overshoot   ● 2015
- C2: return warming to 1.5°C (>50%) after a high overshoot
- C3: limit warming to 2°C (>67%)

Figure 6.33 | Regional average annual investments from 2023 to 2052 (undiscounted, in USD billion yr⁻¹) for four of the largest sub-sectors of the energy system in scenarios that limit warming to 2°C (>67%) or lower (C1–C3) (Source: AR6 Scenarios Database and Chapter 3). Historical investments are also shown for comparison (Source: IEA, 2016). T&D: transmission and distribution of electricity. Extr.: extraction of fossil fuels. Bars show median values across models-scenarios, and whiskers the inter-quartile ranges. See Chapters 3 and 15 for additional information on investments and finance.

Investments into end-use energy efficiency are projected to also be substantial in mitigation pathways, potentially upwards of several hundred USD billion yr⁻¹ on average to 2050, compared to USD270 billion yr⁻¹ in 2019 (McCollum et al. 2018a; IEA 2021f). However, the literature is inconsistent in how demand-side investments are calculated, as boundary conditions are less clear than for energy supply investments. Taking a broader definition can result in estimates that are an order-of-magnitude higher, meaning as large or larger than supply-side investments (Grubler et al. 2012; IEA 2021f).

Increasing low-carbon investment primarily requires shifting existing capital investment through regulation and incentives as well as removing existing investment barriers (McCollum et al. 2018; Hafner et al. 2020; Ameli, N. et al. 2021). While there is a considerable amount of capital in the world, it is not always available to those wishing to invest in certain projects. Total annual global investment in fixed capital was USD22.4 trillion in 2021, over an order-of-magnitude larger than energy sector investment (World Bank 2021).

Future investment patterns will vary by region, as they do now, due to differences in risk profiles, resource endowments and economic and governance structures (Fizaine et al. 2016; Zhou et al. 2019; Ameli, N. et al. 2021). In rapidly growing countries, investments to support a low-carbon energy system transition will be integrated with those needed to meet rapidly increasing energy demands, irrespective of whether efforts are made to reduce emissions. In less rapidly growing countries (Sun et al. 2019), investments will focus on transitioning current energy systems to low-carbon configurations. Most current energy investments are concentrated in high- and upper-middle-income countries (IEA 2021f), but this will change as investment needs continue to grow in today's lower-middle- and low-income countries (McCollum et al. 2018a; Zhou et al. 2019; Bertram et al. 2021; IEA 2021f).

6.7.3   Energy System Lock-in and Path Dependence

Path dependence refers to resistance to change due to favourable socio-economic conditions with existing systems; decisions made in the past unduly shape future trajectories. Carbon lock-in is a specific type of path dependence (Seto et al. 2016). Given that energy system mitigation will require a major course change from recent history, lock-in is an important issue for emission reductions in the energy sector. While lock-in is typically expressed in terms of physical infrastructure that would need to be retired early to reach mitigation goals, it involves a much broader set of issues that go beyond physical systems and into societal and institutional systems (Table 6.11).

Table 6.11 | Lock-in types and typical mechanisms. Source: Kotilainen et al. 2020), Reproduced under Creative Commons 4.0 International Licence.

Type	Primary lock-in mechanisms	References
Technological (and infrastructural)	– Economies of scale – Economies of scope – Learning effects – Network externalities – Technological interrelatedness	– Arthur (1994); Hughes (1994); Klitkou et al (2015) – David (1985); Panzar and Willig (1981) – Arthur (1994) – David (1985); Katz and Shapiro (1986) – Arrow (1962); Arthur (1994); David (1985); Van den Bergh and Oosterhuis (2008)
Institutional	– Collective action – Complexity and opacity of politics – Differentiation of power and institutions – High density of institutions – Institutional learning effects – Vested interests	– Seto et al (2016) – Foxon (2002); Pierson (2000) – Foxon (2002) – Pierson (2000) – Foxon (2002); Boschma (2005) – Boschma (2005)
Behavioural	– Habituation – Cognitive switching costs – Increasing informational returns	– David (1985); Barnes et al. (2004); Zauberman (2003); Murray and Haubl (2007) – Zauberman (2003); Murray and Haubl (2007); Van den Bergh and Oosterhuis (2008)

6.7.3.1   Societal and Institutional Inertia

A combination of factors – user, business, cultural, regulatory, and transnational – will hinder low-carbon energy transitions. Strong path dependencies, even in early formative stages, can have lasting impacts on energy systems, producing inertia that cuts across technological, economic, institutional and political dimensions (*high confidence*) (Rickards et al. 2014; Vadén et al. 2019) (Chapter 5).

Energy systems exemplify the ways in which massive volumes of labour, capital, and effort become sunk into particular institutional configurations (Bridge et al. 2013, 2018). Several embedded factors affect large-scale transformation of these systems and make technological diffusion a complex process:

- **User environments** affect purchase activities and can involve the integration of new technologies into user practices and the development of new preferences, routines, habits and evenvalues (Kanger et al. 2019).
- **Business environments** can shape the development of industries, business models, supply and distribution chains, instrument constituencies and repair facilities (Béland and Howlett 2016).
- **Culture** can encompass the articulation of positive discourses, narratives, and visions that enhance cultural legitimacy and societal acceptance of new technologies. Regulatory embedding can capture the variety of policies that shape production, markets and use of new technologies.
- **Transnational community** can reflect a shared understanding in a community of global experts related to new technologies that transcends the borders of a single place, often a country.

While low-carbon innovation involves systemic change (Geels et al. 2018), these are typically less popular than energy supply innovations among policymakers and the wider public. Managing low-carbon transitions is therefore not only a techno-managerial challenge (based on targets, policies, and expert knowledge), but also a broader political project that involves the building of support coalitions that include businesses and civil society (*moderate evidence*, *high agreement*).

Low-carbon transitions involve cultural changes extending beyond purely technical developments to include changes in consumer practices, business models, and organisational arrangements. The development and adoption of low-carbon innovations will therefore require sustained and effective policies to create appropriate incentives and support. The implementation of such policies entails political struggles because actors have different understandings and interests, giving rise to disagreements and conflicts.

Such innovation also involves pervasive uncertainty around technical potential, cost, consumer demand, and social acceptance. Such uncertainty carries governance challenges. Policy approaches facing deep uncertainty must protect against and/or prepare for unforeseeable developments, whether it is through resistance (planning for the worst possible case or future situation), resilience (making sure you can recover quickly), or adaptation (changes to policy under changing conditions). Such uncertainty can be hedged in part by learning by firms, consumers, and policymakers. Social interactions and network building (e.g., supply and distribution chains, intermediary actors) and the articulation of positive visions, such as in long-term, low-emission development strategies, all play a crucial role. This uncertainty extends to the impacts of low-carbon innovations on energy demand and other variables, where unanticipated and unintended outcomes are the norm. For instance, rapid investments in public transport networks could restrict car ownership from becoming common in developing countries (Du and Lin 2017).

6.7.3.2   Physical Energy System Lock-In

Current investments in fossil infrastructure have committed 500–700 GtCO$_2$ of emissions, creating significant risks for limiting warming to 1.5°C (Callaghan 2020) (*high confidence*). These current investments combined with emissions from proposed fossil infrastructure exceed the emissions required to limit warming to 1.5°C (*medium confidence*). Existing coal- and gas-fired electricity generation accounts for 200–300 GtCO$_2$ of committed emissions. Emissions from coal generation are larger than for gas plants (Smith et al. 2019; Tong et al. 2019). The lifetime of coal-fired power plants is 25–50 years, creating long-lasting risks to climate goals (Erickson and Tempest 2015). Gas-fired power plants are younger on average than coal-fired power plants. Industry sector lock-in amounts for more than 100 GtCO$_2$, while buildings and transport sector together contribute another 50–100 GtCO$_2$ (Erickson and Tempest 2015).

Lock-in is also relevant to fossil resources. Both coal and gas exploration continue, and new permits are being issued, which may cause economic (Erickson et al. 2018) as well as non-economic issues (Boettcher et al. 2019).

The nature of lock-in varies across the energy system. For example, lock-in in urban and transport sectors is different from the electricity sector. Broadly, urban environments involve infrastructural, institutional, and behavioural lock-in (Ürge-Vorsatz et al. 2018). Addressing lock-in in these sectors requires action by multiple stakeholders and is unlikely with just technological evolution (Table 6.11).

Committed carbon emissions are unevenly distributed. The disproportionate high share of committed emissions in emerging economies is the result of rapid growth in recent years, which has led to a comparably young fossil infrastructure with substantial remaining life (Shearer et al. 2017). Mature industrialised countries tend to have older infrastructures, part of which will be up for retirement in the near

future (Tong et al. 2019). Coal-fired power plants currently planned or under construction are associated with 150–300 GtCO$_2$, of which about 75% and about 10% are located in Asia and the OECD respectively (Edenhofer et al. 2018; Pfeiffer et al. 2018). If implemented, these new fleets will further shorten all coal plants' lifetimes by another 10 years for meeting climate goals (Cui et al. 2019).

Despite the imperative to reduce use of fossil fuels and the multiple health and other benefits from closing coal-based infrastructure (Portugal-Pereira et al. 2018; Liu et al. 2019a; Karlsson et al. 2020; Rauner et al. 2020; Cui et al. 2021), coal power plants have continued to be commissioned globally (Jewell et al. 2019; Jakob et al. 2020), most notably in Asian countries. Gas power plants also continue to be built. In many regions, new fossil electricity generation exceeds needed capacity (Shearer et al. 2017).

Existing policies and the NDCs are insufficient to prevent an increase in fossil infrastructure and associated carbon lock-in (*high confidence*) (Bertram et al. 2015; Johnson et al. 2015). Current investment decisions are critical because there is limited room within the carbon budget required to limit warming to well below 2°C (Kalkuhl et al. 2019; Rosenbloom 2019). Delays in mitigation will increase carbon lock-in and could result in large-scale stranded assets if stringency is subsequently increased to limit warming (Box 6.11). Near-term implementation of stringent GHG mitigation policies are likely to be most effective in reducing carbon lock-in (Haelg et al. 2018). Near-term mitigation policies will also need to consider different energy transition strategies as a result of different resources and carbon budgets between countries (Lucas 2016; Bos and Gupta 2018).

Near-term policy choices are particularly consequential for fast-growing economies. For example, Malik et al. (2020) found that 133 to 227 GW of coal capacity would be stranded after 2030 if India were to delay ambitious mitigation through 2030 and then pursue an ambitious, post-2030 climate strategy. Cui et al. (2021) identified 18% of old, small, inefficient coal plants for rapid near-term retirement in China to help achieve air quality, health, water, and other societal goals and a feasible coal phase-out under climate goals. Comparable magnitudes of stranded assets may also be created in Latin America when adding all announced, authorised, and procured power plants up to 2060 (González-Mahecha et al. 2019). Options to reduce carbon lock-in include reducing fossil fuels subsidies (Box 6.3), building CCS-ready facilities, or ensuring that facilities are appropriately designed for fuel switching (Budinis et al. 2018). Substantial lock-in may necessitate considerable deployment of CDR to compensate for high cumulative emissions.

Past and present energy sector investments have created technological, institutional, and behavioural path dependencies aligned towards coal, oil, and natural gas (*high confidence*). In several emerging economies, large projects are planned that address poverty reduction and economic development. Coal infrastructure may be the default choice for these investments without policies to invest in low-carbon infrastructure instead (Joshua and Alola 2020; Steckel et al. 2020). Path dependencies frequently have sustainability implications beyond carbon emissions. (Box 6.2 and Section 6.7.7).

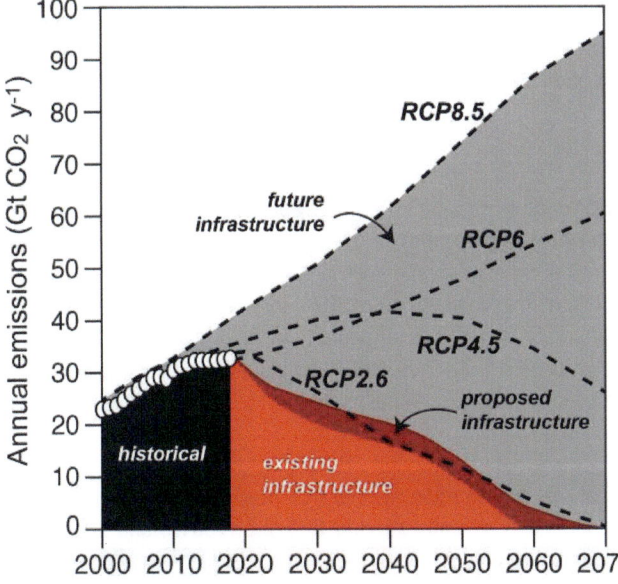

Figure 6.34 | Annual emissions from existing, proposed, and future energy system infrastructure. Source: with permission from Tong et al. 2019.

6

There are several SDG co-benefits associated with decarbonisation of energy systems (Section 6.7.7) (Sörgel et al. 2021). For example, coal

mining communities frequently experience significant health and economic burdens from resource extraction.

Box 6.13 | Stranded Assets

Limiting warming to 2°C (>67%) or lower will result in stranded assets (*high confidence*). Stranded assets can be broadly defined as assets that 'suffer from unanticipated or premature write-offs, downward revaluations or [conversion] to liabilities'. Stranded assets may create risks for financial market stability and macro-economic stability (Battiston et al. 2017; Mercure et al. 2018; Sen and von Schickfus 2020), and they will result in a rapid loss of wealth for the owners of affected assets (Vogt-Schilb and Hallegatte 2017; Ploeg and Rezai 2020).

There are two types of stranded assets: fossil-fuel resources that cannot be burned; and premature retirement of fossil infrastructure (e.g., power plants). About 30% of oil, 50% of gas, and 80% of coal reserves will remain unburnable if warming is limited to 2°C (Meinshausen et al. 2009; Leaton 2011; Leaton Ranger 2013; McGlade and Ekins 2015; Bauer et al. 2016; IRENA 2017b; Pye et al. 2020) (*high confidence*). Significantly more reserves are expected to remain unburned if warming is limited to 1.5°C. Countries with large oil, gas, and coal reserves are most at risk (Caldecott et al. 2017; Ansari and Holz 2020).

About 200 GW of fossil fuel electricity generation per year will likely need to be retired prematurely after 2030 to limit warming to 2°C, even if countries achieve their Nationally Determined Contributions (NDCs) (*medium confidence*) (Iyer et al. 2015; Johnson et al. 2015; Fofrich et al. 2020). Limiting warming to 1.5°C will require significantly more rapid premature retirement of electricity generation capacity (Binsted et al. 2020). Coal- and gas-fired power plants will likely need to retire about 25 years earlier than in the past to limit warming to 2°C, and 30 years earlier to limit warming to 1.5°C (Cui et al. 2019; Fofrich et al. 2020). Coal-fired power plants are at significantly greater risk of stranding compared with gas-fired and oil-fired plants (Iyer et al. 2015; Johnson et al. 2015; Fofrich et al. 2020). The risks of stranded power plants are greatest in countries with newer fossil infrastructure.

If warming is limited to 2°C, the discounted economic impacts of stranded assets, including unburned fossil reserves, could be as high as USD1–4 trillion from 2015 through 2050 (USD10–20 trillion in undiscounted terms) (*medium confidence*) (IRENA, 2017c; Mercure et al. 2018). About 40% of these impacts correspond to unburned fossil reserves (IRENA 2017b). If warming is limited to 1.5°C, the economic impacts of stranded assets are expected to be significantly higher (Binsted et al. 2020).

Stronger near-term mitigation will reduce premature retirements of fossil infrastructure, because more rapid mitigation will decrease new builds of fossil infrastructure that might later be stranded (Johnson et al. 2015; Bertram et al. 2018) (*high confidence*). For example, if warming is limited to 2°C, strengthening the NDC pledges beyond their 2015 levels could decrease stranded electricity sector assets by more than 50% (Iyer et al. 2015). By contrast, if countries fail to meet their NDCs and continue to build fossil infrastructure, mitigation will need to be accelerated beyond 2030, resulting up to double the amount of stranded electricity generation capacity (Iyer et al. 2015). This corresponds to a total undiscounted cost of about USD2 trillion from electricity infrastructure alone, from the period 2015 to 2050 (IRENA 2017). CCS (6.4) could potentially help reduce hundreds of gigawatts stranded power plant capacity along with other fossil-based capital (Clark and Herzog 2014; Iyer et al. 2017; Fan et al. 2018).

6.7.4   Fossil Fuels in a Low-carbon Transition

Global fossil fuel use will need to decline substantially by 2050 to limit warming to 2°C (>67%), and it must decline substantially by 2030 to limit warming to 1.5°C (>50%) with no or limited overshoot (*high confidence*). Failing to reduce global fossil fuel use below today's levels by 2030 will make it more challenging to limit warming to below 2°C (>67%). (*high confidence*). Fossil fuel use declines by 260–330 EJ (52–73% from 2020 levels, interquartile range) through 2050 in scenarios that limit warming to 1.5°C (>50%) with no or limited overshoot, and 124–231 EJ (24–51% reduction compared to 2020 levels) in scenarios that limit warming to 2°C (>67%) with action starting in 2020. This will require a significant reduction in coal, oil and gas investments. Fossil fuels account for about 80% of primary energy today. In scenarios limiting warming to 1.5°C (>50%) with

limited or no overshoot, fossil energy provides 59–69% (interquartile range) of primary energy in 2030 and 25–40% primary energy in 2050 (AR6 Scenarios Database). In scenarios limiting warming to 2°C (>67%) with action starting in 2020, fossil energy provides 71–75% (interquartile range) primary energy in 2030 and 41–57% primary energy in 2050 (AR6 Scenarios Database). The timeline for reducing production and usage varies across coal, oil, and gas due to their differing carbon intensities and uses.

Global coal consumption without CCS needs to be largely eliminated by 2040–2050 to limit warming to 1.5°C (>50%), and 2050–2060 to limit warming to 2°C (>67%) (*high confidence*). New investments in coal-fired electricity without CCS are inconsistent with limiting warming to 2°C (>67%) or lower (*high confidence*) (Edenhofer et al. 2018; Pfeiffer et al. 2018; Spencer et al. 2018; Cui et al. 2019). Coal

6

consumption declines 130 EJ yr^{-1} to 140 EJ yr^{-1} in 2050 (78–99% compared to 2020 levels, interquartile range) in scenarios limiting warming to 1.5°C (>50%) with no or limited overshoot and 118 EJ yr^{-1} to 139 EJ yr^{-1} (65% to 98% compared to 2020 levels) in scenarios limiting warming to 2°C (>67%) with action starting in 2020. Coal consumption without CCS falls by 67% to 82% (interquartile range) in 2030 in scenarios limiting warming to 1.5°C (>50%) with no or limited overshoot. Studies indicate that coal use may decline substantially in the USA and Europe over the coming decade, based on the increasing competitiveness of low-carbon sources and near-term policy actions (Grubert and Brandt 2019; Oei et al. 2020). In several developing economies, the relative youth of the coal-fired electricity fleet will make a complete phase-out before 2050 difficult (Garg and Shukla 2009; Jewell et al. 2016). There are considerable differences in projected coal phase-out timelines in major Asian economies. Some studies suggest that coal may continue to be a part of the Chinese energy mix composing around one-third of the total primary energy consumption by 2050, even if emissions are reduced by 50% by 2030 (He et al. 2020). Others indicate that a strategic transition would decrease the risk of stranded assets and enable a near-complete phase-out by 2050 (Wang et al. 2020a; Cui et al. 2021). This would entail prioritising

earlier retirements of plants based on technical (efficiency), economic (profitability, local employment) and environmental considerations (e.g., water scarcity for cooling).

Natural gas may remain part of energy systems through mid-century, both for electricity generation and use in industry and buildings, and particularly in developed economies, even if warming is limited to 2°C (>67%) or lower (*medium confidence*). The decline in natural gas use from 2020 to 2050 is 38 EJ yr^{-1} to 78 EJ yr^{-1} (21–62% decline from 2020 levels, interquartile range) in scenarios limiting warming to 1.5°C (>50%) with no or limited overshoot and −22 EJ yr^{-1} to 46 EJ yr^{-1} (−14% to 36% decline from 2020 levels, interquartile range) in scenarios limiting warming to 2°C (>67%) with action starting in 2020. Scenarios indicate that gas use in electricity will likely peak around 2035 and 2050 if warming is limited to 1.5°C (>50%) with limited or no overshoot or to 2°C (>67%) with action starting in 2020, respectively. There is variability in the role gas would play in future scenarios based on national climate commitments and availability of cheap renewables (Malik et al. 2020; Vishwanathan and Garg 2020; Vrontisi et al. 2020). Note that these differences are not only present in the electricity sector but also in other end uses.

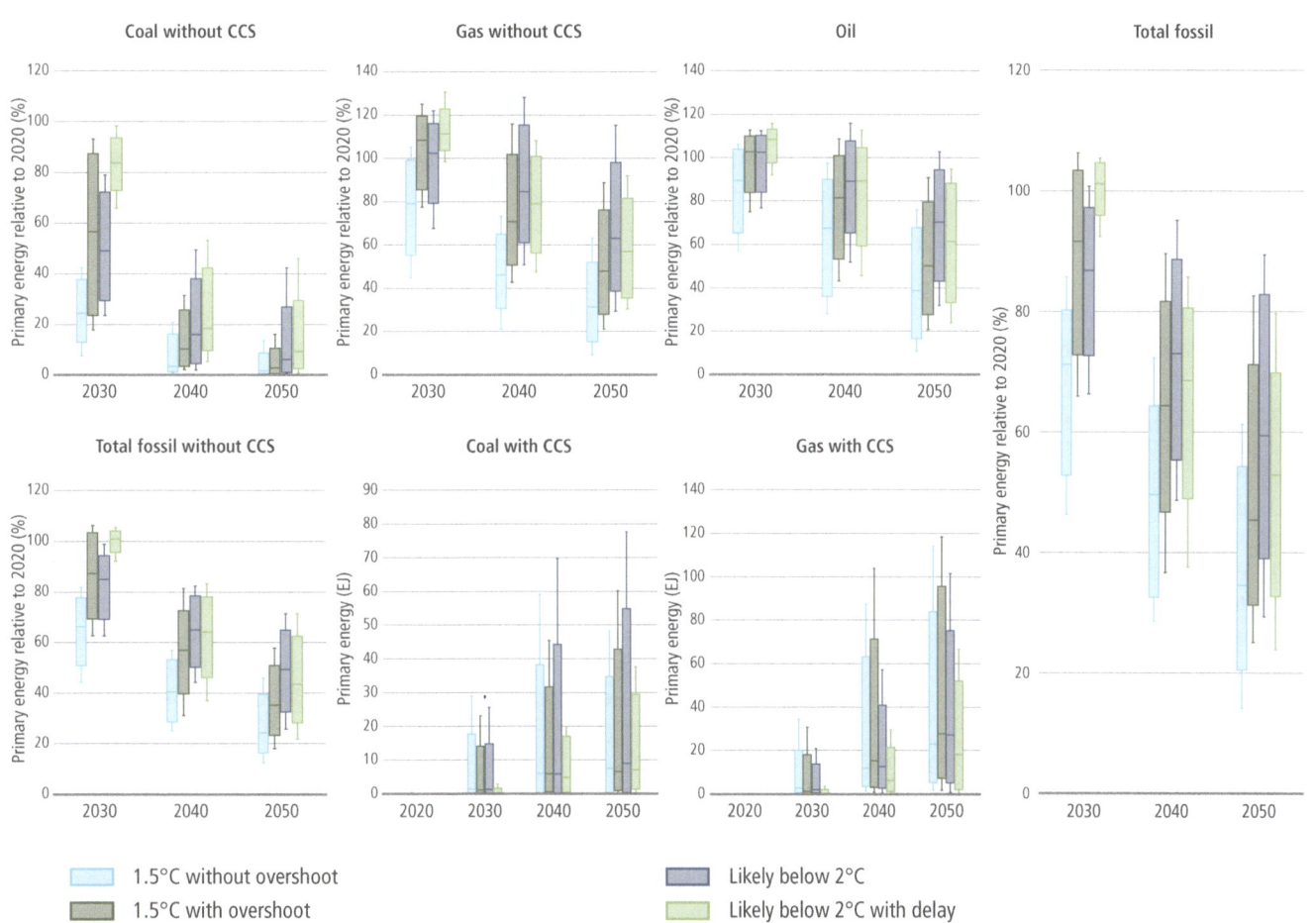

Figure 6.35 | Global fossil fuel pathways for scenarios that limit/return warming to 1.5°C (>50%) with no or limited/after a high, overshoot, and scenarios that limit warming to 2°C (>67%), with action starting in 2020 or NDCs until 2030, during 2030–2050. Boxes indicate 25th and 75th percentiles while whiskers indicate 5th and 95th percentiles. Results for total consumption are expressed as a percentage relative to 2020 consumption. Results for fossil energy with CCS are expressed in total energy consumption. Oil use with CCS is not shown here as it remains below 5% of total use. Source: AR6 Scenarios Database.

While oil use is anticipated to decline substantially, due to changes in the transport sector, its use will likely continue through the mid-century, even if warming is limited to 2°C (>67%) or lower (*medium confidence*). Oil use declines by 73 EJ yr^{-1} to 145 EJ yr^{-1} (30–78% from 2020 levels, interquartile range) in scenarios that limit warming to 1.5°C (>50%) with no or limited overshoot and 26 EJ yr^{-1} to 86 EJ yr^{-1} (14–45% from 2020 levels) by 2050 in scenarios that limit warming to 2°C (>67%) with action starting in 2020. While oil use is anticipated to decline immediately in scenarios limiting warming to 1.5°C (>50%), it is likely to continue to be used through 2050. Oil use continues to be a significant source of transport fuels in most scenarios limiting warming to 2°C (Welsby et al. 2021). Oil use may drop to about half of current levels as a transport fuel by 2050 if warming is limited to 2°C, because of the availability of other options (biofuels, green hydrogen) and rapid deployment of EVs (Feijoo et al. 2020). In the absence of rapid transport electrification, the decline is slower with some studies projecting peak oil use around 2035 (Delgado et al. 2020; Pan et al. 2020).

There is a lack of consensus about how CCS might alter fossil fuel transitions for limiting warming to 2°C (>67%) or lower. CCS deployment will increase the shares of fossil fuels associated with limiting warming, and it can ease the economic transition to a low-carbon energy system (Muratori et al. 2016; Marcucci et al. 2019). While some studies find a significant role for fossil fuels with CCS by 2050 (Koelbl et al. 2014; Eom et al. 2015; Vishwanathan and Garg 2020), others find that retirement of unabated coal far outpaces the deployment of coal with CCS (Budinis et al. 2018; Xie et al. 2020; McJeon et al. 2021) Moreover, several studies also project that, with availability of CO_2 capture technology, BECCS might become significantly more appealing than fossil CCS, even before 2050 (Muratori et al. 2017; Luderer et al. 2018b).

6.7.5   Policy and Governance

Policy and governance frameworks are essential for shaping near- and medium-term low-emissions energy system transitions (*high confidence*). While policy interventions are necessary to achieve low-carbon energy system transitions, appropriate governance frameworks are crucial to ensure policy implementation (*high confidence*). The policy environment in energy transition pathways relate to climate policy goals, the characteristics of the policy regimes and measures to reach the policy goals including implementation limits and obstacles, and the timing of the climate instrument (Kriegler et al. 2014b).

The literature discusses a broad set of policy approaches. Environmental economics focuses mainly on market-based approaches as the least-cost policy to achieve emission reductions (Kube et al. 2018). Many countries, however, have implemented policy mixes with a diverse set of complementary policies to achieve energy and climate policy targets. One example is the German Energiewende, which includes substantial support for renewables, an action plan for energy efficiency, and phase-out processes for nuclear- and coal-based power generation next to carbon pricing (Löschel et al. 2019). The halving of CO_2 emissions in UK power generation reflects multiple policies, particularly within the UK's Climate Change Act 2008 (Grubb and Newbery 2018). More generally, the implementation of the NDCs under the Paris Agreement are all characterised by diverse climate policy mixes.

These policy mixes (or policy packages) are shaped by different factors, including policy goals and objectives (including political, social and technological influences), multiple market, governance or behavioural failures or previous policy choices of earlier policy eras (Rogge 2017). When pursuing multiple policy goals or targeting some type of imperfection, well designed policy mixes can, in principle, reduce mitigation costs (Corradini et al. 2018) or address distributional concerns, especially vulnerable populations. For example, the interaction between carbon pricing and the support for clean energy technologies in the EU clean low-carbon strategy for 2050 can reduce mitigation costs and allow for the early adoption of more stringent climate targets (Vandyck et al. 2016). Policy efforts to promote adoption of low-carbon technologies are more successful if they focus not only on economic incentives but include behavioural interventions that target relevant cognitive and motivational factors (Mundaca et al. 2019; Khanna et al. 2021) (Section 6.7.6). Overlapping nudges might not necessarily lead to lower effectiveness (Brandon et al. 2019).

Well-designed policy mixes can support the pursuit of multiple policy goals, target effectively different types of imperfections and framework conditions and take into account the technological, economical, and societal situation (*high confidence*). Accounting for the different development stages of new technologies will enhance low-emissions transitions (Graaf and Sovacool 2020). For prototype technologies and technologies in the demonstration phase, research subsidies and demonstration projects are most important. For technologies experiencing early adoption, infrastructure development and strengthening of markets are increasingly important, while retiring or repurposing of existing assets is important for mature technologies (IEA 2020h) Effective policy mixes will address different market frictions and deal with various uncertainties, for example, those pertaining to technological, climate, and socio-economic developments (Aldy 2020), but also with respect to outcomes of individual policies (e.g., Borenstein et al. 2019). Therefore, policy mixes may balance the trade-off between stability and the flexibility to change individual policies (Gawel and Lehmann 2019) and the policy mix over time (Rayner et al. 2017). Some policy instruments may become feasible over time, for example, as technological advancements reduce the transaction costs of comprehensive market-based approaches (Andoni et al. 2019; Di Silvestre et al. 2020), or as weakened barriers to stringency enable policy sequencing (Pahle et al. 2018). Energy system policy mixes often include sector-specific regulation. Compared to economy-wide approaches, sectoral policies may be able to directly target specific sectors or mitigation options. However, uncoordinated implementation or limited coordination across sectors may lead to efficiency losses (e.g. Rosendahl et al. 2017). These losses also depend on other policies, such as pre-existing taxes (Goulder et al. 2016; Marten et al. 2018) or research and development policies (Acemoglu et al. 2016). Moreover, unilateral policies – those taken by individual countries in the absence of coordination with other countries – could raise carbon leakage risks, while balancing potential issues of (industrial) competitiveness (Martin et al. 2014; Rosendahl et al. 2017). Energy leakage may become more important during low-carbon energy systems. Numerous studies have identified pathways for carbon leakage in electricity markets with incomplete emission markets (Caron et al. 2015; Murray and Maniloff 2015; Thurber et al. 2015; Duan et al. 2017; Fell and Maniloff 2017; Qian et al. 2018). Well-designed policy mixes will need to target the whole lifecycle or value chains, for example, through policies on limiting fossil fuel extraction (Asheim et al. 2019), or they will need to include measures to limit carbon leakage (e.g. Cosbey et al. 2019).

Interactions between policy measures including their scope, stringency, and timing, influence the costs of reducing emissions (Corradini et al. 2018). In particular, some policy instruments may lead to lock-in effects (Section 6.7.3), compete with other regulations (Graaf and Sovacool 2020), or trigger negative policy interactions (Perino 2015; Jarke-Neuert and Perino 2020). Existing policy mixes often reflect different political economy constraints, and sometimes not well coordinated goals. The resulting policy mixes are often economically inefficient. However, comprehensive evaluation of policy mixes requires a broader set of criteria that reflect different considerations, such as broader goals (e.g., SDGs) and the feasibility of policies (*high confidence*).

Policy mixes might rather emerge piece-by-piece over time out of individual policy interventions rather than be designed as a whole from the outset (Howlett 2014; Rogge 2017) and may reflect differences across jurisdictions and sectors (Howlett 2014). For example, taking into account country-specific objectives, failures, and limitations, carbon prices may be only one part of a broader policy mix, and thereby may not be uniform across countries (Bataille 2020). This lack of consistency makes it more difficult to assess economic outcomes since costs of complementary policies are often less visible and are often targeted at high-cost mitigation options (Borenstein et al. 2019).

Effective assessment of policy mixes requires comprehensive, validated international data, methodologies, and indicators. Existing policy mixes are difficult to evaluate because they target multiple objectives, and the evaluation must consider various criteria (Chapter 13 and Section 6.7.7), such as environmental and economic effectiveness, distributional effects, transformative potential, institutional requirements, and feasibility. Economic outcomes depend on policy goals and implementation. Existing studies on policy mixes suggest the benefits of a comprehensive approach (Rosenow et al. 2017), while also highlighting that an 'excessive' number of instruments may reduce overall effectiveness (Costantini et al. 2017). Combining environmental regulation and innovation policies may be of particular importance to tackle both emissions and innovation market failures (Fabrizi et al. 2018). The consistency and credibility of policy mixes is positively associated with green innovation (Rogge and Schleich 2018).

Potential future policies are difficult to evaluate due to methodological challenges (*high confidence*). Recent model-based analyses of future policy mixes based on 'current policy scenarios' try to implement existing policies besides explicit or implicit carbon prices (den Elzen et al. 2016; Rogelj et al. 2016; van Soest et al. 2017; Roelfsema et al. 2020). Many assessments of future low-carbon energy transitions are still based on cost-optimal evaluation frameworks and include only limited analysis of interactions between policy measures. Hence they are often not describing real-world energy transitions properly, but rather differences in implied carbon prices, constraints in technology deployment, and timing of policies (Trutnevyte 2016).

6.7.6   Behaviour and Societal Integration

Members of societies, including individuals, civil society, and businesses, will all need to engage with, and be affected by, low-carbon energy system transitions (*high confidence*). This raises questions about the extent to which different strategies and policy would effectively promote mitigation behaviours and the factors that increase the social acceptability of mitigation options, policies, and system changes.

6.7.6.1   Strategies to Encourage Climate Mitigation Actions

Climate policy will be particularly effective if it targets key factors inhibiting, enabling, and motivating mitigation behaviours. As barriers differ across mitigation options, regions, and groups, tailored approaches are more effective (Grubb et al. 2017). When people face important barriers to change (e.g., high costs, legal barriers), policy would be needed make low-carbon actions more attractive, or to make high-carbon actions less attractive. As people generally face multiple barriers for change, combinations of policies would be more effective (Rosenow et al. 2017).

Financial incentives can motivate mitigation actions (Santos 2008; Thøgersen 2009; Bolderdijk et al. 2011; Eliasson 2014; Maki et al. 2016), particularly when actions are costly (Mundaca 2007). In many countries, more residential solar PV were installed after the introduction of favourable financial schemes such as feed-in-tariffs, federal income tax credits, and net metering (Wolske and Stern 2018). Similarly, many programs have promoted the installation of lower-carbon household options such as heat pumps, district heating, or solar water heaters across Europe, the Asia-Pacific and Africa (Hu et al. 2012; Sovacool and Martiskainen 2020; Ahmed et al. 2021). Yet, financial incentives may underperform expectations when other factors are overlooked. For example, people may not respond to financial incentives when they do not trust the organisation sponsoring the programme, or when it takes too much effort to receive the incentive (Mundaca 2007; Stern et al. 2016a). Financial incentives are more effective if combined with strategies addressing non-financial barriers.

Communicating financial consequences of behaviour seems less effective than emphasising social rewards (Handgraaf et al. 2013) or benefits of actions for people (e.g., public health, comfort) and the environment (Bolderdijk et al. 2013; Asensio and Delmas 2015, 2016; Schwartz et al. 2015; Ossokina 2020). Financial appeals may have limited effects because they reduce people's focus on environmental consequences, weaken intrinsic motivation to engage in mitigation actions, provide a licence to pollute (Agrawal et al. 2015; Bolderdijk and Steg 2015; Schwartz et al. 2015), and because pursuing small financial gains is perceived not worth the effort (Bolderdijk et al. 2013; Dogan et al. 2014).

Providing information on the causes and consequences of climate change or on effective mitigation actions increases people's knowledge and awareness, but generally does not promote mitigation actions by individuals (Abrahamse et al. 2005) or organisations (Anderson and Newell 2004). Fear-inducing representations of climate change may inhibit action when they make people feel helpless (O'Neill and Nicholson-Cole 2009). Energy-related advice and feedback can promote energy savings, load shifting in electricity use and sustainable travel, particularly when framed in terms of losses rather than gains (Gonzales et al. 1988; Wolak 2011; Bradley et al. 2016; Bager and Mundaca 2017). Also, credible and targeted information at the point of decision can promote action (Stern et al. 2016a). Information is more effective when delivered by a trusted source, such as peers (Palm 2017), advocacy groups (Schelly 2014), and community organisations (Noll et al. 2014), and when tailored to actors' personal situations and core values (Daamen et al. 2001; Abrahamse et al. 2007; Bolderdijk et al. 2013; Boomsma and Steg 2014; Wolsko et al. 2016; van den Broek et al. 2017). This explains why home energy audits promoted energy savings (Delmas et al. 2013; Alberini and Towe 2015), and investments in resource efficiency and renewable energy generation (Kastner and Stern 2015).

Energy use feedback can promote energy saving behaviour within households (Fischer 2008; Grønhøj and Thøgersen 2011; Delmas et al. 2013; Karlin et al. 2015; Zangheri et al. 2019) and at work (Young et al. 2015), particularly when provided in real time or immediately after the action so that people learn the impact of different actions (Abrahamse et al. 2005; Faruqui et al. 2009; Delmas et al. 2013; Yu et al. 2015; Stern et al. 2016a; Tiefenbeck et al. 2016). Energy labels (Banerjee and Solomon 2003; Stadelmann 2017), visualisation techniques (Pahl et al. 2016), and ambient persuasive technology (Midden and Ham 2012) can encourage energy savings as they immediately make sense and hardly require users' conscious attention. Feedback can make people aware of their previous mitigation behaviours, which can strengthen their environmental self-identity, and motivate them to engage in other mitigation actions, to act in line with their self-image (Van der Werff et al. 2014).

Social influence approaches that communicate what other people do or think can encourage mitigation actions (Clayton et al. 2015), as can social models of desired actions (Osbaldiston and Schott 2012; Abrahamse and Steg 2013; Sussman and Gifford 2013; Wolske et al. 2020). Feedback on one's own energy use relative to others can be effective (Nolan et al. 2008; Allcott 2011; Schultz et al. 2015), although not always, and effect sizes are small (Abrahamse and Steg 2013) compared to other types of feedback (Karlin et al. 2015).

Interventions that capitalise on people's motivation to be consistent can promote mitigation actions (Steg 2016). Examples are commitment strategies where people pledge to act (Abrahamse and Steg 2013; Lokhorst et al. 2013), implementation intentions where they additionally explicate how and when they will perform the relevant action and how they would cope with possible barriers (Bamberg 2000, 2002; Rees et al. 2018), and hypocrisy-related strategies that make people aware of inconsistencies between their attitudes and behaviour (Osbaldiston and Schott 2012).

Bottom-up approaches can promote mitigation action (Abrahamse and Steg 2013). Indeed, community energy initiatives can encourage members' low-carbon behaviour (Middlemiss 2011; Seyfang and Haxeltine 2012; Abrahamse and Steg 2013; Sloot et al. 2018). Organisations can promote mitigation behaviour among their employees and customers by communicating their mission and strategies to mitigate climate change (Ruepert et al. 2017; van der Werff et al. 2021).

Default options, where a preset choice is implemented if users do not select another option, can promote mitigation actions such as energy savings, green electricity uptake, and meat-free options (Pichert and Katsikopoulos 2008; Bessette et al. 2014; Campbell-Arvai et al. 2014; Kunreuther and Weber 2014; Ölander and Thøgersen 2014; Ebeling and Lotz 2015; Liebe et al. 2018; Liebe et al. 2021).

6.7.6.2 Acceptability of Policy, Mitigation Options and System Changes

Public acceptability reflects the extent to which the public evaluates climate policy, mitigation options, and system changes (un)favourably, which can shape, enable, or prevent low-carbon energy system transitions. Public acceptability of policy and mitigation options is higher when people expect these have more positive and less negative consequences for self, others, and the environment (Perlaviciute and Steg 2014; Demski et al. 2015; Drews and Van den Bergh 2016). Public opposition may result when a culturally valued landscape is affected by renewable energy development (Warren et al. 2005; Devine-Wright and Howes 2010), particularly when place-based identities are threatened (Devine-Wright 2009, 2013; Boudet 2019). Acceptability can increase after a policy or change has been implemented and the consequences appear to be more positive than expected (Schuitema et al. 2010; Eliasson 2014; Weber 2015; Carattini et al. 2018); effective policy trials can thus build public support.

Next, climate policy and low-carbon options are evaluated as more fair and acceptable when costs and benefits are distributed equally, and when nature, the environment and future generations are protected (Schuitema et al. 2011; Drews and Van den Bergh 2016). Compensating affected groups for losses due to policy or systems changes enhanced public acceptability in some cases (Perlaviciute and Steg 2014), but people may disagree on which compensation would be worthwhile (Aitken 2010b; Cass et al. 2010), on the distribution of compensation (Devine-Wright and Sherry-Brennan 2019; Leer Jørgensen et al. 2020), or feel they are being bribed (Cass et al. 2010; Perlaviciute and Steg 2014). Pricing policies are more acceptable when revenues are earmarked for environmental purposes (Steg et al. 2006; Sælen and Kallbekken 2011) or redistributed towards those affected (Schuitema and Steg 2008).

Climate policy and mitigation options, such as renewable energy projects, are also perceived as more fair and acceptable when the public (Dietz 2013; Bidwell 2014; Bernauer et al. 2016b) or public society organisations (Terwel et al. 2010; Bernauer et al. 2016b) could participate in the decision-making (Arvai 2003; Devine-Wright 2005;

6

Terwel et al. 2012; Walker and Baxter 2017; Perlaviciute and Squintani 2020). People are more motivated to participate in decision-making on local projects than on national or general policy goals (Perlaviciute and Squintani 2020). Public acceptability is also higher when people can influence major rather than only minor decisions, particularly when trust in responsible parties is low (Liu et al. 2019a). Public participation can enhance the quality and legitimacy of decisions by including local knowledge and views that may otherwise be missed (Dietz 2013; Bidwell 2016).

Public support is higher when people trust responsible parties (Perlaviciute and Steg 2014; Drews and Van den Bergh 2016; Michaels and Parag 2016; Jiang et al. 2018; Liu et al. 2019a). Public support for unilateral climate policy is rather strong and robust (Bernauer et al. 2016a), even in the absence of reciprocal commitments by other states (Bernauer and Gampfer 2015).

Public acceptability of climate policy and low-carbon options differs across individuals. Climate policy and low-carbon options are more acceptable when people strongly value protecting other people and the environment, and support egalitarian worldviews, left-wing or green political ideologies, while acceptability is lower when people strongly endorse self-centred values, and support individualistic worldviews (Dietz et al. 2007; Perlaviciute and Steg 2014; Drews and Van den Bergh 2016). Similarly, public decision-makers support climate policy more when they endorse environmental values (Nilsson et al. 2016). Climate and energy policy is more acceptable when people are more concerned about climate change (Hornsey et al. 2016), when they believe their actions would help mitigate climate change, and feel responsible to mitigate climate change (Steg 2005; Eriksson et al. 2006; Jakovcevic and Steg 2013; Drews and Van den Bergh 2016; Kim and Shin 2017; Ünal et al. 2019).

6.7.7 The Costs and Benefits of Low-carbon Energy System Transitions in the Context of Sustainable Development

The attractiveness of energy sector mitigation ultimately depends on the way that it provides benefits and reduces the costs for the many different priorities that societies value (Yang et al. 2018a; Wei et al. 2018, 2020). While costs and benefits of climate mitigation are often considered in the context of pure economic outcomes – for example, GDP effects or changes in value of consumption – costs and benefits should be viewed with a broader lens that accounts for the many ways that the energy system interacts with societal priorities (Karlsson et al. 2020). Climate mitigation is not separate from countries' broader growth and development strategies, but rather as a key element of those strategies.

Cost reductions in key technologies, particularly in electricity and light-duty transport, have increased the economic attractiveness of near-term low-carbon energy system transitions (*high confidence*). The near-term, economic outcomes of low-carbon energy system transitions in some sectors and regions may be on par with or superior to those of an emissions-intensive future (*high confidence*). Even in cases when system costs are higher for low-carbon transitions, these

transitions may still be economically favourable when accounting for health impacts and other co-benefits (Gielen et al. 2019). Past assessments have quantified the aggregate economic costs for climate change mitigation using different metrics, for example, carbon prices, GDP losses, investments in energy infrastructure, and energy system costs. Assessments of mitigation costs from integrated assessment and energy system models vary widely. For example, scenarios include carbon prices in 2030 of less than USD20 tCO_2^{-1}, but also more than USD400 tCO_2^{-1} depending on the region, sector boundary, and methodology (e.g., Bauer et al. 2016; Brouwer et al. 2016; Oshiro et al. 2017; Vaillancourt et al. 2017; Chen et al. 2019). Those arise both from different methodologies (Guivarch and Rogelj 2017) and assumptions about uncertainties in key factors that drive costs (Meyer et al. 2021).

Recent developments, however, raise the prospect that economic outcomes could be substantially superior to prior estimates, particularly if key technologies continue to improve rapidly. In some regions and circumstances, particularly in the electricity sector, near-term mitigation may lead to superior economic outcomes than continuing to invest in and utilise emissions-intensive infrastructure (e.g. Brown et al. 2017; Kumar et al. 2020). Given the importance of electricity decarbonisation in near-term mitigation strategies (Section 6.7.1), decreasing costs of solar PV, wind power, and batteries to support their integration, have an outsized influence on near-term economic outcomes from mitigation. At the same time, economic outcomes may vary across regions depending, among other things, on the characteristics of the current energy systems, energy resources, and needs for integrating VRE technologies.

The long-term economic characteristics of low-emissions energy system transitions are not well understood, and they depend on policy design and implementation along with future costs and availability of technologies in key sectors (e.g., process heat, long-distance transport), and the ease of electrification in end-use sectors (*high confidence*). The long-term aggregate economic outcomes from a low-emissions future are not likely to be substantially worse than in an emissions-intensive future and may prove superior (Child et al. 2019, Farmer et al. 2020; Bogdanov et al. 2021) (*medium confidence*). For the whole economy, the interquartile range of estimated mitigation costs is between 140 USD2015 and 340 USD2015 tCO_2^{-1} in 2050 in scenarios limiting warming to 2°C (>67%) and between 430 USD2015 and 990 USD2015 tCO_2^{-1} in scenarios limiting warming to 1.5°C (>50%) with no or limited overshoot (Chapter 3). For energy sectors in various regions and globally, different scenarios show a wide range of implied carbon prices in 2050 to limit warming to 1.5°C, from below USD50 tCO_2^{-1} to more than USD900 tCO_2^{-1} (Brouwer et al. 2016; Rogelj et al. 2018a). Mitigation costs for scenarios limiting warming to 2°C (>67%) were 3–11% in consumption losses in AR5, but the median in newer studies is about 3% in GDP losses (Su et al. 2018; Gambhir et al. 2019).

Estimates of long-run mitigation costs are highly uncertain and depend on various factors. Both faster technological developments and international cooperation are consistently found to improve economic outcomes (Paroussos et al. 2019). Long-term mitigation is likely to be more challenging than near-term mitigation because low-

6

cost opportunities get utilised first and later efforts would require mitigation in more challenging sectors (Section 6.6). Advances in low-carbon energy resources and carriers such as next-generation biofuels, hydrogen produced from electrolysis, synthetic fuels, and carbon-neutral ammonia would substantially improve the economics of net-zero energy systems (*high confidence*). Current estimates of cumulative mitigation costs are comparably high for developing countries, amounting to up to 2–3% of GDP, indicating difficulties for mitigation without adequate support from developed countries (Dorband et al. 2019; Fujimori et al. 2020). In scenarios involving large amounts of stranded assets, the overall costs of low-carbon transitions also include the additional costs of early retirements (Box 6.11).

Focusing only on aggregate economic outcomes neglects distributional impacts, impacts on broader SDGs, and other outcomes of broad societal importance. Strategies to increase energy efficiency and energy conservation are, in most instances, mutually reinforcing with strategies to support sustainable development. Improving efficiency and energy conservation will promote sustainable consumption and production of energy and associated materials (SDG 12) (*high confidence*). Contrastingly, successful implementation of demand-side options requires sustainable partnerships (SDG 17) between different actors in energy systems, for example, governments, utilities, distributors, and consumers. Many authors have argued that energy efficiency has a large untapped potential in both supply and demand (Lovins 2018; Méjean et al. 2019). For example, improved fossil power plant efficiency has been estimated to lower the costs of CCS from USD80–100 tCO$_2^{-1}$ for a subcritical plant to <USD40 tCO$_2^{-1}$ for a high-efficiency plant (Hu and Zhai 2017; Singh et al. 2017). This could enhance energy access and affordability. Eliminating electricity

transmission losses has been estimated to mitigate 500 MtCO$_2$ per year globally (Surana and Jordaan 2019). For several other options, such as methane mitigation from the natural gas sector, the costs of infrastructure refurbishing could be offset with the value of the recovered natural gas (Kang et al. 2019).

Efficient end-use technologies are likely to be particularly cost-effective in developing countries where new infrastructure is rapidly getting built and there is an opportunity to create positive path dependencies (Section 6.7.3). Aside from reducing energy consumption, efficient end-use technologies reduce resource extraction, for example, fossil fuel extraction or mining for materials used in wind turbines or solar PV cells (Luderer et al. 2019). Reduced resource extraction is an important precursor to SDG 12 on sustainable consumption and production of minerals. End-use efficiency strategies also reduce the need for, and therefore SDG trade-offs associated with, CDR towards the end of the century and avoid temperature overshoot (van Vuuren et al. 2018). But fully leveraging the demand-side efficiency would entail behavioural changes and thus rely on strong partnerships with communities (SDG 17). For instance, approaches that inform households of the economic value of conservation strategies at home could be particularly useful (Niamir et al. 2018). Improved energy efficiency is interlinked with higher economic growth in Africa (Lin and Abudu 2020; Ohene-Asare et al. 2020). An important distinction here between SDGs focusing on infrastructural and behavioural interventions is the temporal context. Improving building heat systems or the electricity grid with reduced T&D losses would provide climate mitigation with one-time investments and minor maintenance over decades. On the other hand, behavioural changes would be an ongoing process involving sustained, long-term societal interactions.

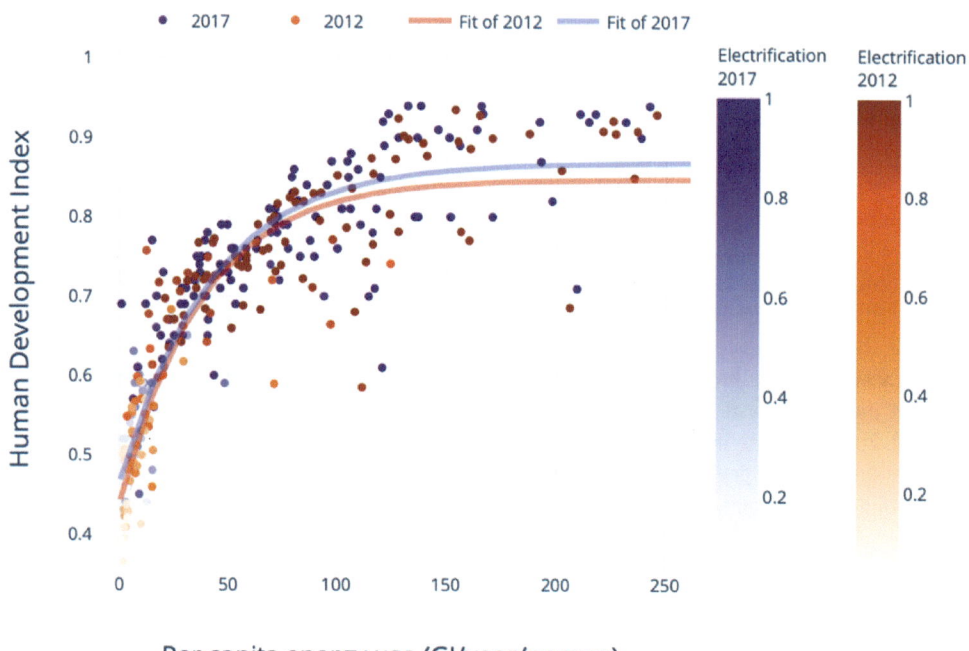

Figure 6.36 | The relationship between total per capita energy use, rate of electrification and human development index (HDI). Improved efficiency has lowered the energy demand required for meeting a threshold HDI during 2012–2017.

Figure 6.37 | Nature of the interactions between SDG 7 (Energy) and the non-energy SDGs. Source: McCollum et al. 2018c, reproduced under Creative Commons 3.0 Licence.

Increasing electrification will support and reduce the costs of key elements of human development, such as education, health, and employment (*high confidence*). Greater access to electricity might offer greater access to irrigation opportunities for agricultural communities (Peters and Sievert 2016) which could have the potential for increasing farmer incomes in support of SDG 1. Coordinated electrification policies also improve enrolment for all forms of education (Kumar and Rauniyar 2018; López-González et al. 2020). Empirical evidence from India suggests that electrification reduced the time for biomass collection, and thus increased the time children have available for schooling (SDGs 4 and 5) (Khandker et al. 2014). Reduced kerosene use in developing countries has improved indoor air quality (SDG 3) (Barron and Torero 2017; Lewis and Severnini 2020). These positive linkages between climate change mitigation and other goals have improved perceptions of solar PV among the public and policymakers. 'Goodwill' towards solar PV is the highest among all the major mitigation options considered in this chapter (Section 6.4.2).

Past trends have also indicated that, in some Asian countries, electrification has been obtained at lower income levels as compared to developed countries (Rao and Pachauri 2017), with corresponding impacts for development goals. For example, a human development index (HDI) greater than 0.7 (Figure 6.36) which signifies high development is now possible at close to 30 GJ yr^{-1} per person. This was attainable only at the energy consumption of 50 GJ yr^{-1} per person in preceding decades.

Electrification also improves energy efficiency, with corresponding implications for development goals. For example, the availability of electric cooking may reduce the cooking primary energy requirement considerably compared to traditional stoves (Yang and Yang 2018; Batchelor et al. 2019; Khan and Alam 2020) while also promoting improved indoor air quality (SDG 3). Similarly, PV-powered irrigation and water pumping reduces pumping energy demands, which has

the added advantage of promoting SDG 6 on clean water (Rathore et al. 2018; Elkadeem et al. 2019).

Phasing out fossil fuels in favour of low-carbon sources is likely to have considerable SDG benefits, particularly if trade-offs such as unemployment to fossil fuel workers are minimised (*high confidence*). A phase-out of coal (Box 6.2) will support SDGs 3, 7 and 14, but it is also anticipated to create large job losses if not properly managed. At the same time, there are large potential employment opportunities that may be created in alternative sectors such as renewables and bioenergy for both skilled and unskilled workers. 'Sustainable transition' pathways have indicated a complete fossil phase-out which could entail numerous other co-benefits. For instance, fossil fuels are estimated to generate only 2.65 jobs per million USD as compared to projected 7.49 from renewables (Garrett-Peltier 2017). Similar synergies may also emerge for nuclear power in the long term, though the high costs create trade-offs in developing country contexts (Agyekum et al. 2020; Castor et al. 2020). While bioenergy production may create jobs, it may also be problematic for SDG 2 on zero hunger by affecting the supplies and prices of food. Phasing out of fossil fuels will also improve air quality (SDG 3) and premature deaths by reducing PM2.5 emissions, (He et al. 2020; Li et al. 2020c). Energy transitions from fossil fuels to renewables, as well as within fossil fuels (coal to gas switching), are already occurring in some regions, spurred by climate concerns, health concerns, market dynamics, or consumer choice (e.g., in the transport sector).

CDR and CCS can create significant land and water trade-offs (*high confidence*). For large-scale CDR and CCS deployment to not conflict with development goals requires efforts to reduce implications on water and food systems. The water impacts of carbon capture are large, but these impacts can be strategically managed (Magneschi et al. 2017; Liu et al. 2019a; Realmonte et al. 2019; Giannaris et al. 2020c). In addition, high-salinity brines are produced from geologic carbon storage, which may be a synergy or trade-off depending on the energy intensity of the treatment process and the reusability of the treated waters (Klapperich et al. 2014; Arena et al. 2017); if the produced brine from geologic formations can be treated via desalination technologies, there is an opportunity to keep the water intensity of electricity as constant (Section 6.4.2.5). Both implications of CCS and CDR are related to SDG 6 on clean water. CDR discussions in the context of energy systems frequently pertains to BECCS which could affect food prices based on land management approaches (Daioglou et al. 2020a). Several CDR processes also require considerable infrastructure refurbishment and electrification to reduce upstream CO_2 emissions (Singh and Colosi 2021). Large-scale CDR could also open the potential for low-carbon transport and urban energy (by offsetting emissions in these sectors) use that would create synergies with SDG 11 (sustainable cities and communities). Effective siting of CDR infrastructure therefore requires consideration of trade-offs with other priorities. At the same time, several SDG synergies have also been reported to accompany CCS projects, such as with reduced air pollution (SDG 3) (Mikunda et al. 2021).

Greater energy system integration (Sections 6.4.3 and 6.6.2) would enhance energy-SDG synergies while eliminating trade-offs associated with deploying mitigation options (*high confidence*). Energy system integration strategies focus on codependence of individual technologies in ways that optimise system performance. Accordingly, they can improve economic outcomes and reduce negative implications for SDGs. For example, VRE electricity options raise intermittency concerns and hydrogen can be expensive due to the costs of electricity. Both are relevant to SDG 7 on affordable and reliable energy access. Routing excess solar generation during daytime for hydrogen production will improve grid stability as lower hydrogen costs (Tarroja et al. 2015). Due to the varying patterns of solar and wind energy, these two energy sources could be operated in tandem, thus reducing the material needs for their construction and for storage, thus promoting SDG 12 on sustainable production (Weitemeyer et al. 2015; Wang et al. 2019d). For CCS facilities, co-firing of fossil fuels and biomass could enable a more gradual, near-term low-carbon transition (Lu et al. 2019). This could enable early retirements (associated with SDG 1) while also providing air pollution reductions (associated with SDG 3).

Overall, the scope for positive interactions between low-carbon energy systems and SDGs is considerably larger than the trade-offs (Figure 6.37) (McCollum et al. 2018b). Some critical trade-offs include impact to biodiversity due to large-scale mineral mining needed for renewable infrastructure (Sonter et al. 2020).

Frequently Asked Questions

FAQ 6.1 | Will energy systems that emit little or no CO$_2$ be different than those of today?

Low-carbon energy systems will be similar to those of today in that they will provide many of the same services as today – for example, heating and cooling homes, travelling to work or on vacation, transporting goods and services, and powering manufacturing. But future energy systems may be different in that people may also demand new services that aren't foreseen today, just as people now use energy for many information technology uses that were not anticipated 50 years ago. More importantly, low-carbon energy systems will be different in the way that energy is produced, transformed, and used to provide these services. In the future, almost all electricity will be produced from sources that emit little or no CO$_2$, such as solar power, wind power, nuclear power, bioenergy, hydropower, geothermal power, or fossil energy in which the CO$_2$ is captured and stored. Electricity, hydrogen, and bioenergy will be used in many situations where fossil fuels are used today, for example, in cars or heating homes. And energy is likely to be used more efficiently than today, for example, through more efficient cars, trucks, and appliances, buildings that use very little energy, and greater use or public transportation. All of these changes may require new policies, institutions, and even new ways for people to live their lives. And fundamental to all of these changes is that low-carbon energy systems will use far less fossil fuel than today.

FAQ 6.2 | Can renewable sources provide all the energy needed for energy systems that emit little or no CO$_2$?

Renewable energy technologies harness energy from natural sources that are continually replenished, for example, from the sun (solar energy), the wind (wind energy), plants (bioenergy), rainfall (hydropower), or even the ocean. The energy from these sources exceeds the world's current and future energy needs many times. But that does not mean that renewable sources will provide all energy in future low-carbon energy systems. Some countries have a lot of renewable energy, whereas others do not, and other energy sources, such as nuclear power or fossil energy in which CO$_2$ emissions are captured and stored (carbon dioxide capture and storage, or CCS) can also contribute to low-carbon energy systems. The energy from sources such as solar energy, wind energy, and hydropower can vary throughout the day or over seasons or years. All low-carbon energy sources have other implications for people and countries, some of which are desirable, for example, reducing air pollution or making it easy to provide electricity in remote locations, and some of which are undesirable, for example decreasing biodiversity or mining of minerals to produce low-emissions technologies. For all of these reasons, it is unlikely that all low-carbon energy systems around the world will rely entirely on renewable energy sources.

FAQ 6.3 | What are the most important steps to decarbonise the energy system?

To create a low-carbon energy system, emissions must be reduced across all parts of the system, and not just one or two. This means, for example, reducing the emissions from producing electricity, driving cars, hauling freight, heating and cooling buildings, powering data centres, and manufacturing goods. There are more opportunities to reduce emissions over the next decade in some sectors compared to others. For example, it is possible to substantially reduce electricity emissions over the next decade by investing in low-carbon electricity sources, while at the same time halting the construction of new coal-fired power plants, retiring existing coal-fired power plants or retrofitting them with carbon capture and storage (CCS), and limiting the construction of new gas-fired power plants. There are also opportunities to increase the number of electric cars, trucks, and other vehicles on the road, or to use electricity rather than natural gas or coal to heat homes. And across the whole energy system, emissions can be reduced by using more efficient technologies. While these and other actions will be critical over the coming decade, it is also important to remember that the low-carbon energy transition needs to extend for many decades into the future to limit warming. This means that it is important now to improve and test options that could be useful later on, for example, producing hydrogen from low-carbon sources or producing bioenergy from crops that require less land than today.

6

References

Abanades, J.C. et al., 2015: Emerging CO_2 capture systems. *Int. J. Greenh. Gas Control*, **40**, 126–166, doi:10.1016/j.ijggc.2015.04.018.

Abdella, J. and K. Shuaib, 2018: Peer to Peer Distributed Energy Trading in Smart Grids: A Survey. Energies, **11**, 1560, doi:10.3390/en11061560.

Abdin, Z. et al., 2020: Hydrogen as an energy vector. *Renew. Sustain. Energy Rev.*, **120**, 109620, doi:10.1016/j.rser.2019.109620.

Abotalib, M., F. Zhao, and A. Clarens, 2016: Deployment of a Geographical Information System Life Cycle Assessment Integrated Framework for Exploring the Opportunities and Challenges of Enhanced Oil Recovery Using Industrial CO_2 Supply in the United States. *ACS Sustain. Chem. Eng.*, **4(9)**, 4743–4751, doi:10.1021/acssuschemeng.6b00957.

Abousahl, S. et al., 2021: Technical assessment of nuclear energy with respect to the 'do no significant harm' criteria of Regulation (EU) 2020/852 ('Taxonomy Regulation'). EUR 30777 EN, Publications Office of the European Union, Luxembourg, doi:10.2760/207251.

Abraham, J., 2017: Just Transitions for the Miners: Labor Environmentalism in the Ruhr and Appalachian Coalfields. *New Polit. Sci.*, **39(2)**, 218–240, doi:10.1080/07393148.2017.1301313.

Abrahamse, W. and L. Steg, 2013: Social influence approaches to encourage resource conservation: A meta-analysis. *Glob. Environ. Change*, **23(6)**, 1773–1785, doi:10.1016/j.gloenvcha.2013.07.029.

Abrahamse, W., L. Steg, C. Vlek, and T. Rothengatter, 2005: A review of intervention studies aimed at household energy conservation. *J. Environ. Psychol.*, **25(3)**, 273–291, doi:10.1016/j.jenvp.2005.08.002.

Abrahamse, W., L. Steg, C. Vlek, and T. Rothengatter, 2007: The effect of tailored information, goal setting, and tailored feedback on household energy use, energy-related behaviors, and behavioral antecedents. *J. Environ. Psychol.*, **27(4)**, 265–276, doi:10.1016/j.jenvp.2007.08.002.

Abrell, J. and S. Rausch, 2016: Cross-country electricity trade, renewable energy and European transmission infrastructure policy. *J. Environ. Econ. Manage.*, **79**, 87–113, doi:10.1016/j.jeem.2016.04.001.

Abrell, J., M. Kosch, and S. Rausch, 2019: Carbon abatement with renewables: Evaluating wind and solar subsidies in Germany and Spain. *J. Public Econ.*, **169**, 172–202, doi:10.1016/j.jpubeco.2018.11.007.

Abreu, E.F.M., P. Canhoto, V. Prior, and R. Melicio, 2018: Solar resource assessment through long-term statistical analysis and typical data generation with different time resolutions using GHI measurements. *Renew. Energy*, **127**, 398–411, doi:10.1016/j.renene.2018.04.068.

Acemoglu, D., U. Akcigit, D. Hanley, and W. Kerr, 2016: Transition to Clean Technology. *J. Polit. Econ.*, **124(1)**, 52–104, doi:10.1086/684511.

ACOLA, 2017: *The Role of Energy Storage in Australia's Future Energy Supply Mix*. https://acola.org/hs1-energy-storage-australia/.

Adenle, A.A., D.T. Manning, and J. Arbiol, 2017: Mitigating Climate Change in Africa: Barriers to Financing Low-Carbon Development. *World Dev.*, **100**, 123–132, doi:10.1016/j.worlddev.2017.07.033.

Afif, A. et al., 2016: Ammonia-fed fuel cells: a comprehensive review. *Renew. Sustain. Energy Rev.*, **60**, 822–835, doi:10.1016/j.rser.2016.01.120.

Aghahosseini, A. and C. Breyer, 2018: Assessment of geological resource potential for compressed air energy storage in global electricity supply. *Energy Convers. Manag.*, **169**, 161–173, doi:10.1016/j.enconman.2018.05.058.

Agnew, S. and P. Dargusch, 2017: Consumer preferences for household-level battery energy storage. *Renew. Sustain. Energy Rev.*, **75**, 609–617, doi:10.1016/j.rser.2016.11.030.

Agrawal, A., A. Chhatre, and E.R. Gerber, 2015: Motivational Crowding in Sustainable Development Interventions. *Am. Polit. Sci. Rev.*, **109(3)**, 470–487, doi:10.1017/S0003055415000209.

Aguilar, F.X., A. Mirzaee, R.G. McGarvey, S.R. Shifley, and D. Burtraw, 2020: Expansion of US wood pellet industry points to positive trends but the need

for continued monitoring. *Sci. Rep.*, **10(1)**, 18607, doi:10.1038/s41598-020-75403-z.

Agyekum, E.B., M.N.S. Ansah, and K.B. Afornu, 2020: Nuclear energy for sustainable development: SWOT analysis on Ghana's nuclear agenda. *Energy Reports*, **6**, 107–115, doi:10.1016/J.EGYR.2019.11.163.

Ahl, A., M. Goto, and M. Yarime, 2020: Smart technology applications in the woody biomass supply chain: interview insights and potential in Japan. *Sustain. Sci.*, **15(5)**, 1531–1553, doi:10.1007/s11625-019-00728-2.

Ahmad, A., 2021: Increase in frequency of nuclear power outages due to changing climate. *Nat. Energy*, **6(7)**, 755–762, doi:10.1038/s41560-021-00849-y.

Ahmad, S.I. et al., 2020: Development of quantitative SHE index for waste to energy technology selection. *Energy*, **191**, 116534, doi:10.1016/j.energy.2019.116534.

Ahmed, S.F. et al., 2021: Recent progress in solar water heaters and solar collectors: A comprehensive review. *Thermal Science and Engineering Progress*, **25**, 100981, doi:10.1016/j.tsep.2021.100981.

Aitken, M., 2010a: Wind power and community benefits: Challenges and opportunities. *Energy Policy*, **38(10)**, 6066–6075, doi:10.1016/j.enpol.2010.05.062.

Aitken, M., 2010b: Why we still don't understand the social aspects of wind power: A critique of key assumptions within the literature. *Energy Policy*, **38(4)**, 1834–1841, doi:10.1016/j.enpol.2009.11.060.

Aklin, M., P. Bayer, S.P. Harish, and J. Urpelainen, 2017: Does basic energy access generate socioeconomic benefits? A field experiment with off-grid solar power in India. *Sci. Adv.*, **3(5)**, doi:10.1126/sciadv.1602153.

Al-Qahtani, A., B. Parkinson, K. Hellgardt, N. Shah, and G. Guillen-Gosalbez, 2021: Uncovering the true cost of hydrogen production routes using life cycle monetisation. *Appl. Energy*, **281**, 115958, doi:10.1016/j.apenergy.2020.115958.

Al Shaqsi, A.Z., K. Sopian, and A. Al-Hinai, 2020: Review of energy storage services, applications, limitations, and benefits. *Energy Reports*, **6**, 288–306, doi:10.1016/j.egyr.2020.07.028.

Alassi, A., S. Bañales, O. Ellabban, G. Adam, and C. MacIver, 2019: HVDC Transmission: Technology Review, Market Trends and Future Outlook. *Renew. Sustain. Energy Rev.*, **112**, 530–554, doi:10.1016/j.rser.2019.04.062.

Alberini, A. and C. Towe, 2015: Information v. energy efficiency incentives: Evidence from residential electricity consumption in Maryland. *Energy Econ.*, **52**, S30–S40, doi:10.1016/j.eneco.2015.08.013.

Albertus, P., J.S. Manser, and S. Litzelman, 2020: Long-Duration Electricity Storage Applications, Economics, and Technologies. *Joule*, **4(1)**, 21–32, doi:10.1016/j.joule.2019.11.009.

Alcalde, J. et al., 2018: Estimating geological CO_2 storage security to deliver on climate mitigation. *Nat. Commun.*, **9(1)**, 2201, doi:10.1038/s41467-018-04423-1.

Alcalde, J. et al., 2019: Acorn: Developing full-chain industrial carbon capture and storage in a resource- and infrastructure-rich hydrocarbon province. *J. Clean. Prod.*, **233**, 963–971, doi:10.1016/j.jclepro.2019.06.087.

Aldy, J.E., 2020: Carbon Tax Review and Updating: Institutionalizing an Act-Learn-Act Approach to U.S. Climate Policy. *Rev. Environ. Econ. Policy*, **14(1)**, 76–94, doi:10.1093/reep/rez019.

Allcott, H., 2011: Social norms and energy conservation. *J. Public Econ.*, **95(9–10)**, 1082–1095, doi:10.1016/j.jpubeco.2011.03.003.

Allen, P. and T. Chatterton, 2013: Carbon reduction scenarios for 2050: An explorative analysis of public preferences. *Energy Policy*, **63**, 796–808, doi:10.1016/j.enpol.2013.08.079.

Alrashed, F. and U. Zahid, 2021: Comparative analysis of conventional steam methane reforming and PdAu membrane reactor for the hydrogen production. *Comput. Chem. Eng.*, **154**, 107497, doi:10.1016/j.compchemeng.2021.107497.

Alsaleh, M. and A. Abdul-Rahim, 2018: The Economic Determinants of Bioenergy Trade Intensity in the EU-28: A Co-Integration Approach. *Sustainability*, **10(2)**, 565, doi:10.3390/su10020565.

Alvarez, R.A. et al., 2018: Assessment of methane emissions from the U.S. oil and gas supply chain. *Science.*, **361**, 186–188, doi:10.1126/science.aar7204.

Ambrosio-Albala, P., P. Upham, C.S.E. Bale, and P.G. Taylor, 2020: Exploring acceptance of decentralised energy storage at household and neighbourhood scales: A UK survey. *Energy Policy*, **138**(December 2019), 111194, doi:10.1016/j.enpol.2019.111194.

Ameli, H., M. Qadrdan, and G. Strbac, 2017: Value of gas network infrastructure flexibility in supporting cost effective operation of power systems. *Appl. Energy*, **202**, 571–580, doi:10.1016/j.apenergy.2017.05.132.

Ameli, H., M. Qadrdan, and G. Strbac, 2019: Coordinated operation strategies for natural gas and power systems in presence of gas-related flexibilities. *IET Energy Syst. Integr.*, **1(1)**, 3–13, doi:10.1049/iet-esi.2018.0047.

Ameli, H., M. Qadrdan, and G. Strbac, 2020: Coordinated Operation of Gas and Electricity Systems for Flexibility Study. *Front. Energy Res.*, **8**, 120, doi:10.3389/fenrg.2020.00120.

Amirante, R., E. Cassone, E. Distaso, and P. Tamburrano, 2017: Overview on recent developments in energy storage: Mechanical, electrochemical and hydrogen technologies. *Energy Convers. Manag.*, **132**, 372–387, doi:10.1016/j.enconman.2016.11.046.

Amiryar, M. and K. Pullen, 2017: A Review of Flywheel Energy Storage System Technologies and Their Applications. *Appl. Sci.*, **7(3)**, 286, doi:10.3390/app7030286.

Andadari, R.K., P. Mulder, and P. Rietveld, 2014: Energy poverty reduction by fuel switching. Impact evaluation of the LPG conversion program in Indonesia. *Energy Policy*, **66**, 436–449, doi:10.1016/j.enpol.2013.11.021.

Anderson, S.T. and R.G. Newell, 2004: Information programs for technology adoption: The case of energy-efficiency audits. *Resour. Energy Econ.*, **26(1)**, 27–50, doi:10.1016/j.reseneeco.2003.07.001.

Andersson, J., and S. Grönkvist, 2019: Large-scale storage of hydrogen. *Int. J. Hydrogen Energy*, **44**, 11901–11919, doi:10.1016/j.ijhydene.2019.03.063.

Andoni, M. et al., 2019: Blockchain technology in the energy sector: A systematic review of challenges and opportunities. *Renew. Sustain. Energy Rev.*, **100**, 143–174, doi:10.1016/j.rser.2018.10.014.

Andor, M. and A. Voss, 2016: Optimal renewable-energy promotion: Capacity subsidies vs. generation subsidies. *Resour. Energy Econ.*, **45**, 144–158, doi:10.1016/j.reseneeco.2016.06.002.

Andrews-Speed, P., 2016: Applying institutional theory to the low-carbon energy transition. *Energy Res. Soc. Sci.*, **13**, 216–225, doi:10.1016/j.erss.2015.12.011.

Andrews-Speed, P. and G. Ma, 2016: Household Energy Saving in China: The Challenge of Changing Behaviour. In: *China's Energy Efficiency and Conservation* [Su, B. and E. Thomson, (eds.)]. Springer, Singapore, pp. 23–39.

Ansari, D. and F. Holz, 2020: Between stranded assets and green transformation: Fossil-fuel-producing developing countries towards 2055. *World Dev.*, **130**, 104947, doi:10.1016/j.worlddev.2020.104947.

Antosiewicz, M., A. Nikas, A. Szpor, J. Witajewski-Baltvilks, and H. Doukas, 2020: Pathways for the transition of the Polish power sector and associated risks. *Environ. Innov. Soc. Transitions*, **35**, 271–291, doi:10.1016/j.eist.2019.01.008.

Arbabzadeh, M., R. Sioshansi, J.X. Johnson, and G.A. Keoleian, 2019: The role of energy storage in deep decarbonization of electricity production. *Nat. Commun.*, **10**, doi:10.1038/s41467-019-11161-5.

Ardente, F., C.E.L. Latunussa, and G.A. Blengini, 2019: Resource efficient recovery of critical and precious metals from waste silicon PV panel recycling. *Waste Manag.*, **91**, 156–167, doi:10.1016/j.wasman.2019.04.059.

Ardizzon, G., G. Cavazzini, and G. Pavesi, 2014: A new generation of small hydro and pumped-hydro power plants: Advances and future challenges. *Renew. Sustain. Energy Rev.*, **31**, 746–761, doi:10.1016/j.rser.2013.12.043.

ARENA, 2020: South Australian battery grows bigger and better. https://arena.gov.au/blog/south-australian-battery-grows-bigger-and-better/.

Arena, J.T. et al., 2017: Management and dewatering of brines extracted from geologic carbon storage sites. *Int. J. Greenh. Gas Control*, **63**, 194–214, doi:10.1016/j.ijggc.2017.03.032.

Arenas, L.F. et al., 2018: The characteristics and performance of hybrid redox flow batteries with zinc negative electrodes for energy storage. *Renew. Sustain. Energy Rev.*, **90**, 992–1016, doi:10.1016/j.rser.2018.03.016.

Arnaiz del Pozo, C., S. Cloete, and Á. Jiménez Álvaro, 2021: Carbon-negative hydrogen: Exploring the techno-economic potential of biomass co-gasification with CO_2 capture. *Energy Convers. Manag.*, **247**, 114712, doi:10.1016/j.enconman.2021.114712.

Arndt, C., S. Msangi, and J. Thurlow, 2011: Are biofuels good for African development? An analytical framework with evidence from Mozambique and Tanzania. *Biofuels*, **2**, 221–234, doi:10.4155/bfs.11.1.

Arning, K. et al., 2019: Same or different? Insights on public perception and acceptance of carbon capture and storage or utilization in Germany. *Energy Policy*, **125**, 235–249, doi:10.1016/j.enpol.2018.10.039.

Arshad, M., et al., 2019: A Techno-Economic Concept of EGS Power Generation in Pakistan. Proceedings 44th Workshop on Geothermal Reservoir Engineering, February 2019, Stanford, CA, USA, 7 pp.

Arvai, J.L., 2003: Using risk communication to disclose the outcome of a participatory decision-making process: Effects on the perceived acceptability of risk-policy decisions. *Risk Anal.*, **23(2)**, 281–289, doi:10.1111/1539-6924.00308.

Asensio, O.I. and M.A. Delmas, 2015: Nonprice incentives and energy conservation. *Proc. Natl. Acad. Sci.*, **112(6)**, E510–515, doi:10.1073/pnas.1401880112.

Asensio, O.I. and M.A. Delmas, 2016: The dynamics of behavior change: Evidence from energy conservation. *J. Econ. Behav. Organ.*, **126**, 196–212, doi:10.1016/j.jebo.2016.03.012.

Asheim, G.B. et al., 2019: The case for a supply-side climate treaty. *Science*, **365(6451)**, 325–327, doi:10.1126/science.aax5011.

Auffhammer, M., P. Baylis, and C.H. Hausman, 2017: Climate change is projected to have severe impacts on the frequency and intensity of peak electricity demand across the United States. *Proc. Natl. Acad. Sci.*, **114(8)**, 1886–1891, doi:10.1073/pnas.1613193114.

Auger, T., J. Trüby, P. Balcombe, and I. Staffell, 2021: The future of coal investment, trade, and stranded assets. *Joule*, **5(6)**, 1462–1484, doi:10.1016/j.joule.2021.05.008.

Aunedi, M. and G. Strbac, 2020: Whole-system Benefits of Vehicle-to-Grid Services from Electric Vehicle Fleets. *2020 Fifteenth International Conference on Ecological Vehicles and Renewable Energies (EVER)*, IEEE, Monte Carlo, Monaco, 9 pp.

Avraam, C., D. Chu, and S. Siddiqui, 2020: Natural gas infrastructure development in North America under integrated markets. *Energy Policy*, **147**, 111757, doi:10.1016/j.enpol.2020.111757.

Awasthi, M.K. et al., 2019: Global Status of Waste-to-Energy Technology. In: *Current Developments in Biotechnology and Bioengineering*, Elsevier, Amsterdam, Netherlands, pp. 31–52.

Ayodele, T.R., A.S.O. Ogunjuyigbe, and M.A. Alao, 2018: Economic and environmental assessment of electricity generation using biogas from organic fraction of municipal solid waste for the city of Ibadan, Nigeria. *J. Clean. Prod.*, **203**, 718–735, doi:10.1016/J.JCLEPRO.2018.08.282.

Azevedo, I., C. Bataille, J. Bistline, L. Clarke, and S. Davis, 2021: Net-zero emissions energy systems: What we know and do not know. *Energy Clim. Change*, **2**, 100049, doi:10.1016/j.egycc.2021.100049.

Bager, S. and L. Mundaca, 2017: Making 'Smart Meters' smarter? Insights from a behavioural economics pilot field experiment in Copenhagen, Denmark. *Energy Res. Soc. Sci.*, **28**(April), 68–76, doi:10.1016/j.erss.2017.04.008.

Baik, E. et al., 2018: Geospatial analysis of near-term potential for carbon-negative bioenergy in the United States. *Proc. Natl. Acad. Sci.*, **115(13)**, 3290–3295, doi:10.1073/pnas.1720338115.

Baik, E. et al., 2021: What is different about different net-zero carbon electricity systems? *Energy Clim. Change*, **2**, 100046, doi:10.1016/J.EGYCC.2021.100046.

Baker, S.E. et al., 2020: *Getting to Neutral: Options for Negative Carbon Emissions in California*. Lawrence Livermore National Laboratory, Livermore, CA, USA, 178 pp.

Balcombe, P., D. Rigby, and A. Azapagic, 2013: Motivations and barriers associated with adopting microgeneration energy technologies in the UK. *Renew. Sustain. Energy Rev.*, **22**, 655–666, doi:10.1016/j.rser.2013.02.012.

Balducci, P.J., M.J.E. Alam, T.D. Hardy, and D. Wu, 2018: Assigning value to energy storage systems at multiple points in an electrical grid. *Energy Environ. Sci.*, **11(8)**, 1926–1944, doi:10.1039/c8ee00569a.

Balijepalli, N., S.S. Venkata, C.W. Richter, R.D. Christie, and V.J. Longo, 2005: Distribution system reliability assessment due to lightning storms. *IEEE Trans. Power Deliv.*, **20(3)**, 2153–2159, doi:10.1109/TPWRD.2005.848724.

Ballarino, A. et al., 2016: The BEST PATHS Project on MgB 2 Superconducting Cables for Very High Power Transmission. *IEEE Trans. Appl. Supercond.*, **26(3)**, 1–6, doi:10.1109/TASC.2016.2545116.

Bamberg, S., 2000: The promotion of new behavior by forming an implementation intention: Results of a field experiment in the domain of travel mode choice. *J. Appl. Soc. Psychol.*, **30(9)**, 1903–1922, doi:10.1111/j.1559-1816.2000.tb02474.x.

Bamberg, S., 2002: Effects of implementation intentions on the actual performance of new environmentally friendly behaviours – Results of two field experiments. *J. Environ. Psychol.*, **22(4)**, 399–411, doi:10.1006/jevp.2002.0278.

Banerjee, A. and B.D. Solomon, 2003: Eco-labeling for energy efficiency and sustainability: A meta-evaluation of US programs. *Energy Policy*, **31(2)**, 109–123, doi:10.1016/S0301-4215(02)00012-5.

Banerjee, T., M. Kumar, R.K. Mall, and R.S. Singh, 2017: Airing 'clean air' in Clean India Mission. *Environ. Sci. Pollut. Res.*, **24(7)**, 6399–6413, doi:10.1007/s11356-016-8264-y.

Barbose, G. et al., 2016: A retrospective analysis of benefits and impacts of US renewable portfolio standards. *Energy Policy*, **96**, 645–660, doi:10.1016/j.enpol.2016.06.035.

Barbour, E., I.A.G. Wilson, J. Radcliffe, Y. Ding, and Y. Li, 2016: A review of pumped hydro energy storage development in significant international electricity markets. *Renew. Sustain. Energy Rev.*, **61**, 421–432, doi:10.1016/j.rser.2016.04.019.

Barney, J.N. and J.M. DiTomaso, 2010: Bioclimatic predictions of habitat suitability for the biofuel switchgrass in North America under current and future climate scenarios. *Biomass and Bioenergy*, **34(1)**, 124–133, doi:10.1016/j.biombioe.2009.10.009.

Baron, R., 2016: *The Role of Public Procurement in Low-carbon Innovation*. Organisation for Economic Co-operation and Development, Paris, France, 32 pp. https://www.oecd.org/sd-roundtable/papersandpublications/The Role of Public Procurement in Low-carbon Innovation.pdf.

Barra, P.H.A., W.C. de Carvalho, T.S. Menezes, R.A.S. Fernandes, and D.V. Coury, 2021: A review on wind power smoothing using high-power energy storage systems. *Renew. Sustain. Energy Rev.*, **137**(October 2020), 110455, doi:10.1016/j.rser.2020.110455.

Barron-Gafford, G.A. et al., 2016: The Photovoltaic Heat Island Effect: Larger solar power plants increase local temperatures. *Sci. Rep.*, **6(1)**, 35070, doi:10.1038/srep35070.

Barron-Gafford, G.A. et al., 2019: Agrivoltaics provide mutual benefits across the food–energy–water nexus in drylands. *Nat. Sustain.*, **2(9)**, 848–855, doi:10.1038/s41893-019-0364-5.

Barron, M. and M. Torero, 2017: Household electrification and indoor air pollution. *J. Environ. Econ. Manage.*, **86**, 81–92, doi:10.1016/j.jeem.2017.07.007.

Barthelmie, R.J. and S.C. Pryor, 2021: Climate Change Mitigation Potential of Wind Energy. *Climate*, **9(9)**, doi:10.3390/cli9090136.

Bartholomew, T.V. and M.S. Mauter, 2016: Multiobjective optimization model for minimizing cost and environmental impact in shale gas water and wastewater management. *ACS Sustain. Chem. Eng.*, **4(7)**, 3728–3735, doi:10.1021/acssuschemeng.6b00372.

Bartók, B. et al., 2017: Projected changes in surface solar radiation in CMIP5 global climate models and in EURO-CORDEX regional climate models for Europe. *Clim. Dyn.*, **49(7–8)**, 2665–2683, doi:10.1007/s00382-016-3471-2.

Bartos, M. et al., 2016: Impacts of rising air temperatures on electric transmission ampacity and peak electricity load in the United States. *Environ. Res. Lett.*, **11(11)**, 114008, doi:10.1088/1748-9326/11/11/114008.

Bataille, C., H. Waisman, M. Colombier, L. Segafredo, and J. Williams, 2016: The Deep Decarbonization Pathways Project (DDPP): insights and emerging issues. *Clim. Policy*, **16 (sup1)**, S1–S6, doi:10.1080/14693062.2016.1179620.

Bataille, C., C. Guivarch, S. Hallegatte, J. Rogelj, and H. Waisman, 2018: Carbon prices across countries. *Nat. Clim. Change*, **8(8)**, 648–650, doi:10.1038/s41558-018-0239-1.

Bataille, C. et al., 2020: *Net-zero Deep Decarbonization Pathways in Latin America: Challenges and Opportunities*. Elsevier, Washington, DC, USA, 36 pp.

Bataille, C.G.F., 2020: Physical and policy pathways to net-zero emissions industry. *WIREs Clim. Change*, **11(2)**, doi:10.1002/wcc.633.

Batchelor, S., E. Brown, N. Scott, and J. Leary, 2019: Two birds, one stone-reframing cooking energy policies in Africa and Asia. *Energies*, **12(9)**, 1591, doi:10.3390/en12091591.

Bates, A. and J. Firestone, 2015: A comparative assessment of proposed offshore wind power demonstration projects in the United States. *Energy Res. Soc. Sci.*, **10**, 192–205, doi:10.1016/j.erss.2015.07.007.

Bauer, N. et al., 2016: Global fossil energy markets and climate change mitigation – an analysis with REMIND. *Clim. Change*, **136(1)**, 69–82, doi:10.1007/s10584-013-0901-6.

Bauer, N. et al., 2017: Shared Socio-Economic Pathways of the Energy Sector – Quantifying the Narratives. *Glob. Environ. Change*, **42**, 316–330, doi:10.1016/j.gloenvcha.2016.07.006.

Bauer, N., C. McGlade, J. Hilaire, and P. Ekins, 2018: Divestment prevails over the green paradox when anticipating strong future climate policies. *Nat. Clim. Change*, **8(2)**, 130–134, doi:10.1038/s41558-017-0053–1.

Bauer, N. et al., 2020: Global energy sector emission reductions and bioenergy use: overview of the bioenergy demand phase of the EMF-33 model comparison. *Clim. Change*, **163(3)**, 1553–1568, doi:10.1007/s10584-018-2226-y.

Baxter, J., Y. Ho, Y. Rollins, and V. Maclaren, 2016: Attitudes toward waste to energy facilities and impacts on diversion in Ontario, Canada. *Waste Manag.*, **50**, 75–85, doi:10.1016/J.WASMAN.2016.02.017.

Bednar, J., M. Obersteiner, and F. Wagner, 2019: On the financial viability of negative emissions. *Nat. Commun.*, **10(1783)**, 1–4, doi:10.1038/s41467-019-09782-x.

BEIS, 2021: *Hydrogen Production Costs*. Department for Business, Energy & Industrial Strategy, Longdon, UK. https://assets.publishing.service.gov.uk/government/uploads/system/uploads/attachment_data/file/1011506/Hydrogen_Production_Costs_2021.pdf.

Beiter, P. et al., 2021: Wind power costs driven by innovation and experience with further reductions on the horizon. *Wiley Interdiscip. Rev. Energy Environ.*, **10(5)**, 1–20, doi:10.1002/wene.398.

Béland, D. and M. Howlett, 2016: The Role and Impact of the Multiple-Streams Approach in Comparative Policy Analysis. *J. Comp. Policy Anal. Res. Pract.*, **18(3)**, 221–227, doi:10.1080/13876988.2016.1174410.

Belderbos, A., E. Delarue, and W. D'haeseleer, 2016: Calculating the levelized cost of electricity storage. *Energy: Expectations and Uncertainty, 39th IAEE International Conference, Jun 19-22, 2016*.

Bell, T.E. and L. Torrente-Murciano, 2016: H2 Production via Ammonia Decomposition Using Non-Noble Metal Catalysts: A Review. *Top. Catal.*, **59(15–16)**, 1438–1457, doi:10.1007/s11244-016-0653-4.

Bellarby, J., M. Wattenbach, G. Tuck, M.J. Glendining, and P. Smith, 2010: The potential distribution of bioenergy crops in the UK under present and future climate. *Biomass and Bioenergy*, **34(12)**, 1935–1945, doi:10.1016/j.biombioe.2010.08.009.

Beringer, T., W. Lucht, and S. Schaphoff, 2011: Bioenergy production potential of global biomass plantations under environmental and agricultural constraints. *GCB Bioenergy*, **3(4)**, 299–312, doi:10.1111/j.1757-1707.2010.01088.x.

Bernauer, T. and R. Gampfer, 2015: How robust is public support for unilateral climate policy? *Environ. Sci. Policy*, **54**, 316–330, doi:10.1016/j.envsci.2015.07.010.

Bernauer, T., L. Dong, L.F. McGrath, I. Shaymerdenova, and H. Zhang, 2016a: Unilateral or reciprocal climate policy? Experimental evidence from China. *Polit. Gov.*, **4(3)**, 152–171, doi:10.17645/pag.v4i3.650.

Bernauer, T., R. Gampfer, T. Meng, and Y.S. Su, 2016b: Could more civil society involvement increase public support for climate policy-making? Evidence from a survey experiment in China. *Glob. Environ. Change*, **40**, 1–12, doi:10.1016/j.gloenvcha.2016.06.001.

Berthelemy, M. and L.E. Rangel, 2015: Nuclear reactors' construction costs: The role of lead-time, standardization and technological progress. *Energy Policy*, **82**, 118–130, doi:10.1016/j.enpol.2015.03.015.

Bertram, C. et al., 2015: Complementing carbon prices with technology policies to keep climate targets within reach. *Nat. Clim. Change*, **5(3)**, 235–239, doi:10.1038/nclimate2514.

Bertram, C. et al., 2018: Targeted policies can compensate most of the increased sustainability risks in 1.5°C mitigation scenarios. *Environ. Res. Lett.*, **13(6)**, doi:10.1088/1748-9326/aac3ec.

Bertram, C. et al., 2021: Energy system developments and investments in the decisive decade for the Paris Agreement goals. *Environ. Res. Lett.*, **16(7)**, 74020, doi:10.1088/1748-9326/ac09ae.

Bertsch, V., M. Hall, C. Weinhardt, and W. Fichtner, 2016: Public acceptance and preferences related to renewable energy and grid expansion policy: Empirical insights for Germany. *Energy*, **114**, 465–477, doi:10.1016/j.energy.2016.08.022.

Bertsch, V., M. Hyland, and M. Mahony, 2017: What drives people's opinions of electricity infrastructure? Empirical evidence from Ireland. *Energy Policy*, **106**, 472–497, doi:10.1016/j.enpol.2017.04.008.

Besharat, F., A.A. Dehghan, and A.R. Faghih, 2013: Empirical models for estimating global solar radiation: A review and case study. *Renew. Sustain. Energy Rev.*, **21**, 798–821, doi:10.1016/j.rser.2012.12.043.

Bessette, D.L. and J.L. Arvai, 2018: Engaging attribute tradeoffs in clean energy portfolio development. *Energy Policy*, **115**(October 2017), 221–229, doi:10.1016/j.enpol.2018.01.021.

Bessette, D.L., J. Arvai, and V. Campbell-Arvai, 2014: Decision support framework for developing regional energy strategies. *Environ. Sci. Technol.*, **48(3)**, 1401–1408, doi:10.1021/es4036286.

Best, R. and P.J. Burke, 2018: Adoption of solar and wind energy: The roles of carbon pricing and aggregate policy support. *Energy Policy*, **118**, 404–417, doi:10.1016/j.enpol.2018.03.050.

Bhagwat, P.C., J.C. Richstein, E.J.L. Chappin, K.K. Iychettira, and L.J. De Vries, 2017: Cross-border effects of capacity mechanisms in interconnected power systems. *Util. Policy*, **46**, 33–47, doi:10.1016/j.jup.2017.03.005.

Bhave, A. et al., 2017: Screening and techno-economic assessment of biomass-based power generation with CCS technologies to meet 2050 CO_2 targets. *Appl. Energy*, **190**, 481–489, doi:10.1016/j.apenergy.2016.12.120.

Biddau, F., A. Armenti, and P. Cottone, 2016: Socio-psychological aspects of grassroots participation in the transition movement: An Italian case study. *J. Soc. Polit. Psychol.*, **4(1)**, 142–165, doi:10.5964/jspp.v4i1.518.

Bidwell, D., 2014: The Effects of Information on Public Attitudes Toward Renewable Energy. *Environ. Behav.*, **48(6)**, 743–768, doi:10.1177/0013916514554696.

Bidwell, D., 2016: Thinking through participation in renewable energy decisions. *Nat. Energy*, **1(5)**, 16051, doi:10.1038/nenergy.2016.51.

Bidwell, D., 2017: Ocean beliefs and support for an offshore wind energy project. *Ocean Coast. Manag.*, **146**, 99–108, doi:10.1016/j.ocecoaman.2017.06.012.

Bindoff, N.L., W.W.L. Cheung, J.G. Kairo, J. Arístegui, V.A. Guinder, R. Hallberg, N. Hilmi, N. Jiao, M.S. Karim, L. Levin, S. O'Donoghue, S.R. Purca Cuicapusa, B. Rinkevich, T. Suga, A. Tagliabue, and P. Williamson, 2019: Changing Ocean, Marine Ecosystems, and Dependent Communities. In: *IPCC Special Report on the Ocean and Cryosphere in a Changing Climate* [H.-O. Pörtner, D.C. Roberts, V. Masson-Delmotte, P. Zhai, M. Tignor, E. Poloczanska, K. Mintenbeck, A. Alegría, M. Nicolai, A. Okem, J. Petzold, B. Rama, N.M. Weyer (eds.)]. Cambridge University Press, Cambridge, UK and New York, NY, USA, pp. 447–588.

Binsted, M. et al., 2020: Stranded asset implications of the Paris Agreement in Latin America and the Caribbean. *Environ. Res. Lett.*, **15(4)**, 44026, doi:10.1088/1748-9326/ab506d.

Bird, D.K., K. Haynes, R. van den Honert, J. McAneney, and W. Poortinga, 2014: Nuclear power in Australia: A comparative analysis of public opinion regarding climate change and the Fukushima disaster. *Energy Policy*, **65**, 644–653, doi:10.1016/j.enpol.2013.09.047.

Bistline, J., 2021a: Variability in Deeply Decarbonized Electricity Systems. *Environ. Sci. & Technol.*, **55(9)**, 5629–5635, doi:10.1021/acs.est.0c06708.

Bistline, J., N. Santen, and D. Young, 2019: The economic geography of variable renewable energy and impacts of trade formulations for renewable mandates. *Renew. Sustain. Energy Rev.*, **106**, 79–96, doi:10.1016/j.rser.2019.02.026.

Bistline, J. et al., 2020a: Energy storage in long-term system models: a review of considerations, best practices, and research needs. *Prog. Energy*, **2(3)**, 32001, doi:10.1088/2516-1083/ab9894.

Bistline, J.E., 2017: Economic and technical challenges of flexible operations under large-scale variable renewable deployment. *Energy Econ.*, **64**, 363–372, doi:10.1016/j.eneco.2017.04.012.

Bistline, J.E., 2019: Turn Down for What? The Economic Value of Operational Flexibility in Electricity Markets. *IEEE Trans. Power Syst.*, **34(1)**, 527–534, doi:10.1109/TPWRS.2018.2856887.

Bistline, J.E. and F. de la Chesnaye, 2017: Banking on banking: does 'when' flexibility mask the costs of stringent climate policy? *Clim. Change*, **144(4)**, 597–610, doi:10.1007/s10584-017-2053-6.

Bistline, J.E. et al., 2018: Electric sector policy, technological change, and U.S. emissions reductions goals: Results from the EMF 32 model intercomparison project. *Energy Econ.*, **73**, 307–325, doi:10.1016/j.eneco.2018.04.012.

Bistline, J.E.T., 2021b: Roadmaps to net-zero emissions systems: Emerging insights and modeling challenges. *Joule*, **5(10)**, 2551–2563, doi:10.1016/j.joule.2021.09.012.

Bistline, J.E.T., 2021c: The importance of temporal resolution in modeling deep decarbonization of the electric power sector. *Environ. Res. Lett.*, **16(8)**, 84005, doi:10.1088/1748-9326/ac10df.

Bistline, J.E.T. and D.T. Young, 2019: Economic drivers of wind and solar penetration in the US. *Environ. Res. Lett.*, **14(12)**, doi:10.1088/1748-9326/ab4e2d.

Bistline, J.E.T. and G.J. Blanford, 2020: Value of technology in the U.S. electric power sector: Impacts of full portfolios and technological change on the costs of meeting decarbonization goals. *Energy Econ.*, **86**, 104694, doi:10.1016/j.eneco.2020.104694.

Bistline, J.E.T. and D.T. Young, 2020: Emissions impacts of future battery storage deployment on regional power systems. *Appl. Energy*, **264**, 114678, doi:10.1016/j.apenergy.2020.114678.

Bistline, J.E.T. and G.J. Blanford, 2021a: Impact of carbon dioxide removal technologies on deep decarbonization of the electric power sector. *Nat. Commun.*, **12(1)**, 3732, doi:10.1038/s41467-021-23554-6.

Bistline, J.E.T. and G.J. Blanford, 2021b: The role of the power sector in net-zero energy systems. *Energy Clim. Change*, **2**, 100045, doi:10.1016/J.EGYCC.2021.100045.

6

Bistline, J.E.T., M. Brown, S.A. Siddiqui, and K. Vaillancourt, 2020b: Electric sector impacts of renewable policy coordination: A multi-model study of the North American energy system. *Energy Policy*, **145**, 111707, doi:10.1016/j.enpol.2020.111707.

Bistline, J.E.T., C.W. Roney, D.L. McCollum, and G.J. Blanford, 2021: Deep decarbonization impacts on electric load shapes and peak demand. *Environ. Res. Lett.*, **16(9)**, 94054, doi:10.1088/1748-9326/ac2197.

Blakers, A., 2019: Development of the PERC Solar Cell. *IEEE J. Photovoltaics*, **9(3)**, 629–635, doi:10.1109/JPHOTOV.2019.2899460.

Blanc, P. et al., 2020: *Five steps to energy storage-Innovation Insights Brief-2020*. World Energy Council, Paris, France, 75 pp.

Blanco, H. and A. Faaij, 2018: A review at the role of storage in energy systems with a focus on Power to Gas and long-term storage. *Renew. Sustain. Energy Rev.*, **81**, 1049–1086, doi:10.1016/j.rser.2017.07.062

Blanford, G., T. Wilson, and J. Bistline, 2021: *Powering Decarbonization: Strategies for Net-Zero CO₂ Emissions*. Electric Power Research Institute, Washington DC, USA, 21 pp.

Blanford, G.J., J.H. Merrick, J.E.T. Bistline, and D.T. Young, 2018: Simulating Annual Variation in Load, Wind, and Solar by Representative Hour Selection. *Energy J.*, **39(3)**, doi:10.5547/01956574.39.3.gbla.

Blarke, M.B. and H. Lund, 2007: Large-scale heat pumps in sustainable energy systems: System and project perspectives. *Therm. Sci.*, **11(3)**, 143–152, doi:10.2298/TSCI0703143B.

Bloemendal, M., M. Jaxa-Rozen, and T. Olsthoorn, 2018: Methods for planning of ATES systems. *Appl. Energy*, **216**, 534–557, doi:10.1016/j.apenergy.2018.02.068.

Blomgren, G.E., 2017: The Development and Future of Lithium Ion Batteries. *J. Electrochem. Soc.*, **164(1)**, A5019–A5025, doi:10.1149/2.0251701jes.

Blondeel, M. and T. Van de Graaf, 2018: Toward a global coal mining moratorium? A comparative analysis of coal mining policies in the USA, China, India and Australia. *Clim. Change*, **150(1–2)**, 89–101, doi:10.1007/s10584-017-2135-5.

Blondeel, M., T. Van de Graaf, and T. Haesebrouck, 2020: Moving beyond coal: Exploring and explaining the Powering Past Coal Alliance. *Energy Res. Soc. Sci.*, **59**, 101304, doi:10.1016/J.ERSS.2019.101304.

Bloom, A. et al., 2020: *The Value of Increased HVDC Capacity Between Eastern and Western U.S. Grids: The Interconnections Seam Study: Preprint*. National Renewable Energy Laboratory (NREL), Golden, CO, USA, 11 pp.

Bloomberg Energy Finance, 2019: A Behind the Scenes Take on Lithium-ion Battery Prices. https://about.bnef.com/blog/behind-scenes-take-lithium-ion-battery-prices/.

Blumer, Y.B., L. Braunreiter, A. Kachi, R. Lordan-Perret, and F. Oeri, 2018: A two-level analysis of public support: Exploring the role of beliefs in opinions about the Swiss energy strategy. *Energy Res. Soc. Sci.*, **43**(May), 109–118, doi:10.1016/j.erss.2018.05.024.

Bodenhamer, A., 2016: King Coal: A Study of Mountaintop Removal, Public Discourse, and Power in Appalachia. *Soc. Nat. Resour.*, **29(10)**, 1139–1153, doi:10.1080/08941920.2016.1138561.

Boehringer, C. and M. Behrens, 2015: Interactions of emission caps and renewable electricity support schemes. *J. Regul. Econ.*, **48**, doi:10.1007/s11149-015-9279-x.

Boettcher, C. et al., 2019: Fugitive Emissions. In: *2019 Refinement to the 2006 IPCC Guidelines for National Greenhouse Gas Inventories*. [Calvo Buendia, E., Tanabe, K., Kranjc, A., Baasansuren, J., Fukuda, M., Ngarize, S., Osako, A., Pyrozhenko, Y., Shermanau, P. and Federici, S. (eds).]. IPCC, Geneva, Switzerland.

Bogdanov, D. et al., 2019: Radical transformation pathway towards sustainable electricity via evolutionary steps. *Nat. Commun.*, **10(1)**, 1077, doi:10.1038/s41467-019-08855-1.

Bogdanov, D., A. Gulagi, M. Fasihi, and C. Breyer, 2021: Full energy sector transition towards 100% renewable energy supply: Integrating power, heat, transport and industry sectors including desalination. *Appl. Energy*, **283**, 116273, doi:10.1016/j.apenergy.2020.116273.

Böhringer, C. and T.F. Rutherford, 2008: Combining bottom-up and top-down. *Energy Econ.*, **30(2)**, 574–596, doi:10.1016/j.eneco.2007.03.004.

Bolderdijk, J. and L. Steg, 2015: Promoting sustainable consumption: the risks of using financial incentives. In: *Handbook of research in sustainable consumption* [Reisch, L.A. and J. Thøgersen, (eds.)]. Edward Elgar Publishing, Cheltenham, UK, pp. 328–342.

Bolderdijk, J.W., J. Knockaert, E.M. Steg, and E.T. Verhoef, 2011: Effects of Pay-As-You-Drive vehicle insurance on young drivers' speed choice: Results of a Dutch field experiment. *Accid. Anal. Prev.*, **43(3)**, 1181–1186, doi:10.1016/j.aap.2010.12.032.

Bolderdijk, J.W., L. Steg, E.S. Geller, P.K. Lehman, and T. Postmes, 2013: Comparing the effectiveness of monetary versus moral motives in environmental campaigning. *Nat. Clim. Change*, **3(4)**, 413–416, doi:10.1038/nclimate1767.

Bollen, J. and C. Brink, 2014: Air pollution policy in Europe: Quantifying the interaction with greenhouse gases and climate change policies. *Energy Econ.*, **46(2014)**, 202–215, doi:10.1016/j.eneco.2014.08.028.

Bolsen, T. and F.L. Cook, 2008: The polls – Trends: Public opinion on energy policy: 1974–2006. *Public Opin. Q.*, **72**, 364–388, doi:10.1093/poq/nfn019.

Bonjean Stanton, M.C., S. Dessai, and J. Paavola, 2016: A systematic review of the impacts of climate variability and change on electricity systems in Europe. *Energy*, **109**, 1148–1159, doi:10.1016/j.energy.2016.05.015.

Bonou, A., A. Laurent, and S.I. Olsen, 2016: Life cycle assessment of onshore and offshore wind energy-from theory to application. *Appl. Energy*, **180**, 327–337, doi:10.1016/j.apenergy.2016.07.058.

Boomsma, C. and L. Steg, 2014: The effect of information and values on acceptability of reduced street lighting. *J. Environ. Psychol.*, **39**, 22–31, doi:10.1016/j.jenvp.2013.11.004.

Booth, M.S., 2018: Not carbon neutral: Assessing the net emissions impact of residues burned for bioenergy. *Environ. Res. Lett.*, **13(3)**, 35001, doi:10.1088/1748-9326/aaac88.

Borenstein, S., J. Bushnell, F.A. Wolak, and M. Zaragoza-Watkins, 2019: Expecting the Unexpected: Emissions Uncertainty and Environmental Market Design. *Am. Econ. Rev.*, **109(11)**, 3953–3977, doi:10.1257/aer.20161218.

Boretti, A. and B.K. Banik, 2021: Advances in Hydrogen Production from Natural Gas Reforming. *Adv. Energy Sustain. Res.*, **2(11)**, 2100097, doi:10.1002/aesr.202100097.

Bos, K. and J. Gupta, 2018: Climate change: the risks of stranded fossil fuel assets and resources to the developing world. *Third World Q.*, **39(3)**, 436–453, doi:10.1080/01436597.2017.1387477.

Bosch, J., I. Staffell, and A.D. Hawkes, 2017: Temporally-explicit and spatially-resolved global onshore wind energy potentials. *Energy*, **131**, 207–217, doi:10.1016/j.energy.2017.05.052.

Bosch, J., I. Staffell, and A.D. Hawkes, 2018: Temporally explicit and spatially resolved global offshore wind energy potentials. *Energy*, **163**, 766–781, doi:10.1016/j.energy.2018.08.153.

Boudet, H.S., 2019: Public perceptions of and responses to new energy technologies. *Nat. Energy*, **4(6)**, 446–455, doi:10.1038/s41560-019-0399-x.

Bouman, T. and L. Steg, 2019: Motivating Society-wide Pro-environmental Change. *One Earth*, **1(1)**, 27–30, doi:10.1016/j.oneear.2019.08.002.

Boyd, A.D., J. Liu, and J.D. Hmielowski, 2019: Public support for energy portfolios in Canada: How information about cost and national energy portfolios affect perceptions of energy systems. *Energy Environ.*, **30(2)**, 322–340, doi:10.1177/0958305X18790958.

BP, 2020: Statistical Review of World Energy, 2020 | 69th Edition. BP, London, UK, 66 pp.

Brack, D. and R. King, 2020: *Net-zero and Beyond: What Role for Bioenergy with Carbon Capture and Storage?* Chatham House, London, UK, 25 pp.

Bradley, P., A. Coke, and M. Leach, 2016: Financial incentive approaches for reducing peak electricity demand, experience from pilot trials with a UK energy provider. *Energy Policy*, **98**, 108–120, doi:10.1016/j.enpol.2016.07.022.

Brändle, G., M. Schönfisch, and S. Schulte, 2021: Estimating long-term global supply costs for low-carbon hydrogen. *Appl. Energy*, **302**, 117481, doi:10.1016/j.apenergy.2021.117481.

Brandon, A., J.A. List, R.D. Metcalfe, M.K. Price, and F. Rundhammer, 2019: Testing for crowd out in social nudges: Evidence from a natural field experiment in the market for electricity. *Proc. Natl. Acad. Sci.*, **116(12)**, 5293 LP – 5298, doi:10.1073/pnas.1802874115.

Brandon, G. and A. Lewis, 1999: Reducing household energy consumption: A qualitative and quantitative field study. *J. Environ. Psychol.*, **19(1)**, 75–85, doi:10.1006/jevp.1998.0105.

Brandon, N.P. et al. 2015: *UK Research Needs in Grid Scale Energy Storage Technologies*. Energy Storage Research Network, UK, 92 pp. https://energysuperstore.org/wp-content/uploads/2016/04/IMPJ4129_White_Paper_UK-Research-Needs-in-Grid-Scale-Energy-Storage-Technologies_WEB.pdf.

Brauers, H. and P.-Y. Oei, 2020: The political economy of coal in Poland: Drivers and barriers for a shift away from fossil fuels. *Energy Policy*, **144**, 111621, doi:10.1016/j.enpol.2020.111621.

Breyer, C., S. Khalili, and D. Bogdanov, 2019: Solar photovoltaic capacity demand for a sustainable transport sector to fulfil the Paris Agreement by 2050. *Prog. Photovoltaics Res. Appl.*, **27(11)**, 978–989, doi:10.1002/pip.3114.

Bridge, G., S. Bouzarovski, M. Bradshaw, and N. Eyre, 2013: Geographies of energy transition: Space, place and the low-carbon economy. *Energy Policy*, **53**, 331–340, doi:10.1016/j.enpol.2012.10.066.

Bridge, G., S. Barca, B. Özkaynak, E. Turhan, and R. Wyeth, 2018: Towards a political ecology of EU energy policy. In: *Advancing Energy Policy: Lessons on the Integration of Social Sciences and Humanities* [Foulds, C. and R. Robison (eds.)]. Palgrave Pivot Cham, Switzerland, pp. 163–175.

Brinkman, M.L. J., B. Wicke, A.P.C. Faaij, and F. van der Hilst, 2019: Projecting socio-economic impacts of bioenergy: Current status and limitations of ex-ante quantification methods. *Renew. Sustain. Energy Rev.*, **115**, 109352, doi:10.1016/j.rser.2019.109352.

Brockway, P.E., A. Owen, L.I. Brand-Correa, and L. Hardt, 2019: Estimation of global final-stage energy-return-on-investment for fossil fuels with comparison to renewable energy sources. *Nat. Energy*, **4(7)**, 612–621, doi:10.1038/s41560-019-0425-z.

Bronfman, N.C., R.B. Jiménez, P.C. Arévalo, and L.A. Cifuentes, 2012: Understanding social acceptance of electricity generation sources. *Energy Policy*, **46**, 246–252, doi:10.1016/j.enpol.2012.03.057.

Bronfman, N.C., R.B. Jiménez, P.C. Arevalo, and L.A. Cifuentes, 2015: Public Acceptance of Electricity Generation Sources: The Role of Trust in Regulatory Institutions. *Energy Environ.*, **26(3)**, 349–368, doi:10.1260/0958-305x.26.3.349.

Brook, B.W. and C.J.A. Bradshaw, 2015: Key role for nuclear energy in global biodiversity conservation. *Conserv. Biol.*, **29(3)**, 702–712, doi:10.1111/cobi.12433.

Brosch, T., M.K. Patel, and D. Sander, 2014: Affective influences on energy-related decisions and behaviors. *Front. Energy Res.*, **2**(March), 1–12, doi:10.3389/fenrg.2014.00011.

Brouwer, A.S., M. van den Broek, Ö. Özdemir, P. Koutstaal, and A. Faaij, 2016: Business case uncertainty of power plants in future energy systems with wind power. *Energy Policy*, **89**, 237–256, doi:10.1016/j.enpol.2015.11.022.

Brown, D.A., 2011: Comparative ethical issues entailed in the geological disposal of radioactive waste and carbon dioxide in the light of climate change. *Geological disposal of carbon dioxide and radioactive waste: A comparative assessment*, Springer, Cham, Switzerland, pp. 317–337.

Brown, M.A., G. Kim, A.M. Smith, and K. Southworth, 2017: Exploring the impact of energy efficiency as a carbon mitigation strategy in the U.S. *Energy Policy*, **109**, 249–259, doi:10.1016/j.enpol.2017.06.044.

Brown, T., D. Schlachtberger, A. Kies, S. Schramm, and M. Greiner, 2018: Synergies of sector coupling and transmission reinforcement in a cost-optimised, highly renewable European energy system. *Energy*, **160**, 720–739, doi:10.1016/j.energy.2018.06.222.

Bruce, S., M. Temminghoff, J. Hayward, E. Schmidt, C. Munnings, D. Palfreyman, and P. Hartley, *2018: National hydrogen roadmap*. CSIRO, Australia. https://einow.org/s/18-00314_EN_NationalHydrogenRoadmap_WEB_180823.pdf.

Bruninx, K., D. Madzharov, E. Delarue, and W. D'Haeseleer, 2013: Impact of the German nuclear phase-out on Europe's electricity generation-A comprehensive study. *Energy Policy*, **60**, 251–261, doi:10.1016/j.enpol.2013.05.026.

Buckley, T., 2019: *Over 100 Global Financial Institutions Are Exiting Coal, With More to Come. IEEFA*. Institute for Energy Economics and Financial Analysis, Lakewood, Ohio, USA, 35 pp.

Budinis, S. et al., 2017: Can Carbon Capture and Storage Unlock 'Unburnable Carbon'? *Energy Procedia*, **114**, 7504–7515, doi:10.1016/j.egypro.2017.03.1883.

Budinis, S., S. Krevor, N. Mac Dowell, N. Brandon, and A. Hawkes, 2018: An assessment of CCS costs, barriers and potential. *Energy Strateg. Rev.*, **22**, 61–81, doi:10.1016/j.esr.2018.08.003.

Bui, M. et al., 2018: Carbon capture and storage (CCS): the way forward. *Energy Environ. Sci.*, **11(5)**, 1062–1176, doi:10.1039/C7EE02342A.

Busby, J. W. et al., 2021: Cascading risks: Understanding the 2021 winter blackout in Texas. *Energy Res. Soc. Sci.*, **77**, 102106, doi:10.1016/j.erss.2021.102106.

Buttler, A. and H. Spliethoff, 2018: Current status of water electrolysis for energy storage, grid balancing and sector coupling via power-to-gas and power-to-liquids: A review. *Renew. Sustain. Energy Rev.*, **82**, 2440–2454, doi:10.1016/j.rser.2017.09.003.

Caglayan, D. G. et al., 2019: Technical Potential of Salt Caverns for Hydrogen Storage in Europe. *Int. J. Hydrogen Energy*, **45(11)**, 6793–6805, doi:10.20944/preprints201910.0187.v1.

Caldecott, B., D. Saygin, J. Rigter, and D. Gielen, 2017: *Stranded Assets and Renewables: How the energy transition affects the value of energy reserves, buildings and capital stock*. International Renewable Energy Agency, Abu Dhabi, 46 pp.

Calvin, K. et al., 2013: Implications of simultaneously mitigating and adapting to climate change: Initial experiments using GCAM. *Clim. Change*, **117(3)**, 545–560, doi:10.1007/s10584-012-0650-y.

Calvin, K. et al., 2019: Characteristics of human-climate feedbacks differ at different radiative forcing levels. *Glob. Planet. Change*, **180**, 126–135, doi:10.1016/j.gloplacha.2019.06.003.

Cambini, C., R. Congiu, T. Jamasb, M. Llorca, and G. Soroush, 2020: Energy Systems Integration: Implications for public policy. *Energy Policy*, **143**, 111609, doi:10.1016/j.enpol.2020.111609.

Campbell-Arvai, V., J. Arvai, and L. Kalof, 2014: Motivating Sustainable Food Choices: The Role of Nudges, Value Orientation, and Information Provision. *Environ. Behav.*, **46(4)**, 453–475, doi:10.1177/0013916512469099.

Campiglio, E., 2016: Beyond carbon pricing: The role of banking and monetary policy in financing the transition to a low-carbon economy. *Ecol. Econ.*, **121**, 220–230, doi:10.1016/j.ecolecon.2015.03.020.

Cano, Z. et al., 2018: Batteries and fuel cells for emerging electric vehicle markets. *Nat. Energy*, **3**, 279–289, doi:10.1038/s41560-018-0108–1.

Capellán-Pérez, I., C. de Castro, and I. Arto, 2017: Assessing vulnerabilities and limits in the transition to renewable energies: Land requirements under 100% solar energy scenarios. *Renew. Sustain. Energy Rev.*, **77**, 760–782, https://doi.org/10.1016/j.rser.2017.03.137.

Capros, P. et al., 2019: Energy-system modelling of the EU strategy towards climate-neutrality. *Energy Policy*, **134**, 110960, doi:10.1016/J.ENPOL.2019.110960.

Carattini, S., A. Baranzini, and R. Lalive, 2018: Is Taxing Waste a Waste of Time? Evidence from a Supreme Court Decision. *Ecol. Econ.*, **148**, 131–151, doi:10.1016/J.ECOLECON.2018.02.001.

Carbon Trust and Imperial College London, 2016: *Can storage help reduce the cost of a future UK electricity system?* Carbon Trust and Imperial College London, London, 120 pp.

6

Caron, J., S. Rausch, and N. Winchester, 2015: Leakage from Sub-national Climate Policy: The Case of California's Cap-and-Trade Program. *Energy J.*, **36**, doi:10.5547/01956574.36.2.8.

Carrus, G., P. Passafaro, and M. Bonnes, 2008: Emotions, habits and rational choices in ecological behaviours: The case of recycling and use of public transportation. *J. Environ. Psychol.*, **28(1)**, 51–62, doi:10.1016/j.jenvp.2007.09.003.

Carvalho, D., A. Rocha, M. Gómez-Gesteira, and C. Silva Santos, 2017: Potential impacts of climate change on European wind energy resource under the CMIP5 future climate projections. *Renew. Energy*, **101**, 29–40, doi:10.1016/j.renene.2016.08.036.

Cass, N., G. Walker, and P. Devine-Wright, 2010: Good neighbours, public relations and bribes: The politics and perceptions of community benefit provision in renewable energy development in the UK. *J. Environ. Policy Plan.*, **12(3)**, 255–275, doi:10.1080/1523908X.2010.509558.

Castillo, A. and D.F. Gayme, 2014: Grid-scale energy storage applications in renewable energy integration: A survey. *Energy Convers. Manag.*, **87**, 885–894, doi:10.1016/j.enconman.2014.07.063.

Castor, J., K. Bacha, and F. Fuso Nerini, 2020: SDGs in action: A novel framework for assessing energy projects against the sustainable development goals. *Energy Res. Soc. Sci.*, **68**, 101556, doi:10.1016/J.ERSS.2020.101556.

Catolico, A.C.C., M. Maestrini, J.C.M. Strauch, F. Giusti, and J. Hunt, 2021: Socioeconomic impacts of large hydroelectric power plants in Brazil: A synthetic control assessment of Estreito hydropower plant. *Renew. Sustain. Energy Rev.*, **151**, 111508, doi:10.1016/j.rser.2021.111508.

CEA, 2019: *Annual Report 2018–19*. Government of India, Ministry of Power.

Cerniauskas, S. et al., 2020: Options of natural gas pipeline reassignment for hydrogen: Cost assessment for a Germany case study. *Int. J. Hydrogen Energy*, **45**, 12095–12107, doi:10.1016/j.ijhydene.2020.02.121.

Chadwick, A. et al., 2008: *Best practice for the storage of CO₂ in saline aquifers – observations and guidelines from the SACS and CO2STORE projects*. British Geological Survey, Nottingham, UK, 267 pp.

Chaffey, G., 2016: The Impact of Fault Blocking Converters on HVDC Protection. PhD Thesis, Imperial College London, 325 pp.

Chamorro, H. R. et al., 2020: Innovative primary frequency control in low-inertia power systems based on wide-area RoCoF sharing. *IET Energy Syst. Integr.*, **2(2)**, 151–160, doi:10.1049/iet-esi.2020.0001.

Chan, H.R., B.A. Chupp, M.L. Cropper, and N.Z. Muller, 2018: The impact of trading on the costs and benefits of the Acid Rain Program. *J. Environ. Econ. Manage.*, **88**, 180–209, doi:10.1016/j.jeem.2017.11.004.

Chang, K.C., W.M. Lin, T.S. Lee, and K.M. Chung, 2009: Local market of solar water heaters in Taiwan: Review and perspectives. *Renew. Sustain. Energy Rev.*, **13(9)**, 2605–2612, doi:10.1016/j.rser.2009.01.031.

Chang, N. L. et al., 2017: A manufacturing cost estimation method with uncertainty analysis and its application to perovskite on glass photovoltaic modules. *Prog. Photovoltaics Res. Appl.*, **25(5)**, 390–405, doi:10.1002/pip.2871.

Chang, N.L. et al., 2018: Manufacturing cost and market potential analysis of demonstrated roll-to-roll perovskite photovoltaic cell processes. *Sol. Energy Mater. Sol. Cells*, **174**, 314–324, doi:10.1016/j.solmat.2017.08.038.

Chatziaras, N., C.S. Psomopoulos, and N.J. Themelis, 2016: Use of waste derived fuels in cement industry: a review. *Manag. Environ. Qual. An Int. J.*, **27(2)**, 178–193, doi:10.1108/MEQ-01-2015-0012.

Chen, H., L. Wang, and W. Chen, 2019: Modeling on building sector's carbon mitigation in China to achieve the 1.5°C climate target. *Energy Effic.*, **12(2)**, 483–496, doi:10.1007/s12053-018-9687-8.

Chen, L., 2020: Impacts of climate change on wind resources over North America based on NA-CORDEX. *Renew. Energy*, **153**, 1428–1438, doi:10.1016/j.renene.2020.02.090.

Chen, M.F., 2015: Self-efficacy or collective efficacy within the cognitive theory of stress model: Which more effectively explains people's self-reported proenvironmental behavior? *J. Environ. Psychol.*, **42**, 66–75, doi:10.1016/j.jenvp.2015.02.002.

Cheng, V.K.M. and G.P. Hammond, 2017: Life-cycle energy densities and land-take requirements of various power generators: A UK perspective. *J. Energy Inst.*, **90(2)**, 201–213, doi:10.1016/j.joei.2016.02.003.

Cherubini, A., A. Papini, R. Vertechy, and M. Fontana, 2015: Airborne Wind Energy Systems: A review of the technologies. *Renew. Sustain. Energy Rev.*, **51**, 1461–1476, doi:10.1016/j.rser.2015.07.053.

Chiaramonti, D., 2019: Sustainable Aviation Fuels: the challenge of decarbonization. *Energy Procedia*, **158**, 1202–1207, doi:10.1016/j.egypro.2019.01.308.

Child, M., C. Kemfert, D. Bogdanov, and C. Breyer, 2019: Flexible electricity generation, grid exchange and storage for the transition to a 100% renewable energy system in Europe. *Renew. Energy*, **139**, 80–101, doi:10.1016/j.renene.2019.02.077.

Christensen, A., 2020: *Assessment of hydrogen production costs from electrolysis: United States and Europe*. International Council on Clean Transport, USA, 73 pp.

Clark, R.-J., A. Mehrabadi, and M. Farid, 2020: State of the art on salt hydrate thermochemical energy storage systems for use in building applications. *J. Energy Storage*, **27**, 101145, doi:10.1016/j.est.2019.101145.

Clark, V.R. and H.J. Herzog, 2014: Can 'stranded' Fossil Fuel Reserves Drive CCS Deployment? *Energy Procedia*, **63**, 7261–7271, doi:10.1016/j.egypro.2014.11.762.

Clarke, C.E. et al., 2016: How geographic distance and political ideology interact to influence public perception of unconventional oil/natural gas development. *Energy Policy*, **97**, 301–309, doi:10.1016/j.enpol.2016.07.032.

Clayton, S. et al., 2015: Psychological research and global climate change. *Nat. Clim. Change*, **5(7)**, 640–646, doi:10.1038/nclimate2622.

Clegg, S. and P. Mancarella, 2016a: Storing renewables in the gas network: modelling of power-to-gas seasonal storage flexibility in low-carbon power systems. *IET Gener. Transm. Distrib.*, **10(3)**, 566–575, doi:10.1049/iet-gtd.2015.0439.

Clegg, S. and P. Mancarella, 2016b: Integrated Electrical and Gas Network Flexibility Assessment in Low-Carbon Multi-Energy Systems. *IEEE Trans. Sustain. Energy*, **7**, 718–731, doi:10.1109/TSTE.2015.2497329.

Coady, D., I. Parry, and L. Sears, 2017: How large are global fossil fuel subsidies? *World Dev.*, **91**, 11–17, doi.org/10.1016/j.worlddev.2016.10.004.

Coady, D., I. Parry, N. Le, and B. Shang, 2019: *Global Fossil Fuel Subsidies Remain Large: An Update Based on Country-Level Estimates*. International Monetary Fund, Washington, DC, USA, 36 pp.

Cochran, J., T. Mai, and M. Bazilian, 2014: Meta-analysis of high penetration renewable energy scenarios. *Renew. Sustain. Energy Rev.*, **29**, 246–253, doi:10.1016/j.rser.2013.08.089.

Cock, J., 2019: Resistance to coal inequalities and the possibilities of a just transition in South Africa. *Dev. South. Afr.*, **36(6)**, 860–873, doi:10.1080/0376835X.2019.1660859.

Coker, P.J., H.C. Bloomfield, D.R. Drew, and D.J. Brayshaw, 2020: Interannual weather variability and the challenges for Great Britain's electricity market design. *Renew. Energy*, **150**, 509–522, doi:10.1016/j.renene.2019.12.082.

Cole, W. et al., 2017: *Variable Renewable Energy in Long-Term Planning Models: A Multi-Model Perspective*. National Renewable Energy Laboratory, Golden, CO, USA, 43 pp.

Cole, W.J. et al., 2021: Quantifying the challenge of reaching a 100% renewable energy power system for the United States. *Joule*, **5(7)**, 1732–1748, doi:10.1016/J.JOULE.2021.05.011.

Collins, S. et al., 2017: Integrating short term variations of the power system into integrated energy system models: A methodological review. *Renew. Sustain. Energy Rev.*, **76**, 839–856, doi:10.1016/j.rser.2017.03.090.

Collodi, G., G. Azzaro, N. Ferrari, and S. Santos, 2017: Techno-economic Evaluation of Deploying CCS in SMR Based Merchant H2 Production with NG as Feedstock and Fuel. *Energy Procedia*, **114**, 2690–2712, doi:10.1016/j.egypro.2017.03.1533.

Colmer, J., R. Martin, M. Muls, and U.J. Wagner, 2020: *Does Pricing Carbon Mitigate Climate Change? Firm-Level Evidence from the European Union Emissions Trading Scheme*, Centre for Economic Performance, London, UK, 68 pp.

Committee on Climate Change (CCC), 2018: *Hydrogen in a low carbon economy*. Committee on Climate Change, London, UK, 128 pp.

Conant, R. T. et al., 2018: Northern Great Plains. In: *Impacts, Risks, and Adaptation in the United States: Fourth National Climate Assessment* [Reidmiller, D.R., C.W. Avery, D.R. Easterling, K.E. Kunkel, K.L.M. Lewis, T.K. Maycock, and B.C. Stewart, (eds.)]. Vol. II. U.S. Global Change Research Program, Washington DC, USA.

Corner, A. et al., 2011: Nuclear power, climate change and energy security: Exploring British public attitudes. *Energy Policy*, **39(9)**, 4823–4833, doi:10.1016/j.enpol.2011.06.037.

Corradini, M., V. Costantini, A. Markandya, E. Paglialunga, and G. Sforna, 2018: A dynamic assessment of instrument interaction and timing alternatives in the EU low-carbon policy mix design. *Energy Policy*, **120**, 73–84, doi:10.1016/J.ENPOL.2018.04.068.

Cosbey, A., S. Droege, C. Fischer, and C. Munnings, 2019: Developing Guidance for Implementing Border Carbon Adjustments: Lessons, Cautions, and Research Needs from the Literature. *Rev. Environ. Econ. Policy*, **13(1)**, 3–22, doi:10.1093/reep/rey020.

Cosentino, S.L., G. Testa, D. Scordia, and E. Alexopoulou, 2012: Future yields assessment of bioenergy crops in relation to climate change and technological development in Europe. *Ital. J. Agron.*, **7(2)**, 154–166, doi:10.4081/ija.2012.e22.

Costantini, V., F. Crespi, and A. Palma, 2017: Characterizing the policy mix and its impact on eco-innovation: A patent analysis of energy-efficient technologies. *Res. Policy*, **46(4)**, 799–819, doi:10.1016/j.respol.2017.02.004.

Costoya, X., M. DeCastro, D. Carvalho, and M. Gómez-Gesteira, 2020: On the suitability of offshore wind energy resource in the United States of America for the 21st century. *Appl. Energy*, **262**(October 2019), 114537, doi:10.1016/j.apenergy.2020.114537.

Court, V. and F. Fizaine, 2017: Long-Term Estimates of the Energy-Return-on-Investment (EROI) of Coal, Oil, and Gas Global Productions. *Ecol. Econ.*, **138**, 145–159, doi:10.1016/j.ecolecon.2017.03.015.

Crabtree, G., E. Kócs, and L. Trahey, 2015: The energy-storage frontier: Lithium-ion batteries and beyond. *MRS Bull.*, **40(12)**, 1067–1078, doi:10.1557/mrs.2015.259.

Craig, M.T., I. Losada Carreño, M. Rossol, B.-M.M. Hodge, and C. Brancucci, 2019: Effects on power system operations of potential changes in wind and solar generation potential under climate change. *Environ. Res. Lett.*, **14(3)**, 034014, doi:10.1088/1748-9326/aaf93b.

Cremer, J.L., I. Konstantelos, and G. Strbac, 2019: From Optimization-Based Machine Learning to Interpretable Security Rules for Operation. *IEEE Trans. Power Syst.*, **34(5)**, 3826–3836, doi:10.1109/TPWRS.2019.2911598.

Creutzig, F. et al., 2015: Bioenergy and climate change mitigation: an assessment. *GCB Bioenergy*, **7(5)**, 916–944, doi:10.1111/gcbb.12205.

Creutzig, F. et al., 2017: The underestimated potential of solar energy to mitigate climate change. *Nat. Energy*, **2(9)**, doi:10.1038/nenergy.2017.140.

Creutzig, F. et al., 2018: Towards demand-side solutions for mitigating climate change. *Nat. Clim. Change*, **8(4)**, 260–263, doi:10.1038/s41558-018-0121-1.

Creutzig, F. et al., 2019: The mutual dependence of negative emission technologies and energy systems. *Energy Environ. Sci.*, **12(6)**, 1805–1817, doi:10.1039/C8EE03682A.

Crippa, M. et al., 2021: *EDGAR v6.0 Greenhouse Gas Emissions*. European Commission, Luxembourg. http://data.europa.eu/89h/97a67d67-c62e-4826-b873-9d972c4f670b.

Croce, P. et al., 2018: The snow load in Europe and the climate change. *Clim. Risk Manag.*, **20**, 138–154, doi:10.1016/J.CRM.2018.03.001.

Cronin, J., G. Anandarajah, and O. Dessens, 2018: Climate change impacts on the energy system: a review of trends and gaps. *Clim. Change*, **151(2)**, 79–93, doi:10.1007/s10584-018-2265-4.

Cudjoe, D., M.S. Han, and A.P. Nandiwardhana, 2020: Electricity generation using biogas from organic fraction of municipal solid waste generated in provinces of China: Techno-economic and environmental impact analysis. *Fuel Process. Technol.*, **203**, 106381, doi:10.1016/J.FUPROC.2020.106381.

Cui, R. Y. et al., 2019: Quantifying operational lifetimes for coal power plants under the Paris goals. *Nat. Commun.*, **10(1)**, 4759, doi:10.1038/s41467-019-12618-3.

Cui, R.Y. et al., 2021: A plant-by-plant strategy for high-ambition coal power phaseout in China. *Nat. Commun.*, **12(1)**, 1468, doi:10.1038/s41467-021-21786-0.

Culver, W.J. and M. Hong, 2016: Coal's decline: Driven by policy or technology? *Electr. J.*, **29**, 50–61, doi:org/10.1016/j.tej.2016.08.008.

Daamen, D., M. de Best-Waldhober, K. Damen, and A. Faaij, 2006: Pseudo-opinions on CCS technologies. *Proceedings of 8th International Conference on Greenhause Gas Control Technologies (GHGT-8), June 19-22*, Trondheim, Norway, pp. 1–5.

Daamen, D.D.L., H. Staats, H.A.M. Wilke, and M. Engelen, 2001: Improving environmental behavior in companies. The effectiveness of tailored versus nontailored interventions. *Environ. Behav.*, **33(2)**, 229–248, doi:10.1177/00139160121972963.

Daggash, H.A., C.F. Heuberger, and N. Mac Dowell, 2019: The role and value of negative emissions technologies in decarbonising the UK energy system. *Int. J. Greenh. Gas Control*, **81**, 181–198, doi:10.1016/j.ijggc.2018.12.019.

Dahash, A., F. Ochs, M.B. Janetti, and W. Streicher, 2019: Advances in seasonal thermal energy storage for solar district heating applications: A critical review on large-scale hot-water tank and pit thermal energy storage systems. *Appl. Energy*, **239**, 296–315, doi:10.1016/j.apenergy.2019.01.189.

Daioglou, V. et al., 2017: Greenhouse gas emission curves for advanced biofuel supply chains. *Nat. Clim. Change*, **7(12)**, 920–924, doi:10.1038/s41558-017-0006-8.

Daioglou, V. et al., 2020a: Bioenergy technologies in long-run climate change mitigation: results from the EMF-33 study. *Clim. Change*, **163(3)**, 1603–1620, doi:10.1007/s10584-020-02799-y.

Daioglou, V. et al., 2020b: Implications of climate change mitigation strategies on international bioenergy trade. *Clim. Change*, **163(3)**, 1639–1658, doi:10.1007/s10584-020-02877–1.

Daiyan, R., I. MacGill, and R. Amal, 2020: Opportunities and Challenges for Renewable Power-to-X. *ACS Energy Lett.*, **5(12)**, 3843–3847, doi:10.1021/acsenergylett.0c02249.

Damgaard, C., D. McCauley, and J. Long, 2017: Assessing the energy justice implications of bioenergy development in Nepal. *Energy. Sustain. Soc.*, **7**, 8, doi:10.1186/s13705-017-0111-6.

Darton, R.C. and A. Yang, 2018: Removing carbon dioxide from the atmosphere – Assessing the technologies. *Chem. Eng. Trans.*, **69**, 91–96, doi:10.3303/CET1869016.

Das, S., E. Hittinger, and E. Williams, 2020: Learning is not enough: Diminishing marginal revenues and increasing abatement costs of wind and solar. *Renew. Energy*, **156**, 634–644, doi:10.1016/j.renene.2020.03.082.

Davis, L.W. and P.J. Gertler, 2015: Contribution of air conditioning adoption to future energy use under global warming. *Proc. Natl. Acad. Sci.*, **112(19)**, 5962–5967, doi:10.1073/pnas.1423558112.

Davis, N.N., Ø. Byrkjedal, A.N. Hahmann, N.-E. Clausen, and M. Žagar, 2016: Ice detection on wind turbines using the observed power curve. *Wind Energy*, **19(6)**, doi:10.1002/we.1878.

Davis, S.J. et al., 2018: Net-zero emissions energy systems. *Science*, **360(6396)**, doi:10.1126/science.aas9793.

Dawood, F., M. Anda, and G.M. Shafiullah, 2020: Hydrogen production for energy: An overview. *Int. J. Hydrogen Energy*, **45(7)**, 3847–3869, doi:10.1016/j.ijhydene.2019.12.059.

Dean, M. and O. Tucker, 2017: A risk-based framework for Measurement, Monitoring and Verification (MMV) of the Goldeneye storage complex for the Peterhead CCS project, UK. *Int. J. Greenh. Gas Control*, **61**, 1–15, doi:10.1016/j.ijggc.2017.03.014.

6

De Best-Waldhober, M. et al., 2009: Informed public opinions on CCS in comparison to other mitigation options. *Energy Procedia*, **1(1)**, 4795–4802, doi:10.1016/j.egypro.2009.02.306.

De Cian, E. and I. Sue Wing, 2019: Global Energy Consumption in a Warming Climate. *Environ. Resour. Econ.*, **72(2)**, 365–410, doi:10.1007/s10640-017-0198-4.

de Faria, F.A.M., A. Davis, E. Severnini, and P. Jaramillo, 2017: The local socio-economic impacts of large hydropower plant development in a developing country. *Energy Econ.*, **67**, 533–544, doi:10.1016/j.eneco.2017.08.025.

de Groot, J.I.M. and L. Steg, 2011: Psychological Perspectives on the Geological Disposal of Radioactive Waste and Carbon Dioxide. In: *Geological Disposal of Carbon Dioxide and Radioactive Waste: A Comparative Assessment* [Toth, F.L., (ed.)], Vol. 44 of *Advances in Global Change Research*, Springer, Dordrecht, Netherlands, pp. 339–363.

de Groot, J.I.M., L. Steg, and W. Poortinga, 2013: Values, Perceived Risks and Benefits, and Acceptability of Nuclear Energy. *Risk Anal.*, **33(2)**, 307–317, doi:10.1111/j.1539-6924.2012.01845.x.

de Jong, P. et al., 2019: Estimating the impact of climate change on wind and solar energy in Brazil using a South American regional climate model. *Renew. Energy*, **141**, 390–401, doi:10.1016/j.renene.2019.03.086.

de Lucas, M., M. Ferrer, M.J. Bechard, and A.R. Muñoz, 2012: Griffon vulture mortality at wind farms in southern Spain: Distribution of fatalities and active mitigation measures. *Biol. Conserv.*, **147(1)**, 184–189, doi:10.1016/j.biocon.2011.12.029.

De Sa, A. and S. Al Zubaidy, 2011: Gas turbine performance at varying ambient temperature. *Appl. Therm. Eng.*, **31(14)**, 2735–2739, doi:10.1016/j.applthermaleng.2011.04.045.

de Sisternes, F.J., J.D. Jenkins, and A. Botterud, 2016: The value of energy storage in decarbonizing the electricity sector. *Appl. Energy*, **175**, 368–379, doi:10.1016/j.apenergy.2016.05.014.

de Wild-Scholten, M.J., 2013: Energy payback time and carbon footprint of commercial photovoltaic systems. *Sol. Energy Mater. Sol. Cells*, **119**, 296–305, doi:10.1016/j.solmat.2013.08.037.

DeAngelo, J. et al., 2021: Energy systems in scenarios at net-zero CO2 emissions. *Nat. Commun.*, **12(1)**, 6096, doi:10.1038/s41467-021-26356-y.

Deason, W., 2018: Comparison of 100% renewable energy system scenarios with a focus on flexibility and cost. *Renew. Sustain. Energy Rev.*, **82**, 3168–3178, doi:10.1016/J.RSER.2017.10.026.

Deetjen, T.A. and I.L. Azevedo, 2020: Climate and Health Benefits of Rapid Coal-to-Gas Fuel Switching in the U.S. Power Sector Offset Methane Leakage and Production Cost Increases. *Environ. Sci. Technol.*, **54(18)**, 11494–11505, doi:10.1021/acs.est.9b06499.

Dehghani-Sanij, A.R., E. Tharumalingam, M.B. Dusseault, and R. Fraser, 2019: Study of energy storage systems and environmental challenges of batteries. *Renew. Sustain. Energy Rev.*, **104**, 192–208, doi:10.1016/j.rser.2019.01.023.

Delgado, R., T.B. Wild, R. Arguello, L. Clarke, and G. Romero, 2020: Options for Colombia's mid-century deep decarbonization strategy. *Energy Strateg. Rev.*, **32**, 100525, doi:10.1016/j.esr.2020.100525.

Delmas, M.A., M. Fischlein, and O.I. Asensio, 2013: Information strategies and energy conservation behavior: A meta-analysis of experimental studies from 1975 to 2012. *Energy Policy*, **61**, 729–739, doi:10.1016/j.enpol.2013.05.109.

Del Rio, P., 2017: Why does the combination of the European Union Emissions Trading Scheme and a renewable energy target makes economic sense? *Renew. Sustain. Energy Rev.*, **74**, 824–834, doi:10.1016/j.rser.2017.01.122.

Demski, C., C. Butler, K.A. Parkhill, A. Spence, and N.F. Pidgeon, 2015: Public values for energy system change. *Glob. Environ. Change*, **34**, 59–69, doi:10.1016/j.gloenvcha.2015.06.014.

Demski, C., A. Spence, and N. Pidgeon, 2017: Effects of exemplar scenarios on public preferences for energy futures using the my2050 scenario-building tool. *Nat. Energy*, **2(4)**, 1–7, doi:10.1038/nenergy.2017.27.

DENA, 2017: *The potential of electricity-based fuels for low-emission transport in the EU An expertise by LBST and dena.* Deutsche Energie-Agentur GmbH (dena), Berlin, Germany, 176 pp.

Deng, R., N. L. Chang, Z. Ouyang, and C.M. Chong, 2019: A techno-economic review of silicon photovoltaic module recycling. *Renew. Sustain. Energy Rev.*, **109**, 532–550, doi:10.1016/j.rser.2019.04.020.

Deng, Y. Y. et al., 2015: Quantifying a realistic, worldwide wind and solar electricity supply. *Glob. Environ. Change*, **31**, 239–252, doi:10.1016/j.gloenvcha.2015.01.005.

Dengiz, T., P. Jochem, and W. Fichtner, 2019: Demand response with heuristic control strategies for modulating heat pumps. *Appl. Energy*, **238**, 1346–1360, doi:10.1016/j.apenergy.2018.12.008.

Denholm, P. and T. Mai, 2019: Timescales of energy storage needed for reducing renewable energy curtailment. *Renew. Energy*, **130**, 388–399, doi:10.1016/j.renene.2018.06.079.

Denholm, P., G. Brinkman, and T. Mai, 2018: How low can you go? The importance of quantifying minimum generation levels for renewable integration. *Energy Policy*, **115**, 249–257, doi:10.1016/j.enpol.2018.01.023.

Denholm, P. et al., 2021: The challenges of achieving a 100% renewable electricity system in the United States. *Joule*, **5(6)**, 1331–1352, doi:10.1016/J.JOULE.2021.03.028.

Detz, R.J., J.N.H. Reek, and B.C.C. Van Der Zwaan, 2018: The future of solar fuels: When could they become competitive? *Energy Environ. Sci.*, **11(7)**, 1653–1669, doi:10.1039/c8ee00111a.

Devine-Wright, P., 2005: Beyond NIMBYism: Towards an integrated framework for understanding public perceptions of wind energy. *Wind Energy*, **8(2)**, 125–139, doi:10.1002/we.124.

Devine-Wright, P., 2009: Rethinking NIMBYism: The role of place attachment and place identity in explaining place-protective action. *J. Community Appl. Soc. Psychol.*, **19(6)**, 426–441, doi:10.1002/casp.1004.

Devine-Wright, P., 2013: Think global, act local? The relevance of place attachments and place identities in a climate changed world. *Glob. Environ. Change*, **23(1)**, 61–69, doi:10.1016/j.gloenvcha.2012.08.003.

Devine-Wright, P. and Y. Howes, 2010: Disruption to place attachment and the protection of restorative environments: A wind energy case study. *J. Environ. Psychol.*, **30(3)**, 271–280, doi:10.1016/j.jenvp.2010.01.008.

Devine-Wright, P. and F. Sherry-Brennan, 2019: Where do you draw the line? Legitimacy and fairness in constructing community benefit fund boundaries for energy infrastructure projects. *Energy Res. Soc. Sci.*, **54**, 166–175, doi:10.1016/J.ERSS.2019.04.002.

Devine-Wright, P. and B. Wiersma, 2020: Understanding community acceptance of a potential offshore wind energy project in different locations: An island-based analysis of 'place-technology fit.' *Energy Policy*, **137**(March 2019), 111086, doi:10.1016/j.enpol.2019.111086.

Devis, A., N.P.M. Van Lipzig, and M. Demuzere, 2018: Should future wind speed changes be taken into account in wind farm development? *Environ. Res. Lett.*, **13(6)**, 064012, doi:10.1088/1748-9326/aabff7.

Di Silvestre, M. L. et al., 2020: Blockchain for power systems: Current trends and future applications. *Renew. Sustain. Energy Rev.*, **119**, 109585, doi:10.1016/j.rser.2019.109585.

Diagne, M., M. David, P. Lauret, J. Boland, and N. Schmutz, 2013: Review of solar irradiance forecasting methods and a proposition for small-scale insular grids. *Renew. Sustain. Energy Rev.*, **27**, 65–76, doi:10.1016/j.rser.2013.06.042.

Dian, S. et al., 2019: Integrating Wildfires Propagation Prediction Into Early Warning of Electrical Transmission Line Outages. *IEEE Access*, **7**, 27586–27603, doi:10.1109/ACCESS.2019.2894141.

Dietz, T., 2013: Bringing values and deliberation to science communication. *Proc. Natl. Acad. Sci.*, **110(sup3)**, 14081–14087, doi:10.1073/pnas.1212740110.

Dietz, T. and P. Stern, 2008: *Public Participation in Environmental Assessment and Decision Making.* National Academies Press, Washington, DC, USA, 322 pp.

Dietz, T., A. Dan, and R. Shwom, 2007: Support for Climate Change Policy: Social Psychological and Social Structural Influences. *Rural Sociol.*, **72(2)**, 185–214, doi:10.1526/003601107781170026.

Dietz, T., K.A. Frank, C.T. Whitley, J. Kelly, and R. Kelly, 2015: Political influences on greenhouse gas emissions from US states. *Proc. Natl. Acad. Sci.*, **112(27)**, 8254–8259, doi:10.1073/pnas.1417806112.

Diluiso, F. and Coauthors, 2021: Coal transitions—part 1: a systematic map and review of case study learnings from regional, national, and local coal phase-out experiences. *Environ. Res. Lett.*, **16**, 113003, doi:10.1088/1748-9326/ac1b58.

Dinesh, H. and J. M. Pearce, 2016: The potential of agrivoltaic systems. *Renew. Sustain. Energy Rev.*, **54**, 299–308, doi:10.1016/j.rser.2015.10.024.

Diógenes, J.R.F., J. Claro, J.C. Rodrigues, and M.V. Loureiro, 2020: Barriers to onshore wind energy implementation: A systematic review. *Energy Res. Soc. Sci.*, **60**(December 2019), 101337, doi:10.1016/j.erss.2019.101337.

Djapic, P., G. Strbac, and G. Britain, 2008: *Cost benefit methodology for optimal design of offshore transmission systems*. Department for Business, Enterprise & Regulatory Reform, London, UK, 86 pp.

do Sacramento, E.M., P.C.M. Carvalho, L.C. de Lima, and T.N. Veziroglu, 2013: Feasibility study for the transition towards a hydrogen economy: A case study in Brazil. *Energy Policy*, **62**, 3–9, doi:10.1016/j.enpol.2013.06.071.

DOE, 2018: Technical targets for hydrogen productrion from electrolysis. U.S. Department of Energy, https://www.energy.gov/eere/fuelcells/doe-technical-targets-hydrogen-production-electrolysis.

DOE, 2020a: *Department of Energy Hydrogen Program Plan*. U.S. Department of Energy, Washington, DC, USA, 56 pp.

DOE, 2020b: *Cost of Electrolytic Hydrogen Production with Existing Technology*. U.S. Department of Energy, 5 pp.

Dogan, E., J.W. Bolderdijk, and L. Steg, 2014: Making Small Numbers Count: Environmental and Financial Feedback in Promoting Eco-driving Behaviours. *J. Consum. Policy*, **37(3)**, 413–422, doi:10.1007/s10603-014-9259-z.

Dohi, H., M. Kasai, and K. Onoue, 2016: Hydrogen Infrastructure. In: *Hydrogen Energy Engineering Green Energy and Technology* [Sasaki, K., H.-W. Li, A. Hayashi, J. Yamabe, T. Ogura, and S.M. Lyth, (eds.)]. Springer, Tokyo, Japan, pp. 537–547.

Dolan, K.A., P.C. Stoy, and B. Poulter, 2020: Land management and climate change determine second-generation bioenergy potential of the US Northern Great Plains. *GCB Bioenergy*, **12(7)**, 491–509, doi:10.1111/gcbb.12686.

Dong, Z. et al., 2019: Modelling and simulation of ternary pumped storage hydropower for power system studies. *IET Gener. Transm. Distrib.*, **13(19)**, 4382–4390, doi:10.1049/iet-gtd.2018.5749.

Dorband, I.I., M. Jakob, M. Kalkuhl, and J.C. Steckel, 2019: Poverty and distributional effects of carbon pricing in low- and middle-income countries – A global comparative analysis. *World Dev.*, **115**, 246–257, doi:10.1016/j.worlddev.2018.11.015.

Dörenkämper, M. et al., 2020: The Making of the New European Wind Atlas – Part 2: Production and evaluation. *Geosci. Model Dev.*, **13(10)**, 5079–5102, doi:10.5194/gmd-13-5079-2020.

Doukas, D.I., 2019: Superconducting Transmission Systems: Review, Classification, and Technology Readiness Assessment. *IEEE Trans. Appl. Supercond.*, **29(5)**, 1–5, doi:10.1109/TASC.2019.2895395.

Dowd, A.M., N. Boughen, P. Ashworth, and S. Carr-Cornish, 2011: Geothermal technology in Australia: Investigating social acceptance. *Energy Policy*, **39(10)**, 6301–6307, doi:10.1016/j.enpol.2011.07.029.

Dowling, J. A. et al., 2020: Role of Long-Duration Energy Storage in Variable Renewable Electricity Systems. *Joule*, **4(9)**, 1907–1928, doi:10.1016/j.joule.2020.07.007.

Dragoni, E., 2019: Mechanical design of flywheels for energy storage: A review with state-of-the-art developments. *Proc. Inst. Mech. Eng. Part L J. Mater. Des. Appl.*, **233(5)**, 995–1004, doi:10.1177/1464420717729415.

Drews, S. and J.C.J.M. Van den Bergh, 2016: What explains public support for climate policies? A review of empirical and experimental studies. *Clim. Policy*, **16(7)**, 855–876, doi:10.1080/14693062.2015.1058240.

Dreyfus, G., Borgford-Parnell, J. Fahey, B. Peters, and Xu, 2020: Assessment of Climate and Development Benefits of Efficient and Climate-Friendly Cooling.

Du, Z., 2009: *Study on Strategic Planning of Ultra High Voltage Grid Development in China*. PhD Thesis, Shandong University.

Du, Z. and B. Lin, 2017: How oil price changes affect car use and purchase decisions? Survey evidence from Chinese cities. *Energy Policy*, **111**, 68–74, doi:10.1016/j.enpol.2017.09.017.

Duan, H. et al., 2021: Assessing China's efforts to pursue the 1.5°C warming limit. *Science*, **372(6540)**, 378–385, doi:10.1126/science.aba8767.

Duan, M., Z. Tian, Y. Zhao, and M. Li, 2017: Interactions and coordination between carbon emissions trading and other direct carbon mitigation policies in China. *Energy Res. Soc. Sci.*, **33**, 59–69, https://doi.org/10.1016/j.erss.2017.09.008.

Dubois, A., S. Holzer, G. Xexakis, J. Cousse, and E. Trutnevyte, 2019: Informed Citizen Panels on the Swiss Electricity Mix 2035: Longer-Term Evolution of Citizen Preferences and Affect in Two Cities. *Energies*, **12(22)**, 4231, doi:10.3390/en12224231.

Dupont, E., R. Koppelaar, and H. Jeanmart, 2020: Global available solar energy under physical and energy return on investment constraints. *Appl. Energy*, **257**, 113968, doi:10.1016/j.apenergy.2019.113968.

Dupraz, C. et al., 2011: Combining solar photovoltaic panels and food crops for optimising land use: Towards new agrivoltaic schemes. *Renew. Energy*, **36(10)**, 2725–2732, doi:10.1016/j.renene.2011.03.005.

Dworkin, M.H., R.V. Sidortsov, and B.K. Sovacool, 2013: Rethinking the scale, structure & scope of U.S. energy institutions. *Daedalus J. Am. Acad. Arts Sci.*, **142(1)**, 129–145, doi:10.1162/DAED_a_00190.

Dyrstad, J.M., A. Skonhoft, M.Q. Christensen, and E.T. Ødegaard, 2019: Does economic growth eat up environmental improvements? Electricity production and fossil fuel emission in OECD countries 1980–2014. *Energy Policy*, **125**, 103–109, doi:10.1016/j.enpol.2018.10.051.

E3G, 2021: *Offshore Wind in the North Seas From Ambition To Delivery*. London, UK, pp. 1–33. https://9tj4025ol53byww26jdkao0x-wpengine.netdna-ssl.com/wp-content/uploads/Offshore-wind-in-the-North-Seas-from-ambition-to-delivery-report.pdf.

Ebeling, F. and S. Lotz, 2015: Domestic uptake of green energy promoted by opt-out tariffs. *Nat. Clim. Change*, **5(9)**, 868–871, doi:10.1038/nclimate2681.

Ebinger, J. and W. Vergara, 2011: *Climate Impacts on Energy Systems: Key Issues for Energy Sector Adaptation*. The World Bank, Washington DC, USA, 224 pp.

EC, 2019: *Orientations towards the first Strategic Plan for Horizon Europe*. European Commission, Luxembourg, 164 pp.Edenhofer, O., 2015: King coal and the queen of subsidies. *Science*, **349(6254)**, 1286–1287, doi:10.1126/science.aad0674.

Edenhofer, O., J.C. Steckel, M. Jakob, and C. Bertram, 2018: Reports of coal's terminal decline may be exaggerated. *Environ. Res. Lett*, **13**, 1–9, doi:10.1088/1748-9326/aaa3a2.

Edwards, R.W.J. and M.A. Celia, 2018: Infrastructure to enable deployment of carbon capture, utilization, and storage in the United States. *Proc. Natl. Acad. Sci.*, **115(38)**, E8815–E8824, doi:10.1073/pnas.1806504115.

EERE, 2020: Hydrogen Production: Thermochemical Water Splitting. Office of Energy Efficiency & Renewable Energy, Washington, DC, USA. https://www.energy.gov/eere/fuelcells/hydrogen-production-thermochemical-water-splitting.

EIA, 2020: Hydrogen explained use of hydrogen. U.S. Energy Information Administration (EIA), Washington, DC, USA. https://www.eia.gov/energy explained/hydrogen/use-of-hydrogen.php.

Eisenack, K., 2016: Institutional adaptation to cooling water scarcity for thermoelectric power generation under global warming. *Ecol. Econ.*, **124**, 153–163, doi:10.1016/j.ecolecon.2016.01.016.

Eitan, A. and I. Fischhendler, 2021: The social dimension of renewable energy storage in electricity markets: The role of partnerships. *Energy Res. Soc. Sci.*, **76**, 102072, doi:10.1016/j.erss.2021.102072.

Ek, K., 2005: Public and private attitudes towards 'green' electricity: The case of Swedish wind power. *Energy Policy*, **33(13)**, 1677–1689, doi:10.1016/j.enpol.2004.02.005.

6

El Bassam, N., P. Maegaard, and M.L. Schlichting, 2013: Hydropower. In: *Distributed renewable energies for off-grid communities: strategies and technologies toward achieving sustainability in energy generation and supply* [El Bassam, N., P. Maegaard, and M.L. Schlichting, (eds.)]. Elsevier, Oxford, UK, pp. 167–174.

Elamri, Y. et al., 2018: Rain concentration and sheltering effect of solar panels on cultivated plots. *Hydrol. Earth Syst. Sci.*, **22(2)**, 1285–1298, doi:10.5194/hess-22-1285-2018.

Elberry, A.M., J. Thakur, A. Santasalo-Aarnio, and M. Larmi, 2021: Large-scale compressed hydrogen storage as part of renewable electricity storage systems. *Int. J. Hydrogen Energy*, **46(29)**, 15671–15690, doi:10.1016/j.ijhydene.2021.02.080.

Element Energy, 2017: *Hybird Heat Pumps final report*. Element Energy, Cambridge, UK, 146 pp.

Eliasson, J., 2014: The role of attitude structures, direct experience and reframing for the success of congestion pricing. *Transp. Res. Part A Policy Pract.*, **67**, 81–95, doi:10.1016/j.tra.2014.06.007.

Elkadeem, M.R., S. Wang, S.W. Sharshir, and E.G. Atia, 2019: Feasibility analysis and techno-economic design of grid-isolated hybrid renewable energy system for electrification of agriculture and irrigation area: A case study in Dongola, Sudan. *Energy Convers. Manag.*, **196**, 1453–1478, doi:10.1016/j.enconman.2019.06.085.

Elshout, P.M. F. et al., 2015: Greenhouse-gas payback times for crop-based biofuels. *Nat. Clim. Change*, **5(6)**, 604–610, doi:10.1038/nclimate2642.

Elzen, M. den et al. 2016: Greenhouse gas emissions from current and enhanced policies of China until 2030: Can emissions peak before 2030? *Energy Policy*, **89**, 224–236, doi:10.1016/j.enpol.2015.11.030.EMBER, 2020: *Global Electricity Review 2020*. EMBER, India, 43 pp.

Emenike, O. et al., 2020: Initial techno-economic screening of BECCS technologies in power generation for a range of biomass feedstock. *Sustain. Energy Technol. Assessments*, **40**, 100743, doi:10.1016/j.seta.2020.100743.

Emmerich, P., A.G. Hülemeier, D. Jendryczko, M.J. Baumann, M. Weil, and D. Baur, 2020: Public acceptance of emerging energy technologies in context of the German energy transition. *Energy Policy*, **142**, 111516, doi:10.1016/j.enpol.2020.111516.

Emmerling, J. et al., 2019: The role of the discount rate for emission pathways and negative emissions. *Environ. Res. Lett.*, **14(10)**, 104008, doi:10.1088/1748-9326/ab3cc9.

Emodi, N.V., T. Chaiechi, and A.B.M.R.A. Beg, 2019: The impact of climate variability and change on the energy system: A systematic scoping review. *Sci. Total Environ.*, **676**, 545–563, doi:10.1016/j.scitotenv.2019.04.294.

Entriken, R. and R. Lordan, 2012: *Impacts of extreme events on transmission and distribution systems*. 2012 IEEE Power and Energy Society General Meeting, IEEE, San Diego, USA, 1–10.

Eom, J. et al., 2015: The impact of near-term climate policy choices on technology and emission transition pathways. *Technol. Forecast. Soc. Change*, **90**(PA), 73–88, doi:10.1016/j.techfore.2013.09.017.

EPA, 2001: *Hazards of Ammonia Releases at Ammonia Refrigeration Facilities (Update)*. United States Environmental Protection Agency, Washington DC, USA, 358–362 pp.

EPA, 2019: *Energy and the environment, electricity storage*. Environment Protection Agency, USA. https://www.epa.gov/energy/electricity-storage.

EPCC, 2017: *European Perceptions of Climate Change (EPCC) About the EPCC project*. European Perceptions of Climate Change, Cardiff, UK, pp. 1–72. https://orca.cardiff.ac.uk/98660/7/EPCC.pdf.

EPRI, 2017: *The Integrated Energy Network*. Electric Power Research Institute, Palo Alto, CA, USA, 21 pp.

EPRI, 2018: *Developing a Framework for Integrated Energy Network Planning (IEN-P)*. Electric Power Research Institute, Palo Alto, CA, USA, 10 pp.

EPRI, 2019a: *Program on Technology Innovation: Grid Operation with 100% Inverter-Based Resources: Final Report*. Electric Power Research Institute, Palo Alto, CA, USA, 124 pp.

EPRI, 2019b: *U.S. National Electrification Assessment*. Electric Power Research Institute, Palo Alto, CA, USA, 64 pp.

Erickson, P. and K. Tempest, 2015: *Keeping cities green: Avoiding carbon lock-in due to urban development*. Stockholm Environmental Institute, Seattle, WA, USA, 28 pp. https://mediamanager.sei.org/documents/Publications/Climate/SEI-WP-2015-11-C40-Cities-carbon-lock-in.pdf.

Erickson, P., M. Lazarus, and G. Piggot, 2018: Limiting fossil fuel production as the next big step in climate policy. *Nat. Clim. Change*, **8(12)**, 1037–1043, doi:10.1038/s41558-018-0337-0.

Eriksson, L., J. Garvill, and A.M. Nordlund, 2006: Acceptability of travel demand management measures: The importance of problem awareness, personal norm, freedom, and fairness. *J. Environ. Psychol.*, **26(1)**, 15–26, doi:10.1016/j.jenvp.2006.05.003.

ESA, 2019: Energy Storage Association. https://energystorage.org/.

ESFRI, 2018: Strategy Report on Research Infrastructures. *EU, Roadmap 2018*. European Strategy Forum on Research Infrastructures, 229 pp. http://roadmap2018.esfri.eu/.

ESMAP, 2019: *Global Solar Atlas 2.0. Technical Report*. World Bank, Washington, DC, USA, 39 pp.

Esposito, R.A., V.A. Kuuskraa, C.G. Rossman, and M.M. Corser, 2019: Reconsidering CCS in the US fossil-fuel fired electricity industry under section 45Q tax credits. *Greenh. Gases Sci. Technol.*, **9(6)**, 1288–1301, doi:10.1002/ghg.1925.

Eurek, K. et al., 2017: An improved global wind resource estimate for integrated assessment models. *Energy Econ.*, **64**, 552–567, doi:10.1016/j.eneco.2016.11.015.

European Commission Joint Research Centre (EU JRC), 2021: *Technical assessment of nuclear energy with respect to the 'do no significant harm' criteria of Regulation (EU) 2020/852 ('Taxonomy Regulation'). JRC124193*. European Commission, Petten, Netherlands, 387 pp.

Fabrizi, A., G. Guarini, and V. Meliciani, 2018: Green patents, regulatory policies and research network policies. *Res. Policy*, **47(6)**, 1018–1031, doi:10.1016/j.respol.2018.03.005.

Faiers, A. and C. Neame, 2006: Consumer attitudes towards domestic solar power systems. *Energy Policy*, **34(14)**, 1797–1806, doi:10.1016/j.enpol.2005.01.001.

Fajardy, M. and N. Mac Dowell, 2017: Can BECCS deliver sustainable and resource efficient negative emissions? *Energy Environ. Sci.*, **10(6)**, 1389–1426, doi:10.1039/c7ee00465f.

Fajardy, M. and N. Mac Dowell, 2018: The energy return on investment of BECCS: is BECCS a threat to energy security? *Energy Environ. Sci.*, **11(6)**, 1581–1594, doi:10.1039/C7EE03610H.

Fajardy, M. and N. Mac Dowell, 2020: Recognizing the Value of Collaboration in Delivering Carbon Dioxide Removal. *One Earth*, **3(2)**, 214–225, doi:10.1016/j.oneear.2020.07.014.

Fan, J.-L., M. Xu, F. Li, L. Yang, and X. Zhang, 2018: Carbon capture and storage (CCS) retrofit potential of coal-fired power plants in China: The technology lock-in and cost optimization perspective. *Appl. Energy*, **229**, 326–334, doi:10.1016/j.apenergy.2018.07.117.

Fan, J.-L. et al., 2020: Impacts of climate change on hydropower generation in China. *Math. Comput. Simul.*, **167**, 4–18, doi:10.1016/j.matcom.2018.01.002.

Fan, Y. Van, J.J. Klemeš, and C.H. Ko, 2021: Bioenergy carbon emissions footprint considering the biogenic carbon and secondary effects. *Int. J. Energy Res.*, **45(1)**, 283–296, doi:10.1002/er.5409.

Fang, D. et al., 2019: Clean air for some: Unintended spillover effects of regional air pollution policies. *Sci. Adv.*, **5(4)**, doi:10.1126/sciadv.aav4707.

Farfan, J. and C. Breyer, 2018: Combining Floating Solar Photovoltaic Power Plants and Hydropower Reservoirs: A Virtual Battery of Great Global Potential. *Energy Procedia*, **155**, 403–411, doi:10.1016/J.EGYPRO.2018.11.038.

Farfan Orozco, F., 2017: Structural changes of global power generation capacity towards sustainability and the risk of stranded investments supported by a sustainability indicator. *J. Clean. Prod.*, **141**, 370–384, doi:10.1016/j.jclepro.2016.09.068.

Fargione, J., 2010: Is bioenergy for the birds? An evaluation of alternative future bioenergy landscapes. *Proc. Natl. Acad. Sci.*, **107(44)**, 18745 LP – 18746, doi:10.1073/pnas.1014045107.

Farrow, K., G. Grolleau, and L. Ibanez, 2017: Social Norms and Pro-environmental Behavior: A Review of the Evidence. *Ecol. Econ.*, **140**, 1–13, doi:10.1016/j.ecolecon.2017.04.017.

Faruqui, A., S. Sergici, and A. Sharif, 2009: The impact of informational feedback on energy consumption: A survey of the experimental evidence. *Energy*, **35(4)**, 1598–1608, doi:10.1016/j.energy.2009.07.042.

Fasihi, M. and C. Breyer, 2020: Baseload electricity and hydrogen supply based on hybrid PV-wind power plants. *J. Clean. Prod.*, **243**, 118466, doi:10.1016/j.jclepro.2019.118466.

Fasihi, M., D. Bogdanov, and C. Breyer, 2016: Techno-Economic Assessment of Power-to-Liquids (PtL) Fuels Production and Global Trading Based on Hybrid PV-Wind Power Plants. *Energy Procedia*, **99**, 243–268, doi:10.1016/j.egypro.2016.10.115.

Fasihi, M., O. Efimova, and C. Breyer, 2019: Techno-economic assessment of CO_2 direct air capture plants. *J. Clean. Prod.*, **224**, 957–980, doi:10.1016/j.jclepro.2019.03.086.

Feijoo, F., G. Iyer, M. Binsted, and J. Edmonds, 2020: US energy system transitions under cumulative emissions budgets. *Clim. Change*, **162(4)**, 1947–1963, doi:10.1007/s10584-020-02670-0.

Fell, H. and J. Linn, 2013: Renewable electricity policies, heterogeneity, and cost effectiveness. *J. Environ. Econ. Manage.*, **66(3)**, 688–707, doi:10.1016/j.jeem.2013.03.004.

Fell, H. and P. Maniloff, 2017: Leakage in Regional Environmental Policy: The Case of the Regional Greenhouse Gas Initiative. *J. Environ. Econ. Manage.*, **87**, doi:10.1016/j.jeem.2017.10.007.

Feng, X. et al., 2015: A risk evaluation method for cascading failure considering transmission line icing. *2015 IEEE Innovative Smart Grid Technologies – Asia, ISGT ASIA 2015*, Institute of Electrical and Electronics Engineers Inc, pp. 1–4.

Fennell, P.S., S.J. Davis, and A. Mohammed, 2021: Decarbonizing cement production. *Joule*, **5(6)**, 1305–1311, doi:10.1016/J.JOULE.2021.04.011.

Ferrari, N. et al., 2017: Oxy-turbine for Power Plant with CO2 Capture. *Energy Procedia*, **114**, 471–480, doi:10.1016/j.egypro.2017.03.1189.

Fiehn, A. et al., 2020: Estimating CH_4, CO_2 and CO emissions from coal mining and industrial activities in the Upper Silesian Coal Basin using an aircraft-based mass balance approach. *Atmos. Chem. Phys.*, **20(21)**, 12675–12695, doi:10.5194/acp-20-12675-2020.

Field, C.B. and K.J. Mach, 2017: Rightsizing carbon dioxide removal. *Science*, **356(6339)**, 706 LP – 707, doi:10.1126/science.aam9726.

Fielding, K.S. and M.J. Hornsey, 2016: A social identity analysis of climate change and environmental attitudes and behaviors: Insights and opportunities. *Front. Psychol.*, **7(February)**, 1–12, doi:10.3389/fpsyg.2016.00121.

Finon, D., 2019: Carbon policy in developing countries: Giving priority to non-price instruments. *Energy Policy*, **132**, 38–43, doi:10.1016/J.ENPOL.2019.04.046.

Fisch-Romito, V., C. Guivarch, F. Creutzig, J.C. Minx, and M.W. Callaghan, 2020: Systematic map of the literature on carbon lock-in induced by long-lived capital. *Environ. Res. Lett.*, **16(5)**, doi:10.1088/1748-9326/aba660.

Fischer, C., 2008: Feedback on household electricity consumption: A tool for saving energy? *Energy Effic.*, **1(1)**, 79–104, doi:10.1007/s12053-008-9009-7.

Fischer, D., T. Wolf, J. Wapler, R. Hollinger, and H. Madani, 2017: Model-based flexibility assessment of a residential heat pump pool. *Energy*, **118**, 853–864, doi:10.1016/j.energy.2016.10.111.

Fischereit, J., R. Brown, X G. Larsén, J. Badger, and G. Hawkes, 2021: Review of Mesoscale Wind-Farm Parametrizations and Their Applications. *Boundary-Layer Meteoro.*, **182(2)**, 1–50, doi:10.1007/s10546-021-00652-y.

Fisher, S. et al., 2021: Air pollution and development in Africa: impacts on health, the economy, and human capital. *Lancet Planet. Heal.*, **5(10)**, e681–e688, doi:10.1016/S2542-5196(21)00201-1.

Flannigan, M. et al., 2013: Global wildland fire season severity in the 21st century. *For. Ecol. Manage.*, **294**, 54–61, doi:10.1016/j.foreco.2012.10.022.

Fluixá-Sanmartín, J., L. Altarejos-García, A. Morales-Torres, and I. Escuder-Bueno, 2018: Review article: Climate change impacts on dam safety. *Nat. Hazards Earth Syst. Sci.*, **18(9)**, 2471–2488, doi:10.5194/nhess-18-2471-2018.

Fofrich, R. et al., 2020: Early retirement of power plants in climate mitigation scenarios. *Environ. Res. Lett.*, **15(9)**, 1–13, doi:10.1088/1748-9326/ab96d3.

Fotouhi, A., D.J. Auger, L. O'Neill, T. Cleaver, and S. Walus, 2017: Lithium-Sulfur Battery Technology Readiness and Applications—A Review. *Energies*, **10(12)**, doi:10.3390/en10121937.

Fox, T.A., T.E. Barchyn, D. Risk, A.P. Ravikumar, and C.H. Hugenholtz, 2019: Erratum: A review of close-range and screening technologies for mitigating fugitive methane emissions in upstream oil and gas (2019 Environ. Res. Lett. 14 053002). *Environ. Res. Lett.*, **14(6)**, 1–2, doi:10.1088/1748-9326/ab20f1.

Franck, C.M., R. Smeets, A. Adamczyk, and H. Bahirat, 2017: *Technical requirements and specifications of state-of-the-art HVDC switching equipment*. Cigré Technical Brochure.

Frankfurt School-UNEP Centre, and BNEF, 2020: *Global Trends In Renewable Energy Investment 2020*. Frankfurt School-UNEP Centre, Frankfurt am Main, Germany, 80 pp.

Frederiks, E.R., K. Stenner, and E.V. Hobman, 2015: Household energy use: Applying behavioural economics to understand consumer decision-making and behaviour. *Renew. Sustain. Energy Rev.*, **41**, 1385–1394, doi:10.1016/j.rser.2014.09.026.

Frew, B.A., S. Becker, M.J. Dvorak, G.B. Andresen, and M.Z. Jacobson, 2016: Flexibility mechanisms and pathways to a highly renewable US electricity future. *Energy*, **101**, 65–78, doi:10.1016/j.energy.2016.01.079.

Fricko, O. et al., 2016: Energy sector water use implications of a 2 degrees C climate policy. *Environ. Res. Lett.*, **11(3)**, doi:10.1088/1748-9326/11/3/034011.

Fridahl, M., and M. Lehtveer, 2018: Bioenergy with carbon capture and storage (BECCS): Global potential, investment preferences, and deployment barriers. *Energy Res. Soc. Sci.*, **42**, 155–165, doi:10.1016/j.erss.2018.03.019.

Fridriksson, T., A. Mateos, P. Audinet, and Y. Orucu, 2016: *Greenhouse Gases from Geothermal Power Production*. World Bank, Washington, DC, USA, 52 pp.

Fthenakis, V. and H.C. Kim, 2009: Land use and electricity generation: A life-cycle analysis. *Renew. Sustain. Energy Rev.*, **13(6–7)**, 1465–1474, doi:10.1016/j.rser.2008.09.017.

FTI Consulting, 2018: *Pathways to 2050: The role of nuclear in a low-carbon Europe*. FTI Consulting, Washington, DC, USA, 76 pp.

Fu, F.Y. et al., 2021: The dynamic role of energy security, energy equity and environmental sustainability in the dilemma of emission reduction and economic growth. *J. Environ. Manage.*, **280**, 111828, doi:10.1016/j.jenvman.2020.111828.

Fu, P., D. Pudjianto, X. Zhang, and G. Strbac, 2020: Integration of Hydrogen into Multi-Energy Systems Optimisation. *Energies*, **13(7)**, 1606, doi:10.3390/en13071606.

Fu, R., D. Feldman, and R. Margolis, 2018: *U.S. Solar Photovoltaic System Cost Benchmark: Q1 2018*. National Renewable Energy Laboratory, Golden, CO, USA, 1–47 pp.

Fujimori, S., T. Hasegawa, and K. Oshiro, 2020: An assessment of the potential of using carbon tax revenue to tackle poverty. *Environ. Res. Lett.*, **15(11)**, 114063, doi:10.1088/1748-9326/abb55d.

Fulton, L.M., L.R. Lynd, A. Körner, N. Greene, and L.R. Tonachel, 2015: The need for biofuels as part of a low carbon energy future. *Biofuels, Bioprod. Biorefining*, **9(5)**, 476–483, doi:10.1002/bbb.1559.

Fuss, S. et al., 2014: Betting on negative emissions. *Nat. Clim. Change*, **4(10)**, 850–853, doi:10.1038/nclimate2392.

Fuss, S. et al., 2018: Negative emissions – Part 2: Costs, potentials and side effects. *Environ. Res. Lett.*, **13(6)**, doi:10.1088/1748-9326/aabf9f.

Gabrielli, P. et al., 2020: Seasonal energy storage for zero-emissions multi-energy systems via underground hydrogen storage. *Renew. Sustain. Energy Rev.*, **121**, 109629, doi:10.1016/j.rser.2019.109629.

6

Gaffney, F., J.P. Deane, G. Drayton, J. Glynn, and B.P.Ó. Gallachóir, 2020: Comparing negative emissions and high renewable scenarios for the European power system. *BMC Energy*, **2(1)**, 3, doi:10.1186/s42500-020-00013-4.

Gagnon, L. and J.F. van de Vate, 1997: Greenhouse gas emissions from hydropower. *Energy Policy*, **25(1)**, 7–13, doi:10.1016/S0301-4215(96)00125-5.

Gajardo, G. and S. Redón, 2019: Andean hypersaline lakes in the Atacama Desert, northern Chile: Between lithium exploitation and unique biodiversity conservation. *Conserv. Sci. Pract.*, **1(9)**, e94–e94, doi:10.1111/csp2.94.

Gallo, A.B.B., J.R.R. Simões-Moreira, H.K.M.K.M. Costa, M.M.M. Santos, and E. Moutinho dos Santos, 2016: Energy storage in the energy transition context: A technology review. *Renew. Sustain. Energy Rev.*, **65**, 800–822, doi:10.1016/j.rser.2016.07.028.

Gambhir, A., J. Rogelj, G. Luderer, S. Few, and T. Napp, 2019: Energy system changes in 1.5°C, well below 2°C and 2°C scenarios. *Energy Strateg. Rev.*, **23**, 69–80, doi:10.1016/j.esr.2018.12.006.

García-Gil, A. et al., 2020: Nested Shallow Geothermal Systems. *Sustain.*, **12(12)**, doi:10.3390/su12125152.

Garg, A. and P.R. Shukla, 2009: Coal and energy security for India: Role of carbon dioxide (CO_2) capture and storage (CCS). *Energy*, **34(8)**, 1032–1041, doi:10.1016/j.energy.2009.01.005.

Garg, A., P.R. Shukla, S. Parihar, U. Singh, and B. Kankal, 2017a: Cost-effective architecture of carbon capture and storage (CCS) grid in India. *Int. J. Greenh. Gas Control*, **66**(June), 129–146, doi:10.1016/j.ijggc.2017.09.012.

Garg, A., V. Tiwari, and S. Vishwanathan, 2017b: *Relevance of Clean Coal Technology for India's Energy Security: A Policy Perspective*. IOP Conference Series: Earth and Environmental Science, Vol. 76, Institute of Physics Publishing, UK, doi:10.1088/1755-1315/76/1/012001.

Garrett-Peltier, H., 2017: Green versus brown: Comparing the employment impacts of energy efficiency, renewable energy, and fossil fuels using an input-output model. *Econ. Model.*, **61**, 439–447, doi:10.1016/j.econmod.2016.11.012.

Gass, P., H. Duan, and I. Gerasimchuk, 2016: *Stories of Coal Phase-Out: Lessons learned for China*. International Institute for Sustainable Development, Winnipeg, Canada, 26 pp.

Gawel, E. and P. Lehmann, 2019: Should renewable energy policy be 'renewable'? *Oxford Rev. Econ. Policy*, **35(2)**, 218–243, doi:10.1093/oxrep/grz002.

GE, 2020: *Hydrogen fueled gas turbines*. GE Reports.

Ge, T. S. et al., 2018: Solar heating and cooling: Present and future development. *Renew. Energy*, **126**, 1126–1140, doi:10.1016/j.renene.2017.06.081.

Gea-Bermúdez, J. et al., 2021: The role of sector coupling in the green transition: A least-cost energy system development in Northern-central Europe towards 2050. *Appl. Energy*, **289**, 116685, doi:10.1016/j.apenergy.2021.116685.

Geels, F.W., T. Schwanen, S. Sorrell, K. Jenkins, and B.K. Sovacool, 2018: Reducing energy demand through low carbon innovation: A sociotechnical transitions perspective and thirteen research debates. *Energy Res. Soc. Sci.*, **40**, 23–35, doi:10.1016/j.erss.2017.11.003.

Geiger, J.L., L. Steg, E. van der Werff, and A.B. Ünal, 2019: A meta-analysis of factors related to recycling. *J. Environ. Psychol.*, **64**(March), 78–97, doi:10.1016/j.jenvp.2019.05.004.

Gerboni, R., D. Grosso, A. Carpignano, and B. Dalla Chiara, 2017: Linking energy and transport models to support policy making. *Energy Policy*, **111**, 336–345, doi:10.1016/j.enpol.2017.09.045.

Germeshausen, R., 2020: The European Union emissions trading scheme and fuel efficiency of fossil fuel power plants in Germany. *J. Assoc. Environ. Resour. Econ.*, **7(4)**, 751–777, doi:10.7910/DVN/4NUU2J.

Gerten, D. et al., 2020: Feeding ten billion people is possible within four terrestrial planetary boundaries. *Nat. Sustain.*, **3(3)**, 200–208, doi:10.1038/s41893-019-0465-1.

Giannaris, S., C. Bruce, B. Jacobs, W. Srisang, and D. Janowczyk, 2020: Implementing a second generation CCS facility on a coal fired power station – results of a feasibility study to retrofit SaskPower's Shand power station with CCS. *Greenh. Gases Sci. Technol.*, **13(2020)**, 1–13, doi:10.1002/ghg.1989.

Gibon, T., E.G. Hertwich, A. Arvesen, B. Singh, and F. Verones, 2017: Health benefits, ecological threats of low-carbon electricity. *Environ. Res. Lett.*, **12(3)**, doi:10.1088/1748-9326/aa6047.

Gils, H.C., Y. Scholz, T. Pregger, D. Luca de Tena, and D. Heide, 2017: Integrated modelling of variable renewable energy-based power supply in Europe. *Energy*, **123**, 173–188, doi:10.1016/j.energy.2017.01.115.

Gleick, P.H., 2016: *Impacts of California's Ongoing Drought: Hydroelectricity Generation*. Pacific Institute, Oakland, CA, USA, 1–14 pp.

Global CCS Institute, 2020: *The Global Status of CCS: 2020*. The Global CCS Institute, Melbourne, Australia, 44 pp. https://www.globalccsinstitute.com/resources/global-status-report/.

Global Energy Monitor, 2021: *Global Coal Plant Tracker*. Global Energy Monitor, San Francisco, CA, USA. https://endcoal.org/tracker/.

Global Energy Monitor et al., 2021: *Boom and Bust 2021: tracking the global coal plant pipeline*. Global Energy Monitor Sierra Club CREA GreenID Ekosfer Climate Risk Horizons, USA, 23 pp.

Goldemberg, J., J. Martinez-Gomez, A. Sagar, and K.R. Smith, 2018: Household air pollution, health, and climate change: Cleaning the air. *Environ. Res. Lett.*, **13(3)**, 030201, doi:10.1088/1748-9326/aaa49d.

Goldmann, A. and F. Dinkelacker, 2018: Approximation of laminar flame characteristics on premixed ammonia/hydrogen/nitrogen/air mixtures at elevated temperatures and pressures. *Fuel*, **224**, 366–378, doi:10.1016/j.fuel.2018.03.030.

Golley, J. and X. Meng, 2012: Income inequality and carbon dioxide emissions: The case of Chinese urban households. *Energy Econ.*, **34(6)**, 1864–1872, doi:10.1016/j.eneco.2012.07.025.

Gong, J., S.B. Darling, and F. You, 2015: Perovskite photovoltaics: life-cycle assessment of energy and environmental impacts. *Energy Environ. Sci.*, **8(7)**, 1953–1968, doi:10.1039/C5EE00615E.

Gonzales, M.H., E. Aronson, and M.A. Costanzo, 1988: Using Social Cognition and Persuasion to Promote Energy Conservation: A Quasi-Experiment. *J. Appl. Soc. Psychol.*, **18(12)**, 1049–1066, doi:10.1111/j.1559-1816.1988.tb01192.x.

González-Mahecha, E., O. Lecuyer, M. Hallack, M. Bazilian, and A. Vogt-Schilb, 2019: Committed emissions and the risk of stranded assets from power plants in Latin America and the Caribbean. *Environ. Res. Lett.*, **14(12)**, 124096, doi:10.1088/1748-9326/ab5476.

Gonzalez, A., E. Goikolea, A. Barrena, and R. Mysyk, 2016: Review on supercapacitors: Technologies and materials. *Renew. Sustain. Energy Rev.*, **58**, doi:10.1016/j.rser.2015.12.249.

Goodale, M.W. and A. Milman, 2016: Cumulative adverse effects of offshore wind energy development on wildlife. *J. Environ. Plan. Manag.*, **59(1)**, 1–21, doi:10.1080/09640568.2014.973483.

Gormally, A.M., C.G. Pooley, J.D. Whyatt, and R.J. Timmis, 2014: 'They made gunpowder… yes down by the river there, that's your energy source': attitudes towards community renewable energy in Cumbria. *Local Environ.*, **19(8)**, 915–932, doi:10.1080/13549839.2013.810206.

Gorman, W., A. Mills, and R. Wiser, 2019: Improving estimates of transmission capital costs for utility-scale wind and solar projects to inform renewable energy policy. *Energy Policy*, **135**, 110994, doi:10.1016/j.enpol.2019.110994.

Gould, C., 2018: LPG as a Clean Cooking Fuel: Adoption, Use, and Impact in Rural India. *Energy Policy*, **122**, 395–408, doi:10.1016/j.enpol.2018.07.042.

Goulder, L.H. and R.D. Morgenstern, 2018: China's Rate-Based Approach to Reducing CO_2 Emissions: Attractions, Limitations, and Alternatives. *AEA Pap. Proc.*, **108**, 458–462, doi:10.1257/pandp.20181028.

Goulder, L.H., M.A.C. Hafstead, and R.C. Williams III, 2016: General Equilibrium Impacts of a Federal Clean Energy Standard. *Am. Econ. J. Econ. Policy*, **8(2)**, 186–218, doi:10.1257/pol.20140011.

Government of Canada, 2018: Canada's coal power phase-out reaches another milestone. News release, Environment and Climate Change Canada. https://www.canada.ca/en/environment-climate-change/news/2018/12/canadas-coal-power-phase-out-reaches-another-milestone.html.

Gowdy, J., 2008: Behavioral Economics and Climate Change Policy. *J. Econ. Behav. Organ.*, **68**, 632–644, doi:10.1016/j.jebo.2008.06.011.

Gowrisankaran, G., S.S. Reynolds, and M. Samano, 2016: Intermittency and the Value of Renewable Energy. *J. Polit. Econ.*, **124(4)**, 1187–1234, doi:10.1086/686733.

Gracey, E. O. and F. Verones, 2016: Impacts from hydropower production on biodiversity in an LCA framework—review and recommendations. *Int. J. Life Cycle Assess.*, **21**, 412–428, doi:10.1007/s11367-016-1039-3.

Grant, C.A. and A. L. Hicks, 2020: Effect of manufacturing and installation location on environmental impact payback time of solar power. *Clean Technol. Environ. Policy*, **22(1)**, 187–196, doi:10.1007/s10098-019-01776-z.

Graves, C., S.D. Ebbesen, M. Mogensen, and K.S. Lackner, 2011: Sustainable hydrocarbon fuels by recycling CO_2 and H_2O with renewable or nuclear energy. *Renew. Sustain. Energy Rev.*, **15(1)**, 1–23, doi:10.1016/j.rser.2010.07.014.

Green, F. and A. Gambhir, 2020: Transitional assistance policies for just, equitable and smooth low-carbon transitions: who, what and how? *Clim. Policy*, **20(8)**, 902–921, doi:10.1080/14693062.2019.1657379.

Green, M.A., 2015: The Passivated Emitter and Rear Cell (PERC): From conception to mass production. *Sol. Energy Mater. Sol. Cells*, **143**, 190–197, doi:10.1016/j.solmat.2015.06.055.

Green, M.A., 2016: Commercial progress and challenges for photovoltaics. *Nat. Energy*, **1**, 15015, doi:10.1038/nenergy.2015.15.

Green, M.A., 2019: How Did Solar Cells Get So Cheap? *Joule*, **3(3)**, 631–633, doi:10.1016/j.joule.2019.02.010.

Green, M.A. et al., 2019: Solar cell efficiency tables (version 54). *Prog. Photovoltaics Res. Appl.*, **27(7)**, 565–575, doi:10.1002/pip.3171.

Greenberg, P., 2018: Coal Waste, Socioeconomic Change, and Environmental Inequality in Appalachia: Implications for a Just Transition in Coal Country. *Soc. Nat. Resour.*, **31(9)**, 995–1011, doi:10.1080/08941920.2018.1456593.

Griffiths, S., B.K. Sovacool, J. Kim, M. Bazilian, and J.M. Uratani, 2021: Industrial decarbonization via hydrogen: A critical and systematic review of developments, socio-technical systems and policy options. *Energy Res. Soc. Sci.*, **80**, 102208, doi:10.1016/j.erss.2021.102208.

Griskevicius, V., J.M. Tybur, and B. Van den Bergh, 2010: Going Green to Be Seen: Status, Reputation, and Conspicuous Conservation. *J. Pers. Soc. Psychol.*, **98(3)**, 392–404, doi:10.1037/a0017346.

Grønhøj, A. and J. Thøgersen, 2011: Feedback on household electricity consumption: learning and social influence processes. *Int. J. Consum. Stud.*, **35(2)**, 138–145, doi:10.1111/j.1470-6431.2010.00967.x.

Grubb, M. and D. Newbery, 2018: UK electricity market reform and the energy transition: Emerging lessons. *Energy J.*, **39(6)**, 1–25, doi:10.5547/01956574.39.6.mgru.

Grubb, M., W. McDowall, and P. Drummond, 2017: On order and complexity in innovations systems: Conceptual frameworks for policy mixes in sustainability transitions. *Energy Res Soc. Sci.*, **33**, 21–34, doi:10.1016/j.erss.2017.09.016.

Grubert, E., 2020: Fossil electricity retirement deadlines for a just transition. *Science*, **370(6521)**, 1171 LP – 1173, doi:10.1126/science.abe0375.

Grubert, E.A. and A.R. Brandt, 2019: Three considerations for modeling natural gas system methane emissions in life cycle assessment. *J. Clean. Prod.*, **222**, 760–767, doi:10.1016/j.jclepro.2019.03.096.

Grubler, A. et al., 2012: Global Energy Assessment-Toward a Sustainable Future. International Institute for Applied Systems Analysis. Cambridge University Press, Cambridge, UK, pp. 1307–1400.

Grubler, A. et al., 2018: A low energy demand scenario for meeting the 1.5°C target and sustainable development goals without negative emission technologies. *Nat. Energy*, **3(6)**, 515–527, doi:10.1038/s41560-018-0172-6.

Gu, T., C. Yin, W. Ma, and G. Chen, 2019: Municipal solid waste incineration in a packed bed: A comprehensive modeling study with experimental validation. *Appl. Energy*, **247**, 127–139, doi:10.1016/j.apenergy.2019.04.014.

Guerrero-Lemus, R., R. Vega, T. Kim, A. Kimm, and L.E. Shephard, 2016: Bifacial solar photovoltaics – A technology review. *Renew. Sustain. Energy Rev.*, **60**, 1533–1549, doi:10.1016/j.rser.2016.03.041.

Guivarch, C. and J. Rogelj, 2017: *Carbon price variations in 2°C scenarios explored*, Carbon Pricing Leadership Coalition, USA, pp. 1–15.

Gumber, S., and A.V.P. Gurumoorthy, 2018: Methanol Economy Versus Hydrogen Economy. In: *Methanol* [Basile, A. and F.B.T.-M. Dalena, (eds.)]. Elsevier, New York, NY, USA, pp. 661–674.

Gupta, D., A. Das, and A. Garg, 2019a: Financial support vis-à-vis share of wind generation: Is there an inflection point? *Energy*, **181**, 1064–1074, doi:10.1016/J.ENERGY.2019.05.221.

Gupta, K., M.C. Nowlin, J.T. Ripberger, H.C. Jenkins-Smith, and C.L. Silva, 2019b: Tracking the nuclear 'mood' in the United States: Introducing a long term measure of public opinion about nuclear energy using aggregate survey data. *Energy Policy*, **133**(December 2018), 110888, doi:10.1016/j.enpol.2019.110888.

Gur, T.M., 2018: Review of electrical energy storage technologies, materials and systems: challenges and prospects for large-scale grid storage. *Energy Environ. Sci.*, **11(2696–2768)**, doi:10.1039/C8EE01419A.

Haberl, H., T. Beringer, S.C. Bhattacharya, K.-H. Erb, and M. Hoogwijk, 2010: The global technical potential of bio-energy in 2050 considering sustainability constraints. *Curr. Opin. Environ. Sustain.*, **2(5–6)**, 394–403, doi:10.1016/j.cosust.2010.10.007.

Haberl, H. et al., 2011: Global bioenergy potentials from agricultural land in 2050: Sensitivity to climate change, diets and yields. *Biomass and Bioenergy*, **35(12)**, 4753–4769, doi:10.1016/j.biombioe.2011.04.035.

Hackmann, H., S.C. Moser, and A.L. St. Clair, 2014: The social heart of global environmental change. *Nat. Clim. Change*, **4(8)**, 653–655, doi:10.1038/nclimate2320.

Haegel, N.M. et al., 2019: Terawatt-scale photovoltaics: Transform global energy. *Science*, **364**, 836–838, doi:10.1126/science.aaw1845.

Haelg, L., M. Waelchli, and T.S. Schmidt, 2018: Supporting energy technology deployment while avoiding unintended technological lock-in: a policy design perspective. *Environ. Res. Lett.*, **13(10)**, 104011, doi:10.1088/1748-9326/aae161.

Hager, H.A., S.E. Sinasac, Z. Gedalof, and J.A. Newman, 2014: Predicting potential global distributions of two Miscanthus grasses: Implications for horticulture, biofuel production, and biological invasions. *PLoS One*, **9(6)**, doi:10.1371/journal.pone.0100032.

Hahn, H.J., 1983: Organisation for economic cooperation and development, Nuclear Energy Agency. In: *International Organizations in General Universal International Organizations and Cooperation*, Elsevier, New York, NY, USA, pp. 222–224.

Haikola, S., A. Hansson, and J. Anshelm, 2019: From polarization to reluctant acceptance–bioenergy with carbon capture and storage (BECCS) and the post-normalization of the climate debate. *J. Integr. Environ. Sci.*, **16(1)**, 45–69, doi:10.1080/1943815X.2019.1579740.

Hakimi, S.M., A. Hasankhani, M. Shafie-khah, and J.P.S. Catalão, 2020: Demand response method for smart microgrids considering high renewable energies penetration. *Sustain. Energy, Grids Networks*, **21**, 100325, doi:10.1016/j.segan.2020.100325.

Halawa, E., G. James, X. Shi, N. Sari, and R. Nepal, 2018: The Prospect for an Australian–Asian Power Grid: A Critical Appraisal. *Energies*, **11(1)**, 200, doi:10.3390/en11010200.

Hale, E., H. Horsey, N. Merket, B. Stoll, and A. Nag, 2017: *Demand response resource quantification with detailed building energy models*. INFORMS Annual Meeting, Session MB09 – Development of Electricity Systems, NREL, Nashville, USA, 37 pp.

6

Hall, C.A.S., J.G. Lambert, and S.B. Balogh, 2014: EROI of different fuels and the implications for society. *Energy Policy*, **64**, 141–152, doi:10.1016/j.enpol.2013.05.049.

Hammond, G.P. and T. Hazeldine, 2015: Indicative energy technology assessment of advanced rechargeable batteries. *Appl. Energy*, **138**, 559–571, doi:10.1016/j.apenergy.2014.10.037.

Hamududu, B. and A. Killingtveit, 2012: Assessing climate change impacts on global hydropower. *Energies*, **5(2)**, 305–322, doi:10.3390/en5020305.

Handgraaf, M.J.J., M.A. Van Lidth de Jeude, and K.C. Appelt, 2013: Public praise vs. private pay: Effects of rewards on energy conservation in the workplace. *Ecol. Econ.*, **86**, 86–92, doi:10.1016/j.ecolecon.2012.11.008.

Hanger, S. et al., 2016: Community acceptance of large-scale solar energy installations in developing countries: Evidence from Morocco. *Energy Res. Soc. Sci.*, **14**, 80–89, doi:10.1016/j.erss.2016.01.010.

Hänggi, S. et al., 2019: A review of synthetic fuels for passenger vehicles. *Energy Reports*, **5**, 555–569, doi:10.1016/j.egyr.2019.04.007.

Hansen, K., C. Breyer, and H. Lund, 2019: Status and perspectives on 100% renewable energy systems. *Energy*, **175**, 471–480, https://doi.org/10.1016/j.energy.2019.03.092.

Hansen, O.R., 2020: Hydrogen infrastructure—Efficient risk assessment and design optimization approach to ensure safe and practical solutions. *Process Saf. Environ. Prot.*, **143**, 164–176, doi:10.1016/j.psep.2020.06.028.

Hansgen, D., D. Vlachos, and J. Chen, 2010: Using first principles to predict bimetallic catalysts for the ammonia decomposition reaction. *Nat. Chem.*, **2**, 484–489, doi:10.1038/nchem.626.

Hanssen, S.V. et al., 2020: The climate change mitigation potential of bioenergy with carbon capture and storage. *Nat. Clim. Change*, **10(11)**, 1023–1029, doi:10.1038/s41558-020-0885-y.

Haraguchi, M., A. Siddiqi, and V. Narayanamurti, 2019: Stochastic cost-benefit analysis of urban waste-to-energy systems. *J. Clean. Prod.*, **224**, 751–765, doi:10.1016/j.jclepro.2019.03.099.

Harfoot, M.B.J. et al., 2018: Present and future biodiversity risks from fossil fuel exploitation. *Conserv. Lett.*, **11(4)**, e12448, doi:10.1111/conl.12448.

Harland, P., H. Staats, and H.A.M. Wilke, 1999: Explaining proenvironmental intention and behavior by personal norms and the theory of planned behavior. *J. Appl. Soc. Psychol.*, **29(12)**, 2505–2528, doi:10.1111/j.1559–1816.1999.tb00123.x.

Harmsen, J.H.M. et al., 2019: Long-term marginal abatement cost curves of non-CO_2 greenhouse gases. *Environ. Sci. Policy*, **99**(March), 136–149, doi:10.1016/j.envsci.2019.05.013.

Harper, A.B. et al., 2018: Land-use emissions play a critical role in land-based mitigation for Paris climate targets. *Nat. Commun.*, **9(1)**, doi:10.1038/s41467-018-05340-z.

Harper, G. et al., 2019: Recycling lithium-ion batteries from electric vehicles. *Nature*, **575(7781)**, 75–86, doi:10.1038/s41586-019-1682-5.

Harris, M., M. Beck, and I. Gerasimchuk, 2015: *The End of Coal: Ontario's coal phase-out*. International Institute for Sustainable Development, Winnipeg, Canada, 32 pp.

Harvey, B.J., L.C. Shaffrey, and T.J. Woollings, 2014: Equator-to-pole temperature differences and the extra-tropical storm track responses of the CMIP5 climate models. *Clim. Dyn.*, **43(5–6)**, 1171–1182, doi:10.1007/s00382-013-1883-9.

Hassanpour Adeh, E., J.S. Selker, and C.W. Higgins, 2018: Remarkable agrivoltaic influence on soil moisture, micrometeorology and water-use efficiency. *PLoS One*, **13(11)**, e0203256, doi:10.1371/journal.pone.0203256.

Hastings, A., and P. Smith, 2020: Achieving Net-zero Emissions Requires the Knowledge and Skills of the Oil and Gas Industry. *Front. Clim.*, **2**, 22, doi:10.3389/fclim.2020.601778.

Haszeldine, R.S., 2016: Can CCS and NET enable the continued use of fossil carbon fuels after COP21? *Oxford Rev. Econ. Policy*, **32(2)**, 304–322, doi:10.1093/oxrep/grw013.

Haupt, S.E. et al., 2016: A Method to Assess the Wind and Solar Resource and to Quantify Interannual Variability over the United States under Current and Projected Future Climate. *J. Appl. Meteorol. Climatol.*, **55(2)**, 345–363, doi:10.1175/JAMC-D-15-0011.1.

Haya, B. et al., 2020: Managing uncertainty in carbon offsets: insights from California's standardized approach. *Clim. Policy*, **20(9)**, 1112–1126, doi:10.1080/14693062.2020.1781035.

Hayes, D.S. et al., 2019: Life Stage-Specific Hydropeaking Flow Rules. *Sustain.*, **11(6)**, 1547, doi:10.3390/su11061547.

Hazboun, S.O. and H.S. Boudet, 2020: Public preferences in a shifting energy future: Comparing public views of eight energy sources in North America's Pacific Northwest. *Energies*, **13(8)**, 1–21, doi:10.3390/en13081940.

He, G. et al., 2020: Enabling a Rapid and Just Transition away from Coal in China. *One Earth*, **3(2)**, 187–194, doi:10.1016/j.oneear.2020.07.012.

Heath, G.A. et al., 2020: Research and development priorities for silicon photovoltaic module recycling to support a circular economy. *Nat. Energy*, **5(7)**, 502–510, doi:10.1038/s41560-020-0645-2.

Heck, V., D. Gerten, W. Lucht, and A. Popp, 2018: Biomass-based negative emissions difficult to reconcile with planetary boundaries. *Nat. Clim. Change*, **8(2)**, 151–155, doi:10.1038/s41558-017-0064-y.

Hedlund, M., J. Lundin, J. de Santiago, J. Abrahamsson, and H. Bernhoff, 2015: Flywheel Energy Storage for Automotive Applications. *Energies*, **8(10)**, 10636–10663, doi:10.3390/en81010636.

Heffron, R.J., M.F. Körner, M. Schöpf, J. Wagner, and M. Weibelzahl, 2021: The role of flexibility in the light of the COVID-19 pandemic and beyond: Contributing to a sustainable and resilient energy future in Europe. *Renew. Sustain. Energy Rev.*, **140**(December 2020), doi:10.1016/j.rser.2021.110743.

Heide, D. et al., 2010: Seasonal optimal mix of wind and solar power in a future, highly renewable Europe. *Renew. Energy*, **35(11)**, 2483–2489, doi:10.1016/j.renene.2010.03.012.

Heinen, S., D. Burke, and M. O'Malley, 2016: Electricity, gas, heat integration via residential hybrid heating technologies – An investment model assessment. *Energy*, **109**, 906–919, doi:10.1016/j.energy.2016.04.126.

Heleno, M., M.A. Matos, and J.A.P. Lopes, 2015: Availability and Flexibility of Loads for the Provision of Reserve. *IEEE Trans. Smart Grid*, **6(2)**, 667–674, doi:10.1109/TSG.2014.2368360.

Helistö, N., J. Kiviluoma, H. Holttinen, J.D. Lara, and B.M. Hodge, 2019: Including operational aspects in the planning of power systems with large amounts of variable generation: A review of modeling approaches. *Wiley Interdiscip. Rev. Energy Environ.*, **8(5)**, e341.1–e341.34, doi:10.1002/wene.341.

Henry, R.C. et al., 2018: Food supply and bioenergy production within the global cropland planetary boundary. *PLoS One*, **13(3)**, e0194695, doi:10.1371/journal.pone.0194695.

Hepburn, C. et al., 2019: The technological and economic prospects for CO_2 utilization and removal. *Nature*, **575(7781)**, 87–97, doi:10.1038/s41586-019-1681-6.

Heptonstall, P.J., and R.J.K. Gross, 2021: A systematic review of the costs and impacts of integrating variable renewables into power grids. *Nat. Energy*, **6**, 72–83, doi:10.5286/ukerc.edc.000010.

Hernandez, R.R. et al., 2014: Environmental impacts of utility-scale solar energy. *Renew. Sustain. Energy Rev.*, **29**, 766–779, doi:10.1016/j.rser.2013.08.041.

Hernandez, R.R., M.K. Hoffacker, M.L. Murphy-Mariscal, G.C. Wu, and M.F. Allen, 2015: Solar energy development impacts on land cover change and protected areas. *Proc. Natl. Acad. Sci.*, **112(44)**, 13579–13584, doi:10.1073/pnas.1517656112.

Heymann, F. and R. Bessa, 2015: *Power-to-Gas potential assessment of Portugal under special consideration of LCOE*. 2015 IEEE Eindhoven PowerTech, IEEE, Eindhoven, Netherlands, 5 pp.

Hirth, L., 2013: The market value of variable renewables: The effect of solar wind power variability on their relative price. *Energy Econ.*, **38**, 218–236, doi:10.1016/j.eneco.2013.02.004.

Hirth, L., 2015: The Optimal Share of Variable Renewables: How the Variability of Wind and Solar Power affects their Welfare-optimal Deployment. *Energy J.*, **36(1)**, 127–162, doi:10.5547/01956574.36.1.5.

Hirth, L., 2016: The benefits of flexibility: The value of wind energy with hydropower. *Appl. Energy*, **181**, 210–223, doi:10.1016/j.apenergy.2016.07.039.

Hirth, L., F. Ueckerdt, and O. Edenhofer, 2015: Integration costs revisited – An economic framework for wind and solar variability. *Renew. Energy*, **74**, 925–939, doi:10.1016/j.renene.2014.08.065.

Hittinger, E. and R. Lueken, 2015: Is inexpensive natural gas hindering the grid energy storage industry? *Energy Policy*, **87**(December), 140–152, doi:10.1016/j.enpol.2015.08.036.

Hmiel, B. et al., 2020: Preindustrial 14CH4 indicates greater anthropogenic fossil CH_4 emissions. *Nature*, **578(7795)**, 409–412, doi:10.1038/s41586-020-1991-8.

Ho, H.-J., A. Iizuka, and E. Shibata, 2019: Carbon Capture and Utilization Technology without Carbon Dioxide Purification and Pressurization: A Review on Its Necessity and Available Technologies. *Ind. Eng. Chem. Res.*, **58(21)**, 8941–8954, doi:10.1021/acs.iecr.9b01213.

Hobman, E.V. and P. Ashworth, 2013: Public support for energy sources and related technologies: The impact of simple information provision. *Energy Policy*, **63**, 862–869, doi:10.1016/j.enpol.2013.09.011.

Hock, R., G. Rasul, C. Adler, B. Cáceres, S. Gruber, Y. Hirabayashi, M. Jackson, A. Kääb, S. Kang, S. Kutuzov, A. Milner, U. Molau, S. Morin, B. Orlove, and H. Steltzer, 2019: High Mountain Areas. In: *IPCC Special Report on the Ocean and Cryosphere in a Changing Climate* [H.-O. Pörtner, D.C. Roberts, V. Masson-Delmotte, P. Zhai, M. Tignor, E. Poloczanska, K. Mintenbeck, A. Alegría, M. Nicolai, A. Okem, J. Petzold, B. Rama, N.M. Weyer (eds.)]. Cambridge University Press, Cambridge, UK and New York, NY, USA, 131–202 pp.

Hodbod, J. and J. Tomei, 2013: Demystifying the Social Impacts of Biofuels at Local Levels: Where is the Evidence? *Geogr. Compass*, **7**, 478–488, doi:10.1111/gec3.12051.

Hoegh-Guldberg, O., E. Northrop, and J. Lubchenco, 2019: The ocean is key to achieving climate and societal goals. *Science*, **365(6460)**, 1372–1374, doi:10.1126/science.aaz4390.

Hoen, B. et al., 2019: Attitudes of U.S. Wind Turbine Neighbors: Analysis of a Nationwide Survey. *Energy Policy*, **134**(October 2018), 110981, doi:10.1016/j.enpol.2019.110981.

Hoes, O.A.C., L.J.J. Meijer, R.J. van der Ent, and N.C. van de Giesen, 2017: Systematic high-resolution assessment of global hydropower potential. *PLoS One*, **12(2)**, e0171844, doi:10.1371/journal.pone.0171844.

Höglund-Isaksson, L., A. Gómez-Sanabria, Z. Klimont, P. Rafaj, and W. Schöpp, 2020: Technical potentials and costs for reducing global anthropogenic methane emissions in the 2050 timeframe – results from the GAINS model. *Environ. Res. Commun.*, **2(2)**, 025004, doi:10.1088/2515-7620/ab7457.

Homagain, K., C. Shahi, N. Luckai, and M. Sharma, 2015: Life cycle environmental impact assessment of biochar-based bioenergy production and utilization in Northwestern Ontario, Canada. *J. For. Res.*, **26(4)**, 799–809, doi:10.1007/s11676-015-0132-y.

Hooper, T., N. Beaumont, and C. Hattam, 2017: The implications of energy systems for ecosystem services: A detailed case study of offshore wind. *Renew. Sustain. Energy Rev.*, **70**(December 2015), 230–241, doi:10.1016/j.rser.2016.11.248.

Hoppe, W., N. Thonemann, and S. Bringezu, 2018: Life Cycle Assessment of Carbon Dioxide–Based Production of Methane and Methanol and Derived Polymers. *J. Ind. Ecol.*, **22(2)**, 327–340, doi:10.1111/jiec.12583.

Hornsey, M.J., E.A. Harris, P.G. Bain, and K.S. Fielding, 2016: Meta-analyses of the determinants and outcomes of belief in climate change. *Nat. Clim. Change*, **6(6)**, 622–626, doi:10.1038/nclimate2943.

Hossein Motlagh, N., M. Mohammadrezaei, J. Hunt, and B. Zakeri, 2020: Internet of Things (IoT) and the energy sector. *Energies*, **13(2)**, 494, doi:10.3390/en13020494.

Hou, G. et al., 2016: Life cycle assessment of grid-connected photovoltaic power generation from crystalline silicon solar modules in China. *Appl. Energy*, **164**, 882–890, doi:10.1016/j.apenergy.2015.11.023.

Howlett, M., 2014: From the 'Old' to the 'New' Policy Design: Design Thinking Beyond Markets and Collaborative Governance. *Policy Sci.*, **47**, 187–207, doi:10.1007/s11077-014-9199-0.

Hu, A. et al., 2016: Impact of solar panels on global climate. *Nat. Clim. Change*, **6(3)**, 290–294, doi:10.1038/nclimate2843.

Hu, B. and H. Zhai, 2017: The cost of carbon capture and storage for coal-fired power plants in China. *Int. J. Greenh. Gas Control*, **65**, 23–31, doi:10.1016/j.ijggc.2017.08.009.

Hu, J., R. Harmsen, W. Crijns-Graus, E. Worrell, and M. van den Broek, 2018: Identifying barriers to large-scale integration of variable renewable electricity into the electricity market: A literature review of market design. *Renew. Sustain. Energy Rev.*, **81**, 2181–2195, doi:10.1016/j.rser.2017.06.028.

Hu, Q., Y. Shen, J.W. Chew, T. Ge, and C.-H. Wang, 2020: Chemical looping gasification of biomass with Fe_2O_3/CaO as the oxygen carrier for hydrogen-enriched syngas production. *Chem. Eng. J.*, **379**, 122346, doi:10.1016/j.cej.2019.122346.

Hu R., Sun P., Wang Z, 2012: An overview of the development of solar water heater industry in China. Energy policy, 51: 46-51, doi:10.1016/j.enpol.2012.03.081.

Hughes, L. and J. Urpelainen, 2015: Interests, institutions, and climate policy: Explaining the choice of policy instruments for the energy sector. *Environ. Sci. Policy*, **54**, 52–63, doi:10.1016/J.ENVSCI.2015.06.014.

Hunt, J.D., E. Byers, and A.S. Sánchez, 2019: Technical potential and cost estimates for seawater air conditioning. *Energy*, **166**, 979–988, doi:10.1016/j.energy.2018.10.146.

Hunt, T.M., 2001: *Five Lectures on Environmental Effects of Geothermal Utilization*. United Nations University, Geothermal Training Programme, Reykjavík, Iceland, 109 pp.

Huntington, H. et al., 2020: Key findings from the core North American scenarios in the EMF34 intermodel comparison. *Energy Policy*, **144**, 111599, doi:10.1016/j.enpol.2020.111599.

Hwang, J.-Y., S.-T. Myung, and Y.-K. Sun, 2017: Sodium-ion batteries: present and future. *Chem. Soc. Rev.*, **46(12)**, 3529–3614, doi:10.1039/C6CS00776G.

IAEA, 2005: *Thorium fuel cycle: Potential benefits and challenges*. International Atomic Energy Agency, Vienna, Austria, 112 pp.

IAEA, 2009: *Nuclear Technology and Economic Development in the Republic of Korea*. International Atomic Energy Agency, Vienna, Austria, 148 pp.

IAEA, 2014: *Safety of Nuclear Fuel Cycle Facilities*. International Atomic Energy Agency, Vienna, Austria, 102 pp.

IAEA, 2016: *Nuclear power and sustainable development*. International Atomic Energy Agency, Vienna, Austria, 116 pp.

IAEA, 2018: *Economic Assessment of the Long Term Operation of Nuclear Power Plants: Approaches and Experience*. International Atomic Energy Agency, Vienna, Austria, pp. 35–37.

IAEA, 2019: *International Safeguards in the Design of Reprocessing Plants*. International Atomic Energy Agency, Vienna, Austria, 62 pp.

IAEA, 2020: *Advances in Small Modular Reactor Technology Developments*. International Atomic Energy Agency, Vienna, Austria, 150 pp.

IAEA PRIS, 2021: Power Reactor Information System (PRIS) (2021). https://www.iaea.org/resources/databases/power-reactor-information-system-pris.

IEA, 1999: *World Energy Outlook, 1999 Insights – Looking at Energy Subsidies: Getting the Prices Right*. International Energy Agency, Paris, France, 210 pp.

IEA, 2014a: *The power of transformation Wind, Sun and the Economics of Flexible Power Systems*. International Energy Agency, Paris, France, 160–179 pp.

IEA, 2014b: *Energy Technology Perspectives 2014*. International Energy Agency, Paris, France, 382 pp.

IEA, 2017: *Energy Access Outlook 2017*. International Energy Agency, Paris, France, 1–143 pp. https://www.iea.org/reports/energy-access-outlook-2017.

IEA, 2018a: *Global Energy & CO2 Status Report*. International Energy Agency, Paris, France, 28 pp.

IEA, 2018b: *World Energy Outlook 2018*. International Energy Agency, Paris, France, 661 pp.

IEA, 2018c: *Hydrogen from biomass*. International Energy Agency, Paris, France, 265–271 pp.

IEA, 2018d: *The Future of Cooling*. OECD, International Energy Agency, Paris, France, 92 pp.

IEA, 2019a: *Renewables 2019 – Analysis - IEA*. International Energy Agency, Paris, France, 204 pp.

IEA, 2019b: *Africa Energy Outlook 2019*. International Energy Agency, Paris, France, 288 pp.

IEA, 2019c: *Nuclear power in a clean energy system*. International Energy Agency, Paris, France, 103 pp.

IEA, 2019d: *The Future of Hydrogen. Seizing today's opportunities*. International Energy Agency, Paris, France, 203 pp.

IEA, 2019e: *Tracking Transport*. International Energy Agency, Paris, France.

IEA, 2019f: *Renewables 2019*. International Energy Agency, Paris, France, 204 pp. https://www.iea.org/renewables2019/.

IEA, 2020a: *Methane Tracker 2020*. International Energy Agency, Paris, France. https://www.iea.org/reports/methane-tracker-2020.

IEA, 2020b: *Energy efficiency*. International Energy Agency, Paris, France, 105 pp.

IEA, 2020c: *World Energy Outlook 2020*, International Energy Agency, Paris, France.

IEA, 2020d: *Coal Information Overview*. International Energy Agency, Paris, France. https://www.iea.org/reports/coal-information-overview.

IEA, 2020e: *Clean energy progress after the Covid-19 crisis will need reliable supplies of critical minerals* – Analysis, International Energy Agency, Paris, France. https://www.iea.org/articles/clean-energy-progress-after-the-covid-19-crisis-will-need-reliable-supplies-of-critical-minerals.

IEA, 2020f: *Global EV Outlook 2020*. International Energy Agency, Paris, France. 276 pp.

IEA, 2020g: *Hydropower Special Market Report – Analysis and forecast to 2030*. International Energy Agency, Paris, 126 pp.

IEA, 2020h: *Advanced Biofuels – Potential for Cost Reduction*. International Energy Agency, Paris, France, 88 pp.

IEA, 2020i: *Energy Technology Perspectives 2020*. International Energy Agency, Paris, France, 400 pp.

IEA, 2020j: *Projected Costs of Generating Electricity 2020*. Paris, France. https://www.iea.org/reports/projected-costs-of-generating-electricity-2020.

IEA, 2021a: *Global Energy Review 2021*. International Energy Agency, Paris, France, 36 pp.

IEA, 2021b: *Net-zero by 2050: A Roadmap for the Global Energy Sector*. International Energy Agency, Paris, France, 224 pp.

IEA, 2021c: *Global EV Outlook 2021*. International Energy Agency, Paris, France, 101 pp.

IEA, 2021d: *The Role of Critical Minerals in Clean Energy Transitions*. International Energy Agency, Paris, France, 287 pp.

IEA, 2021e: *Curtailing Methane Emissions from Fossil Fuel Operations*. International Energy Agency, Paris, France, 56 pp.

IEA, 2021f: *World Energy Investment 2021*. International Energy Agency, Paris, France, 64 pp.

IEA, IRENA, UNSD, and World Bank, 2020: *Tracking SDG 7: The Energy Progress Report (2020)*. The World Bank, Washington, DC, USA, 204 pp.

IEA WEO, 2019: *World Energy Outlook 2019*. OECD Publishing, Paris, France, 810 pp.

IHA, 2019: *Hydropower Sector Climate Resilience Guide*. IHA, London, UK, 75 pp.

IHA, 2021: *Pumped storage hydropower*. IHA, London, UK. https://www.hydropower.org/factsheets/pumped-storage.

Imelda, B., M. Fripp, and M.J. Roberts, 2018: *Variable Pricing and the Cost of Renewable Energy*.

Immerzeel, D. J., P.A. Verweij, F. van der Hilst, and A. P. C. Faaij, 2014: Biodiversity impacts of bioenergy crop production: a state-of-the-art review. *GCB Bioenergy*, **6(3)**, 183–209, doi:10.1111/gcbb.12067.

Ioannidis, R., and D. Koutsoyiannis, 2020: A review of land use, visibility and public perception of renewable energy in the context of landscape impact. *Appl. Energy*, **276**, 115367, doi:10.1016/j.apenergy.2020.115367.

Ioulia V. Ossokina, S.K. en T.A.A., 2020: Verduurzaming van de huurwoningen: rol van motivatie en communicatie. *Real Estate Research Quarterly*, **(1)**, 1–10.

IPCC, 2011: Summary for Policymakers. In: *Special Report on Renewable Energy Sources and Climate Change Mitigation* [Edenhofer, O., R. Pichs-Madruga, Y. Sokona, K. Seyboth, P. Matschoss, S. Kadner, T. Zwickel, P. Eickemeier, G. Hansen, S. Schlömer, C. von Stechow, (eds.)]. Cambridge University Press, Cambridge, UK, and New York, NY, USA, 12 pp.

IPCC, 2018: *Global Warming of 1.5°C: an IPCC special report on the impacts of global warming of 1.5°C above pre-industrial levels and related global greenhouse gas emission pathways, in the context of strengthening the global response to the threat of climate change.* [Masson-Delmotte, V., P. Zhai, H.-O. Pörtner, D. Roberts, J. Skea, P.R. Shukla, A. Pirani, W. Moufouma-Okia, C. Péan, R. Pidcock, S. Connors, J.B.R. Matthews, Y. Chen, X. Zhou, M.I. Gomis, E. Lonnoy, T. Maycock, M. Tignor, and T. Waterfield, (eds.)]. Cambridge University Press, Cambridge, UK and New York, NY, USA.

IPCC, 2019: *Refinement to the 2006 IPCC Guidelines for National Greenhouse Gas Inventories*, [Calvo Buendia, E., Tanabe, K., Kranjc, A., Baasansuren, J., Fukuda, M., Ngarize, S., Osako, A., Pyrozhenko, Y., Shermanau, P. and Federici, S. (eds)]. IPCC, Geneva, Switzerland.

IPCC, 2020: Climate Change and Land Ice. 1–15 pp.

IPSOS, 2010: *The Reputation of Energy Sources: American Public Opinion in a Global Context*. Ipsos Public Affairs, Toronto Canada, 7 pp. https://www.ipsos.com/sites/default/files/publication/2004-12/IpsosPA_POV_ReputationofEnergySources.pdf.

IRENA, 2015: *Hydropower Technology Brief*. IRENA, 19 pp.

IRENA, 2017a: *Geothermal Power*. International Renewable Energy Agency, Abu Dhabi, UAE, 28 pp.

IRENA, 2017b: *Electricity Storage and Renewables: Costs and Markets to 2030*. International Renewable Energy Agency, Abu Dhabi, UAE, 132 pp.

IRENA, 2017c: *Stranded assets and renewables: how the energy transition affects the value of energy reserves, buildings and capital stock*. International Renewable Energy Agency, Abu Dhabi. www.irena.org/remap.

IRENA, 2018: *Develop bankable renewable energy projects*. International Renewable Energy Agency, Abu Dhabi, UAE, 8 pp.

IRENA, 2019a: *Innovation landscape brief: Utility-scale batteries*. International Renewable Energy Agency, Abu Dhabi, UAE, 7 pp.

IRENA, 2019b: *Renewable Power Generation Costs in 2018*. International Renewable Energy Agency, Abu Dhabi, UAE, 88 pp.

IRENA, 2019c: *Future of wind: Deployment, investment, technology, grid integration and socio-economic aspects (A Global Energy Transformation paper)*. International Renewable Energy Agency, Abu Dhabi, UAE, 88 pp.

IRENA, 2019d: *Hydrogen: A Renewable Energy Perspective*. International Renewable Energy Agency, Abu Dhabi, UAE, 52 pp.

IRENA, 2020a: *Renewable Capacity Statistics 2020*. International Renewable Energy Agency, Abu Dhabi, UAE, 66 pp.

IRENA, 2020b: *Innovation Outlook – Ocean Energy Technologies*. International Renewable Energy Agency, Abu Dhabi, UAE, 112 pp.

IRENA, 2020c: *Green Hydrogen Cost Reduction: Scaling up Electrolysers to Meet the 1.5°C Climate Goal*. International Renewable Energy Agency, Abu Dhabi, UAE, 105 pp.

IRENA, 2021a: *Renewable Capacity Statistics 2021*. International Renewable Energy Agency, Abu Dhabi, UAE, 64 pp.

IRENA, 2021b: *Renewable Power Generation Costs in 2020*. International Renewable Energy Agency, Abu Dhabi, UAE, 180 pp.

Iribarren, D., M. Martín-Gamboa, J. Manzano, and J. Dufour, 2016: Assessing the social acceptance of hydrogen for transportation in Spain: An unintentional focus on target population for a potential hydrogen economy. *Int. J. Hydrogen Energy*, **41(10)**, 5203–5208, doi:10.1016/j.ijhydene.2016.01.139.

Ishaq, H. and I. Dincer, 2021: Comparative assessment of renewable energy-based hydrogen production methods. *Renew. Sustain. Energy Rev.*, **135**, 110192, doi:10.1016/j.rser.2020.110192.

Islam, M.T., N. Huda, A.B. Abdullah, and R. Saidur, 2018: A comprehensive review of state-of-the-art concentrating solar power (CSP) technologies: Current status and research trends. *Renew. Sustain. Energy Rev.*, **91**(April), 987–1018, doi:10.1016/j.rser.2018.04.097.

Ito, S., S. El Khatib, and M. Nakayama, 2016: Conflict over a hydropower plant project between Tajikistan and Uzbekistan. *Int. J. Water Resour. Dev.*, **32(5)**, 692–707, doi:10.1080/07900627.2015.1076381.

Iyer, G. et al., 2017: Measuring progress from nationally determined contributions to mid-century strategies. *Nat. Clim. Change*, **7(12)**, 871–874, doi:10.1038/s41558-017-0005-9.

Iyer, G. et al., 2021: The role of carbon dioxide removal in net-zero emissions pledges. *Energy Clim. Change*, **2**, 100043, doi:10.1016/J.EGYCC.2021.100043.

Iyer, G.C. et al., 2015: Improved representation of investment decisions in assessments of CO_2 mitigation. *Nat. Clim. Change*, **5(5)**, 436–440, doi:10.1038/nclimate2553.

Izquierdo, U. et al., 2012: Hydrogen production from methane and natural gas steam reforming in conventional and microreactor reaction systems. *Int. J. Hydrogen Energy*, **37(8)**, 7026–7033, doi:10.1016/j.ijhydene.2011.11.048.

Jackson, N.D. and T. Gunda, 2021: Evaluation of extreme weather impacts on utility-scale photovoltaic plant performance in the United States. *Appl. Energy*, **302**(June), 117508, doi:10.1016/j.apenergy.2021.117508.

Jacobson, M.Z. and M.A. Delucchi, 2011: Providing all global energy with wind, water, and solar power, Part I: Technologies, energy resources, quantities and areas of infrastructure, and materials. *Energy Policy*, **39**, 1154–1169, doi:10.1016/j.enpol.2010.11.040.

Jacobson, M.Z. and C.L. Archer, 2012: Saturation wind power potential and its implications for wind energy. *Proc. Natl. Acad. Sci.*, **109(39)**, 15679–15684, doi:10.1073/pnas.1208993109.

Jacobson, M.Z. et al., 2019: Impacts of Green New Deal Energy Plans on Grid Stability, Costs, Jobs, Health, and Climate in 143 Countries. *One Earth*, **1(4)**, 449–463, doi:10.1016/j.oneear.2019.12.003.

Jäger-Waldau, A., 2020: The Untapped Area Potential for Photovoltaic Power in the European Union. *Clean Technol. 2020*, **2(4)**, 440–446, doi:10.3390/CLEANTECHNOL2040027.

Jakob, M., C. Chen, S. Fuss, A. Marxen, and O. Edenhofer, 2015: Development incentives for fossil fuel subsidy reform. *Nat. Clim. Change*, **5(8)**, 709–712, doi:10.1038/nclimate2679.

Jakob, M. et al., 2020: The future of coal in a carbon-constrained climate. *Nat. Clim. Change*, **10(8)**, 704–707, doi:10.1038/s41558-020-0866-1.

Jakovcevic, A. and L. Steg, 2013: Sustainable transportation in Argentina: Values, beliefs, norms and car use reduction. *Transp. Res. Part F Traffic Psychol. Behav.*, **20**, 70–79, doi:10.1016/j.trf.2013.05.005.

Janek, J. and W.G. Zeier, 2016: A solid future for battery development. *Nat. Energy*, **1(9)**, 16141, doi:10.1038/nenergy.2016.141.

Jans, L., T. Bouman, and K. Fielding, 2018: A Part of the Energy 'In Crowd' Changing people's Energy Behavior via group based Approaches. *IEEE power energy Electr. power Prof.*, **16(1)**, 35–41.

Jarke-Neuert, J. and G. Perino, 2020: Energy efficiency promotion backfires under cap-and-trade. *Resour. Energy Econ.*, **62**, 101189, doi:10.1016/j.reseneeco.2020.101189.

Jaszczur, M., M.A. Rosen, T. Śliwa, M. Dudek, and L. Pieńkowski, 2016: Hydrogen production using high temperature nuclear reactors: Efficiency analysis of a combined cycle. *Int. J. Hydrogen Energy*, **41(19)**, 7861–7871, doi:10.1016/j.ijhydene.2015.11.190.

Jayadev, G., B.D. Leibowicz, and E. Kutanoglu, 2020: U.S. electricity infrastructure of the future: Generation and transmission pathways through 2050. *Appl. Energy*, **260**(November 2019), 114267, doi:10.1016/j.apenergy.2019.114267.

Jenkins, J. et al., 2018a: The benefits of nuclear flexibility in power system operations with renewable energy. *Appl. Energy*, **222**(April), 872–884, doi:10.1016/j.apenergy.2018.03.002.

Jenkins, J.D., M. Luke, and S. Thernstrom, 2018b: Getting to Zero Carbon Emissions in the Electric Power Sector. *Joule*, **2(12)**, 2498–2510, doi:10.1016/j.joule.2018.11.013.

Jensen, C.B. and J.J. Spoon, 2011: Testing the 'Party Matters' Thesis: Explaining Progress towards Kyoto Protocol Targets. *Polit. Stud.*, **59(1)**, 99–115, doi:10.1111/j.1467-9248.2010.00852.x.

Jentsch, M., T. Trost, and M. Sterner, 2014: Optimal Use of Power-to-Gas Energy Storage Systems in an 85% Renewable Energy Scenario. *Energy Procedia*, **46**, 254–261, doi:10.1016/j.egypro.2014.01.180.

Jerez, S. et al., 2015: The impact of climate change on photovoltaic power generation in Europe. *Nat. Commun.*, **6**, doi:10.1038/ncomms10014.

Jewell, J. et al., 2016: Comparison and interactions between the long-term pursuit of energy independence and climate policies. *Nat. Energy*, **1(6)**, 16073, doi:10.1038/nenergy.2016.73.

Jewell, J. et al., 2018: Limited emission reductions from fuel subsidy removal except in energy-exporting regions. *Nature*, **554(7691)**, 229–233, doi:10.1038/nature25467.

Jewell, J., V. Vinichenko, L. Nacke, and A. Cherp, 2019: Prospects for powering past coal. *Nat. Clim. Change*, **9(8)**, 592–597, doi:10.1038/s41558-019-0509-6.

Jiang, K. et al., 2018: Transition scenarios of power generation in China under global 2°C and 1.5°C targets. *Glob. Energy Interconnect.*, **1(4)**, 477–486, doi:10.14171/j.2096-5117.gei.2018.04.008.

Jiao, F. and B. Xu, 2018: Electrochemical Ammonia Synthesis and Ammonia Fuel Cells. *Adv. Mater.*, **31**, doi:10.1002/adma.201805173.

Jin, E. and J.W. Sutherland, 2018: An integrated sustainability model for a bioenergy system: Forest residues for electricity generation. *Biomass and Bioenergy*, **119**, 10–21, doi:10.1016/j.biombioe.2018.09.005.

Jin, Y., P. Behrens, A. Tukker, and L. Scherer, 2019: Water use of electricity technologies: A global meta-analysis. *Renew. Sustain. Energy Rev.*, **115**, 109391, doi:10.1016/j.rser.2019.109391.

Jobin, M. and M. Siegrist, 2018: We choose what we like – Affect as a driver of electricity portfolio choice. *Energy Policy*, **122**(August), 736–747, doi:10.1016/j.enpol.2018.08.027.

Jobin, M., V.H.M. Visschers, O.P.R. van Vliet, J. Árvai, and M. Siegrist, 2019: Affect or information? Examining drivers of public preferences of future energy portfolios in Switzerland. *Energy Res. Soc. Sci.*, **52**(December 2018), 20–29, doi:10.1016/j.erss.2019.01.016.

Johnson, D.L., and R.J. Erhardt, 2016: Projected impacts of climate change on wind energy density in the United States. *Renew. Energy*, **85**, 66–73, doi:10.1016/j.renene.2015.06.005.

Johnson, N. et al., 2015: Stranded on a low-carbon planet: Implications of climate policy for the phase-out of coal-based power plants. *Technol. Forecast. Soc. Change*, **90**(PA), 89–102, doi:10.1016/j.techfore.2014.02.028.

Johnstone, P. and S. Hielscher, 2017: Phasing out coal, sustaining coal communities? Living with technological decline in sustainability pathways. *Extr. Ind. Soc.*, **4(3)**, 457–461, doi:10.1016/j.exis.2017.06.002.

Jones, C.R., J.R. Eiser, and T.R. Gamble, 2012: Assessing the impact of framing on the comparative favourability of nuclear power as an electricity generating option in the UK. *Energy Policy*, **41**, 451–465, doi:10.1016/j.enpol.2011.11.006.

Jones, C.R., D. Kaklamanou, W.M. Stuttard, R.L. Radford, and J. Burley, 2015: Investigating public perceptions of carbon dioxide utilisation (CDU) technology: A mixed methods study. *Faraday Discuss.*, **183**, 327–347, doi:10.1039/c5fd00063g.

Jones, C.R., J. Gaede, S. Ganowski, and I.H. Rowlands, 2018: Understanding lay-public perceptions of energy storage technologies: Results of a questionnaire conducted in the UK. *Energy Procedia*, **151**, 135–143, doi:10.1016/j.egypro.2018.09.038.

Joshua, U. and A.A. Alola, 2020: Accounting for environmental sustainability from coal-led growth in South Africa: the role of employment and FDI. *Environ. Sci. Pollut. Res.*, **27(15)**, 17706–17716, doi:10.1007/s11356-020-08146-z.

6

Jouin, M. et al., 2016: Estimating the end-of-life of PEM fuel cells: Guidelines and metrics. *Appl. Energy*, **177**, 87–97, doi:10.1016/j.apenergy.2016.05.076.

Junginger, M., E. Hittinger, E. Williams, and R. Wiser, 2020a: Chapter 6 – Onshore wind energy. In: *Technological Learning in the Transition to a Low-Carbon Energy System* [Junginger, M., E. Hittinger, and E. Williams, (eds.)]. Academic Press, MA, USA pp. 87–102.

Junginger, M. et al., 2020b: Chapter 7 – Offshore wind energy. In: *Technological Learning in the Transition to a Low-Carbon Energy System* [Junginger, M., E. Hittinger, and E. Williams, (eds.)]. Academic Press, MA, USA pp. 103–117.

Kabir, E., P. Kumar, S. Kumar, A.A. Adelodun, and K.-H. Kim, 2018: Solar energy: Potential and future prospects. *Renew. Sustain. Energy Rev.*, **82**, 894–900, doi:10.1016/j.rser.2017.09.094.

Kaldellis, J.K. and D. Apostolou, 2017: Life cycle energy and carbon footprint of offshore wind energy. Comparison with onshore counterpart. *Renew. Energy*, **108**, 72–84, doi:10.1016/j.renene.2017.02.039.

Kaldellis, J.K., M. Kapsali, E. Kaldelli, and E. Katsanou, 2013: Comparing recent views of public attitude on wind energy, photovoltaic and small hydro applications. *Renew. Energy*, **52(2013)**, 197–208, doi:10.1016/j.renene.2012.10.045.

Kalkuhl, M. et al., 2019: Successful coal phase-out requires new models of development. *Nat. Energy*, **4(11)**, 897–900, doi:10.1038/s41560-019-0500-5.

Kallbekken, S., H. Sælen, and E.A.T. Hermansen, 2013: Bridging the Energy Efficiency Gap: A Field Experiment on Lifetime Energy Costs and Household Appliances. *J. Consum. Policy*, **36(1)**, 1–16, doi:10.1007/s10603-012-9211-z.

Kallitsis, E., A. Korre, G. Kelsall, M. Kupfersberger, and Z. Nie, 2020: Environmental life cycle assessment of the production in China of lithium-ion batteries with nickel-cobalt-manganese cathodes utilising novel electrode chemistries. *J Clean. Prod.*, **254**, 120067, doi:10.1016/j.jclepro.2020.120067.

Kang, J.-N. et al., 2020: The Prospects of Carbon Capture and Storage in China's Power Sector under the 2°C Target: A Component-based Learning Curve Approach. *Int. J. Greenh. Gas Control*, **101**, 103149, https://doi.org/10.1016/j.ijggc.2020.103149.

Kang, M., D.L. Mauzerall, D.Z. Ma, and M.A. Celia, 2019: Reducing methane emissions from abandoned oil and gas wells: Strategies and costs. *Energy Policy*, 132 (2019), pp. 594–601, doi:10.1016/j.enpol.2019.05.045.

Kanger, L., F.W. Geels, B. Sovacool, and J. Schot, 2019: Technological diffusion as a process of societal embedding: Lessons from historical automobile transitions for future electric mobility. *Transp. Res. Part D Transp. Environ.*, **71**, 47–66, doi:10.1016/j.trd.2018.11.012.

Kar, A., S. Pachauri, R. Bailis, and H. Zerriffi, 2019: Using sales data to assess cooking gas adoption and the impact of India's Ujjwala programme in rural Karnataka. *Nat. Energy*, **4(9)**, 806–814, doi:10.1038/s41560-019-0429-8.

Kardooni, R., S.B. Yusoff, and F.B. Kari, 2016: Renewable energy technology acceptance in Peninsular Malaysia. *Energy Policy*, **88(2016)**, 1–10, doi:10.1016/j.enpol.2015.10.005.

Karlin, B., J.F. Zinger, and R. Ford, 2015: The effects of feedback on energy conservation: A meta-analysis. *Psychol. Bull.*, **141(6)**, 1205–1227, doi:10.1037/a0039650.

Karlstrøm, H., and M. Ryghaug, 2014: Public attitudes towards renewable energy technologies in Norway. The role of party preferences. *Energy Policy*, **67**, 656–663, doi:10.1016/j.enpol.2013.11.049.

Karnauskas, K.B., J.K. Lundquist, and L. Zhang, 2018: Southward shift of the global wind energy resource under high carbon dioxide emissions. *Nat. Geosci.*, **11(1)**, 38–43, doi:10.1038/s41561-017-0029-9.

Karytsas, S., O. Polyzou, and C. Karytsas, 2019: Social Aspects of Geothermal Energy in Greece. In: *Lecture Notes in Energy* [Manzella, A., A. Allansdottir, and A. Pellizzone, (eds.)]. Springer, Cham, Switzerland, pp. 123–144.

Kasaeian, A.B., S. Molana, K. Rahmani, and D. Wen, 2017: A review on solar chimney systems. *Renew. Sustain. Energy Rev.*, **67**, 954–987, doi:10.1016/j.rser.2016.09.081.

Kastner, I. and P.C. Stern, 2015: Examining the decision-making processes behind household energy investments: A review. *Energy Res. Soc. Sci.*, **10**, 72–89, doi:10.1016/j.erss.2015.07.008.

Kastner, I. and E. Matthies, 2016: Investments in renewable energies by German households: A matter of economics, social influences and ecological concern? *Energy Res. Soc. Sci.*, **17**, 1–9, doi:10.1016/j.erss.2016.03.006.

Kätelhön, A., R. Meys, S. Deutz, S. Suh, and A. Bardow, 2019: Climate change mitigation potential of carbon capture and utilization in the chemical industry. *Proc. Natl. Acad. Sci.*, **116(23)**, 11187–11194, doi:10.1073/pnas.1821029116.

Katz, C., 2020: In *Boost for Renewables, Grid-Scale Battery Storage Is on the Rise*. https://e360.yale.edu/features/in-boost-for-renewables-grid-scale-battery-storage-is-on-the-rise.

Kavvadias, K.C. and I. Khamis, 2014: Sensitivity analysis and probabilistic assessment of seawater desalination costs fueled by nuclear and fossil fuel. *Energy Policy*, **74**, S24–S30, doi:10.1016/j.enpol.2014.01.033.

Kayfeci, M., A. Keçebaş, and M. Bayat, 2019: Hydrogen Production. In: *Solar hydrogen production: processes, systems and technologies* [Calise, F., M.D. D'Accadia, M. Santarelli, A. Lanzini, and D. Ferrero, (eds.)]. Academic Press, MA, USA, pp. 45–83.

Kazhamiaka, F., P. Jochem, S. Keshav, and C. Rosenberg, 2017: On the influence of jurisdiction on the profitability of residential photovoltaic-storage systems: A multi-national case study. *Energy Policy*, **109**, 428–440, doi:10.1016/j.enpol.2017.07.019.

Kearns, D.T., 2019: *Waste-to-Energy with CCS: A pathway to carbon-negative power generation*. Global CCS Institute, Washington DC, USA, 11 pp.

Keith, D.W., G. Holmes, D. St. Angelo, and K. Heidel, 2018: A Process for Capturing CO_2 from the Atmosphere. *Joule*, **2(10)**, 1573–1594, doi:10.1016/j.joule.2018.09.017.

Keles, D. and H. Ü. Yilmaz, 2020: Decarbonisation through coal phase-out in Germany and Europe — Impact on Emissions, electricity prices and power production. *Energy Policy*, **141**, 111472, doi:10.1016/j.enpol.2020.111472.

Kelzenberg, M.D. et al., 2018: Design and Prototyping Efforts for the Space Solar Power Initiative, 2017 IEEE 44th Photovoltaic Specialist Conference (PVSC). IEEE, Piscataway, NJ, USA, pp. 558–561.

Khalili, S., E. Rantanen, D. Bogdanov, and C. Breyer, 2019: Global Transportation Demand Development with Impacts on the Energy Demand and Greenhouse Gas Emissions in a Climate-Constrained World. *Energies*, **12(20)**, 3870, doi:10.3390/en12203870.

Khan, M.R. and I. Alam, 2020: A Solar PV-Based Inverter-Less Grid-Integrated Cooking Solution for Low-Cost Clean Cooking. *Energies*, **13(20)**, 5507, doi:10.3390/en13205507.

Khandker, S.R., H.A. Samad, R. Ali, and D.F. Barnes, 2014: Who Benefits Most from Rural Electrification? Evidence in India. *Energy J.*, **35(2)**, doi:10.5547/01956574.35.2.4.

Khanna, T.M. et al., 2021: A multi-country meta-analysis on the role of behavioural change in reducing energy consumption and CO_2 emissions in residential buildings. *Nat. Energy*, **6(9)**, 925–932, doi:10.1038/s41560-021-00866-x.

Kholod, N. et al., 2020: Global methane emissions from coal mining to continue growing even with declining coal production. *J. Clean. Prod.*, **256**, 120489, doi:10.1016/j.jclepro.2020.120489.

Killingtveit, Å., 2020: Hydroelectric Power. In: *Future Energy* [Letcher, T.M.B.T.-F.E. (Third E., (ed.)], Elsevier, New York, NY, USA, pp. 315–330.

Kim, S. and W. Shin, 2017: Understanding American and Korean Students' Support for Pro-environmental Tax Policy: The Application of the Value–Belief–Norm Theory of Environmentalism. *Environ. Commun.*, **11(3)**, 311–331, doi:10.1080/17524032.2015.1088458.

Kimemia, D. and H. Annegarn, 2016: Domestic LPG interventions in South Africa: Challenges and lessons. *Energy Policy*, **93**, 150–156, doi:10.1016/j.enpol.2016.03.005.

Kitzing, L., C. Mitchell, and P.E. Morthorst, 2012: Renewable energy policies in Europe: Converging or diverging? *Energy Policy*, **51**, 192–201, doi:10.1016/j.enpol.2012.08.064.

Kitzing, L., O. Fitch-Roy, M. Islam, and C. Mitchell, 2020: An evolving risk perspective for policy instrument choice in sustainability transitions. *Environ. Innov. Soc. Transitions*, **35**, 369–382, doi:10.1016/j.eist.2018.12.002.

Klapperich, R.J. et al., 2014: The Nexus of Water and CCS: A Regional Carbon Sequestration Partnership Perspective. *Energy Procedia*, **63**, 7162–7172, doi:10.1016/j.egypro.2014.11.752.

Kleidon, A. and L. Miller, 2020: The Kinetic Energy Budget of the Atmosphere (KEBA) model 1.0: A simple yet physical approach for estimating regional wind energy resource potentials that includes the kinetic energy removal effect by wind turbines. *Geosci. Model Dev. Discuss.*, **2019**, 1–20, doi:10.5194/gmd-2020-77.

Kobayashi, H., A. Hayakawa, K.D.K.A. Somarathne, and E.C. Okafor, 2019: Science and technology of ammonia combustion. *Proc. Combust. Inst.*, **37(1)**, 109–133, doi:10.1016/j.proci.2018.09.029.

Koch, H., S. Vögele, F. Hattermann, and S. Huang, 2014: Hydro-climatic conditions and thermoelectric electricity generation – Part II: Model application to 17 nuclear power plants in Germany. *Energy*, **69**, 700–707, doi:10.1016/j.energy.2014.03.071.

Koelbl, B.S., M.A. van den Broek, B.J. van Ruijven, A.P.C. Faaij, and D.P. van Vuuren, 2014: Uncertainty in the deployment of Carbon Capture and Storage (CCS): A sensitivity analysis to techno-economic parameter uncertainty. *Int. J. Greenh. Gas Control*, **27**, 81–102, doi:10.1016/j.ijggc.2014.04.024.

Kommalapati, R., A. Kadiyala, M. Shahriar, and Z. Huque, 2017: Review of the Life Cycle Greenhouse Gas Emissions from Different Photovoltaic and Concentrating Solar Power Electricity Generation Systems. *Energies*, **10(3)**, 350, doi:10.3390/en10030350.

Kondash, A.J., N.E. Lauer, and A. Vengosh, 2018: The intensification of the water footprint of hydraulic fracturing. *Sci. Adv.*, **4(8)**, doi:10.1126/sciadv.aar5982.

Kondash, A.J., D. Patino-Echeverri, and A. Vengosh, 2019: Quantification of the water-use reduction associated with the transition from coal to natural gas in the US electricity sector. *Environ. Res. Lett.*, **14(12)**, 124028, doi:10.1088/1748-9326/ab4d71.

Kondziella, H. and T. Bruckner, 2016: Flexibility requirements of renewable energy based electricity systems – A review of research results and methodologies. *Renew. Sustain. Energy Rev.*, **53**, 10–22, doi:10.1016/j.rser.2015.07.199.

Konstantelos, I. et al., 2017: Integrated North Sea grids: The costs, the benefits and their distribution between countries. *Energy Policy*, **101**, 28–41, doi:10.1016/j.enpol.2016.11.024.

Korcaj, L., U.J.J. Hahnel, and H. Spada, 2015: Intentions to adopt photovoltaic systems depend on homeowners' expected personal gains and behavior of peers. *Renew. Energy*, **75**, 407–415, doi:10.1016/j.renene.2014.10.007.

Kotilainen, K. et al., 2019: From path dependence to policy mixes for Nordic electric mobility: Lessons for accelerating future transport transitions. *Policy Sci.*, **52(4)**, 573–600, doi:10.1007/s11077-019-09361-3.

Kougias, I. et al., 2019: Analysis of emerging technologies in the hydropower sector. *Renew. Sustain. Energy Rev.*, **113**, 109257, doi:10.1016/j.rser.2019.109257.

Kraemer, S., 2018: Missing link for solar hydrogen is… ammonia? *SolarPACES*, https://www.solarpaces.org/missing-link-solar-hydrogen-ammonia/.

Kramer, I.J. et al., 2015: Efficient Spray-Coated Colloidal Quantum Dot Solar Cells. *Adv. Mater.*, **27(1)**, 116–121, doi:10.1002/adma.201403281.

Kreuz, S. and F. Müsgens, 2017: The German Energiewende and its roll-out of renewable energies: An economic perspective. *Front. Energy*, **11(2)**, 126–134, doi:10.1007/s11708-017-0467-5.

Krey, V. et al., 2019: Looking under the hood: A comparison of techno-economic assumptions across national and global integrated assessment models. *Energy*, **172**, 1254–1267, doi:10.1016/j.energy.2018.12.131.

Kriegler, E., K. Riahi, N. Bauer, V.J. Schwanitz, and M. Schaeffer, 2013: Making or breaking climate targets: The AMPERE study on staged accession scenarios for climate policy. *Technol. Forecast. Soc. Change*, **90**, 24–44.

Kriegler, E. et al., 2014a: The role of technology for achieving climate policy objectives: Overview of the EMF 27 study on global technology and climate policy strategies. *Clim. Change*, **123(3–4)**, 353–367, doi:10.1007/s10584-013-0953-7.

Kriegler, E. et al., 2014b: A new scenario framework for climate change research: The concept of shared climate policy assumptions. *Clim. Change*, **122(3)**, 401–414, doi:10.1007/s10584-013-0971-5.

Kriegler, E. et al., 2017: Fossil-fueled development (SSP5): An energy and resource intensive scenario for the 21st century. *Glob. Environ. Change*, **42**, 297–315, doi:10.1016/j.gloenvcha.2016.05.015.

Kriegler, E. et al., 2018: Short term policies to keep the door open for Paris climate goals. *Environ. Res. Lett.*, **13(7)**, 074022, doi:10.1088/1748-9326/aac4f1.

Kroposki, B. et al., 2012: *Energy systems integration: a convergence of ideas*. National Renewable Energy Lab, Golden, CO, USA, 9 pp.

Kube, R., A. Löschel, H. Mertens, and T. Requate, 2018: Research trends in environmental and resource economics: Insights from four decades of JEEM. *J. Environ. Econ. Manage.*, **92**, 433–464, doi:10.1016/J.JEEM.2018.08.001.

Kuckshinrichs, W., T. Ketelaer, and J.C. Koj, 2017: Economic Analysis of Improved Alkaline Water Electrolysis. *Front. Energy Res.*, **5**, doi:10.3389/fenrg.2017.00001.

Kuik, O., F. Branger, and P. Quirion, 2019: Competitive advantage in the renewable energy industry: Evidence from a gravity model. *Renew. Energy*, **131**, 472–481, doi:10.1016/j.renene.2018.07.046.

Kumar, D., V. Mishra, and A.R. Ganguly, 2015: Evaluating wind extremes in CMIP5 climate models. *Clim. Dyn.*, **45(1)**, 441–453, doi:10.1007/s00382-014-2306-2.

Kumar, S. and G. Rauniyar, 2018: The impact of rural electrification on income and education: Evidence from Bhutan. *Rev. Dev. Econ.*, **22(3)**, 1146–1165, doi:10.1111/rode.12378.

Kumar, S., S. Managi, and R.K. Jain, 2020: CO_2 mitigation policy for Indian thermal power sector: Potential gains from emission trading. *Energy Econ.*, **86**, 104653, doi:10.1016/j.eneco.2019.104653.

Kungl, G., 2015: Stewards or sticklers for change? Incumbent energy providers and the politics of the German energy transition. *Energy Res. Soc. Sci.*, **8**, 13–23, doi:10.1016/j.erss.2015.04.009.

Kunreuther, H. and E. U. Weber, 2014: Aiding Decision Making to Reduce the Impacts of Climate Change. *J. Consum. Policy*, **37(3)**, 397–411, doi:10.1007/s10603-013-9251-z.

Kurosaki, 2018: Introduction of Liquid Organic Hydrogen Carrier and the Global Hydrogen Supply Chain Project. September. Chiyoda Corporation, Japan, 22 pp.

Kurtz, J.M., S. Sprik, G. Saur, and S. Onorato, 2019: *Fuel cell electric vehicle durability and fuel cell performance*. National Renewable Energy Laboratory, Golden, CO, USA, 20 pp.

Kuzemko, C., C. Mitchell, M. Lockwood, and R. Hoggett, 2017: Policies, politics and demand side innovations: The untold story of Germany's energy transition. *Energy Res. Soc. Sci.*, **28**, 58–67, doi:10.1016/j.erss.2017.03.013.

Kyle, P., C. Müller, K. Calvin, and A. Thomson, 2014: Meeting the radiative forcing targets of the representative concentration pathways in a world with agricultural climate impacts. *Earth's Future*, **2(2)**, 83–98, doi:10.1002/2013ef000199.

L'Orange Seigo, S., S. Dohle, and M. Siegrist, 2014: Public perception of carbon capture and storage (CCS): A review. *Renew. Sustain. Energy Rev.*, **38**, 848–863, doi:10.1016/j.rser.2014.07.017.

La Viña, A.G., J.M. Tan, T.I.M. Guanzon, M.J. Caleda, and L. Ang, 2018: Navigating a trilemma: Energy security, equity, and sustainability in the Philippines' low-carbon transition. *Energy Res. Soc. Sci.*, **35**(October), 37–47, doi:10.1016/j.erss.2017.10.039.

6

Lacasse, K., 2015: The Importance of Being Green: The Influence of Green Behaviors on Americans' Political Attitudes Toward Climate Change. *Environ. Behav.*, **47(7)**, 754–781, doi:10.1177/0013916513520491.

Lacasse, K., 2016: Don't be satisfied, identify! Strengthening positive spillover by connecting pro-environmental behaviors to an 'environmentalist' label. *J. Environ. Psychol.*, **48**, 149–158, doi:10.1016/j.jenvp.2016.09.006.

Lacombe, G. et al., 2014: Are hydropower and irrigation development complements or substitutes? The example of the Nam Ngum River in the Mekong Basin. *Water Int.*, **39**, doi:10.1080/02508060.2014.956205.

Lade, S.J. et al., 2020: Human impacts on planetary boundaries amplified by Earth system interactions. *Nat. Sustain.*, **3(2)**, 119–128, doi:10.1038/s41893-019-0454-4.

Lamas, M.I. and C.G. Rodriguez, 2019: NOx Reduction in Diesel-Hydrogen Engines Using Different Strategies of Ammonia Injection. *Energies*, **12(7)**, 1255, doi:10.3390/en12071255.

Lamb, W.F. et al., 2021: A review of trends and drivers of greenhouse gas emissions by sector from 1990 to 2018. *Environ. Res. Lett.*, **16(7)**, 073005.

Lamers, P., E. Searcy, J.R. Hess, and H. Stichnothe, 2016: *Developing the global bioeconomy: technical, market, and environmental lessons from bioenergy*. Academic Press, MA, USA, 197 pp.

Lan, R., and S. Tao, 2014: Ammonia as a Suitable Fuel for Fuel Cells. *Front. Energy Res.*, **2**, 35, doi:10.3389/fenrg.2014.00035.

Lan, R., J.T.S. Irvine, and S. Tao, 2012: Ammonia and related chemicals as potential indirect hydrogen storage materials. *Int. J. Hydrogen Energy*, **37(2)**, 1482–1494, doi:10.1016/j.ijhydene.2011.10.004.

Latunussa, C.E.L., F. Ardente, G.A. Blengini, and L. Mancini, 2016: Life Cycle Assessment of an innovative recycling process for crystalline silicon photovoltaic panels. *Sol. Energy Mater. Sol. Cells*, **156**, 101–111, doi:10.1016/j.solmat.2016.03.020.

Lauren, N., K.S. Fielding, L. Smith, and W.R. Louis, 2016: You did, so you can and you will: Self-efficacy as a mediator of spillover from easy to more difficult pro-environmental behaviour. *J. Environ. Psychol.*, **48**, 191–199, doi:10.1016/j.jenvp.2016.10.004.

Laurens, L., 2017: *State of Technology Review – Algae Bioenergy, Bioenergy*. IEA Bioenergy, Paris, France, 158 pp.

Laurent, A., N. Espinosa, and M.Z. Hauschild, 2018: LCA of Energy Systems. In: *Life Cycle Assessment: Theory and Practice* [Hauschild, M.Z., R.K. Rosenbaum, and S.I. Olsen, (eds.)]. Springer International Publishing, Cham, Switzerland, pp. 633–668.

Lazard, 2021: *Levelized Costs of Energy Analysis, Version 15.0*. https://www.lazard.com/media/451881/lazards-levelized-cost-of-energy-version-150-vf.pdf.

Lazarus, M., and H. van Asselt, 2018: Fossil fuel supply and climate policy: exploring the road less taken. *Clim. Change*, **150(1–2)**, doi:10.1007/s10584-018-2266-3.

Leaton, J., 2011: *Unburnable Carbon: Are the World's Financial Markets Carrying a Carbon Bubble?* Carbon Tracker, 36 pp. https://www.lazard.com/perspective/levelized-cost-of-energy-levelized-cost-of-storage-and-levelized-cost-of-hydrogen/.

Leaton, J., N. Ranger, B. Ward, L. Sussams, and M. Brown, 2013: *Unburnable Carbon 2013: Wasted capital and stranded assets*. Carbon Tracker & The Grantham Research Institute, LSE, London, UK, 40 pp.

Lebel, L., A. Haefner, C. Pahl-Wostl, and A. Baduri, 2020: Governance of the water-energy-food nexus: insights from four infrastructure projects in the Lower Mekong Basin. *Sustain. Sci.*, **15**, 885–900, doi:10.1007/s11625-019-00779-5.

Lee, J.C.Y., and J.K. Lundquist, 2017: Observing and Simulating Wind-Turbine Wakes During the Evening Transition. *Boundary-Layer Meteorol.*, **164(3)**, 449–474, doi:10.1007/s10546-017-0257-y.

Lee, N. et al., 2020: Hybrid floating solar photovoltaics-hydropower systems: Benefits and global assessment of technical potential. *Renew. Energy*, **162**, 1415–1427, doi:10.1016/j.renene.2020.08.080.

Lee, R.A., and J.-M. Lavoie, 2013: From first- to third-generation biofuels: Challenges of producing a commodity from a biomass of increasing complexity. *Anim. Front.*, **3(2)**, 6–11, doi:10.2527/af.2013-0010.

Lee, Y., U. Lee, and K. Kim, 2021: A comparative techno-economic and quantitative risk analysis of hydrogen delivery infrastructure options. *Int. J. Hydrogen Energy*, **46(27)**, 14857–14870, doi:10.1016/j.ijhydene.2021.01.160.

Leer Jørgensen, M., H.T. Anker, and J. Lassen, 2020: Distributive fairness and local acceptance of wind turbines: The role of compensation schemes. *Energy Policy*, **138**(January), 111294, doi:10.1016/j.enpol.2020.111294.

Lehtveer, M., S. Brynolf, and M. Grahn, 2019: What Future for Electrofuels in Transport? Analysis of Cost Competitiveness in Global Climate Mitigation. *Environ. Sci. Technol.*, **53(3)**, 1690–1697, doi:10.1021/acs.est.8b05243.

Leijten, F.R.M. et al., 2014: Factors that influence consumers' acceptance of future energy systems: the effects of adjustment type, production level, and price. *Energy Effic.*, **7(6)**, 973–985, doi:10.1007/s12053-014-9271-9.

Lerer, L.B., and T. Scudder, 1999: Health impacts of large dams. *Environ. Impact Assess. Rev.*, **19(2)**, 113–123, doi:10.1016/S0195-9255(98)00041-9.

Lesser, J.A., 2019: *Is There A Future For Nuclear Power In The United States?* The Manhattan Institute. Continental Economics, USA, 36 pp.

Levesque, A. et al., 2018: How much energy will buildings consume in 2100? A global perspective within a scenario framework. *Energy*, **148**, 514–527, doi:10.1016/j.energy.2018.01.139.

Levin, K., D. Rich, K. Ross, T. Fransen, and C. Elliott, 2020: *Designing and Communicating Net-Zero Targets*. 30 pp. https://www.wri.org/research/designing-and-communicating-net-zero-targets?utm_source=twitter&utm_medium=promoted&utm_campaign=socialmedia&utm_term=video.

Lewis, J. and E. Severnini, 2020: Short- and long-run impacts of rural electrification: Evidence from the historical rollout of the U.S. power grid. *J. Dev. Econ.*, **143**(November 2019), 102412, doi:10.1016/j.jdeveco.2019.102412.

Lewis, N.S., 2007: Toward Cost-Effective Solar Energy Use. *Science*, **315(5813)**, 798–801, doi:10.1126/science.1137014.

Li, G. et al., 2017: Optimal dispatch strategy for integrated energy systems with CCHP and wind power. *Appl. Energy*, **192**, 408–419, doi:10.1016/j.apenergy.2016.08.139.

Li, G. et al., 2020a: Building integrated solar concentrating systems: A review. *Appl. Energy*, **260**, 114288, doi:10.1016/j.apenergy.2019.114288.

Li, J. et al., 2020b: Critical Rare-Earth Elements Mismatch Global Wind-Power Ambitions. *One Earth*, **3(1)**, 116–125, doi:10.1016/j.oneear.2020.06.009.

Li, J. et al., 2020c: Incorporating Health Cobenefits in Decision-Making for the Decommissioning of Coal-Fired Power Plants in China. *Environ. Sci. Technol.*, **54(21)**, 13935–13943, doi:10.1021/acs.est.0c03310.

Li, M. et al., 2019: Comprehensive Life Cycle Evaluation of Jet Fuel from Biomass Gasification and Fischer–Tropsch Synthesis Based on Environmental and Economic Performances. *Ind. Eng. Chem. Res.*, **58(41)**, 19179–19188, doi:10.1021/acs.iecr.9b03468.

Li, Y., M. Han, Z. Yang, and G. Li, 2021a: Coordinating Flexible Demand Response and Renewable Uncertainties for Scheduling of Community Integrated Energy Systems With an Electric Vehicle Charging Station: A Bi-Level Approach. *IEEE Trans. Sustain. Energy*, **12(4)**, 2321–2331, doi:10.1109/TSTE.2021.3090463.

Li, Y. et al., 2021b: Conception and policy implications of photovoltaic modules end-of-life management in China. *WIREs Energy Environ.*, **10(1)**, doi:10.1002/wene.387.

Li, Z., W. Wu, M. Shahidehpour, J. Wang, and B. Zhang, 2016: Combined heat and power dispatch considering pipeline energy storage of district heating network. *IEEE Trans. Sustain. Energy*, **7(1)**, 12–22, doi:10.1109/TSTE.2015.2467383.

Liebe, U. and G.M. Dobers, 2019: Decomposing public support for energy policy: What drives acceptance of and intentions to protest against renewable energy expansion in Germany? *Energy Res. Soc. Sci.*, **47**(August 2018), 247–260, doi:10.1016/j.erss.2018.09.004.

Liebe, U., J. Gewinner, and A. Diekmann, 2018: What is missing in research on non-monetary incentives in the household energy sector? *Energy Policy*, **123**(May), 180–183, doi:10.1016/j.enpol.2018.08.036.

Liebe, U., J. Gewinner, and A. Diekmann, 2021: Large and persistent effects of green energy defaults in the household and business sectors. *Nat. Hum. Behav.*, **5(5)**, 576–585, doi:10.1038/s41562-021-01070-3.

Lienert, P., B. Suetterlin, and M. Siegrist, 2015: Public acceptance of the expansion and modification of high-voltage power lines in the context of the energy transition. *Energy Policy*, **87**(November 2017), 573–583, doi:10.1016/j.enpol.2015.09.023.

Lilliestam, J., L. Ollier, M. Labordena, S. Pfenninger, and R. Thonig, 2021: The near- to mid-term outlook for concentrating solar power: mostly cloudy, chance of sun. *Energy Sources, Part B Econ. Planning, Policy*, **16(1)**, 23–41, doi:10.1080/15567249.2020.1773580.

Limberger, J. et al., 2018: Geothermal energy in deep aquifers: A global assessment of the resource base for direct heat utilization. *Renew. Sustain. Energy Rev.*, **82**, Part 1, 961–975, doi:10.1016/j.rser.2017.09.084.

Lin, B. and H. Abudu, 2020: Can energy conservation and substitution mitigate CO_2 emissions in electricity generation? Evidence from Middle East and North Africa. *J. Environ. Manage.*, **275**, 111222, doi:10.1016/j.jenvman.2020.111222.

Lin, C., W. Wu, B. Zhang, and Y. Sun, 2017: Decentralized Solution for Combined Heat and Power Dispatch Through Benders Decomposition. *IEEE Trans. Sustain. Energy*, **8(4)**, 1361–1372, doi:10.1109/TSTE.2017.2681108.

Lindberg, O., J. Arnqvist, J. Munkhammar, and D. Lingfors, 2021: Review on power-production modeling of hybrid wind and PV power parks. *J. Renew. Sustain. Energy*, **13(4)**, 42702, doi:10.1063/5.0056201.

Littlecott, C. et al., 2021: *No new coal by 2021: the collapse of the global coal pipeline*. E3G, 60 pp. https://9tj4025ol53byww26jdkao0x-wpengine. netdna-ssl.com/wp-content/uploads/No-New-Coal-by-2021-the-collapse-of-the-global-pipeline.pdf.

Liu, L., T. Bouman, G. Perlaviciute, and L. Steg, 2019a: Effects of trust and public participation on acceptability of renewable energy projects in the Netherlands and China. *Energy Res. Soc. Sci.*, **53**, 137–144, doi:10.1016/j.erss.2019.03.006.

Liu, L., M. Hejazi, G. Iyer, and B.A. Forman, 2019b: Implications of water constraints on electricity capacity expansion in the United States. *Nat. Sustain.*, **2(3)**, 206–213, doi:10.1038/s41893-019-0235-0.

Liu, P. and C. Y. Barlow, 2017: Wind turbine blade waste in 2050. *Waste Manag.*, **62**, 229–240, doi:10.1016/j.wasman.2017.02.007.

Liu, Z., 2015: *Global energy interconnection*. Academic Press, MA, USA, 396 pp.

Lizin, S. et al., 2013: Life cycle analyses of organic photovoltaics: a review. *Energy Environ. Sci.*, **6(11)**, 3136, doi:10.1039/c3ee42653j.

Lockwood, M., 2015: Fossil Fuel Subsidy Reform, Rent Management and Political Fragmentation in Developing Countries. *New Polit. Econ.*, **20(4)**, 475–494, doi:10.1080/13563467.2014.923826.

Lohrmann, A., J. Farfan, U. Caldera, C. Lohrmann, and C. Breyer, 2019: Global scenarios for significant water use reduction in thermal power plants based on cooling water demand estimation using satellite imagery. *Nat. Energy*, **4(12)**, 1040–1048, doi:10.1038/s41560-019-0501-4.

Lokhorst, A.M., C. Werner, H. Staats, E. van Dijk, and J.L. Gale, 2013: Commitment and Behavior Change: A Meta-Analysis and Critical Review of Commitment-Making Strategies in Environmental Research. *Environ. Behav.*, **45(1)**, 3–34, doi:10.1177/0013916511411477.

López-González, A., B. Domenech, and L. Ferrer-Martí, 2020: The gendered politics of rural electrification: Education, indigenous communities, and impacts for the Venezuelan Guajira. *Energy Res. Soc. Sci.*, **70**, 101776, doi:10.1016/j.erss.2020.101776.

López Prol, J., and W.-P. Schill, 2021: The Economics of Variable Renewable Energy and Electricity Storage. *Annu. Rev. Resour. Econ.*, **13(1)**, 443–467, doi:10.1146/annurev-resource-101620-081246.

Losada Carreño, I. et al., 2018: Potential impacts of climate change on wind and solar electricity generation in Texas. *Renew. Energy*, 2020, 163(2): 745–766.

Löschel, A., B.J. Lutz, and S. Managi, 2019: The impacts of the EU ETS on efficiency and economic performance – An empirical analyses for German manufacturing firms. *Resour. Energy Econ.*, **56**, 71–95, doi:10.1016/j.reseneeco.2018.03.001.

Louwen, A., W.G.J.H.M. van Sark, A.P.C. Faaij, and R.E.I. Schropp, 2016: Re-assessment of net energy production and greenhouse gas emissions avoidance after 40 years of photovoltaics development. *Nat. Commun. 2016 71*, **7(1)**, 1–9, doi:10.1038/ncomms13728.

Lovins, A.B., 2018: How big is the energy efficiency resource? *Environ. Res. Lett.*, **13(9)**, 090401, doi:10.1088/1748-9326/aad965.

Lu, S., W. Dai, Y. Tang, and M. Guo, 2020: A review of the impact of hydropower reservoirs on global climate change. *Sci. Total Environ.*, **711**, 134996, doi:10.1016/j.scitotenv.2019.134996.

Lu, X. et al., 2019: Gasification of coal and biomass as a net carbon-negative power source for environment-friendly electricity generation in China. *Proc. Natl. Acad. Sci.*, **116(17)**, 8206–8213, doi:10.1073/pnas.1812239116.

Lucas, A., 2016: Stranded assets, externalities and carbon risk in the Australian coal industry: The case for contraction in a carbon-constrained world. *Energy Res. Soc. Sci.*, **11**, 53–66, doi:10.1016/j.erss.2015.08.005.

Luckow, P., T. Vitolo, J.2015: *A Solved Problem: Existing Measures Provide Low-Cost Wind and Solar Integration*. Synapse Energy Economics, MA, USA, 19 pp.

Luderer, G. et al., 2017: Assessment of wind and solar power in global low-carbon energy scenarios: An introduction. *Energy Econ.*, **64**, 542–551, doi:10.1016/j.eneco.2017.03.027.

Luderer, G. et al., 2018: Residual fossil CO_2 emissions in 1.5–2°C pathways. *Nat. Clim. Change*, **8(7)**, 626–633, doi:10.1038/s41558-018-0198-6.

Luderer, G. et al., 2019: Environmental co-benefits and adverse side-effects of alternative power sector decarbonization strategies. *Nat. Commun.*, **10(1)**, 1–13, doi:10.1038/s41467-019-13067-8.

Luderer, G. et al., 2022: Impact of declining renewable energy costs on electrification in low-emission scenarios. *Nat. Energy*, **7(1)**, 32–42, doi:10.1038/s41560-021-00937-z.

Lund, H., 2018: Renewable heating strategies and their consequences for storage and grid infrastructures comparing a smart grid to a smart energy systems approach. *Energy*, **151**, 94–102, doi:10.1016/j.energy.2018.03.010.

Lundquist, J.K., K.K. DuVivier, D. Kaffine, and J.M. Tomaszewski, 2019: Costs and consequences of wind turbine wake effects arising from uncoordinated wind energy development. *Nat. Energy*, **4(1)**, 26–34, doi:10.1038/s41560-018-0281-2.

Luo, X., J. Wang, M. Dooner, J. Clarke, and C. Krupke, 2014: Overview of Current Development in Compressed Air Energy Storage Technology. *Energy Procedia*, **62**, 603–611, doi:10.1016/j.egypro.2014.12.423.

Lynd, L.R., 2017: The grand challenge of cellulosic biofuels. *Nat. Biotechnol.*, **35(10)**, 912–915, doi:10.1038/nbt.3976.

Ma, C. et al., 2015: Consumers' willingness to pay for renewable energy: A meta-regression analysis. *Resour. Energy Econ.*, **42**, 93–109, doi:10.1016/j.reseneeco.2015.07.003.

Ma, L., S. Zhang, J. Wang, Y. Xu, and J. Hou, 2020: Recent advances in non-fullerene organic solar cells: from lab to fab. *Chem. Commun.*, **56(92)**, 14337–14352, doi:10.1039/D0CC05528J.

Ma, S., M. Goldstein, A.J. Pitman, N. Haghdadi, and I. MacGill, 2017: Pricing the urban cooling benefits of solar panel deployment in Sydney, Australia. *Sci. Rep.*, **7(1)**, 43938, doi:10.1038/srep43938.

Ma, Y., X. Cai, and P. Zhao, 2018: China's shale gas exploration and development: Understanding and practice. *Pet. Explor. Dev.*, **45(4)**, 589–603, doi:10.1016/S1876-3804(18)30065-X.

Maavara, T. et al., 2020: River dam impacts on biogeochemical cycling. *Nat. Rev. Earth Environ.*, **1(2)**, 103–116, doi:10.1038/s43017-019-0019-0.

Mac Dowell, N., P.S. Fennell, N. Shah, and G.C. Maitland, 2017: The role of CO_2 capture and utilization in mitigating climate change. *Nat. Clim. Change*, **7(4)**, 243–249, doi:10.1038/nclimate3231.

6

MacDonald, A.E. et al., 2016: Future cost-competitive electricity systems and their impact on US CO_2 emissions. *Nat. Clim. Change*, **6(5)**, 526–531, doi:10.1038/nclimate2921.

Madeddu, S. et al., 2020: The CO_2 reduction potential for the European industry via direct electrification of heat supply (power-to-heat). *Environ. Res. Lett.*, **15(12)**, 124004, doi:10.1088/1748-9326/abbd02.

Magneschi, G., T. Zhang, and R. Munson, 2017: The Impact of CO_2 Capture on Water Requirements of Power Plants. *Energy Procedia*, **114**(November 2016), 6337–6347, doi:10.1016/j.egypro.2017.03.1770.

Mahlknecht, J., R. González-Bravo, and F.J. Loge, 2020: Water-energy-food security: A Nexus perspective of the current situation in Latin America and the Caribbean. *Energy*, **194**, 116824, doi:10.1016/j.energy.2019.116824.

Mahmoudzadeh Andwari, A., A. Pesiridis, S. Rajoo, R. Martinez-Botas, and V. Esfahanian, 2017: A review of Battery Electric Vehicle technology and readiness levels. *Renew. Sustain. Energy Rev.*, **78**, 414–430, doi:10.1016/j.rser.2017.03.138.

Mahmud, M., N. Huda, S. Farjana, and C. Lang, 2018: Environmental Impacts of Solar-Photovoltaic and Solar-Thermal Systems with Life-Cycle Assessment. *Energies*, **11(9)**, 2346, doi:10.3390/en11092346.

Mai, T., et al. 2014: Renewable Electricity Futures for the United States. IEEE Transactions on Sustainable Energy **5**, 372–378, doi:10.2172/1219711.

Mai, T. et al., 2018: The role of input assumptions and model structures in projections of variable renewable energy: A multi-model perspective of the U.S. electricity system. *Energy Econ.*, **76**, 313–324, doi:10.1016/j.eneco.2018.10.019.

Maïzi, N., and V. Mazauric, 2019: From centralized to decentralized power systems: The shift on finitude constraints. *Energy Procedia*, **158**, 4262–4267, doi:10.1016/j.egypro.2019.01.800.

Maki, A., R.J. Burns, L. Ha, and A.J. Rothman, 2016: Paying people to protect the environment: A meta-analysis of financial incentive interventions to promote proenvironmental behaviors. *J. Environ. Psychol.*, **47**, 242–255, doi:10.1016/j.jenvp.2016.07.006.

Malhotra, A. and T.S. Schmidt, 2020: Accelerating Low-Carbon Innovation. *Joule*, **4**, 2259–2267, doi:10.1016/j.joule.2020.09.004.Malik, A. et al., 2020: Reducing stranded assets through early action in the Indian power sector. *Environ. Res. Lett.*, **15(9)**, 094091, doi:10.1088/1748-9326/ab8033.

Månberger, A. and B. Stenqvist, 2018: Global metal flows in the renewable energy transition: Exploring the effects of substitutes, technological mix and development. *Energy Policy*, **119**, 226–241, doi:10.1016/j.enpol.2018.04.056.

Mani, S., A. Jain, S. Tripathi, and C.F. Gould, 2020: The drivers of sustained use of liquified petroleum gas in India. *Nat. Energy*, **5(6)**, 450–457, doi:10.1038/s41560-020-0596-7.

Mantripragada, H.C., H. Zhai, and E.S. Rubin, 2019: Boundary Dam or Petra Nova – Which is a better model for CCS energy supply? *Int. J. Greenh. Gas Control*, **82**, 59–68, doi:10.1016/j.ijggc.2019.01.004.

Manzetti, S. and F. Mariasiu, 2015: Electric vehicle battery technologies: From present state to future systems. *Renew. Sustain. Energy Rev.*, **51**, 1004–1012, doi:10.1016/j.rser.2015.07.010.

Marcucci, A., E. Panos, S. Kypreos, and P. Fragkos, 2019: Probabilistic assessment of realizing the 1.5°C climate target. *Appl. Energy*, **239**, 239–251, doi:10.1016/j.apenergy.2019.01.190.

Marten, A.L., R. Garbaccio, and A. Wolverton, 2019: Exploring the General Equilibrium Costs of Sector-Specific Environmental Regulations. *J. Assoc. Environ. Resour. Econ.*, **6(6)**, 1065–1104, doi:10.1086/705593.

Martin-Roberts, E. et al., 2021: Carbon capture and storage at the end of a lost decade. *One Earth*, **4(11)**, 1569–1584, doi:10.1016/j.oneear.2021.10.002.

Martin, G. and E. Saikawa, 2017: Effectiveness of state climate and energy policies in reducing power-sector CO2 emissions. *Nat. Clim. Change*, **7(12)**, 912–919, doi:10.1038/s41558-017-0001-0.

Martin, R., M. Muûls, L.B. de Preux, and U.J. Wagner, 2014: Industry Compensation under Relocation Risk: A Firm-Level Analysis of the EU Emissions Trading Scheme. *Am. Econ. Rev.*, **104(8)**, 2482–2508, doi:10.1257/aer.104.8.2482.

Martinez Cesena, E.A., and P. Mancarella, 2019: Energy Systems Integration in Smart Districts: Robust Optimisation of Multi-Energy Flows in Integrated Electricity, Heat and Gas Networks. *IEEE Trans. Smart Grid*, **10(1)**, 1122–1131, doi:10.1109/TSG.2018.2828146.

Mathiesen, B.V. et al., 2015: Smart Energy Systems for coherent 100% renewable energy and transport solutions. *Appl. Energy*, **145**, 139–154, doi:10.1016/j.apenergy.2015.01.075.

Matos, C.R., J.F. Carneiro, and P.P. Silva, 2019: Overview of Large-Scale Underground Energy Storage Technologies for Integration of Renewable Energies and Criteria for Reservoir Identification. *J. Energy Storage*, **21**, 241–258, doi:10.1016/j.est.2018.11.023.

May, G.J., A. Davidson, and B. Monahov, 2018: Lead batteries for utility energy storage: A review. *J. Energy Storage*, **15**, 145–157, doi:10.1016/j.est.2017.11.008.

Mbow, C., C. Rosenzweig, L.G. Barioni, T.G. Benton, M. Herrero, M. Krishnapillai, E. Liwenga, P. Pradhan, M.G. Rivera-Ferre, T. Sapkota, F.N. Tubiello, Y. Xu, 2019: Food Security. In: *Climate Change and Land: an IPCC special report on climate change, desertification, land degradation, sustainable land management, food security, and greenhouse gas fluxes in terrestrial ecosystems* [P.R. Shukla, J. Skea, E. Calvo Buendia, V. Masson-Delmotte, H.-O. Pörtner, D.C. Roberts, P. Zhai, R. Slade, S. Connors, R. van Diemen, M. Ferrat, E. Haughey, S. Luz, S. Neogi, M. Pathak, J. Petzold, J. Portugal Pereira, P. Vyas, E. Huntley, K. Kissick, M. Belkacemi, J. Malley, (eds.)]. Cambridge University Press, Cambridge, UK and New York, NY, USA, pp. 437–550.

McCartney, M., 2009: Living with dams: managing the environmental impacts. *Water Policy*, **11(sup1)**, 121–139, doi:10.2166/wp.2009.108.

McCauley, D. et al., 2019: Energy justice in the transition to low carbon energy systems: Exploring key themes in interdisciplinary research. *Appl. Energy*, **233–234**(November 2018), 916–921, doi:10.1016/j.apenergy.2018.10.005.

McColl, L. et al., 2012: Assessing the potential impact of climate change on the UK's electricity network. *Clim. Change*, **115(3–4)**, 821–835, doi:10.1007/s10584-012-0469-6.

McCollum, D., V. Krey, P. Kolp, Y. Nagai, and K. Riahi, 2014: Transport electrification: A key element for energy system transformation and climate stabilization. *Clim. Change*, **123(3–4)**, 651–664, doi:10.1007/s10584-013-0969-z.

McCollum, D.L. et al., 2018a: Energy investment needs for fulfilling the Paris Agreement and achieving the Sustainable Development Goals. *Nat. Energy*, **3(7)**, 589–599, doi:10.1038/s41560-018-0179-z.

McCollum, D. L. et al. 2018b: Interaction of consumer preferences and climate policies in the global transition to low-carbon vehicles. *Nat. Energy*, **3(8)**, 664–673, doi:10.1038/s41560-018-0195-z.

McCollum, D.L. et al. 2018c: Connecting the sustainable development goals by their energy inter-linkages. *Environ. Res. Lett.*, **13(3)**, 033006.

McGlade, C. and P. Ekins, 2015: The geographical distribution of fossil fuels unused when limiting global warming to 2°C. *Nature*, **517(7533)**, 187–190, doi:10.1038/nature14016.

Mcgowan, F., and R. Sauter, 2005: *Public Opinion on Energy Research: A Desk Study for the Research Councils*. University of Sussex, Brighton, UK, 35 pp.

McKenna, R. et al., 2020: On the socio-technical potential for onshore wind in Europe: A response to Enevoldsen et al. **(2019)**, Energy Policy, 132, 1092–1100. *Energy Policy*, **145**, 111693, doi:10.1016/j.enpol.2020.111693.

McKenna, R. et al., 2022: High-resolution large-scale onshore wind energy assessments: A review of potential definitions, methodologies and future research needs. *Renew. Energy*, **182**, 659–684, doi:10.1016/j.renene.2021.10.027.

McKone, J.R., N.S. Lewis, and H.B. Gray, 2014: Will solar-driven water-splitting devices see the light of day? *Chem. Mater.*, **26(1)**, 407–414, doi:10.1021/cm4021518.

McLaren, D.P., D.P. Tyfield, R. Willis, B. Szerszynski, and N.O. Markusson, 2019: Beyond 'Net-Zero': A Case for Separate Targets for Emissions Reduction and Negative Emissions. *Front. Clim.*, **1**, 4, doi:10.3389/fclim.2019.00004.

6

McPherson, M., M. Mehos, and P. Denholm, 2020: Leveraging concentrating solar power plant dispatchability: A review of the impacts of global market structures and policy. *Energy Policy*, **139**, 111335, doi:10.1016/j.enpol.2020.111335.

Mehos, M. et al., 2017: *Concentrating Solar Power Gen3 Demonstration Roadmap*. National Renewable Energy Laboratory, Golden, CO, USA, 1–140 pp.

Meinshausen, M. et al., 2009: Greenhouse-gas emission targets for limiting global warming to 2°C. *Nature*, **458(7242)**, 1158–1162, doi:10.1038/nature08017.

Méjean, A., C. Guivarch, J. Lefèvre, and M. Hamdi-Cherif, 2019: The transition in energy demand sectors to limit global warming to 1.5°C. *Energy Effic.*, **12(2)**, 441–462, doi:10.1007/s12053-018-9682-0.

Melara, A.J., U. Singh, and L.M. Colosi, 2020: Is aquatic bioenergy with carbon capture and storage a sustainable negative emission technology? Insights from a spatially explicit environmental life-cycle assessment. *Energy Convers. Manag.*, **224**, 113300, doi:10.1016/j.enconman.2020.113300.

Meldrum, J., S. Nettles-Anderson, G. Heath, and J. Macknick, 2013: Life cycle water use for electricity generation: a review and harmonization of literature estimates. *Environ. Res. Lett.*, **8(1)**, 015031, doi:10.1088/1748-9326/8/1/015031.

Melikoglu, M., 2018: Current status and future of ocean energy sources: A global review. *Ocean Eng.*, **148**(June 2017), 563–573, doi:10.1016/j.oceaneng.2017.11.045.

Menefee, A.H., and B.R. Ellis, 2020: Regional-Scale Greenhouse Gas Utilization Strategies for Enhanced Shale Oil Recovery and Carbon Management. *Energy & Fuels*, **34(5)**, 6136–6147, doi:10.1021/acs.energyfuels.0c00562.

Mercure, J.-F. et al., 2018: Macroeconomic impact of stranded fossil fuel assets. *Nat. Clim. Change*, **8**, 588–593, doi:10.1038/s41558-018-0182-1.

Merrick, J., Y. Ye, and R. Entriken, 2018: Assessing the system value of optimal load shifting. *IEEE Trans. Smart Grid*, **9(6)**, 5943–5952, doi:10.1109/TSG.2017.2699921.

Merrill, L., A.M. Bassi, R. Bridle, and L.T. Christensen, 2015: *Tackling Fossil Fuel Subsidies and Climate Change*. Nordic Council of Ministers, Copenhagen, 62 pp.

Metlay, D.S., 2016: Selecting a Site for a Radioactive Waste Repository: A Historical Analysis. *Elements*, **12(4)**, 269–274, doi:10.2113/gselements.12.4.269.

Meyer, M., A. Löschel, and C. Lutz, 2021: Carbon price dynamics in ambitious climate mitigation scenarios: an analysis based on the IAMC 1.5°C scenario explorer. *Environ. Res. Commun.*, **3(8)**, 81007, doi:10.1088/2515-7620/ac02ad.

Mi, Z. et al., 2020: Economic development and converging household carbon footprints in China. *Nat. Sustain.*, **3(7)**, 529–537, doi:10.1038/s41893-020-0504-y.

Miara, A. et al., 2017: Climate and water resource change impacts and adaptation potential for US power supply. *Nat. Clim. Change*, **7(11)**, 793–798, doi:10.1038/nclimate3417.

Michaels, L., and Y. Parag, 2016: Motivations and barriers to integrating 'prosuming' services into the future decentralized electricity grid: Findings from Israel. *Energy Res. Soc. Sci.*, **21**, 70–83, doi:10.1016/j.erss.2016.06.023.

Midden, C.J.H., and J. Ham, 2012: Persuasive technology to promote pro-environmental behaviour. In: *Environmental Psychology: An Introduction* [Steg, L., A.E. van den Berg and J.I.M. de Groot (eds.)]. John Wiley & Sons, Oxford, UK, pp. 243–254.

Middlemiss, L., 2011: The effects of community-based action for sustainability on participants' lifestyles. *Local Environ.*, **16(3)**, 265–280, doi:10.1080/13549839.2011.566850.

Middleton, R.S. and S. Yaw, 2018: The cost of getting CCS wrong: Uncertainty, infrastructure design, and stranded CO_2. *Int. J. Greenh. Gas Control*, **70**, 1–11, doi:10.1016/j.ijggc.2017.12.011.

Mignacca, B. and G. Locatelli, 2020: Economics and finance of Small Modular Reactors: A systematic review and research agenda. *Renew. Sustain. Energy Rev.*, **118**, 109519, doi:10.1016/j.rser.2019.109519.

Mikunda, T. et al., 2021: *Assessing Interactions between Carbon Capture and Storage and the Sustainable Development Goals.* 15th International Conference on Greenhouse Gas Control Technologies, GHGT-15, Abu Dhabi, UAE, pp. 1–10.

Mileva, A., J. Johnston, J.H. Nelson, and D.M. Kammen, 2016: Power system balancing for deep decarbonization of the electricity sector. *Appl. Energy*, **162**, 1001–1009, doi:10.1016/j.apenergy.2015.10.180.

Milinski, M., D. Semmann, H.J. Krambeck, and J. Marotzke, 2006: Stabilizing the Earth's climate is not a losing game: Supporting evidence from public goods experiments. *Proc. Natl. Acad. Sci. U. S. A.*, **103(11)**, 3994–3998, doi:10.1073/pnas.0504902103.

Miller, L.M. et al., 2015: Two methods for estimating limits to large-scale wind power generation. *Proc. Natl. Acad. Sci.*, **112(36)**, 11169–11174, doi:10.1073/pnas.1408251112.

Milligan, M. et al., 2015: *Review and Status of Wind Integration and Transmission in the United States: Key Issues and Lessons Learned*. National Renewable Energy Laboratory, Golden, CO, USA, 48 pp.

Mills, A.D., T. Levin, R. Wiser, J. Seel, and A. Botterud, 2020: Impacts of variable renewable energy on wholesale markets and generating assets in the United States: A review of expectations and evidence. *Renew. Sustain. Energy Rev.*, **120**, 109670, doi:10.1016/j.rser.2019.109670.

Millstein, D., and S. Menon, 2011: Regional climate consequences of large-scale cool roof and photovoltaic array deployment. *Environ. Res. Lett.*, **6(3)**, doi:10.1088/1748-9326/6/3/034001.

Millstein, D. et al., 2021: Solar and wind grid system value in the United States: The effect of transmission congestion, generation profiles, and curtailment. *Joule*, **5(7)**, 1749–1775, doi:10.1016/J.JOULE.2021.05.009.

Minx, J.C. et al., 2021: A comprehensive and synthetic dataset for global, regional, and national greenhouse gas emissions by sector 1970–2018 with an extension to 2019. *Earth Syst. Sci. Data*, **13(11)**, 5213–5252, doi:10.5194/essd–13-5213-2021.

Mishnaevsky, L., 2021: Sustainable End-of-Life Management of Wind Turbine Blades: Overview of Current and Coming Solutions. *Materials (Basel).*, **14(5)**, 1124, doi:10.3390/ma14051124.

MIT, 2018: *The future of nuclear energy in a carbon-constrained world*. MIT, MA, USA, 272 pp.

Mitchell, J.W., 2013: Power line failures and catastrophic wildfires under extreme weather conditions. *Eng. Fail. Anal.*, **35**, 726–735, doi:10.1016/j.engfailanal.2013.07.006.

Moemken, J., M. Reyers, H. Feldmann, and J.G. Pinto, 2018: Future Changes of Wind Speed and Wind Energy Potentials in EURO-CORDEX Ensemble Simulations. *J. Geophys. Res. Atmos.*, **123(12)**, 6373–6389, doi:10.1029/2018JD028473.

Mohammadi, M. and I. Harjunkoski, 2020: Performance analysis of waste-to-energy technologies for sustainable energy generation in integrated supply chains. *Comput. Chem. Eng.*, **140**, 106905, doi:10.1016/j.compchemeng.2020.106905.

Molino, A., V. Larocca, S. Chianese, and D. Musmarra, 2018: Biofuels Production by Biomass Gasification: A Review. *Energies*, **11(4)**, 811, doi:10.3390/en11040811.

Monforti-Ferrario, F., A. Kona, E. Peduzzi, D. Pernigotti, and E. Pisoni, 2018: The impact on air quality of energy saving measures in the major cities signatories of the Covenant of Mayors initiative. *Environ. Int.*, **118**, 222–234, doi:10.1016/j.envint.2018.06.001.

Montoya, J.H., C. Tsai, A. Vojvodic, and J.K. Nørskov, 2015: The challenge of electrochemical ammonia synthesis: A new perspective on the role of nitrogen scaling relations. *ChemSusChem*, **8(13)**, 2180–2186, doi:10.1002/cssc.201500322.

Montoya, J.H. et al., 2017: Materials for solar fuels and chemicals. *Nat. Mater.*, **16(1)**, 70–81, doi:10.1038/nmat4778.

Moore, J., 2017: Thermal Hydrogen: An emissions free hydrocarbon economy. *Int. J. Hydrogen Energy*, **42(17)**, 12047–12063, doi:10.1016/j.ijhydene.2017.03.182.

6

Morakinyo, T.E. et al., 2019: Estimates of the impact of extreme heat events on cooling energy demand in Hong Kong. *Renew. Energy*, **142**, 73–84, doi:10.1016/j.renene.2019.04.077.

Moran, E.F., M.C. Lopez, N. Moore, N. Müller, and D.W. Hyndman, 2018: Sustainable hydropower in the 21st century. *Proc. Natl. Acad. Sci.*, **115**, 11891 LP – 11898, doi:10.1073/pnas.1809426115.

Moreno-Mateos, D. et al., 2020: The long-term restoration of ecosystem complexity. *Nat. Ecol. Evol.*, **4(5)**, 676–685, doi:10.1038/s41559-020–1154–1.

Moreno, R., D. Pudjianto, and G. Strbac, 2012: Integrated reliability and cost–benefit-based standards for transmission network operation. *Proc. Inst. Mech. Eng. Part O J. Risk Reliab.*, **226(1)**, 75–87, doi:10.1177/1748006X11424103.

Mori, A., 2018: Socio-technical and political economy perspectives in the Chinese energy transition. *Energy Res. Soc. Sci.*, **35**, 28–36, doi:10.1016/j.erss.2017.10.043.

Mørk, G., S. Barstow, A. Kabuth, and M.T. Pontes, 2010: *Assessing the Global Wave Energy Potential. 29th International Conference on Ocean, Offshore and Arctic Engineering: Volume 3*. International Conference on Offshore Mechanics and Arctic Engineering, Shanghai, China, pp. 447–454.

Morris, J., H. Scott Matthews, and C. Morawski, 2013: Review and meta-analysis of 82 studies on end-of-life management methods for source separated organics. *Waste Manag.*, **33(3)**, 545–551, doi:10.1016/j.wasman.2012.08.004.

Morrison, M.L., and K. Sinclair, 2004: Wind Energy Technology, Environmental Impacts of. *Encycl. Energy*, **6**, 435–448, doi:10.1016/B0–12–176480-X/00419-8.

Mouratiadou, I. et al., 2016: The impact of climate change mitigation on water demand for energy and food: An integrated analysis based on the Shared Socioeconomic Pathways. *Environ. Sci. Policy*, **64**, 48–58, doi:10.1016/j.envsci.2016.06.007.

Moya, D., C. Aldás, and P. Kaparaju, 2018: Geothermal energy: Power plant technology and direct heat applications. *Renew. Sustain. Energy Rev.*, **94**(June), 889–901, doi:10.1016/j.rser.2018.06.047.

Mu, M., Z. Zhang, X. Cai, and Q. Tang, 2020: A water-electricity nexus model to analyze thermoelectricity supply reliability under environmental regulations and economic penalties during drought events. *Environ. Model. Softw.*, **123**(September 2019), 104514, doi:10.1016/j.envsoft.2019.104514.

Muchunku, C., K. Ulsrud, D. Palit, and W. Jonker-Klunne, 2018: Diffusion of solar PV in East Africa: What can be learned from private sector delivery models? *Wiley Interdisc. Rev. Energy Environ.*, **7(3)**, doi:10.1002/wene.282.

Mukheibir, P., 2013: Potential consequences of projected climate change impacts on hydroelectricity generation. *Clim. Change*, **121(1)**, 67–78, doi:10.1007/s10584-013-0890-5.

Müller, J., D. Folini, M. Wild, and S. Pfenninger, 2019: CMIP-5 models project photovoltaics are a no-regrets investment in Europe irrespective of climate change. *Energy*, **171**, 135–148, doi:10.1016/j.energy.2018.12.139.

Mundaca, G., 2017: How much can CO_2 emissions be reduced if fossil fuel subsidies are removed? *Energy Econ.*, **64**, 91–104, doi:10.1016/j.eneco.2017.03.014.

Mundaca, L., 2007: Transaction costs of Tradable White Certificate schemes: The Energy Efficiency Commitment as case study. *Energy Policy*, **35(8)**, 4340–4354, doi:10.1016/j.enpol.2007.02.029.

Mundaca, L., D. Ürge-Vorsatz, and C. Wilson, 2019: Demand-side approaches for limiting global warming to 1.5°C. *Energy Effic.*, **12(2)**, 343–362, doi:10.1007/s12053-018-9722-9.

Münster, M. et al. 2020: Sector Coupling: Concepts, State-of-the-art and Perspectives. ETIP SNET, https://orbi.uliege.be/handle/2268/244983.

Muratori, M. and T. Mai, 2020: The shape of electrified transportation. *Environ. Res. Lett.*, **16(1)**, 11003, doi:10.1088/1748-9326/abcb38.

Muratori, M., K. Calvin, M. Wise, P. Kyle, and J. Edmonds, 2016: Global economic consequences of deploying bioenergy with carbon capture and storage (BECCS). *Environ. Res. Lett.*, **11(9)**, 095004, doi:10.1088/1748-9326/11/9/095004.

Muratori, M. et al., 2017a: Carbon capture and storage across fuels and sectors in energy system transformation pathways. *Int. J. Greenh. Gas Control*, **57**, 34–41, doi:10.1016/j.ijggc.2016.11.026.

Muratori, M. et al., 2017b: Role of the Freight Sector in Future Climate Change Mitigation Scenarios. *Environ. Sci. Technol.*, **51(6)**, 3526–3533, doi:10.1021/acs.est.6b04515.

Muratori, M., B. Bush, C. Hunter, and M. Melaina, 2018: Modeling Hydrogen Refueling Infrastructure to Support Passenger Vehicles. *Energies*, **11**, 1171, doi:10.3390/en11051171.

Muratori, M. et al., 2020a: EMF-33 insights on bioenergy with carbon capture and storage (BECCS). *Clim. Change*, **163(3)**, 1621–1637, doi:10.1007/s10584-020-02784-5.

Muratori, M. et al., 2020b: Future integrated mobility-energy systems: A modeling perspective. *Renew. Sustain. Energy Rev.*, **119**, 109541, doi:10.1016/j.rser.2019.109541.

Murray, B.C. and P.T. Maniloff, 2015: Why have greenhouse emissions in RGGI states declined? An econometric attribution to economic, energy market, and policy factors. *Energy Econ.*, **51**, 581–589, doi:10.1016/j.eneco.2015.07.013.

Muteri, V. et al., 2020: Review on Life Cycle Assessment of Solar Photovoltaic Panels. *Energies*, **13(1)**, doi:10.3390/en13010252.

Mutz, D., D. Hengevoss, C. Hugi, and T. Gross, 2017: *Waste-to-Energy Options in Municipal Solid Waste Management – A Guide for Decision Makers in Developing and Emerging Countries*. Deutsche Gesellschaft für Internationale Zusammenarbeit (GIZ) GmbH, Bonn, Germany, 58 pp.

Naegele, H. and A. Zaklan, 2019: Does the EU ETS cause carbon leakage in European manufacturing? *J. Environ. Econ. Manage.*, **93**, 125–147, doi:10.1016/J.JEEM.2018.11.004.

Nagashima M, 2018: *Japan's hydrogen strategy and its economic and geopolitical implications*. Etudes de l'Ifri, Ifri, Paris, France, 75 pp.

Nam, S.W. et al., 2018: Ammonia as an efficient COX-free hydrogen carrier: Fundamentals and feasibility analyses for fuel cell applications. *Appl. Energy*, **224**(April), 194–204, doi:10.1016/j.apenergy.2018.04.100.

Namazkhan, M., C. Albers, and L. Steg, 2019: The role of environmental values, socio-demographics and building characteristics in setting room temperatures in winter. *Energy*, **171**, 1183–1192, doi:10.1016/j.energy.2019.01.113.

Narsilio, G.A. and L. Aye, 2018: *Shallow Geothermal Energy: An Emerging Technology BT – Low Carbon Energy Supply: Trends, Technology, Management*. [Sharma, A., A. Shukla, and L. Aye, (eds.)], Springer Singapore, Singapore, pp. 387–411.

NAS, 2016: *Commercial Aircraft Propulsion and Energy Systems Research*. National Academies Press, Washington, DC, USA. 1–122.

National Academies of Sciences, Engineering, and Medicine, 2019: *Negative Emissions Technologies and Reliable Sequestration*. The National Academies Press, Washington, DC, USA.

Navalpotro, P., J. Palma, M. Anderson, and R. Marcilla, 2017: A Membrane-Free Redox Flow Battery with Two Immiscible Redox Electrolytes. *Angew. Chemie Int. Ed.*, **56(41)**, 12460–12465, doi:10.1002/anie.201704318.

NEA, 2019: *Uranium 2018. Resources, production and demand*. OECD, Paris, France, 462 pp.

NEA, 2020: *Unlocking Reductions in the Construction Costs of Nuclear*. OECD, Paris, France, 134 pp.

NEA and OECD, 2015: *Introduction of Thorium in the Nuclear Fuel Cycle*. OECD, Paris, France, 133 pp.

NEA/IAEA, 2021: *Uranium 2020: Resources, Production and Demand*. OECD, Paris, France, 484 pp.

Nemet, G. et al., 2016: *Sources of price dispersion in U.S. residential solar installations*. Lawrence Berkeley National Laboratory, Berkeley, CA, USA, 45 pp.

Nemet, G.F., 2009: Net Radiative Forcing from Widespread Deployment of Photovoltaics. *Environ. Sci. Technol.*, **43(6)**, 2173–2178, doi:10.1021/es801747c.

6

Nemet, G.F., 2019: *How solar energy became cheap: A model for low-carbon innovation*. Routledge, London, UK, 260 pp.

NETL, 2015: *Carbon Storage Atlas: Fifth Edition*. National Energy Technology National Energy Technology Laboratory, Washington, USA, 114 pp.

Newbery, D., M.G. Pollitt, R.A. Ritz, and W. Strielkowski, 2018: Market design for a high-renewables European electricity system. *Renew. Sustain. Energy Rev.*, **91**, 695–707, doi:10.1016/j.rser.2018.04.025.

Newbery, G., D. Strbac, Pudjianto, and P. Noël, 2013: *Benefits of an integrated European Market*, A report for Directorate General Energy European Commission. Booz & Company, Amsterdam, 122 pp.

Newborough, M., and G. Cooley, 2020: Developments in the global hydrogen market: The spectrum of hydrogen colours. *Fuel Cells Bull.*, **2020(11)**, 16–22, doi:10.1016/S1464-2859(20)30546-0.

Nguyen, K.C., J.J. Katzfey, J. Riedl, and A. Troccoli, 2017: Potential impacts of solar arrays on regional climate and on array efficiency. *Int. J. Climatol.*, **37**, 4053–4064, doi:10.1002/joc.4995.

Niamir, L., T. Filatova, A. Voinov, and H. Bressers, 2018: Transition to low-carbon economy: Assessing cumulative impacts of individual behavioral changes. *Energy Policy*, **118**, 325–345, doi:10.1016/j.enpol.2018.03.045.

Nielander, A.C., M.R. Shaner, K.M. Papadantonakis, S.A. Francis, and N.S. Lewis, 2015: A taxonomy for solar fuels generators. *Energy Environ. Sci.*, **8(1)**, 16–25, doi:10.1039/c4ee02251c.

Nielsen, T., N. Baumert, A. Kander, M. Jiborn, and V. Kulionis, 2021: The risk of carbon leakage in global climate agreements. *Int. Environ. Agreements Polit. Law Econ.*, **21(2)**, 147–163, doi:10.1007/s10784-020-09507-2.

Niermann, M., S. Drünert, M. Kaltschmitt, and K. Bonhoff, 2019: Liquid organic hydrogen carriers (LOHCs) – techno-economic analysis of LOHCs in a defined process chain. *Energy Environ. Sci.*, **12(1)**, 290–307, doi:10.1039/C8EE02700E.

Niermann, M., S. Timmerberg, S. Drünert, and M. Kaltschmitt, 2021: Liquid Organic Hydrogen Carriers and alternatives for international transport of renewable hydrogen. *Renew. Sustain. Energy Rev.*, **135**, 110171, doi:10.1016/j.rser.2020.110171.

Nilsson, A., A. Hansla, J.M. Heiling, C.J. Bergstad, and J. Martinsson, 2016: Public acceptability towards environmental policy measures: Value-matching appeals. *Environ. Sci. Policy*, **61**, 176–184, doi:10.1016/j.envsci.2016.04.013.

Nilsson, E.J.K., C. Brackmann, A. Abou-Taouk, J. Larffldt, and D. Moell, 2017: *Hydrogen addition to flames at gas-turbine-relevant conditions*. Energiforsk, Stockholm, Sweden, 70 pp.

Nocera, D.G., 2017: Solar fuels and solar chemicals industry. *Acc. Chem. Res.*, **50(3)**, 616–619, doi:10.1021/acs.accounts.6b00615.

Nolan, J.M., P.W. Schultz, R.B. Cialdini, N.J. Goldstein, and V. Griskevicius, 2008: Normative social influence is underdetected. *Personal. Soc. Psychol. Bull.*, **34(7)**, 913–923, doi:10.1177/0146167208316691.

Noll, D., C. Dawes, and V. Rai, 2014: Solar community organizations and active peer effects in the adoption of residential PV. *Energy Policy*, **67**, 330–343, doi:10.1016/j.enpol.2013.12.050.

Noppers, E.H., K. Keizer, J.W. Bolderdijk, and L. Steg, 2014: The adoption of sustainable innovations: Driven by symbolic and environmental motives. *Glob. Environ. Change*, **25(1)**, 52–62, doi:10.1016/j.gloenvcha.2014.01.012.

NREL, 2014: *Making Sustainable Energy Choices: Insights on the Energy/Water/Land Nexus*. National Renewable Energy Laboratory, Golden, CO, USA, 8 pp.

NREL, 2021: *Electricity Annual Technoloy Baseline (ATB)*. https://atb.nrel.gov/electricity/2021/data.

Nugent, D. and B.K. Sovacool, 2014: Assessing the lifecycle greenhouse gas emissions from solar PV and wind energy: A critical meta-survey. *Energy Policy*, **65(0)**, 229–244, doi:10.1016/j.enpol.2013.10.048.

Núñez-López, V. and E. Moskal, 2019: Potential of CO_2-EOR for Near-Term Decarbonization. *Front. Clim.*, **1**, doi:10.3389/fclim.2019.00005.

Núñez-López, V., R. Gil-Egui, and S. Hosseini, 2019: Environmental and Operational Performance of CO_2-EOR as a CCUS Technology: A Cranfield Example with Dynamic LCA Considerations. *Energies*, **12(3)**, 448, doi:10.3390/en12030448.

Nuytten, T., B. Claessens, K. Paredis, J. Van Bael, and D. Six, 2013: Flexibility of a combined heat and power system with thermal energy storage for district heating. *Appl. Energy*, **104**, 583–591, doi:10.1016/j.apenergy.2012.11.029.

Nykvist, B. and M. Nilsson, 2015: Rapidly falling costs of battery packs for electric vehicles. *Nat. Clim. Change*, **5(4)**, 329–332, doi:10.1038/nclimate2564.

Nykvist, B. and O. Olsson, 2021: The feasibility of heavy battery electric trucks. *Joule*, **5(4)**, 901–913, doi:10.1016/J.JOULE.2021.03.007.

Nyman, J., 2018: Rethinking energy, climate and security: a critical analysis of energy security in the US. *J. Int. Relations Dev.*, **21(1)**, 118–145, doi:10.1057/jird.2015.26.

O'Malley, M. et al., 2016: *Energy systems integration. Defining and describing the value proposition*. International Institute of Energy Systems Integration, Golden, CO, USA, 9 pp.

O'Malley, M.J. et al., 2020: Multicarrier Energy Systems: Shaping Our Energy Future. *Proc. IEEE*, **108(9)**, 1437–1456, doi:10.1109/JPROC.2020.2992251.

O'Shaughnessy, E., G.F. Nemet, J. Pless, and R. Margolis, 2019: Addressing the soft cost challenge in U.S. small-scale solar PV system pricing. *Energy Policy*, **134**, 110956, https://doi.org/10.1016/j.enpol.2019.110956.

O'Neill, S. and S. Nicholson-Cole, 2009: 'Fear won't do it' Promoting Positive Engagement With Climate Change Through Visual and Iconic Representations. *Sci. Commun.*, **30(3)**, 355–379, doi:10.1177/1075547008329201.

Obour, P.B., K. Owusu, E.A. Agyeman, A. Ahenkan, and À.N. Madrid, 2016: The impacts of dams on local livelihoods: a study of the Bui Hydroelectric Project in Ghana. *Int. J. Water Resour. Dev.*, **32(2)**, 286–300, doi:10.1080/07900627.2015.1022892.

Ocko, I.B. and S.P. Hamburg, 2019: Climate Impacts of Hydropower: Enormous Differences among Facilities and over Time. *Environ. Sci. Technol.*, **53**, 14070–14082, doi:10.1021/acs.est.9b05083.

OECD, 2011: *Water Governance in OECD Countries*. OECD, Paris, France, 250 pp.

Oei, P.-Y. et al., 2020: Coal phase-out in Germany – Implications and policies for affected regions. *Energy*, **196**, 117004, https://doi.org/10.1016/j.energy.2020.117004.

Office of Nuclear Energy, 2021: *Benefits of Small Modular Reactors (SMRs)*. https://www.energy.gov/ne/benefits-small-modular-reactors-smrs.

Ohene-Asare, K., E.N. Tetteh, and E.L. Asuah, 2020: Total factor energy efficiency and economic development in Africa. *Energy Effic.*, **13(6)**, 1177–1194, doi:10.1007/s12053-020-09877-1.

Ölander, F. and J. Thøgersen, 2014: Informing Versus Nudging in Environmental Policy. *J. Consum. Policy*, **37(3)**, 341–356, doi:10.1007/s10603-014-9256-2.

Olivetti, E.A., G. Ceder, G.G. Gaustad, and X. Fu, 2017: Lithium-Ion Battery Supply Chain Considerations: Analysis of Potential Bottlenecks in Critical Metals. *Joule*, **1(2)**, 229–243, doi:10.1016/j.joule.2017.08.019.

Ondraczek, J., N. Komendantova, and A. Patt, 2015: WACC the dog: The effect of financing costs on the levelized cost of solar PV power. *Renew. Energy*, **75**, 888–898, doi:10.1016/j.renene.2014.10.053.

Osbaldiston, R. and J.P. Schott, 2012: Environmental sustainability and behavioral science: Meta-analysis of proenvironmental behavior experiments. *Environ. Behav.*, **44(2)**, 257–299, doi:10.1177/0013916511402673.

Oshiro, K., M. Kainuma, and T. Masui, 2017: Implications of Japan's 2030 target for long-term low emission pathways. *Energy Policy*, **110**, 581–587, doi:10.1016/j.enpol.2017.09.003.

Osička, J. et al., 2020: What's next for the European coal heartland? Exploring the future of coal as presented in German, Polish and Czech press. *Energy Res. Soc. Sci.*, **61**, 101316, doi:10.1016/j.erss.2019.101316.

Osman, O. and S. Sgouridis, 2018: Optimizing the production of ammonia as an energy carrier in the UAE. *2018 5th International Conference on Renewable Energy: Generation and Applications (ICREGA)*, IEEE, United Arab Emirates, pp. 277–280.

Ostadi, M., E. Rytter, and M. Hillestad, 2019: Boosting carbon efficiency of the biomass to liquid process with hydrogen from power: The effect of H2/CO ratio to the Fischer-Tropsch reactors on the production and power consumption. *Biomass and Bioenergy*, **127**, 105282, doi:10.1016/j.biombioe.2019.105282.

Owusu, K., A.B. Asiedu, P.W.K. Yankson, and Y.A. Boafo, 2019: Impacts of Ghana's Bui dam hydroelectricity project on the livelihood of downstream non-resettled communities. *Sustain. Sci.*, **14(2)**, 487–499, doi:10.1007/s11625-018-0588-8.

Ozarslan, A., 2012: Large-scale hydrogen energy storage in salt caverns. *Int. J. Hydrogen Energy*, **37**, 14265–14277, doi:10.1016/j.ijhydene.2012.07.111.

Pahl, S., J. Goodhew, C. Boomsma, and S.R.J. Sheppard, 2016: The role of energy visualization in addressing energy use: Insights from the eViz project. *Front. Psychol.*, **7**(February), 1–4, doi:10.3389/fpsyg.2016.00092.

Pahle, M. et al., 2018: Sequencing to ratchet up climate policy stringency. *Nat. Clim. Change*, **8(10)**, 861–867, doi:10.1038/s41558-018-0287-6.

Pai, S., J. Emmerling, L. Drouet, H. Zerriffi, and J. Jewell, 2021: Meeting well-below 2°C target would increase energy sector jobs globally. *One Earth*, **4(7)**, 1026–1036, doi:10.1016/J.ONEEAR.2021.06.005.

Palle, A., 2021: Bringing geopolitics to energy transition research. *Energy Res. Soc. Sci.*, **81**, 102233, doi:10.1016/j.erss.2021.102233.

Palm, A., 2017: Peer effects in residential solar photovoltaics adoption—A mixed methods study of Swedish users. *Energy Res. Soc. Sci.*, **26**, 1–10, doi:10.1016/J.ERSS.2017.01.008.

Palmstrom, A. F. et al., 2019: Enabling Flexible All-Perovskite Tandem Solar Cells. *Joule*, 3(9): 2193–2204, doi:10.1016/j.joule.2019.05.009.

Pampel, F.C., 2011: Support for nuclear energy in the context of climate change: Evidence from the European Union. *Organ. Environ.*, **24(3)**, 249–268, doi:10.1177/1086026611422261.

Pan, J., F. Zhang, and J. Guo, 2021: *New energy technology research: Opportunities and challenges*. Chinese Academy of Sciences, Nature Research Custom Media, Springer Nature, Cham, Switzerland, 25 pp.

Pan, S.-Y. et al., 2019: Establishment of enhanced geothermal energy utilization plans: Barriers and strategies. *Renew. Energy*, **132**, 19–32, doi:10.1016/j.renene.2018.07.126.

Pan, X. et al., 2020: Analysis of China's oil and gas consumption under different scenarios toward 2050: An integrated modeling. *Energy*, **195**, 116991, doi:10.1016/j.energy.2020.116991.

Panteli, M. and P. Mancarella, 2015: Influence of extreme weather and climate change on the resilience of power systems: Impacts and possible mitigation strategies. *Electr. Power Syst. Res.*, **127**, 259–270, doi:10.1016/J.EPSR.2015.06.012.

Paroussos, L. et al., 2019: Climate clubs and the macro-economic benefits of international cooperation on climate policy. *Nat. Clim. Change*, **9(7)**, 542–546, doi:10.1038/s41558-019-0501-1.

Patrizio, P. et al., 2018: Reducing US Coal Emissions Can Boost Employment. *Joule*, **2(12)**, 2633–2648, doi:10.1016/J.JOULE.2018.10.004.

Patterson, M.G., 1996: What is energy efficiency? Concepts, indicators and methodological issues. *Energy Policy*, **24(5)**, 377–390.

Pavel, C.C. et al., 2017: Substitution strategies for reducing the use of rare earths in wind turbines. *Resour. Policy*, **52**(April), 349–357, doi:10.1016/j.resourpol.2017.04.010.

Pavičević, M. et al., 2020: The potential of sector coupling in future European energy systems: Soft linking between the Dispa-SET and JRC-EU-TIMES models. *Appl. Energy*, **267**, 115100, doi:10.1016/j.apenergy.2020.115100.

Pei, Y. et al., 2020: Research on the Training Program and Develop the Curriculum System for HVDC Equipment Maintainer. *IOP Conf. Ser. Earth Environ. Sci.*, **510(2)**, 22033, doi:10.1088/1755-1315/510/2/022033.

Pellegrini, L., M. Arsel, M. Orta-Martínez, C.F. Mena, and G. Muñoa, 2021: Institutional mechanisms to keep unburnable fossil fuel reserves in the soil. *Energy Policy*, **149**, 112029, doi:10.1016/j.enpol.2020.112029.

Pelletier, L.G., K.M. Tuson, I. Green-Demers, K. Noels, and A.M. Beaton, 1998: Why are you doing things for the environment? The Motivation Toward the Environment Scale (MTES). *J. Appl. Soc. Psychol.*, **28(5)**, 437–468, doi:10.1111/j.1559-1816.1998.tb01714.x.

Pellizzone, A., A. Allansdottir, R. De Franco, G. Muttoni, and A. Manzella, 2015: Exploring public engagement with geothermal energy in southern Italy: A case study. *Energy Policy*, **85(2015)**, 1–11, doi:10.1016/j.enpol.2015.05.002.

Peng, W. et al., 2018: Managing China's coal power plants to address multiple environmental objectives. *Nat. Sustain.*, **1(11)**, 693–701, doi:10.1038/s41893-018-0174-1.

Perera, A.T.D., V.M. Nik, D. Chen, J.L. Scartezzini, and T. Hong, 2020: Quantifying the impacts of climate change and extreme climate events on energy systems. *Nat. Energy*, **5(2)**, 150–159, doi:10.1038/s41560-020-0558-0.

Perez, M., R. Perez, K.R. Rábago, and M. Putnam, 2019: Overbuilding & curtailment: The cost-effective enablers of firm PV generation. *Sol. Energy*, **180**, 412–422, doi:10.1016/j.solener.2018.12.074.

Perino, G., 2015: Climate Campaigns, Cap and Trade, and Carbon Leakage: Why Trying to Reduce Your Carbon Footprint Can Harm the Climate. *J. Assoc. Environ. Resour. Econ.*, **2(3)**, 469–495, doi:10.1086/682572.

Perlaviciute, G. and L. Steg, 2014: Contextual and psychological factors shaping evaluations and acceptability of energy alternatives: Integrated review and research agenda. *Renew. Sustain. Energy Rev.*, **35**, 361–381, doi:10.1016/j.rser.2014.04.003.

Perlaviciute, G. and L. Squintani, 2020: Public Participation in Climate Policy Making: Toward Reconciling Public Preferences and Legal Frameworks. *One Earth*, **2(4)**, 341–348, doi:10.1016/j.oneear.2020.03.009.

Perlaviciute, G., L. Steg, N. Contzen, S. Roeser, and N. Huijts, 2018: Emotional responses to energy projects: Insights for responsible decision making in a sustainable energy transition. *Sustainability*, **10(7)**, doi:10.3390/su10072526.

Permadi, D.A., A. Sofyan, and N.T. Kim Oanh, 2017: Assessment of emissions of greenhouse gases and air pollutants in Indonesia and impacts of national policy for elimination of kerosene use in cooking. *Atmos. Environ.*, **154**, 82–94, https://doi.org/10.1016/j.atmosenv.2017.01.041.

Perpiña Castillo, C., F. Batista e Silva, and C. Lavalle, 2016: An assessment of the regional potential for solar power generation in EU-28. *Energy Policy*, doi:10.1016/j.enpol.2015.10.004.

Perry, M., and A. Troccoli, 2015: Impact of a fire burn on solar irradiance and PV power. *Sol. Energy*, **114**, 167–173, doi:10.1016/j.solener.2015.01.005.

Pes, M. P. et al., 2017: Climate trends on the extreme winds in Brazil. *Renew. Energy*, **109**, 110–120, doi:10.1016/j.renene.2016.12.101.

Peters, G.P. et al., 2017: Key indicators to track current progress and future ambition of the Paris Agreement. *Nat. Clim. Change*, **7(2)**, 118–122, doi:10.1038/nclimate3202.

Peters, J. and M. Sievert, 2016: Impacts of rural electrification revisited – the African context. *J. Dev. Eff.*, **8(3)**, 327–345, doi:10.1080/19439342.2016.1178320.

Petersen, E.L. and I. Troen, 2012: Wind conditions and resource assessment. *Wiley Interdiscip. Rev. Energy Environ.*, **1(2)**, 206–217, doi:10.1002/wene.4.

Peterson, D. et al., 2020: *DOE Hydrogen and Fuel Cells Program Record*. U.S. Department of Energy, Washington, DC, USA.

Peterson, T.R., J.C. Stephens, and E.J. Wilson, 2015: Public perception of and engagement with emerging low-carbon energy technologies: A literature review. *MRS Energy Sustain.*, **2**, 1–14, doi:10.1557/mre.2015.12.

Petrus, M.L. et al., 2017: Capturing the Sun: A Review of the Challenges and Perspectives of Perovskite Solar Cells. *Adv. Energy Mater.*, **7(16)**, 1–27, doi:10.1002/aenm.201700264.

Pfeiffer, A., R. Millar, C. Hepburn, and E. Beinhocker, 2016: The '2°C capital stock' for electricity generation: Committed cumulative carbon emissions from the electricity generation sector and the transition to a green economy. *Appl. Energy*, **179**, 1395–1408, doi:10.1016/j.apenergy.2016.02.093.

Pfeiffer, A., C. Hepburn, A. Vogt-Schilb, and B. Caldecott, 2018: Committed emissions from existing and planned power plants and asset stranding required to meet the Paris Agreement. *Environ. Res. Lett.*, **13(5)**, 054019, doi:10.1088/1748-9326/aabc5f.

Pflug, V. et al., 2019: *Power-to-X: The crucial business on the way to a carbon-free world*. Energy Global GmbH & Co. KG, Siemens Energy, Inc, Munich, Germany and Texas, USA, 24 pp.

Philibert, C., 2017: Renewable energy for industry: From green energy to green materials and fuels. International Energy Agency, Paris, France, 72 pp.

Philibert, C., 2019: Direct and indirect electrification of industry and beyond. *Oxford Rev. Econ. Policy*, **35**(2), 197–217, doi:10.1093/oxrep/grz006.

Phyoe, W.W. and F. Wang, 2019: A review of carbon sink or source effect on artificial reservoirs. *Int. J. Environ. Sci. Technol.*, **16**(4), 2161–2174, doi:10.1007/s13762-019-02237-2.

Pichert, D. and K.V. Katsikopoulos, 2008: Green defaults: Information presentation and pro-environmental behaviour. *J. Environ. Psychol.*, **28**(1), 63–73, doi:10.1016/j.jenvp.2007.09.004.

Pimm, A.J., S.D. Garvey, and M. de Jong, 2014: Design and testing of Energy Bags for underwater compressed air energy storage. *Energy*, **66**, 496–508, doi:10.1016/j.energy.2013.12.010.

Pisano, I. and M. Lubell, 2017: Environmental Behavior in Cross-National Perspective. *Environ. Behav.*, **49**(1), 31–58, doi:10.1177/0013916515600494.

Placke, T., R. Kloepsch, S. Dühnen, and M. Winter, 2017: Lithium ion, lithium metal, and alternative rechargeable battery technologies: the odyssey for high energy density. *J. Solid State Electrochem.*, **21**(7), 1939–1964, doi:10.1007/s10008-017-3610-7.

Plate, R.R., M.C. Monroe, and A. Oxarart, 2010: Public Perceptions of Using Woody Biomass as a Renewable Energy Source. *J. Ext.*, **48**(3), 1–15.

Pleßmann, G. and P. Blechinger, 2017: How to meet EU GHG emission reduction targets? A model based decarbonization pathway for Europe's electricity supply system until 2050. *Energy Strateg. Rev.*, **15**, 19–32, doi:10.1016/j.esr.2016.11.003.

Ploeg, F. and A. Rezai, 2020: Stranded Assets in the Transition to a Carbon-Free Economy. *Annu. Rev. Resour. Econ.*, **12**, doi:10.1146/annurev-resource-110519-040938.

Plum, C., R. Olschewski, M. Jobin, and O. van Vliet, 2019: Public preferences for the Swiss electricity system after the nuclear phase-out: A choice experiment. *Energy Policy*, **130**(April), 181–196, doi:10.1016/j.enpol.2019.03.054.

Pohjolainen, P., L. Kukkonen, P. Jokinen, W. Poortinga, and R. Umit, 2018: *Public Perceptions on Climate Change and Energy in Europe and Russia: Evidence from Round 8 of the European Social Survey*. European Social Survey ERIC, London, UK, 16 pp.

Polzin, F., M. Migendt, F.A. Täube, and P. von Flotow, 2015: Public policy influence on renewable energy investments—A panel data study across OECD countries. *Energy Policy*, **80**, 98–111, doi:10.1016/J.ENPOL.2015.01.026.

Poortinga, W., M. Aoyagi, and N.F. Pidgeon, 2013: Public perceptions of climate change and energy futures before and after the Fukushima accident: A comparison between Britain and Japan. *Energy Policy*, **62**, 1204–1211, doi:10.1016/j.enpol.2013.08.015.

Portugal-Pereira, J. et al., 2018: Interactions between global climate change strategies and local air pollution: lessons learnt from the expansion of the power sector in Brazil. *Clim. Change*, **148**(1–2), 293–309, doi:10.1007/s10584-018-2193-3.

Poudineh, R. and A. Rubino, 2017: Business model for cross-border interconnections in the Mediterranean basin. *Energy Policy*, **107**, 96–108, doi:10.1016/j.enpol.2017.04.027.

Poulsen, A.H. et al., 2018a: Short-term nighttime wind turbine noise and cardiovascular events: A nationwide case-crossover study from Denmark. *Environ. Int.*, **114**, 160–166, doi:10.1016/j.envint.2018.02.030.

Poulsen, A.H. et al., 2018b: Long-term exposure to wind turbine noise and redemption of antihypertensive medication: A nationwide cohort study. *Environ. Int.*, **121**, 207–215, doi:10.1016/j.envint.2018.08.054.

Poulsen, A.H. et al., 2019a: Impact of Long-Term Exposure to Wind Turbine Noise on Redemption of Sleep Medication and Antidepressants: A Nationwide Cohort Study. *Environ. Health Perspect.*, **127**(3), 37005, doi:10.1289/EHP3909.

Poulsen, A.H. et al., 2019b: Long-Term Exposure to Wind Turbine Noise and Risk for Myocardial Infarction and Stroke: A Nationwide Cohort Study. *Environ. Health Perspect.*, **127**(3), 37004, doi:10.1289/EHP3340.

Pour, N., P.A. Webley, and P.J. Cook, 2018: Potential for using municipal solid waste as a resource for bioenergy with carbon capture and storage (BECCS). *Int. J. Greenh. Gas Control*, **68**, 1–15, doi:10.1016/j.ijggc.2017.11.007.

Pradhan, S., W.M. Shobe, J. Fuhrman, H. McJeon, M. Binsted, S.C. Doney, and A.F. Clarens, 2021: Effects of Direct Air Capture Technology Availability on Stranded Assets and Committed Emissions in the Power Sector. *Front. Clim.*, **3**, doi:10.3389/fclim.2021.660787.

Prairie, Y.T. et al., 2018: Greenhouse Gas Emissions from Freshwater Reservoirs: What Does the Atmosphere See? *Ecosystems*, **21**(5), 1058–1071, doi:10.1007/s10021-017-0198-9.

Prăvălie, R., C. Patriche, and G. Bandoc, 2019: Spatial assessment of solar energy potential at global scale. A geographical approach. *J. Clean. Prod.*, **209**, 692–721, doi:10.1016/j.jclepro.2018.10.239.

Premalatha, M., Tabassum-Abbasi, T. Abbasi, and S. A. Abbasi, 2014: A critical view on the eco-friendliness of small hydroelectric installations. *Sci. Total Environ.*, **481**(1), 638–643, doi:10.1016/j.scitotenv.2013.11.047.

Preston, B.L., M. Langholtz, L. Eaton, C. Daly, and M. Halbleib, 2016: Climate Sensitivity of Agricultural Energy Crop Productivity. In: *2016 Billion-Ton Report: Advancing Domestic Resources for a Thriving Bioeconomy, Volume 2: Environmental Sustainability Effects of Select Scenarios from Volume 1*. U.S. Department of Energy, Oak Ridge National Laboratory, Oak Ridge, TN, USA, pp. 519–554.

Prieto, C., P. Cooper, A. I. Fernández, and L.F. Cabeza, 2016: Review of technology: Thermochemical energy storage for concentrated solar power plants. *Renew. Sustain. Energy Rev.*, **60**, 909–929, doi:10.1016/j.rser.2015.12.364.

Proskurina, S., M. Junginger, J. Heinimö, and E. Vakkilainen, 2019a: Global biomass trade for energy – Part 1: Statistical and methodological considerations. Biofuels, Bioprod. Biorefining, 13(2), 358–370, doi:10.1002/bbb.1841.

Proskurina, S., M. Junginger, J. Heinimö, B. Tekinel, and E. Vakkilainen, 2019b: Global biomass trade for energy – Part 2: Production and trade streams of wood pellets, liquid biofuels, charcoal, industrial roundwood and emerging energy biomass. *Biofuels, Bioprod. Biorefining*, **13**(2), 371–387, doi:10.1002/bbb.1858.

Prussi, M., A. O'Connell, and L. Lonza, 2019: Analysis of current aviation biofuel technical production potential in EU28. *Biomass and Bioenergy*, **130**, 105371, doi:10.1016/j.biombioe.2019.105371.

Pryor, S.C. and R.J. Barthelmie, 2013: Assessing the vulnerability of wind energy to climate change and extreme events. *Clim. Change*, **121**(1), 79–91, doi:10.1007/s10584-013-0889-y.

Pryor, S.C., R.J. Barthelmie, M.S. Bukovsky, L.R. Leung, and K. Sakaguchi, 2020: Climate change impacts on wind power generation. *Nat. Rev. Earth Environ.*, **2**(1), doi:10.1038/s43017-020-0101-7.

Pye, S. et al., 2020: An equitable redistribution of unburnable carbon. *Nat. Commun.*, **11**(1), 3968, doi:10.1038/s41467-020-17679-3.

Pye, S. et al., 2021: Modelling net-zero emissions energy systems requires a change in approach. *Clim. Policy*, **21**(2), 222–231, doi:10.1080/14693062.2020.1824891.

Qian, H., Y. Zhou, and L. Wu, 2018: Evaluating various choices of sector coverage in China's national emissions trading system (ETS). *Clim. Policy*, **18**(sup1), 7–26, doi:10.1080/14693062.2018.1464894.

Qin, Y. et al., 2018: Air quality–carbon–water synergies and trade-offs in China's natural gas industry. *Nat. Sustain.*, **1**(9), 505–511, doi:10.1038/s41893-018-0136-7.

Qiu, D., Y. Ye, D. Papadaskalopoulos, and G. Strbac, 2021: Scalable coordinated management of peer-to-peer energy trading: A multi-cluster deep reinforcement learning approach. *Appl. Energy*, **292**, 116940, doi:10.1016/j.apenergy.2021.116940.

Quarton, C.J. and S. Samsatli, 2020: Should we inject hydrogen into gas grids? Practicalities and whole-system value chain optimisation. *Appl. Energy*, **275**, 115172, doi:10.1016/j.apenergy.2020.115172.

Rabe, B.G., 2018: *Can we price carbon?*, MIT Press. Cambridge, MA, USA, 349 pp.

Rai, A., R. Esplin, O. Nunn, and T. Nelson, 2019: The times they are a changin': Current and future trends in electricity demand and supply. *Electr. J.*, **32(6)**, 24–32, doi:10.1016/j.tej.2019.05.017.

Rai, V., D.C. Reeves, and R. Margolis, 2016: Overcoming barriers and uncertainties in the adoption of residential solar PV. *Renew. Energy*, **89**, 498–505, doi:10.1016/j.renene.2015.11.080.

Raimi, D., R. Minsk, J. Higdon, and A. Krupnick, 2019: *Economic volatility in oil producing regions: impacts and federal policy options*. Columbia, Center on Global Energy Policy, New York, NY, USA, 53 pp.

Rajagopalan, K. and G.C. Nihous, 2013: An assessment of global Ocean Thermal Energy Conversion resources under broad geographical constraints. *J. Renew. Sustain. Energy*, **5(6)**, doi:10.1063/1.4850521.

Ralston Fonseca, F., P. Jaramillo, M. Bergés, and E. Severnini, 2019: Seasonal effects of climate change on intra-day electricity demand patterns. *Clim. Change*, **154(3–4)**, 435–451, doi:10.1007/s10584-019-02413-w.

Rand, J. and B. Hoen, 2017: Thirty years of North American wind energy acceptance research: What have we learned? *Energy Res. Soc. Sci.*, **29**(February), 135–148, doi:10.1016/j.erss.2017.05.019.

Rao, N.D. and S. Pachauri, 2017: Energy access and living standards: some observations on recent trends. *Environ. Res. Lett.*, **12(2)**, doi:10.1088/1748-9326/aa5b0d.

Rao, P.C. and M. Yoon, 2020: Potential Liquid-Organic Hydrogen Carrier (LOHC) Systems: A Review on Recent Progress. *Energies*, **13(22)**, 6040, doi:10.3390/en13226040.

Rathore, P.K.S., S.S. Das, and D.S. Chauhan, 2018: Perspectives of solar photovoltaic water pumping for irrigation in India. *Energy Strateg. Rev.*, **22**, 385–395, doi:10.1016/j.esr.2018.10.009.

Rauner, S. et al., 2020: Coal-exit health and environmental damage reductions outweigh economic impacts. *Nat. Clim. Change*, **10(4)**, 308–312, doi:10.1038/s41558-020-0728-x.

Ravestein, P., G. van der Schrier, R. Haarsma, R. Scheele, and M. van den Broek, 2018: Vulnerability of European intermittent renewable energy supply to climate change and climate variability. *Renew. Sustain. Energy Rev.*, **97**(October 2017), 497–508, doi:10.1016/j.rser.2018.08.057.

Rayner, J., M. Howlett, and A. Wellstead, 2017: Policy Mixes and their Alignment over Time: Patching and stretching in the oil sands reclamation regime in Alberta, Canada. *Environ. Policy Gov.*, **27(5)**, 472–483, doi:10.1002/eet.1773.

Realmonte, G. et al., 2019: An inter-model assessment of the role of direct air capture in deep mitigation pathways. *Nat. Commun.*, **10(1)**, 1–12, doi:10.1038/s41467-019-10842-5.

Rees, J.H. et al., 2018: Breaking the Habit: On the Highly Habitualized Nature of Meat Consumption and Implementation Intentions as One Effective Way of Reducing It. *Basic Appl. Soc. Psych.*, **40(3)**, 136–147, doi:10.1080/01973533.2018.1449111.

Regen, 2017: *Energy Storage: The Next Wave; Growth prospects and market outlook for energy storage. Regen Transforming Energy*, UK, 40 pp.

Rehman, S., L.M. Al-Hadhrami, and M.M. Alam, 2015: Pumped hydro energy storage system: A technological review. *Renew. Sustain. Energy Rev.*, **44**, 586–598, doi:10.1016/j.rser.2014.12.040.

Ren, X., Y. Che, K. Yang, and Y. Tao, 2016: Risk perception and public acceptance toward a highly protested Waste-to-Energy facility. *Waste Manag.*, **48**, 528–539, doi:10.1016/J.WASMAN.2015.10.036.

REN21, 2019: *Renewables 2019 Global Status Report*. REN21 Secretariat, Paris, France, 336 pp.

Rentier, G., H. Lelieveldt, and G.J. Kramer, 2019: Varieties of coal-fired power phase-out across Europe. *Energy Policy*, **132**, 620–632, doi:10.1016/j.enpol.2019.05.042.

Rentizelas, A., I.C. Melo, P.N. Alves Junior, J.S. Campoli, and D. Aparecida do Nascimento Rebelatto, 2019: Multi-criteria efficiency assessment of international biomass supply chain pathways using Data Envelopment Analysis. *J. Clean. Prod.*, **237**, 117690, doi:10.1016/j.jclepro.2019.117690.

Rentschler, J., and M. Bazilian, 2017: Reforming fossil fuel subsidies: drivers, barriers and the state of progress. *Clim. Policy*, **17(7)**, 891–914, doi:10.1080/14693062.2016.1169393.

Reyers, M., J. Moemken, and J.G. Pinto, 2016: Future changes of wind energy potentials over Europe in a large CMIP5 multi-model ensemble. *Int. J. Climatol.*, **36(2)**, 783–796, doi:10.1002/joc.4382.

Riahi, K. et al., 2012: Chapter 17 – Energy Pathways for Sustainable Development. In: *Global Energy Assessment – Toward a Sustainable Future* [Johansson, T.B., N. Nakicenovic, A. Patwardhan, and L. Gomez-Echeverri, (eds.)]. Cambridge University Press, Cambridge, UK, pp. 1203–1306.

Riahi, K. et al., 2017: The Shared Socioeconomic Pathways and their energy, land use, and greenhouse gas emissions implications: An overview. *Glob. Environ. Change*, **42**, 153–168, doi:10.1016/j.gloenvcha.2016.05.009.

Riahi, K. et al., 2021: Long-term economic benefits of stabilizing warming without overshoot – the ENGAGE model intercomparison. *Nat. Clim. Change*, doi:10.21203/rs.3.rs-127847/v1.

Rickards, L., J. Wiseman, and Y. Kashima, 2014: Barriers to effective climate change mitigation: the case of senior government and business decision makers. *Wiley Interdiscip. Rev. Clim. Change*, **5(6)**, 753–773, doi:10.1002/wcc.305.

Riede, M., D. Spoltore, and K. Leo, 2021: Organic Solar Cells—The Path to Commercial Success. *Adv. Energy Mater.*, **11(1)**, 2002653, doi:10.1002/AENM.202002653.

Rietzler, A.C., C.R. Botta, M.M. Ribeiro, O. Rocha, and A.L. Fonseca, 2018: Accelerated eutrophication and toxicity in tropical reservoir water and sediments: an ecotoxicological approach. *Environ. Sci. Pollut. Res.*, **25(14)**, 13292–13311, doi:10.1007/s11356-016-7719-5.

Rissman, J. et al., 2020: Technologies and policies to decarbonize global industry: Review and assessment of mitigation drivers through 2070. *Appl. Energy*, **266**. https://doi.org/10.1016/j.apenergy.2020.114848.

Robinius, M. et al., 2017: Linking the Power and Transport Sectors—Part 1: The Principle of Sector Coupling. *Energies*, **10(7)**, 956, doi:10.3390/en10070956.

Rockström, J. et al., 2017: A roadmap for rapid decarbonization. *Science*, **355(6331)**, 1269–1271, doi:10.1126/science.aah3443.

Roddis, P., S. Carver, M. Dallimer, and G. Ziv, 2019: Accounting for taste? Analysing diverging public support for energy sources in Great Britain. *Energy Res. Soc. Sci.*, **56**, 101226, doi:10.1016/j.erss.2019.101226.

Roe, S. et al., 2021: Land-based measures to mitigate climate change: Potential and feasibility by country. *Glob. Change Biol.*, (December 2020), 1–34, doi:10.1111/gcb.15873.

Roelfsema, M. et al., 2020: Taking stock of national climate policies to evaluate implementation of the Paris Agreement. *Nat. Commun.*, **11(1)**, 2096, doi:10.1038/s41467-020–15414-6.

Rogelj, J. et al., 2015a: Energy system transformations for limiting end-of-century warming to below 1.5°C. *Nat. Clim. Change*, **5(6)**, 519–527, doi:10.1038/nclimate2572.

Rogelj, J. et al., 2015b: Zero emission targets as long-term global goals for climate protection. *Environ. Res. Lett.*, **10(105007)**, 1–11, doi:10.1088/1748-9326/10/10/105007.

Rogelj, J. et al., 2016: Paris Agreement climate proposals need a boost to keep warming well below 2°C. *Nature*, **534(7609)**, 631–639, doi:10.1038/nature18307.

Rogelj, J. et al., 2018a: Scenarios towards limiting global mean temperature increase below 1.5°C. *Nat. Clim. Change*, **8(4)**, 325–332, doi:10.1038/s41558-018-0091-3.

Rogers, J.N. et al., 2017: An assessment of the potential products and economic and environmental impacts resulting from a billion ton bioeconomy. *Biofuels, Bioprod. Biorefining*, **11(1)**, 110–128, doi:10.1002/bbb.1728.

Rogge, K.S., 2017: Conceptual and empirical advances in analysing policy mixes for energy transitions. *Energy Res. Soc. Sci.*, **33**, 1–10, doi:10.1016/J.ERSS.2017.09.025.

Rogge, K.S., and J. Schleich, 2018: Do policy mix characteristics matter for low-carbon innovation? A survey-based exploration of renewable power generation technologies in Germany. *Res. Policy*, **47(9)**, 1639–1654, https://doi.org/10.1016/j.respol.2018.05.011.

Rohrig, K. et al., 2019: Powering the 21st century by wind energy—Options, facts, figures. *Appl. Phys. Rev.*, **6(3)**, 031303, doi:10.1063/1.5089877.

Romps, D.M., J.T. Seeley, D. Vollaro, and J. Molinari, 2014: Projected increase in lightning strikes in the United States due to global warming. *Science*, **346(6211)**, 851–854, doi:10.1126/science.1259100.

Roques, F. and D. Finon, 2017: Adapting electricity markets to decarbonisation and security of supply objectives: Toward a hybrid regime? *Energy Policy*, **105**, 584–596, doi:10.1016/j.enpol.2017.02.035.

Rosa, L., J.A. Reimer, M.S. Went, and P. D'Odorico, 2020a: Hydrological limits to carbon capture and storage. *Nat. Sustain.*, **3(8)**, 658–666, doi:10.1038/s41893-020-0532-7.

Rosa, L., D.L. Sanchez, G. Realmonte, D. Baldocchi, and P. D'Odorico, 2020b: The water footprint of carbon capture and storage technologies. *Renew. Sustain. Energy Rev.*, (**April**), 110511, doi:10.1016/j.rser.2020.110511.

Rosenbloom, D., 2019: A clash of socio-technical systems: Exploring actor interactions around electrification and electricity trade in unfolding low-carbon pathways for Ontario. *Energy Res. Soc. Sci.*, **49**, 219–232, doi:10.1016/j.erss.2018.10.015.

Rosendahl, K., C. Böhringer, and H. Storrøsten, 2017: Robust policies to mitigate carbon leakage. *J. Public Econ.*, **149**, 35–46, doi:10.1016/j.jpubeco.2017.03.006.

Rosenow, J., F. Kern, and K. Rogge, 2017: The need for comprehensive and well targeted instrument mixes to stimulate energy transitions: The case of energy efficiency policy. *Energy Res. Soc. Sci.*, **33**, 95–104, doi:10.1016/j.erss.2017.09.013.

Rubin, E.S., C. Chen, and A.B. Rao, 2007: Cost and performance of fossil fuel power plants with CO_2 capture and storage. *Energy Policy*, **35**, 4444–4454, doi:10.1016/j.enpol.2007.03.009.

Rubin, E.S., J.E. Davison, and H.J. Herzog, 2015: The cost of CO_2 capture and storage. *Int. J. Greenh. Gas Control*, **40**, 378–400, doi:10.1016/j.ijggc.2015.05.018.

Rubio, G. and A. Tricot, 2016: *SMR Techno-Economic Assessment—Project 1: Comprehensive Analysis and Assessment*. Atkins, Bristol, UK, 121 pp.

Rudolf, M., R. Seidl, C. Moser, P. Krütli, and M. Stauffacher, 2014: Public preference of electricity options before and after Fukushima. *J. Integr. Environ. Sci.*, **11(1)**, 1–15, doi:10.1080/1943815X.2014.881887.

Rudolph, D., C. Haggett, and M. Aitken, 2018: Community benefits from offshore renewables: The relationship between different understandings of impact, community, and benefit. *Environ. Plan. C Polit. Sp.*, **36(1)**, 92–117, doi:10.1177/2399654417699206.

Ruepert, A.M., K. Keizer, and L. Steg, 2017: The relationship between Corporate Environmental Responsibility, employees' biospheric values and pro-environmental behaviour at work. *J. Environ. Psychol.*, **54**, 65–78, doi:10.1016/j.jenvp.2017.10.006.

Ruffato-Ferreira, V. et al., 2017: A foundation for the strategic long-term planning of the renewable energy sector in Brazil: Hydroelectricity and wind energy in the face of climate change scenarios. *Renew. Sustain. Energy Rev.*, **72**(July 2016), 1124–1137, doi:10.1016/j.rser.2016.10.020.

Ruosteenoja, K., P. Räisänen, S. Devraj, S.S. Garud, and A.V. Lindfors, 2019: Future changes in incident surface solar radiation and contributing factors in India in CMIP5 climate model simulations. *J. Appl. Meteorol. Climatol.*, **58(1)**, 19–35, doi:10.1175/JAMC-D-18-0013.1.

Russell, A., J. Firestone, D. Bidwell, and M. Gardner, 2020: Place meaning and consistency with offshore wind: An island and coastal tale. *Renew. Sustain. Energy Rev.*, **132**, 110044, doi:10.1016/j.rser.2020.110044.

Ruth, M.F. and B. Kroposki, 2014: Energy Systems Integration: An Evolving Energy Paradigm. *Electr. J.*, **27(6)**, 36–47, doi:10.1016/j.tej.2014.06.001.

Saba, S.M., M. Müller, M. Robinius, and D. Stolten, 2018: The investment costs of electrolysis – A comparison of cost studies from the past 30 years. *Int. J. Hydrogen Energy*, **43(3)**, 1209–1223, doi:10.1016/j.ijhydene.2017.11.115.

Sachs, J.D., G. Schmidt-Traub, and J. Williams, 2016: Pathways to zero emissions. *Nat. Geosci.*, **9(11)**, 799–801, doi:10.1038/ngeo2826.

Sachs, J.D. et al., 2019: Six Transformations to achieve the Sustainable Development Goals. *Nat. Sustain.*, **2(9)**, 805–814, doi:10.1038/s41893-019-0352-9.

Sælen, H. and S. Kallbekken, 2011: A choice experiment on fuel taxation and earmarking in Norway. *Ecol. Econ.*, **70(11)**, 2181–2190, doi:10.1016/j.ecolecon.2011.06.024.

Saha, M. and M.J. Eckelman, 2018: Geospatial assessment of regional scale bioenergy production potential on marginal and degraded land. *Resour. Conserv. Recycl.*, **128**, 90–97, doi:10.1016/j.resconrec.2017.09.008.

Sahu, A., N. Yadav, and K. Sudhakar, 2016: Floating photovoltaic power plant: A review. *Renew. Sustain. Energy Rev.*, **66**, 815–824, doi:10.1016/j.rser.2016.08.051.

Sakai, P. and Coauthors, 2020: Understanding the Implications of Alternative Bioenergy Crops to Support Smallholder Farmers in Brazil. *Sustainability*, **12**, 2146, doi:10.3390/su12052146.

Salman, C.A., E. Thorin, and J. Yan, 2020: Opportunities and limitations for existing CHP plants to integrate polygeneration of drop-in biofuels with onsite hydrogen production. *Energy Convers. Manag.*, **221**, 113109, doi:10.1016/j.enconman.2020.113109.

Salmon, N., R. Bañares-Alcántara, and R. Nayak-Luke, 2021: Optimization of green ammonia distribution systems for intercontinental energy transport. *iScience*, **24(8)**, 102903, doi:10.1016/j.isci.2021.102903.

Sánchez-Bastardo, N., R. Schlögl, and H. Ruland, 2020: Methane Pyrolysis for CO_2-Free H_2 Production: A Green Process to Overcome Renewable Energies Unsteadiness. *Chemie Ing. Tech.*, **92(10)**, 1596–1609, doi:10.1002/cite.202000029.

Sanchez, D.L., N. Johnson, S.T. McCoy, P.A. Turner, and K.J. Mach, 2018: Near-term deployment of carbon capture and sequestration from biorefineries in the United States. *Proc. Natl. Acad. Sci.*, **115(19)**, 4875 LP – 4880, doi:10.1073/pnas.1719695115.

Santen, N., J. Bistline, G. Blanford, and F. de la Chesnaye, 2017: *Systems Analysis in Electric Power Sector Modeling: A Review of the Recent Literature and Capabilities of Selected Capacity Planning Tools*. Electric Power Research Institute, Palo Alto, CA, USA, 62 pp.

Santillán Vera, M., A. de la Vega Navarro, and J. Islas Samperio, 2021: Climate change and income inequality: An I-O analysis of the structure and intensity of the GHG emissions in Mexican households. *Energy Sustain. Dev.*, **60**, 15–25, doi:10.1016/j.esd.2020.11.002.

Santos, G., 2008: The London experience. In: Pricing in Road Transport. In: *Pricing in road transport: A multi-disciplinary perspective* [Verhoef, E., M.C.J. Bliemer, L. Steg, and B. van Wee, (ed.)]. Edward Elgar Publishing, Cheltenham, UK, pp. 273–292.

Sanusi, Y.S. and E.M.A. Mokheimer, 2019: Thermo-economic optimization of hydrogen production in a membrane-SMR integrated to ITM-oxy-combustion plant using genetic algorithm. *Appl. Energy*, **235**, 164–176, doi:10.1016/j.apenergy.2018.10.082.

Sanz Rodrigo, J. et al., 2016: Mesoscale to microscale wind farm flow modeling and evaluation. *Wiley Interdiscip. Rev. Energy Environ.*, **6**(April), e214, doi:10.1002/wene.214.

Satchwell, A. et al., 2021: *A National Roadmap for Grid-Interactive Efficient Buildings*. U.S. Department of Energy, Washington, USA, 166 pp.

Saunders, H.D. et al., 2021: Energy Efficiency: What Has Research Delivered in the Last 40 Years? *Annu. Rev. Environ. Resour.*, **46(1)**, 135–165, doi:10.1146/annurev-environ-012320-084937.

Savvanidou, E., E. Zervas, and K.P. Tsagarakis, 2010: Public acceptance of biofuels. *Energy Policy*, **38**, 3482–3488, doi:10.1016/j.enpol.2010.02.021.

6

Saygin, D., J. Rigter, B. Caldecott, N. Wagner, and D. Gielen, 2019: Power sector asset stranding effects of climate policies. *Energy Sources, Part B Econ. Plan. Policy*, **14(4)**, 99–124, doi:10.1080/15567249.2019.1618421.

Scaccabarozzi, R., M. Gatti, and E. Martelli, 2016: Thermodynamic analysis and numerical optimization of the NET Power oxy-combustion cycle. *Appl. Energy*, **178**, 505–526, doi:10.1016/j.apenergy.2016.06.060.

Scanlon, B.R., R.C. Reedy, F. Male, and M. Walsh, 2017: Water Issues Related to Transitioning from Conventional to Unconventional Oil Production in the Permian Basin. *Environ. Sci. Technol.*, **51(18)**, 10903–10912, doi:10.1021/acs.est.7b02185.

Schaeffer, R. et al., 2012: Energy sector vulnerability to climate change: A review. *Energy*, **38(1)**, 1–12, doi:10.1016/j.energy.2011.11.056.

Schaeffer, R. et al., 2020: Comparing transformation pathways across major economies. *Clim. Change*, **162(4)**, 1787–1803, doi:10.1007/s10584-020-02837-9.

Schäfer, S., 2019: Decoupling the EU ETS from subsidized renewables and other demand side effects: lessons from the impact of the EU ETS on CO_2 emissions in the German electricity sector. *Energy Policy*, **133**, 110858, doi:10.1016/j.enpol.2019.06.066.

Scheer, D., W. Konrad, and O. Scheel, 2013: Public evaluation of electricity technologies and future low-carbon portfolios in Germany and the USA. *Energy. Sustain. Soc.*, **3(1)**, 8, doi:10.1186/2192-0567-3-8.

Schelly, C., 2014: Residential solar electricity adoption: What motivates, and what matters? A case study of early adopters. *Energy Res. Soc. Sci.*, **2**, 183–191, doi:10.1016/j.erss.2014.01.001.

Schemme, S., R.C. Samsun, R. Peters, and D. Stolten, 2017: Power-to-fuel as a key to sustainable transport systems – An analysis of diesel fuels produced from CO2 and renewable electricity. *Fuel*, **205**, 198–221, doi:10.1016/j.fuel.2017.05.061.

Schenker, O., S. Koesler, and A. Löschel, 2018: On the effects of unilateral environmental policy on offshoring in multi-stage production processes. *Can. J. Econ. Can. d'économique*, **51(4)**, 1221–1256, doi:10.1111/caje.12354.

Schill, W.P., 2020: Electricity Storage and the Renewable Energy Transition. *Joule*, **4(10)**, 2059–2064, doi:10.1016/J.JOULE.2020.07.022.

Schlachtberger, D.P., T. Brown, S. Schramm, and M. Greiner, 2017: The benefits of cooperation in a highly renewable European electricity network. *Energy*, **134**, 469–481, doi:10.1016/j.energy.2017.06.004.

Schmalensee, R. and R.N. Stavins, 2017: Lessons Learned from Three Decades of Experience with Cap and Trade. *Rev. Environ. Econ. Policy*, **11(1)**, 59–79, doi:10.1093/reep/rew017.

Schmid, E., A. Pechan, M. Mehnert, and K. Eisenack, 2017: Imagine all these futures: On heterogeneous preferences and mental models in the German energy transition. *Energy Res. Soc. Sci.*, **27**, 45–56, doi:10.1016/j.erss.2017.02.012.

Schmidt, O. et al., 2017: Future cost and performance of water electrolysis: An expert elicitation study. *Int. J. Hydrogen Energy*, **42(52)**, 30470–30492, doi:10.1016/j.ijhydene.2017.10.045.

Schönauer, A.-L. and S. Glanz, 2021: Hydrogen in future energy systems: Social acceptance of the technology and its large-scale infrastructure. *Int. J. Hydrogen Energy*, **47(24)**, 12251–12263, doi:10.1016/j.ijhydene.2021.05.160.

Schreyer, F. et al., 2020: Common but differentiated leadership: strategies and challenges for carbon neutrality by 2050 across industrialized economies. *Environ. Res. Lett.*, **15(11)**, 114016, doi:10.1088/1748-9326/abb852.

Schuitema, G. and L. Steg, 2008: The role of revenue use in the acceptability of transport pricing policies. *Transp. Res. Part F Traffic Psychol. Behav.*, **11(3)**, 221–231, doi:10.1016/j.trf.2007.11.003.

Schuitema, G., L. Steg, and S. Forward, 2010: Explaining differences in acceptability before and acceptance after the implementation of a congestion charge in Stockholm. *Transp. Res. Part A Policy Pract.*, **44(2)**, 99–109, doi:10.1016/j.tra.2009.11.005.

Schuitema, G., L. Steg, and M. van Kruining, 2011: When Are Transport Pricing Policies Fair and Acceptable? *Soc. Justice Res.*, **24(1)**, 66–84, doi:10.1007/s11211-011-0124-9.

Schultz, P.W., M. Estrada, J. Schmitt, R. Sokoloski, and N. Silva-Send, 2015: Using in-home displays to provide smart meter feedback about household electricity consumption: A randomized control trial comparing kilowatts, cost, and social norms. *Energy*, **90**, 351–358, doi:10.1016/j.energy.2015.06.130.

Schwartz, D., W.B. De Bruin, B. Fischhoff, and L. Lave, 2015: Advertising energy saving programs: The potential environmental cost of emphasizing monetary savings. *J. Exp. Psychol. Appl.*, **21(2)**, 158–166, doi:10.1037/xap0000042.

Schyns, J.F., A.Y. Hoekstra, M.J. Booij, R.J. Hogeboom, and M.M. Mekonnen, 2019: Limits to the world's green water resources for food, feed, fiber, timber, and bioenergy. *Proc. Natl. Acad. Sci.*, **116(11)**, 4893–4898, doi:10.1073/pnas.1817380116.

Scott, A. et al., 2016: *Accelerating access to electricity in Africa with off-grid solar for solar household solutions: Executive summary*. Overseas Development Institute, London, UK, 7 pp. http://www.odi.org/publications/10200-accelerating-access-electricity-africa-off-grid-solar.

Scott, M. and G. Powells, 2020: Towards a new social science research agenda for hydrogen transitions: Social practices, energy justice, and place attachment. *Energy Res. Soc. Sci.*, **61**, 101346, doi:10.1016/j.erss.2019.101346.

Selosse, S. and O. Ricci, 2017: Carbon capture and storage: Lessons from a storage potential and localization analysis. *Appl. Energy*, **188**, 32–44, doi:10.1016/j.apenergy.2016.11.117.

Sepulveda, N.A., J.D. Jenkins, F.J. de Sisternes, and R.K. Lester, 2018: The Role of Firm Low-Carbon Electricity Resources in Deep Decarbonization of Power Generation. *Joule*, **2(11)**, 2403–2420, doi:10.1016/j.joule.2018.08.006.

Sepulveda, N.A., J.D. Jenkins, A. Edington, D.S. Mallapragada, and R.K. Lester, 2021: The design space for long-duration energy storage in decarbonized power systems. *Nat. Energy*, **6(5)**, 506–516, doi:10.1038/s41560-021-00796-8.

Seto, K.C. et al., 2016: Carbon Lock-In: Types, Causes, and Policy Implications. *Annu. Rev. Environ. Resour.*, **41(1)**, 425–452, doi:10.1146/annurev-environ-110615-085934.

Seyfang, G. and A. Haxeltine, 2012: Growing grassroots innovations: Exploring the role of community-based initiatives in governing sustainable energy transitions. *Environ. Plan. C Gov. Policy*, **30(3)**, 381–400, doi:10.1068/c10222.

Shakoor, A. et al., 2017: *Roadmap for Flexibility Services to 2030: A report to the Committee on Climate Change*. Poyry and Imperial College London, London, UK, 92 pp.

Shaner, M.R., S.J. Davis, N.S. Lewis, and K. Caldeira, 2018: Geophysical constraints on the reliability of solar and wind power in the United States. *Energy Environ. Sci.*, **11(4)**, 914–925, doi:10.1039/C7EE03029K.

Sharma, A., J. Parikh, and C. Singh, 2019: Transition to LPG for cooking: A case study from two states of India. *Energy Sustain. Dev.*, **51**, 63–72, doi:10.1016/j.esd.2019.06.001.

Sharma, D., K. Ravindra, M. Kaur, S. Prinja, and S. Mor, 2020: Cost evaluation of different household fuels and identification of the barriers for the choice of clean cooking fuels in India. *Sustain. Cities Soc.*, **52**, 101825, doi:10.1016/j.scs.2019.101825.

Sharma, T. and Y. Xu, 2021: Domestic and international CO_2 source-sink matching for decarbonizing India's electricity. *Resour. Conserv. Recycl.*, **174**(July), 105824, doi:10.1016/j.resconrec.2021.105824.

Sharmina, M., C. McGlade, P. Gilbert, and A. Larkin, 2017: Global energy scenarios and their implications for future shipped trade. *Mar. Policy*, **84**, 12–21, doi:10.1016/j.marpol.2017.06.025.

Shearer, C., R. Fofrich, and S.J. Davis, 2017: Future CO_2 emissions and electricity generation from proposed coal-fired power plants in India. *Earth's Future*, **5(4)**, 408–416, doi:10.1002/2017EF000542.

6

Sherwin, E.D., 2021: Electrofuel Synthesis from Variable Renewable Electricity: An Optimization-Based Techno-Economic Analysis. *Environ. Sci. Technol.*, **55(11)**, 7583–7594, doi:10.1021/acs.est.0c07955.

Shih, C.F., T. Zhang, J. Li, and C. Bai, 2018: Powering the Future with Liquid Sunshine. *Joule*, **2(10)**, 1925–1949, doi:10.1016/j.joule.2018.08.016.

Shindell, D., G. Faluvegi, K. Seltzer, and C. Shindell, 2018: Quantified, localized health benefits of accelerated carbon dioxide emissions reductions. *Nat. Clim. Change*, **8**, 291–295, doi:10.1038/s41558-018-0108-y.

Shu, K., U.A. Schneider, and J. Scheffran, 2017: Optimizing the bioenergy industry infrastructure: Transportation networks and bioenergy plant locations. *Appl. Energy*, **192**, 247–261, doi:10.1016/j.apenergy.2017.01.092.

Shukla, A.K., K. Sudhakar, and P. Baredar, 2016: A comprehensive review on design of building integrated photovoltaic system. *Energy Build.*, **128**, 99–110, doi:10.1016/j.enbuild.2016.06.077.

Siciliano, G., F. Urban, M. Tan-Mullins, and G. Mohan, 2018: Large dams, energy justice and the divergence between international, national and local developmental needs and priorities in the global South. *Energy Res. Soc. Sci.*, **41**, 199–209, doi:10.1016/j.erss.2018.03.029.

Siegrist, M. and V.H.M. Visschers, 2013: Acceptance of nuclear power: The Fukushima effect. *Energy Policy*, **59**, 112–119, doi:10.1016/j.enpol.2012.07.051.

Singh, A.K., 2019: Better accounting of greenhouse gas emissions from Indian coal mining activities — A field perspective. *Environ. Pract.*, doi:10.1080/14660466.2019.1564428.

Singh, A.K. and P.N. Hajra, 2018: *Coalbed Methane in India: Opportunities, Issues and Challenges for Recovery and Utilizatione*. Springer International Publishing, Cham, Switzerland, 98 pp.

Singh, A.K. and J.N. Sahu, 2018: Coal mine gas: a new fuel utilization technique for India. *Int. J. Green Energy*, **15(12)**, 732–743, doi:10.1080/15435075.2018.1529572.

Singh, U. and A.B. Rao, 2015: Integrating SO_2 and NOx control systems in Indian coal-fired power plants. *DECISION*, **42(2)**, 191–209, doi:10.1007/s40622-015-0083-3.

Singh, U. and L.M. Colosi, 2019: Water–energy sustainability synergies and health benefits as means to motivate potable reuse of coalbed methane-produced waters. *Ambio*, **48(7)**, 752–768, doi:10.1007/s13280-018-1098-8.

Singh, U. and L.M. Colosi, 2021: The case for estimating carbon return on investment (CROI) for CCUS platforms. *Appl. Energy*, **285**, 116394, doi:10.1016/j.apenergy.2020.116394.

Singh, U., A. B. Rao, and M.K. Chandel, 2017: Economic Implications of CO_2 Capture from the Existing as Well as Proposed Coal-fired Power Plants in India under Various Policy Scenarios. *Energy Procedia*, Vol. 114, Elsevier Ltd, New York, NY, USA, pp. 7638–7650.

Singh, U., E.M. Loudermilk, and L.M. Colosi, 2021: Accounting for the role of transport and storage infrastructure costs in carbon negative bioenergy deployment. *Greenh. Gases Sci. Technol.*, **11(1)**, 144–164, doi:10.1002/ghg.2041.

Sjoberg, L., 2004: Local Acceptance of a High-Level Nuclear Waste Repository. *Risk Anal.*, **24(3)**, 737–749, doi:10.1111/j.0272-4332.2004.00472.x.

Sklarew, J.F., 2018: Power fluctuations: How Japan's nuclear infrastructure priorities influence electric utilities' clout. *Energy Res. Soc. Sci.*, **41**(April), 158–167, doi:10.1016/j.erss.2018.04.036.

Sloot, D., L. Jans, and L. Steg, 2018: Can community energy initiatives motivate sustainable energy behaviours? The role of initiative involvement and personal pro-environmental motivation. *J. Environ. Psychol.*, **57**(November 2017), 99–106, doi:10.1016/j.jenvp.2018.06.007.

Smallbone, A., V. Jülch, R. Wardle, and A.P. Roskilly, 2017: Levelised Cost of Storage for Pumped Heat Energy Storage in comparison with other energy storage technologies. *Energy Convers. Manag.*, **152**, 221–228, doi:10.1016/j.enconman.2017.09.047.

Sminchak, J.R., S. Mawalkar, and N. Gupta, 2020: Large CO_2 Storage Volumes Result in Net Negative Emissions for Greenhouse Gas Life Cycle Analysis Based on Records from 22 Years of CO_2 –Enhanced Oil Recovery Operations. *Energy & Fuels*, **34(3)**, 3566–3577, doi:10.1021/acs.energyfuels.9b04540.

Smith, C. J. et al., 2019: Current fossil fuel infrastructure does not yet commit us to 1.5°C warming. *Nat. Commun.*, **10(1)**, 101, doi:10.1038/s41467-018-07999-w.

Smith, C.M., R.J. Barthelmie, and S.C. Pryor, 2013: In situ observations of the influence of a large onshore wind farm on near-surface temperature, turbulence intensity and wind speed profiles. *Environ. Res. Lett.*, **8(3)**, 034006, doi:10.1088/1748-9326/8/3/034006.

Smith, K. et al., 2015: Pilot plant results for a precipitating potassium carbonate solvent absorption process promoted with glycine for enhanced CO_2 capture. *Fuel Process. Technol.*, **135**, 60–65, doi:10.1016/j.fuproc.2014.10.013.

Smith, P. et al., 2016: Biophysical and economic limits to negative CO_2 emissions. *Nat. Clim. Change*, **6(1)**, 42–50, doi:10.1038/nclimate2870.

Smith, P., J. Price, A. Molotoks, R. Warren, and Y. Malhi, 2018: Impacts on terrestrial biodiversity of moving from a 2°C to a 1.5°C target. *Philos. Trans. R. Soc. A Math. Phys. Eng. Sci.*, **376**, 20160456, doi:10.1098/rsta.2016.0456.

Smith, S.M., C.P. Haugtvedt, and R.E. Petty, 1994: Attitudes and recycling: Does the measurement of affect enhance behavioral prediction? *Psychol. Mark.*, **11(4)**, 359–374, doi:10.1002/mar.4220110405.

Soergel, B. et al., 2021: A sustainable development pathway for climate action within the UN 2030 Agenda. *Nat. Clim. Change*, **11(8)**, 656–664, doi:10.1038/s41558-021-01098-3.

Solaun, K. and E. Cerdá, 2017: The impact of climate change on the generation of hydroelectric power-a case study in southern Spain. *Energies*, **10(9)**, doi:10.3390/en10091343.

Solaun, K. and E. Cerdá, 2019: Climate change impacts on renewable energy generation. A review of quantitative projections. *Renew. Sustain. Energy Rev.*, **116**, doi:10.1016/j.rser.2019.109415.

Solomon, A.A., D. Bogdanov, and C. Breyer, 2019: Curtailment-storage-penetration nexus in the energy transition. *Appl. Energy*, **235**, 1351–1368, doi:10.1016/j.apenergy.2018.11.069.

Soloveichik, G., 2016: *Ammonia as Virtual Hydrogen Carrier*. H2@ Scale Workshop. 2016: 19.

Somanathan E., T. Sterner, T. Sugiyama, D. Chimanikire, N.K. Dubash, J. Essandoh-Yeddu, S. Fifita, L. Goulder, A. Jaffe, X. Labandeira, S. Managi, C. Mitchell, J.P. Montero, F. Teng, and T. Zylicz, 2014: National and Sub-national Policies and Institutions. In: *Climate Change 2014: Mitigation of Climate Change*. Contribution of Working Group III to the Fifth Assessment Report of the Intergovernmental Panel on Climate Change [Edenhofer, O., R. Pichs-Madruga, Y. Sokona, E. Farahani, S. Kadner, K. Seyboth, A. Adler, I. Baum, S. Brunner, P. Eickemeier, B. Kriemann, J. Savolainen, S. Schlömer, C. von Stechow, T. Zwickel and J.C. Minx (eds.)]. Cambridge University Press, Cambridge, UK and New York, NY, USA, pp. 1141–1206.

Song, X. et al., 2018: Analysis on the fault characteristics of three-phase short-circuit for half-wavelength AC transmission lines. *Glob. Energy Interconnect.*, **1(2)**, 115–121, https://doi.org/10.14171/j.2096-5117.gei.2018.02.002.

Soni, A., 2018: Out of sight, out of mind? Investigating the longitudinal impact of the Fukushima nuclear accident on public opinion in the United States. *Energy Policy*, **122**, 169–175, doi:10.1016/j.enpol.2018.07.024.

Sonter, L.J., M.C. Dade, J.E.M. Watson, and R.K. Valenta, 2020: Renewable energy production will exacerbate mining threats to biodiversity. *Nat. Commun.*, **11(1)**, 4174, doi:10.1038/s41467-020-17928-5.

Sorrell, S., 2015: Reducing energy demand: A review of issues, challenges and approaches. *Renew. Sustain. Energy Rev.*, **47**, 74–82, doi:10.1016/j.rser.2015.03.002.

Sovacool, B.K., 2017: Reviewing, Reforming, and Rethinking Global Energy Subsidies: Towards a Political Economy Research Agenda. *Ecol. Econ.*, **135**, 150–163, doi:10.1016/j.ecolecon.2016.12.009.

6

Sovacool, B.K., and S. Griffiths, 2020: The cultural barriers to a low-carbon future: A review of six mobility and energy transitions across 28 countries. *Renew. Sustain. Energy Rev.*, **119**, 109569, doi:10.1016/j.rser.2019.109569.

Sovacool, B.K., M.A. Munoz Perea, A.V. Matamoros, and P. Enevoldsen, 2016: Valuing the manufacturing externalities of wind energy: assessing the environmental profit and loss of wind turbines in Northern Europe. *Wind Energy*, **19**, 1623–1647, doi:10.1002/we.1941.

Sovacool, B.K. et al., 2020: Sustainable minerals and metals for a low-carbon future. *Science*, **367(6473)**, 30–33, doi:10.1126/science.aaz6003.

Sovacool, B.K. et al., 2020: Hot transformations: Governing rapid and deep household heating transitions in China, Denmark, Finland and the United Kingdom, Energy Policy, Volume 139, 111330, doi:10.1016/j.enpol.2020.111330.

Spagnolo, S., G. Chinellato, S. Cristiano, A. Zucaro, and F. Gonella, 2020: Sustainability assessment of bioenergy at different scales: An emergy analysis of biogas power production. *J. Clean. Prod.*, **277**, 124038, doi:10.1016/j.jclepro.2020.124038.

Spalding-Fecher, R. et al., 2016: The vulnerability of hydropower production in the Zambezi River Basin to the impacts of climate change and irrigation development. *Mitig. Adapt. Strateg. Glob. Change*, **21(5)**, 721–742, doi:10.1007/s11027-014-9619-7.

Spence, A., C. Demski, C. Butler, K. Parkhill, and N. Pidgeon, 2015: Public perceptions of demand-side management and a smarter energy future. *Nat. Clim. Change*, **5**, 550–554, https://doi.org/10.1038/nclimate2610.

Spencer, T. et al., 2018: The 1.5°C target and coal sector transition: at the limits of societal feasibility. *Clim. Policy*, **18(3)**, 335–351, doi:10.1080/14693062.2017.1386540.

Spittler, N. et al., 2020: The role of geothermal resources in sustainable power system planning in Iceland. *Renew. Energy*, **153**, 1081–1090, doi:10.1016/j.renene.2020.02.046.

Srinivasan, T.N., and T.S. Gopi Rethinaraj, 2013: Fukushima and thereafter: Reassessment of risks of nuclear power. *Energy Policy*, **52**, 726–736, doi:10.1016/j.enpol.2012.10.036.

Stadelmann, M., 2017: Mind the gap? Critically reviewing the energy efficiency gap with empirical evidence. *Energy Res. Soc. Sci.*, **27**, 117–128, doi:10.1016/j.erss.2017.03.006.

Staffell, I. and M. Rustomji, 2016: Maximising the value of electricity storage. *J. Energy Storage*, **8**, 212–225, doi:10.1016/j.est.2016.08.010.

Staffell, I. and S. Pfenninger, 2018: The increasing impact of weather on electricity supply and demand. *Energy*, **145**, 65–78, doi:10.1016/j.energy.2017.12.051.

Staffell, I. et al., 2018: The role of hydrogen and fuel cells in the global energy system. *Energy Environ. Sci.*, **12**, doi:10.1039/C8EE01157E.

Staples, M.D., R. Malina, and S.R.H. Barrett, 2017: The limits of bioenergy for mitigating global life-cycle greenhouse gas emissions from fossil fuels. *Nat. Energy*, **2(2)**, 16202, doi:10.1038/nenergy.2016.202.

Staples, M.D., R. Malina, P. Suresh, J.I. Hileman, and S.R.H. Barrett, 2018: Aviation CO_2 emissions reductions from the use of alternative jet fuels. *Energy Policy*, **114**, 342–354, doi:10.1016/j.enpol.2017.12.007.

Steckel, J.C., O. Edenhofer, and M. Jakob, 2015: Drivers for the renaissance of coal. *Proc. Natl. Acad. Sci.*, **112(29)**, E3775–E3781, doi:10.1073/pnas.1422722112.

Steckel, J.C., J. Hilaire, M. Jakob, and O. Edenhofer, 2020: Coal and carbonization in sub-Saharan Africa. *Nat. Clim. Change*, **10(1)**, 83–88, doi:10.1038/s41558-019-0649-8.

Steel, B.S., J.C. Pierce, R.L. Warner, and N.P. Lovrich, 2015: Environmental Value Considerations in Public Attitudes About Alternative Energy Development in Oregon and Washington. *Environ. Manage.*, **55(3)**, 634–645, doi:10.1007/s00267-014-0419-3.

Steg, L., 2005: Car use: Lust and must. Instrumental, symbolic and affective motives for car use. *Transp. Res. Part A Policy Pract.*, **39(2–3 Spec. Iss.)**, 147–162, doi:10.1016/j.tra.2004.07.001.

Steg, L., 2016: Values, Norms, and Intrinsic Motivation to Act Proenvironmentally. *Annu. Rev. Environ. Resour.*, **41(1)**, 277–292, doi:10.1146/annurev-environ-110615-085947.

Steg, L., 2018: Limiting climate change requires research on climate action. *Nat. Clim. Change*, **8(9)**, 759–761, doi:10.1038/s41558-018-0269-8.

Steg, L. and C. Vlek, 2009: Encouraging pro-environmental behaviour: An integrative review and research agenda. *J. Environ. Psychol.*, **29(3)**, 309–317, doi:10.1016/j.jenvp.2008.10.004.

Steg, L. and J. de Groot, 2010: Explaining prosocial intentions: Testing causal relationships in the norm activation model. *Br. J. Soc. Psychol.*, **49(4)**, 725–743, doi:10.1348/014466609X477745.

Steg, L., L. Dreijerink, and W. Abrahamse, 2006: Why are energy policies acceptable and effective? *Environ. Behav.*, **38(1)**, 92–111, doi:10.1177/0013916505278519.

Steg, L., G. Perlaviciute, and E. van der Werff, 2015: Understanding the human dimensions of a sustainable energy transition. *Front. Psychol.*, **6**(June), 1–17, doi:10.3389/fpsyg.2015.00805.

Stegemann, L. and M. Ossewaarde, 2018: A sustainable myth: A neo-Gramscian perspective on the populist and post-truth tendencies of the European green growth discourse. *Energy Res. Soc. Sci.*, **43**, 25–32, doi:10.1016/j.erss.2018.05.015.

Steinhauser, G., A. Brandl, and T.E. Johnson, 2014: Comparison of the Chernobyl and Fukushima nuclear accidents: A review of the environmental impacts. *Sci. Total Environ.*, **470–471**, 800–817, doi:10.1016/j.scitotenv.2013.10.029.

Stern, P.C. et al., 2016a: Opportunities and insights for reducing fossil fuel consumption by households and organizations. *Nat. Energy*, **1**(May), doi:10.1038/nenergy.2016.43.

Stern, P.C., B.K. Sovacool, and T. Dietz, 2016b: Towards a science of climate and energy choices. *Nat. Clim. Change*, **6(6)**, 547–555, doi:10.1038/nclimate3027.

Stiglitz, J.E. and N. Stern, 2017: *Report of the High-Level Commission on Carbon Prices*. World Bank, Washington DC, USA pp. 1–61.

Stokes, L.C., and H.L. Breetz, 2018: Politics in the U.S. energy transition: Case studies of solar, wind, biofuels and electric vehicles policy. *Energy Policy*, **113**, 76–86, doi:10.1016/j.enpol.2017.10.057.

Stoknes, P.E. and J. Rockström, 2018: Redefining green growth within planetary boundaries. *Energy Res. Soc. Sci.*, **44**, 41–49, doi:10.1016/j.erss.2018.04.030.

Stolz, P. and R. Frischknecht, 2017: *Life Cycle Assessment of Current Photovoltaic Module Recycling*. International Energy Agency, Paris, France, 37 pp.

Stout, S., N. Lee, S. Cox, J. Elsworth, and J. Leisch, 2019: *Power Sector Resilience Planning Guidebook: A Self-Guided Reference for Practitioners*. National Renewable Energy Laboratory & Resilient Energy Platform, USA, 82 pp.

Strachinescu, A., 2017: *The role of the storage in the future European energy system*. Power and Transportation Electrification (ACEPT). IEEE, 7 pp. http://www.europeanenergyinnovation.eu/Articles/Spring-2017/The-role-of-the-storage-in-the-future-European-energy-system.

Strambo, C., J. Burton, and A. Atteridge, 2019: *The end of coal? Planning of a 'just transition' in South Africa*. Stockholm Environment Institute, Stockholm, Sweden, 16 pp.

Strapasson, A., J. Woods, H. Chum, N. Kalas, N. Shah, and F. Rosillo-Calle, 2017: On the global limits of bioenergy and land use for climate change mitigation. *GCB Bioenergy*, **9**, 1721–1735, doi:10.1111/gcbb.12456.

Strbac, G. and M. Aunedi, 2016: *Whole-system cost of variable renewables in future GB electricity system*. Imperial College London, London, UK, 108 pp.

Strbac, G., R. Moreno, I. Konstantelos, D. Pudjianto, and M. Aunedi, 2014: *Strategic Development of North Sea Grid Infrastructure to Facilitate Least – Cost Decarbonisation*. Imperial College London, London, UK, 49 pp, https://www.e3g.org/docs/NorthSeaGrid_Imperial_E3G_Technical_Report_July_2014.pdf.

Strbac, G. et al., 2015b: *Value of Flexibility in a Decarbonised Grid and System Externalities of Low-Carbon Generation Technologies*. Imperial College London; NERA Economic Consulting, London, UK, 139 pp.

Strbac, G. et al., 2020: Role and value of flexibility in facilitating cost-effective energy system decarbonisation. *Prog. Energy*, **2(4)**, 042001 1–33, doi:10.1088/2516-1083/abb216.

Strefler, J. et al., 2018: Between Scylla and Charybdis: Delayed mitigation narrows the passage between large-scale CDR and high costs. *Environ. Res. Lett.*, **13(4)**, 044015, doi:10.1088/1748-9326/aab2ba.

Su, Q., H. Dai, Y. Lin, H. Chen, and R. Karthikeyan, 2018: Modeling the carbon-energy-water nexus in a rapidly urbanizing catchment: A general equilibrium assessment. *J. Environ. Manage.*, **225**, 93–103, doi:10.1016/j.jenvman.2018.07.071.

Sugiyama, M., 2012: Climate change mitigation and electrification. *Energy Policy*, **44**, 464–468, doi:10.1016/j.enpol.2012.01.028.

Sun Cable, 2021: *Australia-ASEAN Power Link, Sun Cable's vision is to see the Indo-Pacific region powered by renewable energy harnessing high-quality solar resources*. https://suncable.sg/australia-asia-power-link/.

Sun, C.H. et al., 2019a: Life-cycle assessment of biofuel production from microalgae via various bioenergy conversion systems. *Energy*, **171**, 1033–1045, doi:10.1016/j.energy.2019.01.074.

Sun, H., S. Niu, and X. Wang, 2019b: Future Regional Contributions for Climate Change Mitigation: Insights from Energy Investment Gap and Policy Cost. *Sustainability*, **11**, 3341, doi:10.3390/su11123341.

Sun, X., H. Hao, F. Zhao, and Z. Liu, 2017: Tracing global lithium flow: A trade-linked material flow analysis. *Resour. Conserv. Recycl.*, **124**, 50–61, doi:10.1016/j.resconrec.2017.04.012.

Sundt, S. and K. Rehdanz, 2015: Consumers' willingness to pay for green electricity: A meta-analysis of the literature. *Energy Econ.*, **51**(SEP.), 1–8, doi:10.1016/j.eneco.2015.06.005.

Sunny, N., N. Mac Dowell, and N. Shah, 2020: What is needed to deliver carbon-neutral heat using hydrogen and CCS? *Energy Environ. Sci.*, **13(11)**, 4204–4224, doi:10.1039/d0ee02016h.

Surana, K. and S.M. Jordaan, 2019: The climate mitigation opportunity behind global power transmission and distribution. *Nat. Clim. Change*, **9(9)**, 660–665, doi:10.1038/s41558-019-0544-3.

Sussman, R. and R. Gifford, 2013: Be the Change You Want to See: Modeling Food Composting in Public Places. *Environ. Behav.*, **45(3)**, 323–343, doi:10.1177/0013916511431274.

Sven, T., P. Thomas, S. Sonja, and N. Tobias, 2018: High renewable energy penetration scenarios and their implications for urban energy and transport systems. *Curr. Opin. Environ. Sustain.*, **2018**, 89–102.

Swilling, M., J. Musango, and J. Wakeford, 2016: Developmental states and sustainability transitions: Prospects of a just Transition in South Africa. *J. Environ. Policy Plan.*, **18(5)**, 650–672, doi:10.1080/1523908X.2015.1107716.

Taha, H., 2013: The potential for air-temperature impact from large-scale deployment of solar photovoltaic arrays in urban areas. *Sol. Energy*, **91**, 358–367, doi:10.1016/j.solener.2012.09.014.

Takle, E.S., D.A. Rajewski, and S.L. Purdy, 2019: The Iowa Atmospheric Observatory: Revealing the Unique Boundary Layer Characteristics of a Wind Farm. *Earth Interact.*, **23(2)**, 1–27, doi:10.1175/EI-D-17-0024.1.

Tampakis, S., G. Tsantopoulos, G. Arabatzis, and I. Rerras, 2013: Citizens' views on various forms of energy and their contribution to the environment. *Renew. Sustain. Energy Rev.*, **20**, 473–482, doi:10.1016/j.rser.2012.12.027.

Tanaka, K., O. Cavalett, W.J. Collins, and F. Cherubini, 2019: Asserting the climate benefits of the coal-to-gas shift across temporal and spatial scales. *Nat. Clim. Change*, **9(5)**, 389–396, doi:10.1038/s41558-019-0457-1.

Tang, B., Y. Zou, B. Yu, Y. Guo, and G. Zhao, 2021: Clean heating transition in the building sector: The case of Northern China. *J. Clean. Prod.*, **307**, 127206, doi:10.1016/j.jclepro.2021.127206.

Tang, Y., Z. Zhang, and Z. Xu, 2021: DRU Based Low Frequency AC Transmission Scheme for Offshore Wind Farm Integration. *IEEE Trans. Sustain. Energy*, **12(3)**, 1512–1524, doi:10.1109/TSTE.2021.3053051.

Tanzer, S.E. and A. Ramírez, 2019: When are negative emissions negative emissions? *Energy Environ. Sci.*, **12(4)**, 1210–1218, doi:10.1039/C8EE03338B.

Tapia, J.F.D., J.-Y. Lee, R.E.H. Ooi, D.C.Y. Foo, and R.R. Tan, 2018: A review of optimization and decision-making models for the planning of CO2 capture, utilization and storage (CCUS) systems. *Sustain. Prod. Consum.*, **13**, 1–15, doi:10.1016/j.spc.2017.10.001.

Tarroja, B., B. Shaffer, and S. Samuelsen, 2015: The importance of grid integration for achievable greenhouse gas emissions reductions from alternative vehicle technologies. *Energy*, **87**, 504–519, doi:10.1016/j.energy.2015.05.012.

Taufik, D., J.W. Bolderdijk, and L. Steg, 2015: Acting green elicits a literal warm glow. *Nat. Clim. Change*, **5(1)**, 37–40, doi:10.1038/nclimate2449.

Taufik, D., J.W. Bolderdijk, and L. Steg, 2016: Going green? The relative importance of feelings over calculation in driving environmental intent in the Netherlands and the United States. *Energy Res. Soc. Sci.*, **22**, 52–62, doi:10.1016/j.erss.2016.08.012.

Taylor, A.L., S. Dessai, and W. Bruine de Bruin, 2014: Public perception of climate risk and adaptation in the UK: A review of the literature. *Clim. Risk Manag.*, **4**, 1–16, doi:10.1016/j.crm.2014.09.001.

Taylor, P. et al., 2012: *Pathways for Energy Storage in the UK*. Centre for Low Carbon Futures, York, UK, 57 pp.

Tayyebi, A., D. Gross, A. Anta, F. Kupzog, and F. Dörfler, 2019: *Interactions of grid-forming power converters and synchronous machines – A comparative study*. 26 pp.

Tcvetkov, P., A. Cherepovitsyn, and S. Fedoseev, 2019: Public perception of carbon capture and storage: A state-of-the-art overview. *Heliyon*, **5(12)**, e02845, doi:10.1016/j.heliyon.2019.e02845.

Teng, F., F. Jotzo, and X. Wang, 2017: Interactions between Market Reform and a Carbon Price in China's Power Sector. *Econ. Energy Environ. Policy*, **6**, doi:10.5547/2160-5890.6.1.ften.

Terwel, B.W., F. Harinck, N. Ellemers, and D.D.L. Daamen, 2010: Voice in political decision-making: The effect of group voice on perceived trustworthiness of decision makers and subsequent acceptance of decisions. *J. Exp. Psychol. Appl.*, **16(2)**, 173–186, doi:10.1037/a0019977.

Terwel, B.W., E. Ter Mors, and D.D.L. Daamen, 2012: It's not only about safety: Beliefs and attitudes of 811 local residents regarding a CCS project in Barendrecht. *Int. J. Greenh. Gas Control*, **9**, 41–51, doi:10.1016/j.ijggc.2012.02.017.

Teufel, B., A. Sentic, and M. Barmet, 2019: Blockchain Energy: Blockchain in Future Energy Systems. *Journal of Electronic Science and Technology*, **017(004)**, P.317–331.

Thapar, S., S. Sharma, and A. Verma, 2018: Analyzing solar auctions in India: Identifying key determinants. *Energy Sustain. Dev.*, **45**, 66–78, doi:10.1016/j.esd.2018.05.003.

The White House, 2021: *Fact Sheet: President Biden Sets 2030 Greenhouse Gas Pollution Reduction Target Aimed at Creating Good-Paying Union Jobs and Securing U.S. Leadership on Clean Energy Technologies*. The White House, Washington, DC, USA, https://www.whitehouse.gov/briefing-room/statements-releases/2021/04/22/fact-sheet-president-biden-sets-2030-greenhouse-gas-pollution-reduction-target-aimed-at-creating-good-paying-union-jobs-and-securing-u-s-leadership-on-clean-energy-technologies/.

Thema, M., F. Bauer, and M. Sterner, 2019: Power-to-Gas: Electrolysis and methanation status review. *Renew. Sustain. Energy Rev.*, **112**, 775–787, doi:10.1016/j.rser.2019.06.030.

Thiel, G.P. and A.K. Stark, 2021: To decarbonize industry, we must decarbonize heat. *Joule*, **5(3)**, 531–550, doi:10.1016/j.joule.2020.12.007.

Thoday, K., P. Benjamin, M. Gan, and E. Puzzolo, 2018: The Mega Conversion Program from kerosene to LPG in Indonesia: Lessons learned and recommendations for future clean cooking energy expansion. *Energy Sustain. Dev.*, **46**, 71–81, doi:10.1016/j.esd.2018.05.011.

6

Thøgersen, J., 2009: Promoting public transport as a subscription service: Effects of a free month travel card. *Transp. Policy*, **16(6)**, 335–343, doi:10.1016/j.tranpol.2009.10.008.

Thomas, G., C. Demski, and N. Pidgeon, 2019: Deliberating the social acceptability of energy storage in the UK. *Energy Policy*, **133**, doi:10.1016/j.enpol.2019.110908.

Thonig, R., 2020: *Niche adaptation in policy driven transitions: secondary innovation in Concentrating Solar Power technologies*. ETH Academy on Sustainability and Technology, IASS Potsdam, 20 pp.

Thornton, P.E. et al., 2017: Biospheric feedback effects in a synchronously coupled model of human and Earth systems. *Nat. Clim. Change*, **7(7)**, 496–500, doi:10.1038/nclimate3310.

Thurber, M. C., T. L. Davis, and F. A. Wolak, 2015: Simulating the Interaction of a Renewable Portfolio Standard with Electricity and Carbon Markets. *Electr. J.*, **28(4)**, 51–65, doi:10.1016/j.tej.2015.04.007.

Thurber, M. C. and R. K. Morse (eds.), 2020: *The Global Coal Market: Supplying the Major Fuel for Emerging Economies*. Cambridge University Press, Cambridge, UK, 72 pp.

Tian, Z. et al., 2019: Large-scale solar district heating plants in Danish smart thermal grid: Developments and recent trends. *Energy Convers. Manag.*, **189**, 67–80, doi:10.1016/j.enconman.2019.03.071.

Tiefenbeck, V. et al., 2016: Overcoming salience bias: How real-time feedback fosters resource conservation. *Manage. Sci.*, **64(3)**, 1458–1476, doi:10.1287/mnsc.2016.2646.

Tilman, D. et al., 2009: Beneficial biofuels – The food, energy, and environment trilemma. *Science*, **325(5938)**, 270–271, doi:10.1126/science.1177970.

Timilsina, G. and K. Shah, 2020: Are Renewable Energy Technologies Competitive? *2020 International Conference and Utility Exhibition on Energy, Environment and Climate Change (ICUE)*, IEEE, Pattaya City, Thailand, 15 pp.

Toft, L., C. Beaton, and L. Lontoh, 2016: *International experiences with LPG subsidy reform*. International Institute for Sustainable Development, Winnipeg, Canada, 48 pp.

Toke, D. and S.-E. Vezirgiannidou, 2013: The relationship between climate change and energy security: key issues and conclusions. *Env. Polit.*, **22(4)**, 537–552, doi:10.1080/09644016.2013.806631.

Torvanger, A., 2019: Governance of bioenergy with carbon capture and storage (BECCS): accounting, rewarding, and the Paris agreement. *Clim. Policy*, **19**, 329–341, doi:10.1080/14693062.2018.1509044.

Tong, D. et al., 2019: Committed emissions from existing energy infrastructure jeopardize 1.5°C climate target. *Nature*, **572(7769)**, 373–377, doi:10.1038/s41586-019-1364-3.

Tota, V., F. Viganò, and M. Gatti, 2021: *Application of CCUS to the WtE sector*. Proceedings of the 15th Greenhouse Gas Control Technologies Conference, March 2021, Abu Dhabi, *SSRN Electronic Journal*, pp. 15–18.

Towler, B.F., 2014: Chapter 10 – Hydroelectricity. In: *The Future of Energy* [Towler, B.F. (ed.)]. Academic Press, Boston, MA, USA, pp. 215–235.

Trainor, A.M., R.I. McDonald, and J. Fargione, 2016: Energy Sprawl is the Largest Driver of Land Use Change in United States. *PLoS One*, **11**, e0162269, doi:10.1371/journal.pone.0162269.

Transport and Environment, 2018: *How to decarbonise European transport by 2050*. European Federation for Transport and Environment AISBL. Brussels, Belgium, 1–26.

Tremblay, A., L. Varfalvy, M. Garneau, and C. Roehm, 2005: *Greenhouse gas Emissions-Fluxes and Processes: hydroelectric reservoirs and natural environments*. Springer Science & Business Media, 148 pp.

Treyer, K., C. Bauer, and A. Simons, 2014: Human health impacts in the life cycle of future European electricity generation. *Energy Policy*, **74**, S31–S44, doi:10.1016/j.enpol.2014.03.034.

Tröndle, T., 2020: Supply-side options to reduce land requirements of fully renewable electricity in Europe. *PLoS One*, **15(8)**, e0236958, doi:10.1371/journal.pone.0236958.

Trutnevyte, E., 2016: Does cost optimization approximate the real-world energy transition? *Energy*, **106**, 182–193, doi:10.1016/j.energy.2016.03.038.

Tsoutsos, T. et al., 2015: Photovoltaics competitiveness in Middle East and North Africa countries the European project PV PARITY. *Int. J. Sustain. Energy*, **34(3–4)**, 202–210, doi:10.1080/14786451.2013.863774.

Tsujikawa, N., S. Tsuchida, and T. Shiotani, 2016: Changes in the Factors Influencing Public Acceptance of Nuclear Power Generation in Japan Since the 2011 Fukushima Daiichi Nuclear Disaster. *Risk Anal.*, **36(1)**, 98–113, doi:10.1111/risa.12447.

Tuck, G., M.J. Glendining, P. Smith, J.I. House, and M. Wattenbach, 2006: The potential distribution of bioenergy crops in Europe under present and future climate. *Biomass and Bioenergy*, **30(3)**, 183–197, doi:10.1016/j.biombioe.2005.11.019.

Turner, S.W.D., M. Hejazi, S.H. Kim, L. Clarke, and J. Edmonds, 2017: Climate impacts on hydropower and consequences for global electricity supply investment needs. *Energy*, **141**, 2081–2090, doi:10.1016/j.energy.2017.11.089.

U.S. Energy Information Administration, 2021: *Levelized Costs of New Generation Resources in the Annual Energy Outlook*. Washington: US Energy Information Administration, 26 pp. https://www.eia.gov/outlooks/aeo/pdf/electricity_generation.pdf.

Ueckerdt, F. et al., 2021: Potential and risks of hydrogen-based e-fuels in climate change mitigation. *Nat. Clim. Change*, **11(5)**, 384–393, doi:10.1038/s41558-021-01032-7.

Ünal, A.B., L. Steg, and J. Granskaya, 2019: 'To support or not to support, that is the question'. Testing the VBN theory in predicting support for car use reduction policies in Russia. *Transp. Res. Part A Policy Pract.*, **119**(October 2018), 73–81, doi:10.1016/j.tra.2018.10.042.

UNECE, 2020: Guidelines on promoting People-first Public-Private Partnership Waste-to-Energy Projects for the Circular Economy. *Oxford Handb. United Nations*, 14898(November), doi:10.1093/oxfordhb/9780199560103.003.0007.

United Nations, 2021: *The UN Security Council and Climate Change*. UN Security Council, New York, NY, USA, 28 pp.

Unsal, D.B., T.S. Ustun, S.M.S. Hussain, and A. Onen, 2021: Enhancing Cybersecurity in Smart Grids: False Data Injection and Its Mitigation. *Energies*, **14(9)**, doi:10.3390/en14092657.

Ürge-Vorsatz, D. et al., 2018: Locking in positive climate responses in cities. *Nat. Clim. Change*, **8(3)**, 174–177, doi:10.1038/s41558-018-0100-6.

Ustun, T.S., and S.M.S. Hussain, 2019: *A Review of Cybersecurity Issues in Smartgrid Communication Networks. 2019 International Conference on Power Electronics, Control and Automation (ICPECA)*, IEEE, New Delhi, India, 6 pp.

Vadén, T. et al., 2019: To continue to burn something? Technological, economic and political path dependencies in district heating in Helsinki, Finland. *Energy Res. Soc. Sci.*, **58**, 101270, doi:10.1016/j.erss.2019.101270.

Vaillancourt, K., O. Bahn, E. Frenette, and O. Sigvaldason, 2017: Exploring deep decarbonization pathways to 2050 for Canada using an optimization energy model framework. *Appl. Energy*, **195**, 774–785, doi:10.1016/j.apenergy.2017.03.104.

Vakulchuk, R., I. Overland, and D. Scholten, 2020: Renewable energy and geopolitics: A review. *Renew. Sustain. Energy Rev.*, **122**, 109547, doi:10.1016/j.rser.2019.109547.

Valavi, M. and A. Nysveen, 2018: Variable-Speed Operation of Hydropower Plants: A Look at the Past, Present, and Future. *IEEE Ind. Appl. Mag.*, **24(5)**, 18–27, doi:10.1109/MIAS.2017.2740467.

Valera-Medina, A. et al., 2017: Ammonia–methane combustion in tangential swirl burners for gas turbine power generation. *Appl. Energy*, **185**, 1362–1371, doi:10.1016/j.apenergy.2016.02.073.

Van de Graaf, T., 2013: *The Politics and Institutions of global Energy Governance*. Palgrave Macmillan UK, London, 190 pp.

van de Graaf, T. and B. Sovacool, 2020: Global Energy Politics. *Polity*, Cambridge, UK and Medford, USA, 240 pp.

van den Berg, N. J. et al., 2020: Implications of various effort-sharing approaches for national carbon budgets and emission pathways. *Clim. Change*, **162**(4), 1805–1822, doi:10.1007/s10584-019-02368-y.

Van den Broek, K., J.W. Bolderdijk, and L. Steg, 2017: Individual differences in values determine the relative persuasiveness of biospheric, economic and combined appeals. *J. Environ. Psychol.*, **53**, 145–156, doi:10.1016/j.jenvp.2017.07.009.

Van Der Kroon, B., R. Brouwer, and P.J.H. Van Beukering, 2013: The energy ladder: Theoretical myth or empirical truth? Results from a meta-analysis. *Renew. Sustain. Energy Rev.*, **20**, 504–513, doi:10.1016/j.rser.2012.11.045.

van der Spek, M. et al., 2020: Uncertainty analysis in the techno-economic assessment of CO_2 capture and storage technologies. Critical review and guidelines for use. *Int. J. Greenh. Gas Control*, **100**, 103113, https://doi.org/10.1016/j.ijggc.2020.103113.

Van der Werff, E., L. Steg, and A. Ruepert, 2021: My company is green, so am I: the relationship between perceived environmental responsibility of organisations and government, environmental self-identity, and pro-environmental behaviours. *Energy Effic.*, **14(5)**, 50, doi:10.1007/s12053-021-09958-9.

Van der Werff, E., L. Steg, and K. Keizer, 2014: Follow the signal: When past pro-environmental actions signal who you are. *J. Environ. Psychol.*, **40**, 273–282, doi:10.1016/j.jenvp.2014.07.004.

Van der Werff, E. and L. Steg, 2015: One model to predict them all: Predicting energy behaviours with the norm activation model. *Energy Res. Soc. Sci.*, **6**, 8–14, doi:10.1016/j.erss.2014.11.002.

Van der Wiel, K. et al., 2019: Meteorological conditions leading to extreme low variable renewable energy production and extreme high energy shortfall. *Renew. Sustain. Energy Rev.*, **111**, 261–275, doi:10.1016/j.rser.2019.04.065.

van Dyk, S., J. Su, J.D. McMillan, and J. (John) N. Saddler, 2019: *'DROP-IN' BIOFUELS: The key role that co-processing will play in its production*. IEA Bioenergy, 156 pp. www.ieabioenergy.com/wp-content/uploads/2019/09/Task-39-Drop-in-Biofuels-Full-Report-January-2019.pdf.

Van Heek, J., K. Arning, and M. Ziefle, 2017: Differences between Laypersons and Experts in Perceptions and Acceptance of CO_2-utilization for Plastics Production. *Energy Procedia*, **114**, 7212–7223, doi:10.1016/j.egypro.2017.03.1829.

Van Noorden, R., 2014: The rechargeable revolution: A better battery. *Nature*, **507**, 26–28, doi:10.1038/507026a.

Van Rijnsoever, F.J., A. Van Mossel, and K.P.F. Broecks, 2015: Public acceptance of energy technologies: The effects of labeling, time, and heterogeneity in a discrete choice experiment. *Renew. Sustain. Energy Rev.*, **45**, 817–829, doi:10.1016/j.rser.2015.02.040.

van Ruijven, B.J., E. De Cian, and I. Sue Wing, 2019: Amplification of future energy demand growth due to climate change. *Nat. Commun.*, **10(1)**, 1–12, doi:10.1038/s41467-019-10399-3.

Van Sluisveld, M.A.E., H.S. de Boer, V. Daioglou, A.F. Hof, and D.P. van Vuuren, 2021: A race to zero – Assessing the position of heavy industry in a global net-zero CO2 emissions context. *Energy Clim. Change*, **2**, 100051, doi:10.1016/J.EGYCC.2021.100051.

van Soest, H.L. et al., 2017: Early action on Paris Agreement allows for more time to change energy systems. *Clim. Change*, **144(2)**, 165–179, doi:10.1007/s10584-017-2027-8.

van Soest, H.L., M.G.J. den Elzen, and D.P. van Vuuren, 2021: Net-zero emission targets for major emitting countries consistent with the Paris Agreement. *Nat. Commun.*, **12**, 2140, doi:10.1038/s41467-021-22294-x.

van Vliet, M.T.H., J. Sheffield, D. Wiberg, and E.F. Wood, 2016a: Impacts of recent drought and warm years on water resources and electricity supply worldwide. *Environ. Res. Lett.*, **11(12)**, doi:10.1088/1748-9326/11/12/124021.

van Vliet, M.T.H. et al., 2016b: Multi-model assessment of global hydropower and cooling water discharge potential under climate change. *Glob. Environ. Change*, **40**, 156–170, doi:10.1016/j.gloenvcha.2016.07.007.

van Vliet, M.T.H., D. Wiberg, S. Leduc, and K. Riahi, 2016c: Power-generation system vulnerability and adaptation to changes in climate and water resources. *Nat. Clim. Change*, **6(4)**, 375–380, doi:10.1038/nclimate2903.

van Vuuren, D.P. et al., 2018: Alternative pathways to the 1.5°C target reduce the need for negative emission technologies. *Nat. Clim. Change*, **8(5)**, 391–397, doi:10.1038/s41558-018-0119-8.

Vandyck, T., K. Keramidas, B. Saveyn, A. Kitous, and Z. Vrontisi, 2016: A global stocktake of the Paris pledges: Implications for energy systems and economy. *Glob. Environ. Change*, **41**, 46–63, doi:10.1016/j.gloenvcha.2016.08.006.

Vartiainen, E., G. Masson, C. Breyer, D. Moser, and E. Román Medina, 2020: Impact of weighted average cost of capital, capital expenditure, and other parameters on future utilityscale PV levelised cost of electricity. *Prog. Photovoltaics Res. Appl.*, **28(6)**, 439–453, doi:10.1002/pip.3189.

Vasseur, V. and R. Kemp, 2015: The adoption of PV in the Netherlands: A statistical analysis of adoption factors. *Renew. Sustain. Energy Rev.*, **41**, 483–494, doi:10.1016/j.rser.2014.08.020.

Vautard, R. et al., 2014: Regional climate model simulations indicate limited climatic impacts by operational and planned European wind farms. *Nat. Commun.*, **5**, 1–9, doi:10.1038/ncomms4196.

Veers, P. et al., 2019: Grand challenges in the science of wind energy. *Science*, **366(6464)**, doi:10.1126/science.aau2027.

Velazquez Abad, A. and P.E. Dodds, 2017: Production of Hydrogen. In: *Encyclopedia of Sustainable Technologies*, Elsevier, New York, NY, USA, pp. 293–304.

Venkataramani, G., P. Parankusam, V. Ramalingam, and J. Wang, 2016: A review on compressed air energy storage – A pathway for smart grid and polygeneration. *Renew. Sustain. Energy Rev.*, **62**, 895–907, doi:10.1016/j.rser.2016.05.002.

Verma, A. and A. Kumar, 2015: Life cycle assessment of hydrogen production from underground coal gasification. *Appl. Energy*, **147**, 556–568, doi:10.1016/j.apenergy.2015.03.009.

Victoria, M. et al., 2021: Solar photovoltaics is ready to power a sustainable future. *Joule*, **5(5)**, 1041–1056, doi:10.1016/J.JOULE.2021.03.005.

Vidal, O., B. Goffé, and N. Arndt, 2013: Metals for a low-carbon society. *Nat. Geosci.*, **6(11)**, 894–896, doi:10.1038/ngeo1993.

Vince, G., 2010: Dams for Patagonia. *Science*, **329(5990)**, 382–385, doi:10.1126/science.329.5990.382.

Vinichenko, V., A. Cherp, and J. Jewell, 2021: Historical precedents and feasibility of rapid coal and gas decline required for the 1.5°C target. *One Earth*, **4**, 1477–1490, doi:10.1016/j.oneear.2021.09.012.

Vishwanathan, S.S. and A. Garg, 2020: Energy system transformation to meet NDC, 2°C, and well below 2 °C targets for India. *Clim. Change*, **162(4)**, 1877–1891, doi:10.1007/s10584-019-02616-1.

Vistra Corp., 2021: *The Sustainability Report: 2020*. Vistra Corp., Texas, USA, 72 pp.

Vivid Economics, 2019: *The Future of Carbon Pricing in the UK*. Vivid Economics, London, UK, 115 pp. https://www.theccc.org.uk/wp-content/uploads/2019/08/Vivid-Economics-The-Future-of-Carbon-Pricing-in-the-UK.pdf.

Vivoda, V., 2019: LNG import diversification and energy security in Asia. *Energy Policy*, **129**, 967–974, doi:10.1016/j.enpol.2019.01.073.

Vogl, V., M. Åhman, and L.J. Nilsson, 2018: Assessment of hydrogen direct reduction for fossil-free steelmaking. *J. Clean. Prod.*, **203**, 736–745, https://doi.org/10.1016/j.jclepro.2018.08.279.

Vogt-Schilb, A. and S. Hallegatte, 2017: Climate policies and nationally determined contributions: reconciling the needed ambition with the political economy: Climate policies and nationally determined contributions. *Wiley Interdiscip. Rev. Energy Environ.*, **6**, e256, doi:10.1002/wene.256.

Voldsund, M., K. Jordal, and R. Anantharaman, 2016: Hydrogen production with CO_2 capture. *Int. J. Hydrogen Energy*, **41(9)**, 4969–4992, doi:10.1016/j.ijhydene.2016.01.009.

Volken, S.P., G. Xexakis, and E. Trutnevyte, 2018: Perspectives of Informed Citizen Panel on Low-Carbon Electricity Portfolios in Switzerland and Longer-Term Evaluation of Informational Materials. *Environ. Sci. Technol.*, **52(20)**, 11478–11489, doi:10.1021/acs.est.8b01265.

6

Volker, P.J.H., A.N. Hahmann, J. Badger, and H.E. Jørgensen, 2017: Prospects for generating electricity by large onshore and offshore wind farms. *Environ. Res. Lett.*, **12(3)**, 034022, doi:10.1088/1748-9326/aa5d86.

Von Wald, G.A., M.S. Masnadi, D.C. Upham, and A.R. Brandt, 2020: Optimization-based technoeconomic analysis of molten-media methane pyrolysis for reducing industrial sector CO_2 emissions. *Sustain. Energy Fuels*, **4(9)**, 4598–4613, doi:10.1039/D0SE00427H.

Vrontisi, Z., K. Fragkiadakis, M. Kannavou, and P. Capros, 2020: Energy system transition and macroeconomic impacts of a European decarbonization action towards a below 2°C climate stabilization. *Clim. Change*, **162(4)**, 1857–1875, doi:10.1007/s10584-019-02440-7.

Wachtmeister, H., and M. Höök, 2020: Investment and production dynamics of conventional oil and unconventional tight oil: Implications for oil markets and climate strategies. *Energy Clim. Change*, **1**, 100010, doi:10.1016/j.egycc.2020.100010.

Wainaina, S., M.K. Awasthi, I.S. Horváth, and M.J. Taherzadeh, 2020: Anaerobic digestion of food waste to volatile fatty acids and hydrogen at high organic loading rates in immersed membrane bioreactors. *Renew. Energy*, **152**, 1140–1148, doi:10.1016/j.renene.2020.01.138.

Waisman, H., H. De Coninck, and J. Rogelj, 2019: Key technological enablers for ambitious climate goals: insights from the IPCC special report on global warming of 1.5°C. *Environ. Res. Lett.*, **14(11)**, 111001, doi:10.1088/1748-9326/ab4c0b.

Waite, M. and V. Modi, 2020: Electricity Load Implications of Space Heating Decarbonization Pathways. *Joule*, **4(2)**, 376–394, doi:10.1016/j.joule.2019.11.011.

Walker, C. and J. Baxter, 2017: Procedural justice in Canadian wind energy development: A comparison of community-based and technocratic siting processes. *Energy Res. Soc. Sci.*, **29**, 160–169, doi:10.1016/j.erss.2017.05.016.

Walker, G., 1995: Renewable energy and the public. *Land use policy*, **12(1)**, 49–59, doi:10.1016/0264-8377(95)90074-C.

Wall, R., S. Grafakos, A. Gianoli, and S. Stavropoulos, 2019: Which policy instruments attract foreign direct investments in renewable energy? *Clim. Policy*, **19(1)**, 59–72, doi:10.1080/14693062.2018.1467826.

Wang Y.,G. Zhou, T. Li, and X. Wei, 2019d: Comprehensive Evaluation of the Sustainable Development of Battery Electric Vehicles in China. *Sustainability*, **11(20)**, 5635, doi:10.3390/su11205635.

Wang, F. et al., 2017a: Latest advances in supercapacitors: from new electrode materials to novel device designs. *Chem. Soc. Rev.*, **46(22)**, 6816–6854, doi:10.1039/C7CS00205J.

Wang, H. et al., 2020a: Early transformation of the Chinese power sector to avoid additional coal lock-in. *Environ. Res. Lett.*, **15(2)**, 024007, doi:10.1088/1748-9326/ab5d99.

Wang, J. et al., 2017b: Overview of Compressed Air Energy Storage and Technology Development. *Energies*, **10**, 991, doi:10.3390/en10070991.

Wang, J. et al., 2017c: Current research and development trend of compressed air energy storage. *Syst. Sci. Control Eng.*, **5(1)**, 434–448, doi:10.1080/21642583.2017.1377645.

Wang, J., S. Yang, C. Jiang, Y. Zhang, and P.D. Lund, 2017d: Status and future strategies for Concentrating Solar Power in China. *Energy Sci. Eng.*, **5(2)**, 100–109, doi:10.1002/ese3.154.

Wang, M., P. Ullrich, and D. Millstein, 2020b: Future projections of wind patterns in California with the variable-resolution CESM: a clustering analysis approach. *Clim. Dyn.*, **54(3–4)**, 2511–2531, doi:10.1007/s00382-020-05125-5.

Wang, Q., B. Mao, S. I. Stoliarov, and J. Sun, 2019a: A review of lithium ion battery failure mechanisms and fire prevention strategies. *Prog. Energy Combust. Sci.*, **73**, 95–131, doi:10.1016/j.pecs.2019.03.002.

Wang, R. et al., 2019b: A Review of Perovskites Solar Cell Stability. *Adv. Funct. Mater.*, **29(47)**, doi:10.1002/adfm.201808843.

Wang, S., S. Wang, and P. Smith, 2015: Ecological impacts of wind farms on birds: Questions, hypotheses, and research needs. *Renew. Sustain. Energy Rev.*, **44**, 599–607, doi:10.1016/j.rser.2015.01.031.

Wang, W. et al., 2014a: Predicting the impacts of climate change on the potential distribution of major native non-food bioenergy plants in China. *PLoS One*, **9(11)**, 1–11, doi:10.1371/journal.pone.0111587.

Wang, Y. et al., 2019c: Vulnerability of existing and planned coal-fired power plants in Developing Asia to changes in climate and water resources. *Energy Environ. Sci.*, **12(10)**, 3164–3181, doi:10.1039/c9ee02058f.

Wang, Y., J. Gu, and J. Wu, 2020c: Explaining local residents' acceptance of rebuilding nuclear power plants: The roles of perceived general benefit and perceived local benefit. *Energy Policy*, **140**, 111410, doi:10.1016/j.enpol.2020.111410.

Wang, Z., J.B. Dunn, J. Han, and M.Q. Wang, 2014b: Effects of co-produced biochar on life cycle greenhouse gas emissions of pyrolysis-derived renewable fuels. *Biofuels, Bioprod. Biorefining*, **8(2)**, 189–204, https://doi.org/10.1002/bbb.1447.

Warren, C.R., C. Lumsden, S. O'Dowd, and R.V. Birnie, 2005: 'Green on green': Public perceptions of wind power in Scotland and Ireland. *J. Environ. Plan. Manag.*, **48(6)**, 853–875, doi:10.1080/09640560500294376.

Watson, S. et al., 2019: Future emerging technologies in the wind power sector: A European perspective. *Renew. Sustain. Energy Rev.*, **113**(July), 109270, doi:10.1016/j.rser.2019.109270.

Watts, N. et al., 2019: The 2019 report of The Lancet Countdown on health and climate change: ensuring that the health of a child born today is not defined by a changing climate. *Lancet*, **394(10211)**, 1836–1878, doi:10.1016/S0140-6736(19)32596-6.

Weber, E.U., 2015: Climate Change Demands Behavioral Change: What Are the Challenges? *Soc. Res. (New York).*, **82(3)**, 561–580.

Weber, J. et al., 2018: Impact of climate change on backup energy and storage needs in wind-dominated power systems in Europe. *PLoS One*, **13(8)**, e0201457, doi:10.1371/journal.pone.0201457.

Wei, Y.-M. et al., 2018: An integrated assessment of INDCs under Shared Socioeconomic Pathways: an implementation of C^3IAM. *Natural Hazards*, **92**, 585–618, doi:10.1007/s11069-018.

Wei, Y.-M. et al., 2020: Self-preservation strategy for approaching global warming targets in the post-Paris Agreement era. *Nat. Commun.*, **11(1)**, 1624, doi:10.1038/s41467-020–15453-z.

Wei, Y.-M. et al., 2021: A proposed global layout of carbon capture and storage in line with a 2°C climate target. *Nat. Clim. Change*, **11**, 112–118, doi:10.1038/s41558-020-00960-0.

Weitemeyer, S., D. Kleinhans, T. Vogt, and C. Agert, 2015: Integration of Renewable Energy Sources in future power systems: The role of storage. *Renew. Energy*, **75**, 14–20, doi:10.1016/j.renene.2014.09.028.

Westlén, D., 2018: *Nuclear power and high sea water temperatures*. Analysgruppen, Stockholm, Sweden, 45–47 pp.

Wetzel, T. and S. Borchers, 2015: Update of energy payback time and greenhouse gas emission data for crystalline silicon photovoltaic modules. *Prog. Photovoltaics Res. Appl.*, **23(10)**, 1429–1435, doi:10.1002/PIP.2548.

Whitley, S., L. Van Der Burg, L. Worrall, and S. Patel, 2017: *Cutting Europe's lifelines to coal Tracking subsidies in 10 countries Policy briefing Shaping policy for development* odi.org *Key findings*. Overseas Development Institute, London, UK, 14 pp.

Whitmarsh, L., G. Seyfang, and S. O'Neill, 2011a: Public engagement with carbon and climate change: To what extent is the public 'carbon capable'? *Glob. Environ. Change*, **21(1)**, 56–65, doi:10.1016/j.gloenvcha.2010.07.011.

Whitmarsh, L. et al., 2011b: *Public Attitudes, Understanding, and Engagement in relation to Low- Carbon Energy: A selective review of academic and non-academic literatures*. Research Councils UK, London, UK, 180 pp.

Wiedenhofer, D. et al., 2017: Unequal household carbon footprints in China. *Nat. Clim. Change*, **7(1)**, 75–80, doi:10.1038/nclimate3165.

Wienchol, P., A. Szlęk, and M. Ditaranto, 2020: Waste-to-energy technology integrated with carbon capture – Challenges and opportunities. *Energy*, **198**, 117352, doi:10.1016/J.ENERGY.2020.117352.

Wiese, C., A. Larsen, and L.-L. Pade, 2018: Interaction effects of energy efficiency policies: a review. *Energy Effic.*, **11**, doi:10.1007/s12053-018-9659-z.

Williams, J.H. et al., 2012: The Technology Path to Deep Greenhouse Gas Emissions Cuts by 2050: The Pivotal Role of Electricity. *Science*, **335(6064)**, 53–59, doi:10.1126/science.1208365.

Williams, J.H. et al., 2014: *Pathways to Deep Decarbonization in the United States*. Sustainable Development Solutions Network, New York, NY, USA, 200 pp.

Williams, J.H. et al., 2021a: Carbon-Neutral Pathways for the United States. *AGU Adv.*, **2(1)**, e2020AV000284-e2020AV000284, doi:10.1029/2020AV000284.

Williams, J.P., A. Regehr, and M. Kang, 2021b: Methane Emissions from Abandoned Oil and Gas Wells in Canada and the United States. *Environ. Sci. Technol.*, **55(1)**, 563–570, doi:10.1021/acs.est.0c04265.

Williams, P.J.L.B. and L.M.L. Laurens, 2010: Microalgae as biodiesel & biomass feedstocks: Review & analysis of the biochemistry, energetics & economics. *Energy Environ. Sci.*, **3(5)**, 554–590, doi:10.1039/b924978h.

Wiloso, E.I., R. Heijungs, G. Huppes, and K. Fang, 2016: Effect of biogenic carbon inventory on the life cycle assessment of bioenergy: challenges to the neutrality assumption. *J. Clean. Prod.*, **125**, 78–85, doi:10.1016/j.jclepro.2016.03.096.

Wiser, R. et al., 2021: Expert elicitation survey predicts 37% to 49% declines in wind energy costs by 2050. *Nat. Energy*, **6(5)**, 555–565, doi:10.1038/s41560-021-00810-z.

Wiser, R.H., A. Mills, J. Seel, T. Levin, and A. Botterud, 2017: *Impacts of Variable Renewable Energy on Bulk Power System Assets, Pricing, and Costs*. Lawrence Berkeley National Laboratory, Berkeley, CA, USA, pp. 1–105.

Wohland, J., M. Reyers, J. Weber, and D. Witthaut, 2017: More homogeneous wind conditions under strong climate change decrease the potential for inter-state balancing of electricity in Europe. *Earth Syst. Dyn.*, **8(4)**, 1047–1060, doi:10.5194/esd-8-1047-2017.

Wohland, J., M. Reyers, C. Märker, and D. Witthaut, 2018: Natural wind variability triggered drop in German redispatch volume and costs from 2015 to 2016. *PLoS One*, **13**, e0190707, doi:10.1371/journal.pone.0190707.

Wohland, J., N. Eddine Omrani, N. Keenlyside, and D. Witthaut, 2019a: Significant multidecadal variability in German wind energy generation. *Wind Energy Sci.*, **4(3)**, 515–526, doi:10.5194/wes-4-515-2019.

Wohland, J., N. Omrani, D. Witthaut, and N.S. Keenlyside, 2019b: Inconsistent Wind Speed Trends in Current Twentieth Century Reanalyses. *J. Geophys. Res. Atmos.*, **124(4)**, 1931–1940, doi:10.1029/2018JD030083.

Wohlfahrt, G., E. Tomelleri, and A. Hammerle, 2021: The albedo–climate penalty of hydropower reservoirs. *Nat. Energy*, **6(4)**, 372–377, doi:10.1038/s41560-021-00784-y.

Wolak, F.A., 2011: Do residential customers respond to hourly prices? Evidence from a dynamic pricing experiment. *Am. Econ. Rev.*, **101(3)**, 83–87, doi:10.1257/aer.101.3.83.

Wolsink, M., 2020: Distributed energy systems as common goods: Socio-political acceptance of renewables in intelligent microgrids. *Renew. Sustain. Energy Rev.*, **127**, 109841, doi:10.1016/j.rser.2020.109841.

Wolske, K.S. and P.C. Stern, 2018: *Contributions of psychology to limiting climate change: Opportunities through consumer behavior*. Elsevier Inc., New York, NY, USA, 127–160 pp.

Wolske, K.S., P.C. Stern, and T. Dietz, 2017: Explaining interest in adopting residential solar photovoltaic systems in the United States: Toward an integration of behavioral theories. *Energy Res. Soc. Sci.*, **25**, 134–151, doi:10.1016/j.erss.2016.12.023.

Wolske, K.S., K.T. Gillingham, and P.W. Schultz, 2020: Peer influence on household energy behaviours. *Nat. Energy*, **5(3)**, 202–212, doi:10.1038/s41560-019-0541-9.

Wolsko, C., H. Ariceaga, and J. Seiden, 2016: Red, white, and blue enough to be green: Effects of moral framing on climate change attitudes and conservation behaviors. *J. Exp. Soc. Psychol.*, **65**, 7–19, doi:10.1016/j.jesp.2016.02.005.

Woolf, D., J. Lehmann, and D.R. Lee, 2016: Optimal bioenergy power generation for climate change mitigation with or without carbon sequestration. *Nat. Commun.*, **7**, 13160, doi:10.1038/ncomms13160.

World Bank, 2019: *State and Trends of Carbon Pricing 2019*. World Bank, Washington DC, USA, 97 pp.

World Bank, 2020: *Climate-smart mining: Minerals for climate action*. World Bank, Washington DC, USA, 112 pp.

World Bank, Ecofys, and Vivid Economics, 2017: *State and Trends of Carbon Pricing 2017*. World Bank, Washington DC, USA. https://openknowledge.worldbank.org/handle/10986/28510.

World Energy Council and Oliver Wyman, 2020: *World Energy Trilemma Index 2020*. World Energy Council, London, UK, pp. 1–69.

Wu, J. et al., 2015: Integrating solar PV (photovoltaics) in utility system operations: Analytical framework and Arizona case study. *Energy*, **85**, 1–9, doi:10.1016/j.energy.2015.02.043.

Wu, Y., F. Zhao, S. Liu, L. Wang, L. Qiu, G. Alexandrov, and V. Jothiprakash, 2018: Bioenergy production and environmental impacts. *Geosci. Lett.*, **5**, 14, doi:10.1186/s40562-018-0114-y.

Xenias, D. and L. Whitmarsh, 2018: Carbon capture and storage (CCS) experts' attitudes to and experience with public engagement. *Int. J. Greenh. Gas Control*, **78**, 103–116, doi:10.1016/j.ijggc.2018.07.030.

Xia, G., L. Zhou, J.R. Minder, R.G. Fovell, and P.A. Jimenez, 2019: Simulating impacts of real-world wind farms on land surface temperature using the WRF model: physical mechanisms. *Clim. Dyn.*, **53(3–4)**, 1723–1739, doi:10.1007/s00382-019-04725-0.

Xiang, X., M.M.C. Merlin, and T.C. Green, 2016: Cost Analysis and Comparison of HVAC, LFAC and HVDC for Offshore Wind Power Connection. *12th IET International Conference on AC and DC Power Transmission (ACDC 2016)*, IET, Institution of Engineering and Technology, 6 pp.

Xiang, X. et al., 2021: Comparison of cost-effective distance for LFAC with HVAC and HVDC in connections of offshore and remote onshore wind energy. *CSEE J. Power Energy Syst.*, **7(5)**, 954–975, doi:10.17775/CSEEJPES.2020.07000.

Xie, Y., X. Liu, Q. Chen, and S. Zhang, 2020: An integrated assessment for achieving the 2°C target pathway in China by 2030. *J. Clean. Prod.*, **268**, 122238, doi:10.1016/j.jclepro.2020.122238.

Xiong, Y., X. Xin, and X. Kou, 2019: Simulation and Projection of Near-Surface Wind Speeds in China by BCC-CSM Models. *J. Meteorol. Res.*, **33(1)**, 149–158, doi:10.1007/s13351-019-8043-z.

Xu, H., R. Zhang, X. Li, and Y. Yan, 2019: Fault Tripping Criteria in Stability Control Device Adapting to Half-Wavelength AC Transmission Line. *IEEE Trans. Power Deliv.*, **34(4)**, 1619–1625, doi:10.1109/TPWRD.2019.2916107.

Yaji, K., H. Homma, G. Sakata, and M. Watanabe, 2014: Evaluation on flashover voltage property of snow accreted insulators for overhead transmission lines, part I – field observations and laboratory tests to evaluate snow accretion properties. *IEEE Trans. Dielectr. Electr. Insul.*, **21(6)**, 2549–2558, doi:10.1109/TDEI.2014.004564.

Yalew, S.G. et al., 2020: Impacts of climate change on energy systems in global and regional scenarios. *Nat. Energy*, **5(10)**, 794–802, doi:10.1038/s41560-020-0664-z.

Yamashita, S., Y. Yoshino, K. Yoshimura, K. Shindo, and E. Harada, 2019: Feasibility Study on the Hydrogen Energy Supply Chain for Low Carbon Society. *Jpn. Soc. Energy Resour.*, **35**, 33–38, doi:10.24778/jjser.35.2_33.

yan Nie, P., Y. hua Chen, Y. cong Yang, and X.H. Wang, 2016: Subsidies in carbon finance for promoting renewable energy development. *J. Clean. Prod.*, **139**, 677–684, doi:10.1016/j.jclepro.2016.08.083.

Yan, X., V. Thieu, and J. Garnier, 2021: Long-Term Evolution of Greenhouse Gas Emissions From Global Reservoirs. *Front. Environ. Sci.*, **9**, 289, doi:10.3389/fenvs.2021.705477.

Yang, B., Y.-M. Wei, Y. Hou, H. Li, and P. Wang, 2019: Life cycle environmental impact assessment of fuel mix-based biomass co-firing plants with CO_2 capture and storage. *Appl. Energy*, **252**, 113483, doi:10.1016/j.apenergy.2019.113483.

Yang, F. and M. Yang, 2018: Rural electrification in sub-Saharan Africa with innovative energy policy and new financing models. *Mitig. Adapt. Strateg. Glob. Change*, **23(6)**, 933–952, doi:10.1007/s11027-017-9766-8.

Yang, L. et al., 2020: Whether CCS technologies will exacerbate the water crisis in China? A full life-cycle analysis. *Renew. Sustain. Energy Rev.*, **134**, 110374, doi:10.1016/j.rser.2020.110374.

Yang, P. et al., 2018a: Social cost of carbon under shared socioeconomic pathways. *Glob. Environ. Change*, **53**, 225–232, doi:10.1016/j.gloenvcha.2018.10.001.

Yang, W. et al., 2018b: Burden on hydropower units for short-term balancing of renewable power systems. *Nat. Commun.*, **9(1)**, 2633, doi:10.1038/s41467-018-05060-4.

Yang, Y., Y. Zhang, B. Duan, D. Wang, and X. Li, 2016: A novel design project for space solar power station (SSPS-OMEGA). *Acta Astronaut.*, **121**, 51–58, doi:10.1016/j.actaastro.2015.12.029.

You, Y. and A. Manthiram, 2018: Progress in High-Voltage Cathode Materials for Rechargeable Sodium-Ion Batteries. *Adv. Energy Mater.*, **8(2)**, 1701785, doi:10.1002/aenm.201701785.

Young, W. et al., 2015: Changing Behaviour: Successful Environmental Programmes in the Workplace. *Bus. Strateg. Environ.*, **24(8)**, 689–703, doi:10.1002/bse.1836.

Yu, B., Y. Tian, and J. Zhang, 2015: A dynamic active energy demand management system for evaluating the effect of policy scheme on household energy consumption behavior. *Energy*, **91**, 491–506, doi:10.1016/j.energy.2015.07.131.

Yu, B., Y.-M. Wei, G. Kei, and Y. Matsuoka, 2018: Future scenarios for energy consumption and carbon emissions due to demographic transitions in Chinese households. *Nat. Energy*, **3(2)**, 109–118, doi:10.1038/s41560-017-0053-4.

Yu, B., G. Zhao, and R. An, 2019: Framing the picture of energy consumption in China. *Nat. Hazards*, **99(3)**, 1469–1490, doi:10.1007/s11069-019-03576-6.

Yulong, P., A. Cavagnino, S. Vaschetto, C. Feng, and A. Tenconi, 2017: *Flywheel Energy Storage Systems for Power Systems Application.* 6th International Conference on Clean Electrical Power (ICCEP), IEEE, Santa Margherita Ligure, Italy, pp. 492–501.

Zamfirescu, C. and I. Dincer, 2008: Using ammonia as a sustainable fuel. *J. Power Sources*, **185(1)**, 459–465, doi:10.1016/j.jpowsour.2008.02.097.

Zanchi, G., N. Pena, and N. Bird, 2012: Is woody bioenergy carbon neutral? A comparative assessment of emissions from consumption of woody bioenergy and fossil fuel. *GCB Bioenergy*, **4(6)**, 761–772, https://doi.org/10.1111/j.1757-1707.2011.01149.x.

Zangheri, P., T. Serrenho, and P. Bertoldi, 2019: Energy savings from feedback systems: A meta-studies' review. *Energies*, **12(19)**, doi:10.3390/en12193788.

Zappa, W., M. Junginger, and M. van den Broek, 2019: Is a 100% renewable European power system feasible by 2050? *Appl. Energy*, **233–234**(August 2018), 1027–1050, doi:10.1016/j.apenergy.2018.08.109.

Zarfl, C., J. Berlekamp, F. He, S.C. Jähnig, W. Darwall, and K. Tockner, 2019: Future large hydropower dams impact global freshwater megafauna. *Sci. Rep.*, **9**, 18531, doi:10.1038/s41598-019-54980-8.

Zaunbrecher, B.S., T. Bexten, M. Wirsum, and M. Ziefle, 2016: What is Stored, Why, and How? Mental Models, Knowledge, and Public Acceptance of Hydrogen Storage. *Energy Procedia*, **99**, 108–119, doi:10.1016/j.egypro.2016.10.102.

Zavala-Araiza, D. et al., 2015: Reconciling divergent estimates of oil and gas methane emissions. *Proc. Natl. Acad. Sci.*, **112(51)**, 201522126, doi:10.1073/pnas.1522126112.

Zeman, F.S., and D.W. Keith, 2008: Carbon neutral hydrocarbons. *Philos. Trans. R. Soc. A Math. Phys. Eng. Sci.*, **366(1882)**, 3901–3918, doi:10.1098/rsta.2008.0143.

Zengel, D. et al., 2020: Emission of Toxic HCN During NOx Removal by Ammonia SCR in the Exhaust of Lean-Burn Natural Gas Engines. *Angew. Chemie Int. Ed.*, **59(34)**, 14423–14428, doi:10.1002/anie.202003670.

Zhai, H. and E.S. Rubin, 2016: A Techno-Economic Assessment of Hybrid Cooling Systems for Coal- and Natural-Gas-Fired Power Plants with and without Carbon Capture and Storage. *Environ. Sci. Technol.*, **50(7)**, 4127–4134, doi:10.1021/acs.est.6b00008.

Zhang, C., H. Liao, and Z. Mi, 2019a: Climate impacts: temperature and electricity consumption. *Nat. Hazards*, **99(3)**, 1259–1275, doi:10.1007/s11069-019-03653-w.

Zhang, D. et al., 2020: Unlocking the potential of BECCS with indigenous sources of biomass at a national scale. *Sustain. Energy Fuels*, **4(1)**, 226–253, doi:10.1039/C9SE00609E.

Zhang, R. and S. Fujimori, 2020: The role of transport electrification in global climate change mitigation scenarios. *Environ. Res. Lett.*, **15(3)**, doi:10.1088/1748-9326/ab6658.

Zhang, X., G. Strbac, F. Teng, and P. Djapic, 2018: Economic assessment of alternative heat decarbonisation strategies through coordinated operation with electricity system – UK case study. *Appl. Energy*, **222**, 79–91, doi:10.1016/j.apenergy.2018.03.140.

Zhang, X., G. Strbac, N. Shah, F. Teng, and D. Pudjianto, 2019b: Whole-System Assessment of the Benefits of Integrated Electricity and Heat System. *IEEE Trans. Smart Grid*, **10(1)**, 1132–1145, doi:10.1109/TSG.2018.2871559.

Zhao, G., B. Yu, R. An, Y. Wu, and Z. Zhao, 2021: Energy system transformations and carbon emission mitigation for China to achieve global 2°C climate target. *J. Environ. Manage.*, **292**, 112721, doi:10.1016/j.jenvman.2021.112721.

Zhao T., L. Bell, M.W. Horner, J. Sulik, and J. Zhang, 2012. Consumer responses towards home energy financial incentives: A survey-based study. *J. Energy Policy*, **47**, 291–297.

Zhao, X, gang G, wu Jiang, A. Li, and L. Wang, 2016: Economic analysis of waste-to-energy industry in China. *Waste Manag.*, **48**, 604–618, doi:10.1016/J.WASMAN.2015.10.014.

Zhou, F. et al., 2016: Recent developments in coal mine methane extraction and utilization in China: A review. *J. Nat. Gas Sci. Eng.*, **31**, 437–458, doi:10.1016/j.jngse.2016.03.027.

Zhou, W. et al., 2019: A comparison of low carbon investment needs between China and Europe in stringent climate policy scenarios. *Environ. Res. Lett.*, **14(5)**, 054017, doi:10.1088/1748-9326/ab0dd8.

Zhou, Y. et al., 2015: A comprehensive view of global potential for hydro-generated electricity. *Energy Environ. Sci.*, **8(9)**, 2622–2633, doi:10.1039/C5EE00888C.

Zhou, Y., H. Li, A. Ravey, and M.-C. Péra, 2020: An integrated predictive energy management for light-duty range-extended plug-in fuel cell electric vehicle. *J. Power Sources*, **451**, 227780, doi:10.1016/j.jpowsour.2020.227780.

Zhu, Y., S. Poddar, L. Shu, Y. Fu, and Z. Fan, 2020: Recent Progress on Interface Engineering for High-Performance, Stable Perovskites Solar Cells. *Adv. Mater. Interfaces*, **7(11)**, 2000118, doi:10.1002/admi.202000118.

Ziegler, M.S. and J.E. Trancik, 2021: Re-examining rates of lithium-ion battery technology improvement and cost decline. *Energy Environ. Sci.*, **14(4)**, 1635–1651, doi:10.1039/D0EE02681F.

Zou, C. et al., 2015: Formation, distribution, potential and prediction of global conventional and unconventional hydrocarbon resources. *Pet. Explor. Dev.*, **42(1)**, 14–28, doi:10.1016/S1876-3804(15)60002-7.

6

7

Agriculture, Forestry and Other Land Uses (AFOLU)

Coordinating Lead Authors:

Gert-Jan Nabuurs (the Netherlands), Rachid Mrabet (Morocco)

Lead Authors:

Assem Abu Hatab (Egypt/Sweden), Mercedes Bustamante (Brazil), Harry Clark (New Zealand), Petr Havlík (the Czech Republic), Joanna I. House (United Kingdom), Cheikh Mbow (Senegal), Karachepone N. Ninan (India), Alexander Popp (Germany), Stephanie Roe (the Philippines/ the United States of America), Brent Sohngen (the United States of America), Sirintornthep Towprayoon (Thailand)

Contributing Authors:

Lillian Aoki (the United States of America), Göran Berndes (Sweden), Katherine Calvin (the United States of America), Annette Cowie (Australia), Vassilis Daioglou (Greece), Andre Deppermann (Germany), Jeremy P. Emmet-Booth (Ireland/New Zealand), Shinichiro Fujimori (Japan), Giacomo Grassi (Italy/European Union), Viola Heinrich (United Kingdom/Germany), Florian Humpenöder (Germany), J. Boone Kauffman (the United States of America), William F. Lamb (Germany/United Kingdom), William Laurance (Australia), Sinead Leahy (New Zealand), Sebastiaan Luyssaert (Belgium), Deissy Martínez-Barón (Colombia), Suvadip Neogi (India), Michael O'Sullivan (United Kingdom), Joeri Rogelj (Belgium/United Kingdom), Todd Rosenstock (the United States of America), Pete Smith (United Kingdom), Jonas Steinfeld (Germany/Brazil), Francesco N. Tubiello (Italy), Pieter Johannes Verkerk (the Netherlands)

Review Editors:

Denis Angers (Canada), Nijavalli Hanumantharao Ravindranath (India)

Chapter Scientists:

Fernando Ayala-Niño (Mexico), Jeremy P. Emmet-Booth (Ireland/New Zealand)

This chapter should be cited as:

Nabuurs, G-J., R. Mrabet, A. Abu Hatab, M. Bustamante, H. Clark, P. Havlík, J. House, C. Mbow, K.N. Ninan, A. Popp, S. Roe, B. Sohngen, S. Towprayoon, 2022: Agriculture, Forestry and Other Land Uses (AFOLU). In IPCC, 2022: *Climate Change 2022: Mitigation of Climate Change. Contribution of Working Group III to the Sixth Assessment Report of the Intergovernmental Panel on Climate Change* [P.R. Shukla, J. Skea, R. Slade, A. Al Khourdajie, R. van Diemen, D. McCollum, M. Pathak, S. Some, P. Vyas, R. Fradera, M. Belkacemi, A. Hasija, G. Lisboa, S. Luz, J. Malley, (eds.)]. Cambridge University Press, Cambridge, UK and New York, NY, USA. doi: 10.1017/9781009157926.009

Table of Contents

Executive Summary

The Agriculture, Forestry and Other Land Use[1] (AFOLU) sector encompasses managed ecosystems and offers significant mitigation opportunities while delivering food, wood and other renewable resources as well as biodiversity conservation, provided the sector adapts to climate change. Land-based mitigation measures represent some of the most important options currently available. They can both deliver carbon dioxide removal (CDR) and substitute for fossil fuels, thereby enabling emissions reductions in other sectors. The rapid deployment of AFOLU measures is essential in all pathways staying within the limits of the remaining budget for a 1.5°C target (*high confidence*). Where carefully and appropriately implemented, AFOLU mitigation measures are uniquely positioned to deliver substantial co-benefits and help address many of the wider challenges associated with land management. If AFOLU measures are deployed badly then, when taken together with the increasing need to produce sufficient food, feed, fuel and wood, they may exacerbate trade-offs with the conservation of habitats, adaptation, biodiversity and other services. At the same time the capacity of the land to support these functions may be threatened by climate change itself (*high confidence*). {IPCC AR6 WGI, Figure SPM.7; IPCC AR6 WGII, 7.1, 7.6}

The AFOLU (managed land) sector, on average, accounted for 13–21% of global total anthropogenic greenhouse gas (GHG) emissions in the period 2010–2019 (*medium confidence*). At the same time managed and natural terrestrial ecosystems were a carbon sink, absorbing around one third of anthropogenic CO_2 emissions (*medium confidence*). Estimated anthropogenic net CO_2 emissions from AFOLU (based on book-keeping models) result in a net source of +5.9 ± 4.1 $GtCO_2$ yr^{-1} between 2010 and 2019 with an unclear trend. Based on FAOSTAT or national GHG inventories, the net CO_2 emissions from AFOLU were 0.0 to +0.8 $GtCO_2$ yr^{-1} over the same period. There is a discrepancy in the reported CO_2 AFOLU emissions magnitude because alternative methodological approaches that incorporate different assumptions are used. If the managed and natural responses of all land to both anthropogenic environmental change and natural climate variability, estimated to be a *gross* sink of −12.5 ± 3.2 $GtCO_2$ yr^{-1} for the period 2010–2019, are included with land use emissions, then land overall, constituted a *net* sink of −6.6 ± 5.2 $GtCO_2$ yr^{-1} in terms of CO_2 emissions (*medium confidence*). {7.2, 7.2.2.5, Table 7.1; IPCC AR6 WGI}

AFOLU CO_2 emissions fluxes are mainly driven by land use change (CO_2 LULUCF), and account for about half of total net AFOLU emissions. The rate of deforestation has generally declined, while global tree cover and global forest growing stock levels are likely increasing (*medium confidence*). There are substantial regional differences, with losses of carbon generally observed in tropical regions and gains in temperate and

boreal regions. Agricultural methane (CH_4) and nitrous oxide (N_2O) emissions are estimated to average 157 ± 47.1 $MtCH_4$ yr^{-1} and 6.6 ± 4.0 MtN_2O yr^{-1} or 4.2 ± 1.3 and 1.8 ± 1.1 $GtCO_2$-eq yr^{-1} (using IPCC AR6 GWP100 values for CH_4 and N_2O) respectively between 2010 and 2019. AFOLU CH_4 emissions continue to increase (*high confidence*), the main source of which is enteric fermentation from ruminant animals (*high confidence*). Similarly, AFOLU N_2O emissions are increasing, dominated by agriculture, notably from manure application, nitrogen deposition, and nitrogen fertiliser use (*high confidence*). In addition to being a source and sink for GHG emissions, land plays an important role in climate through albedo effects, evapotranspiration and volatile organic compounds (VOCs) and their mix, although the combined role in total climate forcing is unclear and varies strongly with bioclimatic region and management type. {2.4.2.5, 7.2, 7.2.1, 7.2.3, 7.3}

The AFOLU sector offers significant near-term mitigation potential at relatively low cost but cannot compensate for delayed emission reductions in other sectors (*high evidence, medium agreement*). The AFOLU sector can provide 20–30% (interquartile range) of the global mitigation needed for a 1.5°C or 2°C pathway towards 2050 (*robust evidence, medium agreement*), though there are highly variable mitigation strategies for how AFOLU potential can be deployed for achieving climate targets. The estimated *likely* economic (<USD100 tCO_2-eq^{-1}) AFOLU sector mitigation potential is 8 to 14 $GtCO_2$-eq yr^{-1} between 2020 and 2050, with the bottom end of this range representing the mean from integrated assessment models (IAMs) and the upper end representing the mean estimate from global sectoral studies. The economic potential is about half of the technical potential from AFOLU, and about 30–50% could be achieved under USD20 tCO_2-eq^{-1}. The implementation of robust measurement, reporting and verification processes is paramount to improving the transparency of net-carbon-stock changes per land unit to prevent misleading assumptions or claims on mitigation. {7.1, 7.4, 7.5}

Between 2020 and 2050, mitigation measures in forests and other natural ecosystems provide the largest share of the economic (up to USD100 tCO_2-eq^{-1}) AFOLU mitigation potential, followed by agriculture and demand-side measures (*high confidence*). In the global sectoral studies, the protection, improved management, and restoration of forests, peatlands, coastal wetlands, savannas and grasslands have the potential to reduce emissions and/or sequester 7.3 mean (3.9–13.1 range) $GtCO_2$-eq yr^{-1}. Agriculture provides the second largest share of the mitigation potential, with 4.1 (1.7–6.7) $GtCO_2$-eq yr^{-1} (up to USD100 tCO_2-eq^{-1}) from cropland and grassland soil carbon management, agroforestry, use of biochar, improved rice cultivation, and livestock and nutrient management. Demand-side measures including shifting to sustainable healthy diets, reducing food waste, and building with wood and biochemicals and bio-textiles have a mitigation potential of 2.2 (1.1–3.6) $GtCO_2$-eq yr^{-1}.

---

[1] Global databases make different choices about which emissions and removals occurring on land are considered anthropogenic. Currently, net CO_2 land fluxes from land reported by global book-keeping models used here differ from those from the aggregate global net emissions based on national GHG inventories. This difference, which has been considered in the literature, mainly reflects differences in how anthropogenic forest sinks and areas of managed land are defined. Other reasons for this difference, which are more difficult to quantify, can arise from the limited representation of land management in global models and varying levels of accuracy and completeness of estimated LULUCF fluxes in national GHG inventories. Neither method is inherently preferable. This chapter reports estimates from different databases and approaches, but uses CO_2 LULUCF from book-keeping models to report overall emissions to ensure consistency and comparability across chapters.

Most mitigation options are available and ready to deploy. Emissions reductions can be unlocked relatively quickly, whereas CDR needs upfront investment. Sustainable intensification in agriculture, shifting diets, and reducing food waste could enhance efficiencies and reduce agricultural land needs, and are therefore critical for enabling supply-side measures such as reforestation, restoration, as well as decreasing CH_4 and N_2O emissions from agricultural production. In addition, emerging technologies (e.g., vaccines or inhibitors) have the potential to substantially increase CH_4 mitigation potential beyond current estimates. AFOLU mitigation is not only relevant in countries with large land areas. Many smaller countries and regions, particularly with wetlands, have disproportionately high levels of AFOLU mitigation potential density. {7.4, 7.5}

The economic and political feasibility of implementing AFOLU mitigation measures is hampered by persistent barriers. Assisting countries to overcome barriers will help to achieve significant short-term mitigation (*medium confidence*). Finance forms a critical barrier to achieving these gains as currently mitigation efforts rely principally on government sources and funding mechanisms which do not provide sufficient resources to enable the economic potential to be realised. Differences in cultural values, governance, accountability and institutional capacity are also important barriers. Climate change could also emerge as a barrier to AFOLU mitigation, although the IPCC AR6 WGI contribution to AR6 indicated that an increase in the capacity of natural sinks may occur, despite changes in climate (*medium confidence*). The continued loss of biodiversity makes ecosystems less resilient to climate change extremes and this may further jeopardise the achievement of the AFOLU mitigation potentials indicated in this chapter (IPCC AR6 WGII and IPBES) (*high confidence*). {7.4, 7.6; IPCC AR6 WGI, Figure SPM.7}

Bioenergy and other bio-based options represent an important share of the total mitigation potential. The range of recent estimates for the technical bioenergy potential when constrained by food security and environmental considerations is 5–50 and 50–250 EJ yr^{-1} by 2050 for residues and dedicated biomass production system respectively. These estimates fall within previously estimated ranges (*medium agreement*). Poorly planned deployment of biomass production and afforestation options for in-forest carbon sequestration may conflict with environmental and social dimensions of sustainability (*high confidence*). The global technical CDR potential of BECCS by 2050 (considering only the technical capture of CO_2 and storage underground) is estimated at 5.9 mean (0.5–11.3) GtCO$_2$ yr^{-1}, of which 1.6 (0.8–3.5) GtCO$_2$ yr^{-1} is available at below USD100 tCO$_2^{-1}$ (*medium confidence*). Bioenergy and other bio-based products provide additional mitigation through the substitution of fossil fuels fossil-based products (*high confidence*). These substitution effects are reported in other sectors. Wood used in construction may reduce emissions associated with steel and concrete use. The agriculture and forestry sectors can devise management approaches that enable biomass production and use for energy in conjunction with the production of food and timber, thereby reducing the conversion pressure on natural ecosystems (*medium confidence*). {7.4}

The deployment of all land-based mitigation measures can provide multiple co-benefits, but there are also risks and trade-offs from misguided or inappropriate land management (*high confidence*). Such risks can best be managed if AFOLU mitigation is pursued in response to the needs and perspectives of multiple stakeholders to achieve outcomes that maximise synergies while limiting trade-offs (*medium confidence*). The results of implementing AFOLU measures are often variable and highly context specific. Depending on local conditions (e.g., ecosystem, climate, food system, land ownership) and management strategies (e.g., scale, method), mitigation measures have the potential to positively or negatively impact biodiversity, ecosystem functioning, air quality, water availability and quality, soil productivity, rights infringements, food security, and human well-being. Mitigation measures addressing GHGs may also affect other climate forcers such as albedo and evapotranspiration. Integrated responses that contribute to mitigation, adaptation, and other land challenges will have greater likelihood of being successful (*high confidence*); measures which provide additional benefits to biodiversity and human well-being are sometimes described as 'Nature-Based Solutions'. {7.1, 7.4, 7.6}

AFOLU mitigation measures have been well understood for decades but deployment remains slow and emissions trends indicate unsatisfactory progress despite beneficial contributions to global emissions reduction from forest-related options (*high confidence*). Globally, the AFOLU sector has so far contributed modestly to net mitigation, as past policies have delivered about 0.65 GtCO$_2$ yr^{-1} of mitigation during 2010–2019 or 1.4% of global gross emissions (*high confidence*). The majority (>80%) of emission reduction resulted from forestry measures (*high confidence*). Although the mitigation potential of AFOLU measures is large from a biophysical and ecological perspective, its feasibility is hampered by lack of institutional support, uncertainty over long-term additionality and trade-offs, weak governance, fragmented land ownership, and uncertain permanence effects. Despite these impediments to change, AFOLU mitigation options are demonstrably effective and with appropriate support can enable rapid emission reductions in most countries. {7.4, 7.6}

Concerted, rapid and sustained effort by all stakeholders, from policy makers and investors to land owners and managers is a pre-requisite to achieving high levels of mitigation in the AFOLU sector (*high confidence*). To date USD0.7 billion yr^{-1} is estimated to have been spent on AFOLU mitigation. This is well short of the more than USD400 billion yr^{-1} that is estimated to be necessary to deliver the up to 30% of global mitigation effort envisaged in deep mitigation scenarios (*medium confidence*). This estimate of the global funding requirement is smaller than current subsidies provided to agriculture and forestry. Making this funding available would require a change in flows of money and determination of who pays. A gradual redirection of existing agriculture and forestry subsidies would greatly advance mitigation. Effective policy interventions and national (investment) plans as part of Nationally Determined Contributions (NDCs), specific to local circumstances and needs, are urgently needed to accelerate the deployment of AFOLU mitigation options. These interventions are effective when they include funding schemes and long-term consistent support for implementation with governments taking the initiative together with private funders and non-state actors. {7.6}

Realising the mitigation potential of the AFOLU sector depends strongly on policies that directly address emissions and drive the deployment of land-based mitigation options, consistent with carbon prices in deep mitigation scenarios (*high confidence*). Examples of successful policies and measures include establishing and respecting tenure rights and community forestry, improved agricultural management and sustainable intensification, biodiversity conservation, payments for ecosystem services, improved forest management and wood chain usage, bioenergy, voluntary supply chain management efforts, consumer behaviour campaigns, private funding and joint regulatory efforts to avoid, for example, leakage. The efficacy of different policies, however, will depend on numerous region-specific factors. In addition to funding, these factors include governance, institutions, long-term consistent execution of measures, and the specific policy setting (*high confidence*). {7.6}

There is a discrepancy, equating to 5.5 $GtCO_2$ yr^{-1} between alternative methods of accounting for anthropogenic land CO_2 fluxes. Reconciling these methods greatly enhances the credibility of AFOLU-based emissions offsetting. It would also assist in assessing collective progress in a global stocktake (*high confidence*). The principal accounting approaches are national GHG inventories (NGHGI) and global modelling approaches. NGHGI, based on IPCC guidelines, consider a much larger area of forest to be under human management than global models. NGHGI consider the fluxes due to human-induced environmental change on this area to be anthropogenic and are thus reported. Global models,[2] in contrast, consider these fluxes to be natural and are excluded from the total reported anthropogenic land CO_2 flux. To enable a like-with-like comparison, the remaining cumulative global CO_2 emissions budget can be adjusted (*medium confidence*). In the absence of these adjustments, collective progress would appear better than it is. {Cross-Chapter Box 6 in this chapter, 7.2}

Addressing the many knowledge gaps in the development and testing of AFOLU mitigation options can rapidly advance the likelihood of achieving sustained mitigation (*high confidence*). Research priorities include improved quantification of anthropogenic and natural GHG fluxes and emissions modelling, better understanding of the impacts of climate change on the mitigation potential, permanence and additionality of estimated mitigation actions, and improved (real time and cheap) measurement, reporting and verification. There is a need to include a greater suite of mitigation measures in IAMs, informed by more realistic assessments that take into account local circumstances and socio-economic factors and cross-sector synergies and trade-offs. Finally, there is a critical need for more targeted research to develop appropriate country-level, locally specific, policy and land management response options. These options could support more specific NDCs with

AFOLU measures that enable mitigation while also contributing to biodiversity conservation, ecosystem functioning, livelihoods for millions of farmers and foresters, and many other Sustainable Development Goals (SDGs) (*high confidence*). {7.7}

---

[2]   Bookkeeping models and dynamic global vegetation models.

7.1 Introduction

7.1.1 Key Findings from Previous Reports

Agriculture, Forestry and Other Land Uses (AFOLU) is unique due to its capacity to mitigate climate change through greenhouse gas (GHG) emission reductions, as well as enhance removals (IPCC 2019). However, despite the attention on AFOLU since early 1990s it was reported in the IPCC Special Report on Climate Change and Land (SRCCL) as accounting for almost a quarter of anthropogenic emission (IPCC, 2019), with three main GHGs associated with AFOLU; carbon dioxide (CO_2), methane (CH_4) and nitrous oxide (N_2O). Overall emission levels had remained similar since the publication of AR4 (Nabuurs et al. 2007). The diverse nature of the sector, its linkage with wider societal, ecological and environmental aspects and the required coordination of related policy, was suggested to make implementation of known and available supply- and demand-side mitigation measures particularly challenging (IPCC 2019). Despite such implementation barriers, the considerable mitigation potential of AFOLU as a sector on its own and its capacity to contribute to mitigation within other sectors was emphasised, with land-related measures, including bioenergy, estimated as capable of contributing between 20% and 60% of the total cumulative abatement to 2030 identified within transformation pathways (IPCC 2018). However, the vast mitigation potential from AFOLU initially portrayed in literature and in Integrated Assessment Models (IAMs), as explored in the IPCC Special Report on Climate Change of 1.5°C (SR1.5), is being questioned in terms of feasibility (Roe et al. 2021) and a more balanced perspective on the role of land in mitigation is developing, while at the same time, interest by private investors in land-based mitigation is increasing fast.

The SRCCL (IPCC 2019) outlined with *medium evidence* and *medium agreement* that supply-side agriculture and forestry measures had an economic (at USD100 tCO_2-eq^{-1}) mitigation potential of 7.2–10.6 $GtCO_2$-eq^{-1} in 2030 (using GWP100 and multiple IPCC values for CH_4 and N_2O) of which about a third was estimated as achievable at <USD20 tCO_2-eq^{-1}. Agricultural measures were reported as sensitive to carbon price, with cropland and grazing land soil organic carbon management having the greatest potential at USD20 tCO_2-eq^{-1} and restoration of organic soils at USD100 tCO_2-eq^{-1}. Forestry measures were less sensitive to carbon price, but varied regionally, with reduced deforestation, forest management and afforestation having the greatest potential depending on region. Although demand-side measures related to food could in theory make a large contribution to mitigation, in reality the contribution has been very small. Overall, the dependency of mitigation within AFOLU on a complex range of factors, from population growth, economic and technological developments, to the sustainability of mitigation measures and impacts of climate change, was suggested to make realisation highly challenging (IPCC 2019).

Land can only be part of the solution alongside rapid emission reduction in other sectors (IPCC 2019). It was recognised that land supports many ecosystem services on which human existence, well-being and livelihoods ultimately depend. Yet over-exploitation of land resources was reported as driving considerable and unprecedented rate of biodiversity loss, and wider environmental degradation (IPBES 2019b; IPCC 2019). Urgent action to reverse this trend was deemed crucial in helping to accommodate the increasing demands on land and enhance climate change adaptation capacity. There was *high confidence* that global warming was already causing an increase in the frequency and intensity of extreme weather and climate events, impacting ecosystems, food security, disturbances and production processes, with existing (and new) carbon stocks in soils and biomass at serious risk. The impact of land cover on regional climate (through biophysical effects) was also highlighted, although there was no confidence regarding impacts on global climate.

Since the IPCC Fifth Assessment Report (AR5), the share of AFOLU to anthropogenic GHG emissions had remained largely unchanged at 13–21% of total GHG emissions (*medium confidence*), though uncertainty in estimates of both sources and sinks of CO_2, exacerbated by difficulties in separating natural and anthropogenic fluxes, was emphasised. Models indicated land (including the natural sink) to have *very likely* provided a net removal of CO_2 between 2007 and 2016. As in AR5, land cover change, notably deforestation, was identified as a major driver of anthropogenic CO_2 emissions while agriculture was a major driver of the increasing anthropogenic CH_4 and N_2O emissions.

In terms of mitigation, without reductions in overall anthropogenic emissions, increased reliance on large-scale land-based mitigation was predicted, which would add to the many already competing demands on land. However, some mitigation measures were suggested to not compete with other land uses, while also having multiple co-benefits, including adaptation capacity and potential synergies with some Sustainable Development Goals (SDGs). As in AR5, there was large uncertainty surrounding mitigation within AFOLU, in part because current carbon stocks and fluxes are unclear and subject to temporal variability. Additionally, the non-additive nature of individual measures that are often inter-linked and the highly context specific applicability of measures, causes further uncertainty. Many AFOLU measures were considered well-established and some achievable at low to moderate cost, yet contrasting economic drivers, insufficient policy, lack of incentivisation and institutional support to stimulate implementation among the many stakeholders involved, in regionally diverse contexts, was recognised as hampering realisation of potential.

None the less, the importance of mitigation within AFOLU was highlighted in all IPCC reports, with modelled scenarios demonstrating the considerable potential role and land-based mitigation forming an important component of pledged mitigation in Nationally Determined Contributions (NDCs) under the Paris Agreement. The sector was identified as the only one in which large-scale carbon dioxide removal (CDR) may currently and at short term be possible (e.g., through afforestation/reforestation or soil organic carbon management). This CDR component was deemed crucial to limit climate change and its impacts, which would otherwise lead to enhanced release of carbon from land. However, the SRCCL emphasised that mitigation cannot be pursued in isolation. The need for integrated response options, that mitigate and adapt to climate change, but also deal with land degradation and desertification, while enhancing food and fibre security, biodiversity and contributing to other SDGs has been made clear (IPCC 2019; IPBES 2019a; IPBES-IPCC 2021).

7.1.2 Boundaries, Scope and Changing Context of the Current Report

This chapter assesses GHG fluxes between land and the atmosphere due to AFOLU, the associated drivers behind these fluxes, mitigation response options and related policy, at time scales of 2030 and 2050. Land and its management has important links with other sectors and therefore associated chapters within this report, notably concerning the provision of food, feed, fuel or fibre for human consumption and societal well-being (Chapter 5), for bioenergy (Chapter 6), the built environment (Chapter 9), transport (Chapter 10) and industry (Chapter 11). Mitigation within these

sectors may in part, be dependent on contributions from land and the AFOLU sector, with interactions between all sectors discussed in Chapter 12. This chapter also has important links with IPCC AR6 WGII regarding climate change impacts and adaptation. Linkages are illustrated in Figure 7.1.

As highlighted in both AR5 and the SRCCL, there is a complex interplay between land management and GHG fluxes as illustrated in Figure 7.2, with considerable variation in management regionally, as a result of geophysical, climatic, ecological, economic, technological, institutional and socio-cultural diversity. The capacity for land-based mitigation varies accordingly. The principal focus of this chapter is therefore, on evaluating regional land-based mitigation potential, identifying applicable AFOLU mitigation measures, estimating associated costs and exploring policy options that could enable implementation.

Figure 7.1 | Linkage between Chapter 7 and other chapters within this report, as well as to IPCC AR6 WGII. Mitigation potential estimates in this chapter consider potential emission reductions and removals only within the AFOLU sector itself, and not the substitution effects from biomass and bio-based products in sectors such as Energy, Transport, Industry, Buildings, nor biophysical effects of, for example, cooling of cities. These are covered in their respective chapters.

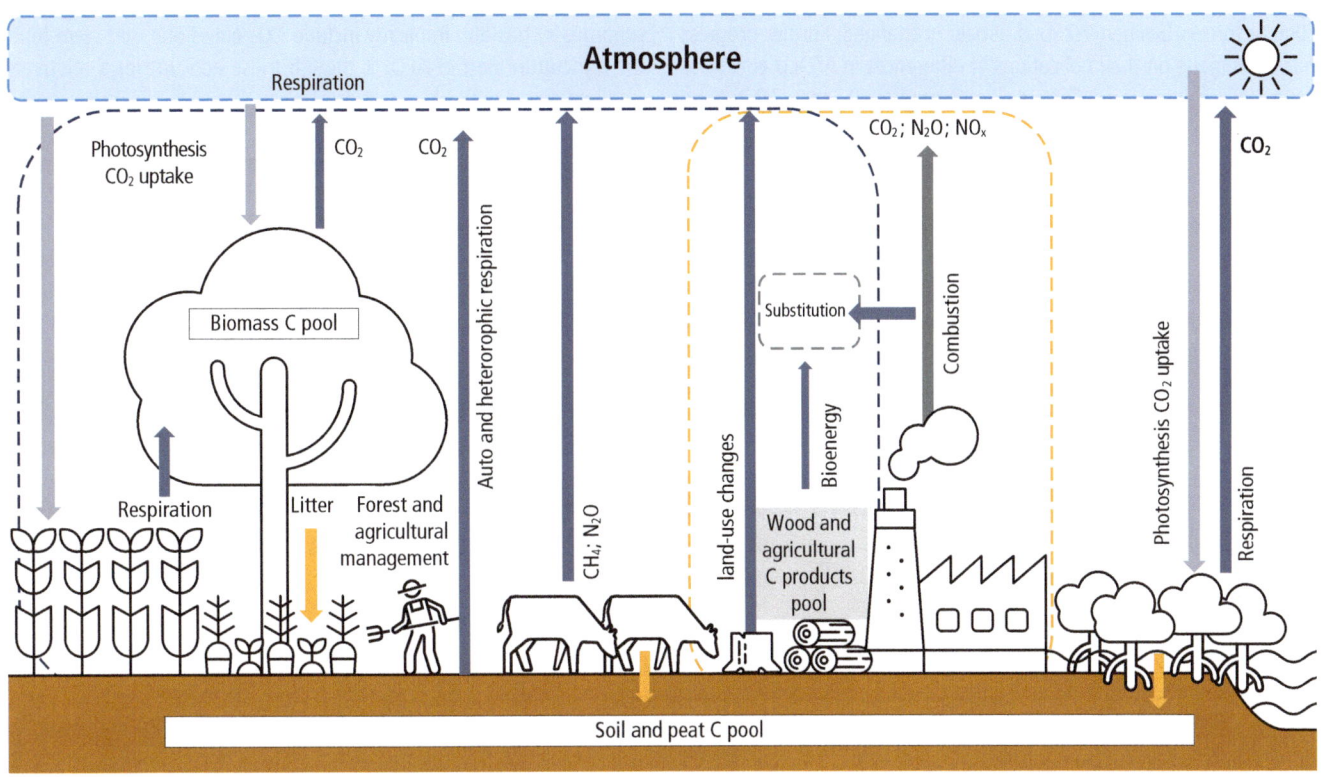

Figure 7.2 | Summarised representation of interactions between land management, its products in terms of food and fibre, and land–atmospheric GHG fluxes. For legibility reasons only a few of the processes and management measures are depicted.

Mitigation measures are broadly categorised as those relating to (i) forests and other ecosystems (ii) agriculture (iii) biomass production for products and bioenergy and (iv) demand-side levers. Assessment is made in the context that land-mitigation is expected to contribute roughly 25% of the 2030 mitigation pledged in Nationally Determined Contributions (NDCs) under the Paris Agreement (Grassi et al. 2017), yet very few countries have provided details on how this will be achieved. In light of AR5 and the SRCCL findings, that indicate large land-based mitigation potential, considerable challenges to its realisation, but also a clear nexus at which humankind finds itself, whereby current land management, driven by population growth and consumption patterns, is undermining the very capacity of land, a finite resource, to support wider critical functions and services on which humankind depends. Mitigation within AFOLU is occasionally and wrongly perceived as an opportunity for in-action within other sectors. AFOLU simply cannot compensate for mitigation shortfalls in other sectors. As the outcomes of many critical challenges (UNEP 2019), including biodiversity loss (IPBES 2019a) and soil degradation (FAO and ITPS 2015), are inextricably linked with how we manage land, the evaluation and assessment of AFOLU is crucial. This chapter aims to address three core topics:

1. What is the latest estimated (economic) mitigation potential of AFOLU measures according to both sectoral studies and integrated assessment models, and how much of this may be realistic within each global region?
2. How do we realise the mitigation potential, while minimising trade-offs and risks and maximising co-benefits that can enhance food and fibre security, conserve biodiversity and address other land challenges?

3. How effective have policies been so far and what additional policies or incentives might enable realisation of mitigation potential and at what costs?

This chapter first outlines the latest trends in AFOLU fluxes and the methodology supporting their estimation (Section 7.2). Direct and indirect drivers behind emission trends are discussed in Section 7.3. Mitigation measures, their costs, co-benefits, trade-offs, estimated regional potential and contribution within integrated global mitigation scenarios, is presented in Sections 7.4 and 7.5 respectively. Assessment of associated policy responses and links with SDGs are explored in Section 7.6. The chapter concludes with gaps in knowledge (Section 7.7) and frequently asked questions.

7.2   Historical and Current Trends in GHG Emission and Removals; Their Uncertainties and Implications for Assessing Collective Climate Progress

The biosphere on land and in wetlands is a source and sink of CO_2 and CH_4, and a source of N_2O due to both natural and anthropogenic processes that happen simultaneously and are therefore difficult to disentangle (IPCC 2010; Angelo and Du Plesis 2017; IPCC 2019). AFOLU is the only GHG sector to currently include anthropogenic sinks. A range of methodological approaches and data have been applied to estimating AFOLU emissions and removals, each developed for their own purposes, with estimates varying accordingly. Since the SRCCL (Jia et al. 2019), emissions estimates have been updated (Sections 7.2.2 and 7.2.3), while the assessment of biophysical processes and short-lived climate forcers (Section 7.2.4) is largely unchanged. Further progress has been made on the implications of differences in AFOLU emissions estimates for assessing collective climate progress (Section 7.2.2.2 and Cross-Chapter Box 6 in this chapter).

7.2.1   Total Net GHG Flux from AFOLU

National greenhouse gas inventory (NGHGI) reporting following the IPCC 1996 guidelines (IPCC 1996), separates the total anthropogenic AFOLU flux into: (i) net anthropogenic flux from Land Use, Land-Use Change, and Forestry (LULUCF) due to both change in land cover and land management; and (ii) the net flux from Agriculture. While fluxes of CO_2 (Section 7.2.2) are predominantly from LULUCF and fluxes of CH_4 and N_2O (Section 7.2.3) are predominantly from agriculture, fluxes of all three gases are associated with both sub-sectors. However, not all methods separate them consistently according to these sub-sectors, thus here we use the term AFOLU,

separate by gas and implicitly include CO_2 emissions that stem from the agriculture part of AFOLU, though these account for a relatively small portion.

Total global net anthropogenic GHG emissions from AFOLU were 11.9 ± 4.4 GtCO$_2$-eq yr^{-1} on average over the period 2010–2019, around 21% of total global net anthropogenic GHG emissions (Table 7.1 and Figure 7.3, using the sum of bookkeeping models for the CO_2 component). When using FAOSTAT/NGHGIs CO_2 flux data, then the contribution of AFOLU to total emissions amounts to 13% of global emissions.

This AFOLU flux is the net of anthropogenic emissions of CO_2, CH_4 and N_2O, and anthropogenic removals of CO_2. The contribution of AFOLU to total emissions varies regionally with highest in Latin America and Caribbean with 58% and lowest in Europe and North America with each 7% (Chapter 2, Section 2.2.3). There is a discrepancy in the reported CO_2 AFOLU emissions magnitude because alternative methodological

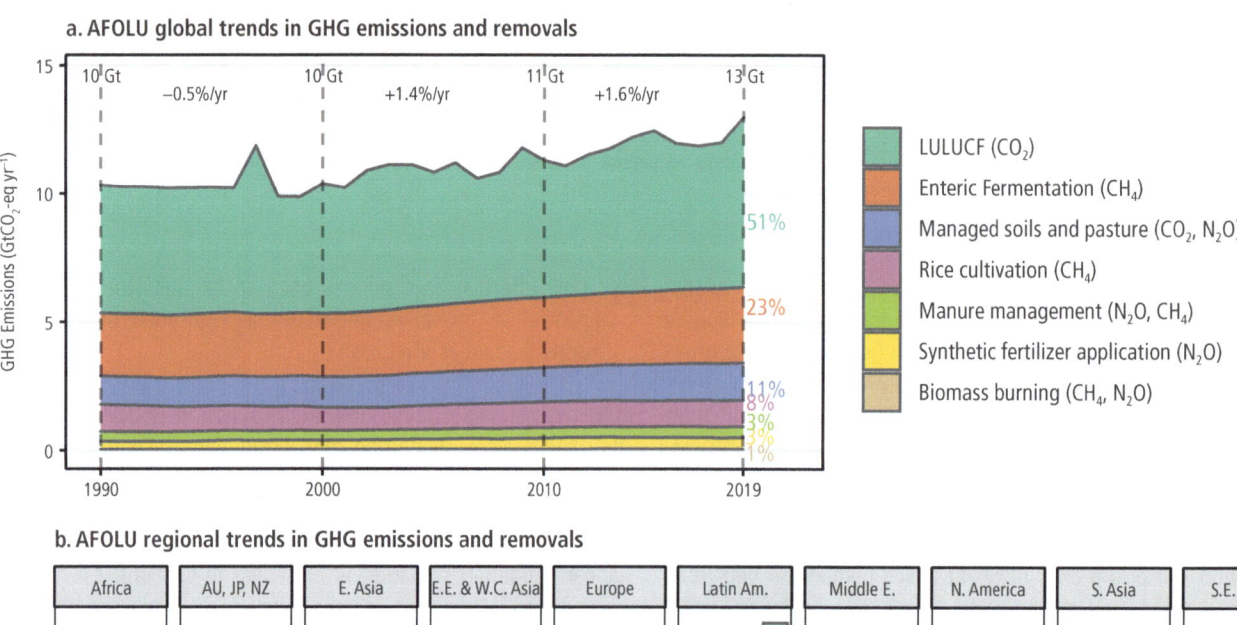

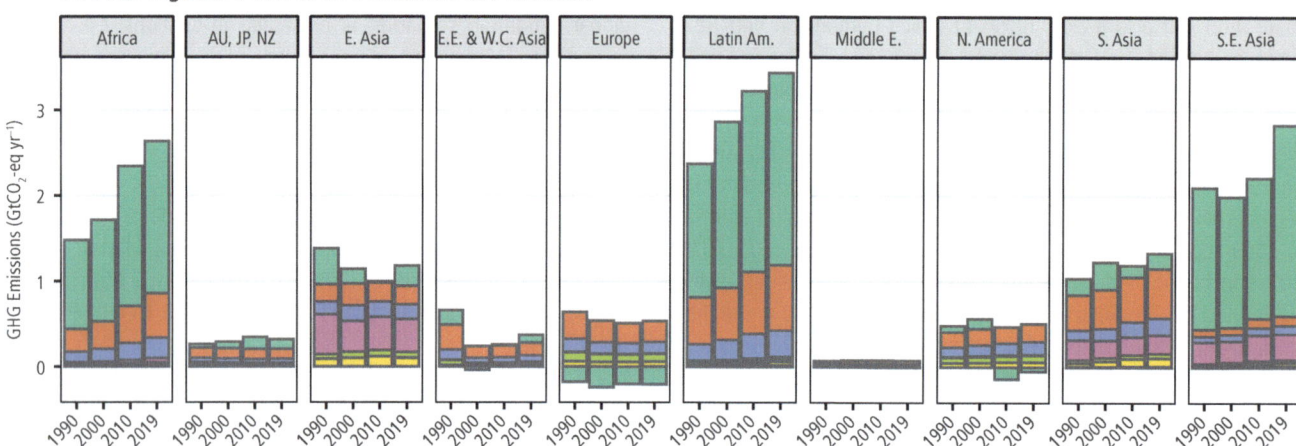

Figure 7.3 | Subdivision of the total AFOLU emissions from Table 7.1 by activity and gas for the period 1990 to 2019. Positive values are emissions from land to atmosphere, negative values are removals. Panel A shows emissions divided into major activity and gases. Note that 'biomass burning' is only the burning of agriculture residues in the fields. The indicated growth rates between 1990–2000, 2000–2010, 2010–2019 are annualised across each time period. Panel B illustrates regional emissions in the years 1990, 2000, 2010, 2019 AFOLU CO_2 (green shading) represents all AFOLU CO_2 emissions. It is the mean from three bookkeeping models (Hansis et al. 2015; Houghton and Nassikas 2017; Gasser et al. 2020) as presented in the Global Carbon Budget (Friedlingstein et al. 2020) and is *not directly comparable to LULUCF in NGHGIs* (Section 7.2.2). Data on CH_4 and N_2O emissions are from the EDGAR database (Crippa et al. 2021). See Sections 7.2.2 and 7.2.3 for comparison of different datasets. All values expressed are as CO_2-eq with GWP100 values: $CH_4 = 27$, $N_2O = 273$.

Table 7.1 | Net anthropogenic emissions (annual averages for 2010–2019[a]) from Agriculture, Forestry and Other Land Use (AFOLU). For context, the net flux due to the natural response of land to climate and environmental change is also shown for CO_2 in column E. Positive values represent emissions, negative values represent removals.

Gas	Units	Anthropogenic				Natural response	Natural and anthropogenic
		AFOLU Net anthropogenic emissions [h]	Non-AFOLU anthropogenic GHG emissions [d, f]	Total net anthropogenic emissions (AFOLU + non-AFOLU) by gas	AFOLU as a % of total net anthropogenic emissions by gas	Natural land sinks including natural response of land to anthropogenic environmental change and climate variability [e]	Net land-atmosphere CO_2 flux (i.e., anthropogenic AFOLU + natural fluxes across entire land surface
		A	B	C = A+B	D = (A/C) *100	E	F=A+E
CO_2	$GtCO_2$-eq yr^{-1}	5.9 ± 4.1 [b, f] (book-keeping models, managed soils and pasture). 0 to 0.8 (NGHGI/FAOSTAT data)	36.2 ± 2.9	42.0 ± 29.0	14%	−12.5 ± 3.2	−6.6 ± 4.6
CH$_4$	MtCH$_4$ yr^{-1}	157.0 ± 47.1 [c]	207.5 ± 62.2	364.4 ± 109.3		– [i]	
	$GtCO_2$-eq yr^{-1}	4.2 ± 1.3 [g]	5.9 ± 1.8	10.2 ± 3.0	41%		
N$_2$O	MtN$_2$O yr^{-1}	6.6 ± 4.0 [c]	2.8 ± 1.7	9.4 ± 5.6			
	$GtCO_2$-eq yr^{-1}	1.8 ± 1.1 [g]	0.8 ± 0.5	2.6 ± 1.5	69%		
Total [j]	$GtCO_2$-eq yr^{-1}	11.9 ± 4.4 (CO_2 component based on book-keeping models, managed soils and pasture)	44 ± 3.4	55.9 ± 6.1	21%		

[a] Estimates are given until 2019 as this is the latest date when data are available for all gases, consistent with Chapter 2, this report. Positive fluxes are emission from land to the atmosphere. Negative fluxes are removals.

[b] Net anthropogenic flux of CO_2 are due to land-use change such as deforestation and afforestation and land management, including wood harvest and regrowth, peatland drainage and fires, cropland and grassland management. Average of three bookkeeping models (Hansis et al. 2015; Houghton and Nassikas 2017; Gasser et al. 2020), complemented by data on peatland drainage and fires from FAOSTAT (Prosperi et al. 2020) and GFED4s (van der Werf et al. 2017). Bookkeeping based CO_2-LULUCF emissions (5.7±4.0) are consistent with AR6 WGI and Chapter 2 of this report. The value of 5.9(±4.1) includes CO_2 emissions from urea application to managed soils and pasture. Comparisons with other estimates are discussed in 7.2.2. Based on NGHGIs and FAOSTAT, the range is 0 to 0.8 $GtCO_2$ yr^{-1}.

[c] CH$_4$ and N$_2$O emission estimates and assessed uncertainty of 30 and 60% respectively, are based on Emissions Database for Global Atmospheric Research (EDGAR) data (Crippa et al. 2021) in accordance with Chapter 2, this report (Sections 2.2.1.3 and 2.2.1.4). Both FAOSTAT (Tubiello 2019; USEPA 2019; FAO 2021a) and the USA EPA (USEPA 2019) also provide data on agricultural non-CO_2 emissions, however, mean global CH$_4$ and N$_2$O values considering the three databases are within the uncertainty bounds of EDGAR. EDGAR only considers agricultural and not overall AFOLU non-CO_2 emissions. Agriculture is estimated to account for approximately 89 and 96% of total AFOLU CH$_4$ and N$_2$O emissions respectively. See Section 7.2.3 for further discussion.

[d] Total non-AFOLU emissions are the sum of total CO_2-eq emissions values for energy, industrial sources, waste and other emissions with data from the Global Carbon Project for CO_2, including international aviation and shipping, and from the PRIMAP database for CH$_4$ and N$_2$O averaged over 2007–2014, as that was the period for which data were available.

[e] The modelled CO_2 estimates include natural processes in vegetation and soils and how they respond to both natural climate variability and to human-induced environmental changes, for example, the response of vegetation and soils to environmental changes such as increasing atmospheric CO_2 concentration, nitrogen deposition, and climate change (indirect anthropogenic effects) on *both managed and unmanaged lands*. The estimate shown represents the average from 17 Dynamic Global Vegetation Models with 1SD uncertainty (Friedlingstein et al. 2020).

[f] The NGHGIs take a different approach to calculating 'anthropogenic' CO_2 fluxes than the models (Section 7.2.2). In particular the sinks due to environmental change (indirect anthropogenic fluxes) on managed lands are generally treated as anthropogenic in NGHGIs and non-anthropogenic in models such as bookkeeping and IAMs. A reconciliation of the results between IAMs and NGHGIs is presented in Cross-Chapter Box 6 in this chapter. If applied to this table, it would transfer approximately −5.5 $GtCO_2$ yr^{-1} (a sink) from Column E (which would become −7.0 $GtCO_2$ yr^{-1}) to Column A (which would then be 0.4 $GtCO_2$ yr^{-1}).

[g] All values expressed in units of CO_2-eq are based on IPCC AR6 100-year Global Warming Potential (GWP100) values with climate-carbon feedbacks (CH$_4$ = 27, N$_2$O = 273) (Chapter 2, Supplementary Material 2.SM.3; IPCC AR6 WGI Section 7.6).

[h] For assessment of cross-sector fluxes related to the food sector, see Chapter 12.

[i] While it is acknowledged that soils are a natural CH$_4$ sink (Jackson et al. 2020) with soil microbial removals estimated to be 30 ± 19 MtCH$_4$ yr^{-1} for the period 2008–2017 (according to bottom-up estimates), natural CH$_4$ sources are considerably greater (371 (245–488) MtCH$_4$ yr^{-1}) resulting in natural processes being a net CH$_4$ source (IPCC AR6 WGI Section 5.2.2). The soil CH$_4$ sink is therefore omitted from Column E.

[j] Total GHG emissions concerning non-AFOLU sectors and all sectors combined (Columns B and C) include fluorinated gases in addition to CO_2, CH$_4$ and N$_2$O. Therefore, total values do not equal the sum of estimates for CO_2, CH$_4$ and N$_2$O.

approaches that incorporate different assumptions are used (Section 7.2.2.2). While there is *low agreement* in the trend of global AFOLU CO_2 emissions over the past few decades (Section 7.2.2), they have remained relatively constant (*medium confidence*) (Chapter 2). Average non-CO_2 emission (aggregated using GWP100 IPCC AR6 values) from agriculture have risen from 5.2 ± 1.4 GtCO$_2$-eq yr^{-1} for the period 1990 to 1999, to 6.0 ± 1.7 GtCO$_2$-eq yr^{-1} for the period 2010 to 2019 (Crippa et al. 2021) (Section 7.2.3).

To present a fuller understanding of land–atmosphere interactions, Table 7.1 includes an estimate of the natural sink of land to atmospheric CO_2 (Jia et al. 2019) (IPCC AR6 WGI Chapter 5). Land fluxes respond naturally to human-induced environmental change (e.g., climate change, and the fertilising effects of increased atmospheric CO_2 concentration and nitrogen deposition), known as 'indirect anthropogenic effects', and also to 'natural effects' such as climate variability (IPCC 2010) (Table 7.1 and Section 7.2.2). This showed a removal of -12.5 ± 3.2 GtCO$_2$ yr^{-1} (*medium confidence*) from the atmosphere during 2010–2019 according to global dynamic global vegetation model (DGVM) models (Friedlingstein et al. 2020) 31% of total anthropogenic net emissions of CO_2 from all sectors. It is likely that the NGHIs and FAOSTAT implicitly cover some part of this sink and thus provide a net CO_2 AFOLU balance with some 5 GtCO$_2$ lower net emissions than according to bookkeeping models, with the overall net CO_2 value close to being neutral. Model results

and atmospheric observations concur that, when combining both anthropogenic (AFOLU) and natural processes on the entire land surface (the total 'land–atmosphere flux'), the land was a global net sink for CO_2 of -6.6 ± 4.6 GtCO$_2$ yr^{-1} with a range for 2010 to 2019 from -4.4 to -8.4 GtCO$_2$ yr^{-1}. (Rödenbeck et al. 2003, 2018; Chevallier et al. 2005; Feng et al. 2016; van der Laan-Luijkx et al. 2017; Niwa et al. 2017; Patra et al. 2018). The natural land sink is *highly likely* to be affected by both future AFOLU activity and climate change (IPCC AR6 WGI Box 5.1 and Figure SPM. 7), whereby under more severe climate change, the amount of carbon stored on land would still increase although the relative share of the emissions that land takes up, declines.

7.2.2 Flux of CO_2 from AFOLU, and the Non-anthropogenic Land Sink

7.2.2.1 Global Net AFOLU CO_2 Flux

Comparison of estimates of the global net AFOLU flux of CO_2 from diverse approaches (Figure 7.4) show differences on the order of several GtCO$_2$ yr^{-1}. When considering the reasons for the differences, and an approach to reconcile them (Grassi et al. 2021) (Section 7.2.2.3), there is *medium confidence* in the magnitude of the net AFOLU CO_2 flux. There is a discrepancy in the reported CO_2

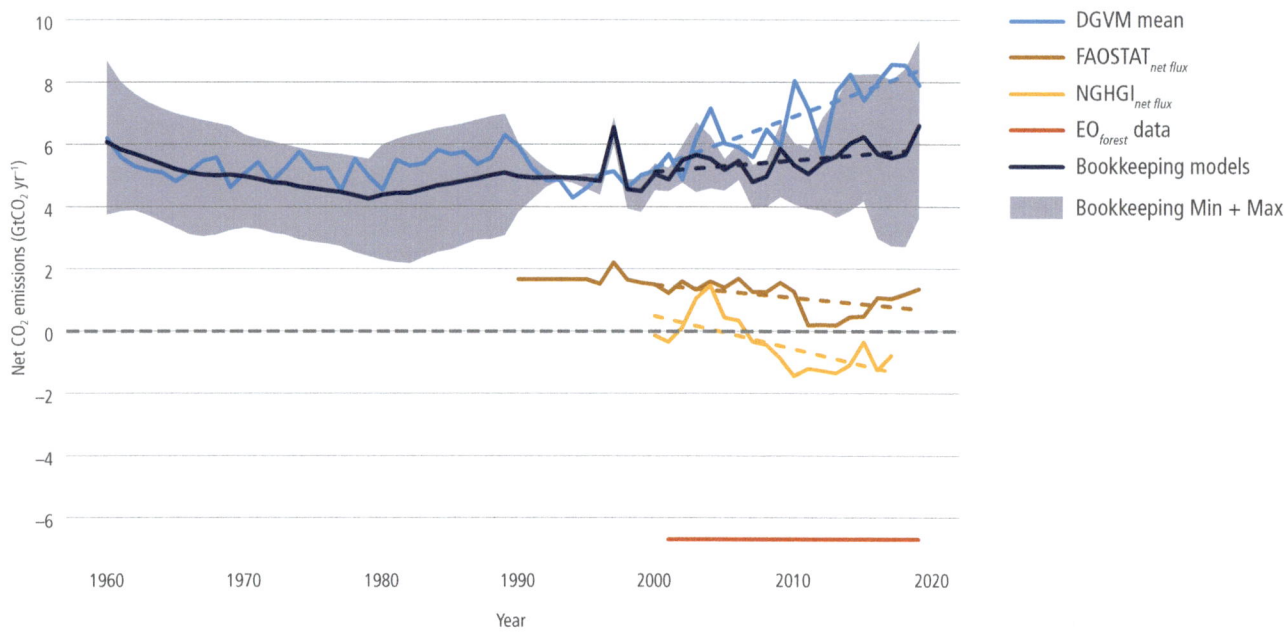

Figure 7.4 | Global net CO_2 flux due to AFOLU estimated using different methods for the period 1960 to 2019 (GtCO$_2$ yr^{-1}). Positive numbers represent emissions. **Light-blue line:** The mean from 17 DGVMs all using the same driving data under TrendyV9 used within the Global Carbon Budget 2020 and including different degrees of management (Bastos et al. 2020; Friedlingstein et al. 2020). **Brown line:** Data downloaded 6 June 2021 from FAOSTAT (FAO 2021b; http://www.fao.org/faostat/) comprising: net emissions from (i) forest land converted to other land, (ii) net emissions from organic soils in cropland, grassland and from biomass burning, including peat fires and peat draining (Prosperi et al. 2020) and (iii) net emissions from forest land remaining forest land, which includes managed forest lands (Tubiello et al. 2020). **Yellow line:** Net flux estimate from National Greenhouse Gas Inventories (NGHGI) based on country reports to the UNFCCC for LULUCF (Grassi et al. 2021) which include land-use change, and flux in managed lands. **Red EO line:** The 2001–2019 average net CO_2 flux from non-intact forest-related emissions and removals based on ground and Earth Observation data (EO) (Harris et al. 2021). Data to mask non-intact forest were used in the tropics (Turubanova et al. 2018) and extra-tropics (Potapov et al. 2017). **Dark blue line:** the mean estimate and minimum and maximum (dark-blue shading) from three bookkeeping models (Hansis et al. 2015; Houghton and Nassikas 2017; Gasser et al. 2020). These include land cover change (e.g., deforestation, afforestation), forest management including wood harvest and land degradation, shifting cultivation, regrowth of forests following wood harvest or abandonment of agriculture, grassland management, agricultural management. Emissions from peat burning and draining are added from external datasets (see text). Both the DGVM and bookkeeping global data is available at: https://www.icos-cp.eu/science-and-impact/global-carbon-budget/2020 (accessed on 4 October 2021). Data consistent with IPCC AR6 WGI Chapter 5. Dotted lines denote the linear regression from 2000 to 2019. Trends are statistically significant (P <0.05) with exception for the NGHGI trend (P <0.01).

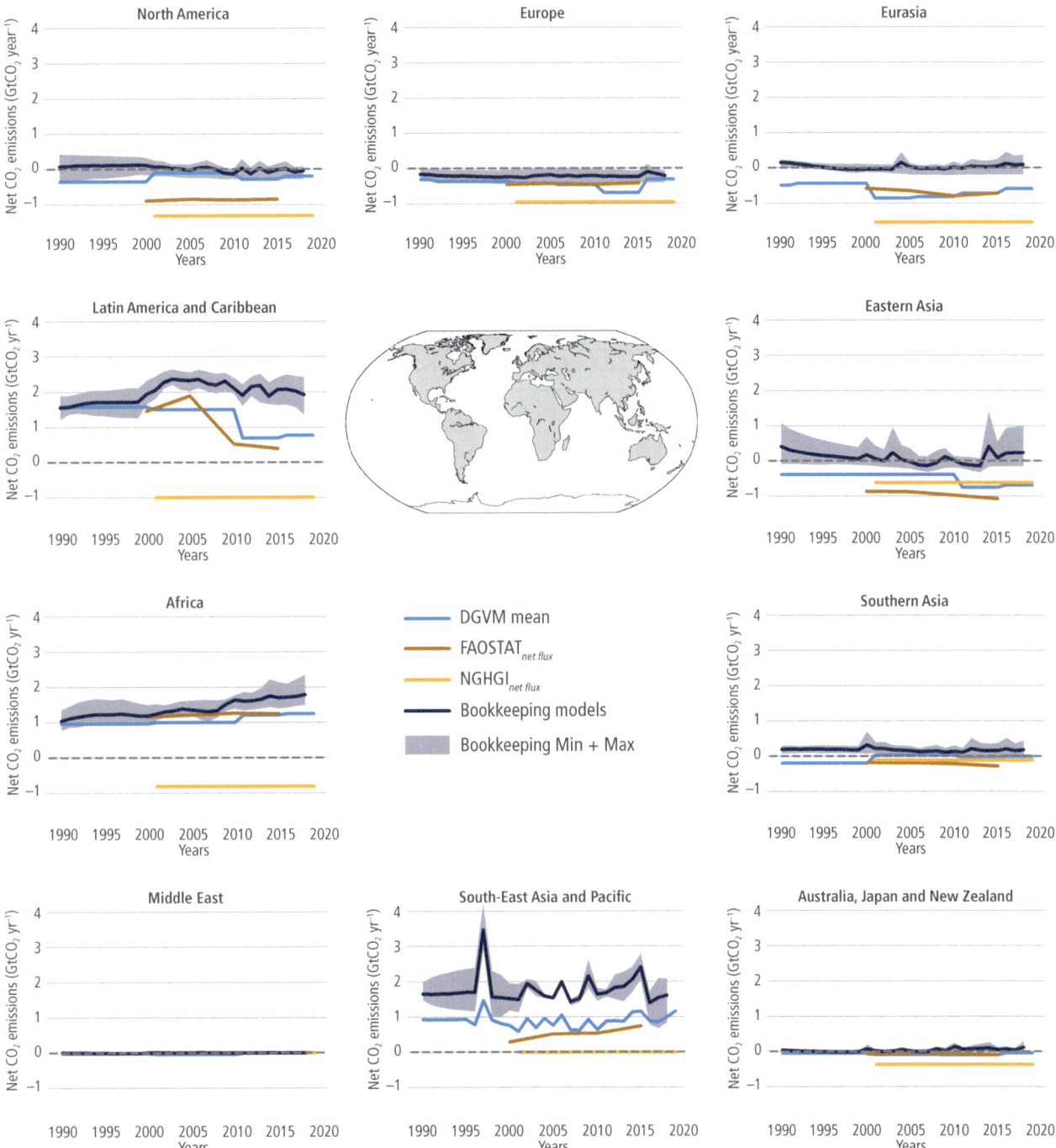

Figure 7.5 | Regional net flux of CO$_2$ due to AFOLU estimated using different methods for the period 1990–2019 (GtCO$_2$ yr^{-1}). Positive numbers represent emissions. The upper-central panel depicts the world map shaded according to the IPCC AR6 regions corresponding to the individual graphs. For each regional panel; **brown line:** Total net flux data from FAOSTAT (Tubiello et al. 2020); **yellow line:** Net emissions estimates from National Greenhouse Gas Inventories based on country reports to the UNFCCC for LULUCF (Grassi et al. 2021); **dark-blue line:** The mean estimate and minimum and maximum (dark-blue shading) from three bookkeeping models. (Hansis et al. 2015; Houghton and Nassikas 2017; Gasser et al. 2020). Regional estimates from bookkeeping models are available at: https://zenodo.org/record/5548333#. YVwJB2LMJPY (Minx et al. 2021). See the legend in Figure 7.4 for a detailed explanation of flux components for each dataset.

AFOLU emissions magnitude because alternative methodological approaches that incorporate different assumptions are used (Section 7.2.2.2). While the mean of the bookkeeping and DGVM model's show a small increase in global CO$_2$ net emissions since year 2000, individual models suggest opposite trends (Friedlingstein et al. 2020). The latest FAOSTAT and NGHGI estimates show a small reduction in net emission. Overall, the trends are unclear.

Regionally (Figure 7.5), there is *high confidence* of net emissions linked to deforestation in Latin America, Africa and South-East Asia from 1990 to 2019. There is *medium confidence* in trends indicating a decrease in net emissions in Latin America since 2005 linked to reduced gross deforestation emissions, and a small increase in net emissions related to increased gross deforestation emissions in Africa since 2000 (Figure 7.5). There is *high confidence* regarding the net

AFOLU CO$_2$ sink in Europe due to forest regrowth and known other sinks in managed forests, and *medium confidence* of a net sink in North America and Eurasia since 2010.

7.2.2.2   Why Do Various Methods Deliver Difference in Results?

The processes responsible for fluxes from land have been divided into three categories (IPCC 2006, 2010): (i) the *direct human-induced effects* due to changing land cover and land management; (ii) the *indirect human-induced effects* due to anthropogenic environmental change, such as climate change, CO$_2$ fertilisation, nitrogen deposition, and so on; and (iii) *natural effects,* including climate variability and a background natural disturbance regime (e.g., wildfires, windthrows, diseases or insect outbreaks).

Global models estimate the anthropogenic land CO$_2$ flux considering only the impact of direct effects, and only those areas that were subject to intense and direct management such as clear-cut harvest. It is important to note, that DGVMs also estimate the non-anthropogenic land CO$_2$ flux (Land Sink) that results from indirect and natural effects (Table 7.1). In contrast, estimates of the anthropogenic land CO$_2$ flux in NGHGIs (LULUCF) include the impact of direct effects and, in most cases, of indirect effects on a much greater area considered 'managed' than global models (Grassi et al. 2021).

The approach used by countries follows the IPCC methodological guidance for NGHGIs (IPCC 2006, 2019). Since separating direct, indirect and natural effects on the land CO$_2$ sink is impossible with direct observation such as national forest inventories (IPCC 2010), upon which most NGHGIs are based, the IPCC adopted the 'managed land' concept as a pragmatic proxy to facilitate NGHGI reporting. Anthropogenic land GHG fluxes (direct and indirect effects) are defined as all those occurring on managed land, that is, where human interventions and practices have been applied to perform production, ecological or social functions (IPCC 2006, 2019). GHG fluxes from unmanaged land are not reported in NGHGIs because they are assumed to be non-anthropogenic. Countries report NGHGI data with a range of methodologies, resolution and completeness, dependent on capacity and available data, consistent with IPCC guidelines (IPCC 2006, 2019) and subject to an international review or assessment processes.

The FAOSTAT approach is conceptually similar to NGHGIs. FAOSTAT data on forests are based on country reports to FAO-FRA 2020 (FAO 2020a), and include changes in biomass carbon stock in 'forest land' and 'net forest conversions' in five-year intervals. 'Forest land' may include unmanaged natural forest, leading to possible overall overestimation of anthropogenic fluxes for both sources and sinks, though emissions from deforestation are likely underestimated (Tubiello et al. 2020). FAOSTAT also estimate emissions from forest fires and other land uses (organic soils), following IPCC methods (Prosperi et al. 2020). The FAO-FRA 2020 (FAO 2020b) update leads to estimates of larger sinks in Russia since 1991, and in China and the USA from 2011, and larger deforestation emissions in Brazil and smaller in Indonesia than FRA 2015 (FAO 2015; Tubiello et al. 2020).

The bookkeeping models by Houghton and Nassikas (2017), Hansis et al. (2015), and Gasser et al. (2020) and the DGVMs used in the Global Carbon Budget (Friedlingstein et al. 2020) use either the LUH2 dataset (Hurtt et al. 2020), HYDE (Goldewijk et al. 2017), FRA 2015 (FAO 2015) or a combination. The LUH2 dataset includes a new wood harvest reconstruction, new representation of shifting cultivation, crop rotations, and management information including irrigation and fertiliser application. The area of forest subject to harvest in LUH2 is much less than the area of forest considered 'managed' in the NGHGIs (Grassi et al. 2018). The model datasets do not yet include the FAO FRA 2020 update (FAO 2020a). The DGVMs consider CO$_2$ fertilisation effects on forest growth that are sometimes confirmed from the ground-based forest inventory networks (Nabuurs et al. 2013) and sometimes not at all (van der Sleen et al. 2015).

Further, the DGVMs and bookkeeping models do not include a wide range of practices which are implicitly covered by the inventories; for example: forest dynamics (Pugh et al. 2019; Le Noë et al. 2020), forest management including wood harvest (Nabuurs, et al. 2013; Arneth et al. 2017), agricultural and grassland practices (Pugh et al. 2015; Sanderman et al. 2017; Pongratz et al. 2018); or, for example, fire management (Andela et al. 2017; Arora and Melton 2018).

Increasingly, higher emissions estimates are expected from DGVMs compared to bookkeeping models, because DGVMs include a loss of additional sink capacity of 3.3 ± 1.1 GtCO$_2$ yr^{-1} on average over 2009–2018, which is increasing with larger climate and CO$_2$ impacts (Friedlingstein et al. 2020). This arises because the DGVM methodological setup requires a reference simulation including climate and environmental changes but without any land-use change such as deforestation, so DGVMs implicitly include the sink capacity forests would have developed in response to environmental changes on areas that in reality have been cleared (Gitz and Ciais 2003; Pongratz et al. 2014) (IPCC AR6 WGI Chapter 5).

Carbon emissions from peat burning have been estimated based on the Global Fire Emission Database (GFED4s; van der Werf et al. 2017). These were included in the bookkeeping model estimates and added 2.0 GtC over 1960–2019 (e.g., causing the peak in South-East Asia in 1998) (Figure 7.5). Within the Global Carbon Budget (Friedlingstein et al. 2020), peat drainage from agriculture accounted for an additional 8.6 GtC from 1960–2019 according to FAOSTAT (Conchedda and Tubiello, 2020) used by two of the bookkeeping models (Hansis et al. 2015; Gasser et al. 2020).

Remote-sensing products provide valuable spatial and temporal land-use and biomass data globally (including in remote areas), at potentially high spatial and temporal resolutions, that can be used to calculate CO$_2$ fluxes, but have mostly been applied only to forests at the global or even regional scale. While such data can strongly support monitoring reporting and verification, estimates of forest carbon fluxes directly from Earth Observation (EO) data vary considerably in both their magnitude and sign (i.e., whether forests are a net source or sink of carbon). For the period 2005–2017, net tropical forest carbon fluxes were estimated as –0.4 GtCO$_2$ yr^{-1} (Fan et al. 2019); 0.58 GtCO$_2$ yr^{-1} (Grace et al. 2014); 1.6 GtCO$_2$yr^{-1} (Baccini et al. 2017) and 2.87 GtCO$_2$ yr^{-1} (Achard et al. 2014). Differences can in part be explained by spatial resolution of the datasets, the definition of 'forest' and the inclusion of processes and methods used to determine degradation and growth in intact and secondary forests, or the changes in algorithm over time (Palahí et al. 2021). A recent global study integrated ground observations and remote sensing data to map forest-related GHG emissions and removals at a high spatial resolution (30 m spatial scale), although it only provides an average estimate of annual carbon loss over 2001–2019 (Harris et al. 2021). The estimated net global forest carbon sink globally was -7.66 GtCO$_2$ yr^{-1}, being -1.7 GtCO$_2$yr^{-1} in the tropics only.

Remote sensing products can help to attribute changes to anthropogenic activity or natural inter-annual climate variability (Fan et al. 2019; Wigneron et al. 2020). Products with higher spatial resolution make it easier to determine forest and carbon dynamics in relatively small-sized managed forests (e.g., Y. Wang et al. 2020;

Heinrich et al. 2021; Reiche et al. 2021). For example, secondary forest regrowth in the Brazilian Amazon offset 9 to 14% of gross emissions due to deforestation[1] (Aragão et al. 2018; Silva Junior et al. 2021). Yet disturbances such as fire and repeated deforestation cycles due to shifting cultivation over the period 1985 to 2017, were found to reduce the regrowth rates of secondary forests by 8 to 55% depending on the climate region of regrowth (Heinrich et al. 2021).

7.2.2.3 Implications of Differences in AFOLU CO$_2$ Fluxes Between Global Models and National Greenhouse Gas Inventories (NGHGIs), and Reconciliation

There is about 5.5 GtCO$_2$ yr^{-1} difference in the anthropogenic AFOLU estimates between NGHGIs and global models (this number relates to an IAMs comparison for the period 2005–2015 – see Cross-Chapter Box 6 in this chapter; for comparison with other

a) 'Anthropogenic CO$_2$ flux' conceptual inconsistency problem

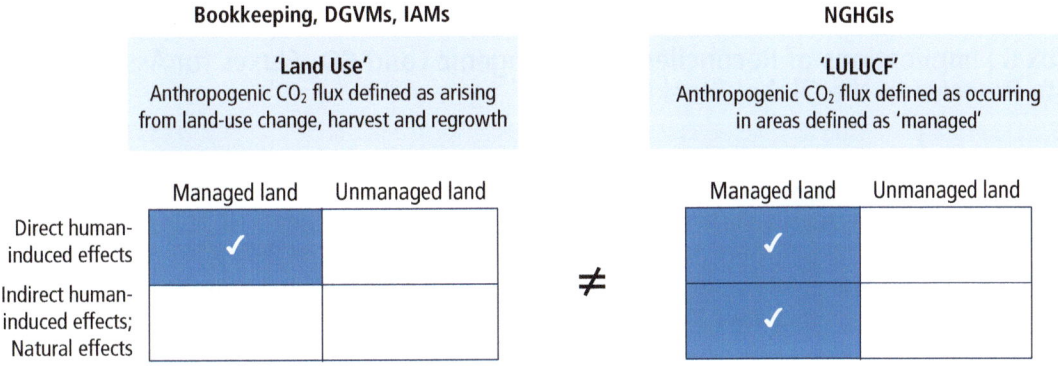

b) Solution via disaggregation of DGVM results

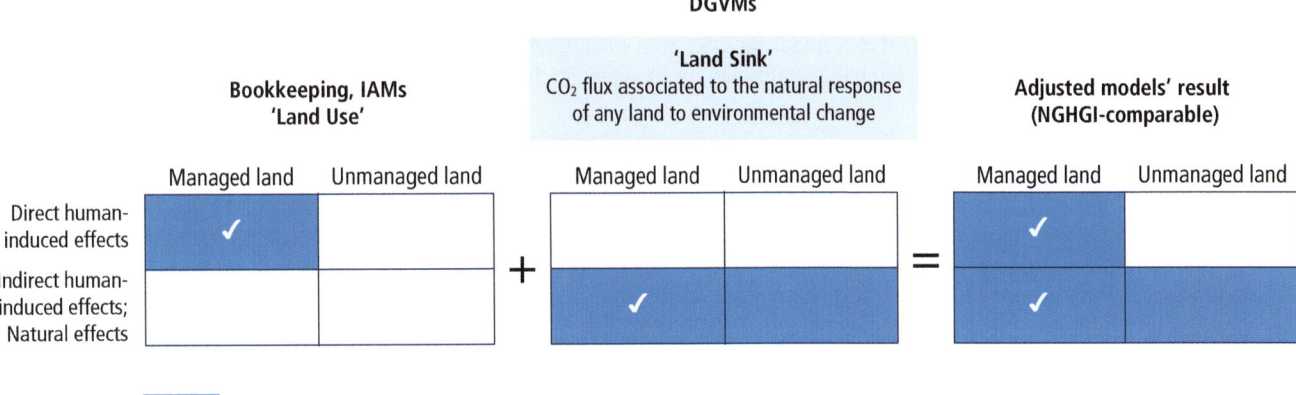

Figure 7.6 | Main conceptual differences between global models (bookkeeping models, IAMs and DGVMs) and NGHGIs definitions of what is considered the 'anthropogenic' land CO$_2$ flux, and proposed solution (from Grassi et al. 2021). (a) Differences in defining the anthropogenic land CO$_2$ flux by global models ('land use') and NGHGIs ('LULUCF'), including the attribution of processes responsible for land fluxes (IPCC 2006; 2010) in managed and unmanaged lands. The anthropogenic land CO$_2$ flux by global models typically includes only the CO$_2$ flux due to 'direct effects' (land-use change, harvest, regrowth). By contrast, most NGHGIs consider anthropogenic all fluxes occurring in areas defined as 'managed', including also the sink due to 'indirect effects' (climate change, atmospheric CO$_2$ increase, N deposition etc.) and due to 'natural effects' (climate variability, background natural disturbances). **(b)** Proposed solution to the inconsistency, via disaggregation of the 'Land Sink' flux from DGVMs into CO$_2$ fluxes occurring in managed and in unmanaged lands. The sum of 'land use' flux (direct effects from bookkeeping models or IAMs) and the 'Land Sink' (indirect effects from DGVMs) in managed lands produces an adjusted global model CO$_2$ flux which is conceptually more comparable with LULUCF fluxes from NGHGIs. Note that the figure may in some cases be an oversimplification, in other words, not all NGHGIs include all recent indirect effects.

models see Figure 7.4). Reconciling the differences, in other words, making estimates comparable, can build confidence in land-related CO_2 estimates, for example for the purpose of assessing collective progress in the context of the Global Stocktake (Cross-Chapter Box 6 in this chapter). The difference largely results from greater estimated CO_2 in NGHGIs, mostly occurring in forests (Grassi et al. 2021). This difference is potentially a consequence of: (i) simplified and/or incomplete representation of management in global models (Popp et al. 2017; Pongratz et al. 2018), for example, concerning impacts of forest management in biomass expansion and thickening (Nabuurs et al. 2013; Grassi et al. 2017), (ii) inaccurate and/or incomplete estimation of LULUCF fluxes in NGHGIs (Grassi et al. 2017), especially in developing countries, primarily in non-forest land uses and in soils, and (iii) conceptual differences in how global models and NGHGIs define 'anthropogenic' CO_2 flux from land (Grassi et al. 2018). The impacts of (i) and (ii) are difficult to quantify and result in uncertainties that will decrease slowly over time through improvements of both models and NGHGIs. By contrast, the inconsistencies in (iii) and its resulting biases were assessed as explained below.

Since changing the NGHGIs' approach is impractical, an interim method to translate and adjust the output of global models was outlined for reconciling a bookkeeping model and NGHGIs (Grassi et al. 2018). More recently, an improved version of this approach has been applied to the future mitigation pathways estimated by IAMs (Grassi et al. 2021), with the implications for the Global Stocktake discussed in Cross-Chapter Box 6 in this chapter. This method implies a post-processing of current global models' results that addresses two components of the conceptual differences in the 'anthropogenic' CO_2 flux; (i) how the impact of human-induced environmental changes (indirect effects) are considered, and (ii) the extent of forest area considered 'managed'. Essentially, this approach adds DGVM estimates of CO_2 fluxes due to indirect effects from countries' managed forest area (using non-intact forest area maps as a proxy) to the original global models' anthropogenic land CO_2 fluxes (Figure 7.6).

Cross-Chapter Box 6 | Implications of Reconciled Anthropogenic Land CO_2 Fluxes for Assessing Collective Climate Progress in the Global Stocktake

Authors: Giacomo Grassi (Italy/European Union), Joeri Rogelj (Belgium/Austria), Joanna I. House (United Kingdom), Alexander Popp (Germany), Detlef van Vuuren (the Netherlands), Katherine Calvin (the United States of America), Shinichiro Fujimori (Japan), Petr Havlík (Austria/the Czech Republic), Gert-Jan Nabuurs (the Netherlands)

The Global Stocktake aims to assess countries' collective progress towards the long-term goals of the Paris Agreement in the light of the best available science. Historic progress is assessed based on NGHGIs, while expectations of future progress are based on country climate targets (e.g., NDCs for 2025 or 2030 and long-term strategies for 2050). Scenarios consistent with limiting warming well-below 2°C and 1.5°C developed by IAMs (Chapter 3) are expected to play a key role as benchmarks against which countries' aggregated future mitigation pledges will be assessed. This, however, implies that estimates by IAMs and country data used to measure progress are comparable.

In fact, there is about 5.5 $GtCO_2$ yr^{-1} difference during 2005–2015 between global anthropogenic land CO_2 net flux estimates of IAMs and aggregated NGHGIs, due to different conceptual approaches to what is 'anthropogenic'. This approach and its implications when comparing climate targets with global mitigation pathways are illustrated in this Box Figure 1a–e.

By adjusting the original IAM output (Cross-Chapter Box 6, Figure 1a) with the indirect effects from countries' managed forest (Cross-Chapter Box 6, Figure 1b, estimated by DGVMs, see also Figure 7.6), NGHGI-comparable pathways can be derived (Cross-Chapter Box 6, Figure 1c). The resulting apparent increase in anthropogenic sink reflects simply a reallocation of a CO_2 flux previously labelled as natural, and thus does not reflect a mitigation action. These changes do not affect non-LULUCF emissions. However, since the atmosphere concentration is a combination of CO_2 emissions from LULUCF and from fossil fuels, the proposed land-related adjustments also influence the NGHGI-comparable economy-wide (all sector) CO_2 pathways (Cross-Chapter Box 6, Figure 1d).

This approach does not imply a change in the original decarbonisation pathways, nor does it suggest that indirect effects should be considered in the mitigation efforts. It simply ensures that a like-with-like comparison is made: if countries' climate targets use the NGHGI definition of anthropogenic emissions, this same definition can be applied to derive NGHGI-comparable future CO_2 pathways. This would have an impact on the NGHGI-comparable remaining carbon or GHG budget (i.e., the allowable emissions until net zero CO_2 or GHG emissions consistent with a certain climate target). For example, for SSP2-1.9 and SSP2-2.6 (representing pathways in line with 1.5°C and well-below 2°C limits under SSP2 assumptions), carbon budget is 170 $GtCO_2$-eq lower than the original remaining carbon budget according to the models' approach (Cross-Chapter Box 6, Figure 1e). Similarly, the remaining carbon (or GHG) budgets in Chapter 3 (this report), as well as the net zero carbon (or GHG) targets, could only be used in combination with the definition of anthropogenic emissions as used by the IAMs (Cross-Chapter Box 3 in Chapter 3). In the absence of these adjustments, collective progress would appear better than it is.

Cross-Chapter Box 6 (continued)

The UNEP's annual assessment of the global 2030 'emission gap' between aggregated country NDCs and specific target mitigation pathways (UNEP 2020), is only affected to a limited degree. This is because some estimates of global emissions under the NDCs already use the same land-use definitions as the IAM mitigation pathways (Rogelj et al. 2017), and because historical data of global NDC estimates is typically harmonised to the historical data of global mitigation pathway projections (Rogelj et al. 2011). This latter procedure, however, is agnostic to the reasons for the observed mismatch, and often uses a constant offset. The adjustment described here allows this mismatch to be resolved by drawing on a scientific understanding of the underlying reasons, and thus provides a more informed and accurate basis for estimating the emission gap.

The approach to deriving a NGHGI-comparable emission pathways presented here can be further refined with improved estimates of the future forest sink. Its use would enable a more accurate assessment of the collective progress achieved and of mitigation pledges under the Paris Agreement.

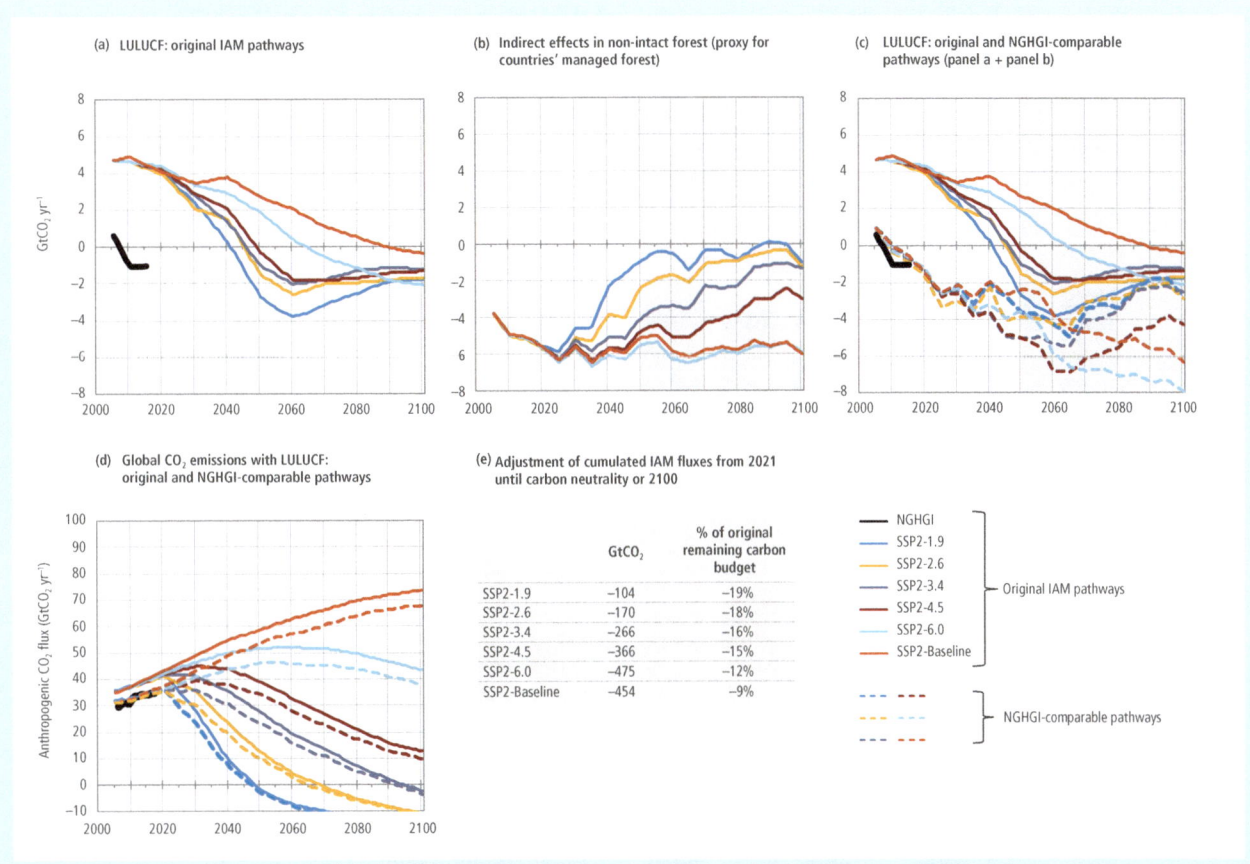

Cross-Chapter Box 6, Figure 1 | Impact on global mitigation pathways of adjusting the modelled anthropogenic land CO$_2$ fluxes to be comparable with National Greenhouse Gas Inventories (NGHGIs) (from Grassi et al. 2021). (a) The mismatch between global historical LULUCF CO$_2$ net flux from NGHGIs (black), and the original (un-adjusted) modelled flux historically and under future mitigation pathways for SSP2 scenarios from Integrated Assessment Models (IAMs, Chapter 3). **(b)** Fluxes due to indirect effects of environmental change on areas equivalent to countries' managed forest (i.e., those fluxes generally considered 'anthropogenic' by countries and 'natural' by global models). **(c)** Original modelled (solid line) LULUCF mitigation pathways adjusted to be NGHGI-comparable (dashed line), for example, by adding the indirect effects in panel b. The indirect effects in panel b decline over time with increasing mitigation ambition, mainly because of the weaker CO$_2$ fertilisation effect. In panel c, the dependency of the adjusted LULUCF pathways on the target becomes less evident after 2030, because the indirect effects in countries' managed forest (which are progressively more uncertain with time, as highlighted by the grey areas) compensate the effects of the original pathways. **(d)** NGHGI-comparable pathways for global CO$_2$ emissions from all sectors including LULUCF (obtained by combining global CO$_2$ pathways without LULUCF – where no adjustment is needed – and the NGHGI-comparable CO$_2$ pathways for LULUCF (Gütschow et al. 2019; Grassi et al. 2017). **(e)** Cumulative impact of the adjustments from 2021 until net zero CO$_2$ emissions or 2100 (whatever comes first) on the remaining carbon budget.

7.2.3   CH$_4$ and N$_2$O Flux From AFOLU

Trends in atmospheric CH$_4$ and N$_2$O concentrations and the associated sources, including land and land use are discussed in Sections 5.2.2 and 5.2.3 of the IPCC AR6 WGI. Regarding AFOLU, the SRCCL and AR5 (Jia et al. 2019; Smith et al. 2014) identified three global non-CO$_2$ emissions data sources: EDGAR (Crippa et al. 2021), FAOSTAT (FAO 2021a; Tubiello, 2019) and the USA EPA (USEPA 2019). Methodological differences have been previously discussed (Jia et al. 2019). In accordance with Chapter 2, this report, EDGAR data are used in Table 7.1 and Figure 7.3. It is important to note that in terms of AFOLU sectoral CH$_4$ and N$_2$O emissions, only FAOSTAT provides data on AFOLU emissions, while EDGAR and USEPA data consider just the agricultural component. However, the mean of values across the three databases for both CH$_4$ and N$_2$O, fall within the assessed uncertainty bounds (30 and 60% for CH$_4$ and N$_2$O respectively, Section 2.2.1, in this report) of EDGAR data. NGHGIs annually submitted to the UNFCCC (Section 7.2.2.3) provide national AFOLU CH$_4$ and N$_2$O data, as included in the SRCCL (Jia et al. 2019). Aggregation of NGHGIs to indicate global emissions must be considered with caution, as not

all countries compile inventories, nor submit annually. Additionally, NGHGIs may incorporate a range of methodologies for CH$_4$ and N$_2$O accounting (e.g., van der Weerden et al. 2016; Ndung'u et al. 2019; Thakuri et al. 2020), making comparison difficult. The analysis of complete AFOLU emissions presented here, is based on FAOSTAT data. For agricultural specific discussion, analysis considers EDGAR, FAOSTAT and USEPA data.

7.2.3.1   Global AFOLU CH$_4$ and N$_2$O Emissions

Using FAOSTAT data, the SRCCL estimated average CH$_4$ emissions from AFOLU to be 161.2 ± 43 MtCH$_4$ yr^{-1} for the period 2007–2016, representing 44% of total anthropogenic CH$_4$ emissions, with agriculture accounting for 88% of the AFOLU component (Jia et al. 2019). The latest data (FAO 2021a, 2020b) highlight a trend of growing AFOLU CH$_4$ emissions, with a 10% increase evident between 1990 and 2019, despite year-to-year variation. Forestry and other land use (FOLU) CH$_4$ emission sources include biomass burning on forest land and combustion of organic soils (peatland fires) (FAO 2020c). The agricultural share of AFOLU CH$_4$ emissions remains relatively

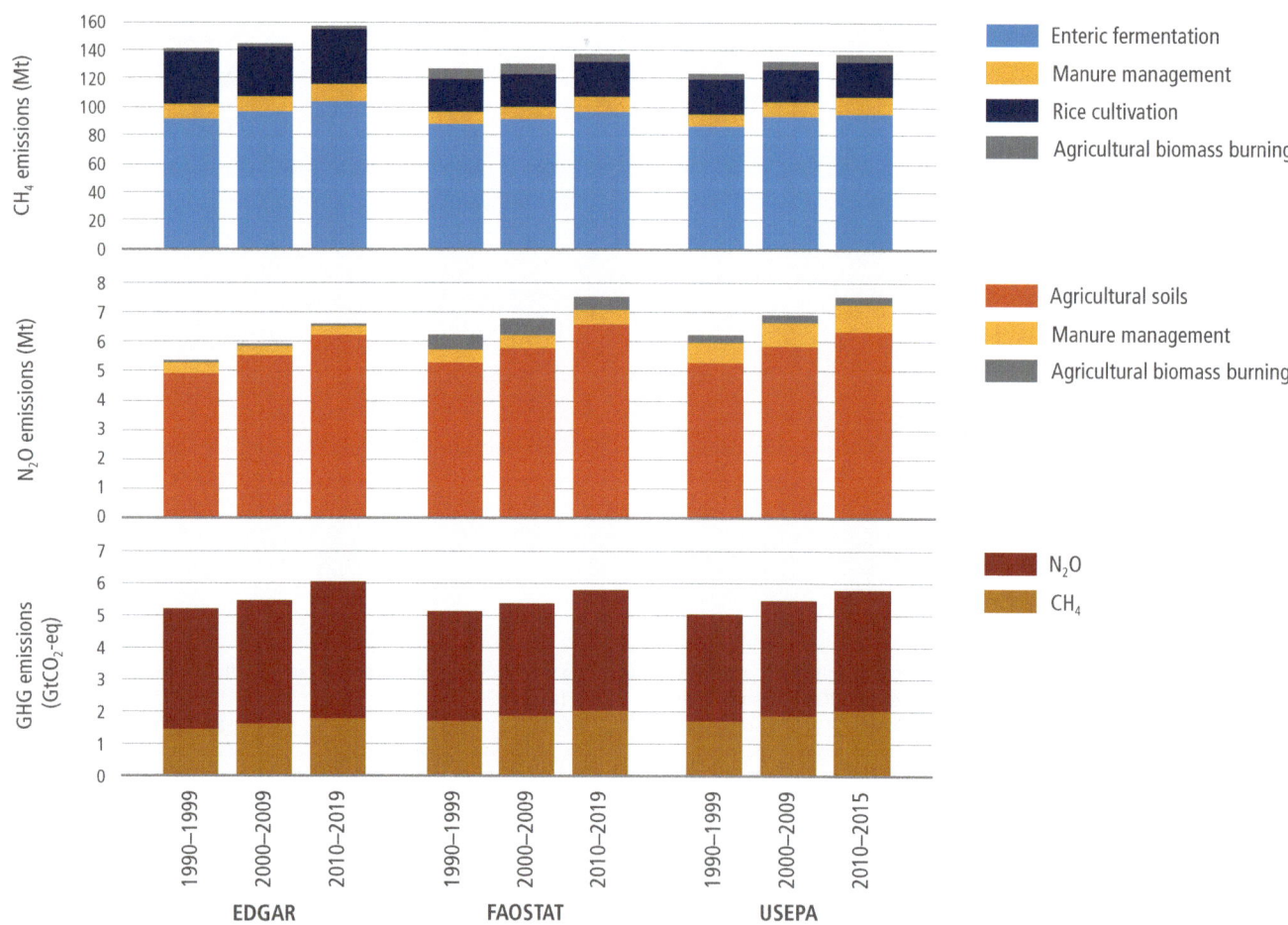

Figure 7.7 | Estimated global mean agricultural CH$_4$ (top), N$_2$O (middle) and aggregated CH$_4$ and N$_2$O (using CO$_2$-eq according to GWP100 AR6 values). (Bottom) emissions for three decades according to EDGAR v6.0 (Crippa et al. 2021), FAOSTAT (FAO 2021a) and USEPA (USEPA 2019) databases. Latest versions of databases indicate historic emissions to 2019, 2019 and 2015 respectively, with average values for the post–2010 period calculated accordingly. For CH$_4$, emissions classified as 'Other Ag.' within USEPA data, are re-classified as 'Agricultural Biomass Burning'. Despite CH$_4$ emissions from agricultural soils also being included, this category was deemed to principally concern biomass burning on agricultural land and classified accordingly. For N$_2$O, emissions classified within EDGAR as direct and indirect emissions from managed soils, and indirect emissions from manure management are combined under 'Agricultural Soils'. Emissions classified by FOASTAT as from manure deposition and application to soils, crop residues, drainage of organic soils and synthetic fertilisers are combined under 'Agricultural Soils', while emissions reported as 'Other Ag.' under USEPA data are re-classified as 'Agricultural Biomass Burning'.

unchanged, with the latest data indicating agriculture to have accounted for 89% of emissions on average between 1990 and 2019. The SRCCL reported with *medium evidence* and *high agreement* that ruminants and rice production were the most important contributors to overall growth trends in atmospheric CH_4 (Jia et al. 2019). The latest data confirm this in terms of agricultural emissions, with agreement between databases that agricultural CH_4 emissions continue to increase and that enteric fermentation and rice cultivation remain the main sources (Figure 7.7). The proportionally higher emissions from rice cultivation indicated by EDGAR data compared to the other databases, may result from the use of a Tier 2 methodology for this source within EDGAR (Janssens-Maenhout et al. 2019).

The SRCCL also noted a trend of increasing atmospheric N_2O concentration, with *robust evidence* and *high agreement* that agriculture accounted for approximately two-thirds of overall global anthropogenic N_2O emissions. Average AFOLU N_2O emissions were reported to be 8.7 ± 2.5 MtN_2O yr^{-1} for the period 2007–2016, accounting for 81% of total anthropogenic N_2O emissions, with agriculture accounting for 95% of AFOLU N_2O emissions (Jia et al. 2019). A recent comprehensive review confirms agriculture as the principal driver of the growing atmospheric N_2O concentration (Tian et al. 2020). The latest FAOSTAT data (FAO 2020b, 2021a) document a 25% increase in AFOLU N_2O emissions between 1990 and 2019,

with the average share from agriculture remaining approximately the same (96%). Agricultural soils were identified in the SRCCL and in recent literature as a dominant emission source, notably due to nitrogen fertiliser and manure applications to croplands, and manure production and deposition on pastures (Jia et al. 2019; Tian et al. 2020). There is agreement within latest data that agricultural soils remain the dominant source (Figure 7.7).

Aggregation of CH_4 and N_2O to CO_2 equivalence (using GWP100 IPCC AR6 values), suggests that AFOLU emissions increased by 15% between 1990 and 2019, though emissions showed trend variability year to year. Agriculture accounted for 91% of AFOLU emissions on average over the period (FAO 2020b, 2021a). EDGAR (Crippa et al. 2021), FAOSTAT (FAO 2021a) and USEPA (USEPA 2019) data suggest aggregated agricultural emissions (CO_2-eq) to have increased since 1990, by 19% (1990–2019), 15% (1990–2019) and 21% (1990–2015) respectively, with all databases identifying enteric fermentation and agricultural soils as the dominant agricultural emissions sources.

7.2.3.2   Regional AFOLU CH_4 and N_2O Emissions

FAOSTAT data (FAO 2020b, 2021a) indicate Africa (+44%), followed by Southern Asia (+29%) to have the largest growth in AFOLU CH_4 emissions between 1990 and 2019 (Figure 7.8). Eurasia was

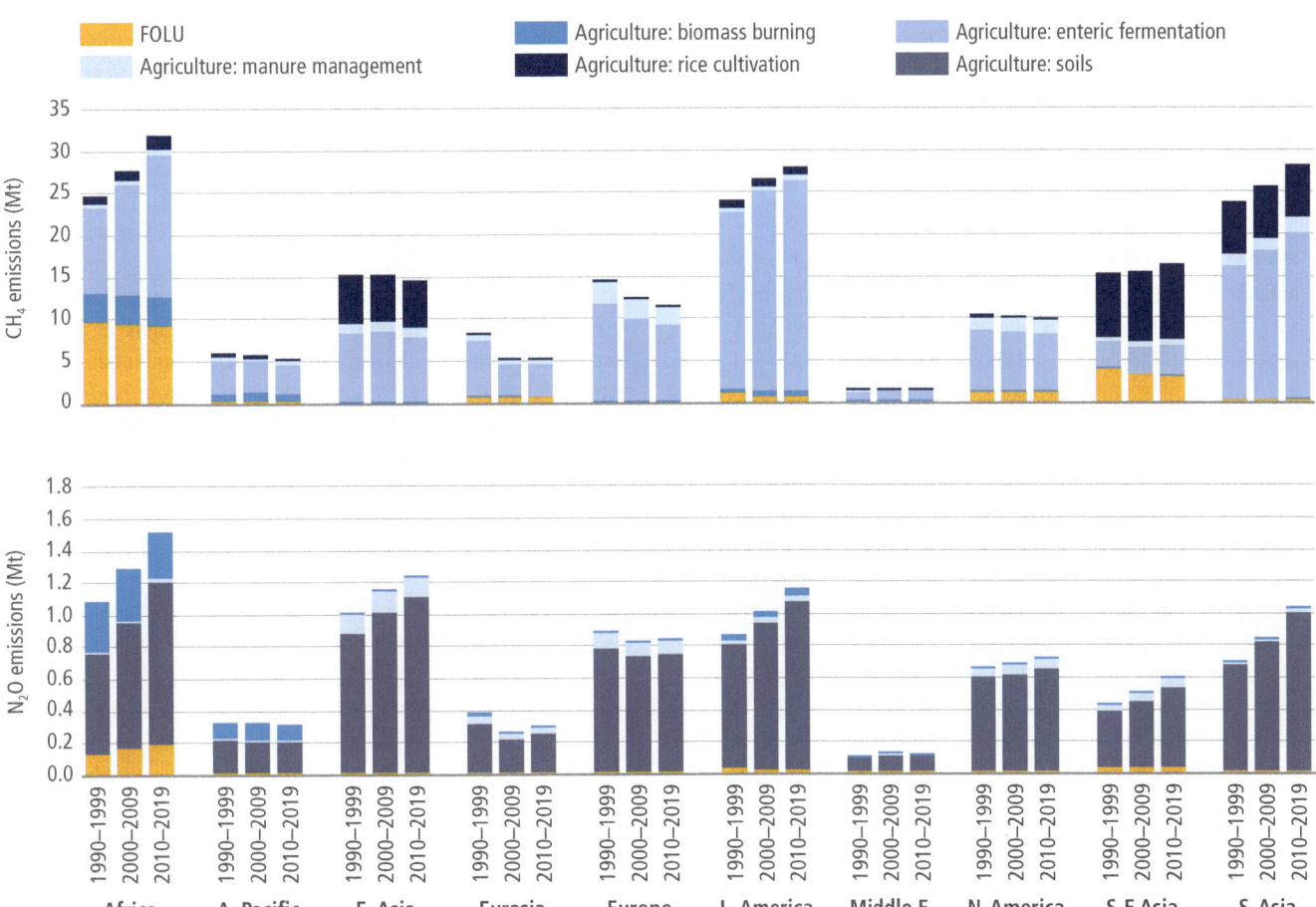

Figure 7.8 | Estimated average AFOLU CH_4 (top) and N_2O (bottom) emissions for three decades according to FAOSTAT data by ten global regions, with disaggregation of agricultural emissions (FAO 2020b; 2021a). Note for N_2O: emissions from manure deposition and application to soils, crop residues and synthetic fertilisers are combined under 'Agriculture: Soils'.

characterised by notable emission reductions (–58%), principally as a result of a sharp decline (–63%) between 1990 and 1999. The average agricultural share of AFOLU emissions between 1990 and 2019 ranged from 66% in Africa to almost 100% in the Middle East.

In agreement with AR5 (Smith et al. 2014), the SRCCL identified Asia as having the largest share (37%) of emissions from enteric fermentation and manure management since 2000, but Africa to have the fastest growth rate. Asia was identified as responsible for 89% of rice cultivation emissions, which were reported as increasing (Jia et al. 2019). Considering classification by ten IPCC regions, data suggest enteric fermentation to have dominated emissions in all regions since 1990, except in South-East Asia and Pacific, where rice cultivation forms the principal source (FAO 2021; USEPA 2019). The different databases broadly indicate the same regional CH_4 emission trends, though the indicated absolute change differs due to methodological differences (Section 7.2.3.1). All databases indicate considerable emissions growth in Africa since 1990 and that this region recorded the greatest regional increases in emissions from both enteric fermentation and rice cultivation since 2010. Additionally, FAOSTAT data suggest that emissions from agricultural biomass burning account for a notably high proportion of agricultural CH_4 emissions in Africa (Figure 7.8).

The latest data suggest growth in AFOLU N_2O emissions in most regions between 1990 and 2019, with Southern Asia demonstrating highest growth (+74%) and Eurasia, greatest reductions (–51%), the latter mainly a result of a 61% reduction between 1990 and 2000 (FAO 2020b, 2021a). Agriculture was the dominant emission source in all regions, its proportional average share between 1990 and 2019 ranging from 87% in Africa, to almost 100% in the Middle East (Figure 7.8).

The SRCCL provided limited discussion on regional variation in agricultural N_2O emissions but reported with *medium confidence* that certain regions (North America, Europe, East and South Asia) were notable sources of grazing land N_2O emissions (Jia et al. 2019). The AR5 identified Asia as the largest source and as having the highest growth rate of N_2O emissions from synthetic fertilisers between 2000 and 2010 (Smith et al. 2014). Latest data indicate agricultural N_2O emission increases in most regions, though variation between databases prevents definitive conclusions on trends, with Africa, Southern Asia, and Eastern Asia suggested to have had greatest growth since 1990 according to EDGAR (Crippa et al. 2021), FAOSTAT (FAO 2021a) and USEPA (USEPA 2019) data respectively. However, all databases indicate that emissions declined in Eurasia and Europe from 1990 levels, in accordance with specific environmental regulations put in place since the late 1980s (Tubiello 2019; European Environment Agency 2020; Tian et al. 2020), but generally suggest increases in both regions since 2010.

7.2.4 Biophysical Effects and Short-lived Climate Forcers

Despite new literature, general conclusions from the SRCCL and WGI-AR6 on biophysical effects and short-lived climate forcers remain the same. Changes in land conditions from land cover change or land management jointly affect water, energy, and aerosol fluxes (biophysical fluxes) as well as GHG fluxes (biogeochemical fluxes) exchanged between the land and atmosphere (*high agreement, robust evidence*) (Anderson et al. 2011; O'Halloran et al. 2012; Alkama and Cescatti 2016; Naudts et al. 2016; Erb et al. 2017). There is *high confidence* that changes in land condition do not just have local impacts but also have non-local impacts in adjacent and more distant areas (Pielke et al. 2011; Mahmood et al. 2014) which may contribute to surpassing climate tipping points (Nepstad et al. 2008; Brando et al. 2014). Non-local impacts may occur through: GHG fluxes and subsequent changes in radiative transfer, changes in atmospheric chemistry, thermal, moisture and surface pressure gradients creating horizontal transport (advection) (de Vrese et al. 2016; Davin and de Noblet-Ducoudré 2010) and vertical transport (convection and subsidence) (Devaraju et al. 2018). Although regional and global biophysical impacts emerge from model simulations (Davin and de Noblet-Ducoudré 2010; de Vrese et al. 2016; Devaraju et al. 2018), especially if the land condition has changed over large areas, there is *very low agreement* on the location, extent and characteristics of the non-local effects across models. Recent methodological advances, empirically confirmed changes in temperature and precipitation owing to distant changes in forest cover (Cohn et al. 2019; Meier et al. 2021).

Following changes in land conditions, CO_2, CH_4 and N_2O fluxes are quickly mixed into the atmosphere and dispersed, resulting in the biogeochemical effects being dominated by the biophysical effects at local scales (*high confidence*) (Y. Li et al. 2015; Alkama and Cescatti 2016). Afforestation/reforestation (Lejeune et al. 2018; Strandberg and Kjellström 2019), urbanisation (Li and Bou-Zeid 2013) and irrigation (Mueller et al. 2016 and Thiery et al. 2017) modulate the likelihood, intensity, and duration of many extreme events including heatwaves (*high confidence*) and heavy precipitation events (*medium confidence*) (Haberlie et al. 2015). There is *high confidence* and *high agreement* that afforestation in the tropics (Perugini et al. 2017), irrigation (Alter et al. 2015; Mueller et al. 2016) and urban greening result in local cooling, *high agreement* and *medium confidence* on the impact of tree growth form (deciduous vs evergreen) (Naudts et al. 2016; Luyssaert et al. 2018 and Schwaab et al. 2020), and *low agreement* on the impact of wood harvest, fertilisation, tillage, crop harvest, residue management, grazing, mowing, and fire management on the local climate.

Studies of biophysical effects have increased since AR5 reaching *high agreement* for the effects of changes in land condition on surface albedo (Leonardi et al. 2015). *Low confidence* remains in proposing specific changes in land conditions to achieve desired impacts on local, regional and global climates due to: a poor relationship between changes in surface albedo and changes in surface temperature (Davin and de Noblet-Ducoudré 2010), compensation and feedbacks among biophysical processes (Bonan 2016; Kalliokoski et al. 2020), climate and seasonal dependency of the biophysical effects (Bonan 2016), omittance of short-lived chemical forcers (Unger 2014; Kalliokoski et al. 2020), and study domains often being too small to document possible conflicts between local and non-local effects (Swann et al. 2012; Hirsch et al. 2018).

7.3   Drivers

Since AR5 several global assessments (IPBES 2018a; NYDF Assessment Partners 2019; UNEP 2019; IPCC 2019) and studies (e.g., Tubiello 2019; Tian et al. 2020) have reported on drivers (natural and anthropogenic factors that affect emissions and sinks of the land-use sector) behind AFOLU emissions trends, and associated projections for the coming decades. The following analysis aligns with the drivers typology used by IPBES (2019b) and the Global Environmental Outlook (UNEP 2019). Drivers are divided into direct drivers resulting from human decisions and actions concerning land use and land-use change, and indirect drivers that operate by altering the level or rate of change of one or more direct drivers. Although drivers of emissions in agriculture and FOLU are presented separately, they are interlinked, operating in many complex ways at different temporal and spatial scales, with outcomes depending on their interactions. For example, deforestation in tropical forests is a significant component of sectorial emissions. A review of deforestation drivers' studies published between 1996 and 2013, indicated a wide range of factors associated with deforestation rates across many analyses and studies, covering different regions (Busch and Ferretti-Gallon 2017) (Figure 7.9). Higher agricultural prices were identified as a key driver of deforestation, while law enforcement, area protection, and ecosystem services payments were found to be important drivers of reduced deforestation, while timber activity did not show a consistent impact.

7.3.1   Anthropogenic Direct Drivers: Deforestation, Conversion of Other Ecosystems, and Land Degradation

The global forest area in 2020 is estimated at 4.1 billion ha, representing 31% of the total land area (FAO 2020a). Most forests are situated in the tropics (45%), followed by boreal (27%), temperate (16%) and subtropical (11%) domains. Considering regional distribution of global forest area, Europe and the Russian Federation accounts for 25%, followed by South America (21%), North and Central America (19%), Africa (16%), Asia (15%) and Oceania (5%). However, a significant share (54%) of the world's forest area concerns five countries – The Russian Federation, Brazil, Canada, the USA and China (FAO 2020a). Forest loss rates differ among regions though the global trend is towards a net forest loss (UNEP 2019). The global forest area declined by about 178 Mha in the 30 years from 1990 to 2020 (FAO 2020a). The rate of net forest loss has decreased since 1990, a result of reduced deforestation in some countries and forest gains in others. The annual net loss of forest area declined from 7.8 Mha in 1990–2000, to 5.2 Mha in 2000–2010, to 4.7 Mha in 2010–2020, while the total growing stock in global forests increased (FAO 2020a). The rate of decline in net forest loss during the last decade was due mainly to an increase in the rate of forest gain (i.e., afforestation and the natural expansion of forests).

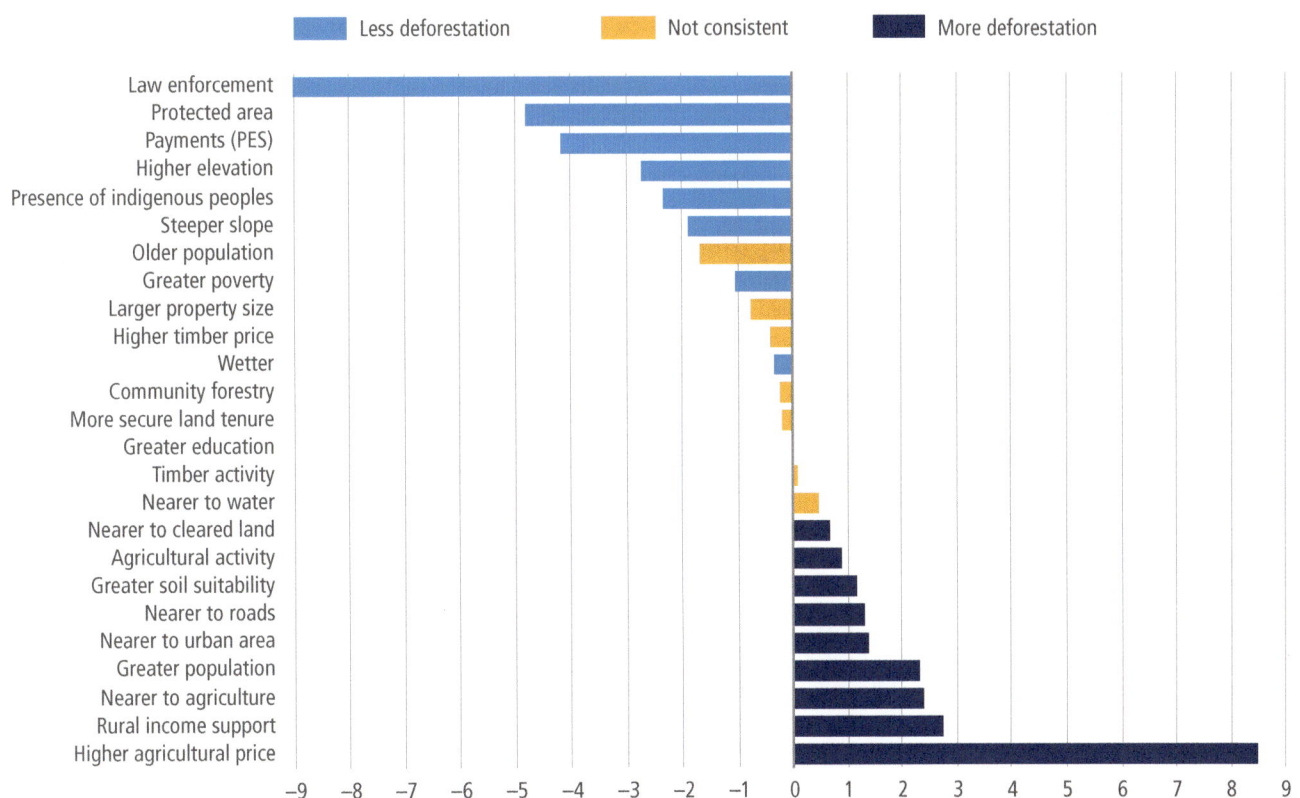

For each category of explanatory variables (left-hand side), the meta-analysis determined whether the driver variables in that category were consistently associated with higher rates of deforestation, lower rates of deforestation, or neither (not consistent). For example, a ratio of –4x indicates that a variable is associated with less deforestation four times as often as it is associated with more deforestation.

Figure 7.9 | Association of driver variables with more or less deforestation. Source: reproduced with permission from Busch and Ferretti-Gallon (2017).

Globally, the area of the more open, other wooded land is also of significant importance, with almost 1 billion hectares (FAO 2020a). The area of other wooded land decreased by 30.6 Mha between 1990 and 2020 with larger declines between 1990–2000 (FAO 2020a). There are still significant challenges in monitoring the area of other wooded land, largely associated with difficulties in measuring tree-canopy cover in the range of 5–10%. The global area of mangroves, one of the most productive terrestrial ecosystems (Neogi 2020a), has also experienced a significant decline (Thomas et al. 2017; Neogi 2020b), with a decrease of 1.0 Mha between 1990 and 2020 (FAO 2020a) due to agriculture and aquaculture (Bhattarai 2011; Ajonina et al. 2014; Webb et al. 2014; Giri et al. 2015; Thomas et al. 2017; Fauzi et al. 2019). Some relevant direct drivers affecting emissions and removal in forests and other ecosystems are discussed in proceeding sections.

7.3.1.1 Conversion of Natural Ecosystems to Agriculture

Previous IPCC reports identify land-use change as an important driver of emissions and agriculture as a key driver of land-use change, causing both deforestation and wetland drainage (P. Smith et al. 2019a). The AR5 reported a trend of declining global agricultural land area since 2000 (Smith et al. 2014). The latest data (FAO 2021b) indicate a 2% reduction in the global agricultural area between 2000 and 2019 (Figure 7.10). This area includes (though is not limited to) land under permanent and temporary crops or pasture, temporary fallow and natural meadows and pasture utilised for grazing or agricultural purposes (FAO 2021b), although the extent of land used for grazing may not be fully captured (Fetzel et al. 2017). Data indicate changes in how agricultural land is used. Between 2000 and 2019, the area classified as permanent meadow and pasture decreased (–6%) while cropland area (under arable production and temporary crops) increased (+2%). A key driver of this change has been a general trend of intensification, including in livestock production (Barger et al. 2018; OECD/FAO 2019; UNEP 2019), whereby less grazing land is supporting increasing livestock numbers in conjunction with greater use of crops as livestock feed (Barger et al. 2018). The share of feed crops, such as maize and soybean, of global crop production is projected to grow as the demand for animal feed increases with further intensification of livestock production (OECD/FAO 2019). Despite increased demand for food, feed, fuel and fibre from a growing human population (FAO 2019b), global agricultural land area is projected to remain relatively stable during the next decade, with increases in production expected to result from agricultural intensification (OECD/FAO 2019).

Despite a decline in global agricultural area, the latest data document some regional expansion between 2000 and 2019, specifically in Africa (+3%) and Asia and the Pacific (+1%). Agricultural area declined in all other regions, notably in developed countries (–9%), due to multiple factors including among others, urbanisation (see Section 7.3.1.2).

7.3.1.2 Infrastructure Development and Urbanisation

Although built-up areas (defined as cities, towns, villages and human infrastructure) occupy a relatively small fraction of land (around 1% of global land), since 1975 urban clusters (i.e., urban centres as well as surrounding suburbs) have expanded approximately 2.5 times (UNEP 2019; Chapter 8, this report). Regional differences are striking. Between 1975 and 2015, built-up areas doubled in size in Europe while urban population remained relatively constant. In Africa built-up areas grew approximately fourfold, while urban population tripled (UNEP 2019). Trends indicate that rural-to-urban migration will continue and accelerate in developing countries increasing environmental pressure in spite of measures to mitigate some of the impacts (e.g., by preserving or enhancing natural systems within cities, for example, lakes or natural and urban green infrastructures (UNEP 2019). If current population densities within cities remain stable, the extent of built-up areas in developed countries is expected to increase by 30% and triple in developing countries between 2000 and 2050 (Barger et al. 2018).

Urban expansion leads to landscape fragmentation and urban sprawl with effects on forest resources and land use (Ünal et al. 2019) while interacting with other drives. For example, in the Brazilian Amazon, the most rapid urban growth occurs within cities that are located near rural areas that produce commodities (minerals or crops) and are connected to export corridors (Richards and VanWey 2015). Urbanisation, coastal development and industrialisation also play crucial roles in the significant loss of mangrove forests (Hirales-Cota 2010; Richards and Friess 2016; Rivera-Monroy et al. 2017). Among infrastructural developments, roads are one of the most consistent and most considerable factors in deforestation, particularly in tropical frontiers (Pfaff et al. 2007; Rudel et al. 2009; Ferretti-Gallon and Busch 2014). The development of roads may also bring subsequent impacts on further development intensity due to increasing economic activities (see Chapter 8) mostly in the tropics and subtropics, where the expansion of road networks increases access to remote forests that act as refuges for biodiversity (Campbell et al. 2017) (Box 7.1). Logging is one of the main drivers of road construction in tropical forests (Kleinschroth and Healey 2017) which leads to more severe long-term impacts that include increased fire incidence, soil erosion, landslides, and sediment accumulation in streams, biological invasions, wildlife poaching, illicit land colonisation, illegal logging and mining, land grabbing and land speculation (Laurance et al. 2009; Alamgir et al. 2017).

Box 7.1 | Case Study: Reducing the Impacts of Roads on Deforestation

Summary
Rapidly expanding roads, particularly in tropical regions, are linked to forest loss, degradation, and fragmentation because the land becomes more generally accessible. Increase of land values of areas adjacent to roads also drives speculation and deforestation related to land tenure (Fearnside 2015). If poorly planned, infrastructure can facilitate fires, illegal mining, and wildlife poaching with consequences for GHG emissions and biodiversity conservation. However, some initiatives are providing new approaches for better planning and then limit environmental and societal impacts.

Background
Although the number and extent of protected areas has increased markedly in recent decades (Watson et al. 2014), many other indicators reveal that nature is in broad retreat. For example, the total area of intact wilderness is declining rapidly worldwide (Watson et al. 2016), 70% of the world's forests are now less than 1 km from a forest edge (Haddad et al. 2015), the extent of tropical forest fragmentation is accelerating exponentially (Taubert et al. 2018). One of the most direct and immediate driver of deforestation and biodiversity decline is the dramatic expansion of roads and other transportation infrastructure (Laurance et al. 2014a; Laurance and Arrea 2017; Alamgir et al. 2017).

Case description
From 2010 to 2050, the total length of paved roads is projected to increase by 25 million km (Dulac 2013) including large infrastructure-expansion schemes in Asia (Laurance and Arrea 2017; Lechner et al. 2018) and in South America (Laurance et al. 2001; Killeen 2007), as well as widespread illegal or unplanned road building (Laurance et al. 2009; Barber et al. 2014). For example, in the Amazon, 95% of all deforestation occurs within 5.5 km of a road, and for every km of legal road there are nearly three km of illegal roads (Barber et al. 2014).

Interactions and limitations
More than any other proximate factor, the dramatic expansion of roads is determining the pace and patterns of habitat disruption and its impacts on biodiversity (Laurance et al. 2009; Laurance and Arrea 2017). Much road expansion is poorly planned. Environmental Impact Assessments (EIAs) for roads and other infrastructure are typically too short term and superficial to detect rare species or assess long-term or indirect impacts of projects (Flyvbjerg 2009; Laurance and Arrea 2017). Another limitation is the consideration of each project in isolation from other existing or planned developments (Laurance et al. 2014b). Hence, EIAs alone are inadequate for planning infrastructure projects and assessing their broader environmental, social, and financial impacts and risks (Laurance et al. 2015a; Alamgir et al. 2017, 2018).

Lessons
The large-scale, proactive land-use planning is an option for managing the development of modern infrastructure. Approaches such as the 'Global Roadmap' scheme (Laurance and Balmford 2013; Laurance et al. 2014a) Strategic Environmental Assessments (Fischer 2007) can be used to evaluate the relative costs and benefits of infrastructure projects, and to spatially prioritise land uses to optimise human benefits while limited new infrastructure in areas of intact or critical habitats. For example, the Global Roadmap strategy has been used in parts of South-East Asia (Sloan et al. 2018), Indochina (Balmford et al. 2016), and sub-Saharan Africa (Laurance et al. 2015b) to devise land-use zoning that can help optimise the many risks and rewards of planned infrastructure projects.

7.3.1.3   Extractive Industry Development

The extent and scale of mining is growing due to increased global demand (UNEP 2019). Due to declining ore grades, more ore needs to be processed to meet demand, with extensive use of open cast mining. A low-carbon future may be more mineral intensive with, for example, clean energy technologies requiring greater inputs in comparison to fossil-fuel-based technologies (Hund et al. 2020). Mining presents cumulative environmental impacts, especially in intensively mined regions (UNEP 2019). The impact of mining on deforestation varies considerably across minerals and countries. Mining causes significant changes to the environment, for example, through mining infrastructure establishment, soil erosion, urban expansion to support a growing workforce and development of mineral commodity supply chains (Sonter et al. 2015). The increasing consumption of gold in developing countries, increased prices, and uncertainty in financial markets is identified as driving gold mining and associated deforestation in the Amazon region (Alvarez-Berrios and Mitchell Aide 2015; Dezécache et al. 2017; Asner and Tupayachi 2017; Espejo et al. 2018). The total estimated area of gold mining throughout the region increased by about 40% between 2012 and 2016 (Asner and Tupayachi 2017). In the Brazilian Amazon, mining significantly increased forest loss up to 70 km beyond mining lease boundaries, causing 11,670 km^2 of deforestation between 2005 and 2015, representing 9% of all Amazon forest loss during this time (Sonter et al. 2015).

Mining is also an important driver of deforestation in African and Asian countries. In the Democratic Republic of Congo, where the second-largest area of tropical forest in the world occurs, mining-related deforestation exacerbated by violent conflict (Butsic et al. 2015). In India, mining has contributed to deforestation at a district level, with coal, iron and limestone having had the most adverse impact on forest area loss (Ranjan 2019). Gold mining is also identified as a driver of deforestation in Myanmar (Papworth et al. 2017).

7.3.1.4   Fire Regime Changes

Wildland fires account for approximately 70% of the global biomass burned annually (van der Werf et al. 2017) and constitute a large global source of atmospheric trace gases and aerosols (Gunsch et al. 2018) (IPCC WGI AR6). Although fires are part of the natural system, the frequency of fires has increased in many areas, exacerbated by decreases in precipitation, including in many regions with humid and temperate forests that rarely experience large-scale fires naturally. Natural and human-ignited fires affect all major biomes, from peatlands through shrublands to tropical and boreal forests, altering ecosystem structure and functioning (Argañaraz et al. 2015; Nunes et al. 2016; Remy et al. 2017; Mancini et al. 2018; Aragão et al. 2018; Engel et al. 2019; Rodríguez Vásquez et al. 2021). However, the degree of incidence and regional trends are quite different and a study over 14 years indicated, on average, the largest fires in Australia, boreal North America and Northern Hemisphere Africa (Andela et al. 2019). More than half of the terrestrial surface of the Earth has fire regimes outside the range of natural variability, with changes in fire frequency and intensity posing major challenges for land restoration and recovery (Barger et al. 2018). In some ecosystems, fire prevention might lead to accumulation of large fuel loads that enable wildfires (Moreira et al. 2020a).

About 98 Mha of forest and savannahs are estimated to have been affected by fire in 2015 (FAO and UNEP 2020). Fire is a prevalent forest disturbance in the tropics where about 4% of the total forest and savannah area in that year was burned and more than two-thirds of the total area affected was in Africa and South America; mostly open savanna types (FAO and UNEP 2020). Fires have many different causes, with land clearing for agriculture the primary driver in tropical regions, for example, clearance for industrial oil-palm and paper-pulp plantations in Indonesia (Chisholm et al. 2016), or for pastures in the Amazon (Barlow et al. 2020). Other socio-economic factors are also associated with wildfire regimes such as land-use conflict and socio-demographic aspects (Nunes et al. 2016; Mancini et al. 2018). Wildfire regimes are also changing by the influence of climate change, with wildfire seasons becoming longer, wildfire average size increases in many areas and wildfires occurring in areas where they did not occur before (Jolly et al. 2015; Artés et al. 2019). Human influence has likely increased fire weather in some regions of all inhabited continents (IPCC AR6 WGI Technical Summary) and, in the last years, fire seasons of unprecedented magnitude occurred in diverse regions as California (Goss et al. 2020), the Mediterranean basin (Ruffault et al. 2020), Canada (Kirchmeier-Young et al. 2019) with unprecedented fires in British Columbia in 2021, the Arctic and Siberia (McCarty et al. 2020), Brazilian Amazon (Silva et al. 2021) and Pantanal (Leal Filho et al. 2021), Chile (Bowman et al. 2019) and

Australia (Ward et al. 2020; Gallagher et al. 2021). Lightning plays an important role in the ignition of wildfires, with the incidence of lightning igniting wildfires predicted to increase with rises in global average air temperature (Worden et al. 2017).

7.3.1.5   Logging and Fuelwood Harvest

The area of forest designated for production has been relatively stable since 1990. Considering forest uses, about 30% (1.2 billion ha) of all forests is used primarily for production (wood and non-wood forest products), about 10% (424 Mha) is designated for biodiversity conservation, 398 Mha for the protection of soil and water, and 186 Mha is allocated for social services (recreation, tourism, education research and the conservation of cultural and spiritual sites) (FAO and UNEP 2020). While the rate of increase in the area of forest allocated primarily for biodiversity conservation has slowed in the last ten years, the rate of increase in the area of forest allocated for soil and water protection has grown since 1990, and notably in the last ten years. Global wood harvest (including from forests, other wooded land and trees outside forests) was estimated to be almost 4.0 billion m^3 in 2018 (considering both industrial roundwood and fuelwood) (FAO, 2019). Overall, wood removals are increasing globally as demand for, and the consumption of wood products grows annually by 1% in line with growing populations and incomes with this trend expected to continue in coming decades. When done in a sustainable way, more regrowth will occur and is stimulated by management, resulting in a net sink. However illegal and unsustainable logging (i.e., harvesting of timber in contravention of the laws and regulations of the country of harvest) is a global problem with significant negative economic (e.g., lost revenue), environmental (e.g., deforestation, forest degradation, GHG emissions and biodiversity losses) and social impact (e.g., conflicts over land and resources, disempowerment of local and indigenous communities) (World Bank 2019). Many countries around the world have introduced regulations for the international trade of forest products to reduce illegal logging, with significant and positive impacts (Guan et al. 2018).

Over-extraction of wood for timber and fuelwood is identified as an important driver of mangrove deforestation and degradation (Bhattarai 2011; Ajonina et al. 2014; Webb et al. 2014; Giri et al. 2015; Thomas et al. 2017; Fauzi et al. 2019). Unsustainable selective logging and over-extraction of wood is a substantial form of forest and mangrove degradation in many tropical and developing countries, with emissions associated with the extracted wood, incidental damage to the surrounding forest and from logging infrastructure (Bhattarai 2011; Ajonina et al. 2014; Webb et al. 2014; Pearson et al. 2014, Giri et al. 2015; Thomas et al. 2017; Fauzi et al. 2019). Traditional fuelwood and charcoal continue to represent a dominant share of total wood consumption in low-income countries (Barger et al. 2018). Regionally, the percentage of total wood harvested used as fuelwood varies from 90% in Africa, 62% in Asia, 50% in South America to less than 20% in Europe, North America and Oceania. Under current projections, efforts to intensify wood production in plantation forests, together with increases in fuel-use efficiency and electrification, are suggested to only partly alleviate the pressure on native forests (Barger et al. 2018). Nevertheless, the area of forest under management plans has increased in all regions since 2000 by 233 Mha (FAO 2020e). In regions representing the majority of industrial wood production, forests certified under sustainable forest management programmes accounted for 51% of total managed forest area in 2017, an increase from 11% in 2000 (ICFPA 2021).

7.3.2   Anthropogenic Direct Drivers – Agriculture

7.3.2.1   Livestock Populations and Management

Enteric fermentation dominates agricultural CH_4 emissions (Section 7.2.3) with emissions being a function of both ruminant animal numbers and productivity (output per animal). In addition to enteric fermentation, both CH_4 and N_2O emissions from manure management (i.e., manure storage and application) and deposition on pasture, make livestock the main agricultural emissions source (Tubiello 2019). The AR5 reported increases in populations of all major livestock categories between the 1970s and 2000s, including ruminants, with increasing numbers directly linked with increasing CH_4 emissions (Smith et al. 2014). The SRCCL identified managed pastures as a disproportionately high N_2O emissions source within grazing lands, with *medium confidence* that increased manure production and deposition was a key driver (Jia et al. 2019). The latest data (FAO 2021c) indicate continued global livestock population growth between 1990 and 2019 (Figure 7.10), including increases of 18% in cattle and buffalo numbers, and 30% in sheep and goat numbers, corresponding with CH_4 emission trends. Data also indicate increased productivity per animal for example, average increases of 16% in beef, 17% in pig meat and 70% in whole (cow) milk per respective animal between 1990 and 2019 (FAO 2021c). Despite these advances leading to reduced emissions per unit of product (calories, meat and milk) (FAO 2016; Tubiello 2019), increased individual animal productivity generally requires increased inputs (e.g., feed) and this generates increased emissions (Beauchemin et al. 2020). Manipulation of livestock diets, or improvements in animal genetics or health may counteract some of this. In addition, the production of inputs to facilitate increased animal productivity, may indirectly drive further absolute GHG emissions along the feed supply chain.

Although there are several potential drivers (McDermott et al. 2010; Alary et al. 2015), increased livestock production is principally in response to growth in demand for animal-sourced food, driven by a growing human population (FAO, 2019) and increased consumption resulting from changes in affluence, notably in middle-income countries (Godfray et al. 2018). Available data document increases in total meat and milk consumption by 24 and 22% respectively between 1990 and 2013, as indicated by average annual per capita supply (FAO 2017a). Updated data indicate that trends of increasing consumption continued between 2014 and 2018 (FAO 2021d). Sustained demand for animal-sourced food is expected to drive further livestock sector growth, with global production projected to expand by 14% by 2029, facilitated by maintained product prices and lower feed prices (OECD/FAO 2019).

7.3.2.2   Rice Cultivation

In addition to livestock, both AR5 and the SRCCL identified paddy rice cultivation as an important emissions source (Smith et al. 2014), with *medium evidence* and *high agreement* that its expansion is a key driver of growing trends in atmospheric CH_4 concentration (Jia et al. 2019). The latest data indicate the global harvested area of rice to have grown by 11% between 1990 and 2019, with total paddy production increasing by 46%, from 519 Mt to 755 Mt (FAO 2021c). Global rice production is projected to increase by 13% by 2028 compared to 2019 levels (OECD/FAO 2019). However, yield increases are expected to limit cultivated area expansion, while dietary shifts from rice to protein as a result of increasing per capita income, is expected to reduce demand in certain regions, with a slight decline in related emissions projected to 2030 (USEPA 2019).

Between 1990 and 2019, Africa recorded the greatest increase (+160%) in area under rice cultivation, followed by Asia and the Pacific (+6%), with area reductions evident in all other regions (FAO 2021c) broadly corresponding with related regional CH_4 emission (Figures 7.3 and 7.8). Data indicate the greatest growth in consumption (average annual supply per capita) between 1990 and 2013 to have occurred in Eastern Europe and West Central Asia (+42%) followed by Africa (+25%), with little change (+1%) observed in Asia and the Pacific (FAO 2017a). Most of the projected increase in global rice consumption is in Africa and Asia (OECD/FAO 2019).

7.3.2.3   Synthetic Fertiliser Use

Both AR5 and the SRCCL described considerable increases in global use of synthetic nitrogen fertilisers since the 1970s, which was identified to be a major driver of increasing N_2O emissions (Jia et al. 2019). The latest data document a 41% increase in global nitrogen fertiliser use between 1990 and 2019 (FAO 2021e) corresponding with associated increased N_2O emissions (Figure 7.3). Increased fertiliser use has been driven by pursuit of increased crop yields, with for example, a 61% increase in average global cereal yield per hectare observed during the same period (FAO 2021c), achieved through both increased fertiliser use and varietal improvements. Increased yields are in response to increased demand for food, feed, fuel and fibre crops which in turn has been driven by a growing human population (FAO, 2019), increased demand for animal-sourced food and bioenergy policy (OECD/FAO 2019). Global crop production is projected to increase by almost 15% over the next decade, with low income and emerging regions with greater availability of land and labour resources expected to experience the strongest growth, and account for about 50% of global output growth (OECD/FAO 2019). Increases in global nitrogen fertiliser use are also projected, notably in low income and emerging regions (USEPA 2019).

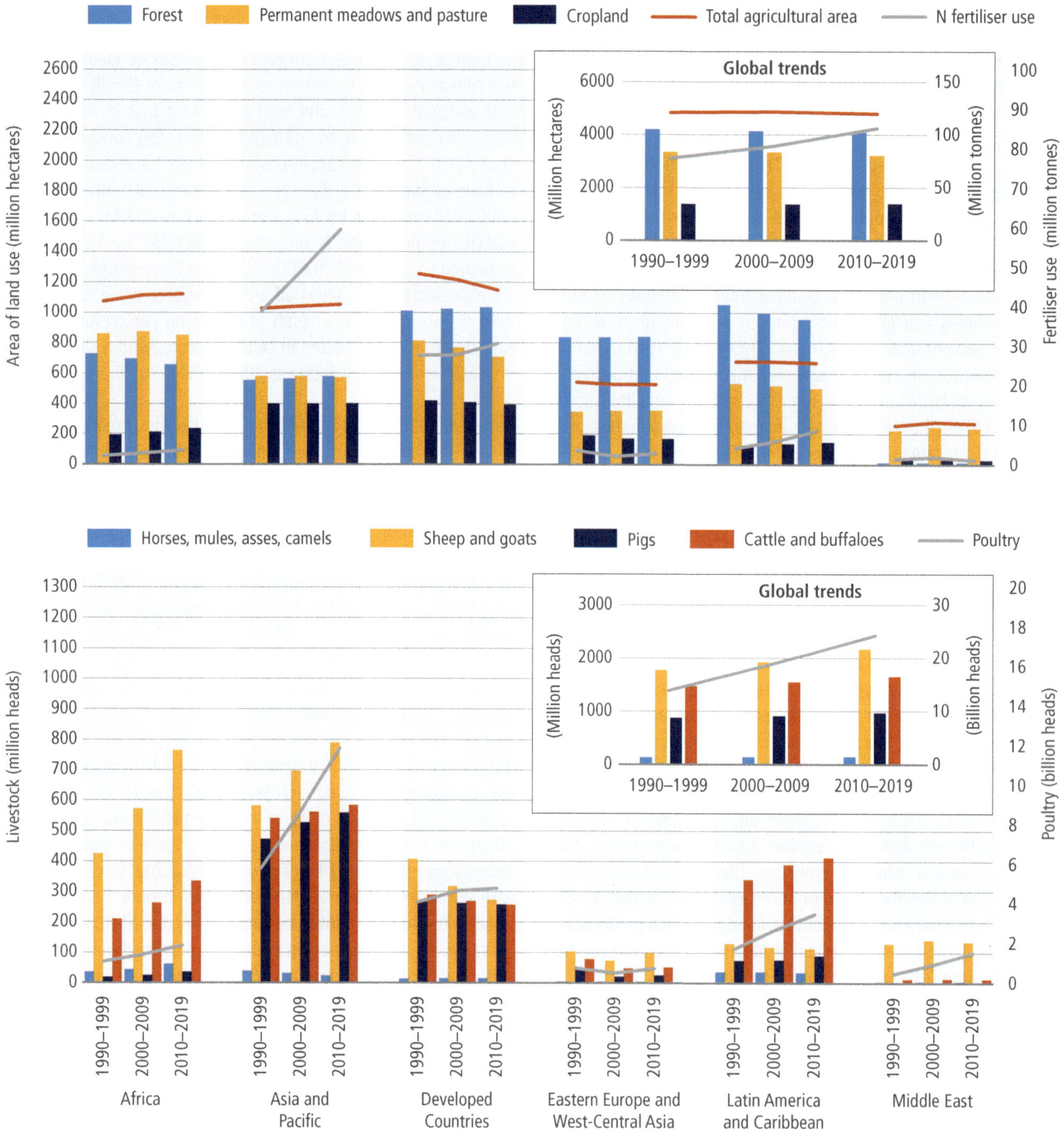

Figure 7.10 | Trends in average global and regional land area under specific land uses (FAO 2021b), inorganic nitrogen fertiliser use (FAO 2021e) (top) and number of livestock (FAO 2021c) (bottom) for three decades. For land use classification 'cropland' represents the FAOSTAT category 'arable land' which includes land under temporary crops, meadow, pasture and fallow. 'Forest' and 'permanent meadow and pasture' follow FAOSTAT categories.

7.3.3　Indirect Drivers

The indirect drivers behind how humans both use and impact natural resources are outlined in Table 7.2. Specifically; demographic, economic and cultural, scientific and technological, and institutional and governance drivers. These indirect drivers not only interact with each other at different temporal and spatial scales but are also subject to impacts and feedbacks from the direct drivers (Barger et al. 2018).

Table 7.2 | Indirect drivers of anthropogenic land and natural resource use patterns.

Demography	**Global and regional trends in population growth:** There was a 43% increase in global population between 1990 and 2018. The greatest growth was observed in Africa and the Middle East (+104%) and least growth in Eastern Europe and West-Central Asia (+7%) (FAO 2019b).
	Global and regional projections: Population is projected to increase by 28% between 2018 and 2050 reaching 9.7 billion (FAO 2019). The world's population is expected to become older, more urbanised and live in smaller households (UNEP 2019).
	Human migration: Growing mobility and population are linked to human migration, a powerful driver of changes in land and resource use patterns at decadal time scales, with the dominant flow of people being from rural areas to urban settlements over the past few decades, notably in the developing world (Adger et al. 2015; Barger et al. 2018).
Economic development and cultural factors	Changes in land use and management come from individual and social responses to economic opportunities (e.g., demand for a particular commodity or improved market access), mediated by institutions and policies (e.g., agricultural subsidies and low-interest credit or government-led infrastructure projects) (Barger et al. 2018).
	Projections on consumption: If the future global population adopts a per capita consumption rate similar to that of the developed world, the global capacity to provide land-based resources will be exceeded (Barger et al. 2018). Economic growth in the developing world is projected to double the global consumption of forest and wood products by 2030, with demand likely to exceed production in many developing and emerging economies in Asia and Africa within the next decade (Barger et al. 2018).
	Global trade: Market distorting agricultural subsidies and globalisation increases pressure on land systems and functions, with global trade and capital flow influencing land use, notably in developing countries (Furumo and Aide 2017; Yao et al. 2018; Pendrill et al. 2019a; UNEP 2019, OECD/FAO 2019). Estimates suggest that between 29 and 39% of emissions from deforestation in the tropics resulted from the international trade of agricultural commodities (Pendrill et al. 2019a).
Science and technology	Technological factors operates in conjunction with economic drivers of land use and management, whether through intensified farming techniques and biotechnology, high-input approaches to rehabilitating degraded land (e.g., Lin et al. 2017; Guo et al. 2020) or through new forms of data collection and monitoring (e.g., Song et al. 2018; Thyagharajan and Vignesh 2019; Arévalo et al. 2020).
	Changes in farming and forestry systems: Changes can have both positive and negative impacts regarding multiple factors, including GHG emission trends. Fast advancing technologies shape production and consumption, and drive land-use patterns and terrestrial ecosystems at various scales. Innovation is expected to help drive increases in global crop production during the next decade (OECD/FAO 2019). For example, emerging gene editing technologies, may advance crop breeding capabilities, though are subject to biosafety, public acceptance and regulatory approval (Jaganathan et al. 2018; Chen et al. 2019; Schmidt et al. 2020). Technological changes were significant for the expansion of soybean in Brazil by adapting to different soils and photoperiods (Abrahão and Costa 2018). In Asia, technological development changed agriculture with significant improvements in production and adaptation to climate change (Thomson et al. 2019; Giller and Ewert 2019; Anderson et al. 2020; Cassman and Grassini 2020). Developments such as precision agriculture and drip irrigation have facilitated more efficient agrochemical and water use (UNEP 2019).
	Research and development are central to forest restoration strategies that have become increasingly important around the world as costs vary depending on methods used, from natural regeneration with native tree species to active restoration using site preparation and planting (Löf et al. 2019). In addition, climate change poses the challenge about tree species selection in the future. Innovations in the forest sector also form the basis of a bioeconomy associated with bioproducts and new processes (Verkerk et al. 2020) (Cross-Working Group Box 3 in Chapter 12).
	Emerging mitigation technologies: Chemically synthesised methanogen inhibitors for ruminants are expected to be commercially available in some countries within the next two years and have considerable CH_4 mitigation potential (McGinn et al. 2019; Melgar et al. 2020; Beauchemin et al. 2020; Reisinger et al. 2021) (Section 7.4.3). There is growing literature (in both academic and non-academic spheres) on the biological engineering of protein. Although in its infancy and subject to investment, technological development, regulatory approval and consumer acceptance, it is suggested to have the potential to disrupt current livestock production systems and land use (Stephens et al. 2018; Ben-Arye and Levenberg 2019; RethinkX 2019; Post et al. 2020). The extent to which this is possible and the overall climate benefits are unclear (Lynch and Pierrehumbert 2019; Chriki and Hocquette 2020).
Institutions and governance	Institutional factors often moderate the relevance and impact of changes in economic and demographic variables related to resource exploitation and use. Institutions encompass the rule of law, legal frameworks and other social structures (e.g., civil society networks and movements) determining land management (e.g., formal and informal property rights, regimes and their enforcement); information and knowledge exchange systems; local and traditional knowledge and practice systems (Barger et al. 2018).
	Land rights: Land tenure often allows communities to exercise traditional governance based on traditional ecological knowledge, devolved and dynamic access rights, judicious use, equitable distribution of benefits (Mantyka-Pringle et al. 2017; Wynberg 2017; Thomas et al. 2017), biodiversity (Contreras-Negrete et al. 2014) and fire and grazing management (Levang et al. 2015; Varghese et al. 2015).
	Agreements and Finance: Since AR5, global agreements were reached on climate change, sustainable development goals, and the mobilisation of finance for development and climate action. Several countries adopted policies and commitments to restore degraded land (Barger et al. 2018). The UN Environment Programme (UNEP) and the Food and Agriculture Organization of the UN (FAO), launched the UN Decade on Ecosystem Restoration (https://www.decadeonrestoration.org/).
	Companies have also made pledges to reduce impacts on forests and on the rights of local communities as well as eliminating deforestation from their supply chains. The finance sector, a crucial driver behind action (Section 7.6, Box 7.12), has also started to make explicit commitments to avoiding environmental damage (Barger et al. 2018) and net zero targets (Forest Trends Ecosystem Marketplace 2021), though investment is sensitive to market outlook.

7.4 Assessment of AFOLU Mitigation Measures Including Trade-offs and Synergies

AFOLU mitigation or land-based climate change mitigation (used in this chapter interchangeably) are a variety of land management or demand management practices that reduce GHG emissions and/or enhance carbon sequestration within the land system (i.e., in forests, wetlands, grasslands, croplands and pasturelands). If implemented with benefits to human well-being and biodiversity, land-based mitigation measures are often referred to as nature-based solutions and/or natural climate solutions (Glossary). Measures that result in a net removal of GHGs from the atmosphere and storage in either living or dead organic material, or in geological stores, are known as CDR, and in previous IPCC reports were sometimes referred to as greenhouse gas removal (GGR) or negative emissions technologies (NETs) (Rogelj et al. 2018a; Jia et al. 2019). This section evaluates current knowledge and latest scientific literature on AFOLU mitigation measures and potentials, including land-based CDR measures. Section 7.4.1 provides an overview of the approaches for estimating mitigation potential, the co-benefits and risks from land-based mitigation measures, estimated global and regional mitigation potential and associated costs according to literature published over the last decade. Subsequent subsections assess literature on 20 key AFOLU mitigation measures specifically providing:

- A description of activities, co-benefits, risks and implementation opportunities and barriers.
- A summary of conclusions in the IPCC Fifth Assessment Report (AR5) and IPCC Special Reports (Special Report on Climate Change of 1.5°C (SR1.5), Special Report on the Ocean and Cryosphere in a Changing Climate (SROCC) and Special Report on Climate Change and Land (SRCCL)).
- An overview of literature and developments since the AR5 and IPCC Special Reports.
- An assessment and conclusion based on current evidence.

Measures are categorised as supply-side activities in: (i) forests and other ecosystems (Section 7.4.2); (ii) agriculture (Section 7.4.3); (iii) bioenergy and other land-based energy technologies (Section 7.4.4); as well as (iv) demand-side activities (Section 7.4.5 and Figure 7.11). Several information boxes are dispersed within the section and provide supporting material, including case studies exploring a range of topics from climate-smart forestry in Europe (Box 7.2), agroforestry in Brazil (Box 7.3), climate-smart village approaches (Box 7.4), farm systems approaches (Box 7.5), mitigation within Indian agriculture (Box 7.6), and bioenergy and BECCS mitigation calculations (Box 7.7). Novel measures, including enhanced weathering and novel foods are covered in Chapter 12, this report. In addition, as mitigation within AFOLU concerns land management and use of land resources, AFOLU measures impact other sectors. Accordingly, AFOLU measures are also discussed in other sectoral chapters within this report, notably demand-side solutions (Chapter 5), bioenergy and bioenergy with carbon capture and storage (BECCS) (Chapter 6), the use of wood products and biomass in buildings (Chapter 9), and CDR measures, food systems and land related impacts, risks and opportunities of mitigation measures (Chapter 12).

7.4.1 Introduction and Overview of Mitigation Potential

7.4.1.1 Estimating Mitigation Potentials

Mitigation potentials for AFOLU measures are estimated by calculating the scale of emissions reductions or carbon sequestration against a counterfactual scenario without mitigation activities. The types of mitigation potential estimates in recent literature include: (i) technical potential (the biophysical potential or amount possible with current technologies); (ii) economic potential (constrained by costs, usually by a given carbon price (Table 7.3); (iii) sustainable potential (constrained by environmental safeguards and/or natural resources, e.g., limiting natural forest conversion), and (iv) feasible potential (constrained by environmental, socio-cultural, and/or institutional barriers), however, there are no set definitions used in literature. In addition to types of mitigation estimates, there are two AFOLU mitigation categories often calculated: supply-side measures (land management interventions) and demand-side measures (interventions that require a change in consumer behaviour).

Two main approaches to estimating mitigation potentials include: (i) studies on individual measures and/or sectors – henceforth referred to as sectoral assessments, and (ii) integrated assessment models (IAM). Sectoral assessments include studies focusing on one activity (e.g., agroforestry) based on spatial and biophysical data, as well as econometric and optimisation models for a sector, for example, the forest or agriculture sector, and therefore cover a large suite of practices and activities while representing a broad body of literature. Sectoral assessments, however, rarely capture cross-sector interactions or impacts, making it difficult to completely account for land competition, trade-offs, and double counting when aggregating sectoral estimates across different studies and methods (Smith et al. 2014; Jia et al. 2019). On the other hand, IAMs assess the climate impact of multiple and interlinked practices across sectors and therefore, can account for interactions and trade-offs (including land competition, use of other resources and international trade) between them. However, the number of land-based measures used in IAMs are limited compared with the sectoral portfolio (Figure 7.11). The resolution of land-based measures in IAMs are also generally coarser compared to some sectoral estimates, and as such, may be less robust for individual measures (Roe et al. 2021). Given the differences between and strengths and weaknesses of the two approaches, it is helpful to compare the estimates from both. We combine estimates from both approaches to establish an updated range of global land-based mitigation potential.

For the 20 land-based mitigation measures outlined in this section, the mitigation potential estimates are largely derived from sectoral approaches, and where data is available, are compared to IAM estimates. Integrated assessment models and the emissions trajectories, cost-effectiveness and trade-offs of various mitigation pathways are detailed in Section 7.5. It should be noted that the underlying literature for sectoral as well as IAM mitigation estimates consider GWP100 IPCC AR5 values ($CH_4 = 28$, $N_2O = 265$) as well as GWP100 IPCC AR4 values ($CH_4 = 25$, $N_2O = 298$) to convert CH_4 and N_2O to CO_2-eq. Where possible, we note the various GWP100 values (in IAM estimates, and the wetlands and agriculture sections), however in some instances, the varying GWP100 values used across studies prevents description of non-CO_2 gases in native units as well as conversion to AR6 GWP100 ($CH_4 = 27$, $N_2O = 273$) CO_2-eq values to aggregate sectoral assessment estimates.

7.4.1.2   Co-benefits and Risks

Land interventions have interlinked implications for climate mitigation, adaptation, food security, biodiversity, ecosystem services, and other environmental and societal challenges (Section 7.6.5). Therefore, it is important to consider the net effect of mitigation measures for achieving both climate and non-climate goals (Section 7.1).

While it is helpful to assess the general benefits, risks and opportunities possible for land-based mitigation measures (L.G. Smith et al. 2019), their efficacy and scale of benefit or risk largely depends on the type of activity undertaken, deployment strategy (e.g., scale, method), and context (e.g., soil, biome, climate, food system, land ownership) that vary geographically and over time (*robust evidence, high agreement*) (L.G. Smith et al. 2019; P. Smith et al. 2019a; Hurlbert et al. 2019) (Section 12.5). Impacts of land-based mitigation measures are therefore highly context specific and conclusions from specific studies may not be universally applicable. If implemented at appropriate scales and in a sustainable manner, land-based mitigation practices have the capacity to reduce emissions and sequester billions of tonnes of carbon from the atmosphere over coming decades, while also preserving or enhancing biodiversity, water quality and supply, air quality, soil fertility, food and wood security, livelihoods, resilience to droughts, floods and other natural disasters, and positively contributing to ecosystem health and human well-being (*high confidence*) (Toensmeier 2016; Karlsson et al. 2020).

Overall, measures in the AFOLU sector are uniquely positioned to deliver substantial co-benefits. However, the negative consequences of inappropriate or misguided design and implementation of measures may be considerable, potentially impacting for example, mitigation permanence, longevity, and leakage, biodiversity, wider ecosystem functioning, livelihoods, food security and human well-being (Section 7.6) (AR6 WGII, Box 2.2). Land-based mitigation may also face limitations and trade-offs in achieving sustained emission reductions and/or removals due to other land challenges including climate change impacts. It is widely recognised that land-use planning that is context-specific, considers other sustainable development goals, and is adaptable over time can help achieve land-based mitigation that maximises co-benefits, avoids or limits trade-offs, and delivers on international policy goals including the SDGs, Land Degradation Neutrality, and Convention on Biological Diversity (Section 7.6; Chapter 12).

Potential co-benefits and trade-offs are outlined for each of the 20 land-based mitigation measures in the proceeding sub-sections and summarised in Figure 7.12. Section 7.6.5. discusses general links with ecosystem services, human well-being and adaptation, while Chapter 12 (Section 12.5) provides an in-depth assessment of the land related impacts, risks and opportunities associated with mitigation

options across sectors, including positive and negative effects on land resources, water, biodiversity, climate, and food security.

7.4.1.3   Overview of Global and Regional Technical and Economic Potentials in AFOLU

IPCC AR5 (2014). In the AR5, the economic mitigation potential of supply-side measures in the AFOLU sector was estimated at 7.18–10.60 $GtCO_2$-eq yr^{-1} in 2030 with carbon prices up to USD100 tCO_2-eq^{-1}, about a third of which could be achieved at <USD20 tCO_2-eq^{-1} (*medium evidence, medium agreement*) (Smith et al. 2014). The AR5 provided a summary table of individual AFOLU mitigation measures, but did not conduct a detailed assessment for each.

IPCC SRCCL (2019). The SRCCL assessed the full range of technical, economic and sustainability mitigation potentials in AFOLU for the period 2030–2050 and identified reduced deforestation and forest degradation to have greatest potential for reducing supply-side emissions (0.4 to 5.8 $GtCO_2$-eq yr^{-1}) (*high confidence*) followed by combined agriculture measures, 0.3 to 3.4 $GtCO_2$-eq yr^{-1} (*medium confidence*) (Jia et al. 2019). For the demand-side estimates, shifting towards healthy, sustainable diets (0.7 to 8.0 $GtCO_2$-eq yr^{-1}) (*high confidence*) had the highest potential, followed by reduced food loss and waste (0.8 to 4.5 $GtCO_2$-eq yr^{-1}) (*high confidence*). Measures with greatest potential for CDR were afforestation/reforestation (0.5 to 10.1 $GtCO_2$-eq yr^{-1}) (*medium confidence*), soil carbon sequestration in croplands and grasslands (0.4 to 8.6 $GtCO_2$-eq yr^{-1}) (*medium confidence*) and BECCS (0.4 to 11.3 $GtCO_2$-eq yr^{-1}) (*medium confidence*). The SRCCL did not explore regional potential, associated feasibility nor provide detailed analysis of costs.

IPCC AR6. This assessment concludes the likely range of global land-based mitigation potential is approximately 8–14 $GtCO_2$-eq yr^{-1} between 2020–2050 with carbon prices up to USD100 tCO_2-eq^{-1}, about half of the technical potential (*medium evidence, medium agreement*). About 30–50% could be achieved <USD20 tCO_2-eq^{-1} (Table 7.3). The global economic potential estimates in this assessment are slightly higher than the AR5 range. Since AR5, there have been numerous new global assessments of sectoral land-based mitigation potential (Fuss et al. 2018; Griscom et al. 2017, 2020; Roe et al. 2019; Jia et al. 2019; Griscom et al. 2020; Roe et al. 2021) as well as IAM estimates of mitigation potential (Riahi et al. 2017; Popp et al. 2017; Rogelj et al. 2018a; Frank et al. 2019; Johnston and Radeloff 2019; Baker et al. 2019), expanding the scope of AFOLU mitigation measures included and substantially improving the robustness and spatial resolution of mitigation estimates. A recent development is an assessment of country-level technical and economic (USD100 tCO_2-eq^{-1}) mitigation potential for 20 AFOLU measures, including for demand-side and soil organic carbon sequestration in croplands and grasslands, not estimated before (Roe et al. 2021). Estimates on costs, feasibility, sustainability, benefits, and risks have also been developed for some mitigation measures, and they continue to be active areas of research. Developing more refined sustainable potentials at a country-level will be an important next step. Although most mitigation estimates still do not consider the impact of future climate change, there are some emerging studies

that do (Sonntag et al. 2016; Doelman et al. 2019). Given the IPCC WG1 finding that the land sink is continuing to increase although its efficiency is decreasing with climate change, it will be critical to better understand how future climate will affect mitigation potentials, particularly from CDR measures.

Across global sectoral studies, the economic mitigation potential (up to USD100 tCO_2-eq^{-1}) of supply-side measures in AFOLU for the period 2020–2050 is 11.4 mean (5.6–19.8 full range) $GtCO_2$-eq yr^{-1},

about 50% of the technical potential of 24.2 (4.9–58) $GtCO_2$-eq yr^{-1} (Table 7.3). Adding 2.1 $GtCO_2$-eq yr^{-1} from demand-side measures (accounting only for diverted agricultural production to avoid double counting with land-use change effects), total land-based mitigation potential up to USD100 tCO_2-eq^{-1} is 13.6 (6.7–23.4) $GtCO_2$-eq yr^{-1}. This estimate aligns with the most recent regional assessment (Roe et al. 2021), which found the aggregate global mitigation potential of supply and demand-side measures to be 13.8 ± 3.1 $GtCO_2$-eq yr^{-1} up to USD100 tCO_2-eq^{-1} for the period 2020–2050. Across integrated

Table 7.3 | Estimated annual mitigation potential ($GtCO_2$-eq yr^{-1}) in 2020–2050 of AFOLU mitigation options by carbon price. Estimates reflect sectoral studies based on a comprehensive literature review updating data from (Roe et al. 2019) and integrated assessment models using the IPCC AR6 database (Section 7.5). Values represent the mean, and full range of potential. Sectoral mitigation estimates are averaged for the years 2020–2050 to capture a wider range of literature, and the IAM estimates are given for 2050 as many model assumptions delay most land-based mitigation to mid-century. The sectoral potentials are the sum of global estimates for the individual measures listed for each option. IAM potentials are given for mitigation options with available data; for example, net land-use CO_2 for total forests and other ecosystems, and land sequestration from A/R, but not reduced deforestation (protect). Sectoral estimates predominantly use GWP100 IPCC AR5 values ($CH_4 = 28$, $N_2O = 265$), although some use GWP100 IPCC AR4 values ($CH_4 = 25$, $N_2O = 298$); and the IAMs use GWP100 IPCC AR6 values ($CH_4 = 27$, $N_2O = 273$). The sectoral and IAM estimates reflected here do not account for the substitution effects of avoiding fossil fuel emissions nor emissions from other more energy intensive resources/materials. For example, BECCS estimates only consider the carbon dioxide removal (CDR) via geological storage component and not potential mitigation derived from the displacement of fossil fuel use in the energy sector. Mitigation potential from substitution effects are included in the other sectoral chapters like energy, transport, buildings and industry. The total AFOLU sectoral estimate aggregates potential from agriculture, forests and other ecosystems, and diverted agricultural production from avoided food waste and diet shifts (excluding land-use impacts to avoid double counting). Because of potential overlaps between measures, sectoral values from BECCS and the full value chain potential from demand-side measures are not summed with AFOLU. IAMs account for land competition and resource optimisation and can therefore sum across all available categories to derive the total AFOLU potential. Key: ND = no data; Sectoral = as assessed by sectoral literature review; IAM = as assessed by integrated assessment models; EJ = exajoule primary energy.

Mitigation option	Estimate type	<USD20 tCO_2-eq^{-1}	<USD50 tCO_2-eq^{-1}	<USD100 tCO_2-eq^{-1}	Technical
Agriculture total	Sectoral	0.9 (0.5–1.4)	1.6 (1–2.4)	4.1 (1.7–6.7)	11.2 (1.6–28.5)
	IAM	0.9 (0–3.1)	1.3 (0–3.2)	1.8 (0.7–3.3)	ND
Agriculture – Carbon sequestration (Soil carbon management in croplands and grasslands, agroforestry, and biochar)	Sectoral	0.5 (0.4–0.6)	1.2 (0.9–1.6)	3.4 (1.4–5.5)	9.5 (1.1–25.3)
	IAM	ND	ND	ND	ND
Agriculture – Reduce CH_4 and N_2O emissions (Improve enteric fermentation, manure management, nutrient management, and rice cultivation)	Sectoral	0.4 (0.1–0.8)	0.4 (0.1–0.8)	0.6 (0.3–1.3)	1.7 (0.5–3.2)
	IAM	0.9 (0–3.1)	1.3 (0–3.2)	1.8 (0.7–3.3)	ND
Forests and other ecosystems total	Sectoral	2.9 (2.2–3.5)	3.1 (1.4–5.1)	7.3 (3.9–13.1)	13 (5–29.5)
	IAM	2.4 (0–10.5)	3.3 (0–9.9)	4.2 (0–12.1)	ND
Forests and other ecosystems – Protect (Reduce deforestation, loss and degradation of peatlands, coastal wetlands, and grasslands)	Sectoral	2.3 (1.7–2.9)	2.4 (1.2–3.6)	4.0 (2.5–7.4)	6.2 (2.8–14.4)
	IAM	ND	ND	ND	ND
Forests and other ecosystems – Restore (Afforestation, reforestation, peatland restoration, coastal wetland restoration)	Sectoral	0.15	0.7 (0.2–1.5)	2.1 (0.8–3.8)	5 (1.1–12.3)
	IAM (A/R)	0.6 (0.2–6.5)	0.6 (0.01–8.3)	0.7 (0.07–6.8)	ND
Forests and other ecosystems – Manage (Improve forest management, fire management)	Sectoral	0.4 (0.3–0.4)	ND	1.2 (0.6–1.9)	1.8 (1.1–2.8)
	IAM	ND	ND	ND	ND
Demand-side measures (Shift to sustainable healthy diets, reduce food waste, and enhanced and improved use of wood products) *For all three only the direct avoided emissions; land-use effects are in measures above*	Sectoral	ND	ND	*2.2 (1.1–3.6)**	*4.2 (2.2–7.1)**
	IAM	ND	ND	ND	ND
BECCS (Only the CDR component, for example, the geological storage. Substitution effects are accounted in other sectoral chapters e.g: Energy (ch 6), Transport (ch 10))	Sectoral	ND	ND	1.6 (0.5–3.5)	5.9 (0.5–11.3)
	IAM	0.08 (0–0.7)	0.5 (0–6)	1.8 (0.2–9.9)	ND
Bioenergy from residues	Sectoral	ND	ND	ND	Up to 57 EJ yr^{-1}
TOTAL AFOLU (Agriculture, forests and other ecosystems, diverted agricultural production from demand-side)	Sectoral	3.8 (2.7–4.9)	4.3 (2.3–6.7)	13.6 (6.7–23.4)	28.4 (8.8–65.1)
TOTAL AFOLU (Agriculture, forests and other ecosystems, BECCS)	IAM	3.4 (0–14.6)	5.3 (0.6–19.4)	7.9 (4.1–17.3)	ND

assessment models (IAMs), the economic potential for land-based mitigation (Agriculture, LULUCF and BECCS) for USD100 tCO_2-eq^{-1} is 7.9 mean (4.1–17.3 range) $GtCO_2$-eq yr^{-1} in 2050 (Table 7.3). We add the estimate for BECCS here to provide the full land-based potential, as IAMs optimise land allocation based on costs, which displaces land-based CDR activities for BECCS. Combining both IAM and sectoral approaches, the likely range is therefore 7.9–13.6 (rounded to 8–14) $GtCO_2$-eq yr^{-1} up to USD100 tCO_2-eq^{-1} between 2020–2050. Considering both IAM and sectoral economic potential estimates, land-based mitigation could have the capacity to make the AFOLU sector net negative in GHG emissions from 2036 (Figure 7.12), although there are highly variable mitigation strategies for how AFOLU potential can be deployed for achieving climate targets (Illustrative Mitigation Pathways in Section 7.5.5). Economic potential estimates, which reflect a public willingness to pay, may be more relevant for policy making compared with technical potentials which reflect a theoretical maximum that may not be feasible or sustainable.

Among the mitigation options, the protection, improved management, and restoration of forests and other ecosystems (wetlands, savannas and grasslands) have the largest potential to reduce emissions and/or sequester carbon at 7.3 (3.9–13.1) $GtCO_2$-eq yr^{-1} (up to USD100 tCO_2-eq^{-1}), with measures that 'protect' having the single highest total mitigation and mitigation densities (mitigation per area) in AFOLU (Table 7.3 and Figure 7.11). Agriculture provides the second largest share of mitigation, with 4.1 (1.7–6.7) $GtCO_2$-eq yr^{-1} potential (up to USD100 tCO_2-eq^{-1}), from soil carbon management in croplands and grasslands, agroforestry, biochar, rice cultivation, and livestock and nutrient management (Table 7.3 and Figure 7.11). Demand-side measures including shifting to sustainable healthy diets, reducing food waste, and improving wood products can mitigate 2.2 (1.1–3.6) $GtCO_2$-eq yr^{-1} when accounting only for diverted agricultural production from diets and food waste to avoid double counting with measures in forests and other ecosystems (Table 7.3 and Figure 7.11). The potential of demand-side measures increases three-fold, to 6.5 (4–9.5) $GtCO_2$-eq yr^{-1} when accounting for the entire value chain including land-use effects, but would overlap with other measures and is therefore not additive.

Most mitigation options are available and ready to deploy. Emissions reductions can be unlocked relatively quickly, whereas CDR need upfront investment to generate sequestration over time. The protection of natural ecosystems, carbon sequestration in agriculture, sustainable healthy diets and reduced food waste have especially high co-benefits and cost efficiency. Avoiding the conversion of carbon-rich primary peatlands, coastal wetlands and forests is particularly important as most carbon lost from those ecosystems are irrecoverable through restoration by the 2050 timeline of achieving net zero carbon emissions (Goldstein et al. 2020). Sustainable intensification, shifting diets, reducing food waste could enhance efficiencies and reduce agricultural land needs, and are therefore critical for enabling supply-side measures such as reduced deforestation, restoration, as well as reducing N_2O and CH_4 emissions from agricultural production – as seen in the Illustrative Mitigation Pathway (IMP-SP) (Section 7.5.6). Although agriculture measures that reduce non-CO_2, particularly of CH_4, are important for

near-term emissions reductions, they have less economic potential due to costs. Demand-side measures may be able to deliver non-CO_2 emissions reductions more cost efficiently.

Regionally, economic mitigation potential up to USD100 tCO_2-eq^{-1} is estimated to be greatest in tropical countries in Asia and Pacific (34%), Latin America and the Caribbean (24%), and Africa and the Middle East (18%) because of the large potential from reducing deforestation and sequestering carbon in forests and agriculture (Figure 7.11). However, there is also considerable potential in Developed Countries (18%) and more modest potential in Eastern Europe and West-Central Asia (5%). These results are in line with the IAM regional mitigation potentials (Figure 7.11). The protection of forests and other ecosystems is the dominant source of mitigation potential in tropical regions, whereas carbon sequestration in agricultural land and demand-side measures are important in Developed Countries and Asia and Pacific. The restoration and management of forests and other ecosystems is more geographically distributed, with all regions having significant potential. Regions with large livestock herds (Developed Countries, Latin America) and rice paddy fields (Asia and Pacific) have potential to reduce CH_4. As expected, the highest total potential is associated with countries and regions with large land areas, however when considering mitigation density (total potential per hectare), many smaller countries, particularly those with wetlands have disproportionately high levels of mitigation for their size (Roe et al. 2021). As global commodity markets connect regions, AFOLU measures may create synergies and trade-offs across the world, which could make national demand-side measures for example, important in mitigating supply-side emissions elsewhere (Kallio et al. 2018).

Although economic potentials provide more realistic, near-term climate mitigation compared to technical potentials, they still do not account for feasibility barriers and enabling conditions that vary by region and country. For example, according to most models, including IAMs, avoided deforestation is the cheapest land-based mitigation option (Table 7.3, Sections 7.5.3 and 7.5.4), however implementing interventions aimed at reducing deforestation (including REDD+) often have higher transaction and implementation costs than expected due to various barriers and enabling conditions (Luttrell et al. 2018) (Section 7.6). The feasibility of implementing AFOLU mitigation measures, including those with multiple co-benefits, depends on varying economic, technological, institutional, socio-cultural, environmental and geophysical barriers (*high confidence*) (L.G. Smith et al. 2019). The section for each individual mitigation measure provides an overview of co-benefits and risks associated with the measure and Section 7.6.6 outlines key enabling factors and barriers for implementation.

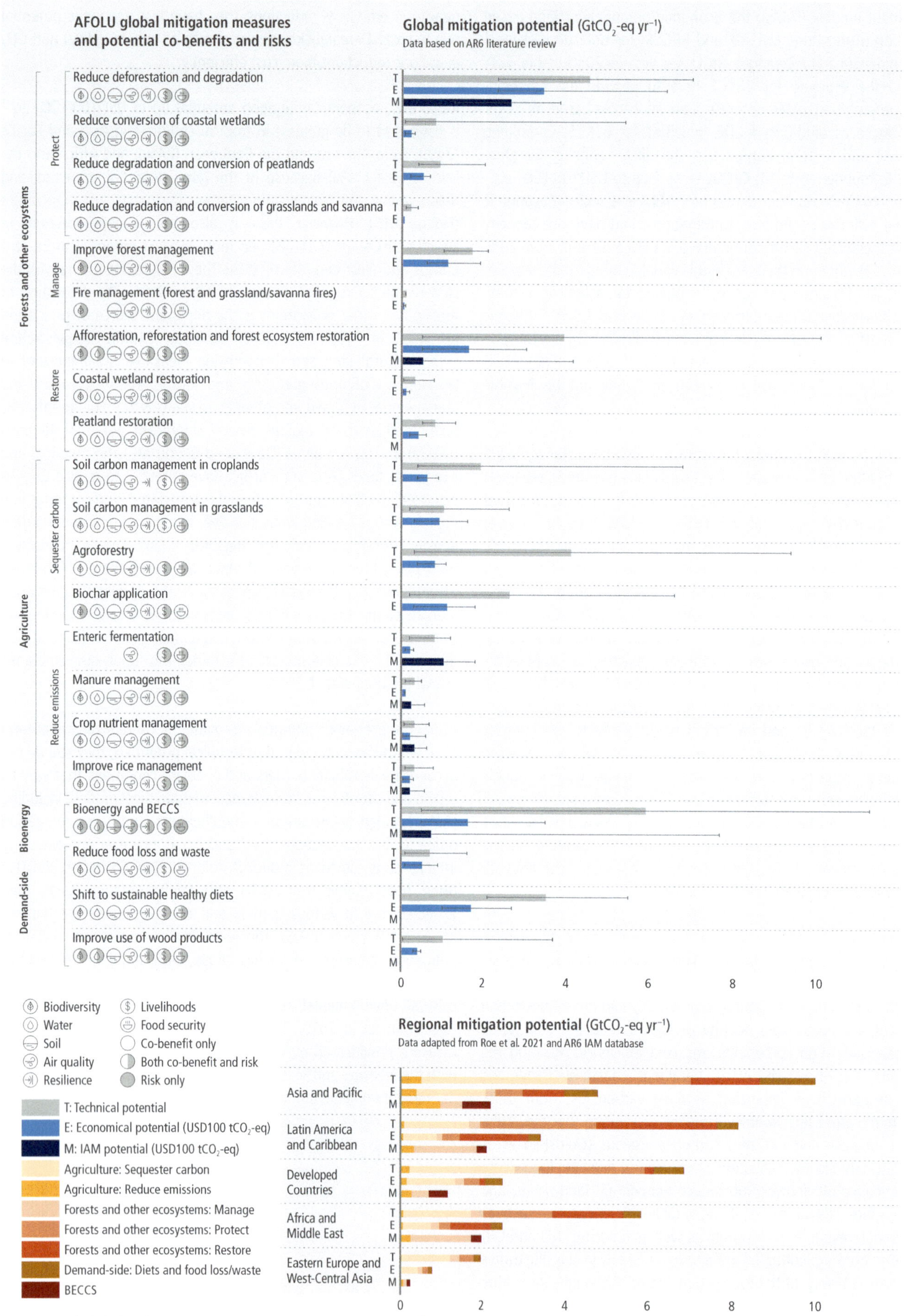

Figure 7.11 | Global and regional mitigation potential (GtCO₂-eq yr⁻¹) in 2020–2050 for 20 land-based measures.

Figure 7.11 (continued): Global and regional mitigation potential (GtCO$_2$-eq yr^{-1}) in 2020–2050 for 20 land-based measures. (a) Global estimates represent the mean (bar) and full range (error bars) of the economic potential (up to USD100 tCO$_2$-eq^{-1}) based on a comprehensive literature review of sectoral studies (references are outlined in the sub-section for each measure in Sections 7.4.2–7.4.5). Potential co-benefits and trade-offs for each of the 20 measures are summarised in icons. **(b)** Regional estimates illustrate the mean technical (T) and economic (E) (up to USD100 tCO$_2$-eq^{-1}) sectoral potential based on data from (Roe et al. 2021). IAM economic potential (M) (USD100 tCO$_2$-eq^{-1}) data is from the IPCC AR6 database.

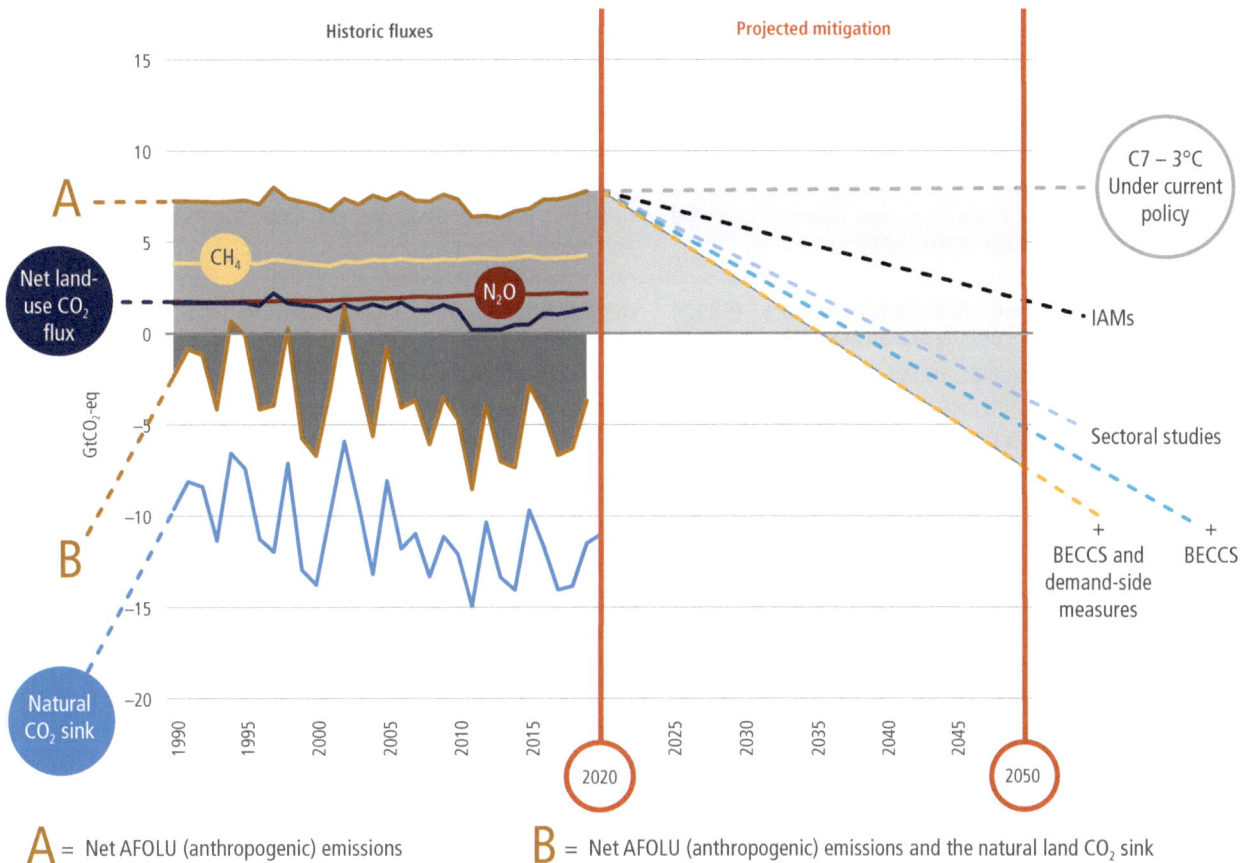

A = Net AFOLU (anthropogenic) emissions   B = Net AFOLU (anthropogenic) emissions and the natural land CO$_2$ sink

Figure 7.12 | Historic land sector GHG flux estimates and illustrative AFOLU mitigation pathways to 2050, based on data presented in Sections 7.2, 7.4 and 7.5. Historic trends consider both **A** anthropogenic (AFOLU) GHG fluxes (GtCO$_2$-eq yr^{-1}) according to FAOSTAT (FAO 2021a; 2021b) and **B** the estimated natural land CO$_2$ sink according to (Friedlingstein et al. 2020). Note that for the anthropogenic net land CO$_2$ flux component, several approaches and methods are described within the literature (Section 7.2.2) with a wide range in estimates. For clarity, only one dataset (FAOSTAT) is illustrated here. It is not intended to indicate preference for one particular method over others. Historic flux trends are illustrated to 2019, the latest year for which data is available. Projected economic mitigation potential (at costs of up to USD100 tCO$_2$-eq^{-1}) includes estimates from IAMs and sectoral studies (Table 7.3). The 'sectoral studies' are disaggregated into several cumulative parts: first 'sectoral studies' involves measures in agriculture, forests and other ecosystems, then an additional BECCS share ('+ BECCS'), then the additional effect of demand-side measures and BECCS ('+BECCS and demand-side measures'). The latter only accounting for diverted agricultural production to avoid double counting. Projected mitigation assumes adoption of measures to achieve increasing, linear mitigation, reaching average annual potential in 2050, although this does not reflect deployment rates for most measures. For illustrative purposes, a pathway to projected emissions in 2050 according to a scenario of current policy (C7 – above 3.0°C – Model: GCAM 5.3) is additionally included for reference.

7.4.2   Forests and Other Ecosystems

7.4.2.1   Reduce Deforestation and Degradation

Activities, co-benefits, risks and implementation opportunities and barriers. Reducing deforestation and forest degradation conserves existing carbon pools in forest vegetation and soil by avoiding tree cover loss and disturbance. Protecting forests involves controlling the drivers of deforestation (such as commercial and subsistence agriculture, mining, urban expansion) and forest degradation (such as overharvesting including fuelwood collection, poor harvesting practices, overgrazing, pest outbreaks, and extreme wildfires), as well as by establishing well designed, managed and funded protected areas (Barber et al. 2014), improving law

enforcement, forest governance and land tenure, supporting community forest management and introducing forest certification (P. Smith et al. 2019a). Reducing deforestation provides numerous and substantial co-benefits, preserving biodiversity and ecosystem services (e.g., air and water filtration, water cycling, nutrient cycling) more effectively and at lower costs than afforestation/reforestation (Jia et al. 2019). Potential adverse side effects of these conservation measures include reducing the potential for agriculture land expansion, restricting the rights and access of local people to forest resources, or increasing the dependence of local people to insecure external funding. Barriers to implementation include unclear land tenure, weak environmental governance, insufficient funds, and increasing pressures associated to agriculture conversion, resource exploitation and infrastructure development (Sections 7.3 and 7.6).

Conclusions from AR5 and IPCC Special Reports (SR1.5, SROCC and SRCCL); mitigation potential, costs, and pathways. Reducing deforestation and forest degradation represents one of the most effective options for climate change mitigation, with technical potential estimated at 0.4–5.8 $GtCO_2$ yr^{-1} by 2050 (*high confidence*) (SRCCL, Chapters 2 and 4, and Table 6.14). The higher technical estimate represents a complete halting of land-use conversion in forests and peatland forests (i.e., assuming recent rates of carbon loss are saved each year) and includes vegetation and soil carbon pools. Ranges of economic potentials for forestry ranged in AR5 from 0.01–1.45 $GtCO_2$ yr^{-1} for USD20 tCO_2^{-1} to 0.2–13.8 $GtCO_2$ yr^{-1} for USD100 tCO_2^{-1} by 2030 with reduced deforestation dominating the forestry mitigation potential LAM and MAF, but very little potential in OECD-1990 and EIT (IPCC AR5).

Developments since AR5 and IPCC Special Reports (SR1.5, SROCC and SRCCL). Since the SRCCL, several studies have provided updated and convergent estimates of economic mitigation potentials by region (Busch et al. 2019; Griscom et al. 2020; Austin et al. 2020; Roe et al. 2021). Tropical forests and savannas in Latin America provide the largest share of mitigation potential (3.9 $GtCO_2$ yr^{-1} technical, 2.5 $GtCO_2$ yr^{-1} at USD100 tCO_2^{-1}) followed by South-East Asia (2.2 $GtCO_2$ yr^{-1} technical, 1.5 $GtCO_2$ yr^{-1} at USD100 tCO_2^{-1}) and Africa (2.2 $GtCO_2$ yr^{-1} technical, 1.2 $GtCO_2$ yr^{-1} at USD100 tCO_2^{-1}) (Roe et al. 2021). Tropical forests continue to account for the highest rates of deforestation and associated GHG emissions. While deforestation shows signs of decreasing in several countries, in others, it continues at a high rate or is increasing (Turubanova et al. 2018). Between 2010–2020, the rate of net forest loss was 4.7 Mha yr^{-1} with Africa and South America presenting the largest shares (3.9 Mha and 2.6 Mha, respectively) (FAO 2020a).

A major uncertainty in all studies on avoided deforestation potential is their reliance on future reference levels that vary across studies and approaches. If food demand increases in the future, for example, the area of land deforested will likely increase, suggesting more technical potential for avoiding deforestation. Transboundary leakage due to market adjustments could also increase costs or reduce effectiveness of avoiding deforestation (e.g., Ingalls et al. 2018; Gingrich et al. 2019). Regarding forest regrowth, there are uncertainties about the time for the secondary forest carbon saturation (Houghton and Nassikas 2017; Zhu et al. 2018). Permanence of avoided deforestation may also be a concern due to the impacts of climate change and disturbance of other biogeochemical cycles on the world's forests that can result in future potential changes in terrestrial ecosystem productivity, climate-driven vegetation migration, wildfires, forest regrowth and carbon dynamics (Ballantyne et al. 2012; Kim et al. 2017b; Lovejoy and Nobre 2018; Aragão et al. 2018).

Critical assessment and conclusion. Based on studies since AR5, the technical mitigation potential for reducing deforestation and degradation is significant, providing 4.5 (2.3–7) $GtCO_2$ yr^{-1} globally by 2050, of which 3.4 (2.3–6.4) $GtCO_2$ yr^{-1} is available at below USD100 tCO_2^{-1} (*medium confidence*) (Figure 7.11). Over the last decade, hundreds of subnational initiatives that aim to reduce deforestation related emissions have been implemented across the tropics (Section 7.6). Reduced deforestation is a significant piece of the NDCs in the Paris Agreement (Seddon et al. 2020) and keeping the temperature below 1.5°C (Crusius 2020). Conservation of forests

provides multiple co-benefits linked to ecosystem services, biodiversity and sustainable development (Section 7.6.). Still, ensuring good governance, accountability (e.g., enhanced monitoring and verification capacity; Bos 2020), and the rule of law are crucial for implementing forest-based mitigation options. In many countries with the highest deforestation rates, insecure land rights often are significant barriers for forest-based mitigation options (Gren and Zeleke 2016; Essl et al. 2018).

7.4.2.2   Afforestation, Reforestation and Forest Ecosystem Restoration

Activities, co-benefits, risks and implementation opportunities and barriers. Afforestation and reforestation (A/R) are activities that convert land to forest, where reforestation is on land that has previously contained forests, while afforestation is on land that historically has not been forested (Box 7.2). Forest restoration refers to a form of reforestation that gives more priority to ecological integrity as well, even though it can still be a managed forest. Depending on the location, scale, and choice and management of tree species, A/R activities have a wide variety of co-benefits and trade-offs. Well-planned, sustainable reforestation and forest restoration can enhance climate resilience and biodiversity, and provide a variety of ecosystem services including water regulation, microclimatic regulation, soil erosion protection, as well as renewable resources, income and livelihoods (Locatelli et al. 2015; Stanturf et al. 2015; Ellison et al. 2017; Verkerk et al. 2020). Afforestation, when well planned, can help address land degradation and desertification by reducing runoff and erosion and lead to cloud formation however, when not well planned, there are localised trade-offs such as reduced water yield or biodiversity (Teuling et al. 2017; Ellison et al. 2017). The use of non-native species and monocultures may have adverse impacts on ecosystem structure and function, and water availability, particularly in dry regions (Ellison et al. 2017). A/R activities may change the surface albedo and evapotranspiration regimes, producing net cooling in the tropical and subtropical latitudes for local and global climate and net warming at high latitudes (Section 7.4.2). Very large-scale implementation of A/R may negatively affect food security since an increase in global forest area can increase food prices through land competition (Kreidenweis et al. 2016).

Conclusions from AR5 and IPCC Special Reports (SR1.5, SROCC and SRCCL); mitigation potential, costs, and pathways. The AR5 did not provide a new specification of A/R potential, but referred to IPCC AR4 mostly for forestry measures (Nabuurs et al. 2007). The AR5 did view the feasible A/R potential from a diets change scenario that released land for reforestation and bioenergy crops. The AR5 provided top-down estimates of costs and potentials for forestry mitigation options – including reduced deforestation, forest management, afforestation, and agroforestry, estimated to contribute between 1.27 and 4.23 $GtCO_2$ yr^{-1} of economically viable abatement in 2030 at carbon prices up to USD100 tCO_2-eq^{-1} (Smith et al. 2014).

The SRCCL remained with a reported wide range of mitigation potential for A/R of 0.5–10.1 $GtCO_2$ yr^{-1} by 2050 (*medium confidence*) (Kreidenweis et al. 2016; Griscom et al. 2017; Hawken 2017; Fuss et al. 2018; Roe et al. 2019) (SRCCL Chapters 2 and 6). The higher estimate represents a technical potential of reforesting all areas where forests are the native cover type (reforestation), constrained by food security and biodiversity considerations, considering above and below-ground carbon pools and implementation on a rather theoretical maximum of 678 Mha of land (Griscom et al. 2017; Roe et al. 2019). The lower estimates represent the minimum range from an Earth System Model and a sustainable global CDR potential (Fuss et al. 2018). Climate change will affect the mitigation potential of reforestation due to impacts in forest growth and composition, as well as changes in disturbances including fire. However, none of the mitigation estimates included in the SRCCL account for climate impacts.

Developments since AR5 and IPCC Special Reports (SR1.5, SROCC and SRCCL). Since SRCCL, additional studies have been published on A/R mitigation potential by Bastin et al. (2019), Lewis et al. (2019), Doelman et al. (2019), Favero et al. (2020) and Austin et al. (2020). These studies are within the range reported in the SRCCL stretching the potentials at the higher range. The rising public interest in nature-based solutions, along with high profile initiatives being launched (UN Decade on Restoration announced in 2019, the Bonn challenge on 150 million ha of restored forest in 2020 and the one trillion trees campaign launched by the World Economic Forum in 2020), has prompted intense discussions on the scale, effectiveness, and pitfalls of A/R and tree planting for climate mitigation (Luyssaert et al. 2018; Bond et al. 2019; Anderegg et al. 2020; Heilmayr et al. 2020; Holl and Brancalion 2020). The sometimes sole attention on afforestation and reforestation – suggesting it may solve the climate problem to large extent, in combination with the very high estimates of potentials – have led to polarisation in the debate, resulting in criticism to these measures or an emphasis on nature restoration only (Lewis et al. 2019). Our assessment based on most recent literature produced regional economic mitigation potential at USD100 tCO_2^{-1} estimate of 100–400 $MtCO_2$ yr^{-1} in Africa, 210–266 $MtCO_2$ yr^{-1} in Asia and Pacific, 291 $MtCO_2$-eq yr^{-1} in Developed Countries (87% in North America), 30 $MtCO_2$-eq yr^{-1} in Eastern Europe and West-Central Asia, and 345–898 $MtCO_2$-eq yr^{-1} in Latin America and Caribbean (Roe et al. 2021), which totals to about 1200 $MtCO_2$ yr^{-1}, leaning to the lower range of the potentials in earlier IPCC reports. A recent global assessment of the aggregate costs for afforestation and reforestation suggests that at USD100 tCO_2^{-1}, 1.6 $GtCO_2$ yr^{-1} could be sequestered globally for an annual cost of USD130 billion (Austin et al. 2020). Sectoral studies that are able to deal with local circumstances and limits estimate A/R potentials at 20 $MtCO_2$ yr^{-1} in Russia (Eastern Europe and West-Central Asia) (Romanovskaya et al. 2020) and 64 $MtCO_2$ yr^{-1} in Europe (Nabuurs et al. 2017). (Domke et al. 2020) estimated for the USA an additional 20% sequestration rate from tree planting to achieve full stocking capacity of all understocked productive forestland, in total reaching 187 $MtCO_2$ yr^{-1} sequestration. A new study on costs in the USA estimates 72–91 $MtCO_2$ yr^{-1} could be sequestered between now and 2050 for USD100 tCO_2^{-1} (Wade et al. 2019). The tropical and subtropical latitudes are the most effective for forest restoration in terms of carbon sequestration because of the rapid growth and lower albedo of the land surface compared with high latitudes (Lewis et al. 2019). Costs may be higher if albedo is considered in North America, Russia, and Africa (Favero et al. 2017). In addition, a wide variety of sequestration rates have been collected and published in the IPCC Good Practice Guidance for the AFOLU sector (IPCC 2006).

Critical assessment and conclusion. There is *medium confidence* that the global technical mitigation potential

of afforestation and reforestation activities by 2050 is 3.9 (0.5–10.1) $GtCO_2$ yr^{-1}, and the economic mitigation potential (<USD100 tCO_2^{-1}) is 1.6 (0.5–3.0) $GtCO_2$ yr^{-1} (requiring about 200 Mha). Per hectare a long (about 100 year) sustained effect of 5–10 t CO_2 ha^{-1} yr^{-1} is realistic with ranges between 1–20 t(CO_2) ha^{-1} yr^{-1}. Not all sectoral studies rely on economic models that account for leakage (Murray et al. 2004; Sohngen and Brown 2004), suggesting that technical potential may be overestimated.

7.4.2.3 Improved Forest Management

Activities, co-benefits, risks and implementation opportunities and barriers. Improved sustainable forest management of already managed forests can lead to higher forest carbon stocks, better quality of produced wood, continuously produced wood, while maintaining and enhancing the forest carbon stock, and can also partially prevent and counteract the impacts of disturbances (Kurz et al. 2008; Marlon et al. 2012; Abatzoglou and Williams 2016; Seidl et al. 2017; Nabuurs et al. 2017; Tian et al. 2018; Ekholm 2020). Furthermore, it can provide benefits for climate change adaptation, biodiversity conservation, microclimatic regulation, soil erosion protection and water and flood regulation with reduced lateral carbon fluxes (Ashton et al. 2012; Martínez-Mena et al. 2019; Verkerk et al. 2020). Often, in existing (managed) forests with existing carbon stocks, large changes per hectare cannot be expected, although many forest owners may respond to carbon price incentives (Favero et al. 2020; Ekholm 2020). The full mitigation effects can be assessed in conjunction with the overall forest and wood use system i.e., carbon stock changes in standing trees, soil, harvested wood products (HWPs) and its bioenergy component with the avoided emissions through substitution. Forest management strategies aimed at increasing the biomass stock may have adverse side effects, such as decreasing the stand-level structural complexity, large emphasis on pure fast-growing stands, risks for biodiversity and resilience to natural disasters.

Generally, measures can consist of one or combination of longer rotations, less intensive harvests, continuous-cover forestry, mixed stands, more adapted species, selected provenances, high quality wood assortments, and so on. Further, there is a trade-off between management in various parts of the forest product value chain, resulting in a wide range of results on the role of managed forests in mitigation (Agostini et al. 2013; Braun et al. 2016; Soimakallio et al. 2016; Gustavsson et al. 2017; Erb et al. 2017; Favero et al. 2020; Hurmekoski et al. 2020). Some studies conclude that reduction in forest carbon stocks due to harvest exceeds for decades the joint sequestration of carbon in harvested wood product stocks and emissions avoided through wood use (Soimakallio et al. 2016; Seppälä et al. 2019), whereas others emphasise country level examples where investments in forest management have led to higher growing stocks while producing more wood (Schulze et al. 2020; Ouden et al. 2020; Cowie et al. 2021).

Conclusions from AR5 and IPCC Special Reports (SR1.5, SROCC and SRCCL); mitigation potential, costs, and pathways. In the SRCCL, forest management activities have the potential to mitigate 0.4–2.1 $GtCO_2$-eq yr^{-1} by 2050 (*medium confidence*) (SRCCL: Griscom et al. 2017; Roe et al. 2019). The higher estimate stems from assumptions of applications on roughly 1.9 billion ha of already managed forest which can be seen as very optimistic. It combines both natural forest management as well as improved plantations, on average with a small net additional effect per hectare, not including substitution effects in the energy sector nor the buildings sector.

Developments since AR5 and IPCC Special Reports (SR1.5, SROCC and SRCCL). The area of forest under management plans has increased in all regions since 2000 by 233 Mha (FAO 2020e). The roughly 1 billion ha of secondary and degraded forests would be ideal to invest in and develop a sustainable sector that pays attention to biodiversity, wood provision and climate mitigation at the same time. This all depends on the effort made, the development of expertise, know-how in the field, nurseries with adapted provenances, etc as was also found for Russian climate-smart forestry options (Leskinen et al. 2020). Regionally, recently updated economic mitigation potential at USD100 tCO_2^{-1} have 179–186 $MtCO_2$-eq yr^{-1} in Africa, 193–313 $MtCO_2$-eq yr^{-1} in Asia and Pacific, 215–220 $MtCO_2$-eq yr^{-1} in Developed Countries , 82–152 $MtCO_2$-eq yr^{-1} in Eastern Europe and West-Central Asia, and 62–204 $MtCO_2$-eq yr^{-1} in Latin America and Caribbean (Roe et al. 2021).

Regional studies can take into account the local situation better: Russia Romanovskaya et al. (2020) estimate the potential of forest fires management at 220–420 $MtCO_2$ yr^{-1}, gentle logging technology at 15–59, reduction of wood losses at 61–76 $MtCO_2$ yr^{-1}. In North America, (Austin et al. 2020) estimate that in the next 30 years, forest management could contribute 154 $MtCO_2$ yr^{-1} in the USA and Canada with 81 $MtCO_2$ yr^{-1} available at less than USD100 tCO_2^{-1}. In one production region (British Columbia) a cost-effective portfolio of scenarios was simulated that directed more of the harvested wood to longer-lived wood products, stopped burning of harvest residues and instead produced bioenergy to displace fossil fuel burning, and reduced harvest levels in regions with low disturbance rates. Net GHG emissions were reduced by an average of −9 $MtCO_2$-eq yr^{-1}

(Smyth et al. 2020). In Europe, climate-smart forestry could mitigate an additional 0.19 $GtCO_2$ yr^{-1} by 2050 (Nabuurs et al. 2017), in line with the regional estimates in (Roe et al. 2021).

In the tropics, estimates of the pantropical climate mitigation potential of natural forest management (a light intensity management in secondary forests), across three tropical regions (Latin America, Africa, Asia), is around 0.66 $GtCO_2$-eq yr^{-1} with Asia responding for the largest share followed by Africa and Latin America (Roe et al. 2021). Selective logging occurs in at least 20% of the world's tropical forests and causes at least half of the emissions from tropical forest degradation (Asner et al. 2005; Blaser and Küchli 2011; Pearson et al. 2017). Reduced-impact logging for climate (RIL-C; promotion of reduced wood waste, narrower haul roads, and lower impact skidding equipment) has the potential to reduce logging emissions by 44% (Ellis et al. 2019), while also providing timber production.

Critical assessment and conclusion. There is *medium confidence* that the global technical mitigation potential for improved forest management by 2050 is 1.7 (1–2.1) $GtCO_2$ yr^{-1}, and the economic mitigation potential (<USD100 tCO_2^{-1}) is 1.1 (0.6–1.9) $GtCO_2$ yr^{-1}. Efforts to change forest management do not only require, for example, a carbon price incentive, but especially require knowledge, institutions, skilled labour, good access and so on. These requirements outline that although the potential is of medium size, we estimate a feasible potential towards the lower end. The net effect is also difficult to assess, as management changes impact not only the forest biomass, but also the wood chain and substitution effects. Further, leakage can arise from efforts to change management for carbon sequestration. Efforts, for example to set aside large areas of forest, may be partly counteracted by higher harvesting pressures elsewhere (Kallio et al. 2018). Studies such as (Austin et al. 2020) implicitly account for leakage and thus suggest higher costs than other studies. We therefore judge the mitigation potential at medium potential with medium agreement.

Box 7.2 | Climate-smart Forestry in Europe

Summary

European forests have been regarded as prospering and increasing for the last five decades. However, these views also changed recently. Climate change is putting a large pressure on mono species and high stocked areas of Norway spruce in Central Europe (Hlásny et al. 2021; Senf and Seidl 2021) with estimates of mortality reaching 200 million m³, biodiversity under pressure, the Mediterranean area showing a weak sector and harvesting pressure in the Baltics and north reaching maxima achievable. A European strategy for unlocking the EU's forests and forest sector potential was needed at the time of developing the LULUCF regulation and was based on the concept of 'climate-smart forestry' (CSF) (Nabuurs et al. 2017; Verkerk et al. 2020).

Background

The idea behind CSF is that it considers the whole value chain from forest to wood products and energy, illustrating that a wide range of measures can be applied to provide positive incentives for more firmly integrating climate objectives into the forest and forest sector framework. CSF is more than just storing carbon in forest ecosystems; it builds upon three main objectives; (i) reducing and/ or removing GHG emissions; (ii) adapting and building diverse forests for forest resilience to climate change; and (iii) sustainably increasing forest productivity and incomes. These three CSF objectives can be achieved by tailoring policy measures and actions to regional circumstances in member states' forest sectors.

Box 7.2 (continued)

Case description

The 2015 annual mitigation effect of EU-28 forests via contributions to the forest sink, material substitution and energy substitution is estimated at 569 MtCO$_2$ yr^{-1}, or 13% of total current EU emissions. With the right set of incentives in place at EU and member states levels, it was found that the EU-28 has the potential to achieve an additional combined mitigation impact through the implementation of CSF of 441 MtCO$_2$ yr^{-1} by 2050. Also, with the Green Deal and its biodiversity and forest strategy, more emphasis will be placed on forests, forest management and the provision of renewables. It is the diversity of measures (from strict reserves to more intensively managed systems while adapting the resource) that will determine the success. Only with co-benefits in, for example, nature conservation, soil protection, and provision of renewables, wood for buildings and income, the mitigation and adaptation measures will be successful.

Interactions, limitations and lessons

Climate-smart forestry is now taking shape across Europe with various research and implementation projects (Climate Smart Forest and Nature Management, 2021). Pilots and projects are being implemented by a variety of forest owners, some with more attention on biodiversity and adaptation, some with more attention on production functions. They establish examples and in longer term the outreach to the 16 million private owners in Europe. However, the right triggers and incentives are often still lacking. For example, adapting the spruce forest areas in Central Europe to climate change requires knowledge about different species, biodiversity and different management options and eventually use in industry. It requires alternative species to be available from the nurseries, as well as improved monitoring to assess the success and steer activities.

7.4.2.4 Fire Management (Forest and Grassland/ Savanna Fires)

Activities, co-benefits, risks and implementation opportunities and barriers. Fire management objectives include safeguarding life, property, and resources through the prevention, detection, control, restriction, and management of fire for diverse purposes in natural ecosystems (SRCCL, Chapter 6). Controlled burning is an effective economic method of reducing fire danger and stimulating natural regeneration. Co-benefits of fire management include reduced air pollution compared to much larger, uncontrolled fires, prevention of soil erosion and land degradation, biodiversity conservation in rangelands, and improvement of forage quality (Hurteau and Brooks 2011; Falk 2017; Hurteau et al. 2019). Fire management is still challenging because it is not only fire suppression at times of fire, but especially proper natural resource management in between fire events. Furthermore, it is challenging because of legal and policy issues, equity and rights concerns, governance, capacity, and research needs (Wiedinmyer and Hurteau 2010; Goldammer 2016; Russell-Smith et al. 2017). It will increasingly be needed under future enhanced climate change.

Conclusions from AR5 and IPCC Special Reports (SR1.5, SROCC and SRCCL); mitigation potential, costs, and pathways. In the SRCCL, fire management is among the nine options that can deliver medium-to-large benefits across multiple land challenges (climate change mitigation, adaptation, desertification, land degradation, and food security) (*high confidence*). Total emissions from fires have been on the order of 8.1 GtCO$_2$-eq yr^{-1} in terms of gross biomass loss for the period 1997–2016 (SRCCL, Chapter 2, and Cross-Chapter Box 3 in Chapter 2). Reduction in fire CO$_2$ emissions was calculated to enhance land carbon sink by 0.48 GtCO$_2$-eq yr^{-1} for the 1960–2009 period (Arora and Melton 2018) (SRCCL, Table 6.16).

Developments since AR5 and IPCC Special Reports (SR1.5, SROCC and SRCCL)

Savannas. Savannas constitute one of the most fire-prone vegetation types on Earth and are a significant source of GHG emissions. Savanna fires contributed 62% (4.92 PgCO$_2$-eq yr$^{-1)}$) of gross global mean fire emissions between 1997 and 2016. Regrowth from vegetation postfire sequesters the CO$_2$ released into the atmosphere, but not the CH$_4$ and N$_2$O emissions which contributed an approximate net of 2.1 PgCO$_2$-eq yr^{-1} (Lipsett-Moore et al. 2018). Therefore, implementing prescribed burning with low intensity fires, principally in the early dry season, to effectively manage the risk of wildfires occurring in the late dry season is associated with reducing emissions (Whitehead et al. 2014). Considering this fire management practice, estimates of global opportunities for emissions reductions were estimated at 69.1 MtCO$_2$-eq yr^{-1} in Africa (29 countries, with 20 least developed African countries accounting for 74% of the mitigation potential), 13.3 MtCO$_2$-eq yr^{-1} in South America (six countries), and 6.9 MtCO$_2$-eq yr^{-1} in Australia and Papua New Guinea (Lipsett-Moore et al. 2018). In Australia, savanna burning emissions abatement methodologies have been available since 2012, and abatement has exceeded 9.3 MtCO$_2$-eq mainly through the management of low intensity early dry season fire. Until September 2021, 78 projects were registered (Australian Government, Clean Energy Regulator, 2021).

Forests. Fire is also a prevalent forest disturbance (Falk et al. 2011; Scott et al. 2014; Andela et al. 2019). About 98 Mha of forest were affected by fire in 2015, affecting about 4% of the tropical (dry) forests, 2% of the subtropical forests, and 1% of temperate and boreal forests (FAO 2020a). Between 2001–2018, remote sensing data showed that tree-covered areas correspond to about 29% of the total area burned by wildfires, most in Africa. Prescribed fires are also applied routinely in forests worldwide for fuel reduction and ecological reasons (Kalies and Yocom Kent 2016). Fire resilience is increasingly managed in Southwestern USA forest landscapes, which have experienced droughts and widespread, high-severity wildfires (Keeley et al. 2019). In these forests, fire exclusion management, coupled with a warming climate, has led to increasingly severe wildfires (Hurteau et al. 2014). However, the impacts of prescribed fires in forests in reducing carbon emissions are still inconclusive. Some positive impacts of prescribed fires are associated with other fuel reduction techniques (Loudermilk et al. 2017; Flanagan et al. 2019; Stephens et al. 2020), leading to maintaining carbon stocks and reducing carbon emissions in the future where extreme fire weather events are more frequent (Krofcheck et al. 2018, 2019; Hurteau et al. 2019; Bowman et al. 2020a,b; Goodwin et al. 2020). Land management approaches will certainly need to consider the new climatic conditions (e.g., the proportion of days in fire seasons with the potential for unmanageable fires more than doubling in some regions in northern and eastern boreal forest) (Wotton et al. 2017).

Critical assessment and conclusion. There is *low confidence* that the global technical mitigation potential for grassland and savanna fire management by 2050 is 0.1 (0.09–0.1) GtCO$_2$ yr^{-1}, and the economic mitigation potential (<USD100 tCO$_2$$^{-1}$) is 0.05 (0.03–0.07) GtCO$_2$ yr^{-1}. Savanna fires produce significant emissions globally, but prescribed fires in the early dry season could mitigate emissions in different regions, particularly Africa. Evidence is less clear for fire management of forests, with the contribution of GHG mitigation depending on many factors that affect the carbon balance (e.g., Simmonds et al. 2021). Although prescribed burning is promoted to reduce uncontrolled wildfires in forests, the benefits for the management of carbon stocks are unclear, with different studies reporting varying results especially concerning its long-term effectiveness (Wotton et al. 2017; Bowman et al. 2020b). Under increasing climate change however, an increased attention on fire management will be necessary.

7.4.2.5 Reduce Degradation and Conversion of Grasslands and Savannas

Activities, co-benefits, risks and implementation opportunities and barriers. Grasslands cover approximately 40.5% of the terrestrial area (i.e., 52.5 million km^2) divided as 13.8% woody savanna and savanna; 12.7% open and closed shrub; 8.3% non-woody grassland; and 5.7% is tundra (White et al. 2000). Sub-Saharan Africa and Asia have the most extensive total area, 14.5 and 8.9 million km^2, respectively. A review by Conant et al. (2017) reported based on data on grassland area (FAO 2013) and grassland soil carbon stocks (Sombroek et al. 1993) a global estimate of about 343 PgC (in the top 1 m), nearly 50% more than is stored in forests worldwide (FAO 2007). Reducing the conversion of grasslands and savannas to croplands prevents soil carbon losses by oxidation, and to a smaller extent, biomass carbon loss due to vegetation clearing (SRCCL, Chapter 6). Restoration of grasslands through enhanced soil carbon sequestration, including (i) management of vegetation, (ii) animal management, and (iii) fire management, was also included in the SRCCL and is covered in Section 7.4.3.1. Similar to other measures that reduce conversion, conserving carbon stocks in grasslands and savannas can be achieved by controlling conversion

drivers (e.g., commercial and subsistence agriculture, see Section 7.3) and improving policies and management. In addition to mitigation, conserving grasslands provide various socio-economic, biodiversity, water cycle and other environmental benefits (Claassen et al. 2010; Ryals et al. 2015; Bengtsson et al. 2019). Annual operating costs, and opportunity costs of income foregone by undertaking the activities needed for avoiding conversion of grasslands making costs one of the key barriers for implementation (Lipper et al. 2010).

Conclusions from AR5 and IPCC Special Reports (SR1.5, SROCC and SRCCL); mitigation potential, costs, and pathways. The SRCCL reported a mitigation potential for reduced conversion of grasslands and savannas of 0.03–0.12 GtCO$_2$-eq yr^{-1} (Griscom et al. 2017; IPCC 2019) considering the higher loss of soil organic carbon in croplands (Sanderman et al. 2017). Assuming an average starting soil organic carbon stock of temperate grasslands (Poeplau et al. 2011), and the mean annual global cropland conversion rates (1961–2003) (Krause et al. 2017), the equivalent loss of soil organic carbon over 20 years would be 14 GtCO$_2$-eq, for example, 0.7 GtCO$_2$ yr^{-1} (SRCCL, Chapter 6). IPCC AR5 and AR4 did not explicitly consider the mitigation potential of avoided conversion of grasslands-savannas but the management of grazing land is accounted for considering plant, animal, and fire management with a mean mitigation potential of 0.11–0.80 tCO$_2$-eq ha^{-1} yr^{-1} depending on the climate region. This resulted in 0.25 GtCO$_2$-eq yr^{-1} at USD20 tCO$_2$$^{-1}$ to 1.25 GtCO$_2$-eq yr^{-1} at USD100 tCO$_2$$^{-1}$ by 2030.

Developments since AR5 and IPCC Special Reports (SR1.5, SROCC and SRCCL). Unlike most of the measures covered in Section 7.4, there are currently no global, spatially explicit mitigation potential estimates for reduced grassland conversion to generate technical and economic potentials by region. Literature developments since AR5 and SRCCL are studies that provide mitigation estimates in one or a few countries or regions. Modelling experiments comparing Californian forests and grasslands found that grasslands resulted in a more resilient carbon sink than forests to future climate change (Dass et al. 2018). However, previous studies indicated that precipitation is a key controller of the carbon storage in these grasslands, with the grassland became a carbon sink in 2005, when the region received relatively high spring precipitation (Ma et al. 2007). In North America, grassland conversion was the source for 77% of all new croplands from 2008–2012 (Lark et al. 2015). Avoided conversion of North American grasslands to croplands presents an economic mitigation potential of 0.024 GtCO$_2$-eq yr^{-1} and technical potential of 0.107 GtCO$_2$-eq yr^{-1} (Fargione et al. 2018). This potential is related mainly to root biomass and soils (81% of emissions from soils). Estimates of GHG emissions from any future deforestation in Australian savannas also point to the potential mitigation of around 0.024 GtCO$_2$-eq yr^{-1} (Bristow et al. 2016). The expansion of the Soy Moratorium (SoyM) from the Brazilian Amazon to the Cerrado (Brazilian savannas) would prevent the direct conversion of 3.6 Mha of native vegetation to soybeans by 2050 and avoid the emission of 0.02 GtCO$_2$-eq yr^{-1} (Soterroni et al. 2019).

Critical assessment and conclusion. There is *low confidence* that the global technical mitigation potential for reduced grassland and savanna conversion by 2050 is 0.2 (0.1–0.4) GtCO$_2$ yr^{-1}, and the economic mitigation potential (<USD100 tCO_2^{-1}) is 0.04 $GtCO_2$ yr^{-1}. Most of the carbon sequestration potential is in below-ground biomass and soil organic matter. However, estimates of potential are still based on few studies and vary according to the levels of soil carbon, and ecosystem productivity (e.g., in response to rainfall distribution). Conservation of grasslands presents significant benefits for desertification control, especially in arid areas (SRCCL, Chapter 3). Policies supporting avoided conversion can help protect at-risk grasslands, reduce GHG emissions, and produce positive outcomes for biodiversity and landowners (Ahlering et al. 2016). In comparison to tropical rainforest regions that have been the primary target for mitigation policies associated to natural ecosystems (e.g., REDD+), conversion grasslands and savannas has received less national and international attention, despite growing evidence of concentrated cropland expansion into these areas with impacts of carbon losses.

7.4.2.6 Reduce Degradation and Conversion of Peatlands Activities, Co-benefits, Risks and Implementation Barriers

Peatlands are carbon-rich wetland ecosystems with organic soil horizons in which soil organic matter concentration exceeds 30% (dry weight) and soil carbon concentrations can exceed 50% (Page and Baird 2016, Boone Kauffman et al. 2017). Reducing the conversion of peatlands avoids emissions of above- and below-ground biomass and soil carbon due to vegetation clearing, fires, and peat decomposition from drainage. Similar to deforestation, peatland carbon stocks can be conserved by controlling the drivers of conversion and degradation (e.g., commercial and subsistence agriculture, mining, urban expansion) and improving governance and management. Reducing conversion is urgent because peatland carbon stocks accumulate slowly and persist over millennia; loss of existing stocks cannot be easily reversed over the decadal time scales needed to meet the Paris Agreement (Goldstein et al. 2020). The main co-benefits of reducing conversion of peatlands include conservation of a unique biodiversity including many critically endangered species, provision of water quality and regulation, and improved public health through decreased fire-caused pollutants (Griscom et al. 2017). Although reducing peatland conversion will reduce land availability for alternative uses including agriculture or other land-based mitigation, drained peatlands constitute a small share of agricultural land globally while contributing significant emissions (Joosten 2009). Mitigation through reduced conversion of peatlands therefore has a high potential of avoided emissions per hectare (Roe et al. 2019).

Conclusions from AR5 and IPCC Special Reports (SR1.5, SROCC and SRCCL); mitigation potential, costs, and pathways. In the SRCCL (Chapters 2 and 6), it was estimated that avoided peat impacts could deliver 0.45–1.22 $GtCO_2$-eq yr^{-1} technical potential by 2030–2050 (*medium confidence*) (Hooijer et al. 2010; Griscom et al. 2017; Hawken 2017). The mitigation potential estimates cover tropical peatlands and include CO_2, N_2O and CH_4 emissions. The mitigation potential is derived from quantification of losses of carbon stocks due to land conversion, shifts in GHG fluxes, alterations in net ecosystem productivity, input factors such as fertilisation needs, and biophysical climate impacts (e.g., shifts in albedo, water cycles, etc.). Tropical peatlands account for only about 10% of peatland area

and about 20% of peatland carbon stock but about 80% of peatland carbon emissions, primarily from peatland conversion in Indonesia (about 60%) and Malaysia (about 10%) (Hooijer et al. 2010; Page et al. 2011; Leifeld and Menichetti 2018). While the total mitigation potential of peatland conservation is considered moderate, the per hectare mitigation potential is the highest among land-based mitigation measures (Roe et al. 2019).

Developments since AR5 and IPCC Special Reports (SR1.5, SROCC and SRCCL). Recent studies continue to report high carbon stocks in peatlands and emphasise the vulnerability of peatland carbon after conversion. The carbon stocks of tropical peatlands are among the highest of any forest, 1,211–4,257 tCO_2-eq ha^{-1} in the Peruvian Amazon (Bhomia et al. 2019) and 1,956–14,757 tCO_2-eq ha^{-1} in Indonesia (Novita et al. 2021). Ninety percent of tropical peatland carbon stocks are vulnerable to emission during conversion and may not be recoverable through restoration; in contrast, boreal and temperate peatlands hold similar carbon stocks (1,439–5,619 tCO_2-eq ha^{-1}) but only 30% of northern carbon stocks are vulnerable to emission during conversion and irrecoverable through restoration (Goldstein et al. 2020). A recent study shows global mitigation potential of about 0.2 $GtCO_2$-eq yr^{-1} at costs up to USD100 tCO_2^{-1} (Roe et al. 2021). Another study estimated that 72% of mitigation is achieved through avoided soil carbon impacts, with the remainder through avoided impacts to vegetation (Bossio et al. 2020). Recent model projections show that both peatland protection and peatland restoration (Section 7.4.2.7) are needed to achieve a 2°C mitigation pathway and that peatland protection and restoration policies will have minimal impacts on regional food security (Leifeld et al. 2019, Humpenöder et al. 2020). Global studies have not accounted for extensive peatlands recently reported in the Congo Basin, estimated to cover 145,500 km^2 and contain 30.6 PgC, as much as 29% of total tropical peat carbon stock (Dargie et al. 2017). These Congo peatlands are relatively intact; continued preservation is needed to prevent major emissions (Dargie et al. 2019). In northern peatlands that are underlain by permafrost roughly 50% of the total peatlands north of 23° latitude, (Hugelius et al. 2020), climate change (i.e., warming) is the major driver of peatland degradation (e.g., through permafrost thaw) (Schuur et al. 2015, Goldstein et al. 2020). However, in non-permafrost boreal and temperate peatlands, reduction of peatland conversion is also a cost-effective mitigation strategy. Peatlands are sensitive to climate change and there is *low confidence* about the future peatland sink globally (SRCCL, Chapter 2). Permafrost thaw may shift northern peatlands from a net carbon sink to net source (Hugelius et al. 2020). Uncertainties in peatland extent and the magnitude of existing carbon stocks, in both northern (Loisel et al. 2014) and tropical (Dargie et al. 2017) latitudes limit understanding of current and future peatland carbon dynamics (Minasny et al. 2019).

Critical assessment and conclusion. Based on studies to date, there is *medium confidence* that peatland conservation has a technical potential of 0.86 (0.43–2.02) $GtCO_2$-eq yr^{-1} of which 0.48 (0.2–0.68) $GtCO_2$-eq yr^{-1} is available at USD100 tCO_2^{-1} (Figure 7.11). High per hectare mitigation potential and high rate of co-benefits particularly in tropical countries, support the effectiveness of this mitigation strategy (Roe et al. 2019). Feasibility of reducing peatland conversion may depend on countries' governance, financial capacity and political will.

7.4.2.7   Peatland Restoration

Activities, co-benefits, risks and implementation barriers. Peatland restoration involves restoring degraded and damaged peatlands, for example through rewetting and revegetation, which both increases carbon accumulation in vegetation and soils and avoids ongoing CO_2 emissions. Peatlands only account for about 3% of the terrestrial surface, predominantly occurring in boreal ecosystems (78%), with a smaller proportion in tropical regions (13%), but may store about 600 GtC or 21% of the global total soil organic carbon stock of about 3000 Gt (Page et al. 2011; Leifeld and Menichetti 2018). Peatland restoration delivers co-benefits for biodiversity, as well as regulating water flow and preventing downstream flooding, while still allowing for extensive management such as paludiculture (Tan et al. 2021). Rewetting of peatlands also reduces the risk of fire, but may also mobilise salts and contaminants in soils (van Diggelen et al. 2020) and in severely degraded peatlands, restoration of peatland hydrology and vegetation may not be feasible (Andersen et al. 2017). At a local level, restoration of peatlands drained for agriculture could displace food production and damage local food supply, although impacts to regional and global food security would be minimal (Humpenöder et al. 2020). Collaborative and transparent planning processes are needed to reduce conflict between competing land uses (Tanneberger et al. 2020b). Adequate resources for implementing restoration policies are key to engage local communities and maintain livelihoods (Resosudarmo et al. 2019; Ward et al. 2021).

Conclusions from AR5 and IPCC Special Reports (SR1.5, SROCC and SRCCL); mitigation potential, costs, and pathways. Large areas (0.51 Mkm²) of global peatlands are degraded of which 0.2 Mkm² are tropical peatlands (Griscom et al. 2017; Leifeld and Menichetti 2018). According the SRCCL, peatland restoration could deliver technical mitigation potentials of 0.15 – 0.81 GtCO$_2$-eq yr^{-1} by 2030–2050 (*low confidence*) (Couwenberg et al. 2010; Griscom et al. 2017) (Chapters 2 and 6 of the SRCCL), though there could be an increase in methane emissions after restoration (Jauhiainen et al. 2008). The mitigation potential estimates cover global peatlands and include CO_2, N_2O and CH_4 emissions. Peatlands are highly sensitive to climate change (*high confidence*), however there are currently no studies that estimate future climate effects on mitigation potential from peatland restoration.

Developments since AR5 and IPCC Special Reports (SR1.5, SROCC and SRCCL). The most recent literature and reviews indicate with *high confidence* that restoration would decrease CO_2 emissions and with *medium confidence* that restoration would decrease net GHG emissions from degraded peatlands (Wilson et al. 2016; Ojanen and Minkkinen 2020; van Diggelen et al. 2020). Although rewetting of drained peatlands increases CH_4 emissions, this effect is often outweighed by decreases in CO_2 and N_2O emissions but depends very much on local circumstances (Günther et al. 2020). Restoration and rewetting of almost all drained peatlands is needed by 2050 to

meet 1.5°C–2°C pathways which is unlikely to happen (Leifeld et al. 2019); immediate rewetting and restoration minimises the warming from cumulative CO_2 emissions (Nugent et al. 2019).

According to recent data, the technical mitigation potential for global peatland restoration is estimated at 0.5–1.3 GtCO$_2$-eq yr^{-1} (Leifeld and Menichetti 2018; Griscom et al. 2020; Bossio et al. 2020; Roe et al. 2021) (Figure 7.11), with 80% of the mitigation potential derived from improvements to soil carbon (Bossio et al. 2020). The regional mitigation potentials of all peatlands outlined in Roe et al. (2021) reflect the country-level estimates from (Humpenöder et al. 2020).

Climate mitigation effects of peatland rewetting depend on the climate zone and land use. Recent analysis shows the strongest mitigation gains from rewetting drained temperate and boreal peatlands used for agriculture and drained tropical peatlands (Ojanen and Minkkinen 2020). However, estimates of emission factors from rewetting drained tropical peatlands remain uncertain (Wilson et al. 2016; Murdiyarso et al. 2019). Topsoil removal, in combination with rewetting, may improve restoration success and limit CH_4 emissions during restoration of highly degraded temperate peatlands (Zak et al. 2018). In temperate and boreal regions, co-benefits mentioned above are major motivations for peatland restoration (Chimner et al. 2017; Tanneberger et al. 2020a).

Critical assessment and conclusion. Based on studies to date, there is *medium confidence* that peatland restoration has a technical potential of 0.79 (0.49–1.3) GtCO$_2$-eq yr^{-1} (median) of which 0.4 (0.2–0.6) GtCO$_2$-eq yr^{-1} is available up to USD100 tCO$_2$$^{-1}$. The large land area of degraded peatlands suggests that significant emissions reductions could occur through large-scale restoration especially in tropical peatlands. There is *medium confidence* in the large carbon stocks of tropical peat forests (1956–14,757 tCO$_2$-eq ha^{-1}) and large rates of carbon loss associated with land cover change (640–1650 tCO$_2$-eq ha^{-1}) (Goldstein et al. 2020; Novita et al. 2021). However, large-scale implementation of tropical peatland restoration will likely be limited by costs and other demands for these tropical lands.

7.4.2.8   Reduce Conversion of Coastal Wetlands

Activities, co-benefits, risks and implementation barriers. Reducing conversion of coastal wetlands, including mangroves, marshes and seagrass ecosystems, avoids emissions from above and below ground biomass and soil carbon through avoided degradation and/or loss. Coastal wetlands occur mainly in estuaries and deltas, areas that are often densely settled, with livelihoods closely linked to coastal ecosystems and resources (Moser et al. 2012). The carbon stocks of these highly productive ecosystems are sometimes referred to as 'blue carbon'. Loss of existing stocks cannot be easily reversed over decadal time scales (Goldstein et al. 2020). The main drivers of conversion include intensive aquaculture, agriculture, salt ponds, urbanisation and infrastructure development, the extensive use of fertilisers, and extraction of water resources (Lovelock et al. 2018). Reduced conversion of coastal wetlands has many co-benefits, including biodiversity conservation, fisheries production, soil stabilisation, water flow and water quality regulation, flooding and storm surge prevention, and increased resilience to cyclones (Windham-Myers et al. 2018a; UNEP 2020). Risks associated with the mitigation potential of coastal wetland conservation include uncertain permanence under future climate scenarios, including the effects of coastal squeeze, where coastal wetland area may be lost if upland area is not available for migration as sea levels rise (Lovelock and Reef 2020) (AR6 WGII, Section 3.4.2.5). Preservation of coastal wetlands also conflicts with other land use in the coastal zone, including aquaculture, agriculture, and human development; economic incentives are needed to prioritise wetland preservation over more profitable short-term land use. Integration of policies and efforts aimed at coastal climate mitigation, adaptation, biodiversity conservation, and fisheries, for example through integrated coastal zone management and marine spatial planning, will bundle climate mitigation with co-benefits and optimise outcomes (Herr et al. 2017).

Conclusions from AR5 and IPCC Special Reports (SR1.5, SROCC and SRCCL); mitigation potential, costs, and pathways. Coastal wetlands contain high, yet variable, organic carbon stocks, leading to a range of estimates of the global mitigation potential of reduced conversion. The SRCCL (Chapter 2) and SROCC (Chapter 5), report a technical mitigation potential of 0.15–5.35 $GtCO_2$-eq yr^{-1} by 2050 (Pendleton et al. 2012; Lovelock et al. 2017; Howard et al. 2017; Griscom et al. 2017). The mitigation potential is derived from quantification of losses of carbon stocks in vegetation and soil due to land conversion, shifts in GHG fluxes associated with land use, and alterations in net ecosystem productivity. The wide range in estimates mostly relate to the scope (all coastal ecosystems vs mangroves only) and different assumptions on decomposition rates. Loss rates of coastal wetlands have been estimated at 0.2–3% yr^{-1}, depending on the vegetation type and location (Atwood et al. 2017; Howard et al. 2017).

Developments since AR5 and IPCC Special Reports (SR1.5, SROCC and SRCCL). Global technical mitigation potential for conservation of coastal wetlands from recent literature have focused on protection of mangroves; estimates range from 0.06–2.25 $GtCO_2$-eq yr^{-1} (Griscom et al. 2020; Bossio et al. 2020) with 80% of the mitigation potential derived from improvements to soil carbon (Bossio et al. 2020). Regional potentials (Roe et al. 2021) reflect mangrove protection; marsh and seagrass protection were not included due to lack of country-level data on marsh and seagrass distribution and conversion.

Global estimates show mangroves have the largest per hectare carbon stocks (see IPCC AR6 WGII Box 3.4 for estimates of carbon stocks, burial rates and ecosystem extent for coastal wetland ecosystems). Mean ecosystem carbon stock in mangroves is 3131 tCO_2-eq ha^{-1} among the largest carbon stocks on Earth. Recent studies emphasise the variability in total ecosystem carbon stocks for each wetland type, based on species and climatic and edaphic conditions (Kauffman et al. 2020; Bedulli et al. 2020; Ricart et al. 2020; Alongi et al. 2020; F. Wang et al. 2021), and highlight the vulnerability of soil carbon below 1 m depth (Arifanti et al. 2019). Sea level strongly influences coastal wetland distribution, productivity, and sediment accretion; therefore, sea level rise will impact carbon accumulation and

persistence of existing carbon stocks (Macreadie et al. 2019) (IPCC AR6 WGII Box 3.4).

Recent loss rates of mangroves are 0.16–0.39% yr^{-1} and are highest in South-East Asia (Hamilton and Casey 2016; Friess et al. 2019; Hamilton and Casey 2016). Assuming loss of soil carbon to 1 m depth after deforestation, avoiding mangrove conversion has the technical potential to mitigate approximately 23.5–38.7 $MtCO_2$-eq yr^{-1} (Ouyang and Lee 2020); note, this potential is additional to reduced conversion of forests (Griscom et al. 2020) (Section 7.4.2.1). Regional estimates show that about 85% of mitigation potential for avoided mangrove conversion is in South-East Asia and Pacific (32 $MtCO_2$-eq yr^{-1} at USD100 $tCO_2$$^{-1}$), 10% is in Latin American and the Caribbean (4 $MtCO_2$-eq yr^{-1}), and approximately 5% in other regions (Griscom et al. 2020; Roe et al. 2021).

Key uncertainties remain in mapping extent and conversion rates for salt marshes and seagrasses (McKenzie et al. 2020). Seagrass loss rates were estimated at 1–2% yr^{-1} (Dunic et al. 2021) with stabilisation in some regions (de los Santos et al. 2019) (AR6 WGII, Section 3.4.2.5); however, loss occurs non-linearly and depends on site-specific context. Tidal marsh extent and conversion rates remains poorly estimated, outside of the USA, Europe, South Africa, and Australia (Mcowen et al. 2017; Macreadie et al. 2019).

Critical assessment and conclusion. There is *medium confidence* that coastal wetland protection has a technical potential of 0.8 (0.06–5.4) $GtCO_2$-eq yr^{-1} of which 0.17 (0.06–0.27) $GtCO_2$-eq yr^{-1} is available up to USD100 $tCO_2$$^{-1}$. There is a *high certainty* (*robust evidence, high agreement*) that coastal ecosystems have among the largest carbon stocks of any ecosystem. As these ecosystems provide many important services, reduced conversion of coastal wetlands is a valuable mitigation strategy with numerous co-benefits. However, the vulnerability of coastal wetlands to climatic and other anthropogenic stressors may limit the permanence of climate mitigation.

7.4.2.9 Coastal Wetland Restoration

Activities, co-benefits, risks and implementation barriers. Coastal wetland restoration involves restoring degraded or damaged coastal wetlands including mangroves, salt marshes, and seagrass ecosystems, leading to sequestration of 'blue carbon' in wetland vegetation and soil (SRCCL, Chapter 6; SROCC, Chapter 5). Successful approaches to wetland restoration include: (i) passive restoration, the removal of anthropogenic activities that are causing degradation or preventing recovery; and (ii) active restoration, purposeful manipulations to the environment in order to achieve recovery to a naturally functioning system (Elliott et al. 2016) (IPCC AR6 WGII Chapter 3). Restoration of coastal wetlands delivers many valuable co-benefits, including enhanced water quality, biodiversity, aesthetic values, fisheries production (food security), and protection from rising sea levels and storm impacts (Barbier et al. 2011; Hochard et al. 2019; Sun and Carson 2020; Duarte et al. 2020). Of the 0.3 Mkm^2 coastal wetlands globally, 0.11 Mkm^2 of mangroves are considered feasible for restoration (Griscom et al. 2017). Risks associated with coastal wetland restoration include uncertain permanence under future climate scenarios (IPCC AR6 WGII, Box 3.4), partial offsets of mitigation

7

through enhanced methane and nitrous oxide release and carbonate formation, and competition with other land uses, including aquaculture and human settlement and development in the coastal zone (SROCC, Chapter 5). To date, many coastal wetland restoration efforts do not succeed due to failure to address the drivers of degradation (van Katwijk et al. 2016). However, improved frameworks for implementing and assessing coastal wetland restoration are emerging that emphasise the recovery of ecosystem functions (Zhao et al. 2016; Cadier et al. 2020). Restoration projects that involve local communities at all stages and consider both biophysical and socio-political context are more likely to succeed (Brown et al. 2014; Wylie et al. 2016).

Conclusions from AR5 and IPCC Special Reports (SR1.5, SROCC and SRCCL); mitigation potential, costs, and pathways. The SRCCL reported that mangrove restoration has the technical potential to mitigate 0.07 $GtCO_2$ yr^{-1} through rewetting (Crooks et al. 2011) and take up 0.02–0.84 $GtCO_2$ yr^{-1} from vegetation biomass and soil enhancement through 2030 (*medium confidence*) (Griscom et al. 2017). The SROCC concluded that cost-effective coastal blue carbon restoration had a potential of about 0.15–0.18 $GtCO_2$-eq yr^{-1}, a low global potential compared to other ocean-based solutions but with extensive co-benefits and limited adverse side effects (Gattuso et al. 2018).

Developments since AR5 and IPCC Special Reports (SR1.5, SROCC and SRCCL). Recent studies emphasise the time frame needed to achieve the full mitigation potential (Duarte et al. 2020; Taillardat et al. 2020). The first project-derived estimate of the net GHG benefit from seagrass restoration found 1.54 tCO_2-eq (0.42 MgC) ha^{-1} yr^{-1} 10 years after restoration began (Oreska et al. 2020); comparable to the default emission factor in the Wetlands Supplement (Kennedy et al. 2014). Recent studies of rehabilitated mangroves also indicate that annual carbon sequestration rates in biomass and soils can return to natural levels within decades of restoration (Cameron et al. 2019; Sidik et al. 2019). A meta-analysis shows increasing carbon sequestration rates over the first 15 years of mangrove restoration with rates stabilising at 25.7 ± 7.7 tCO_2-eq (7.0 ± 2.1 MgC) ha^{-1} yr^{-1} through forty years, although success depends on climate, sediment type, and restoration methods (Sasmito et al. 2019). Overall, 30% of mangrove soil carbon stocks and 50–70% of marsh and seagrass carbon stocks are unlikely to recover within 30 years of restoration, underscoring the importance of preventing conversion of coastal wetlands (Goldstein et al. 2020) (Section 7.4.2.8).

According to recent data, the technical mitigation potential for global coastal wetland restoration is 0.04–0.84 $GtCO_2$-eq yr^{-1} (Griscom et al. 2020; Bossio et al. 2020; Roe et al. 2021) with 60% of the mitigation potential derived from improvements to soil carbon (Bossio et al. 2020). Regional potentials based on country-level estimates from Griscom et al. (2020) show the technical and economic (up to USD100 tCO_2^{-1}) potential of mangrove restoration; seagrass and marsh restoration was not included due to lack of country-level data on distribution and conversion (but see McKenzie et al. 2020 for updates on global seagrass distribution). Although global potential is relatively moderate, mitigation can be quite significant for countries with extensive coastlines (e.g., Indonesia, Brazil) and for small island states where coastal wetlands have been shown to comprise 24–34%

of their total national carbon stock (Donato et al. 2012). Furthermore, non-climatic co-benefits can strongly motivate coastal wetland restoration worldwide (UNEP 2021a). Major successes in both active and passive restoration of seagrasses have been documented in North America and Europe (Lefcheck et al. 2018; de los Santos et al. 2019; Orth et al. 2020); passive restoration may also be feasible for mangroves (Cameron et al. 2019).

There is high site-specific variation in carbon sequestration rates and uncertainties regarding the response to future climate change (Jennerjahn et al. 2017; Nowicki et al. 2017) (IPCC AR6 WGII Box 3.4). Changes in distributions (Kelleway et al. 2017; Wilson and Lotze 2019), methane release (Al-Haj and Fulweiler 2020), carbonate formation (Saderne et al. 2019), and ecosystem responses to interactive climate stressors are not well-understood (Short et al. 2016; Fitzgerald and Hughes 2019; Lovelock and Reef 2020).

Critical assessment and conclusion. There is *medium confidence* that coastal wetland restoration has a technical potential of 0.3 (0.04–0.84) $GtCO_2$-eq yr^{-1} of which 0.1 (0.05–0.2) $GtCO_2$-eq yr^{-1} is available up to USD100 tCO_2^{-1}. There is *high confidence* that coastal wetlands, especially mangroves, contain large carbon stocks relative to other ecosystems and *medium confidence* that restoration will reinstate pre-disturbance carbon sequestration rates. There is *low confidence* on the response of coastal wetlands to climate change; however, there is *high confidence* that coastal wetland restoration will provide a suite of valuable co-benefits.

7.4.3 Agriculture

7.4.3.1 Soil Carbon Management in Croplands and Grasslands

Activities, co-benefits, risks and implementation opportunities and barriers. Increasing soil organic matter in croplands are agricultural management practices that include (i) crop management: for example, high input carbon practices such as improved crop varieties, crop rotation, use of cover crops, perennial cropping systems (including agroforestry; see Section 7.4.3.3), integrated production systems, crop diversification, agricultural biotechnology; (ii) nutrient management including fertilisation with organic amendments/green manures (Section 7.4.3.6); (iii) reduced tillage intensity and residue retention, (iv) improved water management: including drainage of waterlogged mineral soils and irrigation of crops in arid/semi-arid conditions, (v) improved rice management (Section 7.4.3.5) and (vi) biochar application (P. Smith et al. 2019a) (Section 7.4.3.2). For increased soil organic matter in grasslands, practices include (i) *management of vegetation*: including improved grass varieties/ sward composition, deep rooting grasses, increased productivity, and nutrient management, (ii) *livestock management*: including appropriate stocking densities fit to carrying capacity, fodder banks, and fodder diversification, and (iii) *fire management*: improved use of fire for sustainable grassland management, including fire prevention and improved prescribed burning (Smith et al. 2014, 2019b). All these measures are recognised as Sustainable Soil Management Practices by FAO (Baritz et al. 2018). While there are co-benefits for livelihoods, biodiversity, water provision and food security (P. Smith et al. 2019a), and impacts on leakage, indirect land-use change and foregone sequestration do not apply (since production in not displaced), the climate benefits of soil carbon sequestration in croplands can be negated if achieved through additional fertiliser inputs (potentially causing increased N_2O emissions; (Guenet et al. 2021), and both saturation and permanence are relevant concerns. When considering implementation barriers, soil carbon management in croplands and grasslands is a low-cost option at a high level of technology readiness (it is already widely deployed globally) with low socio-cultural and institutional barriers, but with difficulty in monitoring and verification proving a barrier to implementation (Smith et al. 2020a).

Conclusions from AR5 and IPCC Special Reports (SR1.5, SROCC and SRCCL); mitigation potential, costs, and pathways. Building on AR5, the SRCCL reported the global mitigation potential for soil carbon management in croplands to be 1.4–2.3 $GtCO_2$-eq yr^{-1} (Smith et al. 2014), though the full literature range was 0.3–6.8 $GtCO_2$-eq yr^{-1} (Sommer and Bossio 2014; Powlson et al. 2014; Dickie et al. 2014b; Henderson et al. 2015; Herrero et al. 2016; Paustian et al. 2016; Zomer et al. 2016; Frank et al. 2017; Conant et al. 2017; Griscom et al. 2017; Hawken 2017; Sanderman et al. 2017; Fuss et al. 2018; Roe et al. 2019). The global mitigation potential for soil organic carbon management in grasslands was assessed to be 1.4–1.8 $GtCO_2$-eq yr^{-1}, with the full literature range being 0.1–2.6 $GtCO_2$-eq yr^{-1} (Herrero et al. 2013; 2016; Conant et al. 2017; Roe et al. 2019). Lower values in the range represented economic potentials, while higher values represented technical potentials – and uncertainty was expressed by reporting the whole range of estimates. The SR1.5 outlined associated costs reported in literature to range from USD –45 to 100 tCO_2^{-1}, describing enhanced soil carbon sequestration as a cost-effective measure (IPCC 2018). Despite significant mitigation potential, there is limited inclusion of soil carbon sequestration as a response option within IAM mitigation pathways (Rogelj et al. 2018a).

Developments since AR5 and IPCC Special Reports (SR1.5, SROCC and SRCCL). No recent literature has been published which conflict with the mitigation potentials reported in the SRCCL. Relevant papers include Lal et al. (2018) which estimated soil carbon sequestration potential to be 0.7–4.1 $GtCO_2$-eq yr^{-1} for croplands and 1.1–2.9 $GtCO_2$-eq yr^{-1} for grasslands. Bossio et al. (2020) assessed the contribution of soil carbon sequestration to natural climate solutions and found the potential to be 5.5 $GtCO_2$ yr^{-1} across all ecosystems, with only small portions of this (0.41 $GtCO_2$-eq yr^{-1} for cover cropping in croplands; 0.23, 0.15, 0.15 $GtCO_2$-eq yr^{-1} for avoided grassland conversion, optimal grazing intensity and legumes in pastures, respectively) arising from croplands and grasslands. Regionally, soil carbon management in croplands is feasible anywhere, but effectiveness can be limited in very dry regions (Sanderman et al. 2017). For soil carbon management in grasslands the feasibility is greatest in areas where grasslands have been degraded (e.g., by overgrazing) and soil organic carbon is depleted. For well managed grasslands, soil carbon stocks are already high and the potential for additional carbon storage is low. Roe et al. (2021) estimate the greatest economic (up to USD100 tCO_2^{-1}) potential between 2020 and 2050 for croplands to be in Asia and the Pacific (339.7 $MtCO_2$ yr^{-1}) and for grasslands, in Developed Countries (253.6 $MtCO_2$ yr^{-1}).

Critical assessment and conclusion. In conclusion, there is *medium confidence* that enhanced soil carbon management in croplands has a global technical mitigation potential of 1.9 (0.4–6.8) $GtCO_2$ yr^{-1}, and in grasslands of 1.0 (0.2–2.6) $GtCO_2$ yr^{-1}, of which, 0.6 (04–0.9) and 0.9 (0.3–1.6) $GtCO_2$ yr^{-1} is estimated to be available at up to USD100 tCO_2^{-1} respectively. Regionally, soil carbon management in croplands and grasslands is feasible anywhere, but effectiveness can be limited in very dry regions, and for grasslands it is greatest in areas where degradation has occurred (e.g., by overgrazing) and soil organic carbon is depleted. Barriers to implementation include regional capacity for monitoring and verification (especially in developing countries), and more widely through concerns over saturation and permanence.

7.4.3.2　Biochar

Activities, co-benefits, risks and implementation opportunities and barriers. Biochar is produced by heating organic matter in oxygen-limited environments (pyrolysis and gasification) (Lehmann and Joseph 2012). Feedstocks include forestry and sawmill residues, straw, manure and biosolids. When applied to soils, biochar is estimated to persist from decades to thousands of years, depending on feedstock and production conditions (J. Wang et al. 2016; Singh et al. 2015). Biochar systems producing biochar for soil application plus bioenergy, generally give greater mitigation than bioenergy alone and other uses of biochar, and are recognised as a CDR strategy. Biochar persistence is increased through interaction with clay minerals and soil organic matter (Fang et al. 2015). Additional CDR benefits arise through 'negative priming' whereby biochar stabilises soil carbon and rhizodeposits (Weng et al. 2015; J. Wang et al. 2016; Archanjo et al. 2017; Hagemann et al. 2017; Han Weng et al. 2017; Weng et al. 2018). Besides CDR, additional mitigation can arise from displacing fossil fuels with pyrolysis gases, lower soil N_2O emissions (Cayuela et al. 2014, 2015; Song et al. 2016; He et al. 2017; Verhoeven et al. 2017; Borchard et al. 2019), reduced nitrogen fertiliser requirements due to reduced nitrogen leaching and volatilisation from soils (Liu et al. 2019; Borchard et al. 2019), and reduced GHG emissions from compost when biochar is added (Agyarko-Mintah et al. 2017; Wu et al. 2017). Biochar application to paddy rice has resulted in substantial reductions (20–40% on average) in N_2O (Song et al. 2016; Awad et al. 2018; Liu et al. 2018) (Section 7.4.3.5) and smaller reduction in CH_4 emissions (Song et al. 2016; Kammann et al. 2017; Kim et al. 2017a; He et al. 2017; Awad et al. 2018). Potential co-benefits include yield increases particularly in sandy and acidic soils with low cation exchange capacity (Woolf et al. 2016; Jeffery et al. 2017); increased soil water-holding capacity (Omondi et al. 2016), nitrogen use efficiency (Liu et al. 2019; Borchard et al. 2019), biological nitrogen fixation (Van Zwieten et al. 2015); adsorption of organic pollutants and heavy metals (e.g., Silvani et al. 2019); odour reduction from manure handling (e.g., Hwang et al. 2018) and managing forest fuel loads (Puettmann et al. 2020). Due to its dark colour, biochar could decrease soil albedo (Meyer et al. 2012), though this is insignificant under recommended rates and application methods. Biochar could reduce enteric CH_4 emissions when fed to ruminants (Section 7.4.3.4). Barriers to upscaling include insufficient investment, limited large-scale production facilities, high production costs at small scale, lack of agreed approach to monitoring, reporting and verification, and limited knowledge, standardisation and quality control, restricting user confidence (Gwenzi et al. 2015).

Conclusions from AR5 and IPCC Special Reports (SR1.5, SROCC and SRCCL); mitigation potential, costs, and pathways. Biochar is discussed as a mitigation option in AR5 and CDR strategy in the SR1.5. Consideration of potential was limited as biochar is not included in IAMs. The SRCCL estimated mitigation potential of 0.03–6.6 $GtCO_2$-eq yr^{-1} by 2050 based on studies with widely varying assumptions, definitions of potential, and scope of mitigation processes included (SRCCL, Chapters 2 and 4: (Roberts et al. 2010; Pratt and Moran 2010; Hristov et al. 2013; Lee and Day 2013; Dickie et al. 2014a; Hawken 2017; Fuss et al. 2018; Powell and Lenton 2012; Woolf et al. 2010).

Developments since AR5 and IPCC Special Reports (SR1.5, SROCC and SRCCL). Developments include mechanistic understanding of 'negative priming' and biochar-soil-microbes-plant interactions (DeCiucies et al. 2018; Fang et al. 2019). Indirect climate benefits are associated with persistent yield response to biochar (Kätterer et al. 2019; Ye et al. 2020), improved crop water use efficiency (Du et al. 2018; Gao et al. 2020) and reduced GHG and ammonia emissions from compost and manure (Sanchez-Monedero et al. 2018; Bora et al. 2020a,b; Zhao et al. 2020). A quantification method based on biochar properties is included in the IPCC guidelines for NGHGIs (Domke et al. 2019). Studies report a range of biochar responses, from positive to occasionally adverse impacts, including on GHG emissions, and identify risks (Tisserant and Cherubini 2019). This illustrates the expected variability (Lehmann and Rillig 2014) of responses, which depend on the biochar type and climatic and edaphic characteristics of the site (Zygourakis 2017). Biochar properties vary with feedstock, production conditions and post-production treatments, so mitigation and agronomic benefits are maximised when biochars are chosen to suit the application context (Mašek et al. 2018). A recent assessment finds greatest economic potential (up to USD100 tCO_2^{-1}) between 2020 and 2050 to be in Asia and the Pacific (793 $MtCO_2$ yr^{-1}) followed by Developed Countries (447 $MtCO_2$ yr^{-1}) (Roe et al. 2021). Mitigation through biochar will be greatest where biochar is applied to responsive soils (acidic, low fertility), where soil N_2O emissions are high (intensive horticulture, irrigated crops), and where the syngas co-product displaces fossil fuels. Due to the early stage of commercialisation, mitigation estimates are based pilot-scale facilities, leading to uncertainty. However, the long-term persistence of biochar carbon in soils has been widely studied (Singh et al. 2012; Fang et al. 2019; Zimmerman and Ouyang 2019). The greatest uncertainty is the availability of sustainably-sourced biomass for biochar production.

Critical assessment and conclusion. Biochar has significant mitigation potential through CDR and emissions reduction, and can also improve soil properties, enhancing productivity and resilience to climate change (*medium agreement, robust evidence*). There is *medium evidence* that biochar has a technical potential of 2.6 (0.2–6.6) $GtCO_2$-eq yr^{-1}, of which 1.1 (0.3–1.8) $GtCO_2$-eq yr^{-1} is available up to USD100 tCO_2^{-1}. However, mitigation and agronomic co-benefits depend strongly on biochar properties and the soil to which biochar is applied (*strong agreement, robust evidence*). While biochar could provide moderate to large mitigation potential, it is not yet included in IAMs, which has restricted comparison and integration with other CDR strategies.

7.4.3.3   Agroforestry

Activities, co-benefits, risks and implementation opportunities and barriers. Agroforestry is a set of diverse land management systems that integrate trees and shrubs with crops and/or livestock in space and/or time. Agroforestry accumulates carbon in woody vegetation and soil (Ramachandran Nair et al. 2010) and offers multiple co-benefits such as increased land productivity, diversified livelihoods, reduced soil erosion, improved water quality, and more hospitable regional climates (Ellison et al. 2017; Kuyah et al. 2019; Mbow et al. 2020; Zhu et al. 2020). Incorporation of trees and shrubs in agricultural systems, however, can affect food production, biodiversity, local hydrology and contribute to social inequality (Amadu et al. 2020; Fleischman et al. 2020; Holl and Brancalion 2020). To minimise risks and maximise co-benefits, agroforestry should be implemented as part of support systems that deliver tools, and information to increase farmers' agency. This may include reforming policies, strengthening extension systems and creating market opportunities that enable adoption (Jamnadass et al. 2020; Sendzimir et al. 2011; P. Smith et al. 2019a). Consideration of carbon sequestration in the context of food and fuel production, as well as environmental co-benefits at the farm, local, and regional scales can further help support decisions to plant, regenerate and maintain agroforestry systems (Kumar and Nair 2011; Miller et al. 2020). In spite of the advantages, biophysical and socio-economic factors can limit the adoption (Pattanayak et al. 2003). Contextual factors may include, but are not limited to; water availability, soil fertility, seed and germplasm access, land policies and tenure systems affecting farmer agency, access to credit, and to information regarding the optimum species for a given location.

Conclusions from AR5 and IPCC Special Reports (SR1.5, SROCC and SRCCL); mitigation potential, costs, and pathways. The SRCCL estimated the global technical mitigation potential of agroforestry, with medium confidence, to be between 0.08 and 5.6 $GtCO_2$-eq yr^{-1} by 2050 (Griscom et al. 2017; Dickie et al. 2014a; Zomer et al. 2016; Hawken 2017). Estimates are derived from syntheses of potential area available for various agroforestry systems, for example, windbreaks, farmer managed natural regeneration, and alley cropping and average annual rates of carbon accumulation. The cost-effective economic potential, also with medium confidence, is more limited at 0.3–2.4 $GtCO_2$-eq yr^{-1} (Zomer et al. 2016; Griscom et al. 2017; Roe et al. 2019). Despite this potential, agroforestry is currently not considered in integrated assessment models used for mitigation pathways (Section 7.5).

Developments since AR5 and IPCC Special Reports (SR1.5, SROCC and SRCCL). Updated estimates of agroforestry's technical mitigation potential and synthesised estimates of carbon sequestration across agroforestry systems have since been published. The most recent global analysis estimates technical potential of 9.4 $GtCO_2$-eq yr^{-1} (Chapman et al. 2020) of agroforestry on 1.87 and 1.89 billion ha of crop and pasture lands below median carbon content, respectively. This estimate is at least 68% greater than the largest estimate reported in the SRCCL (Hawken 2017) and represents a new conservative upper bound as Chapman et al. (2020) only accounted for above-ground carbon. Considering both above- and below-ground carbon of windbreaks, alley cropping and silvopastoral systems at a more limited areal extent (Griscom et al. 2020), the economic potential of agroforestry was estimated to be only about 0.8 $GtCO_2$-eq yr^{-1}. Variation in estimates primarily result from assumptions on the agroforestry systems including, extent of implementation and estimated carbon sequestration potential when converting to agroforestry.

Regional estimates of mitigation potential are scant with agroforestry options differing significantly by geography (Feliciano et al. 2018). For example, multi-strata shaded coffee and cacao are successful in the humid tropics (Somarriba et al. 2013; Blaser et al. 2018), silvopastoral systems are prevalent in Latin American (Peters et al. 2013; Landholm et al. 2019) while agrosilvopastoral systems, shelterbelts, hedgerows, and windbreaks are common in Europe (Joffre et al. 1988; Rigueiro-Rodriguez 2009). At the field scale, agroforestry accumulates between 0.59 and 6.24 t ha^{-1} yr^{-1} of carbon above-ground. Below-ground carbon often constitutes 25% or more of the potential carbon gains in agroforestry systems (De Stefano and Jacobson 2018; Cardinael et al. 2018). Roe et al. (2021) estimate greatest regional economic (up to USD100 tCO_2^{-1}) mitigation potential for the period 2020–2050 to be in Asia and the Pacific (368.4 $MtCO_2$-eq yr^{-1}) and Developed Countries (264.7 $MtCO_2$-eq yr^{-1}).

Recent research has also highlighted co-benefits and more precisely identified implementation barriers. In addition to aforementioned co-benefits, evidence now shows that agroforestry can improve soil health, regarding infiltration and structural stability (Muchane et al. 2020); reduces ambient temperatures and crop heat stress (Arenas-Corraliza et al. 2018; Sida et al. 2018); increases groundwater recharge in drylands when managed at moderate density (Ilstedt et al. 2016; Bargués-Tobella et al. 2020); positively influences human health (Rosenstock et al. 2019); and can improve dietary diversity (McMullin et al. 2019). Along with previously mentioned barriers, low social capital, assets, and labour availability have been identified as pertinent to adoption. Practically all barriers are interdependent and subject to the context of implementation.

Critical assessment and conclusion. There is medium confidence that agroforestry has a technical potential of 4.1 (0.3–9.4) $GtCO_2$-eq yr^{-1} for the period 2020–2050, of which 0.8 (0.4–1.1) $GtCO_2$-eq yr^{-1} is available at USD100 tCO_2^{-1}. Despite uncertainty around global estimates due to regional preferences for management systems, suitable land availability, and growing conditions, there is high confidence in agroforestry's mitigation potential at the field scale. With countless options for farmers and land managers to implement agroforestry, there is medium confidence in the feasibility of achieving estimated regional mitigation potential. Appropriately matching agroforestry options, to local biophysical and social contexts is important in maximising mitigation and co-benefits, while avoiding risks (Sinclair and Coe 2019).

Box 7.3 | Case Study: Agroforestry in Brazil – CANOPIES

Summary
Brazilian farmers are integrating trees into their croplands in various ways, ranging from simple to highly complex agroforestry systems. While complex systems are more effective in the mitigation of climate change, trade-offs with scalability need to be resolved for agroforestry systems to deliver on their potential. The Brazilian-Dutch CANOPIES project (Janssen 2020) is exploring transition pathways to agroforestry systems optimised for local ecological and socio-economic conditions.

Background
The climate change mitigation potential of agroforestry systems is widely recognised (Zomer et al. 2016; FAO 2017b) and Brazilian farmers and researchers are pioneering diverse ways of integrating trees into croplands, from planting rows of eucalyptus trees in pastures up to highly complex agroforests consisting of >30 crop and tree species. The degree of complexity influences the multiple functions that farmers and societies can attain from agroforestry: the more complex it is, the more it resembles a natural forest with associated benefits for its carbon storage capacity and its habitat quality for biodiversity (Santos et al. 2019). However, trade-offs exist between the complexity and scalability of agroforestry as complex systems rely on intensive manual labour to achieve high productivity (Tscharntke et al. 2011). To date, mechanisation of structurally diverse agroforests is scarce and hence, efficiencies of scale are difficult to achieve.

Case description
These synergies and trade-offs between complexity, multifunctionality and scalability are studied in the CANOPIES (Co-existence of Agriculture and Nature: Optimisation and Planning of Integrated Ecosystem Services) project, a collaboration between Wageningen University (NL), the University of São Paulo and EMBRAPA (both Brazil). Soil and management data are collected on farms of varying complexity to evaluate carbon sequestration and other ecosystem services, economic performance and labour demands.

Interactions and limitations
The trade-off between complexity and labour demand is less pronounced in EMBRAPA's integrated crop-livestock-forestry (ICLF) systems, where grains and pasture are planted between widely spaced tree rows. Here, barriers for implementation relate mostly to livestock and grain farmers' lack of knowledge on forestry management and financing mechanisms[5] (Gil et al. 2015). Additionally, linking these financing mechanisms to carbon sequestration remains a Monitoring, Reporting and Verification challenge (Smith et al. 2020b).

Box 7.3 (continued)

Lessons
Successful examples of how more complex agroforestry can be upscaled do exist in Brazil. For example, on farm trials and consistent investments over several years have enabled Rizoma Agro to develop a citrus production system that integrates commercial and native trees in a large-scale multi-layered agroforestry system. The success of their transition resulted in part from their corporate structure that allowed them to tap into the certified Green Bonds market (CBI 2020). However, different transition strategies need to be developed for family farmers and their distinct socio-economic conditions.

7.4.3.4   Enteric Fermentation

Activities, co-benefits, risks and implementation opportunities and barriers. Mitigating CH_4 emissions from enteric fermentation can be direct (i.e., targeting ruminal methanogenesis and emissions per animal or unit of feed consumed) or indirect, by increasing production efficiency (i.e., reducing emission intensity per unit of product). Measures can be classified as those relating to (i) feeding, (ii) supplements, additives and vaccines, and (iii) livestock breeding and wider husbandry (Jia et al. 2019). Co-benefits include enhanced climate change adaptation and increased food security associated with improved livestock breeding (Smith et al. 2014). Risks include mitigation persistence, ecological impacts associated with improving feed quality and supply, or potential toxicity and animal welfare issues concerning feed additives. Implementation barriers include feeding/administration constraints, the stage of development of measures, legal restrictions on emerging technologies and negative impacts, such as the previously described risks (Smith et al. 2014; Jia et al. 2019; P. Smith et al. 2019a).

Conclusions from AR5 and IPCC Special Reports (SR1.5, SROCC and SRCCL); mitigation potential, costs, and pathways. The AR5 indicated medium (5–15%) technical mitigation potential from both feeding and breeding related measures (Smith et al. 2014). More recently, the SRCCL estimated with *medium confidence*, a global potential of 0.12–1.18 $GtCO_2$-eq yr^{-1} between 2020 and 2050, with the range reflecting technical, economic and sustainability constraints (SRCCL, Chapter 2: Hristov et al. 2013; Dickie et al. 2014a; Herrero et al. 2016; Griscom et al. 2017). The underlying literature used a mixture of IPCC GWP100 values for CH_4, preventing conversion of CO_2-eq to CH_4. Improved livestock feeding and breeding were included in IAM emission pathway scenarios within the SRCCL and SR1.5, although it was suggested that the full mitigation potential of enteric CH_4 measures is not captured in current models (Rogelj et al. 2018b; IPCC 2018).

Developments since AR5 and IPCC Special Reports (SR1.5, SROCC and SRCCL). Recent reviews generally identify the same measures as those outlined in the SRCCL, with the addition of early life manipulation of the ruminal biome (Grossi et al. 2019; Eckard and Clark 2020; Thompson and Rowntree 2020; Beauchemin et al. 2020; Ku-Vera et al. 2020; Honan et al. 2021). There is *robust evidence* and *high agreement* that chemically synthesised inhibitors are promising emerging near-term measures (Patra 2016; Jayanegara et al. 2018; Van Wesemael et al. 2019; Beauchemin et al.

2020) with high (e.g., 16–70% depending on study) mitigation potential reported (e.g., Hristov et al. 2015; McGinn et al. 2019; Melgar et al. 2020) and commercial availability expected within two years in some countries (Reisinger et al. 2021). However, their mitigation persistence (McGinn et al. 2019), cost (Carroll and Daigneault 2019; Alvarez-Hess et al. 2019) and public acceptance (Jayasundara et al. 2016) or regulatory approval is currently unclear while administration in pasture-based systems is likely to be challenging (Patra et al. 2017; Leahy et al. 2019). Research into other inhibitors/feeds containing inhibitory compounds, such as macroalga or seaweed (Chagas et al. 2019; Kinley et al. 2020; Roque et al. 2019), shows promise, although concerns have been raised regarding palatability, toxicity, environmental impacts and the development of industrial-scale supply chains (Abbott et al. 2020; Vijn et al. 2020). In the absence of CH_4 vaccines, which are still under development (Reisinger et al. 2021) pasture-based and non-intensive systems remain reliant on increasing production efficiency (Beauchemin et al. 2020). Breeding of low emitting animals may play an important role and is a subject under ongoing research (Pickering et al. 2015; Jonker et al. 2018; López-Paredes et al. 2020).

Approaches differ regionally, with more focus on direct, technical options in Developed Countries, and improved efficiency in developing countries (Caro Torres et al. 2016; Mottet et al. 2017b; MacLeod et al. 2018; Frank et al. 2018). A recent assessment finds greatest economic (up to USD100 tCO_2-eq^{-1}) potential (using the IPCC AR4 GWP100 value for CH_4) for 2020–2050 in Asia and the Pacific (32.9 $MtCO_2$-eq yr^{-1}) followed by Developed Countries (25.5 $MtCO_2$-eq yr^{-1}) (Roe et al. 2021). Despite numerous country and sub-sector specific studies, most of which include cost analysis (Hasegawa and Matsuoka 2012; Hoa et al. 2014; Jilani et al. 2015; Eory et al. 2015; Pradhan et al. 2017; Pellerin et al. 2017; Ericksen and Crane 2018; Habib and Khan 2018; Kashangaki and Ericksen 2018; Salmon et al. 2018; Brandt et al. 2019b; Kiggundu et al. 2019; Kavanagh et al. 2019; Mosnier et al. 2019; Pradhan et al. 2019; Sapkota et al. 2019; Carroll and Daigneault 2019; Leahy et al. 2019; Dioha and Kumar 2020), sectoral assessment of regional technical and notably economic (Beach et al. 2015; USEPA 2019) potential is restricted by lack comprehensive and comparable data. Therefore, verification of regional estimates indicated by global assessments is challenging. Feed quality improvement, which may have considerable potential in developing countries (Caro et al. 2016; Mottet et al. 2017a), may have negative wider impacts. For example, potential land-use change and greater emissions associated with production of concentrates (Brandt et al. 2019b).

Critical review and conclusion. Based on studies to date, using a range of IPCC GWP100 values for CH_4, there is *medium confidence* that activities to reduce enteric CH_4 emissions have a global technical potential of 0.8 (0.2–1.2) $GtCO_2$-eq yr^{-1}, of which 0.2 (0.1–0.3) $GtCO_2$-eq yr^{-1} is available up to USD100 tCO_2-eq^{-1} (Figure 7.11). The CO_2-eq value may also slightly differ if the GWP100 IPCC AR6 CH_4 value was uniformly applied within calculations. Lack of comparable country and sub-sector studies to assess the context applicability of measures, associated costs and realistic adoption likelihood, prevents verification of estimates.

7.4.3.5 Improve Rice Management

Activities, co-benefits, risks and implementation opportunities and barriers. Emissions from rice cultivation mainly concern CH_4 associated with anaerobic conditions, although N_2O emission also occur via nitrification and denitrification processes. Measures to reduce CH_4 and N_2O emissions include (i) improved water management (e.g., single drainage and multiple drainage practices), (ii) improved residue management, (iii) improved fertiliser application (e.g., using slow release fertiliser and nutrient specific application), and (iv) soil amendments (including biochar and organic amendments) (Pandey et al. 2014; Kim et al. 2017b; Yagi et al. 2020; Sriphirom et al. 2020). These measures not only have mitigation potential but can improve water use efficiency, reduce overall water use, enhance drought adaptation and overall system resilience, improve yield, reduce production costs from seed, pesticide, pumping and labour, increase farm income, and promote sustainable development (Quynh and Sander 2015; Yamaguchi et al. 2017; Tran et al. 2018; Sriphirom et al. 2019). However, in terms of mitigation of CH_4 and N_2O, antagonistic effects can occur, whereby water management can enhance N_2O emissions due to creation of alternate wet and dry conditions (Sriphirom et al. 2019), with trade-offs between CH_4 and N_2O during the drying period potentially offsetting some mitigation benefits. Barriers to adoption may include site-specific limitations regarding soil type, percolation and seepage rates or fluctuations in precipitation, water canal or irrigation infrastructure, paddy surface level and rice field size, and social factors including farmer perceptions, pump ownership, and challenges in synchronising water management between neighbours and pumping stations (Quynh and Sander 2015; Yamaguchi et al. 2017; Yamaguchi et al. 2019).

Conclusions from AR5 and IPCC Special Reports (SR1.5, SROCC and SRCCL); mitigation potential, costs, and pathways. The AR5 outlined emissions from rice cultivation of 0.49–0.723 $GtCO_2$-eq yr^{-1} in 2010 with an average annual growth of 0.4% yr^{-1}. The SRCCL estimated a global mitigation potential from improved rice cultivation of 0.08–0.87 $GtCO_2$-eq yr^{-1} between 2020 and 2050, with the range representing the difference between technical and economic constraints, types of activities included (e.g., improved water management and straw residue management) and GHGs considered (Dickie et al. 2014a; Beach et al. 2015; Paustian et al. 2016; Griscom et al. 2017; Hawken 2017) (SRCCL, Chapter 2).

Developments since AR5 and IPCC Special Reports (SR1.5, SROCC and SRCCL). Since AR5 and the SRCCL, studies on mitigation have principally focused on water and nutrient management practices with the aim of improving overall sustainability as well as measurements of site-specific emissions to help improve the resolution of regional estimates. Intensity of emissions show considerable spatial and temporal variation, dependent on site specific factors including degradation of soil organic matter, management of water levels in the field, the types and amount of fertilisers applied, rice variety and local cultivation practices. Variation in CH_4 emissions have been found to range from 0.5–41.8 mg m^2 hr^{-1} in South-East Asia (Sander et al. 2014; Chidthaisong et al. 2018; Setyanto et al. 2018; Sibayan et al. 2018; J. Wang et al. 2018; Maneepitak et al. 2019), 0.5–37.0 mg m^2 hr^{-1} in Southern and Eastern Asia (Zhang et al. 2010; Wang et al. 2012; Oo et al. 2018; J. Wang et al. 2018; Takakai et al. 2020), and 0.5–10.4 mg m^2 hr^{-1} in North America (J. Wang et al. 2018). Current studies on emissions of N_2O also showed high variation in the range of 0.13–654 ug/m^2/hr (Akiyama et al. 2005; Islam et al. 2018; Kritee et al. 2018; Zschornack et al. 2018; Oo et al. 2018).

Recent studies on water management have highlighted the potential to mitigate GHG emissions, while also enhancing water use efficiency (Tran et al. 2018). A meta-analysis on multiple drainage systems found that Alternative Wetting and Drying (AWD) with irrigation management, can reduce CH_4 emissions by 20–30% and water use by 25.7%, though this resulted in a slight yield reduction (5.4%) (Carrijo et al. 2017). Other studies have described improved yields associated with AWD (Tran et al. 2018). Water management for both single and multiple drainage can (most likely) reduce methane emissions by about 35% but increase N_2O emissions by about 20% (Yagi et al. 2020). However, N_2O emissions occur only under dry conditions, therefore total reduction in terms of net GWP is approximately 30%. Emissions of N_2O are higher during dry seasons (Yagi et al. 2020) and depend on site specific factors as well as the quantity of fertiliser and organic matter inputs into the paddy rice system. Variability of N_2O emissions from single and multiple drainage can range from 0.06–33 kg/ha (Hussain et al. 2015; Kritee et al. 2018). AWD in Vietnam was found to reduce both CH_4 and N_2O emissions by 29–30 and 26–27% respectively with the combination of net GWP about 30% as compared to continuous flooding (Tran et al. 2018). Overall, greatest average economic mitigation potential (up to USD100 tCO_2-eq^{-1}) between 2020 and 2050 is estimated to be in Asia and the Pacific (147.2 $MtCO_2$-eq yr^{-1}) followed by Latin America and the Caribbean (8.9 $MtCO_2$-eq yr^{-1}) using the IPCC AR4 GWP100 value for CH_4 (Roe et al. 2021).

Critical assessment and conclusion. There is *medium confidence* that improved rice management has a technical potential of 0.3 (0.1–0.8) $GtCO_2$-eq yr^{-1} between 2020 and 2050, of which 0.2 (0.05–0.3) $GtCO_2$-eq yr^{-1} is available up to USD100 tCO_2-eq^{-1} (Figure 7.11). Improving rice cultivation practices will not only reduce GHG emissions, but also improve production sustainability in terms of resource utilisation including water consumption and fertiliser application. However, emission reductions show high variability and are dependent on site specific conditions and cultivation practices.

7.4.3.6   Crop Nutrient Management

Activities, co-benefits, risks and implementation opportunities and barriers. Improved crop nutrient management can reduce N_2O emissions from cropland soils. Practices include optimising fertiliser application delivery, rates and timing, utilising different fertiliser types (i.e., organic manures, composts and synthetic forms), and using slow or controlled-released fertilisers or nitrification inhibitors (Smith et al. 2014; Griscom et al. 2017; P. Smith et al. 2019a). In addition to individual practices, integrated nutrient management that combines crop rotations including intercropping, nitrogen biological fixation, reduced tillage, use of cover crops, manure and bio-fertiliser application, soil testing and comprehensive nitrogen management plans, is suggested as central for optimising fertiliser use, enhancing nutrient uptake and potentially reducing N_2O emissions (Bationo et al. 2012; Lal et al. 2018; Bolinder et al. 2020; Jensen et al. 2020; Namatsheve et al. 2020). Such practices may generate additional mitigation by indirectly reducing synthetic fertiliser manufacturing requirements and associated emissions, though such mitigation is accounted for in the Industry Sector and not considered in this chapter. Tailored nutrient management approaches, such as 4R nutrient stewardship, are implemented in contrasting farming systems and contexts and supported by best management practices to balance and match nutrient supply with crop requirements, provide greater stability in fertiliser performance and to minimise N_2O emissions and nutrient losses from fields and farms (Fixen 2020; Maaz et al. 2021). Co-benefits of improved nutrient management can include enhanced soil quality (notably when manure, crop residues or compost is utilised), carbon sequestration in soils and biomass, soil water holding capacity, adaptation capacity, crop yields, farm incomes, water quality (from reduced nitrate leaching and eutrophication), air quality (from reduced ammonia emissions) and in certain cases, it may facilitate land sparing (Sapkota et al. 2014; Johnston and Bruulsema 2014; Zhang et al. 2017; P. Smith et al. 2019a; Mbow et al. 2019).

A potential risk under certain circumstances, is yield reduction, while implementation of practices should consider current soil nutrient status. There are significant regional imbalances, with some regions experiencing nutrient surpluses from over fertilisation and others, nutrient shortages and chronic deficiencies (FAO 2021e). Additionally, depending on context, practices may be inaccessible, expensive or require expertise to implement (Hedley 2015; Benson and Mogues 2018) while impacts of climate change may influence nutrient use efficiency (Amouzou et al. 2019) and therefore, mitigation potential.

Conclusions from AR5 and IPCC Special Reports (SR1.5, SROCC and SRCCL); mitigation potential, costs, and pathways. The SRCCL broadly identified the same practices as outlined in AR5 and estimated that improved cropland nutrient management could mitigate between 0.03 and 0.71 $GtCO_2$-eq yr^{-1} between 2020 and 2050 (SRCCL Chapter 2) (Dickie et al. 2014a; Beach et al. 2015; Paustian et al. 2016; Griscom et al. 2017; Hawken 2017).

Developments since AR5 and IPCC Special Reports (SR1.5, SROCC and SRCCL). Research since the SRCCL highlights the mitigation potential and co-benefits of adopting improved nutrient management strategies, notably precision fertiliser application methods and nutrient expert systems, and applicability in both large-scale mechanised and small-scale systems (USEPA 2019; Hijbeek et al. 2019; Griscom et al. 2020; Tian et al. 2020; Aryal et al. 2020; Sapkota et al. 2021). Improved crop nutrient management is feasible in all regions, but effectiveness is context dependent. Sub-Saharan Africa has one of the lowest global fertiliser consumption rates, with increased fertiliser use suggested as necessary to meet projected future food requirements (Mueller et al. 2012; ten Berge et al. 2019; Adam et al. 2020; Falconnier et al. 2020). Fertiliser use in Developed Countries is already high (Figure 7.10) with increased nutrient use efficiency among the most promising mitigation measures (Roe et al. 2019; Hijbeek et al. 2019). Considering that Asia and Pacific, and Developed Countries accounted for the greatest share of global nitrogen fertiliser use, it is not surprising that these regions are estimated to have greatest economic mitigation potential (up to USD100 tCO_2-eq^{-1}) between 2020 and 2050, at 161.8 and 37.1 $MtCO_2$-eq yr^{-1} respectively (using the IPCC AR4 GWP100 value for N_2O) (Roe et al. 2021).

Critical assessment and conclusion. There is *medium confidence* that crop nutrient management has a technical potential of 0.3 (0.06–0.7) $GtCO_2$-eq yr^{-1} of which 0.2 (0.05–0.6) $GtCO_2$-eq yr^{-1} is available up to USD100 tCO_2-eq^{-1}. This value is based on GWP100 using a mixture of IPCC values for N_2O and may slightly differ if calculated using AR6 values. The development of national roadmaps for sustainable fertiliser (nutrient) management can help in scaling-up related practices and in realising this potential. Crop nutrient management measures can contribute not only to mitigation, but food and nutrition security and wider environmental sustainability goals.

Box 7.4 | Case Study: The Climate-smart Village Approach

Summary

The climate-smart villages (CSV) approach aims to generate local knowledge, with the involvement of farmers, researchers, practitioners, and governments, on climate change adaptation and mitigation while improving productivity, food security, and farmers' livelihoods (Aggarwal et al. 2018). This knowledge feeds a global network that includes 36 climate-smart villages in South and South-East Asia, West and East Africa, and Latin America.

Background

It is expected that agricultural production systems across the world will change in response to climate change, posing significant challenges to the livelihoods and food security of millions of people (Kennedy et al. 2014). Maintaining agricultural growth while minimising climate shocks is crucial to building a resilient food production system and meeting sustainable development goals in vulnerable countries.

Case description

The CSV approach seeks an integrated vision so that sustainable rural development is the final goal for rural communities. At the same time, it fosters the understanding of climate change with the implementation of adaptation and mitigation actions, as much as possible. Rural communities and local stakeholders are the leaders of this process, where scientists facilitate their knowledge to be useful for the communities and learn at the same time about challenges but also the capacity those communities have built through time. The portfolio includes weather-smart activities, water-smart practices, seed/breed smart, carbon-/nutrient-smart practices, and institutional-/market-smart activities.

Interactions and limitations

The integration of technologies and services that are suitable for the local conditions resulted in many gains for food security and adaptation and for mitigation where appropriate. It was also shown that, in all regions, there is considerable yield advantage when a portfolio of technologies is used, rather than the isolated use of technologies (Govaerts et al. 2005; Zougmoré et al. 2014). Moreover, farmers are using research results to promote their products as climate-smart leading to increases in their income (Acosta-Alba et al. 2019). However, climatic risk sites and socio-economic conditions together with a lack of resource availability are key issues constraining agriculture across all five regions.

Lessons

i. Understanding the priorities, context, challenges, capacity, and characteristics of the territory and the communities regarding climate, as well as the environmental and socio-economic dimensions, is the first step. Then, understanding climate vulnerability in their agricultural systems based on scientific data but also listening to their experience will set the pathway to identify climate-smart agriculture (CSA) options (practices and technologies) to reduce such vulnerability.

ii. Building capacity is also a critical element of the CSV approach, rural families learn about the practices and technologies in a neighbour's house, and as part of the process, families commit to sharing their knowledge with other families, to start a scaling-out process within the communities. Understanding the relationship between climate and their crop is key, as well as the use of weather forecasts to plan their agricultural activities.

The assessment of the implementation of the CSA options should be done together with community leaders to understand changes in livelihoods and climate vulnerability. Also, knowledge appropriation by community leaders has led to farmer-to-farmer knowledge exchange within and outside the community (Ortega Fernandez and Martínez-Barón 2018).

7.4.3.7   Manure Management

Activities, co-benefits, risks and implementation opportunities and barriers. Manure management measures aim to mitigate CH_4 and N_2O emissions from manure storage and deposition. Mitigation of N_2O considers both direct and indirect (i.e., conversion of ammonia and nitrate to N_2O) sources. According to the SRCCL, measures may include (i) anaerobic digestion, (ii) applying nitrification or urease inhibitors to stored manure or urine patches, (iii) composting,

(iv) improved storage and application practices, (v) grazing practices and (vi) alteration of livestock diets to reduce nitrogen excretion (Mbow et al. 2019; Jia et al. 2019). Implementation of manure management with other livestock and soil management measures can enhance system resilience, sustainability, food security and help prevent land degradation (Smith et al. 2014; Mbow et al. 2019; P. Smith et al. 2019a), while potentially benefiting the localised environment, for example, regarding water quality (Di and Cameron 2016). Risks include increased N_2O emission from the application

7

of manure to poorly drained or wet soils, trade-offs between N_2O and ammonia emissions and potential eco-toxicity associated with some measures.

Conclusions from AR5 and IPCC Special Reports (SR1.5, SROCC and SRCCL); mitigation potential, costs, and pathways. The AR5 reported manure measures to have high (>10%) mitigation potential. The SRCCL estimated a technical global mitigation potential between 2020 and 2050 of 0.01–0.26 $GtCO_2$-eq yr^{-1}, with the range depending on economic and sustainable capacity (Dickie et al. 2014a; Herrero et al. 2016) (SRCCL, Chapter 2). Conversion of estimates to native units is restricted as a mixture of GWP100 values was used in underlying studies. Measures considered were typically more suited to confined production systems (Jia et al. 2019; Mbow et al. 2019), while improved manure management is included within IAM emission pathways (Rogelj et al. 2018b).

Developments since AR5 and IPCC Special Reports (SR1.5, SROCC and SRCCL). Research published since SRCCL broadly focuses on measures relevant to intensive or confined systems (e.g., (Hunt et al. 2019; Kavanagh et al. 2019; Sokolov et al. 2020; Im et al. 2020; Adghim et al. 2020; Mostafa et al. 2020), highlighting co-benefits and risks. For example, measures may enhance nutrient recovery, fertiliser value (Sefeedpari et al. 2019; Ba et al. 2020; Yao et al. 2020) and secondary processes such as biogas production (Shin et al. 2019). However, the potential antagonistic relationship between GHG and ammonia mitigation and need for appropriate management is emphasised (Aguirre-Villegas et al. 2019; Grossi et al. 2019; Kupper et al. 2020; Ba et al. 2020). In some circumstances, fugitive emissions may reduce the potential mitigation benefits of biogas production (Scheutz and Fredenslund 2019; Bakkaloglu et al. 2021), while high implementation cost is identified as an adoption barrier, notably of anaerobic digestion (Liu and Liu 2018; Niles and Wiltshire 2019; Ndambi et al. 2019; Ackrill and Abdo 2020; Adghim et al. 2020). Nitrification inhibitors have been found to be effective at reducing N_2O emissions from pasture deposited urine (López-Aizpún et al. 2020), although the use of nitrification inhibitors is restricted in some jurisdictions due to concerns regarding residues in food products (Di and Cameron 2016; Eckard and Clark 2020) while *limited evidence* suggests eco-toxicity risk under certain circumstances (Kösler et al. 2019). Some forage crops may naturally contain inhibitory substances (Simon et al. 2019, 2020; de Klein et al. 2020), though this warrants further research (Podolyan et al. 2020; Gardiner et al. 2020).

Country specific studies provide insight into regionally applicable measures, with emphasis on small-scale anaerobic digestion (e.g., dome digesters), solid manure coverage and daily manure spreading in Asia and the Pacific, and Africa (Hasegawa and Matsuoka 2012; Hoa et al. 2014; Jilani et al. 2015; Hasegawa et al. 2016; Pradhan et al. 2017; Ericksen and Crane 2018; Pradhan et al. 2019; Kiggundu et al. 2019; Dioha and Kumar 2020). Tank/lagoon covers, large-scale anaerobic digestion, improved application timing, nitrogen inhibitor application to urine patches, soil-liquid separation, reduced livestock nitrogen intake, trailing shoe, band or injection slurry spreading and acidification are emphasised in Developed Countries (Kaparaju and Rintala 2011; Eory et al. 2015; Pape et al. 2016; Jayasundara et al. 2016; Pellerin et al. 2017; Liu and Liu 2018; Lanigan et al. 2018; Carroll and Daigneault 2019; Eckard and Clark 2020). Using IPCC AR4 GWP100 values for CH_4 and N_2O, a recent assessment finds 69% (63.4 $MtCO_2$-eq yr^{-1}) of economic potential (up to USD100 tCO_2-eq^{-1}) between 2020–2050, to be in Developed Countries (Roe et al. 2021).

Critical assessment and conclusion. There is *medium confidence* that manure management measures have a global technical potential of 0.3 (0.1–0.5) $GtCO_2$-eq yr^{-1}, (using a range of IPCC GWP100 values for CH_4 and N_2O), of which 0.1 (0.09–0.1) $GtCO_2$-eq yr^{-1} is available at up to USD100 tCO_2-eq^{-1} (Figure 7.11). As with other non-CO_2 GHG mitigation estimates, values may slightly differ depending upon which IPCC GWP100 values were used. There is *robust evidence* and *high agreement* that there are measures that can be applied in all regions, but greatest mitigation potential is estimated in Developed Countries in more intensive and confined production systems.

Box 7.5 | Farming System Approaches and Mitigation

Introduction

There is *robust evidence* and *high agreement* that agriculture needs to change to facilitate environment conservation while maintaining and where appropriate, increase overall production. The SRCCL identified several farming system approaches, deemed alternative to conventional systems (Olsson et al. 2019; Mbow et al. 2019; L.G. Smith et al. 2019). These may incorporate several of the mitigation measures described in Section 7.4.3, while potentially also delivering environmental co-benefits. This Box assesses evidence specifically on the mitigation capacity of some such system approaches. The approaches are not mutually exclusive, may share similar principles or practices and can be complimentary. In all cases, mitigation may result from either (i) emission reductions or (ii) enhanced carbon sequestration, via combinations of management practices as outlined in Figure 1 within this Box. The approaches will have pros and cons concerning multiple factors, including mitigation, yield and co-benefits, with trade-offs subject to the diverse contexts and ways in which they are implemented.

Box 7.5 (continued)

Box 7.5, Figure 1 | Potential mitigation mechanisms and associated management practices. N = nitrogen, SOM = soil organic matter, LUC = land-use change. [a] The farming system approaches outlined are not necessarily mutually exclusive. [b] Only agricultural emissions are considered. Mitigation may also result from reduced production of fertilisers and agrochemicals. [c] Reduced emissions intensity per unit of milk/meat will only result in a reduction in absolute emissions where increased productivity facilitates a reduction in animal numbers. 1 = Altieri et al. 2015; 2 = Altieri and Nicholls 2017; 3 = Powlson et al. 2016; 4 = Corbeels et al. 2019; 5 = Lal 2015; 6 = Gonzalez-Sanchez et al. 2019; 7 = Thierfelder et al. 2017; 8 = Hendrickson et al. 2008; 9 = Weindl et al. 2015; 10 = Thornton and Herrero 2015; 11 = Lal al. 2020; 12 = Scialabba and Müller–Lindenlauf 2010; 13 = Goh 2011; 14 = IFOAM 2016.

Box 7.5 (continued)

Is there evidence that these approaches deliver mitigation?

Agroecology (AE) including Regenerative Agriculture (RA)
There is limited discussion on the mitigation potential of AE (Gliessman 2013; Altieri and Nicholls 2017), but *robust evidence* that AE can improve system resilience and bring multiple co-benefits (Altieri et al. 2015; Mbow et al. 2019; Aguilera et al. 2020; Tittonell 2020; Wanger et al. 2020) (AR6 WGII Box 5.10). *Limited evidence* concerning the mitigation capacity of AE at a system level (Saj et al. 2017; Snapp et al. 2021) makes conclusions difficult, yet studies into specific practices that may be incorporated, suggest AE may have mitigation potential (*medium confidence*) (Section 7.4.3). However, AE, that incorporates management practices used in organic farming (see below), may result in reduced yields, driving compensatory agricultural production elsewhere. Research into GHG mitigation by AE as a system and impacts of wide-scale implementation is required. Despite absence of a universally accepted definition (see Annex I), RA is gaining increasing attention and shares principles of AE. Some descriptions include carbon sequestration as a specific aim (Elevitch et al. 2018). Few studies have assessed mitigation potential of RA at a system level (e.g., Colley et al. 2020). Like AE, it is *likely* that RA can contribute to mitigation, the extent to which is currently unclear and by its case-specific design, will vary (*medium confidence*).

Conservation agriculture (CA)
The SRCCL noted both positive and inconclusive results regarding CA and soil carbon, with sustained sequestration dependent on productivity and residue returns (Jia et al. 2019; Mirzabaev et al. 2019; Mbow et al. 2019). Recent research is in broad agreement (Ogle et al. 2019; Corbeels et al. 2020, 2019; Gonzalez-Sanchez et al. 2019; Munkholm et al. 2020) with greatest mitigation potential suggested in dry regions (Sun et al. 2020). Theoretically, CA may facilitate improved nitrogen use efficiency (*limited evidence*) (Lal 2015; Powlson et al. 2016), though CA appears to have mixed effects on soil N_2O emission (Six et al. 2004; Mei et al. 2018). CA is noted for its adaptation benefits, with *wide agreement* that CA can enhance system resilience to climate related stress, notably in dry regions. There is evidence that CA can contribute to mitigation, but its contribution is depended on multiple factors including climate and residue returns (*high confidence*).

Integrated production systems (IPS)
The integration of different enterprises in space and time (e.g., diversified cropping, crop and livestock production, agroforestry), therefore facilitating interaction and transfer of recourses between systems, is suggested to enhance sustainability and adaptive capacity (Hendrickson et al. 2008; Franzluebbers et al. 2014; Lemaire et al. 2014; Weindl et al. 2015; Gil et al. 2017; Olsson et al. 2019; Peterson et al. 2020; Walkup et al. 2020; Garrett et al. 2020). Research indicates some mitigation potential, including by facilitating sustainable intensification (Box 7.11), though benefits are likely to be highly context specific (Herrero et al. 2013; Carvalho et al. 2014; Piva et al. 2014; de Figueiredo et al. 2017; Rosenstock et al. 2014; Weindl et al. 2015; Thornton and Herrero 2015; Descheemaeker et al. 2016; Lal 2020; Guenet et al. 2021). The other systems outlined within this Box may form or facilitate IPS.

Organic farming (OF)
OF can be considered a form of AE (Lampkin et al. 2017) though it is discussed separately here as it is guided by specific principles and associated regulations (Annex I). OF is perhaps noted more for potential co-benefits, such as enhanced system resilience and biodiversity promotion, than mitigation. Several studies have reviewed the emissions footprint of organic compared to conventional systems (Mondelaers et al. 2009; Tuomisto et al. 2012; Skinner et al. 2014; Meier et al. 2015; Seufert and Ramankutty 2017; Clark and Tilman 2017; Meemken and Qaim 2018; Bellassen et al. 2021). Acknowledging potential assessment limitations (Meier et al. 2015; van der Werf et al. 2020), evidence suggests organic production to typically generate lower emissions per unit of area, while emissions per unit of product vary and depend on the product (*high agreement, medium evidence*). OF has been suggested to increase soil carbon sequestration (Gattinger et al. 2012), though definitive conclusions are challenging (Leifeld et al. 2013). Fewer studies consider impacts of large-scale conversion from conventional to organic production globally. Though context specific (Seufert and Ramankutty 2017), OF is reported to typically generate lower yields (Seufert et al. 2012; De Ponti et al. 2012; Kirchmann 2019; Biernat et al. 2020). Large-scale conversion, without fundamental changes in food systems and diets (Muller et al. 2017; Theurl et al. 2020), may lead to increases in absolute emissions from land-use change, driven by greater land requirements to maintain production (L.G. Smith et al. 2019; Leifeld 2016; Meemken and Qaim 2018).

Box 7.6 | Case Study: Mitigation Options and Costs in the Indian Agricultural Sector

Objective

To assess the technical mitigation potentials of Indian agriculture and costs under a business as usual scenario (BAU) and Mitigation scenario up to 2030 (Sapkota et al. 2019).

Results

The study shows that by 2030 under BAU scenario GHG emissions from the agricultural sector in India would be 515 $MtCO_2$-eq yr^{-1} (using GWP100 and IPCC AR4 values) with a technical mitigation potential of 85.5 $MtCO_2$-eq yr^{-1} through the adoption of various mitigation practices. About 80% of the technical mitigation potential could be achieved by adopting cost-saving measures. Three mitigation options, for example, efficient use of fertiliser, zero-tillage, and rice-water management, could deliver more than 50% of the total technical abatement potential. Under the BAU scenario the projected GHG emissions from major crop and livestock species is estimated at 489 $MtCO_2$-eq in 2030, whereas under mitigation scenario GHG emissions are estimated at 410 $MtCO_2$-eq implying a technical mitigation option of about 78.67 $MtCO_2$-eq yr^{-1} (Box 7.6, Figure 1). Major sources of projected emissions under the BAU scenario, in order of importance, were cattle, rice, buffalo, and small ruminants. Although livestock production and rice cultivation account for a major share of agricultural emissions, the highest mitigation potential was observed in rice (about 36 $MtCO_2$-eq yr^{-1}) followed by buffalo (about 14 $MtCO_2$-eq yr^{-1}), wheat (about 11 $MtCO_2$-eq yr^{-1}) and cattle (about 7 $MtCO_2$-eq yr^{-1}). Crops such as cotton and sugarcane each offered mitigation potential of about 5 $MtCO_2$-eq yr^{-1} while the mitigation potential from small ruminants (goat/sheep) was about 2 $MtCO_2$-eq yr^{-1}.

Sapkota et al. (2019) also estimated the magnitude of GHG savings per year through adoption of various mitigation measures, together with the total cost and net cost per unit of CO_2-eq abated. When the additional benefits of increased yield due to adoption of the mitigation measures were considered, about 80% of the technical mitigation potential (67.5 out of 85.5 $MtCO_2$-eq) could be achieved by cost-saving measures. When yield benefits were considered, green fodder supplements to ruminant diets were the most cost-effective mitigation measure, followed by vermicomposting and improved diet management of small ruminants. Mitigation measures such as fertigation and micro-irrigation, various methods of restoring degraded land and feed additives in livestock appear to be cost-prohibitive, even when considering yield benefits, if any. The study accounted for GHG emissions at the farm level and excluded emissions arising due to processing, marketing or consumption post farm-gate. It also did not include emissions from feed production, since livestock in India mostly rely on crop by-products and concentrates. Further the potential of laser land levelling seems exaggerated which may also be redundant with already accounted potential from 'improved water management in rice'. The mitigation potential of agroecological approaches/technologies such as natural farming which is picking up in India in recent years has also been overlooked.

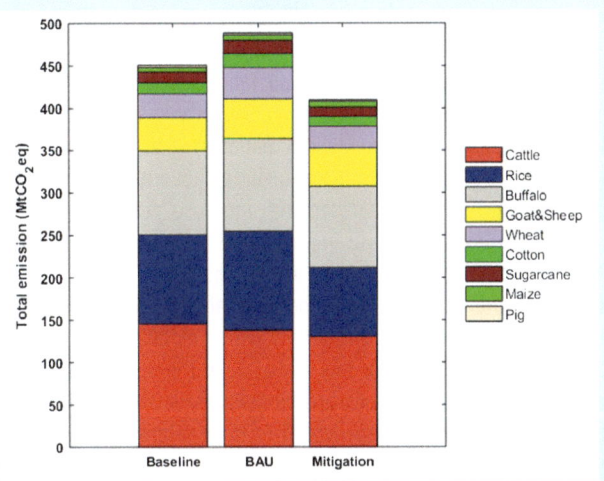

Box 7.6, Figure 1 | Contribution of various crops and livestock species to total agricultural emission in 2012 (baseline) and by 2030 under business as usual (BAU) and mitigation scenarios for Indian agricultural sector. Source: Sapkota et al. (2019). Reprinted from Science of The Total Environment, 655, Sapkota T.B. et al., Cost-effective opportunities for climate change mitigation in Indian agriculture., 2019, with permission from Elsevier.

7.4.4   Bioenergy and BECCS

Activities, co-benefits, risks and implementation opportunities and barriers. Bioenergy refers to energy products (solid, liquid and gaseous fuels, electricity, heat) derived from multiple biomass sources including organic waste, harvest residues and by-flows in the agriculture and forestry sectors, and biomass from tree plantations, agroforestry systems, lignocellulosic crops, and conventional food/feed crops. It may reduce net GHG emissions by displacing the use of coal, oil and natural gas with renewable biomass in the production of heat, electricity, and fuels. When combined with carbon capture and storage (BECCS) and biochar production, bioenergy systems may provide CDR by durably storing biogenic carbon in geological, terrestrial, or ocean reservoirs, or in products, further contributing to mitigation (Chum et al. 2011; Cabral et al. 2019; Hammar and Levihn 2020; Emenike et al. 2020; Moreira et al. 2020b; Y. Wang et al. 2020: Johnsson et al. 2020) (Section 7.4.3.2, Chapters 3, 4, 6 and 12).

This section addresses especially aspects related to land use and biomass supply for bioenergy and BECCS. The mitigation potential presented here and in Table 7.3, includes only the CDR component of

BECCS. The additional mitigation achieved from displacing fossil fuels is covered elsewhere (Chapters 6, 8, 9, 10, 11 and 12).

Modern bioenergy systems (as opposed to traditional use of fuelwood and other low-quality cooking and heating fuels) currently provide approximately 30 EJ yr^{-1} of primary energy, making up 53% of total renewable primary energy supply (IEA 2019). Bioenergy systems are commonly integrated within forest and agriculture systems that produce food, feed, lumber, paper and other bio-based products. They can also be combined with other AFOLU mitigation options: deployment of energy crops, agroforestry and A/R can provide biomass while increasing land carbon stocks (Sections 7.4.2.2 and 7.4.3.3) and anaerobic digestion of manure and wastewater, to reduce methane emissions, can produce biogas and CO_2 for storage (Section 7.4.3.7). But ill-deployment of energy crops can also cause land carbon losses (Hanssen et al. 2020) and increased biomass demand for energy could hamper other mitigation measures such as reduced deforestation and degradation (Sections 7.4.2.1).

Bioenergy and BECCS can be associated with a range of co-benefits and adverse side effects (Smith et al. 2016; Jia et al. 2019; Calvin et al. 2021) (Section 12.5). It is difficult to disentangle bioenergy development from the overall development in the AFOLU sector given its multiple interactions with food, land, and energy systems. It is therefore not possible to precisely determine the scale of bioenergy and BECCS deployment at which negative impacts outweigh benefits. Important uncertainties include governance systems, future food and biomaterials demand, land-use practices, energy systems development, climate impacts, and time scale considered when weighing negative impacts against benefits (Robledo-Abad et al. 2017; Turner et al. 2018b; Daioglou et al. 2019; Wu et al. 2019; Kalt et al. 2020; Hanssen et al. 2020; Calvin et al. 2021; Cowie et al. 2021) (SRCCL, Cross-Chapter Box 7; Box 7.7). The use of municipal organic waste, harvest residues, and biomass processing by-products as feedstock is commonly considered to have relatively lower risk, provided that associated land-use practices are sustainable (Cowie et al. 2021). Deployment of dedicated biomass production systems can have positive and negative implications on mitigation and other sustainability criteria, depending on location and previous land use, feedstock, management practice, deployment strategy and scale (Rulli et al. 2016; Popp et al. 2017; Daioglou et al. 2017; Staples et al. 2017; Carvalho et al. 2017; Humpenöder et al. 2018; Fujimori et al. 2019; Hasegawa et al. 2020; Drews et al. 2020; Schulze et al. 2020; Stenzel et al. 2020; Mouratiadou et al. 2020; Buchspies et al. 2020; Hanssen et al. 2020, IPBES 2019b) (Sections 12.5 and 17.3.3.1).

Conclusions from AR5 and IPCC Special Reports (SR1.5, SROCC and SRCCL); mitigation potential, costs, and pathways. Many more stringent mitigation scenarios in AR5 relied heavily on bioenergy and BECCS. The SR1.5 reported a range for the CDR potential of BECCS (2100) at 0.5 to 5 GtCO$_2$-eq yr^{-1} when applying constraints reflecting sustainability concerns, at a cost of 100–200 USD tCO$_2$$^{-1}$ (Fuss et al. 2018). The SRCCL reported a technical CDR potential for BECCS at 0.4–11.3 GtCO$_2$ yr^{-1} (*medium confidence*), noting that most estimates do not include socio-economic barriers, the impacts of future climate change, or non-GHG climate forcing (IPCC. 2019). The SR1.5 and SRCCL highlighted that bioenergy and BECCS can be

associated with multiple co-benefits and adverse side effects that are context specific.

Developments since AR5 and IPCC Special Reports (SR1.5, SROCC and SRCCL). The role of bioenergy and BECCS in mitigation pathways has been reduced as IAM-based studies have incorporated broader mitigation portfolios and have explored non-CO_2 emissions reduction and a wider variation of underlying assumptions about socio-economic drivers and associated energy and food demand, as well as deployment limits such as land availability for A/R and for cultivation of crops used for bioenergy and BECCS (Grubler et al. 2018; Van Vuuren et al. 2018).

Increased availability of spatially explicit data and advances in the modelling of crop productivity and land use, land carbon stocks, hydrology, and ecosystem properties, have enabled more comprehensive analyses of factors that influence the contribution of bioenergy and BECCS in IAM-based mitigation scenarios, and also associated co-benefits and adverse side effects (Turner et al. 2018a; Wu et al. 2019, Li et al. 2020, Hanssen et al. 2020; Drews et al. 2020; Ai et al. 2021; Hasegawa et al. 2021). Yet, IAMs are still coarse in local land-use practices. (Daioglou et al. 2019; Wu et al. 2019; Moreira et al. 2020b). Literature complementary to IAM studies indicate opportunities for integration of biomass production systems into agricultural landscapes (e.g., agroforestry, double cropping) to produce biomass while achieving co-benefits (Section 12.5). Similarly, climate-smart forestry puts forward measures (Box 7.3) adapted to regional circumstances in forest sectors, enabling co-benefits in nature conservation, soil protection, employment and income generation, and provision of wood for buildings, bioenergy and other bio-based products (Nabuurs et al. 2017).

Studies have also investigated the extent and possible use of marginal, abandoned, and degraded lands, and approaches to help restore the productive value of these lands (Awasthi et al. 2017; Fritsche et al. 2017; Chiaramonti and Panoutsou, 2018; Fernando et al. 2018; Elbersen et al. 2019; Rahman et al. 2019; Næss et al. 2021). In the SRCCL, the presented range for degraded or abandoned land was 32–1400 Mha (Jia et al. 2019). Recent regional assessments not included in the SRCCL found up to 69 Mha in EU-28, 185 Mha in China, 9.5 Mha in Canada, and 127 Mha in the USA (Emery et al. 2017; Liu et al. 2017; Elbersen et al. 2019; Zhang et al. 2020; Vera et al. 2021). The definitions of marginal/abandoned/degraded land, and the methods used to assess such lands remain inconsistent across studies (Jiang et al. 2019), causing large variation amongst them (Jiang et al. 2021). Furthermore, the availability of such lands has been contested since they may serve other functions, such as: subsistence, biodiversity protection, and so on (Baka 2014).

Box 7.7 | Climate Change Mitigation Value of Bioenergy and BECCS

Besides emissions, and possible avoided emissions, related to the supply chain, the GHG effects of using bioenergy depend on: (i) change in GHG emissions when bioenergy substitutes another energy source; and (ii) how the associated land use and possible land-use change influence the amount of carbon that is stored in vegetation and (Calvin et al. 2021) soils over time. Studies arrive at varying mitigation potentials for bioenergy and BECCS due to the large diversity of bioenergy systems, and varying conditions concerning where and how they are deployed (Elshout 2015; Harper et al.2018; Muri 2018; Kalt et al.2019; Brandão et al. 2019; Buchspies et al. 2020; Cowie et al. 2021; Calvin et al. 2021). Important factors include feedstock type, land management practice, energy conversion efficiency, type of bioenergy product (and possible co-products), emissions intensity of the products being displaced, and the land use/cover prior to bioenergy deployment (Zhu et al. 2017; Staples et al. 2017; Daioglou et al. 2017; Carvalho et al. 2017; Hanssen et al. 2020; Mouratiadou et al. 2020). Studies arrive at contrasting conclusions also when similar bioenergy systems and conditions are analysed, due to different methodologies, assumptions, and parametrization (Harper et al.2018; Kalt et al.2019; Brandão et al. 2019; Albers et al. 2019; Buchspies et al. 2020; Bessou et al. 2020; Rolls and Forster 2020; Cowie et al. 2021).

Box 7.7, Figure 1 shows emissions associated with biomass supply (residues and crops grown on cropland not needed for food) in 2050, here designated emission-supply curves. The curves are constructed assuming that additional biomass supply consistently comes from the available land/biomass resource that has the lowest GHG emissions, for example, the marginal GHG emissions increase with increasing biomass use for bioenergy. Net negative emissions indicate cases where biomass production increases land carbon stocks.

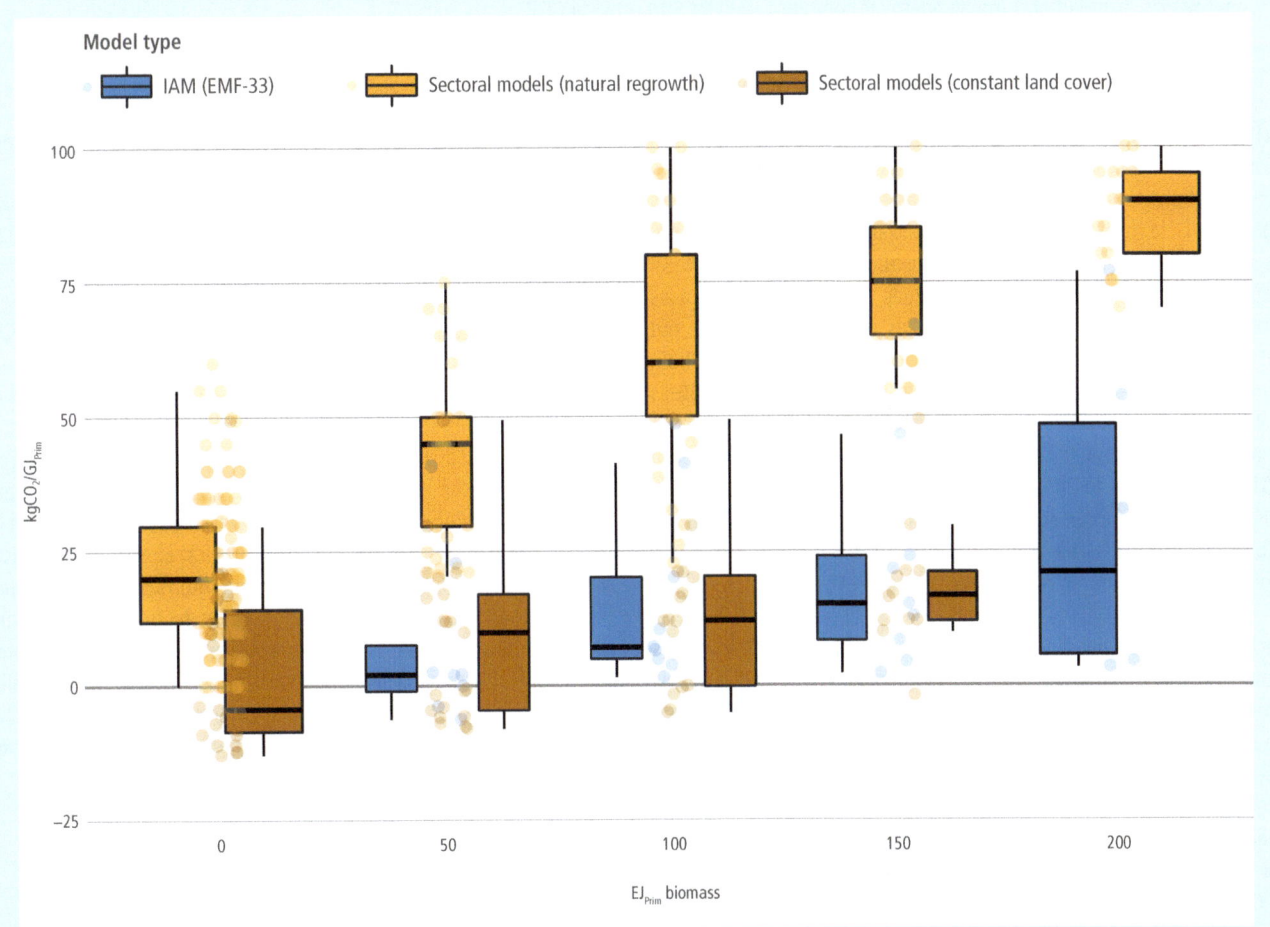

Box 7.7, Figure 1 | Emissions associated with primary biomass supply in 2050 (residues and crops grown on cropland not needed for food), as determined from sectoral models (Daioglou et al. 2017; Kalt et al. 2020), and stylised scenarios from the EMF-33 project using Integrated Assessment Models (Rose et al. 2020). All methods include LUC (direct and indirect) emissions. Emissions associated with *Natural Regrowth* include counterfactual carbon fluxes (see text). The sectoral models include a more detailed representation of the emissions, including lifecycle emissions from fertiliser production. IAM models may include economic feedbacks such as intensification as a result of increasing prices. As an indication: for natural gas the emission factor is around 56, for coal around 95 $kgCO_2\ GJ^{-1}$.

Box 7.7 (continued)

One curve (*EMF-33*) is determined from stylised scenarios using IAMs (Rose et al. 2020). One of the two curves determined from sectoral models, *Constant Land Cover*, reflects supply chain emissions and changes in land carbon storage caused by the biomass supply system itself. These two curves are obtained with modelling approaches compatible with the modelling protocol used for the scenarios in the AR6 database, which accounts for the land-use change and all other GHG emissions along a given transformation trajectory, enabling assessments of the warming level incurred.

The *Natural Regrowth* curve attribute additional 'counterfactual emissions' to the bioenergy system, corresponding to estimated uptake of CO_2 in a counterfactual scenario where land is not used for bioenergy but instead subject to natural vegetation regrowth. This curve does not show actual emissions from the bioenergy system, but it provides insights in the mitigation value of the bioenergy option compared to alternative land-use strategies. To illustrate, if biomass is used instead of a primary energy source with emission factor 75 $kgCO_2$ GJ^{-1}, and the median values in the *Natural Regrowth* curve are adopted, then the curve indicates that up to about 150 EJ of biomass can be produced and used for energy while achieving higher net GHG savings than the alternative to set aside the same land for natural vegetation regrowth (assuming same conversion factor).

The large ranges in the bars signify the importance of uncertainties and how the biomass is deployed. Variation in energy conversion efficiencies and uncertainty about magnitude, timing, and permanence of land carbon storage further complicate the comparison. Finally, not shown in Box 7.7, Figure 1, the emission-supply curves would be adjusted downwards if displacement of emission intensive energy was included or if the bioenergy is combined with CCS to provide CDR.

Critical assessment and conclusion. Recent estimates of technical biomass potentials constrained by food security and environmental considerations fall within previous ranges corresponding to *medium agreement*, (e.g., Turner et al. 2018b; Daioglou et al. 2019; Wu et al. 2019, Hansen et al.2020; Kalt et al. 2020) arriving at 4–57 and 46–245 EJ yr^{-1} by 2050 for residues and dedicated biomass crops, respectively. Based on studies to date, the technical net CDR potential of BECCS (including LUC and other supply chain emissions, but excluding energy carrier substitution) by 2050 is 5.9 (0.5–11.3) $GtCO_2$ yr^{-1} globally, of which 1.6 (0.5–3.5) $GtCO_2$ yr^{-1} is available at below USD100 tCO_2^{-1} (*medium confidence)* (Lenton 2010; Koornneef et al. 2012; McLaren 2012; Powell and Lenton 2012; Fuss et al. 2018; Turner et al. 2018a; Hanssen et al. 2020; Roe et al. 2021) (Figure 7.11). The equivalent economic potential as derived from IAMs is 1.8 (0.2–9.9) $GtCO_2$ yr^{-1} (Table 7.3).

Technical land availability does not imply that dedicated biomass production for bioenergy and BECCS is the most effective use of this land for mitigation. Further, implications of deployment for climate change mitigation and other sustainability criteria are context dependent and influenced by many factors, including rate and total scale. While governance has a critical influence on outcome, larger scale and higher expansion rate generally translates into higher risk for negative outcomes for GHG emissions, biodiversity, food security and a range of other sustainability criteria (Searchinger 2017; Vaughan et al. 2018; Rochedo et al. 2018; de Oliveira Garcia et al. 2018; Daioglou et al. 2019; Junginger et al. 2019; Galik et al. 2020; Stenzel et al. 2020).

However, literature has also highlighted how the agriculture and forestry sectors may respond to increasing demand by devising management approaches that enable biomass production for energy in conjunction with supply of food, construction timber, and other bio-

based products, providing climate change mitigation while enabling multiple co-benefits including for nature conservation (Nabuurs et al. 2017; Parodi et al. 2018; Springmann et al. 2018; Rosenzweig et al. 2020; Clark et al. 2020; Favero et al. 2020; Hanssen et al. 2020) (Section 7.4 and Cross-Working Group Box 3 in Chapter 12).

Strategies to enhance the benefits of bioenergy and BECCS include (i) management practices that protect carbon stocks and the productive and adaptive capacity of lands, as well as their environmental and social functions (van Ittersum et al. 2013, Gerssen-Gondelach et al. 2015; Moreira et al. 2020b) (ii) supply chains from primary production to final consumption that are well managed and deployed at appropriate levels (Fajardy et al. 2018; Donnison et al. 2020); and (iii) development of a cross-sectoral agenda for bio-based production within a circular economy, and international cooperation and governance of global trade in products to maximise synergies while limiting trade-offs concerning environmental, economic and social outcomes (*very high confidence*). Finally, the technical feasibility of BECCS depends on investments in and the roll-out of advanced bioenergy technologies currently not widely available (Baker et al. 2015; Daioglou et al. 2020b).

7.4.5 Demand-side Measures

7.4.5.1 Shift to Sustainable Healthy Diets

Activities, co-benefits, risks and implementation opportunities and barriers. The term 'sustainable healthy diets' refers to dietary patterns that 'promote all dimensions of individuals' health and well-being; have low environmental pressure and impact; are accessible, affordable, safe and equitable; and are culturally acceptable' (FAO and WHO 2019). In addition to climate mitigation gains, a transition towards more plant-based consumption and reduced consumption of animal-based foods, particularly from ruminant animals, could reduce pressure on forests and land used for feed, support the preservation of biodiversity and planetary health (FAO 2018c; Theurl et al. 2020), and contribute to preventing forms of malnutrition (i.e., undernutrition, micronutrient deficiency, and obesity) in developing countries (Section 12.4). Other co-benefits include lowering the risk of cardiovascular disease, type 2 diabetes, and reducing mortality from diet-related non-communicable diseases (Toumpanakis et al. 2018; Satija and Hu 2018; Faber et al. 2020; Magkos et al. 2020). However, transition towards sustainable healthy diets could have adverse impacts on the economic stability of the agricultural sector (MacDiarmid 2013; Aschemann-Witzel 2015; Van Loo et al. 2017). Therefore, shifting toward sustainable and healthy diets requires effective food-system oriented reform policies that integrate agriculture, health, and environment policies to comprehensively address synergies and conflicts in co-lateral sectors (agriculture, trade, health, environment protection etc.) and capture spill-over effects, for example, climate change, biodiversity loss, food poverty (FAO and WHO 2019; Galli et al. 2020).

Conclusions from AR5 and IPCC Special Reports (SR1.5, SROCC and SRCCL); mitigation potential, costs, and pathways. According to the AR5, changes in human diets and consumption patterns can reduce emissions 5.3 to 20.2 $GtCO_2$-eq yr^{-1} by 2050 from diverted agricultural production and avoided land-use change (Smith et al. 2014). In the SRCCL, a 'contract and converge' model of transition to sustainable healthy diets was suggested as an effective approach, reducing food consumption in over-consuming populations and increasing consumption of some food groups in populations where minimum nutritional needs are not met (P. Smith et al. 2019a). The total technical mitigation potential of changes in human diets was estimated as 0.7–8 $GtCO_2$-eq yr^{-1} by 2050 (Tilman and Clark 2014; Springmann et al. 2016; Hawken 2017) (SRCCL, Chapter 2 and 6), ranging from a 50% adoption of healthy diets (<60g of animal-based protein) and only accounting for diverted agricultural production, to the global adoption of a vegetarian diet.

Developments since AR5 and IPCC Special Reports (SR1.5, SROCC and SRCCL). Since the SRCCL, global studies continue to find high mitigation potential from reducing animal-source foods and increasing proportions of plant-rich foods in diets. Springmann et al. (2018) estimated that diet changes in line with global dietary guidelines for total energy intake and consumption of red meat, sugar, fruits, and vegetables, could reduce GHG emissions by 29% and other environmental impacts by 5–9% compared with the baseline in 2050. Poore and Nemecek (2018) revealed that shifting towards diets that exclude animal-source food could reduce land use by 3.1 billion ha, decrease food-related GHG emissions by 6.5 $GtCO_2$-eq yr^{-1}, acidification by 50%, eutrophication by 49%, and freshwater withdrawals by 19% for a 2010 reference year. Frank et al. (2019) estimated non-CO_2 emissions reductions of 0.4 $GtCO_2$-eq yr^{-1} at a carbon price of USD100 tCO_2^{-1} and 0.6 $GtCO_2$-eq yr^{-1} at USD20 tCO_2^{-1} in 2050 from shifting to lower animal-source diets (430 kcal of livestock calorie intake) in developed and emerging countries. From a systematic literature review, Ivanova et al. (2020) found mitigation potentials of 0.4–2.1 tCO_2-eq capita^{-1}

for a vegan diet, of 0.01–1.5 for a vegetarian diet, and of 0.1–2.0 for Mediterranean or similar healthy diet.

Regionally, mitigation potentials for shifting towards sustainable healthy diets (50% convergence to <60g of meat-based protein, only accounting for diverted production) vary across regions. A recent assessment finds greatest economic (up to USD100 tCO_2^{-1}) potential for 2020–2050 in Asia and the Pacific (609 $MtCO_2$-eq yr^{-1}) followed by Developed Countries (322 $MtCO_2$-eq yr^{-1}) based on IPCC AR4 GWP100 values for CH_4 and N_2O) (Roe et al. 2021). In the EU, (Latka et al. 2021) found that moving to healthy diets through price incentives could bring about annual reductions of non-CO_2 emissions from agriculture of 12–111 $MtCO_2$-eq yr^{-1}. At the country level, recent studies show that following National Dietary Guidelines (NDG) would reduce food system GHG emissions by 4–42%, confer large health gains (1.0–1.5 million quality-adjusted life-years) and lower health care system costs (NZD 14–20 billion) in New Zealand Drew et al. (2020); reduce 28% of GHG emissions in Argentina Arrieta and González (2018); about 25% in Portugal Esteve-Llorens et al. (2020) and reduce GHG emissions, land use and blue water footprint by 15–60% in Spain (Batlle-Bayer et al. 2020). In contrast, Aleksandrowicz et al. (2019) found that meeting healthy dietary guidelines in India required increased dietary energy intake overall, which slightly increased environmental footprints by about 3–5% across GHG emissions, blue and green water footprints and land use.

Critical assessment and conclusion. Shifting to sustainable healthy diets has large potential to achieve global GHG mitigation targets as well as public health and environmental benefits (*high confidence*). Based on studies to date, there is *medium confidence* that shifting toward sustainable healthy diets has a technical potential including savings in the full value chain of 3.6 (0.3–8.0) $GtCO_2$-eq yr^{-1} of which 2.5 (1.5–3.9) $GtCO_2$-eq yr^{-1} is considered plausible based on a range of GWP100 values for CH_4 and N_2O. When accounting for diverted agricultural production only, the feasible potential is 1.7 (1–2.7) $GtCO_2$-eq yr^{-1}. A shift to more sustainable and healthy diets is generally feasible in many regions (*medium confidence*). However, potential varies across regions as diets are location- and community- specific, and thus may be influenced by local production practices, technical and financial barriers and associated livelihoods, everyday life and behavioural and cultural norms around food consumption (Meybeck and Gitz 2017; Creutzig et al. 2018; FAO 2018b). Therefore, a transition towards low-GHG emission diets and achieving their mitigation potential requires a combination of appropriate policies, financial and non-financial incentives and awareness-raising campaigns to induce changes in consumer behaviour with potential synergies between climate objectives, health and equity (Rust et al. 2020).

7.4.5.2   Reduce Food Loss and Waste

Activities, co-benefits, risks and implementation opportunities and barriers. Food loss and waste (FLW) refer to the edible parts of plants and animals produced for human consumption that are not ultimately consumed (UNEP 2021b). Food loss occurs through spoilage, spilling or other unintended consequences due to limitations in agricultural infrastructure, storage and packaging (Parfitt et al.

2010). Food waste typically takes place at the distribution (retail and food service) and consumption stages in the food supply chain and refers to food appropriate for human consumption that is discarded or left to spoil (HLPE 2014). Options that could reduce FLW include: investing in harvesting and post-harvesting technologies in developing countries, taxing and other incentives to reduce business and consumer-level waste in developed countries, mandatory FLW reporting and reduction targets for large food businesses, regulation of unfair trading practices, and active marketing of cosmetically imperfect products (van Giesen and de Hooge 2019; Sinclair Taylor et al. 2019). Other studies suggested providing options of longer-lasting products and behavioural changes (e.g., through information provision) that cause dietary and consumption changes and motivate consumers to actively make decisions that reduce FLW. Reductions of FLW along the food chain bring a range of benefits beyond GHG mitigation, including reducing environmental stress (e.g., water and land competition, land degradation, desertification), safeguarding food security, and reducing poverty (Galford et al. 2020; Venkatramanan et al. 2020). Additionally, FLW reduction is crucial for achieving SDG 12 which calls for ensuring 'sustainable consumption and production patterns' through lowering per capita global food waste by 50% at the retail and consumer level and reducing food losses along food supply chains by 2030. In line with these SDG targets, it is estimated that reducing FLW can free up several million km^2 of land (*high confidence*). The interlinkages between reducing FLW and food system sustainability are discussed in Chapter 12. Recent literature identifies a range of barriers to climate change mitigation through FLW reduction, which are linked to technological, biophysical, socio-economic, financial and cultural contexts at regional and local levels (Vogel and Meyer 2018; Gromko and Abdurasalova 2019; Rogissart et al. 2019; Blok et al. 2020). Examples of these barriers include infrastructural and capacity limitations, institutional regulations, financial resources, constraining resources (e.g., energy), information gaps (e.g., with retailers), and consumers' behaviour (Gromko and Abdurasalova 2019; Blok et al. 2020).

Conclusions from AR5 and IPCC Special Reports (SR1.5, SROCC and SRCCL); mitigation potential, costs, and pathways. In AR5, reduced FLW was considered as a mitigation measure that could substantially lower emissions, with estimated mitigation potential of 0.6–6.0 GtCO$_2$-eq yr^{-1} in the food supply chain (Smith et al. 2014). In the SRCCL, the technical mitigation potential of reducing food and agricultural waste was estimated at 0.76–4.5 GtCO$_2$-eq yr^{-1} (Bajželj et al. 2014; Dickie et al. 2014b; Hawken 2017) (SRCCL, Chapter 2 and 6).

Developments since AR5 and IPCC Special Reports (SR1.5, SROCC and SRCCL). Since the SRCCL, there have been very few quantitative estimates of the mitigation potential of FLW reductions. Evidence suggests that reducing FLW together with overall food intake could have substantial mitigation potential, equating to an average of 0.3 tCO$_2$-eq capita^{-1} (Ivanova et al. 2020). Some regional sectoral studies indicate that reducing FLW in the EU can reduce emissions by 186 MtCO$_2$-eq yr^{-1}, the equivalent of around 15% of the environmental impacts (climate, acidification, and eutrophication) of the entire food value chain (Scherhaufer et al. 2018). In the UK, disruptive low-carbon innovations relating to FLW reduction were

found to be associated with potential emissions reductions ranging between 2.6 and 3.6 MtCO$_2$-eq (Wilson et al. 2019). Other studies investigated the effect of tax mechanisms, such as 'pay as you throw' for household waste, on the mitigation potential of reducing FLW. Generally, these mechanisms are recognised as particularly effective in reducing the amount of waste and increasing the recycling rate of households (Carattini et al. 2018; Rogissart et al. 2019). Technological FWL mitigation opportunities exist throughout the food supply chain; post-harvest opportunities for FLW reductions are discussed in Chapter 12. Based on IPCC AR4 GWP100 values for CH$_4$ and N$_2$O, greatest economic mitigation potential (up to USD100 tCO$_2^{-1}$) for the period 2020–2050 from FLW reduction is estimated to be in Asia and Pacific (192.3 GtCO$_2$-eq yr^{-1}) followed by Developed Countries (101.6 GtCO$_2$-eq yr^{-1}) (Roe et al. 2021). These estimates reflect diverted agricultural production and do not capture potential from avoided land-use changes.

Critical assessment and conclusion. There is *medium confidence* that reduced FLW has large global technical mitigation potential of 2.1 (0.1–5.8) GtCO$_2$-eq yr^{-1} including savings in the full value chain and using GWP100 and a range of IPCC values for CH$_4$ and N$_2$O. Potentials at 3.7 (2.2–5.1) GtCO$_2$-eq yr^{-1} are considered plausible. When accounting for diverted agricultural production only, the feasible potential is 0.5 (0.0–0.9) GtCO$_2$-eq yr^{-1}. See the section above for the joint land-use effects of food related demand-side measures which increases three-fold when accounting for the land-use effects as well. But this would overlap with other measures and is therefore not additive. Regionally, FLW reduction is feasible anywhere but its potential needs to be understood in a wider and changing socio-cultural context that determines nutrition (*high confidence*).

7.4.5.3 Improved and Enhanced Use of Wood Products

Activities, co-benefits, risks and implementation opportunities and barriers. The use of wood products refers to the fate of harvested wood for material uses and includes two distinctly different components affecting the carbon cycle, including carbon storage in wood products and material substitution. When harvested wood is used for the manufacture of wood products, carbon remains stored in these products depending on their end use and lifetime. Carbon storage in wood products can be increased through enhancing the inflow of products in use, or effectively reducing the outflow of the products after use. This can be achieved through additional harvest under sustainable management (Pilli et al. 2015; Johnston and Radeloff 2019), changing the allocation of harvested wood to long-lived wood products or by increasing products' lifetime and increasing recycling (Brunet-Navarro et al. 2017; Jasinevičius et al. 2017; Xu et al. 2018; Xie et al. 2021). Material substitution involves the use of wood for building, textiles, or other applications instead of other materials (e.g., concrete or steel, which consume more energy to produce) to avoid or reduce emissions associated with the production, use and disposal of those products it replaces.

The benefits and risks of improved and enhanced improved use of wood products are closely linked to forest management. First of all, the enhanced use of wood products could potentially activate or lead to improved sustainable forest management that can mitigate and adapt (Verkerk et al. 2020). Secondly, carbon storage in wood products and the potential for substitution effects can be increased by additional harvest, but with the risk of decreasing carbon storage in forest biomass when not done sustainably (P. Smith et al. 2019a). Conversely, reduced harvest may lead to gains in carbon storage in forest ecosystems locally, but these gains may be offset through international trade of forest products causing increased harvesting pressure or even degradation elsewhere (Kastner et al. 2011; Kallio et al. 2018; Pendrill et al. 2019b). There are also environmental impacts associated with the processing, manufacturing, use and disposal of wood products (Adhikari and Ozarska 2018; Baumgartner 2019). See Section 9.6.4 of this report for additional discussion on benefits and risks.

Conclusions from AR5 and IPCC Special Reports (SR1.5, SROCC and SRCCL); mitigation potential, costs, and pathways. There is strong evidence at the product level that wood products from sustainably managed forests are associated with less greenhouse emissions in their production, use and disposal over their life-time compared to products made from emission-intensive and non-renewable materials. However, there is still limited understanding of the substitution effects at the level of markets, countries (Leskinen et al. 2018). The AR5 did not report on the mitigation potential of wood products. The SRCCL (Chapters 2 and 6) finds that some studies indicate significant mitigation potentials for material substitution, but concludes that the global, technical mitigation potential for material substitution for construction applications ranges from 0.25–1 $GtCO_2$-eq yr^{-1} (*medium confidence*) (Miner 2010; McLaren 2012; Roe et al. 2019).

Developments since AR5 and IPCC Special Reports (SR1.5, SROCC and SRCCL). Since the SRCCL, several studies have examined the mitigation potential of the enhanced and improved use of wood products. A global forest sector modelling study (Johnston and Radeloff 2019) estimated that carbon storage in wood products represented a net carbon stock increase of 0.34 $GtCO_2$-eq yr^{-1} globally in 2015 and which could provide an average mitigation potential (by increasing the HWP pool) of 0.33–0.41 $GtCO_2$-eq yr^{-1} for the period 2020–2050, based on the future socio-economic development (SSP scenarios) and its effect on the production and consumption of wood products. Traded feedstock provided another 0.071 $GtCO_2$ yr^{-1} of carbon storage in 2015 and 0.12 $GtCO_2$ yr^{-1} by 2065. These potentials exclude the effect of material substitution. Another recent study estimated the global mitigation potential of mid-rise urban buildings designed with engineered wood products at 0.04–3.7 $GtCO_2$ yr^{-1} (Churkina et al. 2020). Another study (Oliver et al. 2014) estimated that using wood to substitute for concrete and steel as building materials could provide a technical mitigation potential of 0.78–1.73 $GtCO_2$ yr^{-1} achieved through carbon storage in wood products and through material and energy substitution.

The limited availability or absence of estimates of the future mitigation potential of improved use of wood products for many world regions represents an important knowledge gap, especially with regards to material substitution effects. At the product level, wood products are often associated with lower fossil-based emissions from production, use and disposal, compared to products made from emission-

intensive and non-renewable materials (Sathre and O'Connor 2010; Geng et al. 2017; Leskinen et al. 2018).

Critical assessment and conclusion. Based on studies to date, there is *strong evidence* and *medium agreement* that the improved use of wood products has a technical potential of 1.0 (0.04–3.7) $GtCO_2$-eq yr^{-1} and economic potential of 0.4 (0.3–0.5) $GtCO_2$-eq yr^{-1}. There is *strong evidence* and *high agreement* at the product level that material substitution provides on average benefits for climate change mitigation as wood products are associated with less fossil-based GHG emissions over their lifetime compared to products made from emission-intensive and non-renewable materials. However, the evidence at the level of markets or countries is uncertain and fairly limited for many parts of the world. There is *medium confidence* that material substitution and carbon storage in wood products contribute to climate change mitigation when also the carbon balances of forest ecosystems are considered of sustainably managed large areas of forests in medium term. The total future mitigation potential will depend on the forest system considered, the type of wood products that are produced and substituted and the assumed production technologies and conversion efficiencies of these products.

7.5　AFOLU Integrated Models and Scenarios

This section assesses the literature and data available on potential future GHG dynamics in the AFOLU sector, the cost-effectiveness of different mitigation measures, and consequences of climate change mitigation pathways on land-use dynamics as well as relevant sustainable development indicators at the regional and global level based on global integrated models.

Land-based mitigation options interact and create various trade-offs, and thus need to be assessed together as well as with mitigation options in other sectors, and in combination with other sustainability goals (Popp et al. 2014; Obersteiner et al. 2016; Roe et al. 2019; Van Vuuren et al. 2019; Prudhomme et al. 2020; Strefler et al. 2021). The assessments of individual mitigation measures or sectoral estimates used to estimate mitigation potential in Section 7.4, when aggregated together, do not account for interactions and trade-offs. Integrative land-use models (ILMs) combine different land-based mitigation options and are partially included in Integrated Assessment Models (IAMs) which combine insights from various disciplines in a single framework and cover the largest sources of anthropogenic GHG emissions from different sectors. Over time, ILMs and IAMs have extended their system coverage (Johnson et al. 2019). However, the explicit modelling and analysis of integrated land-use systems is relatively new compared to other sectoral assessments such as the energy system (Jia et al. 2019). Consequently, ILMs as well as IAMs differ in their portfolio and representation of land-based mitigation options, the representation of sustainability goals other than climate action as well as the interplay with mitigation in other sectors (van Soest et al. 2019; Johnson et al. 2019). These structural differences have implications for the regional and global deployment of different mitigation options as well as their sustainability impacts.

As a consequence of the relative novelty of land-based mitigation assessment in ILMs and IAMs, the portfolio of land-based mitigation options does not cover the full option space as outlined in Section 7.4. The inclusion and detail of a specific mitigation measure differs across models. Land-based mitigation options are only partially included in ILM and IAM analyses, which mostly rely on afforestation/reforestation and bioenergy with CCS (BECCS). Most ILM and IAM scenarios are based on the Shared Socio-economic Pathways (SSPs) (Riahi et al. 2017), which is a set of contrasting future scenarios widely used in the research community such as in the CMIP6 exercise, the SRCCL and the IPBES global assessment. However, the coverage of land-based mitigation options in these scenarios is mostly limited to dietary changes, higher efficiency in food processing (especially in livestock production systems), reduction of food waste, increasing agricultural productivity, methane reductions in rice paddies, livestock and grazing management for reduced methane emissions from enteric fermentation, manure management, improvement of N-efficiency, international trade, first generation of biofuels, avoided deforestation, afforestation, bioenergy and BECCS (Popp et al. 2017; Van Meijl et al. 2018; Frank et al. 2019). Hence, there are mitigation options not being broadly included in integrated pathway modelling as soil carbon, forest management, agroforestry or wetland

management (Humpenöder et al. 2020) which have the potential to alter the contribution of land-based mitigation in terms of timing, potential and sustainability consequences (Frank et al. 2017).

7.5.1 Regional GHG Emissions and Land Dynamics

In most of the assessed mitigation pathways, the AFOLU sector is of great importance for climate change mitigation as it (i) turns from a source into a sink of atmospheric CO_2 due to large-scale afforestation and reforestation, (ii) provides high amounts of biomass for bioenergy with or without CCS and (iii), even under improved agricultural management, still causes residual non-CO_2 emissions from agricultural production and (iv) interplays with sustainability dimensions other than climate action (Popp et al. 2017; Rogelj et al. 2017; Van Vuuren et al. 2018; Frank et al. 2018; Hasegawa et al. 2018; van Soest et al. 2019). Regional AFOLU GHG emissions in scenarios with <4°C warming in 2100 (scenario category C7), as shown in Figure 7.13, are shaped by considerable CH_4 and N_2O emissions throughout 2050 and 2100, mainly from ASIA and AFRICA. CH_4 emissions from enteric fermentation are largely caused by ASIA, followed by AFRICA, while CH_4 emissions from paddy rice

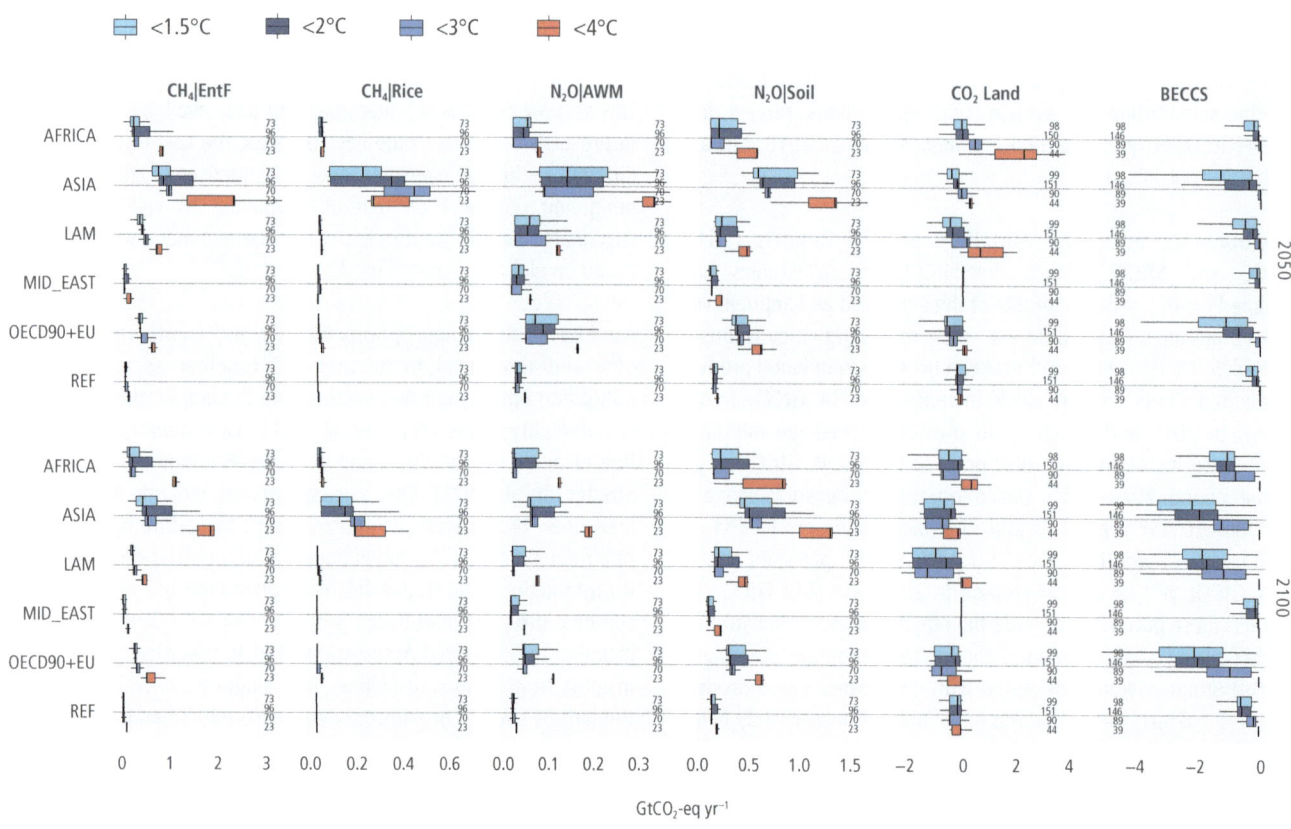

Figure 7.13 | Land-based regional GHG emissions and removals in 2050 (top) and 2100 (bottom) for scenarios from the AR6 Database with <1.5°C (C1, C2), <2°C (C3, C4), <3°C (C5, C6) and <4°C (C7) global warming in 2100 (scenario type is indicated by colour). The categories shown include CH_4 emissions from enteric fermentation (EntF) and rice production (Rice), N_2O emissions from animal waste management (AWM) and fertilisation (Soil). The category CO_2 Land includes CO_2 emissions from land-use change as well as removals due to afforestation/reforestation. BECCS reflects the CO_2 emissions captured from bioenergy use and stored in geological deposits. The annual GHG emission data from various models and scenarios is converted to CO_2 equivalents using GWP factors of 27 for CH_4 and 273 for N_2O. The data is summarised in boxplots (Tukey style), which show the median (vertical line), the interquartile range (IQR box) and the range of values within 1.5 × interquartile range at either end of the box (horizontal lines) across all models and scenarios. The number of data points available for each emission category, scenario type, region and year is shown at the edge of each panel. Regional definitions: AFRICA = sub-Saharan Africa, ASIA = Asia, LAM = Latin America and Caribbean, MID_EAST = Middle East, OECD90+EU = OECD 90 and EU, REF = Reforming Economies of Eastern Europe and the Former Soviet Union.

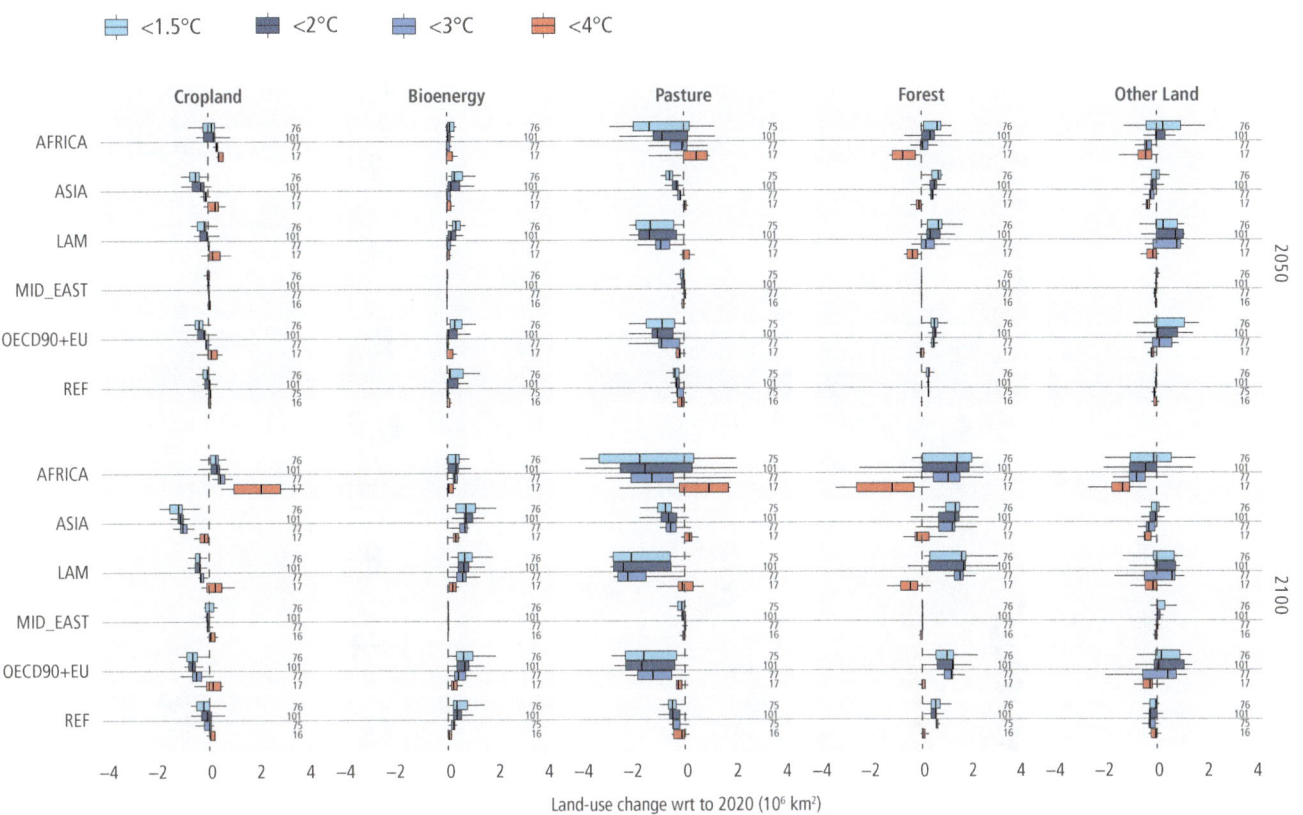

Figure 7.14 | Regional change of major land cover types by 2050 (top) and 2100 (bottom) relative to 2020 for scenarios from the AR6 Database with <1.5°C (C1, C2), <2°C (C3, C4), <3°C (C5, C6) and <4°C (C7) global warming in 2100 (scenario type is indicated by colour). The data is summarised in boxplots (Tukey style), which show the median (vertical line), the interquartile range (IQR box) and the range of values within 1.5 × IQR at either end of the box (horizontal lines) across all models and scenarios. The number of data points available for each land cover type, scenario type, region and year is shown at the right edge of each panel. Regional definitions: AFRICA = sub-Saharan Africa, ASIA = Asia, LAM = Latin America and Caribbean, MID_EAST = Middle East, OECD90+EU = OECD 90 and EU, REF = Reforming Economies of Eastern Europe and the Former Soviet Union.

production are almost exclusively caused by ASIA. N_2O emissions from animal waste management and soils are more equally distributed across region.

In most regions, CH_4 and N_2O emission are both lower in mitigation pathways that limit warming to 3°C (>50%) or lower (C1–C6) compared to scenarios with <4°C (Popp et al. 2017; Rogelj et al. 2018a). In particular, the reduction of CH_4 emissions from enteric fermentation in ASIA and AFRICA is profound. Land-related CO_2 emissions, which include emissions from deforestation as well as removals from afforestation, are slightly negative (i.e., AFOLU systems turn into a sink) in <1.5°C, <2°C and <3°C mitigation pathways compared to <4°C scenarios. Carbon sequestration via BECCS is most prominent in ASIA, LAM, AFRICA and OECD90+EU, which are also the regions with the highest bioenergy area.

Figure 7.14 indicates that regional land-use dynamics in scenarios with <4°C warming in 2100 are characterised by rather static agricultural land (i.e., cropland and pasture) in ASIA, LAM, OECD90+EU and REF, and increasing agricultural land in AFRICA. Bioenergy area is relatively small in all regions. Agricultural land in AFRICA expands at the cost of forests and other natural land.

The overall land dynamics in <1.5°C, <2°C and <3°C mitigation pathways are shaped by land-demanding mitigation options such as bioenergy and afforestation, in addition to the demand for other agricultural and forest commodities. Bioenergy production and afforestation take place largely in the (partly) tropical regions ASIA, LAM and AFRICA, but also in OECD90+EU. Land for dedicated second generation bioenergy crops and afforestation displace agricultural land for food production (cropland and pasture) and other natural land. For instance, in the <1.5°C mitigation pathway in ASIA, bioenergy and forest area together increased by about 2.1 million km^2 between 2020 and 2100, mostly at the cost of cropland and pasture (median values). Such large-scale transformations of land use have repercussions on biogeochemical cycles (e.g., fertiliser and water) but also on the economy (e.g., food prices) and potential socio-political conditions.

7.5.2   Marginal Abatement Costs According to Integrated Assessments

In this section, Integrated Assessment Model (IAM) results from the AR6 database are used to derive marginal abatement costs which indicate the economic mitigation potential for the different gases (N_2O, CH_4, CO_2) related to the AFOLU sector, at the global level and at

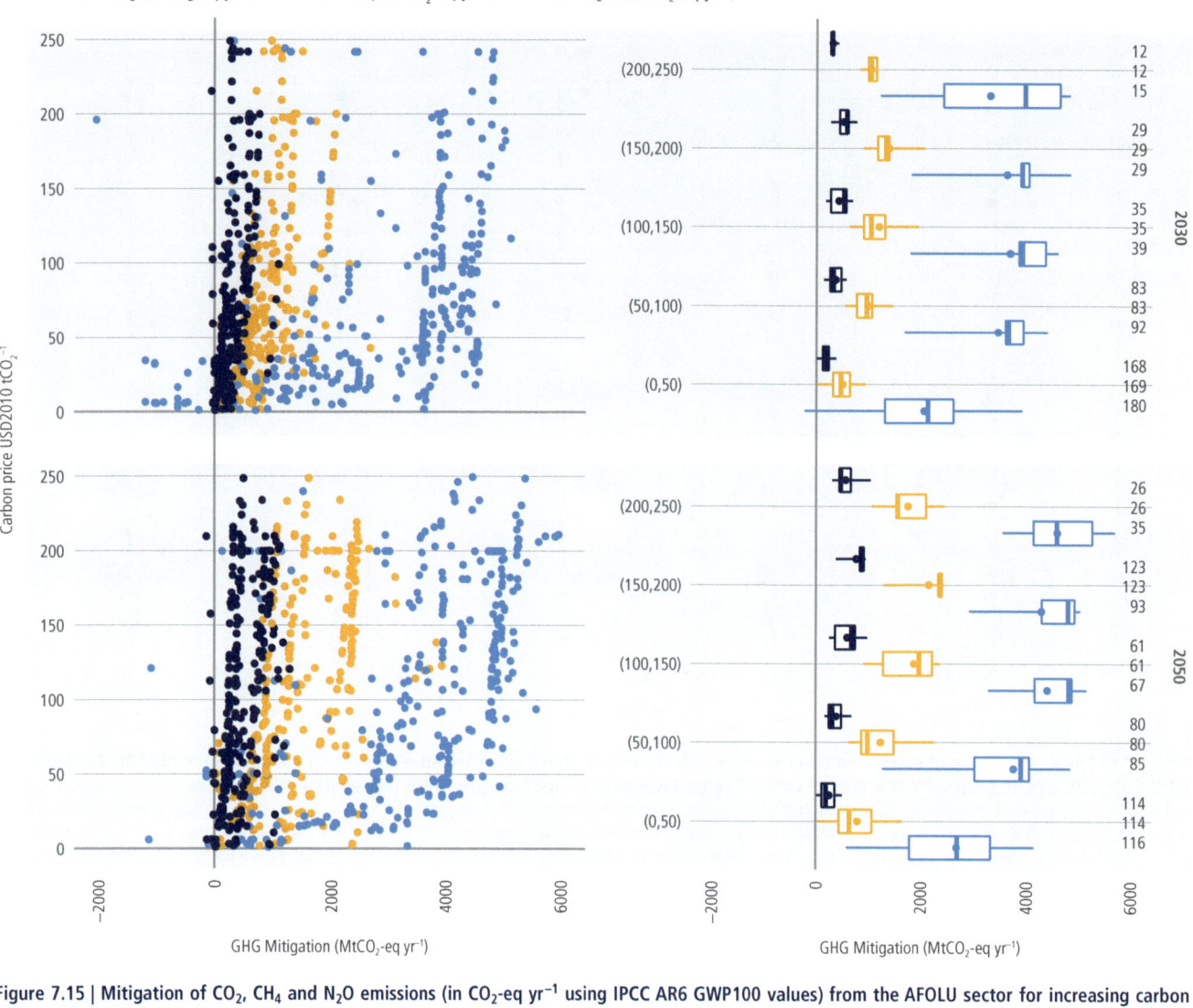

Figure 7.15 | Mitigation of CO₂, CH₄ and N₂O emissions (in CO₂-eq yr⁻¹ using IPCC AR6 GWP100 values) from the AFOLU sector for increasing carbon price levels for 2030 and 2050. In the left-hand panels, single data points are generated by comparing emissions between a policy scenario and a related benchmark scenario, and mapping these differences with the respective carbon price difference. Plots only show the price range of up to 250 USD2010 tCO₂-eq⁻¹ and the mitigation range between −2000 and 6000 MtCO₂-eq yr⁻¹ for better visibility. At the right-hand side, based on the same data as left-hand side panels, boxplots show medians (vertical line within the boxes), means (dots), 33%–66% intervals (box) and 10%–90% intervals (horizontal lines). Numbers on the very right indicate the number of observations falling into the respective price range per variable. A wide range of carbon price induced mitigation options (such as technical, structural and behavioural options in the agricultural sector, afforestation, reforestation, natural re-growth or avoided deforestation in the LULUCF sector, *excluding* carbon capture and sequestration from BECCS) are reflected in different scenarios.

the level of five world regions. This review provides a complementary view on the economic mitigation potentials estimated in Section 7.4 by implicitly taking into account the interlinkages between the land-based mitigation options themselves as well as the interlinkages with mitigation options in the other sectors such as BECCS. The review systematically evaluates a range of possible economic potential estimates across gases, time, and carbon prices.

For different models and scenarios from the AR6 database, the amount of mitigated emissions is presented together with the respective carbon price (Figure 7.15). To determine mitigation

potentials, scenarios are compared to a benchmark scenario which usually assumes business-as-usual trends and no explicit additional mitigation efforts. Scenarios have been excluded, if they do not have an associated benchmark scenario or fail the vetting according to the AR6 scenario database, or if they do not report carbon prices and CO₂ emissions from AFOLU. Scenarios with contradicting assumptions (for example, fixing some of the emissions to baseline levels) are excluded. Furthermore, only scenarios with consistent[3] regional and global level results are considered. Mitigation potentials are computed by subtracting scenario specific emissions and sequestration amounts from their respective benchmark scenario values. This difference

---

[3]   Scenarios are considered consistent between global and regional results (based on R5 regions), if the sum of regional emissions (or sequestration efforts) does not deviate more than 10% from the reported global total. To take into account that small absolute values have a higher sensitivity, a deviation of 90% is allowed for absolute values below 100.

accounts for the mitigation that can be credited to the carbon price which is applied in a scenario. A few benchmark scenarios, however, apply already low carbon prices. For consistency reasons, a carbon price that is applied in a benchmark scenario is subtracted from the respective scenario specific carbon price. This may generate a bias because low carbon prices tend to have a stronger marginal impact on mitigation than high carbon prices. Scenarios with carbon prices which become negative due to the correction are not considered. The analysis considers all scenarios from the AR6 database which pass the criteria and should be considered as an ensemble of opportunity (Huppmann et al. 2018).

This approach is close to integrated assessment marginal abatement cost curves (MACCs) as described in the literature (Fujimori et al. 2016; Frank et al. 2018, 2019; Harmsen et al. 2019) in the sense that it incorporates besides the technical mitigation options also structural options, as well as behavioural changes and market feedbacks. Furthermore, indirect emission changes and interactions with other sectors can be highly relevant (Daioglou et al. 2019; Kalt et al. 2020) and are also accounted for in the presented potentials. Hereby, some sequestration efforts can occur in other sectors, while leading to less mitigation in the AFOLU sector. For instance, as an integral part of many scenarios, BECCS deployment will lead to overall emissions reductions, and even provision of CDR as a result of the interplay between three direct components (i) LULUCF emissions/sinks, (ii) reduction of fossil fuel use/emissions, (iii) carbon capture and sequestration. Since the latter two effects can compensate for the LULUCF effect, BECCS deployment in ambitious stabilisation scenarios may lead to reduced sink/increased emissions in LULUCF (Kalt et al. 2020). The same holds for trade-offs between carbon sequestration in forests versus harvested wood products both for enhancing the HWP pool and for material substitution. The strengths of the competition between biomass use and carbon sequestration will depend on the biomass feedstocks considered (Lauri et al. 2019).

In the individual cases, the accounting of all these effects is dependent on the respective underlying model and its coverage of inter-relations of different sectors and sub-sectors. The presented potentials cover a wide range of models, and additionally, a wide range of background assumptions on macro-economic, technical, and behavioural developments as well as policies, which the models have been fed with. Subsequently, the range of the resulting marginal abatement costs is relatively wide, showing the full range of expected contributions from land-use sector mitigation and sequestration in applied mitigation pathways.

At the global level, the analysis of the economic mitigation potentials from N_2O and CH_4 emissions from AFOLU (which mainly can be related to agricultural activities) and CO_2 emissions (which mainly can be related to LULUCF emissions) reveals a relatively good agreement of models and scenarios in terms of ranking between the gases. On the right-hand side panels of Figure 7.15, only small overlaps between the ranges (showing the 10–90% intervals of observations) and mainly for lower price levels, can be observed, despite all differences in underlying model structure and scenario assumptions.

N_2O emissions show the smallest economic potential of the three different gases in 2030 as well as in 2050. The mitigation potential increases until a price range of USD150–200 and to a median value of around 0.6 $GtCO_2$-eq yr^{-1} mitigation in 2030 and 0.9 $GtCO_2$-eq yr^{-1} in 2050, respectively, while afterwards with higher prices the expansion is very limited. Mitigation of CH_4 emissions has a higher potential, also with increasing mitigation potentials until a price range of USD150–200 in both years, with median mitigation of around 1.3 $GtCO_2$-eq yr^{-1} in 2030 and around 2.4 $GtCO_2$-eq yr^{-1} in 2050, respectively. The highest mitigation potentials are observed for CO_2, but also the highest ranges of observations among the three gases. In 2030, a median of 4 $GtCO_2$-eq yr^{-1} mitigation potential is reported for the price range of USD200–250. In 2050, for the carbon price range of between USD100 and USD200, a median of around 4.8 $GtCO_2$-eq yr^{-1} can be observed.

When compared with the sectoral estimates from Harmsen et al. (2019), the integrated assessment median potentials are broadly comparable for the N_2O mitigation potential; Harmsen et al. 2050 mitigation potential at USD125 is 0.6 $GtCO_2$-eq yr^{-1} while the integrated assessment estimate for the same price range is 0.7 $GtCO_2$-eq yr^{-1}. The difference is substantially larger for the CH_4 mitigation potential; 0.9 $GtCO_2$-eq yr^{-1} in Harmsen et al. while 2 $GtCO_2$-eq yr^{-1} the median integrated assessment estimate. While the Harmsen et al. MACCs consider only technological mitigation options, integrated assessments typically include also demand side response to the carbon price and GHG efficiency improvements through structural change and international trade. These additional mitigation options can represent more than 60% of the total non-CO_2 mitigation potential in the agricultural sector, where they are more important in the livestock sector, and thus the difference between sectoral and integrated assessments is more pronounced for the CH_4 emissions (Frank et al. 2019).

Economic CO_2 mitigation potentials from land-use change and forestry are larger compared to potentials from non-CO_2 gases, and at the same time reveal high levels of variation in absolute terms. The 66th percentile in 2050 goes up to 5.2 $GtCO_2$-eq yr^{-1} mitigation, while the lowest observations are even negative, indicating higher CO_2 emissions from land use in scenarios with carbon price compared to scenarios without (counterintuitive dynamics explained below).

Land use is at the centre of the interdependencies with other sectors, including energy. Some models see a strong competition between BECCS deployment with its respective demand for biomass, and CO_2 mitigation/sequestration potentials in the land sector. Biomass demand may lead to an increase in CO_2 emissions from land use despite the application of a carbon price when land-use expansion for dedicated biomass production, such as energy plantations, comes from carbon rich land use/land cover alternatives, or when increased extraction of biomass from existing land uses, such as forest management, leads to reduction of the carbon sink (Daioglou 2019; Luderer et al. 2018) and can explain the high variety of observations in some cases. Overall, the large variety of observations shows a large variety of plausible results, which can go back to different model structures and assumptions, showing a robust range of plausible outcomes (Kriegler et al. 2015).

7.5.3 Interaction Between Mitigation in the AFOLU Sector and Other SDGs in the Context of Integrated Assessments

Besides the level of biomass supply for bioenergy, the adoption of SDGs may also significantly impact AFOLU emissions and the land-use sector's ability for GHG abatement (Frank et al. 2021). Selected SDGs are found to have positive synergies for AFOLU GHG abatement and to consistently decrease GHG emissions for both agriculture and forestry, thereby allowing for even more rapid and deeper emissions cuts. In particular, the decreased consumption of animal products and less food waste (SDG 12), and the protection of high biodiversity ecosystems such as primary forests (SDG 15) deliver high synergies with GHG abatement. On the other hand, protection of highly biodiverse ecosystems from conversion (SDG 15) limits the global biomass potentials for bioenergy (Frank et al. 2021), and while several forestry measures enhancing woody biomass supply for bioenergy may have synergies with improving ecosystems conditions, many represent a threat to biodiversity (Camia et al. 2020) (Sections 7.6.5 and 17.3.3.7, Figure 17.1 and Supplementary Material Table 17.SM.1).

7.5.4 Regional AFOLU Abatement for Different Carbon Prices

At the regional level (Figure 7.16), the highest potential from non-CO$_2$ emissions abatement, and mostly from CH$_4$, is reported for ASIA with the median of mitigation potential observations from CH$_4$ increasing up to a price of USD200 in the year 2050, reaching a median of 1.2 GtCO$_2$-eq yr^{-1}. In terms of economic potential, ASIA is followed by LAM, AFRICA, and OECD+EU, where emission reduction mainly is achieved in the livestock sector.

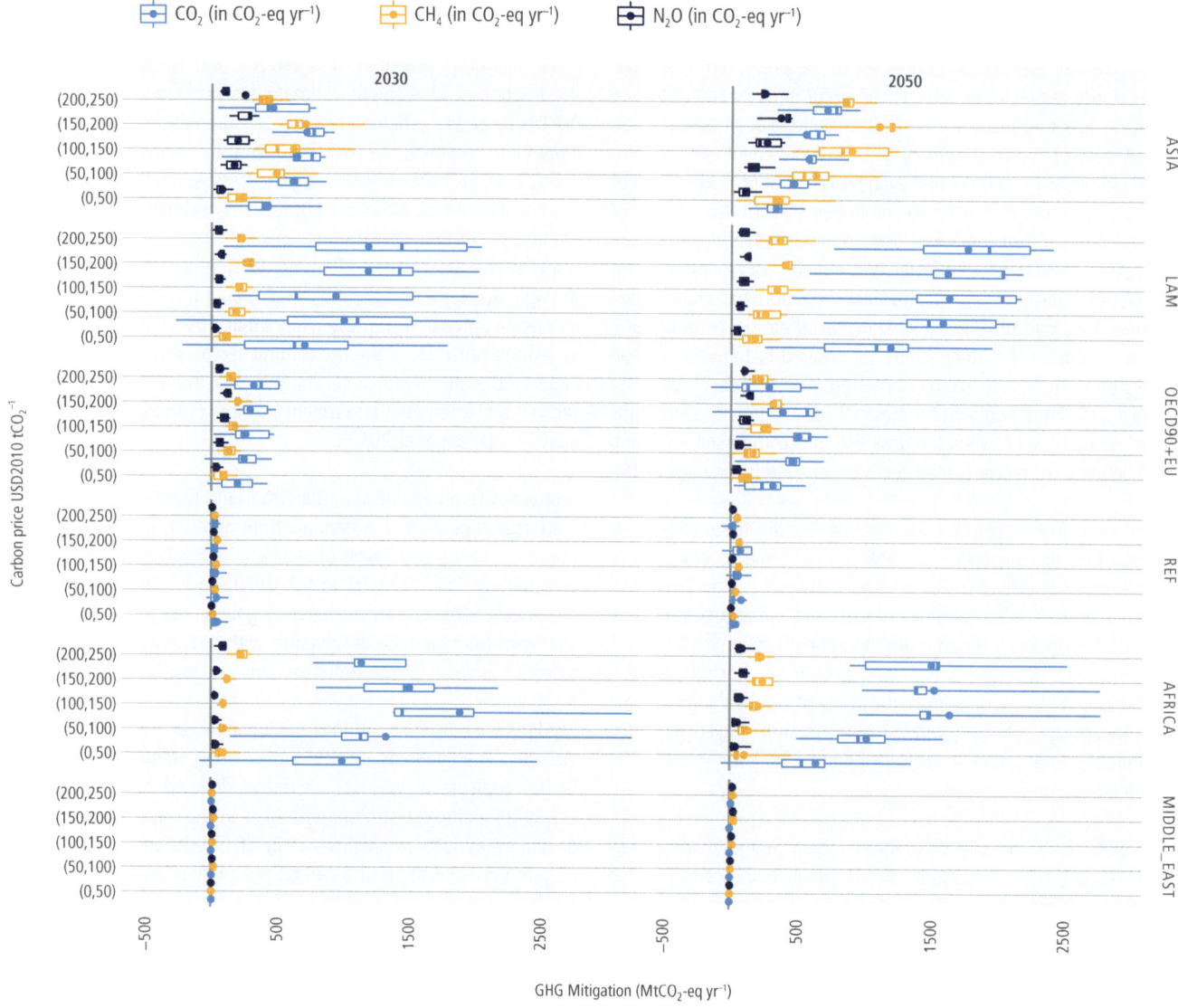

Figure 7.16 | Regional mitigation efforts for CO$_2$, CH$_4$ and N$_2$O emissions (in CO$_2$-eq yr^{-1} using IPCC AR6 GWP100 values) from the AFOLU sector for increasing carbon price levels for 2030 and 2050. Underlying datapoints are generated by comparing emissions between a policy scenario and a related benchmark scenario, mapping these differences with the respective carbon price differences. Boxplots show Medians (vertical line within the boxes), Means (dots), 33%–66% intervals (box) and 10%–90% intervals (horizontal lines) for respective scenarios of carbon prices implemented in intervals of USD50 from a price of USD0 to USD250. Regions: Asia (ASIA), Latin America and Caribbean (LAM), Middle East (MIDDLE_EAST), Africa (AFRICA), Developed Countries (OECD 90 and EU) (OECD+EU) and Reforming Economies of Eastern Europe and the Former Soviet Union (REF).

The highest potentials from land-related CO_2 emissions, including avoided deforestation as well as afforestation, can be observed in LAM and AFRICA with strong responses of mitigation (indicated by the median value) to carbon prices mainly in the lower range of displayed carbon prices. In general, CO_2 mitigation potentials show a wide range of results in comparison to non-CO_2 mitigation potentials, but mostly also a higher median value. The most extreme ranges are reported for the regions LAM and AFRICA. A medium potential is reported for ASIA and OECD+EU, while REF has the smallest potential according to model submissions. These estimates reflect techno-economic potentials and do not necessarily include feasibility constraints which are discussed in Chapter 7.6.

7.5.5　Illustrative Mitigation Pathways

Different mitigation strategies can achieve the net emission reductions that would be required to follow a pathway limiting global warming, with very different consequences for the land system. Figure 7.17 shows Illustrative Mitigation Pathways (IMPs) for achieving different climate targets highlighting AFOLU mitigation strategies, resulting GHG and land-use dynamics as well as the interaction with other sectors. For consistency this chapter discusses IMPs as described in detail in chapters 1 and 3 of this report but focusing on the land-use sector. All pathways are assessed by different IAM realisations and do not only reduce GHG emissions but also use CDR options, whereas

a. Global land-based GHG emissions and removals

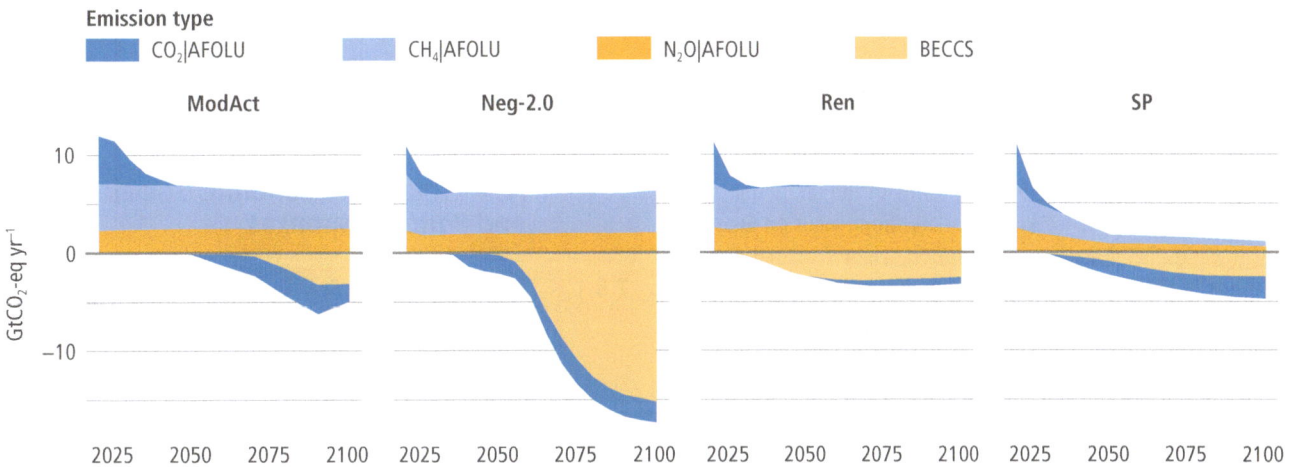

b. Global land-use change compared to 2020

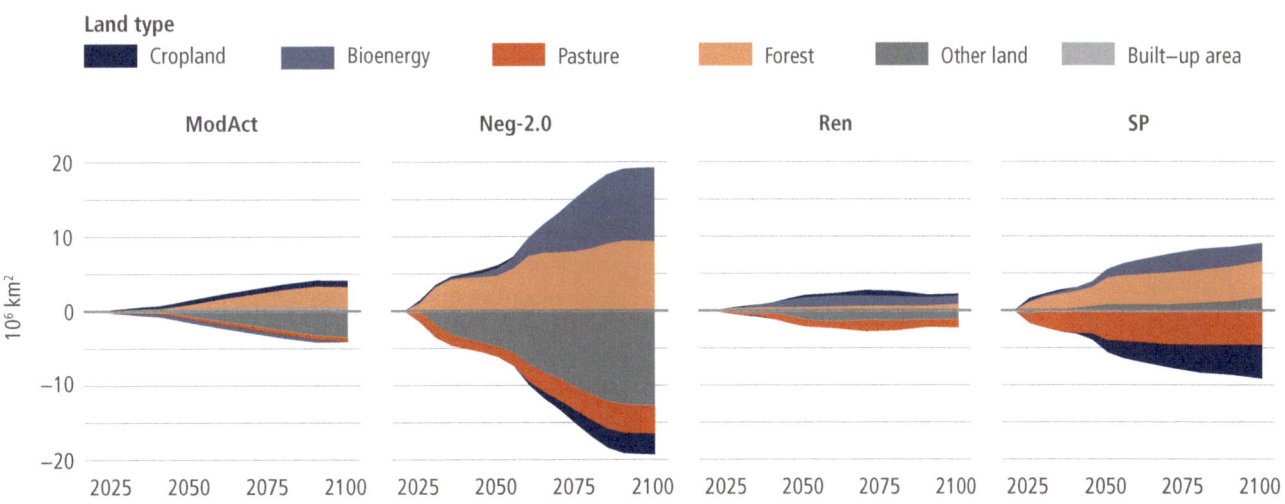

Figure 7.17 | Evolution and breakdown of (a) global land-based GHG emissions and removals and (b) global land-use dynamics under four Illustrative Mitigation Pathways, which illustrate the differences in timing and magnitude of land-based mitigation approaches including afforestation and BECCS. All pathways are based on different IAM realisations: *ModAct* scenario (below 3.0°C, C6) from IMAGE 3.0; *IMP Neg-2.0* (limit warming to 2°C (>67%), C3) from AIM/CGE 2.2; *IMP Ren* (1.5°C with no or low overshoot, C1) from REMIND-MAgPIE 2.1–4.3; *IMP SP* (1.5°C with no or low overshoot, C1) from REMIND-MAgPIE 2.1–4.2. In panel A the categories CO_2 AFOLU, CH_4 AFOLU and N_2O AFOLU include GHG emissions from land-use change and agricultural land use (including emissions related to bioenergy production). In addition, the category CO_2 Land includes removals due to afforestation/reforestation. BECCS reflects the CO_2 emissions captured from bioenergy use and stored in geological deposits. CH_4 and N_2O emissions are converted to CO_2-eq using GWP100 factors of 27 and 273 respectively.

the amount and timing varies across pathways, as do the relative contributions of different land-based CDR options.

The scenario *ModAct* (limit warming to 3°C (>50%), C6) is based on the prolongation of current trends (SSP2) but contains measures to strengthen policies for the implementation of National Determined Contributions (NDCs) in all sectors including AFOLU (Grassi et al. 2018). This pathway shows a strong decrease of CO_2 emissions from land-use change in 2030, mainly due to reduced deforestation, as well as moderately decreasing N_2O and CH_4 emissions from agricultural production due to improved agricultural management and dietary shifts away from emissions-intensive livestock products. However, in contrast to CO_2 emissions, which turn net-negative around 2050 due to afforestation/reforestation, CH_4 and N_2O emissions persist throughout the century due to difficulties of eliminating these residual emissions based on existing agricultural management methods (Frank et al. 2017; Stevanović et al. 2017). Comparably small amounts of BECCS are applied by the end of the century. Forest area increases at the cost of other natural vegetation.

IMP-Neg is similar to *ModAct* scenario in terms of socio-economic setting (SSP2) but differs strongly in terms of the mitigation target (limit warming to 2°C (>67%), C3) and its strong focus on the supply side of mitigation measures with strong reliance on net-negative emissions. Consequently, all GHG emission reductions as well as afforestation/reforestation and BECCS-based CDR start earlier in time at a higher rate of deployment. However, in contrast to CO_2 emissions, which turn net-negative around 2030 due to afforestation/ reforestation, CH_4 and N_2O emissions persist throughout the century, similar to *ModAct*, due to ongoing increasing demand for total calories and animal-based commodities (Bodirsky et al. 2020) and difficulties of eliminating these residual emissions based on existing agricultural management methods (Stevanović et al. 2017; Frank et al. 2017). In addition to abating land-related GHG emissions as well as increasing the terrestrial sink, this example also shows the potential importance of the land sector in providing biomass for BECCS and hence CDR in the energy sector. Cumulative CDR (2020–2100) amounts to 502 $GtCO_2$ for BECCS and 121 $GtCO_2$ for land-use change (including afforestation and reduced deforestation). In consequence, compared to *ModAct* scenario, competition for land is increasing and much more other natural land as well as agricultural land (cropland and pasture land) is converted to forest or bioenergy cropland with potentially severe consequences for various sustainability dimensions such as biodiversity (Hof et al. 2018) and food security (Fujimori et al. 2019).

IMP-Ren is similar to *IMP Neg-2.0* in terms of socio-economic setting (SSP2) but differs substantially in terms of mitigation target and mitigation efforts in the energy sector. Even under the more ambitious climate change mitigation target (1.5°C with no or low overshoot (OS), C1), the high share of renewable energy in *IMP Ren* strongly reduces the need for large-scale land-based CDR, which is reflected in smaller bioenergy and afforestation areas compared to *IMP Neg-2.0*. However, CH_4 and N_2O emissions from AFOLU persist throughout the century, similar to *ModAct* scenario and *IMP Neg-2.0*.

In contrast to *IMPs Neg-2.0* and *Ren*, *IMP SP* (Soergel et al. 2021; 1.5°C with no or low OS, C1) displays a future of generally low resource and energy consumption (including healthy diets with low animal-calorie shares and low food waste) as well as significant but sustainable agricultural intensification in combination with high levels of nature protection. This pathway shows a strong near-term decrease of CO_2 emissions from land-use change, mainly due to reduced deforestation, and in difference to all other IMPs described in this chapter strongly decreasing N_2O and CH_4 emissions from agricultural production due to improved agricultural management but also based on dietary shifts away from emissions-intensive livestock products as well as lower shares of food waste. In consequence, comparably small amounts of land are needed for land demanding mitigation activities such as BECCS and afforestation. In particular, the amount of agricultural land converted to bioenergy cropland is smaller compared to other mitigation pathways. Forest area increases either by regrowth of secondary vegetation following the abandonment of agricultural land or by afforestation/reforestation at the cost of agricultural land.

7.6 Assessment of Economic, Social and Policy Responses

7.6.1 Retrospective in Policy Efforts and Achieved Mitigation Within AFOLU

Since the establishment of the UNFCCC, international agencies, countries, sub-national units and NGO's have developed policies to facilitate and encourage GHG mitigation within AFOLU (Figure 7.18). Early guidance and policies focused on developing GHG inventory methodology with some emphasis on afforestation and reforestation projects, but the Clean Development Mechanism (CDM) in the Kyoto Protocol focused attention on emission reduction projects, mostly outside of AFOLU. As successive IPCC AR6 WGIII reports illustrated large potential for AFOLU mitigation, methods to quantify and verify carbon emission reductions emerged within several projects in the early 2000s, through both voluntary (e.g., the Chicago Climate Exchange (CCX)) and regulated (e.g., New South Wales and California) markets. The CDM dedicated large attention to LULUCF, including dedicated methodologies and bodies. The reasons for limited uptake of CDM afforestation/reforestation projects were multiple and not limited to the regulatory constraints, but also due to the low abatement potential (poor cost/performance ratio) compared to other mitigation opportunities.

Following COP 13 in Bali, effort shifted to advancing policies to reduce deforestation and forest degradation (REDD+) in developing countries. According to Simonet et al. (2019), nearly 65 Mha have been enrolled in REDD+ type programmes or projects funded through a variety of sources, including United Nations Programme on Reducing Emissions from Deforestation and Forest Degradation (UN-REDD), the World Bank Forest Carbon Partnership Facility, and bi-lateral agreements between countries with Norway being the largest donor. While there has been considerable focus on forest and

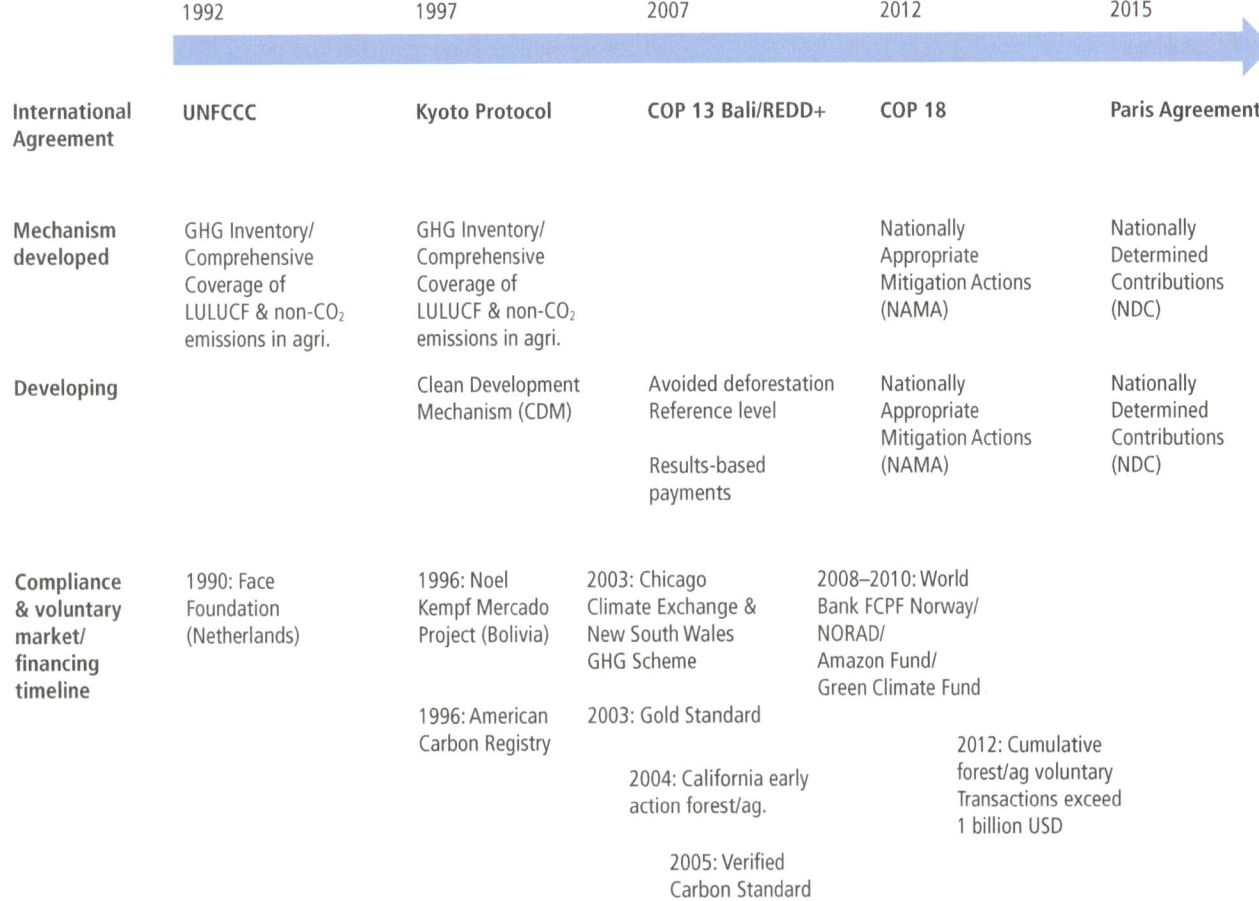

Figure 7.18 | Milestones in policy development for AFOLU measures. 'ag.' and 'agri.' = agriculture.

agricultural project-based mitigation actions, national governments were encouraged to incorporate project-based approaches with other sectoral strategies in their Nationally Appropriate Mitigation Actions (NAMAs) after 2012. NAMAs reflect the country's proposed strategy to reduce net emissions across various sectors within their economy (e.g., forests or agriculture). More recently, Nationally Determined Contributions (NDCs) indicate whether individual countries plan to use forestry and agricultural policies or related projects amongst a set of measures in other sectors, to reduce their net emissions as part of the Paris Agreement (e.g., Forsell et al. 2016; Fyson and Jeffery 2019).

The many protocols now available can be used to quantify the potential mitigation to date resulting from various projects or programs. For instance, carbon registries issue credits using protocols that typically account for additionality, permanence and leakage, thus providing evidence that the projects are a net carbon benefit to the atmosphere. Protocol development engages the scientific community, project developers, and the public over a multi-year period. Some protocols have been revised multiple times, such as the USA State of California's forest carbon protocol, which is in its fifth revision, with the latest in 2019 (see http://www.climateactionreserve.org/how/protocols/forest/). Credits from carbon registries feed into regulatory programs, such as the cap and trade programme in California, or

voluntary offset markets (Hamrick and Gallant 2017a). Although AFOLU measures have been deployed across a range of projects and programmes globally to reduce net carbon emissions, debate about the net carbon benefits of some projects continues (e.g., Krug 2018).

A new assessment of projects over the last two decades finds emission reductions or offsets of at least 7.9 $GtCO_2$-eq (using GWP100 and a mix of IPCC values for CH_4 and N_2O) over the last 12 years due to agricultural and forestry activities (Table 7.4). More than 80% of these emission reductions or offsets have been generated by forest-based activities. The total amounts to 0.66 $GtCO_2$ yr^{-1} for the period 2010–2019, which is 1.2% of total global, and 5.5% of AFOLU emissions reported in Table 7.1, over the same time period (*high confidence*).

The array of activities in Table 7.4 includes the Clean Development Mechanism, REDD+ activities reported in technical annexes of country biennial update reports to the UNFCCC, voluntary market transactions, and carbon stored as a result of carbon markets in Australia, New Zealand and California in the USA. Although other countries and sub-national units have developed programmes and policies, these three regions are presented due to their focus on forest and agricultural carbon mitigation, their use of generally accepted protocols or measures and the availability of data to quantify outcomes.

The largest share of emission reductions or carbon offsets in Table 7.4 has been from slowing deforestation and REDD+, specifically from efforts in Brazil (86% of total), which substantially reduced deforestation rates between 2004 and 2012 (Nepstad et al. 2014), as well as other countries in Latin America. With the exception of Roopsind et al. (2019), estimated reductions in carbon emissions from REDD+ in Table 7.4 are measured relative to a historical baseline. As noted in Brazil's Third Biennial Update Report (Ministry of Foreign Affairs 2019), estimates are made in accordance with established methodologies to determine the benefits of results-based REDD+ payments to Brazil. REDD+ estimates from other countries also have been derived from biennial update reports.

Regulatory markets provide the next largest share of carbon removal to date. Data from the Australia Emissions Reduction Fund are carbon credits issued in for agricultural, and vegetation and savanna burning projects. In the case of California, offset credits from forest and agricultural activities, using methods approved by a third-party certification authority (Climate Action Reserve), have been allowed as part of their state-wide cap and trade system. Transaction prices for forest and agricultural credits in California were around USD13 tCO_2^{-1} in 2018, and represented 7.4% of total market compliance. By the end of 2018, 80 $MtCO_2$ had been used for compliance purposes.

For New Zealand, the carbon reduction in Table 7.4 represents forest removals that were surrendered from post-1989 forests between 2008 and the 2020. Unlike offsets in voluntary markets or in California, where permanence involves long-term contracts or insurance pools, forests in the New Zealand market liable for emissions when harvested or following land-use change. This means sellers account for future emission risks related to harvesting when they enter forests into carbon contracts. Offset prices were around USD13 tCO_2^{-1} in 2016 but have risen to more than USD20 tCO_2^{-1} in 2020.

The voluntary market data in Table 7.4 are offsets developed under the major standard-setting organisations, and issued from 2008–2018 (e.g., Hamrick and Gallant 2018). Note that there is some potential for double counting of voluntary offsets that may have been transacted in the California compliance market, however this would only have applied to transactions of US-issued offsets, and the largest share of annual transactions of voluntary AFOLU credits occurs with credits generated in Latin America, followed by Africa, Asia and North America. Europe and Oceania have few voluntary carbon market transactions. Within forestry and agriculture, most of the voluntary offsets were generated by forestry projects. Using historical transaction data from various *Forest Trends* reports, the offsets generated were valued at USD46.9 million yr^{-1}. Prices for voluntary offset transactions in the period 2014–2016 ranged from USD4.90 to USD5.40 tCO_2^{-1} (Hamrick and Gallant 2017a).

Table 7.4 | Estimates of achieved emission offsets or reductions in AFOLU through 2018. Data include CDM, voluntary carbon standards, compliance markets, and reduced deforestation from official UNFCCC reports. Carbon sequestration due to other government policies not included.

Fund/mechanism	Total emission reductions or offsets (MtCO₂-eq)	Time frame	MtCO₂-eq yr⁻¹	Financing (million USD yr⁻¹)
CDM-forest [a]	11.3	2007–2015	1.3	–
CDM-agriculture [a]	21.8	2007–2015	2.4	–
REDD+ (Guyana) [b]	12.8	2010–2015	2.1	33.0
Reduced Deforestation/REDD+ Brazil [c]	6894.5	2006–2017	574.5	49.2
REDD+ Indonesia [c]	244.9	2013–2017	49.0	13.4
REDD+ Argentina [c]	165.2	2014–2015	55.1	1.4
REDD+ Others [c]	211.8	2010–2017	26.5	46.0
Voluntary Market [d]	95.3	2009–2018	9.5	46.9
Australia ERF [e]	42.7	2012—2019[h]	6.1	53.6
California [f]	122.2	2013–2018	20.4	227.1
New Zealand carbon trading [g]	83.9	2010–2019	8.4	101.7
Total	**7,897.4**	**2007–2018**	**658.1 h**	**569.1**

[a] Clean Development Mechanism Registry: https://cdm.unfccc.int/Registry/index.html (accessed 22 June 2021).

[b] Roopsind et al. 2019.

[c] UNFCCC REDD+ Web Platform (https://redd.unfccc.int/submissions.html) and UNFCCC Biennial Update Report database (https://unfccc.int/BURs).

[d] (Hamrick and Gallant 2017a). State of Forest Carbon Finance. Forest Trends Ecosystem Marketplace. Washington, DC, USA.

[e] Data for Australia carbon credit units (ACCUs) from Australia Emissions Reduction Fund Registry for agricultural and vegetation and savanna burning projects through FY2018/19 (downloaded on 24/10/2019): (http://www.cleanenergyregulator.gov.au/ERF/project-and-contracts-registers/project-register) and from Emissions Reduction Fund auction results to December 2018: (http://www.cleanenergyregulator.gov.au/ERF/auctions-results/december-2018).

[f] Data from the California Air Resources Board Offset Issuance registry (https://ww2.arb.ca.gov/our-work/programs/compliance-offset-program) for forestry and agricultural early action and compliance credits.

[g] Surrendered forest carbon credits from post-1989 forests in New Zealand. Obtained from New Zealand Environmental Protection Authority. ETS Unit Movement interactive report (Excel based). https://www.epa.govt.nz/industry-areas/emissions-trading-scheme/ets-reports/unit-movement/.

[h] Obtained 13/08/2020. All non-CO₂ gases are converted to CO₂-eq using IPCC GWP100 values recommended at the time the project achieved approval by the relevant organisation or agency.

Voluntary finance has amounted to USD0.5 billion over a 10-year period for development of forest and agricultural credits. The three regulatory markets quantified amount to USD2.7 billion in funding from 2010 to 2019. For the most part, this funding has focused on forest projects and programs, with agricultural projects accounting for 5–10% of the total. In total, reported funding for AFOLU projects and programmes has been USD4.4 billion over the past decade, or about USD569 million yr^{-1} (*low confidence*). The largest share of the total carbon includes efforts in the Amazon by Brazil. Government expenditures on regulatory programmes and business expenditures on voluntary programmes in Brazil (e.g., the soy or cattle moratoriums) were not included in financing estimates due to difficulties obtaining that data. If Brazil and CDM (for which we have no cost estimates) are left out of the calculation, average cost per ton has been USD3.20 tCO$_2{}^{-1}$.

The large number of policy approaches described in Table 7.4 combined with efforts by other international actors, such as the Global Environmental Facility (GEF), as well as non-state actors (e.g., eco-labelling programmes and corporate social responsibility initiatives) illustrate significant policy experimentation over the last several decades. Despite widespread effort, AFOLU measures have thus far failed to achieve the large potential for climate mitigation described in earlier IPCC WG III reports (*high confidence*). The limited gains from AFOLU to date appear largely to result from lack of investment and other institutional and social barriers, rather than methodological concerns (*high confidence*).

7.6.2 Review of Observed Policies and Policy Instruments

7.6.2.1 Economic Incentives

Emissions Trading/Carbon Taxes. While emissions trading programmes have been developed across the globe, forest and agriculture have not been included as part of the cap in any of the existing systems. However, offsets from forestry and agriculture have been included in several of the trading programs. New Zealand has a hybrid programme where carbon storage in forests can be voluntarily entered into the carbon trading program, but once entered, forests are counted both as a sink for carbon if net gains are positive, and a source when harvesting occurs. New Zealand is considering rules to include agricultural GHG emissions under a future cap (Henderson et al. 2020; see: https://www.agmatters.nz/topics/he-waka-eke-noa/).

The state of California has developed a formal cap and trade programme that allows a limited number of forest and agricultural offset credits to be used under the cap. All offsets must meet protocols to account for additionality, permanence and leakage. Forest projects used as offsets in California currently are located in the USA, but the California Air Resources Board adopted a tropical forest carbon standard, allowing for avoided deforestation projects from outside the USA to enter the California market (CARB 2019).

Canadian provinces have developed a range of policy options that can include carbon offsets. Quebec has an emissions trading programme that plans to allow forest and agricultural offsets generated within the province to be utilised. Alberta also allows offsets to be utilised by regulated sectors while British Columbia allows offsets to be utilised by the government for its carbon neutrality goals (Government of Alberta, 2021). Over 20 countries and regions have adopted explicit carbon taxes on carbon emission sources and fossil fuels, however, the charges have not been applied to non-CO$_2$ agricultural emissions (OECD 2021a). California may implement regulations on methane emissions from cattle, however, regulations if approved, will not go into effect until 2024. Institutional and trade-related barriers (e.g., leakage) likely will limit widespread implementation of taxes on emissions in the food sector globally. Many countries exempt purchases of fuels used in agricultural or fishery production from fuel or carbon taxes, thus lowering the effective tax rate imposed on those sectors (OECD 2021a). Furthermore, bioenergy, produced from agricultural products, agricultural waste, and wood is often exempted from explicit carbon taxes. Colombia recently implemented a carbon tax on liquid fuels but allowed domestically produced forestry credits to offset the tax. Colombia also is in the process of developing an emissions trading scheme (OECD 2021a).

REDD+/Payment for Ecosystem Services (PES). PES programmes for a variety of ecosystem services have long been utilised for conservation (e.g., Wunder 2007) and may now be as large as USD42 billion yr^{-1} (Salzman et al. 2018). REDD+ emerged in the early 2000s and is a widely recognised example of PES programme focused on conservation of tropical forests (Table 7.4). However, our summation of actually paid funds in Table 7.4 is much smaller than what is portrayed by Salzman et al. (2018). REDD+ may operate at the country level, or for specific programmes or forests within a country. As with other PES programs, REDD+ has evolved towards a results-based programme that involves payments that are conditioned on meeting certain successes or milestones, such as rates of deforestation (Angelsen 2017).

A large literature has investigated whether PES programmes have successfully protected habitats. Studies in the USA found limited additionality for programmes that encouraged conservation tillage practices, but stronger additionality for programmes that encouraged set-asides for grasslands or forests (Woodward et al. 2016; Claassen et al. 2018), although the set-asides led to estimated leakage of 20 up to 100% (Pfaff and Robalino 2017; Kallio et al. 2018; Wu 2000). Evidence from the EU similarly suggests that payments for some agroenvironmental practices may be additional, while others are not (Chabé-Ferret and Subervie 2013). Other studies, in particular in Latin America where many PES programmes have been implemented, have found a wide range of estimates of effectiveness (e.g., Honey-Rosés et al. 2011; Robalino and Pfaff 2013; Alix-Garcia et al. 2015; Robalino et al. 2015; Mohebalian and Aguilar 2016; Jayachandran et al. 2017; Börner et al. 2017; Burivalova et al. 2019). Despite concerns, the many lessons learned from PES programme implementation provide critical information that will help policymakers refine future PES programmes to increase their effectiveness (*medium confidence*).

While expectations that carbon-centred REDD+ would be a simple and efficient mechanism for climate mitigation have not been met (Turnhout et al. 2017; Arts et al. 2019), progress has nonetheless occurred. Measuring, monitoring and verification systems have been developed and deployed, REDD readiness programmes have improved capacity to implement REDD+ on the ground in over 50 countries, and a number of countries now have received results-based payments.

Empirical evidence that REDD+ funding has slowed deforestation is starting to emerge. Simonet et al. (2019) showed that a REDD+ project in Brazil reduced deforestation certainly until 2018, while Roopsind et al. (2019) showed that country-level REDD+ payments to Guyana encouraged reduced deforestation and increased carbon storage. Although more impact evaluation (IE) analysis needs to be conducted on REDD+ payments, these studies support the country-level estimates of carbon benefits from REDD+ shown in Table 7.4. Nearly all of the analysis of PES and REDD+ to date has focused on the presence or absence of forest cover, with little to no analysis having been conducted on forest degradation, conservation, or enhancement of forest stocks.

Agroenvironmental Subsidy Programs/PES. Climate policy for agriculture has developed more slowly than in other sectors due to concerns with food security and livelihoods, political interests, and difficulties in coordinating diffuse and diverse activities and stakeholders (e.g., nutritional health, rural development, and biodiversity conservation) (Leahy et al. 2020). However, a review of the National Adaptation Programme of Action (NAPAs), National Adaptation Plans (NAPs), NAMAs, and NDCs in the Paris Agreement suggest an increasing focus of policy makers on agriculture and food security. The vast majority of parties to the Paris Agreement recognise the significant role of agriculture in supporting a secure sustainable development pathway (Richards and VanWey 2015) with the inclusion of agriculture mitigation in 103 NDCs from a total of 160 NDC submissions. Livestock is the most frequently cited specific agricultural sub-sector, with mitigation activities generally focusing on increasing efficiency and productivity.

Agriculture is one of the most subsidised industries globally, especially in the European Union and the USA. While subsidy payments over the last 20 years have shifted modestly to programmes designed to reduce the environmental impact of the agricultural sector, only 15–20% of the more than USD700 billion spent globally on subsidies are green payments (OECD 2021b). Under the Common Agricultural Policy in the EU, up to 30% of the direct payments to farmers (Pillar 1) have been green payments (Henderson et al. 2020), including some actions that could increase carbon storage or reduce emissions. Similarly, at least 30% of the rural development payments (Pillar 2) are used for measures that reduce environmental impact, including reduction of GHG emissions and carbon storage. There is limited evidence that these policies contributed to the 20% reduction in GHG emissions from the agricultural sector in the EU between 1990 and 2018 (Baudrier et al. 2015; Eurostat 2020).

The USA spends USD4 billion yr^{-1} on conservation programs, or 12% of net farm income (Department of Agriculture 2020). In real terms, this expenditure has remained constant for 15 years, supporting 12 Mha

of permanent grass or woodland cover in the Conservation Reserve Program (CRP), which has increased soil carbon sequestration by 3 tCO$_2$ ha^{-1} yr^{-1} (Conant et al. 2017; Paustian et al. 2019), as well as other practices that could lower net emissions. Gross GHG emissions from the agricultural sector in the US, however, have increased since 1990 (USEPA 2020) due to reductions in the area of land in the US CRP programme and changes in crop rotations, both of which caused soil carbon stocks to decline (USEPA 2020). When combined with increased non-CO$_2$ gas emissions, the emission intensity of US agriculture increased from 1.5 to 1.7 tCO$_2$ ha^{-1} between 2005 and 2018 (*high confidence*).

China has implemented large conservation programmes that have influenced carbon stocks. For example, the Sloping Land Conversion Program, combined with other programs, has increased forest cover and carbon stocks, reduced erosion and increased other ecosystem services in China in recent years (Ouyang et al. 2016). As part of Brazil's national strategy, numerous practices to reduce GHG emissions from agriculture, and in particular from the animal agriculture industry, have been subsidised. Estimates by Manzatto et al. (2020) suggest that the programme may have reduced agricultural emissions by 169 MtCO$_2$ between 2010 and 2020. Given the large technical and economic potential for agroforestry to be deployed in Africa, subsidy approaches could be deployed along with other polices to enhance carbon through innovative practices such as regreening (Box 7.10).

7.6.2.2 Regulatory Approaches

Regulations on land use include direct controls on how land is used, zoning, or legally set limits on converting land from one use to another. Since the early 2000s, Brazil has deployed various regulatory measures to slow deforestation, including enforcement of regulations on land-use change in the legal Amazon area. Enforcement of these regulations, among other approaches is credited with encouraging the large-scale reduction in deforestation and associated carbon emissions after 2004 (Nepstad et al. 2014). Empirical evidence has found that regulations reduced deforestation in Brazil (Arima et al. 2014) but over time, reversals occurred when enforcement was not consistent (Azevedo et al. 2017) (Box 7.9).

Many OECD countries have strong legal frameworks that influence agricultural and forest management on both public and private land. These include for example, legal requirements to protect endangered species, implement conservation tillage, protect riparian areas, replant forests after harvest, maintain historical species composition, forest certification, and other approaches. Increasingly, laws support more widespread implementation of nature-based solutions for a range of environmental issues (e.g., see European Commission-EU 2021). The extent to which the combined influence of these regulations has enhanced carbon storage in ecosystems is not quantified although they are likely to explain some of the persistent carbon sink that has emerged in temperate forests of OECD countries (*high confidence*). In the least developed and developing countries, regulatory approaches face challenges in part because environmental issues are a lower priority than many other socio-economic issues (e.g., poverty, opportunity, essential services), and weak governance (Mayer Pelicice 2019; Walker et al. 2020) (Box 7.2).

Set asides and protected areas have been a widely utilised approach for conservation, and according to (FAO 2020d), 726 Mha (18%) of forests are in protected areas globally. A review of land sparing and land sharing policies in developing countries indicated that most of them follow land sparing models, sometimes in combination with land sharing approaches. However, there is still no clear evidence of which policy provides the best results for ecosystem services provision, conservation, and livelihoods (Mertz and Mertens 2017). The literature contains a wide range of results on the effectiveness of protected areas to reduce deforestation (Burivalova et al. 2019), with studies suggesting that protected areas provide significant protection of forests (e.g., Blackman 2015), modest protection (Andam et al. 2008), as well as increases in deforestation (Blackman 2015) and possible leakage of harvesting to elsewhere (Kallio et al. 2018). An estimate of the contributions of protected areas to mitigation between 2000 and 2012, showed that in the tropics, PAs reduced carbon emissions from deforestation by 4.88 PgC, or around 29%, when compared to the expected rates of deforestation (Bebber and Butt 2017). In that study,

the tropical Americas (368.8 TgC yr^{-1}) had the largest contribution, followed by Asia (25.0 TgC yr^{-1}) and Africa (12.7 TgC yr^{-1}). The authors concluded that local factors had an important influence on the effectiveness of protected areas. For example, in the Brazilian Amazon, protected area effectiveness is affected by the government agency controlling the land (federal indigenous lands, federal PAs, and state PAs) (Herrera et al. 2019). Because protected areas limit not just land-use change, but also logging or harvesting non-timber forest products, they may be relatively costly approaches for forest conservation (*medium confidence*).

Community forest management (CFM) allows less intensive use of forest resources, while at the same time providing carbon benefits by protecting forest cover. Community forest management provides property rights to communities to manage resources in exchange for their efforts to protect those resources. In many cases, the local communities are indigenous people who otherwise would have insecure tenure due to an advancing agricultural frontier or mining

---

Box 7.8 | Management of Native Forests by the Menominee people in North America and Lessons From Forest Owner Associations

Summary of the case. Indigenous peoples include more than 5000 different peoples, with over 370 million people, in 70 countries on five continents (UNIPP 2012). For example, in Latin America and Caribbean, forests cover more than 80% of the area occupied by indigenous peoples (330 million hectares) (FAO and FILAC, 2021) which points to their critical role for forest governance (Garnett et al. 2018; Fa et al. 2020). The Menominee people (Wisconsin, USA) practice sustainable forestry on their reservation according to a land ethic integral to the tribal identity. The Tribe calls themselves 'The Forest Keepers', recognising that the connection of their future to the sustainable management of the forest that allowed the forest volume standing today to be higher than when timber harvesting began more than 160 years ago. Management practices are based on continuous forest inventories (Mausel et al. 2017).

Introduction to the case. Forest management and timber harvesting operations began shortly after the Menominee Indian Reservation was created by treaty in 1854. The Menominee reservation sits on about 95,000 ha of land in Wisconsin that spans multiple forest types and is more diverse than adjacent forests. The collectively maintained reservation has 87% of its land under sustained yield forestry.

Case description. The Tribe, in the 19th century, had already mastered vegetation manipulation with fire, sustainable forestry, multiple-use, ecosystem, and adaptive management. The centrepiece of the Tribe's economy has been its forest product industry, Menominee Tribal Enterprises (MTE) (Pecore 1992). A balance between growth and removals and continuous forest inventories (CFI) are central for forest management for the past 160 years, aiming not at very large volumes, but at very high-quality trees. During this same period, more than 2.3 billion board feet have been harvested from the same area, equivalent to 0.3 m^3 ha^{-1} yr^{-1}.

Interactions and limitations. In 2013, the Menominee Tribe started a collaboration with the US Forest Service to implement climate adaptation measures. The Tribe actively works to reduce the risk of forest damage and decided to further promote diversity by planting tree seedlings adapted to a warming climate (https://toolkit.climate.gov/case-studies/and-trees-will-last-forever). However, new challenges are related to increasing pressures on forest ecosystems such as non-native insects, pathogens, weed invasions, and the costs for continuous forest inventories to support long-term forest management.

Identified lessons. The elements of sustainability are intertwined with Menominee history, culture, spirituality, and ethics. The balance between the environment, community, and economy for the short term as well as future generations is an example of protecting the entire environment as the Menominee land is a non-fragmented remnant of the prehistoric Lake States forest which has been dramatically reduced all around the reserve (Schabel and Pecore 1997). These and other types of community forest owner associations exist all over the world. Examples are Södra in Sweden (with 52,000 forest owners) (Södra, 2021) or Waldbauernverband in North-Rhine Westphalia (with 150,000 forest owners and covering 585,000 ha) (AGDW-The Forest Owners, 2021). These are ways for small forest owners to educate, jointly put wood on the market, employ better forest management, use machinery together, and apply certification jointly. In this manner and with all their diversity of goals, they manage to maintain carbon sinks and stocks, while preserving biodiversity and producing wood.

7

activity. Other examples are forest owner associations like those discussed in Box 7.8. According to the Rights and Resources Initiative (2018), the area of forests under community management increased globally by 152 Mha from 2002 to 2017, with over 500 Mha under community management in 2017. Studies have now shown that improved property rights with community forest management can reduce deforestation and increase carbon storage (Deininger and Minten 2002; Alix-Garcia et al. 2005; Alix-Garcia 2007; Bowler et al. 2012; Blackman 2015; Fortmann et al. 2017; Burivalova et al. 2019). Efforts to expand property rights, especially community forest management, have reduced carbon emissions from deforestation in tropical forests in the last two decades (*high confidence*), although the extent of carbon savings has not been quantified globally.

Bioenergy targets. Multiple policies have been enacted at national and supra-national levels to promote the use of bioenergy in the transport sector, and for bioelectricity production. Existing policies mandate or subsidise the production and use of bioenergy. In the past few years, policies have been proposed, put in place or updated in Australia (Renewable Energy Target), Brazil (RenovaBio, Nationally Determined Contribution), Canada (Clean Fuel Standard), China (Biodiesel Industrial Development Policy, Biodiesel Fuel Blend Standard), the European Union (Renewable Energy Directive II), the USA (Renewable Fuel Standards), Japan (FY2030), Russia (Energy Strategy Bill 2035), India (Revised National Policy on Biofuels), and South Africa (Biofuels Regulatory Framework).

While current policies focus on bioenergy to decarbonise the energy system, some also contain provisions to minimise the potential environmental and social trade-offs from bioenergy production. For instance, the EU Renewable Energy Directive (EU-RED II) and US Renewable Energy Standard (US-RFS) assign caps on the use of biofuels, which are associated with indirect land-use change and food-security concerns. The Netherlands has a stringent set of 36 sustainability criteria to which the certified biomass needs to comply. The EU-RED II also sets a timeline for the complete phase-out of high-risk biofuels (Section 7.4.4).

7.6.2.3   Voluntary Actions and Agreements

Forest certification programs, such as Forest Sustainability Council (FSC) or Programme for the Endorsement of Forest Certification (PEFC), are consumer driven, voluntary programmes that influence timber harvesting practices, and may reduce emissions from forest degradation with reduced impact logging and other approaches (*medium confidence*). Forest certification has expanded globally to over 440 Mha (Kraxner et al. 2017). As the area of land devoted to certification has increased, the amount of timber produced from certified land has increased. In 2018, FSC accounted for harvests of 427 million m^3 and jointly FSC and PEFC accounted for 689 million m^3 in 2016 or around 40% of total industrial wood production (FAO 2018c). There is evidence that reduced impact logging can reduce carbon losses in tropical regions (Pearson et al. 2014; Ellis et al. 2019). However, there is conflicting evidence about whether forest certification reduces deforestation (e.g., Blackman et al. 2018; Tritsch et al. 2020).

Supply chain management in the food sector encourages more widespread use of conservation measures in agriculture (*high confidence*). The number of private commitments to reduce deforestation from supply chains has greatly increased in recent years, with at least 865 public commitments by 447 producers, processors, traders, manufacturers and retailers as of December, 2020 (New York Declaration on Forests 2021). Industry partnerships with NGOs, such as the Roundtable on Sustainable Palm Oil (RSPO), have become more widespread and visible in agricultural production. For example, RSPO certifies members all along the supply chain for palm oil and claims around 19% of total production. Similar sustainability efforts exist for many of the world's major agricultural products, including soybeans, rice, sugar cane, and cattle.

There is evidence that the Amazon Soy Moratorium (ASM), an industry-NGO effort whereby large industry consumers agreed voluntarily not to purchase soybeans grown on land deforested after 2006, reduced deforestation in the legal Amazon (Nepstad et al. 2014; Gibbs et al. 2015). However, recent studies have shown that some deforestation from the Amazon was displaced to the Cerrado (Brazilian savannas) region (Moffette and Gibbs 2021), which is a global hotspot for biodiversity, and has significant carbon stocks. These results illustrate the importance of broadening the scope of supply chain management to minimise or eliminate displacement (Lima et al. 2019). In addition, while voluntary efforts may improve environmental outcomes for a time, it is not clear that they are sufficient to deliver long-term reductions in deforestation, given the increases in deforestation that have occurred in the Amazon in recent years (Box 7.9). Voluntary efforts would be more effective at slowing deforestation if they present stronger linkages to regulatory or other approaches (Lambin et al. 2018).

Box 7.9 | Case Study: Deforestation Control in the Brazilian Amazon

Summary

Between 2000 and 2004, deforestation rates in the Brazilian Legal Amazon (is a socio-geographic division containing all nine Brazilian states in the Amazon basin) increased from 18,226 to 27,772 km^2 yr^{-1} 2008 (INPE, 2021). A set of public policies designed in participatory process involving federal government, states, municipalities, and civil society successfully reduced deforestation rates until 2012. However, deforestation rates increased after 2013, and particularly between 2019 and 2020. Successful deforestation control policies are being negatively affected by changes in environmental governance, weak law enforcement, and polarisation of the national politics.

Box 7.9 (Continued)

Background

In 2004, the Brazilian federal government started the Action Plan for Prevention and Control of Deforestation in the Legal Amazon (PPCDAm) (Ministry of Environment, Government of Brazil, 2018).

The PPCDAm was a benchmark for the articulation of forest conservation policies that included central and state governments, prosecutor offices, and the civil society. The decline in deforestation after 2008 is mostly attributed to these policy options. In 2012, deforestation rates decreased to 4,571 km^2 yr^{-1}.

Case description

Combating deforestation was a theme in several programs, government plans, and projects not being more restricted to the environmental agenda. This broader inclusion resulted from a long process of insertion and articulation in the government dating back to 2003 while elaborating on the Sustainable Amazon Plan. In May 2003, a historic meeting took place in an Amazonian city, with the president of the Republic, state governors, ministers, and various business leaders, civil institutions, and social movements. It was presented and approved the document entitled 'Sustainable Amazonia – Guidelines and Priorities of the Ministry of Environment for the Sustainable Development of the Amazon Brazilian', containing several guidelines for conservation and sustainable use in the region. At the meeting, the Union and some states signed a Cooperation Agreement aiming to elaborate a plan for the Amazon, to be widely discussed with the various sectors of the regional and national society (Ministerio do Meio Ambiente, MMA, 2013).

Interactions and limitations

The PPCDAm had three main lines of action: (i) territorial management and land use; (ii) command and control; and (iii) promotion of sustainable practices. During the execution of the 1st and 2nd phases of the PPCDAm (2004–2011), important results in the territorial management and land-use component included, for example, the creation of 25 Mha of federal Protected Areas (PAs) located mainly in front of the expansion of deforestation, as well as the homologation of 10 Mha of Indigenous Lands. Also, states and municipalities created approximately 25 Mha, so that all spheres of government contributed to the expansion of PAs in the Brazilian Amazon. In the 'command and control' component, agencies performed hundreds of inspection operations against illegal activities (e.g., illegal logging) under strategic planning based on technical and territorial priorities. Besides, there was a significant improvement of the environmental monitoring systems, involving the analysis of satellite images to guide actions on the ground. Another policy was the restriction of public credit to enterprises linked to illegal deforestation following a resolution of the Brazilian Central Bank (2008) (Ministerio do Meio Ambiente, MMA, 2013). Also, in 2008, Brazil created the Amazon Fund, a REDD+ mechanism (Government of Brazil, n.d.).

However, the country's political polarisation has gradually eroded environmental governance, especially after the Brazilian Forest Code changes in 2012 (major environmental law in Brazil), the presidential impeachment in 2016, presidential elections in 2018, and the start of the new federal administration in 2019. Successful deforestation control policies are being negatively affected by critical changes in the political context, and weakening the environmental rule of law, forest conservation, and sustainable development programmes (for example, changes in the Amazon Fund governance in disagreement with the main donors). In 2019, the annual deforestation rate reached 10,129 km^2 being the first time it surpassed 10,000 km^2 since 2008 (INPE, 2021). Besides, there has been no effective transition from the historical economic model to a sustainable one. The lack of clarity in the ownership of land is still a major unresolved issue in the Amazon.

Lessons

The reduction of deforestation in the Brazilian Amazon was possible due to effective political and institutional support for environmental conservation. The initiatives of the Action Plan included the expansion of the protected areas network (conservation unities and indigenous lands), improvement of deforestation monitoring to the enforcement of environmental laws, and the use of economic instruments, for example, by cutting off public credit for municipalities with higher deforestation rates (Ricketts et al. 2010; Souza et al. 2013; Nepstad et al. 2014; Arima et al. 2014; Blackman and Veit 2018).

The array of public policies and social engagement was a historical and legal breakthrough in global protection. However, the broader political and institutional context and actions to reduce the representation and independent control of civil society movements in decision-making bodies weaken this structure with significant increases in deforestation rates, burnings, and forest fires.

Box 7.10 | Regreening the Sahel, Northern Africa

Case description

More than 200 million trees have regenerated on more than 5 Mha in the Sahel (Sendzimir et al. 2011). The Maradi/Zinder region of Niger is the epicentre of experimentation and scale up. This vast geographic extent generates significant mitigation potential despite the relatively modest per unit area increase in carbon of about 0.4 MgC ha^{-1} a^{-1} (Luedeling and Neufeldt 2012). In addition to the carbon benefits, these agroforestry systems decrease erosion, provide animal fodder, recharge groundwater, generate nutrition and income benefits and act as safety nets for vulnerable rural households during climate and other shocks (Bayala et al. 2014, 2015; Binam et al. 2015; Sinare and Gordon 2015; Ilstedt et al. 2016).

Lessons

A mélange of factors contributed to regreening in the Sahel. Increased precipitation, migration, community development, economic volatility and local policy reform have all likely played a role (Haglund et al. 2011; Sendzimir et al. 2011; Brandt et al. 2019a; Garrity and Bayala 2019); the easing of forestry regulations has been particularly critical in giving farmers greater control over the management and use of trees on their land (Garrity et al. 2010). This policy shift was catalysed by greater regional autonomy resulting from economic decline and coincided with successful pilots and NGO-led experimentation, cash-for-work, and training efforts to support changes in land management (Sendzimir et al. 2011). Participation of farmers in planning and implementation helped align actions with local knowledge and goals as well as market opportunities.

Regreening takes place when dormant seed or tree stumps sprout and are cultivated through the technique, called Farmer Managed Natural Regeneration (FMNR). Without planting new trees, FMNR is presumed to be cheaper than other approaches to restoration, though comparative economic analysis has yet to be conducted (Chomba et al. 2020). Relatively lower investment costs are believed to have contributed to the replication across the landscape. These factors worked together to contribute to a groundswell of action that affected rights, access, and use of local resources (Tougiani et al. 2009).

Regreening in the Sahel and the consequent transformation of the landscape has resulted from the actions of hundreds of thousands of individuals responding to social and biophysical signals (Hanan 2018). This is an example for climate change mitigation, where eliminating regulations – versus increasing them – has led to carbon dioxide removal.

7.6.2.4 Mitigation Effectiveness: Additionality, Permanence and Leakage

Additionality, permanence and leakage have been widely discussed in the forestry and agricultural mitigation literature (Murray et al. 2007), including in AR5 (Section 11.3.2 of the AR5WGIII report) and earlier assessment reports. Since the earlier assessment reports, new studies have emerged to provide new insights on the effect of these issues on the credibility of forest and agricultural mitigation. This assessment also provides additional context not considered in earlier assessments.

Typically, carbon registries will require that project developers show additionality by illustrating that the project is not undertaken as a result of a legal requirement, and that the project achieves carbon reductions above and beyond a business as usual. The protocols developed by the California Air Resources Board to ensure permanence and additionality are strong standards and may even limit participation (e.g., Ruseva et al. 2017). The business as usual is defined as past management actions by the same entity that can be verified. Additionality can thus be observed in the future as a difference from historical actions. This approach has been used by several countries in their UNFCCC Biennial Update reports to establish reductions in carbon emissions from avoided deforestation (e.g., Brazil and Indonesia).

However, alternative statistical approaches have been deployed in the literature to assess additionality with a quasi-experimental method that rely on developing a counterfactual (e.g., Andam et al. 2008; Blackman 2015; Sills et al. 2015; Fortmann et al. 2017; Roopsind et al. 2019). In several studies, additionality in avoided deforestation was established after the project had been developed by comparing land-use change in treated plots where the policy or programme was in effect with land-use change in similar untreated plot. Alternatively, synthetic matching statistically compares trends in a treated region (i.e., a region with a policy) to trends in a region without the policy, and has been applied in a region in Brazil (e.g., Sills et al. 2015), and at the country level in Guyana (Roopsind et al. 2019). While these analyses establish that many projects to reduce deforestation have overcome hurdles related to additionality (*high confidence*), there has not been a systematic assessment of the elements of project or programme design that lead to high levels of additionality. Such assessment could help developers design projects to better meet additionality criteria.

The same experimental methods have been applied to analyse additionality of the adoption of soil conservation and nutrient management practices in agriculture. Claassen et al. (2018) find that programmes to promote soil conservation are around 50% additional across the USA (i.e., 50% of the land enrolled in soil conservation programmes would not have been enrolled if not for the programme), while Woodward et al. (2016) find that adoption of conservation tillage is rarely additional. Claassen et al. (2018) find that payments for nutrient management plans are nearly 100% additional, although there is little evidence that farmers reduce nutrient inputs when they adopt plans. It is not clear if the same policy approaches would lead to additionality in other regions.

Permanence focuses on the potential for carbon sequestered in offsets to be released in the future due to natural or anthropogenic disturbances. Most offset registries have strong permanence requirements, although they vary in their specific requirements. The Verified Carbon Standard (VCS) from the Verra programme requires a pool of additional carbon credits that provides a buffer against inadvertent losses. The Climate Action Reserve (CAR) protocol for forests requires carbon to remain on the site for 100 years. The carbon on the site will be verified at pre-determined intervals over the life of the project. If carbon is diminished on a given site, the credits for the site have to be relinquished and the project developer has to use credits from their reserve fund (either other projects or purchased credits) to make up for the loss. Estimates of leakage in forestry projects in AR5 suggest that it can range from 10% to over 90% in the USA (Murray et al. 2004), and 20–50% in the tropics (Sohngen and Brown 2004) for forest set-asides and reduced harvesting. Carbon offset protocols have made a variety of assumptions. The Climate Action Reserve (CAR) assumes it is 20% in the USA. One of the voluntary protocols (Verra) uses specific information about the location of the project to calculate a location specific leakage factor.

More recent literature has developed explicit estimates of leakage based on statistical analysis of carbon projects or programs. The literature suggests that there are two economic pathways for leakage (e.g., (Roopsind et al. 2019), either through a shift in output price that occurs when outputs are affected by the policy or programme implementation, as described in (Wear and Murray 2004; Murray et al. 2004; Sohngen and Brown 2004; Gan and McCarl 2007), or through a shift in input prices and markets, such as for labour or capital, as analysed in (Andam et al. 2008; Alix-Garcia et al. 2012; Honey-Rosés et al. 2011; Fortmann et al. 2017). Estimates of leakage through product markets (e.g., timber prices) have suggested leakage of up to 90% (Sohngen and Brown 2004; Murray et al. 2004; Gan and McCarl 2007; Kallio et al. 2018), while studies that consider shifts in input markets are considerably smaller. The analysis of leakage for the Guyana programme by Roopsind et al. (2019) revealed no statistically significant leakage in Suriname. A key design feature for any programme to reduce leakage is to increase incentives for complementary mitigation policies to be implemented in areas where leakage may occur. Efforts to continue to draw more forests into carbon policy initiatives will reduce leakage over time Roopsind et al. (2019), suggesting that if NDCs continue to encompass a broader selection of policies, measures and forests over time, leakage will decline.

7.6.3   Assessment of Current Policies and Potential Future Approaches

The Paris Agreement encourages a wide range of policy approaches, including REDD+, sustainable management of forests, joint mitigation and adaptation, and emphasises the importance of non-

carbon benefits and equity for sustainable development (Martius et al. 2016). Around USD0.7 billion yr^{-1} has been invested in land-based carbon offsets (Table 7.4), but as noted in Streck (2012), there is a large funding gap between these efforts and the scale of efforts necessary to meet 1.5 or 2.0°C targets outlined in SR1.5. As Box 7.12 discusses, forestry actions could achieve up to 5.8 GtCO$_2$ yr^{-1} with costs rising from USD178 billion yr^{-1} to USD400 billion yr^{-1} by 2050. Over half of this investment is expected to occur in Latin America, with 13% in SE Asia and 17% in sub-Saharan Africa (Austin et al. 2020). Other studies have suggested that similar sized programmes are possible, although they do not quantify total costs (e.g., Griscom et al. 2017; Busch et al. 2019). The currently quantified efforts to reduce net emissions with forests and agricultural actions are helpful, but society will need to quickly ramp up investments to achieve carbon sequestration levels consistent with high levels of mitigation. Only 2.5% of climate mitigation funding goes to land-based mitigation options, an order of magnitude below the potential proportional contribution (Buchner et al. 2015).

To date, there has been significantly less investment in agricultural projects than forestry projects to reduce net carbon emissions (Table 7.4). For example, the economic potential (available up to USD100 tCO$_2^{-1}$) for soil carbon sequestration in croplands is 1.9 (0.4–6.8) GtCO$_2$ yr^{-1} (Section 7.4.3.1), however, less than 2% of the carbon in Table 7.4 is derived from soil carbon sequestration projects. While reductions in CH$_4$ emissions due to enteric fermentation constitute a large share of potential agricultural mitigation reported in Section 7.4, agricultural CH$_4$ emission reductions so far have been relatively modest compared to forestry sequestration. The protocols to quantify emission reductions in the agricultural sector are available and have been tested, and the main limitation appears to be the lack of available financing or the unwillingness to re-direct current subsidies (*medium confidence*).

Although quantified emission reductions in agricultural projects are limited to date, a number of OECD and economy in transition parties have reduced their net emissions through carbon storage in cropland soils since 2000. These reductions in emissions have typically resulted from policy innovations outside of the climate space, or market trends. For example, in the USA, there has been widespread adoption of conservation tillage in the last 30 years as a labour-saving crop management technique. In Europe, agricultural N$_2$O and CH$_4$ emissions have declined due to reductions in nutrient inputs and cattle numbers (Henderson et al. 2020). These reductions may be attributed to mechanism within the Common Agricultural Policy (Section 7.6.2.1), but could also be linked to higher nutrient prices in the 2000–2014 period. Other environmental policies could play a role, for example, efforts to reduce water pollution from phosphorus in The Netherlands, may ultimately reduce cattle numbers, also lowering CH$_4$ emissions.

Numerous developing countries have established policy efforts to abate agricultural emissions or increase carbon storage. Brazil, for instance, developed a subsidy programme in 2010 to promote sustainable development in agriculture, and practices that would reduce GHG emissions. Henderson et al. (2020) report that this programme reduced GHG emission in agricultural by up to

170 MtCO$_2$ between 2010 and 2018. However, the investments in low-carbon agriculture in Brazil amounted only 2% of the total funds for conventional agriculture in 2019. Programmes on deforestation in Brazil had successes and failures, as described in Box 7.9. Indonesia has engaged in a wide range of programmes in the REDD+ space, including a moratorium implemented in 2011 to prevent the conversion of primary forests and peatlands to oil palm and logging concessions (Wijaya et al. 2017; Tacconi and Muttaqin 2019; Henderson et al. 2020). Efforts to restore peatlands and forests have also been undertaken. Indonesia reports that results-based REDD+ programmes have been successful and have led to lower rates of deforestation (Table 7.4).

Existing policies focused on GHG management in agriculture and forestry is less advanced in Africa than in Latin American and Asia, however, Henderson et al. (2020) report on 10 countries in sub-Saharan Africa that have included explicit policy proposals for reducing AFOLU GHG emissions through their NDCs. These include efforts to reduce N$_2$O emission, increase implementation of conservation agriculture, improve livestock management, and implement forestry and grassland practices, including agroforestry

(Box 7.10). Within several of the NDCs, countries have explicitly suggested intensification as an approach to reduce emission in the livestock sector. However, it is important to note caveats associated with pursuing mitigation via intensification (Box 7.11).

The agricultural sector throughout the world is influenced by many policies that affect production practices, crop choices and land use. It is difficult to quantify the effect of these policies on reference level GHG emissions from the sector, as well as the cost estimates presented in Sections 7.4 and 7.5. The presence of significant subsidy programmes intended to improve farmer welfare and rural livelihoods makes it more difficult to implement regulatory programmes aimed at reducing net emissions in agriculture, however, it may increase the potential to implement new subsidy programmes that encourage practices aimed at reducing net emissions (*medium confidence*). For instance, in the USA, crop insurance can influence both crop choices and land use (Miao et al. 2016; Claassen et al. 2017), both of which will affect emission trends. Regulations to limit nutrient applications have not been widely considered, however, federal subsidy programmes have been implemented to encourage farmers to conduct nutrient management planning.

Box 7.11 | Sustainable Intensification Within Agriculture: Evidence and Caveats

Introduction
Sustainable intensification (SI) has received considerable attention as a suggested means of pursuing increased overall production, reducing associated environmental externalities, and potentially releasing agricultural land for alternative uses, such as forestry or rewilding (Godfray and Garnett 2014; Pretty 2018). The concept was explored within the SRCCL (SRCCL (Mbow et al. 2019), Section 5.6.4.4 and Cross-Chapter Box 6 in Chapter 5). SI is context specific and dynamic, with no universally prescribed methodology (HLPE 2019). Equal importance is given to enhancing sustainability as to achieving agricultural intensification. The former aspect is often challenging to realise, measure and maintain.

The extent of sustainable intensification
Total global agricultural land area has remained relatively stable while overall production has increased in recent decades (Section 7.3), indicating that agricultural intensification, as judged by production per unit of land (Petersen and Snapp 2015; OECD and FAO 2019) has taken place. However, changes in agricultural land use and degradation of natural resources (UNEP 2019; IPBES 2019b) suggests that not all of this intensification is sustainable. Although agricultural intensification has led to less GHG emissions compared to a scenario where that intensification had not taken place (Burney et al. 2010), absolute agriculture related emissions have continued to increase (Section 7.2). Active pursuit of SI was found to be expanding, with implementation on an increasing area, notably in developing countries (Pretty et al. 2018), yet regional agricultural area expansion at the expense of native habitat also continues in such regions (Section 7.3). Although there are specific examples of SI (Box 7.13) global progress in achieving SI is acknowledged as slow (Cassman and Grassini 2020) with potentially multiple, context specific geophysical and socio-economic barriers to implementation (Firbank et al. 2018; da Silva et al. 2021).

Preconditions to ensure sustainable intensification
Increasing the total amount of product produced by improving production efficiency (output per unit of input) does not guarantee SI. It will only be successful if increased production efficiency translates into reduced environmental and social impacts as well as increased production. For example, AR5 highlighted a growing emphasis on reducing GHG emissions per unit of product via increasing production efficiency (Smith et al. 2014), but reductions in absolute GHG emissions will only occur when production efficiency increases at a greater rate than the rate at which production increases (Clark et al. 2005).

Defined indicators are required. Measurement of SI requires multiple indicators and metrics. It can be assessed at farm, regional or global scales and temporal aspect must be considered. SI may warrant whole system redesign or land reallocation (Garnett et al. 2013; Pretty et al. 2018). Accordingly, there is *high agreement* concerning the need to consider multiple environmental and social outcomes

Box 7.11 (Continued)

at wider spatial scales, such as catchments or regions (Weltin et al. 2018; Bengochea Paz et al. 2020; Cassman and Grassini 2020). Impacts may be considered in relative terms (per area or product unit), with relationships potentially antagonistic. Both area- and product unit-based metrics are valid, relevant under different contexts and useful in approaching SI, but do not capture overall impacts and trade-offs (Garnett 2014). To reduce the risk of unsustainable intensification, quantitative data and selection of appropriate metrics to identify and guide strategies are paramount (Garnett et al. 2013; Gunton et al. 2016; Cassman and Grassini 2020).

Avoiding unsustainable intensification
It is critical that intensification does not drive expansion of unsustainable practices. Increased productivity with associated economic reward could incentivise and reward agricultural land expansion, or environmentally and socially damaging practices on existing and former agricultural land (Ceddia et al. 2013; Phalan 2018). Accordingly, coordinated policies are crucial to ensuring desired outcomes (Godfray and Garnett 2014; Reddy et al. 2020; Kassam and Kassam 2020). Barretto et al. (2013) found that in agriculturally consolidated areas, land-use intensification coincided with either a contraction of both cropland and pasture areas, or cropland expansion at the expense of pastures, both resulting in a stable farmed area. In contrast, in agricultural frontier areas, land-use intensification coincided with expansion of agricultural lands.

In conclusion, SI within agriculture is needed given the rising global population and the need to address multiple environmental and social externalities associated with agricultural activities. However, implementation requires strong stakeholder engagement, appropriate regulations, rigorous monitoring and verification and comprehensive outreach and knowledge exchange programmes.

A factor that will influence future carbon storage in so-called land-based reservoirs involves considering short- and long-term climate benefits, as well as interactions among various natural climate solution options. The benefits of various natural climate solutions depend on a variety of spatially dependent issues as well as institutional factors, including their management status (managed or unmanaged systems), their productivity, opportunity costs, technical difficulty of implementation, local willingness to consider, property rights and institutions, among other factors. Biomass energy, as described elsewhere in this chapter and in (Cross-Working Group Box 3 in Chapter 12), is a potential example of an option with trade-offs that emerge when policies favour one type of mitigation strategy over another. Bioenergy production needs safeguards to limit negative impacts on carbon stocks on the land base as is already in place in the EU Renewable Energy Directive and several national schemes in Netherlands, UK and Denmark (Buchholz et al. 2016; Khanna et al. 2017; DeCicco and Schlesinger 2018; Favero et al. 2020). It is argued that a carbon tax on only fossil fuel derived emissions, may lead to massive deployment of bioenergy, although the effects of such a policy can be mitigated when combined with policies that encourage sustainable forest management and protection of forest carbon stocks as well as forest management certification (*high confidence*) (Nabuurs et al. 2017, Baker et al. 2019 and Favero et al. 2020).

If biomass energy production expands and shifts to carbon capture and storage (e.g., BECCS) during the century, there could be a significant increase in the area of crop and forestland used for biomass energy production (Sections 7.4 and 7.5). BECCS is not projected to be widely implemented for several decades, but in the meantime, policy efforts to advance land-based measures including reforestation and restoration activities (Strassburg et al.

2020) combined with sustainable management and provision of agricultural and wood products are widely expected to increase the terrestrial pool of carbon (Cross-Working Group Box 3 in Chapter 12). Carbon sequestration policies, sustainable land management (forest and agriculture), and biomass energy policies can be complementary (Favero et al. 2017; Baker et al. 2019). However, if private markets emerge for biomass and BECCS on the scale suggested in the SR1.5, policy efforts must ramp up to substantially value, encourage, and protect terrestrial carbon stocks and ecosystems to avoid outcomes inconsistent with many SDGs (*high confidence*).

7.6.4   Barriers and Opportunities for AFOLU Mitigation

The AR5 and other assessments have acknowledged many barriers and opportunities to effective implementation of AFOLU measures. Many of these barriers and opportunities focus on the context in developing countries, where a significant portion of the world's cost-effective mitigation exists, but where domestic financing for implementation is likely to be limited. The SSPs capture some of this context, and as a result, IAMs (Section 7.5) exhibit a wide range of land-use outcomes, as well as mitigation potential. Potential mitigation, however, will be influenced by barriers and opportunities that are not considered by IAMs or by bottom-up studies reviewed here. For example, more efficient food production systems, or sustainable intensification within agriculture, and globalised trade could enhance the extent of natural ecosystems leading to lower GHG emissions from the land system and lower food prices (Popp et al. 2017), but this (or any) pathway will create new barriers to implementation and encourage new opportunities, negating potential benefits (Box 7.11). It is critically important to consider the current context in any country.

7.6.4.1   Socio-economic Barriers and Opportunities

Design and coverage of financing mechanisms. The lack of resources thus far committed to implementing AFOLU mitigation, income and access to alternative sources of income in rural households that rely on agriculture or forests for their livelihoods remains a considerable barrier to adoption of AFOLU (*high confidence*). Section 7.6.1 illustrates that to date only USD0.7 billion yr^{-1} has been spent on AFOLU mitigation, well short of the more than USD400 billion yr^{-1} that would be needed to achieve the economic potential described in Section 7.4. Despite long-term recognition that AFOLU can play an important role in mitigation, the *economic incentives* necessary to achieve AFOLU aspirations as part of the Paris Agreement or to maintain temperatures below 2.0°C have not emerged. Without quickly ramping up spending, the lack of funding to implement projects remains a substantial barrier (*high confidence*). Investments are critically important in the livestock sector, which has the highest emissions reduction potential among options because actions in the sector influence agriculture specific activities, such as enteric fermentation, as well as deforestation (Mayberry et al. 2019). In many countries with export-oriented livestock industries, livestock farmers control large swaths of forests or re-forestable areas. Incentive mechanisms and funding can encourage adoption of mitigation strategies, but funding is currently too low to make consistent progress.

Scale and accessibility of financing. The largest share of funding to date has been for REDD+, and many of the commitments to date suggest that there will be significant funding in this area for the foreseeable future. Funding for conservation programmes in OECD countries and China affects carbon, but has been driven by other objectives such as water quality and species protection. Considerably less funding has been available for agricultural projects aimed at reducing carbon emissions, and outside of voluntary markets, there do not appear to be large sources of funding emerging either through international organisations, or national programs. In the agricultural sector, funding for carbon must be obtained by redirecting existing resources from non-GHG conservation to GHG measures, or by developing new funding streams (Henderson et al. 2020).

Risk and uncertainty. Most approaches to reduce emissions, especially in agriculture, require new or different technologies that involve significant time or financial investments by the implementing landholders. Adoption rates are often slow due to risk aversion among agricultural operators. Many AFOLU measures require carbon to be compensated to generate positive returns, reducing the likelihood of implementation without clear financial incentives. Research to show costs and benefits is lacking in most parts of the world.

Poverty. Mitigation and adaptation can have important implications for vulnerable people and communities, for example, mitigation activities consistent with scenarios examined in the SR1.5 could raise food and fiber prices globally (Section. 7.5). In the NDCs, 82 Parties included references to social issues (e.g., poverty, inequality, human well-being, marginalisation), with poverty the most cited factor (70 Parties). The number of hungry and food insecure people in the world is growing, reaching 821 million in 2017, or one in every nine people (FAO 2018b), and two-thirds live in rural areas (Laborde Debucquet et al. 2020). Consideration of rural poverty and food insecurity is central in AFOLU mitigation because there are a large number of farms in the world (about 570 million), and most are

---

Box 7.12 | Financing AFOLU Mitigation; What Are the Costs and Who Pays?

Achieving the large contribution to mitigation that the AFOLU sector can make requires public and private investment. Austin et al. (2020) estimate that in forestry, USD178 billion yr^{-1} is needed over the next decade to achieve 5 GtCO$_2$ yr^{-1}, and investments need to ramp up to USD400 billion yr^{-1} by 2050 to expand effort to 6 GtCO$_2$ yr^{-1}. Other land-based options, such as mangrove protection, peatland restoration, and agricultural options would increase this total cost estimate, but have smaller to negligible opportunity costs.

Financing needs in AFOLU, and in particular in forestry, include both the direct effects of any changes in activities – costs of planting or managing trees, net revenues from harvesting, costs of thinning, costs of fire management, and so on – as well as the opportunity costs associated with land-use change. Opportunity costs are a critical component of AFOLU finance, and must be included in any estimate of the funds necessary to carry out projects. They are largest, as share of total costs, in forestry because they play a prominent role in achieving high levels of afforestation, avoided deforestation, and improved forest management. In case of increasing soil carbon in croplands through reduced tillage, there are often cost savings associated with increased residues because there is less effort tilling, but the carbon effects per hectare are also modest. There could, however, be small opportunity costs in cases where residues may otherwise be marketed to a biorefinery. The effect of reduced tillage on yields varies considerably across sites and crop types, but tends to enhance yields modestly in the longer-run.

Opportunity costs are a direct financing costs for activities that require land uses to change. For instance a government can encourage planting forests on agricultural land by (a) requiring it, (b) setting up a market or market-based incentives, or (c) buying the land and doing it themselves. In each case, the required investment is the same – the planting cost plus the net foregone returns of agricultural rents – even though a different entity pays the cost. Private entities that pay for carbon credits will also bear the direct costs of planting plus the opportunity costs. In the case of avoided deforestation, opportunity costs similarly must be paid to individual actors to avoid the deforestation.

smaller than 2 hectares. It is important to better understand how different mitigation policies affect the poor.

Cultural values and social acceptance. Barriers to adoption of AFOLU mitigation will be strongest where historical practices represent long-standing traditions (*high confidence*). Adoption of new mitigation practices, however, may proceed quickly if the technologies can be shown to improve crop yields, reduce costs, or otherwise improve livelihoods (Ranjan 2019). AR6 presents new estimates of the mitigation potential for shifts in diets and reductions in food waste, but given long-standing dietary traditions within most cultures, some of the strongest barriers exist for efforts to change diets (*medium confidence*). Furthermore, the large number of undernourished who may benefit from increased calories and meat will complicate efforts to change diets. Regulatory or tax approaches will face strong resistance, while efforts to use educational approaches and voluntary measures have limited potential to slow changes in consumption patterns due to free-riders, rebound effects, and other limitations. Food loss and waste occurs across the supply chain, creating significant challenges to reduce it (FAO 2019c). Where food loss occurs in the production stage, in other words, in fields at harvest, there may be opportunities to align reductions in food waste with improved production efficiency, however, adoption of new production methods often requires new investments or changes in labour practices, both of which are barriers.

7.6.4.2 Institutional Barriers and Opportunities

Transparent and accountable governance. Good governance and accountability are crucial for implementation of forest and agriculture mitigation. Effective nature-based mitigation will require large-scale estimation, modelling, monitoring, reporting and verification of GHG inventories, mitigation actions, as well as their implications for sustainable development goals and their interactions with climate change impacts and adaptation. Efforts must be made to integrate the accounting from projects to the country level. While global datasets have emerged to measure forest loss, at least temporarily (e.g., Hansen et al. 2013), similar datasets do not yet exist for forest degradation and agricultural carbon stocks or fluxes. Most developing countries have insufficient capacity to address research needs, modelling, monitoring, reporting and data requirements (Ravindranath et al. 2017), compromising transparency, accuracy, completeness, consistency and comparability.

Opportunity for political participation of local stakeholders is barrier in most places where forest ownership rights are not sufficiently documented (Essl et al. 2018). Since incentives for self-enforcement can have an important influence on deforestation rates (Fortmann et al. 2017), weak governance and insecure property rights are significant barriers to introduction of forest carbon offset projects in developing countries, where many of the low-cost options for such projects exist (Gren and Zeleke 2016). Governance challenges exist at all levels of government, with poor coordination, insufficient information sharing, and concerns over accountability playing a prominent role within REDD+ projects and programmes (Ravikumar et al. 2015). In some cases, governments are increasingly centralising REDD+ governance and limiting the distribution of governance

functions between state and non-state actors (Zelli et al. 2017; Phelps et al. 2010). Overlap and duplication in Forest Law Enforcement, Governance and Trade (FLEGT) and REDD+ also limits governance effectiveness (Gupta et al. 2016).

Clear land tenure and land-use rights. Unclear property rights and tenure insecurity undermine the incentives to improve forest and agricultural productivity, lead to food insecurity, undermine REDD+ objectives, discourage adoption of farm conservation practices, discourage tree planting and forest management, and exacerbate conflict between different land users (Antwi-Agyei et al. 2015; Felker et al. 2017; Sunderlin et al. 2018; Borras and Franco 2018; Riggs et al. 2018; Kansanga and Luginaah 2019). Some positive signs exist as over 500 million hectares of forests have been converted to community management with clear property rights in the past two decades (Rights and Resources Initiative 2018), but adoption of forest and agricultural mitigation practices will be limited in large remaining areas with unclear property rights (Gupta et al. 2016).

Lack of institutional capacity. Institutional complexity, or lack thereof, represents a major challenge when implementing large and complex mitigation programmes (e.g., REDD+) in agriculture, forest and other land uses (Bäckstrand et al. 2017). Without sufficient capacity, many synergies between agricultural and forest programs, or mitigation and adaptation opportunities, may be missed (Duguma et al. 2014). Another aspect of institutional complexity is the different biophysical and socio-economic circumstances as well as the public and private financial means involved in the architecture and implementation of REDD+ and other initiatives (Zelli et al. 2017).

7.6.4.3 Ecological Barriers and Opportunities

Availability of land and water. Climate mitigation scenarios in the two recent special reports (SR1.5 and SRCCL) that aim to limit global temperature increase to 2°C or less involve carbon dioxide (CO_2) removal from the atmosphere. To support large-scale CDR, these scenarios involve significant land-use change, due to afforestation/reforestation, avoided deforestation, and deployment of biomass energy with carbon capture and storage (BECCS). While a considerable amount of land is certainly available for new forests or new bioenergy crops, that land has current uses that will affect not only the costs, but also the willingness of current users or owners, to shift uses. Regions with private property rights and a history of market-based transactions may be the most feasible for land-use change or land management change to occur. Areas with less secure tenure or a land market with fewer transactions in general will likely face important hurdles that limit the feasibility of implementing novel nature-based solutions.

Implementation of nature-based solution may have local or regionally important consequences for other ecosystem services, some of which may be negative (*high confidence*). Land-use change has important implications for the hydrological cycle, and the large land-use shifts suggested for BECCS when not carried out in a carefully planned manner, are expected to increase water demands substantially across the globe (Stenzel et al. 2019; Rosa et al. 2020). Afforestation can have minor to severe consequences for surface water acidification, depending on site-specific factors and exposure to air pollution and sea-salts (Futter et al. 2019). The potential effects of coastal afforestation on sea-salt related acidification could lead to re-acidification and damage on aquatic biota.

Specific soil conditions, water availability, GHG emission-reduction potential as well as natural variability and resilience. Recent analysis by (Cook-Patton et al. 2020) illustrates large variability in potential rates of carbon accumulation for afforestation and reforestation options, both within biomes/ecozones and across them. Their results suggest that while there is large potential for afforestation and reforestation, the carbon uptake potential in land-based climate change mitigation efforts is highly dependent on the assumptions related to climate drivers, land use and land management, and soil carbon responses to land-use change. Less analysis has been conducted on bioenergy crop yields, however, bioenergy crop yields are also likely to be highly variable, suggesting that bioenergy supply could exceed or fall short of expectations in a given region, depending on site conditions.

The effects of climate change on ecosystems, including changes in crop yields, shifts in terrestrial ecosystem productivity, vegetation migration, wildfires, and other disturbances also will affect the potential for AFOLU mitigation. Climate is expected to reduce crop yields, increase crop and livestock prices, and increase pressure on undisturbed forest land for food production creating new barriers and increasing costs for implementation of many nature-based mitigation techniques (*medium confidence*) (IPCC AR6 WGII Chapter 5).

The observed increase in the terrestrial sink over the past half century can be linked to changes in the global environment, such as increased atmospheric CO_2 concentrations, N deposition, or changes in climate (Ballantyne et al. 2012), though not always proven from ground-based information (Vandersleen et al. 2015). While the terrestrial sink relies on regrowth in secondary forests (Houghton and Nassikas 2017), there is emerging evidence that the sink will slow in the Northern Hemisphere as forests age (Nabuurs et al. 2013), although saturation may take decades (Zhu et al. 2018). Forest management through replanting, variety selection, fertilisation, and other management techniques, has increased the terrestrial carbon sink over the last century (Mendelsohn and Sohngen 2019). Saturation of the sink in situ may not occur when, for example, substitution effects of timber usage are also considered.

Increasing concentrations of CO_2 are expected to increase carbon stocks globally, with the strongest effects in the tropics (Schimel et al. 2015; Kim et al. 2017a) (IPCC AR6 WGII Chapter 5) and economic models suggest that future sink potential may be robust to the impacts of climate change (Tian et al. 2018). However, it is uncertain if this large terrestrial carbon sink will continue in the future (Aragão et al. 2018), as it is increasingly recognised that gains due to CO_2 fertilisation are constrained by climate and increasing disturbances (Schurgers et al. 2018; Duffy et al. 2021) (IPCC AR6 WGII Chapter 5). Further, negative synergies between local impacts like deforestation and forest fires may interact with global drivers like climate change and lead to tipping points (Lovejoy and Nobre 2018). Factors that reduce permanence or slow forest growth will drive up costs of

forest mitigation measures, suggesting that climate change presents a formidable challenge to implementation of nature-based solutions beyond 2030 (*high confidence*).

In addition to climate change, Dooley and Kartha (2018) also note that technological and social factors could ultimately limit the feasibility of agricultural and forestry mitigation options, especially when deployed at large scale. Concern is greatest with widespread use of bioenergy crops, which could lead to forest losses (Harper et al. 2018). Deployment of BECCS and forest-based mitigation can be complementary (Favero et al. 2017; Baker et al. 2019), but inefficient policy approaches could lead to net carbon emissions if BECCS replaces high-carbon content ecosystems with crops.

Adaptation benefits and biodiversity conservation. Biodiversity may improve resilience to climate change impacts as more-diverse systems could be more resilient to climate change impacts, thereby maintaining ecosystem function and preserving biodiversity (Hisano et al. 2018). However, losses in ecosystem functions due species shifts or reductions in diversity may impair the positive effects of biodiversity on ecosystems. Forest management strategies based on biodiversity and ecosystems functioning interactions can augment the effectiveness of forests in reducing climate change impacts on ecosystem functioning (*high confidence*). In spite of the many synergies between climate policy instruments and biodiversity conservation, however, current policies often fall short of realising this potential (Essl et al. 2018).

7.6.4.4 Technological Barriers and Opportunities

Monitoring, reporting, and verification. Development of satellite technologies to assess potential deforestation has grown in recent years with the release of 30 m data by Hansen et al. (2013), however, this data only captures tree cover loss, and increasing accuracy over time may limit its use for trend analysis (Ceccherini et al. 2020; Palahí et al. 2021). Datasets on forest losses are less well developed for reforestation and afforestation. As Mitchell et al. (2017) point out, there has been significant improvement in the ability to measure changes in tree and carbon density on sites using satellite data, but these techniques are still evolving and improving and they are not yet available for widespread use.

Ground-based forest inventory measurements have been developed in many countries, most prominently in the Northern Hemisphere, but more and more countries are starting to develop and collect national forest inventories. Training and capacity building is going on in many developing countries under UNREDD and FAO programmes. Additional efforts to harmonise data collection methods and to make forest inventory data available to the scientific community would improve confidence in forest statistics, and changes in forest statistics over time. To some extent the Global Forest Biodiversity Initiative fills in this data gap (https://gfbi.udl.cat/).

7.6.5 Linkages to Ecosystem Services, Human Well-being and Adaptation (including SDGs)

The linkage between biodiversity, ecosystem services, human well-being and sustainable development is widely acknowledged (Millenium Ecosystem Assesment 2005; UNEP 2019). Loss of biodiversity and ecosystem services will have an adverse impact on quality of life, human well-being and sustainable development (IPBES 2019a). Such losses will not only affect current economic growth but also impede the capacity for future economic growth.

Population growth, economic development, urbanisation, technology, climate change, global trade and consumption, policy and governance are key drivers of global environmental change over recent decades (Kram et al. 2014; UNEP 2019; WWF 2020). Changes in biodiversity and ecosystem services are mainly driven by habitat loss, climate change, invasive species, over-exploitation of natural resources, and pollution (Millenium Ecosystem Assesment 2005). The relative importance of these drivers varies across biomes, regions, and countries. Climate change is expected to be a major driver of biodiversity loss in the coming decades, followed by commercial forestry and bioenergy production (OECD 2012; UNEP 2019). Population growth along with rising incomes and changes in consumption and dietary patterns, will exert immense pressure on land and other natural resources (IPCC 2019). Current estimates suggest that 75% of the land surface has been significantly anthropogenically altered, with 66% of the ocean area experiencing increasing cumulative impacts and over 85% of wetland area lost (IPBES 2019a). As discussed, in Section 7.3, land-use change is driven amongst others by agriculture, forestry (logging and fuelwood harvesting), infrastructure development and urbanisation, all of which may also generate localised air, water, and soil pollution (IPBES 2019a). Over a third of the world's land surface and nearly three-quarters of available freshwater resources are devoted to crop or livestock production (IPBES 2019a). Despite a slight reduction in global agricultural area since 2000, regional agricultural area expansion has occurred in Latin America and the Caribbean, Africa and the Middle East (FAO 2019c; OECD and FAO 2019). The degradation of tropical forests and biodiversity hotspots, endangers habitat for many threatened and endemic species, and reduces valuable ecosystem services. However, trends vary considerably by region. As noted in Section 7.3, global forest area declined by roughly 178 Mha between 1990 and 2020 (FAO 2020a), though the rate of net forest loss has decreased over the period, due to reduced deforestation in some countries and forest gains in others. Between 1990 to 2015, forest cover fell by almost 13% in South-East Asia, largely due to an increase in timber extraction, large-scale biofuel plantations and expansion of intensive agriculture and shrimp farms, whereas in North-East Asia and South Asia it increased by 23% and 6% respectively, through policy instruments such as joint forest management, payment for ecosystem services, and restoration of degraded forests (IPBES 2018b). It is lamenting that the area under natural forests which are rich in biodiversity and provide diverse ecosystem services decreased by 301 Mha between 1990 and 2020, decreasing in most regions except Europe and Oceania with largest losses reported in sub-Saharan Africa (FAO 2020a). The increasing trend of mining in forest and coastal areas, and in river basins for extracting has had significant negative impacts on biodiversity, air and water quality, water distribution, and on human health (Section 7.3). Freshwater ecosystems equally face a series of combined threats including from land-use change, water extraction, exploitation, pollution, climate change and invasive species (IPBES 2019a).

7.6.5.1 Ecosystem Services

An evaluation of eighteen ecosystem services over the past five decades (1970–2019) found only four (agricultural production, fish harvest, bioenergy production and harvest of materials) to demonstrate increased performance, while the remaining fourteen, mostly concerning regulating and non-material contributions, were found to be in decline (IPBES 2019a). The value of global agricultural output (over USD3.54 trillion in 2018) had increased approximately threefold since 1970, and roundwood production (industrial roundwood and fuelwood) by 27%, between 1980 to 2018, reaching some 4 billion m^3 in 2018. However, the positive trends in these four ecosystem services does not indicate long-term sustainability. If increases in agricultural production are realised through forest clearance or through increasing energy-intensive inputs, gains are likely to be unsustainable in the long run. Similarly, an increase in fish production may involve overfishing, leading to local species declines which also impacts fish prices, fishing revenues, and the well-being of coastal and fishing communities (Sumaila and Lam 2020). Climate change and other drivers are likely to affect future fish catch potential, although impacts will differ across regions (Sumaila et al. 2017; Domke et al. 2019).

The increasing trend in aquaculture production especially in South and South-East Asia through intensive methods affects existing food production and ecosystems by diverting rice fields or mangroves (Bhattacharya and Ninan 2011). Although extensive traditional fish farming of carp in central Europe can contribute to landscape management, enhance biodiversity and provide ecosystem services, there are several barriers to scale up production due to strict EU environmental regulations, vulnerability to extreme weather events, and to avian predators that are protected by EU laws, and disadvantages faced by small-scale enterprises that dominate the sector (European-Commission 2021). Bioenergy production may have high opportunity costs in land-scarce areas and compete with land used for food production which threatens food security and affects the poor and vulnerable. But these impacts will differ across scale, contexts and other factors.

Currently, land degradation is estimated to have reduced productivity in 23% of the global terrestrial area, and between USD235 billion and USD577 billion in annual global crop output is at risk because of pollinator loss (IPBES 2019a). The global trends reviewed above are based on data from 2000 studies. It is not clear whether the assessment included a quality control check of the studies evaluated and suffer from aggregation bias. For instance, a recent meta-analysis of global forest valuation studies noted that many studies reviewed had shortcomings such as failing to clearly mention the methodology and prices used to value the forest ecosystem services, double counting, data errors, and so on (Ninan and Inoue 2013). Furthermore, the criticisms against the paper by (Costanza et al.

1997), such as ignoring ecological feedbacks and non-linearities that are central to the processes that link all species to each other and their habitats, ignoring substitution effects may also apply to the global assessment (Smith 1997; Bockstael et al. 2000; Loomis et al. 2000). Land degradation has had a pronounced impact on ecosystem functions worldwide (IPBES 2018e). Net primary productivity of ecosystem biomass and of agriculture is presently lower than it would have been under a natural state on 23% of the global terrestrial area, amounting to a 5% reduction in total global net primary productivity (IPBES 2018e). Over the past two centuries, soil organic carbon, an indicator of soil health, has seen an estimated 8% loss globally (176 GtC) from land conversion and unsustainable land management practices (IPBES 2018e). Projections to 2050 predict further losses of 36 GtC from soils, particularly in sub-Saharan Africa. These losses are projected to come from the expansion of agricultural land into natural areas (16 GtC), degradation due to inappropriate land management (11 GtC) and the draining and burning of peatlands (9 GtC) and melting of permafrost (IPBES 2018e). Trends in biodiversity measured by the global living planet index between 1970 to 2016 indicate a 68% decline in monitored population of mammals, birds, amphibians, reptiles, and fish (WWF 2020). FAO's recent report on the state of the world's biodiversity for food and agriculture points to an alarming decline in biodiversity for food and agriculture including associated biodiversity such as pollination services, microorganisms which are essential for production systems (FAO 2019d). These suggest that overall ecosystem health is consistently declining with adverse consequences for good quality of life, human well-being, and sustainable development.

Although numerous studies have estimated the value of ecosystem services for different sites, ecosystems, and regions, these studies mostly evaluate ecosystem services at a single point in time (Costanza et al. 1997; Xue and Tisdell 2001; Nahuelhual et al. 2007;

de Groot et al. 2012; Ninan and Kontoleon 2016). The few studies that have assessed the trends in the value of ecosystem services provided by different ecosystems across regions and countries indicate a declining trend (Costanza et al. 2014; Kubiszewski et al. 2017). Land-use change is a major driver behind loss of biodiversity and ecosystem services in most regions (IPBES 2018b; IPBES 2018c, IPBES 2018d, Rice et al. 2018). Projected impacts of land-use change and climate change on biodiversity and ecosystem services (material and regulating services) between 2015 to 2050 were assessed to have relatively less negative impacts under global sustainability scenarios as compared to regional competition and economic optimism scenarios (IPBES 2019a). The projected impacts were based on a subset of Shared Socio-economic Pathway (SSP) scenarios and GHG emissions trajectories (RCP) developed in support of IPCC assessments. There are synergies, trade-offs and co-benefits between ecosystem services and mitigation options with impacts on ecosystem services differing by scale and contexts (*high confidence*). Measures such as conservation agriculture, agroforestry, soil and water conservation, afforestation, adoption of silvopastoral systems, can help minimise trade-offs between mitigations options and ecosystem services (Duguma et al. 2014). Climate-smart agriculture (CSA) is being promoted to enable farmers to make agriculture more sustainable and adapt to climate change (Box 7.4). However, experience with CSA in Africa has not been encouraging. For instance, a study of climate-smart cocoa production in Ghana shows that due to lack of tenure (tree) rights, bureaucratic and legal hurdles in registering trees in cocoa farms, and other barriers small cocoa producers could not realise the project benefits (Box 7.13). Experience of CSA in some other sub-Saharan African countries and other countries such as Belize too has been constrained by weak extension systems and policy implementation, and other barriers (Arakelyan et al. 2017; Kongsager 2017).

Box 7.13 | Case Study: Climate-smart Cocoa Production in Ghana

Policy objectives

i.   To promote sustainable intensification of cocoa production and enhance the adaptive capacity of small cocoa producers.
ii. To reduce cocoa-induced deforestation and GHG emissions.
iii. To improve productivity, incomes, and livelihoods of smallholder cocoa producers.

Policy mix

The climate-smart cocoa (CSC) production programme in Ghana involved distributing shade tree seedlings that can protect cocoa plants from heat and water stress, enhance soil organic matter and water holding capacity of soils, and provide other assistance with agroforestry, giving access to extension services such as agronomic information and agrochemical inputs. The shade tree seedlings were distributed by NGOs, government extension agencies, and the private sector free of charge or at subsidised prices and was expected to reduce pressure on forests for growing cocoa plants. The CSC programme was mainly targeted at small farmers who constitute about 80% of total farm holdings in Ghana. Although the government extension agency (Cocobod) undertook mass spraying or pruning of cocoa farms they found it difficult to access the 800,000 cocoa smallholders spread across the tropical south of the country. The project brought all stakeholders together, in other words, the government, private sector, local farmers and civil society or NGOs to facilitate the sustainable intensification of cocoa production in Ghana. Creation of a community-based governance structure was expected to promote benefit sharing, forest conservation, adaptation to climate change, and enhanced livelihood opportunities.

Box 7.13 (continued)

Governance context

Critical enablers

The role assigned to local government mechanisms such as Ghana's Community Resource Management Area Mechanisms (CREMAs) was expected to give a voice to smallholders who are an important stakeholder in Ghana's cocoa sector. CREMAs are inclusive because authority and ownership of natural resources are devolved to local communities who can thus have a voice in influencing CSC policy thereby ensuring equity and adapting CSC to local contexts. However, ensuring the long-term sustainability of CREMAs will help to make them a reliable mechanism for farmers to voice their concerns and aspirations, and ensure their independence as a legitimate governance structure in the long run. The private sector was assigned an important role to popularise climate-smart cocoa production in Ghana. However, whether this will work to the advantage of smallholder cocoa producers needs to be seen.

Critical barriers

The policy intervention overlooks the institutional constraints characteristic of the cocoa sector in Ghana where small farmers are dominant and have skewed access to resources and markets. Lack of secure tenure (tree rights) where the ownership of shade trees and timber vests with the state, bureaucratic and legal hurdles to register trees in their cocoa farms are major constraints that impede realisation of the expected benefits of the CSC programme. This is a great disincentive for small cocoa producers to implement CSC initiatives and nurture the shade tree seedlings and undertake land improvement measures. The state marketing board has the monopoly in buying and marketing of cocoa beans including exports which impeded CREMAs or farming communities from directly selling their produce to MNCs and traders. However, many MNCs have been involved in setting up of CREMA or similar structures, extending premium prices and non-monetary benefits (access to credit, shade tree seedlings, agrochemicals) thus indirectly securing their cocoa supply chains. A biased ecological discourse about the benefits of climate-smart agriculture and sustainable intensive narrative, complexities regarding the optimal shade levels for growing cocoa, and dependence on agrochemicals are issues that affect the success and sustainability of the project intervention. Dominance of private sector players especially MNCs in the sector may be detrimental to the interests of smallholder cocoa producers (Nasser et al. 2020).

7.6.5.2 Human Well-being and Sustainable Development Goals

Conservation of biodiversity and ecosystem services is part of the larger objective of building climate resilience and promoting good quality of life, human well-being and sustainable development. While two of the 17 SDGs directly relate to nature (SDGs 14 and 15 covering marine and terrestrial ecosystems and biodiversity), most other SDGs relating to poverty, hunger, inequality, health and well-being, clean sanitation and water, energy, and so on, are directly or indirectly linked to nature (Blicharska et al. 2019). A survey among experts to assess how 16 ecosystem services could help in achieving the SDGs relating to good environment and human well-being suggested that ecosystem services could contribute to achieving about 41 targets across 12 SDGs (Wood et al. 2018). They also indicated cross-target interactions and synergetic outcomes across many SDGs. Conservation of biodiversity and ecosystem services is critical to sustaining the well-being and livelihoods of poor and marginalised people, and indigenous communities who depend on natural resources (*high confidence*). Nature provides a broad array of goods and services that are critical to good quality of life and human well-being. Healthy and diverse ecosystems can play an important role in reducing vulnerability and building resilience to disasters and extreme weather events (SCBD 2009; The Royal Society Science Policy Centre 2014; Ninan and Inoue 2017).

Current negative trends in biodiversity and ecosystem services will undermine progress towards achieving 80% (35 out of 44) of the assessed targets of SDGs related to poverty, hunger, health, water, cities, climate, oceans and land (IPBES 2019a). However, Reyers and Selig (2020) note that the assessment by (IPBES 2019a) could only assess the consequences of trends in biodiversity and ecosystem services for 35 out of the 169 SDG targets due to data and knowledge gaps, and lack of clarity about the relationship between biodiversity, ecosystem services and SDGs.

Progress in achieving the 20 Aichi Biodiversity targets which are critical for realising the SDGs has been poor with most of the targets not being achieved or only partially realised (SCBD 2020). There could be synergies and trade-offs between ecosystem services and human well-being. For instance, a study notes that although policy interventions and incentives to enhance supply of provisioning services (e.g., agricultural production) have led to higher GDP, it may have an adverse effect on the regulatory services of ecosystems (Kirchner et al. 2015). However, we are aware of the inadequacies of traditional GDP as an indicator of well-being. In this context the Dasgupta Biodiversity Review argues for using the inclusive wealth approach to accurately measure social well-being by tracking the changes in produced, human and natural capital (Dasgupta 2021). Targets for nature (biodiversity and ecosystem services) should be refined so as to fit in with the metrics tracked by the SDGs (IPBES 2016; Rosa et al. 2017).

7

7.6.5.3   Land-based Mitigation and Adaptation

Combined mitigation and adaptation approaches have been highlighted throughout Section 7.4 regarding specific measures. Land-based mitigation and adaptation to the risks posed by climate change and extreme weather events can have several co-benefits as well as help promote development and conservation goals. Land-based mitigation and adaptation will not only help reduce GHG emissions in the AFOLU sector, but measures are required to closely link up with adaptation. In the central 2°C scenario, improved management of land and more efficient forest practices, a reduction in deforestation and an increase in afforestation, would account for 10% of the total mitigation effort over 2015–2050 (Keramidas et al. 2018). If managed and regulated appropriately, the Land sector could become carbon-neutral as early as 2030–2035, being a key sector for emissions reductions beyond 2025 (Keramidas et al. 2018). Nature-based solutions (NBS) with safeguards has immense potential for cost-effective adaptation to climate change; but their impacts will vary by scale and contexts (*high confidence*). Griscom et al. 2017 estimate this potential to provide 37% of cost-effective CO_2 mitigation until 2030 needed to meet 2°C goals with likely co-benefits for biodiversity. However, due to the time lag for technology deployment and natural carbon gain this mitigation potential of NBS by 2030 or 2050 can be delayed or much lower than the estimated potential (Qin et al. 2021).

7.7   Knowledge Gaps

Closing knowledge gaps and narrowing uncertainties are crucial to advance AFOLU mitigation. Knowledge gaps exist across a range of areas, from emissions accounting and mitigation measure development to integration of scientific and traditional knowledge and development and sustainable implementation strategies. The following are identified as priorities:

- Uncertainty in contemporary emissions and sinks within AFOLU is still high. There is ongoing need to develop and refine emission factors, improve activity data and facilitate knowledge exchange, concerning inventories and accounting. For example, insufficient knowledge on CO_2 emissions relating to forest management and burning or draining of organic soils (wetlands and peatlands), limits certainty on CO_2 and CH_4 fluxes.
- Improved monitoring of the land CO_2 balance is urgently needed, including impacts of land degradation and restoration efforts (e.g., in tropical and boreal regions), making use of combined remote sensing, artificial intelligence, ground-based and modelling tools (Grassi et al. 2021). Improved estimates would provide more reliable projections of nationally determined contributions to emissions reduction and enhancement of sinks, and reconciliation of national accounting and modelling results (Nabuurs et al. 2019).
- The future impacts of climate change on land systems are highly uncertain, for example, the role of permafrost thaw, tipping points, increased disturbances and enhanced CO_2 fertilisation (Friedlingstein et al. 2020). Further research into these

mechanisms is critical to better understand the permanence of mitigation measures in land sector.
- There is need to understand the role of forest management, carbon and nitrogen fertilisation and associated interactions in the current forest carbon sink that has emerged in the last 50 to 70 years. These aspects are likely to explain much of the difference between bookkeeping models and other methodologies.
- Continued research into novel and emerging mitigation measures and associated cost efficiency (e.g., CH_4 inhibitors or vaccines for ruminants) is required. In addition to developing specific measures, research is also needed into best practice regarding implementation and optimal agricultural land and livestock management at regional and country level. Further research into the feasible mitigation potential of sustainable intensification in terms of absolute GHG emissions and appropriate policy mechanisms, is required to implement and advance this strategy.
- Research into accounting systems and policy options that will enable agricultural soil and forest carbon to be utilised as offsets (voluntary or regulatory) is needed to increase financing for land-based CDR. Design of incentives that consider local institutions and novel frameworks for cooperation between private finance and public governance can encourage investment. Equally, research to adjust or remove regulations and subsidy schemes that may hamper land-based mitigation efforts, is urgently required.
- Improving mitigation potential estimates, whether derived from sectoral studies or IAMs to account for biophysical climate effects, and impacts of future climate change (e.g., mitigation permanence), biodiversity loss and corresponding feedbacks is needed. IAM 'usability' can be enhanced by integrating a wider set of measures and incorporating sustainability considerations.
- Research into the feasibility of improving and enhancing sustainable agricultural and forestry value chains, provision of renewable products (building with wood) and the sustainability of bioenergy is critically important. Modelled scenarios do not examine many poverty, employment and development trade-offs, which are highly context specific and vary enormously by region. Trade-off analysis and cost-benefit analysis can assist decision-making and policy.
- In-depth understanding of mitigation-SDG interactions is critical for identifying mitigation options that maximise synergies and minimise trade-offs. Mitigation measures have important synergies, trade-offs and co-benefits, impacting biodiversity and resource-use, human well-being, ecosystem services, adaptation capacity and many SDGs. In addition to exploring localised economic implementation costs, studies are needed to understand how measures will impact and interact with wider environmental and social factors across localities and contexts.

FAQ 7.1 | Why is the Agriculture, Forestry and Other Land Uses (AFOLU) sector unique when considering GHG mitigation?

There are three principal reasons that make the AFOLU sector unique in terms of mitigation:

In contrast to other sectors, AFOLU can facilitate mitigation in several different ways. Specifically, AFOLU can (i) reduce emissions as a sector in its own right, (ii) remove meaningful quantities of carbon from the atmosphere and relatively cheaply, and (iii) provide raw materials to enable mitigation within other sectors, such as energy, industry or the built environment.

The emissions profile of AFOLU differs from other sectors, with a greater proportion of non-CO_2 gases (N_2O and CH_4). The impacts of mitigation efforts within AFOLU can vary according to which gases are targeted, as a result of the differing atmospheric lifetime of the gases and differing global temperature responses to the accumulation of the specific gases in the atmosphere.

In addition to tackling climate change, AFOLU mitigation measures have capacity, where appropriately implemented, to help address some critical, wider challenges, as well as contributing to climate change adaptation. AFOLU is inextricably linked with some of the most serious challenges that are suggested to have ever faced humanity, such as large-scale biodiversity loss, environmental degradation and the associated consequences. As AFOLU concerns land management and utilises a considerable portion of the Earth's terrestrial area, the sector greatly influences soil, water and air quality, biological and social diversity, the provision of natural habitats, and ecosystem functioning, consequently impacting many SDGs.

FAQ 7.2 | What AFOLU measures have the greatest economic mitigation potential?

Economic mitigation potential refers to the mitigation estimated to be possible at an annual cost of up to USD100 tCO_2^{-1} mitigated. This cost is deemed the price at which society is willing to pay for mitigation and is used as a proxy to estimate the proportion of technical mitigation potential that could realistically be implemented. Between 2020 and 2050, measures concerning forests and other ecosystem are estimated to have an average annual mitigation potential of 7.3 (3.9–13.1) $GtCO_2$-eq yr^{-1} at USD100 tCO_2^{-1}. At the same cost, agricultural measures are estimated to have a potential of 4.1 (1.7–6.7) $GtCO_2$-eq yr^{-1}. Emerging technologies, such as CH_4 vaccines and inhibitors, could sustainably increase agricultural mitigation potential in future. The diverted production effects of changes in demand (reduced food losses, diet changes and improved and enhanced wood products use), is estimated to have an economic potential of 2.2 (1.1–3.6) $GtCO_2$-eq yr^{-1}. However, cost forms only one constraint to mitigation, with realisation of economic potential dependent on multiple context-specific environmental and socio-cultural factors.

FAQ 7.3 | What are potential impacts of large-scale establishment of dedicated bioenergy plantations and crops and why is it so controversial?

The potential of bioenergy with carbon capture and storage (BECCS) remains a focus of debate with several studies evaluating the level at which BECCS could be sustainably implemented, published since AR5. BECCS involves sequestering carbon through plant growth (i.e., in trees or crops) and capturing the carbon generated when this biomass is processed for power or fuel. The captured carbon then requires long-term storage in for example, geological, terrestrial or ocean reservoirs, or in products. While appearing to create a net removal of carbon from the atmosphere, BECCS requires land, water and energy which can create adverse side effects at scale. Controversy has arisen because some of the models calculating the energy mix required to keep the temperature to 1.5°C have included BECCS at very large scales as a means of both providing energy and removing carbon from the atmosphere to offset emissions from industry, power, transport or heat. For example, studies have calculated that for BECCS to achieve 11.5 $GtCO_2$-eq per year of carbon removal in 2100, as envisaged in one scenario, 380–700 Mha or 25–46% of all the world's arable and cropland would be needed. In such a situation, competition for agricultural land seriously threatens food production and food security, while also impacting biodiversity, water and soil quality, and landscape aesthetic value. More recently however, the scenarios for BECCS have become much more realistic, though concerns regarding impacts on food security and the environment remain, while the reliability of models is uncertain due to methodological flaws. Improvements to models are required to better capture wider environmental and social impacts of BECCS in order to ascertain its sustainable contribution in emissions pathways. Additionally, the opportunity for other options that could negate very large-scale deployment of BECCS, such as other carbon dioxide removal measures or more stringent emission reductions in other sectors, could be explored within models.

7

References

Abatzoglou, J.T. and A.P. Williams, 2016: Impact of anthropogenic climate change on wildfire across western US forests. *Proc. Natl. Acad. Sci.*, **113(42)**, 11770–11775, doi:10.1073/pnas.1607171113.

Abbott, D.W. et al., 2020: Seaweed and Seaweed Bioactives for Mitigation of Enteric Methane: Challenges and Opportunities. *Animals*, **10(12)**, 2432, doi:10.3390/ani10122432.

Abrahão, G.M. and M.H. Costa, 2018: Evolution of rain and photoperiod limitations on the soybean growing season in Brazil: The rise (and possible fall) of double-cropping systems. *Agric. For. Meteorol.*, **256–257**, 32–45, doi:10.1016/j.agrformet.2018.02.031.

Achard, F. et al., 2014: Determination of tropical deforestation rates and related carbon losses from 1990 to 2010. *Glob. Change Biol.*, **20(8)**, 2540–2554, doi:10.1111/gcb.12605.

Ackrill, R. and H. Abdo, 2020: On-farm anaerobic digestion uptake barriers and required incentives: A case study of the UK East Midlands region. *J. Clean. Prod.*, **264**, 121727, doi:10.1016/j.jclepro.2020.121727.

Acosta-Alba, I., E. Chia, and N. Andrieu, 2019: The LCA4CSA framework: Using life cycle assessment to strengthen environmental sustainability analysis of climate smart agriculture options at farm and crop system levels. *Agric. Syst.*, **171**, 155–170, doi:10.1016/j.agsy.2019.02.001.

Adam, M. et al., 2020: Which is more important to sorghum production systems in the Sudano-Sahelian zone of West Africa: Climate change or improved management practices? *Agric. Syst.*, **185**, 102920, doi:10.1016/j.agsy.2020.102920.

Adger, W.N. et al., 2015: Focus on environmental risks and migration: causes and consequences. *Environ. Res. Lett.*, **10(6)**, 060201, doi:10.1088/1748-9326/10/6/060201.

Adghim, M. et al., 2020: Comparative life cycle assessment of anaerobic co-digestion for dairy waste management in large-scale farms. *J. Clean. Prod.*, **256**, 120320, doi:10.1016/j.jclepro.2020.120320.

Adhikari, S. and B. Ozarska, 2018: Minimizing environmental impacts of timber products through the production process "From Sawmill to Final Products". *Environ. Syst. Res.*, **7(1)**, 6, doi:10.1186/s40068-018-0109-x.

AGDW – The Forest Owners, 2021: The Working Group of German Forest Owner Associations. https://www.waldeigentuemer.de/verband/mitglieder sverbaende_agdw/#nrw (Accessed October 6, 2021).

Aggarwal, P.K. et al., 2018: The climate-smart village approach: framework of an integrative strategy for scaling up adaptation options in agriculture. *Ecol. Soc.*, **23(1)**, art14, doi:10.5751/ES-09844-230114.

Agostini, A., J. Giuntoli, and A. Boulamanti, 2014: *Carbon accounting of forest bioenergy*. Publications Office of the European Union, Luxembourg, 88 pp.

Aguilera, E. et al., 2020: Agroecology for adaptation to climate change and resource depletion in the Mediterranean region. A review. *Agric. Syst.*, **181**, 102809, doi:10.1016/j.agsy.2020.102809.

Aguirre-Villegas, H.A., R.A. Larson, and M.A. Sharara, 2019: Anaerobic digestion, solid-liquid separation, and drying of dairy manure: Measuring constituents and modeling emission. *Sci. Total Environ.*, **696**, 134059, doi:10.1016/j.scitotenv.2019.134059.

Agyarko-Mintah, E. et al., 2017: Biochar increases nitrogen retention and lowers greenhouse gas emissions when added to composting poultry litter. *Waste Manag.*, **61**, 138–149, doi:10.1016/j.wasman.2016.11.027.

Ahlering, M., J. Fargione, and W. Parton, 2016: Potential carbon dioxide emission reductions from avoided grassland conversion in the northern Great Plains. *Ecosphere*, **7(12)**, e01625, doi:10.1002/ecs2.1625.

Ai, Z., N. Hanasaki, V. Heck, T. Hasegawa, and S. Fujimori, 2021: Global bioenergy with carbon capture and storage potential is largely constrained by sustainable irrigation. *Nat. Sustain.*, **4(10)**, 884–891, doi:10.1038/s41893-021-00740-4.

Ajonina, G.N. et al., 2014: Assessment of Mangrove Carbon Stocks in Cameroon, Gabon, the Republic of Congo (RoC) and the Democratic Republic of Congo (DRC) Including their Potential for Reducing Emissions from Deforestation and Forest Degradation (REDD+). In: *The Land/Ocean Interactions in the Coastal Zone of West and Central Africa* [Diop, S., J.-P. Barusseau, and C. Descamps (eds.)]. Springer, Cham, Switzerland, pp. 177–189.

Akiyama, H., K. Yagi, and X. Yan, 2005: Direct N₂O emissions from rice paddy fields: Summary of available data. *Global Biogeochem. Cycles*, **19(1)**, doi:10.1029/2004GB002378.

Al-Haj, A.N. and R.W. Fulweiler, 2020: A synthesis of methane emissions from shallow vegetated coastal ecosystems. *Glob. Change Biol.*, **26(5)**, 2988–3005, doi:10.1111/gcb.15046.

Alamgir, M. et al., 2017: Economic, Socio-Political and Environmental Risks of Road Development in the Tropics. *Curr. Biol.*, **27(20)**, R1130–R1140, doi:10.1016/j.cub.2017.08.067.

Alamgir, M., M.J. Campbell, S. Sloan, W.E. Phin, and W.F. Laurance, 2018: Road risks & environmental impact assessments in Malaysian road infrastructure projects. *Jurutera*, 13–16.

Alary, V. et al., 2015: Roles of small ruminants in rural livelihood improvement – Comparative analysis in Egypt. *Rev Elev Med Vet Pays Trop*, **68(2–3)**, 79–85, doi: https://doi.org/10.19182/remvt.20592.

Albers, A., P. Collet, A. Benoist, and A. Hélias, 2020: Back to the future: dynamic full carbon accounting applied to prospective bioenergy scenarios. *Int. J. Life Cycle Assess.*, **25(7)**, 1242–1258, doi:10.1007/s11367-019-01695-7.

Aleksandrowicz, L. et al., 2019: Environmental impacts of dietary shifts in India: A modelling study using nationally-representative data. *Environ. Int.*, **126**, 207–215, doi:10.1016/j.envint.2019.02.004.

Alix-Garcia, J., 2007: A spatial analysis of common property deforestation. *J. Environ. Econ. Manage.*, **53(2)**, 141–157, doi:10.1016/j.jeem.2006.09.004.

Alix-Garcia, J., A. de Janvry, E. Sadoulet, and J.M. Torres, 2005: *An Assessment of Mexico's Payment for Environmental Services Program*. Food and Agriculture Organiation of the United Nations, Rome, 85 pp.

Alix-Garcia, J.M., E.N. Shapiro, and K.R.E. Sims, 2012: Forest Conservation and Slippage: Evidence from Mexico's National Payments for Ecosystem Services Program. *Land Econ.*, **88(4)**, 613–638, doi:10.3368/le.88.4.613.

Alix-Garcia, J.M., K.R.E. Sims, and P. Yañez-Pagans, 2015: Only One Tree from Each Seed? Environmental Effectiveness and Poverty Alleviation in Mexico's Payments for Ecosystem Services Program. *Am. Econ. J. Econ. Policy*, **7(4)**, 1–40, doi:10.1257/pol.20130139.

Alkama, R. and A. Cescatti, 2016: Biophysical climate impacts of recent changes in global forest cover. *Science*, **351**(6273), 600–604, doi:10.1126/science.aac8083.

Alongi, D.M., 2020: Blue Carbon Coastal Sequestration for Climate Change. Springer Briefs in Climate Studies. 88p. https://doi.org/10.1007/978-3-319-91698-9

Alter, R.E., E.-S. Im, and E.A.B. Eltahir, 2015: Rainfall consistently enhanced around the Gezira Scheme in East Africa due to irrigation. *Nat. Geosci.*, **8(10)**, 763–767, doi:10.1038/ngeo2514.

Altieri, M.A. and C.I. Nicholls, 2017: The adaptation and mitigation potential of traditional agriculture in a changing climate. *Clim. Change*, **140(1)**, 33–45, doi:10.1007/s10584-013-0909-y.

Altieri, M.A., C.I. Nicholls, A. Henao, and M.A. Lana, 2015: Agroecology and the design of climate change-resilient farming systems. *Agron. Sustain. Dev.*, **35(3)**, 869–890, doi:10.1007/s13593-015-0285-2.

Alvarez-Berrios, N.L. and T. Mitchell Aide, 2015: Global demand for gold is another threat for tropical forests. *Environ. Res. Lett.*, **10(1)**, 014006, doi:10.1088/1748-9326/10/1/014006.

Alvarez-Hess, P.S. et al., 2019: A partial life cycle assessment of the greenhouse gas mitigation potential of feeding 3-nitrooxypropanol and nitrate to cattle. *Agric. Syst.*, **169**, 14–23, doi:10.1016/j.agsy.2018.11.008.

Amadu, F.O., D.C. Miller, and P.E. McNamara, 2020: Agroforestry as a pathway to agricultural yield impacts in climate-smart agriculture investments:

Evidence from southern Malawi. *Ecol. Econ.*, **167**, 106443, doi:10.1016/j. ecolecon.2019.106443.

Amouzou, K.A. et al., 2019: Climate change impact on water- and nitrogen-use efficiencies and yields of maize and sorghum in the northern Benin dry savanna, West Africa. *F. Crop. Res.*, **235**, 104–117, doi:10.1016/j.fcr. 2019.02.021.

Andam, K.S., P.J. Ferraro, A. Pfaff, G.A. Sanchez-Azofeifa, and J.A. Robalino, 2008: Measuring the effectiveness of protected area networks in reducing deforestation. *Proc. Natl. Acad. Sci.*, **105(42)**, 16089–16094, doi:10.1073/pnas.0800437105.

Andela, N. et al., 2017: A human-driven decline in global burned area. *Science*, **356(6345)**, 1356–1362, doi:10.1126/science.aal4108.

Andela, N. et al., 2019: The Global Fire Atlas of individual fire size, duration, speed and direction. *Earth Syst. Sci. Data*, **11(2)**, 529–552, doi:10.5194/essd-11-529-2019.

Anderegg, W.R.L. et al., 2020: Climate-driven risks to the climate mitigation potential of forests. *Science*, **368(6497)**, doi:10.1126/science.aaz7005.

Andersen, R. et al., 2017: An overview of the progress and challenges of peatland restoration in Western Europe. *Restor. Ecol.*, **25(2)**, 271–282, doi:10.1111/rec.12415.

Anderson, R., P.E. Bayer, and D. Edwards, 2020: Climate change and the need for agricultural adaptation. *Curr. Opin. Plant Biol.*, **56**, 197–202, doi:10.1016/j.pbi.2019.12.006.

Anderson, R.G. et al., 2011: Biophysical considerations in forestry for climate protection. *Front. Ecol. Environ.*, **9(3)**, 174–182, doi:10.1890/090179.

Angelo, M.J. and A. du Plessis, 2017: *Research Handbook on Climate Change and Agricultural Law*. Edward Elgar Publishing, Cheltenham and Northampton, UK, 488 pp.

Angelsen, A., 2017: REDD+ as Result-based Aid: General Lessons and Bilateral Agreements of Norway. *Rev. Dev. Econ.*, **21(2)**, 237–264, doi:10.1111/rode.12271.

Antwi-Agyei, P., A.J. Dougill, and L.C. Stringer, 2015: Barriers to climate change adaptation: evidence from northeast Ghana in the context of a systematic literature review. *Clim. Dev.*, **7(4)**, 297–309, doi:10.1080/17565529.2014.951013.

Aragão, L.E.O.C. et al., 2018: 21st Century drought-related fires counteract the decline of Amazon deforestation carbon emissions. *Nat. Commun.*, **9(1)**, 536, doi:10.1038/s41467-017-02771-y.

Arakelyan, I., A. Wreford, and D. Moran, 2017: Can agriculture be climate smart? In: *Building a Climate Resilient Economy and Society* [Ninan, K.N. and M. Inoue (eds.)]. Edward Elgar Publishing, Cheltenham and Northampton, UK, pp. 336.

Archanjo, B.S. et al., 2017: Nanoscale analyses of the surface structure and composition of biochars extracted from field trials or after co-composting using advanced analytical electron microscopy. *Geoderma*, **294**, 70–79, doi:10.1016/j.geoderma.2017.01.037.

Arenas-Corraliza, M.G., M.L. López-Díaz, and G. Moreno, 2018: Winter cereal production in a Mediterranean silvoarable walnut system in the face of climate change. *Agric. Ecosyst. Environ.*, **264**, 111–118, doi:10.1016/j. agee.2018.05.024.

Arévalo, P., P. Olofsson, and C.E. Woodcock, 2020: Continuous monitoring of land change activities and post-disturbance dynamics from Landsat time series: A test methodology for REDD+ reporting. *Remote Sens. Environ.*, **238**, 111051, doi:10.1016/j.rse.2019.01.013.

Argañaraz, J.P., G. Gavier Pizarro, M. Zak, M.A. Landi, and L. M. Bellis, 2015: Human and biophysical drivers of fires in Semiarid Chaco mountains of Central Argentina. *Sci. Total Environ.*, **520**, 1–12, doi:10.1016/j. scitotenv.2015.02.081.

Arifanti, V.B., J.B. Kauffman, D. Hadriyanto, D. Murdiyarso, and R. Diana, 2019: Carbon dynamics and land use carbon footprints in mangrove-converted aquaculture: The case of the Mahakam Delta, Indonesia. *For. Ecol. Manage.*, **432**, 17–29, doi:10.1016/j.foreco.2018.08.047.

Arima, E.Y., P. Barreto, E. Araújo, and B. Soares-Filho, 2014: Public policies can reduce tropical deforestation: Lessons and challenges from Brazil. *Land use policy*, **41**, 465–473, doi:10.1016/j.landusepol.2014.06.026.

Arneth, A. et al., 2017: Historical carbon dioxide emissions caused by land-use changes are possibly larger than assumed. *Nat. Geosci.*, **10(2)**, 79, doi:10.1038/ngeo2882.

Arora, V.K. and A. Montenegro, 2011: Small temperature benefits provided by realistic afforestation efforts. *Nat. Geosci.*, **4**, 514–518, doi:10.1038/ngeo1182.

Arora, V.K. and J.R. Melton, 2018: Reduction in global area burned and wildfire emissions since 1930s enhances carbon uptake by land. *Nat. Commun.*, **9(1)**, 1326, doi:10.1038/s41467-018-03838-0.

Arrieta, E.M. and A.D. González, 2018: Impact of current, National Dietary Guidelines and alternative diets on greenhouse gas emissions in Argentina. *Food Policy*, **79**, 58–66, doi:10.1016/j.foodpol.2018.05.003.

Artés, T. et al., 2019: A global wildfire dataset for the analysis of fire regimes and fire behaviour. *Sci. Data*, **6(1)**, 296, doi:10.1038/s41597-019-0312-2.

Arts, B., V. Ingram, and M. Brockhaus, 2019: The Performance of REDD+: From Global Governance to Local Practices. *Forests*, **10(10)**, 837, doi:10.3390/f10100837.

Aryal, J.P., D.B. Rahut, T.B. Sapkota, R. Khurana, and A. Khatri-Chhetri, 2020: Climate change mitigation options among farmers in South Asia. *Environ. Dev. Sustain.*, **22(4)**, 3267–3289, doi:10.1007/s10668-019-00345-0.

Aschemann-Witzel, J., 2015: Consumer perception and trends about health and sustainability: trade-offs and synergies of two pivotal issues. *Curr. Opin. Food Sci.*, **3**, 6–10, doi:10.1016/j.cofs.2014.08.002.

Ashton, M.S., M.L. Tyrrell, D. Spalding, and B. Gentry, 2012: *Managing Forest Carbon in a Changing Climate*. Springer, Dordrecht, The Netherlands, 882 pp.

Asner, G.P. and R. Tupayachi, 2016: Accelerated losses of protected forests from gold mining in the Peruvian Amazon. *Environ. Res. Lett.*, **12(9)**, 094004, doi:10.1088/1748-9326/aa7dab.

Asner, G.P. et al., 2005: Selective Logging in the Brazilian Amazon. *Science*, **310(5747)**, 480–482, doi:10.1126/science.1118051.

Atwood, T.B. et al., 2017: Global patterns in mangrove soil carbon stocks and losses. *Nat. Clim. Change*, **7(7)**, 523–528, doi:10.1038/nclimate3326.

Australian Government- Clean Energy Regulator, 2021: The Emission Reduction Fund Project Maps. http://www.cleanenergyregulator.gov.au/maps/Pages/erf-projects/index.html (Accessed August 21, 2021).

Austin, K.G., et al., 2020: The economic costs of planting, preserving, and managing the world's forests to mitigate climate change. *Nat. Commun.*, **11**, doi:10.1038/s41467-020-19578-z.

Awad, Y.M. et al., 2018: Biochar Effects on Rice Paddy: Meta-analysis. *Advances in Agronomy* [Sparks, D.L. (ed.)]. **148**, 1–32, doi.org/10.1016/bs.agron.2017.11.005.

Awasthi, A., K. Singh, and R.P. Singh, 2017: A concept of diverse perennial cropping systems for integrated bioenergy production and ecological restoration of marginal lands in India. *Ecol. Eng.*, **105**, 58–65, doi:10.1016/j. ecoleng.2017.04.049.

Azevedo, A.A. et al., 2017: Limits of Brazil's Forest Code as a means to end illegal deforestation. *Proc. Natl. Acad. Sci.*, **114(29)**, 7653–7658, doi:10.1073/pnas.1604768114.

Ba, S., Q. Qu, K. Zhang, and J.C.J. Groot, 2020: Meta-analysis of greenhouse gas and ammonia emissions from dairy manure composting. *Biosyst. Eng.*, **193**, 126–137, doi:10.1016/j.biosystemseng.2020.02.015.

Baccini, A. et al., 2017: Tropical forests are a net carbon source based on aboveground measurements of gain and loss. *Science*, **358(6360)**, 230–234, doi:10.1126/science.aam5962.

Bäckstrand, K., J.W. Kuyper, B.-O. Linnér, and E. Lövbrand, 2017: Non-state actors in global climate governance: from Copenhagen to Paris and beyond. *Env. Polit.*, **26(4)**, 561–579, doi:10.1080/09644016.2017.1327485.

Bai, X. et al., 2019: Responses of soil carbon sequestration to climate-smart agriculture practices: A meta-analysis. *Glob. Change Biol.*, **25(8)**, 2591–2606, doi:10.1111/gcb.14658.

7

Bajželj, B. et al., 2014: Importance of food-demand management for climate mitigation. *Nat. Clim. Change*, **4(10)**, 924–929, doi:10.1038/nclimate2353.

Baka, J., 2014: What wastelands? A critique of biofuel policy discourse in South India. *Geoforum*, **54**, 315–323, doi:10.1016/j.geoforum.2013.08.007.

Baker, E., V. Bosetti, L.D. Anadon, M. Henrion, and L. Aleluia Reis, 2015: Future costs of key low-carbon energy technologies: Harmonization and aggregation of energy technology expert elicitation data. *Energy Policy*, **80**, 219–232, doi:10.1016/j.enpol.2014.10.008.

Baker, J.S., C.M. Wade, B.L. Sohngen, S. Ohrel, and A.A. Fawcett, 2019: Potential complementarity between forest carbon sequestration incentives and biomass energy expansion. *Energy Policy*, **126**, 391–401, doi:10.1016/j.enpol.2018.10.009.

Bakkaloglu, S. et al., 2021: Quantification of methane emissions from UK biogas plants. *Waste Manag.*, **124**, 82–93, doi:10.1016/j.wasman.2021.01.011.

Ballantyne, A.P., C.B. Alden, J.B. Miller, P.P. Tans, and J.W.C. White, 2012: Increase in observed net carbon dioxide uptake by land and oceans during the past 50 years. *Nature*, **488(7409)**, 70–72, doi:10.1038/nature11299.

Balmford, A. et al., 2016: Getting Road Expansion on the Right Track: A Framework for Smart Infrastructure Planning in the Mekong. *PLOS Biol.*, **14(12)**, e2000266, doi:10.1371/journal.pbio.2000266.

Barber, C.P., M.A. Cochrane, C.M. Souza, and W.F. Laurance, 2014: Roads, deforestation, and the mitigating effect of protected areas in the Amazon. *Biol. Conserv.*, **177**, 203–209, doi:10.1016/j.biocon.2014.07.004.

Barbier, E.B. et al., 2011: The value of estuarine and coastal ecosystem services. *Ecol. Monogr.*, **81(2)**, 169–193.

Barger, N.N., et al., 2018, Chapter 3: Direct and indirect drivers of land degradation and restoration. In: *The IPBES assessment report on land degradation and restoration* [Montanarella, L., R. Scholes, and A. Brainich (eds.)]. Secretariat of the Intergovernmental Science-Policy Platform on Biodiversity and Ecosystem Services, Bonn, Germany, pp. 137–218.

Bargués-Tobella, A. et al., 2020: Trees in African drylands can promote deep soil and groundwater recharge in a future climate with more intense rainfall. *L. Degrad. Dev.*, **31(1)**, 81–95, doi:10.1002/ldr.3430.

Baritz, R., L. Wiese, I. Verbeke, and R. Vargas, 2018: Voluntary Guidelines for Sustainable Soil Management: Global Action for Healthy Soils. In: *International Yearbook of Soil Law and Policy 2017* [Ginzky, H., E. Dooley, I.L. Heuser, E. Kasimbazi, T. Markus, and T. Qin (eds.)]. Springer, Cham, Switzerland, pp. 17–36.

Barlow, J., E. Berenguer, R. Carmenta, and F. França, 2020: Clarifying Amazonia's burning crisis. *Glob. Change Biol.*, **26(2)**, 319–321, doi:10.1111/gcb.14872.

Barretto, A.G.O.P., G. Berndes, G. Sparovek, and S. Wirsenius, 2013: Agricultural intensification in Brazil and its effects on land-use patterns: an analysis of the 1975-2006 period. *Glob. Change Biol.*, **19(6)**, 1804–1815, doi:10.1111/gcb.12174.

Bastin, J.-F. et al., 2019: The global tree restoration potential. *Science*, **365(6448)**, 76–79, doi:10.1126/science.aax0848.

Bastos, A. et al., 2020: Sources of Uncertainty in Regional and Global Terrestrial CO_2 Exchange Estimates. *Global Biogeochem. Cycles*, **34(2)**, e2019GB006393, doi:10.1029/2019GB006393.

Bationo, A. et al., 2012: Knowing the African Soils to Improve Fertilizer Recommendations. In: *Improving Soil Fertility Recommendations in Africa using the Decision Support System for Agrotechnology Transfer (DSSAT)* [Kihara, J., D. Fatondji, J.W. Jones, G. Hoogenboom, R. Tabo, and A. Bationo (eds.)]. Springer Netherlands, Dordrecht, The Netherlands, pp. 19–42.

Batlle-Bayer, L. et al., 2020: Food affordability and nutritional values within the functional unit of a food LCA. An application on regional diets in Spain. *Resour. Conserv. Recycl.*, **160**, 104856, doi:10.1016/j.resconrec.2020.104856.

Baudrier, M., V. Bellassen, and C. Foucherot, 2015: *Previous Agricultural Emissions Policy (2003-2013) reduced French agricultural emissions*. Climate Brief No. 49, IAEA. pp. 1–31. INIS-FR--16-1150, Paris, France.

Baumgartner, R.J., 2019: Sustainable Development Goals and the Forest Sector—a Complex Relationship. *Forests*, **10(2)**, 152, doi:10.3390/f10020152.

Bayala, J., J. Sanou, Z. Teklehaimanot, A. Kalinganire, and S. Ouédraogo, 2014: Parklands for buffering climate risk and sustaining agricultural production in the Sahel of West Africa. *Curr. Opin. Environ. Sustain.*, **6**, 28–34, doi:10.1016/j.cosust.2013.10.004.

Bayala, J. et al., 2015: Advances in knowledge of processes in soil–tree–crop interactions in parkland systems in the West African Sahel: A review. *Agric. Ecosyst. Environ.*, **205**, 25–35, doi:10.1016/j.agee.2015.02.018.

Beach, R.H. et al., 2015: Global mitigation potential and costs of reducing agricultural non-CO_2 greenhouse gas emissions through 2030. *J. Integr. Environ. Sci.*, **12(sup1)**, 87–105, doi:10.1080/1943815X.2015.1110183.

Beauchemin, K.A., E.M. Ungerfeld, R.J. Eckard, and M. Wang, 2020: Review: Fifty years of research on rumen methanogenesis: lessons learned and future challenges for mitigation. *Animal*, **14**, 2–16, doi:10.1017/S1751731119003100.

Bebber, D.P. and N. Butt, 2017: Tropical protected areas reduced deforestation carbon emissions by one third from 2000–2012. *Sci. Rep.*, **7(1)**, 14005, doi:10.1038/s41598-017-14467-w.

Bedulli, C., P.S. Lavery, M. Harvey, C.M. Duarte, and O. Serrano, 2020: Contribution of Seagrass Blue Carbon Toward Carbon Neutral Policies in a Touristic and Environmentally-Friendly Island. *Front. Mar. Sci.*, **7**, 1–12, doi:10.3389/fmars.2020.00001.

Bellassen, V. et al., 2021: The Carbon and Land Footprint of Certified Food Products. *J. Agric. Food Ind. Organ.*, **19(2)**, 113–126, doi:10.1515/jafio-2019-0037.

Ben-Arye, T. and S. Levenberg, 2019: Tissue Engineering for Clean Meat Production. *Front. Sustain. Food Syst.*, **3**, 1–19, doi:10.3389/fsufs.2019.00046.

Bengochea Paz, D., K. Henderson, and M. Loreau, 2020: Agricultural land use and the sustainability of social-ecological systems. *Ecol. Modell.*, **437**, 109312, doi:10.1016/j.ecolmodel.2020.109312.

Bengtsson, J., et al., 2019: Grasslands—more important for ecosystem services than you might think. *Ecosphere*, **10(2)**, 1–20, doi:10.1002/ecs2.2582.

Benson, T. and T. Mogues, 2018: Constraints in the fertilizer supply chain: evidence for fertilizer policy development from three African countries. *Food Secur.*, **10(6)**, doi:10.1007/s12571-018-0863-7.

Bessou, C. et al., 2020: Accounting for soil organic carbon role in land use contribution to climate change in agricultural LCA: which methods? Which impacts? *Int. J. Life Cycle Assess.*, **25(7)**, 1217–1230, doi:10.1007/s11367-019-01713-8.

Bhattacharya, P. and K.N. Ninan, 2011: Social cost-benefit analysis of intensive versus traditional shrimp farming: A case study from India. *Nat. Resour. Forum*, **35(4)**, 321–333, doi:10.1111/j.1477-8947.2011.01385.x.

Bhattarai, B., 2011: Assessment of mangrove forests in the Pacific region using Landsat imagery. *J. Appl. Remote Sens.*, **5(1)**, 053509, doi:10.1117/1.3563584.

Bhomia, R.K. et al., 2019: Impacts of Mauritia flexuosa degradation on the carbon stocks of freshwater peatlands in the Pastaza-Marañón river basin of the Peruvian Amazon. *Mitig. Adapt. Strateg. Glob. Change*, **24(4)**, 645–668, doi:10.1007/s11027-018-9809-9.

Biernat, L., F. Taube, R. Loges, C. Kluß, and T. Reinsch, 2020: Nitrous Oxide Emissions and Methane Uptake from Organic and Conventionally Managed Arable Crop Rotations on Farms in Northwest Germany. *Sustainability*, **12(8)**, 3240, doi:10.3390/su12083240.

Binam, J.N. et al., 2015: Effects of farmer managed natural regeneration on livelihoods in semi-arid West Africa. *Environ. Econ. Policy Stud.*, **17(4)**, 543–575, doi:10.1007/s10018-015-0107-4.

Blackman, A., 2015: Strict versus mixed-use protected areas: Guatemala's Maya Biosphere Reserve. *Ecol. Econ.*, **112**, 14–24, doi:10.1016/j.ecolecon.2015.01.009.

Blackman, AP. Veit, 2018: Titled Amazon Indigenous Communities Cut Forest Carbon Emissions. *Ecol. Econ.*, **153**, 56–67, doi:10.1016/j.ecolecon.2018.06.016.

Blackman, A., L. Goff, and M. Rivera Planter, 2018: Does eco-certification stem tropical deforestation? Forest Stewardship Council certification in Mexico. *J. Environ. Econ. Manage.*, **89**, 306–333, doi:10.1016/j.jeem.2018.04.005.

Blaser, J. and C. Küchli, 2011: Globale Walderhaltung und -bewirtschaftung und ihre Finanzierung: eine Bestandesaufnahme (Global forest conservation and management and its financing: an appraisal). *Schweizerische Zeitschrift fur Forstwes.*, **162(4)**, 107–116, doi:10.3188/szf.2011.0107.

Blaser, W.J. et al., 2018: Climate-smart sustainable agriculture in low-to-intermediate shade agroforests. *Nat. Sustain.*, **1(5)**, 234–239, doi:10.1038/s41893-018-0062-8.

Blicharska, M. et al., 2019: Biodiversity's contributions to sustainable development. *Nat. Sustain.*, **2(12)**, 1083–1093, doi:10.1038/s41893-019-0417-9.

Blok, K. et al., 2020: Assessment of Sectoral Greenhouse Gas Emission Reduction Potentials for 2030. *Energies*, **13(4)**, 943, doi:10.3390/en13040943.

Bockstael, N.E., A.M. Freeman, R.J. Kopp, P.R. Portney, and V.K. Smith, 2000: On Measuring Economic Values for Nature. *Environ. Sci. Technol.*, **34(8)**, 1384–1389, doi:10.1021/es990673l.

Bodirsky, B.L. et al., 2020: The ongoing nutrition transition thwarts long-term targets for food security, public health and environmental protection. *Sci. Rep.*, **10(1)**, 19778, doi:10.1038/s41598-020-75213-3.

Bolinder, M.A., et al., 2020: The effect of crop residues, cover crops, manures and nitrogen fertilization on soil organic carbon changes in agroecosystems: a synthesis of reviews. *Mitig. Adapt. Strateg. Glob. Change*, **25**, 929–952, doi:10.1007/s11027-020-09916-3.

Bonan, G.B., 2016: Forests, Climate, and Public Policy: A 500-Year Interdisciplinary Odyssey. *Annu. Rev. Ecol. Evol. Syst.*, **47(1)**, 97–121, doi:10.1146/annurev-ecolsys-121415-032359.

Bond, W.J., N. Stevens, G.F. Midgley, and C.E.R. Lehmann, 2019: The Trouble with Trees: Afforestation Plans for Africa. *Trends Ecol. Evol.*, **34(11)**, 963–965, doi:10.1016/j.tree.2019.08.003.

Boone Kauffman, J. et al., 2017: The jumbo carbon footprint of a shrimp: carbon losses from mangrove deforestation. *Front. Ecol. Environ.*, **15(4)**, 183–188, doi:10.1002/fee.1482.

Bora, R.R., M. Lei, J.W. Tester, J. Lehmann, and F. You, 2020a: Life Cycle Assessment and Technoeconomic Analysis of Thermochemical Conversion Technologies Applied to Poultry Litter with Energy and Nutrient Recovery. *ACS Sustain. Chem. Eng.*, **8(22)**, 8436–8447, doi:10.1021/acssuschemeng.0c02860.

Bora, R.R. et al., 2020b: Techno-Economic Feasibility and Spatial Analysis of Thermochemical Conversion Pathways for Regional Poultry Waste Valorization. *ACS Sustain. Chem. Eng.*, **8(14)**, 5763–5775, doi:10.1021/acssuschemeng.0c01229.

Borchard, N. et al., 2019: Biochar, soil and land-use interactions that reduce nitrate leaching and N$_2$O emissions: A meta-analysis. *Sci. Total Environ.*, **651**, 2354–2364, doi:10.1016/j.scitotenv.2018.10.060.

Börner, J. et al., 2017: The Effectiveness of Payments for Environmental Services. *World Dev.*, **96**, 359–374, doi:10.1016/J.WORLDDEV.2017.03.020.

Borras, S.M. and J.C. Franco, 2018: The challenge of locating land-based climate change mitigation and adaptation politics within a social justice perspective: towards an idea of agrarian climate justice. *Third World Q.*, **39(7)**, 1308–1325, doi:10.1080/01436597.2018.1460592.

Bos, A.B., 2020: Towards performance assessment of subnational forest-based climate change mitigation initiatives. PhD Thesis synthesis 24 p., Wageningen University, Wageningen, The Netherlands.

Bossio, D.A. et al., 2020: The role of soil carbon in natural climate solutions. *Nat. Sustain.*, **3(5)**, 391–398, doi:10.1038/s41893-020-0491-z.

Bowler, D.E. et al., 2012: Does community forest management provide global environmental benefits and improve local welfare? *Front. Ecol. Environ.*, **10(1)**, 29–36, doi:10.1890/110040.

Bowman, D.M.J.S. et al., 2019: Human–environmental drivers and impacts of the globally extreme 2017 Chilean fires. *Ambio*, **48(4)**, 350–362, doi:10.1007/s13280-018-1084-1.

Bowman, D.M.J.S. et al., 2020a: Vegetation fires in the Anthropocene. *Nat. Rev. Earth Environ.*, **1(10)**, 500–515, doi:10.1038/s43017-020-0085-3.

Bowman, D.M.J.S., G.J. Williamson, O.F. Price, M.N. Ndalila, and R.A. Bradstock, 2020b: Australian forests, megafires and the risk of dwindling carbon stocks. *Plant. Cell Environ.*, **44(2)**, 347–355, doi:10.1111/pce.13916.

Brandão, M., M.U.F. Kirschbaum, A.L. Cowie, and S. V. Hjuler, 2019: Quantifying the climate change effects of bioenergy systems: Comparison of 15 impact assessment methods. *GCB Bioenergy*, **11(5)**, 727–743, doi:10.1111/gcbb.12593.

Brando, P.M. et al., 2014: Abrupt increases in Amazonian tree mortality due to drought-fire interactions. *Proc. Natl. Acad. Sci.*, **111(17)**, 6347–6352, doi:10.1073/pnas.1305499111.

Brandt, M. et al., 2019a: Changes in rainfall distribution promote woody foliage production in the Sahel. *Commun. Biol.*, **2(1)**, 133, doi:10.1038/s42003-019-0383-9.

Brandt, P., G. Yesuf, M. Herold, and M.C. Rufino, 2019b: Intensification of dairy production can increase the GHG mitigation potential of the land use sector in East Africa. *Glob. Change Biol.*, **26(2)**, 568–585, doi:10.1111/gcb.14870.

Braun, M. et al., 2016: A holistic assessment of greenhouse gas dynamics from forests to the effects of wood products use in Austria. *Carbon Manag.*, **7(5–6)**, 271–283, doi:10.1080/17583004.2016.1230990.

Bristow, M. et al., 2016: Quantifying the relative importance of greenhouse gas emissions from current and future savanna land use change across northern Australia. *Biogeosciences*, **13(22)**, 6285–6303, doi:10.5194/bg-13-6285-2016.

Brown, B., R. Fadillah, Y. Nurdin, I. Soulsby, and R. Ahmad, 2014: Community Based Ecological Mangrove Rehabilitation (CBEMR) in Indonesia. *S.a.p.i.en.s*, **7(2)**, 1–13.

Brunet-Navarro, P., H. Jochheim, and B. Muys, 2017: The effect of increasing lifespan and recycling rate on carbon storage in wood products from theoretical model to application for the European wood sector. *Mitig. Adapt. Strateg. Glob. Change*, **22(8)**, 1193–1205, doi:10.1007/s11027-016-9722-z.

Buchholz, T., M.D. Hurteau, J. Gunn, and D. Saah, 2016: A global meta-analysis of forest bioenergy greenhouse gas emission accounting studies. *GCB Bioenergy*, **8(2)**, 281–289, doi:10.1111/gcbb.12245.

Buchner, B.K., C. Trabacchi, F. Mazza, D. Abramskiehn, and D. Wang, 2015: *A CPI Report – Global Landscape of Climate Finance 2015*. Climate Policy Initiative (CPI), London, UK, 17 pp.

Buchspies, B., M. Kaltschmitt, and M. Junginger, 2020: Straw utilization for biofuel production: A consequential assessment of greenhouse gas emissions from bioethanol and biomethane provision with a focus on the time dependency of emissions. *GCB Bioenergy*, **12(10)**, 789–805, doi:10.1111/gcbb.12734.

Burivalova, Z. et al., 2019: What works in tropical forest conservation, and what does not: Effectiveness of four strategies in terms of environmental, social, and economic outcomes. *Conserv. Sci. Pract.*, **1(6)**, e28, doi:10.1111/csp2.28.

Burney, J.A., S.J. Davis, and D.B. Lobell, 2010: Greenhouse gas mitigation by agricultural intensification. *Proc. Natl. Acad. Sci.*, **107(26)**, 12052–12057, doi:10.1073/pnas.0914216107.

Busch, J. and K. Ferretti-Gallon, 2017: What drives deforestation and what stops it? A meta-analysis. *Rev. Environ. Econ. Policy*, **11**, 3–23, doi:10.1093/reep/rew013.

Busch, J. et al., 2019: Potential for low-cost carbon dioxide removal through tropical reforestation. *Nat. Clim. Change*, **9(6)**, 463–466, doi:10.1038/s41558-019-0485-x.

Butsic, V., M. Baumann, A. Shortland, S. Walker, and T. Kuemmerle, 2015: Conservation and conflict in the Democratic Republic of Congo: The impacts of warfare, mining, and protected areas on deforestation. *Biol. Conserv.*, **191**, 266–273, doi:10.1016/j.biocon.2015.06.037.

Cabral, R.P., M. Bui, and N. Mac Dowell, 2019: A synergistic approach for the simultaneous decarbonisation of power and industry via bioenergy with carbon capture and storage (BECCS). *Int. J. Greenh. Gas Control*, **87**, 221–237, doi:10.1016/j.ijggc.2019.05.020.

Cadier, C., E. Bayraktarov, R. Piccolo, and M.F. Adame, 2020: Indicators of Coastal Wetlands Restoration Success: A Systematic Review. *Front. Mar. Sci.*, **7**, Art 600220. doi:10.3389/fmars.2020.600220.

Calvin, K. et al., 2021: Bioenergy for climate change mitigation: Scale and sustainability. *GCB Bioenergy*, **13(9)**, 1346–1371, doi:10.1111/gcbb.12863.

Cameron, C., L.B. Hutley, D.A. Friess, and B. Brown, 2019: Community structure dynamics and carbon stock change of rehabilitated mangrove forests in Sulawesi, Indonesia. *Ecol. Appl.*, **29(1)**, e1810 doi:10.1002/eap.1810.

Camia, A. et al., 2020: *The use of woody biomass for energy production in the EU*. Publications Office of the European Union, Luxembourg, 182 pp.

Campbell, M., M. Alamgir, and W. Laurance, 2017: Roads to ruin: Can we build roads that benefit people while not destroying nature? *Australas. Sci.*, **38(2)**, 40–41.

Carattini, S., A. Baranzini, and R. Lalive, 2018: Is Taxing Waste a Waste of Time? Evidence from a Supreme Court Decision. *Ecol. Econ.*, **148**, 131–151, doi:10.1016/j.ecolecon.2018.02.001.

CARB, 2019: *California Tropical Forest Standard: Criteria for Assessing Jurisdiction-Scale Programs that Reduce Emissions from Tropical Deforestation*. California Air Resources Board, California, USA, 49 pp.

Cardinael, R. et al., 2018: Revisiting IPCC Tier 1 coefficients for soil organic and biomass carbon storage in agroforestry systems. *Environ. Res. Lett.*, **13(12)**, 124020, doi:10.1088/1748-9326/aaeb5f.

Caro, D., E. Kebreab, and F.M. Mitloehner, 2016: Mitigation of enteric methane emissions from global livestock systems through nutrition strategies. *Clim. Change*, **137(3–4)**, 467–480, doi:10.1007/s10584-016-1686-1.

Caro Torres, P., W. de Jong, A. Denvir, D. Humphreys, and K. McGinley, 2016: *Can Legality Verification enhance local rights to forest resources? Piloting the policy learning protocol in the Peruvian forest context*. International Union of Forest Research Organizations (IUFRO) and Yale University's Governance, Environment and Markets (GEM) Initiative, IUFRO, Vienna, Austria, 113 pp. http://www.iufro.org/science/divisions/division-9/90000/90500/90505/publications/.

Carrijo, D.R., M.E. Lundy, and B.A. Linquist, 2017: Rice yields and water use under alternate wetting and drying irrigation: A meta-analysis. *F. Crop. Res.*, **203**, 173–180, doi:10.1016/j.fcr.2016.12.002.

Carroll, J. and A.J. Daigneault, 2019: Achieving ambitious climate targets: Is it economical for New Zealand to invest in agricultural GHG mitigation? *Environ. Res. Lett.*, 14: 124064 doi:10.1088/1748-9326/ab542a.

Carvalho, J.L.N. et al., 2014: Crop-pasture rotation: A strategy to reduce soil greenhouse gas emissions in the Brazilian Cerrado. *Agric. Ecosyst. Environ.*, **183**, 167–175, doi:10.1016/j.agee.2013.11.014.

Carvalho, J.L.N., T.W. Hudiburg, H.C.J. Franco, and E.H. DeLucia, 2017: Contribution of above- and belowground bioenergy crop residues to soil carbon. *GCB Bioenergy*, **9(8)**, 1333–1343, doi:10.1111/gcbb.12411.

Cassman, K. and P. Grassini, 2020: A global perspective on sustainable intensification research. *Nat. Sustain.*, **3(4)**, 262–268, doi:10.1038/s41893-020-0507-8.

Cayuela, M.L. et al., 2014: Biochar's role in mitigating soil nitrous oxide emissions: A review and meta-analysis. *Agric. Ecosyst. Environ.*, **191(0)**, 5–16, doi:10.1016/j.agee.2013.10.009.

Cayuela, M.L., S. Jeffery, and L. van Zwieten, 2015: The molar H:Corg ratio of biochar is a key factor in mitigating N_2O emissions from soil. *Agric. Ecosyst. Environ.*, **202**, 135–138, doi:10.1016/j.agee.2014.12.015.

CBI, 2020: Climate Bonds Initiative: Certification Ecoagro-Rizoma Agro, Brazil. https://www.climatebonds.net/certification/ecoagro-rizoma. (Accessed April 15, 2021).

Ceccherini, G. et al., 2020: Abrupt increase in harvested forest area over Europe after 2015. *Nature*, **583(7814)**, 72–77, doi:10.1038/s41586-020-2438-y.

Ceddia, M.G., S. Sedlacek, N.O. Bardsley, and S. Gomez-y-Paloma, 2013: Sustainable agricultural intensification or Jevons paradox? The role of

public governance in tropical South America. *Glob. Environ. Change*, **23(5)**, 1052–1063, doi:10.1016/j.gloenvcha.2013.07.005.

Chabé-Ferret, S. and J. Subervie, 2013: How much green for the buck? Estimating additional and windfall effects of French agro-environmental schemes by DID-matching. *J. Environ. Econ. Manage.*, **65(1)**, 12–27, doi:10.1016/j.jeem.2012.09.003.

Chagas, J.C., M. Ramin, and S.J. Krizsan, 2019: In Vitro Evaluation of Different Dietary Methane Mitigation Strategies. *Animals*, **9(12)**, 1120, doi:10.3390/ani9121120.

Chapman, M. et al., 2020: Large climate mitigation potential from adding trees to agricultural lands. *Glob. Change Biol.*, **26(8)**, 4357–4365, doi:10.1111/gcb.15121.

Chen, K., Y. Wang, R. Zhang, H. Zhang, and C. Gao, 2019: CRISPR/Cas Genome Editing and Precision Plant Breeding in Agriculture. *Annu. Rev. Plant Biol.*, **70(1)**, 667–697, doi:10.1146/annurev-arplant-050718-100049.

Cherubini, F. et al., 2009: Energy- and greenhouse gas-based LCA of biofuel and bioenergy systems: Key issues, ranges and recommendations. *Resour. Conserv. Recycl.*, **53(8)**, 434–447, doi:10.1016/j.resconrec.2009.03.013.

Chevallier, F. et al., 2005: Inferring CO_2 sources and sinks from satellite observations: Method and application to TOVS data. *J. Geophys. Res.*, **110(D24)**, D24309, doi:10.1029/2005JD006390.

Chiaramonti, D and C. Panoutsou, 2018: Low-ILUC biofuel production in marginal areas: Can existing EU policies support biochar deployment in EU MED arid lands under desertification? *Chem. Eng. Trans.*, **65**, 841–846, doi:10.3303/CET1865141.

Chidthaisong, A. et al., 2018: Evaluating the effects of alternate wetting and drying (AWD) on methane and nitrous oxide emissions from a paddy field in Thailand. *Soil Sci. Plant Nutr.*, **64(1)**, 31–38, doi:10.1080/00380768.2017.1399044.

Chimner, R.A., D.J. Cooper, F.C. Wurster, and L. Rochefort, 2017: An overview of peatland restoration in North America: where are we after 25 years? *Restor. Ecol.*, **25(2)**, 283–292, doi:10.1111/rec.12434.

Chisholm, R.A., L.S. Wijedasa, and T. Swinfield, 2016: The need for long-term remedies for Indonesia's forest fires. *Conserv. Biol.*, **30(1)**, 5–6, doi:10.1111/cobi.12662.

Chomba, S., F. Sinclair, P. Savadogo, M. Bourne, and M. Lohbeck, 2020: Opportunities and Constraints for Using Farmer Managed Natural Regeneration for Land Restoration in Sub-Saharan Africa. *Front. For. Glob. Change*, **3**, 571679 . doi:10.3389/ffgc.2020.571679.

Chriki, S. and J.-F. Hocquette, 2020: The Myth of Cultured Meat: A Review. *Front. Nutr.*, **7**(February), 1–9, doi:10.3389/fnut.2020.00007.

Chum, H., A. Faaij, J. Moreira, G. Berndes, P. Dhamija, H. Dong, B. Gabrielle, A. Goss Eng, W. Lucht, M. Mapako, O. Masera Cerutti, T. McIntyre, T. Minowa, and K. Pingoud, 2011: Bioenergy. In: *IPCC Special Report on Renewable Energy Sources and Climate Change Mitigation* [Edenhofer, O., R. Pichs-Madruga, Y. Sokona, K. Seyboth, P. Matschoss, S. Kadner, T. Zwickel, P. Eickemeier, G. Hansen, S. Schlömer, and C. von Stechow (eds.)]. Cambridge University Press, Cambridge, UK, and New York, NY, USA, pp. 209–332.

Churkina, G. et al., 2020: Buildings as a global carbon sink. *Nat. Sustain.*, **3(4)**, 269–276, doi:10.1038/s41893-019-0462-4.

Claassen, R., F. Carriazo, and K. Ueda, 2010: Grassland Conversion for Crop Production in the United States: Defining Indicators for Policy Analysis. *OECD Agri-environmental Indicators: Lessons Learned and Future Directions*. Organisation for Economic Co-operation and Development (OECD), Washington, DC, USA, 27.

Claassen, R., C. Langpap, and J. Wu, 2017: Impacts of Federal Crop Insurance on Land Use and Environmental Quality. *Am. J. Agric. Econ.*, **99(3)**, 592–613, doi:10.1093/ajae/aaw075.

Claassen, R., E.N. Duquette, and D.J. Smith, 2018: Additionality in U.S. Agricultural Conservation Programs. *Land Econ.*, **94(1)**, 19–35, doi:10.3368/le.94.1.19.

Clark, H., C. Pinares-Patiño, and C. DeKlein, 2005: Relationships between biodiversity and production in grasslands at local and regional scales.

In: *Grassland: a global resource* [McGilloway, D.A. (ed.)]. Wageningen Academic Publishers, Wageningen, The Netherlands, 279–293 pp.

Clark, M. and D. Tilman, 2017: Comparative analysis of environmental impacts of agricultural production systems, agricultural input efficiency, and food choice. *Environ. Res. Lett.*, **12(6)**, 064016, doi:10.1088/1748-9326/aa6cd5.

Clark, M.A. et al., 2020: Global food system emissions could preclude achieving the 1.5° and 2°C climate change targets. *Science*, **370(6517)**, 705–708, doi:10.1126/science.aba7357.

Climate Smart Forest and Nature Management, 2021: European Network, Climate-Smart Forestry in Europe. https://www.vbne.nl/klimaatslimbosen natuurbeheer/projecten-europa (Accessed April 15, 2021).

Cohn, A.S. et al., 2019: Forest loss in Brazil increases maximum temperatures within 50 km. *Environ. Res. Lett.*, **14(8)**, 084047, doi:10.1088/1748-9326/ab31fb.

Colley, T.A., S.I. Olsen, M. Birkved, and M.Z. Hauschild, 2020: Delta Life Cycle Assessment of Regenerative Agriculture in a Sheep Farming System. *Integr. Environ. Assess. Manag.*, **16(2)**, 282–290, doi:10.1002/ieam.4238.

Conant, R.T., C.E.P. Cerri, B.B. Osborne, and K. Paustian, 2017: Grassland management impacts on soil carbon stocks: a new synthesis. *Ecol. Appl.*, **27(2)**, 662–668, doi:10.1002/eap.1473.

Conchedda, G. and F.N. Tubiello, 2020: Drainage of organic soils and GHG emissions: validation with country data. *Earth Syst. Sci. Data*, **12(4)**, 3113–3137, doi:10.5194/essd-12-3113-2020.

Contreras-Negrete, G. et al., 2014: Genetic diversity and structure of wild and managed populations of Polaskia chende (Cactaceae) in the Tehuacán-Cuicatlán Valley, Central Mexico: insights from SSR and allozyme markers. *Genet. Resour. Crop Evol.*, **62(1)**, 85–101, doi:10.1007/s10722-014-0137-y.

Cook-Patton, S.C. et al., 2020: Mapping carbon accumulation potential from global natural forest regrowth. *Nature*, **585(7826)**, 545–550, doi:10.1038/s41586-020-2686-x.

Corbeels, M., R. Cardinael, K. Naudin, H. Guibert, and E. Torquebiau, 2019: The 4 per 1000 goal and soil carbon storage under agroforestry and conservation agriculture systems in sub-Saharan Africa. *Soil Tillage Res.*, **188**, 16–26, doi:10.1016/j.still.2018.02.015.

Corbeels, M., R. Cardinael, D. Powlson, R. Chikowo, and B. Gerard, 2020: Carbon sequestration potential through conservation agriculture in Africa has been largely overestimated. *Soil Tillage Res.*, **196**, 104300, doi:10.1016/j.still.2019.104300.

Costanza, R. et al., 1997: The value of the world's ecosystem services and natural capital. *Nature*, **387(6630)**, 253–260, doi:10.1038/387253a0.

Costanza, R. et al., 2014: Changes in the global value of ecosystem services. *Glob. Environ. Change*, **26**, 152–158, doi:10.1016/j.gloenvcha.2014.04.002.

Couwenberg, J., R. Dommain, and H. Joosten, 2010: Greenhouse gas fluxes from tropical peatlands in south-east Asia. *Glob. Change Biol.*, **16(6)**, 1715–1732, doi:10.1111/j.1365-2486.2009.02016.x.

Cowie, A.L. et al., 2021: Applying a science-based systems perspective to dispel misconceptions about climate effects of forest bioenergy. *GCB Bioenergy*, **13(8)**, 1210–1231, doi:10.1111/gcbb.12844.

Creutzig, F. et al., 2018: Towards demand-side solutions for mitigating climate change. *Nat. Clim. Change*, **8(4)**, 260–263, doi:10.1038/s41558-018-0121-1.

Crippa, M. et al., 2021: *EDGAR v6.0 Greenhouse Gas Emissions*. European Commission, Joint Research Centre (JRC), Ispra, Italy. https://edgar.jrc.ec.europa.eu/dataset_ghg60 (Accessed May 1, 2021).

Crooks, S., D. Herr, J. Tamelander, D. Laffoley, and J. Vandever, 2011: *Mitigating climate change through restoration and management of coastal wetlands and near-shore marine ecosystems: challenges and opportunities*. The World Bank, Washington, DC, 69 pp, https://openknowledge.worldbank.org/handle/10986/18318.

Crusius, J., 2020: "Natural" Climate Solutions Could Speed Up Mitigation, With Risks. Additional Options Are Needed. *Earth's Futur.*, **8(4)**, doi:10.1029/2019EF001310.

da Silva, S.S. et al., 2021: Burning in southwestern Brazilian Amazonia, 2016–2019. *J. Environ. Manage.*, **286**, 112189, doi:10.1016/j.jenvman.2021.112189.

Daioglou, V., B. Wicke, A.P.C. Faaij, and D.P. van Vuuren, 2015: Competing uses of biomass for energy and chemicals: implications for long-term global CO_2 mitigation potential. *GCB Bioenergy*, **7(6)**, 1321–1334, doi:10.1111/gcbb.12228.

Daioglou, V. et al., 2017: Greenhouse gas emission curves for advanced biofuel supply chains. *Nat. Clim. Change*, **7(12)**, 920–924, doi:10.1038/s41558-017-0006-8.

Daioglou, V., J.C. Doelman, B. Wicke, A. Faaij, and D.P. van Vuuren, 2019: Integrated assessment of biomass supply and demand in climate change mitigation scenarios. *Glob. Environ. Change*, **54**, 88–101, doi:10.1016/j.gloenvcha.2018.11.012.

Daioglou et al., 2020b: Bioenergy technologies in long-run climate change mitigation: results from the EMF-33 study. *Clim. Change*, **163**, 1603–1620, doi:10.1007/s10584-020-02799-y.

Dargie, G.C. et al., 2017: Age, extent and carbon storage of the central Congo Basin peatland complex. *Nature*, **542(7639)**, 86–90, doi:10.1038/nature21048.

Dargie, G.C. et al., 2019: Congo Basin peatlands: threats and conservation priorities. *Mitig. Adapt. Strateg. Glob. Change*, **24(4)**, 669–686, doi:10.1007/s11027-017-9774-8.

Dasgupta, P., 2021: *The Economics of Biodiversity: The Dasgupta Review*. HM Treasury, UK Government, London, UK, 126–145 pp.

Dass, P., B.Z. Houlton, Y. Wang, and D. Warlind, 2018: Grasslands may be more reliable carbon sinks than forests in California. *Environ. Res. Lett.*, **13(7)**, 074027, doi:10.1088/1748-9326/aacb39.

Davin, E.L. and N. de Noblet-Ducoudré, 2010: Climatic Impact of Global-Scale Deforestation: Radiative versus Nonradiative Processes. *J. Clim.*, **23(1)**, 97–112, doi:10.1175/2009JCLI3102.1.

de Figueiredo, E.B. et al., 2017: Greenhouse gas balance and carbon footprint of beef cattle in three contrasting pasture-management systems in Brazil. *J. Clean. Prod.*, **142**, 420–431, doi:10.1016/j.jclepro.2016.03.132.

de Groot, R. et al., 2012: Global estimates of the value of ecosystems and their services in monetary units. *Ecosyst. Serv.*, **1(1)**, 50–61, doi:10.1016/j.ecoser.2012.07.005.

de Klein, C.A.M., T.J. van der Weerden, J. Luo, K.C. Cameron, and H.J. Di, 2020: A review of plant options for mitigating nitrous oxide emissions from pasture-based systems. *New Zeal. J. Agric. Res.*, **63(1)**, 29–43, doi:10.1080/00288233.2019.1614073.

de los Santos, C.B. et al., 2019: Recent trend reversal for declining European seagrass meadows. *Nat. Commun.*, **10(1)**, 3356, doi:10.1038/s41467-019-11340-4.

de Oliveira Garcia, W., T. Amann, and J. Hartmann, 2018: Increasing biomass demand enlarges negative forest nutrient budget areas in wood export regions. *Sci. Rep.*, **8(1)**, 5280, doi:10.1038/s41598-018-22728-5.

de Ponti, T., B. Rijk, and M.K. van Ittersum, 2012: The crop yield gap between organic and conventional agriculture. *Agric. Syst.*, **108**, 1–9, doi:10.1016/j.agsy.2011.12.004.

De Stefano, A., M.G. Jacobson, 2017: Soil carbon sequestration in agroforestry systems: a meta-analysis. *Agrofor. Syst.*, **92(2)**, 285–299, doi:10.1007/s10457-017-0147-9.

de Vrese, P., S. Hagemann, and M. Claussen, 2016: Asian irrigation, African rain: Remote impacts of irrigation. *Geophys. Res. Lett.*, **43(8)**, 3737–3745, doi:10.1002/2016GL068146.

DeCicco, J.M. and W.H. Schlesinger, 2018: Opinion: Reconsidering bioenergy given the urgency of climate protection. *Proc. Natl. Acad. Sci.*, **115(39)**, 9642–9645, doi:10.1073/pnas.1814120115.

DeCiucies, S., T. Whitman, D. Woolf, A. Enders, and J. Lehmann, 2018: Priming mechanisms with additions of pyrogenic organic matter to soil. *Geochim. Cosmochim. Acta*, **238**, 329–342, doi:10.1016/j.gca.2018.07.004.

7

Deininger, K. and B. Minten, 2002: Determinants of Deforestation and the Economics of Protection: An Application to Mexico. *Am. J. Agric. Econ.*, **84(4)**, 943–960, doi:10.1111/1467-8276.00359.

Department of Agriculture, 2020: Farm Income and Wealth Statistics.U.S. Department of Agriculture, https://www.ers.usda.gov/data-products/farm-income-and-wealth-statistics/data-files-us-and-state-level-farm-income-and-wealth-statistics (Accessed March 23, 2021).

Descheemaeker, K. et al., 2016: Climate change adaptation and mitigation in smallholder crop–livestock systems in sub-Saharan Africa: a call for integrated impact assessments. *Reg. Environ. Change*, **16(8)**, 2331–2343, doi:10.1007/s10113-016-0957-8.

Devaraju, N., N. de Noblet-Ducoudré, B. Quesada, and G. Bala, 2018: Quantifying the Relative Importance of Direct and Indirect Biophysical Effects of Deforestation on Surface Temperature and Teleconnections. *J. Clim.*, **31(10)**, 3811–3829, doi:10.1175/JCLI-D-17-0563.1.

Dezécache, C. et al., 2017: Gold-rush in a forested El Dorado: deforestation leakages and the need for regional cooperation. *Environ. Res. Lett.*, **12(3)**, 034013, doi:10.1088/1748-9326/aa6082.

Di, H.J and K.C. Cameron, 2016: Inhibition of nitrification to mitigate nitrate leaching and nitrous oxide emissions in grazed grassland: a review. *J. Soils Sediments*, **16(5)**, 1401–1420, doi:10.1007/s11368-016-1403-8.

Dickie, A. et al., 2014a: *Strategies for Mitigating Climate Change in Agriculture: Recommendations for Philanthropy – Executive Summary*. Climate Focus and California Environmental Associate, Climate and Land Use Alliance, San Francisco, USA. 17 pp.

Dickie, I.A. et al., 2014b: Conflicting values: ecosystem services and invasive tree management. *Biol. Invasions*, **16(3)**, 705–719, doi:10.1007/s10530-013-0609-6.

Dioha, M.O. and A. Kumar, 2020: Exploring greenhouse gas mitigation strategies for agriculture in Africa: The case of Nigeria. *Ambio*, **49(9)**, 1549–1566, doi:10.1007/s13280-019-01293-9.

Doelman, J.C. et al., 2018: Exploring SSP land-use dynamics using the IMAGE model: Regional and gridded scenarios of land-use change and land-based climate change mitigation. *Glob. Environ. Change*, **48**, 119–135, doi:10.1016/j.gloenvcha.2017.11.014.

Doelman, J.C. et al., 2020: Afforestation for climate change mitigation: Potentials, risks and trade-offs. *Glob. Change Biol.*, **26(3)**, 1576–1591, doi:10.1111/gcb.14887.

Domke, G., A. Brandon, R. Diaz-Lasco, S. Federici, E. Garcia-Apaza, G. Grassi, T. Gschwantner, M. Herold, Y. Hirata, Å. Kasimir, M.J. Kinyanjui, H. Krisnawati, A. Lehtonen, R.E. Malimbwi, S. Niinistö, S.M. Ogle, T. Paul, N.H. Ravindranath, J. Rock, C.R. Sanquetta, M.J.S. Sanchez, M. Vitullo, S.J. Wakelin, and J. Zhu., 2019: Refinement to the 2006 IPCC Guidelines for National Greenhouse Gas Inventories. Vol. 4, Agriculture, Forestry and Other Land Use, Chapter 4, Forest Land [Calvo Buendia, E., K. Tanabe, A. Kranjc, J. Baasansuren, M. Fukuda, S. Ngarize, A. Osako, Y. Pyrozhenko, P. Shermanau, and S. Federici (eds.)]. Intergovernmental Panel on Climate Change (IPCC), Geneva, Switzerland, 71 pp.

Domke, G.M., S.N. Oswalt, B.F. Walters, and R.S. Morin, 2020: Tree planting has the potential to increase carbon sequestration capacity of forests in the United States. *Proc. Natl. Acad. Sci.*, **117(40)**, 24649–24651, doi:10.1073/pnas.2010840117.

Donato, D.C., J.B. Kauffman, R.A. Mackenzie, A. Ainsworth, and A.Z. Pfleeger, 2012: Whole-island carbon stocks in the tropical Pacific: Implications for mangrove conservation and upland restoration. *J. Environ. Manage.*, **97**, 89–96, doi:10.1016/j.jenvman.2011.12.004.

Donnison, C. et al., 2020: Bioenergy with Carbon Capture and Storage (BECCS): Finding the win–wins for energy, negative emissions and ecosystem services—size matters. *GCB Bioenergy*, **12(8)**, 586–604, doi:10.1111/gcbb.12695.

Dooley, K. and S. Kartha, 2018: Land-based negative emissions: risks for climate mitigation and impacts on sustainable development. *Int.*

Environ. Agreements Polit. Law Econ., **18(1)**, 79–98, doi:10.1007/s10784-017-9382-9.

Drew, J., C. Cleghorn, A. Macmillan, and A. Mizdrak, 2020: Healthy and Climate-Friendly Eating Patterns in the New Zealand Context. *Environ. Health Perspect.*, **128(1)**, 017007, doi:10.1289/EHP5996.

Drews, M., M.A.D. Larsen, and J.G. Peña Balderrama, 2020: Projected water usage and land-use-change emissions from biomass production (2015–2050). *Energy Strateg. Rev.*, **29**, 100487, doi:10.1016/j.esr.2020.100487.

Du, Y.-D. et al., 2018: Crop yield and water use efficiency under aerated irrigation: A meta-analysis. *Agric. Water Manag.*, **210**, 158–164, doi:10.1016/j.agwat.2018.07.038.

Duarte, C.M. et al., 2020: Rebuilding marine life. *Nature*, **580(7801)**, 39–51, doi:10.1038/s41586-020-2146-7.

Duffy, K.A. et al., 2021: How close are we to the temperature tipping point of the terrestrial biosphere? *Sci. Adv.*, **7(3)**, doi:10.1126/sciadv.aay1052.

Duguma, L.A., P.A. Minang, and M. van Noordwijk, 2014: Climate Change Mitigation and Adaptation in the Land Use Sector: From Complementarity to Synergy. *Environ. Manage.*, **54(3)**, 420–432, doi:10.1007/s00267-014-0331-x.

Dulac, J., 2013: *Global land transport infrastructure requirements. Estimating road and railway infrastructure capacity and costs to 2050*. 54p. International Energy Agency (IEA), Paris, France.

Dunic, J.C., C.J. Brown, R.M. Connolly, M.P. Turschwell, and I.M. Côté, 2021: Long-term declines and recovery of meadow area across the world's seagrass bioregions. *Glob. Change Biol.*, **27(17)**, 4096–4109, doi:10.1111/gcb.15684.

Eckard, R. and H. Clark, 2020: Potential solutions to the major greenhouse-gas issues facing Australasian dairy farming. *Anim. Prod. Sci.*, **60(1)**, 10, doi:10.1071/AN18574.

Ekholm, T., 2020: Optimal forest rotation under carbon pricing and forest damage risk. *For. Policy Econ.*, **115**, 102131, doi:10.1016/j.forpol.2020.102131.

Elbersen, B. et al., 2020: *Definition and classification of marginal lands suitable for industrial crops in Europe*. Wageningen University, Wageningen, The Netherlands, 62 pp.

Elevitch, C., D. Mazaroli, and D. Ragone, 2018: Agroforestry Standards for Regenerative Agriculture. *Sustainability*, **10(9)**, 3337, doi:10.3390/su10093337.

Elliott, M. et al., 2016: Ecoengineering with Ecohydrology: Successes and failures in estuarine restoration. *Estuar. Coast. Shelf Sci.*, **176**, 12–35, doi:10.1016/j.ecss.2016.04.003.

Ellis, P.W. et al., 2019: Reduced-impact logging for climate change mitigation (RIL-C) can halve selective logging emissions from tropical forests. *For. Ecol. Manage.*, **438**, 255–266, doi:10.1016/j.foreco.2019.02.004.

Ellison, D. et al., 2017: Trees, forests and water: Cool insights for a hot world. *Glob. Environ. Change*, **43**, 51–61, doi:10.1016/j.gloenvcha.2017.01.002.

Elshout, P.M.F. et al., 2015: Greenhouse-gas payback times for crop-based biofuels. *Nat. Clim. Change*, **5(6)**, 604–610, doi:10.1038/nclimate2642.

Emenike, O. et al., 2020: Initial techno-economic screening of BECCS technologies in power generation for a range of biomass feedstock. *Sustain. Energy Technol. Assessments*, **40**, 100743, doi:10.1016/j.seta.2020.100743.

Emery, I., S. Mueller, Z. Qin, and J.B. Dunn, 2017: Evaluating the Potential of Marginal Land for Cellulosic Feedstock Production and Carbon Sequestration in the United States. *Environ. Sci. Technol.*, **51(1)**, 733–741, doi:10.1021/acs.est.6b04189.

Engel, R.A., M.E. Marlier, and D.P. Lettenmaier, 2019: On the causes of the summer 2015 Eastern Washington wildfires. *Environ. Res. Commun.*, **1(1)**, 011009, doi:10.1088/2515-7620/ab082e.

Eory, V. et al., 2015: Review and update the UK agriculture MACC to assess the abatement potential for the 5th carbon budget period and to 2050: Final report submitted for the project contract "Provision of services to review and update the UK agriculture MACC and to assess abatement potential for the 5th carbon budget period and to 2050". Prepared for the Climate Change Committee. 274 pp. https://www.theccc.org.uk/publication/scotlands-rural-collage-sruc-ricardo-energy-and-environment2015-review-and-update-of-the-uk-agriculture-macc-to-assess-abatement-potential-for-the-fifth-carbon-budgetperiod-and-to-2050/.

Erb, K.-H., H. Haberl, and C. Plutzar, 2012: Dependency of global primary bioenergy crop potentials in 2050 on food systems, yields, biodiversity conservation and political stability. *Energy Policy*, **47**, 260–269, doi:10.1016/j.enpol.2012.04.066.

Erb, K.-H. et al., 2013: Bias in the attribution of forest carbon sinks. *Nat. Clim. Change*, **3(10)**, 854–856, doi:10.1038/nclimate2004.

Erb, K.-H. et al., 2017: Land management: data availability and process understanding for global change studies. *Glob. Change Biol.*, **23(2)**, 512–533, doi:10.1111/gcb.13443.

Erb, K.-H. et al., 2018: Unexpectedly large impact of forest management and grazing on global vegetation biomass. *Nature*, **553(7686)**, 73–76, doi:10.1038/nature25138.

Ericksen, P. and T. Crane, 2018: *The feasibility of low emissions development interventions for the East African livestock sector: Lessons from Kenya and Ethiopia*. International Livestock Research Institute, Nairobi, Kenya, 25 pp.

Espejo, J.C. et al., 2018: Deforestation and Forest Degradation Due to Gold Mining in the Peruvian Amazon: A 34-Year Perspective. *Remote Sens.*, **10(12)**, 1903, doi:10.3390/rs10121903.

Essl, F., K. Erb, S. Glatzel, and A. Pauchard, 2018: Climate change, carbon market instruments, and biodiversity: focusing on synergies and avoiding pitfalls. *WIREs Clim. Change*, **9(1)**, doi:10.1002/wcc.486.

Esteve-Llorens, X., A.C. Dias, M.T. Moreira, G. Feijoo, and S. González-García, 2020: Evaluating the Portuguese diet in the pursuit of a lower carbon and healthier consumption pattern. *Clim. Change*, **162(4)**, 2397–2409, doi:10.1007/s10584-020-02816-0.

European Commission, 2021: *Freshwater Aquaculture in the EU*. Publications Office of the European Union, Luxembourg, 83 pp.

European Commission-EU, 2021: New EU Forest Strategy for 2030. https://ec.europa.eu/environment/strategy/forest-strategy_en (Accessed October 1, 2021).

European Environment Agency, 2020: *Annual European Union greenhouse gas inventory 1990-2018 and inventory report 2020*. https://www.eea.europa.eu/publications/european-union-greenhouse-gas-inventory-2020. European Environment Agency Copenhagen, Denmark (Accessed Oct 1, 2021).

Eurostat, 2020: Greenhouse gas emissions by source sector. *Eurostat Metadata, Source EEA,*. https://ec.europa.eu/eurostat/cache/metadata/en/env_air_gge_esms.htm (Accessed March 23, 2021).

Fa, J.E. et al., 2020: Importance of Indigenous Peoples' lands for the conservation of Intact Forest Landscapes. *Front. Ecol. Environ.*, **18(3)**, 135–140, doi:10.1002/fee.2148.

Faber, I., N.A. Castellanos-Feijoó, L. Van de Sompel, A. Davydova, and F.J.A. Perez-Cueto, 2020: Attitudes and knowledge towards plant-based diets of young adults across four European countries. Exploratory survey. *Appetite*, **145**, 104498, doi:10.1016/j.appet.2019.104498.

Fajardy, M., S. Chiquier, and N. Mac Dowell, 2018: Investigating the BECCS resource nexus: delivering sustainable negative emissions. *Energy Environ. Sci.*, **11(12)**, 3408–3430, doi:10.1039/C8EE01676C.

Falconnier, G.N. et al., 2020: Modelling climate change impacts on maize yields under low nitrogen input conditions in sub-Saharan Africa. *Glob. Change Biol.*, **26(10)**, 5942–5964, doi:10.1111/gcb.15261.

Falk, D.A., 2017: Restoration Ecology, Resilience, and the Axes of Change. *Ann. Missouri Bot. Gard.*, **102(2)**, 201–216, doi:10.3417/2017006.

Falk, D.A. et al., 2011: Multi-scale controls of historical forest-fire regimes: new insights from fire-scar networks. *Front. Ecol. Environ.*, **9(8)**, 446–454, doi:10.1890/100052.

Fan, L. et al., 2019: Satellite-observed pantropical carbon dynamics. *Nat. Plants*, **5(9)**, 944–951, doi:10.1038/s41477-019-0478-9.

Fang, Y., B. Singh, and B.P. Singh, 2015: Effect of temperature on biochar priming effects and its stability in soils. *Soil Biol. Biochem.*, **80**, 136–145, doi:10.1016/j.soilbio.2014.10.006.

Fang, Y. et al., 2019: Interactive carbon priming, microbial response and biochar persistence in a Vertisol with varied inputs of biochar and labile organic matter. *Eur. J. Soil Sci.*, **70(5)**, 960-974, ejss.12808, doi:10.1111/ejss.12808.

FAO, 2007: *State of the World's Forests 2007*. Food and Agriculture Organization of the United Nations (FAO), Rome, Italy, 157 pp.

FAO, 2013: FAOSTAT-Statistical Database. Food and Agriculture Organization of the United Nations (FAO), Rome, Italy. http://www.fao.org/faostat/en/#home (Accessed September 13, 2021).

FAO, 2015: *Global Forest Resources Assessment 2015*. UN-FAO, Rome, Italy. https://www.fao.org/forest-resources-assessment/en/ (Accessed November 1, 2021).

FAO, 2016: *The State of Food and Agriculture: Climate change, agriculture and food security*. Food and Agriculture Organization of the United Nations (FAO), Rome, Italy. https://www.fao.org/3/i6030e/i6030e.pdf. (Accessed November 1, 2021).

FAO, 2017a: Agroforestry for landscape restoration: Exploring the potential of agroforestry to enhance the sustainability and resilience of degraded landscapes. Food and Agriculture Organization of the United Nations (FAO), Rome, Italy.

FAO, 2017b: FAO Statistics: Food Balances (-2013, old methodology and population). Food and Agriculture Organization of the United Nations (FAO), Rome, Italy. http://www.fao.org/faostat/en/#data/FBSH.

FAO, 2018a: Food supply – livestock and fish primary equivalent. Food and Agriculture Organization of the United Nations (FAO), Rome, Italy. http://www.fao.org/faostat/en/#data/CL.

FAO, 2018b: *The future of food and agriculture – Alternative pathways to 2050*. Global Perspectives Studies. Food and Agriculture Organization of the United Nations (FAO), Rome, Italy. 224 pp.

FAO, 2018c: *The State of the World's Forests 2018: Forest Pathways to Sustainable Development*. Food and Agriculture Organization of the United Nations (FAO), Rome, Italy, 28 pp.

FAO, 2019a: FAO Statistics, Emissions – Agriculture. Food and Agriculture Organization of the United Nations (FAO), Rome, Italy. http://www.fao.org/faostat/en/#data/GT (Accessed March 1, 2021).

FAO, 2019b: FAO Statistics, Annual population. Food and Agriculture Organization of the United Nations (FAO), Rome, Italy. http://www.fao.org/faostat/en/#data/OA.UN-FAO (Accessed October 11, 2021).

FAO, 2019c: *The State of Food and Agriculture 2019: Moving forward on food loss and waste reduction*. Food and Agriculture Organization of the United Nations (FAO), Rome, Italy, 182 pp.

FAO, 2019d: The State of the World's Biodiversity for Food and Agriculture. Food and Agriculture Organization of the United Nations (FAO), Rome, Italy. https://www.fao.org/3/CA3129EN/CA3129EN.pdf (Accessed June 15, 2021).

FAO, 2020a: *Global Forest Resources Assessment 2020*. Food and Agriculture Organization of the United Nations (FAO), Rome, Italy. https://www.fao.org/forest-resources-assessment/2020/en/ (Accessed October 11, 2021).

FAO, 2020b: FAO Statistics: Land use. Food and Agriculture Organization of the United Nations (FAO), Rome, Italy. http://www.fao.org/faostat/en/#data/RL.

FAO, 2020c: FAO Statistics. Emissions – Biomass burning. Food and Agriculture Organization of the United Nations (FAO), Rome, Italy. http://www.fao.org/faostat/en/#data/GI.

FAO, 2020d: *Global Forest Resources Assessment 2020 - Key Findings*. Food and Agriculture Organization of the United Nations (FAO), Rome, Italy, 16 pp. https://www.fao.org/3/CA8753EN/CA8753EN.pdf (Accessed October 11, 2021).

FAO, 2020e: *Global Forest Resources Assessment 2020: Terms and Definition*. Food and Agriculture Organization of the United Nations (FAO), Rome, Italy, 32 pp.

FAO, 2021a: FAO Statistics, Emissions-Total. Food and Agriculture Organization of the United Nations (FAO), Rome, Italy. http://www.fao.org/faostat/en/#data/GT.

FAO, 2021b: FAO Statistics, Land use. Food and Agriculture Organization of the United Nations (FAO), Rome, Italy. http://www.fao.org/faostat/en/#data/RL.

FAO, 2021c: FAO Statistics: Crops and Livestock products. Food and Agriculture Organization of the United Nations (FAO), Rome, Italy. http://www.fao.org/faostat/en/#data/QCL.

FAO, 2021d: FAO Statistics: Food Balances (2014–).Food and Agriculture Organization of the United Nations (FAO), Rome, Italy. http://www.fao.org/faostat/en/#data/FBS.

FAO, 2021e: FAO Statistics: Fertilizers by Nutrient. Food and Agriculture Organization of the United Nations (FAO), Rome, Italy. http://www.fao.org/faostat/en/#data/RFN (Accessed July 21, 2021).

FAO and FILAC, 2021: Forest governance by indigenous and tribal peoples. An opportunity for climate action in Latin America and the Caribbean. Santiago. FAO. https://doi.org/10.4060/cb2953en.

FAO and ITPS, 2015: Status of the World's Soil Resources. Food and Agriculture Organization of the United Nations (FAO), Rome, Italy.

FAO and UNEP, 2020: The State of the World's Forests 2020. Forests, biodiversity and people. Food and Agriculture Organization of the United Nations (FAO), Rome, Italy.

FAO and WHO, 2019: Sustainable Healthy Diets Guiding Principles. Food and Agriculture Organization of the United Nations (FAO), Rome, Italy.

Fargione, J.E. et al., 2018: Natural climate solutions for the United States. Sci. Adv., 4(11), doi:10.1126/sciadv.aat1869.

Fauzi et al., 2019: Contextualizing Mangrove Forest Deforestation in Southeast Asia Using Environmental and Socio-Economic Data Products. Forests, 10(11), 952, doi:10.3390/f10110952.

Favero, A., R. Mendelsohn, and B. Sohngen, 2017: Using forests for climate mitigation: sequester carbon or produce woody biomass? Clim. Change, 144(2), 195–206, doi:10.1007/s10584-017-2034-9.

Favero, A., A. Daigneault, and B. Sohngen, 2020: Forests: Carbon sequestration, biomass energy, or both? Sci. Adv., 6(13), doi:10.1126/sciadv.aay6792.

Fearnside, P.M., 2000: Global Warming and Tropical Land-Use Change: Greenhouse Gas Emissions from Biomass Burning, Decomposition and Soils in Forest Conversion, Shifting Cultivation and Secondary Vegetation. Clim. Change, 46, 115–158, doi.org/10.1023/A:1005569915357.

Fearnside, P.M., 2015: Highway Construction as a Force in the Destruction of the Amazon Forest. In: Handbook of Road Ecology [van der Ree, R., D.J. Smith, and C. Grilo (eds.)]. John Wiley & Sons, New Jersey, USA, pp. 414–424.

Fearnside, P.M. et al., 2009: Biomass and greenhouse-gas emissions from land-use change in Brazil's Amazonian "arc of deforestation": The states of Mato Grosso and Rondônia. For. Ecol. Manage., 258(9), 1968–1978, doi:10.1016/j.foreco.2009.07.042.

Feliciano, D., A. Ledo, J. Hillier, and D.R. Nayak, 2018: Which agroforestry options give the greatest soil and above ground carbon benefits in different world regions? Agric. Ecosyst. Environ., 254(July 2017), 117–129, doi:10.1016/j.agee.2017.11.032.

Felker, M.E., I.W. Bong, W.H. DePuy, and L.F. Jihadah, 2017: Considering land tenure in REDD+ participatory measurement, reporting, and verification: A case study from Indonesia. PLoS One, 12(4), e0167943, doi:10.1371/journal.pone.0167943.

Feng, L. et al., 2016: Estimates of European uptake of CO_2 inferred from GOSAT XCO2 retrievals: sensitivity to measurement bias inside and outside Europe. Atmos. Chem. Phys., 16(3), 1289–1302, doi:10.5194/acp-16-1289-2016.

Fernando, A.L., J. Costa, B. Barbosa, A. Monti, and N. Rettenmaier, 2018: Environmental impact assessment of perennial crops cultivation on marginal soils in the Mediterranean Region. Biomass and Bioenergy, 111, 174–186, doi:10.1016/j.biombioe.2017.04.005.

Ferretti-Gallon, K. and J. Busch, 2014: What Drives Deforestation and What Stops it? A Meta-Analysis of Spatially Explicit Econometric Studies. SSRN Electron. J., 11(1), Working Paper 361, Ctr for Global Development. Doi:10.2139/ssrn.2458040.

Fetzel, T. et al., 2017: Quantification of uncertainties in global grazing systems assessment. Global Biogeochem. Cycles, 31(7), 1089–1102, doi:10.1002/2016GB005601.

Firbank, L.G. et al., 2018: Grand Challenges in Sustainable Intensification and Ecosystem Services. Front. Sustain. Food Syst., 2,7: 2018.00007. doi:10.3389/fsufs.2018.00007.

Fischer, T.B., 2007: The Theory and Practice of Strategic Environmental Assessment. Routledge, Abingdon, Oxfordshire, UK, 218 pp.

FitzGerald, D.M. and Z. Hughes, 2019: Marsh Processes and Their Response to Climate Change and Sea-Level Rise. Annu. Rev. Earth Planet. Sci., 47(1), 481–517, doi:10.1146/annurev-earth-082517-010255.

Fixen, P.E., 2020: A brief account of the genesis of 4R nutrient stewardship. Agron. J., 112(5), 4511–4518, doi:10.1002/agj2.20315.

Flanagan, S.A. et al., 2019: Quantifying carbon and species dynamics under different fire regimes in a southeastern U.S. pineland. Ecosphere, 10(6), doi:10.1002/ecs2.2772.

Fleischman, F. et al., 2020: Pitfalls of Tree Planting Show Why We Need People-Centered Natural Climate Solutions. Bioscience, 70(11), 947–950, doi:10.1093/biosci/biaa094.

Flyvbjerg, B., 2009: Survival of the unfittest: why the worst infrastructure gets built—and what we can do about it. Oxford Rev. Econ. Policy, 25(3), 344–367, doi:10.1093/oxrep/grp024.

Forest Trends Ecosystem Marketplace, 2021: State of Forest Carbon Finance 2021. Forest Trends Ecosystem Marketplace, Washington, DC, USA, 78 pp.

Forsell, N. et al., 2016: Assessing the INDCs' land use, land use change, and forest emission projections. Carbon Balance Manag., 11(1), 26, doi:10.1186/s13021-016-0068-3.

Fortmann, L., B. Sohngen, and D. Southgate, 2017: Assessing the Role of Group Heterogeneity in Community Forest Concessions in Guatemala's Maya Biosphere Reserve. Land Econ., 93(3), 503–526, doi:10.3368/le.93.3.503.

Frank, S. et al., 2017: Reducing greenhouse gas emissions in agriculture without compromising food security? Environ. Res. Lett., 12(10), 105004, doi:10.1088/1748-9326/aa8c83.

Frank, S. et al., 2018: Structural change as a key component for agricultural non-CO_2 mitigation efforts. Nat. Commun., 9(1), 1060, doi:10.1038/s41467-018-03489-1.

Frank, S. et al., 2019: Agricultural non-CO_2 emission reduction potential in the context of the 1.5°C target. Nat. Clim. Change, 9(1), 66–72, doi:10.1038/s41558-018-0358-8.

Frank, S. et al., 2020: Land-based climate change mitigation potentials within the agenda for sustainable development. Environ. Res. Lett., 16(2), 024006, doi:10.1088/1748-9326/abc58a.

Franzluebbers, A.J., G. Lemaire, P.C. de Faccio Carvalho, R.M. Sulc, and B. Dedieu, 2014: Toward agricultural sustainability through integrated crop–livestock systems. II. Production responses. Eur. J. Agron., 57, 1–3, doi:10.1016/j.eja.2014.05.004.

Friedlingstein, P. et al., 2020: Global Carbon Budget 2019. Earth Syst. Sci. Data, 11(4), 1783–1838, doi:10.5194/essd-11-1783-2019.

Friess, D.A. et al., 2019: The State of the World's Mangrove Forests: Past, Present, and Future. Annu. Rev. Environ. Resour., 44(1), 89–115, doi:10.1146/annurev-environ-101718-033302.

Fritsche, U.R. et al., 2017: Energy and Land Use Disclaimer – Global Land Outlook Working Paper. United Nations Convention to Combat Desertification (UNCCD), Bonn, Germany, 60 pp.

Fujimori, S. et al., 2016: Implication of Paris Agreement in the context of long-term climate mitigation goals. Springerplus, 5(1), 1620, doi:10.1186/s40064-016-3235-9.

Fujimori, S. et al., 2019: A multi-model assessment of food security implications of climate change mitigation. Nat. Sustain., 2(5), 386–396, doi:10.1038/s41893-019-0286-2.

Furumo, P.R. and T.M. Aide, 2017: Characterizing commercial oil palm expansion in Latin America: land use change and trade. *Environ. Res. Lett.*, **12(2)**, 024008, doi:10.1088/1748-9326/aa5892.

Fuss, S. et al., 2018: Negative emissions—Part 2: Costs, potentials and side effects. *Environ. Res. Lett.*, **13(6)**, 063002, doi:10.1088/1748-9326/aabf9f.

Futter, M., N. Clarke, Ø. Kaste, and S. Valinia, 2019: *The potential effects on water quality of intensified forest management for climate mitigation in Norway.* Norwegian Institute for Water Research, Oslo, Norway, 7363–2019 pp.

Fyson, C.L. and M.L. Jeffery, 2019: Ambiguity in the Land Use Component of Mitigation Contributions Toward the Paris Agreement Goals. *Earth's Futur.*, **7(8)**, 873–891, doi:10.1029/2019EF001190.

Galford, G.L. et al., 2020: Agricultural development addresses food loss and waste while reducing greenhouse gas emissions. *Sci. Total Environ.*, **699**, 134318, doi:10.1016/j.scitotenv.2019.134318.

Galik, C.S., 2020: A continuing need to revisit BECCS and its potential. *Nat. Clim. Change*, **10(1)**, 2–3, doi:10.1038/s41558-019-0650-2.

Gallagher, R.V. et al., 2021: High fire frequency and the impact of the 2019–2020 megafires on Australian plant diversity. *Divers. Distrib.*, **27(7)**, 1166–1179, doi:10.1111/ddi.13265.

Galli, F. et al., 2020: How can policy processes remove barriers to sustainable food systems in Europe? Contributing to a policy framework for agri-food transitions. *Food Policy*, **96**, 101871, doi:10.1016/j.foodpol.2020.101871.

Gan, J. and B.A. McCarl, 2007: Measuring transnational leakage of forest conservation. *Ecol. Econ.*, **64(2)**, 423–432, doi:10.1016/j.ecolecon.2007.02.032.

Gao, Y. et al., 2020: Effects of biochar application on crop water use efficiency depend on experimental conditions: A meta-analysis. *F. Crop. Res.*, **249**, 107763, doi:10.1016/j.fcr.2020.107763.

Gardiner, C.A., T.J. Clough, K.C. Cameron, H.J. Di, and G.R. Edwards, 2020: Ruminant urine patch nitrification and N_2O flux: effects of urine aucubin rate in a laboratory trial. *New Zeal. J. Agric. Res.*, **63(1)**, 65–72, doi:10.1080/00288233.2019.1626743.

Garnett, S.T. et al., 2018: A spatial overview of the global importance of Indigenous lands for conservation. *Nat. Sustain.*, **1(7)**, 369–374, doi:10.1038/s41893-018-0100-6.

Garnett, T., 2014: Three perspectives on sustainable food security: efficiency, demand restraint, food system transformation. What role for life cycle assessment? *J. Clean. Prod.*, **73**, 10–18, doi:10.1016/j.jclepro.2013.07.045.

Garnett, T. et al., 2013: Sustainable intensification in agriculture: Premises and policies. *Science*, **341(6161)**, 33, doi:10.1126/science.1234485.

Garrett, R.D. et al., 2020: Drivers of decoupling and recoupling of crop and livestock systems at farm and territorial scales. *Ecol. Soc.*, **25(1)**, 24, doi:10.5751/ES-11412-250124.

Garrity, D.P and J. Bayala, 2019: Zinder: farmer-managed natural regeneration of Sahelian parklands in Niger. In: van Noordwijk M, ed. Sustainable development through trees on farms: agroforestry in its fifth decade. Bogor, Indonesia: World Agroforestry (ICRAF) Southeast Asia Regional Program, pp. 153–174.

Garrity, D.P. et al., 2010: Evergreen Agriculture: a robust approach to sustainable food security in Africa. *Food Secur.*, **2(3)**, 197–214, doi:10.1007/s12571-010-0070-7.

Gasser, T. et al., 2020: Historical CO_2 emissions from land use and land cover change and their uncertainty. *Biogeosciences*, **17(15)**, 4075–4101, doi:10.5194/bg-17-4075-2020.

Gattinger, A. et al., 2012: Enhanced top soil carbon stocks under organic farming. *Proc. Natl. Acad. Sci.*, **109(44)**, 18226–18231, doi:10.1073/pnas.1209429109.

Gattuso, J. et al., 2018: Ocean Solutions to Address Climate Change and Its Effects on Marine Ecosystems. *Front. Mar. Sci.*, **5**(October), art337, doi:10.3389/fmars.2018.00337.

Geng, A., H. Yang, J. Chen, and Y. Hong, 2017: Review of carbon storage function of harvested wood products and the potential of wood substitution in greenhouse gas mitigation. *For. Policy Econ.*, **85**, 192–200, doi:10.1016/j.forpol.2017.08.007.

Gerssen-Gondelach, S., B. Wicke, and A. Faaij, 2015: Assessment of driving factors for yield and productivity developments in crop and cattle production as key to increasing sustainable biomass potentials. *Food Energy Secur.*, **4(1)**, 36–75, doi:10.1002/fes3.53.

Gibbs, H.K. et al., 2015: Brazil's Soy Moratorium. *Science*, **347(6220)**, 377–378, doi:10.1126/science.aaa0181.

Gil, J., M. Siebold, and T. Berger, 2015: Adoption and development of integrated crop–livestock–forestry systems in Mato Grosso, Brazil. *Agric. Ecosyst. Environ.*, **199**, 394–406, doi:10.1016/j.agee.2014.10.008.

Gil, J.D.B., A.S. Cohn, J. Duncan, P. Newton, and S. Vermeulen, 2017: The resilience of integrated agricultural systems to climate change. *WIREs Clim. Change*, **8(4)**, doi:10.1002/wcc.461.

Giller, K. and F. Ewert, 2019: Australian wheat beats the heat. *Nat. Clim. Change*, **9(3)**, 189–190, doi:10.1038/s41558-019-0427-7.

Gingrich, S. et al., 2019: Hidden emissions of forest transitions: a socio-ecological reading of forest change. *Curr. Opin. Environ. Sustain.*, **38**, 14–21, doi:10.1016/j.cosust.2019.04.005.

Ginsburg, CS. Keene, 2020: At a crossroads: consequential trends in recognition of community-based forest tenure from 2002-2017. *China Econ. J.*, **13(2)**, 223–248, doi:10.1080/17538963.2020.1755129.

Giri, C. et al., 2015: Distribution and dynamics of mangrove forests of South Asia. *J. Environ. Manage.*, **148**, 101–111, doi:10.1016/j.jenvman.2014.01.020.

Gitz, V. and P. Ciais, 2003: Amplifying effects of land-use change on future atmospheric CO_2 levels. *Global Biogeochem. Cycles*, **17(1)**, 1024 doi:10.1029/2002GB001963.

Gliessman, S., 2013: Agroecology: Growing the Roots of Resistance. *Agroecol. Sustain. Food Syst.*, **1(37)**, 14, doi.org/10.1080/10440046.2012.736927.

Godfray, H.C.J. and T. Garnett, 2014: Food security and sustainable intensification. *Philos. Trans. R. Soc. B Biol. Sci.*, **369(1639)**, 20120273, doi:10.1098/rstb.2012.0273.

Godfray, H.C.J. et al., 2018: Meat consumption, health, and the environment. *Science*, **361(6399)**, doi:10.1126/science.aam5324.

Goh, K.M., 2011: Greater Mitigation of Climate Change by Organic than Conventional Agriculture: A Review. *Biol. Agric. Hortic.*, **27(2)**, 205–229, doi:10.1080/01448765.2011.9756648.

Goldammer, J.G., 2016: Fire Management in Tropical Forests. In: *Tropical Forestry Handbook* [Pancel, L. and M. Köhl (eds.)]. Springer Berlin Heidelberg, Berlin, Heidelberg, Germany, pp. 2659–2710.

Goldewijk, K.K., A. Beusen, J. Doelman, and E. Stehfest, 2017: Anthropogenic land use estimates for the Holocene – HYDE 3.2. *Earth Syst. Sci. Data*, **9(2)**, 927–953, doi:10.5194/essd-9-927-2017.

Goldstein, A. et al., 2020: Protecting irrecoverable carbon in Earth's ecosystems. *Nat. Clim. Change*, **10(4)**, 287–295, doi:10.1038/s41558-020-0738-8.

Gonzalez-Sanchez, E.J. et al., 2019: Meta-analysis on carbon sequestration through Conservation Agriculture in Africa. *Soil Tillage Res.*, **190**, 22–30, doi:10.1016/j.still.2019.02.020.

Goodwin, M.J., M.P. North, H.S.J. Zald, and M.D. Hurteau, 2020: Changing climate reallocates the carbon debt of frequent-fire forests. *Glob. Change Biol.*, **26(11)**, 6180–6189, doi:10.1111/gcb.15318.

Goss, M. et al., 2020: Climate change is increasing the likelihood of extreme autumn wildfire conditions across California. *Environ. Res. Lett.*, **15(9)**, 094016, doi:10.1088/1748-9326/ab83a7.

Govaerts, B., K.D. Sayre, and J. Deckers, 2005: Stable high yields with zero tillage and permanent bed planting? *F. Crop. Res.*, **94(1)**, 33–42, doi:10.1016/j.fcr.2004.11.003.

Government of Alberta, 2021: Alberta Emission Offset System. https://www.alberta.ca/alberta-emission-offset-system.aspx. Edmonton, Alberta, Canada.

Government of Brazil, Amazon Fund. Brasilia, Brazil. http://www.amazonfund.gov.br/en/home/.

7

Grace, J., E. Mitchard, and E. Gloor, 2014: Perturbations in the carbon budget of the tropics. *Glob. Change Biol.*, **20(10)**, 3238–3255, doi:10.1111/gcb.12600.

Grassi, G. et al., 2017: The key role of forests in meeting climate targets requires science for credible mitigation. *Nat. Clim. Change*, **7(3)**, 220–226, doi:10.1038/nclimate3227.

Grassi, G. et al., 2018: Reconciling global-model estimates and country reporting of anthropogenic forest CO_2 sinks. *Nat. Clim. Change*, **8(10)**, 914–920, doi:10.1038/s41558-018-0283-x.

Grassi, G. et al., 2021: Critical adjustment of land mitigation pathways for assessing countries' climate progress. *Nat. Clim. Change*, **11(5)**, 425–434, doi:10.1038/s41558-021-01033-6.

Gren, I.-M. and A.Z. Aklilu, 2016: Policy design for forest carbon sequestration: A review of the literature. *For. Policy Econ.*, **70**, 128–136, doi:10.1016/j.forpol.2016.06.008.

Griscom, B.W. et al., 2017: Natural climate solutions. *Proc. Natl. Acad. Sci.*, **114(44)**, 11645–11650, doi:10.1073/pnas.1710465114.

Griscom, B.W. et al., 2020: National mitigation potential from natural climate solutions in the tropics. *Philos. Trans. R. Soc. B Biol. Sci.*, **375(1794)**, 20190126, doi:10.1098/rstb.2019.0126.

Gromko, D. and G. Abdurasalova, 2019: *Climate change mitigation and food loss and waste reduction: Exploring the business case*. CGIAR Research Program on Climate Change, Agriculture and Food Security (CCAFS), Wageningen, The Netherlands, 46 pp. https://hdl.handle.net/10568/100165.

Grossi, G., P. Goglio, A. Vitali, and A.G. Williams, 2019: Livestock and climate change: impact of livestock on climate and mitigation strategies. *Anim. Front.*, **9(1)**, 69–76, doi:10.1093/af/vfy034.

Grubler, A. et al., 2018: A low energy demand scenario for meeting the 1.5°C target and sustainable development goals without negative emission technologies. *Nat. Energy*, **3(6)**, 515–527, doi:10.1038/s41560-018-0172-6.

Guan, Z., Y. Xu, P. Gong, and J. Cao, 2018: The impact of international efforts to reduce illegal logging on the global trade in wood products. *Int. Wood Prod. J.*, **9(1)**, 28–38, doi:10.1080/20426445.2017.1419541.

Guenet, B. et al., 2021: Can N_2O emissions offset the benefits from soil organic carbon storage? *Glob. Change Biol.*, **27(2)**, 237–256, doi:10.1111/gcb.15342.

Gunsch, M.J. et al., 2018: Ubiquitous influence of wildfire emissions and secondary organic aerosol on summertime atmospheric aerosol in the forested Great Lakes region. *Atmos. Chem. Phys.*, **18(5)**, 3701–3715, doi:10.5194/acp-18-3701-2018.

Günther, A. et al., 2020: Prompt rewetting of drained peatlands reduces climate warming despite methane emissions. *Nat. Commun.*, **11(1)**, 1644, doi:10.1038/s41467-020-15499-z.

Gunton, R.M., L.G. Firbank, A. Inman, and D.M. Winter, 2016: How scalable is sustainable intensification? *Nat. Plants*, **2(5)**, 16065, doi:10.1038/nplants.2016.65.

Guo, K. et al., 2020: Establishment of an integrated decision-making method for planning the ecological restoration of terrestrial ecosystems. *Sci. Total Environ.*, **741**, 139852, doi:10.1016/j.scitotenv.2020.139852.

Gupta, A., T. Pistorius, and M.J. Vijge, 2016: Managing fragmentation in global environmental governance: the REDD+ Partnership as bridge organization. *Int. Environ. Agreements Polit. Law Econ.*, **16(3)**, 355–374, doi:10.1007/s10784-015-9274-9.

Gustavsson, L. et al., 2017: Climate change effects of forestry and substitution of carbon-intensive materials and fossil fuels. *Renew. Sustain. Energy Rev.*, **67**, 612–624, doi:10.1016/j.rser.2016.09.056.

Gütschow, J., L. Jeffery, R. Gieseke, and A. Günther, 2019: The PRIMAP-hist national historical emissions time series v2.1 (1850-2017). *Earth Syst. Sci. Data*, **8**, 571–603, doi.org/10.5194/essd-8-571-2016.

Gwenzi, W., N. Chaukura, F.N.D. Mukome, S. Machado, and B. Nyamasoka, 2015: Biochar production and applications in sub-Saharan Africa: Opportunities, constraints, risks and uncertainties. *J. Environ. Manage.*, **150**, 250–261, doi:10.1016/j.jenvman.2014.11.027.

Haberlie, A.M., W.S. Ashley, and T.J. Pingel, 2015: The effect of urbanisation on the climatology of thunderstorm initiation. *Q.J.R. Meteorol. Soc.*, **141**(688), 663–675, doi:10.1002/qj.2499.

Habib, G. and A.A. Khan, 2018: Assessment and Mitigation of Methane Emissions from Livestock Sector in Pakistan. *Earth Syst. Environ.*, **2(3)**, 601–608, doi:10.1007/s41748-018-0076-4.

Haddad, N.M. et al., 2015: Habitat fragmentation and its lasting impact on Earth's ecosystems. *Sci. Adv.*, **1(2)**, doi:10.1126/sciadv.1500052.

Hagemann, N. et al., 2017: Organic coating on biochar explains its nutrient retention and stimulation of soil fertility. *Nat. Commun.*, **8(1)**, 1089, doi:10.1038/s41467-017-01123-0.

Haglund, E., J. Ndjeunga, L. Snook, and D. Pasternak, 2011: Dry land tree management for improved household livelihoods: Farmer managed natural regeneration in Niger. *J. Environ. Manage.*, **92(7)**, 1696–1705, doi:10.1016/j.jenvman.2011.01.027.

Hamilton, S.E. and D. Casey, 2016: Creation of a high spatio-temporal resolution global database of continuous mangrove forest cover for the 21st century (CGMFC-21). *Glob. Ecol. Biogeogr.*, **25(6)**, 729–738, doi:10.1111/geb.12449.

Hammar, T. and F. Levihn, 2020: Time-dependent climate impact of biomass use in a fourth generation district heating system, including BECCS. *Biomass and Bioenergy*, **138**, 105606, doi:10.1016/j.biombioe.2020.105606.

Hamrick, K. and M. Gallant, 2017a: *State of Forest Carbon Finance. Forest Trends Ecosystem Marketplace*. Forest Trends' Ecosystem Marketplace, Washington, DC, USA, 88 pp. https://www.forest-trends.org/wp-content/uploads/2018/01/doc_5715.pdf (Accessed November 21, 2021).

Hamrick, K. and M. Gallant, 2017b: *Unlocking potential: State of the Voluntary Carbon Markets 2017*. Forest Trends' Ecosystem Marketplace, Washington, DC, USA, 52 pp.

Hamrick, K. and M. Gallant, 2018: *Voluntary Carbon Markets Outlooks and Trends*. https://www.forest-trends.org/publications/voluntary-carbon-markets/ (Accessed September 12, 2021).

Han Weng, Z. et al., 2017: Biochar built soil carbon over a decade by stabilizing rhizodeposits. *Nat. Clim. Change*, **7(5)**, 371–376, doi:10.1038/nclimate3276.

Hanan, N.P., 2018: Agroforestry in the Sahel. *Nat. Geosci.*, **11(5)**, 296–297, doi:10.1038/s41561-018-0112-x.

Hansen, J.H., L. Hamelin, A. Taghizadeh-Toosi, J.E. Olesen, and H. Wenzel, 2020: Agricultural residues bioenergy potential that sustain soil carbon depends on energy conversion pathways. *GCB Bioenergy*, **12(11)**, 1002–1013, doi:10.1111/gcbb.12733.

Hansen, M.C. et al., 2013: High-Resolution Global Maps of 21st-Century Forest Cover Change. *Science*, **342(6160)**, 850–853, doi:10.1126/science.1244693.

Hanssen, S.V. et al., 2020: The climate change mitigation potential of bioenergy with carbon capture and storage. *Nat. Clim. Change*, **10(11)**, 1023–1029, doi:10.1038/s41558-020-0885-y.

Hansis, E., S.J. Davis, and J. Pongratz, 2015: Relevance of methodological choices for accounting of land use change carbon fluxes. *Global Biogeochem. Cycles*, **29**, 1230–1246, doi:10.1002/2014GB004997.

Harmsen, J.H.M. et al., 2019: Long-term marginal abatement cost curves of non-CO_2 greenhouse gases. *Environ. Sci. Policy*, **99**(March), 136–149, doi:10.1016/j.envsci.2019.05.013.

Harper, A.B. et al., 2018: Land-use emissions play a critical role in land-based mitigation for Paris climate targets. *Nat. Commun.*, **9(1)**, 2938, doi:10.1038/s41467-018-05340-z.

Harris, N.L. et al., 2021: Global maps of twenty-first century forest carbon fluxes. *Nat. Clim. Change*, **11(3)**, 234–240, doi:10.1038/s41558-020-00976-6.

Hasegawa, T. and Y. Matsuoka, 2012: Greenhouse gas emissions and mitigation potentials in agriculture, forestry and other land use in Southeast Asia. *J. Integr. Environ. Sci.*, **9(sup1)**, 159–176, doi:10.1080/1943815X.2012.701647.

Hasegawa, T., S. Fujimori, R. Boer, G. Immanuel, and T. Masui, 2016: Land-Based Mitigation Strategies under the Mid-Term Carbon Reduction Targets in Indonesia. *Sustainability*, **8(12)**, 1283, doi:10.3390/su8121283.

Hasegawa, T. et al., 2018: Risk of increased food insecurity under stringent global climate change mitigation policy. *Nat. Clim. Change*, **8(8)**, 699–703, doi:10.1038/s41558-018-0230-x.

Hasegawa, T. et al., 2020: Food security under high bioenergy demand toward long-term climate goals. *Clim. Change*, **163(3)**, 1587–1601, doi:10.1007/s10584-020-02838-8.

Hasegawa, T. et al., 2021: Land-based implications of early climate actions without global net-negative emissions. *Nat. Sustain.*, **4(12)**, 1052–1059, doi:10.1038/s41893-021-00772-w.

Hawken, P., 2017: *Drawdown: the most comprehensive plan ever proposed to reverse global warming*. Penguin, Washington, DC, USA. https://drawdown.org/the-book (Accessed September 12, 2020).

He, Y. et al., 2017: Effects of biochar application on soil greenhouse gas fluxes: a meta-analysis. *GCB Bioenergy*, **9(4)**, 743–755, doi:10.1111/gcbb.12376.

Hedley, C., 2015: The role of precision agriculture for improved nutrient management on farms. *J. Sci. Food Agric.*, **95(1)**, 12–19, doi:10.1002/jsfa.6734.

Heilmayr, R., C. Echeverría, and E.F. Lambin, 2020: Impacts of Chilean forest subsidies on forest cover, carbon and biodiversity. *Nat. Sustain.*, **3(9)**, 701–709, doi:10.1038/s41893-020-0547-0.

Heinrich, V.H.A. et al., 2021: Large carbon sink potential of secondary forests in the Brazilian Amazon to mitigate climate change. *Nat. Commun.*, **12(1)**, 1785, doi:10.1038/s41467-021-22050-1.

Henderson, B., C. Frezal, and E. Flynn, 2020: *A survey of GHG mitigation policies for the agriculture, forestry and other land use sector*. OECD Publishing, Paris, France, 88 pp.

Henderson, B.B. et al., 2015: Greenhouse gas mitigation potential of the world's grazing lands: Modeling soil carbon and nitrogen fluxes of mitigation practices. *Agric. Ecosyst. Environ.*, **207**, 91–100, doi:10.1016/j.agee.2015.03.029.

Hendrickson, J.R., J.D. Hanson, D.L. Tanaka, and G. Sassenrath, 2008: Principles of integrated agricultural systems: Introduction to processes and definition. *Renew. Agric. Food Syst.*, **23(04)**, 265–271, doi:10.1017/S1742170507001718.

Herr, D., M. von Unger, D. Laffoley, and A. McGivern, 2017: Pathways for implementation of blue carbon initiatives. *Aquat. Conserv. Mar. Freshw. Ecosyst.*, **27(sup1)**, 116–129, doi:10.1002/aqc.2793.

Herrera, D., A. Pfaff, and J. Robalino, 2019: Impacts of protected areas vary with the level of government: Comparing avoided deforestation across agencies in the Brazilian Amazon. *Proc. Natl. Acad. Sci.*, **116(30)**, 14916–14925, doi:10.1073/pnas.1802877116.

Herrero, M. et al., 2013: Biomass use, production, feed efficiencies, and greenhouse gas emissions from global livestock systems. *Proc. Natl. Acad. Sci.*, **110(52)**, 20888–20893, doi:10.1073/pnas.1308149110.

Herrero, M. et al., 2016: Greenhouse gas mitigation potentials in the livestock sector. *Nat. Clim. Change*, **6(5)**, 452–461, doi:10.1038/nclimate2925.

Hijbeek, R., M. van Loon, and M. van Ittersum, 2019: *Fertiliser use and soil carbon sequestration: trade-offs and opportunities*. CGIAR Research Program on Climate Change, Agriculture and Food Security, Wageningen, The Netherlands, 23 pp.

Hirales-Cota, M., J. Espinoza-Avalos, B. Schmook, A. Ruiz-Luna, and R. Ramos-Reyes, 2010: Drivers of mangrove deforestation in Mahahual-Xcalak, Quintana Roo, southeast Mexico. *Ciencias Mar.*, **36(2)**, doi:10.7773/cm.v36i2.1653.

Hirsch, A.L. et al., 2018: Modelled biophysical impacts of conservation agriculture on local climates. *Glob. Change Biol.*, **24(10)**, 4758–4774, doi:10.1111/gcb.14362.

Hisano, M., E.B. Searle, and H.Y.H. Chen, 2018: Biodiversity as a solution to mitigate climate change impacts on the functioning of forest ecosystems. *Biol. Rev.*, **93(1)**, 439–456, doi:10.1111/brv.12351.

Hlásny, T. et al., 2021: Bark Beetle Outbreaks in Europe: State of Knowledge and Ways Forward for Management. *Curr. For. Reports*, **7(3)**, 138–165, doi:10.1007/s40725-021-00142-x.

HLPE, 2014: *Food losses and waste in the context of sustainable food systems*. A report by the High Level Panel of Experts (HLPE) on Food Security and Nutrition of the Committee on World Food Security, Rome Italy, 117 pp. http://www.fao.org/3/a-i3901e.pdf (Accessed October 12, 2021).

HLPE, 2019: *Agroecological and other innovative approaches for sustainable agriculture and food systems that enhance food security and nutrition*. Committee on World Food Security, Rome, Italy, 1–9 pp.

Hoa, N.T., T. Hasegawa, and Y. Matsuoka, 2014: Climate change mitigation strategies in agriculture, forestry and other land use sectors in Vietnam. *Mitig. Adapt. Strateg. Glob. Change*, **19**, 15–32, doi:10.1007/s11027-012-9424-0.

Hochard, J.P., S. Hamilton, and E.B. Barbier, 2019: Mangroves shelter coastal economic activity from cyclones. *Proc. Natl. Acad. Sci.*, **116(25)**, 12232–12237, doi:10.1073/pnas.1820067116.

Hof, C. et al., 2018: Bioenergy cropland expansion may offset positive effects of climate change mitigation for global vertebrate diversity. *Proc. Natl. Acad. Sci.*, **115(52)**, 13294–13299, doi:10.1073/pnas.1807745115.

Holl, K.D. and P.H.S. Brancalion, 2020: Tree planting is not a simple solution. *Science*, **368(6491)**, 580–581, doi:10.1126/science.aba8232.

Honan, M., X. Feng, J.M. Tricarico, and E. Kebreab, 2021: Feed additives as a strategic approach to reduce enteric methane production in cattle: modes of action, effectiveness and safety. *Anim. Prod. Sci.*, doi:10.1071/AN20295.

Honey-Roses, J., K. Baylis, and M.I. Ramirez, 2011: A Spatially Explicit Estimate of Avoided Forest Loss. *Conserv. Biol.*, **25(5)**, 1032–1043, doi:10.1111/j.1523-1739.2011.01729.x.

Hooijer, A. et al., 2010: Current and future CO_2 emissions from drained peatlands in Southeast Asia. *Biogeosciences*, **7(5)**, 1505–1514, doi:10.5194/bg-7-1505-2010.

Houghton, R.A and A.A. Nassikas, 2017: Global and regional fluxes of carbon from land use and land cover change 1850-2015. *Global Biogeochem. Cycles*, **31(3)**, 456–472, doi:10.1002/2016GB005546.

Howard, J. et al., 2017: Clarifying the role of coastal and marine systems in climate mitigation. *Front. Ecol. Environ.*, **15(1)**, 42–50, doi:10.1002/fee.1451.

Hristov, A.N. et al., 2013: *Mitigation of Greenhouse gas emissions in livestock production: A review of technical options for non-CO_2 emissions* [Gerber, P.J., B. Henderson, and H.P.S. Makkar (eds.)]. FAO, Rome, Italy, 352 pp. https://dialnet.unirioja.es/servlet/libro?codigo=317825

Hristov, A.N. et al., 2015: An inhibitor persistently decreased enteric methane emission from dairy cows with no negative effect on milk production. *Proc. Natl. Acad. Sci.*, **112(34)**, 10663–10668, doi:10.1073/pnas.1504124112.

Hugelius, G. et al., 2020: Large stocks of peatland carbon and nitrogen are vulnerable to permafrost thaw. *Proc. Natl. Acad. Sci.*, **117(34)**, 20438–20446, doi:10.1073/pnas.1916387117.

Humpenöder, F. et al., 2018: Large-scale bioenergy production: how to resolve sustainability trade-offs? *Environ. Res. Lett.*, **13(2)**, 024011, doi:10.1088/1748-9326/aa9e3b.

Humpenöder, F. et al., 2020: Peatland protection and restoration are key for climate change mitigation. *Environ. Res. Lett.*, **15(10)**, 104093, doi:10.1088/1748-9326/abae2a.

Hund, K., D. La Porta, T.P. Fabregas, T. Laing, and J. Drexhage, 2020: *Minerals for Climate Action: The Mineral Intensity of the Clean Energy Transition*. World Bank, Washington, DC, USA, 112 pp.

Hunt, D., S. Bittman, M. Chantigny, and R. Lemke, 2019: Year-Round N_2O Emissions From Long-Term Applications of Whole and Separated Liquid Dairy Slurry on a Perennial Grass Sward and Strategies for Mitigation. *Front. Sustain. Food Syst.*, **3**, 2019:00086 doi:10.3389/fsufs.2019.00086.

Huppmann, D., J. Rogelj, E. Kriegler, V. Krey, and K. Riahi, 2018: A new scenario resource for integrated 1.5°C research. *Nat. Clim. Change*, **8(12)**, 1027–1030, doi:10.1038/s41558-018-0317-4.

Hurlbert, M., J. Krishnaswamy, E. Davin, F.X. Johnson, C.F. Mena, J. Morton, S. Myeong, D. Viner, K. Warner, A. Wreford, S. Zakieldeen, and Z. Zommers, 2019: Risk Management and Decision making in Relation to Sustainable Development. In: *Climate Change and Land: an IPCC special report on climate change, desertification, land degradation, sustainable land management, food security, and greenhouse gas fluxes in terrestrial ecosystems* [Shukla, P.R., J. Skea, E. Calvo Buendia, V. Masson-Delmotte, H.-O. Pörtner, D.C. Roberts, P. Zhai, R. Slade, S. Connors, R. van Diemen, M. Ferrat, E. Haughey, S. Luz, S. Neogi, M. Pathak, J. Petzold, J. Portugal Pereira, P. Vyas, E. Huntley, K. Kissick, M. Belkacemi, and J. Malley (eds.)]. Cambridge University Press, Cambridge, UK, and New York, NY, USA, pp. 673–800.

Hurmekoski, E. et al., 2020: Impact of structural changes in wood-using industries on net carbon emissions in Finland. *J. Ind. Ecol.*, **24(4)**, 899–912, doi:10.1111/jiec.12981.

Hurteau, M.D. and M.L. Brooks, 2011: Short- and Long-term Effects of Fire on Carbon in US Dry Temperate Forest Systems. *Bioscience*, **61(2)**, 139–146, doi:10.1525/bio.2011.61.2.9.

Hurteau, M.D., J.B. Bradford, P.Z. Fulé, A.H. Taylor, and K.L. Martin, 2014: Climate change, fire management, and ecological services in the southwestern US. *For. Ecol. Manage.*, **327**, 280–289, doi:10.1016/j.foreco.2013.08.007.

Hurteau, M.D., M.P. North, G.W. Koch, and B.A. Hungate, 2019: Opinion: Managing for disturbance stabilizes forest carbon. *Proc. Natl. Acad. Sci.*, **116(21)**, 10193–10195, doi:10.1073/pnas.1905146116.

Hurtt, G.C. et al., 2020: Harmonization of global land use change and management for the period 850–2100 (LUH2) for CMIP6. *Geosci. Model Dev.*, **13(11)**, 5425–5464, doi:10.5194/gmd-13-5425-2020.

Hussain, S. et al., 2015: Rice management interventions to mitigate greenhouse gas emissions: a review. *Environ. Sci. Pollut. Res.*, **22(5)**, 3342–3360, doi:10.1007/s11356-014-3760-4.

Hwang, O. et al., 2018: Efficacy of Different Biochars in Removing Odorous Volatile Organic Compounds (VOCs) Emitted from Swine Manure. *ACS Sustain. Chem. Eng.*, **6(11)**, 14239–14247, doi:10.1021/acssuschemeng.8b02881.

ICFPA, 2021: *ICFPA 2020–2021 Sustainability Progress Report*. International Council of Forest & Paper Associations, 19 pp.

IEA, 2019: *World Energy Outlook 2019 – Analysis – IEA*. International Energy Agency, Paris, France, 810 pp. https://www.iea.org/reports/world-energy-outlook-2019.

IFOAM, 2016: *Organic Farming, climate change mitigation and beyond reducing the environmental impacts of eu agriculture*. IFOAM EU, Brussels, Belgium, 5 pp.

Ilstedt, U. et al., 2016: Intermediate tree cover can maximize groundwater recharge in the seasonally dry tropics. *Sci. Rep.*, **6(1)**, 21930, doi:10.1038/srep21930.

Im, S., S.O. Petersen, D. Lee, and D.-H. Kim, 2020: Effects of storage temperature on CH_4 emissions from cattle manure and subsequent biogas production potential. *Waste Manag.*, **101**, 35–43, doi:10.1016/j.wasman.2019.09.036.

Ingalls, M.L., P. Meyfroidt, P.X. To, M. Kenney-Lazar, and M. Epprecht, 2018: The transboundary displacement of deforestation under REDD+: Problematic intersections between the trade of forest-risk commodities and land grabbing in the Mekong region. *Glob. Environ. Change*, **50**, 255–267, doi:10.1016/j.gloenvcha.2018.04.003.

INPE, 2021: PRODES, Amazon, Monitoring of Deforestation in the Brazilian Amazon Forest by Satellite, Earth Observation, National Institute for Space Research, Government of Brazil. http://www.obt.inpe.br/OBT/assuntos/programas/amazonia/prodes (Accessed April 12, 2021).

IPBES 2016: *The methodological assessment report on scenarios and models of biodiversity and ecosystem services* [S. Ferrier, K.N. Ninan, P. Leadley, R. Alkemade, and L.A. Acosta, et al. (eds.)]. IPBES Secretariat, Bonn, Germany, 348 pp.

IPBES, 2018a: *The IPBES assessment report on land degradation and restoration of the Intergovernmental Science-Policy Platform on Biodiversity and Ecosystem Services* [Montanarella, L., R. Scholes, and A. Brainich (eds.)]. IPBES Secretariat, Bonn, Germany, 744pp.

IPBES, 2018b: *Summary for policymakers of the regional assessment report on biodiversity and ecosystem services for Asia and the Pacific of the Intergovernmental Science-Policy Platform on Biodiversity and Ecosystem Services* [Karki M., S. Senaratna Sellamuttu, S. Okayasu, W. Suzuki, L.A. Acosta, et al. (eds.)]. IPBES secretariat, Bonn, Germany, 41 pp.

IPBES, 2018c: *Summary for policymakers of the regional assessment report on biodiversity and ecosystem services for Africa of the Intergovernmental Science-Policy Platform on Biodiversity and Ecosystem Services* [E. Archer, L.E. Dziba, K.J. Mulongoy, M.A. Maoela, M. Walters, et al. (eds.)]. IPBES secretariat, Bonn, Germany, 49 pp.

IPBES, 2018d: *Summary for policymakers of the regional assessment report on biodiversity and ecosystem services for Europe and Central Asia of the Intergovernmental Science-Policy Platform on Biodiversity and Ecosystem Services* [Fischer M., M. Rounsevell, A. Torre-Marin Rando, A. Mader, A. Church, et al. (eds.)]. IPBES secretariat, Bonn, Germany, 48pp.

IPBES, 2018e: *Summary for Policy Makers of the Assessment Report on Land Degradation and Restoration of the Intergovernmental Science-Policy Platform on Biodiversity and Ecosystem Services* [Scholes, R., L. Montanarella, A. Brainich, N. Barger, B. ten Brink et al., (eds.)]. Intergovernmental Science-Policy Platform on Biodiversity and Ecosystem Services (IPBES), Bonn, Germany.

IPBES, 2019a: *Summary for policymakers of the global assessment report on biodiversity and ecosystem services of the Intergovernmental Science-Policy Platform on Biodiversity and Ecosystem Services* [Díaz, S., J. Settele, E.S. Brondízio, H.T. Ngo, M. Guèze, et al. (eds.)]. IPBES secretariat, Bonn, Germany, 56 pp.

IPBES, 2019b: *Global assessment report on biodiversity and ecosystem services of the Intergovernmental Science-Policy Platform on Biodiversity and Ecosystem Services* [Brondízio E.S, J. Settele, S. Díaz, and H.T. Ngo (eds.)]. IPBES secretariat, Bonn, Germany, 1144 pp.

IPBES-IPCC, 2021: *IPBES-IPCC co-sponsored workshop report on biodiversity and climate change*. IPBES and IPCC, Bonn, Germany, 28 pp.

IPCC, 1996: *Revised 1996 IPCC Guidelines for National Greenhouse Gas Inventories*. IPCC, Geneva, Switzerland, 190 pp.

IPCC, 2006: *2006 IPCC – Guidelines for National Greenhouse Gas Inventories* [Eggleston H.S., L. Buendia, K. Miwa, T. Ngara, and K. Tanabe K. (eds.)]. Prepared by the National Greenhouse Gas Inventories Programme. Institute for Global Environmental Strategies (IGES), Kanagawa, Japan.

IPCC, 2010: *Revisiting the use of managed land as a proxy for estimating national anthropogenic emissions and removals*. [Eggleston, H.S., N. Srivastava, K.Tanabe, and J. Baasansuren (eds.)]. Institute for Global Environmental Strategies (IGES), Kanagawa, Japan, 56 pp.

IPCC, 2018: *Global Warming of 1.5°C. An IPCC Special Report on the impacts of global warming of 1.5°C above pre-industrial levels and related global greenhouse gas emission pathways, in the context of strengthening the global response to the threat of climate change, sustainable development, and efforts to eradicate poverty*. [Masson-Delmotte, V., P. Zhai, H.-O. Pörtner, D. Roberts, J. Skea, P.R. Shukla, A. Pirani, W. Moufouma-Okia, C. Péan, R. Pidcock, S. Connors, J.B.R. Matthews, Y. Chen, X. Zhou, M.I. Gomis, E. Lonnoy, T. Maycock, M. Tignor, and T. Waterfield (eds.)]. Cambridge University Press, Cambridge, UK and New York, NY, USA.

IPCC, 2019: *Climate Change and Land: an IPCC special report on climate change, desertification, land degradation, sustainable land management, food security, and greenhouse gas fluxes in terrestrial ecosystems*. [Shukla, P.R., J. Skea, E. Calvo Buendia, V. Masson-Delmotte, H.-O. Pörtner, D.C. Roberts, P. Zhai, R. Slade, S. Connors, R. van Diemen, M. Ferrat, E. Haughey, S. Luz, S. Neogi, M. Pathak, J. Petzold, J. Portugal Pereira, P. Vyas, E. Huntley, K. Kissick, M. Belkacemi, and J. Malley (eds.)]. Cambridge University Press, Cambridge, UK and New York, NY, USA.

Islam, S.M.M. et al., 2018: Nitrous oxide and nitric oxide emissions from lowland rice cultivation with urea deep placement and alternate wetting and drying irrigation. *Sci. Rep.*, **8(1)**, 17623, doi:10.1038/s41598-018-35939-7.

Ivanova, D. et al., 2020: Quantifying the potential for climate change mitigation of consumption options. *Environ. Res. Lett.*, **15(9)**, 093001, doi:10.1088/1748-9326/ab8589.

Jackson, R.B. et al., 2020: Increasing anthropogenic methane emissions arise equally from agricultural and fossil fuel sources. *Environ. Res. Lett.*, **15(7)**, 071002, doi:10.1088/1748-9326/ab9ed2.

Jaganathan, D., K. Ramasamy, G. Sellamuthu, S. Jayabalan, and G. Venkataraman, 2018: CRISPR for Crop Improvement: An Update Review. *Front. Plant Sci.*, **9**, doi:10.3389/fpls.2018.00985.

Jamnadass, R. et al., 2020: Enhancing African orphan crops with genomics. *Nat. Genet.*, **52(4)**, 356–360, doi:10.1038/s41588-020-0601-x.

Janssen, A., 2020: *These farmers deserve support*. Wageningen World, Wageningen, The Netherlands, 44–45 pp. https://edepot.wur.nl/530828.

Janssens-Maenhout, G. et al., 2019: EDGAR v4.3.2 Global Atlas of the three major greenhouse gas emissions for the period 1970–2012. *Earth Syst. Sci. Data*, **11(3)**, 959–1002, doi:10.5194/essd-11-959-2019.

Jasinevičius, G., M. Lindner, P. Verkerk, and M. Aleinikovas, 2017: Assessing Impacts of Wood Utilisation Scenarios for a Lithuanian Bioeconomy: Impacts on Carbon in Forests and Harvested Wood Products and on the Socio-Economic Performance of the Forest-Based Sector. *Forests*, **8(4)**, 133, doi:10.3390/f8040133.

Jauhiainen, J., S. Limin, H. Silvennoinen, and H. Vasander, 2008: Carbon Dioxide and Methane Fluxes in Drained Tropical Peat Before and After Hydrological Restoration. *Ecology*, **89(12)**, 3503–3514, doi:10.1890/07-2038.1.

Jayachandran, S. et al., 2017: Cash for carbon: A randomized trial of payments for ecosystem services to reduce deforestation. *Science*, **357(6348)**, 267–273, doi:10.1126/science.aan0568.

Jayanegara, A. et al., 2018: Use of 3-nitrooxypropanol as feed additive for mitigating enteric methane emissions from ruminants: a meta-analysis. *Ital. J. Anim. Sci.*, **17(3)**, 650–656, doi:10.1080/1828051X.2017.1404945.

Jayasundara, S., J.A.D. Ranga Niroshan Appuhamy, E. Kebreab, and C. Wagner-Riddle, 2016: Methane and nitrous oxide emissions from Canadian dairy farms and mitigation options: An updated review. *Can. J. Anim. Sci.*, **96(3)**, 306–331, doi:10.1139/cjas-2015-0111.

Jeffery, S. et al., 2017: Biochar boosts tropical but not temperate crop yields. *Environ. Res. Lett.*, **12(5)**, 053001, doi:10.1088/1748-9326/aa67bd.

Jennerjahn, T.C. et al., 2017: Mangrove Ecosystems under Climate Change. In: *Mangrove Ecosystems: A Global Biogeographic Perspective*. Springer International Publishing, Cham, Switzerland, pp. 211–244.

Jensen, E.S., G. Carlsson, and H. Hauggaard-Nielsen, 2020: Intercropping of grain legumes and cereals improves the use of soil N resources and reduces the requirement for synthetic fertilizer N: A global-scale analysis. *Agron. Sustain. Dev.*, **40(1)**, 5, doi:10.1007/s13593-020-0607-x.

Jia, G., E. Shevliakova, P. Artaxo, N. De Noblet-Ducoudré, R. Houghton, J. House, K. Kitajima, C. Lennard, A. Popp, A. Sirin, R. Sukumar, and L. Verchot, 2019: Land–climate interactions. In: *Climate Change and Land: an IPCC special report on climate change, desertification, land degradation, sustainable land management, food security, and greenhouse gas fluxes in terrestrial ecosystems* [Shukla, P.R., J. Skea, E. Calvo Buendia, V. Masson-Delmotte, H.-O. Pörtner, D.C. Roberts, P. Zhai, R. Slade, S. Connors, R. van Diemen, M. Ferrat, E. Haughey, S. Luz, S. Neogi, M. Pathak, J. Petzold, J. Portugal Pereira, P. Vyas, E. Huntley, K. Kissick, M. Belkacemi, and J. Malley (eds.)]. Cambridge University Press, Cambridge, UK and New York, NY, USA, pp. 131–247.

Jiang, C., K. Guan, M. Khanna, L. Chen, and J. Peng, 2021: Assessing Marginal Land Availability Based on Land Use Change Information in the Contiguous United States. *Environ. Sci. Technol.*, **55(15)**, 10794–10804, doi:10.1021/acs.est.1c02236.

Jiang, W., M.G. Jacobson, and M.H. Langholtz, 2019: A sustainability framework for assessing studies about marginal lands for planting perennial energy crops. *Biofuels, Bioprod. Biorefining*, **13(1)**, 228–240, doi:10.1002/bbb.1948.

Jilani, T., T. Hasegawa, and Y. Matsuoka, 2015: The future role of agriculture and land use change for climate change mitigation in Bangladesh. *Mitig. Adapt. Strateg. Glob. Change*, **20(8)**, 1289–1304, doi:10.1007/s11027-014-9545-8.

Joffre, R., J. Vacher, C. de los Llanos, and G. Long, 1988: The dehesa: an agrosilvopastoral system of the Mediterranean region with special reference to the Sierra Morena area of Spain. *Agrofor. Syst.*, **6(1–3)**, 71–96, doi:10.1007/BF02344747.

Johnson, N. et al., 2019: Integrated Solutions for the Water-Energy-Land Nexus: Are Global Models Rising to the Challenge? *Water*, **11(11)**, 2223, doi:10.3390/w11112223.

Johnsson, F., F. Normann, and E. Svensson, 2020: Marginal Abatement Cost Curve of Industrial CO_2 Capture and Storage – A Swedish Case Study. *Front. Energy Res.*, **8**, doi:10.3389/fenrg.2020.00175.

Johnston, A.M. and T.W. Bruulsema, 2014: 4R Nutrient Stewardship for Improved Nutrient Use Efficiency. *Procedia Eng.*, **83**, 365–370, doi:10.1016/j.proeng.2014.09.029.

Johnston, C.M.T. and V.C. Radeloff, 2019: Global mitigation potential of carbon stored in harvested wood products. *Proc. Natl. Acad. Sci.*, **116(29)**, 14526–14531, doi:10.1073/pnas.1904231116.

Jolly, W.M. et al., 2015: Climate-induced variations in global wildfire danger from 1979 to 2013. *Nat. Commun.*, **6(1)**, 7537, doi:10.1038/ncomms8537.

Jonker, A. et al., 2018: Genetic parameters of methane emissions determined using portable accumulation chambers in lambs and ewes grazing pasture and genetic correlations with emissions determined in respiration chambers1. *J. Anim. Sci.*, **96(8)**, 3031–3042, doi:10.1093/jas/sky187.

Joosten, H., 2009: *The Global Peatland CO_2 Picture*. Wetlands International, Wageningen, The Netherlands, 36 pp.

Junginger, H.M. et al., 2019: The future of biomass and bioenergy deployment and trade: a synthesis of 15 years IEA Bioenergy Task 40 on sustainable bioenergy trade. *Biofuels, Bioprod. Biorefining*, **13(2)**, 247–266, doi:10.1002/bbb.1993.

Kalies, E. and L.L. Yocom Kent, 2016: Tamm Review: Are fuel treatments effective at achieving ecological and social objectives? A systematic review. *For. Ecol. Manage.*, **375**, 84–95, doi:10.1016/j.foreco.2016.05.021.

Kalliokoski, T. et al., 2020: Mitigation Impact of Different Harvest Scenarios of Finnish Forests That Account for Albedo, Aerosols, and Trade-Offs of Carbon Sequestration and Avoided Emissions. *Front. For. Glob. Change*, **3**, doi:10.3389/ffgc.2020.562044.

Kallio, I., A. Marrit and B. Solberg, 2018: Leakage of forest harvest changes in a small open economy: case Norway. *Scand. J. For. Res.*, **33(5)**, 502–510, doi:10.1080/02827581.2018.1427787.

Kalt, G. et al., 2019: Natural climate solutions versus bioenergy: Can carbon benefits of natural succession compete with bioenergy from short rotation coppice? *GCB Bioenergy*, **11(11)**, 1283–1297, doi:10.1111/gcbb.12626.

Kalt, G. et al., 2020: Greenhouse gas implications of mobilizing agricultural biomass for energy: a reassessment of global potentials in 2050 under different food-system pathways. *Environ. Res. Lett.*, **15(3)**, 034066, doi:10.1088/1748-9326/ab6c2e.

Kammann, C. et al., 2017: Biochar as a Tool to Reduce the Agricultural Greenhouse Gas Burden – Knowns, Unknowns and Future Research Needs. *J. Environ. Eng. Landsc. Manag.*, **25(2)**, 114–139, doi:10.3846/16486897.2017.1319375.

Kansanga, M.M. and I. Luginaah, 2019: Agrarian livelihoods under siege: Carbon forestry, tenure constraints and the rise of capitalist forest enclosures in Ghana. *World Dev.*, **113**, 131–142, doi:10.1016/j.worlddev.2018.09.002.

7

Kaparaju, P. and J. Rintala, 2011: Mitigation of greenhouse gas emissions by adopting anaerobic digestion technology on dairy, sow and pig farms in Finland. *Renew. Energy*, **36(1)**, 31–41, doi:10.1016/j.renene.2010.05.016.

Karlsson, M., E. Alfredsson, and N. Westling, 2020: Climate policy co-benefits: a review. *Clim. Policy*, **20(3)**, 292–316, doi:10.1080/14693 062.2020.1724070.

Kashangaki, J. and P. Ericksen, 2018: *Cost–benefit analysis of fodder production as a low emissions development strategy for the Kenyan dairy sector*. ILRI, Nairobi, Kenya, 40 pp. http://cgspace.cgiar.org/rest/bitstreams/158438/retrieve.

Kassam, AL. Kassam, 2020: *Rethinking Food and Agriculture: New Ways Forward*. Woodhead Publishing, 476 pp.

Kastner, T., K.-H. Erb, and S. Nonhebel, 2011: International wood trade and forest change: A global analysis. *Glob. Environ. Change*, **21(3)**, 947–956, doi:10.1016/j.gloenvcha.2011.05.003.

Kätterer, T. et al., 2019: Biochar addition persistently increased soil fertility and yields in maize-soybean rotations over 10 years in sub-humid regions of Kenya. *F. Crop. Res.*, **235**, 18–26, doi:10.1016/j.fcr.2019.02.015.

Katwijk, M.M. et al., 2016: Global analysis of seagrass restoration: the importance of large-scale planting. *J. Appl. Ecol.*, **53(2)**, 567–578, doi:10.1111/1365-2664.12562.

Kauffman, J.B. et al., 2020: Total ecosystem carbon stocks of mangroves across broad global environmental and physical gradients. *Ecol. Monogr.*, **90(2)**, doi:10.1002/ecm.1405.

Kavanagh, I. et al., 2019: Mitigation of ammonia and greenhouse gas emissions from stored cattle slurry using acidifiers and chemical amendments. *J. Clean. Prod.*, **237**, 117822, doi:10.1016/j.jclepro.2019.117822.

Keeley, J.E., P. van Mantgem, and D.A. Falk, 2019: Fire, climate and changing forests. *Nat. Plants*, **5(8)**, 774–775, doi:10.1038/s41477-019-0485-x.

Kelleway, J.J. et al., 2017: Review of the ecosystem service implications of mangrove encroachment into salt marshes. *Glob. Change Biol.*, **23(10)**, 3967–3983, doi:10.1111/gcb.13727.

Kennedy, H., D.M. Alongi, A. Karim, G. Chen, G.L. Chmura, S. Crooks, J.G. Kairo, B. Liao, and G. Lin, 2014: Chapter 4: Coastal Wetlands. In: *2013 Supplement to the 2006 IPCC Guidelines for National Greenhouse Gas Inventories: Wetlands*. [Hiraishi, T., T. Krug, K. Tanabe, N. Srivastava, J. Baasansuren, M. Fukuda, and T. Troxler (eds.)]. IPCC, Geneva, Switzerland, pp. 1–55.

Keramidas, K. et al., 2018: *Global Energy and Climate Outlook 2018: Sectoral mitigation options towards a low-emissions economy – Global context to the EU strategy for long-term greenhouse gas emissions reduction*. European Union (EU), Luxembourg, 200 pp.

Khanna, M., P. Dwivedi, and R. Abt, 2017: Is Forest Bioenergy Carbon Neutral or Worse than Coal? Implications of Carbon Accounting Methods. *Int. Rev. Environ. Resour. Econ.*, **10(3–4)**, 299–346, doi:10.1561/101.00000089.

Kiggundu, N. et al., 2019: Greenhouse gas emissions from Uganda's cattle corridor farming systems. *Agric. Syst.*, **176**, 102649, doi:10.1016/j.agsy.2019.102649.

Killeen, T.J., 2007: *A Perfect Storm in the Amazon Wilderness: Success and Failure in the Fight to Save an Ecosystem of Critical Importance to the Planet*. The White Horse Press, Cambridgeshire, UK. 160 p.

Kim, J., G. Yoo, D. Kim, W. Ding, and H. Kang, 2017a: Combined application of biochar and slow-release fertilizer reduces methane emission but enhances rice yield by different mechanisms. *Appl. Soil Ecol.*, **117–118**, 57–62, doi:10.1016/j.apsoil.2017.05.006.

Kim, J.B. et al., 2017b: Assessing climate change impacts, benefits of mitigation, and uncertainties on major global forest regions under multiple socioeconomic and emissions scenarios. *Environ. Res. Lett.*, **12(4)**, 045001, doi:10.1088/1748-9326/aa63fc.

Kinley, R.D. et al., 2020: Mitigating the carbon footprint and improving productivity of ruminant livestock agriculture using a red seaweed. *J. Clean. Prod.*, **259**, 120836, doi:10.1016/j.jclepro.2020.120836.

Kirchmann, H., 2019: Why organic farming is not the way forward. *Outlook Agric.*, **48(1)**, 22–27, doi:10.1177/0030727019831702.

Kirchmeier-Young, M.C., N.P. Gillett, F.W. Zwiers, A.J. Cannon, and F.S. Anslow, 2019: Attribution of the Influence of Human-Induced Climate Change on an Extreme Fire Season. *Earth's Futur.*, **7(1)**, 2–10, doi:10.1029/2018EF001050.

Kirchner, M. et al., 2015: Ecosystem services and economic development in Austrian agricultural landscapes — The impact of policy and climate change scenarios on trade-offs and synergies. *Ecol. Econ.*, **109**, 161–174, doi:10.1016/j.ecolecon.2014.11.005.

Klein, D., C. Wolf, C. Schulz, and G. Weber-Blaschke, 2015: 20 years of life cycle assessment (LCA) in the forestry sector: state of the art and a methodical proposal for the LCA of forest production. *Int. J. Life Cycle Assess.*, **20(4)**, 556–575, doi:10.1007/s11367-015-0847-1.

Kleinschroth, F. and J.R. Healey, 2017: Impacts of logging roads on tropical forests. *Biotropica*, **49(5)**, 620–635, doi:10.1111/btp.12462.

Kongsager, R., 2017: Barriers to the Adoption of Alley Cropping as a Climate-Smart Agriculture Practice: Lessons from Maize Cultivation among the Maya in Southern Belize. *Forests*, **8(7)**, 260, doi:10.3390/f8070260.

Koornneef, J. et al., 2012: Global potential for biomass and carbon dioxide capture, transport and storage up to 2050. *Int. J. Greenh. Gas Control*, **11**, 117–132, doi:10.1016/j.ijggc.2012.07.027.

Kösler, J.E., O.C. Calvo, J. Franzaring, and A. Fangmeier, 2019: Evaluating the ecotoxicity of nitrification inhibitors using terrestrial and aquatic test organisms. *Environ. Sci. Eur.*, **31(1)**, 91, doi:10.1186/s12302-019-0272-3.

Kram, T., D. van Vuuren, and E. Stehfest, 2014: *Drivers, Chapter 3, In: Integrated Assessment of Global Environmental Change with IMAGE 3.0. Model description and policy applications*. [Stehfest, E., D. Van Vuuren, T. Kram, and L. Bouwman (eds.)]. PBL Netherlands Environmental Assessment Agency, The Hague, The Netherlands. 370p.

Krause, A. et al., 2017: Global consequences of afforestation and bioenergy cultivation on ecosystem service indicators. *Biogeosciences*, **14(21)**, 4829–4850, doi:10.5194/bg-14-4829-2017.

Kraxner, F. et al., 2017: Mapping certified forests for sustainable management – A global tool for information improvement through participatory and collaborative mapping. *For. Policy Econ.*, **83**, 10–18, doi:10.1016/j.forpol.2017.04.014.

Kreidenweis, U. et al., 2016: Afforestation to mitigate climate change: impacts on food prices under consideration of albedo effects. *Environ. Res. Lett.*, **11(8)**, 085001, doi:10.1088/1748-9326/11/8/085001.

Kriegler, E. et al., 2015: Diagnostic indicators for integrated assessment models of climate policy. *Technol. Forecast. Soc. Change*, **90(PA)**, 45–61, doi:10.1016/j.techfore.2013.09.020.

Kritee, K. et al., 2018: High nitrous oxide fluxes from rice indicate the need to manage water for both long- and short-term climate impacts. *Proc. Natl. Acad. Sci.*, **115(39)**, 9720–9725, doi:10.1073/pnas.1809276115.

Krofcheck, D.J., M.D. Hurteau, R.M. Scheller, and E.L. Loudermilk, 2018: Prioritizing forest fuels treatments based on the probability of high-severity fire restores adaptive capacity in Sierran forests. *Glob. Change Biol.*, **24(2)**, 729–737, doi:10.1111/gcb.13913.

Krofcheck, D.J., C.C. Remy, A.R. Keyser, and M.D. Hurteau, 2019: Optimizing Forest Management Stabilizes Carbon Under Projected Climate and Wildfires. *J. Geophys. Res. Biogeosciences*, **124(10)**, 3075–3087, doi:10.1029/2019JG005206.

Krug, J.H.A., 2018: Accounting of GHG emissions and removals from forest management: a long road from Kyoto to Paris. *Carbon Balance Manag.*, **13(1)**, 1, doi:10.1186/s13021-017-0089-6.

Ku-Vera, J.C. et al., 2020: Review: Strategies for enteric methane mitigation in cattle fed tropical forages. *Animal*, **14**, s453–s463, doi:10.1017/S1751731120001780.

Kubiszewski, I., R. Costanza, S. Anderson, and P. Sutton, 2017: The future value of ecosystem services: Global scenarios and national implications. *Ecosyst. Serv.*, **26**, 289–301, doi:10.1016/j.ecoser.2017.05.004.

Kumar, B.M. and P.K.R. Nair, 2011: *Carbon Sequestration Potential of Agroforestry Systems*. [Kumar, B.M. and P.K.R. Nair (eds.)]. Springer Netherlands, Dordrecht, The Netherlands. 298 p.

Kupper, T. et al., 2020: Ammonia and greenhouse gas emissions from slurry storage – A review. *Agric. Ecosyst. Environ.*, **300**, 106963, doi:10.1016/j.agee.2020.106963.

Kurz, W.A. et al., 2008: Mountain pine beetle and forest carbon feedback to climate change. *Nature*, **452(7190)**, 987–990, doi:10.1038/nature06777.

Kuyah, S. et al., 2019: Agroforestry delivers a win-win solution for ecosystem services in sub-Saharan Africa. A meta-analysis. *Agron. Sustain. Dev.*, **39(5)**, 47, doi:10.1007/s13593-019-0589-8.

Laborde, D., S. Murphy, M. Parent, J. Porciello, and S.C, 2020: *Ceres2030: Sustainable Solutions to End Hunger – Summary Report*. Cornell University, IFPRI and IISD, New York, USA, 40 pp.

Lai, L. et al., 2016: Carbon emissions from land-use change and management in China between 1990 and 2010. *Sci. Adv.*, **2(11)**, doi:10.1126/sciadv.1601063.

Lal, R., 2015: Sequestering carbon and increasing productivity by conservation agriculture. *J. Soil Water Conserv.*, **70(3)**, 55A–62A, doi:10.2489/jswc.70.3.55A.

Lal, R., 2020: Integrating Animal Husbandry With Crops and Trees. *Front. Sustain. Food Syst.*, **4**, doi:10.3389/fsufs.2020.00113.

Lal, R. et al., 2018: The carbon sequestration potential of terrestrial ecosystems. *J. Soil Water Conserv.*, **73(6)**, 145A–152A, doi:10.2489/jswc.73.6.145A.

Lambin, E.F. et al., 2018: The role of supply-chain initiatives in reducing deforestation. *Nat. Clim. Change*, **8(2)**, 109–116, doi:10.1038/s41558-017-0061-1.

Lampkin, N.H., et al., 2017: The role of agroecology in sustainable intensification. *Asp. Appl. Biol.*, **136**, 53–62.

Landholm, D.M. et al., 2019: Reducing deforestation and improving livestock productivity: greenhouse gas mitigation potential of silvopastoral systems in Caquetá. *Environ. Res. Lett.*, **14(11)**, 114007, doi:10.1088/1748-9326/ab3db6.

Lanigan, G.J. et al., 2018: *An Analysis of Abatement Potential of Greenhouse Gas Emissions in Irish Agriculture 2021-2030*. Agriculture and Food Development Authority, Carlow, Ireland, 1–80 pp.

Lark, T.J., J. Meghan Salmon, and H.K. Gibbs, 2015: Cropland expansion outpaces agricultural and biofuel policies in the United States. *Environ. Res. Lett.*, **10(4)**, 044003, doi:10.1088/1748-9326/10/4/044003.

Latka, C. et al., 2021: Paying the price for environmentally sustainable and healthy EU diets. *Glob. Food Sec.*, **28**, 100437, doi:10.1016/j.gfs.2020.100437.

Laurance, W. and A. Balmford, 2013: A global map for road building. *Nature*, **495(7441)**, 308–309, doi:10.1038/495308a.

Laurance, W.F. and I.B.B. Arrea, 2017: Roads to riches or ruin? *Science*, **358(6362)**, 442–444, doi:10.1126/science.aao0312.

Laurance, W.F. et al., 2001: The Future of the Brazilian Amazon. *Science*, **291(5503)**, 438–439, doi:10.1126/science.291.5503.438.

Laurance, W.F., M. Goosem, and S.G.W. Laurance, 2009: Impacts of roads and linear clearings on tropical forests. *Trends Ecol. Evol.*, **24(12)**, 659–669, doi:10.1016/j.tree.2009.06.009.

Laurance, W.F. et al., 2014a: A global strategy for road building. *Nature*, **513(7517)**, 229–232, doi:10.1038/nature13717.

Laurance, W.F., J. Sayer, and K.G. Cassman, 2014b: Agricultural expansion and its impacts on tropical nature. *Trends Ecol. Evol.*, **29(2)**, 107–116, doi:10.1016/j.tree.2013.12.001.

Laurance, W.F. et al., 2015a: Reducing the global environmental impacts of rapid infrastructure expansion. *Curr. Biol.*, **25(7)**, R259–R262, doi:10.1016/j.cub.2015.02.050.

Laurance, W.F., S. Sloan, L. Weng, and J.A. Sayer, 2015b: Estimating the Environmental Costs of Africa's Massive "Development Corridors". *Curr. Biol.*, **25(24)**, 3202–3208, doi:10.1016/j.cub.2015.10.046.

Lauri, P. et al., 2019: Global Woody Biomass Harvest Volumes and Forest Area Use Under Different SSP-RCP Scenarios. *J. For. Econ.*, **34(3–4)**, 285–309, doi:10.1561/112.00000504.

Le Noë, J. et al., 2020: Modeling and empirical validation of long-term carbon sequestration in forests (France, 1850–2015). *Glob. Change Biol.*, **26(4)**, 2421–2434, doi:10.1111/gcb.15004.

Leahy, S., H. Clark, and A. Reisinger, 2020: Challenges and Prospects for Agricultural Greenhouse Gas Mitigation Pathways Consistent With the Paris Agreement. *Front. Sustain. Food Syst.*, **4**, doi:10.3389/fsufs.2020.00069.

Leahy, S.C., L. Kearney, A. Reisinger, and H. Clark, 2019: Mitigating greenhouse gas emissions from New Zealand pasture-based livestock farm systems. *J. New Zeal. Grasslands*, **81** 101–110, doi:10.33584/jnzg.2019.81.417.

Leal Filho, W., U.M. Azeiteiro, A.L. Salvia, B. Fritzen, and R. Libonati, 2021: Fire in Paradise: Why the Pantanal is burning. *Environ. Sci. Policy*, **123**, 31–34, doi:10.1016/j.envsci.2021.05.005.

Lechner, A.M., F.K.S. Chan, and A. Campos-Arceiz, 2018: Biodiversity conservation should be a core value of China's Belt and Road Initiative. *Nat. Ecol. Evol.*, **2(3)**, 408–409, doi:10.1038/s41559-017-0452-8.

Lee, J.W. and D.M. Day, 2013: Smokeless biomass pyrolysis for producing biofuels and biochar as a possible arsenal to control climate change. In: *Advanced Biofuels and Bioproducts* [Lee, J.W. (ed.)]. Springer, New York, USA, pp. 23–34.

Lefcheck, J.S. et al., 2018: Long-term nutrient reductions lead to the unprecedented recovery of a temperate coastal region. *Proc. Natl. Acad. Sci.*, **115(14)**, 3658–3662, doi:10.1073/pnas.1715798115.

Lehmann, J. and S. Joseph, 2012: *Biochar for Environmental Management*. [Lehmann, J. and S. Joseph (eds.)]. Routledge, Abingdon, Oxfordshire, UK, 976 pp.

Lehmann, J. and M. Rillig, 2014: Distinguishing variability from uncertainty. *Nat. Clim. Change*, **4(3)**, 153–153, doi:10.1038/nclimate2133.

Leifeld, J., 2016: Current approaches neglect possible agricultural cutback under large-scale organic farming. A comment to Ponisio *et al*. *Proc. R. Soc. B Biol. Sci.*, **283(1824)**, 20151623, doi:10.1098/rspb.2015.1623.

Leifeld, J. and L. Menichetti, 2018: The underappreciated potential of peatlands in global climate change mitigation strategies. *Nat. Commun.*, **9(1)**, 1071, doi:10.1038/s41467-018-03406-6.

Leifeld, J. et al., 2013: Organic farming gives no climate change benefit through soil carbon sequestration. *Proc. Natl. Acad. Sci.*, **110(11)**, E984–E984, doi:10.1073/pnas.1220724110.

Leifeld, J., C. Wüst-Galley, and S. Page, 2019: Intact and managed peatland soils as a source and sink of GHGs from 1850 to 2100. *Nat. Clim. Change*, **9(12)**, 945–947, doi:10.1038/s41558-019-0615-5.

Lejeune, Q., E.L. Davin, L. Gudmundsson, J. Winckler, and S.I. Seneviratne, 2018: Historical deforestation locally increased the intensity of hot days in northern mid-latitudes. *Nat. Clim. Change*, **8(5)**, 386–390, doi:10.1038/s41558-018-0131-z.

Lemaire, G., A. Franzluebbers, P.C. de F. Carvalho, and B. Dedieu, 2014: Integrated crop–livestock systems: Strategies to achieve synergy between agricultural production and environmental quality. *Agric. Ecosyst. Environ.*, **190**, 4–8, doi:10.1016/j.agee.2013.08.009.

Lenton, T.M., 2010: The potential for land-based biological CO$_2$ removal to lower future atmospheric CO$_2$ concentration. *Carbon Manag.*, **1(1)**, 145–160, doi:10.4155/cmt.10.12.

Lenton, T.M., 2014: The global potential for carbon dioxide removal. In: *Geoengineering of the Climate System* [Harrison, R.M. and R.E. Hester (eds.)]. Royal Society of Chemistry, Cambridge, UK, pp. 52–79.

Leonardi, S., F. Magnani, A. Nolè, T. Van Noije, and M. Borghetti, 2015: A global assessment of forest surface albedo and its relationships with climate and atmospheric nitrogen deposition. *Glob. Change Biol.*, **21(1)**, 287–298, doi:10.1111/gcb.12681.

Leskinen, P. et al., 2018: *Substitution effects of wood-based products in climate change mitigation*. European Forest Institute (EFI), Joensuu, Finland, 28 pp.

Leskinen, P. et al., 2020: *Russian forests and climate change*. European Forest Institute, Joensuu, Finland, 136 pp.

7

Levang, P., G. Lescuyer, D. Noumbissi, C. Déhu, and L. Broussolle, 2015: Does gathering really pay? Case studies from forest areas of the East and South regions of Cameroon. *For. Trees Livelihoods*, **24(2)**, 128–143, doi:10.1080/14728028.2014.1000980.

Lewis, S.L., C.E. Wheeler, E.T.A. Mitchard, and A. Koch, 2019: Restoring natural forests is the best way to remove atmospheric carbon. *Nature*, **568(7750)**, 25–28, doi:10.1038/d41586-019-01026-8.

Li, D. and E. Bou-Zeid, 2013: Synergistic Interactions between Urban Heat Islands and Heat Waves: The Impact in Cities Is Larger than the Sum of Its Parts. *J. Appl. Meteorol. Climatol.*, **52(9)**, 2051–2064, doi:10.1175/JAMC-D-13-02.1.

Li, W. et al., 2020: Mapping the yields of lignocellulosic bioenergy crops from observations at the global scale. *Earth Syst. Sci. Data*, **12(2)**, 789–804, doi:10.5194/essd-12-789-2020.

Li, Y. et al., 2015: Local cooling and warming effects of forests based on satellite observations. *Nat. Commun.*, **6(1)**, 6603, doi:10.1038/ncomms7603.

Lima, M., C.A. da Silva Junior, L. Rausch, H.K. Gibbs, and J.A. Johann, 2019: Demystifying sustainable soy in Brazil. *Land use policy*, **82**, 349–352, doi:10.1016/j.landusepol.2018.12.016.

Lin, Z. et al., 2017: Overview of Ecological Restoration Technologies and Evaluation Systems. *J. Resour. Ecol.*, **8(4)**, 315–324, doi:10.5814/j.issn.1674-764x.2017.04.002.

Lipper, L., C. Dutilly-Diane, and N. McCarthy, 2010: Supplying Carbon Sequestration From West African Rangelands: Opportunities and Barriers. *Rangel. Ecol. Manag.*, **63(1)**, 155–166, doi:10.2111/REM-D-09-00009.1.

Lipsett-Moore, G.J., N.H. Wolff, and E.T. Game, 2018: Emissions mitigation opportunities for savanna countries from early dry season fire management. *Nat. Commun.*, **9(1)**, 2247, doi:10.1038/s41467-018-04687-7.

Liu, Q. et al., 2018: How does biochar influence soil N cycle? A meta-analysis. *Plant Soil*, **426(1–2)**, 211–225, doi:10.1007/s11104-018-3619-4.

Liu, Q. et al., 2019: Biochar application as a tool to decrease soil nitrogen losses NH3 volatilization, N_2O emissions, and N leaching from croplands: Options and mitigation strength in a global perspective. *Glob. Change Biol.*, **25(6)**, 2077–2093, doi:10.1111/gcb.14613.

Liu, T. et al., 2017: Bioenergy production on marginal land in Canada: Potential, economic feasibility, and greenhouse gas emissions impacts. *Appl. Energy*, **205**, 477–485, doi:10.1016/j.apenergy.2017.07.126.

Liu, Z. and Y. Liu, 2018: Mitigation of greenhouse gas emissions from animal production. *Greenh. Gases Sci. Technol.*, **8(4)**, 627–638, doi:10.1002/ghg.1785.

Locatelli, B. et al., 2015: Tropical reforestation and climate change: beyond carbon. *Restor. Ecol.*, **23(4)**, 337–343, doi:10.1111/rec.12209.

Löf, M., P. Madsen, M. Metslaid, J. Witzell, and D.F. Jacobs, 2019: Restoring forests: regeneration and ecosystem function for the future. *New For.*, **50(2)**, 139–151, doi:10.1007/s11056-019-09713-0.

Loisel, J. et al., 2014: A database and synthesis of northern peatland soil properties and Holocene carbon and nitrogen accumulation. *The Holocene*, **24(9)**, 1028–1042, doi:10.1177/0959683614538073.

Loomis, J., P. Kent, L. Strange, K. Fausch, and A. Covich, 2000: Measuring the total economic value of restoring ecosystem services in an impaired river basin: results from a contingent valuation survey. *Ecol. Econ.*, **33(1)**, 103–117, doi:10.1016/S0921-8009(99)00131-7.

López-Paredes, J. et al., 2020: Mitigation of greenhouse gases in dairy cattle via genetic selection: 1. Genetic parameters of direct methane using noninvasive methods and proxies of methane. *J. Dairy Sci.*, **103(8)**, 7199–7209, doi:10.3168/jds.2019-17597.

López-Aizpún, M. et al., 2020: Meta-analysis of global livestock urine-derived nitrous oxide emissions from agricultural soils. *Glob. Change Biol.*, **26(4)**, 2002–2013, doi:10.1111/gcb.15012.

Loudermilk, E.L., R.M. Scheller, P.J. Weisberg, and A. Kretchun, 2017: Bending the carbon curve: fire management for carbon resilience under climate change. *Landsc. Ecol.*, **32(7)**, 1461–1472, doi:10.1007/s10980-016-0447-x.

Lovejoy, T.E. and C. Nobre, 2018: Amazon Tipping Point. *Sci. Adv.*, **4(2)**, eaat2340, doi:10.1126/sciadv.aat2340.

Lovelock, C. and R. Reef, 2020: Variable Impacts of Climate Change on Blue Carbon. *One Earth*, **3(2)**, 195–211, doi:10.1016/j.oneear.2020.07.010.

Lovelock, C.E., J.W. Fourqurean, and J.T. Morris, 2017: Modeled CO_2 Emissions from Coastal Wetland Transitions to Other Land Uses: Tidal Marshes, Mangrove Forests, and Seagrass Beds. *Front. Mar. Sci.*, **4**, doi:10.3389/fmars.2017.00143.

Lovelock, C.E., Daniel A. Friess, J.B.K.J.W.F., 2018: *A Blue Carbon Primer*. [Windham-Myers, L., S. Crooks, and T.G. Troxler (eds.)]. CRC Press, Boca Raton. 507 pp.

Luedeling, E. and H. Neufeldt, 2012: Carbon sequestration potential of parkland agroforestry in the Sahel. *Clim. Change*, **115(3–4)**, 443–461, doi:10.1007/s10584-012-0438-0.

Luttrell, C., E. Sills, R. Aryani, A.D. Ekaputri, and M.F. Evinke, 2018: Beyond opportunity costs: who bears the implementation costs of reducing emissions from deforestation and degradation? *Mitig. Adapt. Strateg. Glob. Change*, **23(2)**, 291–310, doi:10.1007/s11027-016-9736-6.

Luyssaert, S. et al., 2018: Trade-offs in using European forests to meet climate objectives. *Nature*, **562(7726)**, 259–262, doi:10.1038/s41586-018-0577-1.

Luderer, G., et al., 2021: Impact of declining renewable energy costs on electrification in low emisison scenarios. *Nat. Energy 7:32-42*, doi:10.1038/s41560-021-00937-z.

Lynch, D., J. Russell-Smith, A.C. Edwards, J. Evans, and C. Yates, 2018: Incentivising fire management in Pindan (Acacia shrubland): A proposed fuel type for Australia's Savanna burning greenhouse gas emissions abatement methodology. *Ecol. Manag. Restor.*, **19(3)**, 230–238, doi:10.1111/emr.12334.

Lynch, J. and R. Pierrehumbert, 2019: Climate Impacts of Cultured Meat and Beef Cattle. *Front. Sustain. Food Syst.*, **3**, doi:10.3389/fsufs.2019.00005.

Ma, S., D.D. Baldocchi, L. Xu, and T. Hehn, 2007: Inter-annual variability in carbon dioxide exchange of an oak/grass savanna and open grassland in California. *Agric. For. Meteorol.*, **147(3–4)**, 157–171, doi:10.1016/j.agrformet.2007.07.008.

Maaz, T.M. et al., 2021: Meta-analysis of yield and nitrous oxide outcomes for nitrogen management in agriculture. *Glob. Change Biol.*, **27(11)**, 2343–2360, doi:10.1111/gcb.15588.

Macdiarmid, J.I., 2013: Is a healthy diet an environmentally sustainable diet? *Proc. Nutr. Soc.*, **72(1)**, 13–20, doi:10.1017/S0029665112002893.

MacLeod, M. et al., 2018: Assessing the Greenhouse Gas Mitigation Effect of Removing Bovine Trypanosomiasis in Eastern Africa. *Sustainability*, **10(5)**, 1633, doi:10.3390/su10051633.

Macreadie, P.I. et al., 2019: The future of Blue Carbon science. *Nat. Commun.*, **10(1)**, 3998, doi:10.1038/s41467-019-11693-w.

Magkos, F. et al., 2020: A Perspective on the Transition to Plant-Based Diets: a Diet Change May Attenuate Climate Change, but Can It Also Attenuate Obesity and Chronic Disease Risk? *Adv. Nutr.*, **11(1)**, 1–9, doi:10.1093/advances/nmz090.

Mahmood, R. et al., 2014: Land cover changes and their biogeophysical effects on climate. *Int. J. Climatol.*, **34(4)**, 929–953, doi:10.1002/joc.3736.

Mäkelä, M., 2017: Environmental impacts and aspects in the forest industry: What kind of picture do corporate environmental reports provide? *For. Policy Econ.*, **80**, 178–191, doi:10.1016/j.forpol.2017.03.018.

Mancini, L.D., P. Corona, and L. Salvati, 2018: Ranking the importance of Wildfires' human drivers through a multi-model regression approach. *Environ. Impact Assess. Rev.*, **72**, 177–186, doi:10.1016/j.eiar.2018.06.003.

Maneepitak, S. et al., 2019: Effects of water and rice straw management practices on water savings and greenhouse gas emissions from a double-rice paddy field in the Central Plain of Thailand. *Eur. J. Agron.*, **107**, 18–29, doi:10.1016/j.eja.2019.04.002.

Mantyka-Pringle, C.S. et al., 2017: Bridging science and traditional knowledge to assess cumulative impacts of stressors on ecosystem health. *Environ. Int.*, **102**, 125–137, doi:10.1016/j.envint.2017.02.008.

Marlon, J.R. et al., 2012: Long-term perspective on wildfires in the western USA. *Proc. Natl. Acad. Sci.*, **109(9)**, E535–E543, doi:10.1073/pnas.1112839109.

Martínez-Mena, M. et al., 2019: Fluvial sedimentary deposits as carbon sinks: organic carbon pools and stabilization mechanisms across a Mediterranean catchment. *Biogeosciences*, **16(5)**, 1035–1051, doi:10.5194/bg-16-1035-2019.

Martius, C. et al., 2016: *How to achieve reliable, transparent and independent monitoring of greenhouse gas emissions from land activities for policy support*. 2016 Berlin Conference on Global Transformative Climate Governance, 7 pp.

Mašek, O. et al., 2018: Consistency of biochar properties over time and production scales: A characterisation of standard materials. *J. Anal. Appl. Pyrolysis*, **132**, 200–210, doi:10.1016/j.jaap.2018.02.020.

Mausel, D.L., A. Waupochick, and M. Pecore, 2017: Menominee Forestry: Past, Present, Future. *J. For.*, **115(5)**, 366–369, doi:10.5849/jof.16-046.

Mayberry, D., H. Bartlett, J. Moss, T. Davison, and M. Herrero, 2019: Pathways to carbon-neutrality for the Australian red meat sector. *Agric. Syst.*, **175**, 13–21, doi:10.1016/j.agsy.2019.05.009.

Mayer Pelicice, F., 2019: Weak Democracies, Failed Policies, and the Demise of Ecosystems in Poor and Developing Nations. *Trop. Conserv. Sci.*, **12**, 194008291983990, doi:10.1177/1940082919839902.

Mbow, C., C. Rosenzweig, L.G. Barioni, T.G. Benton, M. Herrero, M. Krishnapillai, E. Liwenga, P. Pradhan, M.G. Rivera-Ferre, T. Sapkota, F.N. Tubiello, Y. Xu, 2019: Food Security. In: *Climate Change and Land: an IPCC special report on climate change, desertification, land degradation, sustainable land management, food security, and greenhouse gas fluxes in terrestrial ecosystems* [Shukla, P.R., J. Skea, E. Calvo Buendia, V. Masson-Delmotte, H.-O. Pörtner, D.C. Roberts, P. Zhai, R. Slade, S. Connors, R. van Diemen, M. Ferrat, E. Haughey, S. Luz, S. Neogi, M. Pathak, J. Petzold, J. Portugal Pereira, P. Vyas, E. Huntley, K. Kissick, M. Belkacemi, and J. Malley (eds.)]. Cambridge University Press, Cambridge, UK and New York, NY, USA, pp. 131–248.

Mbow, C. et al., 2020: Agroforestry as a solution for multiple climate change challenges in Africa. In: *Climate Change and Agriculture* [Deryng, D. (ed.)]. Burleigh Dodds Science Publishing Limited, Cambridge, UK.

McCarty, J.L., T.E.L. Smith, and M.R. Turetsky, 2020: Arctic fires re-emerging. *Nat. Geosci.*, **13(10)**, 658–660, doi:10.1038/s41561-020-00645-5.

McDermott, J.J., S.J. Staal, H.A. Freeman, M. Herrero, and J.A. Van de Steeg, 2010: Sustaining intensification of smallholder livestock systems in the tropics. *Livest. Sci.*, **130(1–3)**, 95–109, doi:10.1016/j.livsci.2010.02.014.

McGinn, S.M., T.K. Flesch, K.A. Beauchemin, A. Shreck, and M. Kindermann, 2019: Micrometeorological Methods for Measuring Methane Emission Reduction at Beef Cattle Feedlots: Evaluation of 3-Nitrooxypropanol Feed Additive. *J. Environ. Qual.*, **48(5)**, 1454–1461, doi:10.2134/jeq2018.11.0412.

McKenzie, L.J. et al., 2020: The global distribution of seagrass meadows. *Environ. Res. Lett.*, **15(7)**, 074041, doi:10.1088/1748-9326/ab7d06.

McLaren, D., 2012: A comparative global assessment of potential negative emissions technologies. *Process Saf. Environ. Prot.*, **90(6)**, 489–500, doi:10.1016/j.psep.2012.10.005.

McMullin, S. et al., 2019: Developing fruit tree portfolios that link agriculture more effectively with nutrition and health: a new approach for providing year-round micronutrients to smallholder farmers. *Food Secur.*, **11(6)**, 1355–1372, doi:10.1007/s12571-019-00970-7.

Mcowen, C. et al., 2017: A global map of saltmarshes. *Biodivers. Data J.*, **5**, e11764, doi:10.3897/BDJ.5.e11764.

Meemken, E.-M. and M. Qaim, 2018: Organic Agriculture, Food Security, and the Environment. *Annu. Rev. Resour. Econ.*, **10(1)**, 39–63, doi:10.1146/annurev-resource-100517-023252.

Mei, K. et al., 2018: Stimulation of N_2O emission by conservation tillage management in agricultural lands: A meta-analysis. *Soil Tillage Res.*, **182**, 86–93, doi:10.1016/j.still.2018.05.006.

Meier, M.S. et al., 2015: Environmental impacts of organic and conventional agricultural products – Are the differences captured by life cycle assessment? *J. Environ. Manage.*, **149**, 193–208, doi:10.1016/j.jenvman.2014.10.006.

Meier, R. et al., 2021: Empirical estimate of forestation-induced precipitation changes in Europe. *Nat. Geosci.*, **14(7)**, 473–478, doi:10.1038/s41561-021-00773-6.

Melgar, A. et al., 2020: Dose-response effect of 3-nitrooxypropanol on enteric methane emissions in dairy cows. *J. Dairy Sci.*, **103(7)**, 6145–6156, doi:10.3168/jds.2019-17840.

Mendelsohn, R. and B. Sohngen, 2019: The Net Carbon Emissions from Historic Land Use and Land Use Change. *J. For. Econ.*, **34(3–4)**, 263–283, doi:10.1561/112.00000505.

Mertz, O. and C.F. Mertens, 2017: Land Sparing and Land Sharing Policies in Developing Countries – Drivers and Linkages to Scientific Debates. *World Dev.*, **98**, 523–535, doi:10.1016/j.worlddev.2017.05.002.

Meybeck, A. and V. Gitz, 2017: Sustainable diets within sustainable food systems. *Proc. Nutr. Soc.*, **76(1)**, 1–11, doi:10.1017/S0029665116000653.

Meyer, S., R.M. Bright, D. Fischer, H. Schulz, and B. Glaser, 2012: Albedo Impact on the Suitability of Biochar Systems To Mitigate Global Warming. *Environ. Sci. Technol.*, **46(22)**, 12726–12734, doi:10.1021/es302302g.

Miao, R., D.A. Hennessy, and H. Feng, 2016: The Effects of Crop Insurance Subsidies and Sodsaver on Land-Use Change. *J. Agric. Resour. Econ.*, **41(2)**, 247–265, doi.org/10.22004/ag.econ.235189.

Millennium Ecosystem Assessment, 2005: *Ecosystems and Human Well-being:Synthesis- a report on the e Millenium Ecosystem Assessment*.Island Press, Washington, DC, USA. 155 pp.

Miller, D.C., J.C. Muñoz-Mora, L. V Rasmussen, and A. Zezza, 2020: Do Trees on Farms Improve Household Well-Being? Evidence From National Panel Data in Uganda. *Front. For. Glob. Change*, **3**, doi:10.3389/ffgc.2020.00101.

Minasny, B. et al., 2019: Digital mapping of peatlands – A critical review. *Earth-Science Rev.*, **196**, 102870, doi:10.1016/j.earscirev.2019.05.014.

Miner, R., 2010: *Impact of the global forest industry on atmospheric greenhouse gases*. Food and Agriculture Organization of the United Nations (FAO), Rome, Italy, 86 pp.

Ministerio do Meio Ambiente (MMA), 2013: *Plano De Acao Para Prevencao E Controle Do Desmatamento Na Amazonia Legal (PPCDAm) Pelo uso sustentável e conservacao da floresta 3ªFase (2012-2015)*. https://www.researchgate.net/publication/273756502_Plano_de_Acao_para_prevencao_e_controle_do_desmatamento_na_Amazonia_Legal_PPCDAm_3_fase_2012-2015_pelo_uso_sustentavel_e_conservacao_da_Floresta (Accessed March 21, 2021).

Ministry of Environment Government of Brazil, 2018: The Action Plan for the Prevention and Control of Deforestation in the Legal Amazon (PPCDAm). http://redd.mma.gov.br/en/legal-and-public-policy-framework/ppcdam (Accessed October 11, 2021).

Ministry of Foreign Affairs, 2019: *Brazil's third biennial update report to the United Nations framework convention on climate change*. Brasilia, Brazil

Minx, J.C. et al., 2021: A comprehensive dataset for global, regional and national greenhouse gas emissions by sector 1970-2019 (Dataset). *Zenodo*, doi:10.5281/zenodo.5053056.

Mirzabaev, A., J. Wu, J. Evans, F. García-Oliva, I.A.G. Hussein, M.H. Iqbal, J. Kimutai, T. Knowles, F. Meza, D. Nedjraoui, F. Tena, M. Türkeş, R.J. Vázquez, M. Weltz, 2019: Desertification. In: *Climate Change and Land: an IPCC special report on climate change, desertification, land degradation, sustainable land management, food security, and greenhouse gas fluxes in terrestrial ecosystems* [Shukla, P.R., J. Skea, E. Calvo Buendia, V. Masson-Delmotte, H.-O. Pörtner, D.C. Roberts, P. Zhai, R. Slade, S. Connors, R. van Diemen, M. Ferrat, E. Haughey, S. Luz, S. Neogi, M. Pathak, J. Petzold, J. Portugal Pereira, P. Vyas, E. Huntley, K. Kissick, M. Belkacemi, and J. Malley (eds.)]. Cambridge University Press, Cambridge, UK and New York, NY, USA, pp. 249–343.

Mitchell, A.L., A. Rosenqvist, and B. Mora, 2017: Current remote sensing approaches to monitoring forest degradation in support of countries measurement, reporting and verification (MRV) systems for REDD+. *Carbon Balance Manag.*, **12(1)**, 9, doi:10.1186/s13021-017-0078-9.

Moffette, F. and H.K. Gibbs, 2021: Agricultural Displacement and Deforestation Leakage in the Brazilian Legal Amazon. *Land Econ.*, **97(1)**, 155–179, doi:10.3368/wple.97.1.040219-0045R.

Mohebalian, P.M. and F.X. Aguilar, 2016: Additionality and design of forest conservation programs: Insights from Ecuador's Socio Bosque Program. *For. Policy Econ.*, **71**, 103–114, doi:10.1016/j.forpol.2015.08.002.

Mondelaers, K., J. Aertsens, and G. Van Huylenbroeck, 2009: A meta-analysis of the differences in environmental impacts between organic and conventional farming. *Br. Food J.*, **111(10)**, 1098–1119, doi:10.1108/00070700910992925.

Moreira, F. et al., 2020a: Wildfire management in Mediterranean-type regions: paradigm change needed. *Environ. Res. Lett.*, **15(1)**, 011001, doi:10.1088/1748-9326/ab541e.

Moreira, M.M.R. et al., 2020b: Socio-environmental and land-use impacts of double-cropped maize ethanol in Brazil. *Nat. Sustain.*, **3(3)**, 209–216, doi:10.1038/s41893-019-0456-2.

Moser, S.C., S. Jeffress Williams, and D.F. Boesch, 2012: Wicked Challenges at Land's End: Managing Coastal Vulnerability Under Climate Change. *Annu. Rev. Environ. Resour.*, **37(1)**, 51–78, doi:10.1146/annurev-environ-021611-135158.

Mosnier, C. et al., 2019: Greenhouse gas abatement strategies and costs in French dairy production. *J. Clean. Prod.*, **236**, 117589, doi:10.1016/j.jclepro.2019.07.064.

Mostafa, E., A. Selders, R.S. Gates, and W. Buescher, 2020: Pig barns ammonia and greenhouse gas emission mitigation by slurry aeration and acid scrubber. *Environ. Sci. Pollut. Res.*, **27(9)**, 9444–9453, doi:10.1007/s11356-020-07613-x.

Mottet, A. et al., 2017a: Livestock: On our plates or eating at our table? A new analysis of the feed/food debate. *Glob. Food Sec.*, **14**, 1–8, doi:10.1016/j.gfs.2017.01.001.

Mottet, A. et al., 2017b: Climate change mitigation and productivity gains in livestock supply chains: insights from regional case studies. *Reg. Environ. Change*, **17(1)**, 129–141, doi:10.1007/s10113-016-0986-3.

Mouratiadou, I. et al., 2020: Sustainable intensification of crop residue exploitation for bioenergy: Opportunities and challenges. *GCB Bioenergy*, **12(1)**, 71–89, doi:10.1111/gcbb.12649.

Muchane, M.N. et al., 2020: Agroforestry boosts soil health in the humid and sub-humid tropics: A meta-analysis. *Agric. Ecosyst. Environ.*, **295**, 106899, doi:10.1016/j.agee.2020.106899.

Mueller, N.D. et al., 2012: Closing yield gaps through nutrient and water management. *Nature*, **490(7419)**, 254–257, doi:10.1038/nature11420.

Mueller, N.D. et al., 2016: Cooling of US Midwest summer temperature extremes from cropland intensification. *Nat. Clim. Change*, **6(3)**, 317–322, doi:10.1038/nclimate2825.

Muller, A. et al., 2017: Strategies for feeding the world more sustainably with organic agriculture. *Nat. Commun.*, **8(1)**, 1290, doi:10.1038/s41467-017-01410-w.

Munkholm, L.J. et al., 2020: *Vidensyntese Om Conservation Agriculture*. Aarhus Universitet, Tjele, Denmark, 134 pp.

Murdiyarso, D., E. Lilleskov, and R. Kolka, 2019: Tropical peatlands under siege: the need for evidence-based policies and strategies. *Mitig. Adapt. Strateg. Glob. Change*, **24(4)**, 493–505, doi:10.1007/s11027-019-9844-1.

Muri, H., 2018: The role of large—scale BECCS in the pursuit of the 1.5°C target: an Earth system model perspective. *Environ. Res. Lett.*, **13(4)**, 044010, doi:10.1088/1748-9326/aab324.

Murray, B.C., B.A. McCarl, and H.-C. Lee, 2004: Estimating Leakage from Forest Carbon Sequestration Programs. *Land Econ.*, **80(1)**, 109–124, doi:10.2307/3147147.

Murray, B.C., B. Sohngen, and M.T. Ross, 2007: Economic consequences of consideration of permanence, leakage and additionality for soil carbon sequestration projects. *Clim. Change*, **80(1–2)**, 127–143, doi:10.1007/s10584-006-9169-4.

Nabuurs, G.J., O. Masera, K. Andrasko, P. Benitez-Ponce, R. Boer, M. Dutschke, E. Elsiddig, J. Ford-Robertson, P. Frumhoff, T. Karjalainen, O. Krankina, W.A. Kurz, M. Matsumoto, W. Oyhantcabal, N.H. Ravindranath, M.J. Sanz Sanchez, X. Zhang, 2007: Forestry. In *Climate Change 2007: Mitigation. Contribution of Working Group III to the Fourth Assessment Report of the Intergovernmental Panel on Climate Change* [Metz, B., O.R. Davidson, P.R. Bosch, R. Dave, L.A. Meyer (eds.)]. Cambridge University Press, Cambridge, UK and New York, NY, USA, pp. 541–584.

Nabuurs, G.-J. et al., 2013: First signs of carbon sink saturation in European forest biomass. *Nat. Clim. Change*, **3(9)**, 792–796, doi:10.1038/nclimate1853.

Nabuurs, G.-J. et al., 2017: By 2050 the Mitigation Effects of EU Forests Could Nearly Double through Climate Smart Forestry. *Forests*, **8(12)**, 484, doi:10.3390/f8120484.

Nabuurs, G.-J. et al., 2019: Next-generation information to support a sustainable course for European forests. *Nat. Sustain.*, **2(9)**, 815–818, doi:10.1038/s41893-019-0374-3.

Næss, J.S., O. Cavalett, and F. Cherubini, 2021: The land—energy—water nexus of global bioenergy potentials from abandoned cropland. *Nat. Sustain.*, **4(6)**, 525–536, doi:10.1038/s41893-020-00680-5.

Nahuelhual, L. et al., 2007: Valuing Ecosystem Services of Chilean Temperate Rainforests. *Environ. Dev. Sustain.*, **9(4)**, 481–499, doi:10.1007/s10668-006-9033-8.

Namatsheve, T., R. Cardinael, M. Corbeels, and R. Chikowo, 2020: Productivity and biological N2-fixation in cereal-cowpea intercropping systems in sub-Saharan Africa. A review. *Agron. Sustain. Dev.*, **40(4)**, 30, doi:10.1007/s13593-020-00629-0.

Nasser, F., V.A. Maguire-Rajpaul, W.K. Dumenu, and G.Y. Wong, 2020: Climate-Smart Cocoa in Ghana: How Ecological Modernisation Discourse Risks Side-Lining Cocoa Smallholders. *Front. Sustain. Food Syst.*, **4**, 1–17. Doi:10.3389/fsufs.2020.00073.

Naudts, K. et al., 2016: Europe's forest management did not mitigate climate warming. *Science*, **351(6273)**, 597–600, doi:10.1126/science.aad7270.

Ndambi, O.A., D.E. Pelster, J.O. Owino, F. de Buisonjé, and T. Vellinga, 2019: Manure Management Practices and Policies in Sub-Saharan Africa: Implications on Manure Quality as a Fertilizer. *Front. Sustain. Food Syst.*, **3**, doi:10.3389/fsufs.2019.00029.

Ndung'u, P.W. et al., 2019: Improved region-specific emission factors for enteric methane emissions from cattle in smallholder mixed crop: livestock systems of Nandi County, Kenya. *Anim. Prod. Sci.*, **59(6)**, 1136, doi:10.1071/AN17809.

Nemecek, T., D. Dubois, O. Huguenin-Elie, and G. Gaillard, 2011: Life cycle assessment of Swiss farming systems: I. Integrated and organic farming. *Agric. Syst.*, **104(3)**, 217–232, doi:10.1016/j.agsy.2010.10.002.

Neogi, S., 2020a: Short Communication Ecosystem Sustainability for Coastal Wetlands. *COJRR*, **2**, 16–17, doi.org/10.31031/COJRR.2020.02.000546

Neogi, S., 2020b: Understanding soil carbon processes in the Indian Sundarbans to abate climate change. *Int. J. Sci. Eng. Res.*, **11(04)**, 1193–1195, doi:10.14299/ijser.2020.04.03.

Nepstad, D. et al., 2014: Slowing Amazon deforestation through public policy and interventions in beef and soy supply chains. *Science*, **344(6188)**, 1118–1123, doi:10.1126/science.1248525.

Nepstad, D.C., C.M. Stickler, B.S.- Filho, and F. Merry, 2008: Interactions among Amazon land use, forests and climate: prospects for a near-term forest tipping point. *Philos. Trans. R. Soc. B Biol. Sci.*, **363(1498)**, 1737–1746, doi:10.1098/rstb.2007.0036.

New York Declaration on Forests, 2021: Progress Report. Update on Goal 2. *Prog. Report. Updat. Goal 2.*, https://forestdeclaration.org/goals/goal-2 (Accessed May 14, 2021).

Niles, M.T. and S. Wiltshire, 2019: Tradeoffs in US dairy manure greenhouse gas emissions, productivity, climate, and manure management strategies. *Environ. Res. Commun.*, **1(7)**, 075003, doi:10.1088/2515-7620/ab2dec.

Ninan, K. N. and M. Inoue, 2017: *Building a Climate Resilient Economy and Society-Challenges and Opportunities*. Edward Elgar Publishing, Cheltenham, UK and Northampton, USA, 336 pp.

Ninan, K.N. and M. Inoue, 2013: Valuing forest ecosystem services: What we know and what we don't. *Ecol. Econ.*, **93**, 137–149, doi:10.1016/j.ecolecon.2013.05.005.

Ninan, K.N. and A. Kontoleon, 2016: Valuing forest ecosystem services and disservices – Case study of a protected area in India. *Ecosyst. Serv.*, **20**, 1–14, doi:10.1016/j.ecoser.2016.05.001.

Niwa, Y. et al., 2017: A 4D-Var inversion system based on the icosahedral grid model (NICAM-TM 4D-Var v1.0) – Part 2: Optimization scheme and identical twin experiment of atmospheric CO_2 inversion. *Geosci. Model Dev.*, **10(6)**, 2201–2219, doi:10.5194/gmd-10-2201-2017.

Novita, N. et al., 2021: Carbon Stocks from Peat Swamp Forest and Oil Palm Plantation in Central Kalimantan, Indonesia. In: *Climate Change Research, Policy and Actions in Indonesia* [Djalante, R., J. Jupesta, and E. Aldrian (eds.)]. Springer, Cham, Switzerland, pp. 203–227.

Nowicki, R., J. Thomson, D. Burkholder, J. Fourqurean, and M. Heithaus, 2017: Predicting seagrass recovery times and their implications following an extreme climate event. *Mar. Ecol. Prog. Ser.*, **567**, 79–93, doi:10.3354/meps12029.

Nugent, K.A. et al., 2019: Prompt active restoration of peatlands substantially reduces climate impact. *Environ. Res. Lett.*, **14(12)**, 124030, doi:10.1088/1748-9326/ab56e6.

Nunes, A.N., L. Lourenço, and A.C.C. Meira, 2016: Exploring spatial patterns and drivers of forest fires in Portugal (1980–2014). *Sci. Total Environ.*, **573**, 1190–1202, doi:10.1016/j.scitotenv.2016.03.121.

NYDF Assessment Partners, 2019: *Protecting and Restoring Forests: A Story of Large Commitments yet Limited Progress. New York Declaration on Forests Five-Year Assessment Report*. Climate Focus, Amsterdam, The Netherlands, 96 pp.

O'Halloran, T.L. et al., 2012: Radiative forcing of natural forest disturbances. *Glob. Change Biol.*, **18(2)**, 555–565, doi:10.1111/j.1365-2486.2011.02577.x.

Obersteiner, M. et al., 2016: Assessing the land resource–food price nexus of the Sustainable Development Goals. *Sci. Adv.*, **2(9)**, e1501499, doi:10.1126/sciadv.1501499.

OECD, 2012: OECD environmental outlook to 2050: the consequences of inaction. *Int. J. Sustain. High. Educ.*, **13(3)**, ijshe.2012.24913caa.010, doi:10.1108/ijshe.2012.24913caa.010.

OECD, 2021a: *Effective Carbon Rates 2021*. OECD Publishing, Paris, France.

OECD, 2021b: *Making Better Policies for Food Systems*. OECD Publishing, Paris, France, 280 pp.

OECD/FAO, 2019: *OECD-FAO Agricultural Outlook 2019-2028*, OECD Publishing, Paris/Food and Agriculture Organization of the United Nations, Rome. https://doi.org/10.4060/CA4076EN.

Ogle, S.M. et al., 2019: Climate and Soil Characteristics Determine Where No-Till Management Can Store Carbon in Soils and Mitigate Greenhouse Gas Emissions. *Sci. Rep.*, **9(1)**, 11665, doi:10.1038/s41598-019-47861-7.

Ojanen, P. and K. Minkkinen, 2020: Rewetting Offers Rapid Climate Benefits for Tropical and Agricultural Peatlands But Not for Forestry-Drained Peatlands. *Global Biogeochem. Cycles*, **34(7)**, doi:10.1029/2019GB006503.

Olsson, L., H. Barbosa, S. Bhadwal, A. Cowie, K. Delusca, D. Flores-Renteria, K. Hermans, E. Jobbagy, W. Kurz, D. Li, D.J. Sonwa, L. Stringer, 2019: Land Degradation. In: *Climate Change and Land: an IPCC special report on climate change, desertification, land degradation, sustainable land management, food security, and greenhouse gas fluxes in terrestrial ecosystems* [Shukla, P.R., J. Skea, E. Calvo Buendia, V. Masson-Delmotte, H.-O. Pörtner, D.C. Roberts, P. Zhai, R. Slade, S. Connors, R. van Diemen, M. Ferrat, E. Haughey, S. Luz, S. Neogi, M. Pathak, J. Petzold, J. Portugal Pereira, P. Vyas, E. Huntley, K. Kissick, M. Belkacemi, and J. Malley, (eds.)]. Cambridge University Press, Cambridge, UK and New York, NY, USA, pp. 345–436.

Oliver, C.D., N.T. Nassar, B.R. Lippke, and J.B. McCarter, 2014: Carbon, Fossil Fuel, and Biodiversity Mitigation With Wood and Forests. *J. Sustain. For.*, **33(3)**, 248–275, doi:10.1080/10549811.2013.839386.

Omondi, M.O. et al., 2016: Quantification of biochar effects on soil hydrological properties using meta-analysis of literature data. *Geoderma*, **274**, 28–34, doi:10.1016/j.geoderma.2016.03.029.

Oo, A.Z. et al., 2018: Methane and nitrous oxide emissions from conventional and modified rice cultivation systems in South India. *Agric. Ecosyst. Environ.*, **252**, 148–158, doi:10.1016/j.agee.2017.10.014.

Oreska, M.P.J. et al., 2020: The greenhouse gas offset potential from seagrass restoration. *Sci. Rep.*, **10(1)**, 7325, doi:10.1038/s41598-020-64094-1.

Ortega, L.A. and D. Martínez-Barón, 2018: Territorio Sostenible Adaptado al Clima – Cauca: Eje articulador del cambio climático con los instrumentos de gestión y política del departamento del Cauca. 23(1), 1–4.

Orth, R.J. et al., 2020: Restoration of seagrass habitat leads to rapid recovery of coastal ecosystem services. *Sci. Adv.*, **6** eabc6434, doi:10.1126/sciadv.abc6434.

Ouden, J. Den et al., 2020: *Kan uitstel van houtoogst bijdragen aan CO_2-mitigatie?* Wageningen University and Research, Wageningen, The Netherlands.

Ouyang, X. and S.Y. Lee, 2020: Improved estimates on global carbon stock and carbon pools in tidal wetlands. *Nat. Commun.*, **11(1)**, 317, doi:10.1038/s41467-019-14120-2.

Ouyang, Z. et al., 2016: Improvements in ecosystem services from investments in natural capital. *Science*, **352(6292)**, 1455–1459, doi:10.1126/science.aaf2295.

Page, S.E. and A.J. Baird, 2016: Peatlands and Global Change: Response and Resilience. *Annu. Rev. Environ. Resour.*, **41(1)**, 35–57, doi:10.1146/annurev-environ-110615-085520.

Page, S.E., J.O. Rieley, and C.J. Banks, 2011: Global and regional importance of the tropical peatland carbon pool. *Glob. Change Biol.*, **17(2)**, 798–818, doi:10.1111/j.1365-2486.2010.02279.x.

Palahí, M. et al., 2021: Concerns about reported harvests in European forests. *Nature*, **592(7856)**, E15–E17, doi:10.1038/s41586-021-03292-x.

Pandey, A. et al., 2014: Organic matter and water management strategies to reduce methane and nitrous oxide emissions from rice paddies in Vietnam. *Agric. Ecosyst. Environ.*, **196**, 137–146, doi:10.1016/j.agee.2014.06.010.

Pape, D. et al., 2016. *Managing Agricultural Land for Greenhouse Gas Mitigation within the United States*. Report prepared by ICF International under USDA Contract No. AG-3144-D-14-0292. July 2016.

Papworth, S. et al., 2017: The impact of gold mining and agricultural concessions on the tree cover and local communities in northern Myanmar. *Sci. Rep.*, **7(1)**, 46594, doi:10.1038/srep46594.

Parfitt, J., M. Barthel, and S. Macnaughton, 2010: Food waste within food supply chains: quantification and potential for change to 2050. *Philos. Trans. R. Soc. B Biol. Sci.*, **365(1554)**, 3065–3081, doi:10.1098/rstb.2010.0126.

Parodi, A. et al., 2018: The potential of future foods for sustainable and healthy diets. *Nat. Sustain.*, **1(12)**, 782–789, doi:10.1038/s41893-018-0189-7.

Patra, A., T. Park, M. Kim, and Z. Yu, 2017: Rumen methanogens and mitigation of methane emission by anti-methanogenic compounds and substances. *J. Anim. Sci. Biotechnol.*, **8(1)**, 13, doi:10.1186/s40104-017-0145-9.

Patra, A.K., 2016: Recent Advances in Measurement and Dietary Mitigation of Enteric Methane Emissions in Ruminants. *Front. Vet. Sci.*, **3**, doi:10.3389/fvets.2016.00039.

Patra, P.K. et al., 2018: Improved Chemical Tracer Simulation by MIROC4.0-based Atmospheric Chemistry-Transport Model (MIROC4-ACTM). *SOLA*, **14**, 91–96, doi:10.2151/sola.2018-016.

Pattanayak, S.K., D.E. Mercer, E. Sills, and J.C. Yang, 2003: Taking stock of agroforestry adoption studies. *Agrofor. Syst.*, **57**, 173–186, doi.org/10.1023/A:1024809108210.

Paustian, K. et al., 2016: Climate-smart soils. *Nature*, **532(7597)**, 49–57, doi:10.1038/nature17174.

Paustian, K., E. Larson, J. Kent, E. Marx, and A. Swan, 2019: Soil C Sequestration as a Biological Negative Emission Strategy. *Front. Clim.*, **1**, doi:10.3389/fclim.2019.00008.

Pearson, T.R.H., S. Brown, and F.M. Casarim, 2014: Carbon emissions from tropical forest degradation caused by logging. *Environ. Res. Lett.*, **9(3)**, 034017, doi:10.1088/1748-9326/9/3/034017.

Pearson, T.R.H., S. Brown, L. Murray, and G. Sidman, 2017: Greenhouse gas emissions from tropical forest degradation: an underestimated source. *Carbon Balance Manag.*, **12(1)**, 3, doi:10.1186/s13021-017-0072-2.

Pellerin, S. et al., 2017: Identifying cost-competitive greenhouse gas mitigation potential of French agriculture. *Environ. Sci. Policy*, **77**, 130–139, doi:10.1016/j.envsci.2017.08.003.

Pendleton, L. et al., 2012: Estimating global "blue carbon" emissions from conversion and degradation of vegetated coastal ecosystems. *PLoS One*, **7(9)**, e43542–e43542, doi:10.1371/journal.pone.0043542.

Pendrill, F., U.M. Persson, J. Godar, and T. Kastner, 2019a: Deforestation displaced: trade in forest-risk commodities and the prospects for a global forest transition. *Environ. Res. Lett.*, **14(5)**, 055003, doi:10.1088/1748-9326/ab0d41.

Pendrill, F. et al., 2019b: Agricultural and forestry trade drives large share of tropical deforestation emissions. *Glob. Environ. Change*, **56**(December 2018), 1–10, doi:10.1016/j.gloenvcha.2019.03.002.

Perugini, L. et al., 2017: Biophysical effects on temperature and precipitation due to land cover change. *Environ. Res. Lett.*, **12(5)**, 053002, doi:10.1088/1748-9326/aa6b3f.

Peters, M. et al., 2013: Challenges and opportunities for improving eco-efficiency of tropical forage-based systems to mitigate greenhouse gas emissions. *Trop. Grasslands - Forrajes Trop.*, **1(2)**, 156, doi:10.17138/TGFT(1)156-167.

Petersen, B. and S. Snapp, 2015: What is sustainable intensification? Views from experts. *Land use policy*, **46**, 1–10, doi:10.1016/j.landusepol.2015.02.002.

Peterson, C.A., L. Deiss, and A.C.M. Gaudin, 2020: Commercial integrated crop-livestock systems achieve comparable crop yields to specialized production systems: A meta-analysis. *PLoS One*, **15(5)**, e0231840, doi:10.1371/journal.pone.0231840.

Pfaff, A. and J. Robalino, 2017: Spillovers from Conservation Programs. *Annu. Rev. Resour. Econ.*, **9(1)**, 299–315, doi:10.1146/annurev-resource-100516-053543.

Pfaff, A. et al., 2007: Road Investments, Spatial Spillovers, and Deforestation in the Brazilian Amazon. *J. Reg. Sci.*, **47(1)**, 109–123, doi:10.1111/j.1467-9787.2007.00502.x.

Phalan, B., 2018: What Have We Learned from the Land Sparing-sharing Model? *Sustainability*, **10(6)**, 1760, doi:10.3390/su10061760.

Phelps, J., E.L. Webb, and A. Agrawal, 2010: Does REDD+ Threaten to Recentralize Forest Governance? *Science*, **328(5976)**, 312–313, doi:10.1126/science.1187774.

Pickering, N.K. et al., 2015: Animal board invited review: genetic possibilities to reduce enteric methane emissions from ruminants. *Animal*, **9(9)**, 1431–1440, doi:10.1017/S1751731115000968.

Pielke, R.A. et al., 2011: Land use/land cover changes and climate: modeling analysis and observational evidence. *WIREs Clim. Change*, **2(6)**, 828–850, doi:10.1002/wcc.144.

Pilli, R., G. Fiorese, and G. Grassi, 2015: EU mitigation potential of harvested wood products. *Carbon Balance Manag.*, **10(1)**, 6, doi:10.1186/s13021-015-0016-7.

Piva, J.T. et al., 2014: Soil gaseous N_2O and CH_4 emissions and carbon pool due to integrated crop-livestock in a subtropical Ferralsol. *Agric. Ecosyst. Environ.*, **190**, 87–93, doi:10.1016/j.agee.2013.09.008.

Podolyan, A., H.J. Di, and K.C. Cameron, 2020: Effect of plantain on nitrous oxide emissions and soil nitrification rate in pasture soil under a simulated urine patch in Canterbury, New Zealand. *J. Soils Sediments*, **20(3)**, 1468–1479, doi:10.1007/s11368-019-02505-1.

Poeplau, C. et al., 2011: Temporal dynamics of soil organic carbon after land-use change in the temperate zone - carbon response functions as a model approach. *Glob. Change Biol.*, **17(7)**, 2415–2427, doi:10.1111/j.1365-2486.2011.02408.x.

Pongratz, J., C.H. Reick, R.A. Houghton, and J.I. House, 2014: Terminology as a key uncertainty in net land use and land cover change carbon flux estimates. *Earth Syst. Dyn.*, **5(1)**, 177–195, doi:10.5194/esd-5-177-2014.

Pongratz, J. et al., 2018: Models meet data: Challenges and opportunities in implementing land management in Earth system models. *Glob. Change Biol.*, **24(4)**, 1470–1487, doi:10.1111/gcb.13988.

Poore, J. and T. Nemecek, 2018: Reducing food's environmental impacts through producers and consumers. *Science*, **360(6392)**, 987–992, doi:10.1126/science.aaq0216.

Popp, A. et al., 2014: Land-use transition for bioenergy and climate stabilization: model comparison of drivers, impacts and interactions with other land use based mitigation options. *Clim. Change*, **123(3–4)**, 495–509, doi:10.1007/s10584-013-0926-x.

Popp, A. et al., 2017: Land-use futures in the shared socio-economic pathways. *Glob. Environ. Change*, **42**, 331–345, doi:10.1016/j.gloenvcha.2016.10.002.

Post, M.J. et al., 2020: Scientific, sustainability and regulatory challenges of cultured meat. *Nat. Food*, **1(7)**, 403–415, doi:10.1038/s43016-020-0112-z.

Potapov, P. et al., 2017: The last frontiers of wilderness: Tracking loss of intact forest landscapes from 2000 to 2013. *Sci. Adv.*, **3(1)**, doi:10.1126/sciadv.1600821.

Powell, T.W.R. and T.M. Lenton, 2012: Future carbon dioxide removal via biomass energy constrained by agricultural efficiency and dietary trends. *Energy Environ. Sci.*, **5(8)**, 8116, doi:10.1039/c2ee21592f.

Powlson, D.S. et al., 2014: Limited potential of no-till agriculture for climate change mitigation. *Nat. Clim. Change*, **4(8)**, 678–683, doi:10.1038/nclimate2292.

Powlson, D.S., C.M. Stirling, C. Thierfelder, R.P. White, and M.L. Jat, 2016: Does conservation agriculture deliver climate change mitigation through soil carbon sequestration in tropical agro-ecosystems? *Agric. Ecosyst. Environ.*, **220**, 164–174, doi:10.1016/j.agee.2016.01.005.

Pradhan, B.B., R.M. Shrestha, N.T. Hoa, and Y. Matsuoka, 2017: Carbon prices and greenhouse gases abatement from agriculture, forestry and land use in Nepal. *Glob. Environ. Change*, **43**, 26–36, doi:10.1016/j.gloenvcha.2017.01.005.

Pradhan, B.B., A. Chaichaloempreecha, and B. Limmeechokchai, 2019: GHG mitigation in Agriculture, Forestry and Other Land Use (AFOLU) sector in Thailand. *Carbon Balance Manag.*, **14(1)**, 3, doi:10.1186/s13021-019-0119-7.

Pratt, K. and D. Moran, 2010: Evaluating the cost-effectiveness of global biochar mitigation potential. *Biomass and Bioenergy*, **34(8)**, 1149–1158, doi:10.1016/j.biombioe.2010.03.004.

Pretty, J., 2018: Intensification for redesigned and sustainable agricultural systems. *Science*, **362(6417)**, doi:10.1126/science.aav0294.

Pretty, J. et al., 2018: Global assessment of agricultural system redesign for sustainable intensification. *Nat. Sustain.*, **1(8)**, 441–446, doi:10.1038/s41893-018-0114-0.

Prosperi, P. et al., 2020: New estimates of greenhouse gas emissions from biomass burning and peat fires using MODIS Collection 6 burned areas. *Clim. Change*, **161(3)**, 415–432, doi:10.1007/s10584-020-02654-0.

Prudhomme, R. et al., 2020: Combining mitigation strategies to increase co-benefits for biodiversity and food security. *Environ. Res. Lett.*, **15(11)**, 114005, doi:10.1088/1748-9326/abb10a.

Puettmann, M., K. Sahoo, K. Wilson, and E. Oneil, 2020: Life cycle assessment of biochar produced from forest residues using portable systems. *J. Clean. Prod.*, **250**, 119564, doi:10.1016/j.jclepro.2019.119564.

Pugh, T.A.M. et al., 2015: Simulated carbon emissions from land-use change are substantially enhanced by accounting for agricultural management. *Environ. Res. Lett.*, **10(12)**, 124008, doi:10.1088/1748-9326/10/12/124008.

Pugh, T.A.M. et al., 2019: Role of forest regrowth in global carbon sink dynamics. *Proc. Natl. Acad. Sci.*, **116(10)**, 4382–4387, doi:10.1073/pnas.1810512116.

Qin, Z. et al., 2021: Delayed impact of natural climate solutions. *Glob. Change Biol.*, **27(2)**, 215–217, doi:10.1111/gcb.15413.

Quynh, V.D. and O. Sander, 2015: *Applying and scaling up Alternate Wetting and Drying for paddy rice in Vietnam*. International Rice Research Institute and the CGIAR Program on Climate Change, Agriculture and Food Security,.

Rahman, S.A. et al., 2019: Integrating bioenergy and food production on degraded landscapes in Indonesia for improved socioeconomic and environmental outcomes. *Food Energy Secur.*, **8(3)**, e00165, doi:10.1002/fes3.165.

Ramachandran Nair, P.K., V.D. Nair, B. Mohan Kumar, and J.M. Showalter, 2010: Carbon Sequestration in Agroforestry Systems. In: *Advances in Agronomy* [Sparks, D.L. (ed.)]. Academic Press, Elsevier, London, UK, pp. 237–307. https://doi.org/10.1016/S0065-2113(10)08005-3.

Ranjan, R., 2019: Assessing the impact of mining on deforestation in India. *Resour. Policy*, **60**, 23–35, doi:10.1016/j.resourpol.2018.11.022.

Ravikumar, A., A.M. Larson, A.E. Duchelle, R. Myers, and J. Gonzales Tovar, 2015: Multilevel governance challenges in transitioning towards a national approach for REDD+: evidence from 23 subnational REDD+ initiatives. *Int. J. Commons*, **9(2)**, 909, doi:10.18352/ijc.593.

Ravindranath, N.H., R.K. Chaturvedi, and P. Kumar, 2017: Paris Agreement; Research, Monitoring and Reporting Requirements for India. *Curr. Sci.*, **112(05)**, 916, doi:10.18520/cs/v112/i05/916-922.

Reddy, V.R., T. Chiranjeevi, and G. Syme, 2020: Inclusive sustainable intensification of agriculture in West Bengal, India: policy and institutional approaches. *Int. J. Agric. Sustain.*, **18(1)**, 70–83, doi:10.1080/14735903.2019.1698489.

Reiche, J. et al., 2021: Forest disturbance alerts for the Congo Basin using Sentinel-1. *Environ. Res. Lett.*, **16(2)**, 024005, doi:10.1088/1748-9326/abd0a8.

Reisinger, A. et al., 2021: How necessary and feasible are reductions of methane emissions from livestock to support stringent temperature goals? *Philos. Trans. R. Soc. A Math. Phys. Eng. Sci.*, **379(2210)**, 20200452, doi:10.1098/rsta.2020.0452.

Remy, C.C. et al., 2017: Different regional climatic drivers of Holocene large wildfires in boreal forests of northeastern America. *Environ. Res. Lett.*, **12(3)**, 035005, doi:10.1088/1748-9326/aa5aff.

Resosudarmo, I.A.P. et al., 2019: Indonesia's land reform: Implications for local livelihoods and climate change. *For. Policy Econ.*, **108**, 101903, doi:10.1016/j.forpol.2019.04.007.

RethinkX, 2019: *Rethinking Food and Agriculture*. RethinkX, 76 pp. https://www.rethinkx.com/food-and-agriculture (Accessed June 12, 2021).

Reyers, B. and E.R. Selig, 2020: Global targets that reveal the social–ecological interdependencies of sustainable development. *Nat. Ecol. Evol.*, **4(8)**, 1011–1019, doi:10.1038/s41559-020-1230-6.

Riahi, K. et al., 2017: The Shared Socioeconomic Pathways and their energy, land use, and greenhouse gas emissions implications: An overview. *Glob. Environ. Change*, **42**, 153–168, doi:10.1016/j.gloenvcha.2016.05.009.

Ricart, A.M. et al., 2020: High variability of Blue Carbon storage in seagrass meadows at the estuary scale. *Sci. Rep.*, **10(1)**, 5865, doi:10.1038/s41598-020-62639-y.

Rice, J., et al., 2018: *Summary for Policy Makers of the Regional Assessment Report on Biodiversity and Ecosystem Services for the Americas*. Intergovernmental Science Policy Platform on Biodiversity and Ecosystem Services (IPBES), Bonn, Germany, 341–356 pp.

Richards, D.R. and D.A. Friess, 2016: Rates and drivers of mangrove deforestation in Southeast Asia, 2000-2012. *Proc. Natl. Acad. Sci.*, **13(2)**, 344–349, doi:10.1073/pnas.1510272113.

Richards, P. and L. VanWey, 2015: Where Deforestation Leads to Urbanization: How Resource Extraction Is Leading to Urban Growth in the Brazilian Amazon. *Ann. Assoc. Am. Geogr.*, **105(4)**, 806–823, doi:10.1080/00045608.2015.1052337.

Ricketts, T.H. et al., 2010: Indigenous Lands, Protected Areas, and Slowing Climate Change. *PLoS Biol.*, **8(3)**, e1000331, doi:10.1371/journal.pbio.1000331.

Riggs, R. et al., 2018: Governance Challenges in an Eastern Indonesian Forest Landscape. *Sustainability*, **10(1)**, 169, doi:10.3390/su10010169.

Rights and Resources Initiative, 2018: *At a Crossroads. Consequential trends in recognition of community-based forest tenure from 2002-2017*. Rights and Resources Initiative, Washington, DC, USA, 60 pp.

Rigueiro-Rodróguez, A., J. McAdam, and M.R. Mosquera-Losada, 2009: *Agroforestry in Europe: Current Status and Future Prospects*. Springer, Dordrecht, The Netherlands. 450p.

Rivera-Monroy, V.H., E. Kristensen, S.Y. Lee, and R.R. Twilley, 2017: *Mangrove Ecosystems: A Global Biogeographic Perspective*. Springer International Publishing, Cham, Switzerland. 415p.

Robalino, J. and A. Pfaff, 2013: Ecopayments and Deforestation in Costa Rica: A Nationwide Analysis of PSA's Initial Years. *Land Econ.*, **89(3)**, 432–448, doi:10.3368/le.89.3.432.

Robalino, J., C. Sandoval, D.N. Barton, A. Chacon, and A. Pfaff, 2015: Evaluating Interactions of Forest Conservation Policies on Avoided Deforestation. *PLoS One*, **10(4)**, e0124910, doi:10.1371/journal.pone.0124910.

Roberts, K.G., B.A. Gloy, S. Joseph, N.R. Scott, and J. Lehmann, 2010: Life Cycle Assessment of Biochar Systems: Estimating the Energetic, Economic, and Climate Change Potential. *Environ. Sci. Technol.*, **44(2)**, 827–833, doi:10.1021/es902266r.

Robledo-Abad, C., et al., 2017: Bioenergy production and sustainable development: science base for policymaking remains limited. *GCB Bioenergy*, **9**, 541–556, doi:10.1111/gcbb.12338.

Rochedo, P.R.R. et al., 2018: The threat of political bargaining to climate mitigation in Brazil. *Nat. Clim. Change*, **8(8)**, 695–698, doi:10.1038/s41558-018-0213-y.

Rödenbeck, C., S. Houweling, M. Gloor, and M. Heimann, 2003: CO_2 flux history 1982–2001 inferred from atmospheric data using a global inversion of atmospheric transport. *Atmos. Chem. Phys.*, **3(6)**, 1919–1964, doi:10.5194/acp-3-1919-2003.

Rödenbeck, C., S. Zaehle, R. Keeling, and M. Heimann, 2018: How does the terrestrial carbon exchange respond to inter-annual climatic variations? A quantification based on atmospheric CO_2 data. *Biogeosciences*, **15(8)**, 2481–2498, doi:10.5194/bg-15-2481-2018.

Rodríguez Vásquez, M.J., A. Benoist, J. -M. Roda, and M. Fortin, 2021: Estimating Greenhouse Gas Emissions From Peat Combustion in Wildfires on Indonesian Peatlands, and Their Uncertainty. *Global Biogeochem. Cycles*, **35(2)**, doi:10.1029/2019GB006218.

Roe, S. et al., 2019: Contribution of the land sector to a 1.5°C world. *Nat. Clim. Change*, **9(11)**, 817–828, doi:10.1038/s41558-019-0591-9.

Roe, S. et al., 2021: Land-based measures to mitigate climate change: Potential and feasibility by country. *Glob. Change Biol.*, **27(23)**, 6025–6058, doi:10.1111/gcb.15873.

Rogelj, J. et al., 2011: Emission pathways consistent with a 2°C global temperature limit. *Nat. Clim. Change*, **1(8)**, 413–418, doi:10.1038/nclimate1258.

Rogelj, J. et al., 2017: Understanding the origin of Paris Agreement emission uncertainties. *Nat. Commun.*, **8(1)**, 15748, doi:10.1038/ncomms15748.

Rogelj, J. et al., 2018a: Scenarios towards limiting global mean temperature increase below 1.5°C. *Nat. Clim. Change*, **8(4)**, 325–332, doi:10.1038/s41558-018-0091-3.

Rogelj, J., D. Shindell, K. Jiang, S. Fifita, P. Forster, V. Ginzburg, C. Handa, H. Kheshgi, S. Kobayashi, E. Kriegler, L. Mundaca, R. Séférian, and M.V. Vilariño, 2018b: Mitigation Pathways Compatible with 1.5°C in the Context of Sustainable Development. In: *Global Warming of 1.5°C. An IPCC Special Report on the impacts of global warming of 1.5°C above pre-industrial levels and related global greenhouse gas emission pathways,*

7

in the context of strengthening the global response to the threat of climate change, sustainable development, and efforts to eradicate poverty [Masson-Delmotte, V., P. Zhai, H.-O. Pörtner, D. Roberts, J. Skea, P.R. Shukla, A. Pirani, W. Moufouma-Okia, C. Péan, R. Pidcock, S. Connors, J.B.R. Matthews, Y. Chen, X. Zhou, M.I. Gomis, E. Lonnoy, T. Maycock, M. Tignor, and T. Waterfield (eds.)]. Cambridge University Press, Cambridge, UK and New York, NY, USA, pp. 93–174.

Rogissart, L., C. Foucherot, and V. Bellassen, 2019: *Food policies and climate: a literature review*. I4CE, Institute for Climate Economics, Paris. https://www.i4ce.org/wp-core/wp-content/uploads/2019/03/0306-I4CE2984-PolitiquesAlimentairesEtClimat-Etude24p-VA_V2.pdf (Accessed March 3, 2021).

Rokityanskiy, D. et al., 2007: Geographically explicit global modeling of land-use change, carbon sequestration, and biomass supply. *Technol. Forecast. Soc. Change*, **74(7)**, 1057–1082, doi:10.1016/j.techfore.2006.05.022.

Rolls, W. and P.M. Forster, 2020: Quantifying forest growth uncertainty on carbon payback times in a simple biomass carbon model. *Environ. Res. Commun.*, **2(4)**, 045001, doi:10.1088/2515-7620/ab7ff3.

Romanovskaya, A.A. et al., 2020: Greenhouse gas fluxes and mitigation potential for managed lands in the Russian Federation. *Mitig. Adapt. Strateg. Glob. Change*, **25(4)**, 661–687, doi:10.1007/s11027-019-09885-2.

Roopsind, A., B. Sohngen, and J. Brandt, 2019: Evidence that a national REDD+ program reduces tree cover loss and carbon emissions in a high forest cover, low deforestation country. *Proc. Natl. Acad. Sci.*, **116(49)**, 24492–24499, doi:10.1073/pnas.1904027116.

Roque, B.M., J.K. Salwen, R. Kinley, and E. Kebreab, 2019: Inclusion of Asparagopsis armata in lactating dairy cows' diet reduces enteric methane emission by over 50 percent. *J. Clean. Prod.*, **234**, 132–138, doi:10.1016/j.jclepro.2019.06.193.

Rosa, I.M.D. et al., 2017: Multiscale scenarios for nature futures. *Nat. Ecol. Evol.*, **1(10)**, 1416–1419, doi:10.1038/s41559-017-0273-9.

Rosa, L., J.A. Reimer, M.S. Went, and P. D'Odorico, 2020: Hydrological limits to carbon capture and storage. *Nat. Sustain.*, **3(8)**, 658–666, doi:10.1038/s41893-020-0532-7.

Rose, S.K. et al., 2020: An overview of the Energy Modeling Forum 33rd study: assessing large-scale global bioenergy deployment for managing climate change. *Clim. Change*, **163(3)**, 1539–1551, doi:10.1007/s10584-020-02945-6.

Rosenstock, T. et al., 2014: Agroforestry with N2-fixing trees: sustainable development's friend or foe? *Curr. Opin. Environ. Sustain.*, **6**, 15–21, doi:10.1016/j.cosust.2013.09.001.

Rosenstock, T.S. et al., 2019: A Planetary Health Perspective on Agroforestry in Sub-Saharan Africa. *One Earth*, **1(3)**, 330–344, doi:10.1016/j.oneear.2019.10.017.

Rosenzweig, C. et al., 2020: Climate change responses benefit from a global food system approach. *Nat. Food*, **1(2)**, 94–97, doi:10.1038/s43016-020-0031-z.

Rudel, T.K., R. Defries, G.P. Asner, and W.F. Laurance, 2009: Changing drivers of deforestation and new opportunities for conservation. *Conserv. Biol.*, 23:1396-1405 , doi:10.1111/j.1523-1739.2009.01332.x.

Ruffault, J. et al., 2020: Increased likelihood of heat-induced large wildfires in the Mediterranean Basin. *Sci. Rep.*, **10(1)**, 13790, doi:10.1038/s41598-020-70069-z.

Rulli, M.C., D. Bellomi, A. Cazzoli, G. De Carolis, and P. D'Odorico, 2016: The water-land-food nexus of first-generation biofuels. *Sci. Rep.*, **6(1)**, 22521, doi:10.1038/srep22521.

Ruseva, T. et al., 2017: Additionality and permanence standards in California's Forest Offset Protocol: A review of project and program level implications. *J. Environ. Manage.*, **198**, 277–288, doi:10.1016/j.jenvman.2017.04.082.

Russell-Smith, J. et al., 2017: Can savanna burning projects deliver measurable greenhouse emissions reductions and sustainable livelihood opportunities in fire-prone settings? *Clim. Change*, **140(1)**, 47–61, doi:10.1007/s10584-013-0910-5.

Rust, N.A. et al., 2020: How to transition to reduced-meat diets that benefit people and the planet. *Sci. Total Environ.*, **718**, 137208, doi:10.1016/j.scitotenv.2020.137208.

Ryals, R., M.D. Hartman, W.J. Parton, M.S. DeLonge, and W.L. Silver, 2015: Long-term climate change mitigation potential with organic matter management on grasslands. *Ecol. Appl.*, **25(2)**, 531–545, doi:10.1890/13-2126.1.

Saderne, V. et al., 2019: Role of carbonate burial in Blue Carbon budgets. *Nat. Commun.*, **10(1)**, 1106, doi:10.1038/s41467-019-08842-6.

Saj, S., E. Torquebiau, E. Hainzelin, J. Pages, and F. Maraux, 2017: The way forward: An agroecological perspective for Climate-Smart Agriculture. *Agric. Ecosyst. Environ.*, **250**, 20–24, doi:10.1016/j.agee.2017.09.003.

Salmon, G.R. et al., 2018: The greenhouse gas abatement potential of productivity improving measures applied to cattle systems in a developing region. *Animal*, **12(4)**, 844–852, doi:10.1017/S1751731117002294.

Salzman, J., G. Bennett, N. Carroll, A. Goldstein, and M. Jenkins, 2018: The global status and trends of Payments for Ecosystem Services. *Nat. Sustain.*, **1(3)**, 136–144, doi:10.1038/s41893-018-0033-0.

Sanchez-Monedero, M.A. et al., 2018: Role of biochar as an additive in organic waste composting. *Bioresour. Technol.*, **247**, 1155–1164, doi:10.1016/j.biortech.2017.09.193.

Sander, B.O., M. Samson, and R.J. Buresh, 2014: Methane and nitrous oxide emissions from flooded rice fields as affected by water and straw management between rice crops. *Geoderma*, 235-236: 355-362, doi:10.1016/j.geoderma.2014.07.020.

Sanderman, J., T. Hengl, and G.J. Fiske, 2017: Soil carbon debt of 12,000 years of human land use. *Proc. Natl. Acad. Sci.*, **114(36)**, 9575–9580, doi:10.1073/pnas.1706103114.

Santos, P.Z.F., R. Crouzeilles, and J.B.B. Sansevero, 2019: Can agroforestry systems enhance biodiversity and ecosystem service provision in agricultural landscapes? A meta-analysis for the Brazilian Atlantic Forest. *For. Ecol. Manage.*, **433**, 140–145, doi:10.1016/j.foreco.2018.10.064.

Sapkota, T.B. et al., 2014: Precision nutrient management in conservation agriculture based wheat production of Northwest India: Profitability, nutrient use efficiency and environmental footprint. *F. Crop. Res.*, **155**, 233–244, doi:10.1016/j.fcr.2013.09.001.

Sapkota, T.B. et al., 2019: Cost-effective opportunities for climate change mitigation in Indian agriculture. *Sci. Total Environ.*, **655**, 1342–1354, doi:10.1016/j.scitotenv.2018.11.225.

Sapkota, T.B. et al., 2021: Crop nutrient management using Nutrient Expert improves yield, increases farmers' income and reduces greenhouse gas emissions. *Sci. Rep.*, **11(1)**, 1564, doi:10.1038/s41598-020-79883-x.

Sasmito, S.D. et al., 2019: Effect of land-use and land-cover change on mangrove blue carbon: A systematic review. *Glob. Change Biol.*, **25(12)**, 4291–4302, doi:10.1111/gcb.14774.

Sathre, R. and J. O'Connor, 2010: Meta-analysis of greenhouse gas displacement factors of wood product substitution. *Environ. Sci. Policy*, **13(2)**, 104–114, doi:10.1016/j.envsci.2009.12.005.

Satija, A. and F.B. Hu, 2018: Plant-based diets and cardiovascular health. *Trends Cardiovasc. Med.*, **28(7)**, 437–441, doi:10.1016/j.tcm.2018.02.004.

SCBD, 2009: *Connecting Biodiversity and Climate Change Mitigation and Adaptation*. Secretariat of the Convention on Biological Diversity, Montreal, Canada, 127 pp.

SCBD, 2020: *Global Biodiversity Outlook 5*. Secretariat of the Convention on Biological Diversity, Montreal, Canada, 212 pp.

Schabel, H.G. and M. Pecore, 1997: Silviculture on Wisconsin's Menominee Indian Reservation—Is it Dauerwald? *Proceedings, XI World Forestry Congress*, Antalya, Turkey. Vol. D. 97–101.

Scherhaufer, S., G. Moates, H. Hartikainen, K. Waldron, and G. Obersteiner, 2018: Environmental impacts of food waste in Europe. *Waste Manag.*, **77**, 98–113, doi:10.1016/j.wasman.2018.04.038.

Scheutz, C. and A.M. Fredenslund, 2019: Total methane emission rates and losses from 23 biogas plants. *Waste Manag.*, **97**, 38–46, doi:10.1016/j.wasman.2019.07.029.

Schimel, D., B.B. Stephens, and J.B. Fisher, 2015: Effect of increasing CO_2 on the terrestrial carbon cycle. *Proc. Natl. Acad. Sci.*, **112(2)**, 436–441, doi:10.1073/pnas.1407302112.

Schmidt, S.M., M. Belisle, and W.B. Frommer, 2020: The evolving landscape around genome editing in agriculture. *EMBO Rep.*, **21(6)**, doi:10.15252/embr.202050680.

Schulze, K., Ž. Malek, and P.H. Verburg, 2020: The Impact of Accounting for Future Wood Production in Global Vertebrate Biodiversity Assessments. *Environ. Manage.*, **66(3)**, 460–475, doi:10.1007/s00267-020-01322-4.

Schurgers, G., A. Ahlström, A. Arneth, T.A.M. Pugh, and B. Smith, 2018: Climate Sensitivity Controls Uncertainty in Future Terrestrial Carbon Sink. *Geophys. Res. Lett.*, **45(9)**, 4329–4336, doi:10.1029/2018GL077528.

Schuur, E.A.G. et al., 2015: Climate change and the permafrost carbon feedback. *Nature*, **520(7546)**, 171–179, doi:10.1038/nature14338.

Schwaab, J. et al., 2020: Increasing the broad-leaved tree fraction in European forests mitigates hot temperature extremes. *Sci. Rep.*, **10(1)**, 14153, doi:10.1038/s41598-020-71055-1.

Scialabba, N.E.-H. and M. Müller-Lindenlauf, 2010: Organic agriculture and climate change. *Renew. Agric. Food Syst.*, **25(2)**, 158–169, doi:10.1017/S1742170510000116.

Scott, A.C., D.M.J.S. Bowman, W.J. Bond, S.J. Pyne, and M.E., 2014: *Fire on Earth: An Introduction*. Wiley-Blackwell, 88–91 pp.

Searchinger, T.D. et al., 2009: Fixing a Critical Climate Accounting Error. *Science*, **326(5952)**, 527–528, doi:10.1126/science.1178797.

Searchinger, T.D., T. Beringer, and A. Strong, 2017: Does the world have low-carbon bioenergy potential from the dedicated use of land? *Energy Policy*, **110**, 434–446, doi:10.1016/j.enpol.2017.08.016.

Seddon, N. et al., 2020: *Nature-based solutions in nationally determined contributions*. IUCN, University of Oxford, Gland and Oxford, UK, 62 pp.

Sefeedpari, P. et al., 2019: Technical, environmental and cost-benefit assessment of manure management chain: A case study of large scale dairy farming. *J. Clean. Prod.*, **233**, 857–868, doi:10.1016/j.jclepro.2019.06.146.

Seidl, R. et al., 2017: Forest disturbances under climate change. *Nat. Clim. Change*, **7(6)**, 395–402, doi:10.1038/nclimate3303.

Sendzimir, J., C.P. Reij, and P. Magnuszewski, 2011: Rebuilding Resilience in the Sahel: Regreening in the Maradi and Zinder Regions of Niger. *Ecol. Soc.*, **16(3)**, art1, doi:10.5751/ES-04198-160301.

Senf, C. and R. Seidl, 2021: Mapping the forest disturbance regimes of Europe. *Nat. Sustain.*, **4(1)**, 63–70, doi:10.1038/s41893-020-00609-y.

Seppälä, J. et al., 2019: Effect of increased wood harvesting and utilization on required greenhouse gas displacement factors of wood-based products and fuels. *J. Environ. Manage.*, **247**, 580–587, doi:10.1016/j.jenvman.2019.06.031.

Setyanto, P. et al., 2018: Alternate wetting and drying reduces methane emission from a rice paddy in Central Java, Indonesia without yield loss. *Soil Sci. Plant Nutr.*, **64(1)**, 23–30, doi:10.1080/00380768.2017.1409600.

Seufert, V. and N. Ramankutty, 2017: Many shades of gray—The context-dependent performance of organic agriculture. *Sci. Adv.*, **3(3)**, doi:10.1126/sciadv.1602638.

Seufert, V., N. Ramankutty, and J.A. Foley, 2012: Comparing the yields of organic and conventional agriculture. *Nature*, **485(7397)**, 229–232, doi:10.1038/nature11069.

Shin, S.-R. et al., 2019: Effects of pig slurry acidification on methane emissions during storage and subsequent biogas production. *Water Res.*, **152**, 234–240, doi:10.1016/j.watres.2019.01.005.

Short, F.T., S. Kosten, P.A. Morgan, S. Malone, and G.E. Moore, 2016: Impacts of climate change on submerged and emergent wetland plants. *Aquat. Bot.*, **135**, 3–17, doi:10.1016/j.aquabot.2016.06.006.

Sibayan, E.B. et al., 2018: Effects of alternate wetting and drying technique on greenhouse gas emissions from irrigated rice paddy in Central Luzon, Philippines. *Soil Sci. Plant Nutr.*, **64(1)**, 39–46, doi:10.1080/00380768.2017.1401906.

Sida, T.S., F. Baudron, H. Kim, and K.E. Giller, 2018: Climate-smart agroforestry: Faidherbia albida trees buffer wheat against climatic extremes in the Central Rift Valley of Ethiopia. *Agric. For. Meteorol.*, **248**, 339–347, doi:10.1016/j.agrformet.2017.10.013.

Sidik, F., M. Fernanda Adame, and C.E. Lovelock, 2019: Carbon sequestration and fluxes of restored mangroves in abandoned aquaculture ponds. *J. Indian Ocean Reg.*, **15(2)**, 177–192, doi:10.1080/19480881.2019.1605659.

Sills, E.O. et al., 2015: Estimating the Impacts of Local Policy Innovation: The Synthetic Control Method Applied to Tropical Deforestation. *PLoS One*, **10(7)**, e0132590, doi:10.1371/journal.pone.0132590.

Silva, J.V. et al., 2021: How sustainable is sustainable intensification? Assessing yield gaps at field and farm level across the globe. *Glob. Food Sec.*, **30**, 100552, doi:10.1016/j.gfs.2021.100552.

Silva Junior, C.H.L. et al., 2021: The Brazilian Amazon deforestation rate in 2020 is the greatest of the decade. *Nat. Ecol. Evol.*, **5(2)**, 144–145, doi:10.1038/s41559-020-01368-x.

Silvani, L. et al., 2019: Can biochar and designer biochar be used to remediate per- and polyfluorinated alkyl substances (PFAS) and lead and antimony contaminated soils? *Sci. Total Environ.*, **694**, 133693, doi:10.1016/j.scitotenv.2019.133693.

Simmonds, M.B. et al., 2021: Impacts of California's climate-relevant land use policy scenarios on terrestrial carbon emissions (CO_2 and CH_4) and wildfire risk. *Environ. Res. Lett.*, **16(1)**, 014044, doi:10.1088/1748-9326/abcc8d.

Simon, P.L., C.A.M. de Klein, W. Worth, A.J. Rutherford, and J. Dieckow, 2019: The efficacy of Plantago lanceolata for mitigating nitrous oxide emissions from cattle urine patches. *Sci. Total Environ.*, **691**, 430–441, doi:10.1016/j.scitotenv.2019.07.141.

Simon, P.L. et al., 2020: Does Brachiaria humidicola and dicyandiamide reduce nitrous oxide and ammonia emissions from cattle urine patches in the subtropics? *Sci. Total Environ.*, **720**, 137692, doi:10.1016/j.scitotenv.2020.137692.

Simonet, G., J. Subervie, D. Ezzine-de-Blas, M. Cromberg, and A.E. Duchelle, 2019: Effectiveness of a REDD+ Project in Reducing Deforestation in the Brazilian Amazon. *Am. J. Agric. Econ.*, **101(1)**, 211–229, doi:10.1093/ajae/aay028.

Sinare, H. and L.J. Gordon, 2015: Ecosystem services from woody vegetation on agricultural lands in Sudano-Sahelian West Africa. *Agric. Ecosyst. Environ.*, **200**, 186–199, doi:10.1016/j.agee.2014.11.009.

Sinclair, F. and R. Coe, 2019: The Options by Context Approach: A Paradigm Shift in Agronomy. *Exp. Agric.*, **55(S1)**, 1–13, doi:10.1017/S0014479719000139.

Singh, B.P., A.L. Cowie, and R.J. Smernik, 2012: Biochar Carbon Stability in a Clayey Soil As a Function of Feedstock and Pyrolysis Temperature. *Environ. Sci. Technol.*, **46(21)**, 11770–11778, doi:10.1021/es302545b.

Singh, B.P. et al., 2015: In Situ Persistence and Migration of Biochar Carbon and Its Impact on Native Carbon Emission in Contrasting Soils under Managed Temperate Pastures. *PLoS One*, **10(10)**, e0141560, doi:10.1371/journal.pone.0141560.

Six, J. et al., 2004: The potential to mitigate global warming with no-tillage management is only realized when practised in the long term. *Glob. Change Biol.*, **10(2)**, 155–160, doi:10.1111/j.1529-8817.2003.00730.x.

Skinner, C. et al., 2014: Greenhouse gas fluxes from agricultural soils under organic and non-organic management — A global meta-analysis. *Sci. Total Environ.*, **468–469**, 553–563, doi:10.1016/j.scitotenv.2013.08.098.

Sloan, S. et al., 2018: Infrastructure development and contested forest governance threaten the Leuser Ecosystem, Indonesia. *Land use policy*, **77**, 298–309, doi:10.1016/j.landusepol.2018.05.043.

Smith, L.G., G.J.D. Kirk, P.J. Jones, and A.G. Williams, 2019: The greenhouse gas impacts of converting food production in England and Wales to organic methods. *Nat. Commun.*, **10(1)**, 4641, doi:10.1038/s41467-019-12622-7.

Smith, P., 2014: Do grasslands act as a perpetual sink for carbon? *Glob. Change Biol.*, **20(9)**, 2708–2711, doi:10.1111/gcb.12561.

7

Smith, P., 2016: Soil carbon sequestration and biochar as negative emission technologies. *Glob. Change Biol.*, **22(3)**, 1315–1324, doi:10.1111/gcb.13178.

Smith, P., D. Powlson, M. Glendining, and J. Smith, 1997: Potential for carbon sequestration in European soils: preliminary estimates for five scenarios using results from long-term experiments. *Glob. Change Biol.*, **3(1)**, 67–79, doi:10.1046/j.1365-2486.1997.00055.x.

Smith, P. et al., 2008: Greenhouse gas mitigation in agriculture. *Philos. Trans. R. Soc. B Biol. Sci.*, **363(1492)**, 789–813, doi:10.1098/rstb.2007.2184.

Smith, P., M. Bustamante, H. Ahammad, H. Clark, H. Dong, E.A. Elsiddig, H. Haberl, R. Harper, J. House, M. Jafari, O. Masera, C. Mbow, N.H. Ravindranath, C.W. Rice, C. Robledo Abad, A. Romanovskaya, F. Sperling, and F. Tubiello, 2014: Agriculture, Forestry and Other Land Use (AFOLU). In: *Climate Change 2014: Mitigation of Climate Change. Contribution of Working Group III to the Fifth Assessment Report of the Intergovernmental Panel on Climate Change* [Edenhofer, O., R. Pichs-Madruga, Y. Sokona, E. Farahani, S. Kadner, K. Seyboth, A. Adler, I. Baum, S. Brunner, P. Eickemeier, B. Kriemann, J. Savolainen, S. Schlömer, C. von Stechow, T. Zwickel, and J.C. Minx (eds.)]. Cambridge University Press, Cambridge, UK and New York, NY, USA, pp. 811–922.

Smith, P. et al., 2016: Biophysical and economic limits to negative CO_2 emissions. *Nat. Clim. Change*, **6(1)**, 42–50, doi:10.1038/nclimate2870.

Smith, P., J. Nkem, K. Calvin, D. Campbell, F. Cherubini, G. Grassi, V. Korotkov, A.L. Hoang, S. Lwasa, P. McElwee, E. Nkonya, N. Saigusa, J.-F. Soussana, and M.A. Taboada, 2019a: Interlinkages Between Desertification, Land Degradation, Food Security and Greenhouse Gas Fluxes: Synergies, Trade-offs and Integrated Response Options. In: *Climate Change and Land: an IPCC special report on climate change, desertification, land degradation, sustainable land management, food security, and greenhouse gas fluxes in terrestrial ecosystems* [Shukla, P.R., J. Skea, E. Calvo Buendia, V. Masson-Delmotte, H.- O. Portner, D. C. Roberts, P. Zhai, R. Slade, S. Connors, R. van Diemen, M. Ferrat, E. Haughey, S. Luz, S. Neogi, M. Pathak, J. Petzold, J. Portugal Pereira, P. Vyas, E. Huntley, K. Kissick, M. Belkacemi, and J. Malley (eds.)]. Cambridge University Press, Cambridge, UK and New York, NY, USA, pp. 551–672.

Smith, P. et al., 2019b: Land-Management Options for Greenhouse Gas Removal and Their Impacts on Ecosystem Services and the Sustainable Development Goals. *Annu. Rev. Environ. Resour.*, **44(1)**, 255–286, doi:10.1146/annurev-environ-101718-033129.

Smith, P. et al., 2020a: Which practices co-deliver food security, climate change mitigation and adaptation, and combat land degradation and desertification? *Glob. Change Biol.*, **26(3)**, 1532–1575, doi:10.1111/gcb.14878.

Smith, P. et al., 2020b: How to measure, report and verify soil carbon change to realize the potential of soil carbon sequestration for atmospheric greenhouse gas removal. *Glob. Change Biol.*, **26(1)**, 219–241, doi:10.1111/gcb.14815.

Smith, V., 1997: Mispriced Planet. *Perspect. Regul.*, **20**, 16–17.

Smyth, C.E., Z. Xu, T.C. Lemprière, and W.A. Kurz, 2020: Climate change mitigation in British Columbia's forest sector: GHG reductions, costs, and environmental impacts. *Carbon Balance Manag.*, **15(1)**, 21, doi:10.1186/s13021-020-00155-2.

Snapp, S. et al., 2021: *Delivering climate change outcomes with agroecology in low- and middle-income countries: evidence and actions needed*. CGIAR Research Program on Climate Change, Agriculture and Food Security (CCAFS), Wageningen, The Netherlands, 16 pp.

Södra, 2021: https://www.sodra.com/sv/se/. Swedish forest owners association, Vaxjo, Sweden.

Soergel, B. et al., 2021: Combining ambitious climate policies with efforts to eradicate poverty. *Nat. Commun.*, **12(1)**, 2342, doi:10.1038/s41467-021-22315-9.

Sohngen, BS. Brown, 2004: Measuring leakage from carbon projects in open economies: a stop timber harvesting project in Bolivia as a case study. *Can. J. For. Res.*, **34(4)**, 829–839, doi:10.1139/x03-249.

Soimakallio, S., L. Saikku, L. Valsta, and K. Pingoud, 2016: Climate Change Mitigation Challenge for Wood Utilization—The Case of Finland. *Environ. Sci. Technol.*, **50(10)**, 5127–5134, doi:10.1021/acs.est.6b00122.

Sokolov, V.K. et al., 2021: Dairy manure acidification reduces CH_4 emissions over short and long-term. *Environ. Technol.*, **42(18)**, 2797–2804, doi:10.1080/09593330.2020.1714744.

Somarriba, E. et al., 2013: Carbon stocks and cocoa yields in agroforestry systems of Central America. *Agric. Ecosyst. Environ.*, **173**, 46–57, doi:10.1016/j.agee.2013.04.013.

Sombroek, W.G., F. Nachtergaele, and A. Hebel, 1993: Amounts, Dynamics and Sequestering of Carbon in Tropical and Subtropical Soils. *Ambio*, **7**, 417–426.

Sommer, R. and D. Bossio, 2014: Dynamics and climate change mitigation potential of soil organic carbon sequestration. *J. Environ. Manage.*, **144**, 83–87, doi:10.1016/j.jenvman.2014.05.017.

Song, X.-P. et al., 2018: Global land change from 1982 to 2016. *Nature*, **560(7720)**, 639–643, doi:10.1038/s41586-018-0411-9.

Song, X., G. Pan, C. Zhang, L. Zhang, and H. Wang, 2016: Effects of biochar application on fluxes of three biogenic greenhouse gases: a meta-analysis. *Ecosyst. Heal. Sustain.*, 2(2):e01202, doi:10.1002/ehs2.1202.

Sonntag, S., J. Pongratz, C.H. Reick, and H. Schmidt, 2016: Reforestation in a high-CO_2 world – higher mitigation potential than expected, lower adaptation potential than hoped for. *Geophys. Res. Lett.*, **43(12)**, 6546–6553, doi:10.1002/2016GL068824.

Sonter, L.J., D.J. Barrett, C.J. Moran, and B.S. Soares-Filho, 2015: Carbon emissions due to deforestation for the production of charcoal used in Brazil's steel industry. *Nat. Clim. Change*, **5(4)**, 359–363, doi:10.1038/nclimate2515.

Soterroni, A.C. et al., 2019: Expanding the Soy Moratorium to Brazil's Cerrado. *Sci. Adv.*, **5(7)**, doi:10.1126/sciadv.aav7336.

Souza, Jr, C.M. et al., 2013: Ten-Year Landsat Classification of Deforestation and Forest Degradation in the Brazilian Amazon. *Remote Sens.*, **5(11)**, 5493–5513, doi:10.3390/rs5115493.

Springmann, M., H.C.J. Godfray, M. Rayner, and P. Scarborough, 2016: Analysis and valuation of the health and climate change cobenefits of dietary change. *Proc. Natl. Acad. Sci.*, **113(15)**, 4146–4151, doi:10.1073/pnas.1523119113.

Springmann, M. et al., 2018: Options for keeping the food system within environmental limits. *Nature*, **562(7728)**, 519–525, doi:10.1038/s41586-018-0594-0.

Sriphirom, P., A. Chidthaisong, and S. Towprayoon, 2019: Effect of alternate wetting and drying water management on rice cultivation with low emissions and low water used during wet and dry season. *J. Clean. Prod.*, **223**, 980–988, doi:10.1016/j.jclepro.2019.03.212.

Sriphirom, P., A. Chidthaisong, K. Yagi, S. Tripetchkul, and S. Towprayoon, 2020: Evaluation of biochar applications combined with alternate wetting and drying (AWD) water management in rice field as a methane mitigation option for farmers' adoption. *Soil Sci. Plant Nutr.*, **66(1)**, 235–246, doi:10.1080/00380768.2019.1706431.

Stanturf, J.A. et al., 2015: *Forest Landscape Restoration as a Key Component of Climate Change Mitigation and Adaptation*. International Union of Forest Research Organizations, Vienna, Austria, 75 pp.

Staples, M.D., R. Malina, and S.R.H. Barrett, 2017: The limits of bioenergy for mitigating global life-cycle greenhouse gas emissions from fossil fuels. *Nat. Energy*, **2(2)**, 16202, doi:10.1038/nenergy.2016.202.

Stenzel, F., D. Gerten, C. Werner, and J. Jägermeyr, 2019: Freshwater requirements of large-scale bioenergy plantations for limiting global warming to 1.5°C. *Environ. Res. Lett.*, **14(8)**, 084001, doi:10.1088/1748-9326/ab2b4b.

Stenzel, F., D. Gerten, and N. Hanasaki, 2020: Global scenarios of irrigation water use for bioenergy production: a systematic review. *Hydrol. Earth Syst. Sci.* 25, 4, 1711-1726, doi:10.5194/hess-2020-338.

Stephens, N. et al., 2018: Bringing cultured meat to market: Technical, socio-political, and regulatory challenges in cellular agriculture. *Trends Food Sci. Technol.*, **78**(June 2017), 155–166, doi:10.1016/j.tifs.2018.04.010.

Stephens, S.L. et al., 2020: Fire and climate change: conserving seasonally dry forests is still possible. *Front. Ecol. Environ.*, **18(6)**, 354–360, doi:10.1002/fee.2218.

Stern, T. et al., 2018: Perceptions on the Importance of Forest Sector Innovations: Biofuels, Biomaterials, or Niche Products? *Forests*, **9(5)**, 255, doi:10.3390/f9050255.

Stevanović, M. et al., 2017: Mitigation Strategies for Greenhouse Gas Emissions from Agriculture and Land-Use Change: Consequences for Food Prices. *Environ. Sci. Technol.*, **51(1)**, 365–374, doi:10.1021/acs.est.6b04291.

Strandberg, G. and E. Kjellström, 2019: Climate Impacts from Afforestation and Deforestation in Europe. *Earth Interact.*, **23(1)**, 1–27, doi:10.1175/EI-D-17-0033.1.

Strassburg, B.B.N. et al., 2020: Global priority areas for ecosystem restoration. *Nature*, **586(7831)**, 724–729, doi:10.1038/s41586-020-2784-9.

Streck, C., 2012: Financing REDD+: matching needs and ends. *Curr. Opin. Environ. Sustain.*, **4(6)**, 628–637, doi:10.1016/j.cosust.2012.10.001.

Strefler, J. et al., 2021: Carbon dioxide removal technologies are not born equal. *Environ. Res. Lett.*, **16(7)**, 074021, doi:10.1088/1748-9326/ac0a11.

Sumaila, U.R. and V.W.Y. Lam, 2020: Climate change and British Columbia's staple seafood supplies and prices. In: *Environmental Assessments: Scenarios, Modelling and Policy* [Ninan, K. (ed.)]. Edward Elgar Publishing, pp. 162–178.

Sumaila, U.R., W.W.L. Cheung, P.M. Cury, and T. Tai, 2017: Climate change, marine ecosystems and global fisheries. In: *Building a Climate Resilient Economy and Society* [Ninan, K.N. and M. Inoue, (eds.)]. Edward Elgar Publishing, Cheltenham, UK and Northampton, USA. pp. 151–163.

Sun, F. and R.T. Carson, 2020: Coastal wetlands reduce property damage during tropical cyclones. *Proc. Natl. Acad. Sci.*, **117(11)**, 5719–5725, doi:10.1073/pnas.1915169117.

Sun, W. et al., 2020: Climate drives global soil carbon sequestration and crop yield changes under conservation agriculture. *Glob. Change Biol.*, **26(6)**, 3325–3335, doi:10.1111/gcb.15001.

Sunderlin, W.D. et al., 2018: Creating an appropriate tenure foundation for REDD+: The record to date and prospects for the future. *World Dev.*, **106**, 376–392, doi:10.1016/j.worlddev.2018.01.010.

Swann, A.L.S., I.Y. Fung, and J.C.H. Chiang, 2012: Mid-latitude afforestation shifts general circulation and tropical precipitation. *Proc. Natl. Acad. Sci.*, **109(3)**, 712–716, doi:10.1073/pnas.1116706108.

Tacconi, L. and M.Z. Muttaqin, 2019: Reducing emissions from land use change in Indonesia: An overview. *For. Policy Econ.*, **108**, 101979, doi:10.1016/j.forpol.2019.101979.

Taillardat, P., B.S. Thompson, M. Garneau, K. Trottier, and D.A. Friess, 2020: Climate change mitigation potential of wetlands and the cost-effectiveness of their restoration. *Interface Focus*, **10(5)**, 20190129, doi:10.1098/rsfs.2019.0129.

Takakai, F., Y. Kominami, S. Ohno, and O. Nagata, 2020: Effect of the long-term application of organic matter on soil carbon accumulation and GHG emissions from a rice paddy field in a cool-temperate region, Japan. I. Comparison of rice straw and rice straw compost. *Soil Sci. Plant Nutr.*, **66(1)**, 84–95, doi:10.1080/00380768.2019.1609335.

Tan, Z.D., M. Lupascu, and L.S. Wijedasa, 2021: Paludiculture as a sustainable land use alternative for tropical peatlands: A review. *Sci. Total Environ.*, **753**, 142111, doi:10.1016/j.scitotenv.2020.142111.

Tanneberger, F. et al., 2020b: Climate Change Mitigation through Land Use on Rewetted Peatlands – Cross-Sectoral Spatial Planning for Paludiculture in Northeast Germany. *Wetlands*, **40(6)**, 2309–2320, doi:10.1007/s13157-020-01310-8.

Tanneberger, F. et al., 2020a: The Power of Nature-Based Solutions: How Peatlands Can Help Us to Achieve Key EU Sustainability Objectives. *Adv. Sustain. Syst.*, **5(1)**, 2000146, doi:10.1002/adsu.202000146.

Taubert, F. et al., 2018: Global patterns of tropical forest fragmentation. *Nature*, **554(7693)**, 519–522, doi:10.1038/nature25508.

Taylor, J.S., J. Parfitt, and D. Jarosz, 2019: *Regulating the role of Unfair Trading Practices in food waste generation*. European Union - EU Horizon 2020 REFRESH Policy Brief, February 2019, 14 pp.

ten Berge, H.F.M. et al., 2019: Maize crop nutrient input requirements for food security in sub-Saharan Africa. *Glob. Food Sec.*, **23**, 9–21, doi:10.1016/j.gfs.2019.02.001.

Teuling, A.J. et al., 2017: Observational evidence for cloud cover enhancement over western European forests. *Nat. Commun.*, **8(1)**, 14065, doi:10.1038/ncomms14065.

Thakuri, S. et al., 2020: Methane emission factors and carbon fluxes from enteric fermentation in cattle of Nepal Himalaya. *Sci. Total Environ.*, **746**, 141184, doi:10.1016/j.scitotenv.2020.141184.

The Royal Society Science Policy Centre, 2014: *Resilience to extreme weather*. The Royal Society, London, UK, 124 pp. https://royalsociety.org/-/media/policy/projects/resilience-climate-change/resilience-full-report.pdf (Accessed February 15, 2021).

Theurl, M.C. et al., 2020: Food systems in a zero-deforestation world: Dietary change is more important than intensification for climate targets in 2050. *Sci. Total Environ.*, **735**, 139353, doi:10.1016/j.scitotenv.2020.139353.

Thierfelder, C. et al., 2017: How climate-smart is conservation agriculture – its potential to deliver on adaptation, mitigation and productivity on smallholder farms in southern Africa. *Food Secur.*, **9(3)**, 537–560, doi:10.1007/s12571-017-0665-3.

Thiery, W. et al., 2017: Present-day irrigation mitigates heat extremes. *J. Geophys. Res. Atmos.*, **122(3)**, 1403–1422, doi:10.1002/2016JD025740.

Thomas, N. et al., 2017: Distribution and drivers of global mangrove forest change, 1996–2010. *PLoS One*, **12(6)**, e0179302, doi:10.1371/journal.pone.0179302.

Thompson, L.R. and J.E. Rowntree, 2020: Invited Review: Methane sources, quantification, and mitigation in grazing beef systems. *Appl. Anim. Sci.*, **36(4)**, 556–573, doi:10.15232/aas.2019-01951.

Thomson, A.M. et al., 2019: Sustainable intensification in land systems: trade-offs, scales, and contexts. *Curr. Opin. Environ. Sustain*. **38**, 37–43, doi:10.1016/j.cosust.2019.04.011.

Thornton, P.K. and M. Herrero, 2015: Adapting to climate change in the mixed crop and livestock farming systems in sub-Saharan Africa. *Nat. Clim. Change*, **5(9)**, 830–836, doi:10.1038/nclimate2754.

Thyagharajan, K.K. and T. Vignesh, 2019: Soft Computing Techniques for Land Use and Land Cover Monitoring with Multispectral Remote Sensing Images: A Review. *Arch. Comput. Methods Eng.*, **26(2)**, 275–301, doi:10.1007/s11831-017-9239-y.

Tian, H. et al., 2020: A comprehensive quantification of global nitrous oxide sources and sinks. *Nature*, **586(7828)**, 248–256, doi:10.1038/s41586-020-2780-0.

Tian, X., B. Sohngen, J. Baker, S. Ohrel, and A.A. Fawcett, 2018: Will U.S. Forests Continue to Be a Carbon Sink? *Land Econ.*, **94(1)**, 97–113, doi:10.3368/le.94.1.97.

Tilman, D. and M. Clark, 2014: Global diets link environmental sustainability and human health. *Nature*, **515(7528)**, 518–522, doi:10.1038/nature13959.

Tisserant, A. and F. Cherubini, 2019: Potentials, Limitations, Co-Benefits, and Trade-Offs of Biochar Applications to Soils for Climate Change Mitigation. *Land*, **8(12)**, 179, doi:10.3390/land8120179.

Tittonell, P., 2020: Assessing resilience and adaptability in agroecological transitions. *Agric. Syst.*, **184**, 102862, doi:10.1016/j.agsy.2020.102862.

Toensmeier, E., 2016: *The carbon farming solution: a global toolkit of perennial crops and regenerative agriculture practices for climate change mitigation and food security*. Chelsea Green Publishing, White River Junction, VT, USA, 480 pp.

Tougiani, A., C. Guero, and T. Rinaudo, 2009: Community mobilisation for improved livelihoods through tree crop management in Niger. *GeoJournal*, **74(5)**, 377–389, doi:10.1007/s10708-008-9228-7.

7

Toumpanakis, A., T. Turnbull, and I. Alba-Barba, 2018: Effectiveness of plant-based diets in promoting well-being in the management of type 2 diabetes: a systematic review. *BMJ Open Diabetes Res. Care*, **6(1)**, e000534, doi:10.1136/bmjdrc-2018-000534.

Tran, D.H., T.N. Hoang, T. Tokida, A. Tirol-Padre, and K. Minamikawa, 2018: Impacts of alternate wetting and drying on greenhouse gas emission from paddy field in Central Vietnam. *Soil Sci. Plant Nutr.*, **64(1)**, 14–22, doi:10.1080/00380768.2017.1409601.

Tritsch, I. et al., 2020: Do forest-management plans and FSC certification help avoid deforestation in the Congo Basin? *Ecol. Econ.*, **175**, 106660, doi:10.1016/j.ecolecon.2020.106660.

Tscharntke, T. et al., 2011: Multifunctional shade-tree management in tropical agroforestry landscapes – a review. *J. Appl. Ecol.*, **48(3)**, 619–629, doi:10.1111/j.1365-2664.2010.01939.x.

Tubiello, F.N., 2019: Greenhouse Gas Emissions Due to Agriculture. In: *Encyclopedia of Food Security and Sustainability, vol. 1* [Ferranti, P., E.M. Berry, and J.R. Anderson (eds.)]. Elsevier, pp. 196–205.

Tubiello, F.N. et al., 2020: Carbon emissions and removals by forests: new estimates, 1990–2020. *Earth Syst. Sci. Data*, doi:10.5194/essd-2020-203.

Tuomisto, H.L., I.D. Hodge, P. Riordan, and D.W. Macdonald, 2012: Does organic farming reduce environmental impacts? – A meta-analysis of European research. *J. Environ. Manage.*, **112**, 309–320, doi:10.1016/j.jenvman.2012.08.018.

Turner, P.A., C.B. Field, D.B. Lobell, D.L. Sanchez, and K.J. Mach, 2018a: Unprecedented rates of land-use transformation in modelled climate change mitigation pathways. *Nat. Sustain.*, **1(5)**, 240–245, doi:10.1038/s41893-018-0063-7.

Turner, P.A. et al., 2018b: The global overlap of bioenergy and carbon sequestration potential. *Clim. Change*, **148(1–2)**, 1–10, doi:10.1007/s10584-018-2189-z.

Turnhout, E. et al., 2017: Envisioning REDD+ in a post-Paris era: between evolving expectations and current practice. *WIREs Clim. Change*, **8(1)**, doi:10.1002/wcc.425.

Turubanova, S., P.V. Potapov, A. Tyukavina, and M.C. Hansen, 2018: Ongoing primary forest loss in Brazil, Democratic Republic of the Congo, and Indonesia. *Environ. Res. Lett.*, **13(7)**, 074028, doi:10.1088/1748-9326/aacd1c.

Ünal, H.E., Ü. Birben, and F. Bolat, 2019: Rural population mobility, deforestation, and urbanization: case of Turkey. *Environ. Monit. Assess.*, **191(1)**, 21, doi:10.1007/s10661-018-7149-6.

UNEP, 2019: Drivers of Environmental Change. In: *Global Environment Outlook – GEO-6: Healthy Planet, Healthy People*.

UNEP, 2020: *Emissions Gap Report 2020*. United Nations Environment Programme (UNEP), Nairobi, Kenya, 112 pp.

UNEP, 2021a: *Becoming #GenerationRestoration: Ecosystem Restoration for People, Nature and Climate*. United Nations Environment Programme, Nairobi, Kenya.56p.

UNEP, 2021b: *Food Waste Index Report 2021*. United Nations Environment Programme (UNEP), Nairobi, Kenya, 3–99 pp.

Unger, N., 2014: Human land-use-driven reduction of forest volatiles cools global climate. *Nat. Clim. Change*, **4(10)**, 907–910, doi:10.1038/nclimate2347.

UNIPP, 2012: *Delivering as One UN at the country level in partnership with indigenous peoples and governments*. 9–10 pp.

USEPA, 2019: *Global Non-CO2 Greenhouse Gas Emission Projections & Mitigation 2015–2050*. US Environmental Protection Agency, Washington, DC, USA, 43 pp.

USEPA, 2020: *Inventory of US greenhouse gas emissions and sinks: 1990–2018*. 733 pp. United States Environmental Protection Agency. https://www.epa.gov/sites/production/files/2020-04/documents/us-ghg-inventory-2020-main-text.pdf (Accessed July 1, 2021).

van der Laan-Luijkx, I.T. et al., 2017: The CarbonTracker Data Assimilation Shell (CTDAS) v1.0: implementation and global carbon balance 2001–2015. *Geosci. Model Dev.*, **10(7)**, 2785–2800, doi:10.5194/gmd-10-2785-2017.

van der Sleen, P. et al., 2015: No growth stimulation of tropical trees by 150 years of CO2 fertilization but water-use efficiency increased. *Nat. Geosci.*, **8(1)**, 24–28, doi:10.1038/ngeo2313.

van der Weerden, T.J. et al., 2016: Refining the New Zealand nitrous oxide emission factor for urea fertiliser and farm dairy effluent. *Agric. Ecosyst. Environ.*, **222**, 133–137, doi:10.1016/j.agee.2016.02.007.

van der Werf, G.R. et al., 2017: Global fire emissions estimates during 1997–2016. *Earth Syst. Sci. Data*, **9(2)**, 697–720, doi:10.5194/essd-9-697-2017.

van der Werf, H.M.G., M.T. Knudsen, and C. Cederberg, 2020: Towards better representation of organic agriculture in life cycle assessment. *Nat. Sustain.*, **3(6)**, 419–425, doi:10.1038/s41893-020-0489-6.

van Diggelen, J.M.H., L.P.M. Lamers, J.H.T. Loermans, W.J. Rip, and A.J.P. Smolders, 2020: Towards more sustainable hydrological management and land use of drained coastal peatlands – a biogeochemical balancing act. *Mires Peat*, **26**, 1–12, doi.org/10.19189/MaP.2019.APG.StA.1771.

van Giesen, R.I. and I.E. de Hooge, 2019: Too ugly, but I love its shape: Reducing food waste of suboptimal products with authenticity (and sustainability) positioning. *Food Qual. Prefer.*, **75**, 249–259, doi:10.1016/j.foodqual.2019.02.020.

van Ittersum, M.K. et al., 2013: Yield gap analysis with local to global relevance—A review. *F. Crop. Res.*, **143**, 4–17, doi:10.1016/j.fcr.2012.09.009.

Van Loo, E.J., C. Hoefkens, and W. Verbeke, 2017: Healthy, sustainable and plant-based eating: Perceived (mis)match and involvement-based consumer segments as targets for future policy. *Food Policy*, **69**, 46–57, doi:10.1016/j.foodpol.2017.03.001.

van Meijl, H. et al., 2018: Comparing impacts of climate change and mitigation on global agriculture by 2050. *Environ. Res. Lett.*, **13(6)**, 064021, doi:10.1088/1748-9326/aabdc4.

van Soest, H.L. et al., 2019: Analysing interactions among Sustainable Development Goals with Integrated Assessment Models. *Glob. Transitions*, **1**, 210–225, doi:10.1016/j.glt.2019.10.004.

van Vuuren, D.P. et al., 2018: Alternative pathways to the 1.5°C target reduce the need for negative emission technologies. *Nat. Clim. Change*, **8(5)**, 391–397, doi:10.1038/s41558-018-0119-8.

Van Vuuren, D.P. et al., 2019: Integrated scenarios to support analysis of the food–energy–water nexus. *Nat. Sustain.*, **2(12)**, 1132–1141, doi:10.1038/s41893-019-0418-8.

Van Wesemael, D. et al., 2019: Reducing enteric methane emissions from dairy cattle: Two ways to supplement 3-nitrooxypropanol. *J. Dairy Sci.*, **102(2)**, 1780–1787, doi:10.3168/jds.2018-14534.

Van Zwieten, L. et al., 2015: Enhanced biological N2 fixation and yield of faba bean (Vicia faba L.) in an acid soil following biochar addition: dissection of causal mechanisms. *Plant Soil*, **395(1–2)**, 7–20, doi:10.1007/s11104-015-2427-3.

Vainer Manzatto, C., et al., 2020: *Mitigação das emissões de Gases de Efeitos Estufa pela adoção das tecnologias do Plano ABC: estimativas parciais*. Brasilia, Brazil, 36 pp. https://www.embrapa.br/meio-ambiente/.Embrapa (Accessed September 1, 2021).

Varghese, A., T. Ticktin, L. Mandle, and S. Nath, 2015: Assessing the Effects of Multiple Stressors on the Recruitment of Fruit Harvested Trees in a Tropical Dry Forest, Western Ghats, India. *PLoS One*, **10(3)**, e0119634, doi:10.1371/journal.pone.0119634.

Vaughan, N.E. et al., 2018: Evaluating the use of biomass energy with carbon capture and storage in low emission scenarios. *Environ. Res. Lett.*, **13(4)**, 044014, doi:10.1088/1748-9326/aaaa02.

Venkatramanan, V., S. Shah, and R. Prasad, 2020: *Global Climate Change: Resilient and Smart Agriculture*. Springer, Singapore. https://doi.org/10.1007/978-981-32-9856-9.

Vera, I., R. Hoefnagels, M. Junginger, and F. Hilst, 2021: Supply potential of lignocellulosic energy crops grown on marginal land and greenhouse gas footprint of advanced biofuels—A spatially explicit assessment under the sustainability criteria of the Renewable Energy Directive Recast. *GCB Bioenergy*, **13(9)**, 1425–1447, doi:10.1111/gcbb.12867.

Verhoeven, E. et al., 2017: Toward a Better Assessment of Biochar-Nitrous Oxide Mitigation Potential at the Field Scale. *J. Environ. Qual.*, **46(2)**, 237–246, doi:10.2134/jeq2016.10.0396.

Verkerk, P.J. et al., 2020: Climate-Smart Forestry: the missing link. *For. Policy Econ.*, **115**, 102164, doi:10.1016/j.forpol.2020.102164.

Vijn, S. et al., 2020: Key Considerations for the Use of Seaweed to Reduce Enteric Methane Emissions From Cattle. *Front. Vet. Sci.*, **7**, Art597430 doi:10.3389/fvets.2020.597430.

Vogel, E. and R. Meyer, 2018: Climate Change, Climate Extremes, and Global Food Production—Adaptation in the Agricultural Sector. *Resilience*.2018: 31–49. https://doi.org/10.1016/B978-0-12-811891-7.00003-7.

Wade, C.M., J.S. Baker, G. Latta, S.B. Ohrel, and J. Allpress, 2019: Projecting the Spatial Distribution of Possible Planted Forest Expansion in the United States. *J. For.*, **117(6)**, 560–578, doi:10.1093/jofore/fvz054.

Walker, W.S. et al., 2020: The role of forest conversion, degradation, and disturbance in the carbon dynamics of Amazon indigenous territories and protected areas. *Proc. Natl. Acad. Sci.*, **117(6)**, 3015–3025, doi:10.1073/pnas.1913321117.

Walkup, J., Z. Freedman, J. Kotcon, and E.M. Morrissey, 2020: Pasture in crop rotations influences microbial biodiversity and function reducing the potential for nitrogen loss from compost. *Agric. Ecosyst. Environ.*, **304**, 107122, doi:10.1016/j.agee.2020.107122.

Wang, F. et al., 2021: Global blue carbon accumulation in tidal wetlands increases with climate change. *Natl. Sci. Rev.*, **8(9)**, doi:10.1093/nsr/nwaa296.

Wang, J., X. Pan, Y. Liu, X. Zhang, and Z. Xiong, 2012: Effects of biochar amendment in two soils on greenhouse gas emissions and crop production. *Plant Soil*, **360(1–2)**, 287–298, doi:10.1007/s11104-012-1250-3.

Wang, J., Z. Xiong, and Y. Kuzyakov, 2016: Biochar stability in soil: meta-analysis of decomposition and priming effects. *GCB Bioenergy*, **8(3)**, 512–523, doi:10.1111/gcbb.12266.

Wang, J., H. Akiyama, K. Yagi, and X. Yan, 2018: Controlling variables and emission factors of methane from global rice fields. *Atmos. Chem. Phys.*, **18(14)**, 10419–10431, doi:10.5194/acp-18-10419-2018.

Wang, Y. et al., 2020: Upturn in secondary forest clearing buffers primary forest loss in the Brazilian Amazon. *Nat. Sustain.*, **3(4)**, 290–295, doi:10.1038/s41893-019-0470-4.

Wanger, T.C. et al., 2020: Integrating agroecological production in a robust post-2020 Global Biodiversity Framework. *Nat. Ecol. Evol.*, **4(9)**, 1150–1152, doi:10.1038/s41559-020-1262-y.

Ward, C. et al., 2021: Smallholder perceptions of land restoration activities: rewetting tropical peatland oil palm areas in Sumatra, Indonesia. *Reg. Environ. Change*, **21(1)**, 1, doi:10.1007/s10113-020-01737-z.

Ward, M. et al., 2020: Impact of 2019–2020 mega-fires on Australian fauna habitat. *Nat. Ecol. Evol.*, **4(10)**, 1321–1326, doi:10.1038/s41559-020-1251-1.

Watson, J.E.M., N. Dudley, D.B. Segan, and M. Hockings, 2014: The performance and potential of protected areas. *Nature*, **515(7525)**, 67–73, doi:10.1038/nature13947.

Watson, J.E.M. et al., 2016: Catastrophic Declines in Wilderness Areas Undermine Global Environment Targets. *Curr. Biol.*, **26(21)**, 2929–2934, doi:10.1016/j.cub.2016.08.049.

Wear, D.N. and B.C. Murray, 2004: Federal timber restrictions, interregional spillovers, and the impact on US softwood markets. *J. Environ. Econ. Manage.*, **47(2)**, 307–330, doi:10.1016/S0095-0696(03)00081-0.

Webb, E.L. et al., 2014: Deforestation in the Ayeyarwady Delta and the conservation implications of an internationally-engaged Myanmar. *Glob. Environ. Change*, **24**, 321–333, doi:10.1016/j.gloenvcha.2013.10.007.

Weindl, I. et al., 2015: Livestock in a changing climate: production system transitions as an adaptation strategy for agriculture. *Environ. Res. Lett.*, **10(9)**, 094021, doi:10.1088/1748-9326/10/9/094021.

Weltin, M. et al., 2018: Conceptualising fields of action for sustainable intensification – A systematic literature review and application to regional case studies. *Agric. Ecosyst. Environ.*, **257**, 68–80, doi:10.1016/j.agee.2018.01.023.

Weng, Z. (Han) et al., 2018: The accumulation of rhizodeposits in organo-mineral fractions promoted biochar-induced negative priming of native soil organic carbon in Ferralsol. *Soil Biol. Biochem.*, **118**, 91–96, doi:10.1016/j.soilbio.2017.12.008.

Weng, Z.H. et al., 2015: Plant-biochar interactions drive the negative priming of soil organic carbon in an annual ryegrass field system. *Soil Biol. Biochem.*, **90**, 111–121, doi:10.1016/j.soilbio.2015.08.005.

White, R.P., S. Murray, and M. Rohwede, 2000: *Pilot Analysis of Global Ecosystems: Grassland Ecosystems*. World Resource Institute. Washington, DC, USA, 81 pp.

Whitehead, P.J., J. Russell-Smith, and C. Yates, 2014: Fire patterns in north Australian savannas: extending the reach of incentives for savanna fire emissions abatement. *Rangel. J.*, **36(4)**, 371, doi:10.1071/RJ13129.

Wiedinmyer, C. and M.D. Hurteau, 2010: Prescribed Fire As a Means of Reducing Forest Carbon Emissions in the Western United States. *Environ. Sci. Technol.*, **44(6)**, 1926–1932, doi:10.1021/es902455e.

Wigneron, J.-P. et al., 2020: Tropical forests did not recover from the strong 2015–2016 El Niño event. *Sci. Adv.*, **6(6)**: eaay4603 doi:10.1126/sciadv.aay4603.

Wijaya, A. et al., 2017: *How Can Indonesia Achieve Its Climate Change Mitigation Goal? An Analysis of Potential Emissions Reductions from Energy and Land-Use Policies*. World Resources Institute, Washington, DC, USA, 36 pp.

Wilson, C., H. Pettifor, E. Cassar, L. Kerr, and M. Wilson, 2019: The potential contribution of disruptive low-carbon innovations to 1.5°C climate mitigation. *Energy Effic.*, **12(2)**, 423–440, doi:10.1007/s12053-018-9679-8.

Wilson, D. et al., 2016: Greenhouse gas emission factors associated with rewetting of organic soils. *Mires Peat*, **17(4)**, 1–28, doi:10.19189/MaP.2016.OMB.222.

Wilson, K. and H. Lotze, 2019: Climate change projections reveal range shifts of eelgrass Zostera marina in the Northwest Atlantic. *Mar. Ecol. Prog. Ser.*, **620**, 47–62, doi:10.3354/meps12973.

Windham-Myers, L. et al., 2018: *Chapter 15: Tidal Wetlands and Estuaries. Second State of the Carbon Cycle Report* [Cavallaro, N., G. Shrestha, R. Birdse, M.A. Mayes, R. Najjar, S. Reed, P. Romero-Lankao, and Z. Zhu, (eds.)]. Washington, DC, USA, 596–648 pp.

Wood, S.L.R. et al., 2018: Distilling the role of ecosystem services in the Sustainable Development Goals. *Ecosyst. Serv.*, **29**, 70–82, doi:10.1016/j.ecoser.2017.10.010.

Woodward, R.T., D.A. Newburn, and M. Mezzatesta, 2016: Additionality and reverse crowding out for pollution offsets in water quality trading. *Ecol. Econ.*, **128**, 224–231, doi:10.1016/j.ecolecon.2016.05.001.

Woolf, D., J.E. Amonette, F.A. Street-Perrott, J. Lehmann, and S. Joseph, 2010: Sustainable biochar to mitigate global climate change. *Nat. Commun.*, **1(1)**, 56, doi:10.1038/ncomms1053.

Woolf, D., J. Lehmann, and D.R. Lee, 2016: Optimal bioenergy power generation for climate change mitigation with or without carbon sequestration. *Nat. Commun.*, **7(1)**, 13160, doi:10.1038/ncomms13160.

Worden, J.R. et al., 2017: Reduced biomass burning emissions reconcile conflicting estimates of the post-2006 atmospheric methane budget. *Nat. Commun.*, **8(1)**, 2227, doi:10.1038/s41467-017-02246-0.

World Bank, 2019: *Illegal Logging, Fishing, and Wildlife Trade: The Cost and How to Combat it*. The World Bank, Washington, DC, USA, 70 pp.

Wotton, B.M., M.D. Flannigan, and G.A. Marshall, 2017: Potential climate change impacts on fire intensity and key wildfire suppression thresholds in Canada. *Environ. Res. Lett.*, **12(9)**, 095003, doi:10.1088/1748-9326/aa7e6e.

Wu, H. et al., 2017: The interactions of composting and biochar and their implications for soil amendment and pollution remediation: a review. *Crit. Rev. Biotechnol.*, **37(6)**, 754–764, doi:10.1080/07388551.2016.1232696.

7

Wu, J., 2000: Slippage Effects of the Conservation Reserve Program. *Am. J. Agric. Econ.*, **82(4)**, 979–992, doi:10.1111/0002-9092.00096.

Wu, W. et al., 2019: Global advanced bioenergy potential under environmental protection policies and societal transformation measures. *GCB Bioenergy*, **11(9)**, gcbb.12614, doi:10.1111/gcbb.12614.

Wunder, S., 2007: The Efficiency of Payments for Environmental Services in Tropical Conservation. *Conserv. Biol.*, **21(1)**, 48–58, doi:10.1111/j.1523-1739.2006.00559.x.

WWF, 2020: *The Living Planet Index 2020: Bending the Curve of Biodiversity Loss-Summary* [Almond, R.E.A., M. Grooten M., and T. Petersen (eds.)]. WWF, Gland, Switzerland, 83 pp.

Wylie, L., A.E. Sutton-Grier, and A. Moore, 2016: Keys to successful blue carbon projects: Lessons learned from global case studies. *Mar. Policy*, **65**, 76–84, doi:10.1016/j.marpol.2015.12.020.

Wynberg, R., 2017: Making sense of access and benefit sharing in the rooibos industry: Towards a holistic, just and sustainable framing. *South African J. Bot.*, **110**, 39–51, doi:10.1016/j.sajb.2016.09.015.

Xie, S.H., W.A. Kurz, and P.N. McFarlane, 2021: Inward- versus outward-focused bioeconomy strategies for British Columbia's forest products industry: a harvested wood products carbon storage and emission perspective. *Carbon Balance Manag.*, **16(1)**, 30, doi:10.1186/s13021-021-00193-4.

Xu, Z., C.E. Smyth, T.C. Lemprière, G.J. Rampley, and W.A. Kurz, 2018: Climate change mitigation strategies in the forest sector: biophysical impacts and economic implications in British Columbia, Canada. *Mitig. Adapt. Strateg. Glob. Change*, **23**, 257–290, doi:10.1007/s11027-016-9735-7.

Xue, D. and C. Tisdell, 2001: Valuing ecological functions of biodiversity in Changbaishan Mountain Biosphere Reserve in Northeast China. *Biodivers. Conserv.*, **10**, 467–481, doi.org/10.1023/A:1016630825913.

Yagi, K. et al., 2020: Potential and promisingness of technical options for mitigating greenhouse gas emissions from rice cultivation in Southeast Asian countries. *Soil Sci. Plant Nutr.*, **66(1)**, 37–49, doi:10.1080/00380768.2019.1683890.

Yamaguchi, T., M.T. Luu, K. Minamikawa, and S. Yokoyama, 2017: Compatibility of Alternate Wetting and Drying Irrigation with Local Agriculture in An Giang Province, Mekong Delta, Vietnam. *Trop. Agric. Dev.*, **61(3)**, 117–127, doi.org/10.11248/jsta.61.117.

Yamaguchi, T., L.M. Tuan, K. Minamikawa, and S. Yokoyama, 2019: Assessment of the relationship between adoption of a knowledge-intensive water-saving technique and irrigation conditions in the Mekong Delta of Vietnam. *Agric. Water Manag.*, **212**, 162–171, doi:10.1016/j.agwat.2018.08.041.

Yao, G., T.W. Hertel, and F. Taheripour, 2018: Economic drivers of telecoupling and terrestrial carbon fluxes in the global soybean complex. *Glob. Environ. Change*, **50**, 190–200, doi:10.1016/j.gloenvcha.2018.04.005.

Yao, Y. et al., 2020: Anaerobic digestion of livestock manure in cold regions: Technological advancements and global impacts. *Renew. Sustain. Energy Rev.*, **119**, 109494, doi:10.1016/j.rser.2019.109494.

Ye, L. et al., 2020: Biochar effects on crop yields with and without fertilizer: A meta-analysis of field studies using separate controls. *Soil Use Manag.*, **36(1)**, 2–18, doi:10.1111/sum.12546.

Zak, D. et al., 2018: Top soil removal reduces water pollution from phosphorus and dissolved organic matter and lowers methane emissions from rewetted peatlands. *J. Appl. Ecol.*, **55(1)**, 311–320, doi:10.1111/1365-2664.12931.

Zelli, F., I. Möller, and H. van Asselt, 2017: Institutional complexity and private authority in global climate governance: the cases of climate engineering, REDD+ and short-lived climate pollutants. *Env. Polit.*, **26(4)**, 669–693, doi:10.1080/09644016.2017.1319020.

Zhang, A. et al., 2010: Effect of biochar amendment on yield and methane and nitrous oxide emissions from a rice paddy from Tai Lake plain, China. *Agric. Ecosyst. Environ.*, **139(4)**, 469–475, doi:10.1016/j.agee.2010.09.003.

Zhang, B., A. Hastings, J.C. Clifton-Brown, D. Jiang, and A.P.C. Faaij, 2020: Modeled spatial assessment of biomass productivity and technical potential of *Miscanthus × giganteus*, *Panicum virgatum L.*, and *Jatropha* on marginal land in China. *GCB Bioenergy*, **12(5)**, 328–345, doi:10.1111/gcbb.12673.

Zhang, J.J. et al., 2017: Nutrient Expert Improves Nitrogen Efficiency and Environmental Benefits for Summer Maize in China. *Agron. J.*, **109(3)**, 1082–1090, doi:10.2134/agronj2016.08.0477.

Zhao, N., J. Lehmann, and F. You, 2020: Poultry Waste Valorization via Pyrolysis Technologies: Economic and Environmental Life Cycle Optimization for Sustainable Bioenergy Systems. *ACS Sustain. Chem. Eng.*, **8(11)**, 4633–4646, doi:10.1021/acssuschemeng.0c00704.

Zhao, Q. et al., 2016: A review of methodologies and success indicators for coastal wetland restoration. *Ecol. Indic.*, **60**, 442–452, doi:10.1016/j.ecolind.2015.07.003.

Zhu, K., J. Zhang, S. Niu, C. Chu, and Y. Luo, 2018: Limits to growth of forest biomass carbon sink under climate change. *Nat. Commun.*, **9(1)**, 2709, doi:10.1038/s41467-018-05132-5.

Zhu, P., Q. Zhuang, J. Eva, and C. Bernacchi, 2017: Importance of biophysical effects on climate warming mitigation potential of biofuel crops over the conterminous United States. *GCB Bioenergy*, **9**, 577–590. https://doi.org/10.1111/gcbb.12370.

Zhu, X. et al., 2020: Reductions in water, soil and nutrient losses and pesticide pollution in agroforestry practices: a review of evidence and processes. *Plant Soil*, **453(1–2)**, 45–86, doi:10.1007/s11104-019-04377-3.

Zimmerman, A.R. and L. Ouyang, 2019: Priming of pyrogenic C (biochar) mineralization by dissolved organic matter and vice versa. *Soil Biol. Biochem.*, **130**, 105–112, doi:10.1016/j.soilbio.2018.12.011.

Zomer, R.J. et al., 2016: Global Tree Cover and Biomass Carbon on Agricultural Land: The contribution of agroforestry to global and national carbon budgets. *Sci. Rep.*, **6(1)**, 29987, doi:10.1038/srep29987.

Zougmoré, R., A. Jalloh, and A. Tioro, 2014: Climate-smart soil water and nutrient management options in semiarid West Africa: a review of evidence and analysis of stone bunds and zaï techniques. *Agric. Food Secur.*, **3(1)**, 16, doi:10.1186/2048-7010-3-16.

Zschornack, T. et al., 2018: Soil CH_4 and N_2O Emissions from Rice Paddy Fields in Southern Brazil as Affected by Crop Management Levels: a Three-Year Field Study. *Rev. Bras. Ciência do Solo*, **42**, doi:10.1590/18069657rbcs20170306.

Zygourakis, K., 2017: Biochar soil amendments for increased crop yields: How to design a "designer" biochar. *AIChE J.*, **63(12)**, 5425–5437, doi:10.1002/aic.15870.

8 Urban Systems and Other Settlements

Coordinating Lead Authors:
Shuaib Lwasa (Uganda), Karen C. Seto (the United States of America)

Lead Authors:
Xuemei Bai (Australia), Hilda Blanco (the United States of America), Kevin R. Gurney (the United States of America), Şiir Kılkış (Turkey), Oswaldo Lucon (Brazil), Jin Murakami (Japan), Jiahua Pan (China), Ayyoob Sharifi (Japan/Iran), Yoshiki Yamagata (Japan)

Contributing Authors:
Vanesa Castán Broto (United Kingdom/Spain), Winston Chow (Singapore), Galina Churkina (the Russian Federation/Germany), Felix Creutzig (Germany), David Dodman (Jamaica/United Kingdom), Burak Güneralp (Turkey/the United States of America), Rafiq Hamdi (Belgium), Bronwyn Hayward (New Zealand), Angel Hsu (the United States of America/Singapore), Lucy Hutyra (the United States of America), Nadja Kabisch (Germany), Meredith Keller (the United States of America), Timon McPhearson (the United States of America), Peter Newman (Australia), David Nowak (the United States of America), Alan Organschi (the United States of America), Minal Pathak (India), Mark Pelling (United Kingdom), Clara Pregitzer (the United States of America), Anu Ramaswami (the United States of America), Mia Reback (the United States of America), Diana Reckien (Germany), Jen Shin (the United States of America), Michael Westphal (the United States of America), Lee White (Australia)

Review Editors:
Carolina Burle Schmidt Dubeux (Brazil), Diana Ürge-Vorsatz (Hungary)

Chapter Scientists:
Meredith Keller (the United States of America), Enock Ssekuubwa (Uganda)

This chapter should be cited as:
Lwasa, S., K.C. Seto, X. Bai, H. Blanco, K.R. Gurney, Ş. Kılkış, O. Lucon, J. Murakami, J. Pan, A. Sharifi, Y. Yamagata, 2022: Urban systems and other settlements. In IPCC, 2022: *Climate Change 2022: Mitigation of Climate Change. Contribution of Working Group III to the Sixth Assessment Report of the Intergovernmental Panel on Climate Change* [P.R. Shukla, J. Skea, R. Slade, A. Al Khourdajie, R. van Diemen, D. McCollum, M. Pathak, S. Some, P. Vyas, R. Fradera, M. Belkacemi, A. Hasija, G. Lisboa, S. Luz, J. Malley, (eds.)]. Cambridge University Press, Cambridge, UK and New York, NY, USA. doi: 10.1017/9781009157926.010

Table of Contents

Executive Summary

Although urbanisation is a global trend often associated with increased incomes and higher consumption, the growing concentration of people and activities is an opportunity to increase resource efficiency and decarbonise at scale (*very high confidence*). The same urbanisation level can have large variations in per capita urban carbon emissions. For most regions, per capita urban emissions are lower than per capita national emissions. {8.1.4, 8.3.3, 8.4, Box 8.1}

Most future urban population growth will occur in developing countries, where per capita emissions are currently low but expected to increase with the construction and use of new infrastructure and the built environment, and changes in incomes and lifestyles (*very high confidence*). The drivers of urban greenhouse gas (GHG) emissions are complex and include an interplay of population size, income, state of urbanisation, and how cities are laid out (i.e. urban form). How new cities and towns are designed, constructed, managed, and powered will lock-in behaviour, lifestyles, and future urban GHG emissions. Low-emission urbanisation can improve well-being while minimising impact on GHG emissions, but there is risk that urbanisation can lead to increased global GHG emissions through increased emissions outside the city's boundaries. {8.1.4, 8.3, Box 8.1, 8.4, 8.6}

The urban share of global GHG emissions (including carbon dioxide (CO_2) and methane (CH_4)) is substantive and continues to increase (*high confidence*). In 2015, urban emissions were estimated to be 25 $GtCO_2$-eq (about 62% of the global share) and in 2020, 29 $GtCO_2$-eq (67–72% of the global share).[1] About 100 of the highest emitting urban areas account for approximately 18% of the global carbon footprint. {8.1.6, 8.3.3}

The urban share of regional GHG emissions increased between 2000 and 2015, with much inter-region variation in the magnitude of the increase (*high confidence*). Globally, the urban share of national emissions increased 6 percentage points, from 56% in 2000 to 62% in 2015. For 2000 to 2015, the urban emissions share across AR6 WGIII regions increased from 28% to 38% in Africa, from 46% to 54% in Asia and Pacific, from 62% to 72% in Developed Countries, from 57% to 62% in Eastern Europe and West-Central Asia, from 55% to 66% in Latin America and Caribbean, and from 68% to 69% in the Middle East. {8.1.6, 8.3.3}

Per capita urban GHG emissions increased between 2000 and 2015, with cities in the Developed Countries region producing nearly seven times more per capita than the lowest emitting region (*medium confidence*). From 2000 to 2015, global urban GHG emissions per capita increased from 5.5 to 6.2 tCO_2-eq per person (an increase of 11.8%); Africa increased from 1.3 to 1.5 tCO_2-eq per person (22.6%); Asia and Pacific increased from 3.0 to 5.1 tCO_2-eq per person (71.7%); Eastern Europe and West-Central Asia increased from 6.9 to 9.8 tCO_2-eq per person (40.9%); Latin America and Caribbean increased from 2.7 to 3.7 tCO_2-eq per person (40.4%); and Middle East increased from 7.4 to 9.6 tCO_2-eq per person (30.1%). Albeit starting from the highest level, Developed Countries had a decline of 11.4 to 10.7 tCO_2-eq per person (−6.5%). {8.3.3}

The global share of future urban GHG emissions is expected to increase through 2050, with moderate to low mitigation efforts, due to growth trends in population, urban land expansion, and infrastructure and service demands, but the extent of the increase depends on the scenario and the scale and timing of urban mitigation action (*medium confidence*). In modelled scenarios, global consumption-based urban CO_2 and CH_4 emissions are projected to rise from 29 $GtCO_2$-eq in 2020 to 34 $GtCO_2$-eq in 2050 with moderate mitigation efforts (intermediate GHG emissions, SSP2–4.5), and up to 40 $GtCO_2$-eq in 2050 with low mitigation efforts (high GHG emissions, SSP3–7.0). With aggressive and immediate mitigation policies to limit global warming to 1.5°C (>50%) with no or limited overshoot by the end of the century (very low emissions, SSP1–1.9), including high levels of electrification, energy and material efficiency, renewable energy preferences, and socio-behavioural responses, urban GHG emissions could approach net-zero and reach a maximum of 3 $GtCO_2$-eq in 2050. Under a scenario with aggressive but not immediate urban mitigation policies to limit global warming to 2°C (>67%) (low emissions, SSP1–2.6), urban emissions could reach 17 $GtCO_2$-eq in 2050.[2] (Figure TS.13) {8.3.4}

Urban land areas could triple between 2015 and 2050, with significant implications for future carbon lock-in. There is a large range in the forecasts of urban land expansion across scenarios and models, which highlights an opportunity to shape future urban development towards low- or net-zero GHG emissions and minimise the loss of carbon stocks and sequestration in the agriculture, forestry and other land use (AFOLU) sector due to urban land conversion (*medium confidence*). By 2050, urban areas could increase up to 211% over the 2015 global urban extent, with the median projected increase ranging from 43% to 106%. While the largest absolute amount of new urban land is forecasted to occur in Asia and Pacific, and in Developed Countries, the highest rate of urban land growth is projected to occur in Africa, Eastern Europe and West-Central Asia, and in the Middle East. The infrastructure that will be constructed concomitant with urban land expansion will lock-in patterns of energy consumption that will persist for decades if not generations. Furthermore, given past trends, the expansion of urban areas is likely to take place on agricultural lands and forests, with implications for the loss of carbon stocks and sequestration. {8.3.1, 8.3.4, 8.4.1, 8.6}

The construction of new, and upgrading of, existing urban infrastructure through 2030 will result in significant emissions (*very high confidence*). The construction of new and upgrading

---

[1] These estimates are based on consumption-based accounting, including both direct emissions from within urban areas, and indirect emissions from outside urban areas related to the production of electricity, goods, and services consumed in cities. Estimates include all CO_2 and CH_4 emission categories except for aviation and marine bunker fuels, land-use change, forestry, and agriculture. {8.1, Annex I: Glossary}

[2] These scenarios have been assessed by WGI to correspond to intermediate, high, and very low GHG emissions.

of existing urban infrastructure using conventional practices and technologies can result in significant committed CO_2 emissions, ranging from 8.5 $GtCO_2$ to 14 $GtCO_2$ annually up to 2030 and more than double annual resource requirements for raw materials to about 90 billion tonnes per year by 2050, up from 40 billion tonnes in 2010 (*medium evidence, high agreement*). {8.4.1, 8.6}

Given the dual challenges of rising urban GHG emissions and future projections of more frequent extreme climate events, there is an urgent need to integrate urban mitigation and adaptation strategies for cities to address climate change and withstand its effects (*very high confidence*). Mitigation strategies can enhance resilience against climate change impacts while contributing to social equity, public health, and human well-being. Urban mitigation actions that facilitate economic decoupling can have positive impacts on employment and local economic competitiveness. {8.2, Cross-Working Group Box 2, 8.4}

Cities can only achieve net-zero GHG emissions through deep decarbonisation and systemic transformation (*very high confidence*). Three broad mitigation strategies have been found to be effective in reducing emissions when implemented concurrently: (i) reducing or changing urban energy and material use towards more sustainable production and consumption across all sectors, including through compact and efficient urban forms and supporting infrastructure; (ii) electrification and switching to net-zero-emissions resources; and (iii) enhancing carbon uptake and storage in the urban environment (*high evidence, high agreement*). Given the regional and global reach of urban supply chains, cities can achieve net-zero emissions only if emissions are reduced within and outside of their administrative boundaries. {8.1.6, 8.3.4, 8.4, 8.6}

Packages of mitigation policies that implement multiple urban-scale interventions can have cascading effects across sectors, reduce GHG emissions outside of a city's administrative boundaries, and reduce more emissions than the net sum of individual interventions, particularly if multiple scales of governance are included (*high confidence*). Cities have the ability to implement policy packages across sectors using an urban systems approach, especially those that affect key infrastructure based on spatial planning, electrification of the urban energy system, and urban green and blue infrastructure. The institutional capacity of cities to develop, coordinate, and integrate sectoral mitigation strategies within their jurisdiction varies by context, particularly those related to governance, the regulatory system, and budgetary control. {8.4, 8.5, 8.6}

Integrated spatial planning to achieve compact and resource-efficient urban growth through co-location of higher residential and job densities, mixed land use, and transit-oriented development (TOD) could reduce GHG emissions between 23% and 26% by 2050 compared to the business-as-usual scenario (*robust evidence, high agreement, very high confidence*). Compact cities with shortened distances between housing and jobs, and interventions that support a modal shift away from private motor vehicles towards walking, cycling, and low-emissions shared and public transportation, passive energy comfort in buildings, and urban green infrastructure can deliver significant public health benefits and have lower GHG emissions. {8.2, 8.3.4, 8.4, 8.6}

Urban green and blue infrastructure can mitigate climate change through carbon sequestration, avoided emissions, and reduced energy use while offering multiple co-benefits (*robust evidence, high agreement*). Urban green and blue infrastructure, including urban forests and street trees, permeable surfaces, and green roofs[3] offer potential to mitigate climate change directly through sequestering and storing carbon, and indirectly by inducing a cooling effect that reduces energy demand and reducing energy use for water treatment. Global urban trees store approximately 7.4 billion tonnes of carbon, and sequester approximately 217 million tonnes of carbon annually, although urban tree carbon storage and sequestration are highly dependent on biome. Among the multiple co-benefits of green and blue infrastructure are reducing the urban heat island (UHI) effect and heat stress, reducing stormwater runoff, improving air quality, and improving mental and physical health of urban dwellers. {8.2, 8.4.4}

The potential and sequencing of mitigation strategies to reduce GHG emissions will vary depending on a city's land use, spatial form, development level, and state of urbanisation (i.e., whether it is an established city with existing infrastructure, a rapidly growing city with new infrastructure, or an emerging city with infrastructure buildup (*high confidence*). New and emerging cities will have significant infrastructure development needs to achieve high quality of life, which can be met through energy-efficient infrastructures and services, and people-centred urban design (*high confidence*). The long lifespan of urban infrastructures locks in behaviour and committed emissions. Urban infrastructures and urban form can enable socio-cultural and lifestyle changes that can significantly reduce carbon footprints. Rapidly growing cities can avoid higher future emissions through urban planning to co-locate jobs and housing to achieve compact urban form, and by leapfrogging to low-carbon technologies. Established cities will achieve the largest GHG emissions savings by replacing, repurposing, or retrofitting the building stock, targeted infilling and densifying, as well as through modal shift and the electrification of the urban energy system. New and emerging cities have unparalleled potential to become low or net-zero GHG emissions while achieving high quality of life by creating compact, co-located, and walkable urban areas with mixed land use and transit-oriented design, that also preserve existing green and blue assets. {8.2, 8.4, 8.6}

With over 880 million people living in informal settlements, there are opportunities to harness and enable informal practices and institutions in cities related to housing, waste, energy, water, and sanitation to reduce resource use and mitigate climate change (*low evidence, medium agreement*). The upgrading of informal settlements and inadequate housing to improve resilience and well-being offers a chance to create a low-carbon transition. However, there is limited quantifiable data on

---

3   These examples are considered to be a subset of nature-based solutions or ecosystem-based approaches.

these practices and their cumulative impacts on GHG emissions. {8.1.4, 8.2.2, Cross-Working Group Box 2, 8.3.2, 8.4, 8.6, 8.7}

Achieving transformational changes in cities for climate change mitigation and adaptation will require engaging multiple scales of governance, including governments and non-state actors, and in connection with substantive financing beyond sectoral approaches (*very high confidence*). Large and complex infrastructure projects for urban mitigation are often beyond the capacity of local municipality budgets, jurisdictions, and institutions. Partnerships between cities and international institutions, national and regional governments, transnational networks, and local stakeholders play a pivotal role in mobilising global climate finance resources for a range of infrastructure projects with low-carbon emissions and related spatial planning programmes across key sectors. {8.4, 8.5}

8.1   Introduction

8.1.1   What Is New Since AR5?

The Fifth Assessment Report (AR5) of the Intergovernmental Panel on Climate Change (IPCC) was the first IPCC report that had a standalone chapter on urban mitigation of climate change. The starting point for that chapter was how the spatial organisation of urban settlements affects greenhouse gas (GHG) emissions and how urban form and infrastructure could facilitate mitigation of climate change. A main finding in AR5 was that urban form shapes urban energy consumption and GHG emissions.

Since AR5, there has been growing scientific literature and policy foci on urban strategies for climate change mitigation. There are three possible reasons for this. First, according to AR5 Working Group III (WGIII) Chapter 12 on Human Settlements, Infrastructure, and Spatial Planning, urban areas generate between 71% and 76% of carbon dioxide (CO_2) emissions from global final energy use and between 67% and 76% of global energy (Seto et al. 2014). Thus, focusing on 'urban systems' (see Annex I: Glossary and Figure 8.15) addresses one of the key drivers of emissions. Second, more than half of the world population lives in urban areas, and by mid-century 7 out of 10 people on the planet will live in a town or a city (UN DESA 2019). Thus, coming up with mitigation strategies that are relevant to urban settlements is critical for successful mitigation of climate change. Third, beyond climate change, there is growing attention on cities as major catalysts of change and to help achieve the objectives outlined in multiple international frameworks and assessments.

Cities are also gaining traction within the work of the IPCC. The IPCC Special Report on Global Warming of 1.5°C (SR1.5 Chapter 4) identified four systems that urgently need to change in fundamental and transformative ways: urban infrastructure, land use and ecosystems, industry, and energy. Urban infrastructure was singled out but urban systems form a pivotal part of the other three systems requiring change (IPCC 2018a) (see 'infrastructure' in Glossary). The IPCC Special Report on Climate Change and Land (SRCCL) identified cities not only as spatial units for land-based mitigation options but also places for managing demand for natural resources including food, fibre, and water (IPCC 2019).

Other international frameworks are highlighting the importance of cities. For example, the Intergovernmental Science-Policy Platform on Biodiversity and Ecosystem Services (IPBES) report on nature's contribution to people is clear: cities straddle the biodiversity sphere in the sense that they present spatial units of ecosystem fragmentation and degradation while at the same time contain spatial units where the concentration of biodiversity compares favourably with some landscapes (IPBES 2019a). Cities are also featured as a key element in the transformational governance to tackle both climate change and biodiversity and ecosystem challenges in the first-ever IPCC-IPBES co-sponsored workshop report (Pörtner et al. 2021) (Section 8.5 and see 'governance' in Glossary).

The UN Sustainable Development Goals (SDGs) further underscore the importance of cities in the international arena with the inclusion of SDG 11 on Sustainable Cities and Communities for 'inclusive, safe, resilient and sustainable' cities and human settlements (United Nations 2015; Queiroz et al. 2017; United Nations 2019). Additionally, UN-Habitat's New Urban Agenda (NUA) calls for various measures, including integrated spatial planning at the city-regional scale, to address the systemic challenges included in greening cities, among which is emissions reduction and avoidance (United Nations 2017).

Since AR5, there has also been an increase in scientific literature on urban mitigation of climate change, including more diversity of mitigation strategies than were covered during AR5 (Lamb et al. 2018), as well as a growing focus on how strategies at the urban scale can have compounding or additive effects beyond urban areas (e.g., in rural areas, land-use planning, and the energy sector).

There is more literature on using a systems approach to understand the interlinkages between mitigation and adaptation, and situating GHG emissions reduction targets within broader social, economic, and human well-being contexts and goals (Bai et al. 2018; Ürge-Vorsatz et al. 2018; Lin et al. 2021). In particular, the nexus approach, such as the water and energy nexus and the water-energy-food nexus, is increasingly being used to understand potential emissions and energy savings from cross-sectoral linkages that occur in cities (Wang and Chen 2016; Engström et al. 2017; Valek et al. 2017). There is also a growing literature that aims to quantify transboundary urban GHG emissions and carbon footprint beyond urban and national administrative boundaries (Chen et al. 2016; Hu et al. 2016). Such a scope provides a more complete understanding of how local urban emissions or local mitigation strategies can have effects on regions' carbon footprint or GHG emissions.

8.1.1.1   City Climate Action

Moreover, cities around the world are putting increasing focus on tackling climate change. Since AR5:

- Climate leadership at the local scale is growing with commitment from city decision-makers and policymakers to implement local-scale mitigation strategies (GCoM 2018, 2019; ICLEI 2019a; C40 Cities 2020a).
- More than 360 cities announced at the Paris Climate Conference that the collective impact of their commitments will lead to a reduction of up to 3.7 $GtCO_2$-eq (CO_2-equivalent) of urban emissions annually by 2030 (Cities for Climate 2015).
- The Global Covenant of Mayors (GCoM), a transnational network of more than 10,000 cities, has made commitments to reduce urban GHG emissions by up to 1.4–2.3 $GtCO_2$-eq annually by 2030 and 2.8–4.2 $GtCO_2$-eq annually by 2050, compared to business-as-usual (GCoM 2018, 2019).
- More than 800 cities have made commitments to achieve net-zero GHG emissions, either economy-wide or in a particular sector (NewClimate Institute and Data-Driven EnviroLab 2020).

Although most cities and other subnational actors are yet to meet their net-zero GHG or CO_2 emissions commitments, the growing numbers of those commitments, alongside organisations enabled to facilitate reaching those targets, underscore the growing support for climate action by city and other subnational leaders.

8.1.1.2 Historical and Future Urban Emissions

One major innovation in this Assessment Report is the inclusion of historical and future urban GHG emissions. Urban emissions based on consumption-based accounting by regions has been put forth for the time frame 1990–2100 using multiple datasets with projections given in the framework of the Shared Socio-economic Pathway (SSP)–Representative Concentration Pathway (RCP) scenarios. This advance has provided a time dimension to urban footprints considering different climate scenarios with implications for urban mitigation, allowing a comparison of the way urban emissions and their reduction can evolve given different scenario contexts (see Glossary for definitions of various 'pathways' and 'scenarios' in the context of climate change mitigation, including 'SSPs' and 'RCPs').

8.1.1.3 Sustainable Development Linkages and Feasibility Assessment

Special emphasis is placed on the co-benefits of urban mitigation options, including an evaluation of linkages with the SDGs based on synergies and/or trade-offs. Urban mitigation options are further evaluated based on multiple dimensions according to the feasibility assessment (see Section 8.5.5 and Figure 8.19, and Section 8. SM.2) indicating the enablers and barriers of implementation. These advances provide additional guidance for urban mitigation.

8.1.2 Preparing for the Special Report on Cities and Climate Change in AR7

At the 43rd Session of the IPCC in 2016, the IPCC approved a Special Report on Climate Change and Cities during the Seventh Assessment Cycle of the IPCC (AR7). To stimulate scientific research knowledge exchange, the IPCC and nine global partners co-sponsored the IPCC Cities and Climate Change Science Conference, which brought together over 700 researchers, policymakers, and practitioners from 80 countries.

The conference identified key research priorities including the need for an overarching systems approach to understanding how sectors interact in cities as drivers for GHG emissions and the relationship between climate and other urban processes, as well as achieving transformation towards low-carbon and resilient futures (Bai et al. 2018). The subsequent report on the global research and action agenda identifies scale, informality, green and blue infrastructure, governance and transformation, as well as financing climate action, as areas for scientific research during the AR6 cycle and beyond (WCRP 2019).

8.1.3 The Scope of the Chapter: A Focus on Urban Systems

This chapter takes an urban systems approach and covers the full range of urban settlements, including towns, cities, and metropolitan areas. By 'urban system' (Figure 8.15), this chapter refers to two related concepts. First, an urban systems approach recognises that cities do not function in isolation. Rather, cities exhibit strong interdependencies across scales, whether it is within a region, a country, a continent, or worldwide. Cities are embedded in broader ecological, economic, technical, institutional, legal, and governance structures that often constrain their systemic function, which cannot be separated from wider power relations (Bai et al. 2016).

The notion of a system of cities has been around for nearly 100 years and recognises that cities are interdependent, in that significant changes in one city, such as economic activities, income, or population, will affect other cities in the system (Christaller 1933; Berry 1964; Marshall 1989). This perspective of an urban system emphasises the connections between a city and other cities, as well as between a city and its hinterlands (Hall and Hay 1980; Ramaswami et al. 2017b; Xu et al. 2018c). An important point is that growth in one city affects growth in other cities in the global, national or regional system of cities (Gabaix 1999; Scholvin et al. 2019; Knoll 2021).

Moreover, there is a hierarchy of cities (Taylor 1997; Liu et al. 2014), with very large cities at the top of the hierarchy concentrating political power and financial resources, but of which there are very few. Rather, the urban system is dominated by small and medium-sized cities and towns. With globalisation and increased interconnectedness of financial flows, labour, and supply chains, cities across the world today have long-distance relationships on multiple dimensions but are also connected to their hinterlands for resources.

The second key component of the urban systems lens identifies the activities and sectors within a city as being inter-connected – that cities are ecosystems (Rees 1997; Grimm et al. 2000; Newman and Jennings 2008; Acuto et al. 2019; Abdullah and Garcia-Chueca 2020; Acuto and Leffel 2021). This urban systems perspective emphasises linkages and interrelations within cities. The most evident example of this is urban form and infrastructure, which refer to the patterns and spatial arrangements of land use, transportation systems, and urban design. Changes in urban form and infrastructure can simultaneously affect multiple sectors, such as buildings, energy, and transport.

This chapter assesses urban systems beyond simply jurisdictional boundaries. Using an urban systems lens has the potential to accelerate mitigation beyond a single sector or purely jurisdictional approach (Section 8.4). An urban systems perspective presents both challenges and opportunities for urban mitigation strategies. It shows that any mitigation option potentially has positive or negative consequences in other sectors, other settlements, cities, or other parts of the world, and requires more careful and comprehensive considerations on the broader impacts, including equity and social justice (see Glossary for a comprehensive definition of 'equity' in the context of mitigation and adaptation). This chapter focuses on cities, city regions, metropolitan regions, megalopolitans, mega-urban regions, towns, and other types of urban configurations because they are the primary sources of urban GHG emissions and tend to be where mitigation action can be most impactful.

There is no internationally agreed upon definition of 'urban', 'urban population', or 'urban area'. Countries develop their own definitions of urban, often based on a combination of population size or density, and other criteria including the percentage of population not employed in agriculture, the availability of electricity, piped water, or other infrastructures, and characteristics of the built environment, such as dwellings and built structures. This chapter assesses urban systems, which includes cities and towns. It uses a similar framework to Chapter 6 of AR6 WGII, referring to cities and urban settlements as 'concentrated human habitation centres that exist along a continuum' (Dodman et al. 2022) (for further definitions of 'urban', 'cities', 'settlements' and related terms, see Glossary, and WGII Chapter 6).

8.1.4   The Urban Century

The 21st century will be the urban century, defined by a massive increase in global urban populations and a significant building up of new urban infrastructure stock to accommodate the growing urban population. Six trends in urbanisation are especially important in the context of climate change mitigation.

First, the size and relative proportion of the urban population is unprecedented and continues to increase. As of 2018, approximately 55% of the global population lives in urban areas (about 4.3 billion people) (UN DESA 2019). It is predicted that 68% of the world population will live in urban areas by 2050. This will mean adding 2.5 billion people to urban areas between 2018 and 2050, with 90% of this increase taking place in Africa and Asia. There is a strong correlation between the level of urbanisation and the level of national income, with considerable variation and complexity in the relationship between the two (UN DESA 2019). In general, countries with levels of urbanisation of 75% or greater all have high national incomes, whereas countries with low levels of urbanisation under 35% have low national incomes (UN DESA 2019). In general, there is a clear positive correlation between the level of urbanisation and income levels (Figure 8.1 and Box 8.1).

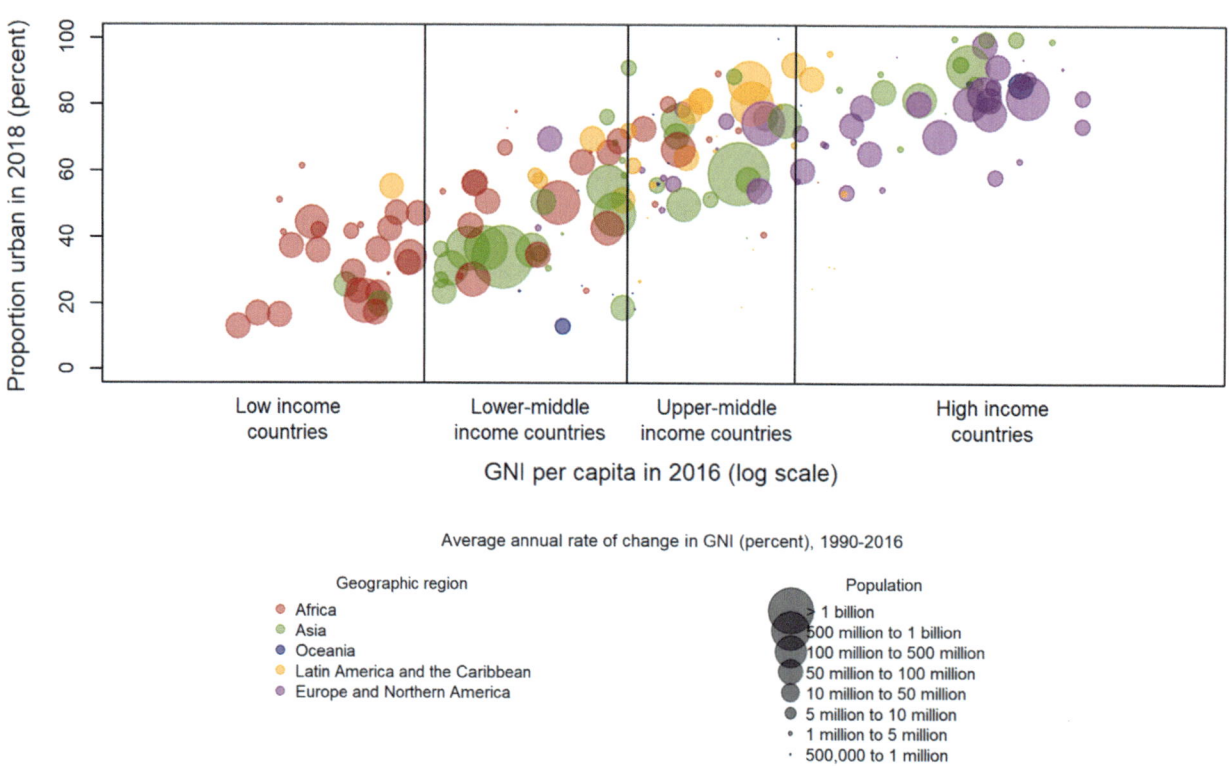

Figure 8.1[4]: Relationship between urbanisation level and gross national income (GNI). There is a positive and strong correlation between the urbanisation level and gross national income. High-income countries have high levels of urbanisation, on average 80%. Low-income countries have low levels of urbanisation, on average 30%. Source: UN DESA 2019, p. 42.

---

[4]   The countries and areas classification in the underlying report for this figure deviates from the standard classification scheme adopted by WGIII as set out in Annex II, Section 1.

Second, the geographic concentration of the world's current urban population is in emerging economies, and the majority of future urban population growth will take place in developing countries and least-developed countries (LDCs). About half of the world's urban population in 2018 lived in just seven countries, and about half of the increase in urban population through 2050 is projected to be concentrated in eight countries (UN DESA 2019) (Figure 8.2). Of these eight, seven are emerging economies where there will be a need for significant financing to construct housing, roads, and other urban infrastructure to accommodate the growth of the urban population. How these new cities of tomorrow will be designed and constructed will lock-in patterns of urban energy behaviour for decades if not generations (Sections 8.3.4 and 8.4). Thus, it is essential that urban

climate change mitigation strategies include solutions appropriate for cities of varying sizes and typologies (Section 8.6 and Figure 8.21).

Third, small and medium-sized cities and towns are a dominant type of urban settlement. In 2018, more than half (58%) of the urban population lived in cities and towns with fewer than 1 million inhabitants and almost half of the world's urban population (48%) lived in settlements with fewer than 500,000 inhabitants (Figure 8.3). Although megacities receive a lot of attention, only about 13% of the urban population worldwide lived in a megacity – an urban area with at least 10 million inhabitants (UN DESA 2019). Thus, there is a need for a wide range of strategies for urban mitigation of climate change that are appropriate for cities of varying levels of development

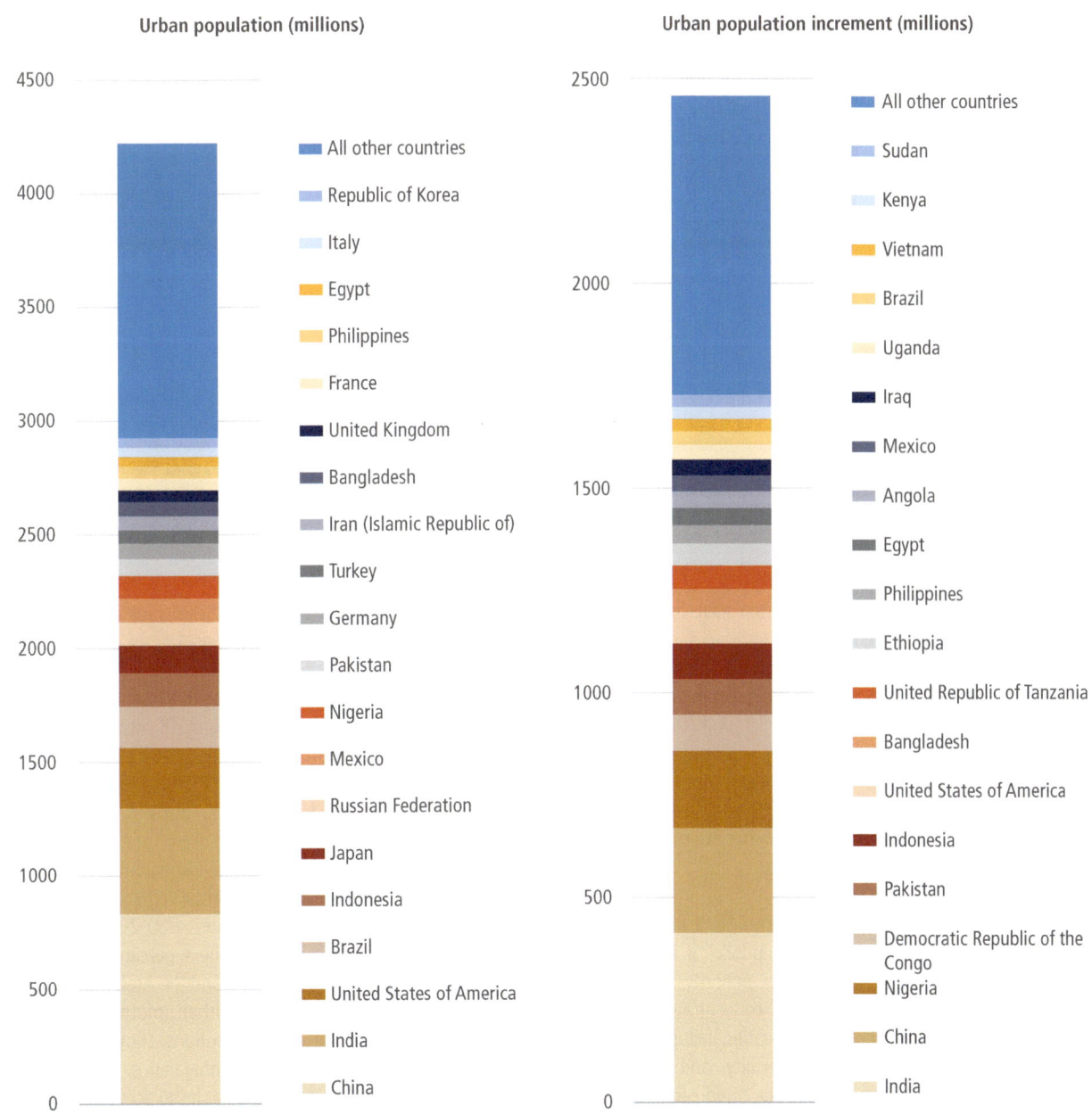

Figure 8.2: Urban population size in 2018 and increase in the projected urban population. In 2018, about half of the world's urban population lived in seven countries, and about half of the increase in urban population through 2050 is forecasted to concentrate in eight countries. Source: UN DESA 2019, p. 44.

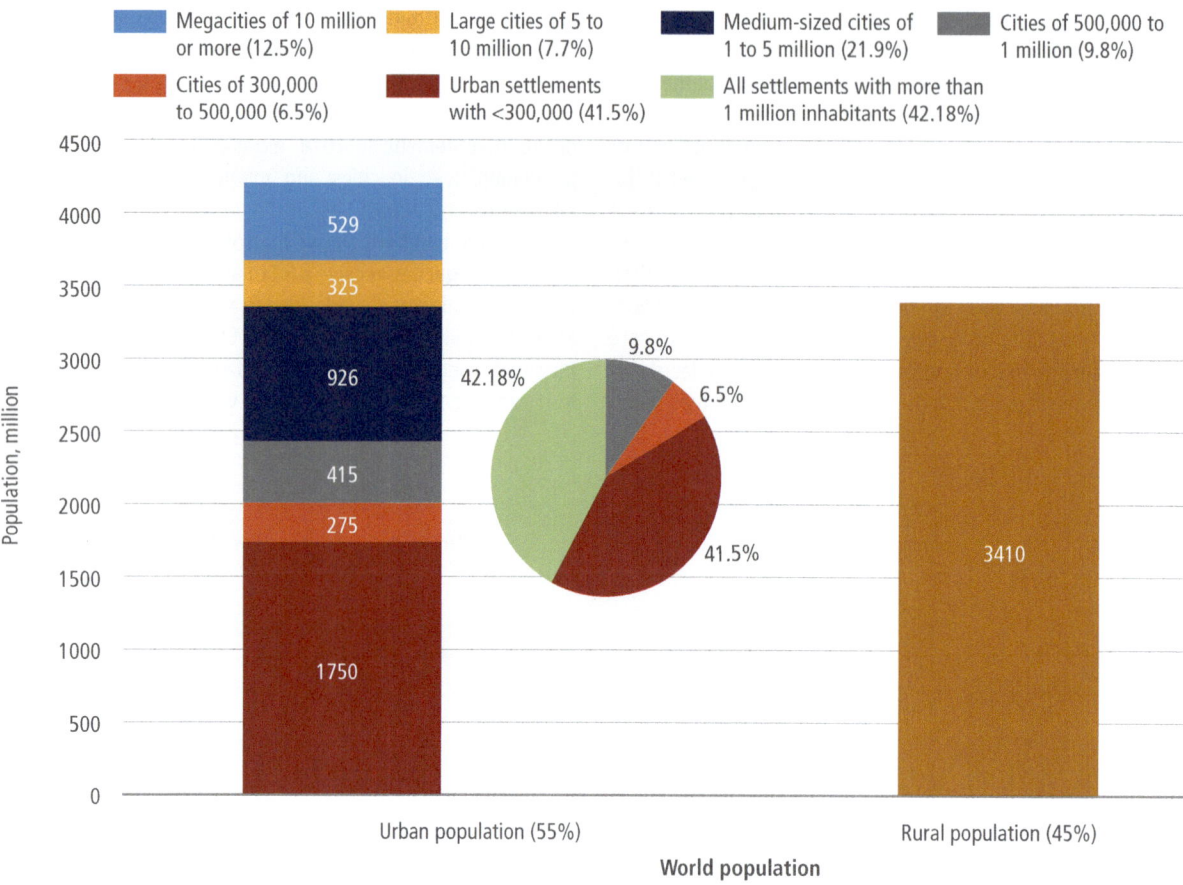

Figure 8.3: Population of the world, by area of residence and size class of urban settlement for 2018. As of 2018, 4.2 billion people or 55% of the world population reside in urban settlements while 45% reside in rural areas. The coloured stacked column for the urban population represents the total number of inhabitants for a given size class of urban settlements. Megacities of 10 million or more inhabitants have a total of only 529 million inhabitants, corresponding to 12.5% of the urban population. In contrast, about 1.8 billion inhabitants reside in urban settlements with fewer than 300,000 inhabitants, corresponding to 41.5% of the urban population. The pie chart represents the respective shares for 2018, with 42% of the urban population residing in settlements with more than 1 million inhabitants, and 58% of the urban population residing in settlements with fewer than 1 million inhabitants. Almost half of the world's urban population (48%) live in settlements with fewer than 500,000 inhabitants. Source: adapted from UN DESA 2019, p. 56.

and size, especially smaller cities which often have lower levels of financial capacities than large cities.

Fourth, another trend is the rise of megacities and extended metropolitan regions. The largest cities around the world are becoming even larger, and there is a growing divergence in economic power between megacities and other large cities (Kourtit et al. 2015; Hoornweg and Pope 2017; Zhao et al. 2017b). Moreover, there is evidence that the largest city in each country has an increasing share of the national population and economy.

Fifth, population declines have been observed for cities and towns across the world, including in Poland, Republic of Korea, Japan, United States, Germany, and Ukraine. The majority of cities that have experienced population declines are concentrated in Europe. Multiple factors contribute to the decline in cities, including declining industries and the economy, declining fertility, and outmigration to larger cities. Shrinking urban populations could offer retrofitting opportunities (UNEP 2019) and increasing greenspaces (Jarzebski

et al. 2021), but the challenges for these cities differ in scope and magnitude from rapidly expanding cities.

Sixth, urbanisation in many emerging economies is characterised by informality and an informal economy (Brown and McGranahan 2016). The urban informal economy includes a wide array of activities, including but not limited to street vending, home-based enterprises, unreported income from self-employment, informal commerce, domestic service, waste-picking, and urban agriculture. The urban informal economy is large and growing. Globally, about 44% of the urban economy is informal, although there is much variation between countries and regions (ILO 2018). Emerging and developing economies have the highest percentage of the urban informal economy, with Africa (76%) and the Arab States (64%) with the largest proportion (ILO 2018). Urban informality also extends to planning, governance and institutions (Roy 2009; EU 2016; Lamson-Hall et al. 2019). Given its prevalence, it is important for urban climate change mitigation strategies to account for informality, especially in emerging and developing countries (Section 8.3.2).

8.1.5   Urbanisation in Developing Countries

Urbanisation in the 21st century will be dominated by population and infrastructure growth in developing countries, and as such it is important to highlight three aspects that are unique and especially relevant for climate change mitigation. First, urbanisation will increase in speed and magnitude. Given their significant impact on emissions, mitigation action in Asian cities, especially the large and rapidly growing cities, will have significant implications on global ambitions (Section 8.3.4).

Second, a number of cities in developing countries lack institutional, financial and technical capacities to enable local climate change action (Sharifi et al. 2017; Fuhr et al. 2018). While these capacities differ across contexts (Hickmann et al. 2017), several governance challenges are similar across cities (Gouldson et al. 2015). These factors also influence the ability of cities to innovate and effectively implement mitigation action (Nagendra et al. 2018) (Chapter 17).

Third, there are sizable economic benefits in developing country cities that can provide an opportunity to enhance political momentum and institutions (Colenbrander et al. 2016). The co-benefits approach (Section 8.2), which frames climate objectives alongside other development benefits, is increasingly seen as an important concept justifying and driving climate change action in developing countries (Sethi and Puppim de Oliveira 2018).

Large-scale system transformations are also deeply influenced by factors outside governance and institutions, such as private interests and power dynamics (Jaglin 2014; Tyfield 2014). In some cases, these private interests are tied up with international flows of capital. In India, adaptation plans involving networks of private actors and related mitigation actions have resulted in the dominance of private interests. This has led to trade-offs and adverse impacts on the poor (Chu 2016; Mehta et al. 2019).

When planning and implementing low-carbon transitions, it is important to consider the socio-economic context. An inclusive approach emphasises the need to engage non-state actors, including businesses, research organisations, non-profit organisations and citizens (Lee and Painter 2015; Hale et al. 2020). For example, engaging people in defining locally relevant mitigation targets and actions has enabled successful transformations in China (Engels 2018), Africa (Göpfert et al. 2019) and Malaysia (Ho et al. 2015). An active research and government collaboration through multiple stakeholder interactions in a large economic corridor in Malaysia led to the development and implementation of a low-carbon blueprint for the region (Ho et al. 2013). Many cities in LDCs and developing countries lack adequate urban infrastructure and housing. An equitable transformation in these cities entails prioritising energy access and basic services, including safe drinking water and sanitation, to meet basic needs of their populations.

8.1.6   Urban Carbon Footprint

Urban areas concentrate GHG fluxes because of the size of the urban population, the size and nature of the urban economy, the energy and GHGs embodied in the infrastructure (see 'embodied emissions' in Glossary), and the goods and services imported and exported to and from cities (USGCRP 2018).

8.1.6.1   Urban Carbon Cycle

In cities, carbon cycles through natural (e.g., vegetation and soils) and managed (e.g., reservoirs and anthropogenic – buildings, transportation) pools. The accumulation of carbon in urban pools, such as buildings or landfills, results from the local or global transfer of carbon-containing energy and raw materials used in the city (Churkina 2008; Pichler et al. 2017; Chen et al. 2020b). Quantitative understanding of these transfers and the resulting emissions and uptake within an urban area is essential for accurate urban carbon accounting (USGCRP 2018). Currently, urban areas are a net source of carbon because they emit more carbon than they uptake. Thus, urban mitigation strategies require a twofold strategy: reducing urban emissions of carbon into the atmosphere, and enhancing uptake of carbon in urban pools (Churkina 2012) (for a broader definition of 'carbon cycle' and related terms such as 'carbon sink,' 'carbon stock,' 'carbon neutrality,' 'GHG neutrality,' and others, see Glossary).

Burning fossil fuels to generate energy for buildings, transportation, industry, and other sectors is a major source of urban GHG emissions (Gurney et al. 2015). At the same time, most cities do not generate within their boundaries all of the resources they use, such as electricity, gasoline, cement, water, and food needed for local homes and businesses to function (Jacobs 1969), requiring consideration of GHG emissions embodied in supply chains serving cities. Furthermore, urban vegetation, soils, and aquatic systems can both emit or remove carbon from the urban atmosphere and are often heavily managed. For example, urban parks, forests, and street trees actively remove carbon from the atmosphere through growing season photosynthesis. They can become a net source of carbon most often during the dormant season or heat waves. Some of the sequestered carbon can be stored in the biomass of urban trees, soils, and aquatic systems. Urban infrastructures containing cement also uptake carbon through the process of carbonation. The uptake of carbon by urban trees is at least two orders of magnitude faster than by cement-containing infrastructures (Churkina 2012) (Section 8.4.4 and Figures 8.17 and 8.18).

8.1.6.2   Urban Emissions Accounting

Urban GHG emissions accounting can determine critical conceptual and quantitative aspects of urban GHG emissions. The accounting framework chosen can therefore predetermine the emissions responsibility, the mitigation options available, and the level of effort required to correctly account for emissions (Afionis et al. 2017).

Two main urban carbon accounting advances have occurred since AR5. The first includes efforts to better understand and clarify how the different urban GHG accounting frameworks that have emerged over the past 15 years are interrelated, require different methodological tools, and reflect differing perspectives on emissions responsibility and quantification effort. The second main advance lies in a series of methodological innovations facilitating practical implementation, emissions verification, and scaling-up of the different GHG accounting approaches. This section provides an overview of the most used GHG urban accounting frameworks followed by a review of the advances since AR5.

Numerous studies have reviewed urban GHG accounting frameworks and methods with somewhat different nomenclatures and categorical divisions (Lin et al. 2015; Lombardi et al. 2017; Chen et al. 2019b; Arioli et al. 2020; Heinonen et al. 2020; Hachaichi and Baouni 2021; Ramaswami et al. 2021). Furthermore, accounting frameworks are reflected in multiple protocols used by urban practitioners (BSI 2013; Fong et al. 2014; ICLEI 2019b). Synthesis of these reviews and protocols, as well as the many individual methodological studies available, point to four general frameworks of urban GHG accounting: (i) territorial accounting (TA); (ii) community-wide infrastructure supply chain footprinting (CIF); and (iii and iv) consumption-based carbon footprint accounting (CBCF; Wiedmann and Minx 2008). The last, CBCF, can be further divided into accounting with a focus on household or personal consumption (iii: the personal carbon footprint, or PCF); and an approach in which one includes final consumption in an area by all consumers (iv: the areal carbon footprint, or ACF) (Heinonen et al. 2020). A number of small variations to these general categories are found in the literature (Lin et al. 2015; Chen et al. 2020a), but these four general frameworks capture the important distinctive (i.e., policy-relevant) features of urban GHG accounting.

All these approaches are foundationally rooted in the concept of urban metabolism, that is, the tracking of material and energy flows into, within, and out of cities (Wolman 1965). These frameworks all aim to quantify urban GHG emissions but reflect different perspectives on where the emission responsibility is allocated in addition to how much and which components of the GHG emissions associated with the import and export of goods and services to and from a city ('transboundary embedded/embodied GHG emissions') are included in a given urban emissions account. The four frameworks share some common, overlapping GHG emission quantities and their interrelationships have been defined mathematically (Chavez and Ramaswami 2013).

A key advance since AR5 lies in understanding the different GHG accounting frameworks in terms of what they imply for responsibility – shared or otherwise – and what they imply for the depth and breadth of GHG emission reductions. TA focuses on in-city direct emission of GHGs to the atmosphere (e.g., combustion, net ecosystem exchange, methane (CH_4) leakage) within a chosen geographic area (Sovacool and Brown 2010; Gurney et al. 2019). CIF connects essential infrastructure use and demand activities in cities with their production, by combining TA emissions with the transboundary supply chain emissions associated with imported electricity, fuels, food, water, building materials, and waste management services used in cities (Ramaswami et al. 2008; Kennedy et al. 2009; Chavez and Ramaswami 2013).

CBCF considers not only the supply-chain-related GHG emissions of key infrastructure, but also emissions associated with all goods and services across a city, often removing emissions associated with goods and services exported from a city (Wiedmann et al. 2016, 2021). The distinction between the PCF and ACF variants of the CBCF is primarily associated with whether the agents responsible for the final demand are confined to only city residents (PCF) or all consumers in a city (ACF), which can include government consumers, capital formation, and other final demand categories (Heinonen et al. 2020).

A recent synthesis of these frameworks in the context of a net-zero GHG emissions target suggests that the four frameworks contribute to different aspects of decarbonisation policy and can work together to inform the overall process of decarbonisation (Ramaswami et al. 2021). Furthermore, the relative magnitude of GHG emissions for a given city resulting from the different frameworks is often a reflection of the city's economic structure as a 'consumer' or 'producer' city (Chavez and Ramaswami 2013; Sudmant et al. 2018).

The TA framework is unique in that it can be independently verified through direct measurement of GHGs in the atmosphere, offering a check on the integrity of emission estimates (Lauvaux et al. 2020; Mueller et al. 2021). It is traditionally simpler to estimate by urban practitioners given the lower data requirements, and it can be relevant to policies aimed specifically at energy consumption and mobility activities within city boundaries. However, it will not reflect electricity imported for use in cities or lifecycle emissions associated with in-city consumption of goods and services.

The CIF framework adds to the TA framework by including GHG emissions associated with electricity imports and the lifecycle GHG emissions associated with key infrastructure provisioning activities in cities, serving all homes, businesses, and industries. This widens both the number of emitting categories and the responsibility for those emissions by including infrastructure-related supply chain emissions. The CIF framework enables individual cities to connect community-wide demand for infrastructure and food with their transboundary production, strategically aligning their net-zero emissions plans with larger-scale net-zero efforts (Ramaswami and Chavez 2013; Ramaswami et al. 2021; Seto et al. 2021).

The PCF version of the CBCF shifts the focus of the consumption and associated supply chain emissions to only household consumption of goods and services (Jones and Kammen 2014). This both reduces the TA emissions considered and the supply chain emissions, excluding all emissions associated with government, capital formation, and exports. The ACF, by contrast, widens the perspective considerably, including the TA and supply chain emissions of all consumers in a city, but often removing emissions associated with exports.

An additional distinction is the ability to sum up accounts from individual cities in a region or country, for example, directly to arrive at a regional or national total. This can only be done for the TA and PCF frameworks. The ACF and CIF frameworks would require adjustment to avoid double-counting emissions (Chen et al. 2020a).

A second major area of advance since AR5 has been in methods to implement, verify and scale up the different GHG footprinting approaches. Advances have been made in six key areas: (i) advancing urban metabolism accounts integrating stocks and flows, and considering biogenic and fossil-fuel-based emissions (Chen et al. 2020b); (ii) improving fine-scale and near-real-time urban use-activity data through new urban data science (Gately et al. 2017; Gurney et al. 2019; Turner et al. 2020; Yadav et al. 2021); (iii) using atmospheric monitoring from the ground, aircraft, and satellites combined with inverse modelling to independently quantify TA emissions (Lamb et al. 2016; Lauvaux et al. 2016, 2020; Davis et al. 2017; Mitchell et al. 2018; Sargent et al. 2018; Turnbull et al. 2019; Wu et al. 2020a); (iv) improving supply chain and input-output modelling, including the use of physically based input-output models (Wachs and Singh 2018); (v) establishing the global multi-region input-output models (Lenzen et al. 2017; Wiedmann et al. 2021); and (vi) generating multi-sector use and supply activity data across all cities in a nation, in a manner where data aggregate consistently across city, province, and national scales (Tong et al. 2021) (Section 8.3).

8.2 Co-benefits and Trade-offs of Urban Mitigation Strategies

Co-benefits are 'the positive effects that a policy or measure aimed at one objective might have on other objectives, thereby increasing the total benefits to the society or environment' (IPCC 2018b). AR5 WGIII Chapter 12 reported a range of co-benefits associated with urban climate change mitigation strategies, including public savings, air quality and associated health benefits, and productivity increases in urban centres (Seto et al. 2014). Since AR5, evidence continues to mount on the co-benefits of urban mitigation. Highlighting co-benefits could make a strong case for driving impactful mitigation action (Bain et al. 2016), especially in developing countries, where development benefits can be the argument for faster implementation (Sethi and Puppim de Oliveira 2018). Through co-benefits, urban areas can couple mitigation, adaptation, and sustainable development while closing infrastructure gaps (Thacker et al. 2019; Kamiya et al. 2020).

The urgency of coupling mitigation and adaptation is emphasised through a special Cross-Working Group Box on 'Cities and Climate Change' (Section 8.2.3 and Cross-Working Group Box 2 in this chapter). This section further addresses synergies and trade-offs for sustainable development with a focus on linkages with the SDGs and perspectives for economic development, competitiveness, and equity.

8.2.1 Sustainable Development

Sustainable development is a broad concept, encompassing socio-economic and environmental dimensions, envisaging long-term permanence and improvement. While long-term effects are more related to resilience – and hence carry co-benefits and synergies with the mitigation of GHG emissions – some short-term milestones were defined by the post-2015 UN Sustainable Development Agenda SDGs, including a specific goal on climate change (SDG 13) and one on making cities inclusive, safe, resilient and sustainable (SDG 11)

(United Nations 2015). The SDGs and related indicators can be an opportunity to improve cities by using science-based decision-making and engaging a diverse set of stakeholders (Simon et al. 2016; Klopp and Petretta 2017; Kutty et al. 2020).

There are multiple ways that development pathways can be shifted towards sustainability (Section 4.3.3, Cross-Chapter Box 5 in Chapter 4, Chapter 17 and Figure 17.1). Urban areas can work to redirect development pathways towards sustainability while increasing co-benefits for urban inhabitants. Figure 8.4 indicates that mitigation options for urban systems can provide synergistic linkages across a wide range of SDGs, and some cases where linkages can produce both synergies and trade-offs. While linkages are based on context and the scale of implementation, synergies can be most significant when urban areas pursue integrated approaches where one mitigation option supports the other (Sections 8.4 and 8.6).

Figure 8.4 summarises an evaluation of the synergies and/or trade-offs with the SDGs for the mitigation options for urban systems based on Supplementary Material 8.SM.1. The evaluations depend on the specific urban context, with synergies and/or trade-offs being more significant in certain contexts than others. Urban mitigation with a view of the SDGs can support shifting pathways of urbanisation towards greater sustainability. The feasibility of urban mitigation options is also malleable and can increase with more 'enabling conditions' (see Glossary), provided, perhaps, through institutional (i.e., financial or governmental) support (Section 8.5). Strengthened institutional capacity that supports the coordination of mitigation options can increase linkages with the SDGs and their synergies. For example, urban land use and spatial planning for walkable and co-located densities, together with electrification of the urban energy system, can hold more benefits for the SDGs than any one of the mitigation options alone (Sections 8.4.2.3, 8.4.3.1 and 8.6).

Evidence on the co-benefits of urban mitigation measures for human health has increased significantly since AR5, especially through the use of health impact assessments, where energy savings and cleaner energy supply structures based on measures for urban planning, heating, and transport have reduced CO_2, nitrogen oxides (NO_x), and coarse particulate matter (PM_{10}) emissions (Diallo et al. 2016). Some measures, especially those related to land-use planning and transportation, have also increased opportunities for physical activity for improved health (Diallo et al. 2016). In developing countries, the co-benefits approach has been effective in justifying climate change mitigation actions at the local level (Puppim de Oliveira and Doll 2016). Mixed-use compact development with sufficient land-use diversity can have a positive influence on urban productivity (Section 8.4.2). Conversely, urban spatial structures that increase walking distances and produce car dependency have negative impacts on urban productivity considering congestion as well as energy costs (Salat et al. 2017).

There is increasing evidence that climate mitigation measures can lower health risks that are related to energy poverty, especially among vulnerable groups such as the elderly and in informal settlements (Monforti-Ferrario et al. 2018). Measures such as renewable energy-based electrification of the energy system not only reduce outdoor air

Figure 8.4: Co-benefits of urban mitigation actions. The first column lists urban mitigation options. The second column indicates synergies with the SDGs. The third column indicates both synergies and/or trade-offs. The dots represent confidence levels with the number of dots representing levels from low to high. In the last column, confidence levels for synergies and/or trade-offs are provided separately. A plus sign (+) represents synergy and a minus sign (−) represents a trade-off. Supplementary Material 8.SM.1 provides 64 references and extends the SDG mappings that are provided in Thacker et al. (2019) and Fuso Nerini et al. (2018). Please see Table 17.SM.1 for details and Annex II for the methodology of the SDG assessment.

pollution, but also enhance indoor air quality by promoting smoke-free heating and cooking in buildings (Kjellstrom and McMichael 2013). The environmental and ecological benefits of electrification of the urban energy system include improved air quality based on a shift to non-polluting energy sources (Jacobson et al. 2018; Ajanovic and Haas 2019; Bagheri et al. 2019; Gai et al. 2020). Across 74 metropolitan areas around the world, an estimated 408,270 lives per year are saved due to air quality improvements that stem from a move to 100% renewable energy (Jacobson et al. 2020). Other studies indicate that there is potential to reduce premature mortality by up to 7000 people in 53 towns and cities, to create 93,000 new jobs, and to lower global climate costs and personal energy costs, through renewable energy transformations (Jacobson et al. 2018).

Across 146 signatories of a city climate network, local energy-saving measures led to 6596 avoided premature deaths and 68,476 years of life saved due to improved air quality (Monforti-Ferrario et al. 2018). Better air quality further reinforces the health co-benefits of climate mitigation measures based on walking and bicycling since evidence suggests that increased physical activity in urban outdoor settings with low levels of black carbon improves lung function (Laeremans et al. 2018). Physical activity can also be fostered through urban design measures and policies that promote the development of ample and well-connected parks and open spaces, and can lead to physical and mental health benefits (Kabisch et al. 2016) (Section 8.4.4 and Figure 8.18).

Cities in India, Indonesia, Vietnam, and Thailand show that reducing emissions from major sources (e.g., transport, residential burning, biomass open burning, and industry) could bring substantial co-benefits of avoided deaths from reduced $PM_{2.5}$ (fine inhalable particulates) emissions and radiative forcing from black carbon (Pathak and Shukla 2016; Dhar et al. 2017; Permadi et al. 2017; Karlsson et al. 2020), reduced noise, and reduced traffic injuries (Kwan and Hashim 2016). Compact city policies and interventions that support a modal shift away from private motor vehicles towards walking, cycling, and low-emission public transport delivers significant public health benefits (Creutzig 2016; Ürge-Vorsatz et al. 2018). Trade-offs associated with compact development include the marginal health costs of transport air pollution (Lohrey and Creutzig 2016) and stress from traffic noise (Gruebner et al. 2017) (Section 8.4.2.3).

Urban green and blue infrastructure – a subset of nature-based solutions (NBS) – acts as both climate mitigation and adaptation measures by reducing heat stress (Kim and Coseo 2018; Privitera and La Rosa 2018; Herath et al. 2021), improving air quality, reducing noise (Scholz et al. 2018; De la Sota et al. 2019), improving urban biodiversity (Hall et al. 2017b), and enhancing well-being, including contributions to local development (Lwasa et al. 2015). Health benefits from urban forestry and green infrastructure include reduced cardiovascular morbidity, improved mental health (van den Bosch and Ode Sang 2017; Vujcic et al. 2017; Al-Kindi et al. 2020; Sharifi et al. 2021), raised birth weight (Dzhambov et al. 2014), and increased life expectancy (Jonker et al. 2014). Urban agriculture, including urban orchards, rooftop gardens, and vertical farming contribute to enhancing food security and fostering healthier diets

(Cole et al. 2018; Petit-Boix and Apul 2018; De la Sota et al. 2019) (Section 8.4.4, Figure 8.18 and Box 8.2).

8.2.2 Economic Development, Competitiveness, and Equity

Sustainable management of urban ecosystems entails addressing economic growth, equity, and good governance. In total, 102 SDG targets (99 synergies and 51 trade-offs) are identified with published evidence of relationships with urban ecosystems – out of the 169 in the 2030 Agenda (Maes et al. 2019). The targets require action in relation to urban ecosystem management, environmental improvements, equality related to basic services, long-term economic growth, economic savings, stronger governance, and policy development at multiple scales.

Mitigation measures related to different sectors can provide co-benefits and reduce social inequities. Transport-related measures, such as transportation demand management, transit-oriented development (TOD), and promotion of active transport modes provide economic co-benefits through, for example, reducing health care costs linked with pollution and cardiovascular diseases, improving labour productivity, and decreasing congestion costs (including waste of time and money) (Sharifi et al. 2021). As a case-in-point, data from cities such as Bangkok, Kuala Lumpur, Jakarta, Manila, Beijing, Mexico City, Dakar, and Buenos Aires indicate that economic costs of congestion account for a considerable share of their gross domestic product (GDP), ranging from 0.7% to 15.0% (Dulal 2017) (Section 8.4.2).

Since policy interventions can result in negative impacts or trade-offs with other objectives, fostering accessibility, equity, and inclusivity for disadvantaged groups is essential (Viguié and Hallegatte 2012; Sharifi 2020; Pörtner et al. 2021). Anti-sprawl policies that aim to increase density, or the introduction of large green areas in cities could increase property prices, resulting in trade-offs with affordable housing and pushing urban poor further away from cities (Reckien et al. 2017; Alves et al. 2019). Deliberate strategies can improve access of low-income populations to jobs, and gender-responsive transport systems that can enhance women's mobility and financial independence (Viguié and Hallegatte 2012; Lecompte and Juan Pablo 2017; Reckien et al. 2017; Priya Uteng and Turner 2019).

Low-carbon urban development that triggers economic decoupling and involves capacity-building measures could have a positive impact on employment and local competitiveness (Dodman 2009; Kalmykova et al. 2015; Chen et al. 2018b; García-Gusano et al. 2018; Hu et al. 2018; Shen et al. 2018). Sustainable and low-carbon urban development that integrates issues of equity, inclusivity, and affordability while safeguarding urban livelihoods, providing access to basic services, lowering energy bills, addressing energy poverty, and improving public health, can also improve the distributional effects of existing and future urbanisation (Friend et al. 2016; Claude et al. 2017; Colenbrander et al. 2017; Ma et al. 2018; Mrówczyńska et al. 2018; Pukšec et al. 2018; Wiktorowicz et al. 2018; Ramaswami 2020).

Depending on the context, green and blue infrastructure can also offer considerable economic co-benefits. For example, green roofs and facades and other urban greening efforts such as urban agriculture and greening streets can improve microclimatic conditions and enhance thermal comfort, thereby reducing utility and health care costs. The presence of green and blue infrastructure may also increase the economic values of nearby properties (Votsis 2017; Alves et al. 2019) (Section 8.4.4 and Figure 8.18).

Studies in the UK show that beneficiaries are willing to pay (WTP) an additional fee (up to 2% more in monthly rent) for proximity to green and blue infrastructure, with the WTP varying depending on the size and nature of the green space (Mell et al. 2013, 2016). Urban agriculture can not only reduce household food expenditure, but also provide additional sources of revenue for the city (Ayerakwa 2017; Alves et al. 2019). Based on the assessed literature, there is *high agreement* on the economic co-benefits of green and blue infrastructure, but supporting evidence is still limited (Section 8.7).

Implementing waste management and wastewater recycling measures can provide additional sources of income for citizens and local authorities. Wastewater recycling can minimise the costs associated with the renewal of centralised wastewater treatment plants (Bernstad Saraiva Schott and Cánovas 2015; Gharfalkar et al. 2015; Gonzalez-Valencia et al. 2016; Herrero and Vilella 2018; Matsuda et al. 2018; Nisbet et al. 2019). Waste management and wastewater recycling is also a pathway for inclusion of the informal sector into the urban economy with *high agreement* and *medium evidence* (Sharifi 2021). Additionally, authorities can sell energy generated from wastewater recycling to compensate for the wastewater management costs (Colenbrander et al. 2017; Gondhalekar and Ramsauer 2017). Another measure that contributes to reducing household costs is the promotion of behavioural measures such as dietary changes that can decrease the demand for costly food sources and reduce health care costs through promoting healthy diets (Hoppe et al. 2016) (Sections 8.4.5 and 8.4.6).

In addition to cost savings, various measures such as stormwater management and urban greening can enhance social equity and environmental justice. For example, the thermal comfort benefits provided by green and blue infrastructure and passive design measures can address issues related to energy poverty and unaffordability of expensive air conditioning systems for some social groups (Sharma et al. 2018; He et al. 2019). To achieve such benefits, however, the costs of integrating green and blue infrastructure and passive design measures into building design would need to be minimised. Another example is the flood mitigation benefits of stormwater management measures that can reduce impacts on urban poor who often reside in flood-prone and low-lying areas of cities (Adegun 2017; He et al. 2019). Generally, the urban poor are expected to be disproportionately affected by climate change impacts. Carefully designed measures that reduce such disproportionate impacts by involving experts, authorities and citizens would enhance social equity (Pandey et al. 2018; He et al. 2019; Mulligan et al. 2020).

8.2.3 Coupling Mitigation and Adaptation

There are numerous synergies that come from coupling urban adaptation and mitigation. A number of studies have developed methods to assess the synergies between mitigation and adaptation strategies, as well as their co-benefits (Solecki et al. 2015; Buonocore et al. 2016; Chang et al. 2017; Helgenberger and Jänicke 2017). Co-benefits occur when implementing mitigation (or adaptation) measures that have positive effects on adaptation (or mitigation) (Sharifi 2021). In contrast, the trade-offs emerge when measures aimed at improving mitigation (adaptation) undermine the ability to pursue adaptation (mitigation) targets (Sharifi 2020). The magnitude of such co-benefits and trade-offs may vary depending on various factors. A systematic review of over 50 climate change articles provides evidence that mitigation can contribute to resilience – especially to temperature changes and flooding – with varying magnitudes, depending on factors such as the type of mitigation measure and the scale of implementation (Sharifi 2019).

Measures from different sectors that can provide both mitigation and adaptation benefits involve urban planning (Section 8.4.2), buildings (Sections 8.4.3.2 and 8.4.4), energy (Section 8.4.3), green and blue infrastructure (Section 8.4.4), transportation (Section 8.4.2), socio-behavioural aspects (Section 8.4.5), urban governance (Section 8.5), waste (Section 8.4.5.2), and water (Section 8.4.6). In addition to their energy-saving and carbon-sequestration benefits, many measures can also enhance adaptation to climate threats, such as extreme heat, energy shocks, floods, and droughts (Sharifi 2021). Existing evidence is mainly related to urban green infrastructure, urban planning, transportation, and buildings. There has been more emphasis on the potential co-benefits of measures, such as proper levels of density, building energy efficiency, distributed and decentralised energy infrastructure, green roofs and facades, and public/active transport modes. Renewable-based distributed and decentralised energy systems improve resilience to energy shocks and can enhance adaptation to water stress considering the water-energy nexus. By further investment on these measures, planners and decision makers can ensure enhancing achievement of mitigation/adaptation co-benefits at the urban level (Sharifi 2021).

As for trade-offs, some mitigation efforts may increase exposure to stressors such as flooding and the urban heat island (UHI) effect (see Glossary), thereby reducing the adaptive capacity of citizens. For instance, in some contexts, high-density areas that lack adequate provision of green and open spaces may intensify the UHI effect (Pierer and Creutzig 2019; Xu et al. 2019). There are also concerns that some mitigation efforts may diminish adaptive capacity of urban poor and marginalised groups through increasing costs of urban services and/or eroding livelihood options. Environmental policies designed to meet mitigation targets through phasing out old vehicles may erode livelihood options of poor households, thereby decreasing their adaptive capacity (Colenbrander et al. 2017). Ambitious mitigation and adaptation plans could benefit private corporate interests resulting in adverse effects on the urban poor (Chu et al. 2018; Mehta et al. 2019).

Urban green and blue infrastructure such as urban trees, greenspaces, and urban waterways can sequester carbon and reduce energy demand, and provide adaptation co-benefits by mitigating the UHI effect (Berry et al. 2015; Wamsler and Pauleit 2016; WCRP 2019) (Section 8.4.4, Figure 8.18 and Box 8.2).

Cross-Working Group Box 2: Cities and Climate Change

Authors: Xuemei Bai (Australia), Vanesa Castán Broto (Spain/United Kingdom), Winston Chow (Singapore), Felix Creutzig (Germany), David Dodman (Jamaica/United Kingdom), Rafiq Hamdi (Belgium), Bronwyn Hayward (New Zealand), Şiir Kılkış (Turkey), Shuaib Lwasa (Uganda), Timon McPhearson (the United States of America), Minal Pathak (India), Mark Pelling (United Kingdom), Diana Reckien (Germany), Karen C. Seto (the United States of America), Ayyoob Sharifi (Iran/Japan), Diana Ürge-Vorsatz (Hungary)

Introduction

This Cross-Working Group Box on Cities and Climate Change responds to the critical role of urbanisation as a megatrend impacting climate adaptation and mitigation. Issues associated with cities and urbanisation are covered in substantial depth within all three Working Groups (including WGI Box TS.14, WGII Chapter 6 'Cities, Settlements and Key Infrastructure', WGII regional chapters, WGII Cross-Chapter Paper 'Cities and Settlements by the Sea', and WGIII Chapter 8 'Urban Systems and Other Settlements'). This Box highlights key findings from WGII and III and substantial gaps in literature where more research is urgently needed relating to policy action in cities. It describes methods of addressing mitigation and adaptation in an integrated way across sectors and cities to advance sustainable development and equity outcomes and assesses the governance and finance solutions required to support climate-resilient responses.

Urbanisation: A megatrend driving global climate risk and potential for low-carbon and resilient futures

Severe weather events, exacerbated by anthropogenic emissions, are already having devastating impacts on people who live in urban areas, on the infrastructure that supports these communities, as well as people living in distant places (*high confidence*) (Cai et al. 2019; Folke et al. 2021). Between 2000 and 2015, the global population in locations that were affected by floods grew by 58–86 million (Tellman et al. 2021). The direct economic costs of all extreme events reached USD210–268 billion in 2020 (Aon 2021; Munich RE 2021; WMO 2021) or about USD0.7 billion per day; this figure does not include knock-on costs in supply chains (Kii 2020) or lost days of work, implying that the actual economic costs could be far higher. Depending on RCP, between half (RCP2.6) and three-quarters (RCP8.5) of the global population could be exposed to periods of life-threatening climatic conditions arising from coupled impacts of extreme heat and humidity by 2100 (Mora et al. 2017; Huang et al. 2019) (see WGII Section 6.2.2.1, WGII Figure 6.3, and WGIII Sections 8.2 and 8.3.4).

Urban systems are now global, as evidenced by the interdependencies between infrastructure, services, and networks driven by urban production and consumption; remittance flows and investments reach into rural places, shaping natural resource use far from the city and bring risk to the city when these places are impacted by climate change (WGIII Section 8.4 and Figure 8.15). This megatrend (Kourtit et al. 2015) amplifies as well as shapes the potential impacts of climate events and integrates the aims and approaches for delivering mitigation, adaptation, and sustainable development (*medium evidence, high agreement*) (Dawson et al. 2018; Tsavdaroglou et al. 2018; Zscheischler et al. 2018). For cities facing flood damage, wide-ranging impacts have been recorded on other urban areas near and far (Carter et al. 2021; Simpson et al. 2021) as production and trade is disrupted (Shughrue et al. 2020). In the absence of integrated mitigation and adaptation across and between infrastructure systems and local places, impacts that bring urban economies to a standstill can extend into supply chains and across energy networks causing power outages.

Urban settlements contribute to climate change, generating about 70% of global CO_2-eq emissions (*high confidence*) (see WGI Box TS.14, WGII Sections 6.1 and 6.2, and WGIII Section 8.3). This global impact feeds back to cities through the exposure of infrastructure, people, and business to the impacts of climate-related hazards. Particularly in larger cities, this climate feedback is exacerbated by local choices in urban design, land use, building design, and human behaviour (Viguié et al. 2020) that shape local environmental conditions. Both the local and global combine to increase hazardousness. Certain configurations of urban form and their elements can add up to 2°C to warming; concretisation of open space can increase run-off, and building height and orientation influences wind direction and strength (see WGII Section 6.3 and WGIII Section 8.4.2).

Cross-Working Group Box 2 (continued)

Designing for resilient and low-carbon cities today is far easier than retrofitting for risk reduction tomorrow. As urbanisation unfolds, its legacy continues to be the locking-in of emissions and vulnerabilities (*high confidence*) (Seto et al. 2016; Ürge-Vorsatz et al. 2018) (see WGIII Section 8.4 and Figure 8.15). Retrofitting, disaster reconstruction, and urban regeneration programmes offer scope for strategic direction changes to low-carbon and high-resilience urban form and function, so long as they are inclusive in design and implementation. Rapid urban growth means new investment, new buildings and infrastructure, new demands for energy and transport and new questions about what a healthy and fulfilling urban life can be. The USD90 trillion expected to be invested in new urban development by 2030 (NCE 2018) is a global opportunity to place adaptation and mitigation directly into urban infrastructure and planning, as well as to consider social policy including education, health care, and environmental management (Ürge-Vorsatz et al. 2018). If this opportunity is missed, and business-as-usual urbanisation persists, social and physical vulnerability will become much more challenging to address.

The benefits of actions taken to reduce GHG emissions and climate stressors diminish with delayed action, indicating the necessity for rapid responses. Delaying the same actions for increasing the resilience of infrastructure from 2020 to 2030 is estimated to have a median cost of at least USD1 trillion (Hallegatte et al. 2019) while also missing the carbon emissions reductions required in the narrowing window of opportunity to limit global warming to 1.5°C (WGI). In contrast, taking integrated actions towards mitigation, adaptation, and sustainable development will provide multiple benefits for the health and well-being of urban inhabitants and avoid stranded assets (see WGII Section 6.3, WGII Chapter 17, Cross-Chapter Box on 'Feasibility' in WGII Chapter 18, WGIII Chapter 5, and WGIII Section 8.2).

The policy-action gap: urban low-carbon and climate-resilient development

Cities are critical places to realise both adaptation and mitigation actions simultaneously with potential co-benefits that extend far beyond cities (*medium evidence, high agreement*) (Göpfert et al. 2019; Grafakos et al. 2020). Given rapid changes in the built environment, transforming the use of materials and the land intensiveness of urban development, including in many parts of the Global South, will be critical in the next decades, as well as mainstreaming low-carbon development principles in new urban development in all regions. Much of this development will be self-built and 'informal' – and new modes of governance and planning will be required to engage with this. Integrating mitigation and adaptation now rather than later, through reshaping patterns of urban development and associated decision-making processes, is a prerequisite for attaining resilient and zero-carbon cities (see WGIII Sections 8.4 and 8.6, and WGIII Figure 8.21).

While more cities have developed plans for climate adaptation and mitigation since AR5, many remain to be implemented (*limited evidence, high agreement*) (Araos et al. 2017; Aguiar et al. 2018; Olazabal and Ruiz De Gopegui 2021). A review of local climate mitigation and adaptation plans across 885 urban areas of the European Union suggests mitigation plans are more common than adaptation plans – and that city size, national legislation, and international networks can influence the development of local climate and adaptation plans with an estimated 80% of those cities with above 500,000 inhabitants having a mitigation and/or an adaptation plan (Reckien et al. 2018).

Integrated approaches to tackle common drivers of emissions and cascading risks provide the basis for strengthening synergies across mitigation and adaptation, and help manage possible trade-offs with sustainable development (*limited evidence, medium agreement*) (Grafakos et al. 2019; Landauer et al. 2019; Pierer and Creutzig 2019). An analysis of 315 local authority emission-reduction plans reveals that the most common policies cover municipal assets and structures (Palermo et al. 2020a). Estimates of emission reductions by non-state and sub-state actors in 10 high-emitting economies projected GHG emissions in 2030 would be 1.2–2.0 GtCO$_2$-eq yr^{-1} or 3.8–5.5% lower compared to scenario projections for current national policies (31.6–36.8 GtCO$_2$-eq yr^{-1}) if the policies are fully implemented and do not change the pace of action elsewhere (Kuramochi et al. 2020). The value of integrating mitigation and adaptation is underscored in the opportunities for decarbonising existing urban areas, and investing in social, ecological, and technological infrastructure resilience (WGII Section 6.4). Integrating mitigation and adaption is challenging (Landauer et al. 2019) but can provide multiple benefits for the health and well-being of urban inhabitants (Sharifi 2021) (See WGIII Section 8.2.3).

Effective climate strategies combine mitigation and adaptation responses, including through linking adaptive urban land use with GHG emission reductions (*medium evidence, high agreement*) (Xu et al. 2019; Patterson 2021). For example, urban green and blue infrastructure can provide co-benefits for mitigation and adaptation (Ürge-Vorsatz et al. 2018) and is an important entry point for integrating adaptation and mitigation at the urban level (Frantzeskaki et al. 2019) (see WGIII Section 8.4.4 and WGIII Figure 8.18). Grey and physical infrastructure, such as sea defences, can immediately reduce risk, but also transfer risk and limit future options. Social policy interventions including social safety nets provide financial security for the most at-risk and can manage vulnerability determined by specific hazards or independently.

Cross-Working Group Box 2 (continued)

Hazard-independent mechanisms for vulnerability reduction – such as population-wide social security – provide resilience in the face of unanticipated cascading impacts or surprise and novel climate-related hazard exposure. Social interventions can also support or be led by ambitions to reach the SDGs (Archer 2016). Climate-resilient development invites planners to develop interventions and monitor the effectiveness of outcomes beyond individual projects and across wider remits that consider sustainable development. Curbing the emission impacts of urban activities to reach net-zero emissions in the next decades, while improving the resilience of urban areas, necessitates an integrated response now.

Key gaps in knowledge include: urban-enabling environments; the role of smaller settlements, low-income communities, and informal settlements, as well as those in rental housing spread across the city; and the ways in which actions to reduce supply chain risk can be supported to accelerate equitable and sustainable adaptation in the face of financial and governance constraints (Birkmann et al. 2016; Shi et al. 2016; Rosenzweig et al. 2018; Dulal 2019).

Enabling action

Innovative governance and finance solutions are required to manage complex and interconnected risks across essential key infrastructures, networks, and services, as well as to meet basic human needs in urban areas (*medium confidence*) (Colenbrander et al. 2018a; Moser et al. 2019). There are many examples of 'ready-to-use' policy tools, technologies, and practical interventions for policymakers seeking to act on adaptation and mitigation (Bisaro and Hinkel 2018; Keenan et al. 2019; Chirambo 2021) (see WGIII Section 8.5.4). Tax and fiscal incentives for businesses and individuals can help support city-wide behavjour change towards low-carbon and risk-reducing choices. Change can start where governments have most control – often in public sector institutions and investment – but the challenge ahead requires partnership with private sector and community actors acting at scale and with accountability. Urban climate governance and finance needs to address urban inequalities at the forefront if the urban opportunity is to realise the ambition of the SDGs.

Increasing the pace of investments will put pressure on governance capability, transparency, and accountability of decision-making (*medium confidence*) (see WGII Section 6.4.5). Urban climate action that actively includes local actors is more likely to avoid unintended, negative maladaptive impacts and mobilise a wide range of local capacities. In the long run, this is also more likely to carry public support, even if some experiments and investments do not deliver the intended social benefits. Legislation, technical capacity, and governance capability are required to be able to absorb additional finance.

In recent years, about USD384 billion of climate finance has been invested in urban areas per year. This remains at about 10% of the annual climate finance that would be necessary for low-carbon and resilient urban development at a global scale (Negreiros et al. 2021). Rapid deployment of funds to stimulate economies in the recovery from COVID-19 has highlighted the pitfalls of funding expansion ahead of policy innovation and capacity building. The result can be an intensification of existing carbon-intensive urban forms – exactly the kinds of 'carbon lock-in' (see WGIII Glossary and WGIII Section 8.4.1) that have contributed to risk creation and its concentration amongst those with little public voice or economic power.

Iterative and experimental approaches to climate adaptation and mitigation decision-making grounded in data and co-generated in partnership with communities can advance low-carbon climate resilience (*medium evidence, high confidence*) (Culwick et al. 2019; Caldarice et al. 2021; van der Heijden and Hong 2021). Conditions of complexity, uncertainty, and constrained resources require innovative solutions that are both adaptive and anticipatory. Complex interactions among multiple agents in times of uncertainty makes decision-making about social, economic, governance, and infrastructure choices challenging and can lead decision-makers to postpone action. This is the case for those balancing household budgets, residential investment portfolios, and city-wide policy responsibilities. Living with climate change requires changes to business-as-usual design-making. Co-design and collaboration with communities through iterative policy experimentation can point the way towards climate-resilient development pathways (Ataöv and Peker 2021). Key to successful learning is transparency in policymaking, inclusive policy processes, and robust local modelling, monitoring, and evaluation, which are not yet widely undertaken (Sanchez Rodriguez et al. 2018; Ford et al. 2019).

The diversity of cities' experiences of climate mitigation and adaptation strategies brings an advantage for those city governments and other actors willing to 'learn together' (*limited evidence, high confidence*) (Bellinson and Chu 2019; Haupt and Coppola 2019). While contexts are varied, policy options are often similar enough for the sharing of experiments and policy champions. Sharing expertise can build on existing regional and global networks, many of which have already placed knowledge, learning, and capacity building at the centre of their agendas. Learning from innovative forms of governance and financial investment, as well as strengthening co-production of policy through inclusive access to knowledge and resources, can help address mismatches in local capacities and strengthen wider SDGs and COVID-19 recovery agendas (*limited evidence, medium agreement*). Perceptions of risk can greatly

8

influence the reallocation of capital and shift financial resources (Battiston et al. 2021). Coupling mitigation and adaptation in an integrated approach offers opportunities to enhance efficiency, increases the coherence of urban climate action, generates cost savings, and provides opportunities to reinvest the savings into new climate action projects to make all urban areas and regions more resilient.

Local governments play an important role in driving climate action across mitigation and adaptation as managers of assets, regulators, mobilisers, and catalysts of action, but few cities are undertaking transformative climate adaptation or mitigation actions (*limited evidence, medium confidence*) (Heikkinen et al. 2019). Local actors are providers of infrastructure and services, regulators of zoning, and can be conveners and champions of an integrated approach for mitigation and adaptation at multiple levels (*limited evidence, high confidence*). New opportunities in governance and finance can enable cities to pool resources together and aggregate interventions to innovate ways of mobilising urban climate finance at scale (Colenbrander et al. 2019; Simpson et al. 2019; White and Wahba 2019). However, research increasingly points towards the difficulties faced during the implementation of climate financing in situ, such as the fragmentation of structures of governance capable of managing large investments effectively (Mohammed et al. 2019) (see WGIII Section 8.5 and WGIII Chapter 13).

Scaling up transformative place-based action for both adaptation and mitigation requires enabling conditions, including land-based financing, intermediaries, and local partnerships (*medium evidence, high agreement*) (Chu et al. 2019; Chaudhuri, 2020) supported by a new generation of big data approaches. Governance structures that combine actors working at different levels with a different mix of tools are effective in addressing challenges related to implementation of integrated action while cross-sectoral coordination is necessary (Singh et al. 2020). Joint institutionalisation of mitigation and adaptation in local governance structures can also enable integrated action (Göpfert et al. 2020; Hurlimann et al. 2021). However, the proportion of international finance that reaches local recipients remains low, despite the repeated focus of climate policy on place-based adaptation and mitigation (Manuamorn et al. 2020). Green financing instruments that enable local climate action without exacerbating current forms of inequality can jointly address mitigation, adaptation, and sustainable development. Climate finance that also reaches beyond larger non-state enterprises (e.g., small and medium-sized enterprises, local communities, or non-governmental organisations (NGOs)), and is inclusive in responding to the needs of all urban inhabitants (e.g., disabled individuals, or citizens of different races or ethnicities) is essential for inclusive and resilient urban development (Colenbrander et al. 2019; Gabaldón-Estevan et al. 2019; Frenova 2021). Developing networks that can exert climate action at scale is another priority for climate finance.

The urban megatrend is an opportunity to transition global society. Enabling urban governance to avert cascading risk and achieve low-carbon, resilient development will involve the co-production of policy and planning, rapid implementation and greater cross-sector coordination, and monitoring and evaluation (*limited evidence, medium agreement*) (Di Giulio et al. 2018; Grafakos et al. 2019). New constellations of responsible actors are required to manage hybrid local-city or cross-city risk management and decarbonisation initiatives (*limited evidence, medium agreement*). These may increasingly benefit from linkages across more urban and more rural space as recognition of cascading and systemic risk brings recognition of supply chains, remittance flows, and migration trends as vectors of risk and resilience. Urban governance will be better prepared in planning, prioritising, and financing the kind of measures that can reduce GHG emissions and improve resilience at scale when they consider a view of cascading risks and carbon lock-ins globally, while also acting locally to address local limitations and capacities, including the needs and priorities of urban citizens (Colenbrander et al. 2018a; Rodrigues 2019).

8.3 Urban Systems and Greenhouse Gas Emissions

This section assesses trends in urban land use, the built environment, and urban GHG emissions, as well as forecasts for urban land use and emissions under certain scenarios to 2050 or 2100. These trends and scenarios hold implications for optimising the approaches to urban climate change mitigation discussed in Sections 8.4 and 8.6.

8.3.1 Trends in Urban Land Use and the Built Environment

Urban land use is one of the most intensive human impacts on the planet (Pouyat et al. 2007; Grimm et al. 2008). Urban land expansion to accommodate a growing urban population has resulted in the conversion of agricultural land (Pandey et al. 2018; Liu et al. 2019), deforestation (van Vliet 2019), habitat fragmentation (Liu et al. 2016b), biodiversity loss (McDonald et al. 2018, 2020), and the modification of urban temperatures and regional precipitation patterns (Li et al. 2017; Krayenhoff et al. 2018; Liu and Niyogi 2019; Zhang et al. 2019).

Urban land use and the associated built environment and infrastructure shape urban GHG emissions through the demand for materials and the ensuing energy-consuming behaviours. In particular, the structure of the built environment (i.e., its density, form, and extent) have long-lasting influence on urban GHG emissions, especially those from transport and building energy use, as well as the embodied emissions of the urban infrastructure (Butler et al. 2014; Salat et al. 2014; Ramaswami et al. 2016; Seto et al. 2016; d'Amour et al. 2017). Thus, understanding trends in urban land use is essential for assessing energy behaviour in cities as well as long-term mitigation potential (Sections 8.4 and 8.6, and Figure 8.21).

This section draws on the literature to discuss three key trends in urban land expansion, and how those relate to GHG emissions.

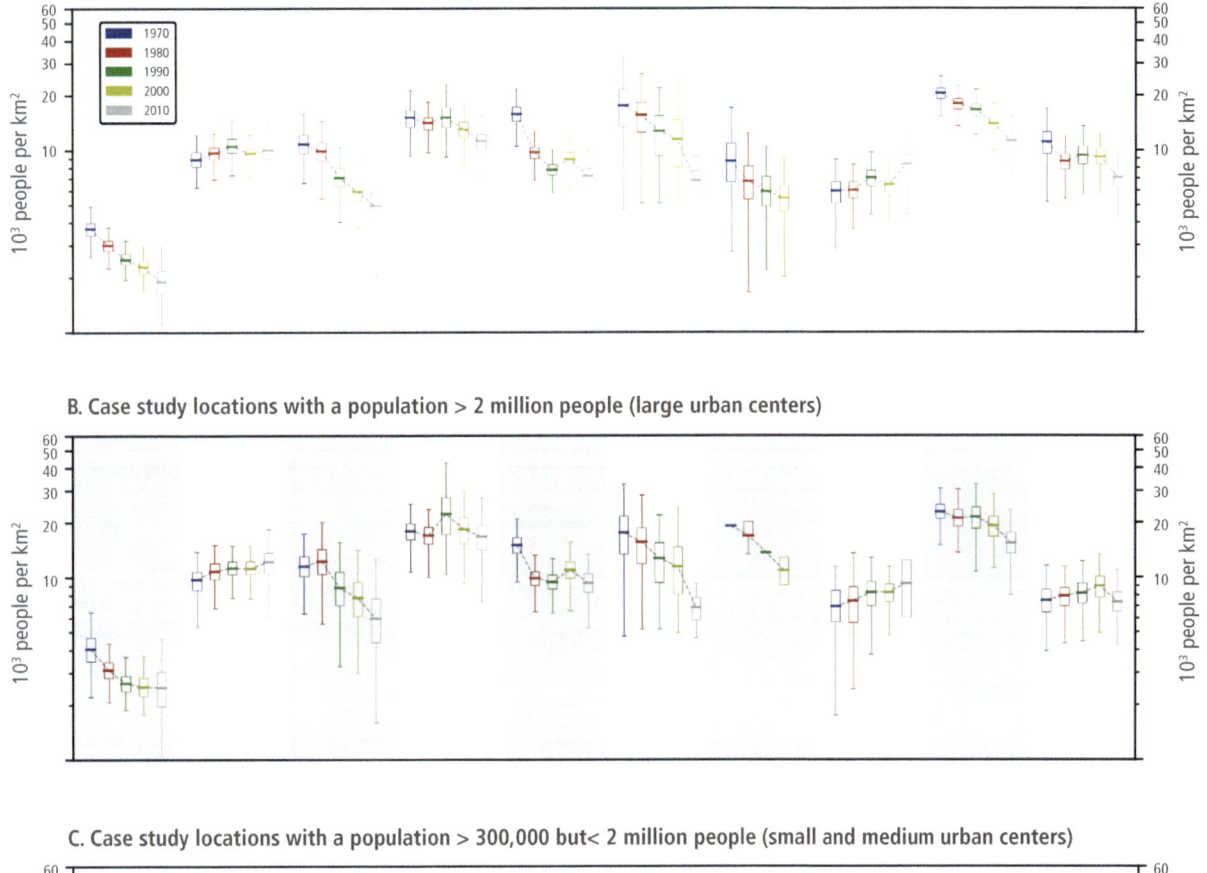

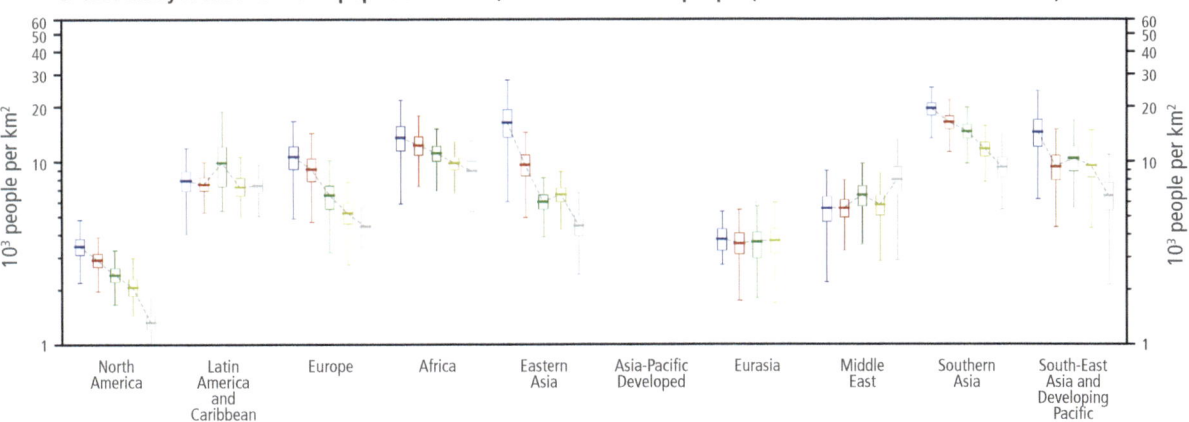

Figure 8.5: Urban population density by decade (1970–2010) grouped by the AR6 WGIII 10-region aggregation. Panel **(a)** displays the results from all case study locations with a population >300,000. Panels **(b)** and **(c)** show results grouped by city size: **(b)** cities with a population >2 million (large urban centres), and **(c)** those with a population >300,000 but <2 million (small and medium urban centres). Box plots show the median, first and third quartiles, and lower and upper mild outlier thresholds of bootstrapped average urban population densities at the turn of each decade. The estimates are shown on a logarithmic scale. The data shows an overall trend of declining urban population densities among all but one region in the last four decades, at varying rates – although the Latin America and Caribbean region indicates relatively constant urban population density over time. The Middle East region is the only region to present with an increase in urban population density across all city sizes. Source: adapted from Güneralp et al. (2020).

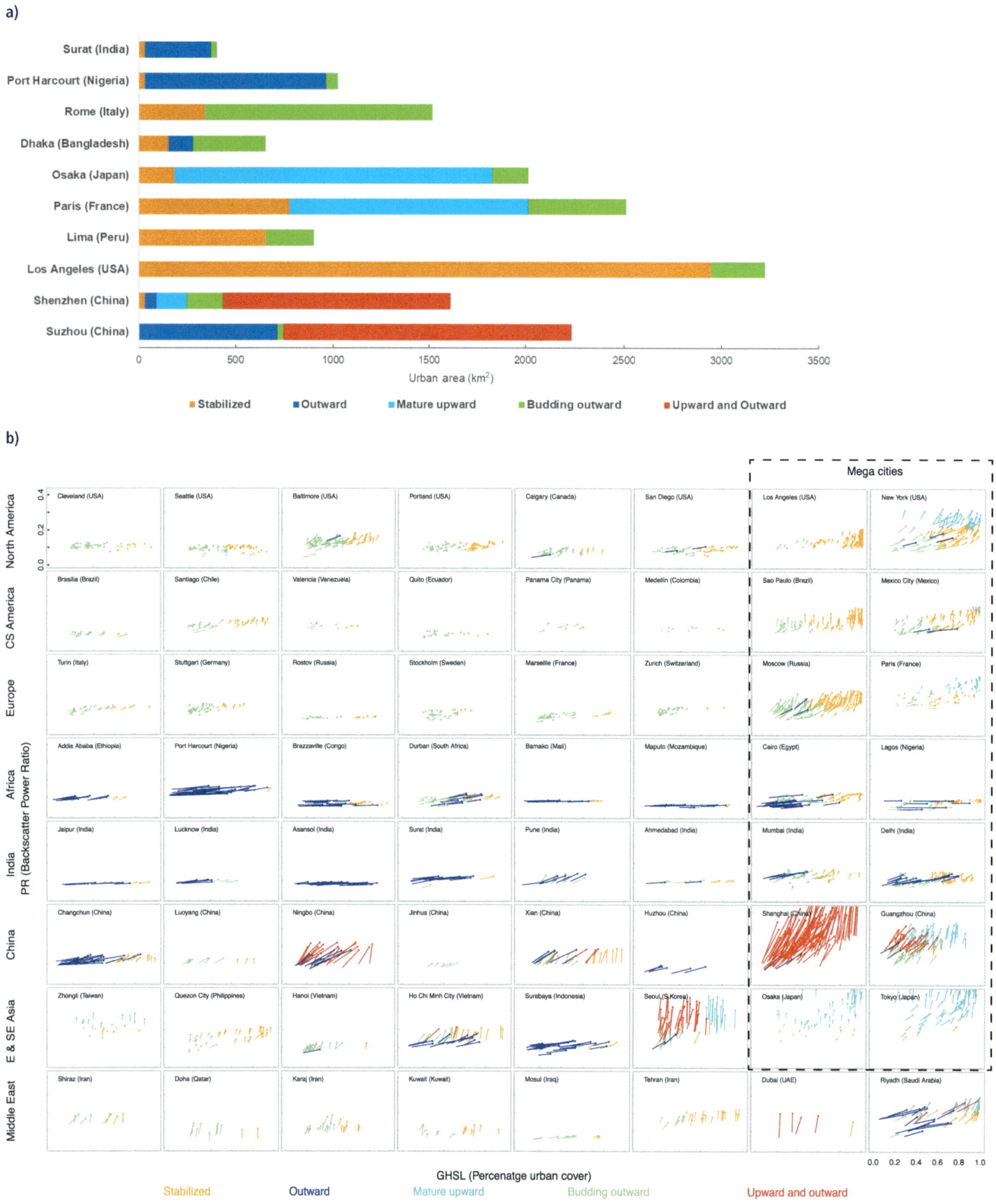

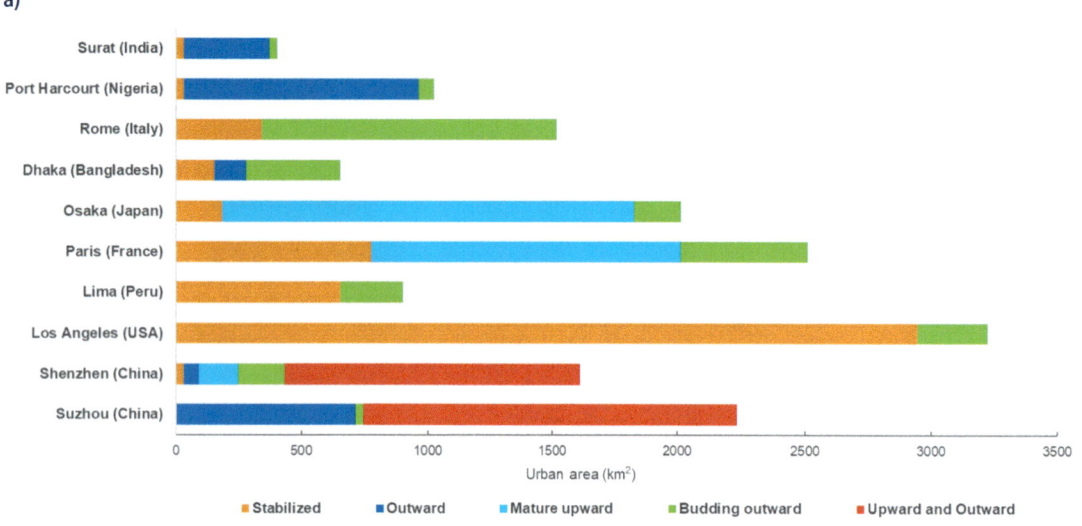

Figure 8.6: (a) Distribution of growth typologies across 10 cities, and (b) sample of 64 cities by region with different patterns of urban growth. The empirical data is based on the Global Human Settlement Layer and backscatter power ratio for different patterns of urban growth across the sample of cities. In (b), the blue arrows indicate outward urban growth. Other urban patterns indicate stabilised (orange), mature upward (light blue), budding outward (green), and upward and outward (red). Note that with few exceptions, each city is comprised of multiple typologies of urban growth. Source: Mahtta et al. (2019).

First, urban land areas are growing rapidly all around the world. From 1975 to 2015, urban settlements expanded in size approximately 2.5 times, accounting for 7.6% of the global land area (Pesaresi et al. 2016). Nearly 70% of the total urban expansion between 1992 and 2015 occurred in Asia and North America (Liu et al. 2020a). By 2015, the extent of urban and built-up lands was between 0.5% and 0.6% of the total 130 Mkm² global ice-free land use, taking up other uses such as fertile cropland and natural ecosystems.

Second, as Figure 8.5 shows, urban population densities are declining, with significant implications for GHG emissions. From 1970 to 2010, while the global urban settlement extent doubled in size (Pesaresi et al. 2016), most regions (grouped by the AR6 WGIII 10-region aggregation) exhibited a trend of decreasing urban population densities, suggesting expansive urban growth patterns. Urban population densities have consistently declined in Australia, Japan and New Zealand, and Europe, North America, and Southern Asia regions, across all city sizes. North America consistently had the lowest urban population densities. Notably, the Middle East region appears to be the only region exhibiting an overall increasing trend across all city-size groups, while Latin America and Caribbean

appears to be relatively stable for all city sizes. While the larger cities in Africa and South-East Asia and Pacific exhibit slightly stable urban population densities, the small and medium-sized cities in those regions trend toward lower urban population densities. In large urban centres of Eastern Asia and North America, rapid decreases in earlier decades seem to have tapered. Compared to larger cities, small-medium urban areas with populations of less than 2 million have more declines in urban population densities and higher rates of urban land expansion (Güneralp et al. 2020).

This decline in urban densities is paralleled by an increase in 'sprawl', or 'outward' urban development. Urban expansion occurs in either one of three dimensions: (i) outward in a horizontal manner; (ii) upward, by way of vertical growth; or (iii) infill development, where unused, abandoned, or underutilised lands within existing urban areas are developed or rehabilitated (Figure 8.20). Outward expansion results in more urban land area and occurs at the expense of other land uses (i.e., the conversion and loss of cropland or forests). Vertical expansion results in more multi-storey buildings and taller buildings, more floor space per area, and an increase in urban built-up density. Every city has some combination of outward and upward

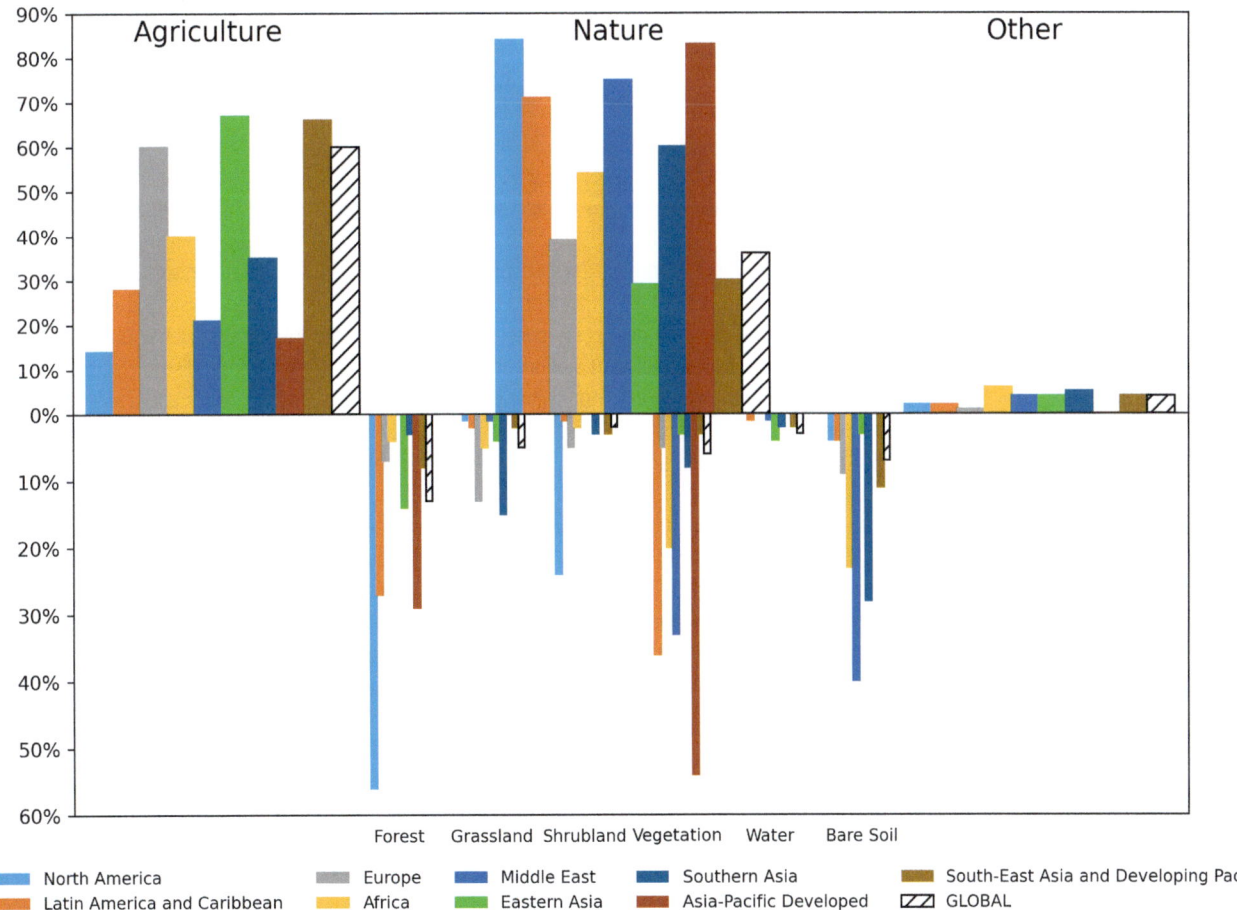

Figure 8.7: Percent of total urban land expansion from other land covers, sorted by the AR6 WGIII 10-region aggregation (1970–2010). As urban land has expanded outward, other forms of land cover, including agriculture, 'nature' (e.g., forest, grassland, shrubland, water, and bare soil, all of which are disaggregated to the bottom half of the plot), and other land covers, have been displaced. Globally, agriculture comprises the majority (about 60%) of the land displaced by urban expansion since 1970. Forests and shrubland vegetation – important carbon stocks – also make up a significant proportion of displacement. The loss of carbon-sequestering land like forests and shrubland independently impacts climate change by reducing global carbon stocks. Eurasia is omitted because there are no case studies from that region that report land conversion data. Source: adapted from Güneralp et al. (2020).

growth in varying degrees (Mahtta et al. 2019) (Figure 8.6). That each city is comprised of different and multiple urban growth typologies suggests the need for differentiated mitigation strategies for different parts of a single city (Section 8.6 and Figure 8.21). Recent research shows that the relative combination of outward versus upward growth is a reflection of its economic and urban development (Lall et al. 2021). That is, how a city grows – whether upward or outward – is a function of its economic development level. Upward growth, or more tall buildings, is a reflection of higher land prices (Ahlfeldt and McMillen 2018; Ahlfeldt and Barr 2020).

An analysis of 478 cities with populations of more than 1 million people found that the predominant urban growth pattern worldwide is outward expansion, suggesting that cities are becoming more expansive than dense (Mahtta et al. 2019) (Figure 8.6). The study also found that cities within a geographic region exhibit remarkably similar patterns of urban growth. Some studies have found a mix of urban forms emerging around the world; an analysis of 194 cities identified an overall trend (from 1990 to 2015) toward urban forms that are a mixture of fragmented and compact (Lemoine-Rodriguez et al. 2020). The exception to this trend is a group of large cities in Australia, New Zealand, and the United States that are still predominantly fragmented. The same study also identified small to medium-sized cities as the most dynamic in terms of their expansion and change in their forms.

A third trend in is urban land growth taking place on agricultural land, carbon stocks, and other land uses (see 'carbon stock' and 'AFOLU' – agriculture, forestry, and other land uses – in Glossary). As Figure 8.7 shows, over 60% of the reported urban expansion (nearly 40,000 km^2) from 1970 to 2010 was formerly agricultural land (Güneralp et al. 2020). This percentage increased to about 70% for global urban expansion that occurred between 1992 and 2015, followed by grasslands (about 12%) and forests (about 9%) (Liu et al. 2020a). In terms of percent of total urban land expansion, the largest conversion of agricultural lands to urban land uses from 1970 to 2010 took place in the Eastern Asia, and South-East Asia and Pacific regions; the largest proportional losses of natural land cover were reported for the North America and Australia, Japan and New Zealand regions (Güneralp et al. 2020). At a sub-regional level, agricultural land constituted the largest proportion of land converted to urban areas in China, India, Europe, Southeast Asian countries and the central United States between 1995 and 2015; in the eastern United States, most new urban land was converted from forests (Liu et al. 2020a). Urban expansion through 2040 may lead to the loss of almost 65 Mt of crop production – a scenario that underscores the ongoing relationship between urbanisation and AFOLU (van Vliet et al. 2017) (Chapter 7).

8.3.2   Informal Urban Settlements

About 880 million people currently live in informal settlements – defined as unplanned areas operating outside of legal and regulatory systems, where residents have no legal claim over their property and have inadequate basic services and infrastructure (United Nations 2018). Furthermore, upgrading informal settlements and inadequate housing is essential for improving resilience to climate change and well-being. Given the ubiquity of informal settlements in developing countries and LDCs, there is potential to harness informality to

accelerate transitions to low-carbon urban development. There are several key reasons for their potential to mitigate GHG emissions. First, informal urban areas may not require large investments in retrofitting as they have developed with minimal investment in large-scale infrastructure. Second, these areas exhibit flexibility of development and can potentially be transformed into an urban form that supports low- or carbon-neutral infrastructure for transportation, energy use in residential buildings, and other sectors (Baurzhan and Jenkins 2016; Henneman et al. 2016; Byrne et al. 2017; Oyewo et al. 2019).

Informal urban areas can avoid the conventional trajectory of urban development by utilising large-scale strategies, such as micro-scale technologies, modal shifts towards compact, walkable urban form, as well as decentralised or meso-scale utilities of water, sanitation, and service centres – thereby mitigating emissions associated with transport and treating wastes (Tongwane et al. 2015; Yang et al. 2018). Some specific mitigation options include spatial adjustments for walkability of neighbourhoods, low-energy-intensive mobility, low-energy-intensive residential areas, low-carbon energy sources at city scale, off-grid utilities, and electrification and enhancement of the urban ecology – all of which have multiple potential benefits (Colenbrander et al. 2017; Fang et al. 2017; Laramee et al. 2018; van der Zwaan et al. 2018; Wu et al. 2018; Silveti and Andersson 2019). Some of the co-benefits of the various mitigation options include more job opportunities and business start-ups, increased incomes, air quality improvement, and enhanced health and well-being (Gebreegziabher et al. 2014; Dagnachew et al. 2018; Keramidas et al. 2018; Adams et al. 2019; Ambole et al. 2019; Boltz et al. 2019; Moncada et al. 2019; Weimann and Oni 2019; Manga et al. 2020) (Section 8.2).

Non-networked and non-centralised urban services and infrastructure in informal settlements, including sanitation, waste, water, and electricity, serve over 60% of the urban population in developing country cities (Lawhon et al. 2018). The alternatives of disruptive, hybrid, largely non-networked multiplicity of technologies applicable at micro to meso scales have potential for low-emissions development in urban areas of developing countries (Narayana 2009; Dávila and Daste 2012; Radomes Jr and Arango 2015; Potdar et al. 2016; Grové et al. 2018). These technologies can be applied in the short term as responses with long-term influence on emissions reduction. The cumulative impact of the disruptive technologies can reduce emissions by 15–25% through enhanced emissions sinks in small and medium-sized cities (Tongwane et al. 2015; du Toit et al. 2018; Nero et al. 2018, 2019; Frantzeskaki et al. 2019; Mantey and Sakyi 2019; Singh and G. 2019).

8.3.3   Trends in Urban Greenhouse Gas Emissions

One major innovation presented in AR6 – particularly in this chapter – is the inclusion of trend data on urban GHG emissions. Using multiple datasets in conjunction with the SSP and RCP scenarios, this chapter provides an estimate of urban GHG emissions from 1990 through 2100, based on a consumption-based approach. This innovation provides, for the first time, a temporal dimension to urban footprints considering different climate scenarios with implications for urban mitigation. The new analysis presents a comparison of ways urban emissions can evolve given different scenario contexts (Section 8.3.4.2). Additionally, new research has quantified trends in urban CO$_2$ emissions and their key drivers across 91 global cities from 2000 to 2018 (Luqman et al. 2021).

Figures 8.8 and 8.9 present key urban emission metrics and trends for six regions (based on the AR6 WGIII regional breakdown) – the first for the year 2015, and the latter for both 2000 and 2015.

The key trends are as follows. First, the urban share of global GHG emissions (including CO$_2$ and CH$_4$) is substantive and continues to increase (Figure 8.9). Total urban CO$_2$-eq emissions based on consumption-based accounting were estimated to be 25 GtCO$_2$-eq, or 62% of the global total in 2015, and increased to an estimated 29 GtCO$_2$-eq in 2020, representing about 67–72% of global emissions. This estimate includes all CO$_2$ and CH$_4$ emissions except aviation, shipping, and biogenic sources (i.e., land-use change, forestry, and agriculture). About 100 of the highest-emitting urban areas account for approximately 18% of the global carbon footprint (Moran et al. 2018). Globally, the urban share of national CO$_2$-eq emissions increased 6 percentage points, from 56% in 2000 to 62% in 2015.

Second, while urban CO$_2$ emissions were increasing in all urban areas, the dominant drivers were dependent upon development level. Emissions growth in urban areas other than in Developed Countries was driven by increases in area and per capita emissions. Across all cities, higher population densities are correlated with lower per capita GHG emissions (Luqman et al. 2021).

Third, the urban share of regional GHG emissions increased between 2000 and 2015, with much inter-region variation in the magnitude of the increase (high confidence) (Figure 8.9). Between 2000 and 2015, the urban emissions share across AR6 WGIII regions (6-region aggregation) increased from 28% to 38% in Africa, from 46% to 54% in Asia and Pacific, from 62% to 72% in Developed Countries, from 57% to 62% in Eastern Europe and West-Central Asia, from 55% to 66% in Latin America and Caribbean, and from 68% to 69% in the Middle East.

Between 2000 and 2015, urban population, urban CO$_2$-eq emissions, and national CO$_2$-eq emissions increased as a share of the global total in the Asia and Pacific region while the share declined for Developed Countries. The urban share of total regional CO$_2$-eq emissions decreased in Developed Countries from 58.2% (2000) to 40.0% (2015). Urban per capita CO$_2$-eq and national per capita CO$_2$-eq also increased in all regions except for the urban per capita CO$_2$-eq value in the Developed Countries region, which declined slightly.

Fourth, the global average per capita urban GHG emissions increased between 2000 and 2015, with cities in the Developed Countries region producing nearly seven times more per capita than the lowest emitting region (medium confidence). From 2000 to 2015, the global urban GHG emissions per capita increased from 5.5 to 6.2 tCO$_2$-eq per person (an increase of 11.8%), with increases across five of the six regions: Africa increased from 1.3 to 1.5 tCO$_2$-eq per person (22.6%); Asia and Pacific increased from 3.0 to 5.1 tCO$_2$-eq per person (71.7%); Eastern Europe and West-Central Asia increased from 6.9 to 9.8 tCO$_2$-eq per person (40.9%); Latin America and Caribbean increased from 2.7 to 3.7 tCO$_2$-eq per person (40.4%); and the Middle East increased from 7.4 to 9.6 tCO$_2$-eq per person (30.1%). Albeit starting from the highest level, Developed Countries had a decline of 11.4 to 10.7 tCO$_2$-eq per person (–6.5%).

In 2015, regional urban per capita consumption-based CO$_2$-eq emissions were lower than regional consumption-based national per capita CO$_2$-eq emissions in five of the six regions. These regions in order of the difference are: Developed Countries (lower by 1.0 tCO$_2$-eq per capita); Latin America and Caribbean (lower by 0.8 tCO$_2$-eq per capita); Eastern Europe and West-Central Asia (lower by 0.7 tCO$_2$-eq per capita); Middle East (lower by 0.4 tCO$_2$-eq per capita); and Africa (lower by 0.2 tCO$_2$-eq per capita); while higher only in the Asia and Pacific region (higher by 0.9 tCO$_2$-eq per capita). All regions show convergence of the urban and national per capita CO$_2$-eq, as the urban share of national emissions increases and dominates the regional total.

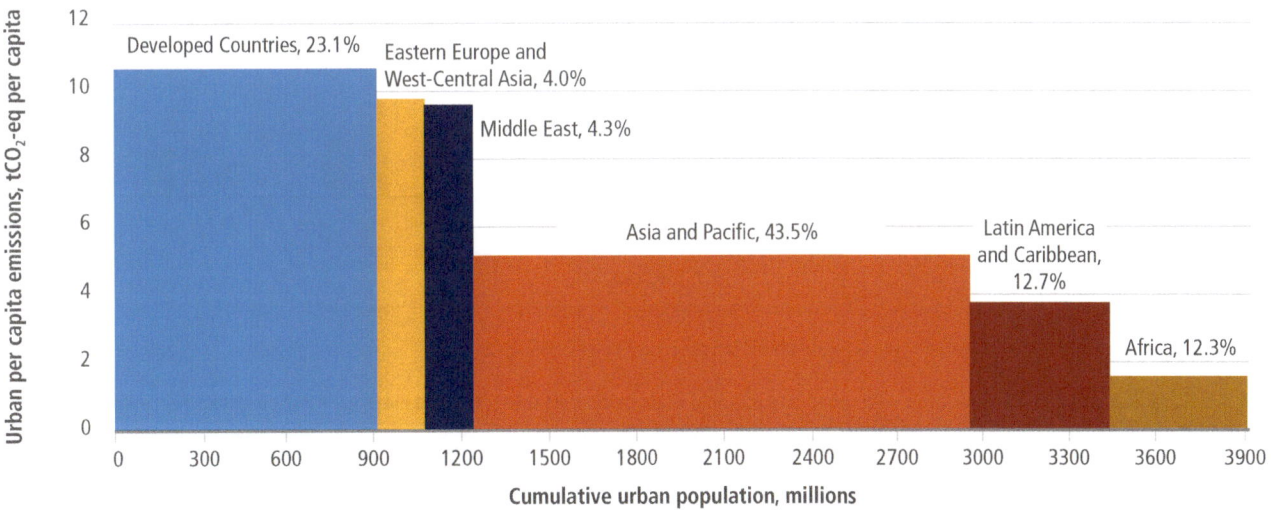

Figure 8.8: 2015 average urban greenhouse gas emissions per capita, considering carbon dioxide (CO$_2$) and methane (CH$_4$) emissions from a consumption-based perspective, alongside urban population, for regions represented in the AR6 WGIII 6-region aggregation. The average urban per capita emissions are given by the height of the bars while the width represents the urban population for a given region, based on 2015 values for both axes. Provided within the bars are the percentage shares of the urban population by region as a share of the total urban population. Source: synthesised based on data from UN DESA (2019) and Gurney et al. (2022).

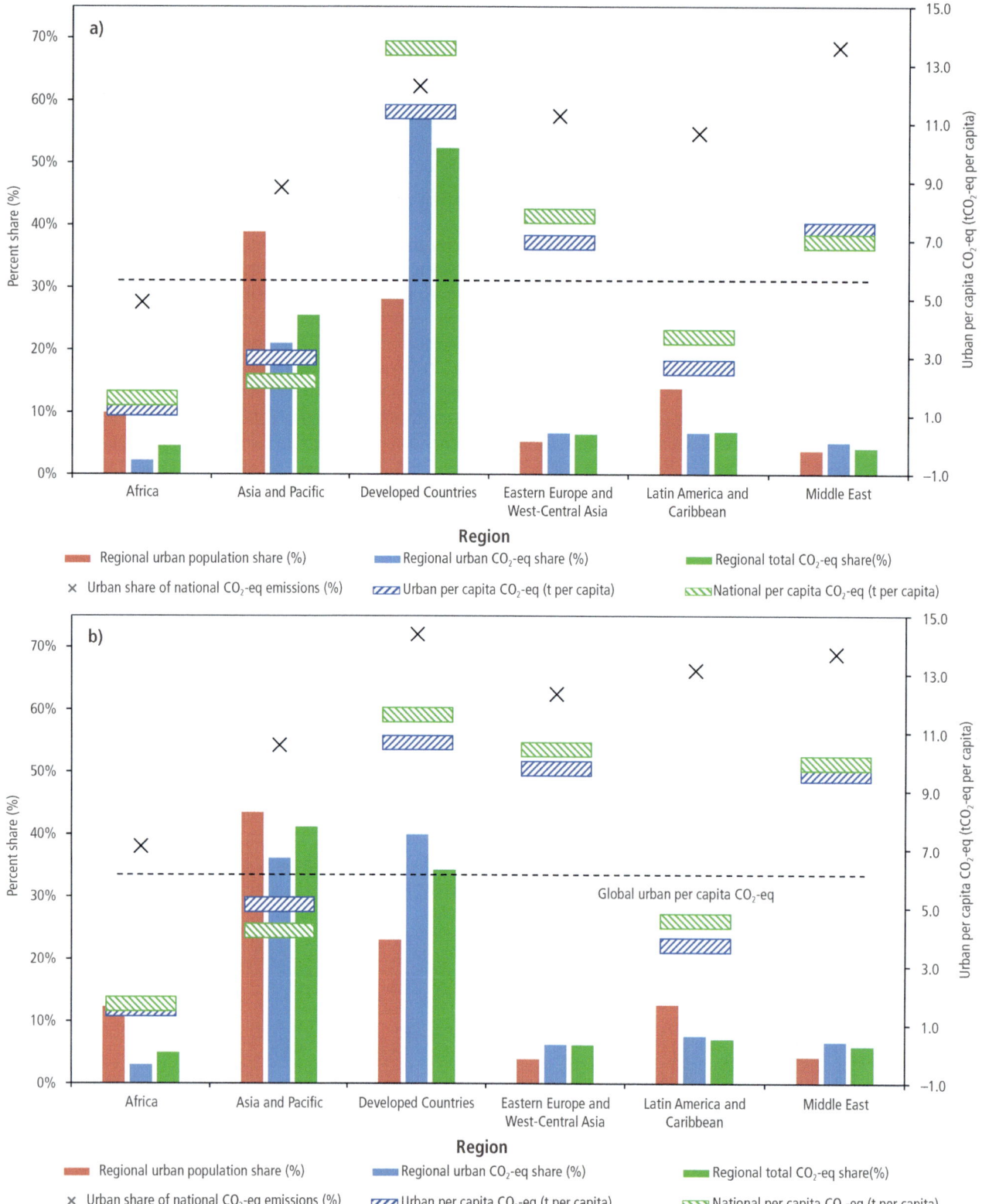

Figure 8.9: Changes in six metrics associated with urban and national-scale carbon dioxide (CO_2) and methane (CH_4) emissions represented in the AR6 WGIII 6-region aggregation, with (a) 2000 and (b) 2015. The trends in Luqman et al. (2021) were combined with the work of Moran et al. (2018) to estimate the regional urban CO_2-eq share of global urban emissions, the urban share of national CO_2-eq emissions, and the urban per capita CO_2-eq emissions by region. This estimate is derived from consumption-based accounting that includes both direct emissions from within urban areas and indirect emissions from outside urban areas related to the production of electricity, goods, and services consumed in cities. It incorporates all CO_2 and CH_4 emissions except aviation, shipping and biogenic sources (i.e., land-use change, forestry, and agriculture). The dashed grey line represents the global average urban per capita CO_2-eq emissions. The regional urban population share, regional CO_2-eq share in total emissions, and national per capita CO_2-eq emissions by region are given for comparison. Source: adapted from Gurney et al. (2022).[5]

5   Figure adapted from *Global Environmental Change*, Vol 73, Gurney et al., Greenhouse gas emissions from global cities under SSP/RCP scenarios, 1990 to 2100, ©2022 with permission from Elsevier.

Box 8.1: Does Urbanisation Drive Emissions?

Urbanisation can drive emissions if the process is accompanied by an income increase and higher levels of consumption (Sudmant et al. 2018). This is typically observed in countries with a large urban-rural disparity in income and basic services, and where urbanisation is accompanied by economic growth that is coupled to emissions. In addition, the outward expansion of urban land areas often results in the conversion and loss of agricultural land (Pandey et al. 2018; Liu et al. 2019), forests (Austin et al. 2019), and other vegetated areas, thereby reducing carbon uptake and storage (Quesada et al. 2018) (Section 8.3.1). Furthermore, the buildup and use of urban infrastructure (e.g., buildings, power, sanitation) requires large amounts of embodied energy and carbon (Figures 8.17 and 8.22). Building new and upgrading existing urban infrastructure could produce cumulative emissions of 226 $GtCO_2$ by 2050 (Bai et al. 2018).

However, for the same level of consumption and basic services, an average urban dweller often requires less energy than their rural counterparts, due to higher population densities that enable sharing of infrastructure and services, and economies of scale. Whether and to what extent such emission reduction potentials can be realised depends on how cities are designed and laid out (i.e., urban form – see Section 8.4.2) as well as how urban infrastructure is built and powered, such as the energy intensity of the city's transportation system, type and level of urban services, the share of renewable energy, as well as the broader national and international economic and energy structure that supports the function of the cities (Sections 8.4.3 and 8.6).

Although population-dense cities can be more efficient than rural areas in terms of per capita energy use, and cities contribute less GHG emissions per person than low-density suburbs (Jones and Kammen 2014), there is some, albeit *limited*, evidence that larger cities are not more efficient than smaller ones (Fragkias et al. 2013; Ribeiro et al. 2019). A number of studies comparing urban and rural residents in the same country have shown that urban residents have higher per capita energy consumption and CO_2 emissions (Chen et al. 2019a; Hachaichi and Baouni 2021). There is some evidence that the benefits of higher urban densities on reducing per capita urban GHG emissions may be offset by higher incomes, smaller household sizes, and, most importantly, higher consumption levels, thus creating a counter-effect that could increase GHG emissions with urbanisation (Gill and Moeller 2018).

Many studies have shown that the relationship between urbanisation and GHG emissions is dependent on the level and stage of urban development, and follows an inverted U-shaped relationship of the environmental Kuznets curve (Wang et al. 2016, 2022; Zhang et al. 2017; Xu et al. 2018a; Zhou et al. 2019) (Sections 8.3.1 and 8.6, and Figure 8.20). Considering existing trends, earlier phases of urbanisation accompanied by rapid industrialisation, development of secondary industries, and high levels of economic growth, are correlated with higher levels of energy consumption and GHG emissions. However, more mature phases of urbanisation, with higher levels of economic development and establishment of the service sector, are correlated with lower levels of energy consumption and GHG emissions (Khan and Su 2021).

8.3.4 Scenarios of Future Urbanisation and Greenhouse Gas Emissions

This section assesses scenarios of future urban land expansion and urban GHG emissions. These scenarios have implications for the urban climate change mitigation strategies discussed in Sections 8.4 and 8.6 – in particular, in the context of the potential mitigation and development pathways for urban areas under certain scenarios.

8.3.4.1 Urban Land Expansion and Greenhouse Gas Emissions

The uncertainties across urban land expansion forecasts, and associated SSPs, highlight an opportunity to pursue compact, low or net-zero GHG emissions development that minimises land-use competition, avoids carbon lock-in, and preserves carbon-sequestering areas like forests and grasslands (Sections 8.4. and 8.6, and Figure 8.21). Among the forecasts available are six global-scale spatially explicit studies of urban land expansion that have been published since AR5; four of the six, which present forecasts for each of the five SSPs, are considered in Table 8.1 and Figure 8.10 (Huang et al. 2019; Li et al. 2019b; Chen et al. 2020a; Gao and O'Neill 2020). All four have forecasts to 2050 but only three to 2100. One of

the two not included here (van Vliet et al. 2017) also forecasts land displacement due to urban land expansion.

Four overarching findings can be gleaned from these studies.

First, urban land areas will expand significantly by 2050 – by as much as 211% (see SSP5 forecast in Huang et al. 2019), but likely within a large potential range of about 43–106% over the 2015 extent by 2050 – to accommodate the growing urban population (Table 8.1). Globally, there are large uncertainties and variations among the studies – and between the SSPs – about the rates and extent of future urban expansion, owing to uncertainties about economic development and population growth (ranges of estimates are provided in Table 8.1). Overall, the largest urban extents are forecasted under SSP5 (fossil fuel-intensive development) for both 2050 and 2100, whereas the smallest forecasted urban extents are under SSP3 ('regional rivalry'). Forecasted global urban extents could reach between 1 and 2.2 million km^2 (median of 1.4 million km^2, a 106% increase) in 2050 under SSP5, and between 0.85 and 1.5 million km^2 (median of 1 million km^2, a 43% increase) in 2050 under SSP3. Under SSP1, which is characterised by a focus on sustainability with more compact, low-emissions development, urban extents could reach

1 million km² (range of 0.9 to 2 million km², a 49% increase) in 2050. By 2100, the forecasted urban extents reach between 1.4 and 3.6 million km² (median 2.5 million km²) under SSP5 and between 1 and 1.5 million km² (median 1.3 million km²) under SSP3. Across the studies, substantially larger amounts of urban land expansion are expected after 2050 under SSP5 compared to other SSPs.

Second, there is a wide variation in estimates of urban land expansion across regions (using the AR6 WGIII 6-region aggregation). Across all four sets of forecasts, current urban land (circa 2015) is the largest in Developed Countries and in the Asia and Pacific region, with approximately two-thirds of the current urban extent occurring in those two regions (Table 8.1 and Figure 8.10). The largest increases in urban land by 2050 are expected in the Asia and Pacific and Developed Countries regions, across all the SSPs. However, the rate of increase in urban land in Eastern Europe and West-Central Asia, Latin America and Caribbean, and the Middle East is significant and urban land could more than double by 2050. One-third of the studies conclude that the United States, China, and India will experience continued urban land expansion at least until 2050 (Huang et al. 2019; Li et al. 2019b). However, Li et al. (2019) report that, after 2050, China could experience a decrease in the rate of urban land expansion, while growth will continue for India. This is not surprising since India's urban demographic transition will only get underway after the middle of the century, when the urban population is expected to exceed the rural population. In contrast, China's urban demographic transition could be nearly complete by 2050.

Third, in spite of these general trends, there are differences in forecasted urban expansion in each region across the SSPs and studies, with Huang et al. (2019) forecasting the most future urban land expansion between 2015 and 2050. The range across

studies is significant. Under SSP1, urban land areas could increase by between 69,000 and 459,000 km² in Developed Countries, 77,000–417,000 km² in Asia and Pacific, and 28,000–216,000 km² in Africa. Under SSP3, where urban land expansion is forecasted to be the lowest, urban land areas could increase by between 23,000 and 291,000 km² in Developed Countries, 57,000–168,000 km² in Asia and Pacific, and 16,000–149,000 km² in Africa. Under SSP5, where urban land expansion is forecasted to be the highest, urban land area could increase by between 129,000 and 573,000 km² in Developed Countries, 83,000–472,000 km² in Asia and Pacific, and 40,000–222,000 km² in Africa (Huang et al. 2019; Li et al. 2019b; Chen et al. 2020a; Gao and O'Neill 2020). By 2100, however, the Developed Countries region is expected to have the most urban expansion only in SSP5. In SSP2 and SSP4, the Developed Countries and Asia and Pacific regions have about equal amounts of new urban land; in SSP3, Asia and Pacific has more new urban land forecasted.

Fourth, both the range of estimates and their implications on land-use competition and urban life point to an opportunity for urban areas to consider their urban form when developing. Under the current urbanisation trajectory, 50–63% of newly expanded urban areas are expected to occur on current croplands (Chen et al. 2020a). However, there is significant regional variation; between 2000 and 2040, 12.5% of cropland in China and 7.5% of cropland in the Middle East and North Africa could potentially be displaced due to urban expansion, compared to the world average of 3.7% (van Vliet et al. 2017). As urban clusters increase in size and greenspace is converted, future urban land expansion is expected to intensify UHIs and exacerbate night-time extreme temperatures. An urban footprint increase of 78–171% by 2050 over the urban footprint in 2015 is expected to result in average summer daytime and night-time warming in air temperature of 0.5°C–0.7°C, even up to about 3°C in certain locations (Huang

Table 8.1: Forecasts of total urban land per AR6 WGIII region (6-region aggregation) in 2050 for each SSP, with the median and range of estimates from four studies: Huang et al. (2019), Li et al. (2019), Chen et al. (2020), and Gao and O'Neill (2020). Median estimates for the 2015 urban extent are based on the mean/median of estimates in Huang et al. (2019) and Chen et al. (2020). Median and range of estimates for each SSP in 2050 are based on values derived from the four studies: Huang et al. (2019), Li et al. (2019), Chen et al. (2020), and Gao and O'Neill (2020). While each study and SSP forecast increases in urban land in each region, the range and magnitude vary. Source: data compiled from Huang et al. (2019), Li et al. (2019), Chen et al. (2020), and Gao and O'Neill (2020).

	2015 median (km²; range)	SSP1 median (km²; range)	SSP2 median (km²; range)	SSP3 median (km²; range)	SSP4 median (km²; range)	SSP5 median (km²; range)
Africa	64,423	97,718	116,486	96,571	119,971	138,604
	(41,472–87,373)	(67,488–303,457)	(59,638–274,683)	(56,071–235,922)	(54,633–344,645)	(79,612–309,532)
Asia and Pacific	241,430	293,647	355,445	296,431	329,485	419,781
	(167,548–315,312)	(244,575–732,303)	(236,677–624,659)	(224,520–483,335)	(240,639–632,678)	(250,670–787,257)
Developed Countries	260,167	459,624	506,301	414,661	496,526	616,847
	(188,660–331,674)	(407,483–648,023)	(431,592–614,592)	(362,063–479,584)	(411,320–586,058)	(510,468–761,275)
Eastern Europe and West-Central Asia	35,970	63,625	65,251	59,779	64,434	76,994
	(27,121–44,819)	(42,990–91,612)	(52,397–91,108)	(44,129–90,794)	(50,806–86,546)	(54,039–93,008)
Latin America and Caribbean	62,613	86,236	88,793	93,804	85,369	102,343
	(60,511–64,716)	(63,507–163,329)	(86,411–162,526)	(65,286–162,669)	(82,148–144,940)	(82,961–167,102)
Middle East	21,192	51,351	51,221	48,032	49,331	55,032
	(19,017–23,366)	(187,68–69,266)	(25,486–69,716)	(19,412–63,236)	(25,415–71,720)	(33,033–75,757)
World	685,795	1,023,220	1,174,742	980,719	1,123,900	1,412,390
	(669,246–702,343)	(919,185–1,991,579)	(927,820–1,819,174)	(850,681–1,493,454)	(922,539–1,851,438)	(1,018,321–2,180,816)

2050 Urban Land Area Forecast

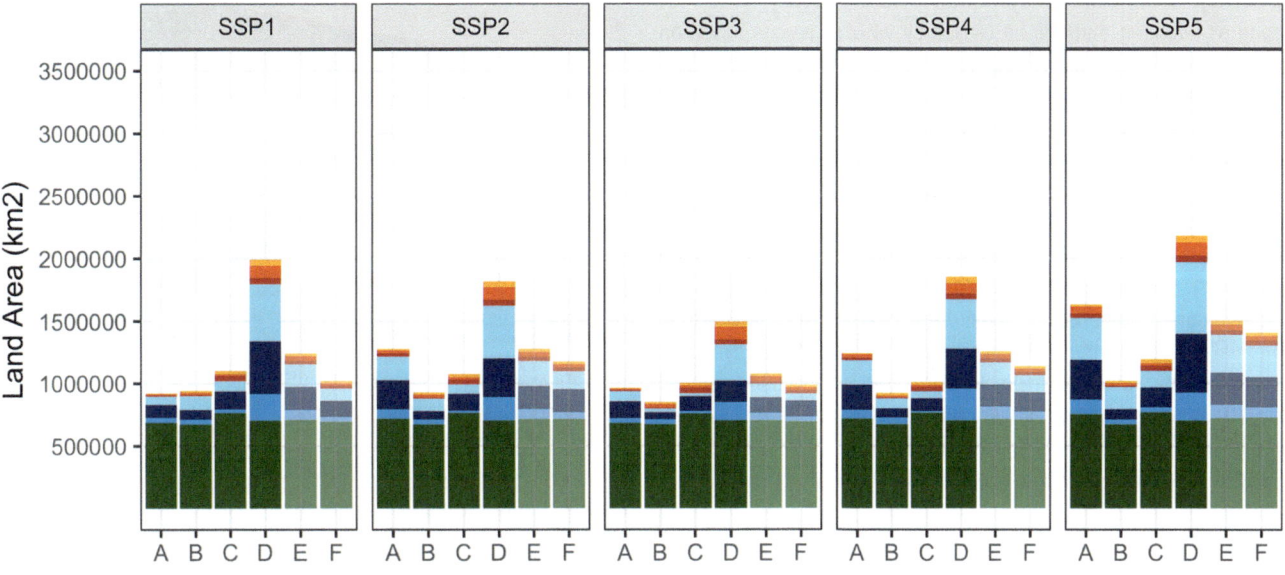

2100 Urban Land Area Forecast

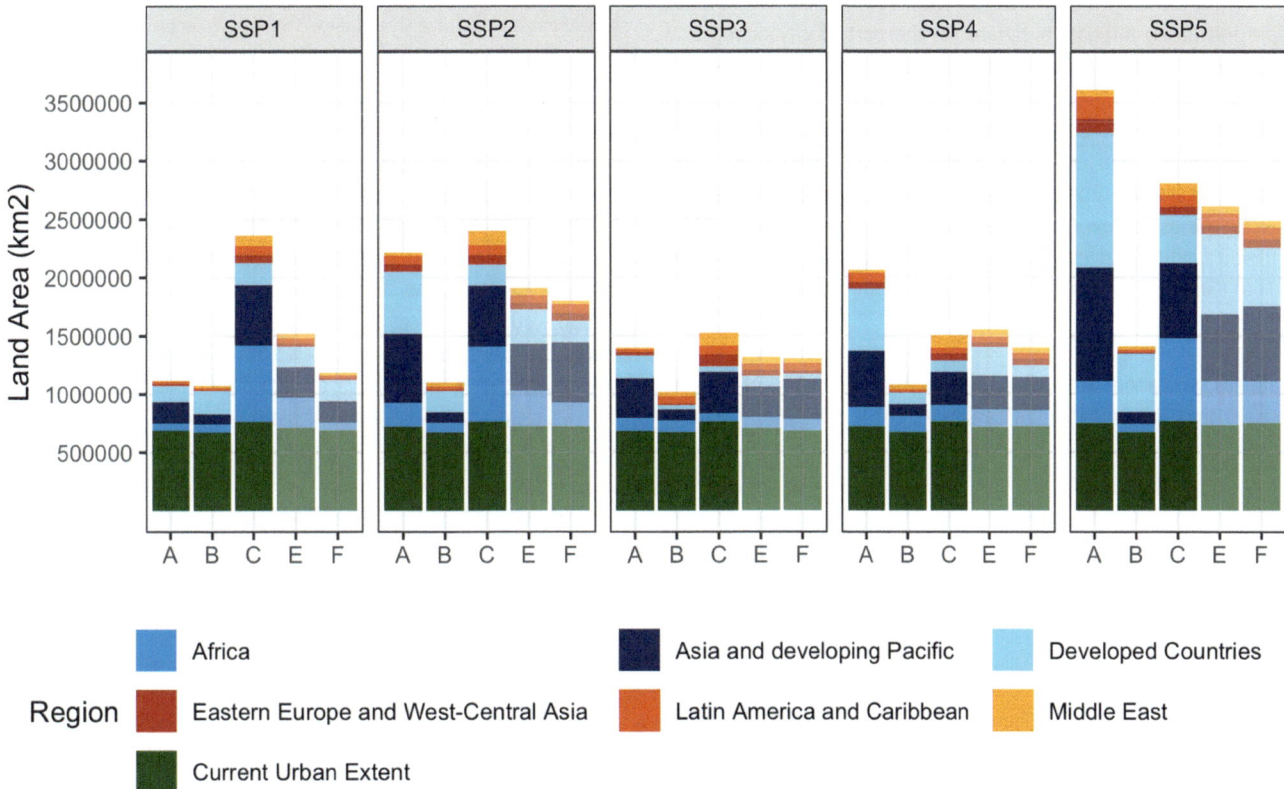

Figure 8.10: Forecasts of urban land expansion in 2050 and 2100 according to each SSP and AR6 WGIII 6-region aggregation, by study, where A: Gao and O'Neill (2020), B: Chen et al. (2020a), C: Li et al. (2019), D: Huang et al. (2019), E: mean across studies, and F: median across all studies. Three studies (Li et al. 2019b; Chen et al. 2020a; Gao and O'Neill 2020) report forecasts of urban land expansion to both 2050 and 2100. One study (Huang et al. 2019) reports the forecast only to 2050. Global current urban extents and the respective initial years vary slightly among the four studies. Years for values of current urban extent range from 2010 to 2020. See Table 8.1 for the range of data across the four studies and across SSPs. Source: data compiled form Huang et al. (2019), Li et al. (2019), Chen et al. (2020), and Gao and O'Neill (2020).

et al. 2019). Furthermore, this urban expansion-induced warming is on average about half – and in certain locations nearly twice – as strong as warming that will be caused by GHG emissions based on the multi-model ensemble average forecasts in RCP4.5. In short, future urban expansion will amplify the background warming caused by GHG emissions, with extreme warming most pronounced during night-time (*very high confidence*) (Huang et al. 2019). These findings corroborate those in the Technical Summary of AR6 WGI (Arias et al. 2021).

The forecasted amounts and patterns of urban expansion presented here bear significant uncertainty due to underlying factors beyond mere methodological differences between the studies. These factors include potential changes in the social, economic, and institutional dynamics that drive urban land development across the world (Güneralp and Seto 2013). Some of these changes may come in the form of sudden shocks such as another global economic crisis or pandemic. The forecasts presented here do not take such factors into account.

8.3.4.2 Scenarios of Future Urban Greenhouse Gas Emissions

There remains little globally comprehensive literature on projections of future baseline GHG emissions from urban areas or scenarios deploying urban mitigation actions on the part of city or regional governments. This dearth of research rests on limited urban emissions data that are consistent and comparable across the globe, making review and synthesis challenging (Creutzig et al. 2016b). Some research has presented urban emissions forecasts and related projections, including estimated urban energy use in 2050 (Creutzig et al. 2015), energy savings for low-carbon development (Creutzig et al. 2016b), emission savings from existing and new infrastructure (Creutzig et al. 2016a) (Figure 8.12), and urban emissions from buildings, transport, industry, and agriculture (IEA 2016a).

In its study of about 700 urban areas with a population of at least 750,000, the Coalition for Urban Transitions (2019), attempts to quantify

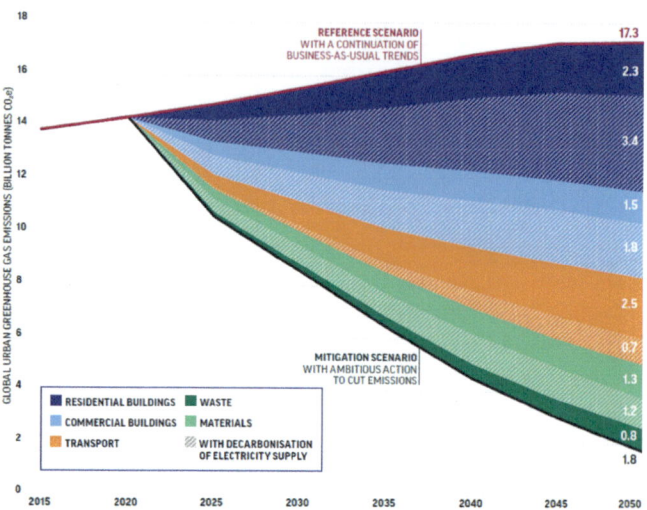

Figure 8.11: Reference scenario and mitigation potential for global urban areas in the residential and commercial building, transport, waste, and material production sectors. The top red line indicates the reference scenario where no further emissions reduction efforts are taken, while the bottom dark line indicates the combined potential of reducing emissions across the sectors displayed. Wedges are provided for potential emissions savings associated with decarbonising residential buildings, commercial buildings, transport, waste, and materials as indicated in the legend. The shaded areas that take place among the wedges with lines indicate contributions from decarbonisation of electricity supply. Source: Re-used with permission from Coalition for Urban Transitions (2019).

the urban portion of global GHG emissions, including the residential and commercial building, transport, waste, and material production (focusing on cement, aluminium, and steel) sectors, along with mitigation wedges aimed at staying below a 2°C level of atmospheric warming (Figure 8.11). Starting in 2015 with a global urban emissions total of almost 14 GtCO$_2$-eq, the study projects an increase to 17.3 GtCO$_2$-eq by 2050 – but this reduces to 1.8 GtCO$_2$-eq by 2050 with the inclusion of mitigation wedges: 58% from buildings, 21% from transport, 15% materials efficiency, and 5% waste, with decarbonisation of electricity supply as a cross-cutting strategy across the wedges.

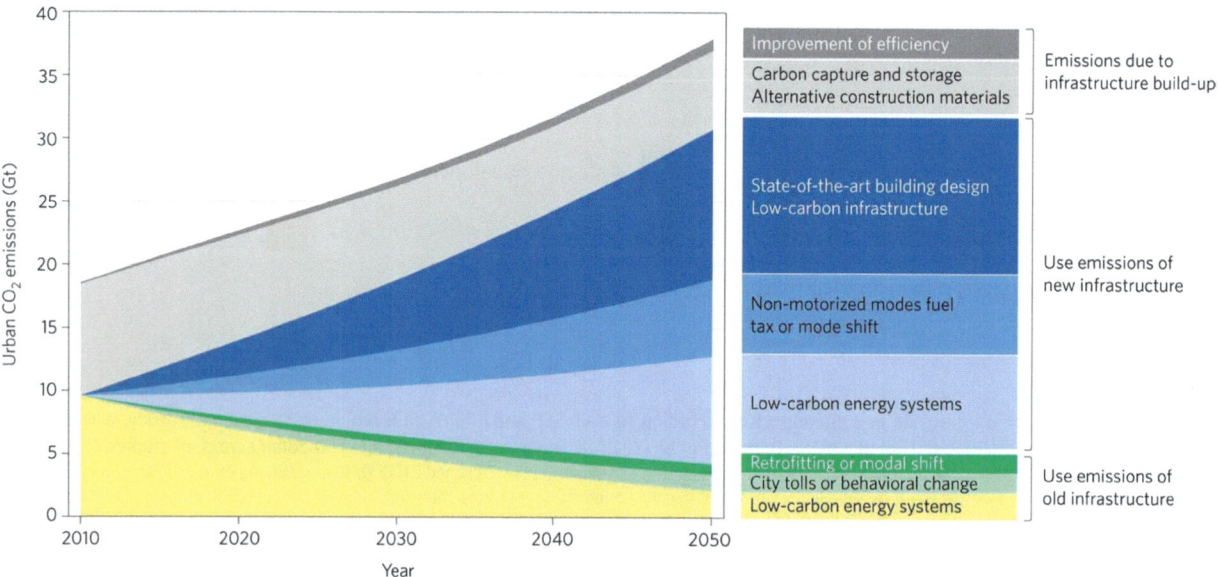

Figure 8.12: Urban infrastructure-based CO$_2$-eq emission mitigation wedges. Urban infrastructure-based CO$_2$-eq emission mitigation wedges across categories of existing (yellow/green), new (blue), and construction (grey) of urban infrastructure. The wedges include low-carbon energy systems and infrastructure, modal shift, tolls/tax, or behavioural change, and reductions from construction materials. Source: re-used with permission from Creutzig et al. (2016a).

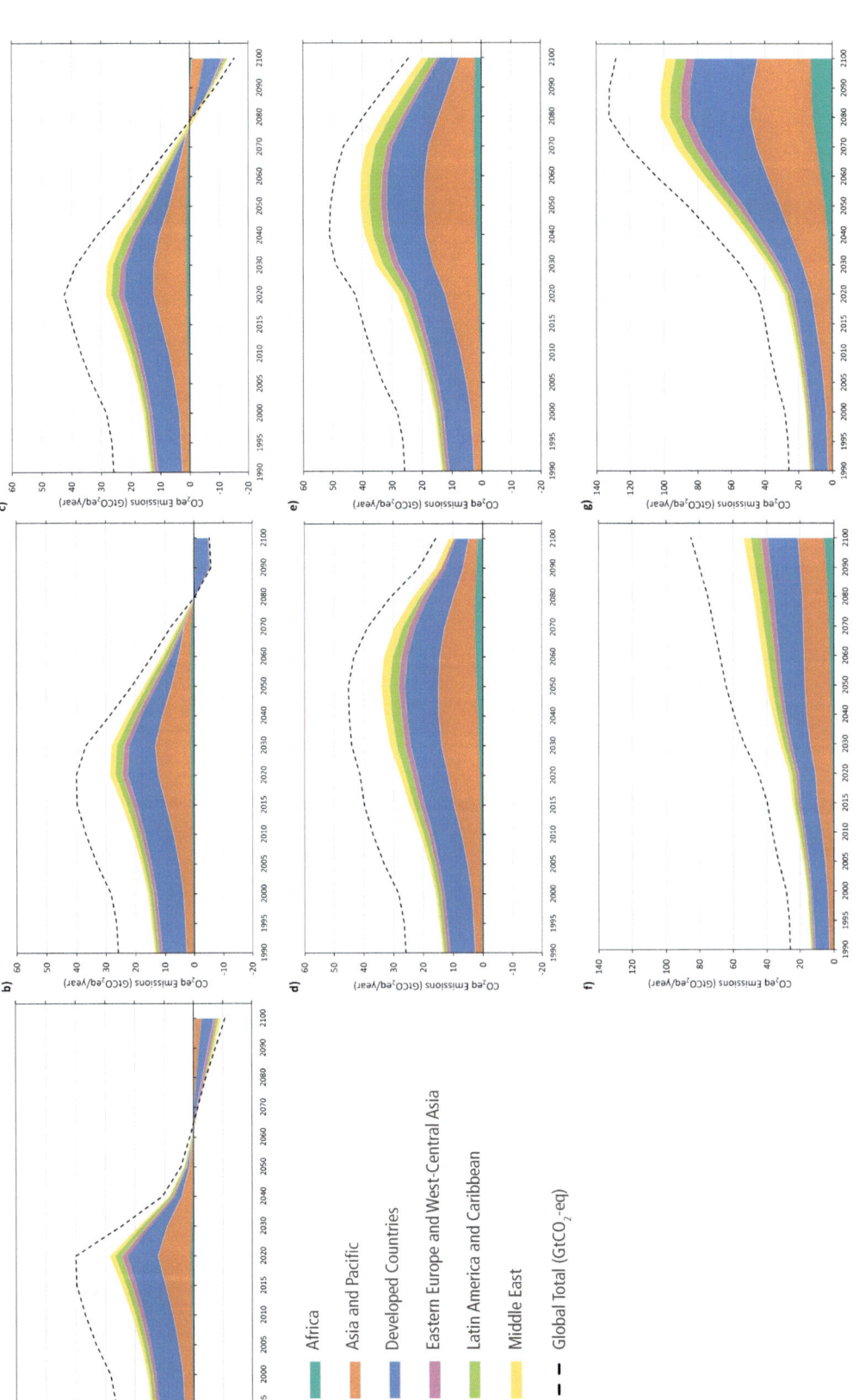

Figure 8.13: Carbon dioxide equivalent (CO₂-eq) emissions from global urban areas in seven SSP-RCP variations spanning the 1990 to 2100 time period. Urban areas are aggregated to six regional domains based on the AR6 WGIII 6-region aggregation. Global total CO₂-eq emissions (CO₂ and CH₄ (methane)) are also shown as marked by the dashed line. Future urban emissions in the context of SSP-RCP-Shared Policy Assumption (SPA) variations correspond to **(a)** SSP1-RCP1.9-SPA1, **(b)** SSP1-RCP2.6-SPA1, **(c)** SSP1-RCP1.9-SPA1, **(d)** SSP2-RCP3.4-SPA4, **(e)** SSP4-RCP3.4-SPA2, **(f)** SSP4-RCP6.0-SPA4, SSP4-RCP6.0-SPA0 and **(g)** SSP5-RCP8.5 based on the marker scenario implementations.[6] The first three scenarios (a–c) with more stringent reduction pathways represent contexts where urban per capita emissions decline rapidly against various increases in urban population and are oriented to reach net-zero emissions within this century at different radiative forcing levels. SSP1 scenarios (a, b) represent contexts where urbanisation takes place rapidly while providing resource efficiency based on compact urban form (Jiang and O'Neill 2017), with high levels of electrification (van Vuuren et al. 2017b; Rogelj et al. 2018). The scenario context of SSP1-RCP1.9 represents a pathway in which there can be a transformative shift towards sustainability. Note that the scale of panels (f) and (g) is different from the other panels.[7] See Table 8.2 detailing the SSP-RCPs. Source: adapted from Gurney et al. (2022).[8]

6   These scenarios have been assessed by WGI to correspond to intermediate, high, and very low GHG emissions.

7   The SSP1-RCP1.9 scenario is aligned with the C1 category of the Illustrative Mitigation Pathways (IMPs) that include IMP-LD, IMP-Ren and IMP-SP. Implications are provided in Table 8.3.

8   Figure adapted from *Global Environmental Change*, Vol 73, Gurney et al., Greenhouse gas emissions from global cities under SSP/RCP scenarios, 1990 to 2100, ©2022 with permission from Elsevier.

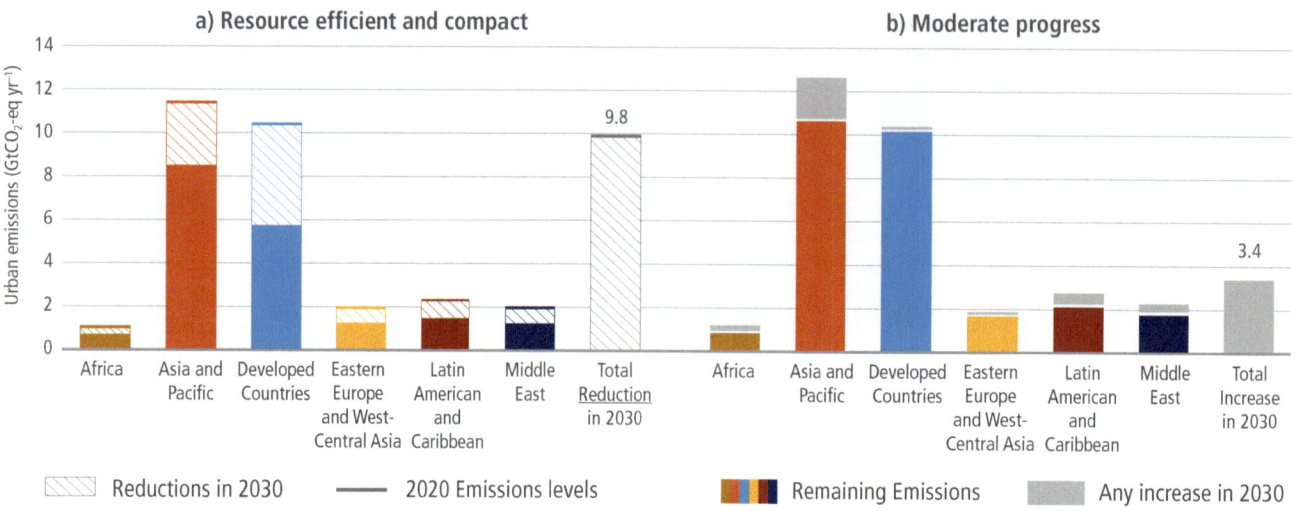

Figure 8.14: Comparison of urban emissions under different urbanisation scenarios (GtCO2-eq yr−1) for the AR6 WGIII 6-region aggregation. The panels represent the estimated urban emissions change in two different scenarios for the time period 2020–2030. Panel (a) represents resource efficient and compact urbanisation while panel (b) represents urbanisation with moderate progress. The two scenarios are consistent with estimated urban emissions under the SSP1-RCP1.9-SPA1 and SSP2-RCP4.5-SPA2 scenarios, respectively (Figure 8.13). In both panels, urban emissions estimates for the year 2020 are marked by the lines for each region. In the resource efficient and compact scenario, various reductions in urban emissions that take place by 2030 are represented by the dashed areas within the bars. The remaining solid shaded areas represent the remaining urban emissions in 2030 for each region on the path towards net-zero emissions. The total reductions in urban emissions worldwide that are given by the last dashed grey bar in panel (a) is estimated to be 9.8 GtCO2-eq yr−1 between 2020 and 2030 in this scenario. In the scenario with moderate progress, there are no regions with reductions in urban emissions. Above the white lines that represent urban emissions in 2020, the grey shaded areas are the estimated increases for each region so that the total urban emissions would increase by 3.4 GtCO2-eq yr−1 from 2020 levels in 2030 under this scenario. The values are based on urban scenario analyses as given in Gurney et al. (2021, 2022). Source: synthesised based on data from Gurney et al. (2022).[9]

Table 8.2: Synthesis of the urbanisation and scenario contexts of the urban emissions scenarios. Descriptions for urbanisation are adapted based on Jiang and O'Neill (2017) while high, medium, low, or mixed levels in the scenario context are drawn from the marker model implementations of SSP1-SSP5 for IMAGE (van Vuuren et al. 2017b; Rogelj et al. 2018), MESSAGE-GLOBIOM (Fricko et al. 2017), AIM/CGE (Fujimori et al. 2017), GCAM (Calvin et al. 2017), and REMIND-MAgPIE (Kriegler et al. 2017). The letters in parentheses refer to the panels in Figure 8.13. Energy and material efficiency relate to energy efficiency improvement and decrease in the intermediate input of materials, including steel and cement. Dietary responses include less meat-intensive diets. Implications for urban areas relate to the mitigation options in Section 8.4. Source: adapted from Gurney et al. (2022).

SSP/RCP framework	Urbanisation context	Scenario context					
		Electrification	Energy and material efficiency	Technology development/ innovation	Renewable energy preferences	Behavioural, lifestyle and dietary responses	Afforestation and re-forestation
SSP1 RCP1.9 (a) RCP2.6 (b)	Resource efficient, walkable and sustainable rapid urbanisation	High	High	High	High	High	High
		Implications for urban climate mitigation include: – Electrification across the urban energy system while supporting flexibility in end-use – Resource efficiency from a consumption-based perspective with cross-sector integration – Knowledge and financial resources to promote urban experimentation and innovation – Empowerment of urban inhabitants for reinforcing positive lock-in for decarbonisation – Integration of sectors, strategies and innovations across different typologies and regions					
SSP2 RCP4.5 (d)	Moderate progress	Medium	Medium	Medium	Medium	Medium	Medium
SSP3 RCP7.0 (f)	Slow urbanisation, inadequate urban planning	Medium	Low	Low	Medium	Low	Low
SSP4 RCP3.4 (c) RCP6.0 (e)	Pace of urbanisation differs with inequalities	Mixed	Mixed	Mixed	Mixed	Mixed	Mixed
SSP5 RCP8.5 (g)	Rapid urbanisation with carbon lock-in	High	Low	High	Low	Low	–

---

[9] Figure adapted from *Global Environmental Change*, Vol 73, Gurney et al., Greenhouse gas emissions from global cities under SSP/RCP scenarios, 1990 to 2100, ©2022 with permission from Elsevier.

Similar analysis by the urban networks C40 and GCoM examine current and future GHG emissions on smaller subsets of global cities, offering further insight on the potential emissions impacts of urban mitigation options. However, this analysis is limited to just a sample of the global urban landscape and primarily focused on cities in the Global North (GCoM 2018, 2019; C40 Cities et al. 2019) with methods to project avoided emissions in development (Kovac et al. 2020). Different scopes of analysis between sectors, as well as limited knowledge of the impact of existing and new urban infrastructure, limit the possibility of direct comparisons in emissions. Still, the shares of urban mitigation potential ranges between 77.7% and 78.9% for combined strategies that involve decarbonised buildings and transport in urban infrastructure, and the wedges approach the remaining emissions reductions also considering construction materials and waste. This data supports urban areas pursuing a package of multiple, integrated mitigation strategies in planning for decarbonisation (Sections 8.4 and 8.6, and Figure 8.21).

The most comprehensive approach to-date for quantifying urban emissions within the global context (Gurney et al. 2021, 2022) combines the per capita carbon footprint estimates for 13,000 cities from Moran et al. (2018) with projections of the share of urban population (Jiang and O'Neill 2017) within the IPCC's SSP-RCP framework (van Vuuren et al. 2014, 2017a; Riahi et al. 2017). Urban emissions in seven SSP-RCP scenarios are shown in Figure 8.13 along with an estimate of the global total CO_2-eq for context.

In 2020, total urban emissions (including CO_2 and CH_4) derived from consumption-based accounting were estimated to be 29 $GtCO_2$-eq, representing between 67% and 72% of global CO_2 and CH_4 emissions, excluding aviation, shipping, and biogenic sources of emissions. By 2050, with moderate to low urban mitigation efforts, urban emissions are projected to rise to 34.0 $GtCO_2$-eq (SSP2-RCP4.5) or 40.2 $GtCO_2$-eq (SSP3-RCP7.0) – driven by growing urban population, infrastructure, and service demands. However, scenarios that involve rapid urbanisation can have different outcomes as seen in SSP1-RCP1.9 based on green growth, versus SSP5-RCP8.5 with the strongest carbon lock-in lacking any decarbonisation. Other scenarios involve mixed and/or low urbanisation, along with other differences, including the implementation of electrification, energy, and material efficiency, technology development and innovation, renewable energy preferences, and behavioural, lifestyle, and dietary responses (Table 8.2). With aggressive and immediate mitigation efforts to limit global warming to 1.5°C (>50%) with no or limited overshoot, urban GHG emissions could approach net-zero and reach a maximum of 3.3 $GtCO_2$-eq in 2050 (SSP1-RCP1.9). Under aggressive but not immediate urban mitigation efforts to limit global warming to 2°C (>67%), urban emissions could reach 17.2 $GtCO_2$-eq in 2050 (SSP1-RCP2.6).

When 2020 levels are compared to the values for the year 2030, urban areas that utilise multiple opportunities towards resource-efficient and walkable urbanisation are estimated to represent a savings potential of 9.8 $GtCO_2$-eq of urban emissions, under SSP1-RCP1.9 scenario conditions, on the path towards net-zero CO_2 and CH_4 emissions. In contrast, urban emissions would increase by 3.4 $GtCO_2$-eq from 2020 levels in 2030 under SSP2-RCP4.5 scenario conditions with moderate changes lacking ambitious mitigation action (Figure 8.14).

Table 8.3: Cross-cutting implications of the reference scenarios and Illustrative Mitigation Pathways (IMPs) for urban areas. The IMPs illustrate key themes of mitigation strategies throughout the WGIII report (Section 3.2.5). The implications of the key themes of the six IMPs (in addition to two pathways illustrative of higher emissions) for mitigation in urban areas are represented based on the main storyline elements that involve energy, land use, food biodiversity and lifestyle, as well as policy and innovation. The cross-cutting implications of these elements for urban areas, where multiple elements interact, are summarised for each reference scenario and the IMPs. IMP-Ren, IMP-LD and IMP-SP represent pathways in the C1 category that also includes SSP1–1.9. Source: adapted from the key themes of the IMPs for urban areas.

Reference scenarios and IMPs	Cross-cutting implications for urban areas
Current Policies (CurPol scenario)	– Urban mitigation is challenged by overcoming lock-in to fossil fuel consumption; also with car-based and low-density urban growth prevailing – Consumption patterns have land impacts, supply chains remain the same, urban inhabitants have limited participation in mitigation options – Progress in low-carbon urban development takes place at a relatively slower pace and there is limited policy learning within climate networks
Moderate Action (ModAct scenarios)	– Renewable energy continues to increase its share that is supported by urban areas to a more limited extent with ongoing lock-in effects – Changes in land use, consumption patterns, and lifestyles mostly continue as before with negligible changes taking place – if any – The fragmented policy landscape also prevails at the urban level with different levels of ambitions and without integration across the urban system
Gradual Strengthening (IMP-GS)	– Urban areas depend upon energy supply from distant power plants or those in rural areas without rapid progress in urban electrification – Afforestation/reforestation is supported with some delay while lower incentives for limiting growth in urban extent provide inconsistencies – The mobilisation of urban actors for GHG emission reductions is strengthened more gradually with stronger coordination taking place after 2030
Net Negative Emissions (IMP-Neg)	– Urban areas depend upon energy supply from distant power plants or those in rural areas with more limited electrification in urban energy systems – Afforestation/reforestation is supported to a certain extent while lower incentives for limiting growth in urban extent provide inconsistencies – Urban areas are less prominent in policy and innovation given emphasis on carbon capture and storage (CCS) options. Rural areas are more prominent considering BECCS
Renewable Energy (IMP-Ren)	– Urban areas support renewable energy penetration with electrification of urban infrastructure and sector coupling for increasing system flexibility – Consumption patterns and urban planning are able to reduce pressures on land use, demand response is increased to support renewables – Urban climate governance is enabling rapid deployment of renewable energy while fostering innovation for sustainable urban planning
Low Demand (IMP-LD)	– Walkable urban form is increased, active and public transport modes are encouraged, low-energy buildings and green-blue infrastructure is integrated – Changes in consumption patterns and urban planning reduce pressures on land use to lower levels while service provisioning is improved – Urban policymaking is used to accelerate solutions that foster innovation and increased efficiencies across all sectors, including material use
Shifting Pathways (IMP-SP)	– Urban areas are transformed to be resource efficient, low demand, and renewable energy supportive with an integrated approach in urban planning – Reinforcing measures enable GHG emission reductions from consumption patterns while also avoiding resource impacts across systems – Urban climate mitigation is best aligned with the SDGs to accelerate GHG emission reductions, increasing both scalability and acceptance

Among the 500 urban areas with the highest consumption-based urban emissions footprint in 2015 (Moran et al. 2018), urban-level emission scenarios under SSP1 conditions are constructed for 420 urban areas located across all regions of the world (Kılkış 2021a). These scenarios are based on urban-level population projections by SSP (Kii 2021), trends in relevant CMIP6 scenarios (Gidden et al. 2019), and a 100% renewable energy scenario (Bogdanov et al. 2021). In the year 2020, the 420 urban areas are responsible for about 10.7 ± 0.32 GtCO$_2$-eq, or 27% of the global total CO$_2$ and CH$_4$ emissions of about 40 GtCO$_2$-eq, excluding aviation, shipping, and biogenic sources. Under three SSP1-based scenarios, the urban emissions of the 420 urban areas in 2030 is projected to be about 7.0 GtCO$_2$-eq in SSP1-RCP1.9, 10.5 GtCO$_2$-eq in SSP1-RCP2.6, and 5.2 GtCO$_2$-eq in the SSP1 renewable energy scenario.

The Illustrative Mitigation Pathways (IMPs) represent different strategies for maintaining temperature goals that are compliant with the Paris Agreement, as well as their comparison with the continuation of current policies (Sections 1.5 and 3.2.5, and Table 8.3). The key characteristics that define the IMPs involve aspects of energy, land use, lifestyle, policy, and innovation. Urban areas provide cross-cutting contexts where each of these key characteristics can be enabled and have a particularly important role in the transformation pathways for renewable energy (IMP-Ren), low demand (IMP-LD), and shifting to sustainability (IMP-SP). Pathways that are compliant with the Paris Agreement include such urban implications as a reversal of decreasing land-use efficiency in urban areas to lower energy demand based on spatial planning for compact urban form (Section 8.4.2), changes in urban infrastructure for supporting demand flexibility to handle variable energy supply (Section 8.4.3), as well as policies and governance that are conducive to innovation in urban areas (Section 8.5). Spatial planning for compact urban form can enable reduced energy demand and changes in service provisioning, including through walkable neighbourhoods and mixed land use, providing venues for socio-behavioural change towards active transport (Section 8.4.5). Electrification and sector coupling in urban infrastructure can, for instance, be an important enabler of supporting higher penetrations of renewable energy in the energy system.

8.4   Urban Mitigation Options

Urban mitigation options can be categorised into three broad strategies: (i) reducing or changing urban energy and material use towards more sustainable production and consumption across all sectors, including through spatial planning and infrastructure; (ii) electrification and switching to net-zero-emissions resources; and (iii) enhancing carbon storage in the urban environment through urban green and blue infrastructure, which can also offer multiple co-benefits. A fourth, socio-behavioural aspects, can shift energy demand and emerge as the result of implementing the strategies. Urban mitigation options covered in this section are organised around these three strategies and can facilitate deep decarbonisation through systemic transformation (see Section 8.6 and Figure 8.21 for prioritising mitigation options based on urban form and urban growth typologies).

Urban areas are systems where multiple mitigation options – especially when integrated – have cascading effects across transport, energy, buildings, land use, and behaviour. These cascading effects take place both within and across urban systems (Figure 8.15). Mitigation actions also occur at multiple urban scales, from households and blocks to districts and city regions, and can be implemented as standalone sectoral strategies, such as increasing energy efficiency for appliances, and also as system-wide actions. In reducing emissions locally, urban areas can help lower emissions outside of their administrative boundaries through their use of materials and resources, and by increasing the efficiency of infrastructure and energy use beyond what is possible with individual sectoral strategies. Urban mitigation policies that implement multiple integrated interventions will provide more emissions savings than the sum of individual interventions (Sethi et al. 2020).

Integrated action also has a key role in providing benefits for human well-being. Urban mitigation options and strategies that are effective, efficient, and fair can also support broader sustainability goals (Güneralp et al. 2017; Kona et al. 2018; Pasimeni et al. 2019). Due to the complex and intensive interactions in urban systems and the interlinked nature of the SDGs, cities can be important intervention points to harness synergies and co-benefits for achieving emissions reductions along with other SDGs (Nilsson et al. 2016; Corbett and Mellouli 2017) (Section 8.2 and Figure 8.4).

8.4.1   Avoiding Carbon Lock-in

Carbon lock-in occurs as the result of interactions between different geographic and administrative scales (institutional lock-in) and across sectors (infrastructural and technological lock-in), which create the conditions for behavioural lock-in covering both individual and social structural behaviours (Seto et al. 2016) (see Glossary for a broader definition of 'lock-in'). The way that urban areas are designed, laid out, and built (i.e., urban form) affects and is affected by the interactions across the different forms of carbon lock-in (Figures 8.15 and 8.16). Cities are especially prone to carbon lock-in because of the multiple interactions of technological, institutional, and behavioural systems, which create inertia and path dependency that are difficult to break. For example, the lock-in of gasoline cars is reinforced by highway and energy infrastructures that are further locked-in by social and cultural preferences for individual mobility options. The dominance of cars and their supporting infrastructures in auto-centric urban forms is further reinforced by zoning and urban development patterns, such as dispersed and low-density housing distantly located from jobs, that create obstacles to creating alternative mobility options (Seto et al. 2016; Linton et al. 2021).

Urban infrastructures and the built environment are long-lived assets, embodying triple carbon lock-ins in terms of their construction, operations, and demolition (Creutzig et al. 2016b; Seto et al. 2016; Ürge-Vorsatz et al. 2018). There is much focus in the climate change literature on the operational lifetimes of the energy sector, especially power plants and the electricity grid, which are between 30 and 60 years (Rode et al. 2017). Yet, in reality, the lifespans of urban

(a)

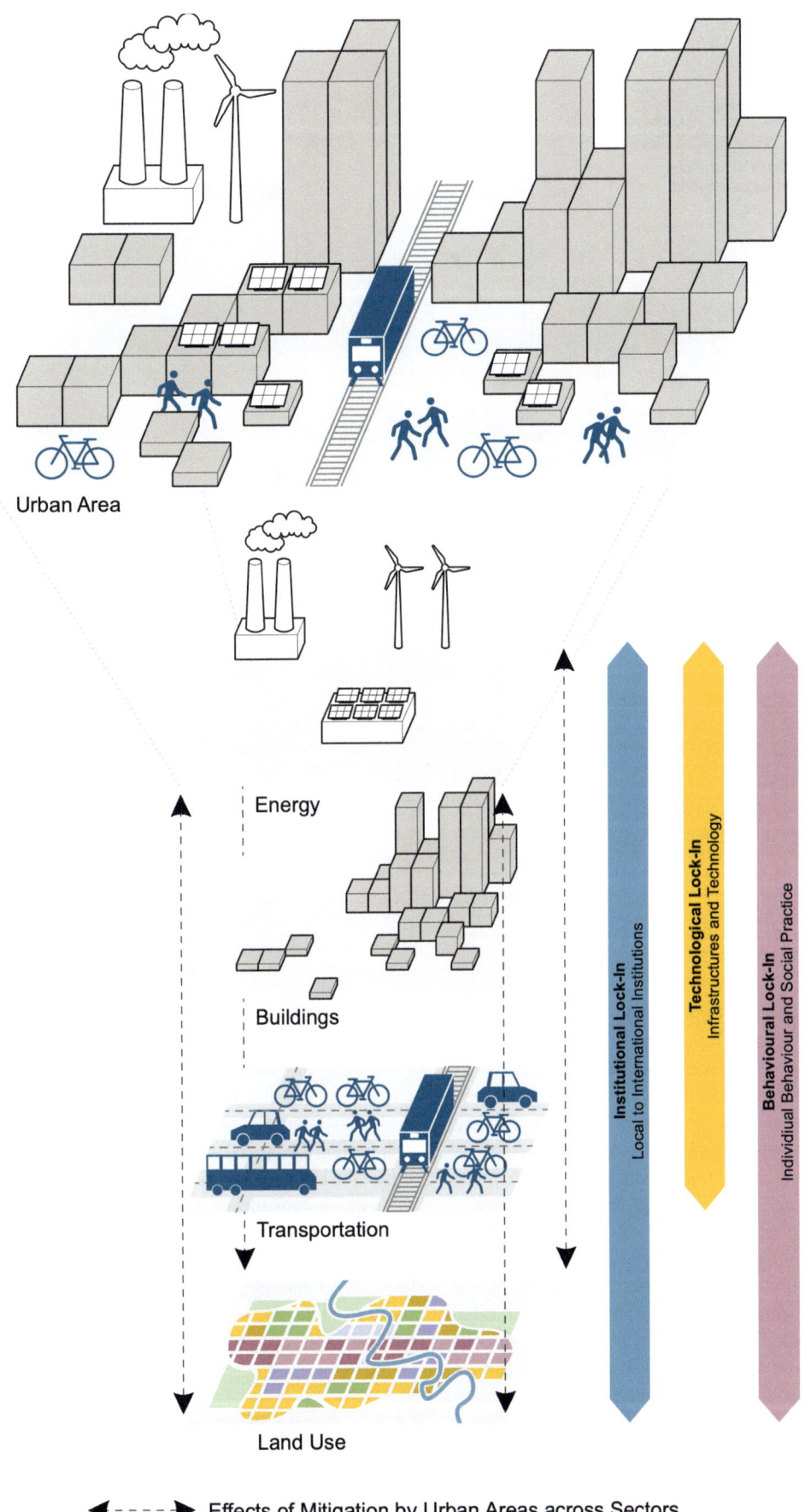

Figure 8.15: Urban systems, lock-in, and cascading effects of mitigation strategies.

(b)

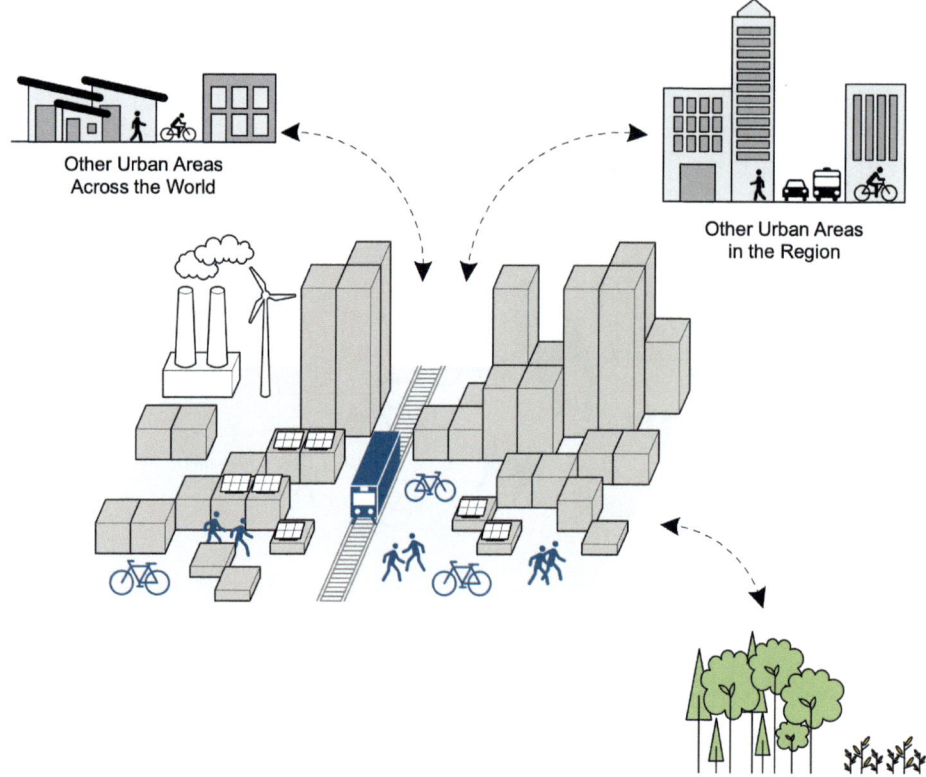

Figure 8.15 (continued): Urban systems, lock-in, and cascading effects of mitigation strategies. Cities are systems of interconnected sectors, activities, and governance structures. Urban-scale mitigation action can have cascading effects across multiple sectors, as shown in panel **(a)**, as well as regional, national, and global impacts through supply chains, resource flows, and institutions, as shown in panel **(b)**. Mitigation efforts implemented at larger scales of governance or in sectors that transcend urban boundaries, like energy and transportation, can also facilitate and amplify mitigation at the urban scale, as shown by the arrows extending in both directions across layers (a). Because urban areas are connected locally and globally, urban mitigation efforts can also impact other cities and surrounding areas (agriculture, forestry and other land use (AFOLU)). Cities are prone to carbon lock-in due to the numerous reinforcing interactions among urban infrastructures and technologies, institutions, and individual and collective behaviours; see the side arrows extending across the layers in panel (a): the yellow arrow represents the infrastructure and technological lock-in involving user technologies and supporting infrastructure, the blue arrow indicates lock-in of local to international institutions, and the pink arrow represents behavioural lock-in for individuals and society. Urban carbon lock-in is strongly determined by urban form, in particular the layout of streets and land-use mix. The different coloured spatial patterns represent varying levels of co-location of housing and jobs, and mobility options (Figure 8.16). Efforts to break urban carbon lock-in require meta-transformations to break inertia in and among infrastructures, institutions, and behaviours. Source: adapted in part from Seto et al. (2016).

infrastructures, especially the basic layout of roadways, are often much longer (Reyna and Chester 2015). A number of detailed case studies on the evolution of urban road networks for cities around the world reveal that the current layout of streets grew out of street networks that were established hundreds of years ago (Strano et al. 2012; Masucci et al. 2013; Mohajeri and Gudmundsson 2014). Furthermore, there is evidence that urban street layout, population growth, urban development, and automobile ownership co-evolve (Li et al. 2019a).

For cities to break out of mutually reinforcing carbon lock-in, it will require systematic transformation and systems-based planning that integrates mitigation strategies across sectors and geopolitical scales. Urban energy demand patterns are locked-in whenever incremental urban design and planning decisions, coupled with investments in long-lasting infrastructure, such as roads and buildings, take place (Seto et al. 2016). The fundamental building blocks of cities are based on the layout of the street network, the size of city blocks, and the density of street intersections. If not significantly altered, these three factors will continue to shape and lock-in energy demand for decades after their initial construction, influencing the mitigation potential of urban areas (Section 8.4.2 and Figure 8.22).

Avoiding carbon lock-in inherently involves decisions that extend beyond the administrative boundaries of cities. This includes pricing of low-emissions technology or materials, such as electric battery or hydrogen vehicles and buses, although cities can support their development and deployment (Cross-Chapter Box 12 in Chapter 16 on Transition Dynamics). In contrast, urban governments in most parts of the world do have powers to set building codes that regulate materials and construction standards for buildings, including heating and cooling technologies, and major appliances. Other examples include zoning that determines the location of buildings, land uses, standards for densities, and the inclusion of energy planning in their building standards and public works, including streets, parks, and open spaces (Blanco et al. 2011; Raven et al. 2018).

8.4.2   Spatial Planning, Urban Form, and Infrastructure

Urban form is the resultant pattern and spatial layout of land use, transportation networks, and urban design elements, including the physical urban extent, configuration of streets and building orientation, and the spatial figuration within and throughout cities and towns (Lynch 1981; Handy 1996). Infrastructure describes the physical structures, social and ecological systems, and corresponding institutional arrangements that provide services and enable urban activity (Dawson et al. 2018; Chester 2019) and comprises services and built-up structures that support urban functioning, including transportation infrastructure, water and wastewater systems, solid waste systems, telecommunications, and power generation and distribution (Seto et al. 2014).

8.4.2.1 Urban Form

The AR5 concluded that infrastructure and four dimensions of urban form are especially important for driving urban energy use: density, land-use mix, connectivity, and accessibility. Specifically, low-carbon cities have the following characteristics: (i) co-located medium to high densities of housing, jobs, and commerce; (ii) high mix of land uses; (iii) high connectivity of streets; and (iv) high levels of accessibility, distinguished by relatively low travel distances and travel times that are enabled by multiple modes of transportation. Urban areas with these features tend to have smaller dwelling units, smaller parcel sizes, walking opportunities, high density of intersections, and are highly accessible to shopping. For brevity, we will refer to these characteristics collectively as 'compact and walkable urban form' (Figure 8.16). Compact and walkable urban form has many co-benefits, including mental and physical health, lower resource demand, and saving land for AFOLU. In contrast, dispersed and auto-centric urban form is correlated with higher GHG emissions, and characterised by separated land uses, low population and job densities, large block size, and low intersection density.

Since AR5, a range of studies have been published on the relationships between urban spatial structures, urban form, and GHG emissions. Multiple lines of evidence reaffirm the key findings from AR5, especially regarding the mitigation benefits associated with reducing vehicle miles or kilometres travelled (VMT/VKT) through

spatial planning. There are important cascading effects not only for transport but also other key sectors and consumption patterns, such as in buildings, households, and energy. However, these benefits can be attained only when the existing spatial structure of an urban area does not limit locational and mobility options, thereby avoiding carbon lock-in through the interaction of infrastructure and the resulting socio-behavioural aspects.

Modifying the layout of emerging urbanisation to be more compact, walkable, and co-located can reduce future urban energy use by 20–25% in 2050 while providing a corresponding mitigation potential of 23–26% (Creutzig et al. 2015, 2016b; Sethi et al. 2020), forming the basis for other urban mitigation options. Cross-Chapter Box 7 in Chapter 10 provides perspectives on simultaneously reducing urban transport emissions, avoiding infrastructure lock-in, and providing accessible services. The systemic nature of compact urban form and integrated spatial planning influences 'Avoid-Shift-Improve' (ASI, see Glossary) options across several sectors simultaneously, including for mobility and shelter (for an in-depth discussion on the integration of service provision solutions within the ASI framework, see Section 5.3).

8.4.2.2 Co-located Housing and Jobs, Mixed Land Use, and High Street Connectivity

Integrated spatial planning, co-location of higher residential and job densities, and systemic approaches are widely identified with development that is characterised by the 5Ds of transit-oriented development (TOD) based on density, diversity (mixed land uses), design (street connectivity), destination accessibility, and distance to transit. Spatial strategies that integrate the 5Ds are shown to reduce VMT/VKT, and thereby transport-related GHG emissions through energy savings. The effect of urban form and built environment strategies on VMT per capita varies by a number of factors (Ewing and Cervero 2010; Stevens 2017; Blanco and Wikstrom 2018). Density and destination accessibility have the highest elasticities, followed by design (Stevens 2017). Population-weighted densities for

Compact and Walkable   **Dispersed and Auto-Centric**

Figure 8.16: **Urban form and implications for GHG emissions.** Compact and walkable urban form is strongly correlated with low GHG emissions and characterised by co-located medium to high densities of housing and jobs, high street density, small block size, and mixed land use (Seto et al. 2014). Higher population densities at places of origin (e.g., home) and destination (e.g., employment, shopping) concentrate demand and are necessary for achieving the Avoid-Shift-Improve (ASI) approach for sustainable mobility (Chapters 5 and 10). Dispersed and auto-centric urban form is strongly correlated with high GHG emissions, and characterised by separated land uses, especially housing and jobs, low street density, large block sizes, and low urban densities. Separated and low densities of employment, retail, and housing increase average travel distances for both work and leisure, and make active transport and modal shift a challenge. Since cities are systems, urban form has interacting implications across energy, buildings, transport, land use, and individual behaviour. Compact and walkable urban form enables effective mitigation while dispersed and auto-centric urban form locks-in higher levels of energy use. The colours represent different land uses and indicate varying levels of co-location and mobility options.

121 metropolitan areas have further found that the concentration of population and jobs along mass transit corridors decreases VMT/VKT significantly when compared to more dispersed metropolitan areas. In this sample, elasticity rates were twice as high for dense metropolitan areas located along mass transit lines (Lee and Lee 2020).

Meta-analyses of the reduction in VMT and the resulting GHG emissions consider the existing and still dominant use of emitting transportation technology, transportation fleets, and urban form characteristics. Varied historical legacies of transportation and the built environment, which can be utilised to develop more sustainable cities (Newman et al. 2016, 2017), are often not taken into account directly. Metropolitan policies and spatial planning, as evident in Copenhagen's Finger Plan, as well as strategic spatial planning in Stockholm and Seoul, have been major tools to restructure urban regions and energy patterns (Sung and Choi 2017). Road prices and congestion charges can provide the conditions for urban inhabitants to shift mobility demands and reduce vehicle use (Section 5.6.2). Surprisingly, even cities with higher population densities and a greater range of land uses can show declines in these important attributes, which can lead to emissions increases, such as found in a study of 323 East and South East Asian cities (Chen et al. 2020c). Conversely, the annual CO_2 emissions reduction of passenger cars in compact versus dispersed urban form scenarios can include at least a 10% reduction by 2030 (Matsuhashi and Ariga 2016). When combined with advances in transport technology, this share increases to 64–70% in 2050 based on compact urban form scenarios for 1727 municipalities (Kii 2020).

As a reaffirmation of AR5, population density reduces emissions per capita in the transport, building, and energy sectors (Baur et al. 2015; Gudipudi et al. 2016; Wang et al. 2017; Yi et al. 2017) (see also Sections 8.3.1 and 8.3.4 on past trends and forecasts of urban population density and land expansion). Urban compactness tends to reduce emissions per capita in the transport sector, especially for commuting (Matsuhashi and Ariga 2016; Lee and Lim 2018; Lee and Lee 2020). The relative accessibility of neighbourhoods to the rest of the region, in addition to the density of individual neighbourhoods, is important (Ewing et al. 2018). Creating higher residential and employment densities, developing smaller block sizes, and increasing housing opportunities in an employment area can significantly reduce household car ownership and car driving, and increase the share of transit, walk, and bicycle commuting (Ding et al. 2018). In addition to population density, land-use mix, rail transit accessibility, and street design reduce emissions from transport (Dou et al. 2016; Cao and Yang 2017; Choi 2018). The impact of population density and urban compactness on emissions per capita in the household or energy sector is also associated with socioeconomic characteristics or lifestyle preferences (Baiocchi et al. 2015; Miao 2017). Changes in the attributes of urban form and spatial structure have influences on overall energy demand across spatial scales, particularly street, block, neighbourhood, and city scales, as well as across the building (housing) and transport (mobility) sectors (Silva et al. 2017). Understanding the existing trade-offs (or synergetic links) between urban form variables across major emissions source sectors, and how they impact the size of energy flows within the urban system, is key to prioritising action for energy-efficient spatial planning strategies, which are likely to vary across urban areas.

8.4.2.3 Urban Form, Growth, and Sustainable Development

Spatial planning for compact urban form is a system-wide intervention (Sethi et al. 2020) and has potential to be combined with sustainable development objectives while pursuing climate mitigation for urban systems (Große et al. 2016; Cheshmehzangi and Butters 2017; Facchini et al. 2017; Lwasa 2017; Stokes and Seto 2019). Compact urban form can enable positive impacts on employment and green growth given that the local economy is decoupled from GHG emissions and related parameters while the concentration of people and activity can increase productivity based on both proximity and efficiency (Lee and Erickson 2017; Salat et al. 2017; Gao and Newman 2018; Han et al. 2018; Li and Liu 2018; Lall et al. 2021).

Public acceptance can have a positive impact on integrated spatial planning especially when there is a process of co-design (Grandin et al. 2018; Webb et al. 2018). The quality of spatial planning can also increase co-benefits for health and well-being, including decisions to balance urban green areas with density (Li et al. 2016; Sorkin 2018; Pierer and Creutzig 2019). The distributional effects of spatial planning can depend on the policy tools that shape the influence of urban densification on affordable housing while evidence for transit-induced gentrification is found to be partial and inconclusive (Chava and Newman 2016; Jagarnath and Thambiran 2018; Padeiro et al. 2019; Debrunner and Hartmann 2020) (Sections 8.2 and 8.4.4).

Reducing GHG emissions across different urban growth typologies (Figure 8.20) depends in part on the ability to integrate opportunities for climate mitigation with co-benefits for health and well-being (Grandin et al. 2018). At the same time, requirements for institutional capacity and governance for cross-sector coordination for integrated urban planning is high given the complex relations between urban mobility, buildings, energy systems, water systems, ecosystem services, other urban sectors, and climate adaptation (Große et al. 2016; Castán Broto 2017a; Endo et al. 2017; Geneletti et al. 2017). The capacity for implementing land-use zoning and regulations in a way that is consistent with supporting spatial planning for compact urban form is not equal across urban areas and depends on different contexts as well as institutional capacities (Bakır et al. 2018; Deng et al. 2018; Shen et al. 2019).

Currently, integrating spatial planning, urban form, and infrastructure in urban mitigation strategies remains limited in mainstream practices, including in urban areas targeting an emissions reduction of 36–80% in the next decades (Asarpota and Nadin 2020). Capacity building for integrated spatial planning for urban mitigation includes increasing collaboration among city departments and with civil society to develop robust mitigation strategies, bringing together civil engineers, architects, urban designers, public policy and spatial planners, and enhancing the education of urban professionals (Asarpota and Nadin 2020) (Section 8.5).

Spatial planning for compact urban form is a prerequisite for efficient urban infrastructure, including district heating and/or cooling networks (Swilling et al. 2018; Möller et al. 2019; Persson et al. 2019; UNEP IRP 2020). District heating and cooling networks benefit from urban design parameters, including density, block area, and elongation that represent the influence of urban density on energy density (Fonseca and Schlueter 2015; Shi et al. 2020). Heat-demand density is a function of both population density and heat demand per capita and can be equally present in urban areas with high population density or high heat demand per capita (Möller et al. 2019; Persson et al. 2019). Low-temperature networks that utilise waste heat or renewable energy can provide an option to avoid carbon lock-in to fossil fuels while layout and eco-design principles can further optimise such networks (Gang et al. 2016; Buffa et al. 2019; Dominković and Krajačić 2019). Replacing gas-based heating and cooling with electrified district heating and cooling networks, for instance, provides 65% emissions reductions also involving carbon-aware scheduling for grid power (De Chalendar et al. 2019). The environmental and ecological benefits increase through the interaction of urban energy and spatial planning (Tuomisto et al. 2015; Bartolozzi et al. 2017; Dénarié et al. 2018; Zhai et al. 2020). These interactions include support for demand-side flexibility, spatial planning using geographic information systems, and access to renewable and urban waste heat sources (Möller et al. 2018; REN21 2020; Sorknæs et al. 2020; Dorotić et al. 2019) (see Table 8.SM.2 for other references).

8.4.3 Electrification and Switching to Net-Zero-Emissions Resources

Pursuing the electrification of mobility, heating, and cooling systems, while decarbonising electricity and energy carriers, and switching to net-zero materials and supply chains, represent important strategies for urban mitigation. Electrification of energy end uses in cities and efficient energy demand for heating, transport, and cooking through multiple options and urban infrastructure, has an estimated mitigation potential of at least 6.9 $GtCO_2$-eq by 2030 and 15.3 $GtCO_2$-eq by 2050 (Coalition for Urban Transitions 2019). Energy efficiency measures in urban areas can be enabled by urban form, building codes, retrofitting and renovation, modal shifts, and other options. Decarbonising electricity supply raises the mitigation potential of efficient buildings and transport in urban areas to about 75% of the total estimate (Coalition for Urban Transitions 2019). In addition, relatively higher-density urban areas enable more cost-effective infrastructure investments, including electric public transport and large-scale heat pumps in districts that support electrification. Urban policymakers can play a key role in supporting carbon-neutral energy systems by acting as target setters and planners, demand aggregators, regulators, operators, conveners, and facilitators for coordinated planning and implementation across sectors, urban form, and demand (IEA 2021a; IRENA 2021).

8.4.3.1 Electrification and Decarbonisation of the Urban Energy System

Urban energy infrastructures often operate as part of larger energy systems that can be electrified, decarbonised, and become enablers of urban system flexibility through demand-side options. With multiple end-use sectors (e.g., transport, buildings) and their interactions with land use drawing on the same urban energy system(s), increasing electrification is essential for rapid decarbonisation, renewable

energy penetration, and demand flexibility (Kammen and Sunter 2016) (see IMPs in Sections 3.2.5 and 8.3.4). The mitigation potential of electrification is ultimately dependent on the carbon intensity of the electricity grid (Kennedy 2015; Hofmann et al. 2016; Peng et al. 2018; Zhang and Fujimori 2020) and starts providing lifecycle emission savings for carbon intensities below a threshold of 600 tCO_2-eq GWh^{-1} (Kennedy et al. 2019). Integrated systems of roof-top photovoltaics (PVs) and all-electric vehicles (EVs) alone could supply affordable carbon-free electricity to cities and reduce CO_2 emissions by 54–95% (Brenna et al. 2014; Kobashi et al. 2021). Furthermore, electrification and decarbonisation of the urban energy system holds widespread importance for climate change mitigation across different urban growth typologies and urban form (Section 8.6 and Figure 8.21) and leads to a multitude of public health co-benefits (see Section 8.2).

Strategies that can bring together electrification with reduced energy demand based on walkable and compact urban form can accelerate and amplify decarbonisation. Taking these considerations – across the energy system, sectors, and land use – contributes to avoiding, or breaking out of, carbon lock-in and allows continued emission savings as the energy supply is decarbonised (Kennedy et al. 2018; Teske et al. 2018; Seto et al. 2021). Indeed, electrification is already transforming urban areas and settlements and has the potential to continue transforming urban areas into net-negative electric cities that may sequester more carbon than emitted (Kennedy et al. 2018; Seto et al. 2021).

In its simplest form, electrification involves the process of replacing fossil fuel-based technologies with electrified innovations such as electric vehicles, buses, streetcars, and trains (Sections 10.3 and 10.4), heat pumps, PVs (Section 6.4.2.1), electric cook-stoves (Section 9.8.2.1), and other technologies (Stewart et al. 2018). Cost-effective decarbonisation of energy use can be supported by electrification in urban areas if there is also demand-side flexibility for power, heat, mobility, and water with sector coupling (Guelpa et al. 2019; Pfeifer et al. 2021). Overall, demand-side flexibility across sectors in urban areas is supported by smart charging, electric mobility, electrified urban rail, power-to-heat, demand side response, and water desalination (Lund et al. 2015; Calvillo et al. 2016; Salpakari et al. 2016; Newman 2017; Meschede 2019).

As an enabler, electrification supports integrating net-zero energy sources in urban infrastructure across sectors, especially when there is more flexible energy demand in mobility, heating, and cooling to absorb greater shares of variable renewable energy. In the transport sector, smart charging can reduce electric vehicle impacts on peak demand by 60% (IEA 2021a). Urban areas that connect efficient building clusters with the operation of smart thermal grids in district heating and cooling networks with large-scale heat pumps can support higher penetrations of variable renewable energy in smart energy systems (Lund et al. 2014, 2017). Higher urban densities provide the advantage of increasing the penetration of renewable power for deep decarbonisation, including mixed-use neighbourhoods for grid balancing and electric public transport (Hsieh et al. 2017; Tong et al. 2017; Fichera et al. 2018; Kobashi et al. 2020). Based on these opportunities, urban areas that provide low-cost options to energy storage for integrating the power sector with multiple demands reduce investment needs in grid electricity storage capacities (Mathiesen et al. 2015; Lund et al. 2018).

Electrification at the urban scale encompasses strategies to aggregate energy loads for demand response in the urban built environment to reduce the curtailment of variable renewable energy and shifting time-of-use based on smart charging for redistributing energy demands (O'Dwyer et al. 2019). Peak shaving or shifting takes place among frequent interventions at the urban level (Sethi et al. 2020). Business models and utility participation, including municipal level demonstrations, can allow for upscaling (Gjorgievski et al. 2020; Meha et al. 2020). The urban system can support increasing demand-side flexibility in energy systems, including in contexts of 100% renewable energy systems (Drysdale et al. 2019; Thellufsen et al. 2020).

Smart grids in the urban system

Smart electricity grids enable peak demand reductions, energy conservation, and renewable energy penetration, and are a subset of smart energy systems. GHG emission reductions from smart grids range from 10 to 180 gCO_2 kWh^{-1} (grams of CO_2 per kilowatt-hour) with a median value of 89 gCO_2 kWh^{-1}, depending on the electricity mix, penetration of renewable energy, and the system boundary (Moretti et al. 2017). Smart electricity grids are characterised by bi-directional flows of electricity and information between generators and consumers, although some actors can be both as 'prosumer' (see Glossary). Two-way power flows can be used to establish peer-to-peer trading (P2P) (Hansen et al. 2020). Business models based on local citizen utilities (Green and Newman 2017; Green et al. 2020; Syed et al. 2020) and community batteries (Mey and Hicks 2019; Green et al. 2020) can support the realisation of distributed energy and solar energy cities (Galloway and Newman 2014; Byrne and Taminiau 2016; Stewart et al. 2018; Allan 2020).

Currently, despite power outages that are costly to local economies, the adoption of smart electricity grids or smart energy systems has been slow in many developing regions, including in Sub-Saharan Africa (Westphal et al. 2017; Kennedy et al. 2019). This is due to a number of different factors, such as unreliable existing infrastructure, fractured fiscal authority, lack of electricity access in urban areas, upfront cost, financial barriers, inefficient pricing of electricity, and low consumer education and engagement (Venkatachary et al. 2018; Acakpovi et al. 2019; Cirolia 2020).

Pathways and trade-offs of electrification in urban systems

Urbanisation and population density are one of the key drivers for enabling access to electricity across the world, with benefits for sustainable development (Aklin et al. 2018). Grid-connected PV systems for urban locations that currently lack electricity access can allow urban areas to leapfrog based on green electrification (Abid et al. 2021). In the Global South, the conversion of public transport to electric transport, especially municipal buses (e.g., Bengaluru, India; Jakarta, Indonesia; Medellín, Colombia; Rio de Janeiro, Brazil; Quito, Ecuador) and micro-mobility (e.g., e-trikes in Manila,

Philippines) have been quantified based on reductions in GHG and $PM_{2.5}$ emissions, avoided premature deaths, and increases in life expectancies (IEA 2014; C40 Cities 2018, 2020b,c,d,e). In 22 Latin American cities, converting 100% of buses and taxis in 2030 to electric was estimated to result in a reduction of 300 $MtCO_2$-eq compared to 2017 (ONU Medio Ambiente 2017). Yet the scaling up of electric vehicles in cities can be examined within a larger set of possible social objectives, such as reducing congestion and the prioritisation of other forms of mobility.

Electrification requires a layering of policies at the national, state, and local levels. Cities have roles as policy architects, including transit planning (e.g., EV targets and low-emission zones, restrictions on the types of energy use in new buildings), implementers (e.g., building codes and compliance checking, financial incentives to encourage consumer uptake of EVs and heat pumps), and complementary partners to national and state policymaking (e.g., permitting or installation of charging infrastructure) (Broekhoff et al. 2015). The number of cities that have instituted e-mobility targets that aim for a certain percentage of EVs sold, in circulation or registered, is increasing (REN21 2021). Realising the mitigation potential of electrification will require fiscal and regulatory policies and public investment (Hall et al. 2017a; Deason and Borgeson 2019; Wappelhorst et al. 2020) (Section 8.5).

EVs are most rapidly deployed when there has been a suite of policies, including deployment targets, regulations and use incentives (e.g., zero-emission zone mandates, fuel economy standards, building codes), financial incentives (e.g., vehicles, chargers), industrial policies (e.g., subsidies), and fleet procurement (IEA 2016b, 2017, 2018, 2020a; Cazzola et al. 2019). The policy mix has included mandates for bus deployment, purchase subsidies, or split ownership of buses and chargers (IEA 2021b) (Chapter 10). Subsidies are often critical to address the often-higher upfront costs of electric devices. In other instances, the uptake of electric induction stoves was increased through government credit and allotment of free electricity (Martínez et al. 2017; Gould et al. 2018).

Bringing multiple stakeholders together in local decision-making for smart energy systems requires effort beyond usual levels while multi-actor settings can be increased to enable institutional conditions (Lammers and Hoppe 2019). Public participation and community involvement in the planning, design and operation of urban energy projects can be an enabler of decarbonising local energy demands (Corsini et al. 2019). Cooperation across institutions is important for municipalities that are engaged in strategic energy planning and implementation for smart energy systems (Krog 2019) (Section 8.5).

Electrification technologies can present potential trade-offs that can be minimised through governance strategies, smart grid technologies, circular economy practices, and international cooperation. One consideration is the increase in electricity demand (Section 5.3.1.1). Across 23 megacities in the world (population greater than 10 million people), electrification of the entire gasoline vehicle fleet could increase electricity demand on average by 18% (Kennedy et al. 2018). How grid capacity will be impacted is dependent on the match between daily electricity loads and supply (Tarroja et al. 2018). Materials recycling of electrification technologies is also key to minimising potential environmental and social costs (Church and Crawford 2018; Gaustad et al. 2018; Sovacool et al. 2020) and can ensure electrification reaches its complete mitigation potential. Circular economy strategies are particularly valuable to this goal by creating closed-loop supply chains through recycling, material recovery, repair, and reuse. For instance, the PV CYCLE programme in Europe prevented more than 30,000 metric tonnes of renewable technology from reaching the waste stream (Sovacool et al. 2020) (Box 10.6 and 'circular economy' in Glossary).

8.4.3.2   Switching to Net-zero-emissions Materials and Supply Chains

For the carbon embodied in supply chains to become net-zero, all key infrastructure and provisioning systems will need to be decarbonised, including electricity, mobility, food, water supply, and construction (Seto et al. 2021). The growth of global urban populations that is anticipated over the next several decades will create significant demand for buildings and infrastructure. As cities expand in size and density, there is an increase in the production of mineral-based structural materials

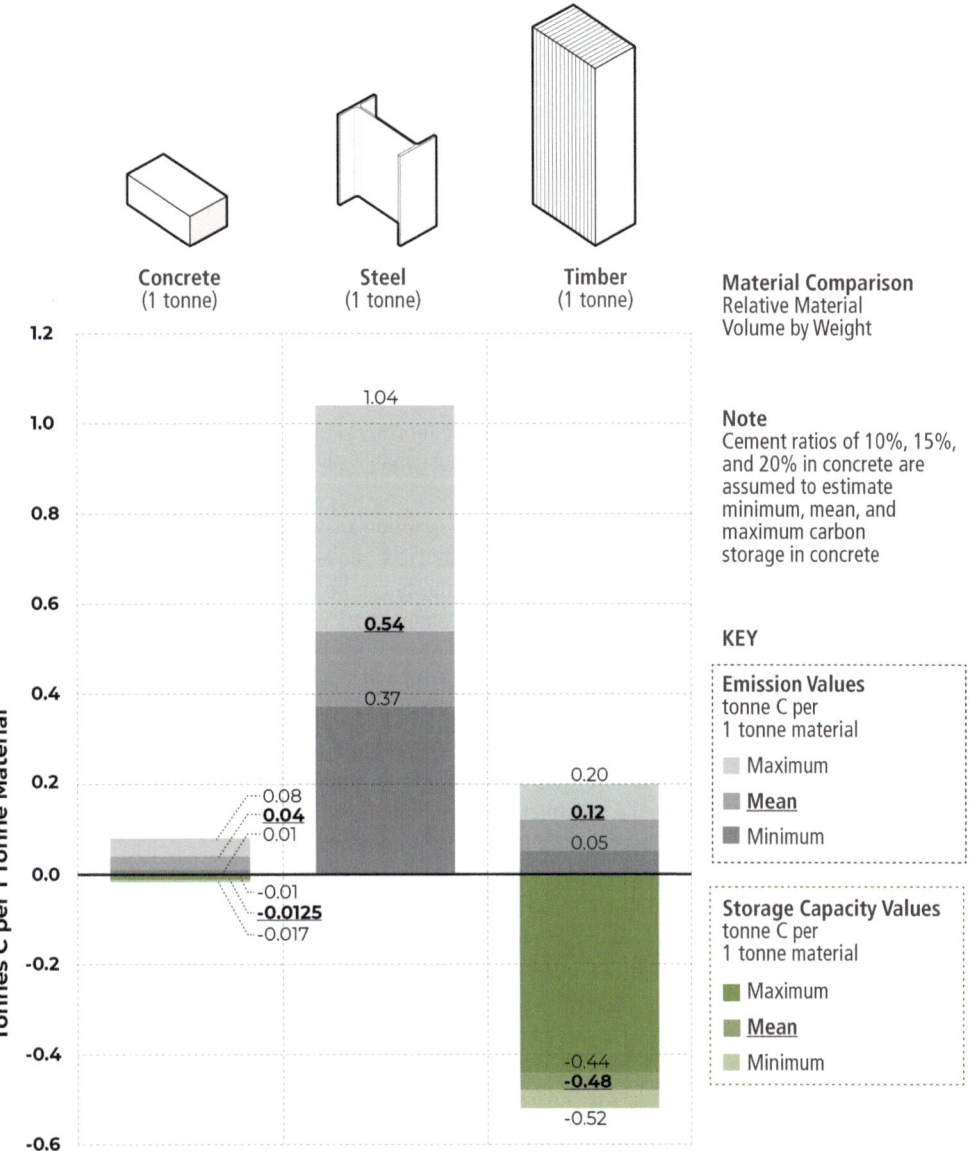

Figure 8.17: Relative volume of a given weight, its carbon emissions, and carbon storage capacity of primary structural materials comparing one tonne of concrete, steel, and timber. Concrete and steel have substantial embodied carbon emissions with minimal carbon storage capacities, while timber stores a considerable quantity of carbon with a relatively small ratio of carbon emissions-to-material volume. The displayed carbon storage of concrete is the theoretical maximum value, which may be achieved after hundreds of years. Cement ratios of 10%, 15%, and 20% are assumed to estimate minimum, mean, and maximum carbon storage in concrete. Carbon storage of steel is not displayed as it is negligible (0.004 tonne C per tonne of steel). The middle-stacked bars represent the mean carbon emission or mean carbon storage values displayed in bold font and underlined. The darker and lighter coloured stacked bars depict the minimum and maximum values. Grey tones represent carbon emissions and green tones are given for storage capacity values. Construction materials have radically different volume-to-weight ratios, as well as material intensity (see representations of structural columns in the upper panel. These differences should be accounted for in the estimations of their carbon storage and emissions (see also Figure 8.22). Source: adapted with permission from Churkina et al. (2020).

and enclosure systems that are conventionally associated with mid- and high-rise urban construction morphologies, including concrete, steel, aluminium, and glass. This will create a significant spike in GHG emissions and discharge of CO_2 at the beginning of each building lifecycle, necessitating alternatives (Churkina et al. 2020).

The initial carbon debt incurred in the production stage, even in sustainable buildings, can take decades to offset through operational stage energy efficiencies alone. Increased reduction in the energy demands and GHG emissions associated with the manufacture of mineral-based construction materials will be challenging, as these industries have already optimised their production processes. Among the category of primary structural materials, it is estimated that final energy demand for steel production can be reduced by nearly 30% compared to 2010 levels, with 12% efficiency improvement for cement (Lechtenböhmer et al. 2016). Even when industries are decarbonised, residual CO_2 emissions will remain from associated chemical reactions that take place in calcination and use of coke from coking coal to reduce iron oxide (Davis et al. 2018). Additionally, carbon sequestration by cement occurs over the course of the building lifecycle in quantities that would offset only a fraction of their production stage carbon spike (Xi et al. 2016; Davis et al. 2018). Moreover, there are collateral effects on the carbon cycle related to modern construction and associated resource extraction. The production of cement, asphalt, and glass requires large amounts of sand extracted from beaches, rivers, and seafloors, disturbing aquatic ecosystems and reducing their capacity to absorb atmospheric carbon. The mining of ore can lead to extensive local deforestation and soil degradation (Sonter et al. 2017). Deforestation significantly weakens the converted land as a carbon sink and in severe cases may even create a net emissions source.

A broad-based substitution of monolithic engineered timber systems for steel and concrete in mid-rise urban buildings offers the opportunity to transform cityscapes from their current status as net sources of GHG emissions into large-scale, human-made carbon sinks. The storage of photosynthetic forest carbon through the substitution of biomass-based structural materials for emissions-intensive steel and concrete is an opportunity for urban infrastructure. The construction of timber buildings for 2.3 billion new urban dwellers from 2020 to 2050 could store between 0.01 and 0.68 $GtCO_2$ per year depending on the scenario and the average floor area per capita. Over 30 years, wood-based construction can accumulate between 0.25 and 20 $GtCO_2$ and reduce cumulative emissions from 4 $GtCO_2$ (range of 7–20 $GtCO_2$) to 2 $GtCO_2$ (range of 0.3–10 $GtCO_2$) (*high confidence*) (Churkina et al. 2020).

Figure 8.17 indicates that new and emerging structural assemblies in engineered timber rival the structural capacity of steel and reinforced concrete while offering the benefit of storing significant quantities of atmospheric carbon (see also Figure 8.22). 'Mass timber' refers to engineered wood products that are laminated from smaller boards or lamella into larger structural components such as glue-laminated (glulam) beams or cross-laminated timber (CLT) panels. Methods of mass-timber production that include finger-jointing, longitudinal and transverse lamination with both liquid adhesive and mechanical fasteners, have allowed for the reformulation of large structural

timbers. The parallel-to-grain strength of mass (engineered) timber is similar to that of reinforced concrete (Ramage et al. 2017). As much as half the weight of a given volume of wood is carbon, sequestered during forest growth as a by-product of photosynthesis (Martin et al. 2018). Mass timber is inflammable, but in large sections forms a self-protective charring layer when exposed to fire that will protect the remaining 'cold wood' core. This property, formed as massive structural sections, is recognised in the fire safety regulations of building codes in several countries, which allow mid- and high-rise buildings in timber. Ongoing studies have addressed associated concerns about the vulnerability of wood to decay and the capacity of structural timber systems to withstand seismic and storm-related stresses.

Transitioning to biomass-based building materials, implemented through the adoption of engineered structural timber products and assemblies, will succeed as a mitigation strategy only if working forests are managed and harvested sustainably (Churkina et al. 2020). Since future urban growth and the construction of timber cities may lead to increased timber demand in regions with low forest cover, it is necessary to systematically analyse timber demand, supply, trade, and potential competition for agricultural land in different regions (Pomponi et al. 2020). The widespread adoption of biomass-based urban construction materials and techniques will demand more robust forest and urban land governance and management policies, as well as internationally standardised carbon accounting methods to properly value and incentivise forest restoration, afforestation, and sustainable silviculture.

Expansion of agroforestry practices may help to reduce land-use conflicts between forestry and agriculture. Harvesting pressures on forests can be reduced through the reuse and recycling of wooden components from dismantled timber buildings. Potential synergies between the carbon sequestration capacity of forests and the associated carbon storage capacity of dense mid-rise cities built from engineered timber offer the opportunity to construct carbon sinks deployed at the scale of landscapes, sinks that are at least as durable as other buildings (Churkina et al. 2020). Policies and practices promoting design for disassembly and material reuse will increase their durability.

8.4.4   Urban Green and Blue Infrastructure

The findings of AR6 WGI and WGII have underscored the importance of urban green and blue infrastructure for reducing the total warming in urban areas due to its local cooling effect on temperature and its benefits for climate adaptation (IPCC 2021; Cross-Working Group Box 2 in this chapter). Urban green and blue infrastructure in the context of nature-based solutions (NBS) involves the protection, sustainable management, and restoration of natural or modified ecosystems while simultaneously providing benefits for human well-being and biodiversity (IUCN 2021) (see Glossary for additional definitions). As an umbrella concept, urban NBS integrates established ecosystem-based approaches that provide multiple ecosystem services and are important in the context of societal challenges related to urbanisation, climate change, and reducing GHG emissions through the conservation and expansion of carbon sinks (Naumann et al. 2014; Raymond et al. 2017) (Section 8.1.6.1).

Urban green and blue infrastructure includes a wide variety of options, from street trees, parks, and sustainable urban drainage systems (Davis and Naumann 2017), to building-related green roofs or green facades, including green walls and vertical forests (Enzi et al. 2017). Figure 8.18 synthesises urban green and blue infrastructure based on urban forests, street trees, green roofs, green walls, blue spaces, greenways, and urban agriculture. Key mitigation benefits, adaptation co-benefits, and SDG linkages are represented by types of green and blue infrastructure. Local implementations of urban green and blue infrastructure can pursue these linkages while progressing toward inclusive sustainable urban planning (SDG 11.3) and the provision of safe, inclusive and accessible green and public spaces for all (SDG 11.7) (Butcher-Gollach 2018; Pathak and Mahadevia 2018; Rigolon et al. 2018; Anguelovski et al. 2019; Buyana et al. 2019; Azunre et al. 2021) (Section 8.2).

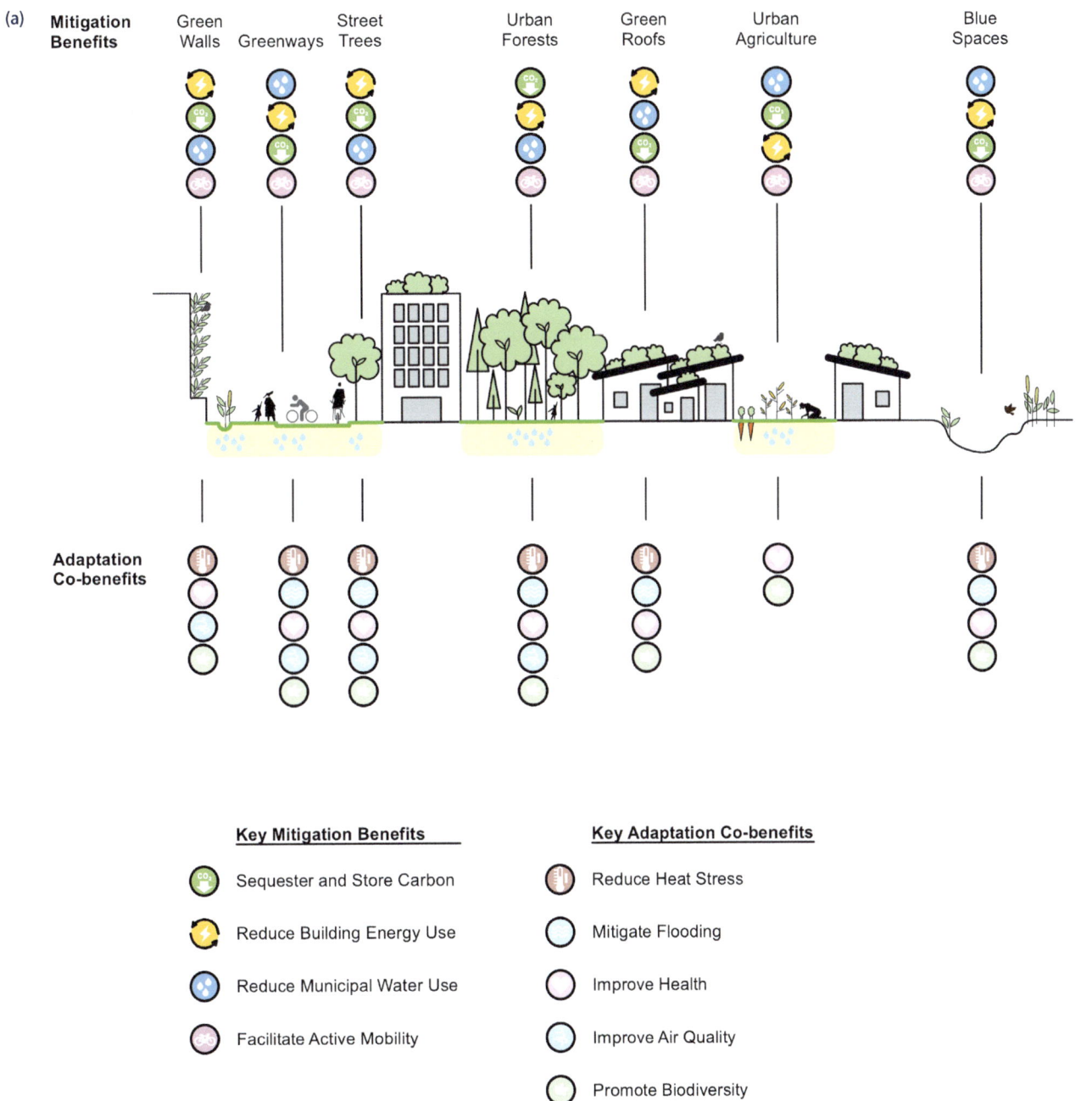

Figure 8.18: Key mitigation benefits, adaptation co-benefits, and SDG linkages of urban green and blue infrastructure. Panel **(a)** illustrates the potential integration of various green and blue infrastructure strategies within an urban system.

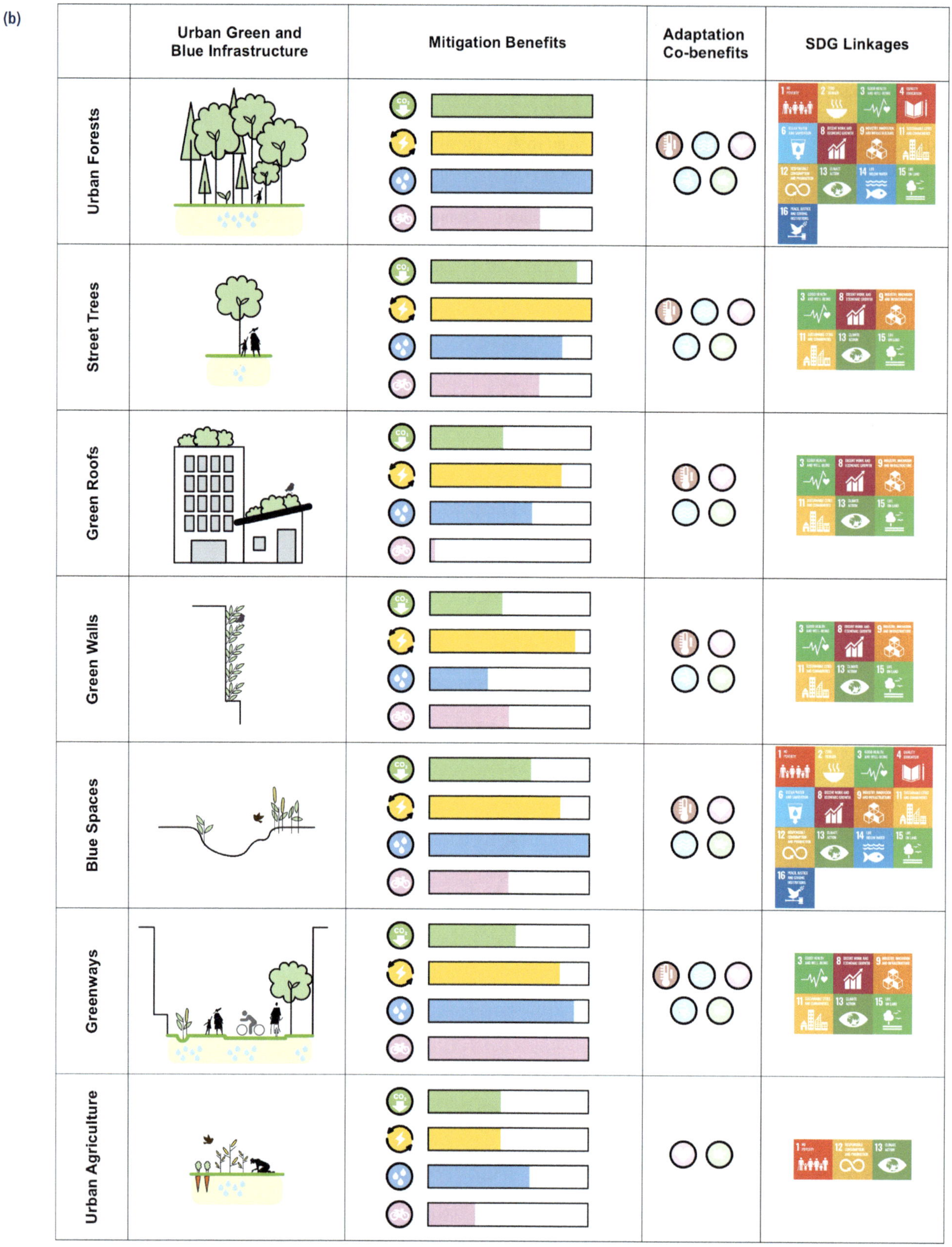

(b)

Figure 8.18: Key mitigation benefits, adaptation co-benefits, and SDG linkages of urban green and blue infrastructure. Panel **(b)** evaluates those strategies in the context of their mitigation benefits, adaptation co-benefits, and linkages to the SDGs. Urban forests and street trees provide the greatest mitigation benefit because of their ability to sequester and store carbon while simultaneously reducing building energy demand. Moreover, they provide multiple adaptation co-benefits and synergies based on the linkages to the SDGs (Figure 8.4). The assessments of mitigation benefits are dependent on context, scale, and spatial arrangement of each green and blue infrastructure type and their proximity to buildings. Mitigation benefits due to reducing municipal water use are based on reducing wastewater loads that reduce energy use in wastewater treatment plants. The sizes of the bars are illustrative and their relative size is based on the authors' best understanding and assessment of the literature.

8.4.4.1 The Mitigation Potential of Urban Trees and Associated Co-benefits

Due to their potential to store relatively high amounts of carbon compared to other types of urban vegetation, as well as their ability to provide many climate mitigation co-benefits (*high agreement, robust evidence*), natural area protection and natural forest management in urban areas is an important priority for cities looking to mitigate climate change. Globally, urban tree cover averages 26.5%, but varies from an average of 12% in deserts to 30.4% in forested regions (Nowak and Greenfield 2020).

Global urban tree carbon storage is approximately 7.4 billion tonnes (GtC) given 363 million hectares of urban land, 26.5% tree cover, and an average carbon storage density of urban tree cover of 7.69 kgC m^{-2} (kilograms carbon per square metre) (Nowak et al. 2013; World Bank et al. 2013). Estimated global annual carbon sequestration by urban trees is approximately 217 million tonnes (MtC) given an average carbon sequestration density per unit urban tree cover of 0.226 kgC m^{-2} (Nowak et al. 2013). With an average plantable (non-tree and non-impervious) space of 48% globally (Nowak and Greenfield 2020), the carbon storage value could nearly triple if all this space is converted to tree cover. In Europe alone, if 35% of the urban surfaces (26,450 km^2) were transformed into green surfaces, the mitigation potential based on carbon sequestration would be an estimated 25.9 MtCO$_2$ yr^{-1} with the total mitigation benefit being 55.8 MtCO$_2$ yr^{-1}, including an energy saving of about 92 TWh yr^{-1} (Quaranta et al. 2021). Other co-benefits include reducing urban runoff by about 17.5% and reducing summer temperatures by 2.5°C–6°C (Quaranta et al. 2021).

Urban tree carbon storage is highly dependent on biome. For example, carbon sequestered by vegetation in Amazonian forests is two to five times higher compared to boreal and temperate forests (Blais et al. 2005). At the regional level, the estimated carbon storage density rates of tree cover include a range of 3.14–14.1 kgC m^{-2} in the United States, 3.85–5.58 kgC m^{-2} in South Korea, 1.53–9.67 kgC m^{-2} in Barcelona, Spain, 28.1–28.9 kgC m^{-2} in Leicester, England, and an estimated 6.82 kgC m^{-2} in Leipzig, Germany and 4.28 kgC m^{-2} in Hangzhou, China (Nowak et al. 2013). At the local scale, above- and below-ground tree carbon densities can vary substantially, as with carbon in soils and dead woody materials. The conservation of natural mangroves has been shown to provide urban mitigation benefits through carbon sequestration, as demonstrated in the Philippines (Abino et al. 2014). Research on urban carbon densities from the Southern Hemisphere will contribute to better estimates.

On a per-tree basis, urban trees offer the most potential to mitigate climate change through both carbon sequestration and GHG emissions reduction from reduced energy use in buildings (Nowak et al. 2017). Maximum possible street tree planting among 245 world cities could reduce residential electricity use by about 0.9–4.8% annually (McDonald et al. 2016). Urban forests in the United States reduce building energy use by 7.2%, equating to an emissions reduction of 43.8 MtCO$_2$ annually (Nowak et al. 2017).

Urban trees can also mitigate some of the impacts of climate change by reducing the UHI effect and heat stress, reducing stormwater runoff, improving air quality, and supporting health and well-being in areas where the majority of the world's population resides (Nowak and Dwyer 2007). Urban forest planning and management can maximise these benefits for present and future generations by sustaining optimal tree cover and health (also see SDG linkages in Figure 8.4). Urban and peri-urban agriculture can also have economic benefits from fruit, ornamental, and medicinal trees (Gopal and Nagendra 2014; Lwasa 2017; Lwasa et al. 2018).

Box 8.2: Urban Carbon Storage: An Example from New York City

The structure, composition, extent, and growing conditions of vegetation in cities has an influence on their potential for mitigating climate change (Pregitzer et al. 2021). Urban natural areas, particularly forested natural areas, grow in patches and contain many of the same components as non-urban forests, such as high tree density, down woody material, and regenerating trees (Box 8.2, Figure 1).

Urban forested natural areas have unique benefits as they can provide habitat for native plants and animals, protecting local biodiversity in a fragmented landscape (Di Giulio et al. 2009). Forests can have a greater cooling effect on cities than designed greenspaces, and the bigger the forest the greater the effect (Jaganmohan et al. 2016). In New York City, urban forested natural areas have been found to account for the majority of trees estimated in the city (69%), but are a minority of the total tree canopy (25%, or 5.5% of the total city land area) (Pregitzer et al. 2019a). In New York City, natural areas are estimated to store a mean of 263.5 MgC ha^{-1} (megagram carbon per hectare), adding up to 1.86 TgC (teragram carbon) across the city, with the majority of carbon (86%) being stored in the trees and soils (Pregitzer et al. 2021). These estimates are similar to per-hectare estimates of carbon storage across different pools in non-urban forest types (Table 1), and 1.5 times greater than estimates for carbon stored in just trees across the entire city (Pregitzer et al. 2021).

Within urban natural areas, the amount of carbon stored varies widely based on vegetation type, tree density, and the species composition (Box 8.2, Figure 1). The oak-hardwood forest type is one of the most abundant in New York City's natural areas and is characterised by large and long-lived native hardwood tree species, with relatively dense wood. These forests store an estimated 311.5 MgC ha^{-1}. However, non-native exotic invasive species can be prevalent in the understory vegetation layer (<1m height), and account for about 50% of cover in New York City (Pregitzer et al. 2019b).

Box 8.2 (continued)

This could lead to a trajectory where exotic understory species, which are often herbaceous, out-compete regenerating trees in the understory layer, alter the soil (Ward et al. 2020), and alter the forest canopy (Matthews et al. 2016). A change in New York City's vegetation structure and composition to a more open vegetation type could reduce the carbon storage by over half (open grassland 120.1 MgC ha^{-1}).

When compared to estimates of carbon storage presented in other studies, the components (pools) of the natural area forests in New York City store carbon in similar proportions to other non-urban forests (see Table 1). This might suggest that in other geographies, similar adjacent non-urban forest types may store similar carbon stocks per unit area (*medium confidence*). However, despite similarities to non-urban forests, the urban context can lead to altered forest function and carbon cycling that should be considered. For example, trees growing in urban areas have been observed to grow at much higher rates due to higher access to light, nutrients, and increased temperatures (Gregg et al. 2003; Reinmann et al. 2020).

Higher growth rates coupled with the UHI effect have also been suggested to yield greater evaporative cooling by urban canopies relative to rural forests (Winbourne et al. 2020). Based on estimates in New York City, it is likely that the majority of tree biomass, and carbon in trees in cities, could be found in urban natural area forest patches (*medium agreement, limited evidence*). More research is needed to map urban natural areas, assess vegetation, and differentiate tree canopy types (natural versus non-natural) at fine scales within many cities and geographies. Accurate maps, as well as greater understanding of definitions of urban canopies and vegetation, could lead to better accounts for carbon stocks and the many other unique benefits they provide (Raciti et al. 2012; Pregitzer et al. 2019a).

Despite this potential, natural areas are inherently a minority land-use type in cities and should be viewed along with other types of urban tree canopy that occur in more designed environments that might out-perform natural areas in other ecosystem services. The mosaic of vegetation characteristics and growing conditions will yield different ecosystem services across cities (Pataki et al. 2011) and should be an important consideration in planning, management, and policy in the future.

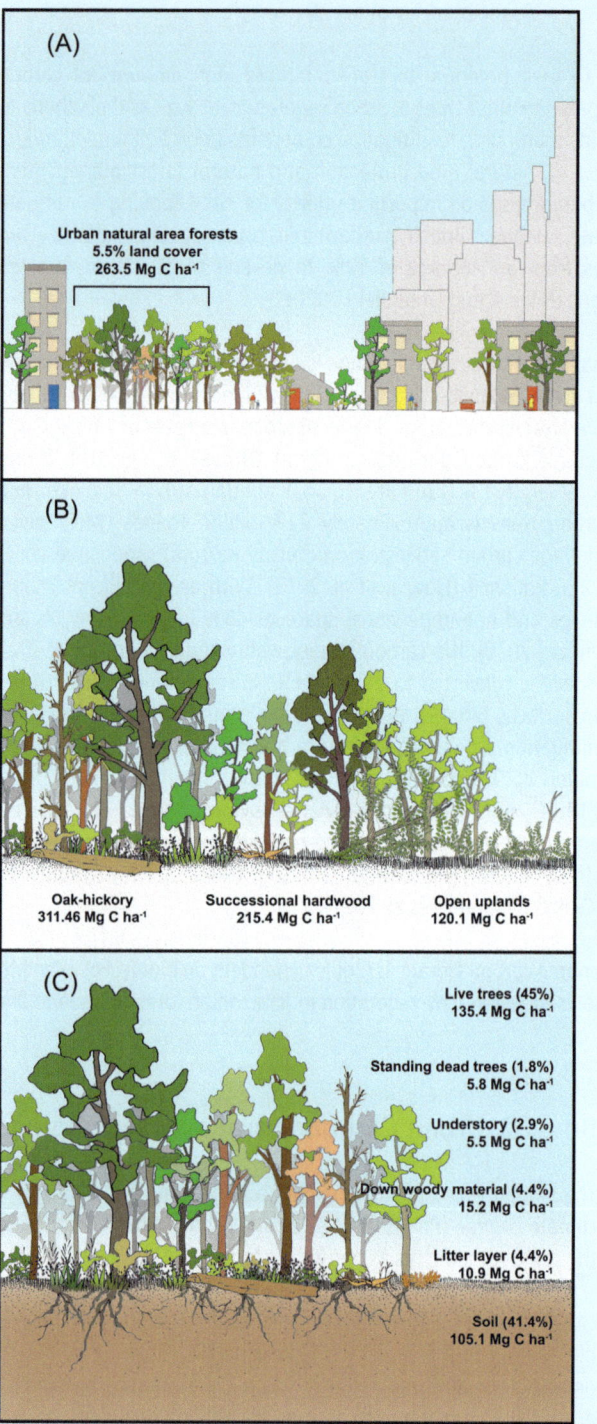

Box 8.2, Figure 1: Estimates for carbon storage in natural area forests in New York City. (a) Mean estimated carbon stock per hectare in natural area forests (Pregitzer et al. 2019a, 2021); **(b)** estimates for carbon stocks vary based on vegetation types; and **(c)** estimates of the amount of carbon stock in different forest pools per hectare. The proportion of the total estimated carbon stock per pool is out of the total estimated for the entire city (1.86 TgC). Source: adapted from Pregitzer et al. (2021).

Box 8.2 (continued)

Box 8.2, Table 1: A selection of benchmark reference estimates of different carbon pools sampled and the related urban considerations to contextualise the results from New York City (NYC), United States (USA) natural area carbon stocks. The benchmark estimates are intended to provide a point of reference to help contextualise the calculations for carbon pools in NYC's forests. Forest carbon is highly variable and dependent on microclimatic conditions such as moisture, microbial communities, and nutrient availability, all of which can be impacted by human activity in urban or altered environments. Standard errors and 95% confidence intervals can be found in Pregitzer et al. (2021). DBH: diameter at breast height; DWM: down woody material; CWM: coarse woody material and FWM: fine woody material. Source: Pregitzer et al. (2021).

Pool considered in NYC natural area	Published estimates of carbon stock (MgC ha^{-1})	NYC estimated carbon stock (MgC ha^{-1})	Urban considerations
Live trees: all trees (>2 cm DBH) including above and below ground	87.1: northeastern USA (Smith et al. 2013) 73.3: NYC assuming 100% cover (Nowak et al. 2013)	135.4	Lower ozone levels, higher CO_2, warmer temperatures, and higher nutrient deposition could lead to increased growth rates and annual carbon sequestration. However, pollutants in soil (e.g., heavy metals), increased pests, and GHGs in the atmosphere (e.g., NO_X and SO_2) could decrease annual tree growth and carbon sequestration (Gregg et al. 2003)
Groundcover: all vegetation growing <1 m height	1.8: northeastern USA (Smith et al. 2013)	5.5	Anthropogenic disturbance creates canopy gaps that accelerate herbaceous growth; invasive vines are prevalent in urban forests that can alter tree survival and growth and soils (Matthews et al. 2016; Ward et al. 2020)
Standing dead trees	5.1: northeastern USA (Smith et al. 2013) 2.59: Massachusetts (Liu et al. 2006)	5.8	Removal may occur due to safety considerations
CWM: coarse (>10 cm) and FWM (>0.1 cm)	9.18: CWM – New York state 2.52: CWM – Massachusetts (Liu et al. 2006) 6.37: FWM – New York (Woodall et al. 2013) 3.67: FWM northern hardwood; 0 to 227.94: Northern USA (Domke et al. 2016)	15.25 (added together DWM and FWM)	Removal may occur due to safety considerations
Litter and duff: depth measured	12: NYC (Pouyat et al. 2002) 9.36: northern hardwood; 0.04: northern USA (Domke et al. 2016)	10.95	Decomposition increases with temperature (Hanson et al. 2003); decreased ozone levels facilitate litter decay (Carreiro et al. 2009)
Mineral soil (organic 30 cm)	104: to 30 cm depth, NYC (Cambou et al. 2018) 50: to 10 cm depth, NYC (Pouyat et al. 2002)	105.11(30 cm) and 77.78 (10 cm)	UHI and pollution alter the litter chemistry, decomposer organisms, conditions, and resources, which all influence respiration rates (Carreiro et al. 2009); earthworms, prevalent in urban areas, accelerate decay, but some carbon is sequestered in passive pools (Pouyat et al. 2002). Soil could be compacted.

8.4.4.2 Benefits of Green Roofs, Green Walls, and Greenways

Green roofs and green walls have potential to mitigate air and surface temperature, improve thermal comfort, and mitigate UHI effects (Jamei et al. 2021; Wong et al. 2021), while lowering the energy demand of buildings (Susca 2019) (Figure 8.18). Green roofs have the highest median cooling effect in dry climates (3°C) and the lowest cooling effect in hot, humid climates (1°C) (Jamei et al. 2021). These mitigation potentials depend on numerous factors and the scale of implementation. The temperature reduction potential for green roofs when compared to conventional roofs can be about 4°C in winter and about 12°C during summer conditions (Bevilacqua et al. 2016). Green roofs can reduce building heating demands by about 10–30% compared to conventional roofs (Besir and Cuce 2018), 60–70% compared to black roofs, and 45–60% compared to white roofs (Silva et al. 2016). Green walls or facades can provide

a temperature difference between air temperature outside and behind a green wall of up to 10°C, with an average difference of 5°C in Mediterranean contexts in Europe (Perini et al. 2017). The potential of saving energy for air conditioning by green facades can be around 26% in summer months. Considerations of the spatial context are essential given their dependence on climatic conditions (Susca 2019). Cities are diverse and emissions savings potentials depend on several factors, while the implementation of green roofs or facades may be prevented in heritage structures.

Green roofs have been shown to have beneficial effects in stormwater reduction (Andrés-Doménech et al. 2018). A global meta-analysis of 75 international studies on the potential of green roofs to mitigate runoff indicate that the runoff retention rate was on average 62% but with a wide range (0–100%) depending on a number of interdependent factors (Zheng et al. 2021). These factors relate to the characteristics of the rainfall event (e.g., intensity) and characteristics of the green roof (e.g., substrate, vegetation type, and size), and of the climate and season type. A hydrologic modelling approach applied to an Italian case demonstrated that implementing green roofs may reduce peak runoff rates and water volumes by up to 35% in a 100% green roof conversion scenario (Masseroni and Cislaghi 2016).

Greenways support stormwater management to mitigate water runoff and urban floods by reducing the water volume (e.g., through infiltration) and by an attenuation or temporal shift of water discharge (Fiori and Volpi 2020; Pour et al. 2020). Using green infrastructure delays the time to runoff and reduces water volume but depends on the magnitude of floods (Qin et al. 2013). Measures are most effective for flood mitigation at a local scale; however, as the size of the catchment increases, the effectiveness of reducing peak discharge decreases (Fiori and Volpi 2020). Reduction of water volume through infiltration can be more effective with rainfall events on a lower return rate. Overall, the required capacity for piped engineered systems for water runoff attenuation and mitigation can be reduced while lowering flow rates, controlling pollution transport, and increasing the capacity to store stormwater (Srishantha and Rathnayake 2017). Benefits for flood mitigation require a careful consideration of the spatial context of the urban area, the heterogeneity of the rainfall events, and characteristics of implementation (Qiu et al. 2021). Maintenance costs and stakeholder coordination are other aspects requiring attention (Mguni et al. 2016).

Providing a connected system of greenspace throughout the urban area may promote active transportation (Nieuwenhuijsen and Khreis 2016), thereby reducing GHG emissions. Soft solutions for improving green infrastructure connectivity for cycling is an urban NBS mitigation measure, although there is *low evidence* for emissions reductions. In the city of Lisbon, Portugal, improvements in cycling infrastructure and bike-sharing system resulted in 3.5 times more cyclists within two years (Félix et al. 2020). In Copenhagen, the cost of cycling (0.08 EUR km^{-1}) is declining and is about six times lower than car driving (Euro 0.50/km) (Vedel et al. 2017). In addition, participants were willing to cycle 1.84 km longer if the route has a designated cycle track and 0.8 km more if there are also green surroundings. Changes in urban landscapes, including through the integration of green infrastructure in sustainable urban and transport planning, can support the transition from private motorised transportation to public and physically active transportation in carbon-neutral, more liveable and healthier cities (Nieuwenhuijsen and Khreis 2016; Nieuwenhuijsen 2020). Car infrastructure can be also transferred into public open and green space, such as in the Superblock model in Barcelona's neighbourhoods (Rueda 2019). Health impact assessment models estimated that 681 premature deaths may be prevented annually with this implementation (Mueller et al. 2020) and the creation of greenways in Maanshan, China has stimulated interest in walking or cycling (Zhang et al. 2020).

8.4.5   Socio-behavioural Aspects

Urban systems shape the behaviour and social structures of their residents through urban form, energy systems, and infrastructure – all of which provide a range of options for consumers to make choices about residential location, mobility, energy sources, and the consumption of materials, food, and other resources. The relative availability of options across these sectors has implications on urban emissions through individual behaviour. In turn, urban GHG emissions, as well as emissions from the supply chains of cities, are driven by the behaviour and consumption patterns of residents, with households accounting for over 60% of carbon emissions globally (Ivanova et al. 2016). The exclusion of consumption-based emissions and emissions that occur outside of city boundaries as a result of urban activities, however, will lead to significant undercounting. For example, a study of 79 major cities found that about 41% of consumption-based carbon footprints (1.8 GtCO$_2$-eq of 4.4 GtCO$_2$-eq) occurred outside of city boundaries.

Changes in behaviour across all areas (e.g., transport, buildings, food) could reduce an individual's emissions by 5.6–16.2% relative to the accumulated GHG emissions from 2011 to 2050 in a baseline scenario modelled with the Global Change Assessment Model (van de Ven et al. 2018). In other models, behaviour change in transport and residential energy use could reduce emissions by 2 GtCO$_2$-eq in 2030 compared to 2019 (IEA 2020b) (Chapter 5). Voluntary behaviour change can support emissions reduction, but behaviours that are not convenient to change are unlikely to shift without changes to policy (Sköld et al. 2018). Cities can increase the capability of citizens to make sustainable choices by making these choices less onerous, through avenues such as changing urban form to increase locational and mobility options and providing feedback mechanisms to support socio-behavioural change.

Transport emissions can be reduced by options including telecommuting (0.3%), taking closer holidays (0.5%), avoiding short flights (0.5%), using public transit (0.7%), cycling (0.6%), car sharing (1.1%), and carpool commuting (1.2%); all reduction estimates reflect cumulative per capita emission savings relative to baseline emissions for the period 2011–2050, and assume immediate adoption of behavioural changes (van de Ven et al. 2018). Cities can support voluntary shift to walking, cycling, and transit instead of car use through changes to urban form, such as TOD (Kamruzzaman et al. 2015), increased density of form with co-location of activities (Ma et al. 2015; Ding et al. 2017; Duranton and Turner 2018; Masoumi 2019), and greater intersection density and street integration (Koohsari et al. 2016). Mechanisms such as providing financial incentives or disincentives for car use can also be effective in reducing emissions (Wynes et al. 2018) (Section 8.4.2).

Adopting energy efficient practices in buildings could decrease global building energy demand in 2050 by 33–44% compared to a business-as-usual scenario (Levesque et al. 2019). Reductions in home energy use can be achieved by reducing floor area (0.5–3.0%), utilising more efficient appliances and lighting (2.7–5.0%), optimising thermostat settings (8.3–11%), using efficient heating and cooling technologies (6.7–10%), improving building insulation (2.9–4.0%), optimising clothes washing (5.0–5.7%), and optimising dishwashing (1–1.1%) (Levesque et al. 2019). Building standards and mandates could work towards making these options required or more readily available and accessible. Residential appliance use, water heating, and thermostat settings can be influenced by feedback on energy use, particularly when paired with real-time feedback and/or instructions on how to reduce energy use (Kastner and Stern 2015; Stern et al. 2016; Wynes et al. 2018; Tiefenbeck et al. 2019). The energy-saving potentials of changing occupant behaviour can range between 10% and 25% for residential buildings, and between 5% and 30% for commercial buildings (Zhang et al. 2018). Households are more likely to invest in energy-related home technologies if they believe it financially benefits (rather than disadvantages) them, increases comfort, or will benefit the natural environment (Kastner and Stern 2015). Social influences and availability of funding for household energy measures also support behaviour change (Kastner and Stern 2015).

8.4.5.1   Increasing Locational and Mobility Options

Spatial planning, urban form, and infrastructure can be utilised to deliberately increase both locational and mobility options for socio-behavioural change in support of urban mitigation. The mitigation impacts of active travel can include a reduction of mobility-related lifecycle CO_2 emissions by about 0.5 tonnes over a year when an average person cycles one trip per day more, and drives one trip per day less, for 200 days a year (Brand et al. 2021). Urban areas that develop and implement effective 15/20-minute city programmes are very likely to reduce urban energy use and multiply emission reductions, representing an important cascading effect.

Accessibility as a criterion widens the focus beyond work trips and VKT/VMT, paying attention to a broader set of destinations beyond workplaces, as well as walking and biking trips or active travel. It holds promise for targeting and obtaining greater reductions in GHG emissions in household travel by providing access through walking, biking, and public transit. Accessibility as a criterion for urban form has been embedded in neighbourhood form models since at least the last century and in more recent decades in the 'urban village' concept of the New Urbanism (Duany and Plater-Zyberck 1991) and TODs (Calthorpe 1993). However, accessibility did not gain much traction in urban planning and transportation until the last decade. The experience of cities and metropolitan areas with the COVID-19 pandemic has led to a further resurgence in interest and importance (Handy 2020; Hu et al. 2020), and it is becoming a criterion at the core of the concept of the 15/20-minute city (Moreno et al. 2021; Pozoukidou and Chatziyiannaki 2021). Initially, neighbourhoods have been designed to provide quality, reliable services within 15 or 20 minutes of active transport (i.e., walking or cycling), as well as a variety of housing options and open space (Portland Bureau of Planning and Sustainability 2012; Pozoukidou and Chatziyiannaki 2021; State Government of Victoria 2021). Community life circles strategy for urban areas has also emphasised walking access and health (Weng et al. 2019; Wu et al. 2021). The growing popularity of the 15/20-minute city movement has significant potential for reducing VMT/VKT and associated GHG emissions.

8.4.5.2   Avoiding, Minimising, and Recycling Waste

The waste sector is a significant source of GHG emissions, particularly CH_4 (Gonzalez-Valencia et al. 2016; Nisbet et al. 2019). Currently, the sector remains the largest contributor to urban emissions after the energy sector, even in low-carbon cities (Lu and Li 2019). Since waste management systems are usually under the control of municipal authorities, they are a prime target for city-level mitigation efforts with co-benefits (EC 2015, 2020; Gharfalkar et al. 2015; Herrero and Vilella 2018; Zaman and Ahsan 2019). Despite general agreement on mitigation impacts, quantification remains challenging due to differing assumptions for system boundaries and challenges related to measuring avoided waste (Zaman and Lehmann 2013; Bernstad Saraiva Schott and Cánovas 2015; Matsuda et al. 2018).

The implementation of the waste hierarchy from waste prevention onward, as well as the effectiveness of waste separation at source, involves socio-behavioural options in the context of urban infrastructure (Sun et al. 2018a; Hunter et al. 2019). Managing and treating waste as close to the point of generation as possible, including distributed waste treatment facilities, can minimise transport-related emissions, congestion, and air pollution. Home composting and compact urban form can also reduce waste transport emissions (Oliveira et al. 2017). Decentralised waste management can reinforce source-separation behaviour since the resulting benefits can be more visible (Eisted et al. 2009; Hoornweg and Bhada-Tata 2012; Linzner and Lange 2013). Public acceptance for waste management is greatest when system costs for citizens are reduced, there is greater awareness of primary waste separation at source, and there are positive behavioural spill-overs across environmental policies (Milutinović et al. 2016; Boyer and Ramaswami 2017; Díaz-Villavicencio et al. 2017; Slorach et al. 2020). In addition to the choice of technology, the costs of waste management options depend on the awareness of system users that can represent time-dependent costs (Khan et al. 2016; Chifari et al. 2017; Ranieri et al. 2018; Tomić and Schneider 2020). Waste management systems and the inclusion of materials from multiple urban sectors for alternative by-products can increase scalability (Eriksson et al. 2015; Boyer and Ramaswami 2017; D'Adamo et al. 2021). As a broader concept, circular economy approaches can contribute to managing waste (Box 12.8) with varying emissions impacts (Section 5.3.4).

The generation and composition of waste varies considerably from region to region and city to city. So do the levels of institutional management, infrastructure, and (informal) work in waste disposal activities. Depending on context, policy priorities are directed towards reducing waste generation and transforming waste to energy or other products in a circular economy (Diaz 2017; Ezeudu and Ezeudu 2019; Joshi et al. 2019; Calderón Márquez and Rutkowski 2020; Fatimah et al. 2020). Similarly, waste generation, waste collection coverage, recycling, and composting rates, as well as the means of waste disposal and treatment, differ widely, including the logistics of urban waste management systems. Multiple factors influence waste generation, and regions with similar urbanisation rates can generate different levels of waste per capita (Kaza et al. 2018).

Under conventional practices, municipal solid waste is projected to increase by about 1.4 Gt between 2016 and 2050, reaching 3.4 Gt in 2050 (Kaza et al. 2018). Integrated policymaking can increase the energy, material, and emissions benefits in the waste management sector (Hjalmarsson 2015; Fang et al. 2017; Jiang et al. 2017). Organisational structure and programme administration poses demands for institutional capacity, governance, and cross-sectoral coordination for obtaining the maximum benefit (Hjalmarsson 2015; Kalmykova et al. 2016; Conke 2018; Marino et al. 2018; Yang et al. 2018).

The informal sector plays a critical role in waste management, particularly but not exclusively in developing countries (Linzner and Lange 2013; Dias 2016). Sharing of costs and benefits, and transforming informality of waste recycling activities into programmes, can support distributional effects (Conke 2018; Grové et al. 2018). Balancing centralised and decentralised waste management options along low-carbon objectives can address potential challenges in transforming informality (de Bercegol and Gowda 2019). Overall, the positive impacts of waste management on employment and economic growth can be increased when informality is transformed to stimulate employment opportunities for value-added products with an estimated 45 million jobs in the waste management sector by 2030 (Alzate-Arias et al. 2018; Coalition for Urban Transitions 2020; Soukiazis and Proença 2020).

8.4.6   Urban-Rural Linkages

Urban-rural linkages, especially through waste, food, and water, are prominent elements of the urban system, given that cities are open systems that depend on their hinterlands for imports and exports (Pichler et al. 2017), and include resources, products for industrial production or final use (Section 8.1.6). As supply chains are becoming increasingly global in nature, so are the resource flows with the hinterlands of cities. In addition to measures within the jurisdictional boundaries of cities, cities can influence large upstream emissions through their supply chains, as well as through activities that rely on resources outside city limits. The dual strategy of implementing local actions and taking responsibility for the entire supply chains of imported and exported goods can reduce GHG emissions outside of a city's administrative boundaries (Figure 8.15).

Waste prevention, minimisation, and management provides the potential of alleviating resource usage and upstream emissions from urban settlements (Swilling et al. 2018; Chen et al. 2020a; Harris et al. 2020). Integrated waste management and zero-waste targets can allow urban areas to maximise the mitigation potential while reducing pressures on land use and the environment. This mitigation option reduces emissions due to (i) avoided emissions upstream in the supply chain of materials based on measures for recycling and the reuse of materials; (ii) avoided emissions due to land-use changes as well as emissions that are released into the atmosphere from waste disposal; and (ii) avoided primary energy (see Glossary) spending and emissions. Socio-behavioural change that reduces waste generation, combined with technology and infrastructure according to the waste hierarchy, can be especially effective. The mitigation potential

of waste-to-energy depends on the technological choices that are undertaken (e.g., anaerobic digestion of the organic fraction), the emissions factor of the energy mix that it replaces, and its broader role within integrated municipal solid management practices (Eriksson et al. 2015; Potdar et al. 2016; Yu and Zhang 2016; Soares and Martins 2017; Alzate-Arias et al. 2018; Islam 2018). The climate mitigation potential of anaerobic digestion plants can increase when power, heat and/or cold is co-produced (Thanopoulos et al. 2020).

Urban food systems, as well as city-regional production and distribution of food, factors into supply chains. Reducing food demand from urban hinterlands can have a positive impact on energy and water demand for food production (Eigenbrod and Gruda 2015) (see 'food system' in Glossary). Managing food waste in urban areas through recycling or reduction of food waste at source of consumption would require behavioural change (Gu et al. 2019). Urban governments could also support shifts towards more climate-friendly diets, including through procurement policies. These strategies have created economic opportunities or have enhanced food security while reducing the emissions that are associated with waste and the transportation of food. Strategies for managing food demand in urban areas would depend on the integration of food systems in urban planning.

Urban and peri-urban agriculture and forestry is pursued by both developing and some developed country cities. There is increasing evidence for economically feasible, socially acceptable, and environmentally supportive urban and peri-urban agricultural enterprises although these differ between cities (Brown 2015; Eigenbrod and Gruda 2015; Blay-Palmer et al. 2019; De la Sota et al. 2019). The pathways include integrated crop-livestock systems, urban agroforestry systems, aquaculture-livestock-crop systems, and crop systems (Lwasa et al. 2015), while the mitigation potential of urban and peri-urban agriculture has *medium agreement* and *low evidence*. Strategies for urban food production in cities have also relied on recycling nutrients from urban waste and utilisation of harvested rainwater or wastewater.

Systems for water reallocation between rural areas and urban areas will require change by leveraging technological innovations for water capture, water purification, and reducing water wastage either by plugging leakages or changing behaviour in regard to water use (Eigenbrod and Gruda 2015; Prior et al. 2018). Reducing energy use for urban water systems involves reducing energy requirements for water supply, purification, distribution, and drainage (Ahmad et al. 2020). Various levels of rainwater harvesting in urban settings for supplying end-use water demands or supporting urban food production can reduce municipal water demands, including by up to 20% or more in Cape Town (Fisher-Jeffes et al. 2017).

8.4.7   Cross-sectoral Integration

There are two broad categories of urban mitigation strategies. One is from the perspective of key sectors, including clean energy, sustainable transport, and construction (Rocha et al. 2017; Álvarez Fernández 2018; Magueta et al. 2018; Seo et al. 2018; Waheed et al. 2018); the coupling of these sectors can be enabled through electrification (Section 8.4.3.1). The other looks at the needs for emissions through a more systematic or fundamental understanding of urban design, urban form, and urban spatial planning (Wang et al. 2017; Privitera et al. 2018), and proposes synergistic scenarios for their integration for carbon neutrality (Ravetz et al. 2020).

Single-sector analysis in low-carbon urban planning examines solutions in supply, demand, operations, and assets management either from technological efficiency or from a system approach. For example, the deployment of renewable energy technologies for urban mitigation can be evaluated in detail and the transition to zero-carbon energy in energy systems and EVs in the transport sector can bring about a broad picture for harvesting substantial low-carbon potentials through urban planning (*high agreement, robust evidence*) (Álvarez Fernández 2018; Tarigan and Sagala 2018).

The effects of urban carbon lock-in on land use, energy demand, and emissions vary depending on national circumstances (Wang et al. 2017; Pan 2020). Systematic consideration of urban spatial planning and urban forms, such as polycentric urban regions and rational urban population density, is essential not only for liveability but also for achieving net-zero GHG emissions as it aims to shorten commuting distances and is able to make use of NBS for energy and resilience (*high agreement, medium evidence*). However, crucial knowledge gaps remain in this field. There is a shortage of consistent and comparable GHG emissions data at the city level and a lack of in-depth understanding of how urban renewal and design can contribute to carbon neutrality (Mi et al. 2019).

An assessment of opportunities suggests that strategies for material efficiency that cross-cut sectors will have greater impact than those that focus one-dimensionally on a single sector (UNEP IRP 2020). In the urban context, this implies using less material by the design of physical infrastructure based on light-weighting and down-sizing, material substitution, prolonged use, as well as enhanced recycling, recovery, remanufacturing, and reuse of materials and related components. For example, light-weight design in residential buildings and passenger vehicles can enable about 20% reductions in lifecycle material-related GHG emissions (UNEP IRP 2020).

The context of urban areas as the nexus of both sectors (i.e., energy, and urban form and planning) underlines the role of urban planning and policies in contributing to reductions in material-related GHG emissions while enabling housing and mobility services for the benefit of inhabitants. In addition, combining resource efficiency measures with strategic densification can increase the GHG reduction potential and lower resource impacts. While resource efficiency measures are estimated to reduce GHG emissions, land use, water consumption, and metal use impacts from a lifecycle assessment perspective by 24–47% over a baseline, combining resource efficiency with strategic densification can increase this range to about 36–54% over the baseline for a sample of 84 urban settlements worldwide (Swilling et al. 2018).

Evidence from a systematic scoping of urban solutions further indicates that the GHG abatement potential of integrating measures across urban sectors is greater than the net sum of individual interventions due to the potential of realising synergies when realised in tandem, such as urban energy infrastructure and renewable energy (Sethi et al. 2020). Similarly, system-wide interventions, such as sustainable urban form, are important for increasing the GHG abatement potential of interventions based on individual sectoral projects (Sethi et al. 2020). Overall, the pursuit of inter-linkages among urban interventions is important for accelerating GHG reductions in urban areas (Sethi et al. 2020); this is also important for reducing reliance on carbon capture and storage technologies (CCS) at the global scale (Figures 8.15 and 8.21).

Currently, cross-sectoral integration is one of the main thematic areas of climate policy strategies among the actions that are adopted by signatories to an urban climate and energy network (Hsu et al. 2020c). Although not as prevalent as those for efficiency, municipal administration, and urban planning measures (Hsu et al. 2020c), strategies that are cross-cutting in nature across sectors can provide important emission-saving opportunities for accelerating the pace of climate mitigation in urban areas. Cross-sectoral integration also involves mobilising urban actors to increase innovation in energy services and markets beyond individual energy efficiency actions (Hsu et al. 2020c). Indeed, single-sector versus cross-sector strategies for 637 cities from a developing country can enable an additional 15–36% contribution to the national climate mitigation reduction potential (Ramaswami et al. 2017a). The strategies at the urban level involved those for energy cascading and exchange of materials that connected waste, heat, and electricity strategies (Section 8.5 and Box 8.4).

The feasibility of upscaling multiple response options depends on the urban context as well as the stage of urban development, with certain stages providing additional opportunities over others (Dienst et al. 2015; Maier 2016; Affolderbach and Schulz 2017; Roldán-Fontana et al. 2017; Zhao et al. 2017a; Beygo and Yüzer 2017; Lwasa 2017; Pacheco-Torres et al. 2017; Alhamwi et al. 2018; Kang and Cho 2018; Lin et al. 2018; Collaço et al. 2019) (Figures 8.19 and 8.21, and Section 8.SM.2).

8.5 Governance, Institutions, and Finance

Governance and other institutions act as core components to urban systems by facilitating and managing linkages between different sectors, geographic regions, and stakeholders. This position renders subnational governments and institutions key enablers of climate change mitigation (Seto et al. 2016, 2021; Hsu et al. 2018, 2020c; Vedeld et al. 2021) (Section 8.4.1). Indeed, since AR5 more research has emerged identifying these actors as vehicles through which to accelerate local-to-global efforts to decarbonise (IPCC 2018a; Hsu et al. 2020b; Salvia et al. 2021; Seto et al. 2021) (Chapter 13, Sections 4.2.3, 14.5.5, 15.6.5 and 16.4.7, and 'subnational actors' in Glossary). The current extent (Section 8.3.3) and projected rise (Section 8.3.4.2) in the urban share of global emissions underscores the transformative global impact of supporting urban climate governance and institutions (Section 8.5.2). Further, the multisector approach to mitigation emphasised in this chapter (Sections 8.4

and 8.6, and Figure 8.21) highlights the need for facilitation across sectors (Figure 8.19).

8.5.1   Multi-level Governance

IPCC SR1.5 identified multi-level governance (see Glossary for full definition) as an enabling condition that facilitates systemic transformation consistent with keeping global temperatures below 1.5°C (IPCC 2018a, pp. 18–19). The involvement of governance at multiple levels is necessary to enable cities to plan and implement emissions reductions targets (*high confidence*) (Seto et al. 2021) (Boxes 8.3 and 8.4). Further, regional, national, and international climate goals are most impactful when local governments are involved alongside higher levels, rendering urban areas key foci of climate governance more broadly (*high confidence*) (Fuhr et al. 2018; Kern 2019; Hsu et al. 2020b).

Since AR5, multi-level governance has grown in influence within the literature and has been defined as a framework for understanding the complex interaction of the many players involved in GHG generation and mitigation across geographic scales – the 'vertical' levels of governance from neighbourhoods to the national and international levels, and those 'horizontal' networks of non-state and subnational actors at various scales (Corfee-Morlot et al. 2009; Seto et al. 2014; Castán Broto 2017b; Fuhr et al. 2018; Peng and Bai 2018; Kern 2019), as well as the complex linkages between them (Vedeld et al. 2021). This more inclusive understanding of climate governance provides multiple pathways through which urban actors can engage in climate policy to reduce emissions.

8.5.1.1   Multi-level, Multi-player Climate Governance in Practice

A multi-level, multi-player framework highlights both the opportunities and constraints on local autonomy to engage in urban mitigation efforts (Castán Broto 2017b; Fuhr et al. 2018; Vedeld et al. 2021). When multiple actors – national, regional, and urban policymakers, as well as non-state actors and civil society – work together to exploit the opportunities, it leads to the most impactful mitigation gains (Melica et al. 2018). This framework also highlights the multiple paths and potential synergies available to actors who wish to pursue mitigation policies despite not having a full slate of enabling conditions (Castán Broto 2017b; Keller 2017; Fuhr et al. 2018; Hsu et al. 2020b,a; Seto et al. 2021).

For example, Sections 8.4.3. and 8.4.5 highlight how instigating the electrification of urban energy systems requires a 'layered' approach to policy implementation across different levels of governance (see Section 8.4.3.1 for specific policy mechanisms associated with electrification), with cities playing a key role in setting standards, particularly through mechanisms like building codes (Hsu et al. 2020c; Salvia et al. 2021), as well as through facilitation between stakeholders (e.g., consumers, government, utilities) to advocate for zero-emissions targets (Linton et al. 2021; Seto et al. 2021). Local governments can minimise trade-offs associated with electrification technologies by enabling circular economy practices and

opportunities (Pan et al. 2015; Gaustad et al. 2018; Sovacool et al. 2020). These include public-private partnerships between consumers and producers, financial and institutional support, and networking for stakeholders like entrepreneurs, so as to increase accessibility and efficiency of recycling for consumers by providing a clear path from consumer waste back to the producers (Pan et al. 2015; Prendeville et al. 2018; Fratini et al. 2019). Box 8.3 discusses the mitigation benefits of coordination between local and central government in the context of Shanghai's GHG emissions reduction goals.

Still, there are constraints on urban autonomy that might limit urban mitigation influence. The capacity of subnational governments to autonomously pursue emissions reductions on their own depends on different political systems and other aspects of multi-level governance, such as innovation, legitimacy, and institutional fit, as well as the resources, capacity, and knowledge available to subnational technicians and other officials (Widerberg and Pattberg 2015; Valente de Macedo et al. 2016; Green 2017; Roger et al. 2017). Financing is considered one of the most crucial facets of urban climate change mitigation. It is also considered one of the biggest barriers, given the limited financial capacities of local and regional governments (Sections 8.5.4 and 8.5.5).

When sufficient local autonomy is present, local policies have the ability to upscale to higher levels of authority, imparting influence at higher geographic scales. Established urban climate leaders with large institutional capacity can influence small and mid-sized cities, or other urban areas with less institutional capacity, to enact effective climate policies, by engaging with those cities through transnational networks and by adopting a public presence of climate leadership (Chan et al. 2015; Kern 2019; Seto et al. 2021) (Section 8.5.3). Increasingly, subnational actors are also influencing their national and international governments through lobbying efforts that call on them to adopt more ambitious climate goals and provide more support for subnational GHG mitigation efforts (Linton et al. 2021; Seto et al. 2021). These dynamics underscore the importance of relative local autonomy in urban GHG mitigation policy. They also highlight the growing recognition of subnational authorities' role in climate change mitigation by national and international authorities.

The confluence of political will and policy action at the local level, and growing resources offered through municipal and regional networks and agreements, have provided a platform for urban actors to engage in international climate policy (Section 8.5.3). This phenomenon is recognised in the Paris Agreement, which, for the first time in a multilateral climate treaty, referenced the crucial role subnational and non-state actors like local communities have in meeting the goals set forth in the agreement (UNFCCC 2015). The Durban Platform for Enhanced Action (Widerberg and Pattberg 2015), as well as UN-Habitat's NUA and the 2030 Development Agenda, are other examples of the international sphere elevating the local level to global influence (Fuhr et al. 2018). Another facet of local-to-global action is the emergence of International Cooperative Initiatives (ICIs) (Widerberg and Pattberg 2015). One such ICI, the City Hall Declaration, was signed alongside the Paris Agreement during the first Climate Summit for Local Leaders. Signatories included hundreds of local government leaders, in partnership with private sector representatives and NGOs, who pledged to enact the goals of the Paris Agreement through their own spheres of influence (Cities for Climate 2015). Similar Summits have been held at each subsequent UNFCCC COP (Hsu et al. 2018). Like transnational climate networks, these platforms provide key opportunities to local governments to further their own mitigation goals, engage in knowledge transfer with other cities and regions, and shape policies at higher levels of authority (Cities for Climate 2015; Castán Broto 2017b).

Box 8.3: Coordination of Fragmented Policymaking for Low-carbon Urban Development: Example from Shanghai, China

As a growing megacity in the Global South, Shanghai represents the challenge of becoming low carbon despite its economic growth and population size (Chen et al. 2017). Shanghai was designated as one of the pilot low-carbon cities by the central government. The city utilised a coordination mechanism for joining fragmented policymaking across the city's economy, energy, and environment. The coordination mechanism was supported by a direct fund that enabled implementation of cross-sector policies beyond a single-sector focus across multiple institutions while increasing capacity for enabling a low-carbon transition for urban sustainability (Peng and Bai 2020).

Implementation and governance process

In Shanghai, coordination between the central and local governments had an instrumental role for encouraging low-carbon policy experimentation. Using a nested governance framework, the central government provided target setting and performance evaluation while the local government initiated pilot projects for low-carbon development. The policy practices in Shanghai surpassed the top-down targets and annual reporting of GHG emissions, including carbon labelling standards at the local level, pilot programme for transitioning sub-urban areas, and the engagement of public utilities (Peng and Bai 2018).

Towards low-carbon urban development

New policy measures in Shanghai were built upon a series of related policies from earlier, ranging from general energy saving measures to air pollution reduction. This provided a continuum of policy learning for implementing low-carbon policy measures. An earlier policy was a green electricity scheme based on the Jade Electricity Program while the need for greater public awareness was one aspect requiring further attention in policy design (Baeumler et al. 2012), supporting policy-learning for policies later on. The key point here is that low-carbon policies were built on and learned from earlier policies with similar goals.

Outcomes and impacts of the policy mix

Trends during 1998 and 2015 indicate that energy intensity decreased from about 130 tonnes per million RMB to about 45 tonnes per million RMB and carbon intensity decreased from about 0.35 Mt per billion RMB to 0.10 Mt per billion RMB (Peng and Bai 2018). These impacts on energy and carbon intensities represent progress, while challenges remain. Among the challenges are the need for investment in low-carbon technology and increases in urban carbon sinks (Yang and Li 2018) while cross-sector interaction and complexity are increasing.

8.5.2   Mitigation Potential of Urban Subnational Actors

A significant research question that has been paid more attention in both the scientific and policy communities is related to subnational actors' role in and contribution to global climate mitigation. The 2018 UN Environment Programme's (UNEP) annual Emissions Gap report in 2018 included for the first time a special chapter on subnational and non-state (i.e., businesses and private) actors and assessed the landscape of studies aiming to quantify their contributions to global climate mitigation. Non-state action on net-zero GHG or CO_2 emissions continues to be emphasised (UNEP 2021) (Box 8.4). There has been an increase in the number of studies aiming to quantify the overall aggregate mitigation impact of subnational climate action globally. Estimates for the significance of their impact vary widely, from up to 30 $MtCO_2$-eq from 25 cities in the United States in 2030 (Roelfsema 2017), to a 2.3 $GtCO_2$-eq reduction in 2030 compared to a current policy scenario from over 10,239 cities participating in GCoM (Hsu et al. 2018; GCoM 2019). For regional governments, the Under 2 Coalition, which includes 260 governments pledging goals to keep global temperature rise below 2°C, is estimated to reduce emissions by 4.2 $GtCO_2$-eq in 2030, compared to a current policy scenario (Kuramochi et al. 2020).

Some studies suggest that subnational mitigation actions (Roelfsema 2017; Kuramochi et al. 2020) are in addition to national government mitigation efforts and can therefore reduce emissions even beyond current national policies, helping to 'bridge the gap' between emissions trajectories consistent with least-cost scenarios for limiting temperature rise below 1.5°C or 2°C (Blok et al. 2012). In some countries, such as the United States, where national climate policies have been curtailed, the potential for cities' and regions' emissions reduction pledges to make up the country's Nationally Determined Contribution under the Paris Agreement is assessed to be significant (Kuramochi et al. 2020).

These estimates are also often contingent on assumptions that subnational actors fulfil their pledges and that these actions do not result in rollbacks in climate action (i.e., weakening of national climate legislation) from other actors or rebound in emissions growth elsewhere, but data tracking or quantifying the likelihood of their implementation remains rare (Chan et al. 2018; Hsu et al. 2019; Hale et al. 2020; Kuramochi et al. 2020). Reporting networks may attract high-performing cities, suggesting an artificially high level of cities interested in taking climate action or piloting solutions that may not be effective elsewhere (van der Heijden 2018). These studies could also present a conservative view of potential mitigation impact because they draw upon publicly reported mitigation actions and inventory data, excluding subnational actors that may be taking actions but not reporting them (Kuramochi et al. 2020). The nuances of likelihood, and the drivers and obstacles of climate action across different contexts is a key source of uncertainty around subnational actors' mitigation impacts.

8.5.3 Urban Climate Networks and Transnational Governance

As of 2019, more than 10,000 cities and regions (Hsu et al. 2020a) have recorded participation in a transnational or cooperative climate action network, which are voluntary membership networks of a range of subnational governments such as cities, as well as regional governments like states and provinces (Hsu et al. 2020a). These organisations, often operating across and between national boundaries, entail some type of action on climate change. Among the most prominent climate networks are GCoM, ICLEI, and C40, all of which ask their members to adopt emission reduction commitments, develop climate action plans, and regularly report on emissions inventories.

Municipal and regional networks and agreements have provided a platform for urban actors to engage in international climate policy (Fraundorfer 2017; Keller 2017; Fuhr et al. 2018; Hsu et al. 2018, 2020b; Westman and Broto 2018; Kern 2019; Seto et al. 2021). Their impact comes through (i) providing resources for cities and regions

to reduce their GHG emissions and improve environmental quality more generally, independent of national policy; (ii) encouraging knowledge transfer between member cities and regions; and (iii) acting as platforms of national and international policy influence (Castán Broto 2017b; Fuhr et al. 2018).

Subnational governments that participate in transnational climate networks, however, are primarily located in developed countries, particularly Europe and North America, with far less representation in developing countries. In one of the largest studies of subnational climate mitigation action, more than 93% of just over 6000 quantifiable subnational climate commitments come from cities and regions based in the European Union (NewClimate Institute et al. 2019). Such gaps in geographic coverage have been attributed to factors such as the dominating role of Global North actors in the convening and diffusion of 'best practices' related to climate action (Bouteligier 2013), or the more limited autonomy or ability of subnational or non-state actors in Global South countries to define boundaries and interests separately from national governments, particularly those that exercise top-down decision-making or have vertically integrated governance structures (Bulkeley et al. 2012). Many of the participating subnational actors from under-represented regions are large megacities (of 10 million people or more) that will play a pivotal role in shaping emissions trajectories (Data Driven Yale et al. 2018; NewClimate Institute et al. 2019).

While these networks have proven to be an important resource in local-level mitigation, their long-term effects and impact at larger scales is less certain (Valente de Macedo et al. 2016; Fuhr et al. 2018). Their influence is most effective when multiple levels of governance are aligned in mitigation policy. Nevertheless, these groups have become essential resources to cities and regions with limited institutional capacity and support (for more on transnational climate networks and transnational governance more broadly, see Sections 13.5 and 14.5).

Box 8.4: Net-zero Targets and Urban Settlements

Around the world, net-zero-emissions targets, whether economy-wide or targeting a specific sector (e.g., transport, buildings) or emissions scope (e.g., direct scope 1, or both scope 1 and 2), have been adopted by at least 826 cities and 103 regions that represent 11% of the global population with 846 million people across six continents (NewClimate Institute and Data-Driven EnviroLab 2020). In some countries, the share of such cities and regions has reached a critical mass by representing more than 70% of their total populations with or without net-zero-emissions targets at the national level.

In some cases, the scope of these targets extends beyond net-zero emissions from any given sector based on direct emissions (see Glossary) and encompass downstream emissions from a consumption-based perspective with 195 targets that are found to represent economy-wide targets. These commitments range from 'carbon neutrality' (see Glossary) or net-zero GHG emissions targets, which entail near elimination of cities' own direct or electricity-based emissions but could involve some type of carbon offsetting, to more stringent net-zero-emissions goals (Data-Driven EnviroLab and NewClimate Institute 2020) (for related definitions, such as 'carbon neutrality', 'net-zero CO_2 emissions', 'net-zero GHG emissions', and 'offset', see Glossary).

Currently, 43% of the urban areas with net-zero-emissions targets have also put into place related action plans while about 24% have integrated net-zero-emissions targets into formal policies and legislation (Data-Driven EnviroLab and NewClimate Institute 2020). Moreover, thousands of urban areas have adopted renewable energy-specific targets for power, heating/cooling and transport and about 600 cities are pursuing 100% renewable energy targets (REN21 2019, 2021) with some cities already achieving it.

Box 8.4 (continued)

The extent of realising and implementing these targets with the collective contribution of urban areas to net-zero-emissions scenarios with sufficient timing and pace of emission reductions will require a coordinated integration of sectors, strategies, and innovations (Swilling et al. 2018; Hsu et al. 2020c; Sethi et al. 2020; UNEP IRP 2020). In turn, the transformation of urban systems can significantly impact net-zero-emissions trajectories within mitigation pathways. Institutional capacity, governance, financing, and cross-sector coordination is crucial for enabling and accelerating urban actions for rapid decarbonisation.

8.5.4 Financing Urban Mitigation

Meeting the goals of the Paris Agreement will require fundamental changes that will be most successful when cities work together with provincial and national leadership and legislation, third-sector leadership, transformative action, and supportive financing. Urban governments often obtain their powers from provincial, state and/or national governments, and are subjected to laws and regulations to regulate development and implement infrastructure. In addition, the sources of revenue are often set at these levels so that many urban governments rely on state/provincial and national government funds for improving infrastructure, especially transit infrastructure. The increasing financialisation of urban infrastructures is another factor that can make it more difficult for local governments to determine infrastructure choices (O'Brien et al. 2019). Urban transit system operations, in particular, are heavily subsidised in many countries, both locally and by higher levels of government. As a result of this interplay of policy and legal powers among various levels of government, the lock-in nature of urban infrastructures and built environments will require multi-level governance responses to ensure meeting decarbonisation targets. The reliance on state and national policy and/or funding can accelerate or impede the decarbonisation of urban environments (McCarney et al. 2011; McCarney 2019).

The world's infrastructure spending is expected to more than double from 2015 to 2030 under a low-carbon and climate-resilient scenario. More than 70% of the infrastructure will concentrate in urban areas by requiring USD4.5–5.4 trillion per year (CCFLA 2015). However, today's climate finance flows for cities or 'urban climate finance', estimated at USD384 billion annually on average in 2017/18, are insufficient to meet the USD4.5–5.4 trillion annual investment needs for urban mitigation actions across key sectors (CCFLA 2015; CPI and World Bank 2021; Negreiros et al. 2021). Low-carbon urban form (e.g., compact, high-density, and mixed-use characteristics) is likely to economise spending in infrastructure along with the application of new technologies and renewable energies that would be able to recover the increasing upfront cost of low-carbon infrastructure from more efficient operating and energy savings (*medium evidence, high agreement*) (Global Commission on the Economy and Climate 2014; Foxon et al. 2015; Bhattacharya et al. 2016; Floater et al. 2017; Colenbrander et al. 2018b).

Governments have traditionally financed a large proportion of infrastructure investment. When budget powers remain largely centralised, intergovernmental transfers will be needed to fund low-carbon infrastructure in cities. During the COVID-19 pandemic, cities tend to rely more on intergovernmental transfers in the form of stimulus packages for economic recovery. Nonetheless, the risk of high carbon lock-ins is likely to increase in rapidly growing cities if long-term urban mitigation strategies are not incorporated into short-term economic recovery actions (Granoff et al. 2016; Floater et al. 2017; Colenbrander et al. 2018b; CPI and World Bank 2021; Negreiros et al. 2021). Indeed, large and complex infrastructure projects for urban mitigation are often beyond the capacity of both national government and local municipality budgets. Additionally, the COVID-19 pandemic necessitates large government expenditures for public health programme and decimates municipal revenue sources for urban infrastructure projects in cities.

To meet the multi-trillion-dollar annual investment needs in urban areas, cities in partnership with international institutions, national governments, and local stakeholders increasingly play a pivotal role in mobilising global climate finance resources for a range of low-carbon infrastructure projects and related urban land use and spatial planning programmes across key sectors (*high confidence*). In particular, national governments are expected to set up enabling conditions for the mobilisation of urban climate finance resource by articulating various goals and strategies, improving pricing, regulation and standards, and developing investment vehicles and risk sharing instruments (Qureshi 2015; Bielenberg et al. 2016; Granoff et al. 2016; Floater et al. 2017; Sudmant et al. 2017; Colenbrander et al. 2018b; Zhan and de Jong 2018; Hadfield and Cook 2019; CPI and World Bank 2021; Negreiros et al. 2021).

Indeed, 75% of the global climate finance for both mitigation and adaptation in 2017 and 2018 took the form of commercial financing (e.g., balance sheets, commercial-rate loans, equity), while 25% came in the form of concessional financing (e.g., grants, below-market-rate loans). However, cities in developing countries are facing difficulty making use of commercial financing and gaining access to international credit markets. Cities without international creditworthiness currently rely on local sources, including domestic commercial banks (*medium evidence, high agreement*) (Global Commission on the Economy and Climate 2014; CCFLA 2015; Floater et al. 2017; Buchner et al. 2019).

Cities with creditworthiness have rapidly become issuers of 'green bonds' eligible for renewable energy, energy efficiency, low-carbon transport, sustainable water, waste, and pollution, and other various climate mitigation projects across the global regions since 2013. The world's green bond market reached USD1 trillion in cumulative issuance, with issuance of USD280 billion in 2020, during the

COVID-19 pandemic. While green municipal bonds still account for a small share of the whole green bond market in 2020, scale is predicted to grow further in emerging markets over the coming years. Green municipal bonds have great potential for cities to expand and diversify their investor base. In addition, the process of issuing green municipal bonds is expected to promote cross-sector cooperation within a city by bringing together various agencies responsible for finance, climate change, infrastructure, planning and design, and operation. Indeed, the demand for green bonds presently outstrips supply as being constantly over-subscribed (*robust evidence*, *high agreement*) (Global Commission on the Economy and Climate 2014; Saha and D'Almeida 2017; Amundi and IFC 2021).

On the other hand, cities without creditworthiness face difficulty making use of commercial financing and getting access to international credit markets (Global Commission on the Economy and Climate 2014; CCFLA 2015; Floater et al. 2017). The lack of creditworthiness is one of the main problems preventing cities from issuing green municipal bonds in developing countries. As a prerequisite for the application of municipal debt-financing, it is an essential condition for cities to ensure sufficient own revenues from low-carbon urbanisation, or the default risk becomes too high for potential investors. Indeed, many cities in developed countries and emerging economies have already accumulated substantial amounts of debts through bond insurances, and ongoing debt payments prevent new investments in low-carbon infrastructure projects.

National governments and multilateral development banks might be able to provide support for debt financing by developing municipal creditworthiness programme and issuing sovereign bonds or providing national guarantees for investors (Floater et al. 2017). Another problem with green municipal bonds is the lack of aggregation mechanisms to support various small-scale projects in cities. Asset-backed securities are likely to reduce the default risk for investors through portfolio diversification and create robust pipelines for a bundle of small-scale projects (Granoff et al. 2016; Floater et al. 2017; Saha and D'Almeida 2017).

In principle, the upfront capital costs of various low-carbon infrastructure projects, including the costs of urban climate finance (dividend and interest payments), are eventually transferred to users and other stakeholders in the forms of taxes, charges, fees, and other revenue sources. Nevertheless, small cities in developing countries are likely to have a small revenue base, most of which is committed to recurring operating costs, associated with weak revenue collection and management systems. In recent years, there has been scope to apply not only user-based but also land-based funding instruments for the recovery of upfront capital costs (Braun and Hazelroth 2015; Kościelniak and Górka 2016; Floater et al. 2017; Colenbrander et al. 2018b; Zhan and de Jong 2018; Zhan et al. 2018a).

In practice, however, the application of land-based or 'land value capture' funding requires cities to arrange various instruments, including property (both land and building taxes), betterment levies/ special assessments, impact fees (exactions), tax increment financing, land readjustment/land pooling, sales of public land/development rights, recurring lease payments, and transfer taxes/stamp duties,

across sectors in different urban contexts (Suzuki et al. 2015; Chapman 2017; Walters and Gaunter 2017; Berrisford et al. 2018). Land value capture is expected not only for cities to generate additional revenue streams but also to prevent low-density urban expansion around city-fringe locations. Inversely, land value capture is supposed to perform well when accompanied by low-carbon urban form and private real estate investments along with the application of green building technologies (*robust evidence*, *high agreement*) (Suzuki et al. 2015; Floater et al. 2017; Colenbrander et al. 2018b).

For the implementation of land-based funding, property rights are essential. However, weak urban-rural governance leads to corruption in land occupancy and administration, especially in developing countries with no land information system or less reliable paper-based land records under a centralised registration system. The lack of adequate property rights seriously discourages low-carbon infrastructure and real estate investments in growing cities.

The emerging application of blockchain technology for land registry and real estate investment is expected to change the governance framework, administrative feasibility, allocative efficiency, public accountability, and political acceptability of land-based funding in cities across developed countries, emerging economies, and developing countries (Graglia and Mellon 2018; Kshetri and Voas 2018). Particularly, the concept of a transparent, decentralised public ledger is adapted to facilitate value-added property transactions on a P2P basis without centralised intermediate parties and produce land-based funding opportunities for low-carbon infrastructure and real estate development district-wide and city-wide in unconventional ways (Veuger 2017; Nasarre-Aznar 2018).

The consolidation of local transaction records into national or supranational registries is likely to support large-scale land formalisation, but most pilot programmes are not yet at the scale (Graglia and Mellon 2018). Moreover, the potential application of blockchain for land-based funding instruments is possibly associated with urban form attributes, such as density, compactness, and land-use mixture, to disincentivise urban expansion and emissions growth around city-fringe locations (*medium confidence*) (Allam and Jones 2019).

8.5.5   Barriers and Enablers for Implementation

Irrespective of geography or development level, many cities face similar climate governance challenges such as lacking institutional, financial, and technical capacities (Gouldson et al. 2015; Hickmann and Stehle 2017; Sharifi et al. 2017; Fuhr et al. 2018). Large-scale system transformations are also deeply influenced by factors outside governance and institutions, such as private interests and power dynamics (Jaglin 2014; Tyfield 2014). In some cases, these private interests are tied up with international flows of capital. At the local level, a lack of empowerment, high upfront costs, inadequate and uncertain funding for mitigation, diverse and conflicting policy objectives, multiple agencies and actors with diverse interests, high levels of informality, and a siloed approach to climate action are constraining factors to mainstreaming climate action (Beermann et al. 2016; Gouldson et al. 2016; Pathak and Mahadevia 2018; Khosla and Bhardwaj 2019).

Yet urban mitigation options that can be implemented to transform urban systems involve the interplay of multiple enablers and barriers. Based on a framework for assessing feasibility from a multi-dimensional perspective, feasibility is malleable and various enablers can be brought into play to increase the implementation of mitigation options. The scope of this assessment enables an approach for considering multiple aspects that have an impact on feasibility as a tool for policy support (Singh et al. 2020). In Figure 8.19, the assessment framework that is based on geophysical, environmental-ecological, technological, economic, socio-cultural, and institutional dimensions is applied to identify the enablers and/or barriers in implementing mitigation options in urban systems. The feasibility of options may differ across context, time, and scale (Section 8.SM.2). The line of sight upon which the assessment is based includes urban case studies (Lamb et al. 2019) and assessments of land use and spatial planning in IPCC SR1.5 (IPCC 2018a).

Across the enablers and barriers of different mitigation options, urban land use and spatial planning for increasing co-located densities in urban areas has positive impacts in multiple indicators, particularly reducing land use and preserving carbon sinks when the growth in urban extent is reduced and avoided, which if brought into interplay in decision-making, can support the enablers for its implementation. Improvements in air quality are possible when higher urban densities are combined with modes of active transport, electrified mobility as well as urban green and blue infrastructure (Sections 8.3.4, 8.4 and 8.6). The demands on geophysical resources, including materials for urban development, will depend on whether additional strategies are in place with largely negative impacts under conventional practices. The technological scalability of multiple urban mitigation options is favourable while varying according to the level of existing urban development and scale of implementation (Tables 8.SM.3 and 8.SM.4).

Similarly, multiple mitigation options have positive impacts on employment and economic growth, especially when urban densities enable productivity. Possible distributional effects, including availability of affordable accommodation and access to greenspace, are best addressed when urban policy packages combine more than one policy objective. Such an approach can provide greater support to urban mitigation efforts with progress towards shifting urban development to sustainability. The electrification of the urban energy system involves multiple enablers that support the feasibility of this mitigation option, including positive impacts on health and well-being. In addition, increases in urban densities can support the planning of district heating and cooling networks that can decarbonize the built environment at scale with technology readiness levels increasing for lower temperature supply options. Preventing, minimising, and managing waste as an urban mitigation option can be enabled when informality in the sector is transformed to secure employment effects and value-addition based on the more circular use of resources (Sections 8.4.3 and 8.4.5, and Tables 8.SM.3 and 8.SM.4 in Supplementary Material 8.2).

As a combined evaluation, integrating multiple mitigation options in urban systems involves the greatest requirement for strengthening institutional capacity and governance through cross-sectoral coordination. Notably, integrated action requires significant effort to coordinate sectors and strategies across urban growth typologies (Sections 8.4 and 8.6, and Figure 8.21). Institutional capacity, if not strengthened to a suitable level to handle this process – especially to break out of carbon lock-in – can fall short of the efforts this entails. These conditions can pose barriers for realising cross-sectoral coordination while the formation of partnerships and stakeholder engagement take place as important enablers. Overcoming institutional challenges for cross-sectoral coordination can support realising synergies among the benefits that each mitigation option can offer within and across urban systems, including for the SDGs. These include those that can be involved in co-located and walkable urban form together with decarbonising and electrifying the urban energy system as well as urban green and blue infrastructure, providing the basis for more liveable, resource efficient and compact urban development with benefits for urban inhabitants (Section 8.2).

Figure 8.19: Feasibility assessment based on the enablers and barriers of implementing mitigation options for urban systems across multiple dimensions. The figure summarises the extent to which different factors would enable or inhibit the deployment of mitigation options in urban systems. These factors are assessed systematically based on 18 indicators in 6 dimensions (geophysical, environmental-ecological, technological, economic, socio-cultural, and institutional dimensions). Blue bars indicate the extent to which the indicator enables the implementation of the option (E) and orange bars indicate the extent to which an indicator is a barrier (B) to the deployment of the option, relative to the maximum possible barriers and enablers assessed. The shading indicates the level of confidence, with darker shading signifying higher levels of confidence. Supplementary Material 8.SM.2 provides an overview of the extent to which the feasibility of options may differ across context, time and scale of implementation (Table 8.SM.3) and includes line of sight upon which the assessment is based (Table 8.SM.4). The line of sight builds upon urban case studies in (Lamb et al. 2019) and assessments for land use and urban planning (IPCC 2018a) involving 414 references. The assessment method is further explained in Annex II, Section 11.

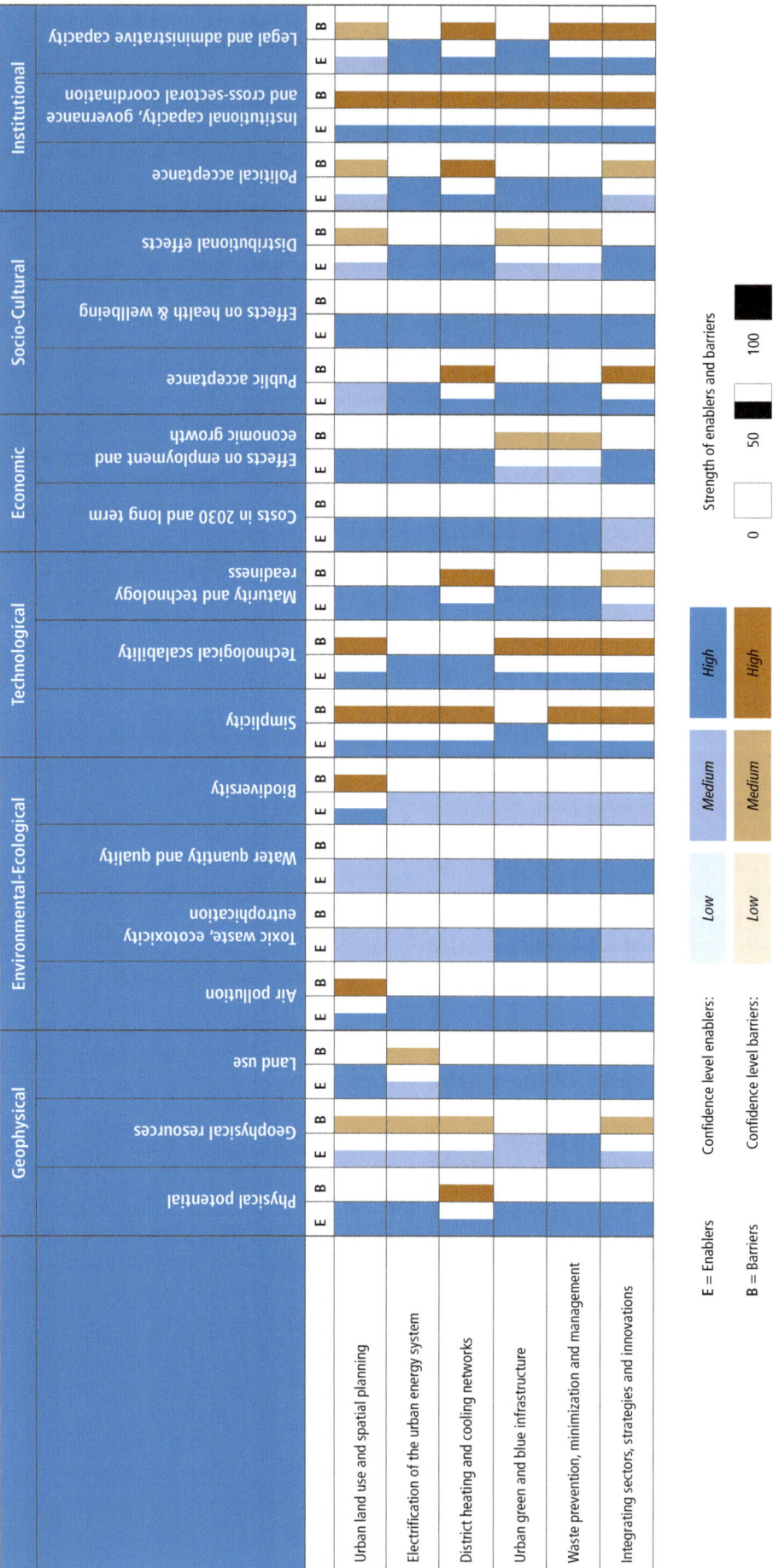

8.6 A Roadmap for Integrating Mitigation Strategies for Different Urbanisation Typologies

The most effective and appropriate packages of mitigation strategies will vary depending on several dimensions of a city. This section brings together the urban mitigation options described in Section 8.4 and assesses the range of mitigation potentials for different types of cities. There is consensus in the literature that mitigation strategies are most effective when multiple interventions are coupled together. Urban-scale interventions that implement multiple strategies concurrently through policy packages are more effective and have greater emissions savings than when single interventions are implemented separately. This is because a city-wide strategy can have cascading effects across sectors, that have multiplicative effects on GHG emissions reduction within and outside a city's administrative boundaries. Therefore, city-scale strategies can reduce more emissions than the net sum of individual interventions, particularly if multiple scales of governance are included (Sections 8.4 and 8.5). Furthermore, cities have the ability to implement policy packages across sectors using an urban systems approach, such as through planning, particularly those that affect key infrastructures (Figures 8.15, 8.17 and 8.22).

The way that cities are laid out and built will shape the entry points for realising systemic transformation across urban form and infrastructure, energy systems, and supply chains. Section 8.3.1 discusses the ongoing trend of rapid urbanisation – and how it varies through different forms of urban development or 'typologies' (Figure 8.6). Below, Figure 8.20 distils the typologies of urban growth across three categories: emerging, rapidly growing, and established. Urban growth is relatively stabilised in established urban areas with mature urban form while newly taking shape in emerging urban areas. In contrast, rapidly growing urban areas experience pronounced changes in outward and/or upward growth. These typologies are not mutually exclusive, and can co-exist within an urban system; cities typically encompass a spectrum of development, with multiple types of urban form and various typologies (Mahtta et al. 2019).

Taken together, urban form (Figure 8.16) and growth typology (Figure 8.20) can act as a roadmap for cities or sub-city communities looking to identify their urban context and, by extension, the mitigation opportunities with the greatest potential to reduce GHG emissions. Specifically, this considers whether a city is established with existing and managed infrastructure; rapidly growing with new and actively developing infrastructure; or emerging with large amounts of infrastructure build-up. The long lifespan of urban infrastructure locks in behaviour and committed emissions. Therefore, the sequencing of mitigation strategies is important for determining emissions savings in the short and long term. Hence, different types of cities will have different mitigation pathways, depending upon a city's urban form and state of that city's urban development and infrastructure; the policy packages and implementation plan that provide the highest mitigation potential for rapidly growing cities with new infrastructures will differ from those for established cities with existing infrastructure.

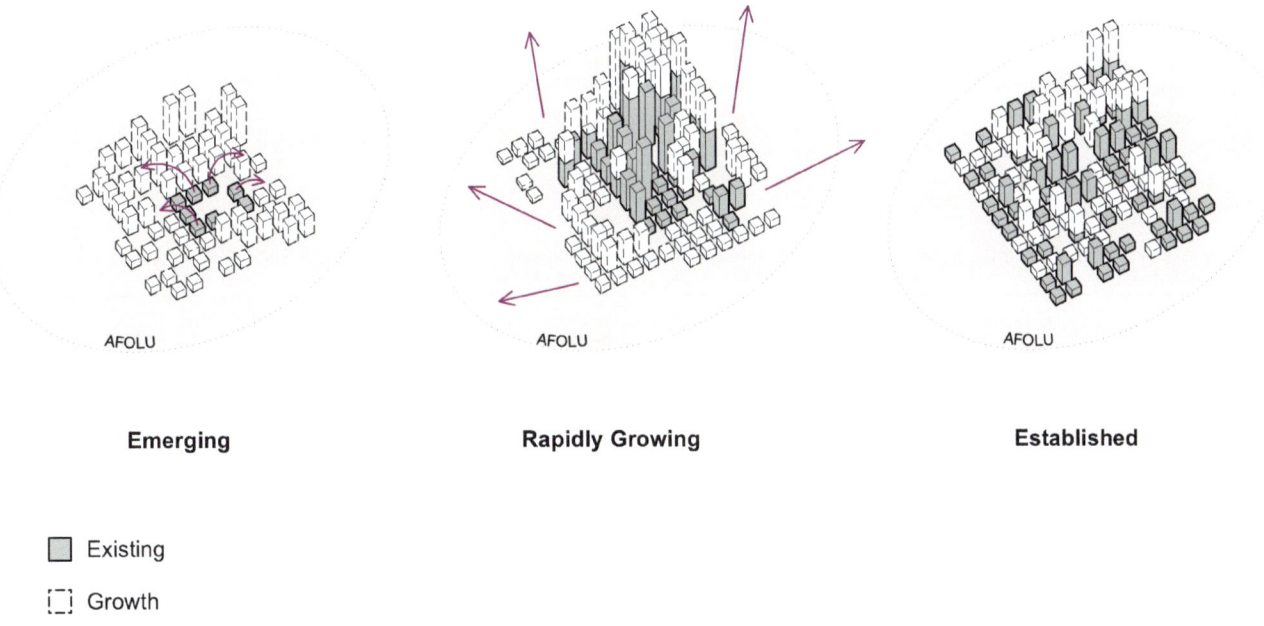

Emerging **Rapidly Growing** **Established**

☐ Existing

⬚ Growth

Figure 8.20: Urban growth typologies define the main patterns of urban development. Emerging urban areas are undergoing the buildup of new infrastructure. These are new urban areas that are budding out. Rapidly growing urban areas are undergoing significant changes in either outward and/or upward growth, accompanied by large-scale development of new urban infrastructure. Established urban areas are relatively stable with mature urban form and existing urban infrastructures. Each of these typologies represents different levels of economic development and state of urbanisation. Rapidly growing urban areas that are building up through vertical development are often those with higher levels of economic development. Rapidly growing urban areas that are building outward through horizontal expansion are found at lower levels of economic development and are land intensive. Like with urban form, different areas of a single city can undergo different growth typologies. Therefore a city will be comprised of multiple urban growth typologies. Source: synthesized from Mahtta et al. (2019) and Lall et al. (2021).

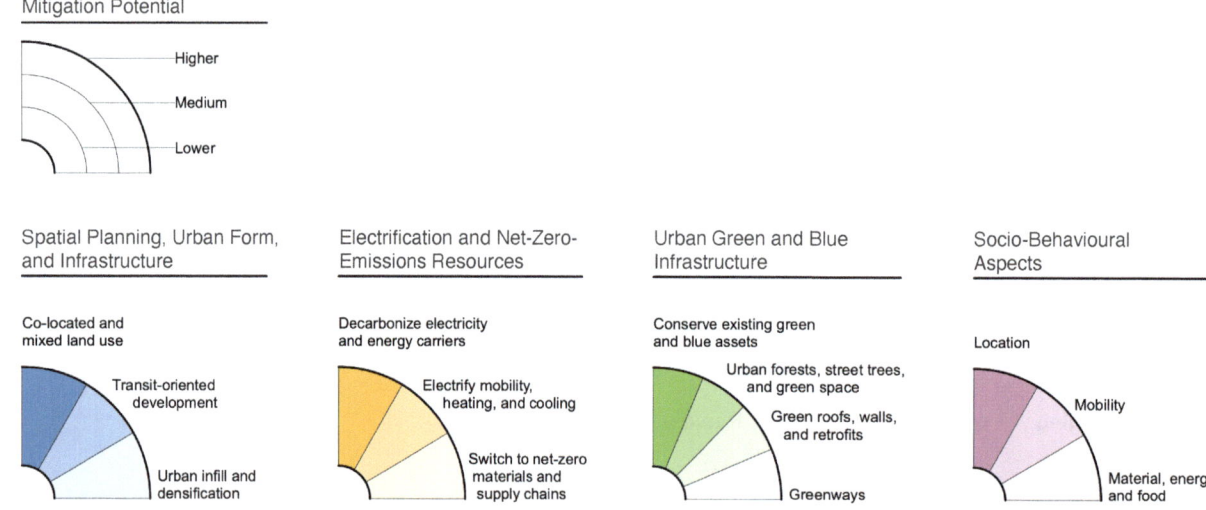

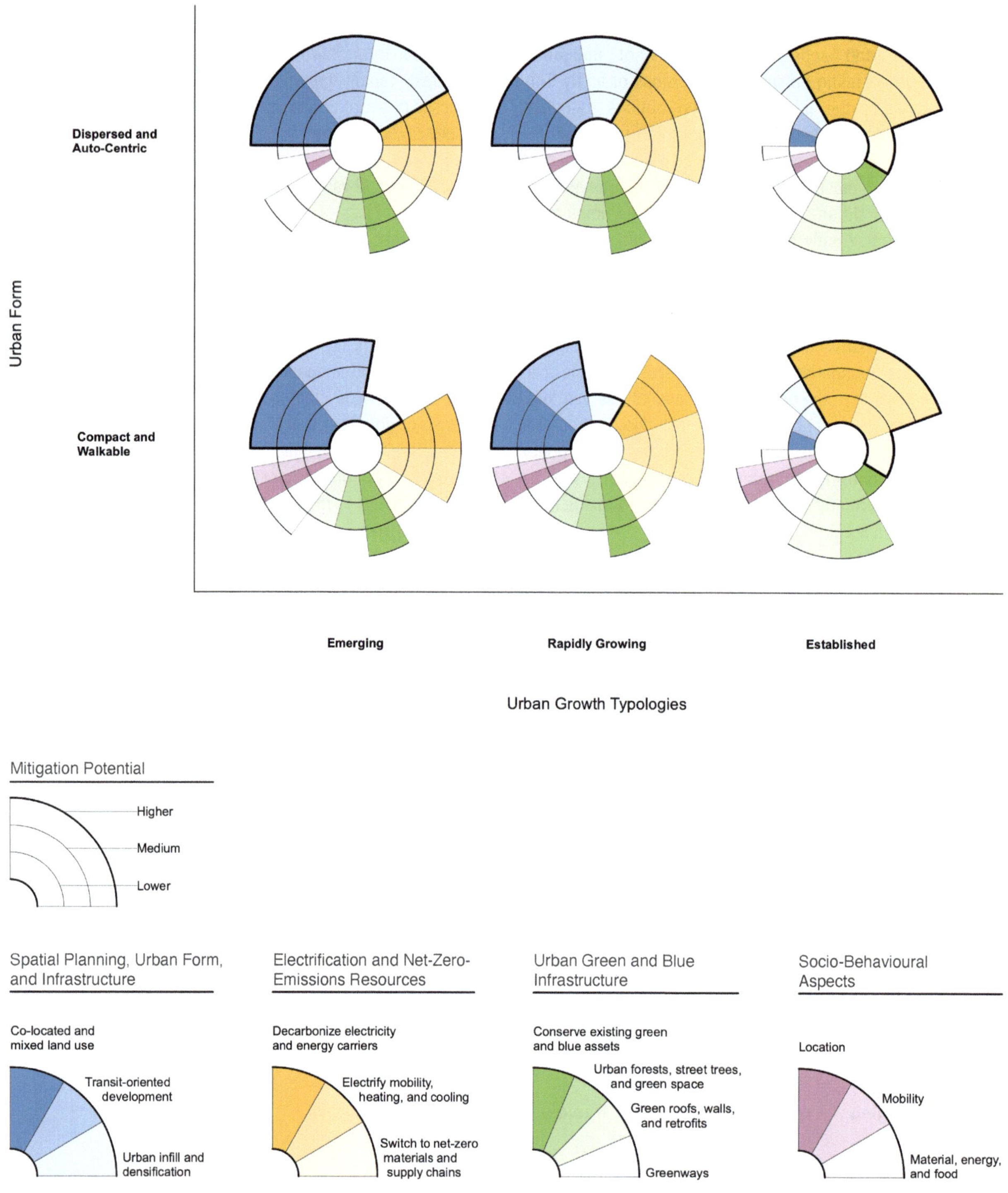

Urban Form

Dispersed and Auto-Centric

Compact and Walkable

Emerging   Rapidly Growing   Established

Urban Growth Typologies

Mitigation Potential

Higher
Medium
Lower

Spatial Planning, Urban Form, and Infrastructure

Co-located and mixed land use

Transit-oriented development

Urban infill and densification

Electrification and Net-Zero-Emissions Resources

Decarbonize electricity and energy carriers

Electrify mobility, heating, and cooling

Switch to net-zero materials and supply chains

Urban Green and Blue Infrastructure

Conserve existing green and blue assets

Urban forests, street trees, and green space

Green roofs, walls, and retrofits

Greenways

Socio-Behavioural Aspects

Location

Mobility

Material, energy, and food

Figure 8.21: Priorities and potentials for packages of urban mitigation strategies across typologies of urban growth (Figure 8.20) and urban form (Figure 8.16). The horizontal axis represents urban growth typologies based on emerging, rapidly growing, and established urban areas. The vertical axis shows the continuum of urban form, from compact and walkable, to dispersed and auto-centric. Urban areas can first locate their relative positioning in this space according to their predominant style of urban growth and urban form. The urban mitigation options are bundled across four broad sectors of mitigation strategies: (i) spatial planning, urban form, and infrastructure (blue); (ii) electrification and net-zero-emissions resources (yellow); (iii) urban green and blue infrastructure (green); and (iv) socio-behavioural aspects (purple). The concentric circles indicate lower, medium, and higher mitigation potential considering the context of the urban area. For each city type (circular graphic) the illustrative urban mitigation strategy that is considered to provide the greatest cascading effects across mitigation opportunities is represented by a section that is larger relative to others; those strategy sections outlined in black are 'entry points' for sequencing of strategies. Within each of the larger strategy sections (i.e., spatial planning, urban green and blue infrastructure, etc.), the size of the sub-strategy sections are equal and do not suggest any priority or sequencing. The relative sizes of the strategies and extent of mitigation potential are illustrative and based on the authors' best understanding and assessment of the literature.

Mitigation options that involve spatial planning, urban form, and infrastructure – particularly co-located and mixed land use, as well as TOD – provide the greatest opportunities when urban areas are rapidly growing or emerging (Section 8.4.2). Established urban areas that are already compact and walkable have captured mitigation benefits from these illustrative strategies to various extents. Conversely, established urban areas that are dispersed and auto-centric have foregone these opportunities, with the exception of urban infill and densification that can be used to transform or continue to transform the existing urban form. Figure 8.21 underscores that urban mitigation options and illustrative strategies differ by urban growth typologies and urban form. Cities can identify their entry points for sequencing mitigation strategies.

The emissions reduction potential of urban mitigation options further varies based on governance contexts, institutional capacity, and economic structure, as well as human and physical geography. According to the development level, for instance, urban form can remain mostly planned or unplanned, taking place spontaneously, with persistent urban infrastructure gaps remaining (Lwasa et al. 2018; Kareem et al. 2020). Measures for closing the urban infrastructure gap while addressing 'leapfrogging' opportunities (see Glossary) for mitigation and providing co-benefits represent possibilities for shifting development paths for sustainability (Cross-Chapter Box 5 in Chapter 4).

8.6.1   Mitigation Opportunities for *Established* Cities

Established cities will achieve the largest GHG emissions savings by replacing, repurposing, or retrofitting the building stock, encouraging modal shift, electrifying the urban energy system, as well as infilling and densifying urban areas.

Shifting pathways to low-carbon development for established cities with existing infrastructures and locked-in behaviours and lifestyles is admittedly challenging. Urban infrastructures such as buildings, roads, and pipelines often have long lifetimes that lock-in emissions, as well as institutional and individual behaviour. Although the expected lifetime of buildings varies considerably by geography, design, and materials, typical lifespans are at minimum 30 years to more than 100 years.

Cities where urban infrastructure has already been built have opportunities to increase energy efficiency measures, prioritise compact and mixed-use neighbourhoods through urban regeneration, advance the urban energy system through electrification, undertake cross-sector synergies, integrate urban green and blue infrastructure, encourage behavioural and lifestyle change to reinforce climate mitigation, and put into place a wide range of enabling conditions as necessary to guide and coordinate actions in the urban system and its impacts in the global system. Retrofitting buildings with state of the art deep-energy retrofit measures could reduce emissions of the existing stock by about 30–60% (Creutzig et al. 2016a) and in some cases up to 80% (Ürge-Vorsatz et al. 2020) (Section 8.4.3).

Established cities that are compact and walkable are likely to have low per capita emissions, and thus can keep emissions low by focusing on electrification of all urban energy services and using urban green and blue infrastructure to sequester and store carbon while reducing urban heat stress. Illustrative mitigation strategies with the highest mitigation potential are decarbonising electricity and energy carriers while electrifying mobility, heating, and cooling (Table 8.3 and Figure 8.19). Within integrated strategies, the importance of urban forests, street trees, and green space as well as green roofs, walls, and retrofits, also have high mitigation potential (Section 8.4.4 and Figure 8.18).

Established cities that are dispersed and auto-centric are likely to have higher per capita emissions and thus can reduce emissions by focusing on creating modal shift and improving public transit systems in order to reduce urban transport emissions, as well as focusing on infilling and densifying. Only then can the urban form constraints on locational and mobility options be effective at reducing transport-based emissions. Among mitigation options based on spatial planning, urban form, and infrastructure, urban infill and densification has priority. For these cities, the use of urban green and blue infrastructure will be essential to offset residual emissions that cannot be reduced because their urban form is already established and difficult to change.

System-wide energy savings and emissions reductions for low-carbon urban development are widely recognised to require both behavioural and structural changes (Zhang and Li 2017). Synergies between social and ecological innovation can reinforce the sustainability of urban systems while decoupling energy usage and economic growth (Hu et al. 2018; Ma et al. 2018). In addition, an integrated sustainable development approach that enables cross-sector energy efficiency, sustainable transport, renewable energy, and local development in urban neighbourhoods can address issues of energy poverty (Pukšec et al. 2018). In this context, cross-sectoral, multi-scale, and public-private collaborative action is crucial to steer societies and cities closer to low-carbon futures (Hölscher et al. 2019). Such actions include guiding residential living area per capita, limiting private vehicle growth, expanding public transport, improving the efficiency of urban infrastructure, enhancing urban carbon pools, and minimising waste through sustainable, ideally circular, waste management (Lin et al. 2018). Through a coordinated approach, urban areas can be transformed into hubs for renewable and distributed energy, sustainable mobility, as well as inclusivity and health (Newman et al. 2017; Newman 2020).

Urban design for existing urban areas includes strategies for urban energy transitions for carbon neutrality based on renewable energy, district heating for the city centre and suburbs, as well as green and blue interfaces (Pulselli et al. 2021). Integrated modelling approaches for urban energy system planning, including land use and transport and flexible demand-side options, is increased when municipal actors are also recognised as energy planners (Yazdanie and Orehounig 2021) (Section 8.4.3). Enablers for action can include the co-design of infill residential development through an inclusive and participatory process with citizen utilities and disruptive innovation that can support net-zero-carbon power while contributing to 1.5°C pathways, the SDGs, and affordable housing simultaneously (Wiktorowicz et al. 2018). Cross-sectoral strategies for established cities, including those taking place among 120 urban areas, also involve opportunities for sustainable development (Kılkış 2019, 2021b).

A shared understanding for urban transformation through a participatory approach can largely avoid maladaptation and contribute to equity (Moglia et al. 2018). Transformative urban futures that are radically different from the existing trajectories of urbanisation, including in developing countries, can remain within planetary boundaries while being inclusive of the urban poor (Friend et al. 2016). At the urban policy level, an analysis of 12,000 measures in urban-level monitoring emissions inventories based on the mode of governance further suggests that local authorities with lower population have primarily relied on municipal self-governing while local authorities with higher population more frequently adopted regulatory measures as well as financing and provision (Palermo et al. 2020b). Policies that relate to education and enabling were uniformly adopted regardless of population size (Palermo et al. 2020b). Multi-disciplinary teams, including urban planners, engineers, architects, and environmental institutions, can support local decision-making capacities, including for increasing energy efficiency and renewable energy considering building intensity and energy use (Mrówczyńska et al. 2021) (Section 8.5).

8.6.2   Mitigation Opportunities for *Rapidly Growing* Cities

Rapidly growing cities with new and actively developing infrastructures can avoid higher future emissions through using urban planning to co-locate jobs and housing, and achieve compact urban form; leapfrogging to low-carbon technologies; electrifying all urban services, including transportation, cooling, heating, cooking, recycling, water extraction, wastewater recycling, and so on; and preserving and managing existing green and blue assets.

Rapidly growing cities have significant opportunities for integrating climate mitigation response options in earlier stages of urban development, which can provide even greater opportunities for avoiding carbon lock-in and shifting pathways towards net-zero GHG emissions. In growing cities that are expected to experience large increases in population, a significant share of urban development remains to be planned and built. The ability to shift these investments towards low-carbon development earlier in the process represents an important opportunity for contributing to net-zero GHG emissions at the global scale. In particular, evidence suggests that investment in low-carbon development measures and reinvestment based on the returns of the measures, even without considering substantial co-benefits, can provide tipping points for climate mitigation action and reaching peak emissions at lower levels while decoupling emissions from economic growth, even in fast-growing megacity contexts with well-established infrastructure (Colenbrander et al. 2017).

At the same time, some of the rapidly growing cities in developing countries can have existing walkable urban design that can be maintained and supported with electrified urban rail plus renewable-energy-based solutions to avoid a shift to private vehicles (Sharma 2018). In addition, community-based distributed renewable electricity can be applicable for the regeneration of informal settlements rather than more expensive informal settlement clearance (Teferi and Newman 2018). Scalable options for decentralised energy, water, and wastewater systems, as well as spatial planning and urban agriculture and forestry, are applicable to urban settlements across multiple regions simultaneously (Lwasa 2017).

Rapidly urbanising areas can experience pressure for rapid growth in urban infrastructure to address growth in population. This challenge can be addressed with coordinated urban planning and support from enabling conditions for pursuing effective climate mitigation (Section 8.5 and Box 8.3). The ability to mobilise low-carbon development will also increase opportunities for capturing co-benefits for urban inhabitants while reducing embodied and operational emissions. Transforming urban growth, including its impacts on energy and materials, can be carefully addressed with the integration of cross-sectoral strategies and policies.

Rapidly growing cities have entry points into an integrated strategy based on spatial planning, urban form and infrastructure (Figure 8.21). For rapidly growing cities that may be co-located and walkable at present, remaining compact is better ensured when co-location and mixed land use, as well as TOD, continues to be prioritised (Section 8.4.2). Concurrently, ensuring that electricity and energy carriers are decarbonised while electrifying mobility, heating and cooling will support the mitigation potential of these cities. Along with an integrated approach across other illustrative strategies, switching to net-zero materials and supply chains holds importance (Section 8.4.3). Cities that remain compact and walkable can provide a greater array of locational and mobility options to the inhabitants that can be adopted for mitigation benefits. Rapidly growing cities that may currently be dispersed and auto-centric can capture high mitigation potential through urban infill and densification. Conserving existing green and blue assets, thereby protecting sources of carbon storage and sequestration, as well as biodiversity, have high potential for both kinds of existing urban form, especially when the rapid growth can be controlled.

8.6.3   Mitigation Opportunities for *New and Emerging* Cities

New and emerging cities have unparalleled potential to become low- or net-zero-emissions urban areas while achieving high quality of life by creating compact, co-located, and walkable urban areas with mixed land use and TOD, that also preserve existing green and blue assets.

The fundamental building blocks that make up the physical attributes of cities, such as the layout of streets, the size of the city blocks, the location of where people live versus where they work, can affect and lock in energy demand for long time periods (Seto et al. 2016)

(Section 8.4.1). A large share of urban infrastructures that will be in place by 2050 has yet to be constructed and their design and implementation will determine both future GHG emissions as well as the ability to meet mitigation goals (Creutzig et al. 2016a) (Figure 8.10 and Table 8.1). Thus, there are tremendous opportunities for new and emerging cities to be designed and constructed to be low-emissions while providing high quality of life for their populations.

The UN International Resource Panel (IRP) estimates that building future cities under conventional practices will require a more than doubling of material consumption, from 40 billion tonnes annually in 2010 to about 90 billion tonnes annually by 2050 (Swilling et al. 2018). Thus, the demand that new and emerging cities will place on natural resource use, materials, and emissions can be minimised and avoided only if urban settlements are planned and built much differently than today, including minimised impacts on land use based on compact urban form, lowered use of materials, and related cross-sector integration, including energy-driven urban design for sustainable urbanisation.

Minimising and avoiding raw material demands depends on alternative options while accommodating the urban population. In addition, operational emissions that can be committed by new urban infrastructure can range between 8.5 $GtCO_2$ and 14 $GtCO_2$ annually up to 2030 (Erickson and Tempest 2015). Buildings and road networks are strongly influenced by urban layouts, densities, and specific uses. Cities that are planned and built much differently than today through light-weighting, material substitution, resource efficiency, renewable energy, and compact urban form, have the potential to support more sustainable urbanisation and provide co-benefits for inhabitants (Figures 8.17 and 8.22).

In this context, illustrative mitigation strategies that can serve as a roadmap for emerging cities includes priorities for co-located and mixed land use, as well as TOD, within an integrated approach (Table 8.3 and Figure 8.19). This has cascading effects, including conserving existing green and blue assets (e.g., forests, grasslands, wetlands), many of which sequester and store carbon. Priorities for decarbonising electricity and energy carriers while electrifying mobility, heating, and cooling take place within the integrated approach (Section 8.4.3). Increasing greenways and permeable surfaces, especially from the design of emerging urban areas onward, can be pursued, also for adaptation co-benefits and linkages with the SDGs (Section 8.4.4 and Figure 8.18).

In low-energy-driven urban design, parameters are evaluated based on the energy performance of the urban area in the early design phase of future urban development (Shi et al. 2017b). Energy-driven urban design generates and optimises urban form according to the energy performance outcome (Shi et al. 2017b). Beyond the impact of urban form on building energy performance, the approach focuses on the interdependencies between urban form and energy infrastructure in urban energy systems. The process can provide opportunities for both passive options for energy-driven urban design, such as the use of solar gain for space heating, or of thermal mass to moderate indoor temperatures, as well as active options that involve the use of energy infrastructure and technologies while recognising interrelations of the system. Future urban settlements can also be planned and built with net-zero CO_2 or net-zero GHG emissions, as well as renewable energy targets, in mind. Energy master planning of urban areas that initially target net-zero operational GHG emissions can be supported with energy master planning from conceptual design to operation, including district-scale energy strategies (Charani Shandiz et al. 2021).

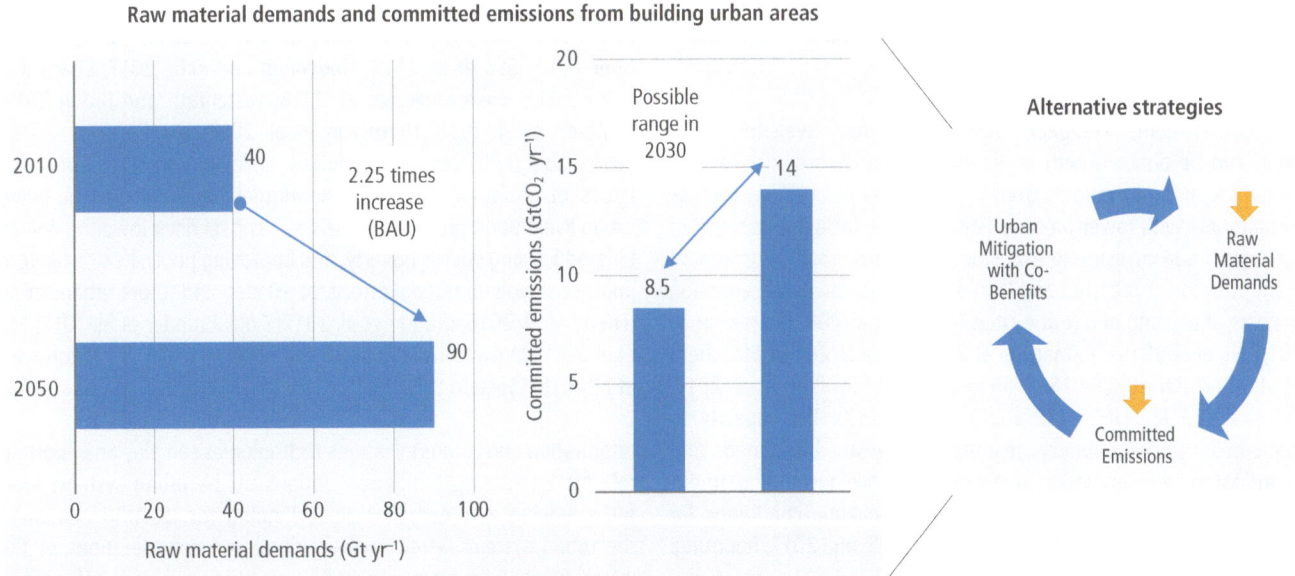

Raw material demands and committed emissions from building urban areas

Figure 8.22: Raw material demands and committed emissions from building urban areas. The horizontal bars represent the projected increase in raw material demands in the year 2050. The vertical bars represent the possible range of committed CO_2 emissions in 2030. The importance of alternative solutions to reduce raw material demands and committed semissions while increasing co-benefits is represented by the circular process on the right-hand side. Ranges for committed emissions from new urban infrastructure are based on Erickson and Tempest (2015) SEI WP 11. Source: drawn using data from Erickson and Tempest (2015) and Swilling et al. (2018).

Integrated scenarios across sectors at the local level can decouple resource usage from economic growth (Hu et al. 2018) and enable 100% renewable energy scenarios (Zhao et al. 2017a; Bačeković and Østergaard 2018). Relative decoupling is obtained (Kalmykova et al. 2015) with increasing evidence for turning points in per capita emissions, total emissions, or urban metabolism (Chen et al. 2018b; Shen et al. 2018). The importance of integrating energy and resource efficiency in sustainable and low-carbon city planning (Dienst et al. 2015), structural changes, as well as forms of disruptive social innovation, such as the 'sharing economy' (see Glossary), is also evident based on analyses for multiple cities, including those that can be used to lower the carbon footprints of urban areas relative to sub-urban areas (Chen et al. 2018a).

To minimise carbon footprints, new cities can utilise new intelligence functions as well as changes in energy sources and material processes. Core design strategies of a compact city can be facilitated by data-driven decision-making so that new urban intelligence functions are holistic and proactive rather than reactive (Bibri 2020). In mainstream practices, for example, many cities use environmental impact reviews to identify potentially negative consequences of individual development projects on environmental conditions on a piecemeal project basis.

New cities can utilise: system-wide analyses of construction materials, or renewable power sources, that minimise ecosystem disruption and energy use, through the use of lifecycle assessments for building types permitted in the new city (Ingrao et al. 2019); urban-scale metabolic impact assessments for neighbourhoods in the city (Pinho and Fernandes 2019); strategic environmental assessments (SEAs) that go beyond the individual project and assess plans for neighbourhoods (Noble and Nwanekezie 2017); or modelling of the type and location of building masses, tree canopies and parks, and temperature (surface conditions) and prevailing winds profiles to reduce the combined effects of climate change and UHI phenomena, thus minimising the need for air conditioning (Matsuo and Tanaka 2019).

Resource-efficient, compact, sustainable, and liveable urban areas can be enabled with an integrated approach across sectors, strategies, and innovations. From a geophysical perspective, the use of materials with lower lifecycle GHG impacts, including the use of timber in urban infrastructure and the selection of urban development plans with lower material and land demand can lower the emission impacts of existing and future cities (Müller et al. 2013; Carpio et al. 2016; Liu et al. 2016a; Ramage et al. 2017; Shi et al. 2017a; Stocchero et al. 2017; Bai et al. 2018; Zhan et al. 2018b; Swilling et al. 2018; Xu et al. 2018b; UNEP IRP 2020) (Figure 8.17). The capacity to implement relevant policy instruments in an integrated and coordinated manner within a policy mix while leveraging multi-level support as relevant can increase the enabling conditions for urban system transformation (Agyepong and Nhamo 2017; Roppongi et al. 2017).

The integration of urban land use and spatial planning, electrification of urban energy systems, renewable energy district heating and cooling networks, urban green and blue infrastructure, and circular economy can also have positive impacts on improving air and environmental quality with related co-benefits for health and well-being (Diallo et al. 2016; Nieuwenhuijsen and Khreis 2016; Shakya 2016; Liu et al. 2017; Ramaswami et al. 2017a; Sun et al. 2018b; Tayarani et al. 2018; Park and Sener 2019; González-García et al. 2021). Low-carbon development options can be implemented in ways that reduce impacts on water use, including water use efficiency, demand management, and water recycling, while increasing water quality (Koop and van Leeuwen 2015; Topi et al. 2016; Drangert and Sharatchandra 2017; Lam et al. 2017, 2018; Vanham et al. 2017; Kim and Chen 2018). The ability to enhance biodiversity while addressing climate change depends on improving urban metabolism and biophilic urbanism towards urban areas that are able to regenerate natural capital (Thomson and Newman 2018; IPBES 2019b).

There are readily available solutions for low-carbon urban development that can be further supported by new and emerging ones, such as tools for optimising the impact of urban form on energy infrastructure (Hu et al. 2015; Shi et al. 2017b; Xue et al. 2017; Dobler et al. 2018; Egusquiza et al. 2018; Pedro et al. 2018; Soilán et al. 2018). The costs of low-carbon urban development are manageable, and enhanced with a portfolio approach for cost-effective, cost-neutral, and reinvestment options with evidence across different urban typologies (Colenbrander et al. 2015, 2017; Gouldson et al. 2015; Nieuwenhuijsen and Khreis 2016; Saujot and Lefèvre 2016; Sudmant et al. 2016; Brozynski and Leibowicz 2018).

Low-carbon urban development that triggers economic decoupling can have a positive impact on employment and local competitiveness (Kalmykova et al. 2015; Chen et al. 2018b; García-Gusano et al. 2018; Hu et al. 2018; Shen et al. 2018). In addition, sustainable urban transformation can be supported with participatory approaches that provide a shared understanding of future opportunities and challenges where public acceptance increases with citizen engagement and citizen empowerment as well as an awareness of co-benefits (Blanchet 2015; Bjørkelund et al. 2016; Flacke and de Boer 2017; Gao et al. 2017; Neuvonen and Ache 2017; Sharp and Salter 2017; Wiktorowicz et al. 2018; Fastenrath and Braun 2018; Gorissen et al. 2018; Herrmann et al. 2018; Moglia et al. 2018). Sustainable and low-carbon urban development that integrates issues of equity, inclusivity, and affordability, while safeguarding urban livelihoods, providing access to basic services, lowering energy bills, addressing energy poverty, and improving public health can also improve the distributional effects of existing and future urbanisation (Friend et al. 2016; Claude et al. 2017; Colenbrander et al. 2017; Ma et al. 2018; Mrówczyńska et al. 2018; Pukšec et al. 2018; Wiktorowicz et al. 2018) (Section 8.2).

Information and communications technologies can play an important role for integrating mitigation options at the urban systems level for achieving zero-carbon cities. Planning for decarbonisation at the urban systems level involves integrated considerations of the interaction among sectors, including synergies and trade-offs among households, businesses, transport, land use, and lifestyles. The utilisation of big data, artificial intelligence and internet of things (IoT) technologies can be used to plan, evaluate and integrate rapidly progressing transport and building technologies, such as autonomous EVs, zero-energy buildings, and districts as an urban system, including energy-driven urban design (Creutzig et al. 2020; Yamagata et al. 2020). Community-level energy sharing systems will contribute to realising the decarbonisation potential of urban systems at community scale, including in smart cities (Section 4.2.5.9, Box 10.1, and Cross-Chapter Box 11 in Chapter 16).

8.7   Knowledge Gaps

While there is growing literature on urban NBS, which encompasses urban green and blue infrastructure in cities, there is still a knowledge gap regarding how these climate mitigation actions can be integrated in urban planning and design, as well as their mitigation potential, especially for cities that have yet to be built. In moving forward with the research agenda on cities and climate change science, transformation of urban systems will be critical; however, understanding this transformation and how best to assess mitigation action remain key knowledge gaps (Butcher-Gollach 2018; Pathak and Mahadevia 2018; Rigolon et al. 2018; Anguelovski et al. 2019; Buyana et al. 2019; Trundle 2020; Azunre et al. 2021).

There is a key knowledge gap in respect to the potential of the informal sector in developing country cities. Informality extends beyond illegality of economic activities to include housing, locally developed off-grid infrastructure, and alternative waste management strategies. Limited literature and understanding of the mitigation potential of enhanced informal sector is highlighted in the key research agenda on cities from the Cities and Climate Change Science Conference (Prieur-Richard et al. 2018).

City-level models and data for understanding of urban systems is another knowledge gap. With increased availability of open data systems, big data and computing capacities, there is an opportunity for analysis of urban systems (Frantzeskaki et al. 2019).

While there is much literature on urban climate governance, there is still limited understanding of the governance models and regimes that support multi-level decision-making for mitigation and climate action in general. Transformative climate action will require changing relationships between actors to utilise the knowledge from data and models and deepen understanding of the urban system to support decision-making.

8.7.1   COVID-19 and Cities

The COVID-19 pandemic has disrupted many aspects of urban life while raising questions about urban densities, transportation, public space, and other urban issues. The impact of COVID-19 on urban activity and urban GHG emissions may offer insights into urban emissions and their behavioural drivers and may include structural shifts in emissions that last into the future. The science is unclear as to the links between urban characteristics and COVID-19, and involves multiple aspects. For example, some research shows higher COVID-19 infection rates with city size (e.g., Dalziel et al. 2018; Stier et al. 2021), as well as challenges to epidemic preparedness due to high population

density and high volume of public transportation (Layne et al. 2020; Lee et al. 2020). Other research from 913 metropolitan areas shows that density is unrelated to COVID-19 infection rates and, in fact, has been inversely related to COVID-19 mortality rates when controlled for metropolitan population.

Densely populated counties are found to have significantly lower mortality rates, possibly due to such advantages as better health care systems, as well as greater adherence to social-distancing measures (Hamidi et al. 2020). Sustainable urbanisation and urban infrastructure that address the SDGs can also improve preparedness and resilience against future pandemics. For example, long-term exposure to air pollution has been found to exacerbate the impacts of COVID-19 infections (Wu et al. 2020b), while urban areas with cleaner air from clean energy and greenspace, can provide advantages.

Some studies indicate that socio-economic factors, such as poverty, racial and ethnic disparities, and crowding are more significant than density in COVID-19 spread and associated mortality rate (Borjas 2020; Maroko et al. 2020; Lamb et al. 2021). The evidence for the connection between household crowding and the risk of contagion from infectious diseases is also strong. A 2018 World Health Organization (WHO) systematic review of the effect of household crowding on health concluded that a majority of studies of the risk of non-tuberculosis infectious diseases, including flu-related illnesses, were associated with household crowding (Shannon et al. 2018).

Though preliminary, some studies suggest that urban areas saw larger overall declines in emissions because of lower commuter activity and associated emissions. For example, researchers have explored the COVID-19 impact in the cities of Los Angeles, Baltimore, Washington, DC, and San Francisco Bay Area in the United States. In the San Francisco region, a decline of 30% in anthropogenic CO_2 was observed, which was primarily due to changes in on-road traffic (Turner et al. 2020). Declines in the Washington, DC/Baltimore region and in the Los Angeles urban area were 33% and 34%, respectively, in the month of April 2020 compared to previous years (Yadav et al. 2021).

At the global scale COVID-related lockdown and travel restrictions reduced daily CO_2 emissions by −17% in early April 2020 compared to 2019 values (Le Quéré et al. 2020; Liu et al. 2020b), though subsequent studies have questioned the accuracy of the indirect proxy data used (Oda et al. 2021). Research at the national scale in the United States found that daily CO_2 emissions declined −15% during the late March to early June time period (Gillingham et al. 2020). Research in China estimated that the first quarter of 2020 saw an 11.5% decline in CO_2 emissions relative to 2019 (Zheng et al. 2020; Han et al. 2021). In Europe, estimates indicated a −12.5% decline in the first half of 2020 compared to 2019 (Andreoni 2021). Rebound to pre-COVID trajectories has been evidenced following the ease of travel restrictions (Le Quéré et al. 2021). It remains unclear to what extent COVID resulted in any structural change in the underlying drivers of urban emissions.

Changes in local air pollution emissions, particularly due to altered transportation patterns, have caused temporary air quality improvements in many cities around the world (see critical review by Adam et al. 2021). Many outdoor air pollutants, such as particulates, nitrogen dioxide, carbon monoxide, and volatile organic compounds declined during national lockdowns. Levels of tropospheric ozone, however, remained constant or increased. A promising transformation that has been observed in many cities is an increase in the share of active travel modes such as cycling and walking (Sharifi and Khavarian-Garmsir 2020). While this may be temporary, other trends, such as increased rates of teleworking and/ or increased reliance on smart solutions that allow remote provision of services provide an unprecedented opportunity to transform urban travel patterns (Belzunegui-Eraso and Erro-Garcés 2020; Sharifi and Khavarian-Garmsir 2020).

Related to the transport sector, the pandemic has resulted in concerns regarding the safety of public transport modes, which has resulted in significant reductions in public transport ridership in some cities (Bucsky 2020; de Haas et al. 2020) while providing opportunities for urban transitions in others (Newman AO 2020). Considering the significance of public transportation for achieving low-carbon and inclusive urban development, appropriate response measures could enhance health safety of public transport modes and regain public trust (Sharifi and Khavarian-Garmsir 2020). Similarly, there is a perceived correlation between the higher densities of urban living and the risk of increased virus transmission (Hamidi et al. 2020; Khavarian-Garmsir et al. 2021).

While city size could be a risk factor with higher transmission in larger cities (Hamidi et al. 2020; Stier et al. 2021), there is also evidence showing that density is not a major risk factor and indeed cities that are more compact have more capacity to respond to and control the pandemic (Hamidi et al. 2020). Considering the spatial pattern of density, even distribution of density can reduce the possibility of crowding that is found to contribute to the scale and length of virus outbreak in cities. Overall, more research is needed to better understand the impacts of density on outbreak dynamics and address public health concerns for resilient cities.

Cities could seize this opportunity to provide better infrastructure to further foster active transportation. This could, for example, involve measures, such as expanding cycling networks and restricting existing streets to make them more pedestrian- and cycling-friendly contributing to health and adaptation co-benefits, as discussed in Section 8.2 (Sharifi 2021). Strengthening the science–policy interface is another consideration that could support urban transformation (Cross-Chapter Box 1 in Chapter 1).

8.7.2   Future Urban Emissions Scenarios

The urban share of global emissions is significant and is expected to increase in the coming decades. This places emphasis on the need to expand development of urban emissions scenarios within climate mitigation scenarios (Gurney et al. 2021, 2022). The literature on globally comprehensive analysis of urban emissions within the existing IPCC scenario framework remains very limited, curtailing understanding of urban emissions tipping points, mitigation opportunities and overall climate policy complexity. A review of the applications of the SSP-RCP scenario framework also recommended downscaling global SSPs to improve the applicability of this framework to regional and local scales (O'Neill et al. 2020). This remains an urgent need and will require multidisciplinary research efforts, particularly as net-zero-emissions targets are emphasised.

8.7.3   Urban Emissions Data

Though there has been a rapid rise in quantification and analysis of urban emissions, gaps remain in comprehensive global coverage, particularly in the Global South, and reliance on standardised frameworks and systematic data are lacking (Gurney and Shepson 2021; Mueller et al. 2021). The development of protocols by (BSI 2013; Fong et al. 2014; ICLEI 2019b) that urban areas can use to organise emissions accounts has been an important step forward, but no single agreed-upon reporting framework exists (Lombardi et al. 2017; Chen et al. 2019b; Ramaswami et al. 2021). Additionally, there is no standardisation of emissions data and limited independent validation procedures (Gurney and Shepson 2021). This is partly driven by the recognition that urban emissions can be conceptualised using different frameworks, each of which has a different meaning for different urban communities (Section 8.1.6.2). Equally important is the recognition that acquisition and analysis of complex data used to populate urban GHG inventory protocols remains a barrier for local practitioners (Creutzig et al. 2019). The limited standardisation has also led to incomparability of the many individual or city cluster analyses that have been accomplished since AR5. Finally, comprehensive, global quantification of urban emissions remains incomplete in spite of recent efforts (Moran et al. 2018; Zheng et al. 2018; Harris et al. 2020; Jiang et al. 2020; Wei et al. 2021; Wiedmann et al. 2021).

Similarly, independent verification or evaluation of urban GHG emissions has seen a large number of research studies (e.g., Wu et al. 2016; Sargent et al. 2018; Whetstone 2018; Lauvaux et al. 2020). This has been driven by the recognition that self-reported approaches may not provide adequate accuracy to track emissions changes and provide confidence for mitigation investment (Gurney and Shepson 2021).

The most promising approach to independent verification of urban emissions has been the use of urban atmospheric monitoring (direct flux and/or concentration) as a means to assess and track urban GHG emissions (Davis et al. 2017). However, like the basic accounting approach itself, standardisation and practical deployment and scaling is an essential near-term need.

Frequently Asked Questions (FAQs)

FAQ 8.1 | Why are urban areas important to global climate change mitigation?

Over half of the world's population currently resides in urban areas – a number forecasted to increase to nearly 70% by 2050. Urban areas also account for a growing proportion of national and global emissions, depending on emissions scope and geographic boundary. These trends are projected to grow in the coming decades; in 2100, some scenarios show the urban share of global emissions above 80%, with 63% being the minimum for any scenario (with the shares being in different contexts of emissions reduction or increase) (Sections 8.3.3 and 8.3.4). As such, urban climate change mitigation considers the majority of the world's population, as well as some of the key drivers of global emissions. In general, emissions scenarios with limited outward urban land expansion are also associated with a smaller rise in global temperature (Section 8.3.4).

The urban share of global emissions and its projected growth stem in part from urban carbon lock-in – that is, the path dependency and inertia of committed emissions through the long lifespan of urban layout, infrastructures, and behaviour. As such, urban mitigation efforts that address lock-in can significantly reduce emissions (Section 8.4.1). Electrification of urban energy systems, in tandem with implementing multiple urban-scale mitigation strategies, could reduce urban emissions by 90% by 2050 – thereby significantly reducing global emissions (Section 8.3.4). Urban areas can also act as points of intervention to amplify synergies and co-benefits for accomplishing the Sustainable Development Goals (Section 8.2).

FAQ 8.2 | What are the most impactful options cities can take to mitigate urban emissions, and how can these be best implemented?

The most impactful urban mitigation plans reduce urban GHG emissions by considering the long lifespan of urban layout and urban infrastructures (Sections 8.4.1 and 8.6). Chapter 8 identifies three overarching mitigation strategies with the largest potential to decrease current, and avoid future, urban emissions: (i) reducing or changing urban energy and material use towards more sustainable production and consumption across all sectors including through spatial planning and infrastructure that supports compact, walkable urban form (Section 8.4.2); (ii) decarbonise through electrification of the urban energy system, and switch to net-zero-emissions resources (i.e., low-carbon infrastructure) (Section 8.4.3); and (iii) enhance carbon sequestration through urban green and blue infrastructure (e.g., green roofs, urban forests and street trees), which can also offer multiple co-benefits like reducing ground temperatures and supporting public health and well-being (Section 8.4.4). Integrating these mitigation strategies across sectors, geographic scales, and levels of governance will yield the greatest emissions savings (Sections 8.4 and 8.5).

A city's layout, patterns, and spatial arrangements of land use, transportation systems, and built environment (urban form), as well as its state and form(s) of development (urban growth typology), can inform the most impactful emissions savings 'entry points' and priorities for urban mitigation strategies (Sections 8.4.2 and 8.6). For rapidly growing and emerging urban areas, there is the opportunity to avoid carbon lock-in by focusing on urban form that promotes low-carbon infrastructure and enables low-impact behaviour facilitated by co-located medium to high densities of jobs and housing, walkability, and transit-oriented development (Sections 8.6.2 and 8.6.3). For established cities, strategies include electrification of the grid and transport, and implementing energy efficiency across sectors (Section 8.6.1).

FAQ 8.3 | How do we estimate global emissions from cities, and how reliable are the estimates?

There are two different emissions estimation techniques applied, individually or in combination, to the four frameworks outlined in Section 8.1.6.2 to estimate urban GHG emissions: 'top-down' and 'bottom-up'. The top-down technique uses atmospheric GHG concentrations and atmospheric modelling to estimate direct (scope 1) emissions (see Glossary). The bottom-up technique estimates emissions using local activity data or direct measurements such as in smokestacks, traffic data, energy consumption information, and building use. Bottom-up techniques will often include indirect emissions (see Glossary) from purchased electricity (scope 2) and the urban supply chain (scope 3). Inclusion of supply-chain emissions often requires additional data such as consumer purchasing data and supply chain emission factors. Some researchers also take a hybrid approach combining top-down and bottom-up estimation techniques to quantify territorial emissions. Individual self-reported urban inventories from cities have shown chronic underestimation when compared to estimates using combined top-down/bottom-up atmospherically calibrated estimation techniques.

No approach has been systematically applied to all cities worldwide. Rather, they have been applied individually or in combination to subsets of global cities. Considerable uncertainty remains in estimating urban emissions. However, top-down approaches have somewhat more objective techniques for uncertainty estimation in comparison to bottom-up approaches. Furthermore, supply chain estimation typically has more uncertainty than direct or territorial emission frameworks.

References

Abdullah, H., and E. Garcia-Chueca, 2020: Cacophony or Complementarity? The Expanding Ecosystem of City Networks Under Scrutiny. In: *City Diplomacy* [Amiri, S. and E. Sevin, (eds.)]. Palgrave Macmillan, Cham, Switzerland, pp. 37–58.

Abid, H., J. Thakur, D. Khatiwada, and D. Bauner, 2021: Energy storage integration with solar PV for increased electricity access: A case study of Burkina Faso. *Energy*, **230**, 120656, doi:10.1016/j.energy.2021.120656.

Abino, A.C., J.A.A. Castillo, and Y.J. Lee, 2014: Assessment of species diversity, biomass and carbon sequestration potential of a natural mangrove stand in Samar, the Philippines. *Forest Sci. Technol.*, **10(1)**, 2–8, doi:10.1080/215 80103.2013.814593.

Acakpovi, A., R. Abubakar, N.Y. Asabere, and I.B. Majeed, 2019: Barriers and prospects of smart grid adoption in Ghana. *Procedia Manuf.*, **35**, 1240–1249, doi:10.1016/j.promfg.2019.06.082.

Acuto, M. and B. Leffel, 2021: Understanding the global ecosystem of city networks. *Urban Stud.*, **58(9)**, 1758–1774, doi:10.1177/0042098020929261.

Acuto, M., K. Steenmans, E. Iwaszuk, and L. Ortega-Garza, 2019: Informing urban governance? Boundary-spanning organisations and the ecosystem of urban data. *Wiley Online Libr.*, **51(1)**, 94–103, doi:10.1111/area.12430.

Adam, M.G., P.T.M. Tran, and R. Balasubramanian, 2021: Air quality changes in cities during the COVID-19 lockdown: A critical review. *Atmos. Res.*, **264**, 105823, doi:10.1016/j.atmosres.2021.105823.

Adams, E.A., H. Price, and J. Stoler, 2019: Urban slums, drinking water, and health: Trends and lessons from Sub-Saharan Africa. In: *Handbook of Global Urban Health* [Vojnovic, I., A.L. Pearson, A. Gershim, G. DeVerteuil, and A. Allen, (eds.)]. Routledge, New York, NY, USA, pp. 533–552.

Adegun, O.B., 2017: Green infrastructure in relation to informal urban settlements. *J. Archit. Urban.*, **41(1)**, 22–33, doi:10.3846/20297 955.2017.1296791.

Affolderbach, J. and C. Schulz, 2017: Positioning Vancouver through urban sustainability strategies? The Greenest City 2020 Action Plan. *J. Clean. Prod.*, **164**, 676–685, doi:10.1016/j.jclepro.2017.06.234.

Afionis, S., M. Sakai, K. Scott, J. Barrett, and A. Gouldson, 2017: Consumption-based carbon accounting: does it have a future? *Wiley Interdiscip. Rev. Clim. Change*, **8**, e438, doi:10.1002/wcc.438.

Aguiar, F.C. et al., 2018: Adaptation to climate change at local level in Europe: An overview. *Environ. Sci. Policy*, **86**, 38–63, doi:10.1016/j.envsci.2018.04.010.

Agyepong, A.O. and G. Nhamo, 2017: Green procurement in South Africa: perspectives on legislative provisions in metropolitan municipalities. *Environ. Dev. Sustain.*, **19(6)**, 2457–2474, doi:10.1007/s10668-016-9865-9.

Ahlfeldt, G.M. and D.P. McMillen, 2018: Tall buildings and land values: Height and construction cost elasticities in Chicago, 1870-2010. *Rev. Econ. Stat.*, **100(5)**, 861–875, doi:10.1162/rest_a_00734.

Ahlfeldt, G.M. and J. Barr, 2020: Viewing urban spatial history from tall buildings. *Reg. Sci. Urban Econ.*, 103618, doi:10.1016/j.regsciurbeco.2020.103618.

Ahmad, S., H. Jia, Z. Chen, Q. Li, and C. Xu, 2020: Water-energy nexus and energy efficiency: A systematic analysis of urban water systems. *Renew. Sustain. Energy Rev.*, **134**, 110381, doi:10.1016/j.rser.2020.110381.

Ajanovic, A., and R. Haas, 2019: On the environmental benignity of electric vehicles. *J. Sustain. Dev. Energy, Water Environ. Syst.*, **7(3)**, 416–431, doi:10.13044/j.sdewes.d6.0252.

Aklin, M., S.P. Harish, and J. Urpelainen, 2018: A global analysis of progress in household electrification. *Energy Policy*, **122**, 421–428, doi:10.1016/j.enpol.2018.07.018.

Al-Kindi, S.G., R.D. Brook, S. Biswal, and S. Rajagopalan, 2020: Environmental determinants of cardiovascular disease: lessons learned from air pollution. *Nat. Rev. Cardiol.*, **17(10)**, doi:10.1038/s41569-020-0371-2.

Alhamwi, A., W. Medjroubi, T. Vogt, and C. Agert, 2018: Modelling urban energy requirements using open source data and models. *Appl. Energy*, **231**, 1100–1108, doi:10.1016/j.apenergy.2018.09.164.

Allam, Z. and D. Jones, 2019: The Potential of Blockchain within Air Rights Development as a Prevention Measure against Urban Sprawl. *Urban Sci.*, **3(1)**, 38, doi:10.3390/urbansci3010038.

Allan, A., 2020: Book Reviews: Resilient Cities: Overcoming Fossil Fuel Dependence. *Urban Policy Res.*, **38(1)**, 74–79, doi:10.1080/08111 146.2019.1687399.

Álvarez Fernández, R., 2018: A more realistic approach to electric vehicle contribution to greenhouse gas emissions in the city. *J. Clean. Prod.*, **172**, 949–959, doi:10.1016/j.jclepro.2017.10.158.

Alves, A., B. Gersonius, Z. Kapelan, Z. Vojinovic, and A. Sanchez, 2019: Assessing the Co-Benefits of green-blue-grey infrastructure for sustainable urban flood risk management. *J. Environ. Manage.*, **239**, 244–254, doi:10.1016/j.jenvman.2019.03.036.

Alzate-Arias, S., Á. Jaramillo-Duque, F. Villada, and B. Restrepo-Cuestas, 2018: Assessment of government incentives for energy from waste in Colombia. *Sustainability*, **10(4)**, 1294, doi:10.3390/su10041294.

Ambole, A. et al., 2019: Mediating household energy transitions through co-design in urban Kenya, Uganda and South Africa. *Energy Res. Soc. Sci.*, **55**, 208–217, doi:10.1016/j.erss.2019.05.009.

Amundi and IFC, 2021: *Emerging Market Green Bonds Report 2020*. Amundi Asset Management (Amundi) and International Finance Corporation (IFC), Washington, DC, USA, 38 pp.

Andreoni, V., 2021: Estimating the European CO_2 emissions change due to COVID-19 restrictions. *Sci. Total Environ.*, **769**, 145115, doi:10.1016/j.scitotenv.2021.145115.

Andrés-Doménech, I., S. Perales-Momparler, A. Morales-Torres, and I. Escuder-Bueno, 2018: Hydrological Performance of Green Roofs at Building and City Scales under Mediterranean Conditions. *Sustainability*, **10(9)**, 3105, doi:10.3390/su10093105.

Anguelovski, I., C. Irazábal-Zurita, and J.J.T. Connolly, 2019: Grabbed Urban Landscapes: Socio-spatial Tensions in Green Infrastructure Planning in Medellín. *Int. J. Urban Reg. Res.*, **43(1)**, 133–156, doi:10.1111/1468-2427.12725.

Aon, 2021: *Weather, Climate & Catastrophe Insight*. 2020 Annual Report, Aon, Chicago, IL, USA, 81 pp. https://www.aon.com/global-weather-catastrophe-natural-disasters-costs-climate-change-2020-annual-report/index.html?utm_source=prnewswire&utm_medium=mediarelease&utm_campaign=natcat21 (Accessed October 22, 2021).

Araos, M., J. Ford, L. Berrang-Ford, R. Biesbroek, and S. Moser, 2017: Climate change adaptation planning for Global South megacities: the case of Dhaka. *J. Environ. Policy Plan.*, **19(6)**, 682–696, doi:10.1080/15239 08X.2016.1264873.

Archer, D., 2016: Building urban climate resilience through community-driven approaches to development. *Int. J. Clim. Change Strateg. Manag.*, **8(5)**, 654–669, doi:10.1108/IJCCSM-03-2014-0035.

Arias, P.A., N. Bellouin, E. Coppola, R.G. Jones, G. Krinner, J. Marotzke, V. Naik, M.D. Palmer, G.-K. Plattner, J. Rogelj, M. Rojas, J. Sillmann, T. Storelvmo, P.W. Thorne, B. Trewin, K. Achuta Rao, B. Adhikary, R.P. Allan, K. Armour, G. Bala, R. Barimalala, S. Berger, J.G. Canadell, C. Cassou, A. Cherchi, W. Collins, W.D. Collins, S.L. Connors, S. Corti, F. Cruz, F.J. Dentener, C. Dereczynski, A. Di Luca, A. Diongue Niang, F.J. Doblas-Reyes, A. Dosio, H. Douville, F. Engelbrecht, V. Eyring, E. Fischer, P. Forster, B. Fox-Kemper, J.S. Fuglestvedt, J.C. Fyfe, N.P. Gillett, L. Goldfarb, I. Gorodetskaya, J.M. Gutierrez, R. Hamdi, E. Hawkins, H.T. Hewitt, P. Hope, A.S. Islam, C. Jones, D.S. Kaufman, R.E. Kopp, Y. Kosaka, J. Kossin, S. Krakovska, J.-Y. Lee, J. Li, T. Mauritsen, T.K. Maycock, M. Meinshausen, S.-K. Min, P.M.S. Monteiro, T. Ngo-Duc, F. Otto, I. Pinto, A. Pirani, K. Raghavan, R. Ranasinghe, A.C. Ruane,

L. Ruiz, J.-B. Sallée, B.H. Samset, S. Sathyendranath, S.I. Seneviratne, A.A. Sörensson, S. Szopa, I. Takayabu, A.-M. Tréguier, B. van den Hurk, R. Vautard, K. von Schuckmann, S. Zaehle, X. Zhang, and K. Zickfeld, 2021: Technical Summary. In *Climate Change 2021: The Physical Science Basis. Contribution of Working Group I to the Sixth Assessment Report of the Intergovernmental Panel on Climate Change* [Masson-Delmotte, V., P. Zhai, A. Pirani, S.L. Connors, C. Péan, S. Berger, N. Caud, Y. Chen, L. Goldfarb, M.I. Gomis, M. Huang, K. Leitzell, E. Lonnoy, J.B.R. Matthews, T.K. Maycock, T. Waterfield, O. Yelekçi, R. Yu, and B. Zhou (eds.)]. Cambridge University Press, Cambridge, UK, and New York, NY, USA.

Arioli, M.S., M. de A. D'Agosto, F.G. Amaral, and H.B.B. Cybis, 2020: The evolution of city-scale GHG emissions inventory methods: A systematic review. *Environ. Impact Assess. Rev.*, **80**, 106316, doi:10.1016/j.eiar.2019.106316.

Asarpota, K. and V. Nadin, 2020: Energy strategies, the Urban dimension, and spatial planning. *Energies*, **13(14)**, 3642, doi:10.3390/en13143642.

Ataöv, A. and E. Peker, 2021: Co-designing Local Climate Action: A Methodological Framework from a Democratic Perspective. In: *Governance of Climate Responsive Cities. The Urban Book Series* [Ataöv, A. and E. Peker, (eds.)]. Springer, Cham, Switzerland, pp. 147–164.

Austin, K.G., A. Schwantes, Y. Gu, and P.S. Kasibhatla, 2019: What causes deforestation in Indonesia? *Environ. Res. Lett.*, **14(2)**, 024007, doi:10.1088/1748-9326/AAF6DB.

Ayerakwa, H.M., 2017: Urban households' engagement in agriculture: implications for household food security in Ghana's medium sized cities. *Geogr. Res.*, **55(2)**, 217–230, doi:10.1111/1745-5871.12205.

Azunre, G.A., O. Amponsah, S.A. Takyi, and H. Mensah, 2021: Informality-sustainable city nexus: The place of informality in advancing sustainable Ghanaian cities. *Sustain. Cities Soc.*, **67**, 102707, doi:10.1016/j.scs.2021.102707.

Bačeković, I. and P.A. Østergaard, 2018: A smart energy system approach vs a non-integrated renewable energy system approach to designing a future energy system in Zagreb. *Energy*, **155**, 824–837, doi:10.1016/j.energy.2018.05.075.

Baeumler, A., E. Ijjasz-Vasquez, and S. Mehndiratta, 2012: *Sustainable Low-Carbon City Development in China*. [Baeumler, A., E. Ijjasz-Vasquez, and S. Mehndiratta, (eds.)]. The World Bank, Washington, DC, USA, 516 pp.

Bagheri, M., S.H. Delbari, M. Pakzadmanesh, and C.A. Kennedy, 2019: City-integrated renewable energy design for low-carbon and climate-resilient communities. *Appl. Energy*, **239**, 1212–1225, doi:10.1016/j.apenergy.2019.02.031.

Bai, X. et al., 2016: Defining and advancing a systems approach for sustainable cities. *Curr. Opin. Environ. Sustain.*, **23**, 69–78, doi:10.1016/j.cosust.2016.11.010.

Bai, X. et al., 2018: Six research priorities for cities and climate change. *Nature*, **555(7694)**, 23–25, doi:10.1038/d41586-018-02409-z.

Bain, P.G. et al., 2016: Co-benefits of addressing climate change can motivate action around the world. *Nat. Clim. Change*, **6(2)**, 154–157, doi:10.1038/nclimate2814.

Baiocchi, G., F. Creutzig, J. Minx, and P.P. Pichler, 2015: A spatial typology of human settlements and their CO2 emissions in England. *Glob. Environ. Change*, **34**, 13–21, doi:10.1016/j.gloenvcha.2015.06.001.

Bakır, Y., D. Neşe, K. Umut, M. Güngör, and B. Bostancı, 2018: Planned development versus unplanned change: The effects on urban planning in Turkey. *Land use policy*, **77**, 310–321, doi:10.1016/j.landusepol.2018.05.036.

Bartolozzi, I., F. Rizzi, and M. Frey, 2017: Are district heating systems and renewable energy sources always an environmental win-win solution? A life cycle assessment case study in Tuscany, Italy. *Renew. Sustain. Energy Rev.*, **80(C)**, 408–420, doi:10.1016/j.rser.2017.05.231.

Battiston, S., I. Monasterolo, K. Riahi, and B.J. van Ruijven, 2021: Accounting for finance is key for climate mitigation pathways. *Science*, **372(6545)**, 918–920, doi:10.1126/science.abf3877.

Baur, A.H., M. Förster, and B. Kleinschmit, 2015: The spatial dimension of urban greenhouse gas emissions: analyzing the influence of spatial structures and LULC patterns in European cities. *Landsc. Ecol.*, **30(7)**, 1195–1205, doi:10.1007/s10980-015-0169-5.

Baurzhan, S. and G.P. Jenkins, 2016: An economic appraisal of solar versus combined cycle electricity generation for African countries that are capital constrained. *Energy Environ.*, **27(2)**, 241–256, doi:10.1177/0958305X15627546.

Beermann, J., A. Damodaran, K. Jörgensen, and M.A. Schreurs, 2016: Climate action in Indian cities: an emerging new research area. *J. Integr. Environ. Sci.*, **13(1)**, 55–66, doi:10.1080/1943815X.2015.1130723.

Bellinson, R. and E. Chu, 2019: Learning pathways and the governance of innovations in urban climate change resilience and adaptation. *J. Environ. Policy Plan.*, **21(1)**, 76–89, doi:10.1080/1523908X.2018.1493916.

Belzunegui-Eraso, A. and A. Erro-Garcés, 2020: Teleworking in the context of the Covid-19 crisis. *Sustainability*, **12(9)**, 3662, doi:10.3390/su12093662.

Bernstad Saraiva Schott, A. and A. Cánovas, 2015: Current practice, challenges and potential methodological improvements in environmental evaluations of food waste prevention – A discussion paper. *Resour. Conserv. Recycl.*, **101**, 132–142, doi:10.1016/j.resconrec.2015.05.004.

Berrisford, S., L.R. Cirolia, and I. Palmer, 2018: Land-based financing in sub-Saharan African cities. *Environ. Urban.*, **30(1)**, 35–52, doi:10.1177/0956247817753525.

Berry, B.L.J., 1964: Cities as Systems within Systems of Cities. *Pap. Reg. Sci. Assoc.*, **13**, 146–163, doi:10.1007/BF01942566.

Berry, P.M. et al., 2015: Cross-sectoral interactions of adaptation and mitigation measures. *Clim. Change*, **128(3)**, 381–393, doi:10.1007/s10584-014-1214-0.

Besir, A.B. and E. Cuce, 2018: Green roofs and facades: A comprehensive review. *Renew. Sustain. Energy Rev.*, **82(Part 1)**, 915–939, doi:10.1016/j.rser.2017.09.106.

Bevilacqua, P., D. Mazzeo, R. Bruno, and A. Natale, 2016: Experimental investigation of the thermal performances of an extensive green roof in the Mediterranean area. *Energy Build.*, **122**, 63–79, doi:10.1016/j.enbuild.2016.03.062.

Beygo, K., and M.A. Yüzer, 2017: Early energy simulation of urban plans and building forms. *A/Z: ITU J. Fac. Archit.*, **14(1)**, 13–23, doi:10.5505/itujfa.2017.67689.

Bhattacharya, A., J. Meltzer, J. Oppenheim, Z. Qureshi, and N. Stern, 2016: *Delivering on Sustainable Infrastructure for Better Development and Better Climate*. The Brookings Institution, The New Climate Economy (NCE), and the Grantham Research Institute on Climate Change and the Environment, Washington, DC, USA, 160 pp. https://www.brookings.edu/wp-content/uploads/2016/12/global_122316_delivering-on-sustainable-infrastructure.pdf (Accessed June 7, 2019).

Bibri, S.E., 2020: Compact urbanism and the synergic potential of its integration with data-driven smart urbanism: An extensive interdisciplinary literature review. *Land use policy*, **97**, 104703, doi:10.1016/j.landusepol.2020.104703.

Bielenberg, A., M. Kerlin, J. Oppenheim, and M. Roberts, 2016: *Financing change: How to mobilize private sector financing for sustainable infrastructure*. McKinsey Center for Business and Environment, Washington DC, USA, 68 pp. https://newclimateeconomy.report/workingpapers/wp-content/uploads/sites/5/2016/04/Financing_change_How_to_mobilize_private-sector_financing_for_sustainable-_infrastructure.pdf (Accessed March 31, 2021).

Birkmann, J., T. Welle, W. Solecki, S. Lwasa, and M. Garschagen, 2016: Boost resilience of small and mid-sized cities. *Nature*, **537**, 605–608, doi:10.1038/537605a.

Bisaro, A. and J. Hinkel, 2018: Mobilizing private finance for coastal adaptation: A literature review. *WIREs Clim. Change*, **9(3)**, doi:10.1002/wcc.514.

Bjørkelund, O.A., H. Degerud, and E. Bere, 2016: Socio-demographic, personal, environmental and behavioral correlates of different modes of transportation to work among Norwegian parents. *Arch. Public Heal.*, **74(43)**, doi:10.1186/s13690-016-0155-7.

Blais, A.-M., S. Lorrain, Y. Plourde, and L. Varfalvy, 2005: Organic Carbon Densities of Soils and Vegetation of Tropical, Temperate and Boreal Forests. In: *Greenhouse Gas Emissions — Fluxes and Processes* [Tremblay, A., L. Varfalvy, C. Roehm, and M. Garneau, (eds.)]. Springer-Verlag, Berlin and Heidelberg, Germany, pp. 155–185.

Blanchet, T., 2015: Struggle over energy transition in Berlin: How do grassroots initiatives affect local energy policy-making? *Energy Policy*, **78**, 246–254, doi:10.1016/j.enpol.2014.11.001.

Blanco, H., and A. Wikstrom, 2018: *Transit-Oriented Development Opportunities Among Failing Malls*. National Center for Sustainable Transportation (NCST), Davis, CA, USA, 25 pp.

Blanco, H., P. McCarney, S. Parnell, M. Schmidt, and K.C. Seto, 2011: The Role of Urban Land in Climate Change. In: *Climate Change and Cities: First Assessment Report of the Urban Climate Change Research Network* [Rosenzweig, C., W.D. Solecki, S.A. Hammer, and S. Mehrotra, (eds.)]. Cambridge University Press, Cambridge, UK, pp. 217–248.

Blay-Palmer, A., D. Conaré, K. Meter, and A. Di Battista, 2019: *Sustainable food system assessment: lessons from global practice*. 1st ed. [Blay-Palmer, A., D. Conaré, K. Meter, A. Di Battista, and J. Carla, (eds.)]. Routledge, London, UK, 282 pp.

Blok, K., N. Höhne, K. van der Leun, and N. Harrison, 2012: Bridging the greenhouse-gas emissions gap. *Nat. Clim. Change*, **2(7)**, 471–474, doi:10.1038/nclimate1602.

Bogdanov, D., A. Gulagi, M. Fasihi, and C. Breyer, 2021: Full energy sector transition towards 100% renewable energy supply: Integrating power, heat, transport and industry sectors including desalination. *Appl. Energy*, **283**, 116273, doi:10.1016/j.apenergy.2020.116273.

Boltz, M., K. Marazyan, and P. Villar, 2019: Income hiding and informal redistribution: A lab-in-the-field experiment in Senegal. *J. Dev. Econ.*, **137**, 78–92, doi:10.1016/j.jdeveco.2018.11.004.

Borjas, G., 2020: *Demographic Determinants of Testing Incidence and COVID-19 Infections in New York City Neighborhoods*. National Bureau of Economic Research (NBER), Cambridge, MA, USA, 29 pp.

Bouteligier, S., 2013: Inequality in new global governance arrangements: the North-South divide in transnational municipal networks. *Innovation*, **26(3)**, 251–267, doi:10.1080/13511610.2013.771890.

Boyer, D. and A. Ramaswami, 2017: What Is the Contribution of City-Scale Actions to the Overall Food System's Environmental Impacts?: Assessing Water, Greenhouse Gas, and Land Impacts of Future Urban Food Scenarios. *Environ. Sci. Technol.*, **51(20)**, 12035–12045, doi:10.1021/acs.est.7b03176.

Brand, C. et al., 2021: The climate change mitigation impacts of active travel: Evidence from a longitudinal panel study in seven European cities. *Glob. Environ. Change*, **67**, 102224, doi:10.1016/j.gloenvcha.2021.102224.

Braun, G. and S. Hazelroth, 2015: Energy Infrastructure Finance: Local Dollars for Local Energy. *Electr. J.*, **28(5)**, 6–21, doi:10.1016/j.tej.2015.05.008.

Brenna, M., A. Dolara, F. Foiadelli, S. Leva, and M. Longo, 2014: Urban Scale Photovoltaic Charging Stations for Electric Vehicles. *IEEE Trans. Sustain. Energy*, **5(4)**, 1234–1241, doi:10.1109/TSTE.2014.2341954.

Broekhoff, D., P. Erickson, and C. Lee, 2015: *What cities do best: Piecing together an efficient global climate governance*. Stockholm Environment Institute (SEI), Seattle, WA, USA, 38 pp. https://mediamanager.sei.org/documents/Publications/Climate/SEI-WP-2015-15-Cities-vertical-climate-governance.pdf (Accessed March 31, 2021).

Brown, A.M., 2015: Sustaining African Cities: Urban Hunger and Sustainable Development in East Africa. *Int. J. Environ. Cult. Econ. Soc. Sustain. Annu. Rev.*, **11**, 1–12, doi:10.18848/1832-2077/cgp/v11/55133.

Brown, D. and G. McGranahan, 2016: The urban informal economy, local inclusion and achieving a global green transformation. *Habitat Int.*, **53**, 97–105, doi:10.1016/j.habitatint.2015.11.002.

Brozynski, M.T. and B.D. Leibowicz, 2018: Decarbonizing power and transportation at the urban scale: An analysis of the Austin, Texas Community Climate Plan. *Sustain. Cities Soc.*, **43**, 41–54, doi:10.1016/j.scs.2018.08.005.

BSI, 2013: *PAS 2070: Incorporating Amendment No. 1: Specification for the assessment of greenhouse gas emissions of a city: direct plus supply chain and consumption-based methodologies*. BSI Standards Limited, London, UK, 26 pp.

Buchner, B. et al., 2019: *Global Landscape of Climate Finance 2019*. Climate Policy Initiative (CPI), London, UK, 36 pp.

Bucsky, P., 2020: Modal share changes due to COVID-19: The case of Budapest. *Transp. Res. Interdiscip. Perspect.*, **8**, 100141, doi:10.1016/j.trip.2020.100141.

Buffa, S., M. Cozzini, M. D'Antoni, M. Baratieri, and R. Fedrizzi, 2019: 5th generation district heating and cooling systems: A review of existing cases in Europe. *Renew. Sustain. Energy Rev.*, **104**, 504–522, doi:10.1016/j.rser.2018.12.059.

Bulkeley, H. et al., 2012: Governing Climate Change Transnationally: Assessing the Evidence from a Database of Sixty Initiatives. *Environ. Plan. C Gov. Policy*, **30(4)**, 591–612, doi:10.1068/c11126.

Buonocore, J.J. et al., 2016: Health and climate benefits of different energy-efficiency and renewable energy choices. *Nat. Clim. Change*, **6**, 100–106, doi:10.1038/nclimate2771.

Butcher-Gollach, C., 2018: Planning and Urban Informality—Addressing Inclusiveness for Climate Resilience in the Pacific. In: *Climate Change Impacts and Adaptation Strategies for Coastal Communities* [Filho, W.L., (ed.)]. Springer International Publishing, Cham, Switzerland, pp. 43–68.

Butler, D. et al., 2014: A New Approach to Urban Water Management: Safe and Sure. *16th Conference on Water Distribution System Analysis*. Procedia Engineering, Vol. 89, Bari, Italy, pp. 347–354.

Buyana, K., D. Byarugaba, H. Sseviiri, G. Nsangi, and P. Kasaija, 2019: Experimentation in an African Neighborhood: Reflections for Transitions to Sustainable Energy in Cities. *Urban Forum*, **30(2)**, 191–204, doi:10.1007/s12132-018-9358-z.

Byrne, J. and J. Taminiau, 2016: A review of sustainable energy utility and energy service utility concepts and applications: realizing ecological and social sustainability with a community utility. *Wiley Interdiscip. Rev. Energy Environ.*, **5(2)**, 136–154, doi:10.1002/wene.171.

Byrne, J., J. Taminiau, K.N. Kim, J. Lee, and J. Seo, 2017: Multivariate analysis of solar city economics: impact of energy prices, policy, finance, and cost on urban photovoltaic power plant implementation. *Wiley Interdiscip. Rev. Energy Environ.*, **6(4)**, doi:10.1002/wene.241.

C40 Cities, 2018: *Benefits of Urban Climate Action: C40 Cities Technical Assistance Report 2018 - Quito*. C40 Cities, 5 pp. https://c40.ent.box.com/s/fpxk4j5xjhxrewbpyer6ciuk38cpc5t2 (Accessed March 28, 2021).

C40 Cities, 2020: 1,000 cities racing to zero emissions. *UNFCCC Race to Zero*, November 9. https://racetozero.unfccc.int/1000-cities-racing-to-zero-emissions/ (Accessed January 6, 2021).

C40 Cities, 2020b: *Benefits of Urban Climate Action: C40 Cities Technical Assistance Report 2019 - Rio de Janeiro*. C40 Cities, 5 pp. https://c40.ent.box.com/s/pllwmupmsdro15jabnmez7lwv3krtl6w (Accessed March 28, 2021).

C40 Cities, 2020c: *Benefits of Urban Climate Action: C40 Cities Technical Assistance Report July 2020 - Bengaluru Electric Buses*. C40 Cities, 5 pp. https://c40.ent.box.com/s/vg8galdyb108lcaar6luwvub4wz78tpm (Accessed March 30, 2021).

C40 Cities, 2020d: *Benefits of Urban Climate Action: C40 Cities Technical Assistance Report 2020 - Jakarta Electric Buses*. C40 Cities, 6 pp. https://c40.ent.box.com/s/5ochjfppuprp7bl08z00w4cl8ybwpjcb (Accessed March 28, 2021).

C40 Cities, 2020e: *Benefits of Urban Climate Action: C40 Cities Technical Assistance Report May 2020 - Medellín Electric Buses*. C40 Cities, 5 pp. https://c40.ent.box.com/s/n8qnv8tbiyc6tlbxibem280p1tlol7yr (Accessed March 28, 2021).

C40 Cities, ARUP, and University of Leeds, 2019: *The Future of Urban Consumption in a 1.5C World - C40 Cities Headline Report*. C40 Cities, ARUP, and the University of Leeds, New York, NY, USA, 133 pp. https://www.c40.org/wp-content/uploads/2021/08/2270_C40_CBE_MainReport_250719.original.pdf (Accessed March 28, 2021).

Cai, B. et al., 2019: China city-level greenhouse gas emissions inventory in 2015 and uncertainty analysis. *Appl. Energy*, **253**, 113579, doi:10.1016/j.apenergy.2019.113579.

Caldarice, O., N. Tollin, and M. Pizzorni, 2021: The relevance of science-policy-practice dialogue. Exploring the urban climate resilience governance in Italy. *City, Territ. Archit.*, **8(9)**, doi:10.1186/s40410-021-00137-y.

Calderón Márquez, A.J. and E.W. Rutkowski, 2020: Waste management drivers towards a circular economy in the global south – The Colombian case. *Waste Manag.*, **110**, 53–65, doi:10.1016/J.WASMAN.2020.05.016.

Calthorpe, P., 1993: *The Next American Metropolis: Ecology, Community, and the American Dream*. Princeton Architectural Press, Princeton, NJ, USA, 180 pp.

Calvillo, C.F., A. Sánchez-Miralles, and J. Villar, 2016: Energy management and planning in smart cities. *Renew. Sustain. Energy Rev.*, **55**, 273–287, doi:10.1016/j.rser.2015.10.133.

Calvin, K. et al., 2017: The SSP4: A world of deepening inequality. *Glob. Environ. Change*, **42**, 284–296, doi:10.1016/j.gloenvcha.2016.06.010.

Cambou, A. et al., 2018: Estimation of soil organic carbon stocks of two cities, New York City and Paris. *Sci. Total Environ.*, **644**, 452–464, doi:10.1016/j.scitotenv.2018.06.322.

Cao, X., and W. Yang, 2017: Examining the effects of the built environment and residential self-selection on commuting trips and the related CO_2 emissions: An empirical study in Guangzhou, China. *Transp. Res. Part D Transp. Environ.*, **52(B)**, 480–494, doi:10.1016/j.trd.2017.02.003.

Carpio, M., J. Roldán-Fontana, R. Pacheco-Torres, and J. Ordóñez, 2016: Construction waste estimation depending on urban planning options in the design stage of residential buildings. *Constr. Build. Mater.*, **113**, 561–570, doi:10.1016/j.conbuildmat.2016.03.061.

Carreiro, M.M., R.V. Pouyat, C.E. Tripler, and W.X. Zhu, 2009: Carbon and nitrogen cycling in soils of remnant forests along urban–rural gradients: Case studies in the New York metropolitan area and Louisville, Kentucky. In: *Ecology of Cities and Towns: A Comparative Approach* [McDonnell, M.J., A.K. Hahs, and J.H. Breuste, (eds.)]. Cambridge University Press, Cambridge, UK, pp. 308–328.

Carter, T.R. et al., 2021: A conceptual framework for cross-border impacts of climate change. *Glob. Environ. Change*, **69**, 102307, doi:10.1016/j.gloenvcha.2021.102307.

Castán Broto, V., 2017a: Energy landscapes and urban trajectories towards sustainability. *Energy Policy*, **108**, 755–764, doi:10.1016/j.enpol.2017.01.009.

Castán Broto, V., 2017b: Urban Governance and the Politics of Climate change. *World Dev.*, **93**, 1–15, doi:10.1016/j.worlddev.2016.12.031.

Cazzola, P. et al., 2019: *Global EV Outlook 2019: Scaling up the transition to electric mobility*. Organisation for Economic Co-operation and Development (OECD) and International Energy Agency (IEA), Paris, France, 232 pp. https://www.iea.org/reports/global-ev-outlook-2019 (Accessed March 31, 2021).

CCFLA, 2015: *The State of City Climate Finance 2015*. Cities Climate Finance Leadership Alliance (CCFLA), New York, NY, USA, 65 pp. https://sustainabledevelopment.un.org/content/documents/2201CCFLA-State-of-City-Climate-Finance-2015.pdf (Accessed March 31, 2021).

Chan, S. et al., 2015: Reinvigorating International Climate Policy: A Comprehensive Framework for Effective Nonstate Action. *Glob. Policy*, **6(4)**, 466–473, doi:10.1111/1758-5899.12294.

Chan, S., R. Falkner, M. Goldberg, and H. van Asselt, 2018: Effective and geographically balanced? An output-based assessment of non-state climate actions. *Clim. Policy*, **18(1)**, 24–35, doi:10.1080/14693062.2016.1248343.

Chang, K.M. et al., 2017: Ancillary health effects of climate mitigation scenarios as drivers of policy uptake: a review of air quality, transportation and diet co-benefits modeling studies. *Environ. Res. Lett.*, **12(11)**, 113001, doi:10.1088/1748-9326/aa8f7b.

Chapman, J., 2017: Value Capture Taxation as an Infrastructure Funding Technique. *Public Work. Manag. Policy*, **22(1)**, 31–37, doi:10.1177/1087724X16670395.

Charani Shandiz, S., B. Rismanchi, and G. Foliente, 2021: Energy master planning for net-zero emission communities: State of the art and research challenges. *Renew. Sustain. Energy Rev.*, **137**, 110600, doi:10.1016/j.rser.2020.110600.

Chava, J., and P. Newman, 2016: Stakeholder deliberation on developing affordable housing strategies: Towards inclusive and sustainable transit-oriented developments. *Sustainability*, **8(10)**, 11–13, doi:10.3390/su8101024.

Chavez, A., and A. Ramaswami, 2013: Articulating a trans-boundary infrastructure supply chain greenhouse gas emission footprint for cities: Mathematical relationships and policy relevance. *Energy Policy*, **54**, 376–384, doi:10.1016/j.enpol.2012.10.037.

Chen, C. et al., 2019a: Energy consumption and carbon footprint accounting of urban and rural residents in Beijing through Consumer Lifestyle Approach. *Ecol. Indic.*, **98**, 575–586, doi:10.1016/j.ecolind.2018.11.049.

Chen, G., T. Wiedmann, Y. Wang, and M. Hadjikakou, 2016: Transnational city carbon footprint networks – Exploring carbon links between Australian and Chinese cities. *Appl. Energy*, **184**, 1082–1092, doi:10.1016/j.apenergy.2016.08.053.

Chen, G., M. Hadjikakou, T. Wiedmann, and L. Shi, 2018a: Global warming impact of suburbanization: The case of Sydney. *J. Clean. Prod.*, **172**, 287–301, doi:10.1016/j.jclepro.2017.10.161.

Chen, G. et al., 2019b: Review on City-Level Carbon Accounting. *Environ. Sci. Technol.*, **53(10)**, 5545–5558, doi:10.1021/acs.est.8b07071.

Chen, G. et al., 2020a: Global projections of future urban land expansion under shared socioeconomic pathways. *Nat. Commun.*, **11**, 537, doi:10.1038/s41467-020-14386-x.

Chen, Q. et al., 2017: CO2 emission data for Chinese cities. *Resour. Conserv. Recycl.*, **126**, 198–208, doi:10.1016/j.resconrec.2017.07.011.

Chen, S., B. Xu, and B. Chen, 2018b: Unfolding the interplay between carbon flows and socioeconomic development in a city: What can network analysis offer? *Appl. Energy*, **211**, 403–412, doi:10.1016/j.apenergy.2017.11.064.

Chen, S. et al., 2020b: Physical and virtual carbon metabolism of global cities. *Nat. Commun.*, **11**, 219–235, doi:10.1038/s41467-019-13757-3.

Chen, T.L., H.W. Chiu, and Y.F. Lin, 2020c: How do East and Southeast Asian cities differ from Western cities? A systematic review of the urban form characteristics. *Sustainability*, **12(6)**, doi:10.3390/su12062423.

Cheshmehzangi, A., and C. Butters, 2017: Chinese urban residential blocks: Towards improved environmental and living qualities. *Urban Des. Int.*, **22(3)**, 219–235, doi:10.1057/s41289-016-0013-9.

Chester, M.V., 2019: Sustainability and infrastructure challenges. *Nat. Sustain.*, **2(4)**, 265–266, doi:10.1038/s41893-019-0272-8.

Chifari, R., S. Lo Piano, S. Matsumoto, and T. Tasaki, 2017: Does recyclable separation reduce the cost of municipal waste management in Japan? *Waste Manag.*, **60**, 32–41, doi:10.1016/j.wasman.2017.01.015.

Chirambo, D., 2021: Corporate Sector Policy Innovations for Sustainable Development Goals (SDGs) Implementation in the Global South: The Case of sub-Saharan Africa. *Hapres J. Sustain. Res.*, **3(2)**, e210011, doi:10.20900/jsr20210011.

Choi, K., 2018: The influence of the built environment on household vehicle travel by the urban typology in Calgary, Canada. *Cities*, **75**, 101–110, doi:10.1016/j.cities.2018.01.006.

Christaller, W., 1933: *Die zentralen Orte in Suddeutschland*. Prentice Hall.

Chu, E., 2016: The political economy of urban climate adaptation and development planning in Surat, India. *Environ. Plan. C Gov. Policy*, **34(2)**, 281–298, doi:10.1177/0263774X15614174.

Chu, E., S. Hughes, and S.G. Mason, 2018: Conclusion: Multilevel Governance and Climate Change Innovations in Cities. In: *Climate Change in Cities: Innovations in Multi-Level Governance* [Hughes, S., E.K. Chu, and S.G. Mason, (eds.)]. Springer, Cham, Switzerland, pp. 361–378.

Chu, E. et al., 2019: *Unlocking the Potential for Transformative Climate Adaptation in Cities*. World Resources Institute (WRI), Washington, DC, USA and Rotterdam, The Netherlands, 76 pp. https://gca.org/wp-content/uploads/2020/12/UnlockingThePotentialForTransformativeAdaptationInCities.pdf (Accessed October 22, 2021).

Church, C., and A. Crawford, 2018: *Green Conflict Minerals: The fuels of conflict in the transition to a low-carbon economy*. International Institute for Sustainable Development (IISD), Winnipeg, Canada, 49 pp. https://www.iisd.org/system/files/publications/green-conflict-minerals.pdf (Accessed March 28, 2021).

Churkina, G., 2008: Modeling the carbon cycle of urban systems. *Ecol. Modell.*, **216(2)**, 107–113, doi:10.1016/j.ecolmodel.2008.03.006.

Churkina, G., 2012: Carbonization of Urban Areas. In: *Recarbonization of the Biosphere: Ecosystems and the Global Carbon Cycle* [Lal, R., K. Lorenz, R.F. Hüttl, B.U. Schneider, and J. Von Braun, (eds.)]. Springer Netherlands, Dordrecht, The Netherlands, pp. 369–382.

Churkina, G. et al., 2020: Buildings as a global carbon sink. *Nat. Sustain.*, **3(4)**, 269–276, doi:10.1038/s41893-019-0462-4.

Cirolia, L.R., 2020: Fractured fiscal authority and fragmented infrastructures: Financing sustainable urban development in Sub-Saharan Africa. *Habitat Int.*, **104**, 102233, doi:10.1016/j.habitatint.2020.102233.

Cities for Climate, 2015: *Paris City Hall Declaration: A Decisive Contribution to COP21*. Climate Summit for Local Leaders, Paris, France, https://www.uclg.org/sites/default/files/climate_summit_final_declaration.pdf (Accessed October 31, 2021).

Claude, S., S. Ginestet, M. Bonhomme, N. Moulène, and G. Escadeillas, 2017: The Living Lab methodology for complex environments: Insights from the thermal refurbishment of a historical district in the city of Cahors, France. *Energy Res. Soc. Sci.*, **32**, 121–130, doi:10.1016/j.erss.2017.01.018.

Coalition for Urban Transitions, 2019: *Climate Emergency, Urban Opportunity*. C40 Cities Climate Leadership Group and World Resources Institute (WRI) Ross Center for Sustainable Cities, London, UK and Washington, DC, USA, 160 pp. https://urbantransitions.global/wp-content/uploads/2019/09/Climate-Emergency-Urban-Opportunity-report.pdf (Accessed March 28, 2021).

Coalition for Urban Transitions, 2020: *Seizing the Urban Opportunity: Supporting National Governments to Unlock the Economic Power of Low Carbon, Resilient and Inclusive Cities*. Coalition for Urban Transitions (CUT), Washington, DC, USA, 48 pp. https://urbantransitions.global/wp-content/uploads/2020/10/Seizing_the_Urban_Opportunity_web_FINAL.pdf (Accessed March 28, 2021).

Cole, M.B., M.A. Augustin, M.J. Robertson, and J.M. Manners, 2018: The science of food security. *npj Sci. Food*, **2**, 14, doi:10.1038/s41538-018-0021-9.

Colenbrander, S., A. Gouldson, A.H. Sudmant, and E. Papargyropoulou, 2015: The economic case for low-carbon development in rapidly growing developing world cities: A case study of Palembang, Indonesia. *Energy Policy*, **80**, 24–35, doi:10.1016/j.enpol.2015.01.020.

Colenbrander, S. et al., 2016: Exploring the economic case for early investment in climate change mitigation in middle-income countries: a case study of Johor Bahru, Malaysia. *Clim. Dev.*, **8(4)**, 351–364, doi:10.1080/17565529.2015.1040367.

Colenbrander, S. et al., 2017: Can low-carbon urban development be pro-poor? The case of Kolkata, India. *Environ. Urban.*, **29(1)**, 139–158, doi:10.1177/0956247816677775.

Colenbrander, S., D. Dodman, and D. Mitlin, 2018a: Using climate finance to advance climate justice: the politics and practice of channelling resources to the local level. *Clim. Policy*, **18(7)**, 902–915, doi:10.1080/14693062.2017.1388212.

Colenbrander, S., M. Lindfield, J. Lufkin, and N. Quijano, 2018b: *Financing Low-Carbon, Climate-Resilient Cities*. Coalition for Urban Transitions (CUT), London, UK and Washington, DC, USA, 44 pp. https://www.researchgate.net/publication/323560614_Financing_Low-Carbon_Climate-Resilient_Cities (Accessed May 20, 2019).

Colenbrander, S., A. Sudmant, N. Chilundika, and A. Gouldson, 2019: The scope for low-carbon development in Kigali, Rwanda: An economic appraisal. *Sustain. Dev.*, **27(3)**, 349–365, doi:10.1002/sd.1906.

Collaço, F.M. de A. et al., 2019: The dawn of urban energy planning – Synergies between energy and urban planning for São Paulo (Brazil) megacity. *J. Clean. Prod.*, **215**, 458–479, doi:10.1016/j.jclepro.2019.01.013.

Conke, L.S., 2018: Barriers to waste recycling development: Evidence from Brazil. *Resour. Conserv. Recycl.*, **134**, 129–135, doi:10.1016/j.resconrec.2018.03.007.

Corbett, J., and S. Mellouli, 2017: Winning the SDG battle in cities: how an integrated information ecosystem can contribute to the achievement of the 2030 sustainable development goals. *Inf. Syst. J.*, **27(4)**, 427–461, doi:10.1111/isj.12138.

Corfee-Morlot, J. et al., 2009: *Cities, Climate Change and Multilevel Governance*. Organisation for Economic Co-operation and Development (OECD), Paris, France, 123 pp. https://www.oecd.org/env/cc/44242293.pdf (Accessed March 20, 2021).

Corsini, F., C. Certomà, M. Dyer, and M. Frey, 2019: Participatory energy: Research, imaginaries and practices on people' contribute to energy systems in the smart city. *Technol. Forecast. Soc. Change*, **142**, 322–332, doi:10.1016/j.techfore.2018.07.028.

CPI and World Bank, 2021: *The State of Cities Climate Finance Executive Summary*. Climate Policy Initiative (CPI) and The World Bank, San Francisco, CA, USA, 16 pp.

Creutzig, F., 2016: Evolving Narratives of Low-Carbon Futures in Transportation. *Transp. Rev.*, **36(3)**, 341–360, doi:10.1080/01441647.2015.1079277.

Creutzig, F., G. Baiocchi, R. Bierkandt, P.-P. Pichler, and K.C. Seto, 2015: Global typology of urban energy use and potentials for an urbanization mitigation wedge. *PNAS*, **112(20)**, 6283–6288, doi:10.1073/pnas.1315545112.

Creutzig, F. et al., 2016a: Urban infrastructure choices structure climate solutions. *Nat. Clim. Change*, **6(12)**, 1054–1056, doi:10.1038/nclimate3169.

Creutzig, F. et al., 2016b: Beyond Technology: Demand-Side Solutions for Climate Change Mitigation. *Annu. Rev. Environ. Resour.*, **41**, 173–198, doi:10.1146/annurev-environ-110615-085428.

Creutzig, F. et al., 2019: Upscaling urban data science for global climate solutions. *Glob. Sustain.*, **2**, e2, doi:10.1017/sus.2018.16.

Creutzig, F., X. Bai, R. Khosla, V. Viguie, and Y. Yamagata, 2020: Systematizing and upscaling urban climate change mitigation. *Environ. Res. Lett.*, **15(10)**, 100202, doi:10.1088/1748-9326/abb0b2.

Culwick, C. et al., 2019: CityLab reflections and evolutions: nurturing knowledge and learning for urban sustainability through co-production experimentation. *Curr. Opin. Environ. Sustain.*, **39**, 9–16, doi:10.1016/j.cosust.2019.05.008.

D'Adamo, I., P.M. Falcone, D. Huisingh, and P. Morone, 2021: A circular economy model based on biomethane: What are the opportunities for the municipality of Rome and beyond? *Renew. Energy*, **163**, 1660–1672, doi:10.1016/j.renene.2020.10.072.

d'Amour, C.B. et al., 2017: Future urban land expansion and implications for global croplands. *Proc. Natl. Acad. Sci.*, **114(34)**, 8939–8944, doi:10.1073/PNAS.1606036114.

Dagnachew, A.G., P.L. Lucas, A.F. Hof, and D.P. van Vuuren, 2018: Trade-offs and synergies between universal electricity access and climate change mitigation in Sub-Saharan Africa. *Energy Policy*, **114**, 355–366, doi:10.1016/j.enpol.2017.12.023.

Dalziel, B.D. et al., 2018: Urbanization and humidity shape the intensity of influenza epidemics in U.S. cities. *Science*, **362(6410)**, 75–79, doi:10.1126/science.aat6030.

Data-Driven EnviroLab and NewClimate Institute, 2020: *Accelerating Net Zero: Exploring Cities, Regions, and Companies' Pledges to Decarbonise*. [Hsu, A. et al., (eds.)]. New Climate Institute, Singapore, 24 pp.

http://datadrivenlab.org/wp-content/uploads/2020/09/Accelerating_Net_Zero_Report_Sept2020.pdf (Accessed March 28, 2021).

Data Driven Yale, NewClimate Institute, and PBL, 2018: *Global climate action of regions, states and businesses*. [Hsu, A. et al., (eds.)]. Data Driven Yale, NewClimate Institute, PBL Netherlands Environmental Assessment Agency, 107 pp. http://bit.ly/yale-nci-pbl-global-climate-action (Accessed March 28, 2021).

Dávila, J.D., and D. Daste, 2012: *Medellín's aerial cable-cars: social inclusion and reduced emissions*. Development Planning Unit, University College London (UCL), London, UK, 4 pp. https://www.ucl.ac.uk/bartlett/development/sites/bartlett/files/davila-daste-2012-unep.pdf (Accessed October 31, 2021).

Davis, K.J. et al., 2017: The Indianapolis Flux Experiment (INFLUX): A test-bed for developing urban greenhouse gas emission measurements. *Elem Sci Anth*, **5**, 21, doi:10.1525/elementa.188.

Davis, M. and S. Naumann, 2017: Making the Case for Sustainable Urban Drainage Systems as a Nature-Based Solution to Urban Flooding. In: *Nature-Based Solutions to Climate Change Adaptation in Urban Areas: Linkages between Science, Policy and Practice* [Kabisch, N., H. Korn, J. Stadler, and A. Bonn, (eds.)]. Springer International Publishing, Cham, Switzerland, pp. 123–137.

Davis, S.J. et al., 2018: Net-zero emissions energy systems. *Science*, **360(6396)**, eaas9793, doi:10.1126/science.aas9793.

Dawson, R.J. et al., 2018: A systems framework for national assessment of climate risks to infrastructure. *Philos. Trans. A. Math. Phys. Eng. Sci.*, **376(2121)**, 20170298, doi:10.1098/rsta.2017.0298.

de Bercegol, R. and S. Gowda, 2019: A new waste and energy nexus? Rethinking the modernisation of waste services in Delhi. *Urban Stud.*, **56(11)**, 2297–2314, doi:10.1177/0042098018770592.

De Chalendar, J.A., P.W. Glynn, and S.M. Benson, 2019: City-scale decarbonization experiments with integrated energy systems. *Energy Environ. Sci.*, **12(5)**, 1695–1707, doi:10.1039/c8ee03706j.

de Haas, M., R. Faber, and M. Hamersma, 2020: How COVID-19 and the Dutch 'intelligent lockdown' change activities, work and travel behaviour: Evidence from longitudinal data in the Netherlands. *Transp. Res. Interdiscip. Perspect.*, **6**, 100150, doi:10.1016/j.trip.2020.100150.

De la Sota, C., V.J. Ruffato-Ferreira, L. Ruiz-García, and S. Alvarez, 2019: Urban green infrastructure as a strategy of climate change mitigation. A case study in northern Spain. *Urban For. Urban Green.*, **40**, 145–151, doi:10.1016/j.ufug.2018.09.004.

Deason, J., and M. Borgeson, 2019: Electrification of Buildings: Potential, Challenges, and Outlook. *Curr. Sustain. Energy Reports*, **6(4)**, 131–139, doi:10.1007/s40518-019-00143-2.

Debrunner, G., and T. Hartmann, 2020: Strategic use of land policy instruments for affordable housing – Coping with social challenges under scarce land conditions in Swiss cities. *Land use policy*, **99**, 104993, doi:10.1016/j.landusepol.2020.104993.

Dénarié, A., M. Calderoni, and M. Aprile, 2018: Multicriteria Approach for a Multisource District Heating. In: *Smart and Sustainable Planning for Cities and Regions* [Bisello, A., D. Vettorato, P. Laconte, and S. Costa, (eds.)]. Springer, Cham, Switzerland, pp. 21–33.

Deng, Y., B. Fu, and C. Sun, 2018: Effects of urban planning in guiding urban growth: Evidence from Shenzhen, China. *Cities*, **83**, 118–128, doi:10.1016/j.cities.2018.06.014.

Dhar, S., M. Pathak, and P.R. Shukla, 2017: Electric vehicles and India's low carbon passenger transport: a long-term co-benefits assessment. *J. Clean. Prod.*, **146**, 139–148, doi:10.1016/j.jclepro.2016.05.111.

Di Giulio, G.M., A.M.B. Bedran-Martins, M. da P. Vasconcellos, W.C. Ribeiro, and M.C. Lemos, 2018: Mainstreaming climate adaptation in the megacity of São Paulo, Brazil. *Cities*, **72**, 237–244, doi:10.1016/j.cities.2017.09.001.

Di Giulio, M., R. Holderegger, and S. Tobias, 2009: Effects of habitat and landscape fragmentation on humans and biodiversity in densely populated landscapes. *J. Environ. Manage.*, **90(10)**, 2959–2968, doi:10.1016/j.jenvman.2009.05.002.

Diallo, T., N. Cantoreggi, and J. Simos, 2016: Health Co-benefits of climate change mitigation policies at local level: Case Study Geneva. *Environnement, Risques et Sante*, **15(4)**, 332–340, doi:10.1684/ers.2016.0890.

Dias, S.M., 2016: Waste pickers and cities. *Environ. Urban.*, **28(2)**, 375–390, doi:10.1177/0956247816657302.

Díaz-Villavicencio, G., S.R. Didonet, and A. Dodd, 2017: Influencing factors of eco-efficient urban waste management: Evidence from Spanish municipalities. *J. Clean. Prod.*, **164**, 1486–1496, doi:10.1016/j.jclepro.2017.07.064.

Diaz, L.F., 2017: Waste management in developing countries and the circular economy. *Waste Manag. Res.*, **35(1)**, 1–2, doi:10.1177/0734242X16681406.

Dienst, C. et al., 2015: Wuxi – a Chinese City on its Way to a Low Carbon Future. *J. Sustain. Dev. Energy, Water Environ. Syst.*, **3(1)**, 12–25, doi:10.13044/j.sdewes.2015.03.0002.

Ding, C., D. Wang, C. Liu, Y. Zhang, and J. Yang, 2017: Exploring the influence of built environment on travel mode choice considering the mediating effects of car ownership and travel distance. *Transp. Res. Part A Policy Pract.*, **100**, 65–80, doi:10.1016/j.tra.2017.04.008.

Ding, C., Y. Wang, T. Tang, S. Mishra, and C. Liu, 2018: Joint analysis of the spatial impacts of built environment on car ownership and travel mode choice. *Transp. Res. Part D Transp. Environ.*, **60**, 28–40, doi:10.1016/j.trd.2016.08.004.

Dobler, C., D. Pfeifer, and W. Streicher, 2018: Reaching energy autonomy in a medium-sized city - three scenarios to model possible future energy developments in the residential building sector. *Sustain. Dev.*, **26(6)**, 859–869, doi:10.1002/sd.1855.

Dodman, D., 2009: Blaming cities for climate change? An analysis of urban greenhouse gas emissions inventories. *Environ. Urban.*, **21(1)**, 185–201, doi:10.1177/0956247809103016.

Dodman, D., B. Hayward, M. Pelling, V. Castan Broto, W. Chow, E. Chu, R. Dawson, L. Khirfan, T. McPhearson, A. Prakash, Y. Zheng, and G. Ziervogel, 2022: Cities, Settlements and Key Infrastructure. In: *Climate Change 2022: Impacts, Adaptation, and Vulnerability. Contribution of Working Group II to the Sixth Assessment Report of the Intergovernmental Panel on Climate Change* [H.-O. Pörtner, D.C. Roberts, M. Tignor, E.S. Poloczanska, K. Mintenbeck, A. Alegría, M. Craig, S. Langsdorf, S. Löschke, V. Möller, A. Okem, B. Rama (eds.)]. Cambridge University Press, Cambridge, UK and New York, NY, USA. In press.

Dominković, D.F. and G. Krajačić, 2019: District cooling versus individual cooling in urban energy systems: The impact of district energy share in cities on the optimal storage sizing. *Energies*, **12(3)**, 407, doi:10.3390/en12030407.

Domke, G.M. et al., 2016: Estimating litter carbon stocks on forest land in the United States. *Sci. Total Environ.*, **557–558**, 469–478, doi:10.1016/j.scitotenv.2016.03.090.

Dorotić, H., T. Pukšec, and N. Duić, 2019: Multi-objective optimization of district heating and cooling systems for a one-year time horizon. *Energy*, **169**, 319–328, doi:10.1016/j.energy.2018.11.149.

Dou, Y. et al., 2016: An empirical study on transit-oriented low-carbon urban land use planning: Exploratory Spatial Data Analysis (ESDA) on Shanghai, China. *Habitat Int.*, **53**, 379–389, doi:10.1016/j.habitatint.2015.12.005.

Drangert, J.-O., and H.C. Sharatchandra, 2017: Addressing urban water scarcity: reduce, treat and reuse – the third generation of management to avoid local resources boundaries. *Water Policy*, **19(5)**, 978–996, doi:10.2166/wp.2017.152.

Drysdale, D., B.V. Mathiesen, and H. Lund, 2019: From carbon calculators to energy system analysis in cities. *Energies*, **12(12)**, 2307, doi:10.3390/en12122307.

du Toit, M.J. et al., 2018: Urban green infrastructure and ecosystem services in sub-Saharan Africa. *Landsc. Urban Plan.*, **180**, 249–261, doi:10.1016/j.landurbplan.2018.06.001.

Duany, A., and E. Plater-Zyberck, 1991: *Towns and town-making principles*. 1st ed. Harvard Graduate School of Design and Rizzoli, Cambridge, MA and New York, NY, USA, 120 pp.

Dulal, H.B., 2017: Making cities resilient to climate change: identifying "win–win" interventions. *Local Environ.*, **22(1)**, 106–125, doi:10.1080/13549 839.2016.1168790.

Dulal, H.B., 2019: Cities in Asia: how are they adapting to climate change? *J. Environ. Stud. Sci.*, **9**, 13–24, doi:10.1007/s13412-018-0534-1.

Duranton, G., and M.A. Turner, 2018: Urban form and driving: Evidence from US cities. *J. Urban Econ.*, **108**, 170–191, doi:10.1016/j.jue.2018.10.003.

Dzhambov, A.M., D.D. Dimitrova, and E.D. Dimitrakova, 2014: Association between residential greenness and birth weight: Systematic review and meta-analysis. *Urban For. Urban Green.*, **13(4)**, 621–629, doi:10.1016/j. ufug.2014.09.004.

EC, 2015: *Closing the loop - An EU action plan for the Circular Economy (Communication from the Commission to the European Parliament, the Council, the European Economic and Social Committee of the Regions)*. COM (2015) 0614 Final, European Commission (EC), Brussels, Belgium, 21 pp. https://eur-lex.europa.eu/resource.html?uri=cellar:8a8ef5e8-99a0-11e5-b3b7-01aa75ed71a1.0012.02/DOC_1&format=PDF (Accessed October 28, 2021).

EC, 2020: *A new Circular Economy Action Plan For a cleaner and more competitive Europe*. European Commission (EC), Brussels, Belgium, 26 pp. https://data.europa.eu/doi/10.2779/05068 (Accessed November 8, 2021).

Egusquiza, A., I. Prieto, J.L. Izkara, and R. Béjar, 2018: Multi-scale urban data models for early-stage suitability assessment of energy conservation measures in historic urban areas. *Energy Build.*, **164**, 87–98, doi:10.1016/j. enbuild.2017.12.061.

Eigenbrod, C. and N. Gruda, 2015: Urban vegetable for food security in cities. A review. *Agron. Sustain. Dev.*, **35**, 483–498, doi:10.1007/s13593-014-0273-y.

Eisted, R., A.W. Larsen, and T.H. Christensen, 2009: Collection, transfer and transport of waste: accounting of greenhouse gases and global warming contribution: *Waste Manag. Res.*, **27(8)**, 738–745, doi:10.1177/0734242X09347796.

Endo, A., I. Tsurita, K. Burnett, and P.M. Orencio, 2017: A review of the current state of research on the water, energy, and food nexus. *J. Hydrol. Reg. Stud.*, **11**, 20–30, doi:10.1016/j.ejrh.2015.11.010.

Engels, A., 2018: Understanding how China is championing climate change mitigation. *Palgrave Commun.*, **4**, 101, doi:10.1057/s41599-018-0150-4.

Engström, R.E. et al., 2017: Connecting the resource nexus to basic urban service provision – with a focus on water-energy interactions in New York City. *Sustain. Cities Soc.*, **31**, 83–94, doi:10.1016/j.scs.2017.02.007.

Enzi, V. et al., 2017: Nature-Based Solutions and Buildings – The Power of Surfaces to Help Cities Adapt to Climate Change and to Deliver Biodiversity. In: *Nature-Based Solutions to Climate Change Adaptation in Urban Areas: Linkages between Science, Policy and Practice* [Kabisch, N., H. Korn, J. Stadler, and A. Bonn, (eds.)]. Springer International Publishing, Cham, Switzerland, pp. 159–183.

Erickson, P. and K. Tempest, 2015: *Keeping cities green: Avoiding carbon lock-in due to urban development*. Stockholm Environment Institute (SEI), Seattle, WA, USA, 28 pp. https://mediamanager.sei.org/documents/Publications/Climate/SEI-WP-2015-11-C40-Cities-carbon-lock-in.pdf (Accessed June 5, 2020).

Eriksson, M., I. Strid, and P.-A. Hansson, 2015: Carbon footprint of food waste management options in the waste hierarchy – a Swedish case study. *J. Clean. Prod.*, **93**, 115–125, doi:10.1016/j.jclepro.2015.01.026.

EU, 2016: *Urban Agenda for the EU 'Pact of Amsterdam'*. Informal Meeting of EU Ministers Responsible for Urban Matters, Amsterdam, The Netherlands, 36 pp. https://ec.europa.eu/regional_policy/sources/policy/themes/urban-development/agenda/pact-of-amsterdam.pdf (Accessed March 31, 2021).

Ewing, R., and R. Cervero, 2010: Travel and the Built Environment. *J. Am. Plan. Assoc.*, **76(3)**, 265–294, doi:10.1080/01944361003766766.

Ewing, R. et al., 2018: Testing Newman and Kenworthy's Theory of Density and Automobile Dependence. *J. Plan. Educ. Res.*, **38(2)**, 167–182, doi:10.1177/0739456X16688767.

Ezeudu, O.B., and T.S. Ezeudu, 2019: Implementation of Circular Economy Principles in Industrial Solid Waste Management: Case Studies from a Developing Economy (Nigeria). *Recycling*, **4(4)**, 42, doi:10.3390/RECYCLING4040042.

Facchini, A., C. Kennedy, I. Stewart, and R. Mele, 2017: The energy metabolism of megacities. *Appl. Energy*, **186(Part 2)**, 86–95, doi:10.1016/j. apenergy.2016.09.025.

Fang, K. et al., 2017: Carbon footprints of urban transition: Tracking circular economy promotions in Guiyang, China. *Ecol. Modell.*, **365**, 30–44, doi:10.1016/j.ecolmodel.2017.09.024.

Fastenrath, S. and B. Braun, 2018: Ambivalent urban sustainability transitions: Insights from Brisbane's building sector. *J. Clean. Prod.*, **176**, 581–589, doi:10.1016/j.jclepro.2017.12.134.

Fatimah, Y.A., K. Govindan, R. Murniningsih, and A. Setiawan, 2020: Industry 4.0 based sustainable circular economy approach for smart waste management system to achieve sustainable development goals: A case study of Indonesia. *J. Clean. Prod.*, **269**, 122263, doi:10.1016/J. JCLEPRO.2020.122263.

Félix, R., P. Cambra, and F. Moura, 2020: Build it and give 'em bikes, and they will come: The effects of cycling infrastructure and bike-sharing system in Lisbon. *Case Stud. Transp. Policy*, **8(2)**, 672–682, doi:10.1016/j. cstp.2020.03.002.

Fichera, A., M. Frasca, V. Palermo, and R. Volpe, 2018: An optimization tool for the assessment of urban energy scenarios. *Energy*, **156**, 418–429, doi:10.1016/j.energy.2018.05.114.

Fiori, A., and E. Volpi, 2020: On the Effectiveness of LID Infrastructures for the Attenuation of Urban Flooding at the Catchment Scale. *Water Resour. Res.*, **56(5)**, e2020WR027121, doi:10.1029/2020WR027121.

Fisher-Jeffes, L., N. Armitage, and K. Carden, 2017: The viability of domestic rainwater harvesting in the residential areas of the Liesbeek River Catchment, Cape Town. *Water SA*, **43(1)**, 81–90, doi:10.4314/wsa.v43i1.11.

Flacke, J., and C. de Boer, 2017: An Interactive Planning Support Tool for Addressing Social Acceptance of Renewable Energy Projects in The Netherlands. *ISPRS Int. J. Geo-Information*, **6(10)**, 313, doi:10.3390/ijgi6100313.

Floater, G. et al., 2017: *Global Review of Finance For Sustainable Urban Infrastructure*. The Coalition for Urban Transitions (CUT), 60 pp. http://newclimateeconomy.report/workingpapers/workingpaper/global-review-of-finance-for-sustainable-urban-infrastructure/ (Accessed March 31, 2021).

Folke, C. et al., 2021: Our future in the Anthropocene biosphere. *Ambio*, **50(4)**, 834–869, doi:10.1007/s13280-021-01544-8.

Fong, W.K. et al., 2014: *Global Protocol for Community-Scale Greenhouse Gas Emission Inventories: An Accounting and Reporting Standard for Cities*. World Resources Institute (WRI), Winnipeg, Canada, C40 Cities, and Local Governments for Sustainability (ICLEI), Bonn, Germany, 176 pp. https://www.ghgprotocol.org/sites/default/files/ghgp/standards/GHGP_GPC_0.pdf (Accessed November 2, 2021).

Fonseca, J.A., and A. Schlueter, 2015: Integrated model for characterization of spatiotemporal building energy consumption patterns in neighborhoods and city districts. *Appl. Energy*, **142**, 247–265, doi:10.1016/j. apenergy.2014.12.068.

Ford, A. et al., 2019: A multi-scale urban integrated assessment framework for climate change studies: A flooding application. *Comput. Environ. Urban Syst.*, **75**, 229–243, doi:10.1016/j.compenvurbsys.2019.02.005.

Foxon, T.J. et al., 2015: Low carbon infrastructure investment: extending business models for sustainability. *Infrastruct. Complex.*, **2**, 4, doi:10.1186/s40551-015-0009-4.

Fragkias, M., J. Lobo, D. Strumsky, and K.C. Seto, 2013: Does Size Matter? Scaling of CO$_2$ Emissions and U.S. Urban Areas. *PLoS One*, **8(6)**, e64727, doi:10.1371/journal.pone.0064727.

Frantzeskaki, N. et al., 2019: Nature-Based Solutions for Urban Climate Change Adaptation: Linking Science, Policy, and Practice Communities for Evidence-Based Decision-Making. *Bioscience*, **69(6)**, 455–466, doi:10.1093/biosci/biz042.

Fratini, C.F., S. Georg, and M.S. Jørgensen, 2019: Exploring circular economy imaginaries in European cities: A research agenda for the governance of urban sustainability transitions. *J. Clean. Prod.*, **228**, 974–989, doi:10.1016/j.jclepro.2019.04.193.

Fraundorfer, M., 2017: The Role of Cities in Shaping Transnational Law in Climate Governance. *Glob. Policy*, **8(1)**, 23–31, doi:10.1111/1758-5899.12365.

Frenova, S., 2021: Orchestrating the Participation of Women Organisations in the UNFCCC Led Climate Finance Decision Making. *Climate*, **9(9)**, 135, doi:10.3390/cli9090135.

Fricko, O. et al., 2017: The marker quantification of the Shared Socioeconomic Pathway 2: A middle-of-the-road scenario for the 21st century. *Glob. Environ. Change*, **42**, 251–267, doi:10.1016/j.gloenvcha.2016.06.004.

Friend, R.M. et al., 2016: Re-imagining Inclusive Urban Futures for Transformation. *Curr. Opin. Environ. Sustain.*, **20**, 67–72, doi:10.1016/j.cosust.2016.06.001.

Fuhr, H., T. Hickmann, and K. Kern, 2018: The role of cities in multi-level climate governance: local climate policies and the 1.5°C target. *Curr. Opin. Environ. Sustain.*, **30**, 1–6, doi:10.1016/j.cosust.2017.10.006.

Fujimori, S. et al., 2017: SSP3: AIM implementation of Shared Socioeconomic Pathways. *Glob. Environ. Change*, **42**, 268–283, doi:10.1016/j.gloenvcha.2016.06.009.

Fuso Nerini, F. et al., 2018: Mapping synergies and trade-offs between energy and the Sustainable Development Goals. *Nat. Energy*, **3**, 10–15, doi:10.1038/s41560-017-0036-5.

Gabaix, X., 1999: Zipf's Law for Cities: An Explanation. *Q. J. Econ.*, **114(3)**, 739–767, doi:10.1162/003355399556133.

Gabaldón-Estevan, D., K. Orru, C. Kaufmann, and H. Orru, 2019: Broader impacts of the fare-free public transportation system in Tallinn. *Int. J. Urban Sustain. Dev.*, **11(3)**, 332–345, doi:10.1080/19463138.2019.1596114.

Gai, Y. et al., 2020: Health and climate benefits of Electric Vehicle Deployment in the Greater Toronto and Hamilton Area. *Environ. Pollut.*, **265**, 114983, doi:10.1016/j.envpol.2020.114983.

Galloway, D., and P. Newman, 2014: How to design a sustainable heavy industrial estate. *Renew. Energy*, **67**, 46–52, doi:10.1016/j.renene.2013.11.018.

Gang, W., S. Wang, F. Xiao, and D.C. Gao, 2016: District cooling systems: Technology integration, system optimization, challenges and opportunities for applications. *Renew. Sustain. Energy Rev.*, **53**, 253–264, doi:10.1016/j.rser.2015.08.051.

Gao, J., and B.C. O'Neill, 2020: Mapping global urban land for the 21st century with data-driven simulations and Shared Socioeconomic Pathways. *Nat. Commun.*, **11**, 2302, doi:10.1038/s41467-020-15788-7.

Gao, J. et al., 2017: Perceptions of Health Co-Benefits in Relation to Greenhouse Gas Emission Reductions: A Survey among Urban Residents in Three Chinese Cities. *Int. J. Environ. Res. Public Health*, **14(3)**, 298, doi:10.3390/ijerph14030298.

Gao, Y., and P. Newman, 2018: Beijing's peak car transition: Hope for emerging cities in the 1.5°C agenda. *Urban Plan.*, **3(2)**, 82–93, doi:10.17645/up.v3i2.1246.

García-Gusano, D., D. Iribarren, and J. Dufour, 2018: Towards Energy Self-sufficiency in Large Metropolitan Areas: Business Opportunities on Renewable Electricity in Madrid. In: *Renewable Energies* [Márquez, F.P.G., A. Karyotakis, and M. Papaelias, (eds.)]. Springer International Publishing, Cham, Switzerland, pp. 17–31.

Gately, C.K., L.R. Hutyra, S. Peterson, and I. Sue Wing, 2017: Urban emissions hotspots: Quantifying vehicle congestion and air pollution using mobile phone GPS data. *Environ. Pollut.*, **229**, 496–504, doi:10.1016/j.envpol.2017.05.091.

Gaustad, G., M. Krystofik, M. Bustamante, and K. Badami, 2018: Circular economy strategies for mitigating critical material supply issues. *Resour. Conserv. Recycl.*, **135**, 24–33, doi:10.1016/j.resconrec.2017.08.002.

GCoM, 2018: *Implementing Climate Ambition: Global Covenant of Mayors 2018 Global Aggregation Report*. The Global Covenant of Mayors for Climate and Energy (GCoM), Brussels, 6 pp. https://www.globalcovenantofmayors.org/wp-content/uploads/2018/09/2018_GCOM_report_web.pdf.

GCoM, 2019: *Climate Emergency: Unlocking the Urban Opportunity Together*. The Global Covenant of Mayors for Climate and Energy (GCoM), Brussels, 37 pp. https://www.globalcovenantofmayors.org/wp-content/uploads/2019/12/2019-GCoM-Aggregation-Report.pdf.

Gebreegziabher, Z., L. Naik, R. Melamu, and B.B. Balana, 2014: Prospects and challenges for urban application of biogas installations in Sub-Saharan Africa. *Biomass and Bioenergy*, **70**, 130–140, doi:10.1016/j.biombioe.2014.02.036.

Geneletti, D., D. La Rosa, M. Spyra, and C. Cortinovis, 2017: A review of approaches and challenges for sustainable planning in urban peripheries. *Landsc. Urban Plan.*, **165**, 231–243, doi:10.1016/j.landurbplan.2017.01.013.

Gharfalkar, M., R. Court, C. Campbell, Z. Ali, and G. Hillier, 2015: Analysis of waste hierarchy in the European waste directive 2008/98/EC. *Waste Manag.*, **39**, 305–313, doi:10.1016/j.wasman.2015.02.007.

Gidden, M.J. et al., 2019: Global emissions pathways under different socioeconomic scenarios for use in CMIP6: A dataset of harmonized emissions trajectories through the end of the century. *Geosci. Model Dev.*, **12(4)**, 1443–1475, doi:10.5194/gmd-12-1443-2019.

Gill, B., and S. Moeller, 2018: GHG Emissions and the Rural-Urban Divide. A Carbon Footprint Analysis Based on the German Official Income and Expenditure Survey. *Ecol. Econ.*, **145**, 160–169, doi:10.1016/j.ecolecon.2017.09.004.

Gillingham, K.T., C.R. Knittel, J. Li, M. Ovaere, and M. Reguant, 2020: The Short-run and Long-run Effects of Covid-19 on Energy and the Environment. *Joule*, **4(7)**, 1337–1341, doi:10.1016/j.joule.2020.06.010.

Gjorgievski, V.Z., N. Markovska, A. Abazi, and N. Duić, 2020: The potential of power-to-heat demand response to improve the flexibility of the energy system: An empirical review. *Renew. Sustain. Energy Rev.*, **138**, 110489, doi:10.1016/j.rser.2020.110489.

Global Commission on the Economy and Climate, 2014: *Better Growth, Better Climate: The New Climate Economy Report - Synthesis Report*. The New Climate Economy (NCE), Global Commission on the Economy and Climate, Washington, DC, USA, 72 pp. https://newclimateeconomy.report/2016/wp-content/uploads/sites/2/2014/08/BetterGrowth-BetterClimate_NCE_Synthesis-Report_web.pdf.

Gondhalekar, D., and T. Ramsauer, 2017: Nexus City: Operationalizing the urban Water-Energy-Food Nexus for climate change adaptation in Munich, Germany. *Urban Clim.*, **19**, 28–40, doi:10.1016/j.uclim.2016.11.004.

González-García, S., M.R. Caamaño, M.T. Moreira, and G. Feijoo, 2021: Environmental profile of the municipality of Madrid through the methodologies of Urban Metabolism and Life Cycle Analysis. *Sustain. Cities Soc.*, **64**, 102546, doi:10.1016/j.scs.2020.102546.

Gonzalez-Valencia, R., F. Magana-Rodriguez, J. Cristóbal, and F. Thalasso, 2016: Hotspot detection and spatial distribution of methane emissions from landfills by a surface probe method. *Waste Manag.*, **55**, 299–305, doi:10.1016/j.wasman.2016.03.004.

Gopal, D., and H. Nagendra, 2014: Vegetation in Bangalore's slums: Boosting livelihoods, well-being and social capital. *Sustainability*, **6(5)**, 2459–2473, doi:10.3390/su6052459.

Göpfert, C., C. Wamsler, and W. Lang, 2019: A framework for the joint institutionalization of climate change mitigation and adaptation in city administrations. *Mitig. Adapt. Strateg. Glob. Change*, **24**, 1–21, doi:10.1007/s11027-018-9789-9.

Göpfert, C., C. Wamsler, and W. Lang, 2020: Enhancing structures for joint climate change mitigation and adaptation action in city administrations – Empirical insights and practical implications. *City Environ. Interact.*, **8**, 100052, doi:10.1016/j.cacint.2020.100052.

Gorissen, L., F. Spira, E. Meynaerts, P. Valkering, and N. Frantzeskaki, 2018: Moving towards systemic change? Investigating acceleration dynamics of urban sustainability transitions in the Belgian City of Genk. *J. Clean. Prod.*, **173**, 171–185, doi:10.1016/j.jclepro.2016.12.052.

Gould, C.F. et al., 2018: Government policy, clean fuel access, and persistent fuel stacking in Ecuador. *Scaling Up Clean Fuel Cook. Programs*, **46**, 111–122, doi:10.1016/j.esd.2018.05.009.

Gouldson, A. et al., 2015: Exploring the economic case for climate action in cities. *Glob. Environ. Change*, **35**, 93–105, doi:10.1016/j.gloenvcha.2015.07.009.

Gouldson, A. et al., 2016: Cities and climate change mitigation: Economic opportunities and governance challenges in Asia. *Cities*, **54**, 11–19, doi:10.1016/j.cities.2015.10.010.

Grafakos, S., K. Trigg, M. Landauer, L. Chelleri, and S. Dhakal, 2019: Analytical framework to evaluate the level of integration of climate adaptation and mitigation in cities. *Clim. Change*, **154(1–2)**, 87–106, doi:10.1007/s10584-019-02394-w.

Grafakos, S. et al., 2020: Integration of mitigation and adaptation in urban climate change action plans in Europe: A systematic assessment. *Renew. Sustain. Energy Rev.*, **121**, 109623, doi:10.1016/j.rser.2019.109623.

Graglia, J.M., and C. Mellon, 2018: Blockchain and Property in 2018: At the End of the Beginning. *Innov. Technol. Governance, Glob.*, **12(1–2)**, 90–116, doi:10.1162/inov_a_00270.

Grandin, J., H. Haarstad, K. Kjærås, and S. Bouzarovski, 2018: The politics of rapid urban transformation. *Curr. Opin. Environ. Sustain.*, **31**, 16–22, doi:10.1016/j.cosust.2017.12.002.

Granoff, I., J.R. Hogarth, and A. Miller, 2016: Nested barriers to low-carbon infrastructure investment. *Nat. Clim. Change*, **6(12)**, 1065–1071, doi:10.1038/nclimate3142.

Green, J., and P. Newman, 2017: Citizen utilities: The emerging power paradigm. *Energy Policy*, **105**, 283–293, doi:10.1016/j.enpol.2017.02.004.

Green, J., P. Newman, and N. Forse, 2020: *RENeW Nexus: Enabling resilient, low cost & localised electricity markets through blockchain P2P & VPP trading*. Power Ledger and Curtin University, Perth, Australia, 62 pp. https://www.powerledger.io/wp-content/uploads/renew-nexus-project-report.pdf.

Green, J.F., 2017: The strength of weakness: pseudo-clubs in the climate regime. *Clim. Change*, **144**, 41–52, doi:10.1007/s10584-015-1481-4.

Gregg, J.W., C.G. Jones, and T.E. Dawson, 2003: Urbanization effects on tree growth in the vicinity of New York City. *Nature*, **424**, 183–187, doi:10.1038/nature01728.

Grimm, N.B., J.M. Grove, S.T.A. Pickett, and C.L. Redman, 2000: Integrated approaches to long-term studies of urban ecological systems. *Bioscience*, **50(7)**, 571–584, doi:10.1641/0006-3568(2000)050[0571:IATLTO]2.0.CO;2.

Grimm, N.B. et al., 2008: Global Change and the Ecology of Cities. *Science*, **319(5864)**, 756–760, doi:10.1126/SCIENCE.1150195.

Große, J., C. Fertner, and N.B. Groth, 2016: Urban Structure, Energy and Planning: Findings from Three Cities in Sweden, Finland and Estonia. *Urban Plan.*, **1(1)**, 24–40, doi:10.17645/up.v1i1.506.

Grové, J., P.A. Lant, C.R. Greig, and S. Smart, 2018: Is MSW derived DME a viable clean cooking fuel in Kolkata, India? *Renew. Energy*, **124**, 50–60, doi:10.1016/j.renene.2017.08.039.

Gruebner, O. et al., 2017: Cities and Mental Health. *Dtsch. Aerzteblatt Online*, **114(121–127)**, doi:10.3238/arztebl.2017.0121.

Gu, B., X. Zhang, X. Bai, B. Fu, and D. Chen, 2019: Four steps to food security for swelling cities. *Nature*, **566**, 31–33, doi:10.1038/d41586-019-00407-3.

Gudipudi, R., T. Fluschnik, A.G.C. Ros, C. Walther, and J.P. Kropp, 2016: City density and CO_2 efficiency. *Energy Policy*, **91**, 352–361, doi:10.1016/j.enpol.2016.01.015.

Guelpa, E., A. Bischi, V. Verda, M. Chertkov, and H. Lund, 2019: Towards future infrastructures for sustainable multi-energy systems: A review. *Energy*, **184**, 2–21, doi:10.1016/j.energy.2019.05.057.

Güneralp, B., and K.C. Seto, 2013: Futures of global urban expansion: Uncertainties and implications for biodiversity conservation. *Environ. Res. Lett.*, **8(1)**, 014025, doi:10.1088/1748-9326/8/1/014025.

Güneralp, B., S. Lwasa, H. Masundire, S. Parnell, and K.C. Seto, 2017: Urbanization in Africa: challenges and opportunities for conservation. *Environ. Res. Lett.*, **13**, 015002, doi:10.1088/1748-9326/aa94fe.

Güneralp, B., M. Reba, B.U. Hales, E.A. Wentz, and K.C. Seto, 2020: Trends in urban land expansion, density, and land transitions from 1970 to 2010: a global synthesis. *Environ. Res. Lett.*, **15(4)**, 044015, doi:10.1088/1748-9326/ab6669.

Gurney, K.R. and P. Shepson, 2021: Opinion: The power and promise of improved climate data infrastructure. *Proc. Natl. Acad. Sci.*, **118(35)**, e2114115118, doi:10.1073/pnas.2114115118.

Gurney, K.R. et al., 2015: Climate change: Track urban emissions on a human scale. *Nature*, **525**, 179–181, doi:10.1038/525179a.

Gurney, K.R. et al., 2019: The Hestia fossil fuel CO2 emissions data product for the Los Angeles megacity (Hestia-LA). *Earth Syst. Sci. Data*, **11(3)**, 1309–1335, doi:10.5194/essd-11-1309-2019.

Gurney, K.R. et al., 2021: Greenhouse gas emissions from global cities under SSP/RCP scenarios, 1990 to 2100. *EarthArXiv*, doi:10.31223/X5Z639.

Gurney, K.R. et al., 2022: Greenhouse gas emissions from global cities under SSP/RCP scenarios, 1990 to 2100. *Glob. Environ. Change*, **73**, 102478, doi:10.1016/j.gloenvcha.2022.102478.

Hachaichi, M., and T. Baouni, 2021: Virtual carbon emissions in the big cities of middle-income countries. *Urban Clim.*, **40**, 100986, doi:10.1016/j.uclim.2021.100986.

Hadfield, P., and N. Cook, 2019: Financing the Low-Carbon City: Can Local Government Leverage Public Finance to Facilitate Equitable Decarbonisation? *Urban Policy Res.*, **37(1)**, 13–29, doi:10.1080/08111146.2017.1421532.

Hale, T.N. et al., 2020: Sub- and non-state climate action: a framework to assess progress, implementation and impact. *Clim. Policy*, **21(3)**, 406–420, doi:10.1080/14693062.2020.1828796.

Hall, D., M. Moultak, and N. Lutsey, 2017a: *Electric vehicle capitals of the world: Demonstrating the path to electric drive*. The International Council on Clean Transportation (ICCT), Washington, DC, USA, 57 pp. https://theicct.org/wp-content/uploads/2021/06/Global-EV-Capitals_White-Paper_06032017_vF.pdf.

Hall, D.M. et al., 2017b: The city as a refuge for insect pollinators. *Conserv. Biol.*, **31(1)**, 24–29, doi:10.1111/cobi.12840.

Hall, P., and D. Hay, 1980: *Growth centres in the European urban system*. Heinemann Educational Books, Ltd, London, UK, 310 pp.

Hallegatte, S., J. Rentschler, and J. Rozenberg, 2019: *Lifelines: The Resilient Infrastructure Opportunity*. The World Bank, Washington, DC, USA, 224 pp. http://hdl.handle.net/10986/31805.

Hamidi, S., S. Sabouri, and R. Ewing, 2020: Does Density Aggravate the COVID-19 Pandemic?: Early Findings and Lessons for Planners. *J. Am. Plan. Assoc.*, **86(4)**, 495–509, doi:10.1080/01944363.2020.1777891.

Han, F., R. Xie, Y. Lu, J. Fang, and Y. Liu, 2018: The effects of urban agglomeration economies on carbon emissions: Evidence from Chinese cities. *J. Clean. Prod.*, **172**, 1096–1110, doi:10.1016/j.jclepro.2017.09.273.

Han, P. et al., 2021: Assessing the recent impact of COVID-19 on carbon emissions from China using domestic economic data. *Sci. Total Environ.*, **750**, 141688, doi:10.1016/J.SCITOTENV.2020.141688.

Handy, S., 1996: Methodologies for exploring the link between urban form and travel behavior. *Transp. Res. Part D Transp. Environ.*, **1(2)**, 151–165, doi:10.1016/S1361-9209(96)00010-7.

Handy, S., 2020: Is accessibility an idea whose time has finally come? *Transp. Res. Part D Transp. Environ.*, **83**, 102319, doi:10.1016/j.trd.2020.102319.

Hansen, P., G.M. Morrison, A. Zaman, and X. Liu, 2020: Smart technology needs smarter management: Disentangling the dynamics of digitalism in the governance of shared solar energy in Australia. *Energy Res. Soc. Sci.*, **60**, 101322, doi:10.1016/j.erss.2019.101322.

Hanson, P.J. et al., 2003: Soil Respiration and Litter Decomposition. In: *North American temperate deciduous forest responses to changing precipitation regimes* [Hanson, P.J. and S.D. Wullschleger, (eds.)]. Springer, New York, NY, USA, pp. 163–189.

Harris, S., J. Weinzettel, A. Bigano, and A. Källmén, 2020: Low carbon cities in 2050? GHG emissions of European cities using production-based and consumption-based emission accounting methods. *J. Clean. Prod.*, **248**, 119206, doi:10.1016/j.jclepro.2019.119206.

Haupt, W., and A. Coppola, 2019: Climate governance in transnational municipal networks: advancing a potential agenda for analysis and typology. *Int. J. Urban Sustain. Dev.*, **11**(2), 123–140, doi:10.1080/19463138.2019.1583235.

He, B.-J. et al., 2019: Co-benefits approach: Opportunities for implementing sponge city and urban heat island mitigation. *Land use policy*, **86**, 147–157, doi:10.1016/j.landusepol.2019.05.003.

Heikkinen, M., T. Ylä-Anttila, and S. Juhola, 2019: Incremental, reformistic or transformational: what kind of change do C40 cities advocate to deal with climate change? *J. Environ. Policy Plan.*, **21**(1), 90–103, doi:10.1080/1523908X.2018.1473151.

Heinonen, J. et al., 2020: Spatial consumption-based carbon footprint assessments - A review of recent developments in the field. *J. Clean. Prod.*, **256**, 120335, doi:10.1016/j.jclepro.2020.120335.

Helgenberger, S., and M. Jänicke, 2017: *Mobilizing the co-benefits of climate change mitigation: Connecting opportunities with interests in the new energy world of renewables*. Institute for Advanced Sustainability Studies (IASS), Postdam, Germany, 20 pp. https://www.iass-potsdam.de/sites/default/files/files/iass_working_paper_co_benefits.pdf

Henneman, L.R.F., P. Rafaj, H.J. Annegarn, and C. Klausbruckner, 2016: Assessing emissions levels and costs associated with climate and air pollution policies in South Africa. *Energy Policy*, **89**, 160–170, doi:10.1016/j.enpol.2015.11.026.

Herath, P., M. Thatcher, H. Jin, and X. Bai, 2021: Effectiveness of urban surface characteristics as mitigation strategies for the excessive summer heat in cities. *Sustain. Cities Soc.*, **72**, 103072, doi:10.1016/j.scs.2021.103072.

Herrero, A., and M. Vilella, 2018: 'We have a right to breathe clean air': the emerging environmental justice movement against waste incineration in cement kilns in Spain. *Sustain. Sci.*, **13**(3), 721–731, doi:10.1007/s11625-017-0473-x.

Herrmann, A. et al., 2018: Household preferences for reducing greenhouse gas emissions in four European high-income countries: Does health information matter? A mixed-methods study protocol. *BMC Public Health*, **18**, 71, doi:10.1186/s12889-017-4604-1.

Hickmann, T., and F. Stehle, 2017: Urban Climate Governance Experiments in South Africa: Insights from Johannesburg, Cape Town, and Durban. *ISA Annual Convention*, Baltimore, MD, USA, 26 pp. https://www.uni-potsdam.de/fileadmin01/projects/fuhr/ISA_Paper_Hickmann__StehleFinal.pdf.

Hickmann, T., H. Fuhr, C. Höhne, M. Lederer, and F. Stehle, 2017: Carbon Governance Arrangements and the Nation-State: The Reconfiguration of Public Authority in Developing Countries. *Public Adm. Dev.*, **37**(5), 331–343, doi:10.1002/pad.1814.

Hjalmarsson, L., 2015: Biogas as a boundary object for policy integration – the case of Stockholm. *J. Clean. Prod.*, **98**, 185–193, doi:10.1016/j.jclepro.2014.10.042.

Ho, C.S., Y. Matsuoka, J. Simson, and K. Gomi, 2013: Low carbon urban development strategy in Malaysia - The case of Iskandar Malaysia development corridor. *Habitat Int.*, **37**(SI), 43–51, doi:10.1016/j.habitatint.2011.12.018.

Ho, C.S., L.W. Chau, B.T. Teh, Y. Matsuoka, and K. Gomi, 2015: "Science to action" of the sustainable low carbon city-region: Lessons learnt from Iskandar Malaysia. In: *Enabling Asia to Stabilise the Climate* [Nishioka, S., (ed.)], Springer Singapore, Singapore, pp. 119–150.

Hofmann, J., D. Guan, K. Chalvatzis, and H. Huo, 2016: Assessment of electrical vehicles as a successful driver for reducing CO2 emissions in China. *Appl. Energy*, **184**, 995–1003, doi:10.1016/j.apenergy.2016.06.042.

Hölscher, K., N. Frantzeskaki, and D. Loorbach, 2019: Steering transformations under climate change: capacities for transformative climate governance and the case of Rotterdam, the Netherlands. *Reg. Environ. Change*, **19**(3), 791–805, doi:10.1007/s10113-018-1329-3.

Hoornweg, D., and P. Bhada-Tata, 2012: *What a Waste: A Global Review of Solid Waste Management*. The World Bank, Washington, DC, USA, 98 pp.

Hoornweg, D., and K. Pope, 2017: Population predictions for the world's largest cities in the 21st century. *Environ. Urban.*, **29**(1), 195–216, doi:10.1177/0956247816663557.

Hoppe, T., A. van der Vegt, and P. Stegmaier, 2016: Presenting a Framework to Analyze Local Climate Policy and Action in Small and Medium-Sized Cities. *Sustainability*, **8**(9), 847, doi:10.3390/su8090847.

Hsieh, S. et al., 2017: Defining density and land uses under energy performance targets at the early stage of urban planning processes. *Energy Procedia*, **122**, 301–306, doi:10.1016/j.egypro.2017.07.326.

Hsu, A. et al., 2018: Bridging the emissions gap - The role of non-state and subnational actors. In: *The Emissions Gap Report 2018*, *A UN Environment Synthesis Report*, United Nations Environment Programme (UNEP), Nairobi, pp. 27.

Hsu, A. et al., 2019: A research roadmap for quantifying non-state and subnational climate mitigation action. *Nat. Clim. Change*, **9**, 11–17, doi:10.1038/s41558-018-0338-z.

Hsu, A. et al., 2020a: ClimActor, harmonized transnational data on climate network participation by city and regional governments. *Sci. Data*, **7**, 374, doi:10.1038/s41597-020-00682-0.

Hsu, A., N. Höhne, T. Kuramochi, V. Vilariño, and B.K. Sovacool, 2020b: Beyond states: Harnessing sub-national actors for the deep decarbonisation of cities, regions, and businesses. *Energy Res. Soc. Sci.*, **70**, 101738, doi:10.1016/j.erss.2020.101738.

Hsu, A. et al., 2020c: Performance determinants show European cities are delivering on climate mitigation. *Nat. Clim. Change*, **10**(11), 1015–1022, doi:10.1038/s41558-020-0879-9.

Hu, J., G. Liu, and F. Meng, 2018: Estimates of The Effectiveness for Urban Energy Conservation and Carbon Abatement Policies: The Case of Beijing City, China. *J. Environ. Account. Manag.*, **6**(3), 199–214, doi:10.5890/JEAM.2018.09.002.

Hu, L., J. Cao, and J. Yang, 2020: Planning for accessibility. *Transp. Res. Part D Transp. Environ.*, **88**, 102575, doi:10.1016/j.trd.2020.102575.

Hu, M.-C., C.-Y. Wu, and T. Shih, 2015: Creating a new socio-technical regime in China: Evidence from the Sino-Singapore Tianjin Eco-City. *Futures*, **70**, 1–12, doi:10.1016/j.futures.2015.04.001.

Hu, Y., J. Lin, S. Cui, and N.Z. Khanna, 2016: Measuring Urban Carbon Footprint from Carbon Flows in the Global Supply Chain. *Environ. Sci. Technol.*, **50**(12), 6154–6163, doi:10.1021/acs.est.6b00985.

Huang, K., X. Li, X. Liu, and K.C. Seto, 2019: Projecting global urban land expansion and heat island intensification through 2050. *Environ. Res. Lett.*, **14**(11), 114037, doi:10.1088/1748-9326/ab4b71.

Hunter, R.G., J.W. Day, A.R. Wiegman, and R.R. Lane, 2019: Municipal wastewater treatment costs with an emphasis on assimilation wetlands in the Louisiana coastal zone. *Ecol. Eng.*, **137**, 21–25, doi:10.1016/j.ecoleng.2018.09.020.

Hurlimann, A., S. Moosavi, and G.R. Browne, 2021: Urban planning policy must do more to integrate climate change adaptation and mitigation actions. *Land use policy*, **101**, 105188, doi:10.1016/j.landusepol.2020.105188.

ICLEI, 2019a: *ICLEI in the urban era – 2019 update*. Local Governments for Sustainability (ICLEI), Bonn, Germany, 140 pp. http://e-lib.iclei.org/wp-content/uploads/2019/07/ICLEI-in-the-Urban-Era-2019-edition.pdf (Accessed March 31, 2021).

ICLEI, 2019b: *U.S. Community Protocol for Accounting and Reporting of Greenhouse Gas Emissions*. Local Governments for Sustainability (ICLEI),

Bonn, Germany, 69 pp. https://icleiusa.org/publications/us-community-protocol/ (Accessed March 30, 2021).

IEA, 2014: *EV City Casebook: 50 Big Ideas Shaping the Future of Electric Mobility*. International Energy Agency (IEA) and Organisation for Economic Co-operation and Development (OECD), Paris, France, 74 pp.

IEA, 2016a: *Energy Technology Perspectives 2016: Towards Sustainable Urban Energy Systems*. International Energy Agency (IEA) and Organisation for Economic Co-operation and Development (OECD), Paris, France, 418 pp.

IEA, 2016b: *Global EV Outlook 2016: Beyond one million electric cars*. International Energy Agency (IEA) and Organisation for Economic Co-operation and Development (OECD), Paris, France, 49 pp.

IEA, 2017: *Global EV Outlook 2017: Two million and counting*. International Energy Agency (IEA) and Organisation for Economic Co-operation and Development (OECD), Paris, France, 71 pp.

IEA, 2018: *Global EV Outlook 2018: Towards cross-modal electrification*. International Energy Agency (IEA) and Organisation for Economic Co-operation and Development (OECD), Paris, France, 141 pp.

IEA, 2020a: *Global EV Outlook 2020: Entering the decade of electric drive?* International Energy Agency (IEA) and Organisation for Economic Co-operation and Development (OECD), Paris, France, 276 pp. https://www.iea.org/reports/global-ev-outlook-2020 (Accessed March 31, 2021).

IEA, 2020b: *World Energy Outlook 2020*. International Energy Agency (IEA), Paris, France, 464 pp. https://www.iea.org/reports/world-energy-outlook-2020 (Accessed October 31, 2021).

IEA, 2021a: *Empowering Cities for a Net Zero Future: Unlocking resilient, smart, sustainable urban energy systems*. International Energy Agency (IEA), Paris, France, 108 pp.

IEA, 2021b: *Global EV Outlook 2021: Accelerating ambitions despite the pandemic*. International Energy Agency (IEA), Paris, France, 101 pp. https://www.iea.org/reports/global-ev-outlook-2021 (Accessed October 31, 2021).

ILO, 2018: *Women and men in the informal economy: A statistical picture*. 3rd ed. International Labour Office (ILO), Geneva, Switzerland, 156 pp. https://www.ilo.org/global/publications/books/WCMS_626831/lang--en/index.htm (Accessed December 30, 2020).

Ingrao, C., A. Messineo, R. Beltramo, T. Yigitcanlar, and G. Ioppolo, 2019: Application of life cycle assessment in buildings: An overview of theoretical and practical information. In: *The Routledge Companion to Environmental Planning* [Davoudi, S., R. Cowell, I. White, and H. Blanco, (eds.)]. Routledge, London, UK, pp. 372–381.

IPBES, 2019a: *Summary for policymakers of the global assessment report on biodiversity and ecosystem services of the Intergovernmental Science-Policy Platform on Biodiversity and Ecosystem Services*. [Díaz, S. et al., (eds.)]. Intergovernmental Science-Policy Platform on Biodiversity and Ecosystem Services (IPBES), Bonn, Germany, 56 pp.

IPBES, 2019b: *Global assessment report on biodiversity and ecosystem services of the Intergovernmental Science-Policy Platform on Biodiversity and Ecosystem Services*. [Brondizio, E.S., J. Settele, S. Díaz, and H.T. Ngo, (eds.)]. Intergovernmental Science-Policy Platform on Biodiversity and Ecosystem Services (IPBES), Bonn, Germany, 1148 pp. https://www.ipbes.net/global-assessment (Accessed March 28).

IPCC, 2018a: *Global Warming of 1.5°C. An IPCC Special Report on the impacts of global warming of 1.5°C above pre-industrial levels and related global greenhouse gas emission pathways, in the context of strengthening the global response to the threat of climate change* [Masson-Delmotte, V., P. Zhai, H.-O. Pörtner, D. Roberts, J. Skea, P.R. Shukla, A. Pirani, W. Moufouma-Okia, C. Péan, R. Pidcock, S. Connors, J.B.R. Matthews, Y. Chen, X. Zhou, M.I. Gomis, E. Lonnoy, T. Maycock, M. Tignor, and T. Waterfield (eds.)]. Cambridge University Press, Cambridge, UK and New York, NY, USA, 630 pp.

IPCC, 2018b: Annex I: Glossary [Matthews, J.B.R. (ed.)]. In: *Global Warming of 1.5°C. An IPCC Special Report on the impacts of global warming of 1.5°C above pre-industrial levels and related global greenhouse gas emission pathways, in the context of strengthening the global response to the threat of climate change, sustainable development, and efforts to eradicate poverty* [Masson-Delmotte, V., P. Zhai, H.-O. Pörtner, D. Roberts, J. Skea, P.R. Shukla, A. Pirani, W. Moufouma-Okia, C. Péan, R. Pidcock, S. Connors, J.B.R. Matthews, Y. Chen, X. Zhou, M.I. Gomis, E. Lonnoy, T. Maycock, M. Tignor, and T. Waterfield (eds.)]. Cambridge University Press, Cambridge, UK, and New York, NY, USA, pp. 541–562.

IPCC, 2018c: Summary for Policymakers. In: *Global warming of 1.5°C. An IPCC Special Report on the impacts of global warming of 1.5°C above pre-industrial levels and related global greenhouse gas emission pathways, in the context of strengthening the global response to the threat of climate change* [Masson-Delmotte, V., P. Zhai, H.-O. Pörtner, D. Roberts, J. Skea, P.R. Shukla, A. Pirani, W. Moufouma-Okia, C. Péan, R. Pidcock, S. Connors, J.B.R. Matthews, Y. Chen, X. Zhou, M.I. Gomis, E. Lonnoy, T. Maycock, M. Tignor, and T. Waterfield (eds.)]. Cambridge University Press, Cambridge, UK and New York, NY, USA, pp. 1–24.

IPCC, 2019: *Climate Change and Land: An IPCC Special Report on climate change, desertification, land degradation, sustainable land management, food security, and greenhouse gas fluxes in terrestrial ecosystems* [P.R. Shukla, J. Skea, E. Calvo Buendia, V. Masson-Delmotte, H.-O. Pörtner, D. C. Roberts, P. Zhai, R. Slade, S. Connors, R. van Diemen, M. Ferrat, E. Haughey, S. Luz, S. Neogi, M. Pathak, J. Petzold, J. Portugal Pereira, P. Vyas, E. Huntley, K. Kissick, M. Belkacemi, J. Malley, (eds.)]. Cambridge University Press, Cambridge, UK and New York, NY, USA, 874 pp.

IPCC, 2021: Climate Change 2021: *The Physical Science Basis. Contribution of Working Group I to the Sixth Assessment Report of the Intergovernmental Panel on Climate Change* [Masson-Delmotte, V., P. Zhai, A. Pirani, S.L. Connors, C. Péan, S. Berger, N. Caud, Y. Chen, L. Goldfarb, M.I. Gomis, M. Huang, K. Leitzell, E. Lonnoy, J.B.R. Matthews, T.K. Maycock, T. Waterfield, O. Yelekçi, R. Yu, and B. Zhou (eds.)]. Cambridge University Press, Cambridge, UK, and New York, NY, USA.

IRENA, 2021: *World Energy Transitions Outlook: 1.5°C Pathway*. International Renewable Energy Agency (IRENA), Abu Dhabi, 312 pp. https://www.irena.org/publications/2021/Jun/World-Energy-Transitions-Outlook (Accessed October 31, 2021).

Islam, K.M.N., 2018: Municipal solid waste to energy generation: An approach for enhancing climate co-benefits in the urban areas of Bangladesh. *Renew. Sustain. Energy Rev.*, **81**, 2472–2486, doi:10.1016/j.rser.2017.06.053.

IUCN, 2021: Nature-based Solutions. International Union for Conservation of Nature (IUCN). https://www.iucn.org/theme/nature-based-solutions (Accessed October 11, 2021).

Ivanova, D. et al., 2016: Environmental Impact Assessment of Household Consumption. *J. Ind. Ecol.*, **20(3)**, 526–536, doi:10.1111/jiec.12371.

Jacobs, J., 1969: *The economy of cities*. Random House, New York, NY, USA, 283 pp.

Jacobson, M.Z. et al., 2018: 100% clean and renewable Wind, Water, and Sunlight (WWS) all-sector energy roadmaps for 53 towns and cities in North America. *Sustain. Cities Soc.*, **42**, 22–37, doi:10.1016/j.scs.2018.06.031.

Jacobson, M.Z. et al., 2020: Transitioning All Energy in 74 Metropolitan Areas, Including 30 Megacities, to 100% Clean and Renewable Wind, Water, and Sunlight (WWS). *Energies*, **13(18)**, 4934, doi:10.3390/en13184934.

Jaganmohan, M., S. Knapp, C.M. Buchmann, and N. Schwarz, 2016: The Bigger, the Better? The Influence of Urban Green Space Design on Cooling Effects for Residential Areas. *J. Environ. Qual.*, **45(1)**, 134–145, doi:10.2134/jeq2015.01.0062.

Jagarnath, M. and T. Thambiran, 2018: Greenhouse gas emissions profiles of neighbourhoods in Durban, South Africa – an initial investigation. *Environ. Urban.*, **30(1)**, 191–214, doi:10.1177/0956247817713471.

Jaglin, S., 2014: Urban Energy Policies and the Governance of Multilevel Issues in Cape Town. *Urban Stud.*, **51(7)**, 1394–1414, doi:10.1177/0042098013500091.

Jamei, E., H.W. Chau, M. Seyedmahmoudian, and A. Stojcevski, 2021: Review on the cooling potential of green roofs in different climates. *Sci. Total Environ.*, **791**, 148407, doi:10.1016/j.scitotenv.2021.148407.

8

Jarzebski, M.P. et al., 2021: Ageing and population shrinking: implications for sustainability in the urban century. *npj Urban Sustain.*, **1(1)**, 17, doi:10.1038/s42949-021-00023-z.

Jiang, L. and B.C. O'Neill, 2017: Global urbanization projections for the Shared Socioeconomic Pathways. *Glob. Environ. Change*, **42**, 193–199, doi:10.1016/j.gloenvcha.2015.03.008.

Jiang, Y., E. van der Werf, E.C. van Ierland, and K.J. Keesman, 2017: The potential role of waste biomass in the future urban electricity system. *Biomass and Bioenergy*, **107**, 182–190, doi:10.1016/j.biombioe.2017.10.001.

Jiang, Y., Y. Long, Q. Liu, K. Dowaki, and T. Ihara, 2020: Carbon emission quantification and decarbonization policy exploration for the household sector - Evidence from 51 Japanese cities. *Energy Policy*, **140**, 111438, doi:10.1016/j.enpol.2020.111438.

Jones, C. and D.M. Kammen, 2014: Spatial distribution of U.S. household carbon footprints reveals suburbanization undermines greenhouse gas benefits of urban population density. *Environ. Sci. Technol.*, **48(2)**, 895–902, doi:10.1021/es4034364.

Jonker, M.F., F.J. van Lenthe, B. Donkers, J.P. Mackenbach, and A. Burdorf, 2014: The effect of urban green on small-area (healthy) life expectancy. *J. Epidemiol. Community Health*, **68(10)**, 999–1002, doi:10.1136/jech-2014-203847.

Joshi, C., J. Seay, and N. Banadda, 2019: A perspective on a locally managed decentralized circular economy for waste plastic in developing countries. *Environ. Prog. Sustain. Energy*, **38(1)**, 3–11, doi:10.1002/EP.13086.

Kabisch, N., M. Strohbach, D. Haase, and J. Kronenberg, 2016: Urban green space availability in European cities. *Ecol. Indic.*, **70**, 586–596, doi:10.1016/j.ecolind.2016.02.029.

Kalmykova, Y., L. Rosado, and J. Patrício, 2015: Urban Economies Resource Productivity and Decoupling: Metabolism Trends of 1996–2011 in Sweden, Stockholm, and Gothenburg. *Environ. Sci. Technol.*, **49(14)**, 8815–8823, doi:10.1021/acs.est.5b01431.

Kalmykova, Y., L. Rosado, and J. Patrício, 2016: Resource consumption drivers and pathways to reduction: economy, policy and lifestyle impact on material flows at the national and urban scale. *J. Clean. Prod.*, **132**, 70–80, doi:10.1016/j.jclepro.2015.02.027.

Kamiya, M., M. Prakash, and H. Berggren, 2020: *Financing Sustainable Urbanization: Counting the Costs and Closing the Gap*. UN-Habitat, Nairobi, Kenya, 8 pp. https://unhabitat.org/sites/default/files/2020/02/financing_sustainable_urbanization_-_counting_the_costs_and_closing_the_gap_february_2020.pdf (Accessed November 1, 2021).

Kammen, D.M., and D.A. Sunter, 2016: City-integrated renewable energy for urban sustainability. *Science*, **352(6288)**, 922–928, doi:10.1126/science.aad9302.

Kamruzzaman, M., F.M. Shatu, J. Hine, and G. Turrell, 2015: Commuting mode choice in transit oriented development: Disentangling the effects of competitive neighbourhoods, travel attitudes, and self-selection. *Transp. Policy*, **42**, 187–196, doi:10.1016/j.tranpol.2015.06.003.

Kang, C.-N., and S.-H. Cho, 2018: Thermal and electrical energy mix optimization (EMO) method for real large-scaled residential town plan. *J. Electr. Eng. Technol.*, **13(1)**, 513–520, doi:10.5370/JEET.2018.13.1.513.

Kareem, B. et al., 2020: Pathways for resilience to climate change in African cities. *Environ. Res. Lett.*, **15(7)**, 73002, doi:10.1088/1748-9326/ab7951.

Karlsson, M., E. Alfredsson, and N. Westling, 2020: Climate policy co-benefits: a review. *Clim. Policy*, **20(3)**, 292–316, doi:10.1080/14693062.2020.1724070.

Kastner, I., and P.C. Stern, 2015: Examining the decision-making processes behind household energy investments: A review. *Energy Res. Soc. Sci.*, **10**, 72–89, doi:10.1016/j.erss.2015.07.008.

Kaza, S., Y. Lisa, P. Bhada-Tata, and F. Van Woerden, 2018: *What a Waste 2.0: A Global Snapshot of Solid Waste Management to 2050*. The World Bank, Washington, DC, USA, 38 pp.

Keenan, J.M., E. Chu, and J. Peterson, 2019: From funding to financing: perspectives shaping a research agenda for investment in urban climate adaptation. *Int. J. Urban Sustain. Dev.*, **11(3)**, 297–308, doi:10.1080/19463138.2019.1565413.

Keller, M., 2017: Multilevel Governance Theory in Practice: How Converging Models Explain Urban Climate Change Mitigation Policy in Bristol. University of Cambridge, Cambridge, UK, 60 pp.

Kennedy, C.A., 2015: Key threshold for electricity emissions. *Nat. Clim. Change*, **5(3)**, 179–181, doi:10.1038/nclimate2494.

Kennedy, C.A. et al., 2009: Greenhouse Gas Emissions from Global Cities. *Environ. Sci. Technol.*, **43(19)**, 7297–7302, doi:10.1021/es900213p.

Kennedy, C.A., I.D. Stewart, M.I. Westphal, A. Facchini, and R. Mele, 2018: Keeping global climate change within 1.5°C through net negative electric cities. *Curr. Opin. Environ. Sustain.*, **30**, 18–25, doi:10.1016/j.cosust.2018.02.009.

Kennedy, C.A., I.D. Stewart, and M.I. Westphal, 2019: *Shifting Currents: Opportunities for Low Carbon Electric Cities in the Global South*. World Resources Institute (WRI), Washington, DC, USA, 36 pp. https://wrirosscities.org/sites/default/files/19_WP_Shifting_Currents_final.pdf (Accessed March 31, 2021).

Keramidas, K. et al., 2018: *Global Energy and Climate Outlook 2018: Sectoral mitigation options towards a low-emissions economy – Global context to the EU strategy for long-term greenhouse gas emissions reduction, EUR 29462 EN*. European Union (EU), Luxembourg, 200 pp.

Kern, K., 2019: Cities as leaders in EU multilevel climate governance: embedded upscaling of local experiments in Europe. *Env. Polit.*, **28**, 125–145, doi:10.1080/09644016.2019.1521979.

Khan, K. and C.-W. Su, 2021: Urbanization and carbon emissions: a panel threshold analysis. *Environ. Sci. Pollut. Res.*, **28(20)**, 26073–26081, doi:10.1007/S11356-021-12443-6.

Khan, M.M., S. Jain, M. Vaezi, and A. Kumar, 2016: Development of a decision model for the techno-economic assessment of municipal solid waste utilization pathways. *Waste Manag.*, **48**, 548–564, doi:10.1016/j.wasman.2015.10.016.

Khavarian-Garmsir, A.R., A. Sharifi, and N. Moradpour, 2021: Are high-density districts more vulnerable to the COVID-19 pandemic? *Sustain. Cities Soc.*, **70**, 102911, doi:10.1016/j.scs.2021.102911.

Khosla, R., and A. Bhardwaj, 2019: Urbanization in the time of climate change: Examining the response of Indian cities. *Wiley Interdiscip. Rev. Clim. Change*, **10(1)**, e560, doi:10.1002/wcc.560.

Kii, M., 2020: Reductions in CO_2 Emissions from Passenger Cars under Demography and Technology Scenarios in Japan by 2050. *Sustainability*, **12(17)**, 6919, doi:10.3390/su12176919.

Kii, M., 2021: Projecting future populations of urban agglomerations around the world and through the 21st century. *npj Urban Sustain.*, **1(1)**, 10, doi:10.1038/s42949-020-00007-5.

Kim, G., and P. Coseo, 2018: Urban Park Systems to Support Sustainability: The Role of Urban Park Systems in Hot Arid Urban Climates. *Forests*, **9(7)**, 439, doi:10.3390/f9070439.

Kim, H., and W. Chen, 2018: Changes in energy and carbon intensity in Seoul's water sector. *Sustain. Cities Soc.*, **41**, 749–759, doi:10.1016/j.scs.2018.06.001.

Kılkış, Ş., 2019: Benchmarking the sustainability of urban energy, water and environment systems and envisioning a cross-sectoral scenario for the future. *Renew. Sustain. Energy Rev.*, **103**, 529–545, doi:10.1016/j.rser.2018.11.006.

Kılkış, Ş., 2021a: Urban-Level-Emission-Scenarios: Urban Level Emission Scenarios. *Zenodo*, doi:10.5281/zenodo.5559792.

Kılkış, Ş., 2021b: Transition towards urban system integration and benchmarking of an urban area to accelerate mitigation towards net-zero targets. *Energy*, **236**, 121394, doi:10.1016/j.energy.2021.121394.

Kjellstrom, T., and A.J. McMichael, 2013: Climate change threats to population health and well-being: the imperative of protective solutions that will last. *Glob. Health Action*, **6(1)**, 20816, doi:10.3402/gha.v6i0.20816.

Klopp, J.M., and D.L. Petretta, 2017: The urban sustainable development goal: Indicators, complexity and the politics of measuring cities. *Cities*, **63**, 92–97, doi:10.1016/j.cities.2016.12.019.

Knoll, M., 2021: *Cities–Regions–Hinterlands: Metabolisms, Markets, and Mobilities Revisited*. [Knoll, M., (ed.)]. StudienVerlag, Innsbruck, Austria, 346 pp.

Kobashi, T. et al., 2020: On the potential of "Photovoltaics + Electric vehicles" for deep decarbonization of Kyoto's power systems: Techno-economic-social considerations. *Appl. Energy*, **275**, 115419, doi:10.1016/j.apenergy.2020.115419.

Kobashi, T., P. Jittrapirom, T. Yoshida, Y. Hirano, and Y. Yamagata, 2021: SolarEV City concept: Building the next urban power and mobility systems. *Environ. Res. Lett.*, **16(2)**, 024042, doi:10.1088/1748-9326/abd430.

Kona, A., P. Bertoldi, F. Monforti-Ferrario, S. Rivas, and J.F. Dallemand, 2018: Covenant of mayors signatories leading the way towards 1.5 degree global warming pathway. *Sustain. Cities Soc.*, **41**, 568–575, doi:10.1016/j.scs.2018.05.017.

Koohsari, M.J. et al., 2016: Street network measures and adults' walking for transport: Application of space syntax. *Heal. Place*, **38**, 89–95, doi:10.1016/j.healthplace.2015.12.009.

Koop, S.H.A., and C.J. van Leeuwen, 2015: Assessment of the Sustainability of Water Resources Management: A Critical Review of the City Blueprint Approach. *Water Resour. Manag.*, **29(15)**, 5649–5670, doi:10.1007/s11269-015-1139-z.

Kościelniak, H. and A. Górka, 2016: Green Cities PPP as a Method of Financing Sustainable Urban Development. *Transp. Res. Procedia*, **16**, 227–235, doi:10.1016/j.trpro.2016.11.022.

Kourtit, K., P. Nijkamp, and H. Scholten, 2015: The Future of the New Urban World. *Int. Plan. Stud.*, **20(1–2)**, 4–20, doi:10.1080/13563475.2014.9387.

Kovac, A., S. Mcdaniel, A. Kona, P. Bertoldi, and C. Chavara, 2020: *Aggregating Cities' GHG Mitigation Targets with Modeled Emissions Scenarios*. World Resources Institute (WRI), Washington, DC, USA, 16 pp. https://files.wri.org/s3fs-public/aggregating-cities-ghg-mitigation-targets.pdf (Accessed March 28, 2021).

Krayenhoff, E.S., M. Moustaoui, A.M. Broadbent, V. Gupta, and M. Georgescu, 2018: Diurnal interaction between urban expansion, climate change and adaptation in US cities. *Nat. Clim. Change*, **8(12)**, 1097–1103, doi:10.1038/s41558-018-0320-9.

Kriegler, E. et al., 2017: Fossil-fueled development (SSP5): An energy and resource intensive scenario for the 21st century. *Glob. Environ. Change*, **42**, 297–315, doi:10.1016/j.gloenvcha.2016.05.015.

Krog, L., 2019: How municipalities act under the new paradigm for energy planning. *Sustain. Cities Soc.*, **47**, 101511, doi:10.1016/j.scs.2019.101511.

Kshetri, N., and J. Voas, 2018: Blockchain in Developing Countries. *IT Prof.*, **20(2)**, 11–14, doi:10.1109/MITP.2018.021921645.

Kuramochi, T. et al., 2020: Beyond national climate action: the impact of region, city, and business commitments on global greenhouse gas emissions. *Clim. Policy*, **20(3)**, 275–291, doi:10.1080/14693062.2020.1740150.

Kutty, A.A., G.M. Abdella, M. Kucukvar, N.C. Onat, and M. Bulu, 2020: A system thinking approach for harmonizing smart and sustainable city initiatives with United Nations sustainable development goals. *Sustain. Dev.*, **28(5)**, 1347–1365, doi:10.1002/sd.2088.

Kwan, S.C. and J.H. Hashim, 2016: A review on co-benefits of mass public transportation in climate change mitigation. *Sustain. Cities Soc.*, **22**, 11–18, doi:10.1016/j.scs.2016.01.004.

Laeremans, M. et al., 2018: Black Carbon Reduces the Beneficial Effect of Physical Activity on Lung Function. *Med. Sci. Sport. Exerc.*, **50(9)**, 1875–1881, doi:10.1249/MSS.0000000000001632.

Lall, S., M. Lebrand, H. Park, D. Sturm, and A.J. Venables, 2021: *Pancakes to Pyramids: City Form to Promote Sustainable Growth*. International Bank for Reconstruction and Development (IBRD) and The World Bank, Washington, DC, USA, 154 pp. https://www.worldbank.org/en/topic/urbandevelopment/publication/pancakes-to-pyramids (Accessed October 21, 2021).

Lam, K.L., S.J. Kenway, and P.A. Lant, 2017: Energy use for water provision in cities. *J. Clean. Prod.*, **143**, 699–709, doi:10.1016/j.jclepro.2016.12.056.

Lam, K.L., P.A. Lant, and S.J. Kenway, 2018: Energy implications of the millennium drought on urban water cycles in Southeast Australian cities. *Water Supply*, **18(1)**, 214–221, doi:10.2166/ws.2017.110.

Lamb, B.K. et al., 2016: Direct and Indirect Measurements and Modeling of Methane Emissions in Indianapolis, Indiana. *Environ. Sci. Technol.*, **50(16)**, 8910–8917, doi:10.1021/acs.est.6b01198.

Lamb, M.R., S. Kandula, and J. Shaman, 2021: Differential COVID-19 case positivity in New York City neighborhoods: Socioeconomic factors and mobility. *Influenza Other Respi. Viruses*, **15(2)**, 209–217, doi:10.1111/irv.12816.

Lamb, W.F., M.W. Callaghan, F. Creutzig, R. Khosla, and J.C. Minx, 2018: The literature landscape on 1.5°C climate change and cities. *Curr. Opin. Environ. Sustain.*, **30**, 26–34, doi:10.1016/j.cosust.2018.02.008.

Lamb, W.F., F. Creutzig, M.W. Callaghan, and J.C. Minx, 2019: Learning about urban climate solutions from case studies. *Nat. Clim. Change*, **9(4)**, 279–287, doi:10.1038/s41558-019-0440-x.

Lammers, I. and T. Hoppe, 2019: Watt rules? Assessing decision-making practices on smart energy systems in Dutch city districts. *Energy Res. Soc. Sci.*, **47**, 233–246, doi:10.1016/j.erss.2018.10.003.

Lamson-Hall, P., S. Angel, D. DeGroot, R. Martin, and T. Tafesse, 2019: A new plan for African cities: The Ethiopia Urban Expansion Initiative. *Urban Stud.*, **56(6)**, 1234–1249, doi:10.1177/0042098018757601.

Landauer, M., S. Juhola, and J. Klein, 2019: The role of scale in integrating climate change adaptation and mitigation in cities. *J. Environ. Plan. Manag.*, **62(5)**, 741–765, doi:10.1080/09640568.2018.1430022.

Laramee, J., S. Tilmans, and J. Davis, 2018: Costs and benefits of biogas recovery from communal anaerobic digesters treating domestic wastewater: Evidence from peri-urban Zambia. *J. Environ. Manage.*, **210**, 23–35, doi:10.1016/j.jenvman.2017.12.064.

Lauvaux, T. et al., 2016: High-resolution atmospheric inversion of urban CO_2 emissions during the dormant season of the Indianapolis flux experiment (INFLUX). *J. Geophys. Res.*, **121(10)**, 5213–5236, doi:10.1002/2015JD024473.

Lauvaux, T. et al., 2020: Policy-Relevant Assessment of Urban CO_2 Emissions. *Environ. Sci. Technol.*, **54(16)**, 10237–10245, doi:10.1021/acs.est.0c00343.

Lawhon, M., D. Nilsson, J. Silver, H. Ernstson, and S. Lwasa, 2018: Thinking through heterogeneous infrastructure configurations. *Urban Stud.*, **55(4)**, 720–732, doi:10.1177/0042098017720149.

Layne, S.P., J.M. Hyman, D.M. Morens, and J.K. Taubenberger, 2020: New coronavirus outbreak: Framing questions for pandemic prevention. *Sci. Transl. Med.*, **12(534)**, eabb1469, doi:10.1126/scitranslmed.abb1469.

Le Quéré, C. et al., 2020: Temporary reduction in daily global CO_2 emissions during the COVID-19 forced confinement. *Nat. Clim. Change*, **10(7)**, 647–653, doi:10.1038/s41558-020-0797-x.

Le Quéré, C. et al., 2021: Fossil CO_2 emissions in the post-COVID-19 era. *Nat. Clim. Change*, **11(3)**, 197–199, doi:10.1038/s41558-021-01001-0.

Lechtenböhmer, S., L.J. Nilsson, M. Åhman, and C. Schneider, 2016: Decarbonising the energy intensive basic materials industry through electrification – Implications for future EU electricity demand. *Energy*, **115**, 1623–1631, doi:10.1016/j.energy.2016.07.110.

Lecompte, M.C. and B.S. Juan Pablo, 2017: Transport systems and their impact con gender equity. *World Conference on Transport Research*, Vol. 25 of, Shanghai, Elsevier B.V., 4245–4257.

Lee, C.M., and P. Erickson, 2017: How does local economic development in cities affect global GHG emissions? *Sustain. Cities Soc.*, **35**, 626–636, doi:10.1016/j.scs.2017.08.027.

Lee, J.H., and S. Lim, 2018: The selection of compact city policy instruments and their effects on energy consumption and greenhouse gas emissions in the transportation sector: The case of South Korea. *Sustain. Cities Soc.*, **37**, 116–124, doi:10.1016/j.scs.2017.11.006.

Lee, S., and B. Lee, 2020: Comparing the impacts of local land use and urban spatial structure on household VMT and GHG emissions. *J. Transp. Geogr.*, **84**, 102694, doi:10.1016/j.jtrangeo.2020.102694.

Lee, T., and M. Painter, 2015: Comprehensive local climate policy: The role of urban governance. *Urban Clim.*, **14**, 566–577, doi:10.1016/j.uclim.2015.09.003.

Lee, V.J. et al., 2020: Epidemic preparedness in urban settings: new challenges and opportunities. *Lancet Infect. Dis.*, **20(5)**, 527–529, doi:10.1016/S1473-3099(20)30249-8.

Lemoine-Rodríguez, R., L. Inostroza, and H. Zepp, 2020: Urban form datasets of 194 cities delineated based on the contiguous urban fabric for 1990 and 2015. *Data Br.*, **33**, 106369, doi:10.1016/J.DIB.2020.106369.

Lenzen, M. et al., 2017: The Global MRIO Lab – charting the world economy. *Econ. Syst. Res.*, **29(2)**, 158–186, doi:10.1080/09535314.2017.1301887.

Levesque, A., R.C. Pietzcker, and G. Luderer, 2019: Halving energy demand from buildings: The impact of low consumption practices. *Technol. Forecast. Soc. Change*, **146**, 253–266, doi:10.1016/j.techfore.2019.04.025.

Li, B. et al., 2016: Spatio-temporal assessment of urbanization impacts on ecosystem services: Case study of Nanjing City, China. *Ecol. Indic.*, **71**, 416–427, doi:10.1016/j.ecolind.2016.07.017.

Li, R. et al., 2019a: Crowded urban traffic: co-evolution among land development, population, roads and vehicle ownership. *Nonlinear Dyn.*, **95(4)**, 2783–2795, doi:10.1007/S11071-018-4722-Z.

Li, X., Y. Zhou, J. Eom, S. Yu, and G.R. Asrar, 2019b: Projecting Global Urban Area Growth Through 2100 Based on Historical Time Series Data and Future Shared Socioeconomic Pathways. *Earth's Future*, **7(4)**, 351–362, doi:10.1029/2019EF001152.

Li, X.X., Y. Zhou, G.R. Asrar, M. Imhoff, and X.X. Li, 2017: The surface urban heat island response to urban expansion: A panel analysis for the conterminous United States. *Sci. Total Environ.*, **605–606**, 426–435, doi:10.1016/j.scitotenv.2017.06.229.

Li, Y., and X. Liu, 2018: How did urban polycentricity and dispersion affect economic productivity? A case study of 306 Chinese cities. *Landsc. Urban Plan.*, **173**, 51–59, doi:10.1016/j.landurbplan.2018.01.007.

Lin, B.B. et al., 2021: Integrating solutions to adapt cities for climate change. *Lancet Planet. Health*, **5(7)**, e479–e486, doi:10.1016/S2542-5196(21)00135-2.

Lin, J., Y. Hu, S. Cui, J. Kang, and A. Ramaswami, 2015: Tracking urban carbon footprints from production and consumption perspectives. *Environ. Res. Lett.*, **10(5)**, 054001, doi:10.1088/1748-9326/10/5/054001.

Lin, J. et al., 2018: Scenario analysis of urban GHG peak and mitigation co-benefits: A case study of Xiamen City, China. *J. Clean. Prod.*, **171**, 972–983, doi:10.1016/j.jclepro.2017.10.040.

Linton, S., A. Clarke, and L. Tozer, 2021: Strategies and governance for implementing deep decarbonization plans at the local level. *Sustainability*, **13(1)**, 1–22, doi:10.3390/su13010154.

Linzner, R., and U. Lange, 2013: Role and size of informal sector in waste management – a review. *Proc. Inst. Civ. Eng. - Waste Resour. Manag.*, **166(2)**, 69–83, doi:10.1680/warm.12.00012.

Liu, F. et al., 2019: Chinese cropland losses due to urban expansion in the past four decades. *Sci. Total Environ.*, **650(1)**, 847–857, doi:10.1016/j.scitotenv.2018.09.091.

Liu, J., and D. Niyogi, 2019: Meta-analysis of urbanization impact on rainfall modification. *Sci. Rep.*, **9**, 7301, doi:10.1038/s41598-019-42494-2.

Liu, M. et al., 2017: Estimating health co-benefits of greenhouse gas reduction strategies with a simplified energy balance based model: The Suzhou City case. *J. Clean. Prod.*, **142**, 3332–3342, doi:10.1016/j.jclepro.2016.10.137.

Liu, W.H. et al., 2006: Woody debris contribution to the carbon budget of selectively logged and maturing mid-latitude forests. *Oecologia*, **148**, 108–117, doi:10.1007/s00442-006-0356-9.

Liu, X., B. Derudder, F. Witlox, and M. Hoyler, 2014: Cities As Networks within Networks of Cities: The Evolution of the City/Firm-Duality in the World City Network, 2000-2010. *Tijdschr. voor Econ. en Soc. Geogr.*, **105(4)**, 465–482, doi:10.1111/tesg.12097.

Liu, X. et al., 2020a: High-spatiotemporal-resolution mapping of global urban change from 1985 to 2015. *Nat. Sustain.*, **3(7)**, 564–570, doi:10.1038/s41893-020-0521-x.

Liu, Y., H. Guo, C. Sun, and W.-S. Chang, 2016a: Assessing Cross Laminated Timber (CLT) as an Alternative Material for Mid-Rise Residential Buildings in Cold Regions in China—A Life-Cycle Assessment Approach. *Sustainability*, **8(10)**, 1047, doi:10.3390/su8101047.

Liu, Z., C. He, and J. Wu, 2016b: The Relationship between Habitat Loss and Fragmentation during Urbanization: An Empirical Evaluation from 16 World Cities. *PLoS One*, **11(4)**, e0154613, doi:10.1371/JOURNAL.PONE.0154613.

Liu, Z. et al., 2020b: Near-real-time monitoring of global CO_2 emissions reveals the effects of the COVID-19 pandemic. *Nat. Commun.*, **11**, 5172, doi:10.1038/s41467-020-18922-7.

Lohrey, S. and F. Creutzig, 2016: A 'sustainability window' of urban form. *Transp. Res. Part D Transp. Environ.*, **45**, 96–111, doi:10.1016/j.trd.2015.09.004.

Lombardi, M., E. Laiola, C. Tricase, and R. Rana, 2017: Assessing the urban carbon footprint: An overview. *Environ. Impact Assess. Rev.*, **66**, 43–52, doi:10.1016/j.eiar.2017.06.005.

Lu, C. and W. Li, 2019: A comprehensive city-level GHGs inventory accounting quantitative estimation with an empirical case of Baoding. *Sci. Total Environ.*, **651**, 601–613, doi:10.1016/j.scitotenv.2018.09.223.

Lund, H. et al., 2014: 4th Generation District Heating (4GDH): Integrating smart thermal grids into future sustainable energy systems. *Energy*, **68**, 1–11, doi:10.1016/J.ENERGY.2014.02.089.

Lund, H., P.A. Østergaard, D. Connolly, and B.V. Mathiesen, 2017: Smart energy and smart energy systems. *Int. J. Sustain. Energy Plan. Manag.*, **11**, 3–14, doi:10.1016/j.energy.2017.05.123.

Lund, H., N. Duic, P.A. Østergaard, and B.V. Mathiesen, 2018: Future district heating systems and technologies: On the role of smart energy systems and 4th generation district heating. *Energy*, **165**, 614–619, doi:10.1016/j.energy.2018.09.115.

Lund, P.D., J. Mikkola, and J. Ypyä, 2015: Smart energy system design for large clean power schemes in urban areas. *J. Clean. Prod.*, **103**, 437–445, doi:10.1016/j.jclepro.2014.06.005.

Luqman, M., P. Rayner, and K.R. Gurney, 2021: On the impact of Urbanisation on CO_2 Emissions. *EarthArXiv*, doi:10.31223/X5D62Z.

Lwasa, S., 2017: Options for reduction of greenhouse gas emissions in the low-emitting city and metropolitan region of Kampala. *Carbon Manag.*, **8(3)**, 263–276, doi:10.1080/17583004.2017.1330592.

Lwasa, S. et al., 2015: A meta-analysis of urban and peri-urban agriculture and forestry in mediating climate change. *Curr. Opin. Environ. Sustain.*, **13**, 68–73, doi:10.1016/j.cosust.2015.02.003.

Lwasa, S., K. Buyana, P. Kasaija, and J. Mutyaba, 2018: Scenarios for adaptation and mitigation in urban Africa under 1.5°C global warming. *Curr. Opin. Environ. Sustain.*, **30**, 52–58, doi:10.1016/j.cosust.2018.02.012.

Lynch, K., 1981: *A Theory of Good City Form*. 1st ed. MIT Press, Cambridge, MA, USA, 532 pp.

Ma, J., Z. Liu, and Y. Chai, 2015: The impact of urban form on CO_2 emission from work and non-work trips: The case of Beijing, China. *Habitat Int.*, **47**, 1–10, doi:10.1016/j.habitatint.2014.12.007.

Ma, Y., K. Rong, D. Mangalagiu, T.F. Thornton, and D. Zhu, 2018: Co-evolution between urban sustainability and business ecosystem innovation: Evidence from the sharing mobility sector in Shanghai. *J. Clean. Prod.*, **188**, 942–953, doi:10.1016/j.jclepro.2018.03.323.

Maes, M.J.A.A., K.E. Jones, M.B. Toledano, and B. Milligan, 2019: Mapping synergies and trade-offs between urban ecosystems and the sustainable development goals. *Environ. Sci. Policy*, **93**, 181–188, doi:10.1016/j.envsci.2018.12.010.

Magueta, D., M. Madaleno, M. Ferreira Dias, and M. Meireles, 2018: New cars and emissions: Effects of policies, macroeconomic impacts and cities characteristics in Portugal. *J. Clean. Prod.*, **181**, 178–191, doi:10.1016/j.jclepro.2017.11.243.

Mahtta, R., A. Mahendra, and K.C. Seto, 2019: Building up or spreading out? Typologies of urban growth across 478 cities of 1 million+. *Environ. Res. Lett.*, **14(12)**, 124077, doi:10.1088/1748-9326/ab59bf.

Maier, S., 2016: Smart energy systems for smart city districts: case study Reininghaus District. *Energy. Sustain. Soc.*, **6**, 23, doi:10.1186/s13705-016-0085-9.

Manga, M., J. Bartram, and B.E. Evans, 2020: Economic cost analysis of low-cost sanitation technology options in informal settlement areas (case study: Soweto, Johannesburg). *Int. J. Hyg. Environ. Health*, **223(1)**, 289–298, doi:10.1016/j.ijheh.2019.06.012.

Mantey, J. and E.K. Sakyi, 2019: A Study of Energy Related Greenhouse Gas Emissions of High Income Urban Residents in the city of Accra, Ghana. *OIDA Int. J. Sustain. Dev.*, **12(2)**, 41–60.

Manuamorn, O.P., R. Biesbroek, and V. Cebotari, 2020: What makes internationally-financed climate change adaptation projects focus on local communities? A configurational analysis of 30 Adaptation Fund projects. *Glob. Environ. Change*, **61**, 102035, doi:10.1016/j.gloenvcha.2020.102035.

Marino, A.L., G. de L.D. Chaves, and J.L. dos Santos Junior, 2018: Do Brazilian municipalities have the technical capacity to implement solid waste management at the local level? *J. Clean. Prod.*, **188**, 378–386, doi:10.1016/j.jclepro.2018.03.311.

Maroko, A.R., D. Nash, and B.T. Pavilonis, 2020: COVID-19 and Inequity: a Comparative Spatial Analysis of New York City and Chicago Hot Spots. *J. Urban Heal.*, **97(4)**, 461–470, doi:10.1007/s11524-020-00468-0.

Marshall, J.U., 1989: *The Structure of Urban Systems*. University of Toronto Press, Toronto, Canada, 394 pp.

Martin, A.R., M. Doraisami, and S.C. Thomas, 2018: Global patterns in wood carbon concentration across the world's trees and forests. *Nat. Geosci.*, **11(12)**, 915–920, doi:10.1038/s41561-018-0246-x.

Martínez, J., J. Martí-Herrero, S. Villacís, A.J. Riofrío, and D. Vaca, 2017: Analysis of energy, CO_2 emissions and economy of the technological migration for clean cooking in Ecuador. *Energy Policy*, **107**, 182–187, doi:10.1016/j.enpol.2017.04.033.

Masoumi, H.E., 2019: A discrete choice analysis of transport mode choice causality and perceived barriers of sustainable mobility in the MENA region. *Transp. Policy*, **79**, 37–53, doi:10.1016/j.tranpol.2019.04.005.

Masseroni, D., and A. Cislaghi, 2016: Green roof benefits for reducing flood risk at the catchment scale. *Environ. Earth Sci.*, **75(7)**, 579, doi:10.1007/s12665-016-5377-z.

Masucci, A.P., K. Stanilov, and M. Batty, 2013: Limited Urban Growth: London's Street Network Dynamics since the 18th Century. *PLoS One*, **8(8)**, e69469, doi:10.1371/JOURNAL.PONE.0069469.

Mathiesen, B.V. et al., 2015: Smart Energy Systems for coherent 100% renewable energy and transport solutions. *Appl. Energy*, **145**, 139–154, doi:10.1016/j.apenergy.2015.01.075.

Matsuda, T. et al., 2018: Monitoring environmental burden reduction from household waste prevention. *Waste Manag.*, **71**, 2–9, doi:10.1016/j.wasman.2017.10.014.

Matsuhashi, K., and T. Ariga, 2016: Estimation of passenger car CO2 emissions with urban population density scenarios for low carbon transportation in Japan. *IATSS Res.*, **39(2)**, 117–120, doi:10.1016/j.iatssr.2016.01.002.

Matsuo, K., and T. Tanaka, 2019: Analysis of spatial and temporal distribution patterns of temperatures in urban and rural areas: Making urban environmental climate maps for supporting urban environmental planning and management in Hiroshima. *Sustain. Cities Soc.*, **47**, 101419, doi:10.1016/j.scs.2019.01.004.

Matthews, E.R., J.P. Schmit, and J.P. Campbell, 2016: Climbing vines and forest edges affect tree growth and mortality in temperate forests of the U.S. Mid-Atlantic States. *For. Ecol. Manage.*, **374**, 166–173, doi:10.1016/j.foreco.2016.05.005.

McCarney, P., 2019: Cities leading: The pivotal role of local governance and planning for sustainable development. In: *The Routledge Companion to Environmental Planning* [Davoudi, S., R. Cowell, I. White, and H. Blanco, (eds.)]. Routledge, London, UK, pp. 200–208.

McCarney, P., H. Blanco, J. Carmin, and M. Colley, 2011: Cities and Climate Change: The challenges for governance. In: *Climate Change and Cities: First Assessment Report of the Urban Climate Change Research Network* [Rosenzweig, C., W.D. Solecki, S.A. Hammer, and S. Mehrotra, (eds.)]. Cambridge University Press, Cambridge, UK, pp. 249–269.

McDonald, R. et al., 2016: *Planting healthy air: A global analysis of the role of urban trees in addressing particulate matter pollution and extreme heat*. The Nature Conservancy (TNC), Arlington, VA, USA, 136 pp. https://www.nature.org/content/dam/tnc/nature/en/documents/20160825_PHA_Report_Final.pdf (Accessed March 28, 2021).

McDonald, R.I., B. Güneralp, C.-W.W. Huang, K.C. Seto, and M. You, 2018: Conservation priorities to protect vertebrate endemics from global urban expansion. *Biol. Conserv.*, **224**, 290–299, doi:10.1016/j.biocon.2018.06.010.

McDonald, R.I. et al., 2020: Research gaps in knowledge of the impact of urban growth on biodiversity. *Nat. Sustain.*, **3**, 16–24, doi:10.1038/s41893-019-0436-6.

Meha, D., A. Pfeifer, N. Duić, and H. Lund, 2020: Increasing the integration of variable renewable energy in coal-based energy system using power to heat technologies: The case of Kosovo. *Energy*, **212**, 118762, doi:10.1016/j.energy.2020.118762.

Mehta, L. et al., 2019: Climate change and uncertainty from 'above' and 'below': perspectives from India. *Reg. Environ. Change*, **19(6)**, 1533–1547, doi:10.1007/s10113-019-01479-7.

Melica, G. et al., 2018: Multilevel governance of sustainable energy policies: The role of regions and provinces to support the participation of small local authorities in the Covenant of Mayors. *Sustain. Cities Soc.*, **39**, 729–739, doi:10.1016/j.scs.2018.01.013.

Mell, I.C., J. Henneberry, S. Hehl-Lange, and B. Keskin, 2013: Promoting urban greening: Valuing the development of green infrastructure investments in the urban core of Manchester, UK. *Urban For. Urban Green.*, **12(3)**, 296–306, doi:10.1016/j.ufug.2013.04.006.

Mell, I.C., J. Henneberry, S. Hehl-Lange, and B. Keskin, 2016: To green or not to green: Establishing the economic value of green infrastructure investments in The Wicker, Sheffield. *Urban For. Urban Green.*, **18**, 257–267, doi:10.1016/j.ufug.2016.06.015.

Meschede, H., 2019: Increased utilisation of renewable energies through demand response in the water supply sector – A case study. *Energy*, **175**, 810–817, doi:10.1016/J.ENERGY.2019.03.137.

Mey, F. and J. Hicks, 2019: Community Owned Renewable Energy: Enabling the Transition Towards Renewable Energy? In: *Decarbonising the Built Environment: Charting the Transition* [Newton, P., D. Prasad, A. Sproul, and S. White, (eds.)]. Palgrave Macmillan, Singapore, pp. 65–82.

Mguni, P., L. Herslund, and M.B. Jensen, 2016: Sustainable urban drainage systems: examining the potential for green infrastructure-based stormwater management for Sub-Saharan cities. *Nat. Hazards*, **82(S2)**, 241–257, doi:10.1007/s11069-016-2309-x.

Mi, Z. et al., 2019: Cities: The core of climate change mitigation. *J. Clean. Prod.*, **207**, 582–589, doi:10.1016/j.jclepro.2018.10.034.

Miao, L., 2017: Examining the impact factors of urban residential energy consumption and CO_2 emissions in China – Evidence from city-level data. *Ecol. Indic.*, **73**, 29–37, doi:10.1016/j.ecolind.2016.09.031.

Milutinović, B., G. Stefanović, S. Milutinović, and Ž. Ćojbašić, 2016: Application of fuzzy logic for evaluation of the level of social acceptance of waste treatment. *Clean Technol. Environ. Policy*, **18(6)**, 1863–1875, doi:10.1007/s10098-016-1211-2.

Mitchell, L.E. et al., 2018: Long-term urban carbon dioxide observations reveal spatial and temporal dynamics related to urban characteristics and growth. *Proc. Natl. Acad. Sci.*, **115(12)**, 2912–2917, doi:10.1073/pnas.1702393115.

Moglia, M. et al., 2018: Urban transformation stories for the 21st century: Insights from strategic conversations. *Glob. Environ. Change*, **50**, 222–237, doi:10.1016/j.gloenvcha.2018.04.009.

Mohajeri, N., and A. Gudmundsson, 2014: The Evolution and Complexity of Urban Street Networks. *Geogr. Anal.*, **46(4)**, 345–367, doi:10.1111/GEAN.12061.

Mohammed, M.U., N.I. Hassan, and M.M. Badamasi, 2019: In search of missing links: urbanisation and climate change in Kano Metropolis, Nigeria. *Int. J. Urban Sustain. Dev.*, **11(3)**, 309–318, doi:10.1080/19463138.2019.1603154.

Möller, B., E. Wiechers, U. Persson, L. Grundahl, and D. Connolly, 2018: Heat Roadmap Europe: Identifying local heat demand and supply areas with a European thermal atlas. *Energy*, **158**, 281–292, doi:10.1016/j.energy.2018.06.025.

Möller, B. et al., 2019: Heat Roadmap Europe: Towards EU-Wide, local heat supply strategies. *Energy*, **177**, 554–564, doi:10.1016/J.ENERGY.2019.04.098.

Moncada, S., H. Bambrick, and M. Briguglio, 2019: The health impacts of a community biogas facility in an informal Urban settlement: does training matter? *J. Dev. Eff.*, **11(2)**, 189–202, doi:10.1080/19439342.2019.1638434.

Monforti-Ferrario, F., A. Kona, E. Peduzzi, D. Pernigotti, and E. Pisoni, 2018: The impact on air quality of energy saving measures in the major cities signatories of the Covenant of Mayors initiative. *Environ. Int.*, **118**, 222–234, doi:10.1016/j.envint.2018.06.001.

Mora, C. et al., 2017: Global risk of deadly heat. *Nat. Clim. Change*, **7(7)**, 501–506, doi:10.1038/nclimate3322.

Moran, D. et al., 2018: Carbon footprints of 13 000 cities. *Environ. Res. Lett.*, **13(6)**, 064041, doi:10.1088/1748-9326/aac72a.

Moreno, C., Z. Allam, D. Chabaud, C. Gall, and F. Pratlong, 2021: Introducing the "15-Minute City": Sustainability, Resilience and Place Identity in Future Post-Pandemic Cities. *Smart Cities*, **4(1)**, 93–111, doi:10.3390/smartcities4010006.

Moretti, M. et al., 2017: A systematic review of environmental and economic impacts of smart grids. *Renew. Sustain. Energy Rev.*, **68**, 888–898, doi:10.1016/j.rser.2016.03.039.

Moser, S.C., J.A. Ekstrom, J. Kim, and S. Heitsch, 2019: Adaptation finance archetypes: local governments' persistent challenges of funding adaptation to climate change and ways to overcome them. *Ecol. Soc.*, **24(2)**, art28, doi:10.5751/ES-10980-240228.

Mrówczyńska, M., M. Skiba, A. Bazan-Krzywoszańska, D. Bazuń, and M. Kwiatkowski, 2018: Social and Infrastructural Conditioning of Lowering Energy Costs and Improving the Energy Efficiency of Buildings in the Context of the Local Energy Policy. *Energies*, **11(9)**, 2302, doi:10.3390/en11092302.

Mrówczyńska, M. et al., 2021: Scenarios as a tool supporting decisions in urban energy policy: The analysis using fuzzy logic, multi-criteria analysis and GIS tools. *Renew. Sustain. Energy Rev.*, **137**, 110598, doi:10.1016/j.rser.2020.110598.

Mueller, K.L. et al., 2021: An emerging GHG estimation approach can help cities achieve their climate and sustainability goals. *Environ. Res. Lett.*, **16(8)**, 084003, doi:10.1088/1748-9326/ac0f25.

Mueller, N. et al., 2020: Changing the urban design of cities for health: The superblock model. *Environ. Int.*, **134**, 105132, doi:10.1016/j.envint.2019.105132.

Müller, D.B. et al., 2013: Carbon Emissions of Infrastructure Development. *Environ. Sci. Technol.*, **47(20)**, 11739–11746, doi:10.1021/es402618m.

Mulligan, J. et al., 2020: Hybrid infrastructures, hybrid governance: New evidence from Nairobi (Kenya) on green-blue-grey infrastructure in informal settlements. *Anthropocene*, **29**, 100227, doi:10.1016/j.ancene.2019.100227.

Munich RE, 2021: Record hurricane season and major wildfires – The natural disaster figures for 2020. https://www.munichre.com/en/company/media-relations/media-information-and-corporate-news/media-information/2021/2020-natural-disasters-balance.html (Accessed October 11, 2021).

Nagendra, H., X. Bai, E.S. Brondizio, and S. Lwasa, 2018: The urban south and the predicament of global sustainability. *Nat. Sustain.*, **1(7)**, 341–349, doi:10.1038/s41893-018-0101-5.

Narayana, T., 2009: Municipal solid waste management in India: From waste disposal to recovery of resources? *Waste Manag.*, **29(3)**, 1163–1166, doi:10.1016/j.wasman.2008.06.038.

Nasarre-Aznar, S., 2018: Collaborative housing and blockchain. *Administration*, **66(2)**, 59–82, doi:10.2478/admin-2018-0018.

Naumann, S., T. Kaphengst, K. McFarland, and J. Stadler, 2014: *Nature-based approaches for climate change mitigation and adaptation: The challenges of climate change - partnering with nature*. German Federal Agency for Nature Conservation (BfN), Ecologic Institute, Bonn, Germany, 22 pp. https://www.ecologic.eu/11240 (Accessed March 28, 2021).

NCE, 2018: *Unlocking the Inclusive Growth Story of the 21st Century: Accelerating Climate Action in Urgent Times - Key Findings & Executive Summary*. The New Climate Economy (NCE), The Global Commission on the Economy and Climate, Washington, DC, USA, 16 pp. https://newclimateeconomy.report/2018/wp-content/uploads/sites/6/2018/09/NCE_2018_ExecutiveSummary_FINAL.pdf (Accessed October 22, 2021).

Negreiros, P. et al., 2021: *The State of Cities Climate Finance Part 1: The Landscape of Urban Climate Finance*. Climate Policy Initiative (CPI), San Francisco, CA, USA, 82 pp.

Nero, B., D. Callo-Concha, and M. Denich, 2018: Structure, Diversity, and Carbon Stocks of the Tree Community of Kumasi, Ghana. *Forests*, **9(9)**, 519, doi:10.3390/f9090519.

Nero, B., D. Callo-Concha, and M. Denich, 2019: Increasing Urbanisation and the Role of Green Spaces in Urban Climate Resilience in Africa. In: *Environmental Change and African Societies* [Haltermann, I. and J. Tischler, (eds.)]. Vol. 5 of *Climate and Culture*, Brill, Leiden, The Netherlands, pp. 265–296.

Neuvonen, A., and P. Ache, 2017: Metropolitan vision making – using backcasting as a strategic learning process to shape metropolitan futures. *Futures*, **86**, 73–83, doi:10.1016/j.futures.2016.10.003.

NewClimate Institute, and Data-Driven EnviroLab, 2020: *Navigating the nuances of net-zero targets*. [Day, T. et al., (eds.)]. NewClimate Institute and Data-Driven EnviroLab, Cologne, Germany, 74 pp. https://newclimate.org/wp-content/uploads/2020/10/NewClimate_NetZeroReport_October2020.pdf (Accessed March 30, 2021).

NewClimate Institute, Data-Driven Lab, German Development Institute/Deutsches Institut für Entwicklungspolitik (DIE), and Blavatnik School of Government University of Oxford, 2019: *Global climate action from cities, regions and businesses: Impact of individual actors and cooperative initiatives on global and national emissions*. [Kuramochi, T. et al., (eds.)]. 2nd ed. NewClimate Institute, Data-Driven Lab, PBL, German Development Institute/Deutsches Institut für Entwicklungspolitik (DIE), Blavatnik School of Government, University of Oxford, 93 pp. https://newclimate.org/wp-content/uploads/2019/09/Report-Global-Climate-Action-from-Cities-Regions-and-Businesses_2019.pdf (Accessed March 28, 2021).

Newman, P., 2020: COVID, CITIES and CLIMATE: Historical Precedents and Potential Transitions for the New Economy. *Urban Sci.*, **4(3)**, 32, doi:10.3390/urbansci4030032.

Newman, P., 2017: The rise and rise of renewable cities. *Renew. Energy Environ. Sustain.*, **2**, 10, doi:10.1051/rees/2017008.

Newman, P., 2020: Cool planning: How urban planning can mainstream responses to climate change. *Cities*, **103**, 102651, doi:10.1016/j.cities.2020.102651.

Newman, P. and I. Jennings, 2008: *Cities as Sustainable Ecosystems: Principles and Practices*. Island Press, Washington, DC, USA, 296 pp.

8

Newman, P., L. Kosonen, and J. Kenworthy, 2016: Theory of urban fabrics: planning the walking, transit/public transport and automobile/motor car cities for reduced car dependency. *Town Plan. Rev.*, **87(4)**, 429–458, doi:10.3828/tpr.2016.28.

Newman, P., T. Beatley, and H. Boyer, 2017: *Resilient Cities, Second Edition: Overcoming Fossil Fuel Dependence*. 2nd ed. Island Press, Washington, DC, USA, 264 pp.

Nieuwenhuijsen, M.J., 2020: Urban and transport planning pathways to carbon neutral, liveable and healthy cities; A review of the current evidence. *Environ. Int.*, **140**, 105661, doi:10.1016/j.envint.2020.105661.

Nieuwenhuijsen, M.J., and H. Khreis, 2016: Car free cities: Pathway to healthy urban living. *Environ. Int.*, **94**, 251–262, doi:10.1016/j.envint.2016.05.032.

Nilsson, M., D. Griggs, and M. Visbeck, 2016: Policy: Map the interactions between Sustainable Development Goals. *Nature*, **534**, 320–322, doi:10.1038/534320a.

Nisbet, E.G. et al., 2019: Very Strong Atmospheric Methane Growth in the 4 Years 2014–2017: Implications for the Paris Agreement. *Global Biogeochem. Cycles*, **33(3)**, 318–342, doi:10.1029/2018GB006009.

Noble, B., and K. Nwanekezie, 2017: Conceptualizing strategic environmental assessment: Principles, approaches and research directions. *Environ. Impact Assess. Rev.*, **62**, 165–173, doi:10.1016/j.eiar.2016.03.005.

Nowak, D.J. and J.F. Dwyer, 2007: Understanding the Benefits and Costs of Urban Forest Ecosystems. In: *Urban and Community Forestry in the Northeast* [Kuser, J.E., (ed.)]. Springer Netherlands, Dordrecht, The Netherlands, pp. 25–46.

Nowak, D.J. and E.J. Greenfield, 2020: The increase of impervious cover and decrease of tree cover within urban areas globally (2012–2017). *Urban For. Urban Green.*, **49**, 126638, doi:10.1016/j.ufug.2020.126638.

Nowak, D.J., E.J. Greenfield, R.E. Hoehn, and E. Lapoint, 2013: Carbon storage and sequestration by trees in urban and community areas of the United States. *Environ. Pollut.*, **178**, 229–236, doi:10.1016/j.envpol.2013.03.019.

Nowak, D.J., N. Appleton, A. Ellis, and E. Greenfield, 2017: Residential building energy conservation and avoided power plant emissions by urban and community trees in the United States. *Urban For. Urban Green.*, **21**, 158–165, doi:10.1016/j.ufug.2016.12.004.

O'Brien, P., P. O'Neill, and A. Pike, 2019: Funding, financing and governing urban infrastructures. *Urban Stud.*, **56(7)**, 1291–1303, doi:10.1177/0042098018824014.

O'Dwyer, E., I. Pan, S. Acha, and N. Shah, 2019: Smart energy systems for sustainable smart cities: Current developments, trends and future directions. *Appl. Energy*, **237**, 581–597, doi:10.1016/j.apenergy.2019.01.024.

O'Neill, B.C. et al., 2020: Achievements and needs for the climate change scenario framework. *Nat. Clim. Change*, **10(12)**, 1074–1084, doi:10.1038/s41558-020-00952-0.

Oda, T., C. Haga, K. Hosomi, T. Matsui, and R. Bun, 2021: Errors and uncertainties associated with the use of unconventional activity data for estimating CO_2 emissions: the case for traffic emissions in Japan. *Environ. Res. Lett.*, **16(8)**, 084058, doi:10.1088/1748-9326/ac109d.

Olazabal, M., and M. Ruiz De Gopegui, 2021: Adaptation planning in large cities is unlikely to be effective. *Landsc. Urban Plan.*, **206**, 103974, doi:10.1016/j.landurbplan.2020.103974.

Oliveira, L.S.B.L., L. Oliveira, B.S. Bezerra, B. Silva Pereira, and R.A.G. Battistelle, 2017: Environmental analysis of organic waste treatment focusing on composting scenarios. *J. Clean. Prod.*, **155(Part I)**, 229–237, doi:10.1016/j.jclepro.2016.08.093.

ONU Medio Ambiente, 2017: *Movilidad eléctrica: Oportunidades para Latinoamérica*. ONU Ambiente / United Nations Environment Programme (UNEP), Panama City, Panama, 82 pp. http://movelatam.org/Movilidad electrica_Oportunidades para AL.pdf (Accessed March 30, 2021).

Oyewo, A.S., A. Aghahosseini, M. Ram, A. Lohrmann, and C. Breyer, 2019: Pathway towards achieving 100% renewable electricity by 2050 for South Africa. *Sol. Energy*, **191**, 549–565, doi:10.1016/j.solener.2019.09.039.

Pacheco-Torres, R., J. Roldán, E.J. Gago, and J. Ordóñez, 2017: Assessing the relationship between urban planning options and carbon emissions at the use stage of new urbanized areas: A case study in a warm climate location. *Energy Build.*, **136**, 73–85, doi:10.1016/j.enbuild.2016.11.055.

Padeiro, M., A. Louro, and N.M. da Costa, 2019: Transit-oriented development and gentrification: a systematic review. *Transp. Rev.*, **39(6)**, 733–754, doi:10.1080/01441647.2019.1649316.

Palermo, V., P. Bertoldi, M. Apostolou, A. Kona, and S. Rivas, 2020a: Assessment of climate change mitigation policies in 315 cities in the Covenant of Mayors initiative. *Sustain. Cities Soc.*, **60**, 102258, doi:10.1016/j.scs.2020.102258.

Palermo, V., P. Bertoldi, M. Apostolou, A. Kona, and S. Rivas, 2020b: Data on mitigation policies at local level within the Covenant of Mayors' monitoring emission inventories. *Data Br.*, **32**, 106217, doi:10.1016/j.dib.2020.106217.

Pan, J., 2020: Target Orientation of Addressing Climate Change during the Period of the 14th Five-Year Plan. *Chinese J. Urban Environ. Stud.*, **8(2)**, 2050007, doi:10.1142/S2345748120500074.

Pan, S.-Y. et al., 2015: Strategies on implementation of waste-to-energy (WTE) supply chain for circular economy system: a review. *J. Clean. Prod.*, **108**, 409–421, doi:10.1016/j.jclepro.2015.06.124.

Pandey, R. et al., 2018: Climate change vulnerability in urban slum communities: Investigating household adaptation and decision-making capacity in the Indian Himalaya. *Ecol. Indic.*, **90**, 379–391, doi:10.1016/j.ecolind.2018.03.031.

Park, E.S. and I.N. Sener, 2019: Traffic-related air emissions in Houston: Effects of light-rail transit. *Sci. Total Environ.*, **651**, 154–161, doi:10.1016/j.scitotenv.2018.09.169.

Pasimeni, M.R., D. Valente, G. Zurlini, and I. Petrosillo, 2019: The interplay between urban mitigation and adaptation strategies to face climate change in two European countries. *Environ. Sci. Policy*, **95**, 20–27, doi:10.1016/j.envsci.2019.02.002.

Pataki, D.E. et al., 2011: Coupling biogeochemical cycles in urban environments: ecosystem services, green solutions, and misconceptions. *Front. Ecol. Environ.*, **9(1)**, 27–36, doi:10.1890/090220.

Pathak, M. and P.R. Shukla, 2016: Co-benefits of low carbon passenger transport actions in Indian cities: Case study of Ahmedabad. *Transp. Res. Part D Transp. Environ.*, **44**, 303–316, doi:10.1016/j.trd.2015.07.013.

Pathak, M. and D. Mahadevia, 2018: Urban Informality and Planning: Challenges to Mainstreaming Resilience in Indian Cities. In: *Resilience-Oriented Urban Planning: Theoretical and Empirical Insights* [Yamagata, Y. and A. Sharifi, (eds.)]. *Lecture Notes in Energy*, Springer International Publishing, Cham, Switzerland, pp. 49–66.

Patterson, J.J., 2021: More than planning: Diversity and drivers of institutional adaptation under climate change in 96 major cities. *Glob. Environ. Change*, **68**, 102279, doi:10.1016/j.gloenvcha.2021.102279.

Pedro, J., C. Silva, and M.D. Pinheiro, 2018: Scaling up LEED-ND sustainability assessment from the neighborhood towards the city scale with the support of GIS modeling: Lisbon case study. *Sustain. Cities Soc.*, **41**, 929–939, doi:10.1016/j.scs.2017.09.015.

Peng, W., J. Yang, X. Lu, and D.L. Mauzerall, 2018: Potential co-benefits of electrification for air quality, health, and CO_2 mitigation in 2030 China. *Appl. Energy*, **218**, 511–519, doi:10.1016/j.apenergy.2018.02.048.

Peng, Y. and X. Bai, 2018: Experimenting towards a low-carbon city: Policy evolution and nested structure of innovation. *J. Clean. Prod.*, **174**, 201–212, doi:10.1016/J.JCLEPRO.2017.10.116.

Peng, Y. and X. Bai, 2020: Financing urban low-carbon transition: The catalytic role of a city-level special fund in Shanghai. *J. Clean. Prod.*, **282**, 124514, doi:10.1016/j.jclepro.2020.124514.

Perini, K., F. Bazzocchi, L. Croci, A. Magliocco, and E. Cattaneo, 2017: The use of vertical greening systems to reduce the energy demand for air conditioning. Field monitoring in Mediterranean climate. *Energy Build.*, **143**, 35–42, doi:10.1016/j.enbuild.2017.03.036.

Permadi, D.A., N.T. Kim Oanh, and R. Vautard, 2017: Assessment of co-benefits of black carbon emission reduction measures in Southeast Asia: Part 2 emission scenarios for 2030 and co-benefits on mitigation of air pollution and climate forcing. *Atmos. Chem. Phys. Discuss.*, 1–21, doi:10.5194/acp-2017-316.

Persson, U., E. Wiechers, B. Möller, and S. Werner, 2019: Heat Roadmap Europe: Heat distribution costs. *Energy*, **176**, 604–622, doi:10.1016/j.energy.2019.03.189.

Pesaresi, M., M. Melchiorri, A. Siragusa, and T. Kemper, 2016: *Atlas of the Human Planet 2016 - Mapping Human Presence on Earth with the Global Human Settlement Layer, EUR 28116 EN*. European Union (EU), Luxembourg, 137 pp.

Petit-Boix, A., and D. Apul, 2018: From Cascade to Bottom-Up Ecosystem Services Model: How Does Social Cohesion Emerge from Urban Agriculture? *Sustainability*, **10(4)**, 998, doi:10.3390/su10040998.

Pfeifer, A., L. Herc, I. Batas Bjelić, and N. Duić, 2021: Flexibility index and decreasing the costs in energy systems with high share of renewable energy. *Energy Convers. Manag.*, **240**, 114258, doi:10.1016/j.enconman.2021.114258.

Pichler, P.-P. et al., 2017: Reducing Urban Greenhouse Gas Footprints. *Sci. Rep.*, **7**, 14659, doi:10.1038/s41598-017-15303-x.

Pierer, C. and F. Creutzig, 2019: Star-shaped cities alleviate trade-off between climate change mitigation and adaptation. *Environ. Res. Lett.*, **14**, 085011, doi:10.1088/1748-9326/ab2081.

Pinho, P. and R. Fernandes, 2019: Urban metabolic impact assessment From concept to practice. In: *The Routledge Companion to Environmental Planning* [Davoudi, S., R. Cowell, I. White, and H. Blanco, (eds.)]. Routledge, London, UK, pp. 358–371.

Pomponi, F., J. Hart, J.H. Arehart, B. D'Amico, and B. D'Amico, 2020: Buildings as a Global Carbon Sink? A Reality Check on Feasibility Limits. *One Earth*, **3(2)**, 157–161, doi:10.1016/j.oneear.2020.07.018.

Portland Bureau of Planning and Sustainability, 2012: *The Portland Plan*. Portland Bureau of Planning and Sustainability (BPS), Portland, OR, USA, 164 pp.https://www.portlandonline.com/portlandplan/index.cfm?c=58776 (Accessed October 27, 2021).

Pörtner, H.O. et al., 2021: *IPBES-IPCC co-sponsored workshop report on biodiversity and climate change*. Intergovernmental Science-Policy Platform on Biodiversity and Ecosystem Services (IPBES) and Intergovernmental Panel on Climate Change (IPCC), Bonn, Germany, 28 pp.

Potdar, A. et al., 2016: Innovation in solid waste management through Clean Development Mechanism in India and other countries. *Process Saf. Environ. Prot.*, **101**, 160–169, doi:10.1016/j.psep.2015.07.009.

Pour, S.H., A.K.A. Wahab, S. Shahid, M. Asaduzzaman, and A. Dewan, 2020: Low impact development techniques to mitigate the impacts of climate-change-induced urban floods: Current trends, issues and challenges. *Sustain. Cities Soc.*, **62**, 102373, doi:10.1016/j.scs.2020.102373.

Pouyat, R., P. Groffman, I. Yesilonis, and L. Hernandez, 2002: Soil carbon pools and fluxes in urban ecosystems. *Environ. Pollut.*, **116(sup1)**, S107–S118, doi:10.1016/S0269-7491(01)00263-9.

Pouyat, R.V. et al., 2007: Effects of Urban Land-Use Change on Biogeochemical Cycles. In: *Terrestrial Ecosystems in a Changing World — The IGBP Series* [Canadell, J.G., D.E. Pataki, and L.F. Pitelka, (eds.)]. Springer Berlin Heidelberg, Berlin, Heidelberg, pp. 45–58.

Pozoukidou, G., and Z. Chatziyiannaki, 2021: 15-Minute City: Decomposing the New Urban Planning Eutopia. *Sustainability*, **13(2)**, 928, doi:10.3390/su13020928.

Pregitzer, C.C. et al., 2019a: Defining and assessing urban forests to inform management and policy. *Environ. Res. Lett.*, **14(8)**, 085002, doi:10.1088/1748-9326/ab2552.

Pregitzer, C.C. et al., 2019b: A cityscale assessment reveals that native forest types and overstory species dominate New York City forests. *Ecol. Appl.*, **29(1)**, e01819, doi:10.1002/eap.1819.

Pregitzer, C.C., C. Hanna, S. Charlop-Powers, and M.A. Bradford, 2021: Estimating carbon storage in urban forests of New York City. *Urban Ecosyst.*, 1–15, doi:10.1007/S11252-021-01173-9.

Prendeville, S., E. Cherim, and N. Bocken, 2018: Circular Cities: Mapping Six Cities in Transition. *Environ. Innov. Soc. Transitions*, **26**, 171–194, doi:10.1016/j.eist.2017.03.002.

Prieur-Richard, A.-H. et al., 2018: Global Research and Action Agenda on Cities and Climate Change Science Urban Crosscutting Cities and Action Integrate Communicate. Intergovernmental Panel on Climate Change (IPCC), 8 pp. https://www.ipcc.ch/site/assets/uploads/2019/07/Research-Agenda-Aug-10_Final_Short-version.pdf (Accessed March 28, 2021).

Prior, J. et al., 2018: Built environment interventions for human and planetary health: integrating health in climate change adaptation and mitigation. *Public Heal. Res. Pract.*, **28(4)**, e2841831, doi:10.17061/phrp2841831.

Privitera, R. and D. La Rosa, 2018: Reducing Seismic Vulnerability and Energy Demand of Cities through Green Infrastructure. *Sustainability*, **10(8)**, 2591, doi:10.3390/su10082591.

Privitera, R., V. Palermo, F. Martinico, A. Fichera, and D. La Rosa, 2018: Towards lower carbon cities: urban morphology contribution in climate change adaptation strategies. *Eur. Plan. Stud.*, **26(4)**, 812–837, doi:10.1080/09654313.2018.1426735.

Priya Uteng, T., and J. Turner, 2019: Addressing the Linkages between Gender and Transport in Low- and Middle-Income Countries. *Sustainability*, **11(17)**, 4555, doi:10.3390/su11174555.

Pukšec, T., P. Leahy, A. Foley, N. Markovska, and N. Duić, 2018: Sustainable development of energy, water and environment systems 2016. *Renew. Sustain. Energy Rev.*, **82**, 1685–1690, doi:10.1016/J.RSER.2017.10.057.

Pulselli, R.M. et al., 2021: Future city visions. The energy transition towards carbon-neutrality: lessons learned from the case of Roeselare, Belgium. *Renew. Sustain. Energy Rev.*, **137**, 110612, doi:10.1016/j.rser.2020.110612.

Puppim de Oliveira, J.A. and C.N.H. Doll, 2016: Governance and networks for health co-benefits of climate change mitigation: Lessons from two Indian cities. *Environ. Int.*, **97**, 146–154, doi:10.1016/j.envint.2016.08.020.

Qin, H.-P., Li, Z.X., and Fu, G., 2013: The effects of low impact development on urban flooding under different rainfall characteristics. *J. Environ. Manage.*, **129**, 577–585, doi:10.1016/j.jenvman.2013.08.026.

Qiu, Y. et al., 2021: Space variability impacts on hydrological responses of nature-based solutions and the resulting uncertainty: a case study of Guyancourt (France). *Hydrol. Earth Syst. Sci.*, **25(6)**, 3137–3162, doi:10.5194/hess-25-3137-2021.

Quaranta, E., C. Dorati, and A. Pistocchi, 2021: Water, energy and climate benefits of urban greening throughout Europe under different climatic scenarios. *Sci. Rep.*, **11**, 12163, doi:10.1038/s41598-021-88141-7.

Queiroz, A., F.T. Najafi, and P. Hanrahan, 2017: Implementation and Results of Solar Feed-In-Tariff in Gainesville, Florida. *J. Energy Eng.*, **143(1)**, 05016005, doi:10.1061/(ASCE)EY.1943-7897.0000373.

Quesada, B., A. Arneth, E. Robertson, and N. De Noblet-Ducoudré, 2018: Potential strong contribution of future anthropogenic land-use and land-cover change to the terrestrial carbon cycle. *Environ. Res. Lett.*, **13(6)**, 064023, doi:10.1088/1748-9326/aac4c3.

Qureshi, Z., 2015: *The Role of Public Policy in Sustainable Infrastructure*. The Brookings Institution, Washington, DC, USA, 19–23 pp. https://www.brookings.edu/wp-content/uploads/2016/07/public-policy-sustainable-infrastructure-qureshi-1.pdf (Accessed March 30, 2021).

Raciti, S.M., L.R. Hutyra, P. Rao, and A.C. Finzi, 2012: Inconsistent definitions of "urban" result in different conclusions about the size of urban carbon and nitrogen stocks. *Ecol. Appl.*, **22(3)**, 1015–1035, doi:10.1890/11-1250.1.

Radomes Jr, A.A., and S. Arango, 2015: Renewable energy technology diffusion: an analysis of photovoltaic-system support schemes in Medellín, Colombia. *J. Clean. Prod.*, **92**, 152–161, doi:10.1016/j.jclepro.2014.12.090.

Ramage, M.H. et al., 2017: The wood from the trees: The use of timber in construction. *Renew. Sustain. Energy Rev.*, **68**, 333–359, doi:10.1016/j.rser.2016.09.107.

Ramaswami, A., 2020: Unpacking the Urban Infrastructure Nexus with Environment, Health, Livability, Well-Being, and Equity. *One Earth*, **2(2)**, 120–124, doi:10.1016/j.oneear.2020.02.003.

Ramaswami, A., and A. Chavez, 2013: What metrics best reflect the energy and carbon intensity of cities? Insights from theory and modeling of 20 US cities. *Environ. Res. Lett.*, **8(3)**, 35011, doi:10.1088/1748-9326/8/3/035011.

Ramaswami, A., T. Hillman, B. Janson, M. Reiner, and G. Thomas, 2008: A Demand-Centered, Hybrid Life-Cycle Methodology for City-Scale Greenhouse Gas Inventories. *Environ. Sci. Technol.*, **42(17)**, 6455–6461, doi:10.1021/es702992q.

Ramaswami, A. et al., 2016: Meta-principles for developing smart, sustainable, and healthy cities. *Science*, **352(6288)**, 940–943, doi:10.1126/science.aaf7160.

Ramaswami, A. et al., 2017a: Urban cross-sector actions for carbon mitigation with local health co-benefits in China. *Nat. Clim. Change*, **7(10)**, 736–742, doi:10.1038/nclimate3373.

Ramaswami, A. et al., 2017b: An urban systems framework to assess the trans-boundary food-energy-water nexus: implementation in Delhi, India. *Environ. Res. Lett.*, **12(2)**, 025008, doi:10.1088/1748-9326/aa5556.

Ramaswami, A. et al., 2021: Carbon analytics for net-zero emissions sustainable cities. *Nat. Sustain.*, **4(6)**, 460–463, doi:10.1038/s41893-021-00715-5.

Ranieri, L., G. Mossa, R. Pellegrino, and S. Digiesi, 2018: Energy Recovery from the Organic Fraction of Municipal Solid Waste: A Real Options-Based Facility Assessment. *Sustainability*, **10(2)**, 368, doi:10.3390/su10020368.

Raven, J. et al., 2018: Urban Planning and Urban Design. In: *Climate Change and Cities: Second Assessment Report of the Urban Climate Change Research Network* [Rosenzweig, C., W.D. Solecki, P. Romero-Lankao, S. Mehrotra, S. Dhakal, and S.A. Ibrahim, (eds.)]. Cambridge University Press, New York, NY, USA, pp. 139–172.

Ravetz, J., A. Neuvonen, and R. Mäntysalo, 2020: The new normative: synergistic scenario planning for carbon-neutral cities and regions. *Reg. Stud.*, **55(1)**, 150–163, doi:10.1080/00343404.2020.1813881.

Raymond, C.M. et al., 2017: A framework for assessing and implementing the co-benefits of nature-based solutions in urban areas. *Environ. Sci. Policy*, **77**, 15–24, doi:10.1016/j.envsci.2017.07.008.

Reckien, D. et al., 2017: Climate change, equity and the Sustainable Development Goals: an urban perspective. *Environ. Urban.*, **29(1)**, 159–182, doi:10.1177/0956247816677778.

Reckien, D. et al., 2018: How are cities planning to respond to climate change? Assessment of local climate plans from 885 cities in the EU-28. *J. Clean. Prod.*, **191**, 207–219, doi:10.1016/j.jclepro.2018.03.220.

Rees, W., 1997: Urban ecosystems: the human dimension. *Urban Ecosyst.*, **1**, 63–75, doi:10.1023/A:1014380105620.

Reinmann, A.B., I.A. Smith, J.R. Thompson, and L.R. Hutyra, 2020: Urbanization and fragmentation mediate temperate forest carbon cycle response to climate. *Environ. Res. Lett.*, **15(11)**, 114036, doi:10.1088/1748-9326/abbf16.

REN21, 2019: *Renewables in Cities: 2019 Global Status Report*. REN21 Secretariat, Paris, France, 174 pp. https://www.ren21.net/wp-content/uploads/2019/05/REC-2019-GSR_Full_Report_web.pdf (Accessed March 31, 2021).

REN21, 2020: *Renewables 2020 Global Status Report*. REN21 Secretariat, Paris, France, 367 pp. https://www.ren21.net/wp-content/uploads/2019/05/gsr_2020_full_report_en.pdf (Accessed March 31, 2021).

REN21, 2021: *Renewables in Cities 2021 Global Status Report*. REN21 Secretariat, Paris, France, 202 pp. https://www.ren21.net/wp-content/uploads/2019/05/REC_2021_full-report_en.pdf (Accessed October 31, 2021).

Reyna, J.L. and M.V Chester, 2015: The Growth of Urban Building Stock: Unintended Lock-in and Embedded Environmental Effects. *J. Ind. Ecol.*, **19(4)**, 524–537, doi:10.1111/jiec.12211.

Riahi, K. et al., 2017: The Shared Socioeconomic Pathways and their energy, land use, and greenhouse gas emissions implications: An overview. *Glob. Environ. Change*, **42**, 153–168, doi:10.1016/j.gloenvcha.2016.05.009.

Ribeiro, H. V, D. Rybski, and J.P. Kropp, 2019: Effects of changing population or density on urban carbon dioxide emissions. *Nat. Commun.*, **10**, 3204, doi:10.1038/s41467-019-11184-y.

Rigolon, A., M. Browning, K. Lee, and S. Shin, 2018: Access to Urban Green Space in Cities of the Global South: A Systematic Literature Review. *Urban Sci.*, **2(3)**, 67, doi:10.3390/urbansci2030067.

Rocha, L.C.S. et al., 2017: Photovoltaic electricity production in Brazil: A stochastic economic viability analysis for small systems in the face of net metering and tax incentives. *J. Clean. Prod.*, **168**, 1448–1462, doi:10.1016/j.jclepro.2017.09.018.

Rode, D.C., P.S. Fischbeck, and A.R. Páez, 2017: The retirement cliff: Power plant lives and their policy implications. *Energy Policy*, **106**, 222–232, doi:10.1016/J.ENPOL.2017.03.058.

Rodrigues, C.U., 2019: Climate change and DIY urbanism in Luanda and Maputo: new urban strategies? *Int. J. Urban Sustain. Dev.*, **11(3)**, 319–331, doi:10.1080/19463138.2019.1585859.

Roelfsema, M., 2017: *Assessment of US City Reduction Commitments, from a Country Perspective*. PBL Netherlands Environmental Assessment Agency, The Hague, The Netherlands, 26 pp. https://www.pbl.nl/sites/default/files/downloads/pbl-2017-assessment-of-us-city-reduction-commitments-from-a-country-perspective-1993.pdf (Accessed January 7, 2021).

Rogelj, J. et al., 2018: Scenarios towards limiting global mean temperature increase below 1.5°C. *Nat. Clim. Change*, **8(4)**, 325–332, doi:10.1038/s41558-018-0091-3.

Roger, C., T. Hale, and L. Andonova, 2017: The Comparative Politics of Transnational Climate Governance. *Int. Interact.*, **43(1)**, 1–25, doi:10.1080/03050629.2017.1252248.

Roldán-Fontana, J., R. Pacheco-Torres, E. Jadraque-Gago, and J. Ordóñez, 2017: Optimization of CO_2 emissions in the design phases of urban planning, based on geometric characteristics: a case study of a low-density urban area in Spain. *Sustain. Sci.*, **12**, 65–85, doi:10.1007/s11625-015-0342-4.

Roppongi, H., A. Suwa, and J.A. Puppim De Oliveira, 2017: Innovating in sub-national climate policy: the mandatory emissions reduction scheme in Tokyo. *Clim. Policy*, **17(4)**, 516–532, doi:10.1080/14693062.2015.1124749.

Rosenzweig, C. et al., 2018: *Climate Change and Cities: Second Assessment Report of the Urban Climate Change Research Network*. [Rosenzweig, C., W. Solecki, P. Romero-Lankao, S. Mehrotra, S. Dhakal, and S.A. Ibrahim, (eds.)]. Cambridge University Press, New York, NY, USA, 311 pp.

Roy, A., 2009: Why India Cannot Plan Its Cities: Informality, Insurgence and the Idiom of Urbanization. *Plan. Theory*, **8(1)**, 76–87, doi:10.1177/1473095208099299.

Rueda, S., 2019: Superblocks for the Design of New Cities and Renovation of Existing Ones: Barcelona's Case. In: *Integrating Human Health into Urban and Transport Planning* [Nieuwenhuijsen, M.J. and H. Khreis, (eds.)]. Springer International Publishing, Cham, Switzerland, pp. 135–153.

Saha, D. and S. D'Almeida, 2017: Green municipal bonds. In: *Finance for City Leaders, 2nd Edition* [Kamiya, M. and L.-Y. Zhang, (eds.)]. UN-Habitat, Nairobi, Kenya, pp. 98–118.

Salat, S., M. Chen, and F.L. Liu, 2014: *Planning Energy Efficient and Livable Cities: Energy Efficient Cities: Mayoral Guidance Note #6*. Energy Sector Management Assistance Program, The World Bank, Washington, DC, USA, 30 pp. https://www.semanticscholar.org/paper/Planning-energy-efficient-and-livable-cities-%3A-Salat-Chen/475a01c0bf911db4a435c1a2a37dabf53ff98f1d (Accessed March 31, 2021).

Salat, S., L. Bourdic, and M. Kamiya, 2017: *Economic Foundations for Sustainable Urbanization: A Study on Three-Pronged Approach: Planned City Extensions, Legal Framework, and Municipal Finance*. UN-Habitat, Nairobi, Kenya, 136 pp. https://unhabitat.org/economic-foundations-for-sustainable-urbanization-a-study-on-three-pronged-approach-planned-city (Accessed March 28, 2021).

Salpakari, J., J. Mikkola, and P.D. Lund, 2016: Improved flexibility with large-scale variable renewable power in cities through optimal demand side management and power-to-heat conversion. *Energy Convers. Manag.*, **126**, 649–661, doi:10.1016/j.enconman.2016.08.041.

Salvia, M. et al., 2021: Will climate mitigation ambitions lead to carbon neutrality? An analysis of the local-level plans of 327 cities in the EU. *Renew. Sustain. Energy Rev.*, **135**, 110253.

Sanchez Rodriguez, R., D. Ürge-Vorsatz, and A.S. Barau, 2018: Sustainable Development Goals and climate change adaptation in cities. *Nat. Clim. Change*, **8(3)**, 181–183, doi:10.1038/s41558-018-0098-9.

Sargent, M. et al., 2018: Anthropogenic and biogenic CO_2 fluxes in the Boston urban region. *Proc. Natl. Acad. Sci. U.S.A.*, **115(29)**, 7491–7496, doi:10.1073/pnas.1803715115.

Saujot, M. and B. Lefèvre, 2016: The next generation of urban MACCs. Reassessing the cost-effectiveness of urban mitigation options by integrating a systemic approach and social costs. *Energy Policy*, **92**, 124–138, doi:10.1016/j.enpol.2016.01.029.

Scholvin, S., M. Breul, and J. Revilla Diez, 2019: Revisiting gateway cities: connecting hubs in global networks to their hinterlands. *Urban Geog.*, **40(9)**, 1291–1309, doi:10.1080/02723638.2019.1585137.

Scholz, T., A. Hof, and T. Schmitt, 2018: Cooling Effects and Regulating Ecosystem Services Provided by Urban Trees—Novel Analysis Approaches Using Urban Tree Cadastre Data. *Sustainability*, **10(3)**, 712, doi:10.3390/su10030712.

Seo, S., G. Foliente, and Z. Ren, 2018: Energy and GHG reductions considering embodied impacts of retrofitting existing dwelling stock in Greater Melbourne. *J. Clean. Prod.*, **170**, 1288–1304, doi:10.1016/j.jclepro.2017.09.206.

Sethi, M. and J.A. Puppim de Oliveira, 2018: Cities and Climate Co-benefits. In: *Mainstreaming Climate Co-Benefits in Indian Cities* [Sethi, M. and J.A. Puppim de Oliveira, (eds.)]. Springer, Singapore, Singapore, pp. 3–45.

Sethi, M., W. Lamb, J. Minx, and F. Creutzig, 2020: Climate change mitigation in cities: a systematic scoping of case studies. *Environ. Res. Lett.*, **15(9)**, 093008, doi:10.1088/1748-9326/ab99ff.

Seto K.C., S. Dhakal, A. Bigio, H. Blanco, G.C. Delgado, D. Dewar, L. Huang, A. Inaba, A. Kansal, S. Lwasa, J.E. McMahon, D.B. Müller, J. Murakami, H. Nagendra, and A. Ramaswami, 2014: Human Settlements, Infrastructure, and Spatial Planning. In: *Climate Change 2014: Mitigation of Climate Change. Contribution of Working Group III to the Fifth Assessment Report of the Intergovernmental Panel on Climate Change* [Edenhofer, O., R. Pichs-Madruga, Y. Sokona, E. Farahani, S. Kadner, K. Seyboth, A. Adler, I. Baum, S. Brunner, P. Eickemeier, B. Kriemann, J. Savolainen, S. Schlömer, C. von Stechow, T. Zwickel and J.C. Minx (eds.)]. Cambridge University Press, Cambridge, UK, and New York, NY, USA, pp. 923–1000.

Seto, K.C. et al., 2016: Carbon Lock-In: Types, Causes, and Policy Implications. *Annu. Rev. Environ. Resour.*, **41**, 425–452, doi:10.1146/annurev-environ-110615-085934.

Seto, K.C. et al., 2021: From Low- to Net-Zero Carbon Cities: The Next Global Agenda. *Annu. Rev. Environ. Resour.*, **46**, 377–415, doi:10.1146/annurev-environ-050120-113117.

Shakya, S.R., 2016: Benefits of Low Carbon Development Strategies in Emerging Cities of Developing Country: a Case of Kathmandu. *J. Sustain. Dev. Energy, Water Environ. Syst.*, **4(2)**, 141–160, doi:10.13044/j.sdewes.2016.04.0012.

Shannon, H. et al., 2018: Web Annex A: report of the systematic review on the effect of household crowding on health. In: *WHO Housing and health guidelines*. World Health Organization (WHO), Geneva, Switzerland, 105 pp.

Sharifi, A., 2019: Resilient urban forms: A review of literature on streets and street networks. *Build. Environ.*, **147**, 171–187, doi:10.1016/j.buildenv.2018.09.040.

Sharifi, A., 2020: Trade-offs and conflicts between urban climate change mitigation and adaptation measures: A literature review. *J. Clean. Prod.*, **276(10)**, 122813, doi:10.1016/j.jclepro.2020.122813.

Sharifi, A., 2021: Co-benefits and synergies between urban climate change mitigation and adaptation measures: A literature review. *Sci. Total Environ.*, **750**, 141642, doi:10.1016/j.scitotenv.2020.141642.

Sharifi, A. and A.R. Khavarian-Garmsir, 2020: The COVID-19 pandemic: Impacts on cities and major lessons for urban planning, design, and management. *Sci. Total Environ.*, **749**, 142391, doi:10.1016/j.scitotenv.2020.142391.

Sharifi, A. et al., 2017: Conceptualizing Dimensions and Characteristics of Urban Resilience: Insights from a Co-Design Process. *Sustainability*, **9(6)**, 1032, doi:10.3390/su9061032.

Sharifi, A., M. Pathak, C. Joshi, and B.-J. He, 2021: A systematic review of the health co-benefits of urban climate change adaptation. *Sustain. Cities Soc.*, **74**, 103190, doi:10.1016/j.scs.2021.103190.

Sharma, A. et al., 2018: Role of green roofs in reducing heat stress in vulnerable urban communities—a multidisciplinary approach. *Environ. Res. Lett.*, **13(9)**, 094011, doi:10.1088/1748-9326/aad93c.

Sharma, R., 2018: Financing Indian urban rail through land development: Case studies and implications for the accelerated reduction in oil associated with 1.5°C. *Urban Plan.*, **3(2)**, 21–34, doi:10.17645/up.v3i2.1158.

Sharp, D. and R. Salter, 2017: Direct Impacts of an Urban Living Lab from the Participants' Perspective: Livewell Yarra. *Sustainability*, **9(10)**, 1699, doi:10.3390/su9101699.

Shen, L. et al., 2018: Analysis on the evolution of low carbon city from process characteristic perspective. *J. Clean. Prod.*, **187**, 348–360, doi:10.1016/j.jclepro.2018.03.190.

Shen, X., X. Wang, Z. Zhang, Z. Lu, and T. Lv, 2019: Evaluating the effectiveness of land use plans in containing urban expansion: An integrated view. *Land use policy*, **80**, 205–213, doi:10.1016/j.landusepol.2018.10.001.

Shi, L. et al., 2016: Roadmap towards justice in urban climate adaptation research. *Nat. Clim. Change*, **6(2)**, 131–137, doi:10.1038/nclimate2841.

Shi, Y., Y.-X. Yun, C. Liu, and Y.-Q. Chu, 2017a: Carbon footprint of buildings in the urban agglomeration of central Liaoning, China. *Chinese J. Appl. Ecol.*, **28(6)**, 2040–2046, doi:10.13287/j.1001-9332.201706.007.

Shi, Z., J.A. Fonseca, and A. Schlueter, 2017b: A review of simulation-based urban form generation and optimization for energy-driven urban design. *Build. Environ.*, **121**, 119–129, doi:10.1016/j.buildenv.2017.05.006.

Shi, Z., S. Hsieh, J.A. Fonseca, and A. Schlueter, 2020: Street grids for efficient district cooling systems in high-density cities. *Sustain. Cities Soc.*, **60**, 102224, doi:10.1016/j.scs.2020.102224.

Shughrue, C., B. Werner, and K.C. Seto, 2020: Global spread of local cyclone damages through urban trade networks. *Nat. Sustain.*, **3(8)**, 606–613, doi:10.1038/s41893-020-0523-8.

Silva, C.M., M.G. Gomes, and M. Silva, 2016: Green roofs energy performance in Mediterranean climate. *Energy Build.*, **116**, 318–325, doi:10.1016/j.enbuild.2016.01.012.

Silva, M., V. Oliveira, and V. Leal, 2017: Urban Form and Energy Demand. *J. Plan. Lit.*, **32(4)**, 346–365, doi:10.1177/0885412217706900.

Silveti, D., and K. Andersson, 2019: Challenges of governing off-grid "Productive" sanitation in peri-urban areas: Comparison of case studies in Bolivia and South Africa. *Sustainability*, **11(12)**, 3468, doi:10.3390/SU11123468.

Simon, D. et al., 2016: Developing and testing the Urban Sustainable Development Goal's targets and indicators – a five-city study. *Environ. Urban.*, **28(1)**, 49–63, doi:10.1177/0956247815619865.

Simpson, N.P., K.J. Simpson, C.D. Shearing, and L.R. Cirolia, 2019: Municipal finance and resilience lessons for urban infrastructure management: a case study from the Cape Town drought. *Int. J. Urban Sustain. Dev.*, **11(3)**, 257–276, doi:10.1080/19463138.2019.1642203.

Simpson, N.P. et al., 2021: A framework for complex climate change risk assessment. *One Earth*, **4(4)**, 489–501, doi:10.1016/j.oneear.2021.03.005.

Singh, C., J. Ford, D. Ley, A. Bazaz, and A. Revi, 2020: Assessing the feasibility of adaptation options: methodological advancements and directions for climate adaptation research and practice. *Clim. Change*, **162(2)**, 255–277, doi:10.1007/s10584-020-02762-x.

Singh, M., and L.G., 2019: Forecasting of GHG emission and linear pinch analysis of municipal solid waste for the city of Faridabad, India. *Energy Sources, Part A Recover. Util. Environ. Eff.*, **41(22)**, 2704–2714, doi:10.1080/15567036.2019.1568642.

Sköld, B. et al., 2018: Household Preferences to Reduce Their Greenhouse Gas Footprint: A Comparative Study from Four European Cities. *Sustainability*, **10(11)**, 4044, doi:10.3390/su10114044.

Slorach, P.C., H.K. Jeswani, R. Cuéllar-Franca, and A. Azapagic, 2020: Environmental sustainability in the food-energy-water-health nexus: A new methodology and an application to food waste in a circular economy. *Waste Manag.*, **113**, 359–368, doi:10.1016/j.wasman.2020.06.012.

Smith, J.E., L.S. Heath, and C.M. Hoover, 2013: Carbon factors and models for forest carbon estimates for the 2005–2011 National Greenhouse Gas Inventories of the United States. *For. Ecol. Manage.*, **307**, 7–19, doi:10.1016/j.foreco.2013.06.061.

Soares, F.R., and G. Martins, 2017: Using Life Cycle Assessment to Compare Environmental Impacts of Different Waste to Energy Options for Sao Paulo's Municipal Solid Waste. *J. Solid Waste Technol. Manag.*, **43(1)**, 36–46, doi:10.5276/JSWTM.2017.36.

Soilán, M., B. Riveiro, P. Liñares, and M. Padín-Beltrán, 2018: Automatic Parametrization and Shadow Analysis of Roofs in Urban Areas from ALS Point Clouds with Solar Energy Purposes. *ISPRS Int. J. Geo-Information*, **7(8)**, 301, doi:10.3390/ijgi7080301.

Solecki, W. et al., 2015: A conceptual framework for an urban areas typology to integrate climate change mitigation and adaptation. *Urban Clim.*, **14**, 116–137, doi:10.1016/j.uclim.2015.07.001.

Sonter, L.J. et al., 2017: Mining drives extensive deforestation in the Brazilian Amazon. *Nat. Commun.*, **8**, 1013, doi:10.1038/s41467-017-00557-w.

Sorkin, M., 2018: Vertical Urbanism. In: *Vertical Urbanism: Designing Compact Cities in China* [Lin, Z. and J.L.S. Gámez, (eds.)]. Routledge, New York, NY, USA, pp. 73–82.

Sorknæs, P. et al., 2020: The benefits of 4th generation district heating in a 100% renewable energy system. *Energy*, **213**, 119030, doi:10.1016/j.energy.2020.119030.

Soukiazis, E., and S. Proença, 2020: The determinants of waste generation and recycling performance across the Portuguese municipalities – A simultaneous equation approach. *Waste Manag.*, **114**, 321–330, doi:10.1016/j.wasman.2020.06.039.

Sovacool, B.K., and M.A. Brown, 2010: Twelve metropolitan carbon footprints: A preliminary comparative global assessment. *Energy Policy*, **38(9)**, 4856–4869, doi:10.1016/j.enpol.2009.10.001.

Sovacool, B.K. et al., 2020: Sustainable minerals and metals for a low-carbon future. *Science*, **367(6473)**, 30–33, doi:10.1126/science.aaz6003.

Srishantha, U., and U. Rathnayake, 2017: Sustainable urban drainage systems (SUDS) – What it is and where do we stand today? *Eng. Appl. Sci. Res.*, **44(4)**, 235–241, doi:10.14456/easr.2017.36.

State Government of Victoria, 2021: 20-minute neighbourhoods. *Plan Melbourne 2017–2050*. https://www.planning.vic.gov.au/policy-and-strategy/planning-for-melbourne/plan-melbourne/20-minute-neighbourhoods (Accessed October 25, 2021).

Stern, P.C. et al., 2016: Opportunities and insights for reducing fossil fuel consumption by households and organizations. *Nat. Energy*, **1**, 16043, doi:10.1038/nenergy.2016.43.

Stevens, M.R., 2017: Does Compact Development Make People Drive Less? *J. Am. Plan. Assoc.*, **83(1)**, 7–18, doi:10.1080/01944363.2016.1240044.

Stewart, I.D., C.A. Kennedy, A. Facchini, and R. Mele, 2018: The Electric City as a Solution to Sustainable Urban Development. *J. Urban Technol.*, **25(1)**, 3–20, doi:10.1080/10630732.2017.1386940.

Stier, A.J., M.G. Berman, and L.M.A. Bettencourt, 2021: Early pandemic COVID-19 case growth rates increase with city size. *npj Urban Sustain.*, **1**, 31, doi:10.1038/s42949-021-00030-0.

Stocchero, A., J.K. Seadon, R. Falshaw, and M. Edwards, 2017: Urban Equilibrium for sustainable cities and the contribution of timber buildings

to balance urban carbon emissions: A New Zealand case study. *J. Clean. Prod.*, **143**, 1001–1010, doi:10.1016/j.jclepro.2016.12.020.

Stokes, E.C. and K.C. Seto, 2019: Characterizing urban infrastructural transitions for the Sustainable Development Goals using multi-temporal land, population, and nighttime light data. *Remote Sens. Environ.*, **234(11)**, 111430, doi:10.1016/j.rse.2019.111430.

Strano, E., V. Nicosia, V. Latora, S. Porta, and M. Barthélemy, 2012: Elementary processes governing the evolution of road networks. *Sci. Reports 2012 21*, **2**, 296, doi:10.1038/srep00296.

Sudmant, A., J. Millward-Hopkins, S. Colenbrander, and A. Gouldson, 2016: Low carbon cities: is ambitious action affordable? *Clim. Change*, **138(3–4)**, 681–688, doi:10.1007/s10584-016-1751-9.

Sudmant, A. et al., 2017: Understanding the case for low-carbon investment through bottom-up assessments of city-scale opportunities. *Clim. Policy*, **17(3)**, 299–313, doi:10.1080/14693062.2015.1104498.

Sudmant, A., A. Gouldson, J. Millward-Hopkins, K. Scott, and J. Barrett, 2018: Producer cities and consumer cities: Using production- and consumption-based carbon accounts to guide climate action in China, the UK, and the US. *J. Clean. Prod.*, **176**, 654–662, doi:10.1016/j.jclepro.2017.12.139.

Sun, L., M. Fujii, T. Tasaki, H. Dong, and S. Ohnishi, 2018a: Improving waste to energy rate by promoting an integrated municipal solid-waste management system. *Resour. Conserv. Recycl.*, **136**, 289–296, doi:10.1016/j.resconrec.2018.05.005.

Sun, L. et al., 2018b: A completive research on the feasibility and adaptation of shared transportation in mega-cities – A case study in Beijing. *Appl. Energy*, **230**, 1014–1033, doi:10.1016/j.apenergy.2018.09.080.

Sung, H., and C.G. Choi, 2017: The link between metropolitan planning and transit-oriented development: An examination of the Rosario Plan in 1980 for Seoul, South Korea. *Land use policy*, **63**, 514–522, doi:10.1016/j.landusepol.2017.01.045.

Susca, T., 2019: Green roofs to reduce building energy use? A review on key structural factors of green roofs and their effects on urban climate. *Build. Environ.*, **162**, 106273, doi:10.1016/j.buildenv.2019.106273.

Suzuki, H., J. Murakami, Y.-H. Hong, and B. Tamayose, 2015: *Financing Transit-Oriented Development with Land Values: Adapting Land Value Capture in Developing Countries*. The World Bank, Washington, DC, USA, 30 pp.

Swilling, M. et al., 2018: *The Weight of Cities: Resource Requirements of Future Urbanization*. United Nations Environment Programme (UNEP), Nairobi, Kenya, 280 pp. https://www.resourcepanel.org/sites/default/files/documents/document/media/the_weight_of_cities_full_report_english.pdf (Accessed March 31, 2021).

Syed, M.M., G.M. Morrison, and J. Darbyshire, 2020: Shared solar and battery storage configuration effectiveness for reducing the grid reliance of apartment complexes. *Energies*, **13(18)**, 4820, doi:10.3390/en13184820.

Tarigan, A.K.M., and S. Sagala, 2018: The pursuit of greenness: explaining low-carbon urban transformation in Indonesia. *Int. Plan. Stud.*, **23(4)**, 408–426, doi:10.1080/13563475.2018.1513360.

Tarroja, B. et al., 2018: Translating climate change and heating system electrification impacts on building energy use to future greenhouse gas emissions and electric grid capacity requirements in California. *Appl. Energy*, **225**, 522–534, doi:10.1016/j.apenergy.2018.05.003.

Tayarani, M., A. Poorfakhraei, R. Nadafianshahamabadi, and G. Rowangould, 2018: Can regional transportation and land-use planning achieve deep reductions in GHG emissions from vehicles? *Transp. Res. Part D Transp. Environ.*, **63**, 222–235, doi:10.1016/j.trd.2018.05.010.

Taylor, P.J., 1997: Hierarchical tendencies amongst world cities: A global research proposal. *Cities*, **14(6)**, 323–332, doi:10.1016/s0264-2751(97)00023-1.

Teferi, Z.A., and P. Newman, 2018: Slum Upgrading: Can the 1.5°C Carbon Reduction Work with SDGs in these Settlements? *Urban Plan.*, **3(2)**, 52–63, doi:10.17645/up.v3i2.1239.

Tellman, B. et al., 2021: Satellite imaging reveals increased proportion of population exposed to floods. *Nature*, **596**, 80–86, doi:10.1038/s41586-021-03695-w.

Teske, S., T. Pregger, S. Simon, and T. Naegler, 2018: High renewable energy penetration scenarios and their implications for urban energy and transport systems. *Curr. Opin. Environ. Sustain.*, **30**, 89–102, doi:10.1016/j.cosust.2018.04.007.

Thacker, S. et al., 2019: Infrastructure for sustainable development. *Nat. Sustain.*, **2(4)**, 324–331, doi:10.1038/s41893-019-0256-8.

Thanopoulos, S. et al., 2020: Analysis of Alternative MSW Treatment Technologies with the Aim of Energy Recovery in the Municipality of Vari-Voula-Vouliagmeni. *Waste Biomass Valor.*, **11(4)**, 1585–1601, doi:10.1007/s12649-018-0388-5.

Thellufsen, J.Z. et al., 2020: Smart energy cities in a 100% renewable energy context. *Renew. Sustain. Energy Rev.*, **129**, 109922, doi:10.1016/j.rser.2020.109922.

Thomson, G. and P. Newman, 2018: Urban fabrics and urban metabolism – from sustainable to regenerative cities. *Resour. Conserv. Recycl.*, **132**, 218–229, doi:10.1016/j.resconrec.2017.01.010.

Tiefenbeck, V., A. Wörner, S. Schöb, E. Fleisch, and T. Staake, 2019: Real-time feedback promotes energy conservation in the absence of volunteer selection bias and monetary incentives. *Nat. Energy*, **4**, 35–41, doi:10.1038/s41560-018-0282-1.

Tomić, T. and D.R. Schneider, 2020: Circular economy in waste management – Socio-economic effect of changes in waste management system structure. *J. Environ. Manage.*, **267**, 110564, doi:10.1016/j.jenvman.2020.110564.

Tong, K., A.S. Nagpure, and A. Ramaswami, 2021: All urban areas' energy use data across 640 districts in India for the year 2011. *Sci. Data 2021 81*, **8**, 104, doi:10.1038/s41597-021-00853-7.

Tong, X., T. Wang, and W. Wang, 2017: Impact of Mixed Function Community on Distributed Photovoltaic Application. *Yingyong Jichu yu Gongcheng Kexue Xuebao/Journal Basic Sci. Eng.*, **25(4)**, 793–804, doi:10.16058/j.issn.1005-0930.2017.04.014.

Tongwane, M., S. Piketh, L. Stevens, and T. Ramotubei, 2015: Greenhouse gas emissions from road transport in South Africa and Lesotho between 2000 and 2009. *Transp. Res. Part D Transp. Environ.*, **37**, 1–13, doi:10.1016/j.trd.2015.02.017.

Topi, C., E. Esposto, and V. Marini Govigli, 2016: The economics of green transition strategies for cities: Can low carbon, energy efficient development approaches be adapted to demand side urban water efficiency? *Environ. Sci. Policy*, **58**, 74–82, doi:10.1016/j.envsci.2016.01.001.

Trundle, A., 2020: Resilient cities in a Sea of Islands: Informality and climate change in the South Pacific. *Cities*, **97**, 102496, doi:10.1016/j.cities.2019.102496.

Tsavdaroglou, M., S.H.S. Al-Jibouri, T. Bles, and J.I.M. Halman, 2018: Proposed methodology for risk analysis of interdependent critical infrastructures to extreme weather events. *Int. J. Crit. Infrastruct. Prot.*, **21**, 57–71, doi:10.1016/j.ijcip.2018.04.002.

Tuomisto, J.T. et al., 2015: Building-related health impacts in European and Chinese cities: a scalable assessment method. *Environ. Heal.*, **14**, 93, doi:10.1186/s12940-015-0082-z.

Turnbull, J.C. et al., 2019: Synthesis of Urban CO_2 Emission Estimates from Multiple Methods from the Indianapolis Flux Project (INFLUX). *Environ. Sci. Technol.*, **53(1)**, 287–295, doi:10.1021/acs.est.8b05552.

Turner, A.J. et al., 2020: Observed Impacts of COVID-19 on Urban CO_2 Emissions. *Geophys. Res. Lett.*, **47(22)**, e2020GL090037, doi:10.1029/2020GL090037.

Tyfield, D., 2014: Putting the Power in 'Socio-Technical Regimes' – E-Mobility Transition in China as Political Process.' *Mobilities*, **9(4)**, 585–603, doi:10.1080/17450101.2014.961262.

UN DESA, 2019: *World Urbanization Prospects: The 2018 Revision*. United Nations Department of Economic and Social Affairs (UN DESA) Population Division, New York, NY, USA, 126 pp. https://population.un.org/wup/Publications/Files/WUP2018-Report.pdf (Accessed July 8, 2019).

UNEP, 2019: *Global Environment Outlook - GEO 6: Healthy Planet, Healthy People*. Cambridge University Press, Nairobi, Kenya, 710 pp.

UNEP, 2021: *Emissions Gap Report 2021: The Heat Is On – A World of Climate Promises Not Yet Delivered – Executive Summary*. United Nations Environment Programme (UNEP), Nairobi, Kenya, 20 pp.

UNEP IRP, 2020: *Resource Efficiency and Climate Change: Material Efficiency Strategies for a Low-Carbon Future, A report of the International Resource Panel*. International Resource Panel (IRP), Nairobi, Kenya, 157 pp. https://www.resourcepanel.org/reports/resource-efficiency-and-climate-change (Accessed March 31, 2021).

UNFCCC, 2015: *Report of the Conference of the Parties on its Twenty-First Session, Held in Paris from 30 November to 13 December 2015 and Action Taken by the Conference of the Parties at its Twenty-First Session, (Paris Agreement)*. United Nations General Assembly, Paris, France, 36 pp.

United Nations, 2015: *Transforming our world: The 2030 agenda for sustainable development, A/RES/70/1*. United Nations General Assembly, New York, NY, USA, 35 pp. https://www.un.org/ga/search/view_doc.asp?symbol=A/RES/70/1&Lang=E (Accessed March 31, 2021).

United Nations, 2017: *New Urban Agenda, A/RES/71/256*. Habitat III and United Nations, New York, NY, USA, 66 pp. http://habitat3.org/wp-content/uploads/NUA-English.pdf (Accessed March 28, 2021).

United Nations, 2018: *Report of the Special Rapporteur on adequate housing as a component of the right to an adequate standard of living, and on the right to non-discrimination in this context, A/73/310/Rev.1*. United Nations General Assembly, New York, NY, USA, 23 pp. https://www.ohchr.org/en/documents/thematic-reports/report-special-rapporteur-adequate-housing-component-right-adequate-1 (Accessed November 2, 2021).

United Nations, 2019: Sustainable Development Goals (SDGs). *Sustainable Development Goals Knowledge Platform*. https://sustainabledevelopment.un.org/sdgs (Accessed October 11, 2021).

Ürge-Vorsatz, D. et al., 2018: Locking in positive climate responses in cities. *Nat. Clim. Change*, **8(3)**, 174–177, doi:10.1038/s41558-018-0100-6.

Ürge-Vorsatz, D. et al., 2020: Advances Toward a Net-Zero Global Building Sector. *Annu. Rev. Environ. Resour.*, **45**, 227–269, doi:10.1146/annurev-environ-012420-045843.

USGCRP, 2018: *Second State of the Carbon Cycle Report (SOCCR2): A Sustained Assessment Report*. US Global Change Research Program (USGCRP), Washington, DC, USA, 878 pp. https://carbon2018.globalchange.gov/ (Accessed March 31, 2021).

Valek, A.M., J. Sušnik, and S. Grafakos, 2017: Quantification of the urban water-energy nexus in México City, México, with an assessment of water-system related carbon emissions. *Sci. Total Environ.*, **590–591**, 258–268, doi:10.1016/J.SCITOTENV.2017.02.234.

Valente de Macedo, L., J. Setzer, and F. Rei, 2016: Transnational Action Fostering Climate Protection in the City of São Paulo and Beyond. *disP - Plan. Rev.*, **52(2)**, 35–44, doi:10.1080/02513625.2016.1195582.

van de Ven, D.J., M. González-Eguino, and I. Arto, 2018: The potential of behavioural change for climate change mitigation: a case study for the European Union. *Mitig. Adapt. Strateg. Glob. Change*, **23(6)**, 853–886, doi:10.1007/s11027-017-9763-y.

van den Bosch, M., and Å. Ode Sang, 2017: Urban natural environments as nature-based solutions for improved public health – A systematic review of reviews. *Environ. Res.*, **158**, 373–384, doi:10.1016/j.envres.2017.05.040.

van der Heijden, J., 2018: City and subnational governance: high ambitions, innovative instruments and polycentric collaborations? In: *Governing Climate Change: Polycentricity in Action?* [Jordan, A., D. Huitema, H. Van Asselt, and J. Forster, (eds.)]. Cambridge University Press, Cambridge, UK, pp. 81–96.

van der Heijden, J. and S.-H. Hong, 2021: Urban Climate Governance Experimentation in Seoul: Science, Politics, or a Little of Both? *Urban Aff. Rev.*, **57(4)**, 1115–1148, doi:10.1177/1078087420911207.

van der Zwaan, B., T. Kober, F.D. Longa, A. van der Laan, and G. Jan Kramer, 2018: An integrated assessment of pathways for low-carbon development in Africa. *Energy Policy*, **117**, 387–395, doi:10.1016/j.enpol.2018.03.017.

van Vliet, J., 2019: Direct and indirect loss of natural area from urban expansion. *Nat. Sustain.*, **2(8)**, 755–763, doi:10.1038/s41893-019-0340-0.

van Vliet, J., D.A. Eitelberg, and P.H. Verburg, 2017: A global analysis of land take in cropland areas and production displacement from urbanization. *Glob. Environ. Change*, **43**, 107–115, doi:10.1016/j.gloenvcha.2017.02.001.

van Vuuren, D.P. et al., 2014: A new scenario framework for Climate Change Research: scenario matrix architecture. *Clim. Change*, **122(3)**, 373–386, doi:10.1007/s10584-013-0906-1.

van Vuuren, D.P. et al., 2017a: The Shared Socio-economic Pathways: Trajectories for human development and global environmental change. *Glob. Environ. Change*, **42**, 148–152, doi:10.1016/j.gloenvcha.2016.10.009.

van Vuuren, D.P. et al., 2017b: Energy, land-use and greenhouse gas emissions trajectories under a green growth paradigm. *Glob. Environ. Change*, **42**, 237–250, doi:10.1016/j.gloenvcha.2016.05.008.

Vanham, D., B.M. Gawlik, and G. Bidoglio, 2017: Food consumption and related water resources in Nordic cities. *Ecol. Indic.*, **74**, 119–129, doi:10.1016/j.ecolind.2016.11.019.

Vedel, S.E., J.B. Jacobsen, and H. Skov-Petersen, 2017: Bicyclists' preferences for route characteristics and crowding in Copenhagen – A choice experiment study of commuters. *Transp. Res. Part A Policy Pract.*, **100**, 53–64, doi:10.1016/j.tra.2017.04.006.

Vedeld, T., H. Hofstad, H. Solli, and G.S. Hanssen, 2021: Polycentric urban climate governance: Creating synergies between integrative and interactive governance in Oslo. *Environ. Policy Gov.*, **31(4)**, 347–360, doi:10.1002/eet.1935.

Venkatachary, S.K., J. Prasad, and R. Samikannu, 2018: Barriers to implementation of smart grids and virtual power plant in sub-saharan region—focus Botswana. *Energy Reports*, **4**, 119–128, doi:10.1016/j.egyr.2018.02.001.

Veuger, J., 2017: Attention to Disruption and Blockchain Creates a Viable Real Estate Economy. *J. US-China Public Adm.*, **14(5)**, 263–285, doi:10.17265/1548-6591/2017.05.003.

Viguié, V., and S. Hallegatte, 2012: Trade-offs and synergies in urban climate policies. *Nat. Clim. Change*, **2(5)**, 334–337, doi:10.1038/nclimate1434.

Viguié, V. et al., 2020: Early adaptation to heat waves and future reduction of air-conditioning energy use in Paris. *Environ. Res. Lett.*, **15(7)**, 75006, doi:10.1088/1748-9326/ab6a24.

Votsis, A., 2017: Planning for green infrastructure: The spatial effects of parks, forests, and fields on Helsinki's apartment prices. *Ecol. Econ.*, **132**, 279–289, doi:10.1016/j.ecolecon.2016.09.029.

Vujcic, M. et al., 2017: Nature based solution for improving mental health and well-being in urban areas. *Environ. Res.*, **158**, 385–392, doi:10.1016/j.envres.2017.06.030.

Wachs, L. and S. Singh, 2018: A modular bottom-up approach for constructing physical input–output tables (PIOTs) based on process engineering models. *J. Econ. Struct.*, **7**, 26, doi:10.1186/s40008-018-0123-1.

Waheed, R., D. Chang, S. Sarwar, and W. Chen, 2018: Forest, agriculture, renewable energy, and CO_2 emission. *J. Clean. Prod.*, **172**, 4231–4238, doi:10.1016/j.jclepro.2017.10.287.

Walters, L. and L.P. Gaunter, 2017: Sharing the Wealth: Private Land Value and Public Benefit. In: *Finance for City Leaders* [Kamiya, M. and L.-Y. Zhang, (eds.)]. 2nd ed. UN-Habitat, Nairobi, Kenya, pp. 192–215.

Wamsler, C. and S. Pauleit, 2016: Making headway in climate policy mainstreaming and ecosystem-based adaptation: two pioneering countries, different pathways, one goal. *Clim. Change*, **137(1–2)**, 71–87, doi:10.1007/s10584-016-1660-y.

Wang, M., M. Madden, and X. Liu, 2017: Exploring the Relationship between Urban Forms and CO_2 Emissions in 104 Chinese Cities. *J. Urban Plan. Dev.*, **143(4)**, 04017014, doi:10.1061/(ASCE)UP.1943-5444.0000400.

Wang, Q., X. Wang, and R. Li, 2022: Does urbanization redefine the environmental Kuznets curve? An empirical analysis of 134 Countries. *Sustain. Cities Soc.*, **76**, 103382, doi:10.1016/J.SCS.2021.103382.

Wang, S. and B. Chen, 2016: Energy–water nexus of urban agglomeration based on multiregional input–output tables and ecological network analysis: A case study of the Beijing–Tianjin–Hebei region. *Appl. Energy*, **178**, 773–783, doi:10.1016/j.apenergy.2016.06.112.

Wang, Y. et al., 2016: Does urbanization lead to more carbon emission? Evidence from a panel of BRICS countries. *Appl. Energy*, **168**, 375–380, doi:10.1016/J.APENERGY.2016.01.105.

Wappelhorst, S., D. Hall, M. Nicholas, and N. Lutsey, 2020: *Analyzing Policies to Grow the Electric Vehicle Market in European Cities*. International Council on Clean Transportation (ICCT), Berlin, Germany, 43 pp. https://theicct.org/publications/electric-vehicle-policies-eu-cities (Accessed March 31, 2021).

Ward, E.B., C.C. Pregitzer, S.E. Kuebbing, and M.A. Bradford, 2020: Invasive lianas are drivers of and passengers to altered soil nutrient availability in urban forests. *Biol. Invasions*, **22(3)**, 935–955, doi:10.1007/s10530-019-02134-2.

WCRP, 2019: *Extended Version: Global Research and Action Agenda on Cities and Climate Change Science*. [Prieur-Richard, A.-H. et al., (eds.)]. World Climate Research Programme (WCRP), Edmonton, Canada, 31 pp.

Webb, R. et al., 2018: Sustainable urban systems: Co-design and framing for transformation. *Ambio*, **47**, 57–77, doi:10.1007/s13280-017-0934-6.

Wei, T., J. Wu, and S. Chen, 2021: Keeping Track of Greenhouse Gas Emission Reduction Progress and Targets in 167 Cities Worldwide. *Front. Sustain. Cities*, **3**, 64, doi:10.3389/frsc.2021.696381.

Weimann, A., and T. Oni, 2019: A Systematised Review of the Health Impact of Urban Informal Settlements and Implications for Upgrading Interventions in South Africa, a Rapidly Urbanising Middle-Income Country. *Int. J. Environ. Res. Public Health*, **16(19)**, 3608, doi:10.3390/ijerph16193608.

Weng, M. et al., 2019: The 15-minute walkable neighborhoods: Measurement, social inequalities and implications for building healthy communities in urban China. *J. Transp. Heal.*, **13**, 259–273, doi:10.1016/j.jth.2019.05.005.

Westman, L., and V.C. Broto, 2018: Climate governance through partnerships: A study of 150 urban initiatives in China. *Glob. Environ. Change*, **50**, 212–221, doi:10.1016/j.gloenvcha.2018.04.008.

Westphal, M.I., S. Martin, L. Zhou, D. Satterthwaite, and S.M.R. Philanthropies, 2017: *Powering Cities in the Global South: How Energy Access for All Benefits the Economy and the Environment*. World Resources Institute (WRI), Washington, DC, USA, 55 pp. https://files.wri.org/s3fs-public/powering-cities-in-the-global-south.pdf (Accessed December 18, 2020).

Whetstone, J.R., 2018: Advances in urban greenhouse gas flux quantification: The Indianapolis Flux Experiment (INFLUX). *Elem Sci Anth*, **6**, 24, doi:10.1525/elementa.282.

White, R., and S. Wahba, 2019: Addressing constraints to private financing of urban (climate) infrastructure in developing countries. *Int. J. Urban Sustain. Dev.*, **11(3)**, 245–256, doi:10.1080/19463138.2018.1559970.

Widerberg, O., and P. Pattberg, 2015: International Cooperative Initiatives in Global Climate Governance: Raising the Ambition Level or Delegitimizing the UNFCCC? *Glob. Policy*, **6(1)**, 45–56, doi:10.1111/1758-5899.12184.

Wiedmann, T., and J. Minx, 2008: A Definition of 'Carbon Footprint'. In: *Ecological Economics Research Trends*. Nova Science Publishers, Hauppauge, NY, USA, pp. 1–11.

Wiedmann, T. et al., 2021: Three-scope carbon emission inventories of global cities. *J. Ind. Ecol.*, **25(3)**, 735–750, doi:10.1111/jiec.13063.

Wiedmann, T.O., G. Chen, and J. Barrett, 2016: The Concept of City Carbon Maps: A Case Study of Melbourne, Australia. *J. Ind. Ecol.*, **20(4)**, 676–691, doi:10.1111/jiec.12346.

Wiktorowicz, J. et al., 2018: WGV: An Australian Urban Precinct Case Study to Demonstrate the 1.5°C Agenda Including Multiple SDGs. *Urban Plan.*, **3(2)**, 64–81, doi:10.17645/up.v3i2.1245.

Winbourne, J.B. et al., 2020: Tree Transpiration and Urban Temperatures: Current Understanding, Implications, and Future Research Directions. *Bioscience*, **70(7)**, 576–588, doi:10.1093/biosci/biaa055.

WMO, 2021: *State of the Global Climate 2021: WMO Provisional Report*. World Meteorological Organization (WMO), 47 pp. https://library.wmo.int/doc_num.php?explnum_id=10859 (Accessed November 5, 2021).

Wolman, A., 1965: The Metabolism of Cities. *Sci. Am.*, **213(3)**, 178–190, doi:10.1038/scientificamerican0965-178.

Wong, N.H., C.L. Tan, D.D. Kolokotsa, and H. Takebayashi, 2021: Greenery as a mitigation and adaptation strategy to urban heat. *Nat. Rev. Earth Environ.*, **2(3)**, 166–181, doi:10.1038/s43017-020-00129-5.

Woodall, C.W. et al., 2013: Biomass and carbon attributes of downed woody materials in forests of the United States. *For. Ecol. Manage.*, **305**, 48–59, doi:10.1016/j.foreco.2013.05.030.

World Bank, CIESIN, and Columbia University, 2013: Urban land area. https://data.worldbank.org/indicator/AG.LND.TOTL.UR.K2 (Accessed January 7, 2020).

Wu, D., J.C. Lin, T. Oda, and E.A. Kort, 2020a: Space-based quantification of per capita CO_2 emissions from cities. *Environ. Res. Lett.*, **15(3)**, 035004, doi:10.1088/1748-9326/ab68eb.

Wu, H., L. Wang, Z. Zhang, and J. Gao, 2021: Analysis and optimization of 15-minute community life circle based on supply and demand matching: A case study of Shanghai. *PLoS One*, **16(8)**, e0256904, doi:10.1371/journal.pone.0256904.

Wu, L. et al., 2016: What would dense atmospheric observation networks bring to the quantification of city CO_2 emissions? *Atmos. Chem. Phys.*, **16(12)**, 7743–7771, doi:10.5194/acp-16-7743-2016.

Wu, Q., H. Ren, W. Gao, P. Weng, and J. Ren, 2018: Coupling optimization of urban spatial structure and neighborhood-scale distributed energy systems. *Energy*, **144**, 472–481, doi:10.1016/j.energy.2017.12.076.

Wu, X., R.C. Nethery, M.B. Sabath, D. Braun, and F. Dominici, 2020b: Air pollution and COVID-19 mortality in the United States: Strengths and limitations of an ecological regression analysis. *Sci. Adv.*, **6(45)**, eabd4049, doi:10.1126/sciadv.abd4049.

Wynes, S., K.A. Nicholas, J. Zhao, and S.D. Donner, 2018: Measuring what works: quantifying greenhouse gas emission reductions of behavioural interventions to reduce driving, meat consumption, and household energy use. *Environ. Res. Lett.*, **13(11)**, 113002, doi:10.1088/1748-9326/aae5d7.

Xi, F. et al., 2016: Substantial global carbon uptake by cement carbonation. *Nat. Geosci.*, **9(12)**, 880–883, doi:10.1038/ngeo2840.

Xu, L. et al., 2019: Identifying the trade-offs between climate change mitigation and adaptation in urban land use planning: An empirical study in a coastal city. *Environ. Int.*, **133**, 105162, doi:10.1016/j.envint.2019.105162.

Xu, Q., Y. Dong, and R. Yang, 2018a: Urbanization impact on carbon emissions in the Pearl River Delta region: Kuznets curve relationships. *J. Clean. Prod.*, **180**, 514–523, doi:10.1016/j.jclepro.2018.01.194.

Xu, Q., Y. Dong, and R. Yang, 2018b: Influence of the geographic proximity of city features on the spatial variation of urban carbon sinks: A case study on the Pearl River Delta. *Environ. Pollut.*, **243**, 354–363, doi:10.1016/j.envpol.2018.08.083.

Xu, Q., X. Zheng, and C. Zhang, 2018c: Quantitative Analysis of the Determinants Influencing Urban Expansion: A Case Study in Beijing, China. *Sustainability*, **10(5)**, 1630, doi:10.3390/su10051630.

Xue, Y. et al., 2017: Transport Emissions and Energy Consumption Impacts of Private Capital Investment in Public Transport. *Sustainability*, **9(10)**, 1760, doi:10.3390/su9101760.

Yadav, V. et al., 2021: The Impact of COVID-19 on CO_2 Emissions in the Los Angeles and Washington DC/Baltimore Metropolitan Areas. *Geophys. Res. Lett.*, **48(11)**, e2021GL,;

Yamagata, Y. et al., 2020: Chapter 2 - Urban systems and the role of big data. In: *Urban Systems Design: Creating Sustainable Smart Cities in the Internet of Things Era* [Yamagata, Y. and P.P.J. Yang, (eds.)]. Elsevier, Amsterdam, The Netherlands, pp. 23–58.

Yang, D., L. Xu, X. Gao, Q. Guo, and N. Huang, 2018: Inventories and reduction scenarios of urban waste-related greenhouse gas emissions for management potential. *Sci. Total Environ.*, **626**, 727–736, doi:10.1016/j.scitotenv.2018.01.110.

Yang, X., and R. Li, 2018: Investigating low-carbon city: Empirical study of Shanghai. *Sustainability*, **10(4)**, 1054, doi:10.3390/su10041054.

Yazdanie, M., and K. Orehounig, 2021: Advancing urban energy system planning and modeling approaches: Gaps and solutions in perspective. *Renew. Sustain. Energy Rev.*, **137**, 110607, doi:10.1016/j.rser.2020.110607.

Yi, Y., S. Ma, W. Guan, and K. Li, 2017: An empirical study on the relationship between urban spatial form and CO_2 in Chinese cities. *Sustainability*, **9(4)**, 672, doi:10.3390/su9040672.

Yu, Y., and W. Zhang, 2016: Greenhouse gas emissions from solid waste in Beijing: The rising trend and the mitigation effects by management improvements. *Waste Manag. Res.*, **34(4)**, 368–377, doi:10.1177/0734242X16628982.

Zaman, A., and T. Ahsan, 2019: *Zero-Waste: Reconsidering Waste Management for the Future*. 1st ed. Routledge, London, UK, 234 pp.

Zaman, A., and S. Lehmann, 2013: The zero waste index: A performance measurement tool for waste management systems in a "zero waste city". *J. Clean. Prod.*, **50**, 123–132, doi:10.1016/j.jclepro.2012.11.041.

Zhai, Y. et al., 2020: Is energy the key to pursuing clean air and water at the city level? A case study of Jinan City, China. *Renew. Sustain. Energy Rev.*, **134**, 110353, doi:10.1016/j.rser.2020.110353.

Zhan, C., and M. de Jong, 2018: Financing eco cities and low carbon cities: The case of Shenzhen International Low Carbon City. *J. Clean. Prod.*, **180**, 116–125, doi:10.1016/J.JCLEPRO.2018.01.097.

Zhan, C., M. de Jong, and H. de Bruijn, 2018a: Funding sustainable cities: A comparative study of Sino-Singapore Tianjin Eco-City and Shenzhen International Low-Carbon City. *Sustainability*, **10(11)**, doi:10.3390/su10114256.

Zhan, J., W. Liu, F. Wu, Z. Li, and C. Wang, 2018b: Life cycle energy consumption and greenhouse gas emissions of urban residential buildings in Guangzhou city. *J. Clean. Prod.*, **194**, 318–326, doi:10.1016/j.jclepro.2018.05.124.

Zhang, F., C.K.L. Chung, and Z. Yin, 2020: Green infrastructure for China's new urbanisation: A case study of greenway development in Maanshan. *Urban Stud.*, **57(3)**, 508–524, doi:10.1177/0042098018822965.

Zhang, H., C. Wu, W. Chen, and G. Huang, 2019: Effect of urban expansion on summer rainfall in the Pearl River Delta, South China. *J. Hydrol.*, **568**, 747–757, doi:10.1016/j.jhydrol.2018.11.036.

Zhang, J., and F. Li, 2017: Energy consumption and low carbon development strategies of three global cities in Asian developing countries. *J. Renew. Sustain. Energy*, **9(2)**, 021402, doi:10.1063/1.4978467.

Zhang, N., K. Yu, and Z. Chen, 2017: How does urbanization affect carbon dioxide emissions? A cross-country panel data analysis. *Energy Policy*, **107**, 678–687, doi:10.1016/j.enpol.2017.03.072.

Zhang, R. and S. Fujimori, 2020: The role of transport electrification in global climate change mitigation scenarios. *Environ. Res. Lett.*, **15(3)**, 034019, doi:10.1088/1748-9326/ab6658.

Zhang, Y., X. Bai, F.P. Mills, and J.C.V.V. Pezzey, 2018: Rethinking the role of occupant behavior in building energy performance: A review. *Energy Build.*, **172**, 279–294, doi:10.1016/J.ENBUILD.2018.05.017.

Zhao, G., J.M. Guerrero, K. Jiang, and S. Chen, 2017a: Energy modelling towards low carbon development of Beijing in 2030. *Energy*, **121**, 107–113, doi:10.1016/j.energy.2017.01.019.

Zhao, S.X., N.S. Guo, C.L.K. Li, and C. Smith, 2017b: Megacities, the World's Largest Cities Unleashed: Major Trends and Dynamics in Contemporary Global Urban Development. *World Dev.*, **98**, 257–289, doi:10.1016/j.worlddev.2017.04.038.

Zheng, B. et al., 2018: Infrastructure Shapes Differences in the Carbon Intensities of Chinese Cities. *Environ. Sci. Technol.*, **52(10)**, 6032–6041, doi:10.1021/acs.est.7b05654.

Zheng, B. et al., 2020: Satellite-based estimates of decline and rebound in China's CO_2 emissions during COVID-19 pandemic. *Sci. Adv.*, **6(49)**, eabd4998, doi:10.1126/SCIADV.ABD4998.

Zheng, X., Y. Zou, A.W. Lounsbury, C. Wang, and R. Wang, 2021: Green roofs for stormwater runoff retention: A global quantitative synthesis of the performance. *Resour. Conserv. Recycl.*, **170**, 105577, doi:10.1016/j.resconrec.2021.105577.

Zhou, C., S. Wang, and J. Wang, 2019: Examining the influences of urbanization on carbon dioxide emissions in the Yangtze River Delta, China: Kuznets curve relationship. *Sci. Total Environ.*, **675**, 472–482, doi:10.1016/J.SCITOTENV.2019.04.269.

Zscheischler, J. et al., 2018: Future climate risk from compound events. *Nat. Clim. Change*, **8(6)**, 469–477, doi:10.1038/s41558-018-0156-3.

9 Buildings

Coordinating Lead Authors:
Luisa F. Cabeza (Spain), Quan Bai (China)

Lead Authors:
Paolo Bertoldi (Italy), Jacob M. Kihila (the United Republic of Tanzania), André F.P. Lucena (Brazil), Érika Mata (Spain/Sweden), Sebastian Mirasgedis (Greece), Aleksandra Novikova (Germany/the Russian Federation), Yamina Saheb (France/Algeria)

Contributing Authors:
Peter Berrill (Germany/Ireland), Lucas R. Caldas (Brazil), Marta Chàfer (Spain), Shan Hu (China), Radhika Khosla (United Kingdom/India), William F. Lamb (Germany/United Kingdom), David Vérez (Cuba/Spain), Joel Wanemark (Sweden)

Review Editors:
Jesse Keenan (the United States of America/Austria), María Isabel Serrano Diná (the Dominican Republic)

Chapter Scientist:
Shan Hu (China)

This chapter should be cited as:
Cabeza, L. F., Q. Bai, P. Bertoldi, J.M. Kihila, A.F.P. Lucena, É. Mata, S. Mirasgedis, A. Novikova, Y. Saheb, 2022: Buildings. In IPCC, 2022: *Climate Change 2022: Mitigation of Climate Change. Contribution of Working Group III to the Sixth Assessment Report of the Intergovernmental Panel on Climate Change* [P.R. Shukla, J. Skea, R. Slade, A. Al Khourdajie, R. van Diemen, D. McCollum, M. Pathak, S. Some, P. Vyas, R. Fradera, M. Belkacemi, A. Hasija, G. Lisboa, S. Luz, J. Malley, (eds.)]. Cambridge University Press, Cambridge, UK and New York, NY, USA. doi: 10.1017/9781009157926.011

Table of Contents

Executive Summary

Global greenhouse gas (GHG) emissions from buildings were in 2019 at 12 GtCO$_2$-eq, equivalent to 21% of global GHG emissions that year, out of which 57% were indirect emissions from offsite generation of electricity and heat, 24% direct emissions produced onsite and 18% were embodied emissions from the use of cement and steel (*high evidence, high agreement*). More than 95% of emissions from buildings were CO$_2$ emissions, CH$_4$ and N$_2$O represented 0.08%, and emissions from halocarbon contributed by 3% to global GHG emissions from buildings. If only CO$_2$ emissions would be considered, the share of CO$_2$ emissions from buildings out of global CO$_2$ emissions increases to 31%. Global final energy demand from buildings reached 128.8 EJ in 2019, and global electricity demand was slightly above 43 EJ. The former accounted for 31% of global final energy demand and the latter for 18% of global electricity demand. Residential buildings consumed 70% of global final energy demand from buildings. Over the period 1990–2019, global CO$_2$ emissions from buildings increased by 50%, global final energy demand grew by 38% and global final electricity demand increased by 161% (*high evidence, high agreement*) {9.3}.

Drivers of GHG emissions in the building sector were assessed using the SER (Sufficiency, Efficiency, Renewables) framework. Sufficiency measures tackle the causes of GHG emissions by avoiding the demand for energy and materials over the lifecycle of buildings and appliances. Sufficiency differs from efficiency in that the latter is about the continuous short-term marginal technological improvements, which allows doing less with more in relative terms without considering the planetary boundaries, while the former is about long-term actions driven by non-technological solutions (i.e., land-use management and planning), which consume less in absolute term and are determined by biophysical processes. Sufficiency addresses the issue of a fair consumption of space and resources. The remaining carbon budget, and its normative target for distributional equity, is the upper limit of sufficiency, while requirements for a decent living standard define the minimum level of sufficiency. The SER framework introduces a hierarchical layering which reduces the cost of constructing and using buildings without reducing the level of comfort of the occupant. Sufficiency interventions in buildings include the optimisation of the use of building, repurposing unused existing buildings, prioritising multi-family homes over single-family buildings, and adjusting the size of buildings to the evolving needs of households by downsizing dwellings. Sufficiency measures do not consume energy during the use phase of buildings.

In most regions, historical improvements in efficiency have been approximately matched by growth in floor area per capita. Implementing sufficiency measures that limit growth in floor area per capita, particularly in developed regions, reduces the dependence of climate mitigation on technological solutions (*medium evidence, medium agreement*). At a global level, up to 17% of the mitigation potential could be captured by 2050 through sufficiency interventions (*medium evidence, medium agreement*). Sufficiency is an opportunity to avoid locking buildings in carbon-intensive solutions. Density, compacity, building typologies, bioclimatic design, multi-functionality of space, circular use of materials, use of

the thermal mass of buildings (to store heat for the cold season and to protect occupants from high temperatures (i.e., heatwaves), when designing energy services, moving from ownership to usership of appliances and towards more shared space, are among the sufficiency measures already implemented in the leading municipalities. At the global level, the main drivers of emissions include (i) population growth, especially in developing countries, (ii) increase in floor area per capita, driven by the increase of the size of dwellings while the size of households kept decreasing, especially in developed countries, (iii) the inefficiency of the newly constructed buildings, especially in developing countries, and the low renovation rates and ambition level in developed countries when existing buildings are renovated, (iv) the increase in use, number and size of appliances and equipment, especially ICT and cooling, driven by the growing welfare (income), and (v) the continued reliance on fossil fuel-based electricity and heat slow decarbonisation of energy supply. These factors taken together are projected to continue driving GHG emissions in the building sector in the future (*high evidence, high agreement*) {9.2, 9.3, 9.4, 9.5, 9.6, and 9.9}.

Bottom-up studies show a mitigation potential up to 85% in Europe and North America and up to 45% in Australia, Japan and New Zealand, compared to the baselines by 2050, even though they sometimes decline (*robust evidence, high agreement*). In developing countries, bottom-up studies estimate the potential of up to 40–80% in 2050, as compared to their sharply growing baselines (*medium evidence, high agreement*). The aggregation of results from all these bottom-up studies translates into a global mitigation potential by 2050 of at least 8.2 GtCO$_2$, which is equivalent to 61% of their baseline scenario. The largest mitigation potential (5.4 GtCO$_2$) is available in developing countries while Developed Countries will be able to mitigate 2.7 GtCO$_2$. These potentials represent the low estimates, and the real potential is likely to be higher. These estimated potentials would be higher if embodied emissions in buildings and those from halocarbons would be included (*low evidence, high agreement*) {9.3, 9.6}.

The development, since the IPCC Fifth Assessment Report (AR5), of integrated approaches to construction and retrofit of buildings has led to the widespread adoption of zero energy/carbon buildings in all climate zones. The complementarity and the interdependency of measures lead to cost reduction while optimising the mitigation potential grasped and avoiding the lock-in-effect. The growing consideration of integrated approach to construction of new buildings as well as to the renovation of existing buildings results in a lower relevance of the step-by-step approach to renovate buildings and to breaking down the potential into cost categories, as to deliver deep mitigation and cost savings technologies and approaches shall be applied together in an integrated and interdependent manner (*medium evidence, high agreement*). The potential associated with the sufficiency measures as well as the exchange of appliances, equipment, and lights with efficient ones is at cost below USD0 tCO$_2^{-1}$ (*high evidence, high agreement*). The construction of high-performance buildings will become by 2050 a business-as-usual technology with costs below USD20 tCO$_2^{-1}$ in developed countries and below USD100 tCO$_2^{-1}$ in developing countries (*medium evidence, high agreement*). For existing buildings, there have been many examples of deep retrofits where additional costs per CO_2 abated are not significantly higher than those of shallow retrofits. However, for the whole stock they tend to be in cost intervals of USD0–200 tCO_2^{-1} and >USD200 tCO_2^{-1} (*medium evidence, medium agreement*). Literature emphasizes the critical role of the decade between in 2020 and 2030 in accelerating the learning of know-how and skills to reduce the costs and remove feasibility constrains for achieving high efficiency buildings at scale and set the sector at the pathway to realise its full potential (*high evidence, high agreement*) {9.6, 9.9}.

The decarbonisation of buildings is constrained by multiple barriers and obstacles as well as limited flow of finance (*robust evidence, high agreement*). The lack of institutional capacity, especially in developing countries, and appropriate governance structures slow down the decarbonisation of the global building stock (*medium evidence, high agreement*). The building sector stands out for its high heterogeneity, with many different building types, sizes, and operational uses. Its segment representing rented property faces principal/agent problems where the tenant benefits from the decarbonisation investment made by the landlord. The organisational context and the governance structure could trigger or hinder the decarbonisation of buildings (*high evidence, high agreement*). Global investment in the decarbonisation of buildings was estimated at USD164 billion in 2020, not enough to close the investment gap (*robust evidence, high agreement*) {9.9}.

Policy packages based on the SER (Sufficiency, Efficiency, Renewables) framework could grasp the full mitigation potential of the global building stock (*medium evidence, high agreement*). Low ambitious policies will lock buildings in carbon for decades as buildings last for decades if not centuries (*high evidence, high agreement*). Building energy codes is the main regulatory instrument to reduce emissions from both new and existing buildings (*high evidence, high agreement*). Most advanced building energy codes include bioclimatic design requirements to capture the sufficiency potential of buildings, efficiency requirements by using the most efficient technologies and requirements to increase the integration of renewable energy solutions to the building shape. Some announced building energy codes extend these requirements from the use phase to the whole building lifecycle. Building energy codes are proven to be especially effective if compulsory and combined with other regulatory instruments such as minimum energy performance standard for appliances and equipment, especially if the performance level is set at the level of the best available technologies in the market (*robust evidence, high agreement*). Market-based instruments such as carbon taxes with recycling of the revenues and personal or building carbon allowances also contribute to foster the decarbonisation of the building sector (*robust evidence, high agreement*). Requirements to limit the use of land and property taxes are also considered effective policies to limit urban sprawl and to prioritise multi-family buildings over single-family homes (*medium evidence, high agreement*) {9.9}.

Actions are needed to adapt buildings to future climate while ensuring well-being for all. The expected heatwaves will inevitably increase cooling needs to limit the health impacts of climate change (*medium evidence, high agreement*). Global warming will impact cooling and heating needs but also the performance, durability and safety of buildings, especially historical and coastal ones, through changes in temperature, humidity, concentrations of CO_2 and chloride, and sea level rise. Adaptation measures to cope with climate change may increase the demand for energy and materials leading to an increase in GHG emissions if not mitigated. Sufficiency measures such as bioclimatic design of buildings, which consider the expected future climate, and includes natural ventilation, white walls and nature-based solutions (e.g., green roofs) will decrease the demand for cooling. Shared cooled spaces with highly efficient cooling solutions are among the mitigation strategies which can limit the effect of the expected heatwaves on people health. Sufficiency, efficiency, and renewable energy can be designed to reduce buildings' vulnerability to climate change impacts (*medium evidence, high agreement*) {9.7, 9.8}.

Well-designed and effectively implemented mitigation actions in the buildings sector have significant potential for achieving the United Nations Sustainable Development Goals. The impacts of mitigation actions in the building sector go far beyond the goal of climate action (SDG 13) and contribute to further meeting fifteen other SDGs. Mitigation actions in the building sector bring health gains through improved indoor air quality and thermal comfort as well as reduced financial stresses in all world regions. Overall decarbonised building stock contribute to well-being and has significant macro- and micro-economic effects, such as increased productivity of labour, job creation, reduced poverty, especially energy poverty, and improved energy security that ultimately reduces net costs of mitigation measures in buildings (*high evidence, high agreement*) {9.8}.

COVID-19 emphasised the importance of buildings for human well-being. However, the lockdown measures implemented to avoid the spread of the virus have also stressed the inequalities in the access for all to suitable and healthy buildings, which provide natural daylight and clean air to their occupants (*low evidence, high agreement*). Meeting the new WHO health requirements, has also put an emphasis on indoor air quality, preventive maintenance of centralised mechanical heating, ventilation, and cooling systems. Moreover, the lockdown measures have led to spreading the South Korean concept of *officetel* (office-hotel) to many countries and to extending it to *officetelschool*. The projected growth, prior to the COVID-19, of 58% of the global residential floor area by 2050 compared to the 290 billion $m^2 \, yr^{-1}$ in 2019 might well be insufficient. Addressing the new needs for more residential buildings may not, necessarily mean constructing new buildings, especially in the global North. Repurposing existing non-residential buildings, no longer in use due to the expected spread of teleworking triggered by the health crisis and enabled by digitalisation, could be the way to overcome the new needs for *officetelschool* buildings triggered by the health crisis (*low evidence, high confidence*) {9.1, 9.2}.

9.1   Introduction

Total GHG emissions in the building sector reached 12 GtCO$_2$-eq in 2019, equivalent to 21% of global GHG emissions that year, of which 57% were indirect CO$_2$ emissions from offsite generation of electricity and heat, followed by 24% of direct CO$_2$ emissions produced on-site and 18% from the production of cement and steel used for construction and/or refurbishment of buildings. If only CO$_2$ emissions would be considered, the share of buildings CO$_2$ emissions increases to 31% out of global CO$_2$ emissions. Energy use in residential and non-residential buildings contributed 50% and 32% respectively, while embodied emissions contributed 18% to global building CO$_2$ emissions. Global final energy demand from buildings reached 128.8 EJ in 2019, equivalent to 31% of global final energy demand. Residential buildings consumed 70% out of global final energy demand from buildings. Electricity demand from buildings was slightly above 43 EJ in 2019, equivalent to more than 18% of global electricity demand. Over the period 1990–2019, global CO$_2$ emissions from buildings increased by 50%, global final energy demand grew by 38%, with 54% increase in non-residential buildings and 32% increase in residential ones. Among energy carriers, the growth in global final energy demand was strongest for electricity, which increased by 161%.

There is growing scientific evidence about the mitigation potential of the building sector and its contribution to the decarbonisation of global and regional energy systems, and to meeting Paris Agreement goals

and Sustainable Development Goals (SDGs) (IPCC, 2018; IEA, 2019c; IEA 2019e). Mitigation interventions in buildings are heterogeneous in many different aspects, from building components (envelope, structure, materials, etc.) to services (shelter, heating, etc.), to building types (residential and non-residential, sometimes also called commercial and public), to building size, function, and climate zone. There are also variations between developed and developing countries in mitigation interventions to implement, as the former is challenged by the renovation of existing buildings while the latter is challenged by the need to accelerate the construction of new buildings.

This chapter aims at updating the knowledge on the building sector since the Intergovernmental Panel on Climate Change Fifth Assessment Report (IPCC AR5) (Lucon et al. 2014). Changes since AR5 are reviewed, including: the latest development of building service and components (Section 9.2), findings of new building related GHG emission trends (Section 9.3), latest technological (Section 9.4) and non-technological (Section 9.5) options to mitigate building GHG emissions, potential emission reduction from these measures at global and regional level (Section 9.6), links to adaptation (Section 9.7) and sustainable development (Section 9.8), and sectoral barriers and policies (Section 9.9).

The chapter introduces the concept of sufficiency, identified in the literature as a mitigation strategy with high potential, and is organised around the Sufficiency, Efficiency, Renewables (SER) framework (Box 9.1).

Box 9.1 | SER (Sufficiency, Efficiency, Renewables) Framework

The SER framework was introduced in the late 1990s by a French NGO (Negawatt 2017) advocating for a decarbonised energy transition. In 2015, the SER framework was considered in the design of the French energy transition law, and the French energy transition agency (ADEME) is developing its 2050 scenario based on the SER framework.

The three pillars of the SER framework include (i) sufficiency, which tackles the causes of the environmental impacts of human activities by avoiding the demand for energy and materials over the lifecycle of buildings and goods, (ii) efficiency, which tackles the symptoms of the environmental impacts of human activities by improving energy and material intensities, and (iii) the renewables pillar, which tackles the consequences of the environmental impacts of human activities by reducing the carbon intensity of energy supply (Box 9.1, Figure 1). The SER framework introduces a hierarchical layering, sufficiency first followed by efficiency and renewable, which reduces the cost of constructing and using buildings without reducing the level of comfort of the occupant.

Sufficiency is not a new concept, its root goes back to the Greek word *sôphrosunè*, which was translated in Latin to *sobrietas*, in a sense of *enough* (Cézard and Mourad 2019). The sufficiency concept was introduced to the sustainability policy debate by (Sachs 1993) and to academia by (Princen 2003). Since 1997, Thailand considers sufficiency, which was framed already in 1974 as Sufficiency Economy Philosophy, as a new paradigm for development with the aim of improving human well-being for all by shifting development pathways towards sustainability (Mongsawad 2012). The Thai approach is based on three principles (i) moderation, (ii) reasonableness, and (iii) self-immunity. Sufficiency goes beyond the dominant framing of energy demand under efficiency and behaviour. Sufficiency is defined as avoiding the demand for materials, energy, land, water and other natural resources while delivering a decent living standard for all within the planetary boundaries (Saheb 2021b, Princen 2005). Decent living standards are a set of essential material preconditions for human well-being which includes shelter, nutrition, basic amenities, health care, transportation, information, education, and public space (Rao and Baer 2012; Rao and Min 2018; Rao et al. 2019). Sufficiency addresses the issue of a fair consumption of space and resources. The remaining carbon budget, and its normative target for distributional equity, is the upper limit of sufficiency, while requirements for a decent living standard define the minimum level of sufficiency. Sufficiency differs from efficiency in that the latter is about the continuous short-term marginal technological improvements which allow doing more

9

Box 9.1 (continued)

with less in relative terms without considering the planetary boundaries, while the former is about long-term actions driven by non-technological solutions (i.e., land-use management and planning), which consume less in absolute-term and are determined by the biophysical processes (Princen 2003).

Box 9.1, Figure 1 | SER framework applied to the building sector. Source: Saheb (2021).

Applying sufficiency principles to buildings requires (i) optimising the use of buildings, (ii) repurposing unused existing ones, (iii) prioritising multi-family homes over single-family buildings, and (iv) adjusting the size of buildings to the evolving needs of households by downsizing dwellings (Wilson and Boehland 2005; Duffy 2009; Fuller and Crawford 2011; Stephan et al. 2013; Huebner and Shipworth 2017; Sandberg 2018; McKinlay et al. 2019; Ellsworth-Krebs 2020; Berrill et al. 2021) (Box 9.1, Figure 2).

Box 9.1 (continued)

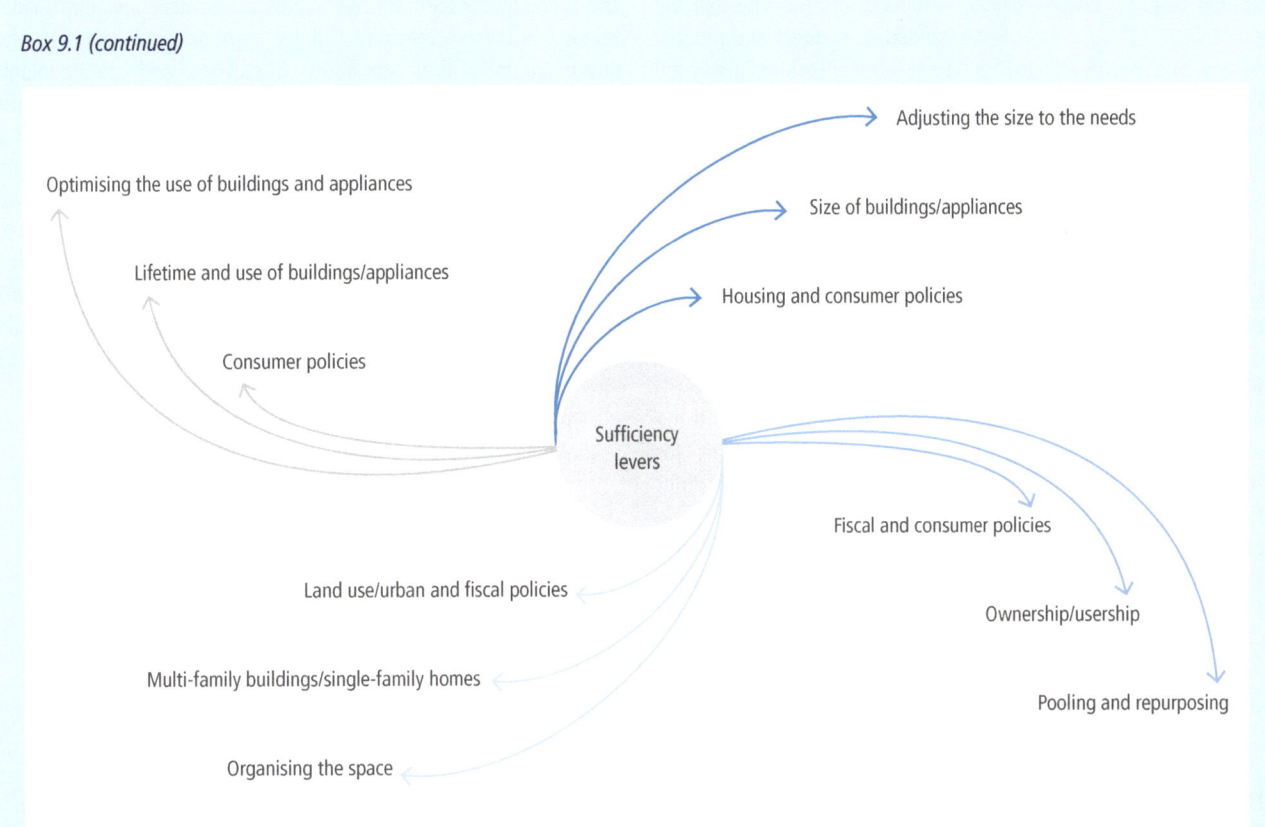

Box 9.1, Figure 2 | Sufficiency interventions and policies in the building sector. Source: Saheb (2021).

Downsizing dwellings through cohousing strategies by repurposing existing buildings and clustering apartments when buildings are renovated and by prioritising multi-family buildings over single-family homes in new developments (Wilson and Boehland 2005; Duffy 2009; Fuller and Crawford 2011; Stephan et al. 2013; Huebner and Shipworth 2017; Sandberg 2018; McKinlay et al. 2019; Ellsworth-Krebs 2020; Ivanova and Büchs 2020; Berrill and Hertwich 2021) are among the sufficiency measures that avoid the demand for materials in the construction phase and energy demand for heating, cooling and lighting in the use phase, especially if the conditioned volume and window areas are reduced (Duffy 2009; Heinonen and Junnila 2014). Less space also means less appliances and equipment and changing preferences towards smaller ones (Aro 2020). Cohousing strategies provide users, in both new and existing buildings, a shared space (i.e., for laundry, offices, guest rooms and dining rooms) to complement their private space. Thus, reducing per capita consumption of resources including energy, water and electricity (Klocker et al. 2012; N. Klocker 2017), while offering social benefits such as limiting loneliness of elderly people and single parents (Wankiewicz 2015; Riedy et al. 2019). Senior cooperative housing communities and eco-villages are considered among the cohousing examples to scale-up (Kuhnhenn et al. 2020). Local authorities have an important role to play in the metamorphosis of housing by proposing communal spaces to be shared (Williams 2008; Marckmann et al. 2012) through urban planning and land-use policies (Duffy 2009; Newton et al. 2017). Thus, encouraging inter-generational cohousing as well as interactions between people with different social backgrounds (Williams 2008; Lietaert 2010). Progressive tax policies based on a cap in the per-capita floor area are also needed to adapt the size of dwellings to households' needs (Murphy 2015; Akenji 2021).

Efficiency, and especially energy efficiency and more recently resource efficiency, and the integration of renewable to buildings are widespread concepts since the oil crisis of the seventies, while only most advanced building energy codes consider sufficiency measures (IEA 2013). Efficiency and renewable technologies and interventions are described in Sections 9.4 and 9.9.

A systematic categorisation of policy interventions in the building sector through the SER framework (Box 9.1, Figure 1) enables identification of the policy areas and instruments to consider for the decarbonisation of the building stock, their overlaps as well as their complementarities. It also shows that sufficiency policies go beyond energy and climate policies to include land-use and urban planning policies as well as consumer policies suggesting a need for a different governance including local authorities and a bottom-up approach driven by citizen engagement.

Compared to AR5, this assessment introduces four novelties (i) the scope of CO_2 emissions has been extended from direct and indirect emissions considered in AR5 to include embodied emissions, (ii) beyond technological efficiency measures to mitigate GHG emissions in buildings, the contribution of non-technological, in particular of sufficiency measures to climate mitigation is also considered, (iii) compared to the IPCC Special Report on Global Warming of 1.5°C (SR1.5), the link to sustainable development, well-being and decent living standard for all has been further developed and strengthened, and finally (iv) the active role of buildings in the energy system by making passive consumers prosumers is also assessed.

COVID-19 emphasised the importance of buildings for human well-being, however, the lockdown measures implemented to avoid the spread of the virus has also stressed the inequalities in the access for all to suitable and healthy buildings, which provide natural daylight and clean air to their occupants (see also Cross-Chapter Box 1 in Chapter 1). COVID-19 and the new health recommendations (World Health Organization 2021) emphasised the importance of ventilation and the importance of indoor air quality (Sundell et al. 2011; Nazaroff 2013; Fisk 2015; Guyot et al. 2018; Wei et al. 2020). The health crisis has also put an emphasis on preventive maintenance of centralised mechanical heating, ventilation, and cooling systems. Moreover, the lockdown measures have led to spreading the South Korean concept of *officetel* (office-hotel) (Gohaud and Baek 2017) to many countries and to extending it to *officetelschool*. Therefore, the projected growth, prior to the COVID-19, of 58% of the global residential floor area by 2050 compared to the 290 billion m² yr⁻¹ in 2019 might well be insufficient. However, addressing the new needs for more residential buildings may not, necessarily mean constructing new buildings. In fact, repurposing existing non-residential buildings, no longer in use due to the expected spread of teleworking triggered by the health crisis and enabled by digitalisation, could be the way to overcome the new needs for *officetelschool* triggered by the health crisis.

The four novelties introduced in this assessment link the building sector to other sectors and call for more sectoral coupling when designing mitigation solutions. Guidelines and methodologies developed in Chapters 1, 2, 3, 4 and 5 are adopted in this chapter. Detailed analysis in building GHG emissions is discussed based on Chapter 2 and scenarios to assess future emissions and mitigation potentials were selected based on Chapters, 3 and 4. There are tight linkages between this chapter and Chapter 6, 7, 8, 10 and 11, which are sectoral sectors. This chapter focusses more on individual buildings and building clusters, while Chapter 8 discusses macro topics in urban areas. Findings of this chapter provides contribution to cross-sectoral prospection (Chapter 12), policies (Chapter 13), international cooperation (Chapter 14), investment and finance (Chapter 15), innovation (Chapter 16), and sustainable development (Chapter 17).

9.2   Services and Components

This section mainly details the boundaries of the building sector; mitigation potentials are evaluated in the following sections.

9.2.1   Building Types

Building types and their composition affect the energy consumption for building operation as well as the GHG emissions (Hachem-Vermette and Singh 2019). They also influence the energy cost (MacNaughton et al. 2015) therefore, an identification of building type is required to understand the heterogeneity of this sector. Buildings are classified as residential and non-residential buildings. Residential buildings can be classified as slums, single-family house and multi-family house or apartment/flats building. Single-family house can be divided between single-family detached (including cottages, house barns, etc.) and

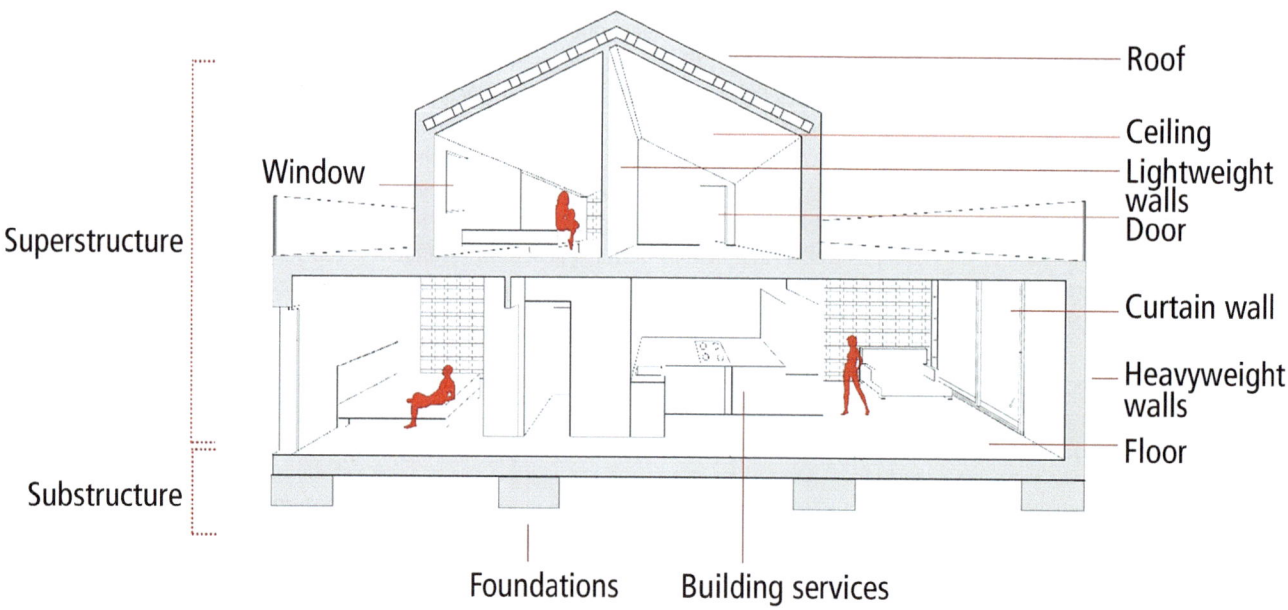

Figure 9.1 | The main building components.

single-family attached (or terrace house, small multi-family, etc.). Another classification is per ownership: owner-occupiers, landlords, and owners' association/condominiums.

Non-residential buildings have a much broader use. They include cultural buildings (which include theatres and performance, museums and exhibits, libraries, and cultural centres), educational buildings (kindergarten, schools, higher education, research centre, and laboratories), sports (recreation and training, and stadiums), healthcare buildings (health, well-being, and veterinary), hospitality (hotel, casino, lodging, nightlife buildings, and restaurants and bars), commercial buildings and offices (institutional buildings, markets, office buildings, retail, and shopping centres), public buildings (government buildings, security, and military buildings), religious buildings (including worship and burial buildings), and industrial buildings (factories, energy plants, warehouses, data centres, transportation buildings, and agricultural buildings).

9.2.2   Building Components and Construction Methods

An understanding of the methods for assembling various materials, elements, and components is necessary during both the design and the construction phase of a building. A building can be broadly divided into parts: the substructure which is the underlying structure forming the foundation of a building, and the superstructure, which is the vertical extension of a building above the foundation.

There is not a global classification for the building components. Nevertheless, Figure 9.1 tries to summarise the building components found in literature (Mañá Reixach 2000; Asbjørn 2009; Ching 2014). The buildings are divided in the substructure and the superstructure. The substructure is the foundation of the building, where the footing, basement, and plinth are found. The superstructure integrates the primary elements (heavyweight walls, columns, floors and ceilings, roofs, sills and lintels, and stairs), the supplementary components (lightweight walls and curtain walls), the completion components (doors and windows), the finishing work (plastering and painting), and the buildings services (detailed in Section 9.3).

At a global level, from historical perspective (from the Neolithic to the present), building techniques have evolved to be able to solve increasingly complex problems. Vernacular architecture has evolved over many years to address problems inherent in housing. Through a process of trial and error, populations have found ways to cope with the extremes of the weather. The industrial revolution was the single most important development in human history over the past three centuries. Previously, building materials were restricted to a few manmade materials (lime mortar and concrete) along with those available in nature as timber and stone. Metals were not available in sufficient quantity or consistent quality to be used as anything more than ornamentation. The structure was limited by the capabilities of natural materials; this construction method is called on-site construction which all the work is done sequentially at the buildings site. The Industrial Revolution changed this situation dramatically, new building materials emerged (cast-iron, glass structures, steel-reinforced concrete,

steel). Iron, steel and concrete were the most important materials of the nineteenth century (Wright 2000; De Villanueva Domínguez 2005). In that context, prefabricated buildings (prefabrication also known as pre-assembly or modularisation) appeared within the so-called off-site construction. Prefabrication has come to mean a method of construction whereby building elements and materials, ranging in size from a single component to a complete building, are manufactured at a distance from the final building location. Prefabricated buildings have been developed rapidly since the Second World War and are widely used all over the world (Pons 2014; Moradibistouni et al. 2018).

Recently, advances in technology have produced new expectations in terms of design possibilities. In that context, 3D printing seems to have arrived. 3D printing may allow in the future to build faster, cheaper and more sustainable (Agustí-Juan et al. 2017; García de Soto et al. 2018). At the same time, it might introduce new aesthetics, new materials, and complex shapes that will be printed at the click of a mouse on our computers. Although 3D printing will not replace architectural construction, it would allow optimisation of various production and assembly processes by introducing new sustainable construction processes and tools (De Schutter et al. 2018). Nevertheless, what is clear is that 3D printing is a technology still in development, with a lot of potentials and that it is advancing quite quickly (Hager et al. 2016; Stute et al. 2018; Wang et al. 2020).

9.2.3   Building Services

Building services make buildings more comfortable, functional, efficient, and safe. In a generic point of view, building services include shelter, nutrition, sanitation, thermal, visual, and acoustic comfort, entertainment, communications, elevators, and illumination. In a more holistic view building services are classified as shown in Figure 9.2.

A building management system is a system of devices configured to control, monitor, and manage equipment in or around a building or building area and is meant to optimise building operations and reduce cost (Schuster et al. 2019). Recent developments include the integration of the system with the renewable energy systems (Arnone et al. 2016), most improved and effective user interface (Rabe et al. 2018), control systems based on artificial intelligence and internet of things (IoT) (Farzaneh et al. 2021).

The use of air conditioning systems in buildings will increase with the experienced rise in temperature (Davis and Gertler 2015; De Falco et al. 2016) (Figure 9.8). This can ultimately lead to high energy consumption rates. Therefore, adoption of energy efficient air conditioning is pertinent to balance the provision of comfortable indoor conditions and energy consumption. Some of the new developments that have been done include ice refrigeration (Xu et al. 2017), the use of solar photovoltaic power in the air conditioning process (Burnett et al. 2014), and use of common thermal storage technologies (De Falco et al. 2016) all of which are geared towards minimising energy consumption and greenhouse gas emissions.

9

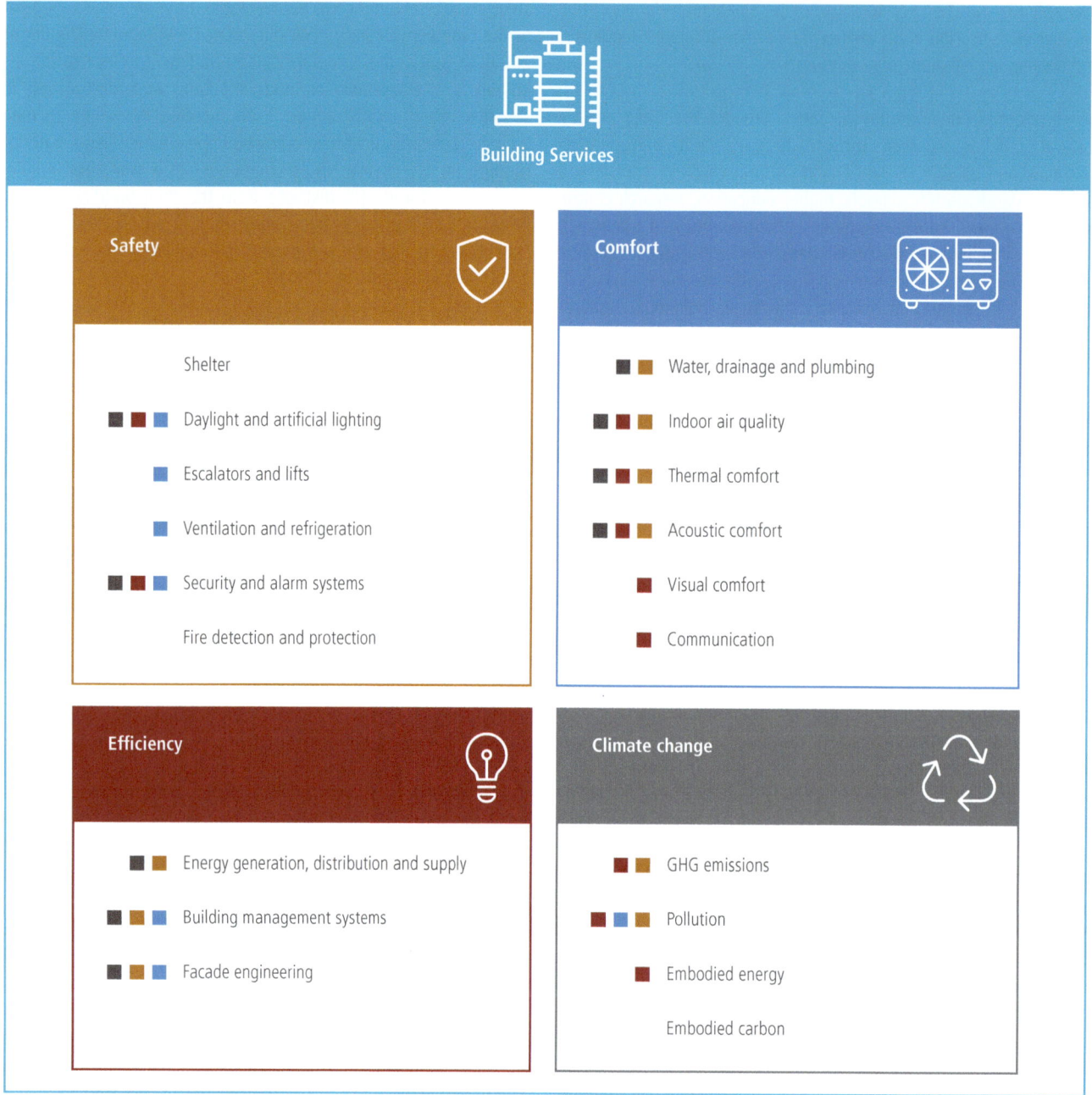

Figure 9.2 | Classification of building services. The coloured small squares to the left of each building service denote to which other classifications that building service may relate to a lesser extent. Source: adapted from Vérez and Cabeza (2021).

Building designs have to consider provision of adequate ventilation. Natural ventilation reduces energy consumption in buildings in warm climates compared to air conditioning systems (Taleb 2015; Azmi et al. 2017). Enhanced ventilation has higher benefits to the public health than the economic costs involved (MacNaughton et al. 2015).

On the refrigeration systems, the recent developments include the use of solar thermoelectric cooling technologies as an energy efficient measure (Liu et al. 2015b); use of nanoparticles for energy saving (Azmi et al. 2017) to mention some.

Lambertz et al. (2019) stated that when evaluating the environmental impact of buildings, building services are only considered in a very simplified way. Moreover, it also highlights that the increasing use of new technologies such as Building Information Modelling (BIM) allows for a much more efficient and easier calculation process for building services, thus enabling the use of more robust and complete models. Furthermore, recent studies on building services related to climate change (Vérez and Cabeza 2021) highlight the importance of embodied energy (Parkin et al. 2019) (Section 9.4).

9.3   New Developments in Emission Trends and Drivers

9.3.1   Past and Future Emission Trends

Total GHG emissions in the building sector reached 12 GtCO$_2$.eq in 2019, equivalent to 21% of global GHG emissions that year. 57% of GHG emissions from buildings were indirect CO$_2$ emissions from generation of electricity and heat off-site, 24% were direct CO$_2$ emissions produced on-site, and 18% were from the production of cement and steel used for construction and refurbishment of buildings (see Cross-Chapter Box 3 and Cross-Working Group Box 1 in Chapter 3, and Figure 9.3a). Halocarbon emissions were equivalent to 3% of global building GHG emissions in 2019. In the absence of the breakdown of halocarbon emissions per end-use sectors, they have been calculated for the purpose of this chapter, by considering that 60% of global halocarbon emissions occur in buildings (Hu et al. 2020). CH$_4$ and N$_2$O emissions were negligible, representing 0.08% each out of the 2019 global building GHG emissions. Therefore, this chapter considers only CO$_2$ emissions from buildings. By limiting the scope of the assessment to CO$_2$ emissions, the share of emissions from buildings increases to 31% of global 2019 CO$_2$ emissions. Energy use in residential and non-residential buildings contributed 50% and 32% respectively, while embodied emissions contributed 18% to global building CO$_2$ emissions.

Over the period 1990–2019, global CO$_2$ emissions from buildings increased by 50%. Global indirect CO$_2$ emissions increased by 92%, driven by the increase of fossil fuels-based electrification, while global direct emissions decreased by 1%. At regional level, emissions in residential buildings decreased in Developed Countries, except in Australia, Japan and New Zealand, while they increased in developing countries. The highest decrease was observed in Europe and Eurasia, with 13.6% decrease of direct emissions and 33% decrease of indirect emissions, while the highest increase of direct emissions occurred in Middle East, 198%, and the highest increase of indirect emissions occurred in Eastern Asia, 2258%. Indirect emissions from non-residential buildings increased in all regions. The highest increase occurred in Eastern Asia, 1202%, and the lowest increase occurred in Europe and Central Asia, 4%, where direct emissions from non-residential buildings decreased by 51%. Embodied emissions have also increased in all regions. The highest increase occurred in Southern Asia, 334%, while the lowest increase occurred in North America, 4% (Figure 9.3b).

Future emissions were assessed using four global scenarios and their respective baselines (Box 9.2). The selection of the scenarios was based on the features of each scenario, the geographic scope, and the data availability to analyse future building emissions based on the SER framework (Box 9.1).

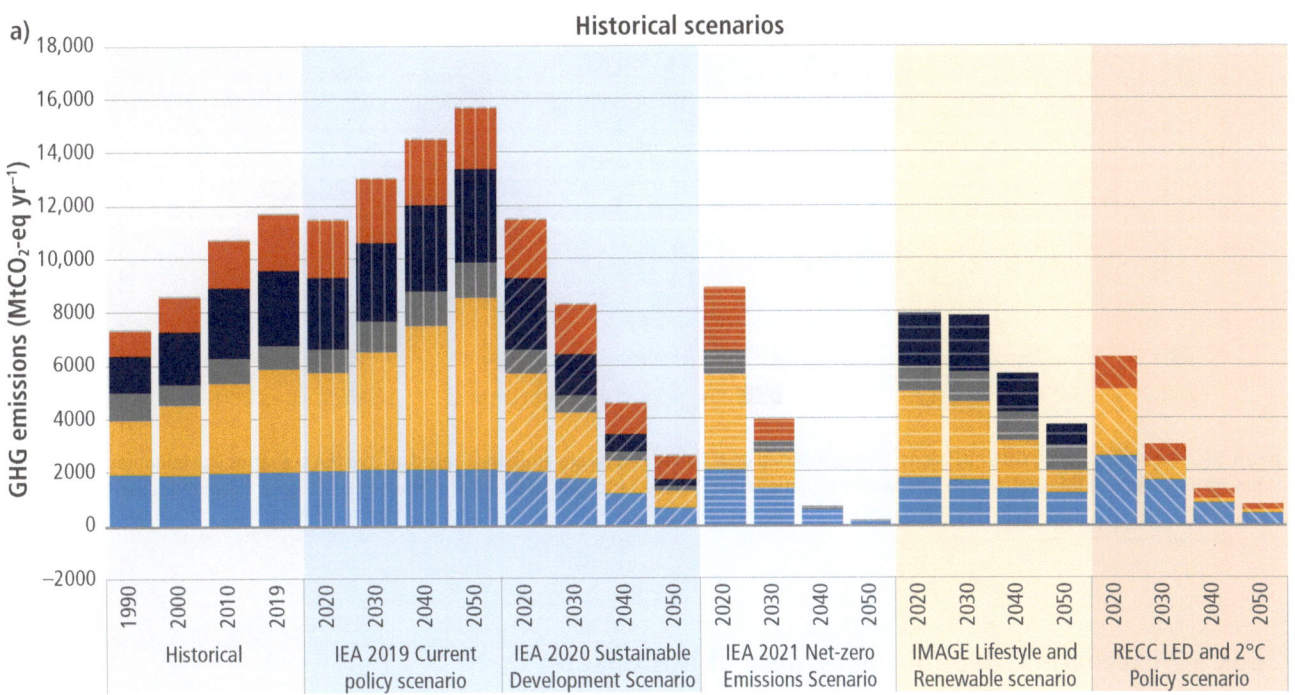

Figure 9.3 | Building GHG emissions: historical based on IEA data and future emissions based on two IEA scenarios (sustainable development, and net zero emissions), IMAGE Lifestyle-Renewable scenario and Resource Efficiency and Climate Change-Low Energy Demand scenario (RECC-LED).

b)

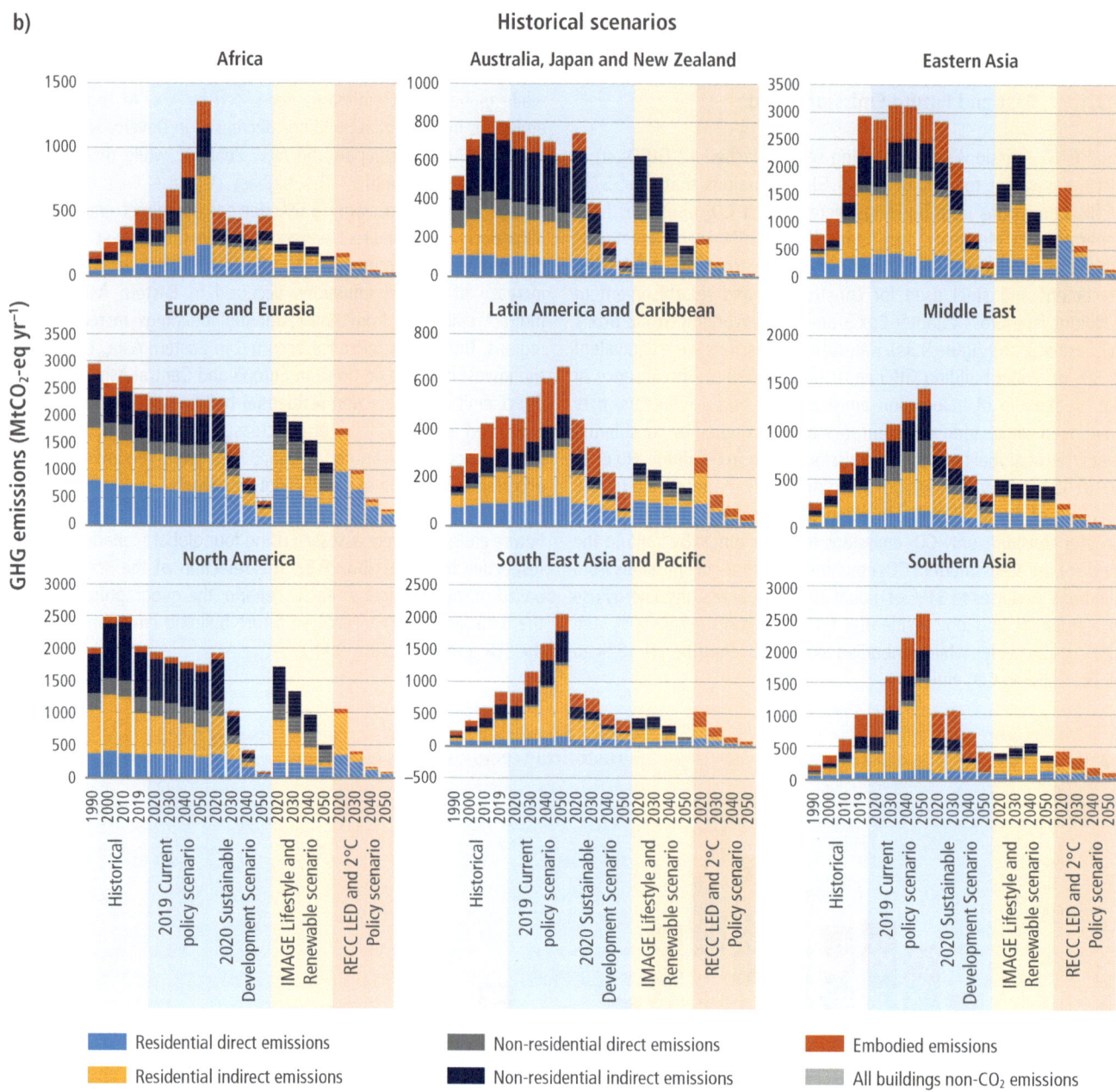

Figure 9.3 (continued): Building GHG emissions: historical based on IEA data and future emissions based on two IEA scenarios (sustainable development, and net zero emissions), IMAGE Lifestyle-Renewable scenario and Resource Efficiency and Climate Change-Low Energy Demand scenario (RECC-LED). RECC-LED data include only space heating and cooling and water heating in residential buildings. The IEA current policies scenario is included as a baseline scenario (IEA current policies scenario).

Box 9.2 | Scenarios Used for the Purpose of This Chapter

Three out of the four scenarios selected, and their related baselines, are based on top-down modelling and were submitted to AR6 scenario database, which includes in total 931 scenarios with a building module (Annex III; see also Boxes 3.1 and 3.2, and Cross-Chapter Box 3 in Chapter 3). A fourth scenario, not included in AR6 scenario database, and based on a bottom-up modelling approach was added.

The main features of these scenarios are shortly described below while the underlying modelling approaches are described in Annex III. Each scenario is assessed compared to its baseline scenario:

International Energy Agency (IEA) scenarios:

2021 Net Zero Emissions by 2050 Scenario (NZE) is a normative scenario, which sets out a narrow but achievable pathway for the global energy sector to achieve net zero CO_2 emissions by 2050 (IEA 2021a).

2020 Sustainable Development Scenario (SDS), which integrates the impact of COVID-19 on health outcomes and economies. It is also a normative scenario, working backwards from climate, clean air, and energy access goals. SDS examines what actions would be necessary to achieve these goals. The near-term detail is drawn from the IEA Sustainable Recovery Plan, which boosts economies and employment while building cleaner and more resilient energy systems (IEA 2020c).

Analysis of the IEA scenarios above was conducted compared to the 2019 Current Policies Scenario, which shows what happens if the world continues along its present path (IEA 2020c), and considered as a baseline scenario.

IMAGE-Lifestyle-Renewable (LiRE) scenario is based on an updated version of the SSP2 baseline, while also meeting the RCP2.6 radiative forcing target using carbon prices, together with the increased adoption of additional lifestyle changes, by limiting the growth in the floor area per capita in Developed Countries as well as the use of appliances. Regarding energy supply, IMAGE-LiRE assumes increased electrification and increased share of renewable in the energy mix (Detlef Van Vuuren et al. 2021).

Resource Efficiency and Climate Change-Low Energy Demand (RECC-LED) scenario is produced by a global bottom-up model, which assesses contributions of resource efficiency to climate change mitigation. RECC-LED estimates the energy and material flows associated with housing stock growth, driven by population and the floor area per capita (Pauliuk et al. 2021). This scenario is informed by the Low Energy Demand Scenario (LED), which seeks convergence between developed and developing countries in the access to decent living standard (Grubler et al. 2018).

For consistency between the four scenarios, aggregation of regions in this chapter differs from the one of the IPCC. Europe and Eurasia have been grouped into one single region.

The IEA-NZE scenario projects emissions from the global building stock to be lowered to 29 $MtCO_2$ by 2050 against 1.7 $GtCO_2$ in the IEA-SDS and 3.7 $GtCO_2$ in IMAGE-LiRE Scenario. These projections can be compared to IEA-CPS in which global emissions from buildings were projected to be at 13.5 $GtCO_2$ in 2050, which is equivalent to the 2018 emissions level (Figure 9.3a). By 2050, direct emissions from residential buildings are projected to be lowered to 108 $MtCO_2$ in the IEA-NZE, this is four times less than the projected direct emissions in RECC-LED scenario, six times less than those under the IEA-SDS and eleven times less than those in the IMAGE-LiRE scenario.

In the IEA-NZE scenario, indirect emissions are projected to be below zero by 2050 for both residential and non-residential buildings, while residual indirect emissions from residential buildings are projected to be 125 $MtCO_2$ in RECC-LED, 634 $MtCO_2$ in IEA-SDS, and 842 $GtCO_2$ in IMAGE-LiRE. Residual indirect emissions from non-residential buildings are projected to be at 1.7 $GtCO_2$ in IEA SDS and double of this in IMAGE-LiRE scenario (Figure 9.3a). Compared to IEA-SDS, the highest decrease of emissions in IEA-NZE is expected to occur after 2030. Direct emissions from residential buildings in IEA-NZE are projected to be, by 2030, at 1.37 $GtCO_2$, against 1.7 $GtCO_2$ in the three other scenarios. The highest cut in emissions in IEA-NZE and in IMAGE-LiRE occur through the decarbonisation of energy supply.

At regional level, by 2050, the lowest emissions are projected to occur in developed Asia and Pacific, with 6.73 $MtCO_2$ under RECC-LED scenario and 12.4 $MtCO_2$ under the IEA-SDS, and the highest emissions are projected to occur in Europe and Eurasia in all three scenarios, with 152 $MtCO_2$ in IEA-SDS, 199 $MtCO_2$ in RECC-LED scenario and 381 $MtCO_2$ in IMAGE-LiRE scenario. Emissions in Africa are projected to decrease to 10 $MtCO_2$ in RECC-LED, this is nine time less than those of 2019, while they are projected to increase by 25% in IEA-SDS compared to those of 2019. Compared to IEA-SDS and IMAGE-LiRE, RECC-LED projects the highest decreases, over the period 2020–2030, of direct emissions in residential buildings in all regions, up to 45% in Australia, Japan and New Zealand, and Eastern Asia and the highest decreases of indirect emissions, ranging from 52% in Eastern Asia to 86% in Latin America and Caribbean. Over the same period, the IEA-SDS projects the highest decreases of indirect emissions to occur in Australia, Japan and New Zealand, and North America. IMAGE-LiRE projects the lowest decreases of emissions over the same decade in almost all regions (Figure 9.3b).

Emissions per capita from residential buildings at a global level reached 0.85 tCO_2 per person in 2019. The four scenarios assessed project a decrease of the global per capita emissions by 2050, ranging from 0 tCO_2 in IEA-NZE 0.21 tCO_2 per person in IMAGE-LiRE, a 75% lower than those of 2019 (Figure 9.4a). There are great

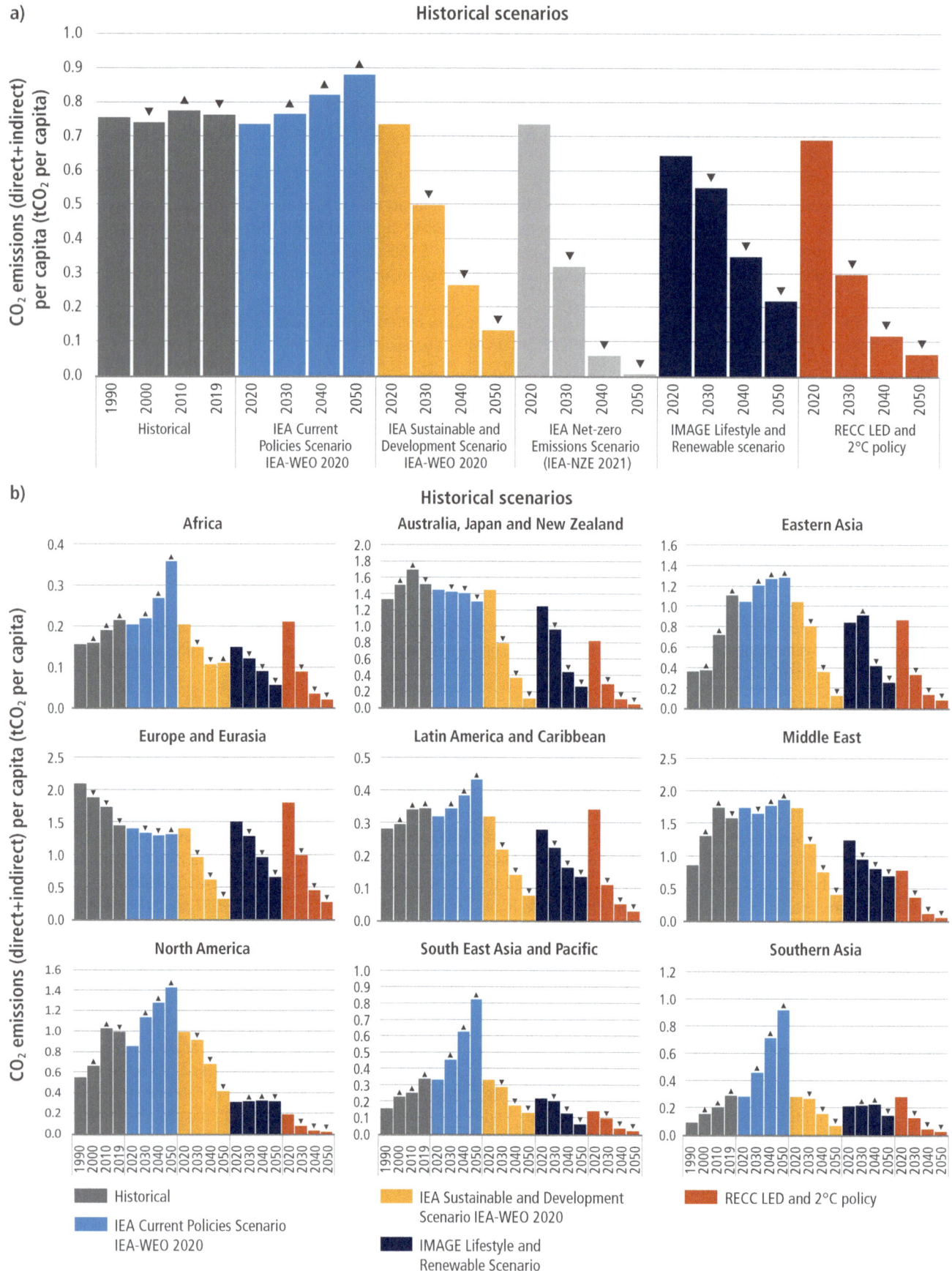

Figure 9.4 | Per capita emissions: historical based on IEA data and future emissions based on two IEA scenarios (sustainable development, and net zero emissions), IMAGE Lifestyle-Renewable scenario and Resource Efficiency and Climate Change-Low Energy Demand scenario (RECC-LED). RECC-LED data include only space heating and cooling and water heating in residential buildings. The IEA current policies scenario is included as a baseline scenario (IEA current policies scenario).

differences in the projected per capita emissions under each scenario different scenarios across the regions (Figure 9.4b). Compared to IEA-SDS and IMAGE-LiRE scenarios, RECC-LED projects the lowest emissions per capita in all regions by 2050. Emissions per capita in Europe and Eurasia are projected to be the highest in all scenarios by 2050, ranging from 0.26 tCO_2 in RECC-LED and 0.31 tCO_2 in IEA-SDS to 0.65 tCO_2 in IMAGE-LiRE.

9.3.2 Drivers of CO_2 Emissions and Their Climate Impact

Building specific drivers of GHG emissions in the four scenarios described above are assessed using an index decomposition analysis with building specific identities and reflecting the three pillars of the Sufficiency, Efficiency, Renewables (SER) framework. Broad drivers of GHG emissions such as GDP and population are analysed using a Kaya decomposition in Chapter 2. Previous decompositions analysing drivers of global GHG emissions in the building sector have either assessed only the impact of GDP and population as drivers of GHG emissions (Lamb et al. 2021) or the impact of building specific drivers on energy demand and not on CO_2 emissions (Lucon et al. 2014; Ürge-Vorsatz et al. 2015; IEA 2020c; ODYSSEE 2020). For this assessment, the decomposition was conducted for energy-related CO_2 emissions for residential buildings only, due to lack of data for non-residential buildings.

The attribution of changes in emissions in the use phase to changes in the drivers of population, sufficiency, efficiency, and carbon intensity of energy supply is calculated using additive log-mean divisia index decomposition analysis (Ang and Zhang 2000). The

decomposition of emissions into four driving factors is shown in Equation 1, where m^2 refers to total floor area, EJ refers to final energy demand, and $MtCO_2$ refers to the sum of direct and indirect CO_2 emissions in the use phase. The allocation of changes in emissions between two cases k and $k–1$ to changes in a single driving factor D is shown in Equation 2. To calculate changes in emissions due to a single driver such as population growth, D will take on the value of population in the two compared cases. The superscript k stands for the case, defined by the time period and scenario of the emissions, for example, IEA-CPS baseline scenario in 2050. When decomposing emissions between two cases k and $k–1$, either the time-period, or the scenario remains constant. The decomposition was done at the highest regional resolution available from each model output, and then aggregated to regional or global level. For changes in emissions within a scenario over time, the decomposition is done for every decade, and the total 2020–2050 decomposition is then produced by summing decompositions of changes in emissions each decade.

$$CO2_{total}^k = Pop \times \frac{m^2}{Pop} \times \frac{EJ}{m^2} \times \frac{Mt_{CO2}}{EJ} = Pop \times Suff \times Eff \times Ren$$

Equation 9.1

$$\Delta CO2_{,D}^{k,k-1} = \frac{CO2 - CO2_{total}^{k-1}}{ln(CO2_{total}^k) - ln(CO2_{total}^{k-1})} \times ln\left(\frac{D^k}{D^{k-1}}\right)$$

Equation 9.2

Over the period 1990–2019, population growth accounted for 28% of the growth in global emissions in residential buildings, the lack of sufficiency policies (growth in floor area per capita) accounted

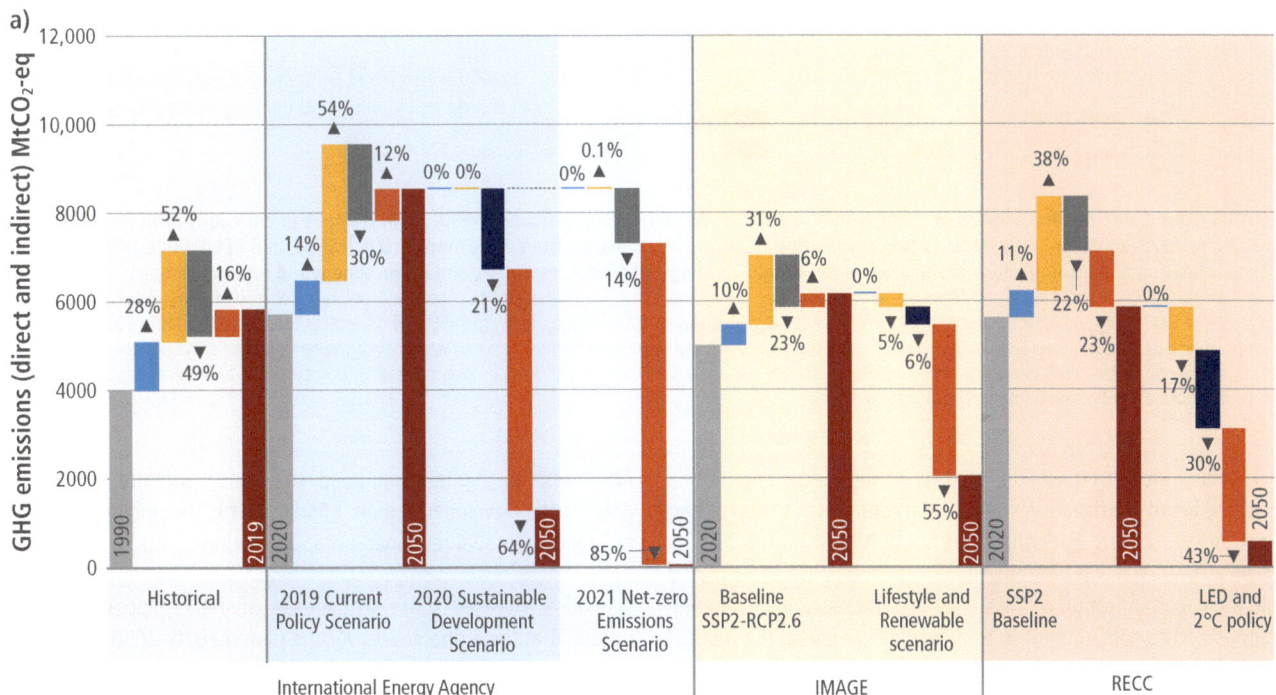

Figure 9.5 | Decompositions of changes in historical residential energy emissions 1990–2019, changes in emissions projected by baseline scenarios for 2020–2050, and differences between scenarios in 2050 using scenarios from three models: IEA, IMAGE, and RECC. RECC-LED data include only space heating and cooling and water heating in residential buildings (a) global resolution, and (b) for nine world regions.

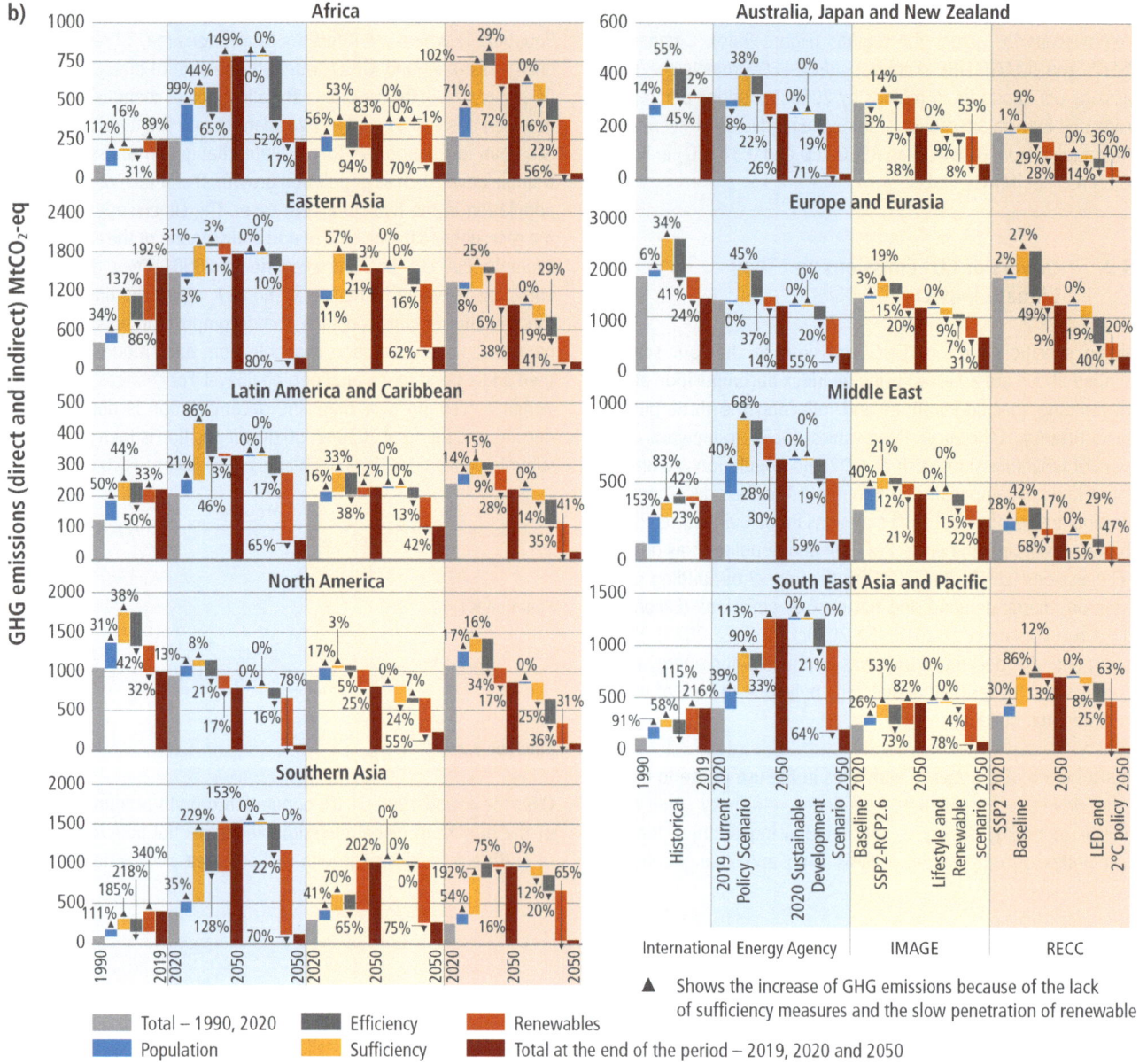

Figure 9.5 (continued): Decompositions of changes in historical residential energy emissions 1990–2019, changes in emissions projected by baseline scenarios for 2020–2050, and differences between scenarios in 2050 using scenarios from three models: IEA, IMAGE, and RECC. RECC-LED data include only space heating and cooling and water heating in residential buildings (a) global resolution, and (b) for nine world regions. Emissions are decomposed based on changes in driver variables of population, sufficiency (floor area per capita), efficiency (final energy per floor area), and renewables (GHG emissions per final energy). 'Renewables' is a summary term describing changes in GHG intensity of energy supply. Emission projections to 2050, and differences between scenarios in 2050, demonstrate mitigation potentials from the dimensions of the SER framework realised in each model scenario. In most regions, historical improvements in efficiency have been approximately matched by growth in floor area per capita. Implementing sufficiency measures that limit growth in floor area per capita, particularly in developed regions, reduces the dependence of climate mitigation on technological solutions.

for 52% and increasing carbon intensity of the global energy mix accounted for 16%. Efficiency improvement contributed to decreasing global emissions from residential buildings by 49% (Figure 9.5a). The sufficiency potential was untapped in all regions over the same period while the decarbonisation of the supply was untapped in developing countries and to some extent in Asia-Pacific Developed. The highest untapped sufficiency and supply decarbonisation potentials occurred in Southern Asia where the lack of sufficiency measures has led to increasing emissions by 185% and the high carbon intensity of the energy mix has led to increasing emissions by 340%. In Developed

Countries, the highest untapped sufficiency potential occurred in Asia-Pacific Developed region. Middle East is the only region where efficiency potential remained untapped (Figure 9.5b).

Scenarios assessed show an increase of the untapped sufficiency potential at the global level over the period 2020–2050. The highest untapped sufficiency potential occurs in IEA scenarios as there are no changes in the floor area per capita across different scenarios. The lack of sufficiency measures in current policies will contribute to increasing emissions by 54%, offsetting the efficiency improvement

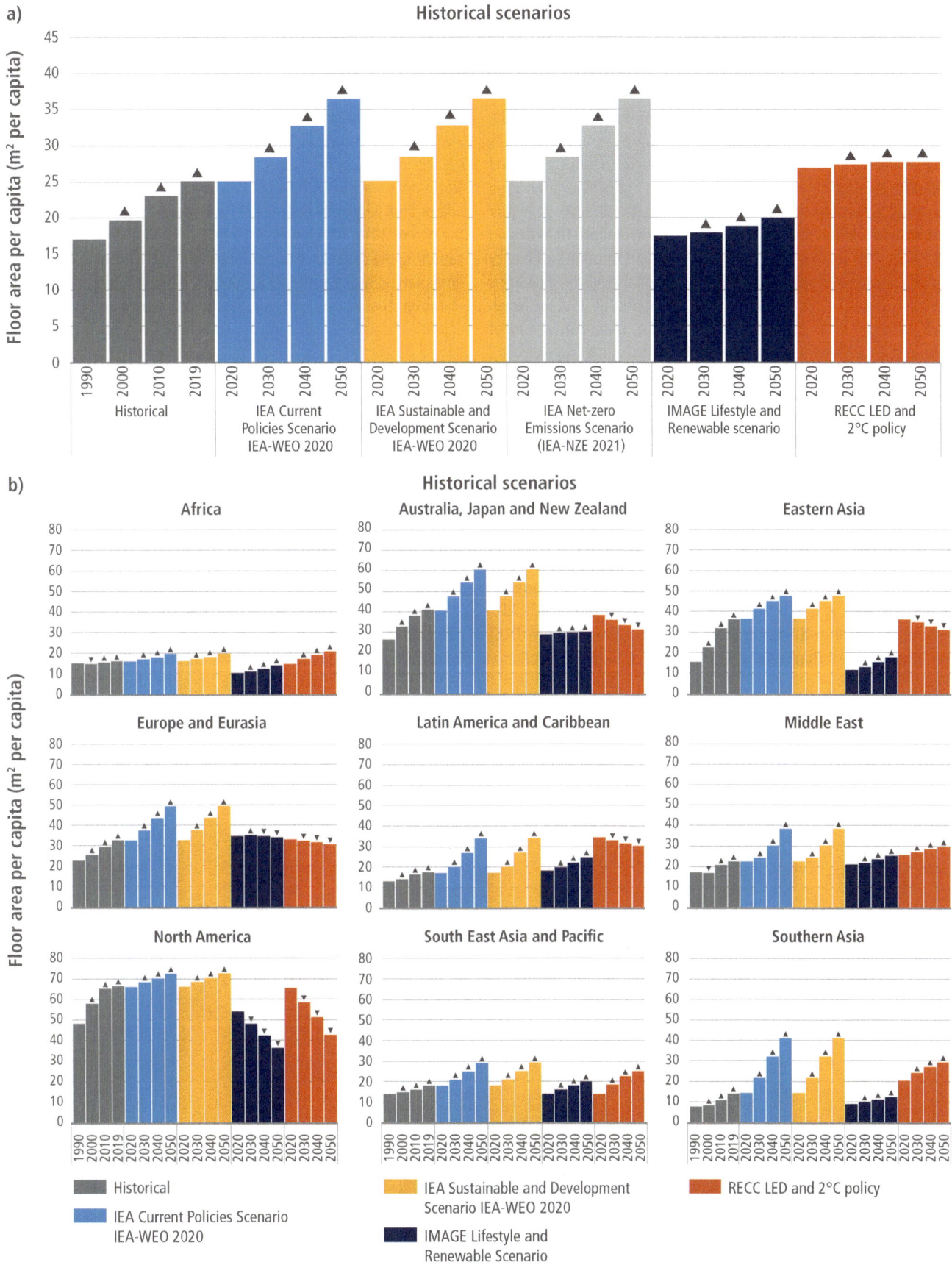

Figure 9.6 | Per capita floor area: historical based on IEA data and future emissions based on two IEA scenarios (sustainable development, and net zero emissions), IMAGE Lifestyle-Renewable scenario and Resource Efficiency and Climate Change-Low Energy Demand scenario (RECC-LED). RECC-LED data include only space heating and cooling and water heating in residential buildings. The IEA current policies scenario is included as a baseline scenario (IEA current policies scenario).

effect. By setting a cap in the growth of the floor area per capita in developed countries, 5% of emission reductions in IMAGE-LiRE scenario derives from sufficiency. However, compared to 2020, the lack of sufficiency measures in the baseline scenario will contribute to increasing emissions by 31%. RECC-LED scenario shows the highest global sufficiency potential captured compared to its baseline scenario in 2050 as this scenario assumes a reduction in the floor area per capita in Developed Countries and slower floor area growth in emerging economies. The four scenarios show a higher contribution of the decarbonisation of energy supply to reducing emissions than the reduction of energy demand through sufficiency and efficiency measures (Figure 9.6a). At regional level, the emissions reduction potential from sufficiency is estimated at 25% in North America under both IMAGE-LiRE and RECC-LED scenarios and at 19% in both Eastern Asia and Europe/Eurasia regions (Figure 9.6b). The highest decarbonisation potential due to growth of renewable energy is 75% in Southern Asia under IMAGE-LiRE scenario.

There is a growing literature on the decarbonisation of end-use sectors while providing decent living standard for all (Rao and Pachauri 2017; Grubler et al. 2018; Rao and Min 2018; Rao et al. 2019; Millward-Hopkins et al. 2020). The floor area per capita is among the gaps identified in the convergence between developed and developing countries in the access to decent living (Kikstra et al. 2021) while meeting energy needs. In the Low Energy Demand (LED) scenario, 30 m² per capita is the converging figure assumed by 2050 (Grubler et al. 2018) while in the Decent Living with minimum Energy (DLE) scenario, (Millward-Hopkins et al. 2020) assumes 15 m² per capita.

Overall, the global residential building stock grew by almost 30% between 2005 and 2019. However, this growth was not distributed

equally across regions and three out of the four scenarios assessed do not assume a convergence, by 2050, in the floor area per capita, between developed and developing countries. Only RECC-LED implements some convergence between Developed Countries and emerging economies to a range of 20–40 m² per capita. IEA scenarios assume a growth in the floor area per capita in all regions with the highest growth in Developed Countries, up to 72 m² per capita in North America from 66 m² per capita in 2019. IMAGE-LiRE projects a floor area per capita in Africa at 14 m² per person. This is lower than the one of 2019, which was at 16 m² per capita (Figure 9.6). Beyond capturing the sufficiency potential by limiting the growth in the floor area per capita in Developed Countries while ensuring decent living standard, the acceptability of the global scenarios by developing countries is getting attraction in academia (Hickel et al. 2021).

9.3.3   Energy Demand Trends

Global final energy demand from buildings reached 128.8 EJ in 2019, equivalent to 31% of global final energy demand. The same year, residential buildings consumed 70% out of global final energy demand from buildings. Over the period 1990–2019, global final energy demand from buildings grew by 38%, with 54% increase in non-residential buildings and 32% increase in residential ones. At regional level, the highest increase of final energy demand occurred in Middle East and Africa in residential buildings and in all South-East Asia and Pacific in non-residential ones. By 2050, global final energy demand from buildings is projected to be at 86 EJ in IEA-NZE, 111 EJ in IEA-SDS and 138 EJ in IMAGE-LiRE. RECC-LED projects the lowest global final energy demand, at 15.7 EJ by 2050, but this refers to water heating, space heating and cooling in residential buildings only (Figure 9.7a).

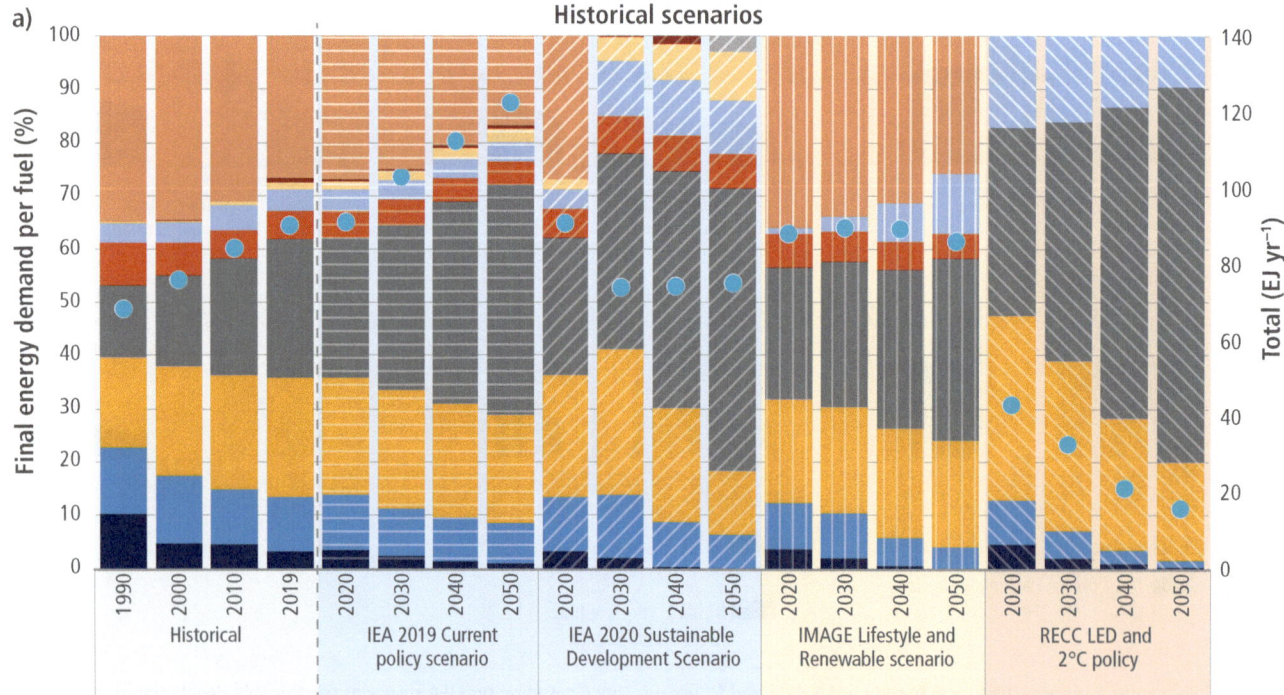

Figure 9.7 | Final energy demand per fuel: historical based on IEA data and future emissions based on two IEA scenarios (sustainable development, and net zero emissions), IMAGE Lifestyle-Renewable scenario and Resource Efficiency and Climate Change-Low Energy Demand scenario (RECC-LED).

b)

Historical scenarios

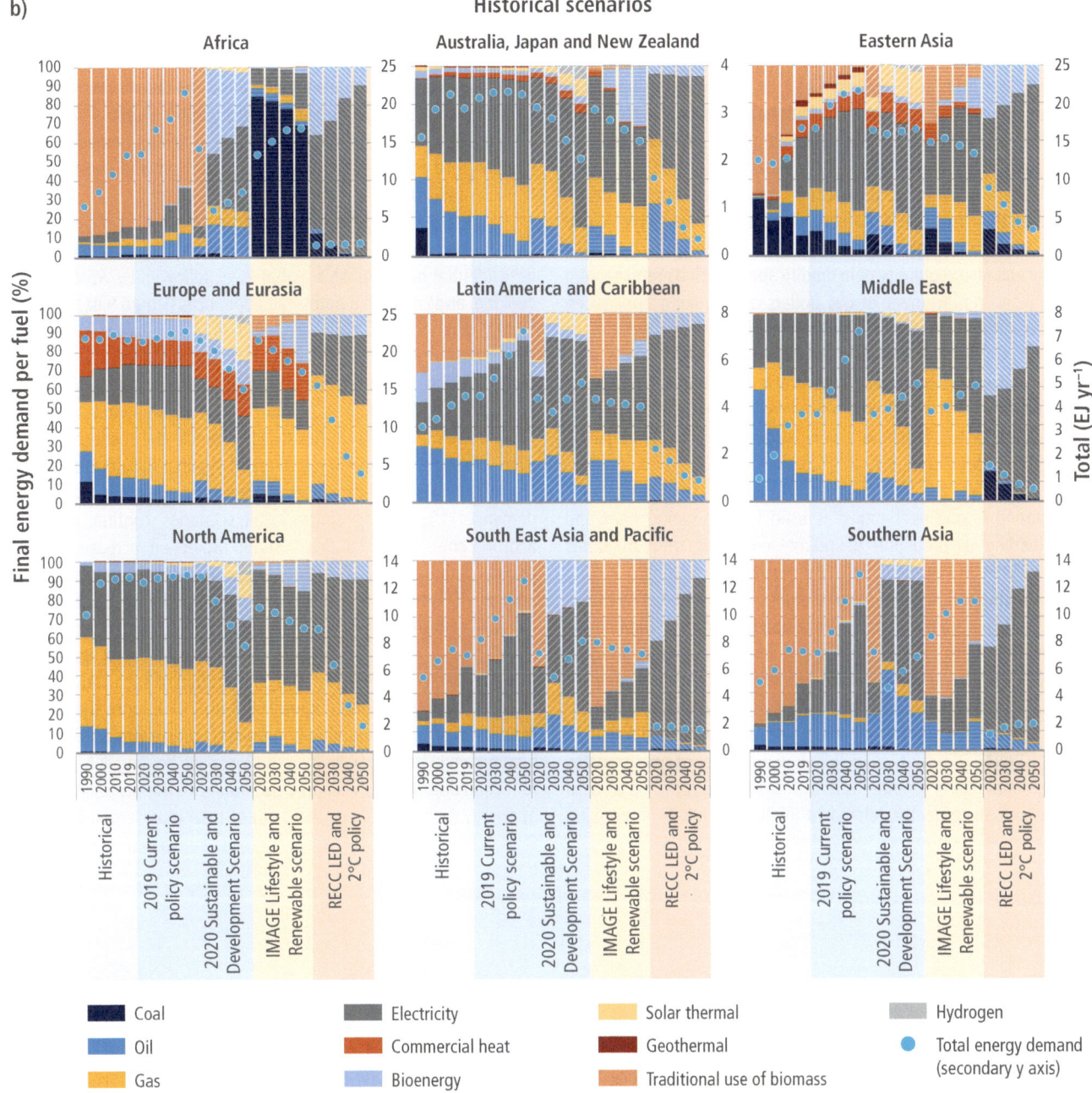

Figure 9.7 (continued): Final energy demand per fuel: historical based on IEA data and future emissions based on two IEA scenarios (sustainable development, and net zero emissions), IMAGE Lifestyle-Renewable scenario and Resource Efficiency and Climate Change-Low Energy Demand scenario (RECC-LED). RECC-LED data include only space heating and cooling and water heating in residential buildings. The IEA current policies scenario is included as a baseline scenario (IEA current policies scenario).

Over the period 1990–2019, the use of coal decreased at a global level by 59% in residential buildings and 52% in non-residential ones. Solar thermal experienced the highest increase, followed by geothermal and electricity. However, by 2019, solar thermal and geothermal contributed by only 1% each to global final energy demand, while electricity contributed by 51% in non-residential buildings and 26% in residential ones. The same year, gas contributed by 26% to non-residential final energy demand and 22% to residential final energy demand, which makes gas the second energy carrier used in buildings after electricity. Over the period 1990–2019, the use of gas grew by 75% in residential buildings and by 46% in non-residential ones. By 2050, RECC-LED projects electricity to contribute by 71% to final energy demand in residential buildings, against 62% in IEA-NZE and 59% in IMAGE-LiRE. IEA-NZE is the only scenario to project less than 1% of gas use by 2050 in residential buildings while the contribution of electricity to energy demand of non-residential buildings is above 60% in all scenarios. At regional level, the use of coal in buildings is projected to disappear while the use of electricity is projected to be above 50% in all regions by 2050 (Figure 9.7b).

Hydrogen emerged in the policy debate as an important energy carrier for the decarbonisation of the energy system. In the case of the building sector, depending on how hydrogen is sourced (Box 12.3), converting gas grids to hydrogen might be an appealing option to decarbonise heat without putting additional stress on the electricity grids. However, according to (Element Energy Ltd 2018; Strbac et al. 2018; Frazer-Nash Consultancy 2018; Broad et al. 2020; Gerhardt et al. 2020) the delivered cost of heat from hydrogen would be much higher than the cost of delivering heat from heat pumps, which could also be used for cooling. Repurposing gas grids for pure hydrogen networks will also require system modifications such as replacement of piping and replacement of gas boilers and cooking appliances, a factor cost to be considered when developing hydrogen roadmaps for buildings. There are also safety and performance concerns with domestic hydrogen appliances (Frazer-Nash Consultancy 2018). Over the period 1990–2019, hydrogen was not used in the building sector and scenarios assessed show a very modest role for hydrogen in buildings by 2050 (Figure 9.7).

In Developed Countries, biomass is used for generating heat and power leading to reduction of indirect emissions from buildings (Ortwein 2016) (IEA et al. 2020 c). However, according to (IEA 2019b) despite the mitigation potential of biomass, if the wood is available locally, its use remains low in Developed Countries. Biomass is also used for efficient cook stoves and for heating using modern appliances such as pellet-fed central heating boilers. In developing countries, traditional use of biomass is characterised by low efficiency of combustion (due to low temperatures) leading to high levels of pollutants and CO output, as well as low efficiency of heat transfer. The traditional use of biomass is associated with public health risks such as premature deaths related to inhaling fumes from cooking

(Dixon et al. 2015; Van de Ven et al. 2019; IEA 2019a; Taylor et al. 2020). According to (Hanna et al. 2016) policies failed in improving the use of biomass. Over the period 1990–2019, the traditional use of biomass decreased by 1% and all scenarios assessed do not project any traditional use of biomass by 2050. Biomass is also used for the construction of buildings, leading to low embodied emissions compared to concrete (Heeren et al. 2015; Hart and Pomponi 2020; Pauliuk et al. 2021).

Over the period 1990–2019, space heating was the dominant end-use in residential buildings at a global level, followed by water heating, cooking, and connected and small appliances (Figure 9.8a). However, energy demand from connected and small appliances experienced the highest increase, 280%, followed by cooking, 89%, cooling, 75%, water heating, 73% and space heating, around 10%. Space heating energy demand is projected to decline over the period 2020–2050 in all scenarios assessed. RECC-LED projects the highest decrease, 77%, of space heating energy demand, against 68% decrease in the IEA-NZE. IMAGE-LiRE projects the lowest decrease of heating energy demand, 21%. To the contrary, all scenarios confirm cooling as a strong emerging trend (Box 9.3) and project an increase of cooling energy demand. IMAGE-LiRE projects the highest increase, 143% against 45% in the IEA-NZE while RECC-LED projects the lowest increase of cooling energy demand, 32%.

There are great differences in the contribution of each end-use to the regional energy demand (Figure 9.8b). In 2019, more than 50% of residential energy demand in Europe and Eurasia was used for space heating while there was no demand for space heating in Middle East, reflecting differences in climatic conditions. To the contrary, the share of energy demand from cooking out of total represented 53% in the

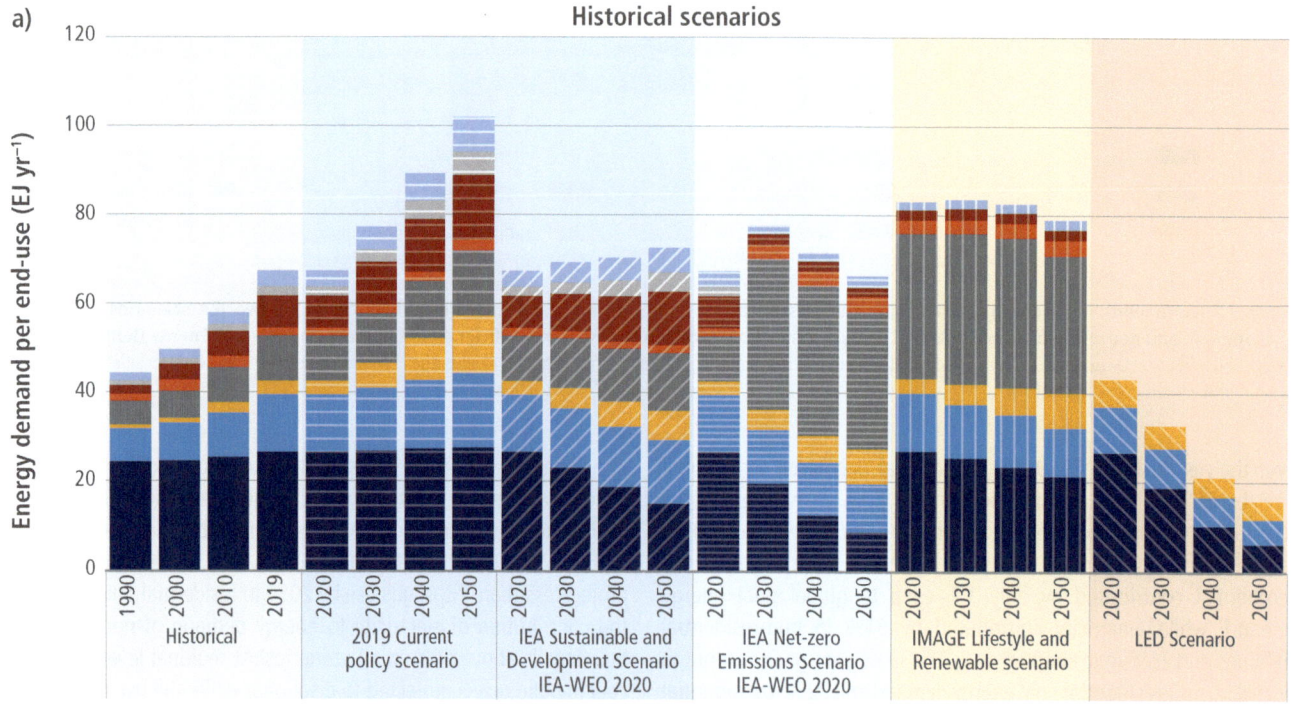

Figure 9.8 | Energy per end use: historical based on IEA data and future emissions based on two IEA scenarios (sustainable development, and net zero emissions), IMAGE Lifestyle-Renewable scenario and Resource Efficiency and Climate Change-Low Energy Demand scenario (RECC-LED).

b)

Historical scenarios

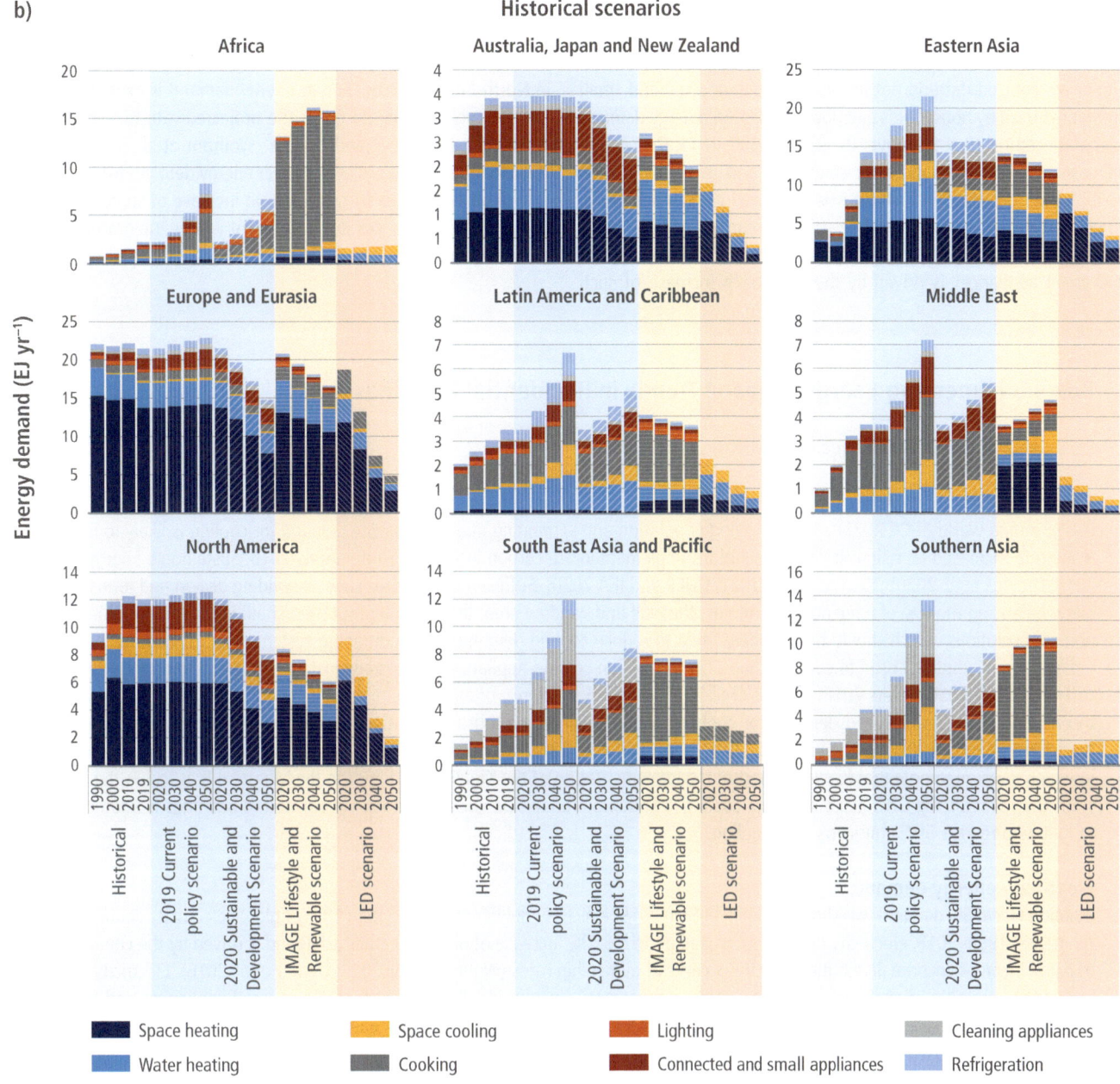

Figure 9.8 (continued): Energy per end use: historical based on IEA data and future emissions based on two IEA scenarios (sustainable development, and net zero emissions), IMAGE Lifestyle-Renewable scenario and Resource Efficiency and Climate Change-Low Energy Demand scenario (RECC-LED). RECC-LED data include only space heating and cooling and water heating. The IEA current policies scenario is included as a baseline scenario (IEA current policies scenario).

Middle East against 5% in Europe and Eurasia reflecting societal organisations. The highest contribution of energy demand from connected and small appliances to the regional energy demand was observed in 2019 in the Asia-Pacific Developed, 24%, followed by the region of Southern Asia, South-East Asia and Developing Pacific, with 17%. Energy demand from cooling was at 9% out of total energy demand of Southern Asia, South-East Asia and Developing Pacific and at 8% in both Middle East and North America while it was at 1% in Europe in 2019.

The increased cooling demand can be partly explained by the increased ownership of room air-conditioners per dwellings in all regions driven by increased wealth and the increased ambient temperatures due to global warming (Cayla et al. 2011; Liddle and Huntington 2021) (Box 9.3). The highest increase, 32%, in ownership of room air-conditioners was observed in Southern Asia and South-East Asia and Developing Pacific while Europe, Latin America and Caribbean countries, Eastern Asia and Africa experienced an increase of 21% in households' ownership of room air-conditioners. The lowest increases in room air-conditioners ownership were observed in the Middle East and North America with 1% and 8% each as these two markets are almost saturated. All scenarios assessed project an increase of ownership of cooling appliances in all regions over the period 2020–2050.

Energy demand from connected and small appliances was, at a global level, above 7 EJ in 2019 (Figure 9.8a). However, it is likely that global energy demand from connected and small appliances is much higher as reported data do not include all the connected and small appliances used by households and does not capture energy demand from data centres (Box 9.3). Over the period 1990–2019, the highest increase of energy demand from connected and small appliances, 4740%, was observed in Eastern Asia, followed by Southern Asia, 1358% while the lowest increase, 99%, occurred in Asia-Pacific Developed countries. The increase of energy demand from connected and small appliances is driven by the ownership increase of such appliances all over the world. The highest increase in ownership of connected appliances, 403%, was observed in Eastern Asia and the lowest increase in ownership of connected appliances was observed in North America, 94%. Future energy demand is expected to occur in the developing world given the projected rate of penetration of household appliances and devices (Wolfram et al. 2012). However, (Grubler et al. 2018) projects a lower energy demand from connected and small appliances by assuming an increase of shared appliances and multiple appliances and equipment will be integrated into units delivering multiple services.

Box 9.3 | Emerging Energy Demand Trends in Residential Buildings

Literature assessed points to three major energy demand trends:

Cooling energy demand

In a warming world (IPCC 2021) with a growing population and expanding middle-class, the demand for cooling is likely to increase leading to increased emissions if cooling solutions implemented are carbon intensive (Santamouris 2016; Sustainable Energy for All 2018; Dreyfus et al. 2020b; Kian Jon et al. 2021; UNEP and IEA 2020). Sufficiency measures such as building design and forms, which allow balancing the size of openings, the volume, the wall and window area, the thermal properties, shading, and orientation are all non-cost solutions, which should be considered first to reduce cooling demand. Air conditioning systems using halocarbons are the most common solutions used to cool buildings. Up to 4 billion cooling appliances are already installed and this could increase to up to 14 billion by 2050 (Peters 2018; Dreyfus et al. 2020b). Energy efficiency of air conditioning systems is of a paramount importance to ensuring that the increased demand for cooling will be satisfied without contributing to global warming through halocarbon emissions (Campbell 2018; Shah et al. 2015, 2019; UNEP and IEA 2020). The installation of highly efficient technological solutions with low global warming potential (GWP), as part of the implementation of the Kigali amendment to the Montreal Protocol, is the second step towards reducing GHG emissions from cooling. Developing renewable energy solutions integrated to buildings is another track to follow to reduce GHG emissions from cooling.

Electricity energy demand

Building electricity demand was slightly above 43 EJ in 2019, which is equivalent to more than 18% of global electricity demand. Over the period 1990–2019, electricity demand increased by 161%. The increase of global electricity demand is driven by the combination of rising incomes, income distribution and the S-curve of ownership rates (Wolfram et al. 2012; Gertler et al. 2016). Electricity is used in buildings for plug-in appliances, in other words, refrigerators, cleaning appliances, connected and small appliances and lighting. An important emerging trend in electricity demand is the use of electricity for thermal energy services (cooking, water and space heating). The increased penetration of heat pumps is the main driver of the use of electricity for heating. Heat pumps used either individually or in conjunction with heat networks can provide heating in cold days and cooling in hot ones. (Lowes et al. 2020) suggests electricity is expected to become an important energy vector to decarbonise heating. However, the use of heat pumps will increase halocarbon emissions (UNEP and IEA 2020). Connolly (2017), Bloess et al. (2018), and Barnes and Bhagavathy (2020) argue for electrification of heat as a cost-effective decarbonisation measure, if electricity is supplied by renewable energy sources (Ruhnau et al. 2020). The electrification of the heat supplied to buildings is likely to lead to an additional electricity demand and consequently additional investment in new power plants. Thomaßen et al. (2021) identifies flexibility as a key enabler of larger heat electrification shares. Importantly, heat pumps work at their highest efficiency level in highly efficient buildings and their market uptake is likely to require incentives due to their high up-front cost (Hannon 2015; Heinen et al. 2017).

Digitalisation energy demand

Energy demand from digitalisation occurs in data centres, which are dedicated buildings or part of buildings for accommodating large amount of information technologies equipment such as servers, data storage and communication devices, and network devices. Data centres are responsible for about 2% of global electricity consumption (Avgerinou et al. 2017; Diguet and Lopez 2019). Energy demand from data centres arises from the densely packed configuration of information technologies, which is up to 100 times higher than a standard office accommodation (Chu and Wang 2019). Chillers combined with air handling units are usually used to provide cooling in data centres. Given the high cooling demand of data centres, some additional cooling strategies, such as free cooling, liquid cooling, low-grade waste heat recovery, absorption cooling and so on, have been adopted. In addition, heat recovery can

Box 9.3 (continued)

provide useful heat for industrial and building applications. More recently, data centres are being investigated as a potential resource for demand response and load balancing (Zheng et al. 2020; Koronen et al. 2020). Supplying data centres with renewable energy sources is increasing (Cook et al. 2014) and is expected to continue to increase (Koomey et al. 2011). Estimates of energy demand from digitalisation (connected and small appliances, data centres, and data networks) combined vary from 5% to 12% of global electricity use (Gelenbe and Caseau 2015; Malmodin and Lundén 2018; Ferreboeuf 2019; Diguet and Lopez 2019). According to (Ferreboeuf 2019) the annual increase of energy demand from digitalisation could be limited to 1.5% against the current 4% if sufficiency measures are adopted along the value chain.

Digitalisation occurs also at the construction stage. (European Union 2019; Witthoeft and Kosta 2017) identified seven digital technologies already in use in the building sector. These technologies include (i) Building Information Modelling/Management (BIM), (ii) additive manufacturing, also known as 3D printing, (iii) robots, (iv) drones, (v) 3D scanning, (vi) sensors, and (vii) internet of things (IoT). BIM supports decision making in the early design stage and allows assessing a variety of design options and their embodied emissions (Basbagill et al. 2013; Röck et al. 2018). 3D printing reduces material waste and the duration of the construction phase as well as labour accidents (Dixit 2019). Coupling 3D printing and robots allows for increasing productivity through fully automated prefabricated buildings. Drones allow for a better monitoring and inspection of construction projects through real-time comparison between planned and implemented solutions. Coupling drones with 3D scanning allows predicting building heights and energy consumption (Streltsov et al. 2020). Sensors offer a continuous data collection and monitoring of end-use services (i.e., heating, cooling, and lighting), thus allowing for preventive maintenance while providing more comfort to end-users. Coupling sensors with IoT, which connects to the internet household appliances and devices such as thermostats, enable demand-response, and flexibility to reduce peak loads (IEA 2017a; Lyons 2019). Overall, connected appliances offer a variety of opportunities for end-users to optimise their energy demand by improving the responsiveness of energy services (IEA 2017a; Nakicenovic et al. 2019) through the use of digital goods and services (Wilson et al., 2020) including peer-to-peer electricity trading (Morstyn et al. 2018).

9.4 Mitigation Technological Options and Strategies Towards Zero Carbon Buildings

Literature in this topic is extensive, but unfortunately, most studies and reviews do not relate themselves to climate change mitigation, therefore there is a clear gap in reporting the mitigation potential of the different technologies (Cabeza et al. 2020). It should be highlighted that when assessing the literature, it is clear that a lot of new research is focused on the improvement of control systems, including the use of artificial intelligence or internet of things (IoT).

This section is organised as follow. First, the key points from AR5 and special reports are summarised, following with a summary of the technological developments since AR5, specially focusing on residential buildings.

9.4.1 Key Points From AR5 and Special Reports

The AR5 WG3 Chapter 9 on Buildings (Lucon et al. 2014) presents mitigation technology options and practices to achieve large reductions in building energy use as well as a synthesis of documented examples of large reductions in energy use achieved in real, new, and retrofitted buildings in a variety of different climates and examples of costs at building level. A key point highlighted is the fact that the conventional process of designing and constructing buildings and its systems is largely linear, losing opportunities for the optimisation

of whole buildings. Several technologies are listed as being able to achieve significant performance improvements and cost potentials (daylighting and electric lighting, household appliances, insulation materials, heat pumps, indirect evaporative cooling, advances in digital building automation and control systems, and smart meters and grids to implement renewable electricity sources).

9.4.2 Embodied Energy and Embodied Carbon

9.4.2.1 Embodied Energy and Embodied Carbon in Building Materials

As building energy demand is decreased the importance of embodied energy and embodied carbon in building materials increases (Ürge-Vorsatz et al. 2020). Buildings are recognised as built following five building frames: concrete, wood, masonry, steel, and composite frames (International Energy Agency 2019a); but other building frames should be considered to include worldwide building construction practice, such as rammed earth and bamboo in vernacular design (Cabeza et al. 2021).

The most prominent materials used following these frames classifications are the following. Concrete, a man-made material, is the most widely used building material. Wood has been used for many centuries for the construction of buildings and other structures in the built environment; and it remains as an important construction material today. Steel is the strongest building material; it is mainly

9

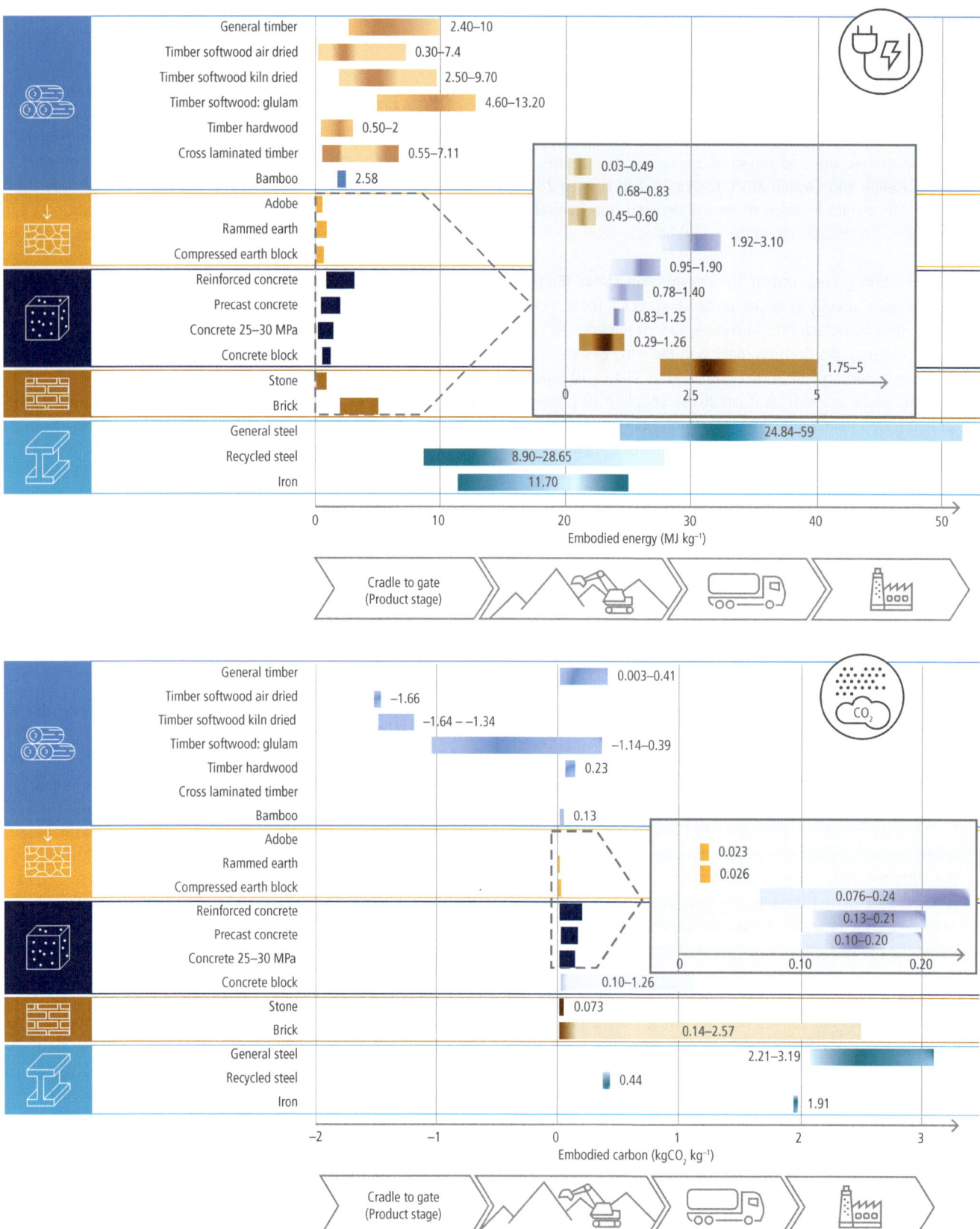

Figure 9.9 | Building materials (a) embodied energy and (b) embodied carbon. Source: Cabeza et al. (2021).

used in industrial facilities and in buildings with big glass envelopes. Masonry is a heterogeneous material using bricks, blocks, and others, including the traditional stone. Composite structures are those involving multiple dissimilar materials. Bamboo is a traditional building material throughout the world tropical and sub-tropical regions. Rammed earth can be considered to be included in masonry construction, but it is a structure very much used in developing countries and it is finding new interest in developed ones (Cabeza et al. 2021).

The literature evaluating the embodied energy in building materials is extensive, but that considering embodied carbon is much more scarce (Cabeza et al. 2021). Recently this evaluation is done using the methodology lifecycle assessment (LCA), but since the boundaries used in those studies are different, varying, for example, in the consideration of cradle to grave, cradle to gate, or cradle to cradle, the comparison is very difficult (Moncaster et al. 2019). A summary of the embodied energy and embodied carbon cradle to gate coefficients reported in the literature are found in Figure 9.9 (Alcorn and Wood 1998; Crawford and Treolar 2010; Vukotic et al. 2010; Symons 2011; Moncaster and Song 2012; Cabeza et al. 2013; De Wolf et al. 2016; Birgisdottir et al. 2017; Pomponi and Moncaster 2016, 2018; Omrany et al. 2020; Cabeza et al. 2021). Steel represents the materials with higher embodied energy, 32–35 MJ kg^{-1}; embodied energy in masonry is higher than in concrete and earth materials, but surprisingly, some types of wood have more embodied energy than expected; there are dispersion values in the literature depending on the material. On the other hand, earth materials and wood have the lowest embodied carbon, with less than 0.01 kgCO$_2$ per kg of material (Cabeza et al. 2021). The concept of buildings as carbon sinks arise from the idea that wood stores considerable quantities of carbon with a relatively small ratio of carbon emissions to material volume and concrete has substantial embodied carbon emissions with minimal carbon storage capacity (Sanjuán et al. 2019; Churkina et al. 2020).

9.4.2.2   Embodied Emissions

Embodied emissions from production of materials are an important component of building sector emissions, and their share is likely to increase as emissions from building energy demand decrease (Röck et al. 2020). Embodied emissions trajectories can be lowered by limiting the amount of new floor area required (Berrill and Hertwich 2021; Fishman et al. 2021), and reducing the quantity and GHG intensity of materials through material efficiency measures such as light-weighting and improved building design, material substitution to lower-carbon alternatives, higher fabrication yields and scrap recovery during material production, and re-use or lifetime extension of building components (Allwood et al. 2011; Heeren et al. 2015; Hertwich et al. 2019; Churkina et al. 2020; Pamenter and Myers 2021; Pauliuk et al. 2021). Reducing the GHG intensity of energy supply to material production activities also has a large influence on reducing overall embodied emissions. Figure 9.10 shows projections of embodied emissions to 2050 from residential buildings in a baseline scenario (SSP2 baseline) and a scenario incorporating multiple material efficiency measures and a much faster decarbonisation of energy supply (LED and 2°C policy) (Pauliuk et al. 2021). Embodied emissions are projected to

be 32% lower in 2050 than 2020 in a baseline scenario, primarily due to a lower growth rate of building floor area per population. This is because the global population growth rate slows over the coming decades, leading to less demand for new floor area relative to total population. Further baseline reductions in embodied emissions between 2020 and 2050 derive from improvements in material production and a gradual decline in GHG intensity of energy supply. In a LED + 2°C policy scenario, 2050 embodied emissions are 86% lower than the baseline. This reduction of 2050 emissions comes from contributions of comparable magnitude from three sources; slower floor area growth leading to less floor area of new construction per capita (sufficiency), reductions in the mass of materials required for each unit of newly built floor area (material efficiency), and reduction in the GHG intensity of material production, from material substitution to lower carbon materials, and faster transition of energy supply.

The attribution of changes in embodied emissions to changes in the drivers of population, sufficiency, material efficiency, and GHG intensity of material production is calculated using additive log-mean divisia index decomposition analysis (Ang and Zhang 2000). The decomposition of emissions into four driving factors is shown in Equation 9.3, where m^2_{NC} refers to floor area of new construction, kg_{Mat} refers to mass of materials used for new construction, and kg_{CO2e} refers to embodied GHG emissions in CO$_{2e}$. The allocation of changes in emissions between two cases k and $k-1$ to changes in a single driving factor D is shown in Equation 9.4. For instance, to calculate changes in emissions due to population growth, D will take on the value of population in the two cases being compared. The superscript k stands for the time period and scenario of the emissions, for example, SSP2 baseline scenario in 2050. When decomposing emissions between two cases k and $k-1$, either the time period or the scenario stays constant. The decomposition is done for every region at the highest regional resolution available, and aggregation (e.g., to global level) is then done by summing over regions. For changes in emissions within a scenario over time (e.g., SSP baseline emissions in 2020 and 2050), the decomposition is made for every decade, and the total 2020–2050 decomposition is then produced by summing decompositions of changes in emissions each decade.

$$GHG^k_{emb} = Pop \times \frac{m^2_{NC}}{Pop} \times \frac{kg_{Mat}}{m^2_{NC}} \times \frac{kg_{CO2e}}{kg_{Mat}} = Pop \times Suff \times Eff \times Ren$$

Equation 9.3

$$\Delta GHG^{k,k-1}_{emb,D} = \frac{GHG^k_{emb} - GHG^{k-1}_{emb}}{ln(GHG^k_{emb}) - ln(GHG^{k-1}_{emb})} \times ln\left(\frac{D^k}{D^{k-1}}\right)$$

Equation 9.4

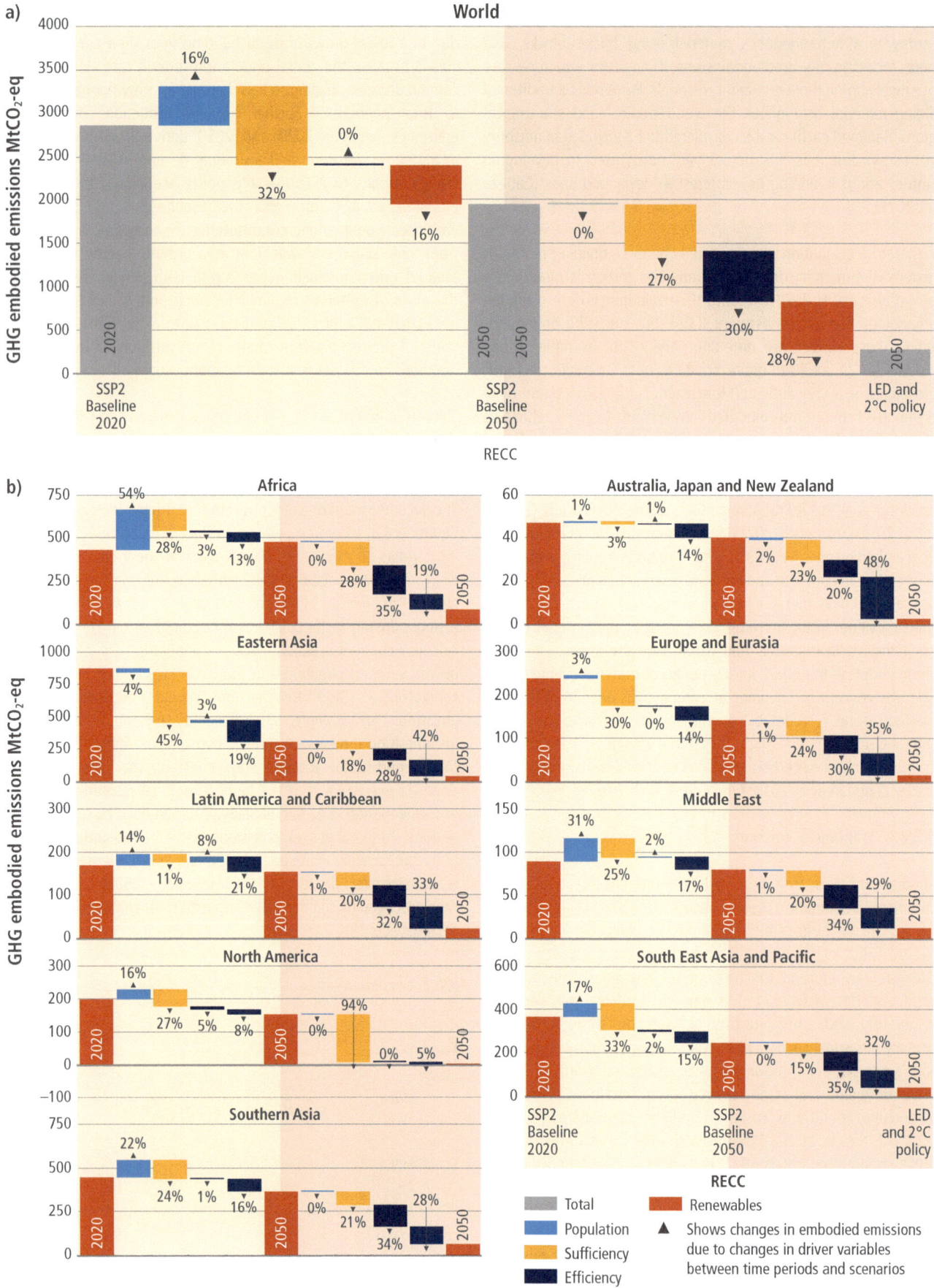

Figure 9.10 | Decompositions of changes in residential embodied emissions projected by baseline scenarios for 2020–2050, and differences between scenarios in 2050 using two scenarios from the RECC model.

Figure 9.10 (continued): Decompositions of changes in residential embodied emissions projected by baseline scenarios for 2020–2050, and differences between scenarios in 2050 using two scenarios from the RECC model. (a) Global resolution, and **(b)** for nine world regions. Emissions are decomposed based on changes in driver variables of population, sufficiency (floor area of new construction per capita), material efficiency (material production per floor area), and renewables (GHG emissions per unit material production). 'Renewables' is a summary term describing changes in GHG intensity of energy supply. Emission projections to 2050, and differences between scenarios in 2050, demonstrate mitigation potentials from the dimensions of the SER framework realised in each model scenario.

9.4.3   Technological Developments Since AR5

9.4.3.1   Overview of Technological Developments

There are many technologies that can reduce energy use in buildings (Finnegan et al. 2018; Kockat et al. 2018a), and those have been extensively investigated. Other technologies that can contribute to achieving carbon zero buildings are less present in the literature. Common technologies available to achieve zero energy buildings were summarised in (Cabeza and Chàfer 2020) and are presented in Tables 9.SM.1 to 9.SM.3 in detail, where Figure 9.11 shows a summary.

Other opportunities exist, such as building light-weighting or more efficient material production, use and disposal (Hertwich et al. 2020), fast-growing biomass sources such as hemp, straw or flax as insulation in renovation processes (Pittau et al. 2019), bamboo-based construction systems as an alternative to conventional high-impact systems in tropical and subtropical climates (Zea Escamilla et al. 2018).

Earth architecture is still limited to a niche (Morel and Charef 2019). See also Cross-Chapter Box 9 in Chapter 13 for carbon dioxide removal and its role in mitigation strategies.

9.4.3.2   Appliances and Lighting

Electrical appliances have a significant contribution to household electricity consumption (Pothitou et al. 2017). Ownership of appliances, the use of appliances, and the power demand of the appliances are key contributors to domestic electricity consumption (Jones et al. 2015). The drivers in energy use of appliances are the appliance type (e.g., refrigerators), number of households, number of appliances per household, and energy used by each appliance (Chu and Bowman 2006; Cabeza et al. 2014; Spiliotopoulos 2019). At the same time, household energy-related behaviours are also a driver of energy use of appliances (Khosla et al. 2019) (Section 9.5). Although new technologies such as IoT linked to the appliances increase flexibility to reduce peak loads and reduce energy demand

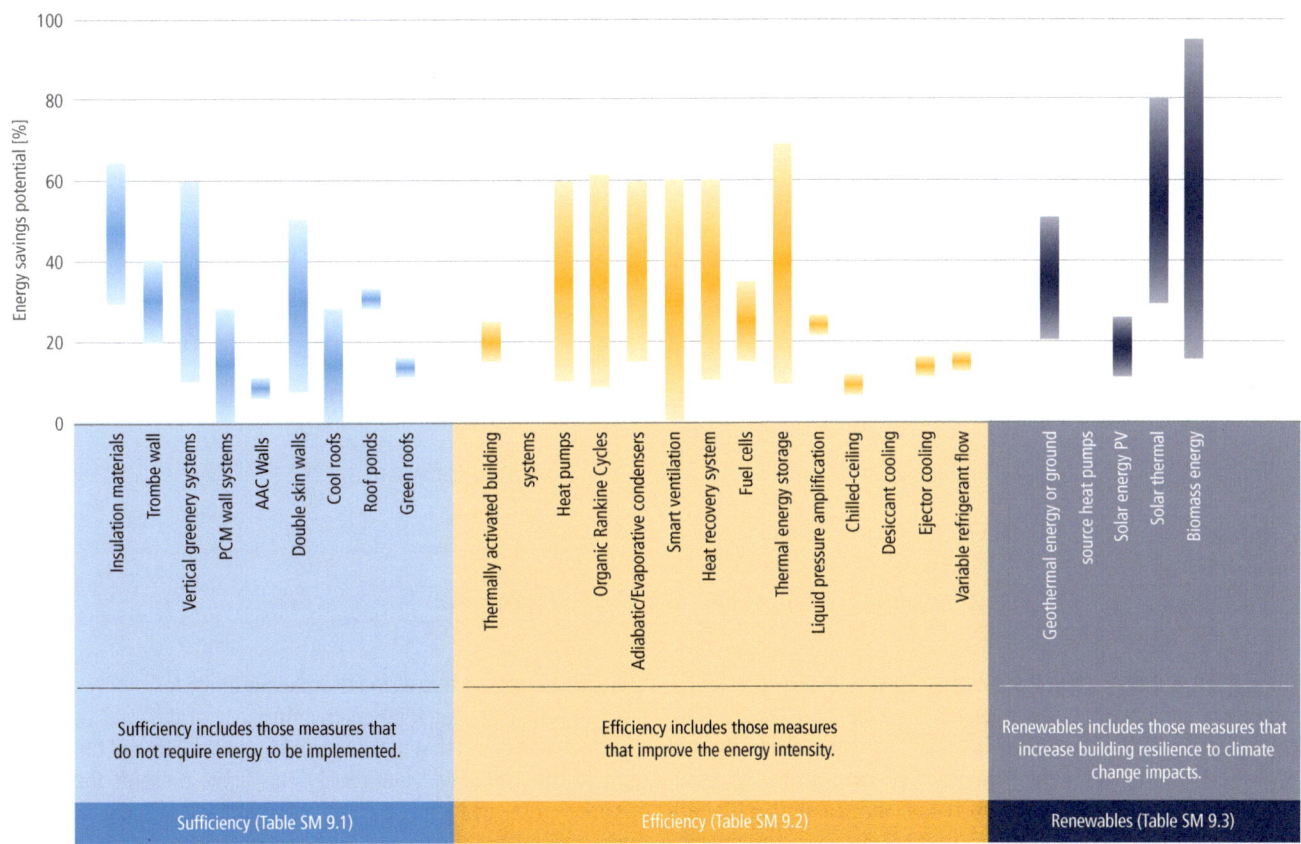

Figure 9.11 | Energy savings potential of technology strategies for climate change mitigation in buildings. Sources: adapted from Imanari et al. (1999); Cabeza et al. (2010); Fallahi et al. (2010); Prívara et al. (2011); Radhi (2011); Asdrubali et al. (2012); Capozzoli et al. (2013); Chen et al. (2013); de Gracia et al. (2013); Seong and Lim (2013); Sourbron et al. (2013); Bojić et al. (2014); Haggag et al. (2014); Sarbu and Sebarchievici (2014); Spanaki et al. (2014); Vakiloroaya et al. (2014); Djedjig et al. (2015); Mujahid Rafique et al. (2015); Yang et al. (2015); Andjelković et al. (2016); Costanzo et al. (2016); Coma et al. (2016); Harby et al. (2016); Navarro et al. (2016); Pomponi et al. (2016); Coma et al. (2017); Khoshbakht et al. (2017); Saffari et al. (2017); Luo et al. (2017); Jedidi and Benjeddou (2018); Romdhane and Louahlia-Gualous (2018); Lee et al. (2018); Alam et al. (2019); Bevilacqua et al. (2019); Gong et al. (2019); Hohne et al. (2019); Irshad et al. (2019); Langevin et al. (2019); Liu et al. (2019); Omara and Abuelnour (2019); Rosado and Levinson (2019); Soltani et al. (2019); Varela Luján et al. (2019); Zhang et al. (2019); Annibaldi et al. (2020); Cabeza and Chàfer (2020); Dong et al. (2020); Nematchoua et al. (2020); Ling et al. (2020); Mahmoud et al. (2020); Peng et al. (2020); Zhang et al. (2020c); Yu et al. (2020).

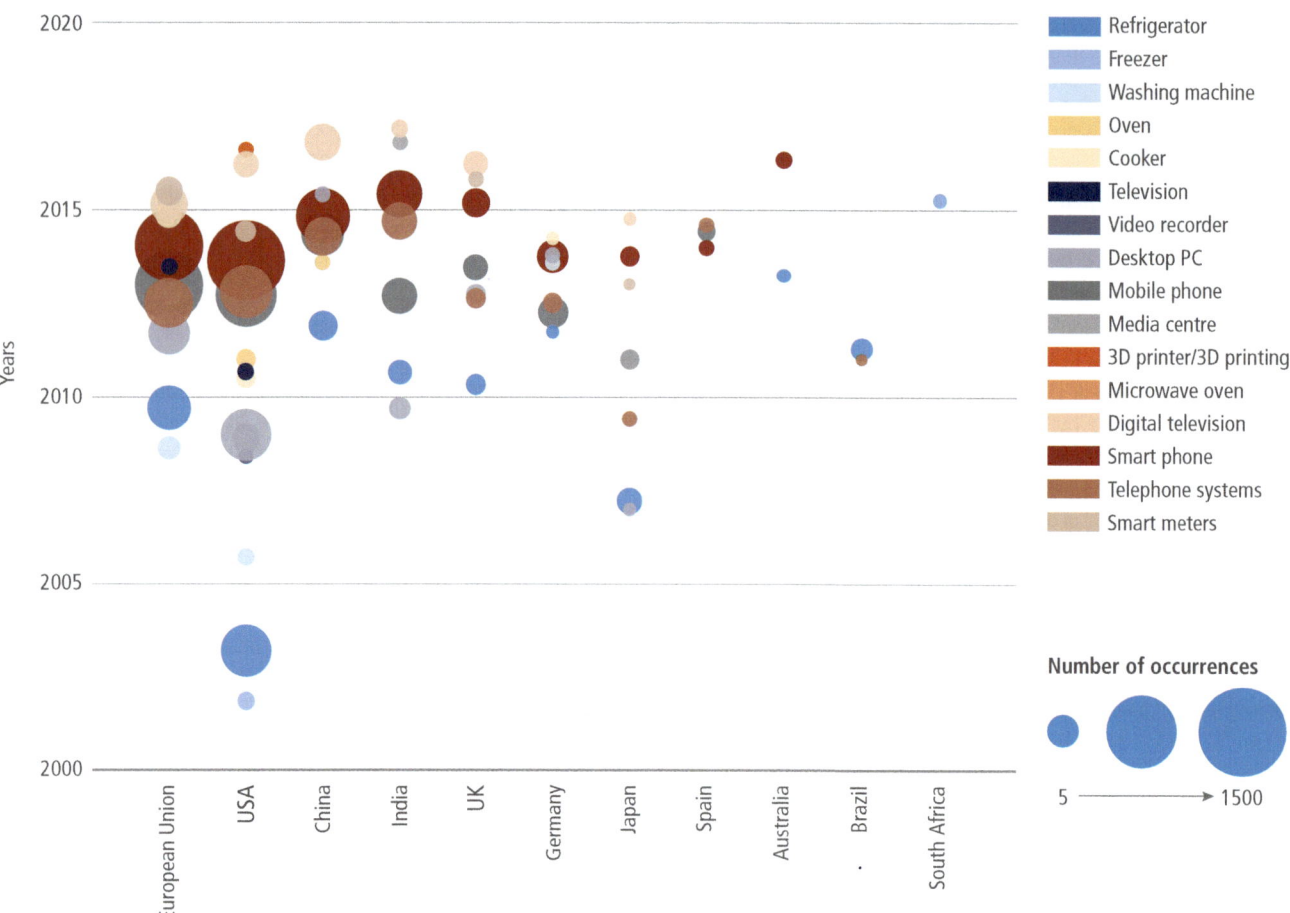

Figure 9.12 | Energy efficiency in appliances research. Year and number of occurrences of different appliances in each studied country/territory.

Table 9.1 | Types of domestic lighting devices and their characteristics. Source: adapted from Attia et al. (2017).

Type of lighting device	Code in plan	Lumens per watt [lm W⁻¹]	Colour temperature [K]	Lifespan [h]	Energy use [W]
Incandescent	InC	13.9	2700	1000	60
Candle incandescent	CnL	14.0	2700	1000	25
Halogen	Hal	20.0	3000	5000	60
Fluorescent TL8	FluT8	80.0	3000–6500	20,000	30–40
Compact fluorescent	CfL	66.0	2700–6500	10,000	20
LED GLS	LeD	100.0	2700–5000	45,000	10
LED spotlight	LeD Pin	83.8	2700–6500	45,000	8
Fluorescent T5	FluT5	81.8	2700–6500	50,000	22
LED DT8	LeDT8	111.0	2700–6500	50,000	15

(Kramer et al. 2020), trends show that appliances account for an increasing amount of building energy consumption (Figure 9.8). Appliances used in Developed Countries consume electricity and not fuels (fossil or renewable), which often have a relatively high carbon footprint. The rapid increase in appliance ownership (Cabeza et al. 2018b) can affect the electricity grid. Moreover, energy intensity improvement in appliances such as refrigerators, washing machines, TVs, and computers has counteracted the substantial increase in ownership and use since the year 2000 (International Energy Agency 2019b).

But appliances are also a significant opportunity for energy efficiency improvement. Research on energy efficiency of different appliances worldwide showed that this research focused in different time frames in different countries (Figure 9.12). This figure presents the number of occurrences of a term (the name of a studied appliance) appearing per year and per country, according to the references obtained from a Scopus search. The figure shows that most research carried out was after 2010. And again, this figure shows that research is mostly carried out for refrigerators and for brown appliances such as smart phones. Moreover, the research carried out worldwide is not only devoted to technological aspects, but also to behavioural aspects and quality of service (such as digital television or smart phones).

Lighting energy accounts for around 19% of global electricity consumption (Attia et al. 2017; Enongene et al. 2017; Baloch et al. 2018). Many studies have reported the correlation between the decrease in energy consumption and the improvement of the energy efficiency of lighting appliances (Table 9.1). Today, the new standards recommend the phase out of incandescent light bulbs, linear fluorescent lamps, and halogen lamps and their substitution by more efficient technologies such as compact fluorescent lighting (CFL) and light-emitting diodes (LEDs) (Figure 9.8). Due to the complexity of these systems, simulation tools are used for the design and study of such systems, which can be summarised in Baloch et al. (2018).

Single-phase induction motors are extensively used in residential appliances and other building low-power applications. Conventional motors work with fixed speed regime directly fed from the grid, giving unsatisfactory performance (low efficiency, poor power factor, and poor torque pulsation). Variable speed control techniques improve the performance of such motors (Jannati et al. 2017).

Within the control strategies to improve energy efficiency in appliances, energy monitoring for energy management has been extensively researched. Abubakar et al. (2017) present a review of those methods. The paper distinguishes between intrusive load monitoring (ILM), with distributed sensing, and non-intrusive load monitoring (NILM), based on a single point sensing.

9.4.4   Case Studies

9.4.4.1   Warehouses

Warehouses are major contributors to the rise of greenhouse gas emissions in supply chains (Bartolini et al. 2019). The expanding e-commerce sector and the growing demand for mass customisation have even led to an increasing need for warehouse space and buildings, particularly for serving the uninterrupted customer demand in the business-to-consumer market. Although warehouses are not specifically designed to provide their inhabitants with comfort because they are mainly unoccupied, the impact of their activities in the global GHG emissions is remarkable. Warehousing activities contribute roughly 11% of the total GHG emissions generated by the logistics sector across the world. Following this global trend, increasing attention to green and sustainable warehousing processes has led to many new research results regarding management concepts, technologies, and equipment to reduce warehouses carbon footprint, that is, the total emissions of GHG in carbon equivalents directly caused by warehouses activities.

9.4.4.2   Historical and Heritage Buildings

Historical buildings, defined as those built before 1945, are usually low-performance buildings by definition from the space heating point of view and represent almost 30–40% of the whole building stock in European countries (Cabeza et al. 2018a). Historical buildings often contribute to townscape character, they create the urban spaces that are enjoyed by residents and attract tourist visitors. They may be protected by law from alteration not only limited to their visual appearance preservation, but also concerning materials and construction techniques to be integrated into original architectures.

On the other hand, a heritage building is a historical building which, for their immense value, is subject to legal preservation. The integration of renewable energy systems in such buildings is more challenging than in other buildings. In the review carried out by Cabeza et al. (2018a) different case studies are presented and discussed, where heat pumps, solar energy and geothermal energy systems are integrated in such buildings, after energy efficiency is considered.

9.4.4.3   Positive Energy or Energy Plus Buildings

The integration of energy generation on-site means further contribution of buildings towards decarbonisation (Ürge-Vorsatz et al. 2020). Integration of renewables in buildings should always come after maximising the reduction in the demand for energy services through sufficiency measures and maximising efficiency improvement to reduce energy consumption, but the inclusion of energy generation would mean a step forward to distributed energy systems with high contribution from buildings, becoming prosumers (Sánchez Ramos et al. 2019). Decrease price of technologies such as photovoltaic (PV) and the integration of energy storage (de Gracia and Cabeza 2015) are essential to achieve this objective. Other technologies that could be used are photovoltaic/thermal (Sultan and Ervina Efzan 2018), solar/biomass hybrid systems (Zhang et al. 2020b), solar thermoelectric (Sarbu and Dorca 2018), solar powered sorption systems for cooling (Shirazi et al. 2018), and on-site renewables with battery storage (Liu et al. 2021).

9.4.4.4   District Energy Networks

District heating networks have evolved from systems where heat was produced by coal or waste and storage was in the form of steam, to much higher energy efficiency networks with water or glycol as the energy carrier and fuelled by a wide range of renewable and low carbon fuels. Common low carbon fuels for district energy systems include biomass, other renewables (i.e., geothermal, PV, and large solar thermal), industry surplus heat or power-to-heat concepts, and heat storage including seasonal heat storage (Lund et al. 2018). District energy infrastructure opens opportunities for integration of several heat and power sources and is 'future proof' in the sense that the energy source can easily be converted or upgraded in the future, with heat distributed through the existing district energy network. Latest developments include the inclusion of smart control and AI (Revesz et al. 2020), and low temperature thermal energy districts. Authors show carbon emissions reduction up to 80% compared to the use of gas boilers.

9.4.5   Low- and Net Zero-energy Buildings – Exemplary Buildings

Nearly zero energy (NZE) buildings or low-energy buildings are possible in all world relevant climate zones (Mata et al. 2020b; Ürge-Vorsatz et al. 2020) (Figure 9.13). Moreover, they are possible both for new and retrofitted buildings. Different envelope design and technologies are needed, depending on the climate and the building shape and orientation. For example, using the Passive House standard an annual heating and cooling energy demand decrease between 75% and 95% compared to conventional values can be achieved. Table 9.2 lists several exemplary low- and NZE-buildings with some of their feature.

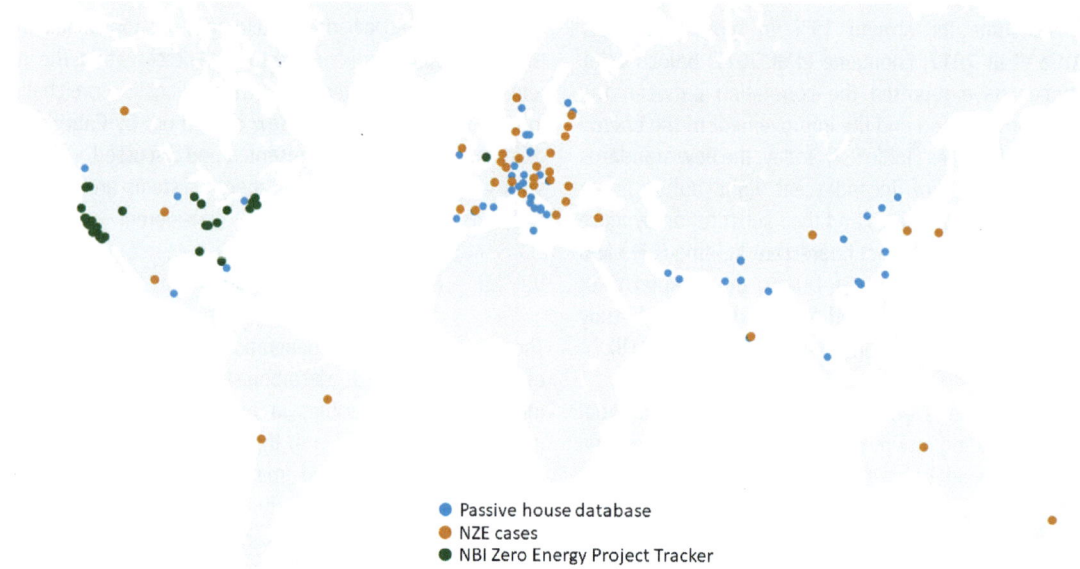

Figure 9.13 | Regional distribution of documented low-energy buildings. Source: New Building Institute (2019); Ürge-Vorsatz et al. (2020).

Table 9.2 | Selected exemplary low- and net zero- energy buildings worldwide. Sources: adapted from Mørck (2017); Schnieders et al. (2020); Ürge-Vorsatz et al. (2020).

Building name and organisation	Location	Building type	Energy efficiency and renewable energy features	Measured energy performance
SDB-10 at the software development company, Infosys	India	Software development block	– Hydronic cooling and a district cooling system with a chilled beam installation – Energy-efficient air conditioning and leveraged load diversity across categorised spaces: comfort air conditioning (workstations, rooms), critical load conditioning (server, hub, UPS, battery rooms), ventilated areas (restrooms, electrical, transformer rooms), and pressurised areas (staircases, lift wells, lobbies) – BMS to control and monitor the HVAC system, reduced face velocity across DOAS filters, and coils that allow for low pressure drop	EPI of 74 kWh m^{-2}, with an HVAC peak load of 5.2 W m^{-2} for a total office area of 47,340 m^2 and total conditioned area of 29,115 m^2
YS Sun Green Building by an electronics manufacturing company Delta Electronics Inc.	Taiwan, Province of China	University research green building	– Low cost and high efficiency are achieved via passive designs, such as large roofs and protruded eaves which are typical shading designs in hot-humid climates and could block around 68% of incoming solar radiation annually – Porous and wind-channelling designs, such as multiple balconies, windowsills, railings, corridors, and make use of stack effect natural ventilation to remove warm indoor air – Passive cooling techniques that help reduce the annual air conditioning load by 30%	EUI of the whole building is 29.53 kWh m^{-2} (82% more energy-saving compared to the similar type of buildings)
BCA Academy Building	Singapore	Academy Building	– Passive design features such a green roof, green walls, daylighting, and stack effect ventilation – Active designs such as energy-efficient lighting, air conditioning systems, building management system with sensors and solar panels – Well-insulated, thermal bridge free building envelope	First net zero energy retrofitted building in Southeast Asia
Energy-Plus Primary School	Germany	School	– Highly insulated Passive House standard – Hybrid (combination of natural and controlled ventilation) ventilation for thermal comfort, air quality, user acceptance and energy efficiency – Integrated photovoltaic plant and wood pellet driven combined heat and power generation – Classrooms are oriented to the south to enable efficient solar shading, natural lighting and passive solar heating – New and innovative building components including different types of innovative glazing, electrochromic glazing, LED lights, filters and control for the ventilation system	Off grid building with an EPI of 23 kWh m^{-2} yr^{-1}
NREL Research Support Facility	USA	Office and research facility	– The design maximises passive architectural strategies such as building orientation, north and south glazing, daylighting which penetrates deep into the building, natural ventilation, and a structure which stores thermal energy – Radiant heating and cooling with radiant piping through all floors, using water as the cooling and heating medium in the majority of workspaces instead of forced air – Roof-mounted photovoltaic system and adjacent parking structures covered with PV panels	EPI of 110 kWh m^{-2} yr^{-1} with a project area of 20,624.5 m^2 to become the then largest commercial net zero energy building in the country
Mohammed Bin Rashid Space Centre (Schnieders et al. 2020)	United Arab Emirates, Dubai	Non-residential, offices	– Exterior walls U-value = 0.08 W m^{-2} K^{-1} – Roof U-value = 0.08 W m^{-2} K^{-1} – Floor slab U-value = 0.108 W m^{-2} K^{-1} – Windows UW = 0.89 W m^{-2} K^{-1} – PVC and aluminium frames, triple solar protective glazing with krypton filling – Ventilation = MVHR, 89% efficiency – Heat pump for cooling with recovery of the rejected heat for DHW and reheating coil	Cooling and dehumidification demand = 40 kWh m^{-2} yr^{-1} sensible cooling +10 kWh m^{-2} yr^{-1} latent cooling Primary energy demand = 143 kWh m^{-2} yr^{-1}
Sems Have (Mørck 2017)	Roskilde, Denmark	Multi-family residential (retrofit)	– Pre-fabricated, lightweight walls – Low-energy glazed windows, basement insulated with expanded clay clinkers under concrete – Balanced mechanical ventilation with heat recovery – PV	Final Energy Use: 24.54 kWh m^{-2} Primary energy use: 16.17 kWh m^{-2}

9.5 Non-technological and Behavioural Mitigation Options and Strategies

Non-technological (NT) measures are key for low-carbon buildings, but still attract less attention than technological measures (Creutzig et al. 2016, 2018; Ruparathna et al. 2016; Mundaca et al. 2019; Vence and Pereira 2019; Cabeza et al. 2020; Mata et al. 2021b). The section is set out to understand, over the building's lifecycle, NT determinants of buildings' energy demand and emissions (Section 9.5.1); to present NT climate mitigation actions (Section 9.5.2); then, to understand how to get these actions implemented (Section 9.5.3). The latter is a starting point in the design of policies (Section 9.9).

9.5.1 Non-technological Determinants of Energy Demand and Carbon Emissions

Buildings climate impact includes CO_2 emissions from operational energy use, carbon footprint, $PM_{2.5}$ concentrations and embodied carbon, and is unequivocally driven by GDP, income, population, buildings floor area, energy price, climate, behaviour, and social and physical environment (Wolske et al. 2020; Mata et al. 2021d).

9.5.1.1 Climate and Physical Environment

Outdoor temperature, heating and cooling degree days, sunshine hours, rainfall, humidity and wind are highly determinant of energy demand (Tol et al. 2012; Rosenberg 2014; Harold et al. 2015; Risch and Salmon 2017; Lindberg et al. 2019). Density, compacity, and spatial effects define the surrounding environment and urban microclimate. Urban residents usually have a relatively affluent lifestyle, but use less energy for heating (Niu et al. 2012; Huang 2015; Rafiee et al. 2019; Ayoub 2019; Oh and Kim 2019). Urbanisation is discussed in Chapter 8.

Climate variability and extreme events may drastically increase peak and annual energy consumption (Hong et al. 2013; Cui et al. 2017; Mashhoodi et al. 2019). Climate change effects on future demand and emissions, are discussed in Section 9.7, and effects of temperature on health and productivity, in Section 9.8.

9.5.1.2 Characteristics of the Building

Building typology and floor area (or e.g., number of bedrooms or lot size) are correlated to energy demand (Manzano-Agugliaro et al. 2015; Moura et al. 2015; Fosas et al. 2018; Morganti et al. 2019; Berrill et al. 2021). Affluence is embedded in these variables as higher-income households have larger homes and lots. Residential consumption increases with the number of occupants but consumption per capita decreases proportionally to it (Serrano et al. 2017). Construction or renovation year has a negative correlation as recently built buildings must comply with increasingly strict standards (Brounen et al. 2012; Kavousian et al. 2015; Österbring et al. 2016). Only for electricity consumption no significant correlation is observed to building age (Kavousian et al. 2013). Material choices, bioclimatic and circular design discussed in Section 9.4.2.

9.5.1.3 Socio-demographic Factors

Income is positively correlated to energy demand (Cayla et al. 2011; Sreekanth et al. 2011; Couture et al. 2012; Moura et al. 2015; Singh et al. 2017; Yu 2017; Bissiri et al. 2019; Mata et al. 2021b). High-income households tend to use more efficient appliances and are likely to be more educated and environmentally sensitive, but their higher living standards require more energy (Harold et al. 2015; Hidalgo et al. 2018). Low-income households are in higher risk of fuel poverty (Section 9.8).

Mixed effects are found for household size, age, gender, ethnicity, education levels and tenancy status (Engvall et al. 2014; Hansen 2016; Lévy and Belaïd 2018; Arawomo 2019; Rafiee et al. 2019). Single-parent and elderly households consume more gas and electricity, and gender has no significant effect (Brounen et al. 2012; Harold et al. 2015; Huang 2015). Similarly, larger families use less electricity per capita (Bedir et al. 2013; Kavousian et al. 2013). Heating expenditure tends to be higher for owners than for renters, despite the formers tendency to have more efficient appliances (Gillingham et al. 2012; Davis, 2012; Kavousian et al. 2015).

9.5.1.4 Behaviour

Occupants presence and movement, interactions with the building, comfort-driven adaptations and cultural practices determine energy consumption (Hong et al. 2017; Yan et al. 2017; D'Oca et al. 2018; Khosla et al. 2019; Li et al. 2019; O'Brien et al. 2020). Households consume more on weekends and public holidays, and households with employed occupants consume less than self-employed occupants, probably because some of the latter jobs are in-house (Harold et al. 2015; Hidalgo et al. 2018). Understanding and accurate modelling of occupant behaviour is crucial to reduce the gap between design and energy performance (Gunay et al. 2013; Yan et al. 2017), especially for more efficient buildings, which rely on passive design features, human-centred technologies, and occupant engagement (Grove-Smith et al. 2018; Pitts 2017).

9.5.2 Insights From Non-technological and Behavioural Interventions

A range of NT actions can substantially reduce buildings energy demand and emissions (Figure 9.14; see Supplementary Material 9.SM.2 for details). The subsections below present insights on the variations depending on the solution, subsector, and region.

9.5.2.1 Passive and Active Design, Management, and Operation

Bioclimatic design and passive strategies for natural heating, cooling and lighting, can greatly reduce buildings' climate impact, and avoid cooling in developing countries (Bienvenido-Huertas et al. 2021, 2020; Amirifard et al. 2019). Design can provide additional small savings, for example, by placing refrigerator away from the oven, radiators or windows (Christidou et al. 2014). Passive management refers to adjustments in human behaviour such as adapted clothing, allocation of activities in the rooms of the building to minimise the

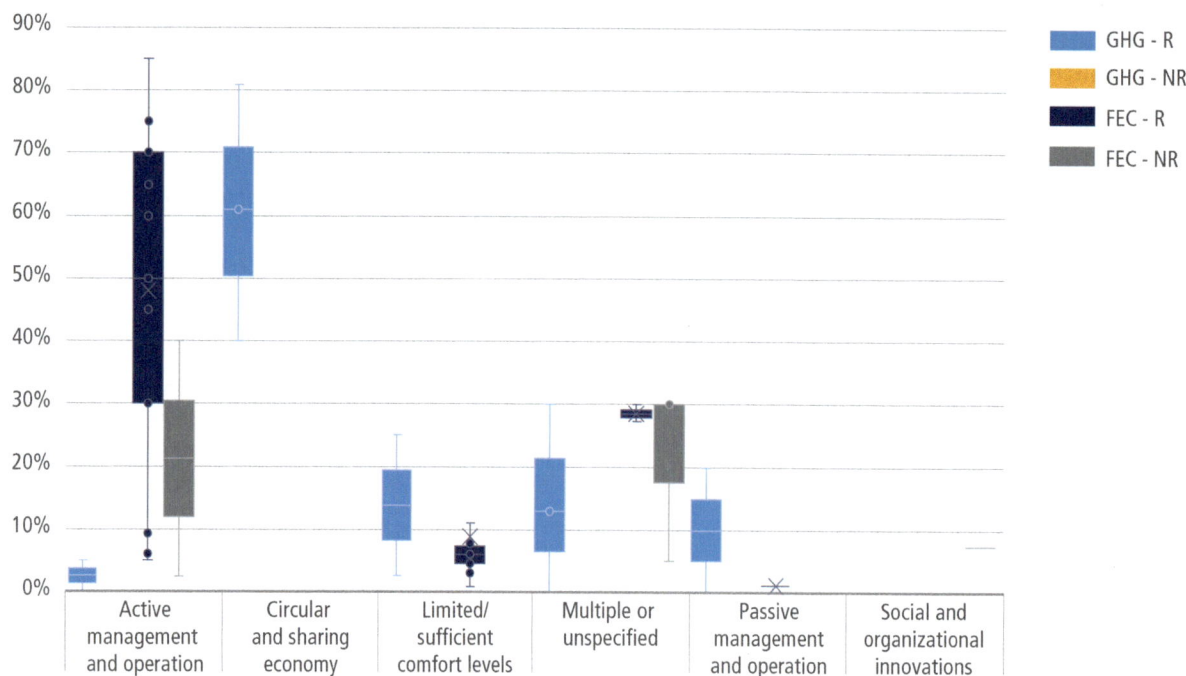

Figure 9.14 | Energy saving and GHG mitigation potentials for categories of NT interventions for Residential (R) and Non-Residential (NR) buildings, from studies with worldwide coverage. Sources: Roussac and Bright (2012); Van Den Wymelenberg (2012); Rupp et al. (2015); Creutzig et al. (2016); Khosrowpour et al. (2016); Ruparathna et al. (2016b); van Sluisveld et al. (2016); Ohueri et al. (2018); Ahl et al. (2019); Bierwirth and Thomas (2019b); Derungs et al. (2019); Grover (2019); Kaminska (2019); Levesque et al. (2019a); Bavaresco et al. (2020); Cantzler et al. (2020); Ivanova and Büchs (2020b); Wilson et al. (2020b); Harris et al. (2021).

energy use (Klein et al. 2012; Rafsanjani et al. 2015) or manual operation of the building envelope (Rijal et al. 2012; Volochovic et al. 2012). Quantitative modelling of such measures is most common for non-residential buildings, in which adaptive behaviours are affected by the office space distribution and interior design, amount of occupants, visual comfort, outdoor view, and easy-to-use control mechanisms (O'Brien and Gunay 2014; Talele et al. 2018). Socio-demographic factors, personal characteristics and contextual factors also influence occupant behaviour and their interactions with buildings (D'Oca et al. 2018b; Hong et al. 2020).

Active management refers to human control of building energy systems. Efficient lighting practices can effectively reduce summer peak demand (Dixon et al. 2015; Taniguchi et al. 2016). On the contrary, the application of the daylight-saving time in the US increases up to 7% lighting consumption (Rakha et al. 2018). Efficient cooking practices for cooking, appliance use (e.g., avoid stand-by regime, select eco-mode), or for hot water can save up to 25% (Peschiera and Taylor 2012; Teng et al. 2012; Abrahamse and Steg 2013; Berezan et al. 2013; Hsiao et al. 2014; Dixon et al. 2015; Reichert et al. 2016). High behavioural control is so far proven difficult to achieve (Ayoub et al. 2014; Sköld et al. 2018). Automated controls and technical measures to trigger occupant operations are addressed in Section 9.4.

9.5.2.2 Limited Demands for Services

Adjustment in the set-point temperature in winter and summer results in savings between 5% and 25% (Ayoub et al. 2014; Christidou et al. 2014; Taniguchi et al. 2016; Sun and Hong 2017). As introduced in Section 9.3, a series of recent works study a cap on the living area (Mata et al. 2021a) or an increase in household size (Berrill et al. 2021). These studies are promising but of limited complexity in terms of rebounds, interactions with other measures, and business models, thus require further investigation. Professional assistance and training on these issues is limited (Maxwell et al. 2018).

Willingness to adopt is found for certain measures (full load to laundry appliances, lid on while cooking, turning lights off, defer electricity usage and HVAC systems, adjust set-point temperature by 1°C) but not for others (appliances on standby, using more clothes, avoid leaving the TV on while doing other things, defer ovens, ironing or heating systems, adjust set-point temperature by 3°C, move to a low energy house or smaller apartment) (Yohanis 2012; Brown et al. 2013; Li et al. 2017; Sköld et al. 2018). A positive synergy with digitalisation and smart home appliances is identified, driven by a combination of comfort requirements and economic interest, confirmed by a willingness to defer electricity usage in exchange for cost savings (Ferreira et al. 2018; Mata et al. 2020c).

9.5.2.3 Flexibility of Demand and Comfort Requirements

In a flexible behaviour, the desired level of service is the same, but it can be shifted over time, typically allowing automated control, for the benefit of the electricity or district heating networks. There are substantial economic, technical, and behavioural benefits from implementing flexibility measures (Mata et al. 2020c), with unknown social impacts.

With demand-side measures (DSM), such as shifting demand a few hours, peak net demand can be reduced by up to 10–20% (Stötzer et al. 2015); a similar potential is available for short-term load shifting during evening hours (Aryandoust and Lilliestam 2017). Although different household types show different consumption patterns and thus an individual availability of DSM capacity during the day (Fischer et al. 2017), there is limited (Shivakumar et al. 2018) or inexistent (Drysdale et al. 2015; Nilsson et al. 2017) information of consumers' response to time of use pricing, specifically among those living in apartments (Bartusch and Alvehag 2014). Behavioural benefits are identified in terms of increased level of energy awareness of the users (Rehm et al. 2018), measured deliberate attempts of the consumers to reduce and/or shift their electricity usage (Bradley et al. 2016). Real-time control and behavioural change influence 40% of the electricity use during the operational life of non-residential buildings (Kamilaris et al. 2014).

9.5.2.4 Circular and Sharing Economy (CSE)

Non-technological CSE solutions, based on the Regenerate, Share, Optimise, Loop, Virtualise, Exchange (ReSOLVE) framework (CE100 2016; ARUP 2018) include sharing, virtualising and exchanging. These are less studied than circular materials, with notably less investigation of existing buildings and sharing solutions (Pomponi and Moncaster 2017; Høibye and Sand 2018; Kyrö 2020; European Commission 2020).

The sharing economy generates an increased utilisation rate of products or systems by enabling or offering shared use, access or ownership of products and assets that have a low ownership or use rate. Measures include conditioned spaces (accommodation, facility rooms, offices) as well as tools and transfer of ownership (i.e., second-hand or donation) (Rademaekers et al. 2017; Mercado 2018; Hertwich et al. 2020; Cantzler et al. 2020; Harris et al. 2021; Mata et al. 2021a). The evidence on the link between user behaviour and net environmental impacts of sharing options is still limited (Laurenti et al. 2019; Mata et al. 2020a; Harris et al. 2021) and even begins to be questioned, due to rebounds that partially or fully offset the benefits (Agrawal and Bellos 2017; Zink and Geyer 2017). For example, the costs savings from reduced ownership can be allocated to activities with a higher carbon intensity, or result in increased mobility. Both reduced ownership and other circular consumption habits show no influence on material footprint, other than mildly positive influence in low-income households (Junnila et al. 2018; Ottelin et al. 2020).

9.5.2.5 Value-chain, Social and Institutional Innovations

Cooperative efforts are necessary to improve buildings energy efficiency (Masuda and Claridge 2014; Kamilaris et al. 2014; Ruparathna et al. 2016). For instance, interdisciplinary understanding of organisational culture, occupant behaviour, and technology adoption is required to set up occupancy/operation best practises (Janda 2014). Similarly, close collaboration of all actors along the value chain can reduce by 50% emissions from concrete use (Habert et al. 2020); such collaboration can be enhanced in a construction project by transforming the project organisation and delivery contract to reduce costs and environmental impact (Hall and Bonanomi 2021). Building commissioning helps to reduce energy consumption by streamlining the systems, but benefits may not persist. Energy communities are discussed later in the chapter.

NT challenges include training and software costs (tailored learning programs, learning-by-doing, human capital mobilisation), client and market demand (service specification, design and provision, market and financial analysis) and legal issues (volatile energy prices, meeting regulation); and partnership, governance and commercialisation. These challenges are identified for Building Information Modelling (BIM) (Oduyemi et al. 2017; Rahman and Ayer 2019), PV industry (Triana et al. 2018), smart living (Solaimani et al. 2015) or circular economy (Vence and Pereira 2019).

9.5.3 Adoption of Climate Mitigation Solutions – Reasons and Willingness

Mixed effects are found for technical issues, attitudes, and values (Table 9.3). In spite of proven positive environmental attitudes and willingness to adopt mitigation solutions, these are outweighed by financial aspects all over the world (Mata et al. 2021b). Adopters in Developed Countries are more sensitive towards financial issues and comfort disruptions; whereas in other world regions techno-economic concerns prevail. Private consumers seem ready to support stronger governmental action, whereas non-private interventions are hindered by constraints in budgets and profits, institutional barriers and complexities (Curtis et al. 2017; Zuhaib et al. 2017; Tsoka et al. 2018; Kim et al. 2019).

A variety of interventions targeted to heterogeneous consumer groups and decision makers is needed to fulfil their diverse needs (Zhang et al. 2012; Haines and Mitchell 2014; Gram-Hanssen 2014; Marshall et al. 2015; Friege et al. 2016; Hache et al. 2017; Liang et al. 2017; Ketchman et al. 2018; Soland et al. 2018). Policy reviews for specific market segments and empirical studies investigating investment decisions would benefit from a multidisciplinary approach to energy consumption patterns and market maturity (Boyd 2016; Heiskanen and Matschoss 2017; Baumhof et al. 2018; Marzano et al. 2018; Wilson et al. 2018).

Table 9.3 | Reasons for Adoption of Climate Mitigation Solutions. The sign represents if the effect is positive (+) or negative (−), and the number of signs represents confidence level (++, many references; +, few references) (Mata et al. 2021a).

	Climate mitigation solutions for buildings							
	Building envelope	Efficient technical systems	On-site renewable energy	Behaviour	Performance standards	Low-carbon materials	Digitalisation and flexibility	Circular and sharing economy
Economic								
Subsidies/microloans*	+	++	++	+	++		+	
Low/high investment costs	−	+/−−	++/−−	+/−	+/−−	+/−	−	−
Short payback period	+	+	+	+	+	+	+	
High potential savings	++	++	++	+	++		++	+
Market-driven demand		+	+		+		+	+
Higher resale value	+	+	+		+		+	
Operating/maintenance costs	+	++/−	++/−	+	+	+	+/−	
Split incentives	−	−	−	−	−		−	
Constrained budgets and profits	−	−−	−		−−	−	−−	−−
Price competitive (overall)		+	+		+	+	+	+
Information and support								
Governmental support and capacity/lack of	+/−	+/−	++/−		++/−	+	+/−	−
Institutional barriers and complexities	−	−	−	−	−−	−	−	−
Information and labelling/lack of	+/−	++/−	++/−	+	++/−		+/−	−
Smart metering		+	+	+			+	
Participative ownership		+	+	+	+	+		
Peer effects	+	+	++		+		+	
Professional advice/lack of	+/−	++/−	++/−	−	+/−−	−	+/−	+/−
Social norm	+	+	+	+	+		+	+
Previous experience with solution/lack of	+/−	+/−	+/−	−	−	−	+/−	+/−
Technical								
Condition of existing elements	+	+	+	+	+		+	
Natural resource availability	+	+	++	+		+		+
Performance and maintenance concerns*	−	−	−−		−−	−	−	−
Low level of control over appliances		−	−	−	−		−	
Limited alternatives available		−				−	−	
Not compatible with existing equipment	−						−	−
Attitudes and values								
Appealing novel technology	+	+	++	+	+	+	++	+
Social and egalitarian world views	+		+	+	+		+	
Willingness to pay		+	++		+		+	
Heritage or aesthetic values	+/−	++/−	+/−		+/−		+/−	
Environmental values	+	+	++	+	++	+	++	+
Status and comfort/Lack of	++	++	++	+	++		+	
Discomfort during the retrofitting period	−	−	−		−		−	
Control, privacy, and security/Lack of*		+/−	+/−	−	−	−	+/−−	
Risk aversion	−	−	−		−	−	−	
Social								
Size factors (household, building)		+/−	++/−	+	+		+	
Status (education, income)	+/−	++/−	+/−	+/−	+/−	+	+/−	
Socio-demographic (age, gender, and ethnicity)	+/−	++/−	+/−	+/−	+/−		+/−	

9.5.3.1   Building Envelope

In North America and Europe, personal attitudes, values, and existing information and support are the most and equally important reasons for improving the building envelope. Consumers have some economic concerns and little technical concerns, the latter related to the performance and maintenance of the installed solutions (Mata et al. 2021a). In other world regions or climate zones the literature is limited.

Motivations are often triggered by urgent comfort or replacement needs. Maintaining the aesthetic value may as well hinder the installation of insulation if no technical solutions are easily available (Haines and Mitchell 2014; Bright et al. 2019). Local professionals and practitioners can both encourage (Friege 2016; Ozarisoy and Altan 2017) and discourage the installation of insulation, according to their knowledge and training (Curtis et al. 2017; Zuhaib et al. 2017; Maxwell et al. 2018; Tsoka et al. 2018). If energy renovations of the buildings envelopes are not normative, cooperative ownership may be a barrier in apartment buildings (Miezis et al. 2016). Similarly, product information and labelling may be helpful or overwhelming (Ozarisoy and Altan 2017; Lilley et al. 2017; Bright et al. 2019). Decisions are correlated to governmental support (Swantje et al. 2015; Tam et al. 2016) and peer information (Friege et al. 2016; Friege 2016).

The intervention is required to be cost efficient, although value could be placed in the amount of energy saved (Mortensen et al. 2016; Lilley et al. 2017; Howarth and Roberts 2018; Kim et al. 2019) or the short payback period (Miezis et al. 2016). Subsidies have a positive effect (Swan et al. 2017).

9.5.3.2   Adoption of Efficient HVAC Systems and Appliances

Mixed willingness is found to adopt efficient technologies. While Developed Countries are positive towards building envelope technologies, appliances such as A-rated equipment or condensing boilers are negatively perceived (Yohanis 2012). In contrast, adopters in Asia are positive towards energy-saving appliances (Liao et al. 2020; Spandagos et al. 2020).

Comfort, economic and ecological aspects, as well as information influence the purchase of a heating system (Claudy et al. 2011; Decker and Menrad 2015). Information and support from different stakeholders are the most relevant aspects in different geographical contexts (Hernandez-Roman et al. 2017; Tumbaz and Moğulkoç 2018; Curtis et al. 2018; Bright et al. 2019; Chu and Wang 2019).

Among high-income countries, economy aspects have positive effects, specially reductions in energy bills and financial incentives or subsidies (Chun and Jiang 2013; Christidou et al. 2014; Mortensen et al. 2016; Clancy et al. 2017; Ketchman et al. 2018). Having complementary technologies already in place also has positively affects adoption (Zografakis et al. 2012; Clancy et al. 2017), but performance and maintenance concerns appear as barriers (Qiu et al. 2014). The solutions are positively perceived as high-technology innovative, to enhance status, and are supported by peers and

own-environmental values (Mortensen et al. 2016; Heiskanen and Matschoss 2017; Ketchman et al. 2018).

9.5.3.3   Installation of Renewable Energy Sources (RES)

Although consumers are willing to install distributed RES worldwide, and information has successfully supported their roll out, economic and governmental support is still necessary for their full deployment. Technical issues remain for either very novel technologies or for the integration of RES in the energy system (Ürge-Vorsatz et al. 2020; Mata et al. 2021a). Capacities are to be built by coordinated actions by all stakeholders (Musonye et al. 2020). To this aim, energy communities and demonstrative interventions at local scale are key to address technical, financial, regulatory and structural barriers and document long-term benefits (von Wirth et al. 2018; Shafique et al. 2020; Fouladvand et al. 2020).

Regarding solar technologies, heterogeneous decisions are formed by socio-demographic, economic and technical predictors interwoven with a variety of behavioural traits (Alipour et al. 2020; Khan 2020). Studies on PV adoption confirm place-specific (various spatial and peer effects), multi-scalar cultural dynamics (Bollinger and Gillingham 2012; Schaffer and Brun 2015; Graziano and Gillingham 2015). Environmental concern and technophilia drive the earliest PV adopters, while later adopters value economic gains (Hampton and Eckermann 2013; Jager-Waldau et al. 2018; Abreu et al. 2019; Palm 2020). Previous experience with similar solutions increases adoption (Baumhof et al. 2018; Qurashi and Ahmed 2019; Bach et al. 2020; Reindl and Palm 2020).

9.5.3.4   Low-carbon Materials

Studies on low-carbon materials tend to focus on wood-based building systems and prefabricated housing construction, mostly in high-income countries, as many sustainable managed forestries and factories for prefabricated housing concentrated in such regions (Mata et al. 2021a). This uneven promotion of wood can lead to its overconsumption (Pomponi et al. 2020).

Although the solutions are not yet implemented at scale, examples include the adoption of low carbon cement in Cuba motivated by the possibility of supplying the rising demand with low initial investment costs (Cancio Díaz et al. 2017) or adoption of bamboo-based social houses in The Philippines motivated by local job creation and typhoon resistance (Zea Escamilla et al. 2016). More generally, low investment costs and high level decision-making, for example, political will and environmental values of society, increase the adoption rate of low-carbon materials (Steinhardt and Manley 2016; Lien and Lolli 2019; Hertwich et al. 2020). In contrast, observed barriers include lobbying by traditional materials industries, short-term political decision making (Tozer 2019) and concerns over technical performance, risk of damage, and limited alternatives available (Thomas et al. 2014).

9.5.3.5   Digitalisation and Demand-supply Flexibility

Demand-supply flexibility measures are experimentally being adopted in North America, Europe, and Asia-Pacific Developed regions.

Changes in the current regulatory framework would facilitate participation based on trust and transparent communication (Wolsink 2012; Nyborg and Røpke 2013; Mata et al. 2020b). However, consumers expect governments and energy utilities to steer the transition (Seidl et al. 2019).

Economic challenges are observed, as unclear business models, disadvantageous market models and high costs of advanced smart metering. Technical challenges include constraints for HPs and seasonality of space heating demands. Social challenges relate to lack of awareness of real-time price information and inadequate technical understanding. Consumers lack acceptance towards comfort changes (noise, overnight heating) and increased automation (Drysdale et al. 2015; Bradley et al. 2016; Sweetnam et al. 2019). Risks identified include higher peaks and congestions in low price-hours, difficulties in designing electricity tariffs because of conflicts with CO_2 intensity, and potential instability in the entire electricity system caused by tariffs coupling to wholesale electricity pricing.

Emerging market players are changing customer utility relationships, as the grid is challenged with intermittent loads and integration needs for ICTs, interfering with consumers requirements of autonomy and privacy (Wolsink 2012; Parag and Sovacool 2016). Although most private PV owners would make their storage system available as balancing load for the grid operator, the acquisition of new batteries by a majority of consumers requires incentives (Gährs et al. 2015). For distributed energy hubs, social acceptance depends on the amount of local benefits in economic, environmental or social terms (Kalkbrenner and Roosen 2015), and increases around demonstration projects (von Wirth et al. 2018).

9.5.3.6 Circular and Sharing Economy

The circular and sharing economy begins to be perceived as organisational and technologically innovative, with the potential to provide superior customer value, response to societal trends and positive marketing (Mercado 2018; Cantzler et al. 2020; Nußholz et al. 2020). Although technical and regulatory challenges remain, there are key difficulties around the demonstration of a business case for both consumers and the supply chain (Pomponi and Moncaster 2017; Hart et al. 2019).

Government support is needed as an initiator but also to reinforce building retrofit targets, promote more stringent energy and material standards for new constructions, and protect consumer interests (Hongping 2017; Fischer and Pascucci 2017; Patwa et al. 2020). Taxes clearly incentivise waste reduction and recycling (Rachel and Travis 2011; Ajayi et al. 2015; Volk et al. 2019). In developing countries, broader, international, market boundaries can allow for a more attractive business model (Mohit et al. 2020). Participative and new ownership models can favour the adoption of prefabricated buildings (Steinhardt and Manley 2016). Needs for improvements are observed, in terms of design for flexibility and deconstruction, procurement and prefabrication and off-site construction, standardisation and dimensional coordination, with differences among solutions (Osmani 2012; Coehlo et al.2013; Lu and Yuan 2013; Cossu and Williams 2015; Schiller et al. 2015, 2017; Ajayi et al. 2017; Bakshan et al. 2017).

Although training is a basic requirement, attitude, past experience, and social pressure can also be highly relevant, as illustrated for waste management in a survey to construction site workers (Amal et al. 2017). Traditional community practices of reuse of building elements are observed to be replaced by a culture of waste (Ajayi et al. 2015; Hongping 2017).

9.6 Global and Regional Mitigation Potentials and Costs

9.6.1 Review of Literature Calculating Potentials for Different World Countries

Section 9.4 provides an update on technological options and practices, which allow constructing and retrofitting individual buildings to produce very low emissions during their operation phase. Since AR5, the world has seen a growing number of such buildings in all populated continents, and a growing amount of literature calculates the mitigation potential for different countries if such technologies and practices penetrate at scale. Figure 9.15 synthesises the results of sixty-seven bottom-up studies, which rely on the bottom-up technology-reach approach and assess the potential of such technologies and practices, aggregated to stock of corresponding products and/or buildings at national level.

The studies presented in Figure 9.15 rely on all, the combination, or either of the following mitigation strategies: the construction of new high energy-performance buildings taking the advantage of building design, forms, and passive construction methods; the thermal efficiency improvement of building envelopes of the existing stock; the installation of advanced HVAC systems, equipment and appliances; the exchange of lights, appliances, and office equipment, including ICT, water heating, and cooking with their efficient options; demand-side management, most often controlling comfort requirements and demand-side flexibility and digitalisation; as well as onsite production and use of renewable energy. Nearly all studies, which assess the technological potential assume such usage of space heating, cooling, water heating, and lighting that does not exceed health, living, and working standards, thus realising at least a part of the non-technological potential, as presented in Figure 9.14. The results presented in Figure 9.15 relate to measures applied within the boundaries of the building sector, including the reduction in direct and indirect emissions. The results exclude the impact of decarbonisation measures applied within the boundaries of the energy supply sector, that is, the decarbonisation of grid electricity and district heat.

The analysis of Figure 9.15 illustrates that there is a large body of literature attesting to mitigation potential in the countries of Europe and North America of up to 55–85% and in Asia-Pacific Developed of up to 45% in 2050, as compared to their sector baseline emissions, even though they sometimes decline. For developing countries, the literature estimates the potential of up to 40–80% in 2050, as compared to their sharply growing baselines. The interpretation of these estimates should be cautious because the studies rely on assumptions with uncertainties and feasibility constrains (see Sections 9.6.4, Figure 9.20 and Supplementary Material Table 9.SM.6).

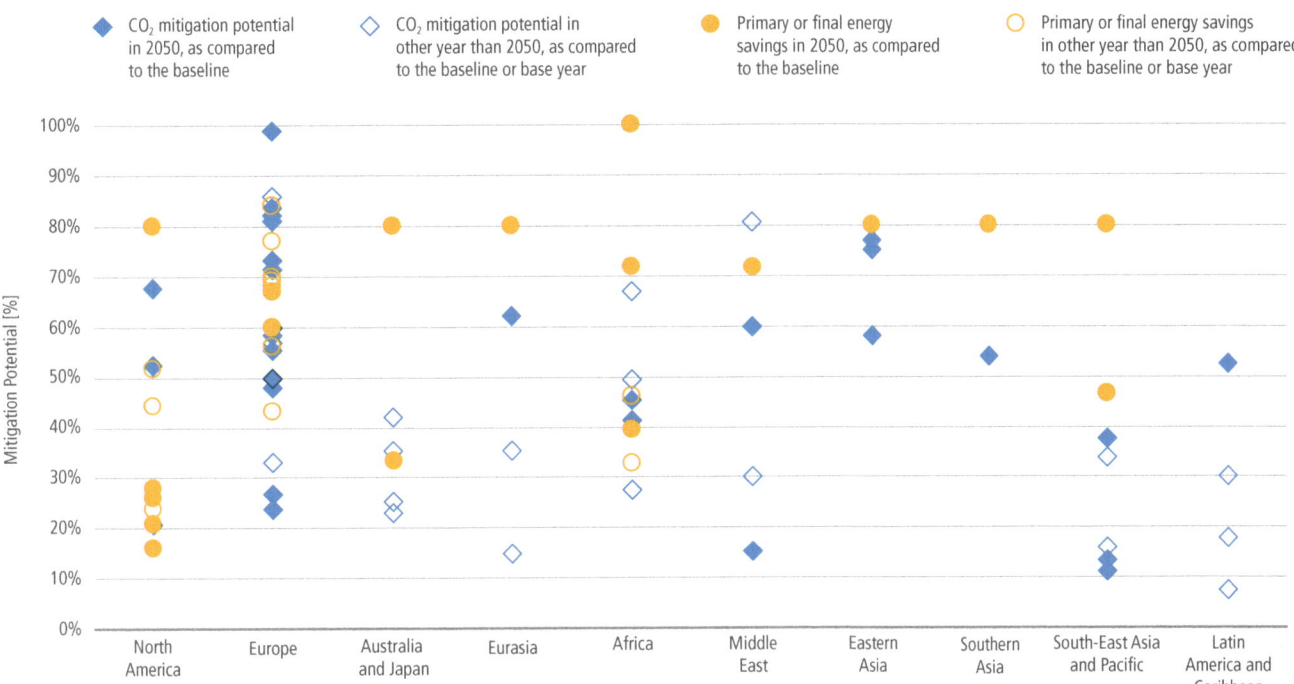

Figure 9.15 | Potential GHG emission reduction in buildings of different world countries grouped by region, as reported by sixty-seven bottom-up studies. Sources: North America: Canada (Trottier 2016; Radpour et al. 2017; Subramanyam et al. 2017a,b; Zhang et al. 2020a), the Unites States of America (Gagnon et al. 2016; Nadel 2016; Yeh et al. 2016; Wilson et al. 2017; Zhang et al. 2020a); Europe: Albania (Novikova et al. 2020, 2018c), Austria (Ploss et al. 2017), Bulgaria, the Czech Republic, Hungary (Csoknyai et al. 2016), France (Ostermeyer et al. 2018b), the European Union (Duscha et al. 2019; Roscini et al. 2020; Brugger et al. 2021), Germany (Markewitz et al. 2015; Bürger et al. 2019; Ostermeyer et al. 2019b), Greece (Mirasgedis et al. 2017), Italy (Calise et al. 2021; Filippi Oberegger et al. 2020), Lithuania (Toleikyte et al. 2018), Montenegro (Novikova et al. 2018c), Netherlands (Ostermeyer et al. 2018c), Norway (Sandberg et al. 2021), Serbia (Novikova et al. 2018a), Switzerland (Iten et al. 2017; Streicher et al. 2017), Poland (Ostermeyer et al. 2019a), the United Kingdom (Ostermeyer et al. 2018a); Eurasia: Armenia, Georgia (Timilsina et al. 2016); the Russian Federation (Bashmakov 2017; Zhang et al. 2020a); Australia (Energetics 2016; Butler et al. 2020; Zhang et al. 2020a), Japan (Momonoki et al. 2017; Wakiyama and Kuramochi 2017; Minami et al. 2019; Zhang et al. 2020a; Sugyiama et al. 2020); Africa: Egypt (Makumbe et al. 2017; Calise et al. 2021), Morocco (Merini et al. 2020), Nigeria (Dioha et al. 2019; Kwag et al. 2019; Onyenokporo and Ochedi 2019), Rwanda (Colenbrander et al. 2019), South Africa (Department of Environmental Affairs 2014), Uganda (de la Rue du Can et al. 2018), Algeria, Egypt, Libya, Morocco, Sudan, Tunisia (Krarti -2019); Middle East – Qatar (Krarti et al. 2017; Kamal et al. 2019), Saudi Arabia (Alaidroos and Krarti 2015; Khan et al. 2017), Bahrain, Iraq, Jordan, Kuwait, Lebanon, Oman, Qatar, Saudi Arabia, State of Palestine, Syrian Arab Republic, United Arab Emirates, Yemen (Krarti 2019); Eastern Asia – China (Tan et al. 2018; Zhou et al. 2018; Xing et al. 2021; Zhang et al. 2020); Southern Asia: India (Yu et al. 2018; de la Rue du Can et al. 2019; Zhang et al. 2020); South-East Asia and Pacific: Indonesia (Kusumadewi and Limmeechokchai 2015, 2017), Thailand (Kusumadewi and Limmeechokchai 2015, 2017; Chaichaloempreecha et al. 2017), Vietnam (ADB 2017), respective countries from the Asia-Pacific Economic Cooperation (APEC) (Zhang et al. 2020a); Latin America and Caribbean: Brazil (de Melo and de Martino Jannuzzi 2015; González-Mahecha et al. 2019), Colombia (Prada-Hernández et al. 2015), Mexico (Grande-acosta and Islas-samperio 2020; Rosas-Flores and Rosas-Flores 2020).

The novelty since AR5 is emerging bottom-up literature, which attempts to account for potential at national and global level from applying the sufficiency approach (see Box 9.1 in Section 9.1 and decomposition analysis in Section 9.3.2). In spite of the reducing energy use per unit of floor area at an average rate of 1.3% per year, the growth of floor area at an average rate of 3% per year causes rising energy demand and GHG emissions because each new square meter must be served with thermal comfort and/or other amenities (International Energy Agency 2017; Ellsworth-Krebs 2020). Nearly all studies reviewed in Figure 9.15 assume the further growth of floor area per capita until 2050, with many studies of developing countries targeting today per capita floor area as in Europe.

Table 9.4 reviews the bottom-up literature, which quantifies the potential from reorganisation of human activities, efficient design, planning, and use of building space, higher density of building and settlement inhabitancy, redefining and downsizing goods and equipment, limiting their use to health, living, and working standards, and their sharing, recognising the number of square meters and devices as a determinant of GHG emissions that could be impacted

via policies and measures. Nearly all national or regional studies originate from Europe and North America recognising challenges, Developed Countries face toward decarbonisation. Thus, Goldstein et al. (2020) suggested prioritising the reduction in floor space of wealthier population and more efficient space planning because grid decarbonisation is not enough to meet the U.S. target by 2050 whereas affluent suburbs may have 15 times higher emission footprints than nearby neighbourhoods. Cabrera Serrenho et al. (2019) argue that reducing the UK floor area is a low cost mitigation option given a low building replacement rate and unreasonably high retrofit costs of existing buildings. Lorek and Spangenberg (2019) discusses the opportunity of reducing building emissions in Germany fitting better the structure of the dwelling stock to the declined average household size, as most dwellings have 3–4 rooms while most households have only one person.

Whereas these studies suggest sufficiency as an important option for Developed Countries, global studies argue that it is also important for the developing world. This is because it provides the means to address inequality, poverty reduction and social inclusion, ensuring

Table 9.4 | Potential GHG emission reduction in the building sector offered by the introduction of sufficiency as a main or additional measure, as reported by bottom-up (or hybrid) literature.

Region	Reference	Scenario and its result	Sufficiency for floor space
Globe	Grubler et al. (2018)	The Low Energy Demand Scenario halves the final energy demand of buildings by 2050, as compared the WEO Current Policy (International Energy Agency 2019c) by modelling the changes in quantity, types, and energy intensity of services.	The scenario assumed a reduction in the residential and non-residential building floor area to 29 and 11 m^2 cap^{-1} respectively.
Globe	Millward-Hopkins et al. (2020)	With the changes in structural and technological intensity, the Decent Living Energy scenario achieved the decent living standard for all while reducing the final energy consumption of buildings by factor three, as compared to the WEO Current Policy Scenario (International Energy Agency 2019c).	The scenario assumed a reduction in floor area to 15 m^2 cap^{-1} across the world.
Globe	Levesque et al. (2019)	Realising both the technological and sufficiency potential, the Low Demand Scenario and the Very Low Demand Scenario calculated a reduction in global building energy demand by 32% and 45% in 2050, as compared to the business-as-usual baseline.	The Low Scenario limited the residential and non-residential floor area to 70 and 23 m^2 cap^{-1}; the Very Low Scenario – to 45 and 15 m^2 cap^{-1}.
EU	Bierwirth and Thomas (2019b)	For the EU residential sector, the authors calculated potential energy savings of 17% and 29% from setting the per capita floor area limits.	A reduction of the residential floor area to 30 m^2 cap^{-1} and 35 m^2 cap^{-1}, respectively.
EU	Roscini et al. (2020)	With the help of technological and non-technological measures, the Responsible Policy Scenario for the EU buildings allows achieving the emission reduction by 60% in 2030, as compared to 2015.	The scenario assumed 6% decrease in the residential per capita floor area (to max. 44.8 m^2 cap^{-1}).
Canada, UK, France, Italy, Japan, USA, Germany	Hertwich et al. (2020)	The potential reduction in GHG emissions from the production of building materials is 56–58% in 2050, as compared to these baseline emissions. The reduction in heating and cooling energy demand is 9–10% in 2050, as compared to its baseline.	Via the efficient use of living space, the scenario assumed its 20% reduction, as compared to its baseline development.
UK	Cabrera Serrenho et al. (2019)	The scenario found that the sufficiency measures allowed mitigating 30% of baseline emissions of the English building sector in 2050, without other additional measures.	The scenario assumed a 10% reduction in the current floor area per capita by 2050.
USA	Goldstein et al. (2020)	The scenario calculated 16% GHG mitigation potential in 2050, as compared to the baseline, on the top of two other scenarios assuming building retrofits and grid decarbonisation already delivering a 42% emission reduction.	The scenario assumed a 10% reduction in per capita floor area and higher penetration of onsite renewable energy.
Switzerland	Roca-Puigròs et al. (2020)	The Green Lifestyle scenario allows achieving 48% energy savings by 2050, as compared to the baseline, due to sufficiency in the floor area among other measures.	The scenario assumed a reduction in residential floor area. from 47 to 41 m^2 cap^{-1}.
France	Negawatt (2017)	The Negawatt scenario assumes that sufficiency behaviour becomes a mainstream across all sectors. In 2050, the final energy savings are 21% and 28% for the residential and tertiary sectors respectively, as compared to their baselines.	The scenario assumes a limit of the residential floor at 42 m^2 cap^{-1} due to apartment sharing and compact urban planning.
France	Virage-Energie Nord-Pas-de-Calais. (2016)	The authors assessed sufficiency opportunities across all sectors for the Nord-Pas-de-Calais region of France. Depending on the level of implementation, sufficiency could reduce the energy consumption of residential and tertiary buildings by 13–30% in 2050, as compared to the baseline.	The scenario assumed sharing spaces, downsizing spaces and sharing equipment from a 'soft' to 'radical' degree.

the provision of acceptable living standards for the entire global population given the planetary boundaries. As Figure 9.6 illustrates, the largest share of current construction occurs in developing countries, while these countries follow a similar demographic track of declining household sizes versus increasing dwelling areas. This trajectory translates into the importance of their awareness of the likely similar forthcoming challenges, and the need in early efficient planning of infrastructure and buildings with a focus on space usage and density.

9.6.2 Assessment of the Potentials at Regional and Global Level

This section presents an aggregation of bottom-up potential estimates for different countries into regional and then global figures for 2050, based on literature presented in Section 9.6.1. First, national potential estimates reported as a share of baseline emissions in 2050 were aggregated into regional potential estimates. Second, the latter were multiplied with regional baseline emissions to calculate the regional potential in absolute numbers. Third, the global potential in absolute numbers was calculated as a sum of

regional absolute potentials. When several bottom-up studies were identified for a region, either a rounded average or a rounded median figure was taken, giving the preference to the one that was closest to the potential estimates of countries with very large contribution to regional baseline emissions in 2050 (e.g., to China in Eastern Asia). Furthermore, we preferred studies, which assessed the whole or a large share of sector emissions and considered a comprehensive set of measures. The regional baseline emissions, refer to the World Energy Outlook (WEO) Current Policy Scenario (International Energy Agency 2019c). The sector mitigation potential reported in Chapter 12 for the year 2030 was estimated in the same manner.

Figure 9.16 presents the mitigation potential in the building sector for the world and each region in 2050, estimated as a result of this aggregation exercise. The potentials presented in the figure are different from those reported in Section 9.3.3, where they are estimated by IEA and IMAGE hybrid model. The figure provides two breakdowns of the potential, into the reduction of direct and indirect emissions as well as into the reduction of emissions from introducing sufficiency, energy efficiency, and renewable energy measures. The potential estimates rely on the incremental stepwise approach, assembling the measures according to the SER framework

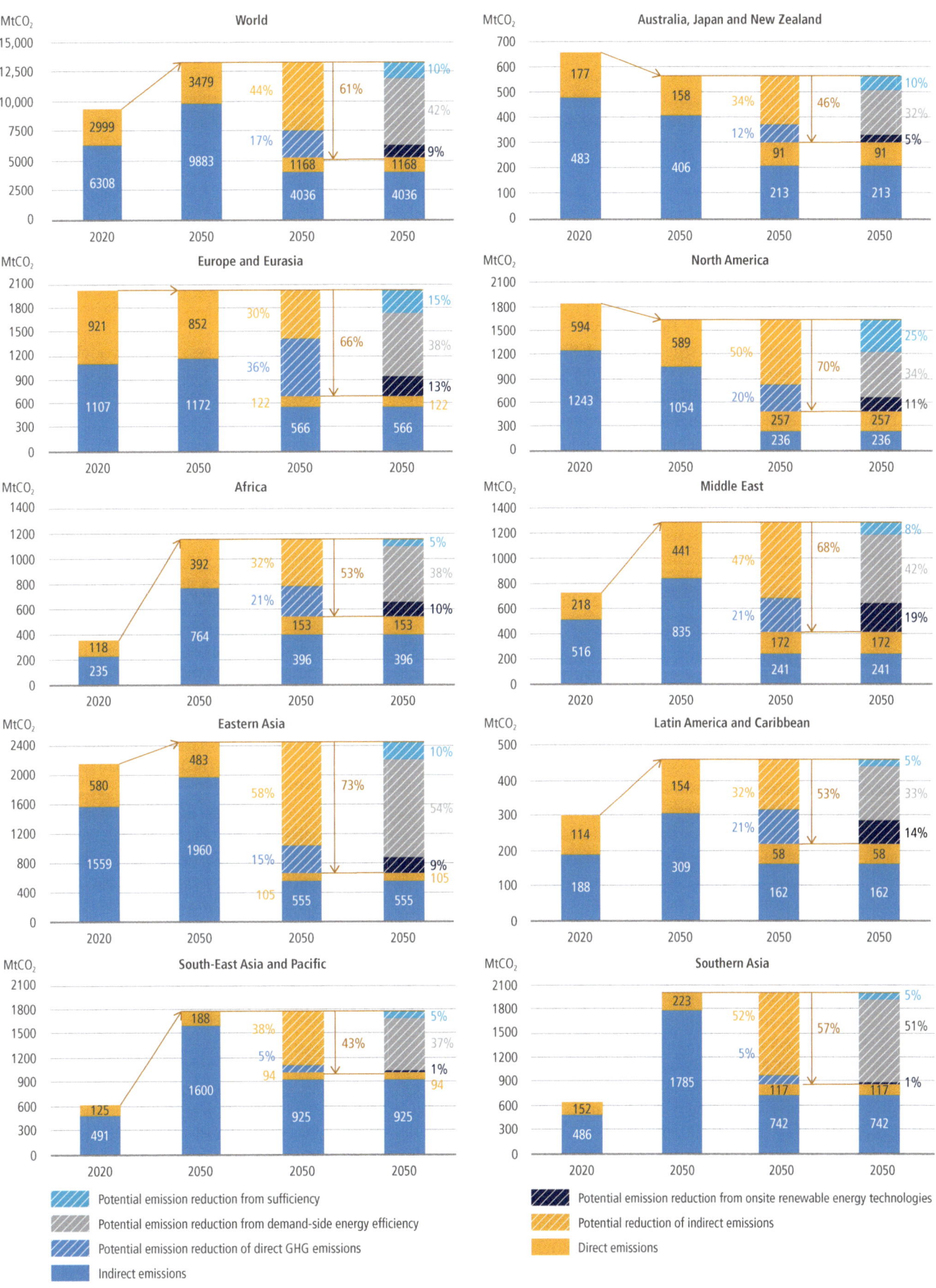

Figure 9.16 | Global and regional estimates of GHG emissions in the building sector in 2020 and 2050, and their potential reduction in 2050 broken down by measure (sufficiency/energy efficiency/renewable energy) and by emission source (direct/indirect). Note: the baseline refers to the WEO Current Policy Scenario (International Energy Agency 2019c). It may differ from other chapters.

(Box 9.1) and correcting the amount of the potential at each step for the interaction of measures. The sequence of energy efficiency and renewable energy measures follow the conclusion of the IPCC Special Report on Global Warming of 1.5°C (SR1.5) (Rogelj et al. 2018) that lower energy demand allows more choice of low-carbon energy supply options, and therefore such sequencing is more beneficial and cost-effective.

Figure 9.16 argues that it is possible to mitigate 8.2 $GtCO_2$ or 61% of global building emissions in 2050, as compared to their baseline. At least 1.4 $GtCO_2$ or 10% of baseline emissions could be avoided introducing the sufficiency approaches. Further 5.6 $GtCO_2$ or 42% of baseline emissions could be mitigated with the help of energy efficiency technologies and practices. Finally, at least 1.1 $GtCO_2$ or 9% of baseline emissions could be reduced through the production and use of onsite renewable energy. Out of the total potential, the largest share of 5.4 $GtCO_2$ will be available in developing countries; these countries will be able to reduce 59% of their baseline emissions. Developed Countries will be able to mitigate 2.7 $GtCO_2$ or 65% of their baseline emissions. Only few potential studies, often with only few mitigation options assessed, were available for the countries of South-East Asia and Pacific, Africa, and Latin America and Caribbean; therefore, the potential estimates represent low estimates, and the real potentials are likely be higher.

9.6.3   Assessment of the Potential Costs

The novelty since AR5 is that a growing number of bottom-up studies considers the measures as an integrated package recognising their technological complementarity and interdependence, rather than the linear process of designing and constructing buildings and their systems, or incremental improvements of individual building components and energy-using devices during building retrofits, losing opportunities for the optimisation of whole buildings. Therefore, integrated measures rather than the individual measures are considered for the estimates of costs and potentials. Figure 9.17 presents the indicative breakdown of the potential reported in Figure 9.16 by measure and cost, to the extent that it was possible to disaggregate and align to common characteristics. Whereas the breakdown per measure was solely based on the literature reviewed in Section 9.6.1, the cost estimates additionally relied on the literature presented in this section, Figure 9.20, and Supplementary Material Table 9.SM.6. The literature reviewed reports fragmented and sometimes contradicting cost-effectiveness information. Despite a large number of exemplary buildings achieving very high performance in all parts of the world, there is a lack of mainstream literature or official studies assessing the costs of these buildings at scale (Lovins 2018; Ürge-Vorsatz et al. 2020).

Figure 9.17 indicates that a very large share of the potential in Developed Countries could be realised through the introduction of sufficiency measures (at least 18% of their baseline emissions). Literature identifies many opportunities, which may help operationalise it. These are reorganisation of human activities, teleworking, coworking, more efficient space design, planning and use, higher density of building and settlement inhabitancy, flexible

space, housing swaps, shared homes and facilities, space and room renting, and others (Bierwirth and Thomas 2019a; Ivanova and Büchs 2020; Ellsworth-Krebs 2020). Whereas literature does not provide a robust cost assessment of the sufficiency potential, it indicates that these measures are likely to be at no or very little cost (Cabrera Serrenho et al. 2019).

The exchange of lights, appliances, and office equipment, including ICT, water heating, and cooking technologies could reduce more than 8% and 13% of the total sector baseline emissions in developed and developing countries respectively, typically at negative cost (Department of Environmental Affairs 2014; de Melo and de Martino Jannuzzi 2015; Prada-Hernández et al. 2015; Subramanyam et al. 2017a,b; González-Mahecha et al. 2019; Grande-Acosta and Islas-Samperio 2020). This cost-effectiveness is, however, often reduced by a larger size of appliances and advanced features, which offset a share of positive economic effects (Molenbroek et al. 2015).

Advanced HVAC technologies backed-up with demand-side management, and onsite integrated renewables backed-up with demand-side flexibility and digitalisation measures are typically a part of the retrofit or construction strategy. Among HVAC technologies, heat pumps are very often modelled to become a central heating and cooling technology supplied with renewable electricity. The estimates of HVAC cost-effectiveness, including heat pumps, vary in modelling results from very cost-effective to medium (Department of Environmental Affairs 2014; Prada-Hernández et al. 2015; Akander et al. 2017; Hirvonen et al. 2020). Among demand-side management, demand-side flexibility and digitalisation options, various sensors, controls, and energy consumption feedback devices have typically negative costs, whereas advanced smart management systems as well as thermal and electric storages linked to fluctuating renewables are not yet cost-effective (Nguyen et al. 2015; Prada-Hernández et al. 2015; Huang et al. 2019; Uchman 2021; Duman et al. 2021; Sharda et al. 2021; Rashid et al. 2021). Several Developed Countries achieved to make onsite renewable energy production and use profitable for at least a part of the building stock (Horváth et al. 2016; Akander et al. 2017; Vimpari and Junnila 2019; Fina et al. 2020), but this is not yet the case for developing countries (Kwag et al. 2019; Cruz et al. 2020; Grande-Acosta and Islas-Samperio 2020). Due to characteristics and parameters of different building types, accommodating the cost-optimal renewables at large scale is especially difficult in non-residential buildings and in urban areas, as compared to residential buildings and rural areas (Horváth et al. 2016; Fina et al. 2020).

Literature agrees that new advanced buildings, using design, form, and passive building construction equipped with demand-side measures, and advanced HVAC technologies can reduce the sector total baseline emissions in developed and developing countries by at least 10% and 25% in 2050, respectively, and renewable energy technologies backed-up with demand-side flexibility and digitalisation measures typically installed in new buildings could further reduce these emissions by at least 11% and 7% (see also Cross-Chapter Box 12 in Chapter 16). The literature, however, provides different and sometimes conflicting information of their cost-effectiveness. Esser et al. (2019) reported that by 2016, the perceived share of buildings similar or close to NZEB in the new construction was just

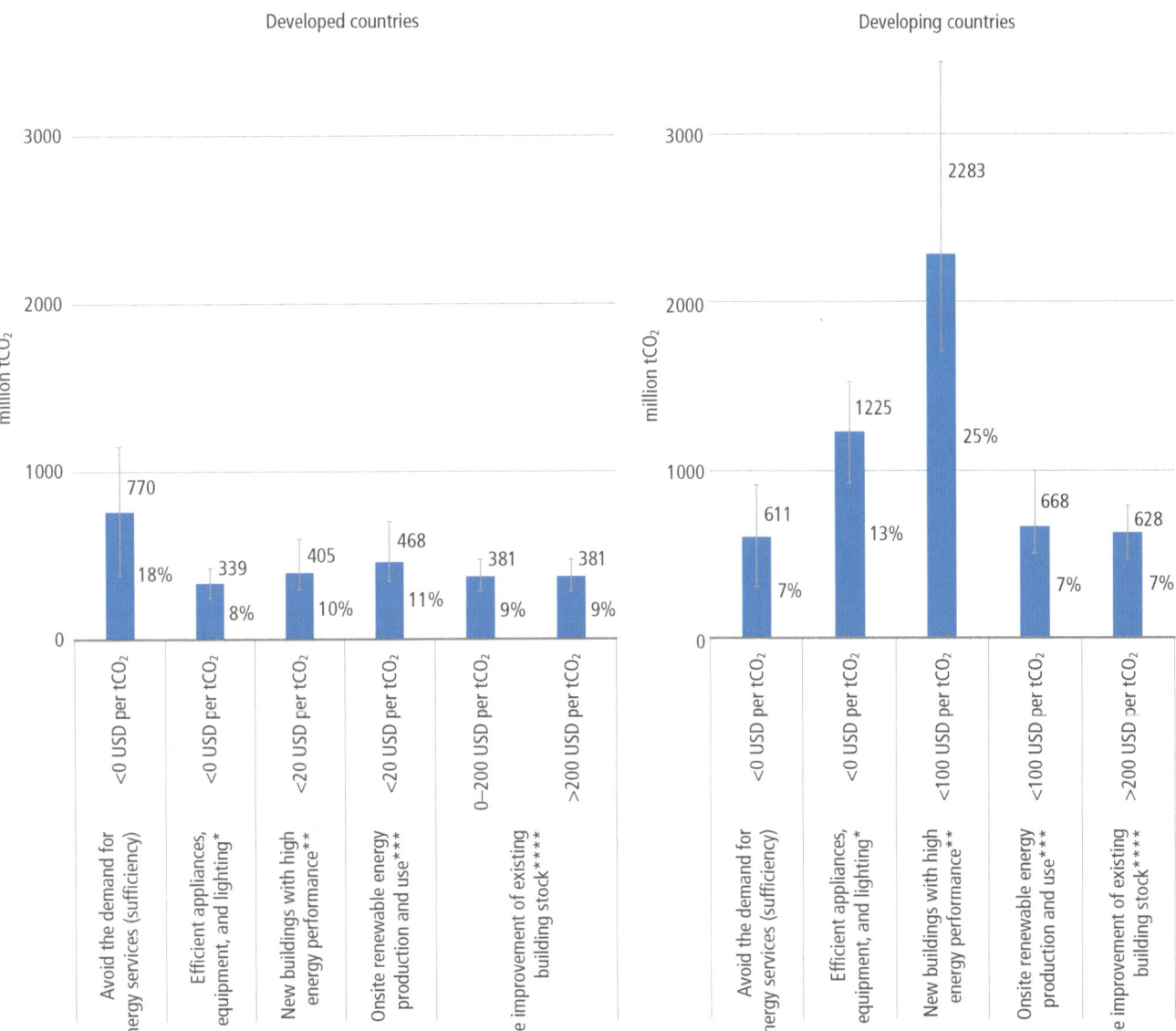

Developed countries   Developing countries

* including ICT, water heating, and cooking.
** including the change in construction methods; management and operation of buildings; and efficient heating, ventilation, and air-conditioning.
*** typically in new high performance buildings.
**** including thermal efficiency of building envelopes; management and operation of buildings; and efficient heating, ventilation, and air-conditioning.

Figure 9.17 | Indicative breakdown of GHG emission reduction potential of the buildings sector in developed and developing countries into measure and costs in 2050, in absolute figures with uncertainty ranges and as a share of their baseline emissions. Notes: (i) The baseline refers to the WEO Current Policy Scenario (International Energy Agency 2019c). It may differ from other chapters. (ii) The figure merged the results of Eurasia into those of Developed Countries.

above 20% across the EU. In this region, additional investment costs were no higher than 15%, as reported for Germany, Italy, Denmark, and Slovenia (Erhorn-Kluttig et al. 2019). Still, the European market experiences challenges which relate to capacity and readiness, as revealed by the Architects' Council of Europe (ACE) (2019), which records a decline in the share of architects who are designing buildings to NZEB standards to more than 50% of their time, from 14% in 2016 to 11% in 2018. In contrast, the APEC countries reported additional investment costs of 67% on average (Xu and Zhang 2017) that makes them a key barrier to the NZEB penetration in developing

countries as of today (Feng et al. 2019). This calls for additional R&D policies and financial incentives to reduce the NZEB costs (Xu and Zhang 2017; Kwag et al. 2019).

Thermal efficiency retrofits of existing envelopes followed up by the exchange of HVAC backed up with demand-side measures could reduce the sector total baseline emissions in developed and developing countries by at least 18% and 7% respectively in 2050. There have been many individual examples of deep building retrofits, which incremental costs are not significantly higher than those of shallow retrofits. However, the literature tends to agree that cost-effective or low cost deep retrofits are not universally applicable for all cases, especially in historically urban areas, indicating a large share of the potential in the high-cost category (Department of Environmental Affairs 2014; Akander et al. 2017; Paduos and Corrado 2017; Semprini et al. 2017; Subramanyam et al. 2017b; Streicher et al. 2017; Mata et al. 2019). Achieving deep retrofits assumes additional measures on the top of business-as-usual retrofits, therefore high rate of deep retrofits at acceptable costs are not possible in case of low business-as-usual rates (Streicher et al. 2020).

For a few studies, which conducted an assessment of the sector transformation aiming at emission reduction of 50–80% in 2050 versus their baseline, the incremental investment need over the modelling period is estimated at 0.4–3.3% of the country annual GDP of the scenario first year (Markewitz et al. 2015; Bashmakov 2017; Novikova et al. 2018c; Kotzur et al. 2020). These estimates represent strictly the incremental share of capital expenditure and sometimes installation costs. Therefore, these figures are not comparable with investment tracked against the regional or national sustainable finance taxonomies, as recently developed in the EU (European Parliament and the Council 2020), Russia (Government of Russian Federation 2021), South Africa (National Treasury of Republic of South Africa 2021), and others, or the growing literature on calculating the recent finance flows (Novikova et al. 2019; Valentova et al. 2019; Kamenders et al. 2019; Macquarie et al. 2020; Hainaut et al. 2021), because they are measured against other methodologies, which are not comparable with the methodologies used to derive the incremental costs by integrated assessment models and bottom-up studies. Therefore, the gap between the investment need and recent investment flows is likely to be higher, than often reported.

9.6.4 Determinants of the Potentials and Costs

The fact that the largest share of the global flow area is still to be built offers a large potential for emission reduction that is, however, only feasible if ambitious building energy codes will be applied to this new stock (see Section 9.9.3 on building codes). The highest demand for additional floor area will occur in developing countries; the building replacement is also the highest in developing countries because their building lifetime could be as short as 30 years (Lixuan et al. 2016; Alaidroos and Krarti 2015). Whereas as of 2018, 73 countries had already had building codes or were developing them, only 41 had mandatory residential codes and 51 had mandatory non-residential codes (Global Alliance for Buildings and Construction et al. 2019). Therefore, the feasibility of capturing this potential is a subject to greater coverage, adoption, and strength of building codes.

Low rates of building retrofits are the major feasibility constraint of building decarbonisation in Developed Countries. Long building lifetime and their slow replacement caused a lock-in of low energy performance in old buildings of Developed Countries, especially in urban areas. A few studies of developing countries, mostly medium and high-income, also considered building retrofits (Prada-Hernández et al. 2015; Yu et al. 2018b; Zhou et al. 2018; Krarti 2019; Kamal et al. 2019). The studies in Developed Countries tend to rely on either of the

strategies: very 'deep' envelope retrofits followed by the exchange of HVAC with various advanced alternatives (Csoknyai et al. 2016; Novikova et al. 2018c,b; Duscha et al. 2019; Filippi Oberegger et al. 2020) or more shallow retrofits followed by switching to low-carbon district heating or by the exchange of current HVAC with heat pumps linked to onsite renewables backed up energy storages (Yeh et al. 2016; Kotzur et al. 2020; Hirvonen et al. 2020). The factors, which impact the feasibility of these strategies, therefore, are the building retrofit rates and replacement rates of building systems. To achieve the building stock decarbonisation by 2050, most studies reviewed in Figure 9.16 assume 'deep' retrofit rates between 2.5% and 5%, and even 10% per annum. Esser et al. (2019) reported that the annual renovation rate in EU-28 is around 0.2%, with relatively small variation across individual EU member states. Sandberg et al. (2016) simulated retrofit rates in eleven European countries and concluded that only minor future increases in the renovation rates of 0.6–1.6% could be expected. Therefore, without strong policies supporting these renovations, the feasibility to achieve such high 'deep' retrofit rates is low.

Among key factors affecting the costs-effectiveness of achieving high-performance buildings remain low energy prices in many countries worldwide (Alaidroos and Krarti 2015; Akander et al. 2017) and high discount rates reflecting low access to capital and high barriers. Copiello et al. (2017) found that the discount rate affects the economic results of retrofits four times higher than the energy price, and therefore the reduction in upfront costs and working out barriers are the feasibility enablers.

The good news is that literature expects a significant cost reduction for many technologies, which are relevant for the construction of high energy-performance buildings and deep retrofits. Applying a technology learning curve to the data available for Europe and reviewing dozens of studies available, Köhler et al. (2018) estimated the cost reduction potential of biomass boilers, heat pumps, ventilation, air conditioning, thermal storages, electricity storages, solar PVs and solar thermal systems of 14%, 20%, 46–52%, 29%, 29%, 65%, 57%, and 43% respectively in 2050; no significant cost reduction potential was found, however, for established and wide-spread insulation technologies. More investment into Research, Development and Demonstration (RD&D) to reduce the technology costs and more financial incentives to encourage uptake of the technologies would allow moving along this learning curve.

Furthermore, some literature argues that the key to cost-effectiveness is not necessarily a reduction in costs of technologies, but a know-how and skills of their choosing, combining, sequencing, and timing to take the most benefits of their interdependence, complementarity, and synergy as illustrated by many examples (Lovins 2018; Ürge-Vorsatz et al. 2020). However, the scenarios reviewed lack such approaches in their cost assessments. Few indicative examples of cost reduction at scale were provided though not by the scenario literature, but case studies of the application of One-Stop Shop (OSS) approach at scale (Section 9.9.4). In 2013, the Dutch Energiesprong network brokered a deal between Dutch building contractors and housing associations to reduce the average retrofit costs from EUR130,000 down to EUR65,000 for 111,000 homes with building prefabrication systems and project delivery models while targeting energy savings of 45–80% (Ürge-Vorsatz et al. 2020); out of which 10,000 retrofits have been realised by 2020. The French Observatory of Low Energy Buildings reported to achieve the cost-effective deep renovations of 818 dwellings and 27 detached houses in France setting a cap for absolute primary energy consumption to achieve after renovation and a cap for the budget to deliver it. The cost-effectiveness was, however, calculated with grants and public subsidies (Saheb 2018).

The literature emphasises the critical role of the time between in 2020 and 2030 for the building sector decarbonisation (IEA 2020a; Roscini et al. 2020). To set the sector at the pathway to realise its whole mitigation potential, it is critical to exponentially accelerate the learning of this know-how and skills to reduce the costs and remove feasibility constraints to enable the penetration of advanced technologies at speed that the world has not seen before. The World Energy Outlook (IEA 2020c) shown in the Net Zero Emissions by 2050 Scenario (Box 9.2) the challenges and commitments the sector will have to address by 2030. These include bringing new buildings and existing buildings to near zero, with a half of existing buildings in Developed Countries and a third of existing buildings in developing countries being retrofitted by 2030. These also mean banning the sale of new fossil fuel-fired boilers, as well as making heat pumps and very efficient appliances standard technologies. The Net Zero Emissions by 2050 Scenario achieves almost fully to decarbonise the sector by 2050, with such commitments reflected neither in the planning and modelling efforts (Section 9.9) nor in policies and commitments (Section 9.9) of most world countries, with the countries of South-East Asia and Pacific, Southern Asia, Africa, and Latin America and Caribbean having the least research.

As discussed in Section 9.6.1, the alternative and low-cost opportunity to reduce the sector emissions in the countries with high floor area per capita and the low stock turnover is offered by the introduction of the sufficiency approach. Section 9.9.3.1 discusses a range of policy instruments, which could support the realisation of the sufficiency potential. As the approach is new, the literature does not yet report experiences of these measures. In the framework of project OptiWohn, the German cities of Göttingen, Köln und Tübingen just started testing the sufficiency approach and policy measures for sufficiency (Stadt Göttingen 2020). Therefore, the feasibility of realising the sufficiency potential depends on its recognition by the energy and climate policy and the introduction of supporting measures (Samadi et al. 2017; Ellsworth-Krebs 2020; Goldstein et al. 2020). More research is needed to understand which measures will work and which will not.

Similar to buildings, the energy consumption and associated emissions of appliances and equipment is driven by the replacement of old appliances and the additional stock due to the increase in penetration and saturation of appliances. The feasibility of appliance stock replacement with efficient options is higher than the feasibility of building stock replacement or retrofit due to their smaller size, shorter lifetime, and cheaper costs (Chu and Bowman 2006; Spiliotopoulos 2019). Some literature argues that once appliances achieve a particular level of efficiency their exchange does not bring benefits from the resource efficiency point of view

(Hertwich et al. 2019). Even through the data records a permanent energy efficiency improvement of individual devices (Figure 9.12), their growing offsets energy savings delivered by this improvement. The emerging literature suggests addressing the growing number of energy services and devices as a part of climate and energy policy (Bierwirth and Thomas 2019b). Section 9.5.2.2 describes measures for limiting demand for these services and Section 9.5.3.6 addresses reducing the number of technologies through their ownership and use patterns. (Grubler et al. 2018) also suggested redefining energy services and aggregating appliances, illustrating the reduction of energy demand by a factor of 30 to substitute over 15 different end-use devices with one integrated digital platform. More research is needed to understand opportunities to realise this sufficiency potential for appliances, and more research is needed to understand policies which may support these opportunities (Bierwirth and Thomas 2019a).

The difference between baselines is among the main reason for difference between the potential estimates in 2030 reported by Chapter 6 on buildings of AR4 (Levine et al. 2017) and the current section of AR6. For Developed Countries, the sector direct and indirect baseline emissions in AR6 are 43% and 28% lower than those in AR4 respectively. For developing countries, the sector direct baseline emissions in AR6 are 47% lower than those in AR4, and the sector indirect baseline emissions are 3% higher than those in AR4. As AR6 is closer to 2030 than AR4 and thus more precise, the likely reason for the difference (besides the fact that some potential was realised) is that AR4 overall overestimated the future baseline emissions, and it underestimated how quickly the fuel switch to electricity from other energy carriers has been happening, especially in developing countries. As illustrated, the baseline is one of determinant of the potential size and hence, all reported estimates shall only be interpreted together with the baseline developments.

The potential is a dynamic value, increasing with the technological progress. Most potential studies reviewed in Section 9.6.1 consider today mature commercialised or near to commercialisation technologies with demonstrated characteristics 'freezing them' in the potential estimates until the study target year. Until 2050, many of these technologies will further improve, and furthermore new advanced technologies may emerge. Therefore, the potential estimates are likely to be low estimates of the real potential volumes. Furthermore, models apply many other assumptions and they cannot always capture right emerging societal or innovation trends; these trends may also significantly impact the potential size into both directions (Brugger et al. 2021).

With the declining amount of emissions during the building operation stage, the share of building embodied emissions in their lifetime emissions will grow, also due to additional building material (Peñaloza et al. 2018; Cabeza et al. 2021). Reviewing 650 lifecycle assessment case studies, Röck et al. (2020) estimated the contribution of embodied emissions to building lifetime emissions up to 45–50% for highly efficient buildings, surpassing 90% in extreme cases.

Recently, a significant body of research has been dedicated to studying the impacts of using bio-based solutions (especially timber)

for building construction instead of conventional materials, such as concrete and steel, because more carbon is stored in bio-based construction materials than released during their manufacturing. Assuming the aggressive use of timber in mid-rise urban buildings, Churkina et al. (2020) estimated the associated mitigation potential between 0.04–3.7 $GtCO_2$ per year depending on how fast countries adopt new building practices and floor area per capita. Based on a simplified timber supply-demand model for timber-based new floor area globally by 2050, Pomponi et al. (2020) showed that the global supply of timber can only be 36% of the global demand for it between 2020 and 2050; especially much more forest areas will be required in Asian countries, such as China and India and American countries, such as the USA, Mexico, and Argentina. Goswein et al. (2021) conducted a similar detailed analysis for Europe and concluded that current European forest areas and wheat plantations are sufficient to provide timber and straw for the domestic construction sector.

The increased use of timber and other bio-based materials in buildings brings not only benefits, but also risks. The increased use of timber can accelerate degradation through poor management and the pressure for deforestation, as already recorded in the Amazon and Siberia forests, and the competition for land and resources (Carrasco et al. 2017; Brancalion et al. 2018; Hart and Pomponi 2020; Pomponi et al. 2020). Churkina et al. (2020) emphasised that promoting the use of more timber in buildings requires the parallel strengthening of legislation for sustainable forest management, forest certification instruments, and care for the people and social organisations that live in forests. In tropical and subtropical countries, the use of bamboo and other fibres brings more benefits and less risks than the use of timber (ibid). One of the main barriers associated with the use of bio-based materials in buildings is fire safety, although there is extensive research on this topic (Östman et al. 2017; Audebert et al. 2019). This is a particularly important criterion for the design of medium and high-rise buildings, which tend to be the most adequate typologies for denser and more compact cities. Overall, more robust models are needed to assess the interlinkages between the enhanced use of bio-based materials in the building stock and economic and social implications of their larger supply, as well as the associated competition between forest and land-use activities (for food), and ecological aspects. Furthermore, more research is required on how to change forest and building legislation and design a combination of policy instruments for the specific political, economic and cultural county characteristics (Hildebrandt et al. 2017). Benefits and risks of enhanced use of wood products in buildings are also discussed in Chapter 7, Section 7.4.5.3.

9.7 Links to Adaptation

Buildings are capital-intensive and long-lasting assets designed to perform under a wide range of climate conditions (Hallegatte 2009; Pyke et al. 2012). Their long lifespan means that the building stock will be exposed to future climate (Hallegatte 2009; de Wilde and Coley 2012; Wan et al. 2012) and, as such, adaptation measures will be necessary.

The impacts of climate change on buildings can affect building structures, building construction, building material properties, indoor climate and building energy use (Andrić et al. 2019). Many of those impacts and their respective adaptation strategies interact with GHG mitigation in different ways.

9.7.1 Climate Change Impacts and Adaptation in Buildings

A large body of literature on climate impacts on buildings focuses on the impacts of climate change on heating and cooling needs (de Wilde and Coley 2012; Wan et al. 2012; Andrić et al. 2019). The associated impacts on energy consumption are expected to be higher in hot summer and warm winter climates, where cooling needs are more relevant (Li et al. 2012; Wan et al. 2012; Andrić et al. 2019). If not met, this higher demand for thermal comfort can impact health, sleep quality and work productivity, having disproportionate effects on vulnerable populations and exacerbating energy poverty (Biardeau et al. 2020; Sun et al. 2020; Falchetta and Mistry 2021) (Section 9.8).

Increasing temperatures can lead to higher cooling needs and, therefore, energy consumption (Li et al. 2012; Schaeffer et al. 2012; Wan et al. 2012; Clarke et al. 2018; International Energy Agency 2018; Andrić et al. 2019). Higher temperatures increase the number of days/hours in which cooling is required and as outdoor temperatures increase, the cooling load to maintain the same indoor temperature will be higher (Andrić et al. 2019). These two effects are often measured by cooling degree-days[1] (CDD) and there is a vast literature on studies at the global (Isaac and van Vuuren 2009; Atalla et al. 2018; Clarke et al. 2018; Mistry 2019; Biardeau et al. 2020) and regional level (Zhou et al. 2014; Bezerra et al. 2021; Falchetta and Mistry 2021). Other studies use statistical econometric analyses to capture the empirical relationship between climate variables and energy consumption (Auffhammer and Mansur 2014; van Ruijven et al. 2019). A third effect is that higher summer temperatures can incentivise the purchase of space cooling equipment (Auffhammer 2014; De Cian et al. 2019; Biardeau et al. 2020), especially in developing countries (Pavanello et al. 2021).

The impacts of increased energy demand for cooling can have systemic repercussions (Ciscar and Dowling 2014; Ralston Fonseca et al. 2019), which in turn can affect the provision of other energy services. Space cooling can be an important determinant of peak demand, especially in periods of extreme heat (International Energy Agency 2018). Warmer climates and higher frequency and intensity of heat waves can lead to higher loads (Dirks et al. 2015; Auffhammer et al. 2017), increasing the risk of grid failure and supply interruptions.

Although heating demand in cold climate regions can be expected to decrease with climate change and, to a certain extent, outweigh the increase in cooling demand, the effects on total primary energy requirements are uncertain (Li et al. 2012; Wan et al. 2012). Studies have found that increases in buildings energy expenditures for cooling

---

[1] CDD can be generally defined as the monthly or annual sum of the difference between an indoor set point temperature and outdoor air temperature whenever the latter is higher than a given threshold temperature (Mistry 2019).

more than compensate the savings from lower heating demands in most regions (Clarke et al. 2018). In addition, climate change may affect the economic feasibility of district heating systems (Andrić et al. 2019).

In cold climates, a warming climate can potentially increase the risk of overheating in high-performance buildings with increased insulation and airtightness to reduce heat losses (Gupta and Gregg 2012). In such situations, the need for active cooling technologies may arise, along with higher energy consumption and GHG emissions (Gupta et al. 2015).

Changes in cloud formation can affect global solar irradiation and, therefore, the output of solar photovoltaic panels, possibly affecting on-site renewable energy production (Burnett et al. 2014). The efficiency of solar photovoltaic panels and their electrical components decreases with higher temperatures (Bahaidarah et al. 2013; Simioni and Schaeffer 2019). However, studies have found that such effects can be relatively small (Totschnig et al. 2017), making solar PV a robust option to adapt to climate change (Shen and Lior 2016; Santos and Lucena 2021) (see Section 9.4).

Climate change can also affect the performance, durability and safety of buildings and their elements (facades, structure, etc.) through changes in temperature, humidity, wind, and chloride and CO_2 concentrations (Bastidas-Arteaga et al. 2010; Bauer et al. 2018; Rodríguez-Rosales et al. 2021; Chen et al. 2021). Historical buildings and coastal areas tend to be more vulnerable to these changes (Huijbregts et al. 2012; Mosoarca et al. 2019; Cavalagli et al. 2019; Rodríguez-Rosales et al. 2021).

Temperature variations affect the building envelope, for example, with cracks and detachment of coatings (Bauer et al. 2016, 2018). Higher humidity (caused by wind-driven rain, snow or floods) hastens deterioration of bio-based materials such as wood and bamboo (Brambilla and Gasparri 2020), also deteriorating indoor air quality and users health (Huijbregts et al. 2012; Grynning et al. 2017; Lee et al. 2020).

Climate change can accelerate the degradation of reinforced concrete structures due to the increase of chloride ingress (Bastidas-Arteaga et al. 2010) and the concentration of CO_2, which increase the corrosion of the embedded steel (Stewart et al. 2012; Peng and Stewart 2016; Chen et al. 2021). Corrosion rates are higher in places with higher humidity and humidity fluctuations (Guo et al. 2019), and degradation could be faster with combined effects of higher temperatures and more frequent and intense precipitations (Bastidas-Arteaga et al. 2010; Chen et al. 2021).

Higher frequency and intensity of hurricanes, storm surges and coastal and non-coastal flooding can escalate economic losses to civil infrastructure, especially when associated with population growth and urbanisation in hazardous areas (Bjarnadottir et al. 2011; Li et al. 2016; Lee and Ellingwood 2017). Climate change should increase the risk and exposure to damage from flood (de Ruig et al. 2019), sea level rise (Bosello and De Cian 2014; Zanetti et al. 2016; Bove et al. 2020) and more frequent wildfires (Barkhordarian et al. 2018; Craig et al. 2020).

9.7.2 Links Between Mitigation and Adaptation in Buildings

Adaptation options interacts with mitigation efforts because measures to cope with climate change impacts can increase energy and material consumption, which may lead to higher GHG emissions (Kalvelage et al. 2014; Davide et al. 2019; Sharifi 2020). Energy consumption is required to adapt to climate change. Mitigation measures, in turn, influence the degree of vulnerability of buildings to future climate and, thus, the adaptation required.

Studies have assessed the increases in energy demand to meet indoor thermal comfort under future climate (de Wilde and Coley 2012; Li et al. 2012; Clarke et al. 2018; Andrić et al. 2019). Higher cooling needs may induce increases in energy demand (Wan et al. 2012; Li et al. 2012), which could lead to higher emissions, when electricity is fossil-based (International Energy Agency 2018; Biardeau et al. 2020), and generate higher loads and stress on power systems (Dirks et al. 2015; Auffhammer et al. 2017). In this regard, increasing energy efficiency of space cooling appliances and adopting dynamic cooling setpoint temperatures, can reduce the energy needs for cooling and limit additional emissions and pressures on power systems (Davide et al. 2019; Bienvenido-Huertas et al. 2020; Bezerra et al. 2021) (Section 9.4, Figure 9.11 and Supplementary Material Tables 9.SM.1 to 9.SM.3). This can also be achieved with on-site renewable energy production, especially solar PV for which there can be a timely correlation between power supply and cooling demand, improving load matching (Salom et al. 2014; Grove-Smith et al. 2018).

Mitigation alternatives through passive approaches may increase resilience to climate change impacts on thermal comfort and reduce active cooling needs (Wan et al. 2012; van Hooff et al. 2016; Andrić et al. 2019; González Mahecha et al. 2020; Rosse Caldas et al. 2020). Combining passive measures can help counteracting climate change driven increases in energy consumption for achieving thermal comfort (Huang and Hwang 2016).

Studies raise the concern that measures aimed at building envelope may increase the risk of overheating in a warming climate (Dodoo and Gustavsson 2016; Fosas et al. 2018) (Section 9.4). If this is the case, there may be a conflict between mitigation through energy efficiency building regulations and climate change adaptation (Fosas et al. 2018). However, while overheating may occur as a result of poor insulation design, better insulation may actually reduce overheating when properly projected and the overheating risk can be overcome by clever designs (Fosas et al. 2018).

Strengthening building structures to increase resilience and reduce exposure to the risk of extreme events, such as draughts, torrential floods, hurricanes and storms, can be partially achieved by improving building standards and retrofitting existing buildings (Bjarnadottir et al. 2011). However, future climate is not yet considered in parameters of existing building energy codes (Steenbergen et al. 2012). While enhancing structural resilience would lead to GHG emissions (Liu and Cui 2018), so would disaster recovery and rebuilding. This adaptation-mitigation trade-off needs to be further assessed.

Since adaptation of the existing building stock may be more expensive and require building retrofit, climate change must be considered in the design of new buildings to ensure performance robustness in both current and future climates, which can have implications for construction costs (Hallegatte 2009; Pyke et al. 2012; de Wilde and Coley 2012; de Rubeis et al. 2020; Picard et al. 2020) and emissions (Liu and Cui 2018). Building energy codes and regulations are usually based on cost-effectiveness and historical climate data, which can lead to the poor design of thermal comfort in future climate (Hallegatte 2009; Pyke et al. 2012; de Wilde and Coley 2012) and non-efficient active adaptive measures based on mechanical air conditioning (De Cian et al. 2019) (Section 9.4, Figure 9.11 and Supplementary Material Tables 9.SM.1 to 9.SM.3). However, uncertainty about future climate change creates difficulties for projecting parameters for the design of new buildings (Hallegatte 2009; de Wilde and Coley 2012). This can be especially relevant for social housing programs (Rubio-Bellido et al. 2017; Triana et al. 2018; González Mahecha et al. 2020) in developing countries.

The impacts on buildings can lead to higher maintenance needs and the consequent embodied environmental impacts related to materials production, transportation and end-of-life, which account for a relevant share of GHG emissions in buildings lifecycle (Rasmussen et al. 2018). Climate change induced biodegradation is especially important for bio-based materials such as wood and bamboo (Brambilla and Gasparri 2020) which are important options for reducing emissions imbued in buildings' construction materials (Peñaloza et al. 2016; Churkina et al. 2020; Rosse Caldas et al. 2020).

Although there can potentially be conflicts between climate change mitigation and adaptation, these can be dealt with proper planning, actions, and policies. The challenge is to develop multifunctional solutions, technologies and materials that can mitigate GHG emissions while improving buildings adaptive capacity. Solutions and technologies should reduce not only buildings' operational emissions, but also embodied emissions from manufacturing and processing of building materials (Röck et al. 2020). For instance, some building materials, such as bio-concrete, can reduce lifecycle emissions of buildings and bring benefits in terms of building thermal comfort in tropical and subtropical climates. Also, energy efficiency, sufficiency and on-site renewable energy production can help to increase building resilience to climate change impacts and reduce pressure on the energy system.

9.8   Links to Sustainable Development

9.8.1   Overview of Contribution of Mitigation Options to Sustainable Development

A growing body of research acknowledges that mitigation actions in buildings may have substantial social and economic value beyond their direct impact of reducing energy consumption and/or GHG emissions (IEA 2014; Ürge-Vorsatz et al. 2016; Deng et al. 2017; Reuter et al. 2017; US EPA 2018; Kamal et al. 2019; Bleyl et al. 2019) (see also Cross-Chapter Box 6 in Chapter 7). In other words, the implementation of these actions in the residential and non-residential sector holds numerous multiple impacts (co-benefits, adverse side-effects, trade-offs, risks, etc.) for the economy, society and end-users, in both developed and developing economies, which can be categorised into the following types (IEA 2014; Ürge-Vorsatz et al. 2016; Ferreira et al. 2017; Thema et al. 2017; Reuter et al. 2017; US EPA 2018; Nikas et al. 2020): (i) health impacts due to better indoor conditions, energy/fuel poverty alleviation, better ambient air quality and reduction of the heat island effect; (ii) environmental benefits such as reduced local air pollution and the associated impact on ecosystems (acidification, eutrophication, etc.) and infrastructures, reduced sewage production, and so on; (iii) improved resource management including water and energy; (iv) impact on social well-being, including changes in disposable income due to decreased energy expenditures and/or distributional costs of new policies, fuel poverty alleviation and improved access to energy sources, rebound effects, increased productive time for women and children, and so on; (v) microeconomic effects (e.g., productivity gains in non-residential buildings, enhanced asset values of green buildings, fostering innovation); (vi) macroeconomic effects, including impact on GDP driven by energy savings and energy availability, creation of new jobs, decreased employment in the fossil energy sector, long-term reductions in energy prices and possible increases in electricity prices in the medium run, possible impacts on public budgets, and so on; and (vii) energy security implications (e.g., access to modern energy resources, reduced import dependency, increase of supplier diversity, smaller reserve requirements, increased sovereignty and resilience).

Well-designed and effectively implemented mitigation actions in the sector of buildings have significant potential for achieving the United Nations (UN) Sustainable Development Goals (SDGs). Specifically, the multiple impacts of mitigation policies and measures go far beyond the goal of climate action (SDG 13) and contribute to further activating a great variety of other SDGs (Figure 9.18 presents some indicative examples). Table 9.5 reviews and updates the analysis carried out in the context of the IPCC Special Report on Global Warming of 1.5°C (SR1.5) (Roy et al. 2018) demonstrating that the main categories of GHG emission reduction interventions in buildings, namely the implementation of energy sufficiency and efficiency improvements as well as improved access and fuel switch to modern low carbon energy, contribute to achieving 16 out of a total of 17 SDGs.

A review of a relatively limited number of studies made by Ürge-Vorsatz et al. (2016) and Payne et al. (2015) showed that the size of multiple benefits of mitigation actions in the sector of buildings may range from 22% up to 7400% of the corresponding energy cost savings. In 7 out of 11 case studies reviewed, the value of the multiple impacts of mitigation actions was equal or greater than the value of energy savings. Even in these studies, several effects have not been measured and consequently the size of multiple benefits of mitigation actions may be even higher. Quantifying and if possible, monetising, these wider impacts of climate action would facilitate their inclusion in cost-benefit analysis, strengthen the adoption of ambitious emissions reduction targets, and improve coordination across policy areas reducing costs (Smith et al. 2016; Thema et al. 2017).

2 hours per day saved for women and girls from collecting fuel in Africa

Up to 90% GHG emissions reduction in developed countries

Up to 80% of GHG emissions reduction in developing countries

24,500 avoided premature deaths and **22,300** disability-adjusted life years (DALYs) of avoided asthma in the EU

1.8 million fewer avoided premature deaths from HAP in developing world in 2030

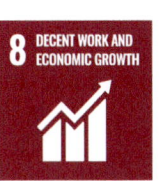

Up to 28% higher selling prices for decarbonised building in developed countries

90% of our time is spent indoors

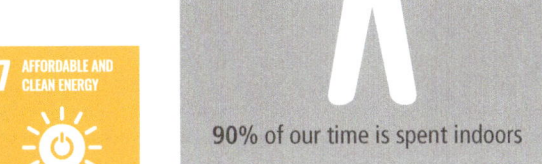

Up to **2.8 billion** people in developing countries lifted from energy poverty

5 to 8 million households in Europe lifted from energy poverty

Up to 30 direct and indirect jobs per million USD invested in building retrofit or new energy efficient buildings

2 million direct jobs from transforming fuel-based lighting to solar LED lighting in developing countries

Key point: Achieving SDG targets requires implementation of ambitious climate mitigation policies which include sufficiency measures to align building design, size and use with SDGs, efficiency measures to ensure high penetration of best available technologies and supplying the remaining energy needs with renewable energy sources.

Figure 9.18 | Contribution of mitigation policies of the building sector to meeting sustainable development goals. Source: based on information from IEA(2019d); IEA (2020b); Mills (2016); European Commission (2016); Rafaj et al. (2018); Mzavanadze (2018a); World Health Organization (2016); and literature review presented in Section 9.8.5.2.

Table 9.5 | Aspects of mitigation actions in buildings and their contributions to the 2030 Sustainable Development Goals. S: enhancement of energy sufficiency; E: energy efficiency improvements; R: improved access and fuel switch to lower carbon and renewable energy.

Level of impact	SDG 1			SDG 2			SDG 3			SDG 4			SDG 5			SDG 6			SDG 7			SDG 8			SDG 9			SDG 10			SDG 11			SDG 12			SDG 13			SDG 14			SDG 15			SDG 16			SDG 17		
	S	E	R	S	E	R	S	E	R	S	E	R	S	E	R	S	E	R	S	E	R	S	E	R	S	E	R	S	E	R	S	E	R	S	E	R	S	E	R	S	E	R	S	E	R	S	E	R	S	E	R
+3																																																				
+2																																																				
+1																																																				
−1																																																				
−2																																																				
−3																																																				
Dimensions of mitigation actions that impact SDGs																																																				
Health impact	●						●			●																																									
Environmental impact		●														●						●												●												●					
Resource efficienvy	●			●												●			●						●						●			●																	
Impact on social well-being	●			●			●						●						●			●			●						●			●									●			●					
Microeconomic effects																●						●			●						●			●																	
Macroeconomic effects																			●						●			●																							
Energy security																			●						●																										

Notes: The strength of interaction between mitigation actions and SDGs is described with a seven-point scale (Nilsson et al., 2016). Also, the blue bullet shows the interactions between co-benefits/risk associated with mitigation actions and the SDGs. **SDG 1:** Sufficiency and efficiency measures result in reduced energy expenditures and other financial savings that further lead to poverty reduction. Access to modern energy forms will largely help alleviate poverty in developing countries as the productive time of women and children will increase, new activities can be developed, and so on. The distributional costs of some mitigation policies promoting energy efficiency and lower carbon energy may reduce the disposable income of the poor. **SDG 2:** Energy sufficiency and efficiency measures result in lower energy bills and avoiding the 'heat or eat' dilemma. Improved cook-stoves provide better food security and reduces the danger of fuel shortages in developing countries; under real-world conditions these impacts may be limited as the households use these stoves irregularly and inappropriately. Green roofs can support food production. Improving energy access enhances agricultural productivity and improves food security; on the other hand, increased bioenergy production may restrict the available land for food production. **SDG 3:** All categories of mitigation action result in health benefits through better indoor air quality, energy/fuel poverty alleviation, better ambient air quality, and reduction of the heat island effect. Efficiency measures with inadequate ventilation may lead to the "sick building" syndrome symptoms. **SDG 4:** Energy efficiency measures result in reduced school absenteeism due to better indoor environmental conditions. Also, fuel poverty alleviation increases the available space at home for reading. Improved access to electricity and clean fuels enables people living in poor developing countries to read, while it is also associated with greater school attendance by children. **SDG 5:** Efficient cook-stoves and improved access to electricity and clean fuels in developing countries will result in substantial time savings for women and children, thus increasing the time for rest, communication, education and productive activities. **SDG 6:** Reduced energy demand due to sufficiency and efficiency measures as well as an upscaling of renewable energy sources (RES) can lead to reduced water demand for thermal cooling at energy production facilities. Also, water savings result through improved conditions and lower space of dwellings. Improved access to electricity is necessary to treat water at homes. In some situations, the switch to bioenergy could increase water use compared to existing conditions. **SDG 7:** All categories of mitigation action result in energy/fuel poverty alleviation in both developed and developing countries as well as in improving the security of energy supply. **SDG 8:** Positive and negative direct and indirect macroeconomic effects (GDP, employment, public budgets) associated with lower energy prices due to the reduced energy demand, energy efficiency and RES investments, improved energy access and fostering innovation. Also, energy efficient buildings with adequate ventilation, result in productivity gains and improve the competitiveness of the economy. **SDG 9:** Adoption of distributed generation and smart grids helps in infrastructure improvement and expansion. Also, the development of 'green buildings' can foster innovation. Reduced energy demand due to sufficiency and efficiency measures as well as an upscaling of RES can lead to early retirement of fossil energy infrastructure. **SDG 10:** Efficient cook-stoves as well as improved access to electricity and clean fuels in developing countries will result in substantial time savings for women and children, thus enhancing education and the development of productive activities. Sufficiency and efficiency measures lead to lower energy expenditures, thus reducing income inequalities. The distributional costs of some mitigation policies promoting energy efficiency and lower carbon energy as well as the need for purchasing more expensive equipment and appliances may reduce the disposable income of the poor and increase inequalities. **SDG 11:** Sufficiency and efficiency measures as well as fuel switching to RES and improvements in energy access would eliminate major sources (both direct and indirect) of poor air quality (indoor and outdoor). Helpful if in-situ production of RES combined with charging electric two, three and four wheelers at home. Buildings with high energy efficiency and/or green features are sold/rented at higher prices than conventional, low energy efficient houses. **SDG 12:** Energy sufficiency and efficiency measures as well as deployment of RES result in reduced consumption of natural resources, namely fossil fuels, metal ores, minerals, water, and so on. Negative impacts on natural resources could be arisen from increased penetration of new efficient appliances and equipment. **SDG 13:** See Sections 9.4–9.6. **SDG 15:** Efficient cookstoves and improved access to electricity and clean fuels in developing countries will result in halting deforestation. **SDG 16:** Building retrofits are associated with lower crime. Improved access to electric lighting can improve safety (particularly for women and children). Institutions that are effective, accountable and transparent are needed at all levels of government for providing energy access and promoting modern renewables as well as boosting sufficiency and efficiency. **SDG 17:** The development of zero energy buildings requires among others capacity building, citizen participation as well as monitoring of the achievements.

Sources: Brounen and Kok (2011); Deng et al. (2012); Zheng et al. (2012); Högberg (2013); Hyland et al. (2013); Kahn and Kok (2014); Koirala et al. (2014); Maidment et al. (2014); Mirasgedis et al. (2014); Scott et al. (2014); Bailis et al. (2015); Boermans et al. (2015); Fuerst et al. (2015, 2016); Galán-Marín et al. (2015); Hasegawa et al. (2015); Hejazi et al. (2015); Holland et al. (2015); Liddell and Guiney (2015); Liu et al. (2015a); Mattioli and Moulinos (2015); Payne et al. (2015); Torero (2015); Willand et al. (2015a); Winter et al. (2015); Baimel et al. (2016); Camarinha-Matos (2016); Cameron et al. (2016); De Ayala et al. (2016); European Commission (2016); Fricko et al. (2016); Hanna et al. (2016); Jensen et al. (2016); Levy et al. (2016); Markovska et al. (2016); Rao et al. (2016); Smith et al. (2016); Sola et al. (2016); Song et al. (2016); Ürge-Vorsatz et al. (2016); Balaban and Puppim de Oliveira (2017); Berrueta et al. (2017); Burney et al. (2017); Mehetre et al. (2017); Mofidi and Akbari (2017); Niemelä et al. (2017); Ortiz et al. (2017); Rao and Pachauri (2017); Thema et al. (2017); Thomson et al. (2017a); Zhao et al. (2017); Barnes and Samad (2018); Cedeño-Laurent et al. (2018); Goldemberg et al. (2018); Grubler et al. (2018); Jeuland et al. (2018); MacNaughton et al. (2018); McCollum et al. (2018); Mzvanadze (2018a); Rosenthal et al. (2018); Saheb et al. (2018b,a); Steenland et al. (2018); Tajani et al. (2018); Venugopal et al. (2018); Walters and Midden (2018); Wierzbicka et al. (2018); Alawneh et al. (2019); Batchelor et al. (2019); Bleyl et al. (2019); Cajias et al. (2019); Marmolejo-Duarte and Chen (2019); Mastrucci et al. (2019); ESMAP et al. (2020); Teubler et al. (2020); Van de Ven et al. (2020); Nikas et al. (2020); Blair et al. (2021).

9.8.2   Climate Mitigation Actions in Buildings and Health Impacts

9.8.2.1   Lack of Access to Clean Energy

In 2018, approximately 2.8 billion people worldwide, most of whom live in Asia and Africa, still use polluting fuels, such as fuelwood, charcoal, dried crops, cow dung, and so on, in low-efficiency stoves for cooking and heating, generating household air pollution (HAP), which adversely affects the health of the occupants of the dwellings, especially children and women (World Health Organization 2016; Rahut et al. 2017; Mehetre et al. 2017; Das et al. 2018; Liu et al. 2018; Quinn et al. 2018; Rosenthal et al. 2018; Xin et al. 2018; IEA 2020a). Exposure to HAP from burning these fuels is estimated to have caused 3.8 million deaths from heart diseases, strokes, cancers, acute lower respiratory infections in 2016 (World Health Organization 2018). It is acknowledged that integrated policies are needed to address simultaneously universal energy access, limiting climate change and reducing air pollution (World Health Organization 2016). Rafaj et al. (2018) showed that a scenario achieving these SDGs in 2030 will imply in 2040 two million fewer premature deaths from HAP

compared to current levels, and 1.5 million fewer premature deaths in relation to a reference scenario, which assumes the continuation of existing and planned policies. The level of incremental investment needed in developing countries to achieve universal access to modern energy was estimated at around USD0.8 trillion cumulatively to 2040 in the scenarios examined (Rafaj et al. 2018).

At the core of these policies is the promotion of improved cook-stoves and other modern energy-efficient appliances to cook (for the health benefits of improved cook-stoves see for example (García-Frapolli et al. 2010; Malla et al. 2011; Aunan et al. 2013; Jeuland et al. 2018), as well as the use of non-solid fuels by poor households in developing countries (Figure 9.19). Most studies agree that the use of non-solid energy options such as LPG, ethanol, biogas, piped natural gas, and electricity is more effective in reducing the health impacts of HAP compared to improved biomass stoves (see for example Larsen 2016; Rosenthal et al. 2018; Steenland et al. 2018; Goldemberg et al. 2018). On the other hand, climate change mitigation policies (e.g., carbon pricing) may increase the costs of some of these clean fuels (e.g., LPG, electricity), slowing down their penetration in the poor segment of the population and restricting the associated health

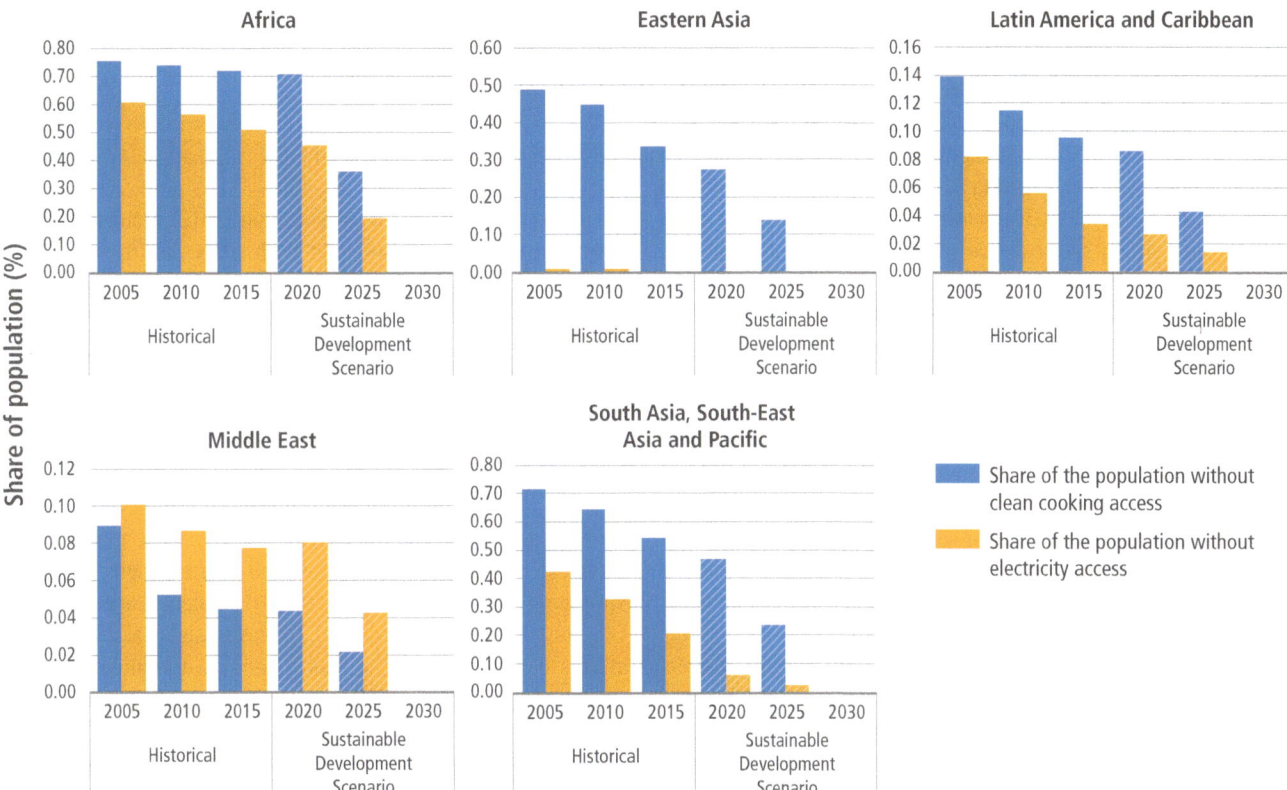

Figure 9.19 | Trends on energy access: historical based on IEA statistics data and scenarios based on IEA WEO data.

benefits (Cameron et al. 2016). In this case, appropriate access policies should be designed to efficiently shield poor households from the burden of carbon taxation (Cameron et al. 2016). The evaluation of the improved biomass burning cook-stoves under real-world conditions has shown that they have lower than expected, and in many cases limited, long-run health and environmental impacts, as the households use these stoves irregularly and inappropriately, fail to maintain them, and their usage decline over time (Patange et al. 2015; Aung et al. 2016; Hanna et al. 2016; Wathore et al. 2017). In this context, the various improved cook-stoves programs should consider the mid- and long-term needs of maintenance, repair, or replacement to support their sustained use (Shankar et al. 2014; Schilmann et al. 2019).

Electrification of households in rural or remote areas results also to significant health benefits. For example, in El Salvador, rural electrification of households leads to reduced overnight air pollutants concentration by 63% due to the substitution of kerosene as a lighting source, and 34–44% less acute respiratory infections among children under six (Torero 2015). In addition, the connection of the health centres to the grid leads to improvements in the quality of health care provided (Lenz et al. 2017).

9.8.2.2 Energy/fuel Poverty, Indoor Environmental Quality and Health

Living in fuel poverty, and particularly in cold and damp housing is related to excess winter mortality and increased morbidity rates due to respiratory and cardiovascular diseases, arthritic and rheumatic

illnesses, asthma, and so on (Lacroix and Chaton 2015; Payne et al. 2015; Camprubí et al. 2016; Wilson et al. 2016; Ormandy and Ezratty 2016; Thema et al. 2017). In addition, lack of affordable warmth can generate stress related to chronic discomfort and high bills, fear of falling into debt, and a sense of lacking control, which are potential drivers of further negative mental health outcomes, such as depression (Howden-Chapman et al. 2012; Liddell and Guiney 2015; Payne et al. 2015; Wilson et al. 2016). Health risks from exposure to cold and inadequate indoor environmental quality may be higher for low-income, energy-poor households, and in particular for those with elderly relatives, young children, and members with existing respiratory illness (Payne et al. 2015; Thomson et al. 2017b; Nunes 2019). High temperatures during summer can also be dangerous for people living in buildings with inadequate thermal insulation and inappropriate ventilation (Ormandy and Ezratty 2016; Sanchez-Guevara et al. 2019; Thomson et al. 2019). Summer fuel poverty (or summer overheating risk) may increase significantly in the coming decades under a warming climate (Section 9.7), with the poorest, who cannot afford to install air conditioning, and the elderly (Nunes 2020) being the most vulnerable.

Improved energy efficiency in buildings contributes in fuel poverty alleviation and brings health gains through improved indoor temperatures and comfort as well as reduced fuel consumption and associated financial stress (Curl et al. 2015; Lacroix and Chaton 2015; Liddell and Guiney 2015; Thomson and Thomas 2015; Willand et al. 2015; Poortinga et al. 2018). On the other hand, households suffering most from fuel poverty experience more barriers for undertaking building retrofits (Braubach and Ferrand 2013; Camprubí et al. 2016;

Charlier et al. 2018), moderating the potential health gains associated with implemented energy efficiency programs. This can be avoided if implemented policies to tackle fuel poverty target the most socially vulnerable households (Lacroix and Chaton 2015; Camprubí et al. 2016). Mzavanadze (2018a) estimated that in EU-28 accelerated energy efficiency policies, reducing the energy demand in residential sector by 333 TWh in 2030 compared to a reference scenario, coupled with strong social policies targeting the most vulnerable households, could deliver additional co-benefits in the year of 2030 of around 24,500 avoided premature deaths due to indoor cold and around 22,300 disability adjusted life years (DALYs) of avoided asthma due to indoor dampness. The health benefits of these policies amount to EUR4.8 billion in 2030. The impacts on inhabitants in developing countries would be much greater than those in EU-28 owing to the much higher prevalence of impoverished household.

Apart from thermal comfort, the internal environment of buildings impacts public health through a variety of pathways including inadequate ventilation, poor indoor air quality, chemical contaminants from indoor or outdoor sources, outdoor noise, or poor lighting. The implementation of interventions aiming to improve thermal insulation of buildings combined with inadequate ventilation may increase the risk of mould and moisture problems due to reduced air flow rates, leading to indoor environments that are unhealthy, with the occupants suffering from the sick building syndrome symptoms (Willand et al. 2015; Cedeño-Laurent et al. 2018; Wierzbicka et al. 2018). On the other hand, if the implementation of energy efficiency interventions or the construction of green buildings is accompanied by adequate ventilation, the indoor environmental conditions are improved through less moisture, mould, pollutant concentrations, and allergens, which result in fewer asthma symptoms, respiratory risks, chronic obstructive pulmonary diseases, heart disease risks, headaches, cancer risks, and so on (Allen et al. 2015; Hamilton et al. 2015; Thomson and Thomas 2015; Cowell 2016; Doll et al. 2016; Wilson et al. 2016; Militello-Hourigan and Miller 2018; Underhill et al. 2018; Cedeño-Laurent et al. 2018). Fisk (2018) showed that increased ventilation rates in residential buildings results in health benefits ranging from 20% to several-fold improvements; however, these benefits do not occur consistently, and ventilation should be combined with other exposure control measures. As adequate ventilation imposes additional costs, the sick building syndrome symptoms are more likely to be seen in low income households (Shrubsole et al. 2016).

The health benefits of residents due to mitigation actions in buildings are significant (for a review see Maidment et al. 2014; Thomson and Thomas 2015; Fisk et al. 2020), and are higher among low income households and/or vulnerable groups, including children, the elderly and those with pre-existing illnesses (Maidment et al. 2014; IEA 2014; Ortiz et al. 2019). Tonn et al. (2018) estimated that the health-related benefits attributed to the two weatherisation programs implemented in the US in 2008 and 2010 exceeds by a factor of 3 the corresponding energy cost savings yield. IEA (2014) also found that the health benefits attributed to energy efficiency retrofit programs may outweigh their costs by up to a factor of 3. Ortiz et al. (2019) estimated that the energy retrofit of vulnerable households in Spain requires an investment of around EUR10.9–12.3 thousands

per dwelling and would generate an average saving to the healthcare system of EUR372 per year and dwelling (due to better thermal comfort conditions in winter).

9.8.2.3   Outdoor Air Pollution

According to World Health Organization (2018) around 4.2 million premature deaths worldwide (in both cities and rural areas) are attributed to outdoor air pollution. According to the results of the quantitative model (Gu et al. 2018), the premature mortalities attributed to $PM_{2.5}$ and O_3 emissions may reach 168000–1796000 (95% CI) in 2010. Mitigation actions in residential and non-residential sectors decrease the amount of fossil fuels burnt either directly in buildings (for heating, cooking, etc.) or indirectly for electricity generation and thereby reduce air pollution (e.g., PM, O_3, SO_2, NO_x), improve ambient air quality and generate significant health benefits through avoiding premature deaths, lung cancers, ischemic heart diseases, hospital admissions, asthma exacerbations, respiratory symptoms, and so on (Levy et al. 2016; Balaban and Puppim de Oliveira 2017; MacNaughton et al. 2018; Karlsson et al. 2020). Several studies have monetised the health benefits attributed to reduced outdoor air pollution due to the implementation of mitigation actions in buildings, and their magnitude expressed as a ratio to the value of energy savings resulting from the implemented interventions in each case, are in the range of 0.08 in EU, 0.18 in Germany, 0.26–0.40 in US, 0.34 in Brazil, 0.47 in Mexico, 0.74 in Turkey, 8.28 in China and 11.67 in India (Joyce et al. 2013; Levy et al. 2016; Diaz-Mendez et al. 2018; MacNaughton et al. 2018). In developed economies, the estimated co-benefits are relatively low due to the fact that the planned interventions influence a quite clean energy source mix (Tuomisto et al. 2015; MacNaughton et al. 2018). On the other hand, the health co-benefits in question are substantially higher in countries and regions with greater dependency on coal for electricity generation and higher baseline morbidity and mortality rates (Kheirbek et al. 2014; MacNaughton et al. 2018).

9.8.3   Other Environmental Benefits of Mitigation Actions

Apart from the health benefits mentioned above, mitigation actions in the buildings sector are also associated with environmental benefits to ecosystems and crops, by avoiding acidification and eutrophication, biodiversity through green roofs and walls, building environment through reduced corrosion of materials, and so on (Thema et al. 2017; Mzavanadze 2018b; Knapp et al. 2019; Mayrand and Clergeau 2018), while some negative effects cannot be excluded (Dylewski and Adamczyk 2016).

Also, very important are the effects of mitigation actions in buildings on the reduction of consumption of natural resources, namely fossil fuels, metal ores, minerals, and so on. These comprise savings from the resulting reduced consumption of fuels, electricity and heat and the lifecycle-wide resource demand for their utilities, as well as potential net savings from the substitution of energy technologies used in buildings – production phase extraction (European Commission 2016; Thema et al. 2017). Teubler et al. (2020) found that the implementation of an energy efficiency scenario in European buildings will result in resource savings (considering only those associated with the generation of final energy products) of 406 kg per MWh lower final energy demand in the residential sector, while the corresponding figure for non-residential buildings was estimated at 706 kg per MWh of reduced energy demand. On the other hand, Smith et al. (2016) claim that a switch to more efficient appliances could result in negative impacts from increased resource use, which can be mitigated by avoiding premature replacement and maximising recycling of old appliances.

Mitigation actions aiming to reduce the embodied energy of buildings through using local and sustainable building materials can be used to leverage new supply chains (e.g., for forestry products), which in turn bring further environmental and social benefits to local communities (Hashemi et al. 2015; Cheong and Storey 2019). Furthermore, improved insulation and the installation of double- or triple-glazed windows result in reduced noise levels. It is worth mentioning that for every 1 dB decrease in excess noise, academic performance in schools and productivity of employees in office buildings increases by 0.7% and 0.3% respectively (Kockat et al. 2018b). Smith et al. (2016) estimated that in the UK the annual noise benefits associated with energy renovations in residential buildings may reach £400 million in 2030 outweighing the benefits of reduced air pollution.

9.8.4   Social Wellbeing

9.8.4.1   Energy/Fuel Poverty Alleviation

In 2018 almost 0.79 billion people in developing countries did not have access to electricity, while approximately 2.8 billion people relied on polluting fuels and technologies for cooking (IEA 2020a). Only in sub-Saharan Africa, about 548 million people (i.e., more than 50% of the population) live without electricity. In developed economies, the EU Energy Poverty Observatory estimated that in EU-28 44.5 million people were unable to keep their homes warm in 2016, 41.5 million had arrears on their utility bills the same year, 16.3% of households faced disproportionately high energy expenditure in 2010, and 19.2% of households reported being uncomfortably hot during summer in 2012 (Thomson and Bouzarovski 2018). Okushima (2016), using the 'expenditure approach', estimated that fuel poverty rates in Japan reached 8.4% in 2013. In the US, in 2015, 17 million households (14.4% of the total) received an energy disconnect/delivery stop notice and 25 million households (21.2% of the total) had to forgo food and medicine to pay energy bills (Bednar and Reames 2020).

The implementation of well-designed climate mitigation measures in buildings can help to reduce energy/fuel poverty and improve living conditions with significant benefits for health (Section 9.8.2) and well-being (Payne et al. 2015; Smith et al. 2016; Tonn et al. 2018). The social implications of energy poverty alleviation for the people in low- and middle-income developing countries with no access to clean energy fuels are further discussed in Section 9.8.4.2. In other developing countries and in developed economies as well, the implementation of mitigation measures can improve the ability of

households to affordably heat/cool a larger area of the home, thus increasing the space available to a family and providing more private and comfortable spaces for several activities like homework (Payne et al. 2015). By reducing energy expenditures and making energy bills more affordable for households, a 'heat or eat' dilemma can be avoided resulting in better nutrition and reductions in the number of low birthweight babies (Payne et al. 2015; Tonn et al. 2018). Also, renovated buildings and the resulting better indoor conditions, can enable residents to avoid social isolation, improve social cohesion, lower crime, and so on (Payne et al. 2015). The European Commission (2016) found that under an ambitious recast of Energy Performance Buildings Directive (EPBD), the number of households that may be lifted from fuel poverty across the EU lies between 5.17 and 8.26 million. To capture these benefits, mitigation policies and particularly energy renovation programmes should target the most vulnerable among the energy-poor households, which very often are ignored by the policy makers. In this context, it is recognised that fuel poverty should be analysed as a multidimensional social problem (Thomson et al. 2017b; Baker et al. 2018; Charlier and Legendre 2019; Mashhoodi et al. 2019), as it is related to energy efficiency, household composition, age and health status of its members, social conditions (single parent families, existence of unemployed and retired people, etc.), energy prices, disposable income, and so on. In addition, the geographical dimension can have a significant impact on the levels of fuel poverty and should be taken into account when formulating response policies (Besagni and Borgarello 2019; Mashhoodi et al. 2019).

9.8.4.2   Improved Access to Energy Sources, Gender Equality and Time Savings

In most low- and middle-income developing countries women and children (particularly girls) spend a significant amount of their time for gathering fuels for cooking and heating (World Health Organization 2016; Rosenthal et al. 2018). For example, in Africa more than 70% of the children living in households that primarily cook with polluting fuels spend at least 15 hours and, in some countries, more than 30 hours per week in collecting wood or water, facing significant safety risks and constraints on their available time for education and rest (World Health Organization 2016; Mehetre et al. 2017). Also, in several developing countries (e.g., in most African countries but also in India, in rural areas in Latin America and elsewhere) women spend several hours to collect fuel wood and cook, thus limiting their potential for productive activities for income generation or rest (García-Frapolli et al. 2010; World Health Organization 2016; Mehetre et al. 2017). Expanding access to clean household energy for cooking, heating and lighting will largely help alleviate these burdens (Malla et al. 2011; World Health Organization 2016; Lewis et al. 2017; Rosenthal et al. 2018). Jeuland et al. (2018) found that the time savings associated with the adoption of cleaner and more fuel-efficient stoves by low-income households in developing countries are amount to USD1.3–1.9 per household per month, constituting the 23–43% of the total social benefits attributed to the promotion of clean stoves.

Electrification of remote rural areas and other regions that do not have access to electricity enables people living in poor developing countries to read, socialise, and be more productive during the evening, while it is also associated with greater school attendance by children (Torero 2015; Rao et al. 2016; Barnes and Samad 2018). Chakravorty et al. (2014) found that a grid connection can increase non-agricultural incomes of rural households in India from 9% up to 28.6% (assuming a higher quality of electricity). On the other hand, some studies clearly show that electricity consumption for connected households is extremely low, with limited penetration of electrical appliances (Cameron et al. 2016; Lee et al. 2017) and low quality of electricity (Chakravorty et al. 2014). The implementation of appropriate policies to overcome bureaucratic red tape, low reliability, and credit constraints, is necessary for maximising the social benefits of electrification.

9.8.5   Economic Implications of Mitigation Actions

9.8.5.1   Buildings-related Labour Productivity

Low-carbon buildings, and particularly well-designed, operated and maintained high-performance buildings with adequate ventilation, may result in productivity gains and improve the competitiveness of the economy through three different pathways (MacNaughton et al. 2015; European Commission 2016; Niemelä et al. 2017; Mofidi and Akbari 2017; Thema et al. 2017; Bleyl et al. 2019): (i) increasing the amount of active time available for productive work by reducing the absenteeism from work due to illness, the presenteeism (i.e., working with illness or working despite being ill), and the inability to work due to chronic diseases caused by the poor indoor environment; (ii) improving the indoor air quality and thermal comfort of non-residential buildings, which can result in better mental well-being of the employees and increased workforce performance; and (iii) reducing the school absenteeism due to better indoor environmental conditions, which may enhance the future earnings ability of the students and restrict the parents absenteeism due to care-taking of sick children.

Productivity gains due to increased amount of active time for work is directly related to acute and chronic health benefits attributed to climate mitigation actions in buildings (Section 9.8.2.2). The bulk of studies quantifying the impact of energy efficiency on productivity focus on acute health effects. Proper ventilation in buildings is of particular importance and can reduce absenteeism due to sick days by 0.6–1.9 days per person per year (MacNaughton et al. 2015; Ben-David et al. 2017; Thema et al. 2017). In a pan-European study, (Chatterjee and Ürge-Vorsatz 2018) showed that deep energy retrofits in residential buildings may increase the number of active days by 1.78–5.27 (with an average of 3.09) per year and person who has actually shifted to a deep retrofitted building. Similarly, the interventions in the non-residential buildings result in increased active days between 0.79 and 2.43 (with an average of 1.4) per year and person shifted to deeply retrofitted non-residential buildings.

As regards improvements in workforce performance due to improved indoor conditions (i.e., air quality, thermal comfort, etc.), (Kozusznik et al. 2019) conducted a systematic review on whether the implementation of energy efficient interventions in office buildings influence well-being and job performance of employees. Among the 34 studies included in this review, 31 found neutral to positive effects of green buildings on productivity and only 3 studies indicated detrimental outcomes for office occupants in terms of job performance. Particularly longitudinal studies, which observe and compare the office users' reactions over time in conventional and green buildings, show that green buildings have neutral to positive effects on occupants well-being and work performance (Thatcher and Milner 2016; Candido et al. 2019; Kozusznik et al. 2019). Bleyl et al. (2019) estimated that deep energy retrofits in office buildings in Belgium would generate a workforce performance increase of EUR10.4 to EUR20.8 m^{-2} renovated. In Europe every 1°C reduction in overheating during the summer period increases students learning performance by 2.3% and workers performance in office buildings by 3.6% (Kockat et al. 2018b). Considering the latter indicator, it was estimated that by reducing overheating across Europe, the overall performance of the workers in office buildings can increase by 7–12% (Kockat et al. 2018b).

9.8.5.2   Enhanced Asset Values of Energy Efficient Buildings

A significant number of studies confirm that homes with high energy efficiency and/or green features are sold at higher prices than conventional, low energy efficient houses. A review of 15 studies from 12 different countries showed that energy efficient dwellings have a price premium ranging between 1.5% and 28%, with a median estimated at 7.8%, for the highest energy efficient category examined in each case study compared to reference houses with the same characteristics but lower energy efficiency (the detailed results of this review are presented in Supplementary Material Table 9.SM.5). In a given real estate market, the higher the energy efficiency of dwellings compared to conventional housing, the higher their selling prices. However, a number of studies show that this premium is largely realised during resale transactions and is smaller or even negative in some cases immediately after the completion of the construction (Deng and Wu 2014; Yoshida and Sugiura 2015). A relatively lower number of studies (also included in Supplementary Material Table 9.SM.5) show that energy efficiency and green features have also a positive effect on rental prices of dwellings (Hyland et al. 2013; Cajias et al. 2019), but this is weaker compared to sales prices, and in a developing country even negative as green buildings, which incorporate new technologies such as central air conditioning, are associated with higher electricity consumption (Zheng et al. 2012).

Regarding non-residential buildings, (European Commission 2016) reviewed a number of studies showing that buildings with high energy efficiency or certified with green certificates present higher sales prices by 5.2–35%, and higher rents by 2.5–11.8%. More recent studies in relation to those included in the review confirm these results (Mangialardo et al. 2018; Ott and Hahn 2018) or project even higher premiums. Chegut et al. (2014) found that green certification in the London office market results in a premium of 19.7% for rents. On the other hand, in Australia, a review study showed mixed evidence regarding price differentials emerged as a function of energy performance of office buildings (Acil Allen Consulting 2015). Other studies have shown that energy efficiency and green certifications have been associated with lower default rates for commercial mortgages (Wallace et al. 2018; An and Pivo 2020; Mathew et al. 2021).

More generally, (Giraudet 2020) based on a meta-analysis of several studies, showed that the capitalisation of energy efficiency is observed in building sales and rental (even in the absence of energy performance certificates), but the resulting market equilibrium can be considered inefficient as rented dwellings are less energy efficient than owner-occupied ones.

9.8.5.3   Macroeconomic Effects

Investments required for the implementation of mitigation actions, create, mainly in the short-run, increase in the economic output and employment in sectors delivering energy efficiency services and products, which are partially counterbalanced by less investments and lower production in other parts of the economy (Yushchenko and Patel 2016; European Commission 2016; Thema et al. 2017; US EPA 2018) (see also Cross-Working Group Box 1 in Chapter 3). The magnitude of these impacts depends on the structure of the economy, the extent to which energy saving technologies are produced domestically or imported from abroad, but also from the growth cycle of the economy with the benefits being maximised when the related investments are realised in periods of economic recession (Mirasgedis et al. 2014; Yushchenko and Patel 2016; Thema et al. 2017). Particularly in developing countries if the mitigation measures and other interventions to improve energy access (Figure 9.19) are carried out by locals, the impact on economy, employment and social well-being will be substantial (Mills 2016; Lehr et al. 2016). As many of these programs are carried out with foreign assistance funds, it is essential that the funds be spent in-country to the full extent possible, while some portion of these funds would need to be devoted to institution building and especially training. (Mills 2016) estimated that a market transformation from inefficient and polluting fuel-based lighting to solar-LED systems to fully serve the 112 million households that currently lack electricity access will create directly 2 million new jobs in these developing countries, while the indirect effects could be even greater. IEA (2020a) estimated that 9–30 jobs would be generated for every million dollars invested in building retrofits or in construction of new energy efficient buildings (gross direct and indirect employment), with the highest employment intensity rates occurring in developing countries. Correspondingly, 7–16 jobs would be created for every million dollars spent in purchasing highly efficient and connected appliances, while expanding clean cooking through LPG could create 16–75 direct local jobs per million dollars invested. Increases in product and employment attributed to energy efficiency investments also affect public budgets by increasing income and business taxation, reducing unemployment benefits, and so on. Thema et al. (2017), thus mitigating the impact on public deficit of subsidising energy saving measures (Mikulić et al. 2016).

Furthermore, energy savings due to the implementation of mitigation actions will result, mainly in the long-run, in increased disposable income for households, which in turn may be spent to buy other goods and services, resulting in economic development, creation of new permanent employment and positive public budget implications (IEA 2014; Thema et al. 2017; US EPA 2018). According to Anderson et al. (2014), the production of these other goods and services is usually more labour-intensive compared to energy production, resulting in net employment benefits of about 8 jobs per million

dollars of consumer bill savings in the US. These effects may again have a positive impact on public budgets. Furthermore, reduced energy consumption on a large scale is likely to have an impact on lower energy prices and hence on reducing the cost of production of various products, improving the productivity of the economy and enhancing security of energy supply (IEA 2014; Thema et al. 2017).

9.8.5.4   Energy Security

GHG emission reduction actions in the sector of buildings affect energy systems by: (i) reducing the overall consumption of energy resources, especially fossil fuels; (ii) promoting the electrification of thermal energy uses; and (iii) enhancing distributed generation through the incorporation of RES and other clean and smart technologies in buildings. Increasing sufficiency, energy efficiency and penetration of RES result in improving the primary energy intensity of the economy and reducing dependence on fossil fuels, which for many countries are imported energy resources (Boermans et al. 2015; Markovska et al. 2016; Thema et al. 2017). The electrification of thermal energy uses is expected to increase the demand for electricity in buildings, which in most cases can be reversed (at national or regional level) by promoting nearly zero energy new buildings and a deep renovation of the existing building stock (Boermans et al. 2015; Couder and Verbruggen 2017). In addition, highly efficient buildings can keep the desired room temperature stable over a longer period and consequently they have the capability to shift heating and cooling operation in time (Boermans et al. 2015). These result in reduced peak demand, lower system losses and avoided generation and grid infrastructure investments. As a significant proportion of the global population, particularly in rural and remote locations, still lack access to modern energy sources, renewables can be used to power distributed generation or micro-grid systems that enable peer-to-peer energy exchange, constituting a crucial component to improve energy security for rural populations (Leibrand et al. 2019; Kirchhoff and Strunz 2019). For successful development of peer-to-peer micro-grids, financial incentives to asset owners are critical for ensuring their willingness to share their energy resources, while support measures should be adopted to ensure that also non-asset holders can contribute to investments in energy generation and storage equipment and have the ability to sell electricity to others (Kirchhoff and Strunz 2019).

9.9   Sectoral Barriers and Policies

9.9.1   Barriers, Feasibility and Acceptance

Understanding the reasons why cost-effective investment in building energy efficiency are not taking place as expected by rational economic behaviour is critical to design effective policies for decarbonise the buildings (Cattano et al. 2013; Cattaneo 2019). Barriers depend from the actors (owner, tenant, utility, regulators, manufacturers, etc.), their role in energy efficiency project and the market, technology, financial economic, social, legal, institutional, regulatory and policy structures (Reddy 1991; Weber 1997; Sorrell et al. 2000; Reddy 2002; Sorrell et al. 2011; Cagno et al. 2012; Bardhan et al., 2014; Bagaini et al. 2020; Vogel et al. 2015; Khosla et al. 2017;

9

Figure 9.20 | Summary of the extent to which different factors would enable or inhibit the deployment of mitigation options in buildings. Blue bars indicate the extent to which the indicator enables the implementation of the option (E) and orange bars indicate the extent to which an indicator is a barrier (B) to the deployment of the option, relative to the maximum possible barriers and enablers assessed. A 'X' signifies the indicator is not applicable or does not affect the feasibility of the option, while a forward slash/indicates that there is no or limited evidence whether the indicator affects the feasibility of the option. The shading indicates the level of confidence, with darker shading signifying higher levels of confidence. Table 9.SM.6 provides an overview of the extent to which the feasibility of options may differ across context (e.g., region), time (e.g., 2030 versus 2050), and scale (e.g., small versus large), and includes a line of sight on which the assessment method is based. The assessment method is explained in Annex II.11.

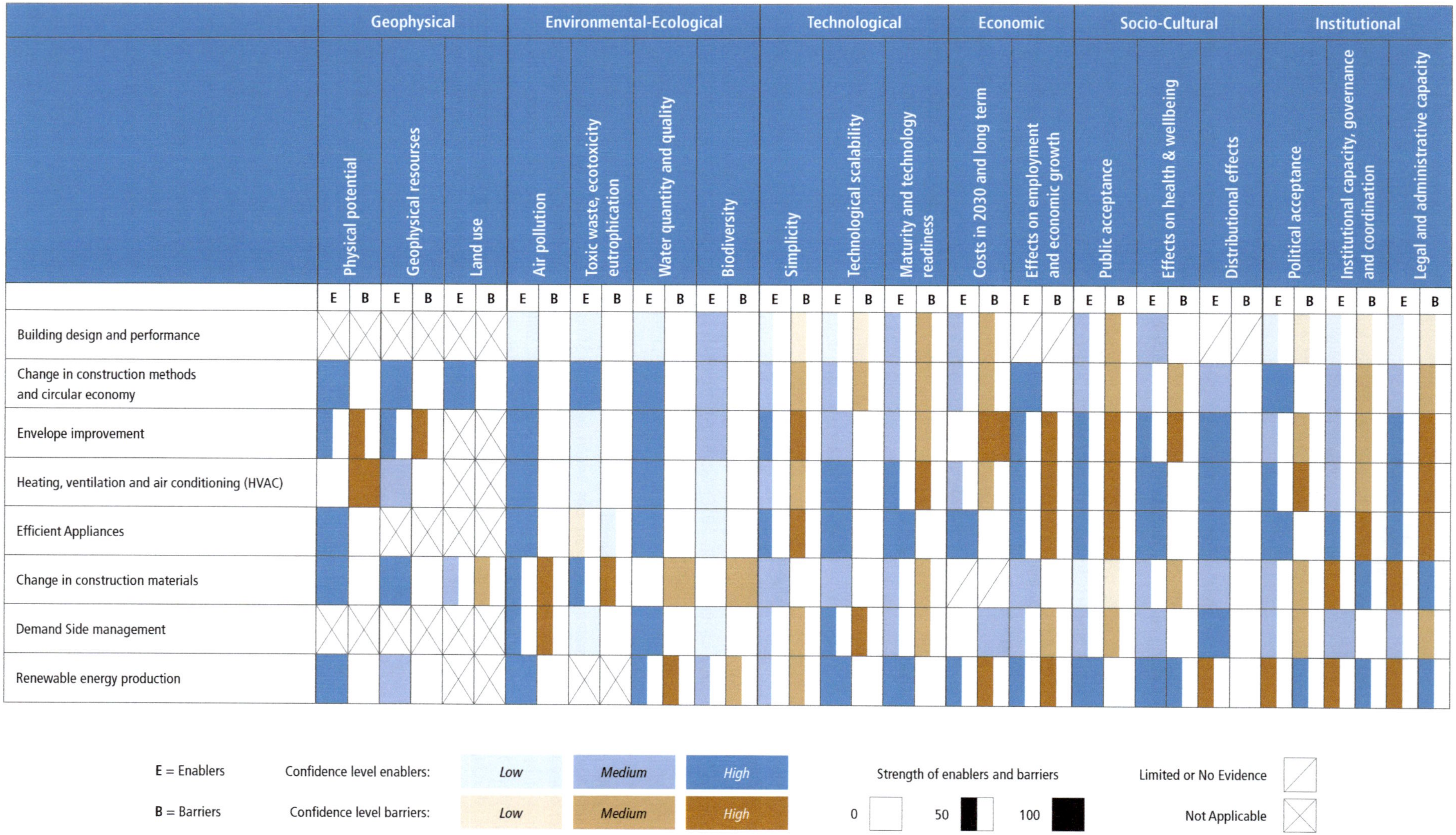

Gupta et al. 2017). Barriers identified for the refurbishment of exiting building or construction of new efficient buildings includes: lack of high-performance products, construction methods, monitoring capacity, investment risks, policies intermittency, information gaps, principal agent problems (both tenant and landlord face disincentives to invest in energy efficiency), skills of the installers, lack of a trained and ready workforce, governance arrangements in collectively owned properties and behavioural anomalies (Gillingham and Palmer 2014; Buessler et al. 2017; Yang et al. 2019; Do et al. 2020; Dutt 2020; Song et al. 2020). A better understanding of behavioural barriers (Frederiks et al. 2015) is essential to design effective policies to decarbonise the building sector. Energy efficiency in buildings faces one additional problem: the sector is highly heterogeneous, with many different building types, sizes and operational uses. Energy efficiency investments do not take place in isolation but in competition with other priorities and as part of a complex, protracted investment process (Cooremans 2011). Therefore, a focus on overcoming barriers is not enough for effective policy. Organisational context is important because the same barrier might have very different organisational effects and require very different policy responses (Mallaburn 2018). Cross-Chapter Box 2 in Chapter 2 presents a summary of methodologies for estimating the macro-level impact of policies on indices of GHG mitigation.

Reaching deep decarbonisation levels throughout the lifecycle of buildings depends on multidimensional criteria for assessing the feasibility of mitigation measures, including criteria related to geophysical, environmental-ecological, technological, economic, socio-cultural and institutional dimensions. An assessment of 16 feasibility criteria for mitigation measures in the buildings sector indicates whether a specific factor, within broader dimensions, acts as a barrier or helps enabling such mitigation measures (Figure 9.20, Supplementary Material Table 9.SM.6, and Annex II.11). Although mitigation measures are aggregated in the assessment of Figure 9.20 and feasibility results can differ for more specific measures, generally speaking, the barriers to mitigation measures in buildings are few, sometimes including technological and socio-cultural challenges. However, many co-benefits could help enable mitigation in the buildings sector. For instance, many measures can have positive effects on the environment, health and well-being, and distributional potential, all of which can boost their feasibility. The feasibility of mitigation measures varies significantly according to socio-economic differences across and within countries.

9.9.2   Rebound Effects

In the buildings sector energy efficiency improvements and promotion of cleaner fuels can lead to all types of rebound effects, while sufficiency measures lead only to indirect and secondary effects (Chitnis et al. 2013). The consideration of the rebound effects as a behavioural economic response of the consumers to cheaper energy services can only partially explain the gap between the expected and actual energy savings (Galvin and Sunikka-Blank 2017). The prebound effect, a term used to describe the situation where there is a significant difference between expected and observed energy consumption of non-refurbished buildings, is usually implicated in

high rebound effects upon retrofitting (Teli et al. 2016; Calì et al. 2016; Galvin and Sunikka-Blank 2017). The access for all to modern energy services such as heating and cooling is one of the well-being objectives governments aim for. However, ensuring this access leads to an increase of energy demand which is considered as a rebound effect by (Chitnis et al. 2013; Orea et al. 2015; Poon 2015; Teli et al. 2016; Seebauer 2018; Sorrell et al. 2018; Berger and Höltl 2019). Aydin et al. (2017) found that in the Netherlands the rebound effect for the lowest wealth quantile is double compared to the highest wealth quantile. Similar, energy access in developing countries leads to an increase consumption compared to very low baselines which is considered by some authors as rebound (Copiello 2017). On the other hand, in households whose members have a higher level of education and/or strong environmental values, the rebound is lower (Seebauer 2018).

Rebound effects in the building sector could be a co-benefit, in cases where the mechanisms involved provide faster access to affordable energy and/or contribute to improved social well-being, or a trade-off, to the extent that the external costs of the increased energy consumption exceed the welfare benefits of the increased energy service consumption (Chan and Gillingham 2015; Borenstein 2015; Galvin and Sunikka-Blank 2017; Sorrell et al. 2018). In cases where rebound effects are undesirable, appropriate policies could be implemented for their mitigation.

There is great variation in estimates of the direct and indirect rebound effects, which stems from the end-uses included in the analysis, differences in definitions and methods used to estimate the rebound effects, the quality of the data utilised, the period of analysis and the geographical area in consideration (International Risk Governance Council 2013; Galvin 2014; Gillingham et al. 2016). Several studies examined in the context of this assessment (see Supplementary Material Table 9.SM.7) showed that direct rebound effects for residential energy consumption, which includes heating, are significant and range between −9% and 127%. The direct rebound effects for energy services other than heating may be lower (Chen et al. 2018; Sorrell et al. 2018). The rebound effects may be reduced with the time as the occupants learn how to optimally use the systems installed in energy renovated buildings (Calì et al. 2016) and seem to be lower in the case of major renovations leading to NZEB (Corrado et al. 2016). The combined direct and indirect or the indirect only rebound effects were found to range between −2% and 80%, with a median at 12% (see Supplementary Material Table 9.SM.7). In non-residential buildings the rebound effects may be smaller, as the commercial sector is characterised by lower price elasticities of energy demand, while the comfort level in commercial buildings before renovation is likely to be better compared to residential buildings (Qiu 2014).

9.9.3   Policy Packages for the Decarbonisation
of Buildings

There is no single energy efficiency policy (Wiese et al. 2018) able to decarbonise the building sector, but a range of polices are needed, often included in a policy package (Kern et al., 2017; Rosenow et al. 2017) to enhance robustness against risks and uncertainties in both short and long-term and addressing the different stakeholder perspectives (Forouli et al. 2019; Nikas et al. 2020; Doukas and Nikas 2020). This is due to: the many barriers; the different types of buildings (residential, non-residential, etc.); the different socio-economic groups of the population (social housing, informal settlement, etc.); the country development status; the local climate (cooling and/or heating), ownership structure (tenant or owner), the age of buildings. Effective policy packages include mandatory standards, codes, the provision of information, carbon pricing, financing, and technical assistance for end-users. Important element related to policy packages is whether the policies reinforce each other or diminish the impact of individual policies, due to policy 'overcrowding'. Examples are the EU policy package for efficiency in buildings (Rosenow and Bayer 2017; BPIE, 2020; Economidou et al. 2020) and China goal of 10 million m² NZEB during the 13th Five-Year Plan, presented in the Supplementary Material (Supplementary Material Section 9.SM.4) (see also Cross-Chapter Box 10 in Chapter 14 for integrated policymaking for sector transitions).

Revisions in tenant and condominium law are necessary for reducing disincentives between landlord and tenant or between multiple owners, these acts alone cannot incentivise them to uptake an energy efficiency upgrade in a property (Economidou and Serrenho, 2019). A package addressing split incentives include regulatory measures, information measures, labels, individual metering rules and financial models designed to distribute costs and benefits to tenants and owners in a transparent and fair way (Bird and Hernández 2012; Economidou and Bertoldi 2015; Castellazi et al. 2017). A more active engagement of building occupants in energy saving practices, the development of agreements benefitting all involved actors, acknowledgement of real energy consumption and establishment of cost recovery models attached to the property instead of the owner are useful measures to address misalignments between actors.

In Developed Countries policy packages are targeted to increase the number and depth of renovations of existing building, while for developing countries policies focus on new construction, including regulatory measures and incentives, while carbon pricing would be more problematic unless there is a strong recycling of the revenues. Building energy codes and labels could be based on LCA emissions, rather than energy consumption during the use phase of buildings, as it is the case in Switzerland and Finland (Kuittinen and Häkkinen 2020).

Policy packages should also combine sufficiency, efficiency, and renewable energy instruments for buildings, for example some national building energy codes already include minimum requirements for the use of renewable energy in buildings.

9.9.3.1　Sufficiency and Efficiency Policies

Recently the concept of sufficiency complementary to energy efficiency has been introduced in policy making (Brischke et al. 2015; Hewitt 2018; Thomas et al. 2019; Bertoldi 2020; Saheb 2021) (Box 9.1).

Lorek and Spangenberg (2019b) investigated the limitations of the theories of planned behaviour and social practice and proposed an approach combining both theories resulting in a heuristic sufficiency policy[2] tool. Lorek and Spangenberg (2019b) showed that increased living area per person counteracts efficiency gains in buildings and called for sufficiency policy instruments to efficiency by limit building size. This could be achieved via mandatory and prescriptive measures, for example, progressive building energy codes (IEA 2013), or financial penalties in the form of property taxation (e.g., non-linear and progressive taxation), or with mandatory limits on building size per capita. Heindl and Kanschik (2016) suggested that voluntary policies promoting sufficiency and proposed that sufficiency should be 'integrated in a more comprehensive normative framework related to welfare and social justice'. Alcott highlighted that in sufficiency there is a loss of utility or welfare (Alcott, 2008). Thomas et al. (2019) described some of the possible policies, some based on the sharing economy principles, for examples co-sharing space, public authorities facilitating the exchange house between young and expanding families with elderly people, with reduced need for space. Policies for sufficiency include land-use and urban planning policies. Berril et al. (2021) proposed removing policies, which support supply of larger home typologies, for example, single-family home or local land-use regulations restricting construction of multifamily buildings. In non-residential building, sufficiency could be implemented through the sharing economy, for example with flexible offices space with hot-desking.

Scholars have identified the 'energy efficiency gap' (Hirst and Brown 1990; Jaffe and Stavins 1994; Alcott and Greenstone 2012; Gillingham and Palmer 2014; Stadelmann 2017) and policies to overcome it. Markandya et al. (2015) and Shen et al. (2016) have classified energy efficiency policies in three broad categories: the command and control (e.g., mandatory building energy codes; mandatory appliances standards, etc.); price instruments (e.g., taxes, subsides, tax deductions, credits, permits and tradable obligations, etc.); and information instruments (e.g., labels, energy audits, smart meters and feed-back, etc.). Based on the EU Energy Efficiency Directive, the MURE and the IEA energy efficiency policy databases (Bertoldi and Mosconi 2020), Bertoldi (2020) proposed six policy categories: regulatory, financial and fiscal; information and awareness; qualification, training and quality assurance; market-based instruments: voluntary action. The categorisation of energy efficiency policies used in this chapter is aligned with the taxonomy used in Chapter 13, sub-section 13.5.1 (economic or market-based instruments, regulatory instruments, and other policies). However, the classification used here is more granular in order to capture the complexity of end-use energy efficiency and buildings.

1.　Regulatory instruments

Building energy codes. Several scholars highlighted the key role of mandatory building energy codes and minimum energy performance requirements for buildings (Enker and Morrison 2017). Wang et al. (2019) finds that, 'Building energy efficiency standards (BEES) are one of the most effective policies to reduce building

---

[2]　Sufficiency policies are a set of measures and daily practices that avoid demand for energy, materials, land and water while delivering human well-being for all within planetary boundaries.

energy consumption, especially in the case of the rapid urbanisation content in China'. *Ex post* policy evaluation shows that stringent buildings' codes reduce energy consumption in buildings and CO_2 emissions and are cost-effective (Aroonruengsawat 2012; Jacobsen and Kotchen 2013; Scott et al. 2015; Levinson 2016; Kotchen 2017; Yu et al. 2017; Yu et al. 2018; Aydin and Brounen 2019). Progressive building energy codes include requirements on efficiency improvement but also on sufficiency and share of renewables (Clune et al. 2012; Rosenberg et al., 2017) and on embodied emissions (Schwarz et al. 2020), for example the 2022 ASHRAE Standard 90.1 includes prescriptive on-site renewable energy requirements for non-residential building. Evans et al. (2017; 2018) calls for strengthen the compliance checks with efficiency requirements or codes when buildings are in operation and highlighted the need for enforcement of building energy codes to achieve the estimate energy and carbon savings recommending actions to improve enforcements, including institutional capacity and adequate resources.

Evans et al. (2017; 2018) identified strengthening the compliance checks with codes when buildings are in operation and the need for enforcement of building energy codes in order to achieve the estimate energy and carbon savings, recommending actions to improve enforcements, including institutional capacity and adequate resources. Another important issue to be addressed by policies is the 'Energy Performance Gap' (EPG), that is, the gap between design and policy intent and actual outcomes. Regulatory and market support regimes are based on predictive models (Cohen and Bordass 2015) with general assumptions about building types, the way they are used and are not covering all energy consumption. In the perspective of moving towards net zero carbon, it is important that policy capture and address the actual in-use performance of buildings (Gupta et al. 2015; Gupta and Kotopouleas 2018). Outcome-based codes are increasingly important because they overcome some limitations of prescriptive building energy codes, which typically do not regulate all building energy uses or do not regulate measured operational energy use in buildings. Regulating all loads, especially plug and process loads, is important because they account for an increasingly large percentage of total energy use as building envelope and space-conditioning equipment are becoming more efficient (Denniston et al. 2011; Colker 2012; Enker and Morrison 2020).

Building codes could also foster the usage of wood and timber as a construction in particular for multi-storey buildings and in the long term penalise carbon intensive building materials (Ludwig 2019) with policies based on environmental performance assessment of buildings and the 'wood first' principle (Ludwig 2019; Ramage et al. 2017).

Retro-commissioning is a cost-effective process to periodically check the energy performance of existing building and assure energy savings are maintained overtime (Kong et al. 2019; Ssembatya et al. 2021).

In countries with low rate of new construction, it is important to consider mandatory building energy codes for existing buildings, but this may also be relevant for countries with high new construction, as they will have soon a large existing building stock. The EU has requirements already in place when building undergo a major renovation (Economidou et al. 2020). Countries considering

mandatory regulations for existing buildings include Canada, the US (specific cities), China and Singapore. Policies include mandating energy retrofits for low performances existing buildings, when sold or rented. In countries with increasing building stock, in particular in developing countries, policies are more effective when targeting new buildings (Kamal et al. 2019).

NZEBs definitions are proposed by (Marszal et al. 2011; Deng and Wu 2014; Zhang and Zhou 2015; Williams et al. 2016; Wells et al. 2018), covering different geographical areas, developing and Developed Countries, and both existing buildings and new buildings. In 2019, China issued the national standard Technical Standard for Nearly Zero Energy Building (MoHURD, 2019). California has also adopted a building energy code mandating for NZEBs for new residential buildings in 2020 and 2030 for commercial buildings (Feng et al. 2019). Several countries have adopted targets, roadmaps or mandatory building energy codes requiring net zero energy buildings (NZEBs) for some classes of new buildings (Feng et al. 2019).

Building labels and Energy Performance Certificates (EPCs). Buildings labels are an important instrument, with some limitations. Li et al. (2019b) reviewed the EU mandatory Energy Performance Certificates for buildings and proposed several measures to make the EPC more effective in driving the markets towards low consumption buildings. Some authors have indicated that the EPC based on the physical properties of the buildings (asset rating) may be misleading due to occupancy behaviour (Cohen and Bordass 2015) and calculation errors (Crawley et al. 2019). Control authorities can have a large impact on the quality of the label (Mallaburn 2018). Labels can also include information on the GHG embedded in building material or be based on LCA.

US EPA Energy Star and NABERS (Gui and Gou, 2020) are building performance labels based on performance, not on modelled energy use. Singapore has mandatory building energy labels, as do many cities in the US, while India and Brazil have mandatory labels for public buildings.

Mandatory energy performance disclosure and benchmarking of building energy consumption is a powerful policy instrument in particular for non-residential buildings (Trencher et al. 2016) and could be more accurate than energy audits. Gabe (2016) showed that mandatory disclosure is more effective than voluntary disclosure. Some US cities (e.g., New York) have adopted Emissions Performance Standards for buildings, capping CO_2 emissions. Accurate statistics related to energy use are very important for reducing GHG in building sector. In 2015, the Republic of Korea stablished the National Building Energy Integrated Management System, where building data and energy consumption information are collected for policy development and public information.

Energy audits. Energy audits, help to overcome the information barriers to efficiency investments, in particular buildings owned or occupied by small companies (Kalantzis and Revoltella, 2019). In the EU energy audits are mandatory for large companies under the Energy Efficiency Directive (Nabitz and Hirzel 2019), with some EU Member States having a long experience with energy audits, as part of national voluntary agreements with the private sector (Rezessy and Bertoldi 2011; Cornelis 2019). Singapore has adopted mandatory audit for buildings (Shen et al. 2016). In the United States, several cities have adopted energy informational policies in recent years, including mandatory buildings audits (Trencher et al. 2016; Kontokosta et al. 2020). The State of New York has in place a subsidised energy audit for residential building since 2010 (Boucher et al. 2018). It is important to assure the training of auditors and the quality of the audit.

Minimum Energy Performance Standards (MEPSs). Mandatory minimum efficiency standards for building technical equipment and appliances (e.g., HVAC, appliances, ICT, lighting, etc.) is a very common, tested and successful policy in most of the OECD countries (e.g., EU, US, Canada, Australia, etc.) for improving energy efficiency (Scott et al. 2015; Wu et al. 2019; Sonnenschein et al. 2019). Brucal and Roberts (2019) showed that efficiency standards reduce product price. McNeil et al. (2019) highlighted how efficiency standards will help developing countries in reducing the power peak demand by a factor of two, thus reducing large investment costs in new generation, transmission, and distribution networks. Mandatory standards have been implemented also other large economies, for example, Russia, Brazil, India, South Africa, China, Ghana, Kenya and Malaysia (Salleh et al. 2019), with an increase in the uptake also in developing countries, for example, Ghana, Kenya, Tunisia, and so on. In Japan, there is a successful voluntary programme the Top Runner, with similar results of mandatory efficiency standards (Inoue and Matsumoto 2019).

Appliance energy labelling. Mandatory energy labelling schemes for building technical equipment and appliances are very often implemented together with minimum efficiency standards, with the mandatory standard pushing the market towards higher efficiency and the label pulling the market (Bertoldi, 2019). OECD countries, and many developing countries (for example China, Ghana, Kenya, India, South Africa, etc.) (Chunekar 2014; Diawuo et al. 2018; Issock et al. 2018) have adopted mandatory energy labelling. Other labelling schemes are of voluntary nature, for example, the Energy Star programme in the US (Ohler et al. 2020), which covers many different appliances.

Information campaign. Provision of information (e.g., public campaigns, targeted technical information, etc.) is a common policy instrument to change end-user behaviour. Many authors agree that the effect of both targeted and general advertisement and campaigns have a short lifetime and the effects tend to decrease over time (Reiss and White 2008; Simcock et al. 2014; Diffney et al. 2013). The meta-analysis carried out by (Delmas et al. 2013) showed that energy audits and personal information were the most effective followed by providing individuals with comparisons with their peers' energy use including 'non-monetary, information-based' (Delmas et al. 2013). An effective approach integrates the social norm as the basis for information and awareness measures on energy behaviour (Schultz et al. 2007; Gifford 2011). Information is more successful when it inspires and engages people: how people feel about a given situation often has a potent influence on their decisions (Slovic and Peters 2006). The message needs to

be carefully selected and kept as simple as possible focusing on the following: entertain, engage, embed and educate (Dewick and Owen 2015).

Energy consumption feedback with smart meters, smart billing and dedicated devices and apps is another instrument recently exploited to reduce energy consumption (Karlin et al. 2015; Buchanan et al. 2018; Zangheri et al. 2019) very often coupled with contest-based interventions or norm-based interventions (Bergquist et al. 2019). Hargreaves et al. (2018) proposes five core types of action to reduce energy use: turn it off, use it less, use it more carefully, improve its performance, and replace it/use an alternative. According to Aydin et al. (2018), technology alone will not be enough to achieve the desired energy savings due to the rebound effect. The lack of interest from household occupants, confusing feedback message and difficulty to relate it to practical intervention, overemphasis on financial savings and the risks of 'fallback effects' where energy use returns to previous levels after a short time or rebound effects has been pointed out (Buchanan et al. 2015) as the main reasons for the failing of traditional feedback. Labanca and Bertoldi (2018) highlight the current limitations of policies for energy conservation and suggests complementary policy approach based on social practices theories.

2. Market-based instruments

Carbon allowances. A number of authors (Raux et al. 2015; Fan et al. 2016; Fawcett and Parag 2017; Li et al. 2015, 2018; Marek et al. 2018; Wadud and Chintakayala 2019) have investigated personal carbon allowances introduced previously (Ayres 1995; Fleming 1997; Raux and Marlot 2005; Bristow et al. 2010; Fawcett 2010; Starkey 2012). Although there is not yet any practical implementation of this policy, it offers an alternative to carbon taxes, although there are some practical issues to be solved before it could be rolled out. Recently the city of Lahti in Finland has introduced a personal carbon allowance in the transport sector (Kuokkanen et al. 2020). Under this policy instrument governments allocate (free allocation, but allowances could also be auctioned) allowances to cover the carbon emission for one year, associated with energy consumption. Trade of allowances between people can be organised. Personal carbon allowances can also foster renewable energies (energy consumption without carbon emissions) both in the grid and in buildings (e.g., solar thermal). Personal carbon allowances can make the carbon price more explicit to consumers, allowing them to know from the market value of each allowance (e.g., 1 kg of CO_2). This policy instrument will shift the responsibility to the individual. Some categories may have limited ability to change their carbon budget or to be engaged by this policy instruments. In addition, in common with many other environmental policies the distributional effects have to be assessed carefully as this policy instrument may favour well off people able to purchase additional carbon allowances or install technologies that reduce their carbon emissions (Burgess 2016; Wang et al. 2017).

The concept of carbon allowances or carbon budget can also be applied to buildings, by assigning a yearly CO_2 emissions budget to each building. This policy would be a less complex than personal allowances as buildings have metered or billed energy sources (e.g., gas, electricity, delivered heat, heating oil, etc.). The scheme stimulates investments in energy efficiency and on-site renewable energies and energy savings resulting from behaviour by buildings occupant. For commercial buildings, similar schemes were implemented in the UK CRC Energy Efficiency Scheme (closed in 2019) or the Tokyo Metropolitan Carbon and Trade Scheme (Nishida and Hua 2011; Bertoldi et al. 2013a). Since 2015 the Republic of Korea implemented an Emission Trading Scheme, covering buildings (Park and Hong 2014; Lee and Yu 2017; Narassimhan et al. 2018). More recently under the New York Climate Mobilization Act enacted in 2019 New York City Local Law 97 established 'Carbon Allowances' for large buildings (Spiegel-Feld 2019; Lee 2020).

Public money can be used to reward and give incentives to energy saved, as a result of technology implementation, and/or as a result of energy conservation and sufficiency (Eyre 2013; Bertoldi et al. 2013b; Prasanna et al. 2018). This can be seen as a core feature of the Energy Savings Feed-in Tariff (ES-FiT). The ES-FiT is a performance-based subsidy, whereby actions undertaken by end-users – for example, investments in energy efficiency technology measures – are awarded based on the real energy savings achieved.

Utilities programmes, energy efficiency resource standard and energy efficiency obligations. Ratepayer-funded efficiency programmes, energy efficiency obligations, energy efficiency resource standards and white certificates have been introduced in some EU Member States, in several US States, Australia, South Korea and Brazil (Bertoldi et al. 2013a; Palmer et al. 2013; Brennan and Palmer 2013; Giraudet and Finon 2015; Wirl 2015; Rosenow and Bayer 2017; Aldrich and Koerner 2018; Choi et al. 2018a; Fawcett and Darby 2018; Fawcett et al. 2019; Nadel, 2019; Sliger and Colburn, 2019; Goldman et al. 2020). This policy instrument helps in improving energy efficiency in buildings, but there is no evidence that it can foster deep renovations of existing buildings. Recently this policy instrument has been investigated is some non-OECD countries such as Turkey, where white certificates could deliver energy savings with some limitations (Duzgun and Komurgoz 2014) and UAE, as a useful instrument to foster energy efficiency in buildings (Friedrich and Afshari 2015). Another similar market based instrument is the energy saving auction mechanism implemented in some US states, Switzerland, and in Germany (Langreder et al. 2019; Rosenow et al. 2019; Thomas and Rosenow 2020). Energy efficiency projects participate in auctions for energy savings based on the cost of the energy saved and receive a financial incentive, if successful.

Energy or carbon taxes. Energy and/or carbon taxes are a climate policy, which can help in reducing energy consumption (Sen and Vollebergh 2018) and manage the rebound effect (Font Vivanco et al. 2016; Peng et al. 2019; Freire-González 2020; Bertoldi 2020). The carbon tax has been adopted mainly in OECD countries and in particular in EU Member States (Sen and Vollebergh 2018; Hájek et al. 2019; Bertoldi 2020). There is high agreement that carbon taxes can be effective in reducing CO_2 emissions (Andersson 2017; IPCC 2018; Hájek et al. 2019). It is hard to define the optimum level of taxation in order to achieve the desired level of energy consumption or CO_2 emission reduction (Weisbach et al. 2009). As for other energy efficiency policy distributional effect and equity considerations have to be carefully considered and mitigated (Borozan 2019). High energy

prices tend to reduce the energy consumption particularly in less affluent households, and thus attention is needed in order to avoid unintended effects such as energy poverty. Bourgeois et al. (2021) showed that using carbon tax revenue to finance energy efficiency investment reduces fuel poverty and increases cost-effectiveness. (Giraudet et al. 2021) assessed the cost-effectiveness of various energy efficiency policies in France, concluding that a carbon tax is the most effective. In particular, revenues could be invested in frontline services that can provide a range of support – including advising householders on how to improve their homes. Hence, the introduction of a carbon tax can be neutral or even positive to the economy, as investments in clean technologies generate additional revenues. In addition, in the long term, a carbon/energy tax could gradually replace the tax on labour reducing labour cost (e.g., the example of the German Eco-tax), thus helping to create additional jobs in the economy. In literature, this is known as double dividend (Murtagh et al. 2013; Freire-González and Ho 2019). Urban economic researches (Creutzig 2014; Borck and Brueckner 2018; Rafaj et al. 2018) have highlighted that higher carbon price would translate in incentives for citizens to live closer to the city centre, which often means less floor space, less commuting distance and thus reduced emissions. Xiang and Lawley (2019) indicated that the carbon tax in British Columbia substantially reduced residential natural gas consumption. Saelim (2019) showed that simulated carbon tax on residential consumption in Thailand will have a low impact on welfare and it will be slightly progressive. Lin and Li (2011) indicate that a carbon tax could reduce the energy consumption and boost the uptake of energy efficiency and renewable energies, while at the same time may impact social welfare and the competitiveness of industry. Solaymani (2017) showed that in Malaysia a tax with revenue recycling increases in the welfare of rural and urban households. Van Heerden et al. (2016) explored economic and environmental effects of the CO_2 tax in South Africa highlighting the negative impact on GDP. This negative impact of the carbon tax on GDP is, however, greatly reduced by the manner in which the tax revenue is recycled. National circumstances shall be taken into consideration in introducing energy taxes, considering the local taxation and energy prices context with regard to sustainable development, justice and equity.

A policy, which can have similar impact to a carbon tax and is the energy price/subsidy reform, which also involves raising energy prices. Energy price/subsidy reform reduces energy consumption and greenhouse gas emissions and encourages investment in energy efficiency (Coady et al. 2018; Aldubyan and Gasim, 2021). In a similar manner, government revenues from subsidies reforms can be used to mitigate the distributional impact on vulnerable population groups, including direct cash transfer programmes (Rentschler and Brazilian 2017; Schaffitzel et al. 2020).

Taxes could also be used to penalise inefficient behaviour and favour the adoption of efficient behaviour and technologies. Taxes are used in some jurisdictions to promote energy efficient appliances with lower VAT. Similarly, the annual building/property tax (and also the purchase tax) could be based on the CO_2 emissions of the buildings, rather than on the value of the building. Tax credits are also an important subsidy for the renovation of buildings in France (Giraudet 2020), Italy (Alberini and Bigano 2015) and other countries.

9.9.4 Financing Mechanisms and Business Models for Reducing Energy Demand

Grants and subsidies are traditional financing instruments used by governments when optimal levels of investments cannot be fully supported by the market alone. They can partly help overcoming the upfront cost barrier as they directly fill an immediate financial gap and thus enable a temporary shift in the market (Newell et al. 2019). These forms of support are usually part of policy mixes including further fiscal and financial instruments such as feed-in tariffs and tax breaks (Polzin et al. 2019). Potential issues with subsidies are the limited availability of public financing, the stop and go due to annual budget and the competition with commercial financing.

Loans provide liquidity and direct access to capital important in deep renovation projects (Rosenow et al. 2014). There is empirical evidence (Giraudet et al. 2021), that banks make large profits on personal loans for renovation purposes. International financing institutions (IFIs) and national governments provided subsidies in public-private partnerships so that financial institutions can offer customers loans with attractive terms (Olmos et al. 2012). Loan guarantees are effective in reducing intervention borrowing costs (Soumaré and Lai 2016). Combination of grants and subsidised loans financed by IFIs could be an effective instrument together with guarantees. An important role in financing energy efficiency can be played by green banks, which are publicly capitalised entities set up to facilitate private investment in low-carbon, including energy efficiency (Bahl 2012; Tu and Yen 2015; Linh and Anh 2017; Khan 2018). Green banks have been established at the national level (e.g., UK, Poland) and in the US at state and city level.

Wholesaling of EE of loans and utilities programmes, are other important financing instruments. Another financing mechanism for building efficiency upgrades, mainly implemented so far in the US, is efficiency-as-a-service under an energy services agreement (ESA), where the building owners or tenant pay to the efficiency service provider a charge based on realised energy savings without any upfront cost (Kim et al. 2012; Bertoldi, 2020). ESA providers give performance guarantees assuming the risk that expected savings would occur (Bertoldi, 2020).

Energy Performance Contracting (EPC) is an agreement between a building owner and Energy Services Company (ESCO) for energy efficiency improvements. EPC is a common financing vehicle for large buildings and it is well developed in several markets (Carvallo et al. 2015; Bertoldi and Boza Kiss, 2017; Stuart et al. 2018; Ruan et al. 2018; Nurchahyanto et al. 2020; Zheng et al. 2021). Quality standards are a part of the EPC (Augustins et al. 2018). Guarantees can facilitate the provision of affordable and sufficient financing for ESCOs (Bullier and Milin 2013). The ESCO guarantees a certain level of energy savings and it shields the client from performance risk. The loan goes on the client's balance sheet and the ESCO assumes full project performance risk (Deng et al. 2015). One of the limitations is on the depth of the energy renovation in existing buildings. According to (Giraudet et al. 2018), EPC is effective at reducing information problems between contractors and investors.

Energy efficient mortgages are mortgages that credits a home energy efficiency by offering preferential mortgage terms to extend existing mortgages to finance efficiency improvements. There are two types of energy mortgages: (i) the Energy Efficient Mortgages (EEMs), and (ii) the Energy Improvement Mortgages (EIMs), both can help in overcoming the main barriers to retrofit policies (Miu et al. 2018). The success depends on the improved energy efficiency with a positive impact on property value and on the reduction of energy bills and the income increase in the household. In the EU, the EeMAP Initiative aims to create a standardised energy efficient mortgage template (Bertoldi et al. 2021).

On-bill financing is a mechanism that reduces first-cost barriers by linking repayment of energy efficiency investments to the utility bill and thereby allowing customers to pay back part or all costs of energy efficiency investments over time (Brown 2009). On-bill finance programmes can be categorised into: (i) on-bill loans (assignment of the obligation to the property) and (ii) on-bill tariffs (payment off in case of ownership transfer) (Eadson et al. 2013). On-bill finance programmes can be more effective when set up as a service rather than a loan (Mundaca and Klocke 2018).

Property Assessed Clean Energy (PACE) is a means of financing energy renovations and renewable energy through the use of specific bonds offered by municipal governments to investors (Mills 2016). Municipalities use the funds raised to loan money towards energy renovations in buildings. The loans are repaid over the assigned long term (15–20 years) via an annual assessment on their property tax bill (Kirkpatrick and Bennear 2014). This model has been subject to consumer protection concerns. Residential PACE programmes in California have been shown to increase PV deployment in jurisdictions that adopt these programs (Kirkpatrick and Bennear 2014; Ameli et al. 2017). In US commercial buildings, PACE volumes and programs, however, continue to grow (Lee 2020).

Revolving funds allow reducing investment requirements and enhancing energy efficiency investment impacts by recovering and reinvesting the savings generated (Setyawan 2014). Revolving fund could make retrofit cost-neutral in the long term and could also dramatically increase low carbon investments, including in developing countries (Gouldson et al. 2015).

Carbon finance, started under the Kyoto Protocol with the flexible mechanisms and further enhanced under the Paris Agreement (Michaelowa et al. 2019), is an activity based on 'carbon emission rights' and its derivatives (Liu et al. 2015a). Carbon finance can promote low-cost emission reductions (Zhou and Li 2019). Under Emission Trading Schemes or other carbon pricing mechanisms, auctioning carbon allowances creates a new revenue stream. Revenues from auctioning could be used to finance energy efficiency projects in buildings with grants, zero interest loans or guarantees (Wiese et al. 2020).

Crowdfunding is a new and rapidly growing form of financial intermediation that channels funds from investors to borrowers (individuals or companies) or users of equity capital (companies) without involving traditional financial organisations such as banks (Miller and Carriveau 2018). Typically, it involves internet-based platforms that link savers directly with borrowers (European Union 2015). It can play a significant role at the start of a renewable and sustainable energy projects (Dilger et al. 2017).

The One-Stop Shop (OSS) service providers for buildings energy renovations are organisations, consortia, projects, independent experts or advisors that usually cover the whole or large part of the customer renovation journey from information, technical assistance, structuring and provision of financial support, to the monitoring of savings (Mahapatra et al. 2019; Bertoldi 2021b). OSSs are transparent and accessible advisory tools from the client perspective and new, innovative business models from the supplier perspective (Boza-Kiss and Bertoldi 2018).

9.9.5   Policies Mechanisms for Financing for On-site Renewable Energy Generation

On-site renewable energy generation is a key component for the building sector decarbonisation, complementing sufficiency and efficiency. Renewable energies (RES) technologies still face barriers due to the upfront investment costs, despite the declining price of some technologies, long pay-back period, unpredictable energy production, policy incertitude, architectural (in particular for built-in PV) and landscape considerations, technical regulations for access to the grid, and future electricity costs (Mah et al. 2018; Agathokleous and Kalogirou 2020).

Several policy instruments for RES have been identified by scholars (Fouquet 2013; Azhgaliyeva et al. 2018; Pitelis et al. 2020): direct investments; feed-in tariffs; grants and subsidies; loans and taxes; (tradable) green certificates or renewable/clean energy portfolio standards; information and education; strategic planning; codes and standards; building codes; priority grid access; research, development and deployment and voluntary approaches. There are specific policies for renewable heating and cooling (Connor et al. 2013). In 2011, the UK introduced the Renewable Heat Incentive (RHI) support scheme (Balta-Ozkan et al. 2015; Connor et al. 2015). The RHI guarantee a fixed payment per unit of heat generated by a renewable heat technology for a specific contract duration (Yılmaz Balaman et al. 2019).

The most common implemented policy instruments are the feed-in tariffs (FiTs) and the Renewable/Energy Portfolio Standards (RPSs) (Xin-gang et al. 2017a; Alizada 2018; Bergquist et al. 2020), with FiTs more suited for small scale generation. More than 60 countries and regions worldwide have implemented one of the two policies (Sun and Nie 2015). FiT is a price policy guaranteeing the purchase of energy generation at a specific fixed price for a fixed period (Barbosa et al. 2018; Xin-gang et al. 2020). RPS is a quantitative policy, which impose mandatory quota of RES generation to power generators (Xin-gang et al. 2020).

A flat rate feed-in tariff (FiT) is a well-tested incentive adopted in many jurisdictions to encourage end-users to generate electricity from RES using rooftop and on-site PV systems (Pacudan 2018). More recently, there has been an increasing interest for dynamic FiTs taking into account electricity costs, hosting capacity, ambient temperature, and time of day (Hayat et al. 2019). Since 2014, EU Member States have been obligated to move from FiT to feed-in premium (FiTP) (Hortay and Rozner 2019); where a FiTP consist in a premium of top of the electricity market price. Lecuyer and Quirion (2019) argued that under uncertainty over electricity prices and renewable production costs a flat FiT results in higher welfare than a FiTP. One of the main concerns with

FiT systems is the increasing cost of policies maintenance (Zhang et al. 2018; Pereira da Silva et al. 2019; Roberts et al. 2019a). In Germany, the financial costs, passed on to consumers in the form a levy on the electricity price have increased substantially in recent years (Winter and Schlesewsky 2019) resulting in opposition to the FiT in particular by non-solar customers. A particular set up of the FiT encourage self-consumption through net metering and net billing, which has a lower financial impact on electricity ratepayers compared with traditional FiTs (Pacudan 2018; Roberts et al. 2019b; Vence and Pereira 2019).

In some countries, for example, Australia (Duong et al. 2019), South Korea (Choi et al. 2018a), China (Yi et al. 2019), there was a transition from subsidies under the FiT to market-based mechanisms, such as RPSs and tendering. Compared with FiT, RPS (or Renewable Obligations) reduce the subsidy costs (Zhang et al. 2018). A number of scholars (Xin-gang et al. 2017; Liu et al. 2018a, 2019a) have highlighted the RPSs' effectiveness in promoting the development of renewable energy. Other authors (Requate 2015; An et al. 2015) have presented possible negative impacts of RPSs.

Both FiT and RPS can support the development of RES. Scholars compared the effectiveness of RPSs and FiTs with mix results and different opinions, with some scholars indicating the advantages of RPS (Ciarreta et al. 2014, 2017; Xin-gang et al. 2017), while Nicolini and Tavoni (2017) showed that in Italy FiTs are outperforming RPSs and Tradable Green Certificates (TGCs). García-Álvarez et al. (2018) carried out an empirical assessment of FiTs and RPSs for PV systems energy in EU over the period 2000–2014 concluding that that FiTs have a significant positive impact on installed PV capacity. This is due to the small size of many rooftop installations and the difficulties in participating in trading schemes for residential end users. Similar conclusions were reached by (Dijkgraaf et al. 2018) assessing 30 OECD countries and concluding that there is a 'positive effect of the presence of a FiT on the development of a country's added yearly capacity of PV'. Other scholars (Lewis and Wiser 2007; Lipp 2007; Cory et al. 2009; Couture and Gagnon 2010) concluded that FiT can create a stable investment framework and long-term policy certainty and it is better than RPS for industrial development and job creation. Ouyang and Lin (2014) highlighted that RPS has a better implementation effect than FiT in China, where FiT required very large subsidy. Ford et al. (2007) showed that TGC is a market-based mechanism without the need for government subsidies. Marchenko (2008) and Wędzik et al. (2017) indicate that the TGCs provide a source of income for investors. Choi et al. (2018a) analysed the economic efficiency of FiT and RPS in the South Korean, where FiT was implemented from 2002 to 2011 followed by an RPS since 2012 (Park and Kim 2018; Choi et al. 2018b). Choi concluded that RPS was more efficient for PV from the government's perspective while from an energy producers' perspective the FiT was more efficient. Some scholars proposed a policy combining FiT and RPS (Cory et al. 2009). Kwon (2015) and del Río et al. (2017) concluded that both FiT and RPS are effective, but policy costs are higher in RPSs than FiTs. RPS, REC trading and FiT subsidy could also be implemented as complementary policies (Zhang et al. 2018).

Tenders are a fast spreading and effective instrument to attract and procure new generation capacity from renewable energy sources (Bayer et al. 2018; Batz and Musgens 2019; Bento et al. 2020;

Ghazali et al. 2020; Haelg 2020). A support scheme based on tenders allows a more precise steering of expansion and lower risk of excessive support (Gephart et al. 2017). Bento et al. (2020) indicated that tendering is more effective in promoting additional renewable capacity comparing to other mechanisms such as FiTs. It is also important to take into account the rebound effect in energy consumption by on-site PV users, which might reduce up to one fifth of the carbon benefit of renewable energy (Deng and Newton 2017).

Financing mechanisms for RES are particularly needed in developing countries. Most of the common supporting mechanisms (FiT, RPSs, PPA, auctions, net metering, etc.) have been implemented in some developing countries (Donastorg et al. 2017). Stable policies and an investment-friendly environment are essential to overcome financing barriers and attract investors (Donastorg et al. 2017). Kimura et al. (2016) identified the following elements as essential for fostering RES in developing countries: innovative business models and financial mechanisms/structures; market creation through the implementation of market-based mechanisms; stability of policies and renewable energy legislation; technical assistance to reduce the uncertainty of renewable energy production; electricity market design, which reflects the impact on the grid capacity and grid balancing; improved availability of financial resources, in particular public, and innovative financial instruments, such as carbon financing (Lim et al. 2013; Park et al. 2018; Kim and Park 2018); green bonds; public foreign exchange hedging facility for renewable energy financing, credit lines; grants and guarantees.

The end-user will be at the centre as a key participant in the future electricity system (Zepter et al. 2019; Lavrijssen and Carrillo Parra, 2017) providing flexibility, storage, energy productions, peer-to-peer trading, electric vehicle charging. Zepter indicates that 'the current market designs and business models lack incentives and opportunities for electricity consumers to become prosumers and actively participate in the market'. Klein et al. (2019) explore the policy options for aligning prosumers with the electricity wholesale market, through price and scarcity signals. Policies should allow for active markets participation of small prosumers (Brown et al. 2019; Zepter et al. 2019), local energy communities and new energy market actors such as aggregators (Iria and Soares 2019; Brown et al. 2019). Energy Communities are new important players in the energy transition (Sokołowski 2020; Gjorgievski et al. 2021). Citizens and local communities can establish local energy communities, providing local RES production to serve the community, alleviate energy poverty and export energy into the grid (DellaValle and Sareen, 2020; Hahnel et al. 2020). Energy Communities have as primary purpose to provide environmental, economic, or social community benefits by engaging in generation, aggregation, energy storage, energy efficiency services and charging services for electric vehicles. Energy communities help in increasing public acceptance and mobilise private funding. Demand response aggregators (Mahmoudi et al. 2017; Henriquez et al. 2018) can aggregate load reductions by a group of consumers, and sell the resulting flexibility to the electricity market (Zancanella et al. 2017). Regulatory frameworks for electricity markets should allow demand response to compete on equal footing in energy markets and encourage new business models for the provision of flexibility to the electricity grid (Shen et al. 2014). Renewable energy and sufficiency requirements could be included in building energy codes and implemented in coordination with each other and with climate policies, for example, carbon pricing (Oikonomou et al. 2014).

9.9.6   Investment in Building Decarbonisation

As Section 9.6.3 points out, the incremental investment cost to decarbonise buildings at national level is up to 3.5% GDP per annum

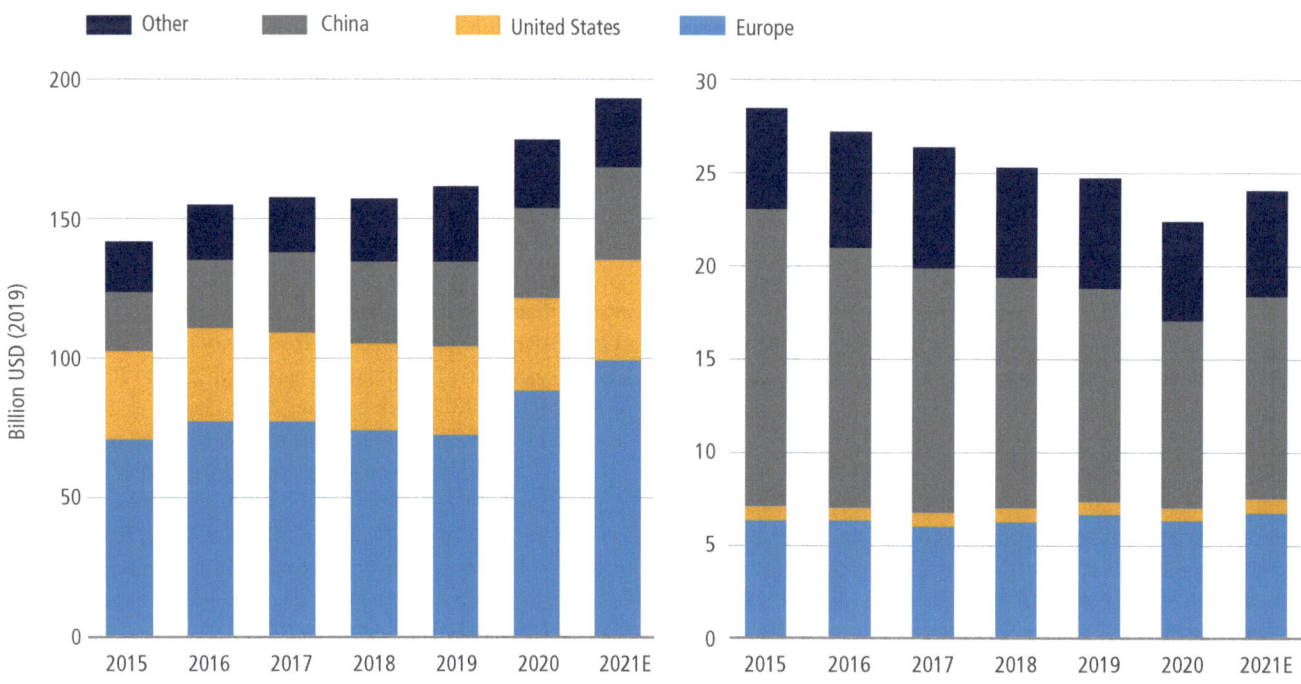

Figure 9.21 | Incremental capital expenditure on energy efficiency investment (left) and renewable heat in buildings, 2015–2021. Notes: (i) An energy efficiency investment is defined as the incremental spending on new energy-efficient equipment or the full cost of refurbishments that reduce energy use. (ii) Renewable heat for end-use include solar thermal applications (for district, space, and water heating), bioenergy and geothermal energy, as well as heat pumps. (iii) The investment in 2021 is an estimate. Source: IEA 2021b.

during the next thirty years (the global GDP in 2019 was USD88 trillion). As the following figures illustrate, only a very small share of it is currently being invested, leaving a very large investment gap still to address. The incremental capital expenditure on energy efficiency in buildings has grown since AR5 to reach the estimated USD193 billion in 2021; Europe was the largest investing region, followed by the USA and China (Figure 9.21). The incremental capital expenditure on renewable energy heat vice versa declined to reach USD24 billion in this year; the leading investor was China, followed by Europe (ibid). The total capital expenditure on distributed small-scale (less than 1MW) solar systems in 2019 was USD52.1 billion, down from the peak of USD71 billion in 2011; most of this capacity is installed in buildings (Frankfurt School-UNEP Centre/BNEF 2020). The US was the largest country market with USD9.6 billion investment; notably USD5 billion was deployed in the Middle East and Africa (ibid). IEA (2021b) provided an estimate of annual average incremental investment needs in building sector decarbonation between 2026 and 2030 of USD711 billion, including USD509 billion in building energy efficiency and USD202 billion in renewable heat for end-use and electrification in buildings. Such investment would allow being on track towards meeting the goals of the WEO Net Zero Emissions Scenario, as presented in Box 9.2. To reach these levels, the respective investment must grow from their average volumes in 2016–2020 factor 3.6 and 4.5 respectively. As the investment needs estimated by (IEA 2021b) are significantly lower the investment intervals reported by bottom-up literature (Section 9.6.3), the actual investment gap is likely to be higher.

9.9.7   Governance and Institutional Capacity

9.9.7.1   Governance

Multi-level and polycentric governance is essential for implementing sufficiency, energy efficiency and renewable energies policies (IPCC 2018). Policies can be implemented at different levels of government and decision making, international, national, regional, and local. Policies for building have be adopted at national level (Enker and Morrison 2017), at state or regional level (Fournier et al. 2019), or at city level (Trencher and van der Heijden 2019). Zhao et al. (2019) find that national policies are instrumental in driving low carbon developments in buildings.

International agreements (Kyoto, Montreal/Kigali, Paris, etc.) play an important role in establishing national energy-efficiency and renewable energy policies in several countries (Dhar et al. 2018; Bertoldi 2018). Under the Paris Agreement, some NDCs contain emission reduction targets for subsectors, for example, buildings, policies for subsectors and energy efficiency and/or renewable targets (see also Cross-Chapter Box 5 in Chapter 4). In the EU since 2007 climate and energy policies are part of a co-ordinated policy package. EU Member States have prepared energy efficiency plans every three years and long-term renovation strategies for buildings (Economidou et al. 2020). Under the new Energy and Climate Governance Regulation EU Member States have submitted at the end of 2020 integrated National Energy and Climate Plans, including energy efficiency and renewable plans. (Oberthur 2019; Schlacke and Knodt 2019). The integration of energy and climate change policies and their governance has been analysed

(von Lüpke and Well 2020), highlighting the need of reinforcing the institutions, anticipatory governance, the inconsistency of energy policies and the emerging multi-level governance.

Some policies are best implemented at international level. Efficiency requirements for traded goods and the associated test methods could be set at global level in order to enlarge the market, avoid technical barriers to trade; reduce the manufacturers design and compliance costs. International standards could be applied to developing countries when specific enabling conditions exist, particularly in regard to technology transfer, assistance for capacity buildings and financial support. This would also reduce the dumping of inefficient equipment in countries with no or lower efficiency requirements. An example is the dumping of new or used inefficient cooling equipment in developing countries, undermining national and local efforts to manage energy, environment, health, and climate goals. Specific regulations can be put in place to avoid such environmental dumping, beginning with the 'prior informed consent' as in the Rotterdam Convention and a later stage with the adoption of minimum efficiency requirements for appliances (Andersen et al. 2018; UNEP 2017). Dreyfus et al. (2020a) indicates that global policies to promote best technologies currently available have the potential to reduce climate emissions from air conditionings and refrigeration equipment by 210–460 GtCO$_2$-eq by 2060, resulting from the phasing down of HFC and from improved energy efficiency. Another example is the commitment by governments in promoting improvements in energy efficiency of cooling equipment in parallel with the phasedown of HFC refrigerants enshrined in the Biarritz Pledge for Fast Action on Efficient Cooling signed in 2019. The policy development and implementation costs will be reduced as the technical analysis leading to the standard could be shared among governments. However, it is important that local small manufacturing companies in developing countries have the capacity to invest in updating production lines for meeting new stringent international efficiency requirements.

Building energy consumption is dependent on local climate and building construction traditions, regional and local government share an important role in promoting energy efficiency in buildings and on-site RES, through local building energy codes, constructions permits and urban planning. In South Korea, there is a green building certification system operated by the government, based on this, Seoul has enacted Seoul's building standard, which includes more stringent requirements. Where it is difficult to retrofit existing buildings, for example, historical buildings, cities may impose target at district level, where RES could be shared among buildings with energy positive buildings compensating for energy consuming buildings. Local climate and urban plans could also contribute to the integration of the building sector with the local transport, water, and energy sectors, requiring, for example, new constructions in areas served by public transport, close to offices or buildings to be ready for e-mobility. Buildings GHG emission reduction shall also be considered in greenfield and brownfield developments and urban expansion (Loo et al. 2017; Salviati and Ricciardo Lamonica 2020), including co-benefits (Zapata-Diomedi et al. 2019).

Energy efficiency, sufficiency, and renewable policies and measures will have a large impact on different stakeholders (citizens, construction companies; equipment manufacturers; utilities, etc.), several studies highlighted the importance of stakeholder consultation and active participation in policy making and policy implementation (Vasileiadou and Tuinstra 2013; Ingold et al. 2020), including voluntary commitments and citizen assemblies. In particular, energy user's role will be transformed from passive role to an active role, as outlined in the concept of energy citizenship (Campos and Marín-González 2020). The energy citizens need and voice should therefore be included in policy processes among traditional business players, such as incumbent centralised power generation companies and utilities (Van Veelen 2018). Architects and engineers play an important role in the decarbonisation of buildings. The professional bodies can mandate their members support energy efficiency and sufficiency. For example, the US AIA states in their code of ethics that architects must inform clients of climate risks and opportunities for sustainability. The capacity and quality of workforce and building construction, retrofit, and service firms are essential to execute the fast transition in building systems (Cross-Chapter Box 12 in Chapter 16).

9.9.7.2   Institutional Capacity

The concept of institutional capacity is increasingly connected with the issue of public governance, emphasising the broad institutional context within which individual policies are adopted. Institutions are durable and are sources of authority (formal or informal) structuring repeated interactions of individuals, companies, civil society groups, governments, and other entities. Thus, institutional capacity also represents a broader 'enabling environment' which forms the basis upon which individuals and organisations interact. In general terms, capacity is 'the ability to perform functions, solve problems and set and achieve objectives' (Fukuda-Parr et al. 2002). Institutional capacity is an important element for regional sustainable development (Farajirad et al. 2015). The role and importance of institutional capacity is fundamental in implementing the building decarbonisation. Central and local governments, regulatory organisations, financial institutions, standardisation bodies, test laboratories, building construction and design companies, qualified workforce and stakeholders are key players in supporting the implementation of building decarbonisation.

Governments (from national to local) planning to introduce efficiency, RES, and sufficiency policies needs technical capacity to set sectoral targets and design policies and introduce effective and enforcement with adequate structure and resources for their implementation. Policies discussed and agreed with stakeholders and based on impartial data and impact assessments, have a higher possibility of success. Public authorities need technical and economics competences to understand complex technical issues and eliminate the knowledge gap in comparison to private sector experts, human and financial resources to design, implement, revise, and evaluate policies. The role of energy efficiency policy evaluation needs to be expanded, including the assessment of the rebound effect (Vine et al. 2013). For developing countries international support for institutional capacity for policy development, implementation and evaluation is of key importance for testing laboratory, standards institute, enforcement and compliances technicians and evaluation

experts. Thus, in development support, addition to technology transfer, also capacity buildings for national and local authorities should be provides. The Paris Agreement Article 11 aims at enhancing the capacity of decision-making institutions in developing countries to support effective implementation.

Enforcement of policies is of key importance. Policies on appliance energy standards need to establish criteria for random checks and tests of compliance, establish penalties and sanctions for non-compliance. For building code compliance there is the need to verify compliance after construction to verify the consistence with building design (Vine et al. 2017). Often local authorities lack resources and technical capacity to carry out inspections to check code compliance. This issue is even more pressing in countries and cities with large informal settlements, where buildings may not be respecting building energy codes for safety and health.

9.10   Knowledge Gaps

Insights from regions, sectors, and communities:

- Due to the dominating amount of literature from Developed Countries and rapidly developing Asia (China), the evidence and therefore conclusions are limited for the developing world. In particular, there is limited evidence on the potential and costs the countries of South-East Asia and Pacific, Africa, and Latin America and Caribbean.
- The contribution of indigenous knowledge in the evolvement of buildings is not well appreciated. There is a need to understand this contribution and provide methodological approaches for incorporation of indigenous knowledge.
- Analysis of emissions and energy demand trends in non-residential buildings is limited due to the number of building types included in this category and the scarcity of data for each building type. The use of new data gathering techniques such as machine learning, GIS combined with digital technologies to fill in this data gap was not identified in the literature. Consideration of embodied emissions from building stock growth has only recently entered the global scenario literature, and more development is expected in this area.

Measures, potentials, and costs:

- There is a lack of scientific reporting of case studies of exemplary buildings, specially from developing countries. Also, there is a lack of identification of researchers on technologies with the mitigation potential of such technologies, bringing a lack in quantification of that potential.
- There is limited evidence on sufficiency measures including those from behavioural energy saving practices: updated categorisations, current adoption rates and willingness to adopt.
- There is limited evidence on circular and shared economy in buildings, including taxonomies, potentials, current adoption rates and willingness to adopt.

- Most of the literature on climate change impacts on buildings is focused on thermal comfort. There is need for further research on climate change impacts on buildings structure, materials and construction and the energy and emissions associated with those impacts. Also, more studies that assess the role of passive energy efficiency measures as adaptation options are needed. Finally, regional studies leave out in depth analyses of specific regions.

Feasibility and policies:

- Applications of human centred profiles for targeted policy making and considering stages of diffusion of innovation, that is: what works (motivation) for whom (different stakeholders, not only households) and when (stages of market maturity).
- The multiple co-benefits of mitigation actions are rarely integrated into decision-making processes. So, there is a need to further develop methodologies to quantify and monetise these externalities as well as indicators to facilitate their incorporation in energy planning.
- Policies for sufficiency have to be further analysed and tested in real situation, including *ex ante* simulation and *ex post* evaluation. The same is also valid for Personable (tradable) Carbon Allowances.

Methods and models:

- There is limited literature on the integration of behavioural measures and lifestyle changes in modelling exercises.
- Mitigation potential resulting from the implementation of sufficiency measures is not identified in global energy/climate and building scenarios despite the growing literature on sufficiency. At the best, mitigation potential from behaviour change is quantified in energy scenarios; savings from structural changes and resource efficiency are not identified in the literature on global and building energy models.
- The actual costs of the potential could be higher to rather optimistic assumptions of the modelling literature, for example, assuming a 2–3% retrofit rate, and even higher, versus the current 1%. The uncertainty ranges of potential costs are not well understood.
- Despite a large number of exemplary buildings achieving very high performance in all parts of the world and a growing amount of modelling literature on the potential, if these will penetrate at scale, there is a lack of modelling literature assessing the costs of respective actions at national, regional, and global level based on comprehensive cost assessments.
- There is a lack of peer-reviewed literature on investment gaps, which compares the investment need in the building sector decarbonisation and recent investment flows into it estimated with the same costing methodologies.

9

Frequently Asked Questions (FAQs)

FAQ 9.1 | To which GHG emissions do buildings contribute?

There are three categories of GHG emissions from buildings:

i.   direct emissions which are defined as all on-site fossil fuel or biomass-based combustion activities (i.e., use of biomass for cooking, or gas for heating and hot water) and F-gas emissions (i.e., use of heating and cooling systems, aerosols, fire extinguishers, soundproof);

ii. indirect emissions which occur off-site and are related to heat and electricity production; and

iii. embodied emissions which are related to extracting, producing, transforming, transporting, and installing the construction material and goods used in buildings.

In 2019, global GHG emissions from buildings were at 12 $GtCO_2$-eq out of which 24% were direct emissions, 57% were indirect emissions, and 18% were embodied emissions. More than 95% of emissions from buildings were CO_2 emissions, CH_4 and N_2O represented 0.08% each and emissions from halocarbon contributed by 3% to global GHG emissions from buildings.

FAQ 9.2 | What are the co-benefits and trade-offs of mitigation actions in buildings?

Mitigation actions in buildings generate multiple co-benefits (e.g., health benefits due to the improved indoor and outdoor conditions, productivity gains in non-residential buildings, creation of new jobs particularly at local level, improvements in social well-being etc.) beyond their direct impact on reducing energy consumption and GHG emissions. Most studies agree that the value of these multiple benefits is greater than the value of energy savings and their inclusion in economic evaluation of mitigation actions may improve substantially their cost-effectiveness. It is also worth mentioning that in several cases the buildings sector is characterised by strong rebound effects, which could be considered as a co-benefit in cases where the mechanisms involved provide faster access to affordable energy but also a trade-off in cases where the external costs of increased energy consumption exceed the welfare benefits of the increased energy service consumption, thus lowering the economic performance of mitigation actions. The magnitude of these co-benefits and trade-offs are characterised by several uncertainties, which may be even higher in the future as mitigation actions will be implemented in a changing climate, with changing building operation style and occupant behaviour. Mitigation measures influence the degree of vulnerability of buildings to future climate change. For instance, temperature rise can increase energy consumption, which may lead to higher GHG emissions. Also, sea level rise, increased storms and rainfall under future climate may impact building structure, materials and components, resulting in increased energy consumption and household expenditure from producing and installing new components and making renovations. Well-planned energy efficiency, sufficiency and on-site renewable energy production can help to increase building resilience to climate change impacts and reduce adaptation needs.

FAQ 9.3 | Which are the most effective policies and measures to decarbonise the building sector?

Several barriers (information, financing, markets, behavioural, etc.) still prevents the decarbonisation of buildings stock, despite the several co-benefits, including large energy savings. Solutions include investments in technological solutions (e.g., insulation, efficient equipment, and low-carbon energies and renewable energies) and lifestyle changes. In addition, the concept of sufficiency is suggested to be promoted and implemented through policies and information, as technological solutions will be not enough to decarbonise the building sector. Due to the different types of buildings, occupants, and development stage there is not a single policy, which alone will reach the building decarbonisation target. A range of policy instruments ranging from regulatory measures such as building energy code for NZEBs and appliance standards, to market-based instruments (carbon tax, personal carbon allowance, renewable portfolio standards, etc.) and information. Financing (grants, loans, performance base incentives, pays as you save, etc.) is another key enabler for energy efficiency technologies and on-site renewables. Finally, effective governance and strong institutional capacity are key to have an effective and successful implementation of policies and financing.

References

Abrahamse, W. and L. Steg, 2013: Social influence approaches to encourage resource conservation: A meta-analysis. *Glob. Environ. Chang.*, **23(6)**, 1773–1785, doi:10.1016/j.gloenvcha.2013.07.029.

Abreu, J., N. Wingartz, and N. Hardy, 2019: New trends in solar: A comparative study assessing the attitudes towards the adoption of rooftop PV. *Energy Policy*, **128** (January), 347–363, doi:10.1016/j.enpol.2018.12.038.

Abubakar, I., S.N. Khalid, M.W. Mustafa, H. Shareef, and M. Mustapha, 2017: Application of load monitoring in appliances' energy management – A review. *Renew. Sustain. Energy Rev.*, **67**, 235–245, doi:10.1016/j.rser.2016.09.064.

ACE, 2019: *The Architectural Professsion in Europe 2018 – A Sector Study*. Architects' Council of Europe, Brussels, Belgium, 106 pp. https://www.ace-cae.eu/activities/publications/sector-study-2018/ (Accessed April 1, 2021).

Acil Allen Consulting, 2015: *Commercial building disclosure – Program Review Final Report*. 130 pp. https://www.cbd.gov.au/sites/default/files/2020-09/cbd_program_review_final_report.pdf.

ADB, 2017: *Pathways to Low-Carbon Development for Viet Nam*. Asian Development Bank, Phillippines, 138 pp. https://www.adb.org/sites/default/files/publication/389826/pathways-low-carbon-devt-viet-nam.pdf.

Agathokleous, R.A. and S.A. Kalogirou, 2020: Status, barriers and perspectives of building integrated photovoltaic systems. *Energy*, **191**, doi:10.1016/j.energy.2019.116471.

Agrawal, V.V, and I. Bellos, 2017: The Potential of Servicizing as a Green Business Model. *Manage. Sci.*, **63(5)**, 1545–1562, doi:10.1287/mnsc.2015.2399.

Agustí-Juan, I., F. Müller, N. Hack, T. Wangler, and G. Habert, 2017: Potential benefits of digital fabrication for complex structures: Environmental assessment of a robotically fabricated concrete wall. *J. Clean. Prod.*, **154**, 330–340, doi:10.1016/j.jclepro.2017.04.002.

Ahl, A., G. Accawi, B. Hudey, M. Lapsa, and T. Nichols, 2019: Occupant Behavior for Energy Conservation in Commercial Buildings: Lessons Learned from Competition at the Oak Ridge National Laboratory. *Sustainability*, **11(12)**, 3297, doi:10.3390/su11123297.

Ajayi, S.O. et al., 2015: Waste effectiveness of the construction industry: Understanding the impediments and requisites for improvements. *Resour. Conserv. Recycl.*, **102**, 101–112, doi:10.1016/j.resconrec.2015.06.001.

Ajayi, S.O. et al., 2017: Attributes of design for construction waste minimization: A case study of waste-to-energy project. *Renew. Sustain. Energy Rev.*, **73** (June 2015), 1333–1341, doi:10.1016/j.rser.2017.01.084.

Akander, J., M. Cehlin, and B. Moshfegh, 2017: Assessing the Myths on Energy Efficiency When Retrofitting Multifamily Buildings in a Northern Region. In: *Sustainable High Rise Buildings in Urban Zones: Advantages, Challenges, and Global Case Studies* [Sayigh, A., (ed.)]. Springer International Publishing, Cham, Switzerland, pp. 139–161.

Akenji, L. et al., 2021: *1.5°C lifestyles report – Policy Approaches For a Fair Consumption Space*. Hot or Cool Institute, Berlin, Germany, 164 pp.

Alaidroos, A. and M. Krarti, 2015: Optimal design of residential building envelope systems in the Kingdom of Saudi Arabia. *Energy Build.*, **86**, 104–117, doi:10.1016/j.enbuild.2014.09.083.

Alam, M., P.X.W. Zou, J. Sanjayan, and S. Ramakrishnan, 2019: Energy saving performance assessment and lessons learned from the operation of an active phase change materials system in a multi-storey building in Melbourne. *Appl. Energy*, **238** (November 2018), 1582–1595, doi:10.1016/j.apenergy.2019.01.116.

Alawneh, R., F. Ghazali, H. Ali, and M. Asif, 2019: A new index for assessing the contribution of energy efficiency in LEED 2009 certified green buildings to achieving UN sustainable development goals in Jordan. *Int. J. Green Energy*, **16(6)**, 490–499, doi:10.1080/15435075.2019.1584104.

Alberini, A. and A. Bigano, 2015: How effective are energy-efficiency incentive programs? Evidence from Italian homeowners. *Energy Econ.*, **52**, S76–S85, doi:10.1016/j.eneco.2015.08.021.

Alcorn, A. and P. Wood, 1998: *Recent work in embodied enrgy analysis of New Zealand building materials*. Centre for Building Performance Research, Victoria University of Wellington, Wellington, New Zealand, 1–23 pp. https://www.wgtn.ac.nz/architecture/centres/cbpr/projects/pdfs/ee-finalreport-vol2.pdf.

Alcott, B., 2008: The sufficiency strategy: Would rich-world frugality lower environmental impact? *Ecol. Econ.*, **64(4)**, 770–786, doi:10.1016/j.ecolecon.2007.04.015.

Aldrich, E.L. and C.L. Koerner, 2018: White certificate trading: A dying concept or just making its debut? Part II: Challenges to trading white certificates. *Electr. J.*, **31(4)**, 41–47, doi:10.1016/j.tej.2018.05.006.

Alexandri, E., et al., 2016: *The Macroeconomic and Other Benefits of Energy Efficiency*. European Union, 138 pp. https://ec.europa.eu/energy/sites/ener/files/documents/final_report_v4_final.pdf.

Aldubyan, M. and A. Gasim, 2021: Energy price reform in Saudi Arabia: Modeling the economic and environmental impacts and understanding the demand response. *Energy Policy*, **148**, 111941, doi:10.1016/j.enpol.2020.111941.

Alipour M., H. Salim, O. Sahin, R.A. Stewart, 2020: Predictors, taxonomy of predictors, and correlations of predictors with the decision behaviour of residential solar photovoltaics adoption: A review. *Renew. Sustain. ENERGY Rev.*, **123**, doi:10.1016/j.rser.2020.109749.

Alizada, K., 2018: Rethinking the diffusion of renewable energy policies: A global assessment of feed-in tariffs and renewable portfolio standards. *Energy Res. Soc. Sci.*, **44**, 346–361, doi:10.1016/j.erss.2018.05.033.

Allen, J.G. et al., 2015: Green Buildings and Health. *Curr. Environ. Heal. Reports*, **2(3)**, 250–258, doi:10.1007/s40572-015-0063-y.

Allwood, J.M., M.F. Ashby, T.G. Gutowski, and E. Worrell, 2011: Material efficiency: A white paper. *Resour. Conserv. Recycl.*, **55(3)**, 362–381, doi:10.1016/j.resconrec.2010.11.002.

Amal, B., S. Issam, C. Ghassan, E.-F. Mutasem, and K. Jalal, 2017: Behavioral determinants towards enhancing construction waste management: A Bayesian Network analysis. *Resour. Conserv. Recycl.*, **117**, 274–284, doi:10.1016/j.resconrec.2016.10.006.

Ameli, N., M. Pisu, and D.M. Kammen, 2017: Can the US keep the PACE? A natural experiment in accelerating the growth of solar electricity. *Appl. Energy*, **191**, 163–169, doi:10.1016/j.apenergy.2017.01.037.

Amirifard, F., S.A. Sharif, and F. Nasiri, 2019: Application of passive measures for energy conservation in buildings – a review. *Adv. Build. Energy Res.*, **13(2)**, 282–315, doi:10.1080/17512549.2018.1488617.

An, X. and G. Pivo, 2020: Green Buildings in Commercial Mortgage-Backed Securities: The Effects of LEED and Energy Star Certification on Default Risk and Loan Terms. *Real Estate Econ.*, **48(1)**, 7–42, doi:10.1111/1540-6229.12228.

An, X., C. Zhao, S. Zhang, and X. Li, 2015: *Joint equilibrium analysis of electricity market with tradable green certificates*. 2015 5th International Conference on Electric Utility Deregulation and Restructuring and Power Technologies (DRPT). IEEE, 29–34, doi:10.1109/DRPT.2015.7432215. https://ieeexplore.ieee.org/document/7432215.

Andersen, S.O. et al., 2018: Defining the Legal and Policy Framework to Stop the Dumping of Environmentally Harmful Products. *Duke Environ. Law Policy Forum*, **29**, 1–48. https://scholarship.law.duke.edu/cgi/viewcontent.cgi?article=1356&context=delpf.

Anderson, D.M., D.B. Belzer, O.V. Livingston, and M.J. Scott, 2014: *Assessing National Employment Impacts of Investment in Residential and Commercial Sector Energy Efficiency: Review and Example Analysis*. Pacific Northwest National Laboratory, Richland, WA, USA, 100 pp.

Andersson, J., 2017: *Cars, carbon taxes and CO₂ emissions*. Centre for Climate Change Economics, London, UK, 42 pp.

Andjelković, A.S., J.R. Petrović, and M.V. Kljajić, 2016: Double or single skin façade in a moderate climate an energyplus assessment. *Therm. Sci.*, **20**, S1501–S1510, doi:10.2298/TSCI16S5501A.

Andrić, I., M. Koc, and S.G. Al-Ghamdi, 2019: A review of climate change implications for built environment: Impacts, mitigation measures and associated challenges in developed and developing countries. *J. Clean. Prod.*, **211**, 83–102, doi:10.1016/j.jclepro.2018.11.128.

Ang, B.W. and F.Q. Zhang, 2000: A survey of index decomposition analysis in energy and environmental studies. *Energy*, **25(12)**, 1149–1176, doi:10.1016/S0360-5442(00)00039-6.

Annibaldi, V., F. Cucchiella, P. De Berardinis, M. Gastaldi, and M. Rotilio, 2020: An integrated sustainable and profitable approach of energy efficiency in heritage buildings. *J. Clean. Prod.*, **251**, 119516, doi:10.1016/j.jclepro.2019.119516.

Arawomo, D.F., 2019: Is Giffen behaviour compatible with residential demand for cooking gas and kerosene? Evidence from a state in Nigeria. *Int. J. Energy Sect. Manag.*, **13(1)**, 45–59, doi:10.1108/IJESM-04-2016-0007.

Arnone, D. et al., 2016: Energy management of multi-carrier smart buildings for integrating local renewable energy system. *5th International Conference on Renewable Energy Research and Applications*, Birmingham, UK, 845–850 pp.

Aro, R., 2020: 'A bigger living room required a bigger TV': Doing and negotiating necessity in well-to-do households. *J. Consum. Cult.*, **20(4)**, 498–520, doi:10.1177/1469540517745706.

Aroonruengsawat, A., 2012: The Impact of State Level Building Codes on Residential Electricity Consumption. *Energy J.*, **33(1)**, doi:10.5547/ISSN0195-6574-EJ-Vol33-No1-2. https://www.iaee.org/energyjournal/article/2466.

ARUP, 2018: *From principles to practices. First steps towards a circular built environment*. ARUP, London, UK, 14 pp.

Aryandoust, A. and J. Lilliestam, 2017: The potential and usefulness of demand response to provide electricity system services. *Appl. Energy*, **204**, 749–766, doi:10.1016/j.apenergy.2017.07.034.

Asbjørn, K., 2009: Classification of Building Element Functions. *26th International Conference on IT in Construction & 1st International Conference on Managing Construction for Tomorrow*. 2009. 301–307 pp.

Asdrubali, F., G. Baldinelli, and F. Bianchi, 2012: A quantitative methodology to evaluate thermal bridges in buildings. *Appl. Energy*, **97**, 365–373, doi:10.1016/j.apenergy.2011.12.054.

Atalla, T., S. Bigerna, C.A. Bollino, and P. Polinori, 2018: An alternative assessment of global climate policies. *J. Policy Model.*, **40(6)**, 1272–1289, doi:10.1016/j.jpolmod.2018.02.003.

Attia, S., M. Hamdy, and S. Ezzeldin, 2017: Twenty-year tracking of lighting savings and power density in the residential sector. *Energy Build.*, **154**, 113–126, doi:10.1016/j.enbuild.2017.08.041.

Audebert, M., D. Dhima, A. Bouchaïr, and A. Frangi, 2019: Review of experimental data for timber connections with dowel-type fasteners under standard fire exposure. *Fire Saf. J.*, **107** (October), 217–234, doi:10.1016/j.firesaf.2019.102905.

Auffhammer, M., 2014: Cooling China: The weather dependence of air conditioner adoption. *Front. Econ. China*, **9(1)**, 70–84, doi:10.3868/s060-003-014-0005-5.

Auffhammer, M. and E.T. Mansur, 2014: Measuring climatic impacts on energy consumption: A review of the empirical literature. *Energy Econ.*, **46**, 522–530, doi:10.1016/j.eneco.2014.04.017.

Auffhammer, M., P. Baylis, and C.H. Hausman, 2017: Climate change is projected to have severe impacts on the frequency and intensity of peak electricity demand across the United States. *Proc. Natl. Acad. Sci.*, **114(8)**, 1886–1891, doi:10.1073/pnas.1613193114.

Augustins, E., D. Jaunzems, C. Rochas, and A. Kamenders, 2018: Managing energy efficiency of buildings: analysis of ESCO experience in Latvia. *Energy Procedia*, **147**, 614–623, doi:10.1016/j.egypro.2018.07.079.

Aunan, K. et al., 2013: Upgrading to cleaner household stoves and reducing chronic obstructive pulmonary disease among women in rural china – a cost-benefit analysis. *Energy Sustain. Dev.*, **17(5)**, 489–496, doi:10.1016/j.esd.2013.06.002.

Aung, T.W. et al., 2016: Health and Climate-Relevant Pollutant Concentrations from a Carbon-Finance Approved Cookstove Intervention in Rural India. *Environ. Sci. Technol.*, **50(13)**, 7228–7238, doi:10.1021/acs.est.5b06208.

Avgerinou, M., P. Bertoldi, and L. Castellazzi, 2017: Trends in Data Centre Energy Consumption under the European Code of Conduct for Data Centre Energy Efficiency. *Energies*, **10(10)**, 1–18, doi:10.3390/en10101470.

Aydin, E., N. Kok, and D. Brounen, 2017: Energy efficiency and household behavior: the rebound effect in the residential sector. *RAND J. Econ.*, **48(3)**, 749–782, doi:10.1111/1756-2171.12190.

Aydin, E., D. Brounen, and N. Kok, 2018: Information provision and energy consumption: Evidence from a field experiment. *Energy Econ.*, **71**, 403–410, doi:10.1016/j.eneco.2018.03.008.

Ayoub, M., 2019: A multivariate regression to predict daylighting and energy consumption of residential buildings within hybrid settlements in hot-desert climates. *Indoor Built Environ.*, **28(6)**, 848–866, doi:10.1177/1420326X18798164.

Ayoub, N., F. Musharavati, S. Pokharel, and H.A. Gabbar, 2014: Energy consumption and conservation practices in Qatar – A case study of a hotel building. *Energy Build.*, **84**, 55–69, doi:10.1016/j.enbuild.2014.07.050.

Ayres, R.U., 1995: Environmental Market Failures: Are There Any Local Market-Based Corrective Mechanisms for Global Problems? *Mitig. Adapt. Strateg. Glob. Chang.*, **1(3)**, 289–309, doi:10.1023/B:MITI.0000018138.12428.65.

Azhgaliyeva, D., M. Belitski, Y. Kalyuzhnova, and M. Romanov, 2018: Policy instruments for renewable energy: an empirical evaluation of effectiveness. *Int. J. Technol. Intell. Plan.*, **12(1)**, 24, doi:10.1504/IJTIP.2018.094409.

Azmi, W.H., M.Z. Sharif, T.M. Yusof, R. Mamat, and A.A.M. Redhwan, 2017: Potential of nanorefrigerant and nanolubricant on energy saving in refrigeration system – A review. *Renew. Sustain. Energy Rev.*, **69** (October 2016), 415–428, doi:10.1016/j.rser.2016.11.207.

Bach, L., D. Hopkins, and J. Stephenson, 2020: Solar electricity cultures: Household adoption dynamics and energy policy in Switzerland. *Energy Res. Soc. Sci.*, **63**, doi:10.1016/j.erss.2019.101395.

Bahaidarah, H., A. Subhan, P. Gandhidasan, and S. Rehman, 2013: Performance evaluation of a PV (photovoltaic) module by back surface water cooling for hot climatic conditions. *Energy*, **59**, 445–453, doi:10.1016/j.energy.2013.07.050.

Bahl, S., 2012: The Role of Green Banking in Sustainable Growth. *Int. J. Mark. Financ. Serv. Manag. Res.*, **1(2)**, 27–35.

Bailis, R., R. Drigo, A. Ghilardi, and O. Masera, 2015: The carbon footprint of traditional woodfuels. *Nat. Clim. Change*, **5(3)**, 266–272, doi:10.1038/nclimate2491.

Baimel, D., S. Tapuchi, and N. Baimel, 2016: Smart Grid Communication Technologies. *J. Power Energy Eng.*, **04(08)**, 1–8, doi:10.4236/jpee.2016.48001.

Baker, K.J., R. Mould, and S. Restrick, 2018: Rethink fuel poverty as a complex problem. *Nat. Energy*, **3(8)**, 610–612, doi:10.1038/s41560-018-0204-2.

Balaban, O. and J.A. Puppim de Oliveira, 2017: Sustainable buildings for healthier cities: assessing the co-benefits of green buildings in Japan. *J. Clean. Prod.*, **163**, S68–S78, doi:10.1016/j.jclepro.2016.01.086.

Baloch, A.A. et al., 2018: Simulation tools application for artificial lighting in buildings. *Renew. Sustain. Energy Rev.*, **82** (March 2017), 3007–3026, doi:10.1016/j.rser.2017.10.035.

Balta-Ozkan, N., J. Yildirim, and P.M. Connor, 2015: Regional distribution of photovoltaic deployment in the UK and its determinants: A spatial econometric approach. *Energy Econ.*, **51** (2015), 417–429, doi:10.1016/j.eneco.2015.08.003.

Barbosa, L., P. Ferrão, A. Rodrigues, and A. Sardinha, 2018: Feed-in tariffs with minimum price guarantees and regulatory uncertainty. *Energy Econ.*, **72**, doi:10.1016/j.eneco.2018.04.028.

Barkhordarian, A., H. von Storch, E. Zorita, P.C. Loikith, and C.R. Mechoso, 2018: Observed warming over northern South America has an anthropogenic origin. *Clim. Dyn.*, **51(5–6)**, 1901–1914, doi:10.1007/s00382-017-3988-z.

Barnes, D.F. and H. Samad, 2018: *Measuring the Benefits of Energy Access: A Handbook for Development Practitioners*. Inter-American Development Bank, Washington, DC, USA, 252 pp.

Barnes, J. and S.M. Bhagavathy, 2020: The economics of heat pumps and the (un)intended consequences of government policy. *Energy Policy*, **138**, 111198, doi:10.1016/j.enpol.2019.111198.

Bartolini, M., E. Bottani, and E.H. Grosse, 2019: Green warehousing: Systematic literature review and bibliometric analysis. *J. Clean. Prod.*, **226**, 242–258, doi:10.1016/j.jclepro.2019.04.055.

Bartusch, C. and K. Alvehag, 2014: Further exploring the potential of residential demand response programs in electricity distribution. *Appl. Energy*, **125**, 39–59, doi:10.1016/j.apenergy.2014.03.054.

Basbagill, J., F. Flager, M. Lepech, and M. Fischer, 2013: Application of life-cycle assessment to early stage building design for reduced embodied environmental impacts. *Build. Environ.*, **60**, 81–92, doi:10.1016/j.buildenv.2012.11.009.

Bashmakov, I., 2017: Improving the Energy Efficiency of Russian Buildings. *Probl. Econ. Transit.*, **58(11–12)**, 1096–1128, doi:10.1080/10611991.2016.1316099.

Bastidas-Arteaga, E., A. Chateauneuf, M. Sánchez-Silva, P. Bressolette, and F. Schoefs, 2010: Influence of weather and global warming in chloride ingress into concrete: A stochastic approach. *Struct. Saf.*, **32(4)**, 238–249, doi:10.1016/j.strusafe.2010.03.002.

Batchelor, S., E. Brown, N. Scott, and J. Leary, 2019: Two birds, one stone-reframing cooking energy policies in Africa and Asia. *Energies*, **12(9)**, 1591, doi:10.3390/en12091591.

Batz, T. and F. Musgens, 2019: *A first analysis of the photovoltaic auction program in Germany*. 16th International Conference on the European Energy Market (EEM), 18–20 September 2019. IEEE Ljubljana, Slovenia. 1–5pp.

Bauer, E., E. Pavón, E. Barreira, and E. Kraus De Castro, 2016: Analysis of building facade defects using infrared thermography: Laboratory studies. *J. Build. Eng.*, **6**, 93–104, doi:10.1016/j.jobe.2016.02.012.

Bauer, E., P.M. Milhomem, and L.A.G. Aidar, 2018: Evaluating the damage degree of cracking in facades using infrared thermography. *J. Civ. Struct. Heal. Monit.*, **8(3)**, 517–528, doi:10.1007/s13349-018-0289-0.

Baumhof, R., T. Decker, H. Röder, and K. Menrad, 2018: Which factors determine the extent of house owners' energy-related refurbishment projects? A Motivation-Opportunity-Ability Approach. *Sustain. Cities Soc.*, **36**, 33–41, doi:10.1016/j.scs.2017.09.025.

Bavaresco, M.V., S. D'Oca, E. Ghisi, and R. Lamberts, 2020: Methods used in social sciences that suit energy research: A literature review on qualitative methods to assess the human dimension of energy use in buildings. *Energy Build.*, **209**, 109702, doi:10.1016/j.enbuild.2019.109702.

Bayer, B., D. Schäuble, and M. Ferrari, 2018: International experiences with tender procedures for renewable energy – A comparison of current developments in Brazil, France, Italy and South Africa. *Renew. Sustain. Energy Rev.*, **95**, 305–327, doi:10.1016/j.rser.2018.06.066.

Bedir, M., E. Hasselaar, and L. Itard, 2013: Determinants of electricity consumption in Dutch dwellings. *Energy Build.*, **58**, 194–207, doi:10.1016/j.enbuild.2012.10.016.

Bednar, D.J. and T.G. Reames, 2020: Recognition of and response to energy poverty in the United States. *Nat. Energy*, **5(6)**, 432–439, doi:10.1038/s41560-020-0582-0.

Ben-David, T., A. Rackes, and M.S. Waring, 2017: Alternative ventilation strategies in U.S. offices: Saving energy while enhancing work performance, reducing absenteeism, and considering outdoor pollutant exposure tradeoffs. *Build. Environ.*, **116**, 140–157, doi:10.1016/j.buildenv.2017.02.004.

Bento, N., M. Borello, and G. Gianfrate, 2020: Market-pull policies to promote renewable energy: A quantitative assessment of tendering implementation. *J. Clean. Prod.*, **248**, doi:10.1016/j.jclepro.2019.119209.

Berezan, O., C. Raab, M. Yoo, and C. Love, 2013: Sustainable hotel practices and nationality: The impact on guest satisfaction and guest intention to return. *Int. J. Hosp. Manag.*, **34(1)**, 227–233, doi:10.1016/j.ijhm.2013.03.010.

Berger, T. and A. Höltl, 2019: Thermal insulation of rental residential housing: Do energy poor households benefit? A case study in Krems, Austria. *Energy Policy*, **127** (October 2018), 341–349, doi:10.1016/j.enpol.2018.12.018.

Bergquist, M., A. Nilsson, and E. Ejelöv, 2019: Contest-Based and Norm-Based Interventions: (How) Do They Differ in Attitudes, Norms, and Behaviors? *Sustainability*, **11(2)**, 425, doi:10.3390/su11020425.

Berrill, P. and E.G. Hertwich, 2021: Material flows and GHG emissions from housing stock evolution in US counties, 2020–60. *Build. Cities*, **2(1)**, 599–617, doi:10.5334/bc.126.

Berrill, P., K.T. Gillingham, and E.G. Hertwich, 2021: Linking Housing Policy, Housing Typology, and Residential Energy Demand in the United States. *Environ. Sci. Technol.*, **55(4)**, doi:10.1021/acs.est.0c05696.

Berrueta, V.M., M. Serrano-Medrano, C. García-Bustamante, M. Astier, and O.R. Masera, 2017: Promoting sustainable local development of rural communities and mitigating climate change: the case of Mexico's Patsari improved cookstove project. *Clim. Change*, **140(1)**, 63–77, doi:10.1007/s10584-015-1523-y.

Bertoldi, P., 2018: The Paris Agreement 1.5°C goal: what it does mean for energy efficiency? *Proceeding of 2018 ACEEE Summer Study on Energy Efficiency in Buildings*. American Council for an Energy-Efficient Economy, Washington, DC, USA, 268 pp.

Bertoldi, P., 2019: Policies, Recommendations and Standards (International Technical Standards, Main Laws and Regulations; EU Directives; Energy Labeling). In: *Handbook of Energy Efficiency in Buildings* [Asdrubali, F. and U. Desideri, (eds.)]. Elsevier, pp. 5–73.

Bertoldi, P., 2020: Overview of the European Union policies to promote more sustainable behaviours in energy end-users. In: *Energy and Behaviour* [Lopes, M., C.H. Antunes, and K.B. Janda, (eds.)]. Academic Press, pp. 451–477.

Bertoldi, P. and B. Boza-Kiss, 2017: Analysis of barriers and drivers for the development of the ESCO markets in Europe. *Energy Policy*, **107**, 345–355, doi:10.1016/j.enpol.2017.04.023.

Bertoldi, P. and R. Mosconi, 2020: Do energy efficiency policies save energy? A new approach based on energy policy indicators (in the EU Member States). *Energy Policy*, **139** (January), 111320, doi:10.1016/j.enpol.2020.111320.

Bertoldi, P., N. Labanca, S. Rezessy, S. Steuwer, and V. Oikonomou, 2013a: Where to place the saving obligation: Energy end-users or suppliers? *Energy Policy*, **63**, 328–337, doi:10.1016/j.enpol.2013.07.134.

Bertoldi, P., S. Rezessy, and V. Oikonomou, 2013b: Rewarding energy savings rather than energy efficiency: Exploring the concept of a feed-in tariff for energy savings. *Energy Policy*, **56**, 526–535, doi:10.1016/j.enpol.2013.01.019.

Bertoldi, P., M. Economidou, V. Palermo, B. Boza-Kiss, and V. Todeschi, 2021: How to finance energy renovation of residential buildings: Review of current and emerging financing instruments in the EU. *WIREs Energy Environ.*, **10(1)**, doi:10.1002/wene.384.

Besagni, G. and M. Borgarello, 2019: The socio-demographic and geographical dimensions of fuel poverty in Italy. *Energy Res. Soc. Sci.*, **49** (October 2018), 192–203, doi:10.1016/j.erss.2018.11.007.

Bevilacqua, P., F. Benevento, R. Bruno, and N. Arcuri, 2019: Are Trombe walls suitable passive systems for the reduction of the yearly building energy requirements? *Energy*, **185**, 554–566, doi:10.1016/j.energy.2019.07.003.

Bezerra, P. et al., 2021: Impacts of a warmer world on space cooling demand in Brazilian households. *Energy Build.*, **234**, 110696, doi:10.1016/j.enbuild.2020.110696.

Biardeau, L.T., L.W. Davis, P. Gertler, and C. Wolfram, 2020: Heat exposure and global air conditioning. *Nat. Sustain.*, **3(1)**, 25–28, doi:10.1038/s41893-019-0441-9.

Bienvenido-Huertas, D., C. Rubio-Bellido, A. Pérez-Fargallo, and J.A. Pulido-Arcas, 2020: Energy saving potential in current and future world built environments based on the adaptive comfort approach. *J. Clean. Prod.*, **249**, 119306, doi:10.1016/j.jclepro.2019.119306.

Bienvenido-Huertas, D., C. Rubio-Bellido, D. Marín-García, and J. Canivell, 2021: Influence of the Representative Concentration Pathways (RCP) scenarios on the bioclimatic design strategies of the built environment. *Sustain. Cities Soc.*, **72**, 103042, doi:10.1016/j.scs.2021.103042.

Bierwirth, A. and S. Thomas, 2019a: *Energy sufficiency in buildings Concept paper*. European Council for an Energy Efficient Economy, 48 pp. https://www.energysufficiency.org/static/media/uploads/site-8/library/papers/sufficiency-buildings-final__v2.pdf.

Bierwirth, A. and S. Thomas, 2019b: *Estimating the sufficiency potential in buildings: the space between under-dimensioned and oversized*. European Council for an Energy Efficient Economy, 12 pp.

Bird, S. and D. Hernández, 2012: Policy options for the split incentive: Increasing energy efficiency for low-income renters. *Energy Policy*, **48**, 506–514, doi:10.1016/j.enpol.2012.05.053.

Birgisdottir, H. et al., 2017: IEA EBC annex 57 'evaluation of embodied energy and CO_2eq for building construction'. *Energy Build.*, **154**, 72–80, doi:10.1016/j.enbuild.2017.08.030.

Bissiri, M., I.F.G. Reis, N.C. Figueiredo, and P. Pereira da Silva, 2019: An econometric analysis of the drivers for residential heating consumption in the UK and Germany. *J. Clean. Prod.*, **228**, 557–569, doi:10.1016/j.jclepro.2019.04.178.

Bjarnadottir, S., Y. Li, and M.G. Stewart, 2011: A probabilistic-based framework for impact and adaptation assessment of climate change on hurricane damage risks and costs. *Struct. Saf.*, **33(3)**, 173–185, doi:10.1016/j.strusafe.2011.02.003.

Blair, M.J., B. Gagnon, A. Klain, and B. Kulišić, 2021: Contribution of biomass supply chains for bioenergy to sustainable development goals. *Land*, **10(2)**, 1–28, doi:10.3390/land10020181.

Bleyl, J.W. et al., 2019: Office building deep energy retrofit: life cycle cost benefit analyses using cash flow analysis and multiple benefits on project level. *Energy Effic.*, **12(1)**, 261–279, doi:10.1007/s12053-018-9707-8.

Bloess, A., W.-P. Schill, and A. Zerrahn, 2018: Power-to-heat for renewable energy integration: A review of technologies, modeling approaches, and flexibility potentials. *Appl. Energy*, **212**, 1611–1626, doi:10.1016/j.apenergy.2017.12.073.

Boermans, T., G. Papaefthymiou, M. Offermann, A. John, and F. Comaty, 2015: *The role of energy efficient buildings in the EUs future power system*. ECOFYS Germany GmbH, 34 pp.

Bojić, M., K. Johannes, and F. Kuznik, 2014: Optimizing energy and environmental performance of passive Trombe wall. *Energy Build.*, **70**, 279–286, doi:10.1016/j.enbuild.2013.11.062.

Bollinger, B. and K. Gillingham, 2012: Peer Effects in the Diffusion of Solar Photovoltaic Panels. *Mark. Sci.*, **31(6)**, 900–912, doi:10.1287/mksc.1120.0727.

Borck, R. and J.K. Brueckner, 2018: Optimal energy taxation in cities. *J. Assoc. Environ. Resour. Econ.*, **5(2)**, 481–516, doi:10.1086/695614.

Borenstein, S., 2015: A microeconomic framework for evaluating energy efficiency rebound and some implications. *Energy J.*, **36(1)**, 1–21, doi:10.5547/01956574.36.1.1.

Borozan, D., 2019: Unveiling the heterogeneous effect of energy taxes and income on residential energy consumption. *Energy Policy*, **129**, 13–22, doi:10.1016/j.enpol.2019.01.069.

Bosello, F. and E. De Cian, 2014: Climate change, sea level rise, and coastal disasters. A review of modeling practices. *Energy Econ.*, **46**, 593–605, doi:10.1016/j.eneco.2013.09.002.

Boucher, J.L., K. Araújo, and E. Hewitt, 2018: Do education and income drive energy audits? A socio-spatial analysis of New York State. *Resour. Conserv. Recycl.*, **136**, 355–366, doi:10.1016/j.resconrec.2018.05.009.

Bourgeois, C., L.G. Giraudet, and P. Quirion, 2019: Social-environmental-economic trade-offs associated with carbon-tax revenue recycling. *ECEEE 2019 Summer Study Proceedings*, 1365–1372.

Bove, G., A. Becker, B. Sweeney, M. Vousdoukas, and S. Kulp, 2020: A method for regional estimation of climate change exposure of coastal infrastructure: Case of USVI and the influence of digital elevation models on assessments. *Sci. Total Environ.*, **710**, 136162, doi:10.1016/j.scitotenv.2019.136162.

Boyd, K., 2016: Policies to reduce urban GHG emissions: Accounting for heterogeneity of demographics, values, and urban form. PhD Thesis, Simon Fraser University, British Columbia, Canada, 95 pp.

Boza-Kiss, B. and P. Bertoldi, 2018: *One-stop-shops for energy renovations of buildings*. European Commission, Ispra, Italy, 69 pp. https://e3p.jrc.ec.europa.eu/publications/one-stop-shops-energy-renovations-buildings.

Bradley, P., A. Coke, and M. Leach, 2016: Financial incentive approaches for reducing peak electricity demand, experience from pilot trials with a UK energy provider. *Energy Policy*, **98**, 108–120, doi:10.1016/j.enpol.2016.07.022.

Brambilla, A. and E. Gasparri, 2020: Hygrothermal behaviour of emerging timber-based envelope technologies in Australia: A preliminary investigation on condensation and mould growth risk. *J. Clean. Prod.*, **276**, 124129, doi:10.1016/j.jclepro.2020.124129.

Brancalion, P.H.S. et al., 2018: Fake legal logging in the Brazilian Amazon. *Sci. Adv.*, **4(8)**, 1–8, doi:10.1126/sciadv.aat1192.

Braubach, M. and A. Ferrand, 2013: Energy efficiency, housing, equity and health. *Int. J. Public Health*, **58(3)**, 331–332, doi:10.1007/s00038-012-0441-2.

Brennan, T.J. and K.L. Palmer, 2013: Energy efficiency resource standards: Economics and policy. *Util. Policy*, **25** (2013), 58–68, doi:10.1016/j.jup.2013.02.001.

Bright, S., D. Weatherall, and R. Willis, 2019: Exploring the complexities of energy retrofit in mixed tenure social housing: a case study from England, UK. *Energy Effic.*, **12(1)**, 157–174, doi:10.1007/s12053-018-9676-y.

Bristow, A.L., M. Wardman, A.M. Zanni, and P.K. Chintakayala, 2010: Public acceptability of personal carbon trading and carbon tax. *Ecol. Econ.*, **69(9)**, doi:10.1016/j.ecolecon.2010.04.021.

Broad, O., G. Hawker, and P.E. Dodds, 2020: Decarbonising the UK residential sector: The dependence of national abatement on flexible and local views of the future. *Energy Policy*, **140**, doi:10.1016/j.enpol.2020.111321.

Brounen, D. and N. Kok, 2011: On the economics of energy labels in the housing market. *J. Environ. Econ. Manage.*, **62(2)**, 166–179, doi:10.1016/j.jeem.2010.11.006.

Brounen, D., N. Kok, and J.M. Quigley, 2012: Residential energy use and conservation: Economics and demographics. *Eur. Econ. Rev.*, **56(5)**, 931–945, doi:10.1016/j.euroecorev.2012.02.007.

Brown, D., S. Hall, and M.E. Davis, 2019: Prosumers in the post subsidy era: an exploration of new prosumer business models in the UK. *Energy Policy*, **135**, doi:10.1016/j.enpol.2019.110984.

Brown, M.H., 2009: *Helping Small Business Reduce Emissions and Energy Use While Improving Profitability On-Bill Financing*. Conover Brown LLC, 32 pp. https://www.ohioenvironmentallawblog.com/wp-content/uploads/sites/576/uploads/file/09OBFNSBA[1].pdf.

Brown, Z., N. Johnstone, I. Haščič, L. Vong, and F. Barascud, 2013: Testing the effect of defaults on the thermostat settings of OECD employees. *Energy Econ.*, **39**, 128–134, doi:10.1016/j.eneco.2013.04.011.

Brucal, A. and M.J. Roberts, 2019: Do energy efficiency standards hurt consumers? Evidence from household appliance sales. *J. Environ. Econ. Manage.*, **96**, 88–107, doi:10.1016/j.jeem.2019.04.005.

Brugger, H., W. Eichhammer, N. Mikova, and E. Dönitz, 2021: Energy Efficiency Vision 2050: How will new societal trends influence future energy demand in the European countries? *Energy Policy*, **152**, doi:10.1016/j.enpol.2021.112216.

Buchanan, K., R. Russo, and B. Anderson, 2015: The question of energy reduction: The problem(s) with feedback. *Energy Policy*, **77**, 89–96, doi:10.1016/j.enpol.2014.12.008.

Buchanan, K., S. Staddon, and D. van der Horst, 2018: Feedback in energy-demand reduction. *Build. Res. Inf.*, **46(3)**, 231–237, doi:10.1080/09613218.2018.1412981.

Bullier, A. and C. Milin, 2013: Alternative financing schemes for energy efficiency in buildings. *ECEE 2013 Summer Study – Rethink, Renew, Restart*. ECEE Summer Study Proceedings, Stockholm, Sweden. ECEE, 10, 952869. 795–805 pp.

Bürger, V., T. Hesse, B. Köhler, A. Palzer, and P. Engelmann, 2019: German Energiewende—different visions for a (nearly) climate neutral building sector in 2050. *Energy Effic.*, **12(1)**, doi:10.1007/s12053-018-9660-6.

Burgess, M., 2016: Personal carbon allowances: A revised model to alleviate distributional issues. *Ecol. Econ.*, **130**, 316–327, doi:10.1016/j.ecolecon.2016.08.002.

Burnett, D., E. Barbour, and G.P. Harrison, 2014: The UK solar energy resource and the impact of climate change. *Renew. Energy*, **71**, 333–343, doi:10.1016/j.renene.2014.05.034.

Burney, J., H. Alaofè, R. Naylor, and D. Taren, 2017: Impact of a rural solar electrification project on the level and structure of women's empowerment. *Environ. Res. Lett.*, **12(9)**, doi:10.1088/1748-9326/aa7f38.

Butler, C. et al., 2020: *Decarbonisation futures: Solutions, actions and benchmarks for a net zero emissions Australia*. ClimateWorks Australia, Melbourne, Australia, 138 pp.

Cabeza, L.F. and M. Chàfer, 2020: Technological options and strategies towards zero energy buildings contributing to climate change mitigation: a systematic review. *Energy Build.*, **219**, 110009, doi:10.1016/j.enbuild.2020.110009.

Cabeza, L.F. et al., 2010: Experimental study on the performance of insulation materials in Mediterranean construction. *Energy Build.*, **42(5)**, 630–636, doi:10.1016/j.enbuild.2009.10.033.

Cabeza, L.F. et al., 2013: Low carbon and low embodied energy materials in buildings: A review. *Renew. Sustain. Energy Rev.*, **23**, 536–542, doi:10.1016/j.rser.2013.03.017.

Cabeza, L.F., D. Urge-Vorsatz, M.A. McNeil, C. Barreneche, and S. Serrano, 2014: Investigating greenhouse challenge from growing trends of electricity consumption through home appliances in buildings. *Renew. Sustain. Energy Rev.*, **36**, 188–193, doi:10.1016/j.rser.2014.04.053.

Cabeza, L.F., A. de Gracia, and A.L. Pisello, 2018a: Integration of renewable technologies in historical and heritage buildings: A review. *Energy Build.*, **177**, 96–111, doi:10.1016/j.enbuild.2018.07.058.

Cabeza, L.F., D. Ürge-Vorsatz, D. Ürge, A. Palacios, and C. Barreneche, 2018b: Household appliances penetration and ownership trends in residential buildings. *Renew. Sustain. Energy Rev.*, **98**, 1–8, doi:10.1016/j.rser.2018.09.006.

Cabeza, L.F., M. Chàfer, and É. Mata, 2020: Comparative Analysis of Web of Science and Scopus on the Energy Efficiency and Climate Impact of Buildings. *Energies*, **13(2)**, 409, doi:10.3390/en13020409.

Cabeza, L.F., L. Boquera, M. Chàfer, and D. Vérez, 2021: Embodied energy and embodied carbon of structural building materials: Worldwide progress and barriers through literature map analysis. *Energy Build.*, **231**, 110612, doi:10.1016/j.enbuild.2020.110612.

Cabrera Serrenho, A., M. Drewniok, C. Dunant, and J.M. Allwood, 2019: Testing the greenhouse gas emissions reduction potential of alternative strategies for the english housing stock. *Resour. Conserv. Recycl.*, **144**, 267–275, doi:10.1016/j.resconrec.2019.02.001.

Cajias, M., F. Fuerst, and S. Bienert, 2019: Tearing down the information barrier: the price impacts of energy efficiency ratings for buildings in the German rental market. *Energy Res. Soc. Sci.*, **47** (May 2017), 177–191, doi:10.1016/j.erss.2018.08.014.

Calì, D., T. Osterhage, R. Streblow, and D. Müller, 2016: Energy performance gap in refurbished German dwellings: Lesson learned from a field test. *Energy Build.*, **127**, 1146–1158, doi:10.1016/j.enbuild.2016.05.020.

Calise, F. et al., 2021: Energy and economic assessment of energy efficiency options for energy districts: Case studies in Italy and Egypt. *Energies*, **14(4)**, 1–24, doi:10.3390/en14041012.

Camarinha-Matos, L.M., 2016: Collaborative smart grids – A survey on trends. *Renew. Sustain. Energy Rev.*, **65**, 283–294, doi:10.1016/j.rser.2016.06.093.

Cameron, C. et al., 2016: Policy trade-offs between climate mitigation and clean cook-stove access in South Asia. *Nat. Energy*, **1(1)**, 1–5, doi:10.1038/nenergy.2015.10.

Campbell, A., 2018: Price and income elasticities of electricity demand: Evidence from Jamaica. *Energy Econ.*, **69**, 19–32, doi:10.1016/j.eneco.2017.10.040.

Campos, I. and E. Marín-González, 2020: People in transitions: Energy citizenship, prosumerism and social movements in Europe. *Energy Res. Soc. Sci.*, **69**, doi:10.1016/j.erss.2020.101718.

Camprubí, L. et al., 2016: Façade insulation retrofitting policy implementation process and its effects on health equity determinants: A realist review. *Energy Policy*, **91**, 304–314, doi:10.1016/j.enpol.2016.01.016.

Cancio Díaz, Y. et al., 2017: Limestone calcined clay cement as a low-carbon solution to meet expanding cement demand in emerging economies. *Dev. Eng.*, **2**, 82–91, doi:10.1016/j.deveng.2017.06.001.

Candido, C. et al., 2019: Designing activity-based workspaces: satisfaction, productivity and physical activity. *Build. Res. Inf.*, **47(3)**, 275–289, doi:10.1080/09613218.2018.1476372.

Cantzler, J. et al., 2020: Saving resources and the climate? A systematic review of the circular economy and its mitigation potential. *Environ. Res. Lett.*, **15(12)**, 123001, doi:10.1088/1748-9326/abbeb7.

Capozzoli, A., A. Gorrino, and V. Corrado, 2013: A building thermal bridges sensitivity analysis. *Appl. Energy*, **107**, 229–243, doi:10.1016/j.apenergy.2013.02.045.

Carrasco, L.R., T.P. Le Nghiem, Z. Chen, and E.B. Barbier, 2017: Unsustainable development pathways caused by tropical deforestation. *Sci. Adv.*, **3(7)**, 1–10, doi:10.1126/sciadv.1602602.

Carvallo, J.P., P.H. Larsen, and C.A. Goldman, 2015: Estimating customer electricity and fuel savings from projects installed by the US ESCO industry. *Energy Effic.*, **8**, 1251–1261, doi:10.1007/s12053-015-9405-8.

Castellazzi, L., P. Bertoldi, and M. Economidou, 2017: *Overcoming the split incentive barrier in the building sector – Unlocking the energy efficiency potential in the rental & multifamily sectors*. Publications Office of the European Union, Luxembourg, 4 pp.

Cattaneo, C., 2019: Internal and external barriers to energy efficiency: which role for policy interventions? *Energy Effic.*, **12(5)**, 1293–1311, doi:10.1007/s12053-019-09775-1.

Cattano, C., R. Valdes-Vasquez, J.M. Plumblee, and L. Klotz, 2013: Potential solutions to common barriers experienced during the delivery of building renovations for improved energy performance: Literature review and case study. *J. Archit. Eng.*, **19(3)**, 164–167, doi:10.1061/(ASCE)AE.1943-5568.0000126.

Cavalagli, N., A. Kita, V.L. Castaldo, A.L. Pisello, and F. Ubertini, 2019: Hierarchical environmental risk mapping of material degradation in historic masonry buildings: An integrated approach considering climate change and structural damage. *Constr. Build. Mater.*, **215**, 998–1014, doi:10.1016/j.conbuildmat.2019.04.204.

Cayla, J.-M., N. Maizi, and C. Marchand, 2011: The role of income in energy consumption behaviour: Evidence from French households data. *Energy Policy*, **39(12)**, 7874–7883, doi:10.1016/j.enpol.2011.09.036.

CE100, 2016: *Capturing the value of Circular Economy through Reverse Logistics*. 1–20 pp. https://www.dpdhl.com/content/dam/dpdhl/en/media-center/media-relations/documents/2018/circular-economy-reverse-logistics-maturity-model-042016.pdf.

Cedeño-Laurent, J.G. et al., 2018: Building Evidence for Health: Green Buildings, Current Science, and Future Challenges. *Annu. Rev. Public Health*, **39(1)**, 291–308, doi:10.1146/annurev-publhealth-031816-044420.

Cézard, F. and M. Mourad, 2019: *Panorama sur la notion de Sobriété – définitions, mises en œuvre, enjeux (rapport final)*. 52 pp.

Chaichaloempreecha, A., P. Winyuchakrit, and B. Limmeechokchai, 2017: Long-term energy savings and GHG mitigations in Thailand's building sector: Impacts of energy efficiency plan. *Energy Procedia*, **138**, 847–852, doi:10.1016/j.egypro.2017.10.110.

9

Chakravorty, U., M. Pelli, and B. Ural Marchand, 2014: Does the quality of electricity matter? Evidence from rural India. *J. Econ. Behav. Organ.*, **107(PA)**, 228–247, doi:10.1016/j.jebo.2014.04.011.

Chan, N.W. and K. Gillingham, 2015: The microeconomic theory of the rebound effect and its welfare implications. *J. Assoc. Environ. Resour. Econ.*, **2(1)**, 133–159, doi:10.1086/680256.

Charlier, D. and B. Legendre, 2019: A Multidimensional Approach to Measuring Fuel Poverty. *Energy J.*, **40(2)**, doi:10.5547/01956574.40.2.bleg.

Charlier, D., A. Risch, and C. Salmon, 2018: Energy Burden Alleviation and Greenhouse Gas Emissions Reduction: Can We Reach Two Objectives With One Policy? *Ecol. Econ.*, **143**, 294–313, doi:10.1016/j.ecolecon.2017.07.002.

Chatterjee, S. and D. Ürge-Vorsatz, 2018: *WP5 Social welfare: Quantification of productivity impacts. D5.4a Final report*. ABUD, Budapest, Hungary, 76 pp.

Chegut, A., P. Eichholtz, and N. Kok, 2014: Supply, Demand and the Value of Green Buildings. *Urban Stud.*, **51(1)**, 22–43, doi:10.1177/0042098013484526.

Chen, G., Y. Lv, Y. Zhang, and M. Yang, 2021: Carbonation depth predictions in concrete structures under changing climate condition in China. *Eng. Fail. Anal.*, **119**, 104990, doi:10.1016/j.engfailanal.2020.104990.

Chen, K., Z. Li, T.-P. Lu, P.-L.P. Rau, and D. Huang, 2018: *Cross-Cultural Design. Applications in Cultural Heritage, Creativity and Social Development*. Springer International Publishing, Cham, Switzerland, 266–274 pp.

Chen, Q., B. Li, and X. Liu, 2013: An experimental evaluation of the living wall system in hot and humid climate. *Energy Build.*, **61**, 298–307, doi:10.1016/j.enbuild.2013.02.030.

Cheong, C. and D. Storey, 2019: *Meeting Global Housing Needs with Low-Carbon Materials*. Global Green Growth Institute, Seoul, South Korea, 38 pp.

Ching, F.D.K., 2014: *Building Construction Illustrated*. 5th ed. John Wiley & Sons, Inc., Hoboken, New Jersey, USA, 480 pp.

Chitnis, M., S. Sorrell, A. Druckman, S.K. Firth, and T. Jackson, 2013: Turning lights into flights: Estimating direct and indirect rebound effects for UK households. *Energy Policy*, **55**, 234–250, doi:10.1016/j.enpol.2012.12.008.

Choi, B.-E. et al., 2018a: Energy Performance Evaluation and Economic Analysis of Insulation Materials of Office Building in Korea. *Adv. Civ. Eng.*, **2018**, 1–8, doi:10.1155/2018/9102391.

Choi, G., S.-Y. Huh, E. Heo, and C.-Y. Lee, 2018b: Prices versus quantities: Comparing economic efficiency of feed-in tariff and renewable portfolio standard in promoting renewable electricity generation. *Energy Policy*, **113**, doi:10.1016/j.enpol.2017.11.008.

Christidou, C., K.P. Tsagarakis, and C. Athanasiou, 2014: Resource management in organized housing settlements, a case study at Kastoria Region, Greece. *Energy Build.*, **74**, 17–29, doi:10.1016/j.enbuild.2014.01.012.

Chu, J. and E. Bowman, 2006: *Long-live the machine. How ecodesign & energy labelling can prevent premature obsolescence of laptops*. ECOS, 1–3 pp. https://ecostandard.org/wp-content/uploads/2020/02/LONG-LIVE-THE-MACHINE-ECOS-REPORT.pdf.

Chu, W.X. and C.C. Wang, 2019: A review on airflow management in data centers. *Appl. Energy*, **240** (February 2019), 84–119, doi:10.1016/j.apenergy.2019.02.041.

Chun, N. and Y. Jiang, 2013: How households in Pakistan take on energy efficient lighting technology. *Energy Econ.*, **40**, 277–284, doi:10.1016/j.eneco.2013.07.006.

Chunekar, A., 2014: Standards and Labeling program for refrigerators: Comparing India with others. *Energy Policy*, **65**, 626–630, doi:10.1016/j.enpol.2013.09.069.

Churkina, G. et al., 2020: Buildings as a global carbon sink. *Nat. Sustain.*, **3(4)**, 269–276, doi:10.1038/s41893-019-0462-4.

Ciarreta, A., M.P. Espinosa, and C. Pizarro-Irizar, 2014: Switching from Feed-in Tariffs to a Tradable Green Certificate Market. In: *The Interrelationship Between Financial and Energy Markets* [Ramos, S. and H. Veiga, (eds.)]. Springer, Berlin Heidelberg, Germany. 261–280.

Ciarreta, A., M.P. Espinosa, and C. Pizarro-Irizar, 2017: Optimal regulation of renewable energy: A comparison of Feed-in Tariffs and Tradable Green Certificates in the Spanish electricity system. *Energy Econ.*, **67** (2017), 387–399, doi:10.1016/j.eneco.2017.08.028.

Ciscar, J.C. and P. Dowling, 2014: Integrated assessment of climate impacts and adaptation in the energy sector. *Energy Econ.*, **46**, 531–538, doi:10.1016/j.eneco.2014.07.003.

Clancy, J.M., J. Curtis, and B.P. O'Gallachóir, 2017: What are the factors that discourage companies in the Irish commercial sector from investigating energy saving options? *Energy Build.*, **146**, 243–256, doi:10.1016/j.enbuild.2017.04.077.

Clarke, L. et al., 2018: Effects of long-term climate change on global building energy expenditures. *Energy Econ.*, **72**, 667–677, doi:10.1016/j.eneco.2018.01.003.

Claudy, M.C., C. Michelsen, and A. O'Driscoll, 2011: The diffusion of microgeneration technologies – assessing the influence of perceived product characteristics on home owners' willingness to pay. *Energy Policy*, **39(3)**, 1459–1469, doi:10.1016/j.enpol.2010.12.018.

Coady, D., I.W.H. Parry, and B. Shang, 2018: Energy Price Reform: Lessons for Policymakers. *Rev. Environ. Econ. Policy*, **12(2)**, 197–219, doi:10.1093/reep/rey004.

Cohen, R. and B. Bordass, 2015: Mandating transparency about building energy performance in use. *Build. Res. Inf.*, **43(4)**, 534–552, doi:10.1080/09613218.2015.1017416.

Colenbrander, S., A. Sudmant, N. Chilundika, and A. Gouldson, 2019: The scope for low-carbon development in Kigali, Rwanda: An economic appraisal. *Sustain. Dev.*, **27(3)**, 349–365, doi:10.1002/sd.1906.

Colker, R.M., 2012: Outcome Based Codes: Answering The Preliminary Questions. *Strateg. Plan. Energy Environ.*, **31(4)**, 35–55, doi:10.1080/10485236.2012.10491662.

Coma, J., G. Pérez, C. Solé, A. Castell, and L.F. Cabeza, 2016: Thermal assessment of extensive green roofs as passive tool for energy savings in buildings. *Renew. Energy*, **85**, 1106–1115, doi:10.1016/j.renene.2015.07.074.

Coma, J. et al., 2017: Vertical greenery systems for energy savings in buildings: A comparative study between green walls and green facades. *Build. Environ.*, **111**, 228–237, doi:10.1016/j.buildenv.2016.11.014.

Connolly, D., 2017: Heat Roadmap Europe: Quantitative comparison between the electricity, heating, and cooling sectors for different European countries. *Energy*, **139**, 580–593, doi:10.1016/j.energy.2017.07.037.

Connor, P., V. Bürger, L. Beurskens, K. Ericsson, and C. Egger, 2013: Devising renewable heat policy: Overview of support options. *Energy Policy*, **59**, 3–16, doi:10.1016/j.enpol.2012.09.052.

Connor, P.M., L. Xie, R. Lowes, J. Britton, and T. Richardson, 2015: The development of renewable heating policy in the United Kingdom. *Renew. Energy*, **75**, doi:10.1016/j.renene.2014.10.056.

Cook, G., T. Dowdall, D. Pomerantz, and Y. Wang, 2014: *Clicking Clean: How Companies are Creating the Green Internet*. Greenpeace International, Washington, DC, USA, 72 pp.

Cooremans, C., 2011: Make it strategic! Financial investment logic is not enough. *Energy Effic.*, **4(4)**, 473–492, doi:10.1007/s12053-011-9125-7.

Copiello, S., 2017: Building energy efficiency: A research branch made of paradoxes. *Renew. Sustain. Energy Rev.*, **69**, 1064–1076, doi:10.1016/j.rser.2016.09.094.

Copiello, S., L. Gabrielli, and P. Bonifaci, 2017: Evaluation of energy retrofit in buildings under conditions of uncertainty: The prominence of the discount rate. *Energy*, **137**, 104–117, doi:10.1016/j.energy.2017.06.159.

Cornelis, E., 2019: History and prospect of voluntary agreements on industrial energy efficiency in Europe. *Energy Policy*, **132**, 567–582, doi:10.1016/j.enpol.2019.06.003.

Corrado, V., I. Ballarini, S. Paduos, E. Primo, and P. Torino, 2016: The Rebound Effect after the Energy Refurbishment of Residential Buildings towards High Performances. *4th International High Performance Buildings Conference*, 2016 Purdue Conferences, 1–10 pp.

Cory, K., T. Couture, and C. Kreycik, 2009: *Feed-in Tariff Policy: Design, Implementation, and RPS Policy Interactions*. National Renewable Energy Laboratory, Golden, CO, USA, 1–17 pp.

Cossu, R. and I.D. Williams, 2015: Urban mining: Concepts, terminology, challenges. *Waste Manag.*, **45**, 1–3, doi:10.1016/j.wasman.2015.09.040.

Costanzo, V., G. Evola, and L. Marletta, 2016: Energy savings in buildings or UHI mitigation? Comparison between green roofs and cool roofs. *Energy Build.*, **114**, 247–255, doi:10.1016/j.enbuild.2015.04.053.

Couder, J. and A. Verbruggen, 2017: *Quantification and monetization of selected energy system and security impacts*. Universiteit Antwerpen, Antwerp, 47 pp.

Couture, S., S. Garcia, and A. Reynaud, 2012: Household energy choices and fuelwood consumption: An econometric approach using French data. *Energy Econ.*, **34(6)**, 1972–1981, doi:10.1016/j.eneco.2012.08.022.

Couture, T. and Y. Gagnon, 2010: An analysis of feed-in tariff remuneration models: Implications for renewable energy investment. *Energy Policy*, **38(2)**, 955–965, doi:10.1016/j.enpol.2009.10.047.

Cowell, S., 2016: *Occupant Health Benefits of Residential Energy Efficiency*. E4The Future, 35 pp.

Craig, C.A., M.W. Allen, S. Feng, and M.L. Spialek, 2020: Exploring the impact of resident proximity to wildfires in the northern Rocky Mountains: Perceptions of climate change risks, drought, and policy. *Int. J. Disaster Risk Reduct.*, **44** (November 2019), 101420, doi:10.1016/j.ijdrr.2019.101420.

Crawford, R.H. and G.J. Treolar, 2010: *Database of embodied energy and water values for materials*. The University of Melbourne, Melbourne, Australia.

Crawley, J. et al., 2019: Quantifying the Measurement Error on England and Wales EPC Ratings. *Energies*, **12(18)**, 3523, doi:10.3390/en12183523.

Creutzig, F., 2014: How fuel prices determine public transport infrastructure, modal shares and urban form. *Urban Clim.*, **10(P1)**, 63–76, doi:10.1016/j.uclim.2014.09.003.

Creutzig, F. et al., 2016: Beyond Technology: Demand-Side Solutions for Climate Change Mitigation. *Annu. Rev. Environ. Resour.*, **41(1)**, 173–198, doi:10.1146/annurev-environ-110615-085428.

Creutzig, F. et al., 2018: Towards demand-side solutions for mitigating climate change. *Nat. Clim. Chang.*, **8(4)**, 260–263, doi:10.1038/s41558-018-0121-1.

Cruz, T., R. Schaeffer, A.F.P. Lucena, S. Melo, and R. Dutra, 2020: Solar water heating technical-economic potential in the household sector in Brazil. *Renew. Energy*, **146**, 1618–1639, doi:10.1016/j.renene.2019.06.085.

Csoknyai, T. et al., 2016: Building stock characteristics and energy performance of residential buildings in Eastern-European countries. *Energy Build.*, **132**, 39–52, doi:10.1016/j.enbuild.2016.06.062.

Cui, Y. et al., 2017: Comparison of typical year and multiyear building simulations using a 55-year actual weather data set from China. *Appl. Energy*, **195**, 890–904, doi:10.1016/j.apenergy.2017.03.113.

Curl, A. et al., 2015: Physical and mental health outcomes following housing improvements: Evidence from the GoWell study. *J. Epidemiol. Community Health*, **69(1)**, 12–19, doi:10.1136/jech-2014-204064.

Curtis, J., A. Walton, and M. Dodd, 2017: Understanding the potential of facilities managers to be advocates for energy efficiency retrofits in mid-tier commercial office buildings. *Energy Policy*, **103** (April 2016), 98–104, doi:10.1016/j.enpol.2017.01.016.

Curtis, J., D. McCoy, and C. Aravena, 2018: Heating system upgrades: The role of knowledge, socio-demographics, building attributes and energy infrastructure. *Energy Policy*, **120** (November 2017), 183–196, doi:10.1016/j.enpol.2018.05.036.

D'Oca, S., T. Hong, and J. Langevin, 2018a: The human dimensions of energy use in buildings: A review. *Renew. Sustain. Energy Rev.*, **81** (May 2017), 731–742, doi:10.1016/j.rser.2017.08.019.

D'Oca, S. et al., 2018b: Human-building interaction at work: Findings from an interdisciplinary cross-country survey in Italy. *Build. Environ.*, **132** (September 2017), 147–159, doi:10.1016/j.buildenv.2018.01.039.

Darby, S. and T. Fawcett, 2018: *Energy sufficiency: an introduction Concept paper*. European Council for an Energy Efficient Economy, European Council for an Energy Efficient Economy, 25 pp. https://www.energysufficiency. org/static/media/uploads/site-8/library/papers/sufficiency-introduction-final-oct2018.pdf.

Das, I., J. Pedit, S. Handa, and P. Jagger, 2018: Household air pollution (HAP), microenvironment and child health: Strategies for mitigating HAP exposure in urban Rwanda. *Environ. Res. Lett.*, **13(4)**, doi:10.1088/1748-9326/aab047.

Davide, M., E. De Cian, and A. Bernigaud, 2019: Building a framework to understand the energy needs of adaptation. *Sustain.*, **11(15)**, 4085, doi:10.3390/su11154085.

Davis, L.W. and P.J. Gertler, 2015: Contribution of air conditioning adoption to future energy use under global warming. *Proc. Natl. Acad. Sci. U. S. A.*, **112(19)**, 5962–5967, doi:10.1073/pnas.1423558112.

De Ayala, A., I. Galarraga, and J.V. Spadaro, 2016: The price of energy efficiency in the Spanish housing market. *Energy Policy*, **94**, 16–24, doi:10.1016/j.enpol.2016.03.032.

De Cian, E., F. Pavanello, T. Randazzo, M.N. Mistry, and M. Davide, 2019: Households' adaptation in a warming climate. Air conditioning and thermal insulation choices. *Environ. Sci. Policy*, **100** (October), 136–157, doi:10.1016/j.envsci.2019.06.015.

De Falco, M., M. Capocelli, and A. Giannattasio, 2016: Performance analysis of an innovative PCM-based device for cold storage in the civil air conditioning. *Energy Build.*, **122**, 1–10, doi:10.1016/j.enbuild.2016.04.016.

de Gracia, A. et al., 2013: Experimental study of a ventilated facade with PCM during winter period. *Energy Build.*, **58**, 324–332, doi:10.1016/j.enbuild. 2012.10.026.

De Gracia, A. and L.F. Cabeza, 2015: Phase change materials and thermal energy storage for buildings. *Energy Build.*, **103**, 414–419, doi:10.1016/j.enbuild.2015.06.007.

de la Rue du Can, S., D. Pudleiner, and K. Pielli, 2018: Energy efficiency as a means to expand energy access: A Uganda roadmap. *Energy Policy*, **120**, 354–364, doi:10.1016/j.enpol.2018.05.045.

de la Rue du Can, S. et al., 2019: Modeling India's energy future using a bottom-up approach. *Appl. Energy*, **238** (December 2018), 1108–1125, doi:10.1016/j.apenergy.2019.01.065.

de Melo, C.A. and G. de Martino Jannuzzi, 2015: Cost-effectiveness of CO_2 emissions reduction through energy efficiency in Brazilian building sector. *Energy Effic.*, **8(4)**, 815–826, doi:10.1007/s12053-014-9322-2.

de Rubeis, T., S. Falasca, G. Curci, D. Paoletti, and D. Ambrosini, 2020: Sensitivity of heating performance of an energy self-sufficient building to climate zone, climate change and HVAC system solutions. *Sustain. Cities Soc.*, **61** (October 2020), 102300, doi:10.1016/j.scs.2020.102300.

de Ruig, L.T., T. Haer, H. de Moel, W.J.W. Botzen, and J.C.J.H. Aerts, 2019: A micro-scale cost-benefit analysis of building-level flood risk adaptation measures in Los Angeles. *Water Resour. Econ.*, **32** (October 2020), 100147, doi:10.1016/j.wre.2019.100147.

De Schutter, G. et al., 2018: Vision of 3D printing with concrete — Technical, economic and environmental potentials. *Cem. Concr. Res.*, **112** (November 2017), 25–36, doi:10.1016/j.cemconres.2018.06.001.

De Villanueva Domínguez, L., 2005: The three ages of construction. *Inf. la Construcción*, **57(498)**, 41–45, doi:10.3989/ic.2005.v57.i498.476.

de Wilde, P. and D. Coley, 2012: The implications of a changing climate for buildings. *Build. Environ.*, **55**, 1–7, doi:10.1016/j.buildenv.2012.03.014.

De Wolf, C. et al., 2016: Material quantities and embodied carbon dioxide in structures. *Proc. Inst. Civ. Eng. Eng. Sustain.*, **169(4)**, 150–161, doi:10.1680/ensu.15.00033.

Decker, T. and K. Menrad, 2015: House owners' perceptions and factors influencing their choice of specific heating systems in Germany. *Energy Policy*, **85**, 150–161, doi:10.1016/j.enpol.2015.06.004.

9

del Río, P. et al., 2017: A techno-economic analysis of EU renewable electricity policy pathways in 2030. *Energy Policy*, **104**, 484–493, doi:10.1016/j.enpol.2017.01.028.

DellaValle, N. and S. Sareen, 2020: Nudging and boosting for equity? Towards a behavioural economics of energy justice. *Energy Res. Soc. Sci.*, **68**, doi:10.1016/j.erss.2020.101589.

Delmas, M.A., M. Fischlein, and O.I. Asensio, 2013: Information strategies and energy conservation behavior: A meta-analysis of experimental studies from 1975 to 2012. *Energy Policy*, **61**, 729–739, doi:10.1016/j.enpol.2013.05.109.

Deng, G. and P. Newton, 2017: Assessing the impact of solar PV on domestic electricity consumption: Exploring the prospect of rebound effects. *Energy Policy*, **110**, doi:10.1016/j.enpol.2017.08.035.

Deng, H.M., Q.M. Liang, L.J. Liu, and L.D. Anadon, 2017: Co-benefits of greenhouse gas mitigation: A review and classification by type, mitigation sector, and geography. *Environ. Res. Lett.*, **12(12)**, doi:10.1088/1748-9326/aa98d2.

Deng, Q., X. Jiang, Q. Cui, and L. Zhang, 2015: Strategic design of cost savings guarantee in energy performance contracting under uncertainty. *Appl. Energy*, **139**, 68–80, doi:10.1016/j.apenergy.2014.11.027.

Deng, Y. and J. Wu, 2014: Economic returns to residential green building investment: The developers' perspective. *Reg. Sci. Urban Econ.*, **47(1)**, 35–44, doi:10.1016/j.regsciurbeco.2013.09.015.

Deng, Y., Z. Li, and J.M. Quigley, 2012: Economic returns to energy-efficient investments in the housing market: Evidence from Singapore. *Reg. Sci. Urban Econ.*, **42(3)**, 506–515, doi:10.1016/j.regsciurbeco.2011.04.004.

Denniston, S., M. Frankel, and D. Hewitt, 2011: Outcome-based Energy Codes On the Way to Net Zero. *Strateg. Plan. Energy Environ.*, **31(2)**, 14–27, doi:10.1080/10485236.2011.10412181.

Department of Environmental Affairs, 2014: *South Africa's Greenhouse Gas (GHG) Mitigation Potential Analysis.*, Pretoria, Department of Environmental Affairs of South Africa, 152 pp. https://www.dffe.gov.za/sites/default/files/docs/mitigationreport.pdf.

Derungs, C., E. Lobsiger-Kägi, U. Tomic, R. Marek, and B. Sütterlin, 2019: Occupant-centred temperature reduction in an energy efficient site. *J. Phys. Conf. Ser.*, **1343**, 12146, doi:10.1088/1742-6596/1343/1/012146.

Dewick, P. and P. Owen, 2015: *How effective is a games-centric approach in changing student eco behaviours?* University of Manchester, Manchester, UK. https://www.research.manchester.ac.uk/portal/files/31873537/FULL_TEXT.PDF (Accessed July 1, 2021).

Dhar, S., M. Pathak, and P.R. Shukla, 2018: Role of Energy Efficiency for Low Carbon Transformation of India. *Chem. Eng. Trans.*, **63**, 307–312, doi:10.3303/CET1863052.

Diawuo, F.A., A. Pina, P.C. Baptista, and C.A. Silva, 2018: Energy efficiency deployment: A pathway to sustainable electrification in Ghana. *J. Clean. Prod.*, **186**, 544–557, doi:10.1016/j.jclepro.2018.03.088.

Diaz-Mendez, S.E. et al., 2018: Economic, environmental and health co-benefits of the use of advanced control strategies for lighting in buildings of Mexico. *Energy Policy*, **113** (November 2017), 401–409, doi:10.1016/j.enpol.2017.11.028.

Diffney, S., S. Lyons, and L. Malaguzzi Valeri, 2013: Evaluation of the effect of the Power of One campaign on natural gas consumption. *Energy Policy*, **62**, 978–988, doi:10.1016/j.enpol.2013.07.099.

Diguet, C. and F. Lopez, 2019: *L'Impact Spatial Et Energetique Des Data*. Rapport Ademe, 2019, 10 pp. https://www.caissedesdepots.fr/sites/default/files/2020-05/data_center_rapport_enernum_final-_1er_mars_2019bis.pdf (Accessed July 1, 2021).

Dijkgraaf, E., T.P. van Dorp, and E. Maasland, 2018: On the effectiveness of feed-in tariffs in the development of solar photovoltaics. *Energy J.*, **39(1)**, doi:10.5547/01956574.39.1.edij.

Dilger, M.G., T. Jovanović, and K.I. Voigt, 2017: Upcrowding energy co-operatives – Evaluating the potential of crowdfunding for business

model innovation of energy co-operatives. *J. Environ. Manage.*, **198**, 50–62, doi:10.1016/j.jenvman.2017.04.025.

Dioha, M.O., N.V. Emodi, and E.C. Dioha, 2019: Pathways for low carbon Nigeria in 2050 by using NECAL2050. *Renew. Energy Focus*, **29** (June 2019), 63–77, doi:10.1016/j.ref.2019.02.004.

Dirks, J.A. et al., 2015: Impacts of climate change on energy consumption and peak demand in buildings: A detailed regional approach. *Energy*, **79(C)**, 20–32, doi:10.1016/j.energy.2014.08.081.

Dixit, M.K., 2019: 3-D Printing in Building Construction: A Literature Review of Opportunities and Challenges of Reducing Life Cycle Energy and Carbon of Buildings. *IOP Conf. Ser. Earth Environ. Sci.*, **290(1)**, 012012, doi:10.1088/1755-1315/290/1/012012.

Dixon, G.N., M.B. Deline, K. McComas, L. Chambliss, and M. Hoffmann, 2015: Using Comparative Feedback to Influence Workplace Energy Conservation: A Case Study of a University Campaign. *Environ. Behav.*, **47(6)**, 667–693, doi:10.1177/0013916513520417.

Djedjig, R., E. Bozonnet, and R. Belarbi, 2015: Analysis of thermal effects of vegetated envelopes: Integration of a validated model in a building energy simulation program. *Energy Build.*, **86**, 93–103, doi:10.1016/j.enbuild.2014.09.057.

Do, T.N., P.J. Burke, K.G.H. Baldwin, and C.T. Nguyen, 2020: Underlying drivers and barriers for solar photovoltaics diffusion: The case of Vietnam. *Energy Policy*, **144** (April), 111561, doi:10.1016/j.enpol.2020.111561.

Dodoo, A. and L. Gustavsson, 2016: Energy use and overheating risk of Swedish multi-storey residential buildings under different climate scenarios. *Energy*, **97**, 534–548, doi:10.1016/j.energy.2015.12.086.

Doll, S.C., E.L. Davison, and B.R. Painting, 2016: Weatherization impacts and baseline indoor environmental quality in low income single-family homes. *Build. Environ.*, **107**, 181–190, doi:10.1016/j.buildenv.2016.06.021.

Donastorg, A., S. Renukappa, and S. Suresh, 2017: Financing Renewable Energy Projects in Developing Countries: A Critical Review. *IOP Conf. Ser. Earth Environ. Sci.*, **83**, 012012, doi:10.1088/1755-1315/83/1/012012.

Dong, H.-W., B.-J. Kim, S.-Y. Yoon, and J.-W. Jeong, 2020: Energy benefit of organic Rankine cycle in high-rise apartment building served by centralized liquid desiccant and evaporative cooling-assisted ventilation system. *Sustain. Cities Soc.*, **60** (July 2019), 102280, doi:10.1016/j.scs.2020.102280.

Doukas, H. and A. Nikas, 2020: Decision support models in climate policy. *Eur. J. Oper. Res.*, **280(1)**, 1–24, doi:10.1016/j.ejor.2019.01.017.

Dreyfus, G. et al., 2020a: *Assessment of climate and development benefits of efficient and climate-friendly cooling*. Molina, M., and Zaelke, D., Steering Committee Co-Chairs., 89 pp.

Dreyfus, G., et al., 2020b: *Assessment of Climate and Development Benefits of Efficient and Climate-Friendly Cooling*. Institute for Governance & Sustainable Development and Centro Mario Molina, 89 pp.

Drysdale, B., J. Wu, and N. Jenkins, 2015: Flexible demand in the GB domestic electricity sector in 2030. *Appl. Energy*, **139**, 281–290, doi:10.1016/j.apenergy.2014.11.013.

Duffy, A., 2009: Land use planning in Ireland-a life cycle energy analysis of recent residential development in the Greater Dublin Area. *Int. J. Life Cycle Assess.*, **14(3)**, 268–277, doi:10.1007/s11367-009-0059-7.

Duman, A.C., H.S. Erden, Ö. Gönül, and Ö. Güler, 2021: A home energy management system with an integrated smart thermostat for demand response in smart grids. *Sustain. Cities Soc.*, **65**, 102639, doi:10.1016/j.scs.2020.102639.

Duong, T.T., T.D. Brewer, J. Luck, and K.K. Zander, 2019: Farmers' assessment of plant biosecurity risk management strategies and influencing factors: A study of smallholder farmers in Australia. *Outlook Agric.*, **48(1)**, 48–57, doi:10.1177/0030727019829754.

Duscha, V., J. Wachsmuth, J. Eckstein, and B. Pfluger, 2019: *GHG-neutral EU2050 – a scenario of an EU with net-zero greenhouse gas emissions and its implications*. Umweltbundesamt, Dessau-Roßlau, Germany, 81 pp.

9

Dutt, D., 2020: Understanding the barriers to the diffusion of rooftop solar: A case study of Delhi (India). *Energy Policy*, **144** (April), 111674, doi:10.1016/j.enpol.2020.111674.

Duzgun, B. and G. Komurgoz, 2014: Turkey's energy efficiency assessment: White certificates systems and their applicability in Turkey. *Energy Policy*, **65**, 465–474, doi:10.1016/j.enpol.2013.10.036.

Dylewski, R. and J. Adamczyk, 2016: The environmental impacts of thermal insulation of buildings including the categories of damage: A Polish case study. *J. Clean. Prod.*, **137**, 878–887, doi:10.1016/j.jclepro.2016.07.172.

Eadson, W., J. Gilbertson, and A. Walshaw, 2013: *Attitudes and Perceptions of the Green Deal amongst private sector landlords in Rotherham Summary Report*. Sheffield Hallam University, Sheffield, UK, 10 pp.

Economidou, M. and P. Bertoldi, 2015: Practices to overcome split incentives in the EU building stock. *ECEEE 2015 Summer Study Proceedings*, 2015, 12.

Economidou, M. and T. Serrenho, 2019: *Assessment of progress made by Member States in relation to Article 19(1) of the Directive 2012/27/EU*. Publications Office of the European Union, Luxembourg, 2019, 62 pp, https://data.europa.eu/doi/10.2760/070440.

Economidou, M. et al., 2020: Review of 50 years of EU energy efficiency policies for buildings. *Energy Build.*, **225**, doi:10.1016/j.enbuild.2020.110322.

Element Energy Ltd, 2018: *Cost analysis of future heat infrastructure options*. Cambridge, UK. 105 pp. https://nic.org.uk/app/uploads/Element-Energy-and-E4techCost-analysis-of-future-heat-infrastructure-Final.pdf.

Ellsworth-Krebs, K., 2020: Implications of declining household sizes and expectations of home comfort for domestic energy demand. *Nat. Energy*, **5(1)**, 20–25, doi:10.1038/s41560-019-0512-1.

Energetics, 2016: *Modelling and analysis of Australia's abatement opportunities*. Energetics, 2016, 60 pp. https://www.readkong.com/page/modelling-and-analysis-of-australia-s-abatement-5655727.

Engvall, K., E. Lampa, P. Levin, P. Wickman, and E. Ofverholm, 2014: Interaction between building design, management, household and individual factors in relation to energy use for space heating in apartment buildings. *Energy Build.*, **81**, 457–465, doi:10.1016/j.enbuild.2014.06.051.

Enker, R.A. and G.M. Morrison, 2017: Analysis of the transition effects of building codes and regulations on the emergence of a low carbon residential building sector. *Energy Build.*, **156**, 40–50, doi:10.1016/j.enbuild.2017.09.059.

Enker, R.A. and G.M. Morrison, 2020: The potential contribution of building codes to climate change response policies for the built environment. *Energy Effic.*, **13(4)**, 789–807, doi:10.1007/s12053-020-09871-7.

Enongene, K.E., P. Murray, J. Holland, and F.H. Abanda, 2017: Energy savings and economic benefits of transition towards efficient lighting in residential buildings in Cameroon. *Renew. Sustain. Energy Rev.*, **78** (April 2016), 731–742, doi:10.1016/j.rser.2017.04.068.

Erhorn-Kluttig, H. et al., 2019: Cost-efficient Nearly Zero-Energy Buildings (NZEBs). *IOP Conf. Ser. Mater. Sci. Eng.*, **609** (2019), 062002, doi:10.1088/1757-899X/609/6/062002.

ESMAP, MECS, and World Bank, 2020: *Cooking with electricity – A cost perspective*. World Bank, Washington, DC, USA.

Esser, A., A. Dunne, T. Meeusen, S. Quaschning, and W. Denis, 2019: *Comprehensive study of building energy renovation activities and the uptake of nearly zero-energy buildings in the EU. Final report*. European Union Publication Office, 87 pp. https://data.europa.eu/doi/10.2833/14675.

European Commission, 2016: *The Macroeconomic and Other Benefits of Energy Efficiency Final report*. European Union Publication Office, 138 pp.

European Commission, 2020: Circular economy action plan: the European Green Deal. European Commission Publication Office.

European Parliament and the Council, 2020: Regulation (EU) 2020/852 of 18 June 2020 on the establishment of a framework to facilitate sustainable investment, and amending Regulation (EU) 2019/2088. *Off. J. Eur. Union*, 13–43.

European Union, 2015: *Crowdfunding from an investor perspective*. Oxera, Luxembourg, 93 pp. doi:10.2874/61896.

European Union, 2019: *Supporting digitalisation of the construction sector and SMEs*. European Union (EU), Luxembourg, 92 pp.

Evans, M., V. Roshchanka, and P. Graham, 2017: An international survey of building energy codes and their implementation. *J. Clean. Prod.*, **158**, 382–389, doi:10.1016/j.jclepro.2017.01.007.

Eyre, N., 2013: Energy saving in energy market reform—The feed-in tariffs option. *Energy Policy*, **52**, doi:10.1016/j.enpol.2012.07.042.

Falchetta, G. and M.N. Mistry, 2021: The role of residential air circulation and cooling demand for electrification planning: Implications of climate change in sub-Saharan Africa. *Energy Econ.*, **99**, 105307, doi:10.1016/j.eneco.2021.105307.

Fallahi, A., F. Haghighat, and H. Elsadi, 2010: Energy performance assessment of double-skin façade with thermal mass. *Energy Build.*, **42(9)**, 1499–1509, doi:10.1016/j.enbuild.2010.03.020.

Fan, J., Y. Li, Y. Wu, S. Wang, and D. Zhao, 2016: Allowance trading and energy consumption under a personal carbon trading scheme: A dynamic programming approach. *J. Clean. Prod.*, **112** (2016), 3875–3883, doi:10.1016/j.jclepro.2015.07.030.

Farajirad, K., G. Kazemian, and Roknoddin Eftekhari A., 2015: Explanatory Model of the Relationship between Regional Governance, Institutional Capacity and Sustainable Development in Iran. *Public Policy Adm. Res.*, **5**, 108–123.

Farzaneh, H. et al., 2021: Artificial intelligence evolution in smart buildings for energy efficiency. *Appl. Sci.*, **11(2)**, 1–26, doi:10.3390/app11020763.

Fawcett, T., 2010: Personal carbon trading: A policy ahead of its time? *Energy Policy*, **38(11)**, 6868–6876, doi:10.1016/j.enpol.2010.07.001.

Fawcett, T. and Y. Parag, 2017: *Personal Carbon Trading*. Climate Policy, 10:4, 329–338, doi:10.3763/cpol.2010.0649.

Fawcett, T., J. Rosenow, and P. Bertoldi, 2019: Energy efficiency obligation schemes: their future in the EU. *Energy Effic.*, **12(1)**, 57–71, doi:10.1007/s12053-018-9657-1.

Feng, W. et al., 2019: A review of net zero energy buildings in hot and humid climates: Experience learned from 34 case study buildings. *Renew. Sustain. Energy Rev.*, **114** (June 2019), 109303, doi:10.1016/j.rser.2019.109303.

Ferreboeuf, H., 2019: *Lean ICT – towards digital sobriety*. The Shift Project, Paris, France, 90 pp.

Ferreira, M., M. Almeida, and A. Rodrigues, 2017: Impact of co-benefits on the assessment of energy related building renovation with a nearly-zero energy target. *Energy Build.*, **152**, 587–601, doi:10.1016/j.enbuild.2017.07.066.

Ferreira, P., A. Rocha, and M. Araujo, 2018: Awareness and attitudes towards demand response programs – a pilot study. *2018 International Conference on Smart Energy Systems and Technologies (SEST)*, IEEE, 1–6 pp.

Fina, B., H. Auer, and W. Friedl, 2020: Cost-optimal economic potential of shared rooftop PV in energy communities: Evidence from Austria. *Renew. Energy*, **152**, 217–228, doi:10.1016/j.renene.2020.01.031.

Finnegan, S., C. Jones, and S. Sharples, 2018: The embodied CO_2e of sustainable energy technologies used in buildings: A review article. *Energy Build.*, **181**, 50–61, doi:10.1016/j.enbuild.2018.09.037.

Fischer, A. and S. Pascucci, 2017: Institutional incentives in circular economy transition: The case of material use in the Dutch textile industry. *J. Clean. Prod.*, **155**, 17–32, doi:10.1016/J.JCLEPRO.2016.12.038.

Fishman, T. et al., 2021: A comprehensive set of global scenarios of housing, mobility, and material efficiency for material cycles and energy systems modeling. *J. Ind. Ecol.*, **25(2)**, 305–320, doi:10.1111/jiec.13122.

Fisk, W.J., 2015: Review of some effects of climate change on indoor environmental quality and health and associated no-regrets mitigation measures. *Build. Environ.*, **86**, 70–80, doi:10.1016/j.buildenv.2014.12.024.

Fisk, W.J., 2018: How home ventilation rates affect health: A literature review. *Indoor Air*, **28(4)**, 473–487, doi:10.1111/ina.12469.

Fisk, W.J., B.C. Singer, and W.R. Chan, 2020: Association of residential energy efficiency retrofits with indoor environmental quality, comfort, and health: A review of empirical data. *Build. Environ.*, **180** (June), 107067, doi:10.1016/j.buildenv.2020.107067.

9

Fleming, D., 1997: Tradable quotas: using information technology to cap national carbon emissions. *Eur. Environ.*, **7(5)**, 139–148, doi:10.1002/(SICI)1099-0976(199709)7:5<139::AID-EET129>3.0.CO;2-C.

Font Vivanco, D., R. Kemp, and E. van der Voet, 2016: How to deal with the rebound effect? A policy-oriented approach. *Energy Policy*, **94**, 114–125, doi:10.1016/j.enpol.2016.03.054.

Ford, A., K. Vogstad, and H. Flynn, 2007: Simulating price patterns for tradable green certificates to promote electricity generation from wind. *Energy Policy*, **35(1)**, doi:10.1016/j.enpol.2005.10.014.

Forouli, A. et al., 2019: Energy efficiency promotion in Greece in light of risk: Evaluating policies as portfolio assets. *Energy*, **170**, 818–831, doi:10.1016/j.energy.2018.12.180.

Fosas, D. et al., 2018: Mitigation versus adaptation: Does insulating dwellings increase overheating risk? *Build. Environ.*, **143** (May), 740–759, doi:10.1016/j.buildenv.2018.07.033.

Fouladvand, J., N. Mouter, A. Ghorbani, and P. Herder, 2020: Formation and Continuation of Thermal Energy Community Systems: An Explorative Agent-Based Model for the Netherlands. *Energies*, **13(11)**, 2829, doi:10.3390/en13112829.

Fouquet, D., 2013: Policy instruments for renewable energy – From a European perspective. *Renew. Energy*, **49**, doi:10.1016/j.renene.2012.01.075.

Fournier, E.D., F. Federico, E. Porse, and S. Pincetl, 2019: Effects of building size growth on residential energy efficiency and conservation in California. *Appl. Energy*, **240** (June 2018), 446–452, doi:10.1016/j.apenergy.2019.02.072.

Frankfurt School-UNEP Centre/BNEF, 2020: *Global Trends Renewable Energy Investment 2020*. Frankfurt School of Finance & Management gGmbH, Frankfurt, Germany, 80 pp.

Frazer-Nash Consultancy, 2018: *Logistics of Domestic Hydrogen Conversion*. Department of Business, Energy & Industrial Strategy, 2018, 58 pp.

Frederiks, E.R., K. Stenner, and E.V. Hobman, 2015: Household energy use: Applying behavioural economics to understand consumer decision-making and behaviour. *Renew. Sustain. Energy Rev.*, **41**, 1385–1394, doi:10.1016/j.rser.2014.09.026.

Freire-González, J., 2020: Energy taxation policies can counteract the rebound effect: analysis within a general equilibrium framework. *Energy Effic.*, **13(1)**, 69–78, doi:10.1007/s12053-019-09830-x.

Freire-González, J. and M.S. Ho, 2019: Carbon taxes and the double dividend hypothesis in a recursive-dynamic CGE model for Spain. *Econ. Syst. Res.*, **31(2)**, 267–284, doi:10.1080/09535314.2019.1568969.

Fricko, O. et al., 2016: Energy sector water use implications of a 2 °C climate policy. *Environ. Res. Lett.*, **11(3)**, 034011, doi:10.1088/1748-9326/11/3/034011.

Friedrich, L. and A. Afshari, 2015: Framework for Energy Efficiency White Certificates in the Emirate of Abu Dhabi. *Energy Procedia*, **75**, 2589–2595, doi:10.1016/j.egypro.2015.07.316.

Friege, J., 2016: Increasing homeowners' insulation activity in Germany: An empirically grounded agent-based model analysis. *Energy Build.*, **128**, 756–771, doi:10.1016/j.enbuild.2016.07.042.

Friege, J., G. Holtz, and É.J.L. Chappin, 2016: Exploring Homeowners' Insulation Activity. *J. Artif. Soc. Soc. Simul.*, **19(1)**, 1–19, doi:10.18564/jasss.2941.

Fuerst, F., P. McAllister, A. Nanda, and P. Wyatt, 2015: Does energy efficiency matter to home-buyers? An investigation of EPC ratings and transaction prices in England. *Energy Econ.*, **48**, 145–156, doi:10.1016/j.eneco.2014.12.012.

Fuerst, F., E. Oikarinen, and O. Harjunen, 2016: Green signalling effects in the market for energy-efficient residential buildings. *Appl. Energy*, **180**, 560–571, doi:10.1016/j.apenergy.2016.07.076.

Fukuda-Parr, S., C. Lopes, and K. Malik, 2002: Overview: Institutional innovations for capacity development. In: *Capacity for Development, New Solutions to Old Problems* [Lopes, C., K. Malik, and S. Fukuda-Parr (eds.)]. Earthscan and UNEP, London and Sterling, UK, pp. 1–22.

Fuller, R.J. and R.H. Crawford, 2011: Impact of past and future residential housing development patterns on energy demand and related emissions. *J. Hous. Built Environ.*, **26(2)**, 165–183, doi:10.1007/s10901-011-9212-2.

Gabe, J., 2016: An empirical comparison of voluntary and mandatory building energy performance disclosure outcomes. *Energy Policy*, **96**, 680–687, doi:10.1016/j.enpol.2016.06.044.

Gagnon, P., R. Margolis, J. Melius, C. Phillips, R. Elmore, 2016: *Rooftop Photovoltaic Technical Potential in the United States: A Detailed Assessment*. National Renewable Energy Laboratory, Golden, USA, 82 pp.

Gährs, S., K. Mehler, M. Bost, and B. Hirschl, 2015: Acceptance of ancillary services and willingness to invest in PV-storage-systems. *Energy Procedia*, **73**, 29–36, doi:10.1016/j.egypro.2015.07.554.

Galán-Marín, C., C. Rivera-Gómez, and A. García-Martínez, 2015: Embodied energy of conventional load-bearing walls versus natural stabilized earth blocks. *Energy Build.*, **97**, 146–154, doi:10.1016/j.enbuild.2015.03.054.

Galvin, R., 2014: Making the 'rebound effect' more useful for performance evaluation of thermal retrofits of existing homes: Defining the 'energy savings deficit' and the 'energy performance gap'. *Energy Build.*, **69**, 515–524, doi:10.1016/j.enbuild.2013.11.004.

Galvin, R. and M. Sunikka-Blank, 2017: Ten questions concerning sustainable domestic thermal retrofit policy research. *Build. Environ.*, **118**, 377–388, doi:10.1016/j.buildenv.2017.03.007.

García-Álvarez, M.T., L. Cabeza-García, and I. Soares, 2018: Assessment of energy policies to promote photovoltaic generation in the European Union. *Energy*, **151**, doi:10.1016/j.energy.2018.03.066.

García-Frapolli, E. et al., 2010: Beyond fuelwood savings: Valuing the economic benefits of introducing improved biomass cookstoves in the Purépecha region of Mexico. *Ecol. Econ.*, **69(12)**, 2598–2605, doi:10.1016/j.ecolecon.2010.08.004.

García de Soto, B. et al., 2018: Productivity of digital fabrication in construction: Cost and time analysis of a robotically built wall. *Autom. Constr.*, **92** (May), 297–311, doi:10.1016/j.autcon.2018.04.004.

Gelenbe, E. and Y. Caseau, 2015: The impact of information technology on energy consumption and carbon emissions. *Ubiquity*, **1530–2180** (June), 1–15, doi:10.1145/2755977.

Gephart, M., C. Klessmann, and F. Wigand, 2017: Renewable energy auctions – When are they (cost-)effective? *Energy Environ.*, **28(1–2)**, doi:10.1177/0958305X16688811.

Gerhardt, N. et al., 2020: *Hydrogen in the energy system of the future: focus on heat in buildings*. Fraunhofer Institute for Energy Economics and Energy System Technology, 2020, Hanover, Germany, 46 pp.

Gertler, P.J., O. Shelef, C.D. Wolfram, and A. Fuchs, 2016: The demand for energy-using assets among the world's rising middle classes. *Am. Econ. Rev.*, **106(6)**, 1366–1401, doi:10.1257/aer.20131455.

Ghazali, F., A.H. Ansari, M. Mustafa, and W.M.Z. Wan Zahari, 2020: Feed-In Tariff, Auctions and Renewable Energy Schemes in Malaysia: Lessons from other Jurisdictions. *IIUM Law J.*, **28(1)**, 113–137, doi:10.31436/iiumlj.v28i1.482.

Gifford, R., 2011: The Dragons of Inaction: Psychological Barriers That Limit Climate Change Mitigation and Adaptation. *Am. Psychol.*, **66(4)**, 290–302, doi:10.1037/a0023566.

Gillingham, K., M. Harding, and D. Rapson, 2012: Split Incentives in Residential Energy Consumption. *Energy J.*, **33(2)**, 37–62, doi:10.5547/01956574.33.2.3.

Gillingham, K., D. Rapson, and G. Wagner, 2016: The Rebound Effect and Energy Efficiency Policy. *Rev. Environ. Econ. Policy*, **10(1)**, 68–88, doi:10.1093/reep/rev017.

Giraudet, L.-G., 2020: Energy efficiency as a credence good: A review of informational barriers to energy savings in the building sector. *Energy Econ.*, **87**, 104698, doi:10.1016/j.eneco.2020.104698.

Giraudet, L.-G. and D. Finon, 2015: European experiences with white certificate obligations: A critical review of existing evaluations. *Econ. Energy Environ. Policy*, **4(1)**, doi:10.5547/2160-5890.4.1.lgir.

Giraudet, L.-G., C. Bourgeois, and P. Quirion, 2018: Long-term efficiency and distributional impacts of energy saving policies in the French residential sector. *Économie & prévision*, **217(1)**, 43–63, doi.org/10.3917/ecop1.217.0044.

Giraudet, L.-G., A. Petronevich, and L. Faucheux, 2019: How Do Lenders Price Energy Efficiency? Evidence From Personal Consumption Loans. *SSRN Electron. J.*, April 2019, 31, doi:10.2139/ssrn.3364243.

Giraudet, L.-G., C. Bourgeois, and P. Quirion, 2021: Policies for low-carbon and affordable home heating: A French outlook. *Energy Policy*, **151**, doi:10.1016/j.enpol.2021.112140.

Gjorgievski, V.Z., S. Cundeva, and G.E. Georghiou, 2021: Social arrangements, technical designs and impacts of energy communities: A review. *Renew. Energy*, **169**, 1138–1156, doi:10.1016/j.renene.2021.01.078.

Global Alliance for Buildings and Construction, International Energy Agency, and United Nations Environment Programme, 2019: *2019 Global Status Report for Buildings and Construction Sector*. United Nations Environment Programme, 2019, 41 pp.

Gohaud, E. and S. Baek, 2017: What is a Korean officetel? Case study on Bundang New Town. *Front. Archit. Res.*, **6(2)**, 261–271, doi:10.1016/j.foar.2017.04.001.

Goldemberg, J., J. Martinez-Gomez, A. Sagar, and K.R. Smith, 2018: Household air pollution, health, and climate change: Cleaning the air. *Environ. Res. Lett.*, **13(3)**, 030201, doi:10.1088/1748-9326/aaa49d.

Goldman, C.A., et al., 2020: What does the future hold for utility electricity efficiency programs? *Electr. J.*, **33**, doi:10.1016/j.tej.2020.106728.

Goldstein, B., D. Gounaridis, and J.P. Newell, 2020: The carbon footprint of household energy use in the United States. *Proc. Natl. Acad. Sci.*, **117(32)**, 19122–19130, doi:10.1073/pnas.1922205117.

Gong, X., N. Wu, C. Li, M. Liang, and Y. Akashi, 2019: Energy performance and CO_2 emissions of fuel cells for residential application in Chinese hot summer and cold winter areas. *IOP Conf. Ser. Earth Environ. Sci.*, **310(2)**, 022057, doi:10.1088/1755-1315/310/2/022057.

González-Mahecha, R.E. et al., 2019: Greenhouse gas mitigation potential and abatement costs in the Brazilian residential sector. *Energy Build.*, **184**, 19–33, doi:10.1016/j.enbuild.2018.11.039.

González Mahecha, R.E. et al., 2020: Constructive systems for social housing deployment in developing countries: A case study using dynamic life cycle carbon assessment and cost analysis in Brazil. *Energy Build.*, **227**, 110395, doi:10.1016/j.enbuild.2020.110395.

Gouldson, A. et al., 2015: Innovative financing models for low carbon transitions: Exploring the case for revolving funds for domestic energy efficiency programmes. *Energy Policy*, **86**, 739–748, doi:10.1016/j.enpol.2015.08.012.

Government of Russian Federation, 2021: *Decree of the Government of the Russian Federation from 21.09.2021 No. 1587 "On approval of the criteria for sustainable (including green) development projects in the Russian Federation and requirem ents for the verification system of sustainable and green development projects in the Russian Federation"*, Russian, 2021. https://www.jdsupra.com/legalnews/russian-sustainable-finance-regulations-3193434/.

Gram-Hanssen, K., 2014: Existing buildings – Users, renovations and energy policy. *Renew. Energy*, **61**, 136–140, doi:10.1016/j.renene.2013.05.004.

Grande-Acosta, G.K. and J.M. Islas-Samperio, 2020: Boosting energy efficiency and solar energy inside the residential, commercial, and public services sectors in Mexico. *Energies*, **13(21)**, 5601, doi:10.3390/en13215601.

Graziano, M. and K. Gillingham, 2015: Spatial patterns of solar photovoltaic system adoption: The influence of neighbors and the built environment. *J. Econ. Geogr.*, **15(4)**, 815–839, doi:10.1093/jeg/lbu036.

Grove-Smith, J., V. Aydin, W. Feist, J. Schnieders, and S. Thomas, 2018: Standards and policies for very high energy efficiency in the urban building sector towards reaching the 1.5°C target. *Curr. Opin. Environ. Sustain.*, **30**, 103–114, doi:10.1016/j.cosust.2018.04.006.

Grover, A.C., 2019: Understanding the role of Occupants in green building energy performance. In: *53rd International Conference of the Architectural Science Association, ANZAScA 2019. Architectural Science Association* [Agrawal, A. and R. Gupta, (eds.)]. pp. 547–556.

Grubler, A. et al., 2018: A low energy demand scenario for meeting the 1.5°C target and sustainable development goals without negative emission technologies. *Nat. Energy*, **3(6)**, 515–527, doi:10.1038/s41560-018-0172-6.

Grynning, S., J.E. Gaarder, and J. Lohne, 2017: Climate Adaptation of School Buildings through MOM – A Case Study. *Procedia Eng.*, **196(1877)**, 864–871, doi:10.1016/j.proeng.2017.08.018.

Gu, Y. et al., 2018: Impacts of sectoral emissions in China and the implications: air quality, public health, crop production, and economic costs. *Environ. Res. Lett.*, **13(8)**, 084008, doi:10.1088/1748-9326/aad138.

Gui, X. and Z. Gou, 2020: Association between green building certification level and post-occupancy performance: Database analysis of the National Australian Built Environment Rating System. *Build. Environ.*, **179**, 106971, doi:10.1016/j.buildenv.2020.106971.

Gunay, H.B., W. O'Brien, and I. Beausoleil-Morrison, 2013: A critical review of observation studies, modeling, and simulation of adaptive occupant behaviors in offices. *Build. Environ.*, **70**, 31–47, doi:10.1016/j.buildenv.2013.07.020.

Guo, L. et al., 2019: The effect of relative humidity change on atmospheric pitting corrosion of stainless steel 304L. *Corros. Sci.*, **150**, 110–120, doi:10.1016/j.corsci.2019.01.033.

Gupta, R. and M. Gregg, 2012: Using UK climate change projections to adapt existing English homes for a warming climate. *Build. Environ.*, **55**, 20–42, doi:10.1016/j.buildenv.2012.01.014.

Gupta, R. and A. Kotopouleas, 2018: Magnitude and extent of building fabric thermal performance gap in UK low energy housing. *Appl. Energy*, **222** (April), 673–686, doi:10.1016/j.apenergy.2018.03.096.

Gupta, R., M. Gregg, and K. Williams, 2015: Cooling the UK housing stock post-2050s. *Build. Serv. Eng. Res. Technol.*, **36(2)**, 196–220, doi:10.1177/0143624414566242.

Guyot, G., M.H. Sherman, and I.S. Walker, 2018: Smart ventilation energy and indoor air quality performance in residential buildings: A review. *Energy Build.*, **165**, 416–430, doi:10.1016/j.enbuild.2017.12.051.

Habert, G. et al., 2020: Environmental impacts and decarbonization strategies in the cement and concrete industries. *Nat. Rev. Earth Environ.*, **1(11)**, 559–573, doi:10.1038/s43017-020-0093-3.

Hache, E., D. Leboullenger, and V. Mignon, 2017: Beyond average energy consumption in the French residential housing market: A household classification approach. *Energy Policy*, **107** (January 2016), 82–95, doi:10.1016/j.enpol.2017.04.038.

Hachem-Vermette, C. and K. Singh, 2019: Optimization of the mixture of building types in a neighborhood and their energy and environmental performance. *Energy Build.*, **204**, doi:10.1016/j.enbuild.2019.109499.

Haelg, L., 2020: Promoting technological diversity: How renewable energy auction designs influence policy outcomes. *Energy Res. Soc. Sci.*, **69**, doi:10.1016/j.erss.2020.101636.

Hager, I., A. Golonka, and R. Putanowicz, 2016: 3D Printing of Buildings and Building Components as the Future of Sustainable Construction? *Procedia Eng.*, **151** (December), 292–299, doi:10.1016/j.proeng.2016.07.357.

Haggag, M., A. Hassan, and S. Elmasry, 2014: Experimental study on reduced heat gain through green façades in a high heat load climate. *Energy Build.*, **82**, 668–674, doi:10.1016/j.enbuild.2014.07.087.

Hahnel, U.J.J., M. Herberz, A. Pena-Bello, D. Parra, and T. Brosch, 2020: Becoming prosumer: Revealing trading preferences and decision-making strategies in peer-to-peer energy communities. *Energy Policy*, **137**, 111098, doi:10.1016/j.enpol.2019.111098.

Hainaut, H., L. Gouiffes, I. Cochran, and M. Ledez, 2021: *Panorama des financements climat. Edition 2020*. Institute for climate economics, Paris, France, 2021.

9

Haines, V. and V. Mitchell, 2014: A persona-based approach to domestic energy retrofit. *Build. Res. Inf.*, **42(4)**, 462–476, doi:10.1080/09613218.2014.893161.

Hájek, M., J. Zimmermannová, K. Helman, and L. Rozenský, 2019: Analysis of carbon tax efficiency in energy industries of selected EU countries. *Energy Policy*, **134** (June 2018), 110955, doi:10.1016/j.enpol.2019.110955.

Hall, D.M. and M.M. Bonanomi, 2021: Governing Collaborative Project Delivery as a Common-Pool Resource Scenario. *Proj. Manag. J.*, **52(3)**, 250–263, doi:10.1177/8756972820982442.

Hallegatte, S., 2009: Strategies to adapt to an uncertain climate change. *Glob. Environ. Chang.*, **19(2)**, 240–247, doi:10.1016/j.gloenvcha.2008.12.003.

Hamilton, I. et al., 2015: Health effects of home energy efficiency interventions in England: A modelling study. *BMJ Open*, **5(4)**, 1–11, doi:10.1136/bmjopen-2014-007298.

Hanna, R., E. Duflo, and M. Greenstone, 2016: Up in Smoke: The Influence of Household Behavior on the Long-Run Impact of Improved Cooking Stoves. *Am. Econ. J. Econ. Policy*, **8(1)**, 80–114, doi:10.1257/pol.20140008.

Hannon, M.J., 2015: Raising the temperature of the UK heat pump market: Learning lessons from Finland. *Energy Policy*, **85**, 369–375, doi:10.1016/j.enpol.2015.06.016.

Hansen, A.R., 2016: The social structure of heat consumption in Denmark: New interpretations from quantitative analysis. *Energy Res. Soc. Sci.*, **11**, 109–118, doi:10.1016/j.erss.2015.09.002.

Harby, K., D.R. Gebaly, N.S. Koura, and M.S. Hassan, 2016: Performance improvement of vapor compression cooling systems using evaporative condenser: An overview. *Renew. Sustain. Energy Rev.*, **58**, 347–360, doi:10.1016/j.rser.2015.12.313.

Hargreaves, T., C. Wilson, and R. Hauxwell-Baldwin, 2018: Learning to live in a smart home. *Build. Res. Inf.*, **46(1)**, 127–139, doi:10.1080/09613218.2017.1286882.

Harold, J., S. Lyons, and J. Cullinan, 2015: The determinants of residential gas demand in Ireland. *Energy Econ.*, **51**, 475–483, doi:10.1016/j.eneco.2015.08.015.

Harris, S., É. Mata, A. Plepys, and C. Katzeff, 2021: Sharing is daring, but is it sustainable? An assessment of sharing cars, electric tools and offices in Sweden. *Resour. Conserv. Recycl.*, **170**, 105583, doi:10.1016/j.resconrec.2021.105583.

Hart, J. and F. Pomponi, 2020: More timber in construction: Unanswered questions and future challenges. *Sustain.*, **12(8)**, doi:10.3390/SU12083473.

Hart, J., K. Adams, J. Giesekam, D.D. Tingley, and F. Pomponi, 2019: Barriers and drivers in a circular economy: The case of the built environment. *Procedia CIRP*, **80**, 619–624, doi:10.1016/j.procir.2018.12.015.

Hasegawa, T. et al., 2015: Consequence of Climate Mitigation on the Risk of Hunger. *Environ. Sci. Technol.*, **49(12)**, 7245–7253, doi:10.1021/es5051748.

Hashemi, A., H. Cruickshank, and A. Cheshmehzangi, 2015: Environmental Impacts and Embodied Energy of Construction Methods and Materials in Low-Income Tropical Housing. *Sustainability*, **7(6)**, 7866–7883, doi:10.3390/su7067866.

Hayat, M.A., F. Shahnia, and G. Shafiullah, 2019: Replacing Flat Rate Feed-In Tariffs for Rooftop Photovoltaic Systems With a Dynamic One to Consider Technical, Environmental, Social, and Geographical Factors. *IEEE Trans. Ind. Informatics*, **15(7)**, doi:10.1109/TII.2018.2887281.

Heeren, N. et al., 2015: Environmental Impact of Buildings—What Matters? *Environ. Sci. Technol.*, **49(16)**, 9832–9841, doi:10.1021/acs.est.5b01735.

Heindl, P. and P. Kanschik, 2016: Ecological sufficiency, individual liberties, and distributive justice: Implications for policy making. *Ecol. Econ.*, **126**, 42–50, doi:10.1016/J.ECOLECON.2016.03.019.

Heinen, S., W. Turner, L. Cradden, F. McDermott, and M. O'Malley, 2017: Electrification of residential space heating considering coincidental weather events and building thermal inertia: A system-wide planning analysis. *Energy*, **127**, 136–154, doi:10.1016/j.energy.2017.03.102.

Heinonen, J. and S. Junnila, 2014: Residential energy consumption patterns and the overall housing energy requirements of urban and rural households in Finland. *Energy Build.*, **76**, 295–303, doi:10.1016/j.enbuild.2014.02.079.

Heiskanen, E. and K. Matschoss, 2017: Understanding the uneven diffusion of building-scale renewable energy systems: A review of household, local and country level factors in diverse European countries. *Renew. Sustain. Energy Rev.*, **75**, 580–591, doi:10.1016/j.rser.2016.11.027.

Hejazi, M.I. et al., 2015: 21st century United States emissions mitigation could increase water stress more than the climate change it is mitigating. *Proc. Natl. Acad. Sci.*, **112(34)**, 10635–10640, doi:10.1073/pnas.1421675112.

Henriquez, R., G. Wenzel, D.E. Olivares, and M. Negrete-Pincetic, 2018: Participation of Demand Response Aggregators in Electricity Markets: Optimal Portfolio Management. *IEEE Trans. Smart Grid*, **9(5)**, 4861–4871, doi:10.1109/TSG.2017.2673783.

Hernandez-Roman, F., C. Sheinbaum-Pardo, and A. Calderon-Irazoque, 2017: "Socially neglected effect" in the implementation of energy technologies to mitigate climate change: Sustainable building program in social housing. *Energy Sustain. Dev.*, **41**, 149–156, doi:10.1016/j.esd.2017.09.005.

Hertwich, E.G. et al., 2019: Material efficiency strategies to reducing greenhouse gas emissions associated with buildings, vehicles, and electronics—a review. *Environ. Res. Lett.*, **14(4)**, 43004, doi:10.1088/1748-9326/ab0fe3.

Hertwich, E.G. et al., 2020: *Resource Efficiency and Climate Change: Material Efficiency Strategies for a Low-Carbon Future*. United Nations Environment Programme, Nairobi, Kenya, 173 pp.

Hewitt, E., 2018: Organizational Characteristics in Residential Rental Buildings: Exploring the Role of Centralization in Energy Outcomes. In: *Handbook of Sustainability and Social Science Research* [Filho, W.L., R.W. Marans, and J. Callewaert, (eds.)]. Springer, Cham, Switzerland, pp. 181–196.

Hickel, J. et al., 2021: Urgent need for post-growth climate mitigation scenarios. *Nat. Energy*, **6(8)**, 766–768, doi:10.1038/s41560-021-00884-9.

Hidalgo, J., S. Coello, and Y. González, 2018: The Determinants of Household Electricity Demand in Marginal Ecuador: "A Case Study at Monte Sinai". In: *16th LACCEI International Multi-Conference for Engineering, Education, and Technology: Innovation in Education and Inclusion*. pp. 19–21. doi:10.18687/LACCEI2018.1.1.312.

Hildebrandt, J., N. Hagemann, and D. Thrän, 2017: The contribution of wood-based construction materials for leveraging a low carbon building sector in europe. *Sustain. Cities Soc.*, **34** (November 2016), 405–418, doi:10.1016/j.scs.2017.06.013.

Hirst, E. and M. Brown, 1990: Closing the efficiency gap: barriers to the efficient use of energy. *Resour. Conserv. Recycl.*, **3(4)**, 267–281, doi:10.1016/0921-3449(90)90023-W.

Hirvonen, J., J. Jokisalo, P. Sankelo, T. Niemelä, and R. Kosonen, 2020: Emission reduction potential of different types of finnish buildings through energy retrofits. *Buildings*, **10(12)**, 234, doi:10.3390/buildings10120234.

Högberg, L., 2013: The impact of energy performance on single-family home selling prices in Sweden. *J. Eur. Real Estate Res.*, **6(3)**, 242–261, doi:10.1108/JERER-09-2012-0024.

Hohne, P.A., K. Kusakana, and B.P. Numbi, 2019: Optimal energy management and economic analysis of a grid-connected hybrid solar water heating system: A case of Bloemfontein, South Africa. *Sustain. Energy Technol. Assessments*, **31** (December 2018), 273–291, doi:10.1016/j.seta.2018.12.027.

Holland, R.A. et al., 2015: Global impacts of energy demand on the freshwater resources of nations. *Proc. Natl. Acad. Sci. U. S. A.*, **112(48)**, E6707–E6716, doi:10.1073/pnas.1507701112.

Hong, T., W.-K. Chang, and H.-W. Lin, 2013: A fresh look at weather impact on peak electricity demand and energy use of buildings using 30-year actual weather data. *Appl. Energy*, **111**, 333–350, doi:10.1016/j.apenergy.2013.05.019.

Hong, T., D. Yan, S. D'Oca, and C. Chen, 2017: Ten questions concerning occupant behavior in buildings: The big picture. *Build. Environ.*, **114**, 518–530, doi:10.1016/j.buildenv.2016.12.006.

Hong, T., C. Chen, Z. Wang, and X. Xu, 2020: Linking human-building interactions in shared offices with personality traits. *Build. Environ.*, **170**, 106602, doi:10.1016/j.buildenv.2019.106602.

Hongping, Y., 2017: Barriers and countermeasures for managing construction and demolition waste: A case of Shenzhen in China. *J. Clean. Prod.*, **157**, 84–93, doi:10.1016/j.jclepro.2017.04.137.

Hortay, O. and B.P. Rozner, 2019: Allocating renewable subsidies. *Econ. Anal. Policy*, **64**, doi:10.1016/j.eap.2019.09.003.

Horváth, M., D. Kassai-Szoó, and T. Csoknyai, 2016: Solar energy potential of roofs on urban level based on building typology. *Energy Build.*, **111**, 278–289, doi:10.1016/j.enbuild.2015.11.031.

Howarth, C. and B.M. Roberts, 2018: The Role of the UK Green Deal in Shaping Pro-Environmental Behaviours: Insights from Two Case Studies. *Sustainability*, **10(6)**, 2107, doi:10.3390/su10062107.

Howden-Chapman, P. et al., 2012: Tackling cold housing and fuel poverty in New Zealand: A review of policies, research, and health impacts. *Energy Policy*, **49**, 134–142, doi:10.1016/j.enpol.2011.09.044.

Hsiao, T.Y., C.M. Chuang, N.W. Kuo, and S.M.F. Yu, 2014: Establishing attributes of an environmental management system for green hotel evaluation. *Int. J. Hosp. Manag.*, **36**, 197–208, doi:10.1016/j.ijhm.2013.09.005.

Hu, S., L.F. Cabeza, and D. Yan, 2020: Review and estimation of global halocarbon emissions in the buildings sector. *Energy Build.*, **225**, 110311, doi:10.1016/j.enbuild.2020.110311.

Huang, K.T. and R.L. Hwang, 2016: Future trends of residential building cooling energy and passive adaptation measures to counteract climate change: The case of Taiwan. *Appl. Energy*, **184**, 1230–1240, doi:10.1016/j.apenergy.2015.11.008.

Huang, P. et al., 2019: Transforming a residential building cluster into electricity prosumers in Sweden: Optimal design of a coupled PV-heat pump-thermal storage-electric vehicle system. *Appl. Energy*, **255**, 113864, doi:10.1016/j.apenergy.2019.113864.

Huang, W., 2015: The determinants of household electricity consumption in Taiwan: Evidence from quantile regression. *Energy*, **87**, 120–133, doi:10.1016/j.energy.2015.04.101.

Huang, Y.-K., J. McDowell, and P. Vargas, 2015: How Old I Feel Matters: Examining Age-Related Differences in Motives and Organizational Citizenship Behavior. *J. Park Recreat. Admi.*, **33(1)**, 20–39.

Huebner, G.M. and D. Shipworth, 2017: All about size? – The potential of downsizing in reducing energy demand. *Appl. Energy*, **186**, 226–233, doi:10.1016/j.apenergy.2016.02.066.

Huijbregts, Z., R.P. Kramer, M.H.J. Martens, A.W.M. van Schijndel, and H.L. Schellen, 2012: A proposed method to assess the damage risk of future climate change to museum objects in historic buildings. *Build. Environ.*, **55**, 43–56, doi:10.1016/j.buildenv.2012.01.008.

Hyland, M., R.C. Lyons, and S. Lyons, 2013: The value of domestic building energy efficiency – evidence from Ireland. *Energy Econ.*, **40**, 943–952, doi:10.1016/j.eneco.2013.07.020.

IEA, 2013: *Policy Pathway – Modernising Building Energy Codes*. International Energy Agency, Paris, France, 9 pp.

IEA, 2014: *Capturing the Multiple Benefits of Energy Efficiency*. International Energy Agency, Paris, France, 232 pp.

IEA, 2017a: *Digitalization & Energy*. International Energy Agency (IEA), 188 pp.

IEA, 2017b: *Energy Technology Perspectives 2017 – Tracking Clean Energy Progress*. International Energy Agency, Paris, France, 116 pp.

IEA, 2018a: *The Future of Cooling*, International Energy Agency, Paris, France.

IEA, 2018b: *Tracking SDG7: The Energy Progress Report 2018*. The World Bank, Washington, DC, USA, 29 pp.

IEA, 2019a: *Africa Energy Outlook 2019 World Energy Outlook Special Report*. International Energy Agency, Paris, France, 288 pp.

IEA, 2019b: *Material efficiency in clean energy*. International Energy Agency, Paris, France.

IEA, 2019c: Perspectives for the Clean Energy Transition — The Critical Role of Buildings. *Perspect. Clean Energy Transit. — Crit. Role Build.*, **53(9)**, 1689–1699, doi:10.1017/CBO9781107415324.004.

IEA, 2019d: *Tracking SDG7: The Energy Progress Report 2019*. The World Bank, Washington, DC, USA, 176 pp.

IEA, 2019e: *World Energy Outlook*. International Energy Agency, Paris, France.

IEA, 2020a: *Sustainable Recovery – World Energy Outlook Special Report*. International Energy Agency, Paris, France, 174 pp.

IEA, 2020b: *Tracking SDG 7: The Energy Progress Report (2020)*. The World Bank, Washington, DC, USA, 204 pp.

IEA, 2020c: *World Energy Outlook 2020*. International Energy Agency, Paris, France, 464 pp.

IEA, 2021a: *Net Zero by 2050: A Roadmap for the Global Energy Sector*. International Energy Agency, Paris, France, 224 pp.

IEA, 2021b: *World Energy Investment 2021*. International Energy Agency, Paris, France, 64 pp.

IEA and UNDP, 2013: *Modernising Building Energy Codes to Secure our Global Energy Future*. IEA and UNDP, Paris, France and New York, USA, 74 pp.

Imanari, T., T. Omori, and K. Bogaki, 1999: Thermal comfort and energy consumption of the radiant ceiling panel system. *Energy Build.*, **30(2)**, 167–175, doi:10.1016/S0378-7788(98)00084-X.

Ingold, K. et al., 2020: Are responses to official consultations and stakeholder surveys reliable guides to policy actors' positions? *Policy Polit.*, **48(2)**, 193–222, doi:10.1332/030557319X15613699478503.

Inoue, N. and S. Matsumoto, 2019: An examination of losses in energy savings after the Japanese Top Runner Program? *Energy Policy*, **124**, 312–319, doi:10.1016/j.enpol.2018.09.040.

International Risk Governance Council, 2013: *The rebound effect: Implications of consumer behaviour for robust energy policies. A review of the literature on the rebound effect in energy efficiency and report from expert workshops*. International Risk Governance Council, 37 pp.

IPCC, 2018: *Global Warming of 1.5°C. An IPCC Special Report on the impacts of global warming of 1.5°C above pre-industrial levels and related global greenhouse gas emission pathways, in the context of strengthening the global response to the threat of climate change, sustainable development, and efforts to eradicate poverty* [Masson-Delmotte, V., P. Zhai, H.-O. Pörtner, D. Roberts, J. Skea, P.R. Shukla, A. Pirani, W. Moufouma-Okia, C. Péan, R. Pidcock, S. Connors, J.B.R. Matthews, Y. Chen, X. Zhou, M.I. Gomis, E. Lonnoy, T. Maycock, M. Tignor, and T. Waterfield (eds.)]. Cambridge University Press, Cambridge, UK, and New York, NY, USA.

IPCC, 2021: Summary for Policymakers. In: *Climate Change 2021: The Physical Science Basis. Contribution of Working Group I to the Sixth Assessment Report of the Intergovernmental Panel on Climate Change* [Masson-Delmotte, V., P. Zhai, A. Pirani, S.L. Connors, C. Péan, S. Berger, N. Caud, Y. Chen, L. Goldfarb, M.I. Gomis, M. Huang, K. Leitzell, E. Lonnoy, J.B.R. Matthews, T.K. Maycock, T. Waterfield, O. Yelekçi, R. Yu, and B. Zhou (eds.)]. Cambridge University Press, Cambridge, UK, and New York, NY, USA, doi:10.1017/9781009157896.001.

Iria, J. and F. Soares, 2019: Real-time provision of multiple electricity market products by an aggregator of prosumers. *Appl. Energy*, **255**, 113792, doi:10.1016/j.apenergy.2019.113792.

Irshad, K., K. Habib, R. Saidur, M.W. Kareem, and B.B. Saha, 2019: Study of thermoelectric and photovoltaic facade system for energy efficient building development: A review. *J. Clean. Prod.*, **209**, 1376–1395, doi:10.1016/j.jclepro.2018.09.245.

Isaac, M. and D.P. van Vuuren, 2009: Modeling global residential sector energy demand for heating and air conditioning in the context of climate change. *Energy Policy*, **37(2)**, 507–521, doi:10.1016/j.enpol.2008.09.051.

Issock, P.B., M. Mpinganjira, and M. Roberts-Lombard, 2018: Drivers of consumer attention to mandatory energy-efficiency labels affixed to home appliances: An emerging market perspective. *J. Clean. Prod.*, **204**, doi:10.1016/j.jclepro.2018.08.299.

Iten, R. et al., 2017: *Auswirkungen eines subsidiären Verbots fossiler Heizungen – Grundlagenbericht für die Klimapolitik nach 2020 [Effects of a subsidiary ban on fossil heating – Background report on climate policy after 2020]*. Infras, TEP Energy iA Bundesamt für Umwelt (BAFU), Zürich/Bern (2017), 104 pp.

Iten R. Catenazzi G, Reiter U., Wunderlich A., Sigrist D., J.M., 2017: *Auswirkungen eines subsidiären Verbots fossiler Heizungen*. Infras, TEP Energy iA Bundesamt für Umwelt (BAFU), Zürich/Bern.

Ivanova, D. and M. Büchs, 2020: Household Sharing for Carbon and Energy Reductions: The Case of EU Countries. *Energies*, **13(8)**, 1909, doi:10.3390/en13081909.

Jacobsen, G.D. and M.J. Kotchen, 2013: Are Building Codes Effective at Saving Energy? Evidence from Residential Billing Data in Florida. *Rev. Econ. Stat.*, **95(1)**, doi:10.1162/REST_a_00243.

Jaffe, A.B. and R.N. Stavins, 1994: The energy-efficiency gap What does it mean? *Energy Policy*, **22(10)**, 804–810, doi:10.1016/0301-4215(94)90138-4.

Jager-Waldau, A. et al., 2018: *Self-consumption of electricity produced from PV systems in apartment buildings – Comparison of the situation in Australia, Austria, Denmark, Germany, Greece, Italy, Spain, Switzerland and the USA*. 2018 IEEE 7th World Conference on Photovoltaic Energy Conversion (WCPEC) (A Joint Conference of 45th IEEE PVSC, 28th PVSEC & 34th EU PVSEC). IEEE, 1424–1430.

Janda, K.B., 2014: Building communities and social potential: Between and beyond organizations and individuals in commercial properties. *Energy Policy*, **67**, 48–55, doi:10.1016/j.enpol.2013.08.058.

Jannati, M. et al., 2017: A review on Variable Speed Control techniques for efficient control of Single-Phase Induction Motors: Evolution, classification, comparison. *Renew. Sustain. Energy Rev.*, **75** (April 2016), 1306–1319, doi:10.1016/j.rser.2016.11.115.

Jedidi, M. and O. Benjeddou, 2018: Effect of Thermal Bridges on the Heat Balance of Buildings. *Int. J. Sci. Res. Civ. Eng.*, **2(5)**, 41–49. https://ijsrce.com/paper/IJSRCE182517.pdf.

Jensen, O.M., A.R. Hansen, and J. Kragh, 2016: Market response to the public display of energy performance rating at property sales. *Energy Policy*, **93**, 229–235, doi:10.1016/j.enpol.2016.02.029.

Jeuland, M., J.S. Tan Soo, and D. Shindell, 2018: The need for policies to reduce the costs of cleaner cooking in low income settings: Implications from systematic analysis of costs and benefits. *Energy Policy*, **121**, 275–285, doi:10.1016/j.enpol.2018.06.031.

Jones, R.V., A. Fuertes, and K.J. Lomas, 2015: The socio-economic, dwelling and appliance related factors affecting electricity consumption in domestic buildings. *Renew. Sustain. Energy Rev.*, **43**, 901–917, doi:10.1016/j.rser.2014.11.084.

Joyce, A., M.B. Hansen, and S. Nass-Schmidt, 2013: Monetising the multiple benefits of energy efficient renovations of the buildings of the EU. *ECEEE 2013 Summer Study Proceedings*, 1497–1507.

Junnila, S., J. Ottelin, and L. Leinikka, 2018: Influence of reduced ownership on the environmental benefits of the circular economy. *Sustain.*, **10(11)**, 4077, doi:10.3390/su10114077.

Kahn, M.E. and N. Kok, 2014: The capitalization of green labels in the California housing market. *Reg. Sci. Urban Econ.*, **47**, 25–34, doi:10.1016/j.regsciurbeco.2013.07.001.

Kalantzis, F. and D. Revoltella, 2019: Do energy audits help SMEs to realize energy-efficiency opportunities? *Energy Econ.*, **83**, 229–239, doi:10.1016/j.eneco.2019.07.005.

Kalkbrenner, B.J. and J. Roosen, 2016: Citizens' willingness to participate in local renewable energy projects: The role of community and trust in Germany. *Energy Res. Soc. Sci.*, **13** (March 2016), 60–70, doi:10.1016/j.erss.2015.12.006.

Kalvelage, K., U. Passe, S. Rabideau, and E.S. Takle, 2014: Changing climate: The effects on energy demand and human comfort. *Energy Build.*, **76**, 373–380, doi:10.1016/j.enbuild.2014.03.009.

Kamal, A., S.G. Al-Ghamdi, and M. Koç, 2019: Role of energy efficiency policies on energy consumption and CO_2 emissions for building stock in Qatar. *J. Clean. Prod.*, **235**, 1409–1424, doi:10.1016/j.jclepro.2019.06.296.

Kamenders, A., C. Rochas, and A. Novikova, 2019: *Investments in Energy Efficiency and Renewable Energy Projects in Latvia in 2018*. Riga Technical University, Riga, Latvia, 1–37 pp.

Kamilaris, A., B. Kalluri, S. Kondepudi, and T. Kwok Wai, 2014: A literature survey on measuring energy usage for miscellaneous electric loads in offices and commercial buildings. *Renew. Sustain. Energy Rev.*, **34**, 536–550, doi:10.1016/j.rser.2014.03.037.

Kaminska, A., 2019: Impact of Heating Control Strategy and Occupant Behavior on the Energy Consumption in a Building with Natural Ventilation in Poland. *Energies*, **12(22)**, 4304, doi:10.3390/en12224304.

Karlin, B., J.F. Zinger, and R. Ford, 2015: The effects of feedback on energy conservation: A meta-analysis. *Psychol. Bull.*, **141(6)**, 1205–1227, doi:10.1037/a0039650.

Karlsson, M., E. Alfredsson, and N. Westling, 2020: Climate policy co-benefits: a review. *Clim. Policy*, **20(3)**, 292–316, doi:10.1080/14693062.2020.1724070.

Kavousian, A., R. Rajagopal, and M. Fischer, 2013: Determinants of residential electricity consumption: Using smart meter data to examine the effect of climate, building characteristics, appliance stock, and occupants' behavior. *Energy*, **55**, 184–194, doi:10.1016/j.energy.2013.03.086.

Kavousian, A., R. Rajagopal, and M. Fischer, 2015: Ranking appliance energy efficiency in households: Utilizing smart meter data and energy efficiency frontiers to estimate and identify the determinants of appliance energy efficiency in residential buildings. *Energy Build.*, **99**, 220–230, doi:10.1016/j.enbuild.2015.03.052.

Kern, F., P. Kivimaa, and M. Martiskainen, 2017: Policy packaging or policy patching? The development of complex energy efficiency policy mixes. *Energy Res. Soc. Sci.*, **23**, 11–25, doi:10.1016/j.erss.2016.11.002.

Ketchman, K.J., D.R. Riley, V. Khanna, and M.M. Bilec, 2018: Survey of Homeowners' Motivations for the Adoption of Energy Efficiency Measures: Evaluating a Holistic Energy Assessment Program. *J. Archit. Eng.*, **24(4)**, 04018024, doi:10.1061/(ASCE)AE.1943-5568.0000310.

Khan, I., 2020: Impacts of energy decentralization viewed through the lens of the energy cultures framework: Solar home systems in the developing economies. *Renew. Sustain. Energy Rev.*, **119**, doi:10.1016/j.rser.2019.109576.

Khan, M.M.A., M. Asif, and E. Stach, 2017: Rooftop PV potential in the residential sector of the kingdom of Saudi Arabia. *Buildings*, **7(2)**, doi:10.3390/buildings7020046.

Khan, S.A., 2018: Green Banking: The Role of Bank for Saving the Environment. *Int. J. Entrep. Dev. Stud.*, **6(2)**, 63–80.

Kheirbek, I. et al., 2014: The public health benefits of reducing fine particulate matter through conversion to cleaner heating fuels in New York city. *Environ. Sci. Technol.*, **48(23)**, 13573–13582, doi:10.1021/es503587p.

Khoshbakht, M., Z. Gou, K. Dupre, and H. Altan, 2017: Thermal Environments of an Office Building with Double Skin Facade. *J. Green Build.*, **12(3)**, 3–22, doi:10.3992/1943-4618.12.3.3.

Khosla, R., N. Sircar, and A. Bhardwaj, 2019: Energy demand transitions and climate mitigation in low-income urban households in India. *Environ. Res. Lett.*, **14(9)**, 095008, doi:10.1088/1748-9326/ab3760.

Khosrowpour, A., T. Duzener, and J.E. Taylor, 2016: Meta-Analysis of Eco-Feedback-Induced Occupant Energy Efficiency Benchmarked with Standard Building Energy Rating Systems. Construction Research Congress 2016, Reston, VA, USA. American Society of Civil Engineers, 1192–1201.

Kian Jon, C., M.R. Islam, N. Kim Choon, and M.W. Shahzad, 2021: Future of Air Conditioning. In: *Green Energy and Technology* [Demirel, Y. ed.]. Springer-Verlag, Berlin and Heidelberg, Germany, pp. 17–52.

Kikstra, J.S., A. Mastrucci, J. Min, K. Riahi, and N.D. Rao, 2021: Decent living gaps and energy needs around the world. *Environ. Res. Lett.*, **16(9)**, doi:10.1088/1748-9326/ac1c27.

Kim, A.A., Y. Sunitiyoso, and L.A. Medal, 2019: Understanding facility management decision making for energy efficiency efforts for buildings at a higher education institution. *Energy Build.*, **199**, 197–215, doi:10.1016/j.enbuild.2019.06.044.

Kim, J. and K. Park, 2018: Effect of the Clean Development Mechanism on the deployment of renewable energy: Less developed vs. well-developed financial markets. *Energy Econ.*, 75(2018), 1–13, doi:10.1016/j.eneco.2018.07.034.

Kimura, F., S. Kimura, Y. Chang, and Y. Li, 2016: Financing renewable energy in the developing countries of the East Asia Summit region: Introduction. *Energy Policy*, **95**, doi:10.1016/j.enpol.2016.04.005.

Kirchhoff, H. and K. Strunz, 2019: Key drivers for successful development of peer-to-peer microgrids for swarm electrification. *Appl. Energy*, **244** (March 2019), 46–62, doi:10.1016/j.apenergy.2019.03.016.

Kirkpatrick, A.J. and L.S. Bennear, 2014: Promoting clean energy investment: An empirical analysis of property assessed clean energy. *J. Environ. Econ. Manage.*, **68(2)**, 357–375, doi:10.1016/j.jeem.2014.05.001.

Klein, L. et al., 2012: Coordinating occupant behavior for building energy and comfort management using multi-agent systems. *Autom. Constr.*, **22**, 525–536, doi:10.1016/j.autcon.2011.11.012.

Klein, M., A. Ziade, and L. de Vries, 2019: Aligning prosumers with the electricity wholesale market – The impact of time-varying price signals and fixed network charges on solar self-consumption. *Energy Policy*, **134**, doi:10.1016/j.enpol.2019.110901.

Klocker, N., 2017: The environmental implications of multigenerational living: are larger households also greener households? *Multigenerational Fam. Living*, first edition, Routledge, 2016, 174–191, doi:10.4324/9781315596266-17.

Klocker, N., C. Gibson, and E. Borger, 2012: Living together but apart: Material geographies of everyday sustainability in extended family households. *Environ. Plan. A*, **44(9)**, 2240–2259, doi:10.1068/a44594.

Knapp, S., S. Schmauck, and A. Zehnsdorf, 2019: Biodiversity impact of green roofs and constructed wetlands as progressive eco-technologies in urban areas. *Sustain.*, **11(20)**, doi:10.3390/su11205846.

Kockat, J., P.V. Dorizas, J. Volt, and D. Staniaszek, 2018: *Building 4 People: Quantifying the benefits of energy renovation investments in schools, offices and hospitals*. Buildings Performance Institute Europe, Brussels and Berlin, Germany, 20 pp.

Köhler, B., M. Stobbe, C. Moser, and F. Garzia, 2018: *Guideline II: nZEB Technologies: Report on cost reduction potentials for technical NZEB solution sets*. AEE INTEC, Gleisdorf, Austria, 74 pp.

Koirala, B.S., A.K. Bohara, and R.P. Berrens, 2014: Estimating the net implicit price of energy efficient building codes on U.S. households. *Energy Policy*, **73**, 667–675, doi:10.1016/j.enpol.2014.06.022.

Kong, K.W., K.W. Lam, C. Chan, and P. Sat, 2019: Retro-Commissioning – Effective Energy Conservation Initiatives in Existing Buildings. *IOP Conf. Ser. Earth Environ. Sci.*, **290**, doi:10.1088/1755-1315/290/1/012099.

Kontokosta, C.E., D. Spiegel-Feld, and S. Papadopoulos, 2020: The impact of mandatory energy audits on building energy use. *Nat. Energy*, **5(4)**, 309–316, doi:10.1038/s41560-020-0589-6.

Koomey, J., S. Berard, M. Sanchez, and H. Wong, 2011: Implications of Historical Trends in the Electrical Efficiency of Computing. *IEEE Ann. Hist. Comput.*, **33(3)**, 46–54, doi:10.1109/MAHC.2010.28.

Koronen, C., M. Åhman, and L.J. Nilsson, 2020: Data centres in future European energy systems—energy efficiency, integration and policy. *Energy Effic.*, **13(1)**, 129–144, doi:10.1007/s12053-019-09833-8.

Kotchen, M.J., 2017: Longer-Run Evidence on Whether Building Energy Codes Reduce Residential Energy Consumption. *J. Assoc. Environ. Resour. Econ.*, **4(1)**, doi:10.1086/689703.

Kotzur, L. et al., 2020: Bottom-up energy supply optimization of a national building stock. *Energy Build.*, **209**, 109667, doi:10.1016/j.enbuild.2019.109667.

Kozusznik, M.W. et al., 2019: Decoupling office energy efficiency from employees' well-being and performance: A systematic review. *Front. Psychol.*, **10** (February), doi:10.3389/fpsyg.2019.00293.

Kramer, H. et al., 2020: *Proving the Business Case for Building Analytics*. Lawrence Berkeley National Laboratory, Berkeley, USA, 41 pp.

Krarti, M., 2019: Evaluation of Energy Efficiency Potential for the Building Sector in the Arab Region. *Energies*, **12(22)**, 4279, doi:10.3390/en12224279.

Krarti, M., F. Ali, A. Alaidroos, and M. Houchati, 2017: Macro-economic benefit analysis of large scale building energy efficiency programs in Qatar. *Int. J. Sustain. Built Environ.*, **6(2)**, 597–609, doi:10.1016/j.ijsbe.2017.12.006.

Kuhnhenn, K., L. Costa, E. Mahnke, L. Schneider, and S. Lange, 2020: *A Societal Transformation Scenario for Staying Below 1.5°C*. Heinrich Böll Foundation, Berlin, Germany, 100 pp.

Kuittinen, M. and T. Häkkinen, 2020: Reduced carbon footprints of buildings: new Finnish standards and assessments. *Build. Cities*, **1(1)**, doi:10.5334/bc.30.

Kuokkanen, A. et al., 2020: A proposal for a novel urban mobility policy: Personal carbon trade experiment in Lahti city. *Util. Policy*, **62**, 100997, doi:10.1016/j.jup.2019.100997.

Kusumadewi, T.V. and B. Limmeechokchai, 2015: Energy Efficiency Improvement and CO_2 Mitigation in Residential Sector: Comparison between Indonesia and Thailand. *Energy Procedia*, **79**, 994–1000, doi:10.1016/j.egypro.2015.11.599.

Kusumadewi, T.V. and B. Limmeechokchai, 2017: CO_2 Mitigation in Residential Sector in Indonesia and Thailand: Potential of Renewable Energy and Energy Efficiency. *Energy Procedia*, **138**, 955–960, doi:10.1016/j.egypro.2017.10.086.

Kwag, B.C., B.M. Adamu, and M. Krarti, 2019: Analysis of high-energy performance residences in Nigeria. *Energy Effic.*, **12(3)**, 681–695, doi:10.1007/s12053-018-9675-z.

Kwon, T., 2015: Is the renewable portfolio standard an effective energy policy?: Early evidence from South Korea. *Util. Policy*, **36**, 46–51, doi:10.1016/j.jup.2015.09.002.

Kyrö, R.K., 2020: Share, Preserve, Adapt, Rethink – a focused framework for circular economy. *IOP Conf. Ser. Earth Environ. Sci.*, **588(4)**, 42034, doi:10.1088/1755-1315/588/4/042034.

Labanca, N. and P. Bertoldi, 2018: Beyond energy efficiency and individual behaviours: policy insights from social practice theories. *Energy Policy*, **115** (February), 494–502, doi:10.1016/j.enpol.2018.01.027.

Lacroix, E. and C. Chaton, 2015: Fuel poverty as a major determinant of perceived health: The case of France. *Public Health*, **129(5)**, 517–524, doi:10.1016/j.puhe.2015.02.007.

Lamb, W.F. et al., 2021: A review of trends and drivers of greenhouse gas emissions by sector from 1990 to 2018. *Environ. Res. Lett.*, **16(7)**, 073005, doi:10.1088/1748-9326/abee4e.

Lambertz, M., S. Theißen, J. Höper, and R. Wimmer, 2019: Importance of building services in ecological building assessments. *E3S Web Conf.*, **111**, 03061, doi:10.1051/e3sconf/201911103061.

Langevin, J., C.B. Harris, and J.L. Reyna, 2019: Assessing the Potential to Reduce U.S. Building CO2 Emissions 80% by 2050. *Joule*, **3(10)**, 2403–2424, doi:10.1016/j.joule.2019.07.013.

Langreder, N., F. Seefeldt, L.-A. Brischke, and T. Chmella, 2019: STEP up! The competitive efficiency tender in Germany – step by step towards an effective new instrument for energy efficiency. *ECEEE 2019 Summer Study Proceedings*, 561–568.

Larsen, B., 2016: *Benefits and costs of household cooking options for air pollution control. Benefits and costs of addressing indoor air pollution challenges in Bangladesh*. Copenhagen Consensus Center, Tewksbury, UK, 38 pp.

Laurenti, R., J. Singh, J.M. Cotrim, M. Toni, and R. Sinha, 2019: Characterizing the Sharing Economy State of the Research: A Systematic Map. *Sustainability*, **11(20)**, 5729, doi:10.3390/su11205729.

Lecuyer, O. and P. Quirion, 2019: Interaction between CO2 emissions trading and renewable energy subsidies under uncertainty: feed-in tariffs as a safety net against over-allocation. *Clim. Policy*, **19(8)**, doi:10.1080/14693062.2019.1625743.

Lee, J. and J. Yu, 2017: Market Analysis during the First Year of Korea Emission Trading Scheme. *Energies*, **10(12)**, 1974, doi:10.3390/en10121974.

Lee, J., S. Wi, S.J. Chang, J. Choi, and S. Kim, 2020: Prediction evaluating of moisture problems in light-weight wood structure: Perspectives on regional climates and building materials. *Build. Environ.*, **168**, 106521, doi:10.1016/j.buildenv.2019.106521.

Lee, J.H., P. Im, and Y. Song, 2018: Field test and simulation evaluation of variable refrigerant flow systems performance. *Energy Build.*, **158**, 1161–1169, doi:10.1016/j.enbuild.2017.10.077.

Lee, J.Y. and B.R. Ellingwood, 2017: A decision model for intergenerational life-cycle risk assessment of civil infrastructure exposed to hurricanes under climate change. *Reliab. Eng. Syst. Saf.*, **159** (August 2016), 100–107, doi:10.1016/j.ress.2016.10.022.

Lee, K., E. Miguel, and C.D. Wolfram, 2017: *The Economics of Rural Electrification: Evidence from Kenya*. International Growth Centre, London, UK, 1–4 pp.

Lee, D., 2020: PACE Financing Emerges as a Valuable Resource for Property Owners Rushing to Comply with NYC's New Climate Mobilization Act. *Cornell Real Estate Rev.*, **18(2020)**, 20. https://hdl.handle.net/1813/70858.

Lehr, U., A. Mönnig, R. Missaoui, S. Marrouki, and G. Ben Salem, 2016: Employment from Renewable Energy and Energy Efficiency in Tunisia – New Insights, New Results. *Energy Procedia*, **93** (March), 223–228, doi:10.1016/j.egypro.2016.07.174.

Leibrand, A., N. Sadoff, T. Maslak, and A. Thomas, 2019: Using Earth Observations to Help Developing Countries Improve Access to Reliable, Sustainable, and Modern Energy. *Front. Environ. Sci.*, **7** (August), 1–14, doi:10.3389/fenvs.2019.00123.

Lenz, L., A. Munyehirwe, J. Peters, and M. Sievert, 2017: Does Large-Scale Infrastructure Investment Alleviate Poverty? Impacts of Rwanda's Electricity Access Roll-Out Program. *World Dev.*, **89**, 88–110, doi:10.1016/j.worlddev.2016.08.003.

Levesque, A., R.C. Pietzcker, and G. Luderer, 2019: Halving energy demand from buildings: The impact of low consumption practices. *Technol. Forecast. Soc. Change*, **146**, 253–266, doi:10.1016/j.techfore.2019.04.025.

Levine, M., D. Ürge-Vorsatz, K. Blok, L. Geng, D. Harvey, S. Lang, G. Levermore, A. Mongameli Mehlwana, S. Mirasgedis, A. Novikova, J. Rilling, H. Yoshino, 2007: Residential and commercial buildings. In *Climate Change 2007: Mitigation. Contribution of Working Group III to the Fourth Assessment Report of the Intergovernmental Panel on Climate Change* [Metz, B., O.R. Davidson, P.R. Bosch, R. Dave, L.A. Meyer (eds)]. Cambridge University Press, Cambridge, UK, and New York, NY, USA, 387–446 pp.

Levinson, A., 2016: How Much Energy Do Building Energy Codes Save? Evidence from California Houses. *Am. Econ. Rev.*, **106(10)**, doi:10.1257/aer.20150102.

Levy, J.I. et al., 2016: Carbon reductions and health co-benefits from US residential energy efficiency measures. *Environ. Res. Lett.*, **11(3)**, 34017, doi:10.1088/1748-9326/11/3/034017.

Lévy, J.P. and F. Belaïd, 2018: The determinants of domestic energy consumption in France: Energy modes, habitat, households and life cycles. *Renew. Sustain. Energy Rev.*, **81** (February), 2104–2114, doi:10.1016/j.rser.2017.06.022.

Lewis, J.I. and R.H. Wiser, 2007: Fostering a renewable energy technology industry: An international comparison of wind industry policy support mechanisms. *Energy Policy*, **35(3)**, 1844–1857, doi:10.1016/j.enpol.2006.06.005.

Lewis, J.J. et al., 2017: Biogas Stoves Reduce Firewood Use, Household Air Pollution, and Hospital Visits in Odisha, India. *Environ. Sci. Technol.*, **51(1)**, 560–569, doi:10.1021/acs.est.6b02466.

Li, D.H.W., L. Yang, and J.C. Lam, 2012: Impact of climate change on energy use in the built environment in different climate zones – A review. *Energy*, **42(1)**, 103–112, doi:10.1016/j.energy.2012.03.044.

Li, J., J. Fan, D. Zhao, and S. Wang, 2015: Allowance price and distributional effects under a personal carbon trading scheme. *J. Clean. Prod.*, **103**, doi:10.1016/j.jclepro.2014.08.081.

Li, J., S. Wang, J. Fan, and L. Liang, 2018: An equilibrium model of consumer energy choice using a personal carbon trading scheme based on allowance price. *J. Clean. Prod.*, **204**, 1087–1096, doi:10.1016/j.jclepro.2018.09.040.

Li, Q., C. Wang, and H. Zhang, 2016: A probabilistic framework for hurricane damage assessment considering non-stationarity and correlation in hurricane actions. *Struct. Saf.*, **59**, 108–117, doi:10.1016/j.strusafe.2016.01.001.

Li, R., G. Dane, C. Finck, and W. Zeiler, 2017: Are building users prepared for energy flexible buildings?—A large-scale survey in the Netherlands. *Appl. Energy*, **203**, 623–634, doi:10.1016/j.apenergy.2017.06.067.

Li, W., C. Lu, and Y.W. Zhang, 2019a: Prospective exploration of future renewable portfolio standard schemes in China via a multi-sector CGE model. *Energy Policy*, **128** (April 2018), 45–56, doi:10.1016/j.enpol.2018.12.054.

Li, Y., S. Kubicki, A. Guerriero, and Y. Rezgui, 2019b: Review of building energy performance certification schemes towards future improvement. *Renew. Sustain. Energy Rev.*, **113** (June), 109244, doi:10.1016/j.rser.2019.109244.

Liang, J., Y. Qiu, and P. Padmanabhan, 2017: Consumers' Attitudes towards Surcharges on Distributed Renewable Energy Generation and Energy Efficiency Programs. *Sustainability*, **9(8)**, 1475, doi:10.3390/su9081475.

Liao, X., S.V. Shen, and X. Shi, 2020: The effects of behavioral intention on the choice to purchase energy-saving appliances in China: the role of environmental attitude, concern, and perceived psychological benefits in shaping intention. *Energy Effic.*, **13(1)**, 33–49, doi:10.1007/s12053-019-09828-5.

Liddell, C. and C. Guiney, 2015: Living in a cold and damp home: Frameworks for understanding impacts on mental well-being. *Public Health*, **129(3)**, 191–199, doi:10.1016/j.puhe.2014.11.007.

Liddle, B. and H. Huntington, 2021: How prices, income, and weather shape household electricity demand in high-income and middle-income countries. *Energy Econ.*, **95**, doi:10.1016/j.eneco.2020.104995.

Lien, A.G. and N. Lolli, 2019: Costs and procurement for cross-laminated timber in mid-rise buildings. *J. Sustain. Archit. Civ. Eng.*, **25(2)**, 43–52, doi:10.5755/j01.sace.25.2.22099.

Lietaert, M., 2010: Cohousing's relevance to degrowth theories. *J. Clean. Prod.*, **18(6)**, 576–580, doi:10.1016/j.jclepro.2009.11.016.

Lilley, S., G. Davidson, and Z. Alwan, 2017: External Wall Insulation (EWI): Engaging social tenants in energy efficiency retrofitting in the North East of England. *Buildings*, **7(4)**, doi:10.3390/buildings7040102.

Lim, X., W.H. Lam, and A.H. Shamsuddin, 2013: Carbon credit of renewable energy projects in Malaysia. *IOP Conf. Ser. Earth Environ. Sci.*, **16**, 012058, doi:10.1088/1755-1315/16/1/012058.

Lin, B. and X. Li, 2011: The effect of carbon tax on per capita CO_2 emissions. *Energy Policy*, **39(9)**, 5137–5146, doi:10.1016/J.ENPOL.2011.05.050.

Lindberg, K.B., S.J. Bakker, and I. Sartori, 2019: Modelling electric and heat load profiles of non-residential buildings for use in long-term aggregate load forecasts. *Util. Policy*, **58** (January), 63–88, doi:10.1016/j.jup.2019.03.004.

Ling, J., H. Tong, J. Xing, and Y. Zhao, 2020: Simulation and optimization of the operation strategy of ASHP heating system: A case study in Tianjin. *Energy Build.*, **226**, 110349, doi:10.1016/j.enbuild.2020.110349.

Linh, D.H. and T. Van Anh, 2017: Impact of stakeholders on the performance of green banking products and services: The case of Vietnamese banks. *Econ. Ann.*, **165(5–6)**, 143–151, doi:10.21003/ea.V165-29.

Lipp, J., 2007: Lessons for effective renewable electricity policy from Denmark, Germany and the United Kingdom. *Energy Policy*, **35(11)**, 5481–5495, doi:10.1016/j.enpol.2007.05.015.

Liu, D. et al., 2018a: Comprehensive effectiveness assessment of renewable energy generation policy: A partial equilibrium analysis in China. *Energy Policy*, **115** (October 2017), 330–341, doi:10.1016/j.enpol.2018.01.018.

Liu, J., B. Hou, X.W. Ma, and H. Liao, 2018b: Solid fuel use for cooking and its health effects on the elderly in rural China. *Environ. Sci. Pollut. Res.*, **25(4)**, 3669–3680, doi:10.1007/s11356-017-0720-9.

Liu, J., X. Chen, H. Yang, and K. Shan, 2021: Hybrid renewable energy applications in zero-energy buildings and communities integrating battery and hydrogen vehicle storage. *Appl. Energy*, **290**, 116733, doi:10.1016/J.APENERGY.2021.116733.

Liu, L., F. Kong, X. Liu, Y. Peng, and Q. Wang, 2015a: A review on electric vehicles interacting with renewable energy in smart grid. *Renew. Sustain. Energy Rev.*, **51**, 648–661, doi:10.1016/j.rser.2015.06.036.

Liu, X. and Q. Cui, 2018: Combining carbon mitigation and climate adaptation goals for buildings exposed to hurricane risks. *Energy Build.*, **177**, 257–267, doi:10.1016/j.enbuild.2018.08.001.

Liu, Z., L. Zhang, G. Gong, H. Li, and G. Tang, 2015b: Review of solar thermoelectric cooling technologies for use in zero energy buildings. *Energy Build.*, **102**, 207–216, doi:10.1016/j.enbuild.2015.05.029.

Liu, Z., W. Li, Y. Chen, Y. Luo, and L. Zhang, 2019: Review of energy conservation technologies for fresh air supply in zero energy buildings. *Appl. Therm. Eng.*, **148** (October 2018), 544–556, doi:10.1016/j.applthermaleng.2018.11.085.

Lixuan, H. et al., 2016: Building stock dynamics and its impacts on materials and energy demand in China. *Energy Policy*, **94** (June 2015), 47–55, doi:10.1016/j.enpol.2016.03.024.

Loo, B.P.Y., A.H.T. Cheng, and S.L. Nichols, 2017: Transit-oriented development on greenfield versus infill sites: Some lessons from Hong Kong. *Landsc. Urban Plan.*, **167**, 37–48, doi:10.1016/j.landurbplan.2017.05.013.

Lorek, S. and J.H. Spangenberg, 2019: Energy sufficiency through social innovation in housing. *Energy Policy*, **126** (February 2018), 287–294, doi:10.1016/j.enpol.2018.11.026.

Lovins, A.B., 2018: How big is the energy efficiency resource? *Environ. Res. Lett.*, **13(9)**, 090401, doi:10.1088/1748-9326/aad965.

Lowes, R., J. Rosenow, M. Qadrdan, and J. Wu, 2020: Hot stuff: Research and policy principles for heat decarbonisation through smart electrification. *Energy Res. Soc. Sci.*, **70**, 101735, doi:10.1016/j.erss.2020.101735.

Lu, W. and H. Yuan, 2013: Investigating waste reduction potential in the upstream processes of offshore prefabrication construction. *Renew. Sustain. Energy Rev.*, **28**, 804–811, doi:10.1016/j.rser.2013.08.048.

Lucon O., D. Ürge-Vorsatz, A. Zain Ahmed, H. Akbari, P. Bertoldi, L.F. Cabeza, N. Eyre, A. Gadgil, L.D.D. Harvey, Y. Jiang, E. Liphoto, S. Mirasgedis, S. Murakami, J. Parikh, C. Pyke, and M.V. Vilariño, 2014: Buildings. In: *Climate Change 2014: Mitigation of Climate Change. Contribution of Working Group III to the Fifth Assessment Report of the Intergovernmental Panel on Climate Change* [Edenhofer, O., R. Pichs-Madruga, Y. Sokona, E. Farahani, S. Kadner, K. Seyboth, A. Adler, I. Baum, S. Brunner, P. Eickemeier, B. Kriemann, J. Savolainen, S. Schlömer, C. von Stechow, T. Zwickel and J.C. Minx (eds.)]. Cambridge University Press, Cambridge, UK, and New York, USA, 671–738 pp.

Ludwig, G., 2019: The Role of Law in Transformative Environmental Policies—A Case Study of "Timber in Buildings Construction in Germany". *Sustainability*, **11(3)**, 842, doi:10.3390/su11030842.

Lund, H. et al., 2018: The status of 4th generation district heating: Research and results. *Energy*, **164**, 147–159, doi:10.1016/j.energy.2018.08.206.

Luo, Y. et al., 2017: A comparative study on thermal performance evaluation of a new double skin façade system integrated with photovoltaic blinds. *Appl. Energy*, **199**, 281–293, doi:10.1016/j.apenergy.2017.05.026.

Lyons, L., 2019: *Digitalisation: Opportunities for heating and cooling*. Publications Office of the European Union, Luxembourg, 58 pp.

MacNaughton, P. et al., 2015: Economic, environmental and health implications of enhanced ventilation in office buildings. *Int. J. Environ. Res. Public Health*, **12(11)**, 14709–14722, doi:10.3390/ijerph121114709.

MacNaughton, P. et al., 2018: Energy savings, emission reductions, and health co-benefits of the green building movement review-article. *J. Expo. Sci. Environ. Epidemiol.*, **28(4)**, 307–318, doi:10.1038/s41370-017-0014-9.

Macquarie, R., B. Naran, P. Rosane, M. Solomon, and C. Wetherbee, 2020: *Updated view on the Global Landscape of Climate Finance 2019*. Climate Policy Initiative, CPI London, London, UK.

Mah, D.N. et al., 2018: Barriers and policy enablers for solar photovoltaics (PV) in cities: Perspectives of potential adopters in Hong Kong. *Renew. Sustain. Energy Rev.*, **92** (February 2017), 921–936, doi:10.1016/j.rser.2018.04.041.

Mahapatra, K., B. Mainali, and G. Pardalis, 2019: Homeowners' attitude towards one-stop-shop business concept for energy renovation of detached houses in Kronoberg, Sweden. *Energy Procedia*, **158**, 3702-3708, doi:10.1016/j.egypro.2019.01.888.

Mahmoud, M. et al., 2020: Recent advances in district energy systems: A review. *Therm. Sci. Eng. Prog.*, **20** (August), 100678, doi:10.1016/j.tsep.2020.100678.

Mahmoudi, N. et al., 2017: A bottom-up approach for demand response aggregators' participation in electricity markets. *Electr. Power Syst. Res.*, **143**, 121–129, doi:10.1016/j.epsr.2016.08.038.

Maidment, C.D., C.R. Jones, T.L. Webb, E.A. Hathway, and J.M. Gilbertson, 2014: The impact of household energy efficiency measures on health: A meta-analysis. *Energy Policy*, **65**, 583–593, doi:10.1016/j.enpol.2013.10.054.

Malla, M.B., N. Bruce, E. Bates, and E. Rehfuess, 2011: Applying global cost-benefit analysis methods to indoor air pollution mitigation interventions in Nepal, Kenya and Sudan: Insights and challenges. *Energy Policy*, **39(12)**, 7518–7529, doi:10.1016/j.enpol.2011.06.031.

Mallaburn, P., 2018: Principles of successful non-residential energy efficiency policy. *ECEEE 2018 Industrial Summer Study Proceedings*, **2018**, 15–22.

Malmodin, J. and D. Lundén, 2018: The Energy and Carbon Footprint of the Global ICT and E&M Sectors 2010–2015. *Sustainability*, **10(9)**, 3027, doi:10.3390/su10093027.

Mañá Reixach, F., 2000: *El Gros de l'obra: uns apunts de construcció*. Edicions UPC, 2020.

Mangialardo, A., E. Micelli, and F. Saccani, 2018: Does Sustainability Affect Real Estate Market Values? Empirical Evidence from the Office Buildings Market in Milan (Italy). *Sustainability*, **11(1)**, 12, doi:10.3390/su11010012.

Mangold, M., M. Österbring, H. Wallbaum, L. Thuvander, and P. Femenias, 2016: Socio-economic impact of renovation and energy retrofitting of the Gothenburg building stock. *Energy Build.*, **123**, 41–49, doi:10.1016/j.enbuild.2016.04.033.

Manzano-Agugliaro, F., F.G. Montoya, A. Sabio-Ortega, and A. García-Cruz, 2015: Review of bioclimatic architecture strategies for achieving thermal comfort. *Renew. Sustain. Energy Rev.*, **49**, 736–755, doi:10.1016/j.rser.2015.04.095.

Marchenko, O.V., 2008: Modeling of a green certificate market. *Renew. Energy*, **33(8)**, doi:10.1016/j.renene.2007.09.026.

Marckmann, B., K. Gram-Hanssen, and T.H. Christensen, 2012: Sustainable living and co-housing: Evidence from a case study of eco-villages. *Built Environ.*, **38(3)**, 413–429, doi:10.2148/benv.38.3.413.

Marek, E., C. Raux, and D. Engelmann, 2018: Personal carbon allowances: Can a budget label do the trick? *Transp. Policy*, **69** (July), 170–178, doi:10.1016/j.tranpol.2018.06.007.

Markandya, A., X. Labandeira, and A. Ramos, 2015: Policy Instruments to Foster Energy Efficiency. In: *Green Energy and Technology* [Ansuategi, A., J. Delgado, and I. Galarraga, (eds.)]. Vol. 164, Springer, Cham, Switzerland, pp. 93–110.

Markewitz, P., P. Hansen, W. Kuckshinrichs, and J.F. Hake, 2015: Strategies for a low carbon building stock in Germany. *8th International Scientific Conference on Energy and Climate Change*, Research Centre Jülich, Institute of Energy and Climate Research, Athens, Greece, 2015.

Markovska, N. et al., 2016: Addressing the main challenges of energy security in the twenty-first century – Contributions of the conferences on Sustainable Development of Energy, Water and Environment Systems. *Energy*, **115**, 1504–1512, doi:10.1016/j.energy.2016.10.086.

Marmolejo-Duarte, C. and A. Chen, 2019: The uneven price impact of energy efficiency ratings on housing segments and implications for public policy and private markets. *Sustain.*, **11(2)**, 372, doi:10.3390/su11020372.

Marshall, R. et al., 2015: Design and evaluation: End users, user datasets and personas. *Appl. Ergon.*, **46(PB)**, 311–317, doi:10.1016/j.apergo.2013. 03.008.

Marszal, A.J. et al., 2011: Zero Energy Building – A review of definitions and calculation methodologies. *Energy Build.*, **43(4)**, 971–979, doi:10.1016/ j.enbuild.2010.12.022.

Marzano, R. et al., 2018: Determinants of the price response to residential water tariffs: Meta-analysis and beyond. *Environ. Model. Softw.*, **101**, 236–248, doi:10.1016/j.envsoft.2017.12.017.

Mashhoodi, B., D. Stead, and A. van Timmeren, 2019: Spatial homogeneity and heterogeneity of energy poverty: a neglected dimension. *Ann. GIS*, **25(1)**, 19–31, doi:10.1080/19475683.2018.1557253.

Mastrucci, A., E. Byers, S. Pachauri, and N.D. Rao, 2019: Improving the SDG energy poverty targets: Residential cooling needs in the Global South. *Energy Build.*, **186**, 405–415, doi:10.1016/j.enbuild.2019.01.015.

Masuda, H. and D.E. Claridge, 2014: Statistical modeling of the building energy balance variable for screening of metered energy use in large commercial buildings. *Energy Build.*, **77**, 292–303, doi:10.1016/j.enbuild.2014.03.070.

Mata, É., J. Wanemark, V.M. Nik, and A. Sasic Kalagasidis, 2019: Economic feasibility of building retrofitting mitigation potentials: Climate change uncertainties for Swedish cities. *Appl. Energy*, **242** (August 2018), 1022–1035, doi:10.1016/j.apenergy.2019.03.042.

Mata, É., S. Harris, A. Novikova, A.F.P. Lucena, and P. Bertoldi, 2020a: Climate Mitigation from Circular and Sharing Economy in the Buildings Sector. *Resour. Conserv. Recycl.*, **158** (March), 104817, doi:10.1016/j.resconrec. 2020.104817.

Mata, É. et al., 2020b: A map of roadmaps for zero and low energy and carbon buildings worldwide. *Environ. Res. Lett.*, **15(11)**, 113003, doi:10.1088/ 1748-9326/abb69f.

Mata, É., J. Ottosson, and J. Nilsson, 2020c: A review of flexibility of residential electricity demand as climate solution in four EU countries. *Environ. Res. Lett.*, **15(7)**, 073001, doi:10.1088/1748-9326/ab7950.

Mata, É. et al., 2021a: Non-technological and behavioral options for decarbonizing buildings – a review of global topics, trends, gaps, and potentials. *Sustain. Prod. Consum.*, **29** (January 2022), 529–545, doi:10.1016/j.spc.2021.10.013.

Mata, É., D. Peñaloza, F. Sandkvist, and T. Nyberg, 2021b: What is stopping low-carbon buildings? A global review of enablers and barriers. *Energy Res. Soc. Sci.*, **82**, 102261, doi:10.1016/j.erss.2021.102261.

Mata, É. et al., 2021c: Systematic map of determinants of buildings' energy demand and CO_2 emissions shows need for decoupling. *Environ. Res. Lett.*, **16(5)**, 55011, doi:10.1088/1748-9326/abe5d7.

Mathew, P., P. Issler, and N. Wallace, 2021: Should commercial mortgage lenders care about energy efficiency? Lessons from a pilot study. *Energy Policy*, **150** (January), 112137, doi:10.1016/j.enpol.2021.112137.

Mattioli, R. and K. Moulinos, 2015: *Communication network dependencies in smart grids*. European Union Agency For Network And Information Security, European Union Agency for Network and Information Security (ENISA), 2015, 54 pp.

Maxwell, K.B. et al., 2018: Chapter 11 : Built Environment, Urban Systems, and Cities. In: *Impacts, Risks, and Adaptation in the United States: The Fourth National Climate Assessment*, Volume II, pp. 438–478, doi:10.7930/ NCA4.2018.CH11.

Mayrand, F. and P. Clergeau, 2018: Green Roofs and Green Walls for Biodiversity Conservation: A Contribution to Urban Connectivity? *Sustainability*, **10(4)**, 985, doi:10.3390/su10040985.

McCollum, D.L. et al., 2018: Connecting the sustainable development goals by their energy inter-linkages. *Environ. Res. Lett.*, **13(3)**, doi:10.1088/1748-9326/aaafe3.

McKinlay, A., C. Baldwin, and N.J. Stevens, 2019: Size Matters: Dwelling Size as a Critical Factor for Sustainable Urban Development. *Urban Policy Res.*, **37(2)**, 135–150, doi:10.1080/08111146.2017.1374944.

McNeil, M.A., N. Karali, and V. Letschert, 2019: Forecasting Indonesia's electricity load through 2030 and peak demand reductions from appliance and lighting efficiency. *Energy Sustain. Dev.*, **49**, 65–77, doi:10.1016/j.esd. 2019.01.001.

Mehetre, S.A., N.L. Panwar, D. Sharma, and H. Kumar, 2017: Improved biomass cookstoves for sustainable development: A review. *Renew. Sustain. Energy Rev.*, **73** (September 2015), 672–687, doi:10.1016/j.rser.2017.01.150.

Meier, H. and K. Rehdanz, 2010: Determinants of residential space heating expenditures in Great Britain. *Energy Econ.*, **32(5)**, 949–959, doi:10.1016/ j.eneco.2009.11.008.

Mercado, J., 2018: *Towards a Circular Building Industry in Berlin-Emerging Concepts from the Circular Economy Kopernikus Projects Enavi Working Package 4 | Task 7 "Technical-systemic analysis with a focus on energy efficiency in buildings"*. IKEM – Institute for Climate Protection, Energy and Mobility, Berlin, Germany, 2018.

Merini, I., A. Molina-García, M. Socorro García-Cascales, M. Mahdaoui, and M. Ahachad, 2020: Analysis and comparison of energy efficiency code requirements for buildings: A Morocco-Spain case study. *Energies*, **13(22)**, 5910, doi:10.3390/en13225979.

Michaelowa, A., I. Shishlov, and D. Brescia, 2019: Evolution of international carbon markets: lessons for the Paris Agreement. *Wiley Interdiscip. Rev. Clim. Chang.*, **10(6)**, doi:10.1002/wcc.613.

Miezis, M., K. Zvaigznitis, N. Stancioff, and L. Soeftestad, 2016: Climate change and buildings energy efficiency – The key role of residents. *Environ. Clim. Technol.*, **17(1)**, 30–43, doi:10.1515/rtuect-2016-0004.

Mikulić, D., I.R. Bakarić, and S. Slijepčević, 2016: The economic impact of energy saving retrofits of residential and public buildings in Croatia. *Energy Policy*, **96** (2016), 630–644, doi:10.1016/j.enpol.2016.06.040.

Militello-Hourigan, R.E. and S.L. Miller, 2018: The impacts of cooking and an assessment of indoor air quality in Colorado passive and tightly constructed homes. *Build. Environ.*, **144** (August), 573–582, doi:10.1016/ j.buildenv.2018.08.044.

Miller, L. and R. Carriveau, 2018: A review of energy storage financing— Learning from and partnering with the renewable energy industry. *J. Energy Storage*, **19** (January), 311–319, doi:10.1016/j.est.2018.08.007.

Mills, E., 2016: Job creation and energy savings through a transition to modern off-grid lighting. *Energy Sustain. Dev.*, **33**, 155–166, doi:10.1016/ j.esd.2016.06.001.

Millward-Hopkins, J., J.K. Steinberger, N.D. Rao, and Y. Oswald, 2020: Providing decent living with minimum energy: A global scenario. *Glob. Environ. Chang.*, **65**, 102168, doi:10.1016/j.gloenvcha.2020.102168.

Mirasgedis, S., C. Tourkolias, E. Pavlakis, and D. Diakoulaki, 2014: A methodological framework for assessing the employment effects associated with energy efficiency interventions in buildings. *Energy Build.*, **82**, 275–286, doi:10.1016/j.enbuild.2014.07.027.

Mirasgedis, S., Y. Sarafidis, and E. Georgopoulou, 2017: *Long-term planning for the energy system of Greece*. WWF, Athens, Greece, 2017.

Mistry, M.N., 2019: Historical global gridded degree-days: A high-spatial resolution database of CDD and HDD. *Geosci. Data J.*, 6(2), 214–221, doi:10.1002/gdj3.83.

Miu, L., N. Wisniewska, C. Mazur, J. Hardy, and A. Hawkes, 2018: A Simple Assessment of Housing Retrofit Policies for the UK: What Should Succeed the Energy Company Obligation? *Energies*, **11(8)**, 2070, doi:10.3390/ en11082070.

Mofidi, F. and H. Akbari, 2017: Personalized energy costs and productivity optimization in offices. *Energy Build.*, **143**, 173–190, doi:10.1016/j.enbuild. 2017.03.018.

Mohit, A., R. Felix, C. Lynette, and S. Arlindo, 2020: Buildings and the circular economy: Estimating urban mining, recovery and reuse potential of building components. *Resour. Conserv. Recycl.*, **154** (October 2019), 104581, doi:10.1016/j.resconrec.2019.104581.

MoHURD, 2019: *Technical Standard for Nearly Zero Energy Building GB 51350-2019*. China Architecture & Building Press, Beijing, China, 135 pp.

9

Molenbroek, E., M. Smith, N. Surmeli, and S. Schimschar, 2015: *Savings and benefits of global regulations for energy efficient products*. European Union, Brussels, Belgium, 2015, 106 pp.

Momonoki, T., A. Taniguchi-Matsuoka, Y. Yamaguchi, and Y. Shimoda, 2017: Evaluation of the greenhouse gas reduction effect in the Japanese residential sector considering the characteristics of regions and households. *Build. Simul. Conf. Proc.*, **1**, 494–501, doi:10.26868/25222708.2017.718.

Moncaster, A.M. and J.Y. Song, 2012: A comparative review of existing data and methodologies for calculating embodied energy and carbon of buildings. *Int. J. Sustain. Build. Technol. Urban Dev.*, **3(1)**, 26–36, doi:10.1080/2093761X.2012.673915.

Moncaster, A.M., F.N. Rasmussen, T. Malmqvist, A. Houlihan Wiberg, and H. Birgisdottir, 2019: Widening understanding of low embodied impact buildings: Results and recommendations from 80 multi-national quantitative and qualitative case studies. *J. Clean. Prod.*, **235**, 378–393, doi:10.1016/j.jclepro.2019.06.233.

Mongsawad, P., 2012: The philosophy of the sufficiency economy: a contribution to the theory of development. *Asia-Pacific Dev. J.*, **17(1)**, 123–143, doi:10.18356/02bd5fb3-en.

Moradibistouni, M., N. Isaacs, and B. Vale, 2018: Learning from the past to build tomorrow: an overview of previous prefabrication schemes. *52nd International Conference of the Architectural Science Association*, 145–152.

Mørck, O.C., 2017: Energy saving concept development for the MORE-CONNECT pilot energy renovation of apartment blocks in Denmark. *Energy Procedia*, **140**, 240–251, doi:10.1016/j.egypro.2017.11.139.

Morel, J.C. and R. Charef, 2019: What are the barriers affecting the use of earth as a modern construction material in the context of circular economy? *IOP Conf. Ser. Earth Environ. Sci.*, **225(1)**, 12053, doi:10.1088/1755-1315/225/1/012053.

Morganti, M., A. Pages-Ramon, H. Coch, and A. Isalgue, 2019: Building mass and Energy Demand in Conventional Housing Typologies of the Mediterranean City. *Sustainability*, **11(13)**, 3540, doi:10.3390/su11133540.

Morstyn, T., N. Farrell, S.J. Darby, and M.D. McCulloch, 2018: Using peer-to-peer energy-trading platforms to incentivize prosumers to form federated power plants. *Nat. Energy*, **3(2)**, doi:10.1038/s41560-017-0075-y.

Mortensen, A., P. Heiselberg, and M. Knudstrup, 2016: Identification of key parameters determining Danish homeowners' willingness and motivation for energy renovations. *Int. J. Sustain. Built Environ.*, **5(2)**, 246–268, doi:10.1016/j.ijsbe.2016.09.002.

Mosoarca, M., A.I. Keller, and C. Bocan, 2019: Failure analysis of church towers and roof structures due to high wind velocities. *Eng. Fail. Anal.*, **100** (February), 76–87, doi:10.1016/j.engfailanal.2019.02.046.

Moura, M.C.P., S.J. Smith, and D.B. Belzer, 2015: 120 Years of U.S. Residential Housing Stock and Floor Space. *PLoS One*, **10(8)**, e0134135–e0134135, doi:10.1371/journal.pone.0134135.

Mujahid Rafique, M., P. Gandhidasan, S. Rehman, and L.M. Al-Hadhrami, 2015: A review on desiccant based evaporative cooling systems. *Renew. Sustain. Energy Rev.*, **45**, 145–159, doi:10.1016/j.rser.2015.01.051.

Mundaca, L., D. Ürge-Vorsatz, and C. Wilson, 2019: Demand-side approaches for limiting global warming to 1.5°C. *Energy Effic.*, **12(2)**, 343–362, doi:10.1007/s12053-018-9722-9.

Mundaca, L. and S. Kloke, 2018: On-Bill Financing Programs to Support Low-Carbon Energy Technologies: An Agent-Oriented Assessment. *Rev. Policy Res.*, 35(4), 502–534, doi:10.1111/ropr.12302.

Murphy, R., 2015: *The Joy of Tax. How a fair tax system can create a better society*. Transworld Publishers, London, UK, 1–250 pp.

Murtagh, N. et al., 2013: Individual energy use and feedback in an office setting: A field trial. *Energy Policy*, **62**, 717–728, doi:10.1016/j.enpol.2013.07.090.

Musonye, X.S., B. Davíðsdóttir, R. Kristjánsson, E.I. Ásgeirsson, and H. Stefánsson, 2020: Integrated energy systems' modeling studies for sub-Saharan Africa: A scoping review. *Renew. Sustain. Energy Rev.*, **128**, doi:10.1016/j.rser.2020.109915.

Mzavanadze, N., 2018a: *Quantifying energy poverty-related health impacts of energy efficiency*. The University of Manchester, Manchester, UK, 66 pp.

Mzavanadze, N., 2018b: *Quantifying air pollution impacts of energy efficiency*. The University of Manchester, Manchester, UK, 32 pp.

Nabitz, L. and S. Hirzel, 2019: Transposing The Requirements of the Energy Efficiency Directive on Mandatory Energy Audits for Large Companies: A Policy-Cycle-based review of the National Implementation in the EU-28 Member States. *Energy Policy*, **125**, 548–561, doi:10.1016/j.enpol.2017.12.016.

Nadel, S., 2016: *Pathway to Cutting Energy Use and Carbon Emissions in Half*. American Council for an Energy-Efficient Economy, Washington, DC, USA, 43 pp.

Nadel, S., 2019: Focusing and improving traditional energy efficiency strategies. *Electr. J.*, **32(7)**, 106620, doi:10.1016/j.tej.2019.106620.

Nakicenovic, N. et al., 2019: *The Digital Revoluion and Sustainable Development: Opportunities and Challenges Report*. International Institute for Applied Systems Analysis, Laxenburg, Austria, 100 pp.

Narassimhan, E., K.S. Gallagher, S. Koester, and J.R. Alejo, 2018: Carbon pricing in practice: a review of existing emissions trading systems. *Clim. Policy*, **18(8)**, 967–991, doi:10.1080/14693062.2018.1467827.

National Treasury of Republic of South Africa, 2021: *Working Draft. Draft Green Finance Taxonomy of South Africa*. NBI, Johannesburg, South Africa, 107 pp.

Navarro, L. et al., 2016: Thermal energy storage in building integrated thermal systems: A review. Part 1. active storage systems. *Renew. Energy*, **88**, 526–547, doi:10.1016/j.renene.2015.11.040.

Nazaroff, W.W., 2013: Exploring the consequences of climate change for indoor air quality. *Environ. Res. Lett.*, **8(1)**, 015022, doi:10.1088/1748-9326/8/1/015022.

Negawatt, 2017: *Scénario négaWatt : Un scénario de transition énergétique*. Negawatt, 4 pp. https://negawatt.org/Scenario-negaWatt-2017-2050.

Nematchoua, M. K., M., J.C. Vanona, and J.A. Orosa, 2020: Energy Efficiency and Thermal Performance of Office Buildings Integrated with Passive Strategies in Coastal Regions of Humid and Hot Tropical Climates in Madagascar. *Appl. Sci.*, **10(7)**, 2438, doi:10.3390/app10072438.

New Building Institute, 2019: Getting to zero buildings database. https://newbuildings.org/resource/getting-to-zero-database/. New buildings Institute, Portland.

Newell, R.G., W.A. Pizer, and D. Raimi, 2019: U.S. federal government subsidies for clean energy: Design choices and implications. *Energy Econ.*, **80**, 831–841, doi:10.1016/j.eneco.2019.02.018.

Newton, P., D. Meyer, and S. Glackin, 2017: Becoming urban: Exploring the transformative capacity for a suburban-to-urban transition in Australia's low-density cities. *Sustain.*, **9(10)**, doi:10.3390/su9101718.

Nguyen, H.T., D.T. Nguyen, and L.B. Le, 2015: Energy management for households with solar assisted thermal load considering renewable energy and price uncertainty. *IEEE Trans. Smart Grid*, **6(1)**, 301–314, doi:10.1109/TSG.2014.2350831.

Nicolini, M. and M. Tavoni, 2017: Are renewable energy subsidies effective? Evidence from Europe. *Renew. Sustain. Energy Rev.*, **74** (December 2016), 412–423, doi:10.1016/j.rser.2016.12.032.

Niemelä, T., K. Levy, R. Kosonen, and J. Jokisalo, 2017: Cost-optimal renovation solutions to maximize environmental performance, indoor thermal conditions and productivity of office buildings in cold climate. *Sustain. Cities Soc.*, **32**, 417–434, doi:10.1016/j.scs.2017.04.009.

Nikas, A. et al., 2020: Barriers to and consequences of a solar-based energy transition in Greece. *Environ. Innov. Soc. Transitions*, **35**, 383–399, doi:10.1016/j.eist.2018.12.004.

Nilsson, A., P. Stoll, and N. Brandt, 2017: Assessing the impact of real-time price visualization on residential electricity consumption, costs, and carbon emissions. *Resour. Conserv. Recycl.*, **124**, 152–161, doi:10.1016/j.resconrec.2015.10.007.

Nishida, Y. and Y. Hua, 2011: Motivating stakeholders to deliver change: Tokyo's Cap-and-Trade Program. *Build. Res. Inf.*, **39(5)**, doi:10.1080/096 13218.2011.596419.

Niu, S., X. Zhang, C. Zhao, and Y. Niu, 2012: Variations in energy consumption and survival status between rural and urban households: A case study of the Western Loess Plateau, China. *Energy Policy*, **49**, 515–527, doi:10.1016/j.enpol.2012.06.046.

Novikova, A., T. Csoknyai, M. Jovanovic-Popovic, B. Stankovic, and Z. Szalay, 2018a: Assessment of decarbonisation scenarios for the residential buildings of Serbia. *Therm. Sci.*, **22(sup4)**, 1231–1247, doi:10.2298/TSCI17 1221229N.

Novikova, A., T. Csoknyai, and Z. Szalay, 2018b: Low carbon scenarios for higher thermal comfort in the residential building sector of South Eastern Europe. *Energy Effic.*, **11(4)**, 845–875, doi:10.1007/s12053-017-9604-6.

Novikova, A., K. Stelmakh, A. Klinge, and I. Stamo, 2019: *Climate and energy investment map of Germany. Status report 2016*. Institute for Climate Protection, Energy and Mobility, Berlin, Germany, 1–109 pp.

Novikova, A. et al., 2020: Assessment of energy-saving potential, associated costs and co-benefits of public buildings in Albania. *Energy Effic.*, **13(7)**, 1387–1407, doi:10.1007/s12053-020-09883-3.

Nunes, A.R., 2020: General and specified vulnerability to extreme temperatures among older adults. *Int. J. Environ. Health Res.*, **30(5)**, 515–532, doi:10.1080/09603123.2019.1609655.

Nurcahyanto, Y. Simsek, and T. Urmee, 2020: Opportunities and challenges of energy service companies to promote energy efficiency programs in Indonesia. *Energy*, **205**, 117603, doi:10.1016/j.energy.2020.117603.

Nußholz, J.L.K., F.N. Rasmussen, K. Whalen, and A. Plepys, 2020: Material reuse in buildings: Implications of a circular business model for sustainable value creation. *J. Clean. Prod.*, **245**, 118546, doi:10.1016/j.jclepro.2019.118546.

Nyborg, S. and I. Røpke, 2013: Constructing users in the smart grid-insights from the Danish eFlex project. *Energy Effic.*, **6(4)**, 655–670, doi:10.1007/s12053-013-9210-1.

Oberegger, F.U., R. Pernetti, and R. Lollini, 2020: Bottom-up building stock retrofit based on levelized cost of saved energy. *Energy Build.*, **210**, 109757, doi:10.1016/j.enbuild.2020.109757.

Oberthür, S., 2019: Hard or Soft Governance? The EU's Climate and Energy Policy Framework for 2030. *Polit. Gov.*, 7(1), 17–27, doi:10.17645/pag.v7i1.1796.

O'Brien, W. and H.B. Gunay, 2014: The contextual factors contributing to occupants' adaptive comfort behaviors in offices – A review and proposed modeling framework. *Build. Environ.*, **77**, 77–87, doi:10.1016/j.buildenv.2014.03.024.

O'Brien, W. et al., 2020: Introducing IEA EBC annex 79: Key challenges and opportunities in the field of occupant-centric building design and operation. *Build. Environ.*, **178**, 106738, doi:10.1016/j.buildenv.2020.106738.

Oduyemi, O., M.I. Okoroh, and O.S. Fajana, 2017: The application and barriers of BIM in sustainable building design. *J. Facil. Manag.*, **15(1)**, 15–34, doi:10.1108/JFM-03-2016-0008.

Oh, M. and Y. Kim, 2019: Identifying urban geometric types as energy performance patterns. *Energy Sustain. Dev.*, **48**, 115–129, doi:10.1016/j.esd.2018.12.002.

Ohler, A.M., D.G. Loomis, and K. Ilves, 2020: A study of electricity savings from energy star appliances using household survey data. *Energy Policy*, **144**, 111607, doi:10.1016/j.enpol.2020.111607.

Ohueri, C.C., W.I. Enegbuma, and R. Kenley, 2018: Energy efficiency practices for Malaysian green office building occupants. *Built Environ. Proj. Asset Manag.*, **8(2)**, 134–146, doi:10.1108/BEPAM-10-2017-0091.

Oikonomou, V., A. Flamos, and S. Grafakos, 2014: Combination of Energy Policy Instruments: Creation of Added Value or Overlapping? *Energy Sources, Part B Econ. Planning, Policy*, **9(1)**, doi:10.1080/15567241003716696.

Okushima, S., 2016: Measuring energy poverty in Japan, 2004–2013. *Energy Policy*, **98** (April 2014), 557–564, doi:10.1016/j.enpol.2016.09.005.

Olmos, L., S. Ruester, and S.J. Liong, 2012: On the selection of financing instruments to push the development of new technologies: Application to clean energy technologies. *Energy Policy*, **43**, 252–266, doi:10.1016/j.enpol.2012.01.001.

Oluleye, G. and R. Smith, 2016: A mixed integer linear programming model for integrating thermodynamic cycles for waste heat exploitation in process sites. *Appl. Energy*, **178**, 434–453, doi:10.1016/j.apenergy.2016.06.096.

Oluleye, G., L. Vasquez, R. Smith, and M. Jobson, 2016: A multi-period Mixed Integer Linear Program for design of residential distributed energy centres with thermal demand data discretisation. *Sustain. Prod. Consum.*, **5**, 16–28, doi:10.1016/j.spc.2015.11.003.

Oluleye, G., J. Allison, N. Kelly, and A.D. Hawkes, 2018: An optimisation study on integrating and incentivising Thermal Energy Storage (TES) in a dwelling energy system. *Energies*, **11(5)**, 1–17, doi:10.3390/en11051095.

Omara, A.A.M. and A.A.A. Abuelnour, 2019: Improving the performance of air conditioning systems by using phase change materials: A review. *Int. J. Energy Res.*, **43(10)**, 5175–5198, doi:10.1002/er.4507.

Omrany, H., V. Soebarto, E. Sharifi, and A. Soltani, 2020: Application of Life Cycle Energy Assessment in Residential Buildings: A Critical Review of Recent Trends. *Sustainability*, **12(1)**, 351, doi:10.3390/su12010351.

Onyenokporo, N.C. and E.T. Ochedi, 2019: Low-cost retrofit packages for residential buildings in hot-humid Lagos, Nigeria. *Int. J. Build. Pathol. Adapt.*, **37(3)**, 250–272, doi:10.1108/IJBPA-01-2018-0010.

Orea, L., M. Llorca, and M. Filippini, 2015: A new approach to measuring the rebound effect associated to energy efficiency improvements: An application to the US residential energy demand. *Energy Econ.*, **49**, 599–609, doi:10.1016/j.eneco.2015.03.016.

Ormandy, D. and V. Ezratty, 2016: Thermal discomfort and health: protecting the susceptible from excess cold and excess heat in housing. *Adv. Build. Energy Res.*, **10(1)**, 84–98, doi:10.1080/17512549.2015.1014845.

Ortiz, J., N. Casquero-Modrego, and J. Salom, 2019: Health and related economic effects of residential energy retrofitting in Spain. *Energy Policy*, **130**, 375–388, doi:10.1016/j.enpol.2019.04.013.

Ortiz, M.A., S.R. Kurvers, and P.M. Bluyssen, 2017: A review of comfort, health, and energy use: Understanding daily energy use and wellbeing for the development of a new approach to study comfort. *Energy Build.*, **152**, 323–335, doi:10.1016/j.enbuild.2017.07.060.

Ortwein, A., 2016: Combined Heat and Power Systems for the Provision of Sustainable Energy from Biomass in Buildings. *E3S Web Conf.*, **10**, 00134, doi:10.1051/e3sconf/20161000134.

Osmani, M., 2012: Construction Waste Minimization in the UK: Current Pressures for Change and Approaches. *Procedia – Soc. Behav. Sci.*, **40**, 37–40, doi:10.1016/j.sbspro.2012.03.158.

Österbring, M. et al., 2016: A differentiated description of building-stocks for a georeferenced urban bottom-up building-stock model. *Energy Build.*, **120**, doi:10.1016/j.enbuild.2016.03.060.

Ostermeyer, Y. et al., 2018a: *Building Market Brief. United Kingdom*. CUES Foundation, Delft, The Netherlands, 70 pp.

Ostermeyer, Y. et al., 2018b: *Building Market Brief. France*. CUES Foundation, Delft, The Netherlands, 70 pp.

Ostermeyer, Y. et al., 2018c: *Building Market Brief. The Netherlands*. CUES Foundation, Delft, The Netherlands, 70 pp.

Ostermeyer, Y. et al., 2019a: *Building Market Brief. Poland*. CUES Foundation, Delft, The Netherlands, 64–75 pp.

Ostermeyer, Y. et al., 2019b: *Building Market Brief. Germany*. CUES Foundation, Delft, The Netherlands, 70 pp.

Östman, B., D. Brandon, and H. Frantzich, 2017: Fire safety engineering in timber buildings. *Fire Saf. J.*, **91** (April), 11–20, doi:10.1016/j.firesaf.2017.05.002.

Ott, C. and J. Hahn, 2018: Green pay off in commercial real estate in Germany: assessing the role of Super Trophy status. *J. Prop. Invest. Financ.*, **36(1)**, 104–124, doi:10.1108/JPIF-03-2017-0019.

Ottelin, J., H. Cetinay, and P. Behrens, 2020: Rebound effects may jeopardize the resource savings of circular consumption: evidence from household material footprints. *Environ. Res. Lett.*, **15(10)**, 104044, doi:10.1088/1748-9326/abaa78.

Ouyang, X. and B. Lin, 2014: Levelized cost of electricity (LCOE) of renewable energies and required subsidies in China. *Energy Policy*, **70**, 64–73, doi:10.1016/j.enpol.2014.03.030.

Ozarisoy, B. and H. Altan, 2017: Adoption of Energy Design Strategies for Retrofitting Mass Housing Estates in Northern Cyprus. *Sustainability*, **9(8)**, 1477, doi:10.3390/su9081477.

Pacudan, R., 2018: Feed-in tariff vs incentivized self-consumption: Options for residential solar PV policy in Brunei Darussalam. *Renew. Energy*, **122**, 362–374, doi:10.1016/j.renene.2018.01.102.

Paduos, S. and V. Corrado, 2017: Cost-optimal approach to transform the public buildings into nZEBs: an European cross-country comparison. *Energy Procedia*, **140**, 314–324, doi:10.1016/j.egypro.2017.11.145.

Palm, A., 2020: Early adopters and their motives: Differences between earlier and later adopters of residential solar photovoltaics. *Renew. Sustain. Energy Rev.*, **133**, 110142, doi:10.1016/j.rser.2020.110142.

Palmer, K.L., S. Grausz, B. Beasley, and T.J. Brennan, 2013: Putting a floor on energy savings: Comparing state energy efficiency resource standards. *Util. Policy*, **25** (2021), 43–57, doi:10.1016/j.jup.2013.02.002.

Pamenter, S. and R.J. Myers, 2021: Decarbonizing the cementitious materials cycle: A whole-systems review of measures to decarbonize the cement supply chain in the UK and European contexts. *J. Ind. Ecol.*, **25(2)**, 359–376, doi:10.1111/jiec.13105.

Parag, Y. and B.K. Sovacool, 2016: Electricity market design for the prosumer era. *Nat. Energy*, **1(4)**, 16032, doi:10.1038/nenergy.2016.32.

Park, E., S. Kim, Y.S. Kim, and S.J. Kwon, 2018: Smart home services as the next mainstream of the ICT industry: determinants of the adoption of smart home services. *Univers. Access Inf. Soc.*, **17(1)**, 175–190, doi:10.1007/s10209-017-0533-0.

Park, H. and W.K. Hong, 2014: Korea's emission trading scheme and policy design issues to achieve market-efficiency and abatement targets. *Energy Policy*, **75** (2014), 73–83, doi:10.1016/j.enpol.2014.05.001.

Park, H. and C. Kim, 2018: Do Shifts in Renewable Energy Operation Policy Affect Efficiency: Korea's Shift from FIT to RPS and Its Results. *Sustainability*, **10(6)**, doi:10.3390/su10061723.

Parkin, A., M. Herrera, and D.A. Coley, 2019: Energy or carbon? Exploring the relative size of universal zero carbon and zero energy design spaces. *Build. Serv. Eng. Res. Technol.*, **40(3)**, 319–339, doi:10.1177/0143624418815780.

Patange, O.S. et al., 2015: Reductions in Indoor Black Carbon Concentrations from Improved Biomass Stoves in Rural India. *Environ. Sci. Technol.*, **49(7)**, 4749–4756, doi:10.1021/es506208x.

Patwa, N. et al., 2021: Towards a circular economy: An emerging economies context. *J. Bus. Res.*, **122**, 725–735, doi:10.1016/j.jbusres.2020.05.015.

Pauliuk, S. et al., 2021: Global scenarios of resource and emission savings from material efficiency in residential buildings and cars. *Nat. Commun.*, **12(1)**, doi:10.1038/s41467-021-25300-4.

Pavanello, F. et al., 2021: Air-conditioning and the adaptation cooling deficit in emerging economies. *Nat. Commun.*, **12(1)**, 6460, doi:10.1038/s41467-021-26592-2.

Payne, J., D. Weatherall, and F. Downy, 2015: Capturing the multiple benefits of energy efficiency in practice: the UK example. *ECEE 2015 Summer Study Proceedings*, 229–238.

Pedzi Makumbe Marwa Moustafa Khalil, and Mohab Hallouda, M.M., 2017: *Energy Efficiency and Rooftop Solar PV Opportunities in Cairo and Alexandria*. Egypt-PV, Dokki, Egypt, 38 pp.

Peñaloza, D., M. Erlandsson, and A. Falk, 2016: Exploring the climate impact effects of increased use of bio-based materials in buildings. *Constr. Build. Mater.*, **125**, 219–226, doi:10.1016/j.conbuildmat.2016.08.041.

Peñaloza, D., M. Erlandsson, J. Berlin, M. Wålinder, and A. Falk, 2018: Future scenarios for climate mitigation of new construction in Sweden: Effects of different technological pathways. *J. Clean. Prod.*, **187**, 1025–1035, doi:10.1016/j.jclepro.2018.03.285.

Peng, J.-T. et al., 2019: Economic and welfare influences of an energy excise tax in Jiangsu province of China: A computable general equilibrium approach. *J. Clean. Prod.*, **211**, 1403–1411, doi:10.1016/j.jclepro.2018.11.267.

Peng, L. and M.G. Stewart, 2016: Climate change and corrosion damage risks for reinforced concrete infrastructure in China. *Struct. Infrastruct. Eng.*, **12(4)**, 499–516, doi:10.1080/15732479.2013.858270.

Peng, P., G. Gong, X. Deng, C. Liang, and W. Li, 2020: Field study and numerical investigation on heating performance of air carrying energy radiant air-conditioning system in an office. *Energy Build.*, **209**, 109712, doi:10.1016/j.enbuild.2019.109712.

Pereira da Silva, P., G. Dantas, G.I. Pereira, L. Câmara, and N.J. De Castro, 2019: Photovoltaic distributed generation – An international review on diffusion, support policies, and electricity sector regulatory adaptation. *Renew. Sustain. Energy Rev.*, **103**, doi:10.1016/j.rser.2018.12.028.

Peschiera, G. and J.E. Taylor, 2012: The impact of peer network position on electricity consumption in building occupant networks utilizing energy feedback systems. *Energy Build.*, **49**, 584–590, doi:10.1016/j.enbuild.2012.03.011.

Peters, T., 2018: *A Cool World Defining the Energy Conundrum of Cooling for All Contributors*. University of Birmingham, Birmingham, UK, 19 pp.

Picard, T., T. Hong, N. Luo, S. Hoon, and K. Sun, 2020: Energy & Buildings Robustness of energy performance of Zero-Net-Energy (ZNE) homes. *Energy Build.*, **224**, 110251, doi:10.1016/j.enbuild.2020.110251.

Pitelis, A., N. Vasilakos, and K. Chalvatzis, 2020: Fostering innovation in renewable energy technologies: Choice of policy instruments and effectiveness. *Renew. Energy*, **151**, doi:10.1016/j.renene.2019.11.100.

Pittau, F., G. Lumia, N. Heeren, G. Iannaccone, and G. Habert, 2019: Retrofit as a carbon sink: The carbon storage potentials of the EU housing stock. *J. Clean. Prod.*, **214**, 365–376, doi:10.1016/j.jclepro.2018.12.304.

Pitts, A., 2017: Passive House and Low Energy Buildings: Barriers and Opportunities for Future Development within UK Practice. *Sustainability*, **9(2)**, 272, doi:10.3390/su9020272.

Ploss, M., T. Hatt, C. Schneider, T. Rosskopf, and M. Braun, 2017: *Modellvorhaben „KliNaWo". Klimagerechter Nachhaltiger Wohnbau*. Energieinstitut Vorarlberg, Dornbirn.

Polzin, F., F. Egli, B. Steffen, and T.S. Schmidt, 2019: How do policies mobilize private finance for renewable energy?—A systematic review with an investor perspective. *Appl. Energy*, **236** (September 2018), 1249–1268, doi:10.1016/j.apenergy.2018.11.098.

Pomponi, F. and A. Moncaster, 2016: Embodied carbon mitigation and reduction in the built environment – What does the evidence say? *J. Environ. Manage.*, **181**, 687–700, doi:10.1016/j.jenvman.2016.08.036.

Pomponi, F. and A. Moncaster, 2017: Circular economy for the built environment: A research framework. *J. Clean. Prod.*, **143**, 710–718, doi:10.1016/j.jclepro.2016.12.055.

Pomponi, F. and A. Moncaster, 2018: Scrutinising embodied carbon in buildings: The next performance gap made manifest. *Renew. Sustain. Energy Rev.*, **81** (February 2017), 2431–2442, doi:10.1016/j.rser.2017.06.049.

Pomponi, F., P.A.E. Piroozfar, R. Southall, P. Ashton, and E.R.P. Farr, 2016: Energy performance of Double-Skin Façades in temperate climates: A systematic review and meta-analysis. *Renew. Sustain. Energy Rev.*, **54**, 1525–1536, doi:10.1016/j.rser.2015.10.075.

Pomponi, F., J. Hart, J.H. Arehart, and B. D'Amico, 2020: Buildings as a Global Carbon Sink? A Reality Check on Feasibility Limits. *One Earth*, **3(2)**, 157–161, doi:10.1016/j.oneear.2020.07.018.

Pons, O., 2014: Assessing the sustainability of prefabricated buildings. In: *Eco-efficient Construction and Building Materials* [Pacheco-Torgal, F., L.F. Cabeza, J. Labrincha, and A. De Magalhães, (eds.)]. Woodhead Publishing, pp. 434–456.

Poon, I., 2015: Incorporation of rebound effect into energy efficient measures cost-benefit analysis model. *2015 IEEE International Conference on Building Efficiency and Sustainable Technologies*. IEEE, 90–94 pp.

Poortinga, W., S. Jiang, C. Grey, and C. Tweed, 2018: Impacts of energy-efficiency investments on internal conditions in low-income households. *Build. Res. Inf.*, **46(6)**, 653–667, doi:10.1080/09613218.2017.1314641.

Pothitou, M., R.F. Hanna, and K.J. Chalvatzis, 2017: ICT entertainment appliances' impact on domestic electricity consumption. *Renew. Sustain. Energy Rev.*, **69** (July 2016), 843–853, doi:10.1016/j.rser.2016.11.100.

Prada-Hernández, A., H. Vargas, A. Ozuna, and J.L. Ponz-tienda, 2015: Marginal Abatement Costs Curve (MACC) for Carbon Emissions Reduction from Buildings: An Implementation for Office Buildings in Colombia. *Int. J. Civ. Struct. Eng.*, **2(1)**, 175–183.

Prasanna, A., J. Mahmoodi, T. Brosch, and M.K. Patel, 2018: Recent experiences with tariffs for saving electricity in households. *Energy Policy*, **115**, doi:10.1016/j.enpol.2018.01.044.

Princen, T., 2003: Principles for Sustainability: From Cooperation and Efficiency to Sufficiency. *Glob. Environ. Polit.*, **3(1)**, 33–50, doi:10.1162/152638003763336374.

Prívara, S., J. Široký, L. Ferkl, and J. Cigler, 2011: Model predictive control of a building heating system: The first experience. *Energy Build.*, **43**(2–3), 564–572, doi:10.1016/j.enbuild.2010.10.022.

Pyke, C.R., S. McMahon, L. Larsen, N.B. Rajkovich, and A. Rohloff, 2012: Development and analysis of Climate Sensitivity and Climate Adaptation opportunities indices for buildings. *Build. Environ.*, **55**, 141–149, doi:10.1016/j.buildenv.2012.02.020.

Qiu, Y., 2014: Energy Efficiency and Rebound Effects: An Econometric Analysis of Energy Demand in the Commercial Building Sector. *Environ. Resour. Econ.*, **59(2)**, 295–335, doi:10.1007/s10640-013-9729-9.

Qiu, Y., G. Colson, and C. Grebitus, 2014: Risk preferences and purchase of energy-efficient technologies in the residential sector. *Ecol. Econ.*, **107**, 216–229, doi:10.1016/j.ecolecon.2014.09.002.

Quinn, A.K. et al., 2018: An analysis of efforts to scale up clean household energy for cooking around the world. *Energy Sustain. Dev.*, **46**, 1–10, doi:10.1016/j.esd.2018.06.011.

Quraishi, K.S. and S. Ahmed, 2019: Analysis of Purchase Behavior of Residential Solar Rooftop PV Adopters. *Int. J. Manag.*, **10(5)**, 28–37, doi:10.34218/IJM.10.5.2019.003.

Rabe, M. et al., 2018: Impact of smart services to current value networks. *J. Mech. Eng.*, **5(4)**, 1–11.

Rachel, B. and W. Travis, 2011: The influence of collection facility attributes on household collection rates of electronic waste: The case of televisions and computer monitors. *Resour. Conserv. Recycl.*, **55(11)**, 1051–1059, doi:10.1016/j.resconrec.2011.05.019.

Rademaekers, K., K. Svatikova, J. Vermeulen, T. Smit, and L. Baroni, 2017: *Environmental potential of the collaborative economy*. Publication Office of the European Union, Luxembourg.

Radhi, H., 2011: Viability of autoclaved aerated concrete walls for the residential sector in the United Arab Emirates. *Energy Build.*, **43(9)**, 2086–2092, doi:10.1016/j.enbuild.2011.04.018.

Radpour, S., M.A. Hossain Mondal, and A. Kumar, 2017: Market penetration modeling of high energy efficiency appliances in the residential sector. *Energy*, **134**, 951–961, doi:10.1016/j.energy.2017.06.039.

Rafaj, P. et al., 2018: Outlook for clean air in the context of sustainable development goals. *Glob. Environ. Chang.*, **53**, 1–11, doi:10.1016/j.gloenvcha.2018.08.008.

Rafiee, A., E. Dias, and E. Koomen, 2019: Analysing the impact of spatial context on the heat consumption of individual households. *Renew. Sustain. Energy Rev.*, **112**(May), 461–470, doi:10.1016/j.rser.2019.05.033.

Rafsanjani, H., C. Ahn, and M. Alahmad, 2015: A Review of Approaches for Sensing, Understanding, and Improving Occupancy-Related Energy-Use Behaviors in Commercial Buildings. *Energies*, **8(10)**, 10996–11029, doi:10.3390/en81010996.

Rahman, R.A. and S.K. Ayer, 2019: Enhancing the non-technological skills required for effective building information modeling through problem-based learning. *J. Inf. Technol. Constr.*, **24** (October 2018), 154–166.

Rahut, D.B., A. Ali, and B. Behera, 2017: Domestic use of dirty energy and its effects on human health: empirical evidence from Bhutan. *Int. J. Sustain. Energy*, **36(10)**, 983–993, doi:10.1080/14786451.2016.1154855.

Rakha, T., Y. Chen, and C. Reinhart, 2018: Do Office Buildings 'Save' Energy in the United States Due To Daylight Saving Time (Dst)? a 50-State Simulation-Based Study. *2018 Building Performance Analysis Conference and Simbuild*, 21–28.

Ralston Fonseca, F., P. Jaramillo, M. Bergés, and E. Severnini, 2019: Seasonal effects of climate change on intra-day electricity demand patterns. *Clim. Change*, **154**(3–4), 435–451, doi:10.1007/s10584-019-02413-w.

Ramage, M.H., et al., 2017: The wood from the trees: The use of timber in construction. *Renew. Sustain. Energy Rev.*, **68**, doi:10.1016/j.rser.2016.09.107.

Rao, N.D. and P. Baer, 2012: "Decent Living" emissions: A conceptual framework. *Sustainability*, **4(4)**, 656–681, doi:10.3390/su4040656.

Rao, N.D. and S. Pachauri, 2017: Energy access and living standards: some observations on recent trends. *Environ. Res. Lett.*, **12(2)**, doi:10.1088/1748-9326/aa5b0d.

Rao, N.D. and J. Min, 2018: Decent Living Standards: Material Prerequisites for Human Wellbeing. *Soc. Indic. Res.*, **138(1)**, 225–244, doi:10.1007/s11205-017-1650-0.

Rao, N.D., A. Agarwal, and D. Wood, 2016: *Impact of small-scale electricity system*. World Resource Institute, Wasgington DC, 66 pp.

Rao, N.D., J. Min, and A. Mastrucci, 2019: Energy requirements for decent living in India, Brazil and South Africa. *Nat. Energy*, **4(12)**, 1025–1032, doi:10.1038/s41560-019-0497-9.

Rashid, M.M.U. et al., 2021: Home energy management for community microgrids using optimal power sharing algorithm. *Energies*, **14(4)**, doi:10.3390/en14041060.

Rasmussen, F.N., T. Malmqvist, A. Moncaster, A.H. Wiberg, and H. Birgisdóttir, 2018: Analysing methodological choices in calculations of embodied energy and GHG emissions from buildings. *Energy Build.*, **158**, 1487–1498, doi:10.1016/j.enbuild.2017.11.013.

Raux, C. and G. Marlot, 2005: A system of tradable CO2 permits applied to fuel consumption by motorists. *Transp. Policy*, **12(3)**, doi:10.1016/j.tranpol.2005.02.006.

Raux, C., Y. Croissant, and D. Pons, 2015: Would personal carbon trading reduce travel emissions more effectively than a carbon tax? *Transp. Res. Part D Transp. Environ.*, **35**, 72–83, doi:10.1016/j.trd.2014.11.008.

Reddy, A.K.N., 1991: Barriers to improvements in energy efficiency. *Energy Policy*, **19(10)**, doi:10.1016/0301-4215(91)90115-5.

Reddy, S.B., 2002: *Barriers to the Diffusion of Renewable Energy Technologies.*, Copenhagen.

Rehm, T.W., T. Schneiders, C. Strohm, and M. Deimel, 2018: Smart Home Field Test – Investigation of Heating Energy Savings in Residential Buildings. *2018 7th International Energy and Sustainability Conference (IESC)*, IEEE, 1–8.

Reichert, G. et al., 2016: Investigation of user behavior and assessment of typical operation mode for different types of firewood room heating appliances in Austria. *Renew. Energy*, **93**(2016), 245–254, doi:10.1016/j.renene.2016.01.092.

Reichmann, J., G. Habert, and F. Pittau, 2021: Land availability in Europe for a radical shift toward bio-based construction Land availability in Europe for a radical shift toward bio-based construction. *Sustain. Cities Soc.*, **70**(April), 102929, doi:10.1016/j.scs.2021.102929.

Reindl, K. and J. Palm, 2020: Energy efficiency in the building sector: A combined middle-out and practice theory approach. *Int. J. Sustain. Energy Plan. Manag.*, **28**, 3–16, doi:10.5278/ijsepm.3426.

Reiss, P.C. and M.W. White, 2008: What changes energy consumption? Prices and public pressures. *RAND J. Econ.*, **39(3)**, 636–663, doi:10.1111/j.1756-2171.2008.00032.x.

Rentschler, J. and M. Bazilian, 2017: Policy Monitor—Principles for Designing Effective Fossil Fuel Subsidy Reforms. *Rev. Environ. Econ. Policy*, **11**(1), 138–155, doi:10.1093/reep/rew016.

Requate, T., 2015: Green tradable certificates versus feed-in tariffs in the promotion of renewable energy shares. *Environ. Econ. Policy Stud.*, **17**(2), 211–239, doi:10.1007/s10018-014-0096-8.

Reuter, M., B. Schlomann, C. Müller, and W. Eichhammer, 2017: A comprehensive indicator set for measuring multiple benefits of energy efficiency. *ECEEE 2017 Summer Study – Consumption, Efficiency & Limits*, 1891–1900.

Revesz, A. et al., 2020: Developing novel 5th generation district energy networks. *Energy*, **201**, 117389, doi:10.1016/j.energy.2020.117389.

Rezessy, S. and P. Bertoldi, 2011: Voluntary agreements in the field of energy efficiency and emission reduction: Review and analysis of experiences in the European Union. *Energy Policy*, **39**(11), 7121–7129, doi:10.1016/j.enpol.2011.08.030.

Riedy, C., L. Wynne, K. McKenna, and M. Daly, 2019: "It's a Great Idea for Other People": Cohousing as a Housing Option for Older Australians. *Urban Policy Res.*, **37**(2), 227–242, doi:10.1080/08111146.2018.1531750.

Rijal, H.B., P. Tuohy, M.A. Humphreys, J.F. Nicol, and A. Samuel, 2012: Considering the impact of situation-specific motivations and constraints in the design of naturally ventilated and hybrid buildings. *Archit. Sci. Rev.*, **55**(1), 35–48, doi:10.1080/00038628.2011.641734.

Risch, A. and C. Salmon, 2017: What matters in residential energy consumption: evidence from France. *Int. J. Glob. Energy Issues*, **40**(1/2), 79, doi:10.1504/IJGEI.2017.080767.

Roberts, M.B., A. Bruce, and I. MacGill, 2019a: A comparison of arrangements for increasing self-consumption and maximising the value of distributed photovoltaics on apartment buildings. *Sol. Energy*, **193**, doi:10.1016/j.solener.2019.09.067.

Roberts, M.B., A. Bruce, and I. MacGill, 2019b: Opportunities and barriers for photovoltaics on multi-unit residential buildings: Reviewing the Australian experience. *Renew. Sustain. Energy Rev.*, **104** (December 2018), 95–110, doi:10.1016/j.rser.2018.12.013.

Roca-Puigròs, M., R.G. Billy, A. Gerber, P. Wäger, and D.B. Müller, 2020: Pathways toward a carbon-neutral Swiss residential building stock. *Build. Cities*, **1**(1), 579–593, doi:10.5334/bc.61.

Röck, M., A. Hollberg, G. Habert, and A. Passer, 2018: LCA and BIM: Visualization of environmental potentials in building construction at early design stages. *Build. Environ.*, **140**, 153–161, doi:10.1016/j.buildenv.2018.05.006.

Röck, M. et al., 2020: Embodied GHG emissions of buildings – The hidden challenge for effective climate change mitigation. *Appl. Energy*, **258** (November 2019), 114107, doi:10.1016/j.apenergy.2019.114107.

Rodríguez-Rosales, B. et al., 2021: Risk and vulnerability assessment in coastal environments applied to heritage buildings in Havana (Cuba) and Cadiz (Spain). *Sci. Total Environ.*, **750**, 141617, doi:10.1016/j.scitotenv.2020.141617.

Rogelj, J., D. Shindell, K. Jiang, S. Fifita, P. Forster, V. Ginzburg, C. Handa, H. Kheshgi, S. Kobayashi, E. Kriegler, L. Mundaca, R. Séférian, and M.V. Vilariño, 2018: Mitigation Pathways Compatible with 1.5°C in the Context of Sustainable Development. In: *Global Warming of 1.5°C. An IPCC Special Report on the impacts of global warming of 1.5°C above pre-industrial levels and related global greenhouse gas emission pathways, in the context of strengthening the global response to the threat of climate change, sustainable development, and efforts to eradicate poverty* [Masson-Delmotte, V., P. Zhai, H.-O. Pörtner, D. Roberts, J. Skea, P.R. Shukla, A. Pirani, W. Moufouma-Okia, C. Péan, R. Pidcock, S. Connors, J.B.R. Matthews, Y. Chen, X. Zhou, M.I. Gomis, E. Lonnoy, T. Maycock, M. Tignor, and T. Waterfield (eds.)]. Cambridge University Press, Cambridge, UK, and New York, NY, USA.

Romdhane, J. and H. Louahlia-Gualous, 2018: Energy assessment of PEMFC based MCCHP with absorption chiller for small scale French residential application. *Int. J. Hydrogen Energy*, **43**(42), 19661–19680, doi:10.1016/j.ijhydene.2018.08.132.

Rosado, P.J. and R. Levinson, 2019: Potential benefits of cool walls on residential and commercial buildings across California and the United States: Conserving energy, saving money, and reducing emission of greenhouse gases and air pollutants. *Energy Build.*, **199**, 588–607, doi:10.1016/j.enbuild.2019.02.028.

Rosas-Flores, J.A. and D. Rosas-Flores, 2020: Potential energy savings and mitigation of emissions by insulation for residential buildings in Mexico. *Energy Build.*, **209**, doi:10.1016/j.enbuild.2019.109698.

Roscini, A.V., O. Rapf, and J. Kockat, 2020: *On the way to a climate-neutral Europe. Contribution from the building sector to a strengthened 2030 climate target*. Buildings Performance Institute Europe, Brussels, 24 pp.

Rosenberg, E., 2014: Calculation method for electricity end-use for residential lighting. *Energy*, **66**, 295–304, doi:10.1016/j.energy.2013.12.049.

Rosenow, J. and E. Bayer, 2017: Costs and benefits of Energy Efficiency Obligations: A review of European programmes. *Energy Policy*, **107** (December 2016), 53–62, doi:10.1016/j.enpol.2017.04.014.

Rosenow, J., R. Platt, and A. Demurtas, 2014: Fiscal impacts of energy efficiency programmes-The example of solid wall insulation investment in the UK. *Energy Policy*, **74**(C), 610–620, doi:10.1016/j.enpol.2014.08.007.

Rosenow, J., F. Kern, and K. Rogge, 2017: The need for comprehensive and well targeted instrument mixes to stimulate energy transitions: The case of energy efficiency policy. *Energy Res. Soc. Sci.*, **33**, 95–104, doi:10.1016/j.erss.2017.09.013.

Rosenow, J., R. Cowart, and S. Thomas, 2019: Market-based instruments for energy efficiency: a global review. *Energy Effic.*, **12**(5), 1379–1398, doi:10.1007/s12053-018-9766-x.

Rosenthal, J., A. Quinn, A.P. Grieshop, A. Pillarisetti, and R.I. Glass, 2018: Clean cooking and the SDGs: Integrated analytical approaches to guide energy interventions for health and environment goals. *Energy Sustain. Dev.*, **42**, 152–159, doi:10.1016/j.esd.2017.11.003.

Rosse Caldas, L., A. Bernstad Saraiva, V.M. Andreola, and R. Dias Toledo Filho, 2020: Bamboo bio-concrete as an alternative for buildings' climate change mitigation and adaptation. *Constr. Build. Mater.*, **263**, 120652, doi:10.1016/j.conbuildmat.2020.120652.

Roussac, A.C. and S. Bright, 2012: Improving environmental performance through innovative commercial leasing: An Australian case study. *Int. J. Law Built Environ.*, **4**(1), 6–22, doi:10.1108/17561451211211714.

Roy, J., P. Tschakert, H. Waisman, S. Abdul Halim, P. Antwi-Agyei, P. Dasgupta, B. Hayward, M. Kanninen, D. Liverman, C. Okereke, P.F. Pinho, K. Riahi, and A.G. Suarez Rodriguez, 2018: Sustainable Development, Poverty Eradication and Reducing Inequalities. In: *Global Warming of 1.5°C. An IPCC Special Report on the impacts of global warming of 1.5°C above pre-industrial levels and related global greenhouse gas emission pathways, in the context of strengthening the global response to the threat of climate change, sustainable development, and efforts to eradicate poverty* [Masson-Delmotte, V., P. Zhai, H.-O. Pörtner, D. Roberts, J. Skea, P.R. Shukla, A. Pirani, W. Moufouma-Okia, C. Péan, R. Pidcock, S. Connors, J.B.R. Matthews, Y. Chen, X. Zhou, M.I. Gomis, E. Lonnoy, T. Maycock, M. Tignor, and T. Waterfield (eds.)]. In PressRuan, H., X. Gao, and C. Mao, 2018: Empirical Study on Annual Energy-Saving Performance of Energy Performance Contracting in China. *Sustainability*, **10**(5), 1666, doi:10.3390/su10051666.

Rubio-Bellido, C., A. Pérez-Fargallo, J.A. Pulido-Arcas, and M. Trebilcock, 2017: Application of adaptive comfort behaviors in Chilean social housing standards under the influence of climate change. *Build. Simul.*, **10**(6), 933–947, doi:10.1007/s12273-017-0385-9.

Ruhnau, O., L. Hirth, and A. Praktiknjo, 2020: Heating with wind: Economics of heat pumps and variable renewables. *Energy Econ.*, **92**, doi:10.1016/j.eneco.2020.104967.

Ruparathna, R., K. Hewage, and R. Sadiq, 2016: Improving the energy efficiency of the existing building stock: A critical review of commercial and institutional buildings. *Renew. Sustain. Energy Rev.*, **53**, 1032–1045, doi:10.1016/j.rser.2015.09.084.

Rupp, R.F., N.G. Vásquez, and R. Lamberts, 2015: A review of human thermal comfort in the built environment. *Energy Build.*, **105**, 178–205, doi:10.1016/j.enbuild.2015.07.047.

Sachs, W., 1993: Die vier E ' s. *Polit. Ökologie*, **33**(33), 69–72.

Saelim, S., 2019: Carbon tax incidence on household consumption: Heterogeneity across socio-economic factors in Thailand. *Econ. Anal. Policy*, **62**, 159–174, doi:10.1016/j.eap.2019.02.003.

Saffari, M., A. de Gracia, C. Fernández, and L.F. Cabeza, 2017: Simulation-based optimization of PCM melting temperature to improve the energy performance in buildings. *Appl. Energy*, **202**, 420–434, doi:10.1016/j.apenergy.2017.05.107.

Saheb, Y., 2018: *Deep Energy Renovation*. OpenExp. https://www.openexp.eu/sites/default/files/publication/files/energy_renovation_trapped_in_overestimated_costs_and_staged_approach.pdf.

Saheb, Y., 2021: COP26: Sufficiency should be first. *Build. Cities.* https://www.buildingsandcities.org/insights/commentaries/cop26-sufficiency.html.

Saheb, Y., H. Ossenbrink, S. Szabo, K. Bódis, and S. Panev, 2018a: Energy transition of Europe's building stock. Implications for EU 2030. Sustainable Development Goals. *Ann. des Mines – Responsab. Environ.*, **90**(2), 62–67, doi:10.3917/re1.090.0062.

Saheb, Y., S. Shnapp, and C. Johnson, 2018b: The Zero Energy concept: making the whole greater than the sum of the parts to meet the Paris Climate Agreement's objectives. *Curr. Opin. Environ. Sustain.*, **30**, 138–150, doi:10.1016/j.cosust.2018.04.014.

Salleh, S.F., M.E.B.M. Roslan, and A.M. Isa, 2019: Evaluating the impact of implementing Minimum Energy Performance Standards appliance regulation in Malaysia. *Int. J. Environ. Technol. Manag.*, **22**(4/5), 257, doi:10.1504/IJETM.2019.104752.

Salom, J., A.J. Marszal, J. Widén, J. Candanedo, and K.B. Lindberg, 2014: Analysis of load match and grid interaction indicators in net zero energy buildings with simulated and monitored data. *Appl. Energy*, **136**, 119–131, doi:10.1016/j.apenergy.2014.09.018.

Salvati, L. and G. Ricciardo Lamonica, 2020: Containing urban expansion: Densification vs greenfield development, socio-demographic transformations and the economic crisis in a Southern European City, 2006–2015. *Ecol. Indic.*, **110**, 105923, doi:10.1016/j.ecolind.2019.105923.

Samadi, S. et al., 2017: Sufficiency in energy scenario studies: Taking the potential benefits of lifestyle changes into account. *Technol. Forecast. Soc. Change*, **124**, 126–134, doi:10.1016/j.techfore.2016.09.013.

Sanchez-Guevara, C., M. Núñez Peiró, J. Taylor, A. Mavrogianni, and J. Neila González, 2019: Assessing population vulnerability towards summer energy poverty: Case studies of Madrid and London. *Energy Build.*, **190**, 132–143, doi:10.1016/j.enbuild.2019.02.024.

Sánchez Ramos, J., Mc.C. Pavón Moreno, L. Romero Rodríguez, Mc.C. Guerrero Delgado, and S. Álvarez Domínguez, 2019: Potential for exploiting the synergies between buildings through DSM approaches. Case study: La Graciosa Island. *Energy Convers. Manag.*, **194** (May), 199–216, doi:10.1016/j.enconman.2019.04.084.

Sandberg, M., 2018: Downsizing of Housing: Negotiating Sufficiency and Spatial Norms. *J. Macromarketing*, **38**(2), 154–167, doi:10.1177/0276146717748355.

Sandberg, N.H. et al., 2016: Dynamic building stock modelling: Application to 11 European countries to support the energy efficiency and retrofit ambitions of the EU. *Energy Build.*, **132**, 26–38, doi:10.1016/j.enbuild.2016.05.100.

Sandberg, N.H., J.S. Næss, H. Brattebø, I. Andresen, and A. Gustavsen, 2021: Large potentials for energy saving and greenhouse gas emission reductions from large-scale deployment of zero emission building technologies in a national building stock. *Energy Policy*, **152**, 112114, doi:10.1016/j.enpol.2020.112114.

Sanjuán, M.Á., E. Estévez, and C. Argiz, 2019: Carbon dioxide absorption by blast-furnace slag mortars in function of the curing intensity. *Energies*, **12**(12), 1–9, doi:10.3390/en12122346.

Santamouris, M., 2016: Cooling the buildings – past, present and future. *Energy Build.*, **128**, 617–638, doi:10.1016/j.enbuild.2016.07.034.

Santos, A.J.L. and A.F.P. Lucena, 2021: Climate change impact on the technical-economic potential for solar photovoltaic energy in the residential sector: a case study for Brazil. *Energy Clim. Chang.*, **2**, 100062, doi:10.1016/j.egycc.2021.100062.

Sarbu, I. and C. Sebarchievici, 2014: General review of ground-source heat pump systems for heating and cooling of buildings. *Energy Build.*, **70**, 441–454, doi:10.1016/j.enbuild.2013.11.068.

Sarbu, I. and A. Dorca, 2018: A comprehensive review of solar thermoelectric cooling systems. *Int. J. Energy Res.*, **42**(2), 395–415, doi:10.1002/er.3795.

Schaeffer, R. et al., 2012: Energy sector vulnerability to climate change: A review. *Energy*, **38**(1), 1–12, doi:10.1016/j.energy.2011.11.056.

Schaffer, A.J. and S. Brun, 2015: Beyond the sun – Socioeconomic drivers of the adoption of small-scale photovoltaic installations in Germany. *Energy Res. Soc. Sci.*, **10**, 220–227, doi:10.1016/j.erss.2015.06.010.

Schaffitzel, F., M. Jakob, R. Soria, A. Vogt-Schilb, and H. Ward, 2020: Can government transfers make energy subsidy reform socially acceptable? A case study on Ecuador. *Energy Policy*, **137**, 111120, doi:10.1016/j.enpol.2019.111120.

Schilmann, A. et al., 2019: A follow-up study after an improved cookstove intervention in rural Mexico: Estimation of household energy use and chronic $PM_{2.5}$ exposure. *Environ. Int.*, **131**, 105013, doi:10.1016/j.envint.2019.105013.

Schlacke, S. and M. Knodt, 2019: The Governance System of the European Energy Union and Climate Action. *J. Eur. Environ. Plan. Law*, **16**(4), 323–339, doi:10.1163/18760104-01604002.

Schnieders, J. et al., 2020: Design and realisation of the Passive House concept in different climate zones. *Energy Effic.*, **13**(8), 1561–1604, doi:10.1007/s12053-019-09819-6.

Schultz, P.W., J.M. Nolan, R.B. Cialdini, N.J. Goldstein, and V. Griskevicius, 2007: The Constructive, Destructive, and Reconstructive Power of Social Norms. *Psychol. Sci.*, **18**(5), 429–434, doi:10.1111/j.1467-9280.2007.01917.x.

Schuster, K. C., Y. Park, and S. R. Sinha, 2019: Building management system with automated vibration data analysis.

Schwarz, M., C. Nakhle, and C. Knoeri, 2020: Innovative designs of building energy codes for building decarbonization and their implementation challenges. *J. Clean. Prod.*, **248**, 119260, doi:10.1016/j.jclepro.2019.119260.

Scott, F.L., C.R. Jones, and T.L. Webb, 2014: What do people living in deprived communities in the UK think about household energy efficiency interventions? *Energy Policy*, **66** (September 2011), 335–349, doi:10.1016/j.enpol.2013.10.084.

Scott, M.J. et al., 2015: Calculating impacts of energy standards on energy demand in U.S. buildings with uncertainty in an integrated assessment model. *Energy*, **90**, 1682–1694, doi:10.1016/j.energy.2015.06.127.

Seebauer, S., 2018: The psychology of rebound effects: Explaining energy efficiency rebound behaviours with electric vehicles and building insulation in Austria. *Energy Res. Soc. Sci.*, **46**, 311–320, doi:10.1016/j.erss.2018.08.006.

Seidl, R., T. von Wirth, and P. Krütli, 2019: Social acceptance of distributed energy systems in Swiss, German, and Austrian energy transitions. *Energy Res. Soc. Sci.*, **54** (April), 117–128, doi:10.1016/j.erss.2019.04.006.

Semprini, G., R. Gulli, and A. Ferrante, 2017: Deep regeneration vs shallow renovation to achieve nearly Zero Energy in existing buildings: Energy saving and economic impact of design solutions in the housing stock of Bologna. *Energy Build.*, **156**, 327–342, doi:10.1016/j.enbuild.2017.09.044.

Sen, S. and H. Vollebergh, 2018: The effectiveness of taxing the carbon content of energy consumption. *J. Environ. Econ. Manage.*, **92**, 74–99, doi:10.1016/j.jeem.2018.08.017.

Seong, Y.-B. and J.-H. Lim, 2013: Energy Saving Potentials of Phase Change Materials Applied to Lightweight Building Envelopes. *Energies*, **6**(10), 5219–5230, doi:10.3390/en6105219.

Serrano, S., D. Ürge-Vorsatz, C. Barreneche, A. Palacios, and L.F. Cabeza, 2017: Heating and cooling energy trends and drivers in Europe. *Energy*, **119**, 425–434, doi:10.1016/j.energy.2016.12.080.

Setyawan, D., 2014: Formulating revolving fund scheme to support energy efficiency projects in Indonesia. *Energy Procedia*, **47**, 37–46, doi:10.1016/j.egypro.2014.01.194.

Shafique, M., X. Luo, and J. Zuo, 2020: Photovoltaic-green roofs: A review of benefits, limitations, and trends. *Sol. ENERGY*, **202**, 485–497, doi:10.1016/j.solener.2020.02.101.

Shah, N., M. Wei, V. Letschert, and A. Phadke, 2015: *Benefits of Leapfrogging to Superefficiency and Low Global Warming Potential Refrigerants in Room Air Conditioning*. Lawrence Berkeley National Laboratory, Berkeley, USA, 58 pp.

Shah, N., M. Wei, V.E. Letschert, and A.A. Phadke, 2019: *Benefits of Energy Efficient and Low-Global Warming Potential Refrigerant Cooling Equipment*. Lawrence Berkeley National Laboratory, Berkeley, USA, 59 pp.

Shankar, A. et al., 2014: Maximizing the benefits of improved cookstoves: moving from acquisition to correct and consistent use. *Glob. Heal. Sci. Pract.*, **2(3)**, 268–274, doi:10.9745/GHSP-D-14-00060.

Sharda, S., K. Sharma, and M. Singh, 2021: A real-time automated scheduling algorithm with PV integration for smart home prosumers. *J. Build. Eng.*, **44**, 102828, doi:10.1016/j.jobe.2021.102828.

Sharifi, A., 2020: Trade-offs and conflicts between urban climate change mitigation and adaptation measures: A literature review. *J. Clean. Prod.*, **276**, 122813, doi:10.1016/j.jclepro.2020.122813.

Shen, L., B. He, L. Jiao, X. Song, and X. Zhang, 2016: Research on the development of main policy instruments for improving building energy-efficiency. *J. Clean. Prod.*, **112** (2016), 1789–1803, doi:10.1016/j.jclepro.2015.06.108.

Shen, P. and N. Lior, 2016: Vulnerability to climate change impacts of present renewable energy systems designed for achieving net-zero energy buildings. *Energy*, **114**, 1288–1305, doi:10.1016/j.energy.2016.07.078.

Shirazi, A., R.A. Taylor, G.L. Morrison, and S.D. White, 2018: Solar-powered absorption chillers: A comprehensive and critical review. *Energy Convers. Manag.*, **171**, 59–81, doi:10.1016/j.enconman.2018.05.091.

Shivakumar, A. et al., 2018: Smart energy solutions in the EU: State of play and measuring progress. *Energy Strateg. Rev.*, **20**, 133–149, doi:10.1016/j.esr.2018.02.005.

Shrubsole, C. et al., 2016: Impacts of energy efficiency retrofitting measures on indoor $PM_{2.5}$ concentrations across different income groups in England: a modelling study. *Adv. Build. Energy Res.*, **10(1)**, 69–83, doi:10.1080/17512549.2015.1014844.

Simcock, N. et al., 2014: Factors influencing perceptions of domestic energy information: Content, source and process. *Energy Policy*, **65**, 455–464, doi:10.1016/j.enpol.2013.10.038.

Simioni, T. and R. Schaeffer, 2019: Georeferenced operating-efficiency solar potential maps with local weather conditions – An application to Brazil. *Sol. Energy*, **184** (October 2018), 345–355, doi:10.1016/j.solener.2019.04.006.

Singh, G., A. Goel, and M. Choudhary, 2017: Analysis of domestic water demand variables of a residential colony in Ajmer, Rajasthan (India). *J. Water Sanit. Hyg. Dev.*, **7(4)**, 568–575, doi:10.2166/washdev.2017.020.

Sköld, B. et al., 2018: Household preferences to reduce their greenhouse gas footprint: A comparative study from four European cities. *Sustain.*, **10(11)**, 4044, doi:10.3390/su10114044.

Sliger, J. and K. Colburn, 2019: Redefining energy efficiency: EE 2.0. *Electr. J.*, **32(7)**, 106619, doi:10.1016/j.tej.2019.106619.

Slovic, P. and E. Peters, 2006: Risk Perception and Affect. *Curr. Dir. Psychol. Sci.*, **15(6)**, doi:10.1111/j.1467-8721.2006.00461.x.

Smith, A.C. et al., 2016: Health and environmental co-benefits and conflicts of actions to meet UK carbon targets. *Clim. Policy*, **16(3)**, 253–283, doi:10.1080/14693062.2014.980212.

Sokołowski, M.M., 2020: Renewable and citizen energy communities in the European Union: how (not) to regulate community energy in national laws and policies. *J. Energy Nat. Resour. Law*, **38(3)**, 289–304, doi:10.1080/02646811.2020.1759247.

Sola, P., C. Ochieng, J. Yila, and M. Iiyama, 2016: Links between energy access and food security in sub Saharan Africa: an exploratory review. *Food Secur.*, **8(3)**, 635–642, doi:10.1007/s12571-016-0570-1.

Solaimani, S., W. Keijzer-Broers, and H. Bouwman, 2015: What we do – And don't – Know about the Smart Home: An analysis of the Smart Home literature. *Indoor Built Environ.*, **24(3)**, 370–383, doi:10.1177/1420326X13516350.

Soland, M., S. Loosli, J. Koch, and O. Christ, 2018: Acceptance among residential electricity consumers regarding scenarios of a transformed energy system in Switzerland—a focus group study. *Energy Effic.*, **11(7)**, 1673–1688, doi:10.1007/s12053-017-9548-x.

Solaymani, S., 2017: Carbon and energy taxes in a small and open country. *Glob. J. Environ. Sci. Manag.*, **3(1)**, 51–62, doi:10.22034/gjesm.2017.03.01.006.

Soltani, M. et al., 2019: A comprehensive study of geothermal heating and cooling systems. *Sustain. Cities Soc.*, **44** (March 2018), 793–818, doi:10.1016/j.scs.2018.09.036.

Song, L. et al., 2020: Contested energy futures, conflicted rewards? Examining low-carbon transition risks and governance dynamics in China's built environment. *Energy Res. Soc. Sci.*, **59** (May 2019), 101306, doi:10.1016/j.erss.2019.101306.

Song, Y. et al., 2016: The Interplay Between Bioenergy Grass Production and Water Resources in the United States of America. *Environ. Sci. Technol.*, **50(6)**, 3010–3019, doi:10.1021/acs.est.5b05239.

Sonnenschein, J., R. Van Buskirk, J.L. Richter, and C. Dalhammar, 2019: Minimum energy performance standards for the 1.5°C target: an effective complement to carbon pricing. *Energy Effic.*, **12(2)**, 387–402, doi:10.1007/s12053-018-9669-x.

Sorrell, S. et al., 2000: *Reducing barriers to energy efficiency in private and public organisations*. Fraunhofer Institute, Brussels, Belgium, 246 pp.

Sorrell, S., A. Mallett, and S. Nye, 2011: *Barriers to industrial energy efficiency: A literature review*. United Nations Industrial Development Organization, Vienna, Austria, 98 pp.

Sorrell, S., B. Gatersleben, and A. Druckman, 2018: *Energy sufficiency and rebound effects. Concept paper*. European Council for an Energy Efficient Economy, 63 pp.

Soumaré, I. and V.S. Lai, 2016: An analysis of government loan guarantees and direct investment through public-private partnerships. *Econ. Model.*, **59**, 508–519, doi:10.1016/j.econmod.2016.08.012.

Sourbron, M., C. Verhelst, and L. Helsen, 2013: Building models for model predictive control of office buildings with concrete core activation. *J. Build. Perform. Simul.*, **6(3)**, 175–198, doi:10.1080/19401493.2012.680497.

Spanaki, A., D. Kolokotsa, T. Tsoutsos, and I. Zacharopoulos, 2014: Assessing the passive cooling effect of the ventilated pond protected with a reflecting layer. *Appl. Energy*, **123**, 273–280, doi:10.1016/j.apenergy.2014.02.040.

Spandagos, C., M. Yarime, E. Baark, and T.L. Ng, 2020: "Triple Target" policy framework to influence household energy behavior: Satisfy, strengthen, include. *Appl. Energy*, **269**, 115117, doi:10.1016/j.apenergy.2020.115117.

Spiegel-Feld, D., 2019: Local Law 97: Emissions Trading for Buildings. *New York Univ. Law Rev. Online*, **94**, 327–347.

Spiliotopoulos, D., 2019: *The future of the MEErP – Reinforcement of circular economy aspects in the methdology*. ECOS and EEB, Brussels, Belgium, 6 pp.

Sreekanth, K.J., S. Jayaraj, and N. Sudarsan, 2011: A meta model for domestic energy consumption. *Int. J. Energy Econ. Policy*, **1(3)**, 69–77.

Stadt Göttingen, 2020: *Quartiersanalyse zur Identifizierung von Flächenoptimierungspotenzialen in Göttingen*. Stadt Göttingen, Germany.

Ssembatya, M., H. Fu, and D.E. Claridge, 2021: Long-term savings persistence from existing building commissioning and retrofits. *Sci. Technol. Built Environ.*, **27(6)**, 730–740, doi:10.1080/23744731.2021.1898820.

Starkey, R., 2012: Personal carbon trading: A critical survey Part 2: Efficiency and effectiveness. *Ecol. Econ.*, **73**, 19–28, doi:10.1016/j.ecolecon.2011.09.018.

9

Steenbergen, R.D.J.M., T. Koster, and C.P.W. Geurts, 2012: The effect of climate change and natural variability on wind loading values for buildings. *Build. Environ.*, **55**, 178–186, doi:10.1016/j.buildenv.2012.03.010.

Steenland, K. et al., 2018: Modeling the potential health benefits of lower household air pollution after a hypothetical liquified petroleum gas (LPG) cookstove intervention. *Environ. Int.*, **111**, 71–79, doi:10.1016/j.envint.2017.11.018.

Steinhardt, D.A. and K. Manley, 2016: Adoption of prefabricated housing-the role of country context. *Sustain. Cities Soc.*, **22**, 126–135, doi:10.1016/j.scs.2016.02.008.

Stephan, A., R.H. Crawford, and K. de Myttenaere, 2013: Multi-scale life cycle energy analysis of a low-density suburban neighbourhood in Melbourne, Australia. *Build. Environ.*, **68**, 35–49, doi:10.1016/j.buildenv.2013.06.003.

Stewart, M.G., X. Wang, and M.N. Nguyen, 2012: Climate change adaptation for corrosion control of concrete infrastructure. *Struct. Saf.*, **35**, 29–39, doi:10.1016/j.strusafe.2011.10.002.

Stötzer, M., I. Hauer, M. Richter, and Z.A. Styczynski, 2015: Potential of demand side integration to maximize use of renewable energy sources in Germany. *Appl. Energy*, **146**, 344–352, doi:10.1016/j.apenergy.2015.02.015.

Strbac, G. et al., 2018: *Analysis of Alternative UK Heat Decarbonisation Pathways*. Imperial College London, London, UK, 159 pp.

Streicher, K.N., D. Parra, M.C. Buerer, and M.K. Patel, 2017: Techno-economic potential of large-scale energy retrofit in the Swiss residential building stock. *Energy Procedia*, **122**, 121–126, doi:10.1016/j.egypro.2017.07.314.

Streicher, K.N., S. Mennel, J. Chambers, D. Parra, and M.K. Patel, 2020: Cost-effectiveness of large-scale deep energy retrofit packages for residential buildings under different economic assessment approaches. *Energy Build.*, **215**, 109870, doi:10.1016/j.enbuild.2020.109870.

Streltsov, A., J.M. Malof, B. Huang, and K. Bradbury, 2020: Estimating residential building energy consumption using overhead imagery. *Appl. Energy*, **280**, doi:10.1016/j.apenergy.2020.116018.

Stute, F., J. Mici, L. Chamberlain, and H. Lipson, 2018: Digital Wood: 3D Internal Color Texture Mapping. *3D Print. Addit. Manuf.*, **5(4)**, 285–291, doi:10.1089/3dp.2018.0078.

Subramanyam, V., M. Ahiduzzaman, and A. Kumar, 2017a: Greenhouse gas emissions mitigation potential in the commercial and institutional sector. *Energy Build.*, **140**, 295–304, doi:10.1016/j.enbuild.2017.02.007.

Subramanyam, V., A. Kumar, A. Talaei, and M.A.H. Mondal, 2017b: Energy efficiency improvement opportunities and associated greenhouse gas abatement costs for the residential sector. *Energy*, **118**, 795–807, doi:10.1016/j.energy.2016.10.115.

Sugiyama, M., Y. Taniguchi-Matsuoka, Ayako Yamaguchi, and Y. Shimoda, 2019: Required Specification of Residential End-use Energy Demand Model for Application to National GHG Mitigation Policy Making – Case Study for the Japanese Plan for Global Warming Countermeasures. *Proceedings of Building Simulation 2019: 16th Conference of IBPSA*, Italy, **6**, 3706–3713, doi:10.26868/25222708.2019.211100.

Sultan, S.M. and M.N. Ervina Efzan, 2018: Review on recent Photovoltaic/Thermal (PV/T) technology advances and applications. *Sol. Energy*, **173**, 939–954, doi:10.1016/j.solener.2018.08.032.

Sun, K. and T. Hong, 2017: A framework for quantifying the impact of occupant behavior on energy savings of energy conservation measures. *Energy Build.*, **146** (October), 383–396, doi:10.1016/j.enbuild.2017.04.065.

Sun, K., M. Specian, and T. Hong, 2020: Nexus of thermal resilience and energy efficiency in buildings: A case study of a nursing home. *Build. Environ.*, **177** (June), 106842, doi:10.1016/j.buildenv.2020.106842.

Sun, P. and P. yan Nie, 2015: A comparative study of feed-in tariff and renewable portfolio standard policy in renewable energy industry. *Renew. Energy*, **74**, 255–262, doi:10.1016/j.renene.2014.08.027.

Sundell, J. et al., 2011: Ventilation rates and health: multidisciplinary review of the scientific literature. *Indoor Air*, **21(3)**, 191–204, doi:10.1111/j.1600-0668.2010.00703.x.

Sustainable Energy for All, 2018: *Chilling prospects: Providing sustainable cooling for all*. SEforALL, Vienna and Washington, DC, USA, 71 pp.

Swan, W., R. Fitton, L. Smith, C. Abbott, and L. Smith, 2017: Adoption of sustainable retrofit in UK social housing 2010-2015. *Int. J. Build. Pathol. Adapt.*, **35(5)**, 456–469, doi:10.1108/IJBPA-04-2017-0019.

Sweetnam, T., M. Fell, E. Oikonomou, and T. Oreszczyn, 2019: Domestic demand-side response with heat pumps: controls and tariffs. *Build. Res. Inf.*, **47(4)**, 344–361, doi:10.1080/09613218.2018.1442775.

Symons, K., 2011: Book review: Embodied Carbon: The Inventory of Carbon and Energy (ICE). A BSRIA Guide Embodied Carbon: The Inventory of Carbon and Energy (ICE). A BSRIA Guide Hammond Professor GeoffJones CraigLowrie FionaTse Peter. University of Bath with BSRIA, Bracknel. *Proc. Inst. Civ. Eng. Energy*, **164(4)**, 206–206, doi:10.1680/ener.2011.164.4.206.

Tajani, F. et al., 2018: Energy retrofit assessment through automated valuation models: An Italian case study. *AIP Conference Proceedings*, **(1982)1**, 020045, doi.org/10.1063/1.5045451.

Taleb, H.M., 2015: Natural ventilation as energy efficient solution for achieving low-energy houses in Dubai. *Energy Build.*, **99**, 284–291, doi:10.1016/j.enbuild.2015.04.019.

Talele, S. et al., 2018: Energy modeling and data structure framework for Sustainable Human-Building Ecosystems (SHBE) — a review. *Front. Energy*, **12(2)**, 314–332, doi:10.1007/s11708-017-0530-2.

Tam, V.W.Y., J. Wang, and K.N. Le, 2016: Thermal insulation and cost effectiveness of green-roof systems: An empirical study in Hong Kong. *Build. Environ.*, **110**, 46–54, doi:10.1016/j.buildenv.2016.09.032.

Tan, X., H. Lai, B. Gu, Y. Zeng, and H. Li, 2018: Carbon emission and abatement potential outlook in China's building sector through 2050. *Energy Policy*, **118** (March), 429–439, doi:10.1016/j.enpol.2018.03.072.

Taniguchi, A. et al., 2016: Estimation of the contribution of the residential sector to summer peak demand reduction in Japan using an energy end-use simulation model. *Energy Build.*, **112**, 80–92, doi:10.1016/j.enbuild.2015.11.064.

Taylor, R., H. Wanjiru, O.W. Johnson, and F.X. Johnson, 2020: Modelling stakeholder agency to investigate sustainable charcoal markets in Kenya. *Environ. Innov. Soc. Transitions*, **35**, 493–508, doi:10.1016/j.eist.2019.10.001.

Teli, D. et al., 2016: Fuel poverty-induced "prebound effect" in achieving the anticipated carbon savings from social housing retrofit. *Build. Serv. Eng. Res. Technol.*, **37(2)**, 176–193, doi:10.1177/0143624415621028.

Teng, C.C., J.S. Horng, M.L.M. Hu, L.H. Chien, and Y.C. Shen, 2012: Developing energy conservation and carbon reduction indicators for the hotel industry in Taiwan. *Int. J. Hosp. Manag.*, **31(1)**, 199–208, doi:10.1016/j.ijhm.2011.06.006.

Teubler, J., S. Kiefer, and K. Bienge, 2020: *WP4 Resources: Methodology and quantification of resource impacts from energy efficiency in Europe – project COMBI*.

Thatcher, A. and K. Milner, 2016: Is a green building really better for building occupants? A longitudinal evaluation. *Build. Environ.*, **108**, 194–206, doi:10.1016/j.buildenv.2016.08.036.

Thema, J. et al., 2017: More than energy savings: quantifying the multiple impacts of energy efficiency in Europe. *ECEEE 2017 Summer Study Proceedings*, 1727–1736.

Thi Thanh Tu, T. and T. Thi Hoang Yen, 2015: Green Bank: International Experiences and Vietnam Perspectives. *Asian Soc. Sci.*, **11(28)**, 188–199, doi:10.5539/ass.v11n28p188.

Thomas, D., G. Ding, and K. Crews, 2014: Sustainable timber use in residential construction: Perception versus reality. *WIT Trans. Ecol. Environ.*, **186**, 399–410, doi:10.2495/ESUS140341.

Thomas, S. and J. Rosenow, 2020: Drivers of increasing energy consumption in Europe and policy implications. *Energy Policy*, **137**, 111108, doi:10.1016/j.enpol.2019.111108.

Thomas, S. et al., 2019: Energy sufficiency policy for residential electricity use and per-capita dwelling size. *Energy Effic.*, **12(5)**, 1123–1149, doi:10.1007/s12053-018-9727-4.

Thomaßen, G., K. Kavvadias, and J.P. Jiménez Navarro, 2021: The decarbonisation of the EU heating sector through electrification: A parametric analysis. *Energy Policy*, **148**, 111929, doi:10.1016/j.enpol.2020.111929.

Thomson, H. and S. Thomas, 2015: Developing empirically supported theories of change for housing investment and health. *Soc. Sci. Med.*, **124**, 205–214, doi:10.1016/j.socscimed.2014.11.043.

Thomson, H. and S. Bouzarovski, 2018: *Addressing Energy Poverty in the European Union: State of Play and Action*. European Commission, Manchester, UK, 54 pp.

Thomson, H., S. Bouzarovski, and C. Snell, 2017a: Rethinking the measurement of energy poverty in Europe: A critical analysis of indicators and data. *Indoor Built Environ.*, **26(7)**, 879–901, doi:10.1177/1420326X17699260.

Thomson, H., C. Snell, and S. Bouzarovski, 2017b: Health, well-being and energy poverty in Europe: A comparative study of 32 European countries. *Int. J. Environ. Res. Public Health*, **14(6)**, 584, doi:10.3390/ijerph14060584.

Thomson, H., N. Simcock, S. Bouzarovski, and S. Petrova, 2019: Energy poverty and indoor cooling: An overlooked issue in Europe. *Energy Build.*, **196**, 21–29, doi:10.1016/j.enbuild.2019.05.014.

Timilsina, G., A. Sikharulidze, E. Karapoghosyan, and S. Shatvoryan, 2016: *How Do We Prioritize the GHG Mitigation Options? Development of a Marginal Abatement Cost Curve for the Building Sector in Armenia and Georgia*. World Bank, Washington, DC, USA, 37 pp.

Tol, R.S.J., S. Petrick, and K. Rehdanz, 2012: *The Impact of Temperature Changes on Residential Energy Use*. University of Sussex, Brighton, UK, 29 pp.

Toleikyte, A., L. Kranzl, and A. Müller, 2018: Cost curves of energy efficiency investments in buildings – Methodologies and a case study of Lithuania. *Energy Policy*, **115**, 148–157, doi:10.1016/j.enpol.2017.12.043.

Tonn, B., E. Rose, and B. Hawkins, 2018: Evaluation of the U.S. department of energy's weatherization assistance program: Impact results. *Energy Policy*, **118** (February), 279–290, doi:10.1016/j.enpol.2018.03.051.

Torero, M., 2015: The Impact of Rural Electrification: Challenges and Ways Forward. *11th Conference AFD PROPARCO/EUDN: Energy for Development*, International Food Policy Research Institute, Washington, Vol. 23, 49–75, doi:10.3917/edd.hs03.0049.

Totschnig, G. et al., 2017: Climate change impact and resilience in the electricity sector: The example of Austria and Germany. *Energy Policy*, **103** (May 2016), 238–248, doi:10.1016/j.enpol.2017.01.019.

Tozer, L., 2019: The urban material politics of decarbonization in Stockholm, London and San Francisco. *Geoforum*, **102** (March), 106–115, doi:10.1016/j.geoforum.2019.03.020.

Trencher, G. and J. van der Heijden, 2019: Instrument interactions and relationships in policy mixes: Achieving complementarity in building energy efficiency policies in New York, Sydney and Tokyo. *Energy Res. Soc. Sci.*, **54** (March), 34–45, doi:10.1016/j.erss.2019.02.023.

Trencher, G. et al., 2016: Innovative policy practices to advance building energy efficiency and retrofitting: Approaches, impacts and challenges in ten C40 cities. *Environ. Sci. Policy*, **66**, 353–365, doi:10.1016/j.envsci.2016.06.021.

Triana, M.A., R. Lamberts, and P. Sassi, 2018: Should we consider climate change for Brazilian social housing? Assessment of energy efficiency adaptation measures. *Energy Build.*, **158**, 1379–1392, doi:10.1016/j.enbuild.2017.11.003.

Trottier, 2016: *Canada's challenge & opportunity. Transformations for major reductions in GHG emissions*. David Suzuki Foundation and partners, Ottawa, Canada, 321 pp.

Tsoka, S., K. Tsikaloudaki, T. Theodosiou, and A. Dugue, 2018: Rethinking user based innovation: Assessing public and professional perceptions of energy efficient building facades in Greece, Italy and Spain. *Energy Res. Soc. Sci.*, **38** (January 2017), 165–177, doi:10.1016/j.erss.2018.02.009.

Tumbaz, M.N.M. and H.T. Moğulkoç, 2018: Profiling energy efficiency tendency: A case for Turkish households. *Energy Policy*, **119** (January), 441–448, doi:10.1016/j.enpol.2018.04.064.

Tuomisto, J.T. et al., 2015: Building-related health impacts in European and Chinese cities: a scalable assessment method. *Environ. Heal.*, **14(1)**, 93, doi:10.1186/s12940-015-0082-z.

Uchman, W., 2021: The cost of increasing prosumer self-sufficiency. *Appl. Therm. Eng.*, **186**, doi:10.1016/j.applthermaleng.2020.116361.

Underhill, L.J. et al., 2018: Modeling the resiliency of energy-efficient retrofits in low-income multifamily housing. *Indoor Air*, **28(3)**, 459–468, doi:10.1111/ina.12446.

UNEP, 2017: *Accelerating the Global Adoption of Climate-Friendly and Energy-Efficient Refrigerators*. United Nations Environment Programme, Paris, France, 80 pp.

UNEP and IEA, 2020: *Cooling Emissions and Policy Synthesis Report: Benefits of cooling efficiency and the Kigali Amendment*. United Nations Environment Programme (UNEP) International Energy Agency (IEA), Paris, France, 50 pp.

Ürge-Vorsatz, D., L.F. Cabeza, S. Serrano, C. Barreneche, and K. Petrichenko, 2015: Heating and cooling energy trends and drivers in buildings. *Renew. Sustain. Energy Rev.*, **41**, 85–98, doi:10.1016/j.rser.2014.08.039.

Ürge-Vorsatz, D. et al., 2016: Measuring multiple impacts of low-carbon energy options in a green economy context. *Appl. Energy*, **179**, 1409–1426, doi:10.1016/j.apenergy.2016.07.027.

Ürge-Vorsatz, D. et al., 2020: Advances Toward a Net-Zero Global Building Sector. *Annu. Rev. Environ. Resour.*, **45(1)**, 227–269, doi:10.1146/annurev-environ-012420-045843.

US EPA, 2018: *Quantifying the Multiple Benefits of Energy Efficiency and Renewable Energy: A Guide for State and Local Governments*. U.S. Environmental Protection Agency, Washington, DC, US.

Vakiloroaya, V., B. Samali, A. Fakhar, and K. Pishghadam, 2014: A review of different strategies for HVAC energy saving. *Energy Convers. Manag.*, **77**, 738–754, doi:10.1016/j.enconman.2013.10.023.

Valentova, M., J. Knapek, and A. Novikova, 2019: *Climate and energy investment map – Czechia*. Czech Technical University, Prague, Czech Republic, 60 pp.

Van de Ven, D.-J. et al., 2019: Integrated policy assessment and optimisation over multiple sustainable development goals in Eastern Africa. *Environ. Res. Lett.*, **14(9)**, 094001, doi:10.1088/1748-9326/ab375d.

Van de Ven, D.-J. et al., 2020: Erratum: Integrated policy assessment and optimisation over multiple sustainable development goals in Eastern Africa (2019 Environ. Res. Lett. 14 094001). *Environ. Res. Lett.*, **15(3)**, 039602, doi:10.1088/1748-9326/ab49ad.

Van Den Wymelenberg, K., 2012: Patterns of occupant interaction with window blinds: A literature review. *Energy Build.*, **51**, 165–176, doi:10.1016/j.enbuild.2012.05.008.

van Heerden, J. et al., 2016: The economic and environmental effects of a carbon tax in South Africa: A dynamic CGE modelling approach. *South African J. Econ. Manag. Sci.*, **19(5)**, 714–732, doi:10.17159/2222-3436/2016/v19n5a3.

van Hooff, T., B. Blocken, H.J.P. Timmermans, and J.L.M. Hensen, 2016: Analysis of the predicted effect of passive climate adaptation measures on energy demand for cooling and heating in a residential building. *Energy*, **94**, 811–820, doi:10.1016/j.energy.2015.11.036.

van Ruijven, B.J., E. De Cian, and I. Sue Wing, 2019: Amplification of future energy demand growth due to climate change. *Nat. Commun.*, **10(1)**, 1–12, doi:10.1038/s41467-019-10399-3.

van Sluisveld, M.A.E., S.H. Martínez, V. Daioglou, and D.P. van Vuuren, 2016: Exploring the implications of lifestyle change in 2°C mitigation scenarios using the IMAGE integrated assessment model. *Technol. Forecast. Soc. Change*, **102**, 309–319, doi:10.1016/j.techfore.2015.08.013.

Van Veelen, B., 2018: Negotiating energy democracy in practice: governance processes in community energy projects. *Env. Polit.*, **27(4)**, 644–665, doi:10.1080/09644016.2018.1427824.

9

Varela Luján, S., C. Viñas Arrebola, A. Rodríguez Sánchez, P. Aguilera Benito, and M. González Cortina, 2019: Experimental comparative study of the thermal performance of the façade of a building refurbished using ETICS, and quantification of improvements. *Sustain. Cities Soc.*, **51** (June), 101713, doi:10.1016/j.scs.2019.101713.

Vasileiadou, E. and W. Tuinstra, 2013: Stakeholder consultations: mainstreaming climate policy in the Energy Directorate? *Env. Polit.*, **22(3)**, 475–495, doi:10.1080/09644016.2012.717376.

Vence, X. and Á. Pereira, 2019: Eco-innovation and Circular Business Models as drivers for a circular economy. *Contaduría y Adm.*, **64(1)**, 64, doi:10.22201/fca.24488410e.2019.1806.

Venugopal, P. et al., 2018: Roadway to self-healing highways with integrated wireless electric vehicle charging and sustainable energy harvesting technologies. *Appl. Energy*, **212**, 1226–1239, doi:10.1016/j.apenergy.2017.12.108.

Vérez, D. and L.F. Cabeza, 2021: Which building services are considered to have impact in climate change? *Build. Serv. Eng. Res. Technol.*, 14(13), 3917, doi:10.3390/en14133917.

Vimpari, J. and S. Junnila, 2019: Estimating the diffusion of rooftop PVs: A real estate economics perspective. *Energy*, **172**, 1087–1097, doi:10.1016/j.energy.2019.02.049.

Vine, E., N. Hall, K.M. Keating, M. Kushler, and R. Prahl, 2013: Emerging evaluation issues: persistence, behavior, rebound, and policy. *Energy Effic.*, **6(2)**, doi:10.1007/s12053-012-9174-6.

Vine, E., A. Williams, and S. Price, 2017: The cost of enforcing building energy codes: an examination of traditional and alternative enforcement processes. *Energy Effic.*, **10(3)**, 717–728, doi:10.1007/s12053-016-9483-2.

Virage-Energie Nord-Pas-de-Calais., 2016: *Mieux Vivre en Région Nord-Pas-de-Calais – Pour un virage énergétique et des transformations sociétales*. Association Virage-énergie Nord-Pas de Calais, Lille, France, 28 pp.

Volk, R., R. Müller, J. Reinhardt, and F. Schultmann, 2019: An Integrated Material Flows, Stakeholders and Policies Approach to Identify and Exploit Regional Resource Potentials. *Ecol. Econ.*, **161**, 292–320, doi:10.1016/j.ecolecon.2019.03.020.

Volochovic, A., Z. Simanaviciene, and D. Streimikiene, 2012: Šiltnamio Efektą Sukeliančių Dujų Emisijų Mažinimas Dėl Elgsenos Pokyčių Lietuvos Namų Ūkiuose. *Eng. Econ.*, **23(3)**, 242–249, doi:10.5755/j01.ee.23.3.1936.

von Lüpke, H. and M. Well, 2020: Analyzing climate and energy policy integration: the case of the Mexican energy transition. *Clim. Policy*, **20(7)**, 832–845, doi:10.1080/14693062.2019.1648236.

von Wirth, T., L. Gislason, and R. Seidl, 2018: Distributed energy systems on a neighborhood scale: Reviewing drivers of and barriers to social acceptance. *Renew. Sustain. Energy Rev.*, **82** (April 2016), 2618–2628, doi:10.1016/j.rser.2017.09.086.

Vukotic, L., R.A. Fenner, and K. Symons, 2010: Assessing embodied energy of building structural elements. *Proc. Inst. Civ. Eng. Eng. Sustain.*, **163(3)**, 147–158, doi:10.1680/ensu.2010.163.3.147.

Vuuren, D. Van et al., 2021: *The 2021 SSP scenarios of the IMAGE 3.2 model*. PBL Netherlands Environmental Assessment Agency, The Hague, The Netherlands, 23 pp.

Wadud, Z. and P.K. Chintakayala, 2019: Personal Carbon Trading: Trade-off and Complementarity Between In-home and Transport Related Emissions Reduction. *Ecol. Econ.*, **156** (December 2016), 397–408, doi:10.1016/j.ecolecon.2018.10.016.

Wakiyama, T. and T. Kuramochi, 2017: Scenario analysis of energy saving and CO_2 emissions reduction potentials to ratchet up Japanese mitigation target in 2030 in the residential sector. *Energy Policy*, **103**, 1–15, doi:10.1016/j.enpol.2016.12.059.

Wallace, N., P. Issler, P. Mathew, and K. Sun, 2018: *Impact of Energy Factors on Default Risk in Commercial Mortgages*. U.S. Department of Energy, Lawrence Berkeley National Laboratory, University of California, USA, 35 pp.

Walters, S.A. and K.S. Midden, 2018: Sustainability of urban agriculture: Vegetable production on green roofs. *Agric.*, **8(11)**, 1–16, doi:10.3390/agriculture8110168.

Wan, K.K.W., D.H.W. Li, W. Pan, and J.C. Lam, 2012: Impact of climate change on building energy use in different climate zones and mitigation and adaptation implications. *Appl. Energy*, **97**, 274–282, doi:10.1016/j.apenergy.2011.11.048.

Wang, M., C.C. Wang, S. Sepasgozar, and S. Zlatanova, 2020: A Systematic Review of Digital Technology Adoption in Off-Site Construction: Current Status and Future Direction towards Industry 4.0. *Buildings*, **10(11)**, 204, doi:10.3390/buildings10110204.

Wang, S., J. Fan, D. Zhao, and Y. Li, 2017: Study on consumers' energy consumption and welfare changes under the personal carbon trading scheme. *Syst. Eng. Theory Pract.*, **37(6)**, 1512–1524, doi:10.12011/1000-6788(2017)06-1512-13.

Wang, Z., Q. Sun, B. Wang, and B. Zhang, 2019: Purchasing intentions of Chinese consumers on energy-efficient appliances: Is the energy efficiency label effective? *J. Clean. Prod.*, **238**, 117896, doi:10.1016/j.jclepro.2019.117896.

Wankiewicz, H., 2015: The potential of cohousing for rural Austria. *Urban Res. Pract.*, **8(1)**, 46–63, doi:10.1080/17535069.2015.1011426.

Wathore, R., K. Mortimer, and A.P. Grieshop, 2017: In-Use Emissions and Estimated Impacts of Traditional, Natural- and Forced-Draft Cookstoves in Rural Malawi. *Environ. Sci. Technol.*, **51(3)**, 1929–1938, doi:10.1021/acs.est.6b05557.

Weber, L., 1997: Some reflections on barriers to the efficient use of energy. *Energy Policy*, **25(10)**, 833–835, doi:10.1016/S0301-4215(97)00084-0.

Wędzik, A., T. Siewierski, and M. Szypowski, 2017: Green certificates market in Poland – The sources of crisis. *Renew. Sustain. Energy Rev.*, **75**, 490–503, doi:10.1016/j.rser.2016.11.014.

Wei, W., P. Wargocki, J. Zirngibl, J. Bendžalová, and C. Mandin, 2020: Review of parameters used to assess the quality of the indoor environment in Green Building certification schemes for offices and hotels. *Energy Build.*, **209**, doi:10.1016/j.enbuild.2019.109683.

Weisbach, D.A. and G.E. Metcalf, 2009: The Design of a Carbon Tax. *33 Harvard Environ. Law Rev.*, **499**, 68. doi:10.2139/ssrn.1327260.

Wells, L., B. Rismanchi, and L. Aye, 2018: A review of Net Zero Energy Buildings with reflections on the Australian context. *Energy Build.*, **158**, 616–628, doi:10.1016/j.enbuild.2017.10.055.

Wierzbicka, A. et al., 2018: Healthy Indoor Environments: The Need for a Holistic Approach. *Int. J. Environ. Res. Public Health*, **15(9)**, 1874, doi:10.3390/ijerph15091874.

Wiese, C., A. Larsen, and L.-L. Pade, 2018: Interaction effects of energy efficiency policies: a review. *Energy Effic.*, **11(8)**, 2137–2156, doi:10.1007/s12053-018-9659-z.

Wiese, C., R. Cowart, and J. Rosenow, 2020: The strategic use of auctioning revenues to foster energy efficiency: status quo and potential within the European Union Emissions Trading System. *Energy Effic.*, **13(8)**, 1677–1688, doi:10.1007/s12053-020-09894-0.

Willand, N., I. Ridley, and C. Maller, 2015: Towards explaining the health impacts of residential energy efficiency interventions – A realist review. Part 1: Pathways. *Soc. Sci. Med.*, **133**, 191–201, doi:10.1016/j.socscimed.2015.02.005.

Williams, J., 2008: Predicting an American future for cohousing. *Futures*, **40(3)**, 268–286, doi:10.1016/j.futures.2007.08.022.

Williams, J. et al., 2016: Less is more: A review of low energy standards and the urgent need for an international universal zero energy standard. *J. Build. Eng.*, **6**, 65–74, doi:10.1016/j.jobe.2016.02.007.

Wilson, A. and J. Boehland, 2005: Small is beautiful: U.S. house size, resource use, and the environment. *J. Ind. Ecol.*, **9(1–2)**, 277–287, doi:10.1162/1088198054084680.

Wilson, C., H. Pettifor, and G. Chryssochoidis, 2018: Quantitative modelling of why and how homeowners decide to renovate energy efficiently. *Appl. Energy*, **212** (November 2017), 1333–1344, doi:10.1016/j.apenergy.2017.11.099.

Wilson, C., L. Kerr, F. Sprei, E. Vrain, and M. Wilson, 2020: Potential Climate Benefits of Digital Consumer Innovations. *Annu. Rev. Environ. Resour.*, **45(1)**, 113–114, doi:10.1146/annurev-environ-012320-082424.

Wilson, E. et al., 2017: *Energy Efficiency Potential in the U.S. Single-Family Housing Stock*. National Renewable Energy Laboratory, Golden, 157 pp.

Wilson, J. et al., 2016: *Home Rx: The Health Benefits of Home Performance*. US Department of Energy, USA, 65 pp.

Winter, E., A. Faße, and K. Frohberg, 2015: Food security, energy equity, and the global commons: a computable village model applied to sub-Saharan Africa. *Reg. Environ. Chang.*, **15(7)**, 1215–1227, doi:10.1007/s10113-014-0674-0.

Winter, S. and L. Schlesewsky, 2019: The German feed-in tariff revisited – an empirical investigation on its distributional effects. *Energy Policy*, **132**, doi:10.1016/j.enpol.2019.05.043.

Wirl, F., 2015: White certificates – Energy efficiency programs under private information of consumers. *Energy Econ.*, **49**, 507–515, doi:10.1016/j.eneco.2015.03.026.

Witthoeft, S. and I. Kosta, 2017: *Shaping the Future of Construction. Inspiring innovators redefine the industry*. World Economic Forum, Cologny/Geneva, Switzerland, 96 pp.

Wolfram, C., O. Sh elef, and P. Gertler, 2012: How will energy demand develop in the developing world? *J. Econ. Perspect.*, **26(1)**, 119–138, doi:10.1257/jep.26.1.119.

Wolsink, M., 2012: The research agenda on social acceptance of distributed generation in smart grids: Renewable as common pool resources. *Renew. Sustain. Energy Rev.*, **16(1)**, 822–835, doi:10.1016/j.rser.2011.09.006.

Wolske, K.S., K.T. Gillingham, and P.W. Schultz, 2020: Peer influence on household energy behaviours. *Nat. Energy*, **5(3)**, 202–212, doi:10.1038/s41560-019-0541-9.

World Health Organization, 2016: *Burning Opportunity: Clean Household Energy for Health, Sustainable Development, and Wellbeing of Women and Children*. WHO Press, Geneva, Switzerland, 130 pp.

WHO, 2018: *World Health Statistics 2018: monitoring health for the SDGs: sustainable development goals.* World Health Organization, Geneva, Switzerland, 86 pp.

WHO, 2021: *Roadmap to improve and ensure good indoor ventilation in the context of COVID-19*. World Health Organization, Geneva, Switzerland, 38 pp.

Wright, G.R., 2000: *Ancient building technology. Volume 3. Construction*. Illustrate. BRILL, Boston, USA, 279 pp.

Wu, J., Z. Xu, and F. Jiang, 2019: Analysis and development trends of Chinese energy efficiency standards for room air conditioners. *Energy Policy*, **125** (June 2018), 368–383, doi:10.1016/j.enpol.2018.10.038.

Xiang, D. and C. Lawley, 2019: The impact of British Columbia's carbon tax on residential natural gas consumption. *Energy Econ.*, **80**, 206–218, doi:10.1016/j.eneco.2018.12.004.

Xin-gang, Z., Z. Yu-zhuo, R. Ling-zhi, Z. Yi, and W. Zhi-gong, 2017: The policy effects of feed-in tariff and renewable portfolio standard: A case study of China's waste incineration power industry. *Waste Manag.*, **68**, 711–723, doi:10.1016/j.wasman.2017.06.009.

Xin-gang, Z., L. Pei-ling, and Z. Ying, 2020: Which policy can promote renewable energy to achieve grid parity? Feed-in tariff vs. renewable portfolio standards. *Renew. Energy*, **162**, 322–333, doi:10.1016/j.renene.2020.08.058.

Xin, L. et al., 2018: Effect of the energy-saving retrofit on the existing residential buildings in the typical city in northern China. *Energy Build.*, **177**, 154–172, doi:10.1016/j.enbuild.2018.07.004.

Xing, R., T. Hanaoka, and T. Masui, 2021: Deep decarbonization pathways in the building sector: China's NDC and the Paris agreement. *Environ. Res. Lett.*, **16(4)**, 044054, doi:10.1088/1748-9326/abe008.

Xu, W. and S. Zhang, 2017: *APEC 100 Best Practice Analysis of Nearly/Net Zero Energy Building*. Asia-Pacific Economic Cooperation, Singapore, 240 pp.

Xu, Y. et al., 2017: Performance analysis of static ice refrigeration air conditioning system driven by household distributed photovoltaic energy system. *Sol. Energy*, **158** (September 2016), 147–160, doi:10.1016/j.solener.2017.09.002.

Yan, D. et al., 2017: IEA EBC Annex 66: Definition and simulation of occupant behavior in buildings. *Energy Build.*, **156**, 258–270, doi:10.1016/j.enbuild.2017.09.084.

Yang, W., Z. Wang, J. Cui, Z. Zhu, and X. Zhao, 2015: Comparative study of the thermal performance of the novel green (planting) roofs against other existing roofs. *Sustain. Cities Soc.*, **16(C)**, 1–12, doi:10.1016/j.scs.2015.01.002.

Yang, X., Zhang, S., Xu, W., 2019: Impact of zero energy buildings on medium-to-long term building energy consumption in China. Energy Policy 129, 574–586. doi:10.1016/j.enpol.2019.02.025

Yeh, S. et al., 2016: A modeling comparison of deep greenhouse gas emissions reduction scenarios by 2030 in California. *Energy Strateg. Rev.*, **13–14** (August 2016), 169–180, doi:10.1016/j.esr.2016.10.001.

Yi, Z., Z. Xin-gang, Z. Yu-zhuo, and Z. Ying, 2019: From feed-in tariff to renewable portfolio standards: An evolutionary game theory perspective. *J. Clean. Prod.*, **213**, 1274–1289, doi:10.1016/j.jclepro.2018.12.170.

Yılmaz Balaman, Ş., J. Scott, A. Matopoulos, and D.G. Wright, 2019: Incentivising bioenergy production: Economic and environmental insights from a regional optimization methodology. *Renew. Energy*, **130** (2019), 867–880, doi:10.1016/j.renene.2018.06.083.

Yohanis, Y.G., 2012: Domestic energy use and householders' energy behaviour. *Energy Policy*, **41**, 654–665, doi:10.1016/j.enpol.2011.11.028.

Yoshida, J. and A. Sugiura, 2015: The Effects of Multiple Green Factors on Condominium Prices. *J. Real Estate Financ. Econ.*, **50(3)**, 412–437, doi:10.1007/s11146-014-9462-3.

Yu, S., 2017: Transition pathways of China and implications for climate change mitigation: evolution of the buildings sector. Thesis, University of Maryland, MD, USA.

Yu, S. et al., 2018: Implementing nationally determined contributions: building energy policies in India's mitigation strategy. *Environ. Res. Lett.*, **13(3)**, 034034, doi:10.1088/1748-9326/aaad84.

Yu, W. et al., 2020: Thermodynamic and thermoeconomic performance analyses and optimization of a novel power and cooling cogeneration system fueled by low-grade waste heat. *Appl. Therm. Eng.*, **179** (May), 115667, doi:10.1016/j.applthermaleng.2020.115667.

Yushchenko, A. and M.K. Patel, 2016: Contributing to a green energy economy? A macroeconomic analysis of an energy efficiency program operated by a Swiss utility. *Appl. Energy*, **179**, 1304–1320, doi:10.1016/j.apenergy.2015.12.028.

Zancanella, P., P. Bertoldi, and B. Boza- Kiss, 2017: Why is demand response not implemented in the EU? Status of demand response and recommendations to allow demand response to be fully integrated in energy markets. *Proceeding ECEEE Summer Study in Energy Efficiency 2017*. ECEEE, Stockholm, Sweden, 457–466.

Zanetti, V., W. de Sousa Junior, and D. De Freitas, 2016: A Climate Change Vulnerability Index and Case Study in a Brazilian Coastal City. *Sustainability*, **8(8)**, 811, doi:10.3390/su8080811.

Zangheri, Serrenho, and Bertoldi, 2019: Energy Savings from Feedback Systems: A Meta-Studies' Review. *Energies*, **12(19)**, 3788, doi:10.3390/en12193788.

Zapata-Diomedi, B. et al., 2019: Physical activity-related health and economic benefits of building walkable neighbourhoods: a modelled comparison between brownfield and greenfield developments. *Int. J. Behav. Nutr. Phys. Act.*, **16(1)**, 11, doi:10.1186/s12966-019-0775-8.

9

Zea Escamilla, E., G. Habert, and E. Wohlmuth, 2016: When CO_2 counts: Sustainability assessment of industrialized bamboo as an alternative for social housing programs in the Philippines. *Build. Environ.*, **103**, 44–53, doi:10.1016/j.buildenv.2016.04.003.

Zea Escamilla, E. et al., 2018: Industrial or Traditional Bamboo Construction? Comparative Life Cycle Assessment (LCA) of Bamboo-Based Buildings. *Sustainability*, **10(9)**, 3096, doi:10.3390/su10093096.

Zepter, J.M., A. Lüth, P. Crespo del Granado, and R. Egging, 2019: Prosumer integration in wholesale electricity markets: Synergies of peer-to-peer trade and residential storage. *Energy Build.*, **184**, 163–176, doi:10.1016/j.enbuild.2018.12.003.

Zhang, C., J. Sun, M. Lubell, L. Qiu, and K. Kang, 2019: Design and simulation of a novel hybrid solar-biomass energy supply system in northwest China. *J. Clean. Prod.*, **233**, 1221–1239, doi:10.1016/j.jclepro.2019.06.128.

Zhang, J. and N. Zhou, 2015: Zero-energy buildings – an overview of terminology and policies in leading world regions. *ECEEE 2015 Summer Study Proceedings*, 1299–1311.

Zhang, Q. et al., 2018: Substitution effect of renewable portfolio standards and renewable energy certificate trading for feed-in tariff. *Appl. Energy*, **227**, 426–435, doi:10.1016/j.apenergy.2017.07.118.

Zhang, S. et al., 2020a: Scenarios of energy reduction potential of zero energy building promotion in the Asia-Pacific region to year 2050. *Energy*, **213**, 118792, doi:10.1016/j.energy.2020.118792.

Zhang, T., P.O. Siebers, and U. Aickelin, 2012: A three-dimensional model of residential energy consumer archetypes for local energy policy design in the UK. *Energy Policy*, **47**, 102–110, doi:10.1016/j.enpol.2012.04.027.

Zhang, X. et al., 2020b: Experimental and analytic study of a hybrid solar/biomass rural heating system. *Energy*, **190**, 116392, doi:10.1016/j.energy.2019.116392.

Zhang, Y. et al., 2020c: Study on model uncertainty of water source heat pump and impact on decision making. *Energy Build.*, **216**, 109950, doi:10.1016/j.enbuild.2020.109950.

Zhao, D., A.P. McCoy, J. Du, P. Agee, and Y. Lu, 2017: Interaction effects of building technology and resident behavior on energy consumption in residential buildings. *Energy Build.*, **134**, 223–233, doi:10.1016/j.enbuild.2016.10.049.

Zhao, Z.-Y., L. Gao, and J. Zuo, 2019: How national policies facilitate low carbon city development: A China study. *J. Clean. Prod.*, **234**, 743–754, doi:10.1016/j.jclepro.2019.06.116.

Zheng, J., A.A. Chien, and S. Suh, 2020: Mitigating Curtailment and Carbon Emissions through Load Migration between Data Centers. *Joule*, **4(10)**, doi:10.1016/j.joule.2020.08.001.

Zheng, S., J. Wu, M.E. Kahn, and Y. Deng, 2012: The nascent market for "green" real estate in Beijing. *Eur. Econ. Rev.*, **56(5)**, 974–984, doi:10.1016/j.euroecorev.2012.02.012.

Zheng, S., R. Wang, T.M.W. Mak, S.-C. Hsu, and D.C.W. Tsang, 2021: How energy service companies moderate the impact of industrialization and urbanization on carbon emissions in China? *Sci. Total Environ.*, **751**, 141610, doi:10.1016/j.scitotenv.2020.141610.

Zhou, K. and Y. Li, 2019: Carbon finance and carbon market in China: Progress and challenges. *J. Clean. Prod.*, **214**, 536–549, doi:10.1016/j.jclepro.2018.12.298.

Zhou, N., N. Khanna, W. Feng, J. Ke, and M. Levine, 2018: Scenarios of energy efficiency and CO 2 emissions reduction potential in the buildings sector in China to year 2050. *Nat. Energy*, **3(11)**, 978–984, doi:10.1038/s41560-018-0253-6.

Zhou, Y. et al., 2014: Modeling the effect of climate change on U.S. state-level buildings energy demands in an integrated assessment framework. *Appl. Energy*, **113**, 1077–1088, doi:10.1016/j.apenergy.2013.08.034.

Zink, T. and R. Geyer, 2017: Circular Economy Rebound. *J. Ind. Ecol.*, **21(3)**, 593–602, doi:10.1111/jiec.12545.

Zografakis, N., K. Karyotakis, and K.P. Tsagarakis, 2012: Implementation conditions for energy saving technologies and practices in office buildings: Part 1. Lighting. *Renew. Sustain. Energy Rev.*, **16(6)**, 4165–4174, doi:10.1016/j.rser.2012.03.005.

Zuhaib, S., R. Manton, M. Hajdukiewicz, M.M. Keane, and J. Goggins, 2017: Attitudes and approaches of Irish retrofit industry professionals towards achieving nearly zero-energy buildings. *Int. J. Build. Pathol. Adapt.*, **35(1)**, 16–40, doi:10.1108/IJBPA-07-2016-0015.